MW00649269

General Industry Regulations
29 CFR PART 1910

with

1903
Inspections, Citations and Proposed Penalties

1904
Recording and Reporting Occupational Injuries

Updated Thru
January 1, 2017

National Safety Compliance

Thank you for purchasing this book.
With this purchase you receive complimentary
access to the online version of the book at:
www.osha29CFR.com/online

® UFCW 888

424 N Cedarbrook Ave.
Springfield, MO 65802
1 877 922 7233
www.osha-safety-training.net

ISBN: 978-1-61946-397-4 Perfect bound
ISBN: 978-1-61946-398-1 Spiral bound
ISBN: 978-1-61946-399-8 Three-ring bound (Premium)

Changes to OSHA Regulations
January 1, 2016 thru January 1, 2017

January 1, 2016

Updated contact information, pamphlets, posters and statistics in the Introduction to OSHA section. Updated OSHA Standard Interpretation footnotes. Additionally, editorial corrections were made to correct minor grammar, punctuation, spelling errors and/or stylistic changes throughout the book.

March 1, 2016

OSHA corrected **§1910.106(a)(14)** reinstating the defnition for **Flammable liquids.**

March 25, 2016

OSHA revised **§1910.6 Incorporation by reference** paragraphs **(e)(69) through (e)(71)** and revised **§1910.133 Eye and face protection paragraph (b)(1).** These changes became effective on April 25, 2016.

March 25, 2016

OSHA revised the **Authority for 1910 Subpart Z, §1910.1000 Air contaminants Table Z-1 & Table Z-3** and added a new **§1910.1053 Respirable Crystalline Silica.** These changes became effective on June 23, 2016. Start-up dates for specifc provisions are set in **§1910.1053(l).** OSHA corrected this revision on May 18, correcting **§1910.1000 Table Z-3**.

May 12, 20, 2016

OSHA revised **§1904.35** & **§1904.36**, added an Authority citation to **Subpart E of §1904**, revised **§1904.41** and added **Appendix A to Subpart E of §1904**. These changes become effective on January 1, 2017, except for **§1904.35** and **§1904.36**, which become effective on August 10, 2016. OSHA corrected an error in this revision on May 20, reinstating **§1904.35(b)(2)**.

July 1, 2016

OSHA revised the **Authority for §1903**, together with **§19032(d)**, **§1903.6(b)**, **§1903.15(a)** and **(b)** and adding paragraph **(d)**, and **§1903.18(d)**. The change became effective August 1, 2016.

July 26, 2016

OSHA amended the table in **§1910.8 OMB control numbers under the Paperwork Reduction Act** by adding the entry "1915.1053'. The change became effective July 26, 2016.

September 1, 2016

OSHA revised the entries for "Silica: Crystalline Quartz (Respirable)", "Silica: Crystalline Cristobalite", and "Silica: Crystalline Tridymite' in **§1910.1000, Table Z-3**. These changes became effective on September 1, 2016.

November 18, 2016

OSHA made a major revision and update of Standards on Walking-Working Surfaces - Subpart D. Headings and contents of most of the Subpart were changed. The change became effective January 17, 2017

December 19, 2016

OSHA amended its recordkeeping regulations to clarify that the duty to make and maintain accurate records of work-related injuries and illnesses is an ongoing obligation. Revised the **Authority** for **§1904**, amended **§1904.0, Subpart C** and **1904.4, §1904.29(b)(3), §1904.32**, the heading and paragraph **(b)** of **§1904.33, §1904.34** and **§1904.35**, and revised the heading of **Subpart E** and paragraph **(a)** of **§1904.40** The changes became effective January 18, 2017.

January 1, 2017

Updated contact information, pamphlets, and statistics in the Introduction to OSHA section (pp. 1-26). Updated OSHA Standard Interpretation footnotes. Additionally, editorial corrections were made to correct minor grammar, punctuation, spelling errors and/or stylistic changes throughout the book.

This page intentionally left blank.

Table of Contents

Table of Contents

Table of Contents

This page intentionally left blank.

Introduction to OSHA

OSHA's Mission

With the Occupational Safety and Health Act of 1970, Congress created the Occupational Safety and Health Administration (OSHA) to assure safe and healthful working conditions for working men and women by setting and enforcing standards and by providing training, outreach, education and assistance.

Organization

OSHA is part of the United States Department of Labor. The Administrator for OSHA is the Assistant Secretary of Labor for Occupational Safety and Health. OSHA's Administrator answers to the Secretary of Labor, who is a member of the cabinet of the President of the United States.

OSHA Coverage

The OSH Act covers most private sector employers and their workers, in addition to some public sector employers and workers in the 50 states and certain territories and jurisdictions under federal authority. Those jurisdictions include the District of Columbia, Puerto Rico, the Virgin Islands, American Samoa, Guam, Northern Mariana Islands, Wake Island, Johnston Island, and the Outer Continental Shelf Lands as defined in the Outer Continental Shelf Lands Act.

Resources:

OSHA General Duty Clause

OSHA AT-A-GLANCE

National and Regional Office Directories

State Occupational Safety and Health Plans

OSHA Consultation Services

OSHA's Top 10 Most Cited Violations

Employer Rights and Responsibilities

OSHA Safety Poster (English & Spanish)

Multi-Employer Citation Policy

–

OSHA Form 300, 300–A, and 301 Instructions
(Following §1904)

OSHA General Duty Clause

Public Law 91-596

84 STAT. 1590

91st Congress, S.2193

December 29, 1970,

as amended through January 1, 2004.

An Act

To assure safe and healthful working conditions for working men and women; by authorizing enforcement of the standards developed under the Act; by assisting and encouraging the States in their efforts to assure safe and healthful working conditions; by providing for research, information, education, and training in the field of occupational safety and health; and for other purposes.

Be it enacted by the Senate and House of Representatives of the United States of America in Congress assembled, **That this Act may be cited as the "Occupational Safety and Health Act of 1970."**

29 USC 654

SEC. 5. Duties

(a) Each employer –

(1) shall furnish to each of his employees employment and a place of employment which are free from recognized hazards that are causing or are likely to cause death or serious physical harm to his employees;

(2) shall comply with occupational safety and health standards promulgated under this Act.

(b) Each employee shall comply with occupational safety and health standards and all rules, regulations, and orders issued pursuant to this Act which are applicable to his own actions and conduct.

OSHA At–A–Glance

AT-A-GLANCE

OSHA®

The *Occupational Safety and Health Act of 1970* (OSH Act) was passed to prevent workers from being killed or seriously harmed at work. This law created the Occupational Safety and Health Administration (OSHA), which sets and enforces protective workplace safety and health standards. OSHA also provides information, training, and assistance to employers and workers.

Under the OSH Act, employers have the responsibility to provide a safe workplace.

RIGHTS AND RESPONSIBILITIES

Employers must:

- Follow all relevant OSHA safety and health standards.
- Find and correct safety and health hazards.
- Inform employees about chemical hazards through training, labels, alarms, color-coded systems, chemical information sheets and other methods.
- As of January 1, 2015, notify OSHA within 8 hours of a workplace fatality or within 24 hours of any work-related inpatient hospitalization, amputation or loss of an eye (1-800-321-OSHA [6742]); www.osha.gov/report_online).
- Provide required personal protective equipment at no cost to workers.*
- Keep accurate records of work-related injuries and illnesses.
- Post OSHA citations, injury and illness summary data, and the OSHA *Job Safety and Health - It's The Law* poster in the workplace where workers will see them.
- Not retaliate against any worker for using their rights under the law.

Employees have the right to:

- Working conditions that do not pose a risk of serious harm.
- Receive information and training (in a language workers can understand) about chemical and other hazards, methods to prevent harm, and OSHA standards that apply to their workplace.
- Review records of work-related injuries and illnesses.
- Get copies of test results done to find and measure hazards in the workplace.
- File a complaint asking OSHA to inspect their workplace if they believe there is a serious hazard or that their employer is not following OSHA rules. When requested, OSHA will keep all identities confidential.
- Use their rights under the law without retaliation. If an employee is fired, demoted, transferred or retaliated against in any way for using their rights under the law, they can file a complaint with OSHA. This complaint must be filed within 30 days of the alleged retaliation.

* Employers must pay for most types of required personal protective equipment.

OSHA Standards

OSHA standards are rules that describe the methods employers are legally required to follow to protect their workers from hazards. Before OSHA can issue a standard, it must go through a very extensive and lengthy process that includes substantial public engagement, notice and comment. The agency must show that a significant risk to workers exists and that there are feasible measures employers can take to protect their workers.

Construction, General Industry, Maritime, and Agriculture standards protect workers from a wide range of serious hazards. These standards limit the amount of hazardous chemicals workers can be exposed to, require the use of certain safe practices and equipment, and require employers to monitor certain workplace hazards.

Examples of OSHA standards include requirements to provide fall protection, prevent trenching cave-ins, prevent exposure to some infectious diseases, ensure the safety of workers who enter confined spaces, prevent exposure to such harmful substances as asbestos and lead, put guards on machines, provide respirators or other safety equipment, and provide training for certain dangerous jobs.

Employers must also comply with the General Duty Clause of the OSH Act. This clause requires employers to keep their workplaces free of serious recognized hazards and is generally cited when no specific OSHA standard applies to the hazard.

Inspections

Inspections are initiated without advance notice, conducted using on-site or telephone and facsimile investigations, performed by highly trained compliance officers, and based on the following priorities:

- Imminent danger.
- Catastrophes – fatalities or hospitalizations.
- Worker complaints and referrals.
- Targeted inspections – particular hazards, high injury rates.
- Follow-up inspections.

On-site inspections can be triggered by a complaint from a current worker or their representative if they believe there is a serious hazard or that their employer is not following OSHA standards or rules. Often the best and fastest way to get a hazard corrected is to notify your supervisor or employer.

When an inspector finds violations of OSHA standards or serious hazards, OSHA may issue citations and fines. A citation includes methods an employer may use to fix a problem and the date by when the corrective actions must be completed.

Employers have the right to contest any part of the citation, including whether a violation actually exists. Workers only have the right to challenge the deadline for when a problem must be resolved. Appeals of citations are heard by the independent Occupational Safety and Health Review Commission.

Help for Employers

OSHA offers free confidential advice. Several programs and services help employers identify and correct job hazards as well as improve their injury and illness prevention programs.

Free On-Site Consultation

OSHA provides a free service, On-Site Consultation, for **small businesses** with fewer than 250 workers at a site (and no more than 500 employees nationwide). On-site Consultation services are separate from enforcement and do not result in penalties or citations. Each year, OSHA makes more than 29,000 consultation visits to small businesses to provide free compliance assistance. By working with the OSHA Consultation Program, certain exemplary employers may request participation in OSHA's Safety and Health Recognition Program, SHARP. To locate the OSHA Consultation Office nearest you, visit www.osha.gov/consultation or call 1-800-321-OSHA (6742).

Compliance Assistance

OSHA has compliance assistance specialists throughout the nation who can provide general information about OSHA standards and compliance assistance resources. Contact your local OSHA office for more information or visit www.osha.gov/dcsp/compliance_assistance/cas.html.

Cooperative Programs

OSHA offers cooperative programs to help prevent fatalities, injuries, and illnesses in the workplace. ***Alliance Program*** – OSHA works with groups committed to worker safety and health to develop compliance assistance resources and educate workers and employers. ***OSHA Strategic Partnerships (OSP)*** – Partnerships are formalized through tailored agreements designed to encourage, assist, and recognize partner efforts to eliminate serious hazards and achieve model workplace safety and health practices. ***Voluntary Protection Programs (VPP)*** – The VPP recognize employers and workers in private industry and federal agencies who have implemented effective safety and health management programs and maintain injury and illness rates below the national average for their respective industries. In VPP, management, labor, and OSHA work cooperatively and proactively to prevent fatalities, injuries, and illnesses.

Information and Education

OSHA Training Institute

The OSHA Training Institute (OTI) Education Centers are a national network of nonprofit organizations authorized by OSHA to deliver occupational safety and health training to private sector workers, supervisors, and employers.

Educational Materials

OSHA has a variety of educational materials and electronic tools available on its website at These include utilities such as expert advisors, electronic compliance assistance, videos and other information for employers and workers. OSHA's software programs and eTools walk you through safety and health issues and common problems to find the best solutions for your workplace.

OSHA's extensive publications help explain OSHA standards, job hazards, and mitigation strategies and provide assistance in developing effective safety and health programs.

Visit www.osha.gov/publications or call 1-800-321-OSHA (6742).

QuickTakes

OSHA's free, twice-monthly online newsletter, *QuickTakes*, offers the latest news about OSHA initiatives and products to assist employers and workers in finding and preventing workplace hazards. To sign up for *QuickTakes*, visit www.osha.gov/quicktakes.

Who Does OSHA Cover

Private Sector Workers

OSHA covers most private sector employers and workers in all 50 states, the District of Columbia, and other U.S. jurisdictions either directly through Federal OSHA or through an OSHA-approved state program. State-run safety and health programs must be at least as effective as the Federal OSHA program.

State and Local Government Workers

State and local government workers are not covered by Federal OSHA, but they do have protections in states that operate their own programs. The following states have approved state programs: AK, AZ, CA, *CT*, HI, IA, *IL*, IN, KY, MD, MI, MN, NC, *NJ*, NM, NV, *NY*, OR, SC, TN, UT, VA, VT, WA, WY, Puerto Rico and the *Virgin Islands*.

Connecticut, Illinois, New Jersey, New York and the Virgin Islands programs cover public sector (state and local government) workers only. Federal OSHA covers private sector workers in these jurisdictions.

Federal Government Workers

OSHA's protection applies to all federal agencies. Although OSHA does not fine federal agencies, it does monitor federal agencies and responds to workers' complaints.

Not Covered by the OSH Act:

Self-employed workers; and workplace hazards regulated by another federal agency (for example, the Mine Safety and Health Administration, the Department of Energy, or Coast Guard).

Contact OSHA

For questions or to get information or advice, to report an emergency, report a fatality or catastrophe, order publications, sign up for OSHA's e-newsletter *QuickTakes*, or to file a confidential complaint, contact your nearest OSHA office, visit www.osha.gov or call OSHA at 1-800-321-OSHA (6742), TTY 1-877-889-5627.

For assistance, contact us.
We are OSHA. We can help.
It's confidential.

U.S. Department of Labor

OSHA®
Occupational Safety and Health Administration
U.S. Department of Labor
www.osha.gov

OSHA 3439-B-12R 2014

National Office Directory

U.S. Department of Labor
Occupational Safety & Health Administration
200 Constitution Avenue
Washington, D.C. 20210

To Report Unsafe Working Conditions
or Safety & Health Violations:

Contact the OSHA Office nearest you, see **Regional Office Directory** below, or, contact the toll free number:
1-800-321-OSHA (6742)
TTY 1-877-889-5627

If you have an **EMERGENCY:**
(EX: to report a fatality or imminent life threatening situation)

Please contact the toll free number immediately:
1-800-321-OSHA (6742)
TTY 1-877-889-5627
DO NOT SEND EMAIL.

If You Have Workplace Safety & Health Related Questions:

[Write To]:
U.S. Department of Labor
Occupational Safety & Health Administration
200 Constitution Avenue
Washington, D.C. 20210

[By Phone]:
1-800-321-OSHA (6742) Toll Free U.S.

[International]:
OSHA International Affairs
U.S. Department of Labor
200 Constitution Avenue, NW
Room: N3641
Washington, D.C. 20210
(202) 693-2400

You can also contact OSHA via email
http://www.osha.gov/ecor_form.html

Regional Office Directory

Region I

Connecticut, Massachusetts, Maine, New Hampshire, Rhode Island, Vermont
25 New Sudbury Street, Room E340
Boston, Massachusetts 02203
(617) 565-9860
(617) 565-9827 Fax

Region II

New Jersey, New York, Puerto Rico, Virgin Islands
201 Varick Street
Room 670
New York, New York 10014
(212) 337-2378
(212) 337-2371 Fax

Region III

District of Columbia, Delaware, Maryland, Pennsylvania, Virginia, West Virginia
The Curtis Center-Suite 740 West
170 S. Independence Mall West
Philadelphia, PA 19106-3309
(215) 861-4900
(215) 861-4904 Fax

Region IV

Alabama, Florida, Georgia, Kentucky, Mississippi, North Carolina, South Carolina, Tennessee
61 Forsyth Street, SW
Room 6T50
Atlanta, Georgia 30303
(678) 237-0400
(678) 237-0447 Fax

Region V

Illinois, Indiana, Michigan, Minnesota, Ohio, Wisconsin
230 South Dearborn Street
Room 3244
Chicago, Illinois 60604
(312) 353-2220
(312) 353-7774 Fax

Region VI

Arkansas, Louisiana, New Mexico, Oklahoma, Texas
525 Griffin Street, Suite 602
Dallas, Texas 75202
(972) 850-4145
(972) 850-4149 Fax
(972) 850-4150 FSO Fax

Region VII

Iowa, Kansas, Missouri, Nebraska
2300 Main Street, Suite 1010
Kansas City, Missouri 64108-2416
(816) 283-8745
(816) 283-0545 Voice
(816) 283-0547 Fax

Region VIII

Colorado, Montana, North Dakota, South Dakota, Utah, Wyoming
Cesar Chavez Memorial Building
1244 Speer Blvd., Suite 551
Denver, CO 80204
720-264-6550
720-264-6585 FAX

Region IX

American Samoa, Arizona, California, Guam, Hawaii, Nevada, North Mariana Islands
90 7th Street, Suite 18100
San Francisco, California 94103
(415) 625-2547 (8AM - 4:30PM Pacific time)
(415) 625-2534 Fax

Region X

Alaska, Idaho, Oregon, Washington
300 Fifth Avenue, Suite 1280
Seattle, Washington 98104
(206) 757-6700
(206) 757-6705 Fax

State Occupational Safety and Health Plans

The Occupational Safety and Health Act of 1970 encourages states to develop and operate their own job safety and health plans under the authority of state law. These plans may cover both private and public sector employment or may be limited to public sector employment only.* OSHA approves and monitors states' plans and provides up to 50 percent of an approved plan's operating costs.

Alaska
Alaska Department of Labor and Workforce Development
1111 W. 8th Street, Room 304
Juneau, AK 99801-1149
(907) 465-2700
(907) 465-2784 Fax

Arizona
Arizona Division of Occupational Safety and Health (ADOSH)
800 W. Washington
Phoenix, AZ 85007-2922
(602) 542-5795
(602) 542-1614 Fax

California
Division of Occupational Safety and Health
1515 Clay Street Suite 1901
Oakland, CA 94612
(510) 286-7000
(510) 286-7037 Fax

Connecticut*
Occupational Safety and Health Division
38 Wolcott Hill Road
Wethersfield, CT 06109
(860) 263-6900
(860) 263-6940 Fax

Hawaii
Hawaii Occupational Safety and Health Division (HIOSH)
830 Punchbowl Street, Suite 423
Honolulu, HI 96813
(808) 586-9100
(808) 586-9104 Fax

Illinois*
Illinois Department of Labor
900 South Spring Street
Springfield, IL 62702
(217) 782-9386
(217) 785-8776 Fax

Indiana
Indiana OSHA (IOSHA)
402 West Washington Street
Room W-195
Indianapolis, IN. 46204-2751
(317) 232-2693
(317) 233-3790 Fax

Iowa
Iowa Occupational Safety and Health Enforcement
1000 E Grand Avenue
Des Moines, IA 50319-0209
(515) 242-5870
(515) 281-7995 Fax

Kentucky
Kentucky Occupational Safety and Health (Kentucky OSH)
1047 US HWY 127 South, Suite 4
Frankfort, KY 40601
(502) 564-3070
(502) 564-1682 Fax

Maine
Maine Occupational Safety and Health (MEOSH)
45 State House Station
Augusta, Maine 04333-0045
(207) 623-7900
(207) 623-7934 Fax

Maryland
Maryland Occupational Safety and Health (MOSH)
10946 Golden West Drive, Suite 160
Hunt Valley, MD 21031
(410) 527-4447
(410) 527-4481 Fax

Michigan
Michigan Occupational Safety and Health Administration (MIOSHA)
7150 Harris Drive
P.O. Box 30643
Lansing, MI 48909-8143
(517) 322-1817
(517) 322-1775 Fax

Minnesota
Minnesota Department of Labor and Industry
443 Lafayette Road North
St. Paul, MN 55155-4307
(651) 284-5050 | (877) 470-6742
(651) 284-5741 Fax

Nevada
Nevada Occupational Safety and Health Administration (Nevada OSHA)
1301 N. Green Valley Parkway, Suite 200
Henderson, NV 89074
(702) 486-9020
(702) 990-0358 Fax

New Jersey*
New Jersey Public Employees Occupational Safety and Health (PEOSH)
P.O. Box 386 Safety, P.O. Box 360 Health
Trenton, New Jersey 08625-0386
(609) 984-1389
(609) 292-3749 Fax

New Mexico
New Mexico Occupational Health and Safety Bureau (OHSB)
525 Camino de los Marquez, Suite3
Santa Fe, NM 87502
(505) 476-8700
(505) 476-8734 Fax

New York*
Public Employee Safety and Health (PESH) Bureau
W. Averell Harriman State Office Campus Building 12, Room 158
Albany, NY 12240
(518) 457-1263
(518) 457-5545 Fax

North Carolina
North Carolina Occupational Safety and Health (OSH)
111 Hillsborough Street
Raleigh, NC 27601
(919) 779-8560
(919) 779-8559 Fax

Oregon
Oregon Occupational Safety and Health Administration (OR-OSHA)
350 Winter Street, NE, Room 430 P.O. Box 14480
Salem, OR 97309-0405
(503) 378-3272 | (800) 922-2689
(503) 947-7461 Fax

Puerto Rico
Puerto Rico Occupational Safety and Health Administration (PR OSHA)
Prudencio Rivera Martinez Building 21st Floor
505 Muñoz Rivera Avenue
Hato Rey, PR 00918
(787) 754-2172
(787) 767-6051 Fax

South Carolina
South Carolina Occupational Safety and Health Plan (SCOSH)
Koger Office Park, Kingstree Building,
110 Centerview Drive, P.O. Box 11329
Columbia, South Carolina 29210-1329
(803) 896-7665
(803) 896-7670 Fax

Tennessee
Tennessee Department of Labor and Workforce Development
220 French Landing Drive
Nashville, TN 37243
(615) 741-2793
(615) 741-3325 Fax

Utah
Utah Occupational Safety and Health (Utah OSHA)
160 East 300 South, 3rd Floor
P.O. Box 146600
Salt Lake City, UT 84114-6600
(801) 530-6901
(801) 536-7906 Fax

Vermont
Vermont Occupational Safety and Health Administration (VOSHA)
5 Green Mountain Drive, P.O. Box 488
Montpelier VT. 05601-0488
(802) 828-2765
(802) 828-2195 Fax

Virgin Islands*
Virgin Islands Division of Occupational Safety and Health (VIDOSH)
4401 Sion Farm
Christiansted, St. Croix VI 00820
(340) 773-1994
(340) 773-0094 Fax

Virginia
Virginia Occupational Safety and Health (VOSH)
600 E Main Street, Suite 207
Richmond, VA 23219
(804) 371-2327
(804) 371-6524

Washington
Washington Division of Occupational Safety and Health (DOSH)
P.O. Box 44600
Olympia, WA 98504-4620
(360) 902-5495
(360) 902-4202 Fax

Wyoming
Wyoming Occupational Safety and Health Administration (Wyoming OSHA)
1510 East Pershing Blvd., West Wing
Cheyenne, WY 82002
(307) 777-7786
(307) 777-3646 Fax

***NOTE:** The Connecticut, Illinois, Maine, New Jersey, New York, and the Virgin Islands plans cover public sector (State & local government) workers only.
More information is available at the OSHA State Occupational Safety and Health Plans web site: http://www.osha.gov/dcsp/osp/

OSHA Consultation Services

Role of the Consultant

Consultants **will**:

- Help employers recognize hazards in the workplace;
- Assist employers in developing or maintaining effective safety and health management programs;
- Suggest general approaches or options for solving a safety or health problem;
- Identify resources available if an employer needs further assistance;
- Provide employers with a written report summarizing findings; and
- Provide safety and health training.

Consultants **will not**:

- Issue citations or propose penalties for violations of OSHA standards.

SAFETY AND HEALTH ACHIEVEMENT RECOGNITION PROGRAM

The On-site Consultation's Safety and Health Achievement Recognition Program (SHARP) recognizes small employers who operate an exemplary safety and health management program.

"Becoming involved with OSHA's On-site Consultation program is one way of giving back to our workers. Our safety and health management system is at the forefront of EWP's business; it has saved us money, resulting in the hiring of new people as EWP expands its business operations."

J. Lynn Greene, Safety Director
Edwards Wood Products, Inc. (EWP)
Marshville, North Carolina
SHARP Participant

If you are an employer who is interested in a free consultation visit, or more information, visit **www.osha.gov**, call 1-800-321-OSHA (6742), or find the local On-site Consultation program in your state at **www.osha.gov/consultation.**

U.S. Department of Labor

For more information

OSHA® Occupational Safety and Health Administration

www.osha.gov (800) 321-OSHA (6742)

OSHA 3357-10R 2012

FREE Safety and Health Consultation Services

Free On-site Safety and Health Services for Small Business

Serving the Small Business Community

OSHA provides free and confidential safety and health advice to small and medium-sized businesses committed to improving workplace safety and health.

ON-SITE CONSULTATION PROGRAM

Workers' comp costs cutting into profits?

Do you worry that a serious workplace injury could disrupt or even shut down your business?

Can't afford to hire a safety consultant?

If so, ***OSHA's FREE and CONFIDENTIAL On-site Consultation Program*** may be perfect for you!

On-site Consultation services are separate from enforcement and do not result in penalties or citations. Each year, our on-site consultants respond to approximately 30,000 requests from businesses looking to improve worker safety and health. At your request, a consultant from a state agency or university will visit your workplace to help you identify hazards and make recommendations on possible solutions.

Benefits

Our consultants are experts in identifying workplace hazards and making recommendations to eliminate these hazards with the goal of improving workplace safety and health.

Businesses have benefited from OSHA's On-site Consultation Program by:

- Reducing worker injury and illness rates;
- Decreasing workers' compensation costs;
- Improving worker morale;
- Increasing productivity;
- Recognizing and removing hazards from your workplace; and
- Improving safety and health management systems.

What Is a Consultation Visit and How Does it Work?

A consultation visit is a voluntary activity conducted at the request of an employer. A telephone call, email message, or request via the OSHA Consultation Program website can initiate the visit. The employer's only obligation is to correct any "serious," unsafe or unhealthful working conditions discovered by the consultant within a reasonable time frame.

- **Request for Services.** The consultant discusses the employer's specific needs and sets a date for a visit that is convenient to both the employer and consultant.
- **Initial Meeting.** The consultant arrives at the worksite for the scheduled visit and conducts an opening conference with the employer and employee representative to explain the consultant's role and the obligations of the employer.
- **Walk-through.** Together, the employer, employee representative, and the consultant examine conditions in the workplace and the consultant evaluates potential hazards, physical work practices and the employer's safety and health management program.
- **Closing Conference and Follow-up.** The consultant reviews detailed findings with the employer and employee representative in a closing conference. The employer will learn not only what improvements are needed but also what is being done right, as well. Following the closing conference, the consultant sends the employer a detailed written report explaining the findings and confirming any abatement schedules.
- **Correcting Hazards.** When a situation is determined as a "serious" hazard, the consultant will assist the employer to develop a specific plan to correct the hazard within a reasonable time frame. In rare instances, where the consultant finds an "imminent danger" situation during the walk-through, the employer must take immediate action to protect workers.

OSHA's Top 10 Most-Cited Standards

The following is OSHA's top 10 most-cited standards violations for fiscal year 2016, as reported October 11, 2016.

1 FALL PROTECTION*

STANDARD: 1926.501 TOTAL VIOLATIONS: 6,906 FISCAL 2015 RANKING: 1 (7,401 violations)

This standard outlines where fall protection is required, which systems are appropriate for given situations, the proper construction and installation of safety systems, and the proper supervision of employees to prevent falls. It is designed to protect employees on walking/working surfaces (horizontal or vertical) with an unprotected side or edge above 6 feet.

2 HAZARD COMMUNICATION STANDARD

STANDARD: 1910.1200 TOTAL VIOLATIONS: 5,665 FISCAL 2015 RANKING: 2 (5,681 violations)

This standard addresses chemical hazards — both chemicals produced in, and those imported into, the workplace. It also governs the communication of those hazards to workers. December 1, 2013 was the first of the phase-in dates required by the revised Standard.**

3 SCAFFOLDING*

STANDARD: 1926.451 TOTAL VIOLATIONS: 3,900 FISCAL 2015 RANKING: 3 (4,681 violations)

This standard covers general safety requirements for scaffolding, which should be designed by a qualified person and constructed and loaded in accordance with that design. Employers must protect construction workers from falls and falling objects while working on or near scaffolding at heights of 10 feet or higher.

4 RESPIRATORY PROTECTION

STANDARD: 1910.134 TOTAL VIOLATIONS: 3,573 FISCAL 2015 RANKING: 4 (3,626 violations)

This standard directs employers in establishing or maintaining a respiratory protection program. It lists requirements for program administration; worksite-specific procedures; respirator selection; employee training; fit testing; medical evaluation; respirator use; and respirator cleaning, maintenance and repair.

5 LOCKOUT/TAGOUT

STANDARD: 1910.147 TOTAL VIOLATIONS: 3,402 FISCAL 2015 RANKING: 5 (2,308 violations)

This standard outlines minimum performance requirements for the control of hazardous energy during service and maintenance of machines and equipment.

6 POWERED INDUSTRIAL TRUCKS

STANDARD: 1910.178 TOTAL VIOLATIONS: 2,855 FISCAL 2015 RANKING: 6 (3,004 violations)

This standard covers the design, maintenance and operation of powered industrial trucks, including forklifts and motorized hand trucks. It also covers operator training requirements.

7 LADDERS*

STANDARD: 1926.1053 TOTAL VIOLATIONS: 2,625 FISCAL 2015 RANKING: 8 (2,732 violations)

This standard covers general requirements for all ladders.

8 MACHINE GUARDING

STANDARD: 1910.212 TOTAL VIOLATIONS: 2,448 FISCAL 2015 RANKING: 9 (2,540 violations)

This standard covers guarding of machinery to protect operators and other employees from hazards, including those created by point of operation, ingoing nip points, rotating parts, flying chips and sparks.

9 ELECTRICAL, WIRING METHODS

STANDARD: 1910.305 TOTAL VIOLATIONS: 1,937 FISCAL 2015 RANKING: 8 (2,624 violations)

This standard covers the grounding of electrical equipment, wiring and insulation. It includes temporary wiring and splicing, such as flexible cords and cables.

10 ELECTRICAL, GENERAL REQUIREMENTS

STANDARD: 1910.303 TOTAL VIOLATIONS: 1,704 FISCAL 2015 RANKING: 10 (2,181 violations)

This standard covers general safety requirements for designing electrical systems.

* Indicates Construction standards

** Phase-in date requirements under the revised Hazard Communication Standard (HCS)

Effective Completion Date	Requirement(s)	Who
December 1, 2013	Train employees on the new label elements and safety data sheet (SDS) format.	Employers
June 1, 2015 December 1, 2015	Compliance with all modified provisions of this final rule, except: The Distributor shall not ship containers labeled by the chemical manufacturer or importer unless it is a GHS label.	Chemical manufacturers, importers, distributors and employers
June 1, 2016	Update alternative workplace labeling and hazard communication program as necessary, and provide additional employee training for newly identified physical or health hazards.	Employers
Transition Period to the effective completion dates.	May comply with either 29 CFR §1910.1200 (the final standard), or the current standard, or both.	Chemical manufacturers, importers, distributors, and employers

Employer Rights and Responsibilities

OSHA® Occupational Safety and Health Administration

www.osha.gov

OSHA®

www.osha.gov

Occupational Safety and Health Act of 1970

"To assure safe and healthful working conditions for working men and women; by authorizing enforcement of the standards developed under the Act; by assisting and encouraging the States in their efforts to assure safe and healthful working conditions; by providing for research, information, education, and training in the field of occupational safety and health..."

This informational booklet provides a general overview of employer rights and responsibilities following a Federal OSHA inspection. It does not alter or determine compliance responsibilities in OSHA standards or the *Occupational Safety and Health Act of 1970.* Because interpretations and enforcement policy may change over time, you should consult current OSHA administrative interpretations and decisions by the Occupational Safety and Health Review Commission and the courts for additional guidance on OSHA compliance requirements.

This information is available to sensory-impaired individuals upon request. Voice phone: (202) 693-1999; teletypewriter (TTY) number: 1-877-889-5627.

OSHA® www.osha.gov

OSHA® www.osha.gov

After a Federal OSHA Inspection

This pamphlet contains important information regarding employer rights and responsibilities following a Federal Occupational Safety and Health Administration (OSHA) inspection under the *Occupational Safety and Health Act of 1970* (OSH Act), as amended. Under the OSH Act, employers have the responsibility to provide a safe workplace.

An OSHA compliance safety and health officer (CSHO) conducts an inspection of your workplace, in accordance with the OSH Act. After the inspection, the CSHO reports the findings to the OSHA area director who evaluates them. If a violation exists, OSHA will issue you a **Citation and Notification of Penalty** detailing the exact nature of the violation(s) and any associated penalties. A citation informs you of the alleged violation, sets a proposed time period within which to correct the violation, and proposes the appropriate dollar penalties.

The information in this booklet can and should be used as a discussion guide during your closing conference with the CSHO. For each apparent violation found during the inspection, the compliance officer has discussed or will discuss the following with you:

- Nature of the violation;
- Possible abatement measures you may take to correct the violative condition;
- Possible abatement dates you may be required to meet; and
- Any penalties that the area director may issue.

The CSHO is a highly trained professional who can help you recognize and evaluate hazards as well as suggest appropriate methods of correcting violations. To minimize worker exposure to possible hazardous conditions, abatement efforts should always begin as soon as possible.

Posting Requirements

When you receive a Citation and Notification of Penalty, you must post the citation (or a copy of it) at or near the place where each violation occurred to make employees aware of the hazards to which they may be exposed. The citation must remain posted in a place where employees can see it, for three working days or until the violation is corrected, whichever is longer. (Saturdays, Sundays, and Federal holidays are not counted as working days.) **You must comply with these posting requirements even if you contest the citation. Failure to follow posting requirements is a violation and can result in a penalty.**

The abatement certification documents – such as abatement certifications, abatement plans and progress reports – also must be posted at or near the place where the violation occurred. For moveable equipment found to be in violation and where the posting of violations would be difficult or impractical, the employer has the option to identify the equipment with a "Warning" tag specified in the abatement verification regulation, Title 29 *Code of Federal Regulations* (CFR) 1903.19(i).

Employer Options

As an employer who has been cited, you may take either of the following courses of action:

- If you agree to the Citation and Notification of Penalty, you must correct the condition by the date set in the citation and pay the penalty, if one is proposed.
- If you do not agree, you have 15 working days from the date you receive the citation to contest in writing any or all of the following:
  - – Citation;
  - – Proposed penalty; and/or
  - – Abatement date.

OSHA encourages you to call the local OSHA area office upon receipt of the citations to discuss any concerns. Before deciding to contest the citation, *you may request an informal conference with the OSHA area director within the 15-working-day period to discuss any issues related to the Citation and Notification of Penalty.* (See the following section on Informal Conference and Settlement).

OSHA will inform the affected employee representatives of the informal conference or contest.

Informal Conference and Settlement

Before deciding whether to file a **Notice of Intent to Contest**, you may request an informal conference with the OSHA area director to discuss the Citation and Notification of Penalty. You may use this opportunity to do any of the following:

- Obtain a better explanation of the violations cited;
- Obtain a more complete understanding of the specific standards that apply;
- Negotiate and enter into an informal settlement agreement;
- Discuss ways to correct violations;
- Discuss issues concerning proposed penalties;
- Discuss proposed abatement dates;
- Resolve disputed citations and penalties, (thereby eliminating the need for the more formal procedures associated with litigation before the Occupational Safety and Health Review Commission); and
- Obtain answers to any other questions you may have.

SHA encourages you to take advantage of the opportunity to have an informal conference if you foresee any difficulties in complying with any part of the citation. **Please note, however, that an informal conference must be held within the 15-working-day Notice of Intent to Contest period and will neither extend the 15-working-day contest period nor take the place of the filing of a written notice if you desire to contest.** Employee representative(s) have the right to participate in any informal conference or negotiations between the regional administrator or area director and the employer.

If you agree that the cited violations exist, but you have a valid reason for wishing to extend the abatement date(s), you may discuss this with the area director in an informal conference. He or she may issue an amended citation that changes the abatement date prior to the expiration of the 15-working-day period without your filing a Notice of Intent to Contest.

If you do not contest within 15 working days, your citation will become a final order not subject to review by any court or agency. After this occurs, the OSHA area director may continue to provide you with information and assistance on how to abate the hazards cited in your citation, but may not amend or change any citation or penalty which has become a final order. The area director may only advise you on abatement methods or extend the time you need to abate the violation. (**See Petition for Modification of Abatement**).

Whenever the employer, an affected employee, or employee representative requests an informal conference, **all** the parties shall be afforded the opportunity to participate fully. If either party chooses not to participate in the informal conference, that party forfeits the right to be consulted before decisions are made that affect the citations. If the requesting party objects to the attendance of the other party, OSHA may hold separate informal conferences. During a joint informal conference, separate or private discussions will be permitted if either party requests them. Informal conferences may be held by any means practical.

Types of Violations

The following general information defines the types of violations and explains the actions you may take if you receive a citation as the result of an inspection.

In settling a penalty, OSHA has a policy of reducing penalties for small employers and those acting in good faith.

Willful: A willful violation exists under the OSH Act where an employer has demonstrated either an intentional disregard for the requirements of the OSH Act or a plain indifference to employee safety and health.

Serious: Section 17(k) of the OSH Act provides that "a serious violation shall be deemed to exist in a place of employment if there is a substantial probability that death or serious physical harm could result from a condition which exists, or from one or more practices, means, methods, operations, or processes which have been adopted or are in use, in such place of employment unless the employer did not, and could not with the exercise of reasonable diligence, know of the presence of the violation." OSHA may propose a penalty for each violation.

Other-Than-Serious: This type of violation is cited in situations where the accident/incident or illness that would be most likely to result from a hazardous condition would probably not cause death or serious physical harm, but would have a direct and immediate relationship to the safety and health of employees. OSHA may impose a penalty for each violation.

De Minimis: *De minimis* conditions are those where an employer has implemented a measure different from one specified in a standard, that has no direct or immediate relationship to safety or health. These conditions do not result in citations or penalties.

Failure to Abate: A failure to abate violation exists when a previously cited hazardous condition, practice or non-complying equipment has not been brought into compliance since the prior inspection (i.e., the violation remains continuously uncorrected) and is discovered at a later inspection. If, however, the violation was corrected, but later reoccurs, the subsequent occurrence is a repeated violation. OSHA may impose a penalty for each violation.

Repeated: An employer may be cited for a repeated violation if that employer has been cited previously, within the last five years, for the same or a substantially similar condition or hazard and the citation has become a final order of the Occupational Safety and Health Review Commission (OSHRC). A citation may become a final order by operation of law when an employer does not contest the citation, or pursuant to court decision or settlement. Repeated violations can bring a civil penalty.

For more information on penalty ranges, see www.osha.gov/penalties.

How to Comply

For violations you do not contest, you must: (1) promptly notify the OSHA area director by letter, signed by a member of management, that you have taken the appropriate corrective action within the time set forth in the citation, and (2) pay any penalties itemized.

The notification you send the area director is referred to as **Abatement Certification**. For Other-Than-Serious violations, this may be a signed letter identifying the inspection number and the citation item number and noting that you corrected the violation by the date specified on the citation. For more serious violations (such as Serious, Willful, Repeated, or Failure to Abate), abatement certification requires more detailed proof.

If the employer has abatement questions after the inspection, the area director must ensure that additional information, if available, is provided to the employer as soon as possible.

Employers also can find guidance on abatement verification on OSHA's website at www.osha.gov/Publications/Abate/abate.html.

When the citation permits an extended time for abatement, you must ensure that employees are adequately protected during this time. For example, the citation may require the immediate use of personal protective equipment by employees while engineering controls are being installed. When indicated on the citation, you must also provide OSHA with an abatement plan (steps you will take to protect employees and correct the hazards) and periodic progress reports on your actions.

The penalties itemized on the Citation and Notification of Penalty are payable within 15 working days of receipt of the penalty notice. If, however, you contest the citation or penalty in good faith, OSHA will suspend abatement and payment of penalties for those items contested until the Occupational Safety and Health Review Commission (OSHRC), or a higher court, issues a final order or decision. The OSHRC is an independent agency and is **not** a part of the U.S. Department of Labor. The final order of OSHRC will either uphold, modify, or eliminate

the citations and/or penalties. Penalties for items not contested, however, are still due within 15 working days. (For further details, see the following section on **How to Contest Citations**.)

Payment should be made by check or money order payable to DOL-OSHA. Please indicate on your payment the OSHA number from the upper right-hand corner of your citation and **send it to the OSHA area office listed on the Citation and Notification of Penalty**.

How to Contest Citations

If you wish to contest any portion of your citation, you must submit a Notice of Intent to Contest in writing to the OSHA area office within 15 working days after receipt of the Citation and Notification of Penalty. This applies even if you have stated your disagreement with a citation, penalty, or abatement date during a telephone conversation or an informal conference.

The Notice of Intent to Contest must clearly state what is being contested – the citation, the penalty, the abatement date, or any combination of these factors. In addition, the notice must state whether all the violations on the citation, or just specific violations, are being contested. (For example, "I wish to contest the citation and penalty proposed for items 3 and 4 of the citation issued June 27, 2011").

Your contest must be made in good faith. OSHA will not consider a contest filed solely to avoid your responsibilities for abatement or payment of penalties.

A proper contest of any item suspends your legal obligation to abate and pay until the item contested has been resolved. If you contest only the dates indicated on the citation or if you contest only some items on the citation, you must correct the other items by the abatement date and pay the corresponding penalties within 15 days of notification.

After you file a Notice of Intent to Contest, your case is officially in litigation. If you wish to settle the case, you may contact the OSHA area director who will give you the name of the attorney handling your case for OSHA. All settlements of contested cases are negotiated between you and the attorney according to the rules of procedure of the OSHRC.

The Contest Process

If you file the written Notice of Intent to Contest within the required 15 working days, the OSHA area director forwards your case to the OSHRC. The OSHRC hears employer contests of OSHA citations. They are an independent agency separate from the Department of Labor. The OSHRC assigns the case to an administrative law judge who usually will schedule a hearing in a public place close to your workplace. Both employers and employees have the right to participate in this hearing, which contains all the elements of a trial, including examination and cross-examination of witnesses. You may choose to represent yourself or have an attorney represent you. The administrative law judge may affirm, modify, or eliminate any contested items of the citation or penalty.

As with any other legal procedure, there is an appeals process. Once the administrative law judge has ruled, any party to the case may request a further review by the full OSHRC. In addition, any of the three commissioners may, on his or her own motion, bring the case before the entire OSHRC for review. The OSHRC's ruling, in turn, may be appealed to the Federal circuit court in which the case arose or for the Federal circuit where the employer has his or her principal office.

For more information, write to:

U.S. Occupational Safety and Health
Review Commission
1120 20th Street, NW, 9th Floor
Washington, DC 20036
Phone: 202-606-5400 Fax: 202-606-5050
www.oshrc.gov

Petition for Modification of Abatement

OSHA assigns abatement dates on the basis of the best information available when issuing the citation. If you are unable to meet an abatement date because of uncontrollable events or other circumstances, and the 15-working-day contest period has expired, you may file a **Petition for Modification of Abatement** (PMA) with the OSHA area director.

The petition must be in writing and must be submitted as soon as possible, **but no later than one working day after the abatement date.** To show clearly that you have made a good-faith effort to comply, the PMA must include all of the following information before OSHA considers it:

- Steps you have taken to achieve compliance, and dates they were taken;
- Additional time you need to comply;
- Why you need additional time;
- Interim steps you are taking to safeguard your workers against the cited hazard(s) until the abatement; and
- A certification that the petition has been posted, the date of posting and, when appropriate, a statement that the petition has

been furnished to an authorized representative of the affected employees. The petition must remain posted for 10 working days, during which employees may file an objection.

The OSHA area director may grant or oppose a PMA. If it is opposed, it automatically becomes a contested case before the OSHRC. If a PMA is granted, OSHA may conduct a monitoring inspection to ensure that conditions are as they have been described and that adequate progress has been made toward abatement. The OSHA area office may provide additional information on PMAs.

What Workers Can Do

Employees or their authorized representatives may contest any or all of the abatement dates set for violations if they believe them to be unreasonable. A written Notice of Intent to Contest must be filed with the OSHA area director within 15 working days after the employer receives the citation.

The filing of an employee contest does not suspend the employer's obligation to abate.

Employees also have the right to object to a PMA. Such objections must be in writing and must be sent to the area office within 10 days of service or posting. OSHA will not make a decision regarding the PMA until the Review Commission resolves the issue.

Follow-up Inspections and Failure to Abate

If you receive a citation, a follow-up inspection may be conducted to verify that you have done the following:

- Posted the citation as required,
- Corrected the violations as required in the citation, and/or

13

- Protected employees adequately and made appropriate progress in correcting hazards during multistep or lengthy abatement periods.

In addition to providing for penalties for failure-to-post citations and failure-to-abate violations, the OSH Act clearly states that you have a **continuing responsibility** to comply with the OSH Act and assure your employees safe and healthful working conditions. OSHA will cite any new violations discovered during a follow-up inspection.

Employer Responsibilities

Employers have the responsibility to provide a safe workplace. Employers MUST provide their employees with a workplace that does not have serious hazards and must follow all OSHA safety and health standards. Employers must find and correct safety and health problems.

Employers MUST also:

- Prominently display the official OSHA *Job Safety and Health – It's the Law* poster that describes rights and responsibilities under the OSH Act. **This poster is free and can be downloaded from www.osha.gov**.
- Inform workers about chemical hazards through training, labels, alarms, color-coded systems, chemical information sheets and other methods.
- Provide safety training to workers in a language and vocabulary they can understand.
- Keep accurate records of work-related injuries and illnesses.
- Perform tests in the workplace, such as air sampling, required by some OSHA standards.
- Provide required personal protective equipment at no cost to workers.*
- Provide hearing exams or other medical tests required by OSHA standards.
- Post OSHA citations and injury and illness data where workers can see them.

14

OSHA® www.osha.gov

- Notify OSHA within 8 hours of a workplace fatality or within 24 hours of any work-related inpatient hospitalization, amputation or loss of an eye (1-800-321-OSHA [6742]).
- Not retaliate against workers for using their rights under the law, including their right to report a work-related injury or illness.

* Employers must pay for most types of required personal protective equipment.

Worker Retaliation

Section 11(c) of the OSH Act prohibits employers from discharging or otherwise retaliating against an employee who has exercised any right under this law, including the right to make safety and health complaints or to request an OSHA inspection. OSHA will investigate complaints from employees who believe they have been retaliated against. If the investigation discloses probable violations of worker rights, court action may follow.

Employees who believe they have been retaliated against must file their complaints with OSHA within **30 calendar days** from the date the retaliatory decision has been both made and communicated to the worker. **No form is needed, but workers must call OSHA within 30 days of the alleged retaliation** (at 1-800-321-OSHA [6742]). In states with OSHA-approved state programs, an employee who believes he/she has been retaliated against under Section 11(c) of the OSH Act is entitled to file a complaint under both state and federal procedures.

Providing False Information

All information employers report to OSHA must be accurate and truthful. Providing false information on efforts to abate cited conditions or in required records is punishable under the OSH Act.

OSHA Assistance, Services and Programs

OSHA has a great deal of information to assist employers in complying with their responsibilities under OSHA law. Several OSHA programs and services can help employers identify and correct job hazards, as well as improve their safety and health program.

Establishing a Safety and Health Program

The key to a safe and healthful work environment is a comprehensive safety and health program.

Safety and health programs are systems that can substantially reduce the number and severity of workplace injuries and illnesses, while reducing costs to employers. Thousands of employers across the United States are already using these programs, and OSHA believes that all employers can and should do the same. Thirty-four states have requirements or voluntary guidelines for safety and health programs. Most successful safety and health programs are based on a common set of key elements. These include management leadership, worker participation, hazard identification, hazard prevention and control, education and training, and program evaluation and improvement. Visit OSHA's Recommended Practices for Safety and Health Programs web page at www.osha.gov/shpguidelines for more information.

Compliance Assistance Specialists

OSHA has compliance assistance specialists throughout the nation located in most OSHA offices. Compliance assistance specialists can provide information to employers and workers about OSHA standards, short educational programs on specific hazards or OSHA rights and responsibilities, and information on additional compliance assistance resources. For more details, visit www.osha.gov/dcsp/compliance_assistance/cas.html or call 1-800-321-OSHA (6742) to contact your local OSHA office.

Free On-site Safety and Health Consultation Services for Small Business

OSHA's On-site Consultation Program offers free and confidential advice to small and medium-sized businesses in all states across the country, with priority given to high-hazard worksites. Each year, responding to requests from small employers looking to create or improve their safety and health management programs, OSHA's On-site Consultation Program conducts over 29,000 visits to small business worksites covering over 1.5 million workers across the nation.

On-site consultation services are separate from enforcement and do not result in penalties or citations. Consultants from state agencies or universities work with employers to identify workplace hazards, provide advice on compliance with OSHA standards, and assist in establishing safety and health management programs.

For more information, to find the local On-site Consultation office in your state, or to request a brochure on Consultation Services, visit www.osha.gov/consultation, or call 1-800-321-OSHA (6742).

Under the consultation program, certain exemplary employers may request participation in OSHA's **Safety and Health Achievement Recognition Program (SHARP)**. Eligibility for participation includes, but is not limited to, receiving a full-service, comprehensive consultation visit, correcting all identified hazards and developing an effective safety and health management program. Worksites that receive SHARP recognition are exempt from programmed inspections during the period that the SHARP certification is valid.

Cooperative Programs

OSHA offers cooperative programs under which businesses, labor groups and other organizations can work cooperatively with OSHA. To find out more about any of the following programs, visit www.osha.gov/cooperativeprograms.

Strategic Partnerships and Alliances

The OSHA Strategic Partnerships (OSP) provide the opportunity for OSHA to partner with employers, workers, professional or trade associations, labor organizations, and/or other interested stakeholders. OSHA Partnerships are formalized through unique agreements designed to encourage, assist, and recognize partner efforts to eliminate serious hazards and achieve model workplace safety and health practices. Through the Alliance Program, OSHA works with groups committed to worker safety and health to prevent workplace fatalities, injuries and illnesses by developing compliance assistance tools and resources to share with workers and employers, and educate workers and employers about their rights and responsibilities.

Voluntary Protection Programs (VPP)

The VPP recognize employers and workers in private industry and federal agencies who have implemented effective safety and health management programs and maintain injury and illness rates below the national average for their respective industries. In VPP, management, labor, and OSHA work cooperatively and proactively to prevent fatalities, injuries, and illnesses through a system focused on: hazard prevention and control, worksite analysis, training, and management commitment and worker involvement.

Occupational Safety and Health Training

The OSHA Training Institute partners with 27 OSHA Training Institute Education Centers at 42 locations throughout the United States to deliver courses on OSHA standards and occupational safety and health topics to thousands of students a year. For more information on training courses, visit www.osha.gov/otiec.

OSHA Educational Materials

OSHA has many types of educational materials in English, Spanish, Vietnamese and other languages available in print or online. These include:

- Brochures/booklets;
- Fact Sheets;
- Guidance documents that provide detailed examinations of specific safety and health issues;
- Online Safety and Health Topics pages;
- Posters;
- Small, laminated QuickCards™ that provide brief safety and health information; and
- *QuickTakes*, OSHA's free, twice-monthly online newsletter with the latest news about OSHA initiatives and products to assist employers and workers in finding and preventing workplace hazards. To sign up for *QuickTakes* visit www.osha.gov/quicktakes.

To view materials available online or for a listing of free publications, visit www.osha.gov/publications. You can also call 1-800-321-OSHA (6742) to order publications.

Select OSHA publications are available in e-Book format. OSHA e-Books are designed to increase readability on smartphones, tablets and other mobile devices. For access, go to www.osha.gov/ebooks.

OSHA's web site also has information on job hazards and injury and illness prevention for employers and workers. To learn more about OSHA's safety and health resources online, visit www.osha.gov or www.osha.gov/html/a-z-index.html.

NIOSH Health Hazard Evaluation Program

Getting Help with Health Hazards

The National Institute for Occupational Safety and Health (NIOSH) is a federal agency that conducts scientific and medical research on workers' safety and health. At no cost to employers or workers, NIOSH can help identify health hazards and recommend ways to reduce or eliminate those hazards in the workplace through its Health Hazard Evaluation (HHE) Program.

Workers, union representatives and employers can request a NIOSH HHE. An HHE is often requested when there is a higher than expected rate of a disease or injury in a group of workers. These situations may be the result of an unknown cause, a new hazard, or a mixture of sources. To request a NIOSH Health Hazard Evaluation go to www.cdc.gov/niosh/hhe/request.html. To find out more, in English or Spanish, about the Health Hazard Evaluation Program:

E-mail HHERequestHelp@cdc.gov or call 800-CDC-INFO (800-232-4636).

OSHA Job Safety and Health Poster

The OSHA Job Safety and Health: It's the Law poster (OSHA 3165; OSHA 3167 - Spanish) is available for free from the OSHA Office of Publications. Employers do not need to replace previous versions of the poster, however, all covered employers are required to display and keep displayed, a poster prepared by the Department of Labor* informing employees of the protections of the Occupational Safety and Health Act P.L. 91-596, December 29, 1970 and its amendments. (* Federal Government Agencies must use the Federal Agency Poster.) Actual poster size is 8½ " x 14".

These posters must be displayed in a conspicuous place where employees and applicants for employment can see them.

U.S. Department of Labor

OSHA® Occupational Safety and Health Administration

Job Safety and Health

IT'S THE LAW!

All workers have the right to:

- A safe workplace.
- Raise a safety or health concern with your employer or OSHA, or report a work-related injury or illness, without being retaliated against.
- Receive information and training on job hazards, including all hazardous substances in your workplace.
- Request an OSHA inspection of your workplace if you believe here are unsafe or unhealthy conditions. OSHA will keep your name confidential. You have the right to have a representative contact OSHA on your behalf.
- Participate (or have your representative participate in an OSHA inspection and speak in private to the inspector.
- File a complaint with OSHA within 30 days (by phone, online or by mail) if you have been retaliated against for using your rights.
- See any OSHA citations issued to your employer.
- Request copies of your medical records, test that measure hazards in the workplace, and the workplace injury illness log.

This poster is available free from OSHA.

Employers must:

- Provide employees a workplace free from recognized hazards. It is illegal to retaliate against an employee for using any of their rights under the law, including raising a health and safety concern with you or with OSHA, or reporting a work-related injury or illness.
- Comply with all applicable OSHA standards.
- Report to OSHA all work-related fatalities within 8 hours, and all inpatient hospitalizations, amputations and losses of an eye within 24 hours.
- Provide required training to all workers in a language and vocabulary they can understand.
- Prominently display this poster in the workplace.
- Post OSHA citations at or near the place of the alleged violations.

FREE ASSISTANCE to identify and correct hazards is available to small and medium-sized employers, without citation or penalty, through OSHA-supported consultation programs in every state.

Contact OSHA. We can help.

1-800-321-OSHA (6742) • TTY 1-877-889-5627 • www.osha.gov

OSHA Job Safety and Health Poster — Spanish

You can DOWNLOAD the poster(s) (3165 for English; 3167 for Spanish) from OSHA (http://osha.gov/pls/oshaweb/searchresults.relevance?p_text=posters&p_osha_filter=PUB_STATIC&p_logger=1). If you would prefer to obtain a pre-printed copy of this poster, you may do so by submitting your order through the Online Publications Order Form (http://www.osha.gov/pls/publications/publication.html). Simply select Publication Number(s) from the list. Actual poster size is 8½" x 14".

These posters must be displayed in a conspicuous place where employees and applicants for employment can see them.

Departamento de Trabajo de los EE. UU.

OSHA®
Administración de Seguridad y Salud Ocupacional

Seguridad y Salud en el Trabajo

¡ES LA LEY!

Todos los trabajadores tienen el derecho a:

- Un lugar de trabajo seguro.
- Decir algo a su empleador o la OSHA sobre preocupaciones de suguridad o salud, o reportar una lesión o enfermedidad en el trabajo sin sufrir represalias.
- Recibir información y entrenamiento sobre los peligros del trabajo, incluyendo sustancias toxicas en su sitio de trabajo.
- Pedirle a la OSHA inspeccionar su lugar de trabajo si usted cree que hay condiciones peligrosas o insalubres. Su inforaciób es confidencial. Algún representante suyo puede comunicarse con OSHA a su nombre.
- Participar (osu representante puede participar) en la inspección de OSHA y hablar en provado con el ispector.
- Presentar un queja con la OSHA dentro de 30 dias (por teléfono, por internet, o por correo) si usted ha sufrido represalias por ejercer sus derechos.
- Ver cualquieras citaciones de la OSHA emtidas a su empleador.
- Pedir copias de sus registros médicos, pruebas que miden los peligros en el trabajo, relacionadas con el trabajo.

Este cartel está disponible de la OSHA para gratis.

Los empleadores deben:

- Proveer a los trabajadores un lugar de trabajo libre de peligros reconocidos. Es ilegal discriminar contra un empleado quien ha ejercido sus derechos bajo la ley, incluyendo hablando sobre preocupaciones de seguriday o salud a used o con la OSHA, o por reportar una lesión o enfermedad relacionada con eltragajo.
- Cumplir con todos las normas aplicables de la OSHA.
- Reportar a la OSHA todas las fatalidades relacionadas con el trabajo dentro de 8 horas, y todas hospitalizaciones, amputaciones y perdidos de un ojo dentro de 24 horas.
- Proporcionar el entrenamiento requerido a todos los trabajadores en un idioma y vocabulario que pueden entender.
- Mostrar claramente este cartel en el lugar de trabajo.
- Mostrar las citaciones de la OSHA acerca del lugar de la violación alegada.

Los empleadores de tamaño pequeño y mediano pueden recibir ASISTENCIA GRATIS para identificar y coregir los peligros sin citatión o multa, a través de los programas de consultación apoyados por la OSHA en cada estado.

Llame OSHA. Podemos ayudar.

1-800-321-OSHA (6742) • TTY 1-877-889-5627 • www.osha.gov/espanol

Multi–Employer Citation Policy

DIRECTIVE NUMBER: CPL 2-0.124

EFFECTIVE DATE: December 10, 1999

SUBJECT: Multi-Employer Citation Policy

ABSTRACT

Purpose:	To Clarify the Agency's multi-employer citation policy
Scope:	OSHA-wide
References:	OSHA Instruction CPL 2.103 (the FIRM)
Suspensions:	Chapter III, Paragraph C. 6. of the FIRM is suspended and replaced by this directive
State Impact:	This Instruction describes a Federal Program Change. Notification of State intent is required, but adoption is not.
Action Offices:	National, Regional, and Area Offices
Originating Office:	Directorate of Compliance Programs
Contact:	Carl Sall (202) 693-2345 Directorate of Construction N3468 FPB 200 Constitution Ave., NW Washington, DC 20210

By and Under the Authority of
R. Davis Layne
Deputy Assistant Secretary, OSHA

TABLE OF CONTENTS

I. Purpose. This Directive clarifies the Agency's multi-employer citation policy and suspends Chapter III. C. 6. of OSHA's Field Inspection Reference Manual (FIRM).

II. Scope. OSHA-Wide

III. Suspension. Chapter III. Paragraph C. 6. of the FIRM (CPL 2.103) is suspended and replaced by this Directive.

IV. References. OSHA Instructions:

- CPL 02-00.103; OSHA Field Inspection Reference Manual (FIRM), September 26, 1994.
- ADM 08-0.1C, OSHA Electronic Directive System, December 19,1997.

V. Action Information

A. Responsible Office. Directorate of Construction

B. Action Offices. National, Regional and Area Offices

C. Information Offices. State Plan Offices, Consultation Project Offices

VI. Federal Program Change. This Directive describes a Federal Program Change for which State adoption is not required. However, the States shall respond via the two-way memorandum to the Regional Office as soon as the State's intent regarding the multi-employer citation policy is known, but no later than 60 calendar days after the date of transmittal from the Directorate of Federal-State Operations.

VII. Force and Effect of Revised Policy. The revised policy provided in this Directive is in full force and effect from the date of its issuance. It is an official Agency policy to be implemented OSHA-wide.

VIII. Changes in Web Version of FIRM. A note will be included at appropriate places in the FIRM as it appears on the Web indicating the suspension of Chapter III paragraph 6. C. and its replacement by this Directive, and a hypertext link will be provided connecting viewers with this Directive.

IX. Background. OSHA's Field Inspection Reference Manual (FIRM) of September 26, 1994 (CPL 2.103), states at Chapter III, paragraph 6. C., the Agency's citation policy for multi-employer worksites. The Agency has determined that this policy needs clarification. This directive describes the revised policy.

A. Continuation of Basic Policy. This revision continues OSHA's existing policy for issuing citations on multi-employer worksites. However, it gives clearer and more detailed guidance than did the earlier description of the policy in the FIRM, including new examples explaining when citations should and should not be issued to exposing, creating, correcting, and controlling employers. These examples, which address common situations and provide general policy guidance, are not intended to be exclusive. In all cases, the decision on whether to issue citations should be based on all of the relevant facts revealed by the inspection or investigation.

B. No Changes in Employer Duties. This revision neither imposes new duties on employers nor detracts from their existing duties under the OSH Act. Those duties continue to arise from the employers' statutory duty to comply with OSHA standards and their duty to exercise reasonable diligence to determine whether violations of those standards exist.

X. Multi-employer Worksite Policy. The following is the multi-employer citation policy:

A. Multi-employer Worksites

On multi-employer worksites (in all industry sectors), more than one employer may be citable for a hazardous condition that violates an OSHA standard. A two-step process must be followed in determining whether more than one employer is to be cited.

1. **Step One**. The first step is to determine whether the employer is a creating, exposing, correcting, or controlling employer. The definitions in paragraphs (B) - (E) below explain and give examples of each. Remember that an employer may have multiple roles (see paragraph H). Once you determine the role of the employer, go to Step Two to determine if a citation is appropriate (**NOTE:** only exposing employers can be cited for General Duty Clause violations).

2. **Step Two**. If the employer falls into one of these categories, it has obligations with respect to OSHA requirements. Step Two is to determine if the employer's actions were sufficient to meet those obligations. The extent of the actions required of employers varies based on which category applies. Note that the extent of the measures that a controlling employer must take to satisfy its duty to exercise reasonable care to prevent and detect violations is less than what is required of an employer with respect to protecting its own employees.

B. The Creating Employer

1. **Step 1**: **Definition**: The employer that caused a hazardous condition that violates an OSHA standard.

2. **Step 2**: **Actions Taken**: Employers must not create violative conditions. An employer that does so is citable even if the only employees exposed are those of other employers at the site.

   a. **Example 1**: Employer Host operates a factory. It contracts with Company S to service machinery. Host fails to cover drums of a chemical despite S's repeated requests that it do so. This results in airborne levels of the chemical that exceed the Permissible Exposure Limit.

   Analysis: **Step 1**: Host is a creating employer because it caused employees of S to be exposed to the air contaminant above the PEL. **Step 2**: Host failed to implement measures to prevent the accumulation of the air contaminant. It could have met its OSHA obligation by implementing the simple engineering control of covering the drums. Having failed to implement a feasible engineering control to meet the PEL, Host is citable for the hazard.

   b. **Example 2**: Employer M hoists materials onto Floor 8, damaging perimeter guardrails. Neither its own employees nor employees of other employers are exposed to the hazard. It takes effective steps to keep all employees, including those of other employers, away from the unprotected edge and informs the controlling employer of the problem. Employer M lacks authority to fix the guardrails itself.

   Analysis: **Step 1**: Employer M is a creating employer because it caused a hazardous condition by damaging the guardrails. **Step 2**: While it lacked the authority to fix the guardrails, it took immediate and effective steps to keep all employees away from the hazard and notified the controlling employer of the hazard. Employer M is not citable since it took effective measures to prevent employee exposure to the fall hazard.

C. The Exposing Employer

1. **Step 1: Definition**: An employer whose own employees are exposed to the hazard. See Chapter III, section (C)(1)(b) for a discussion of what constitutes exposure.

2. **Step 2**: **Actions Taken**: If the exposing employer created the violation, it is citable for the violation as a creating employer. If the violation was created by another employer, the exposing employer is citable if it (1) knew of the hazardous condition or failed to exercise reasonable diligence to discover the condition, and (2) failed to take steps consistent with its authority to protect is employees. If the exposing employer has authority to correct the hazard, it must do so. If the exposing employer lacks the authority to correct the hazard, it is citable if it fails to do each of the following: (1) ask the creating and/or controlling employer to correct the hazard; (2) inform its employees of the hazard; and (3) take reasonable alternative protective measures. In extreme circumstances (e.g., imminent danger situations), the exposing employer is citable for failing to remove its employees from the job to avoid the hazard.

   a. **Example 3**: Employer Sub S is responsible for inspecting and cleaning a work area in Plant P around a large, permanent hole at the end of each day. An OSHA standard requires guardrails. There are no guardrails around the hole and Sub S employees do not use personal fall protection, although it would be feasible to do so. Sub S has no authority to install guardrails. However, it did ask Employer P, which operates the plant, to install them. P refused to install guardrails.

   Analysis: **Step 1**: Sub S is an exposing employer because its employees are exposed to the fall hazard. **Step 2**: While Sub S has no authority to install guardrails, it is required to comply with OSHA requirements to the extent feasible. It must take steps to protect its employees and ask the employer who controls the hazard - Employer P - to correct it. Although Sub S asked for guardrails, since the hazard was not corrected, Sub S was responsible for taking reasonable alternative protective steps, such as providing personal fall protection. Because that was not done, Sub S is citable for the violation.

   b. **Example 4**: Unprotected rebar on either side of an access ramp presents an impalement hazard. Sub E, an electrical subcontractor, does not have the authority to cover the rebar. However, several times Sub E asked the general contractor, Employer GC, to cover the rebar. In the meantime, Sub E instructed its employees to use a different access route that avoided most of the uncovered rebar and required them to keep as far from the rebar as possible.

   Analysis: **Step 1**: Since Sub E employees were still exposed to some unprotected rebar, Sub E is an exposing employer. **Step 2**: Sub E made a good faith effort to get the general contractor to correct the hazard and took feasible measures within its control to protect its employees. Sub E is not citable for the rebar hazard.

D. The Correcting Employer

1. **Step 1: Definition**: An employer who is engaged in a common undertaking, on the same worksite, as the exposing employer and is responsible for correcting a hazard. This usually occurs where an employer is given the responsibility of installing and/or maintaining particular safety/health equipment or devices.

2. **Step 2: Actions taken**: The correcting employer must exercise reasonable care in preventing and discovering violations and meet its obligations of correcting the hazard.

   a. **Example 5**: Employer C, a carpentry contractor, is hired to erect and maintain guardrails throughout a large, 15-story project. Work is proceeding on all floors. C inspects all floors in the morning and again in the afternoon each day. It also inspects areas where material is delivered to the perimeter once the material vendor is finished delivering material to that area. Other subcontractors are required to report damaged/missing guardrails to the general contractor, who forwards those reports to C. C repairs damaged guardrails immediately after finding them and immediately after they are reported. On this project few instances of damaged guardrails have occurred other than where material has been delivered. Shortly after the afternoon inspection of Floor 6, workers moving equipment accidentally damage a guardrail in one area. No one tells C of the damage and C has not seen it. An OSHA inspection occurs at the beginning of the next day, prior to the morning inspection of Floor 6. None of C's own employees are exposed to the hazard, but other employees are exposed.

   Analysis: **Step 1**: C is a correcting employer since it is responsible for erecting and maintaining fall protection equipment. **Step 2**: The steps C implemented to discover and correct damaged guardrails were reasonable in light of the amount of activity and size of the project. It exercised reasonable care in preventing and discovering violations; it is not citable for the damaged guardrail since it could not reasonably have known of the violation.

E. **The Controlling Employer**

1. **Step 1: Definition**: An employer who has general supervisory authority over the worksite, including the power to correct safety and health violations itself or require others to correct them. Control can be established by contract or, in the absence of explicit contractual provisions, by the exercise of control in practice. Descriptions and examples of different kinds of controlling employers are given below.

2. **Step 2: Actions Taken**: A controlling employer must exercise reasonable care to prevent and detect violations on the site. The extent of the measures that a controlling employer must implement to satisfy this duty of reasonable care is less than what is required of an employer with respect to protecting its own employees. This means that the controlling employer is not normally required to inspect for hazards as frequently or to have the same level of knowledge of the applicable standards or of trade expertise as the employer it has hired.

3. **Factors Relating to Reasonable Care Standard**. Factors that affect how frequently and closely a controlling employer must inspect to meet its standard of reasonable care include:

   a. The scale of the project;

   b. The nature and pace of the work, including the frequency with which the number or types of hazards change as the work progresses;

   c. How much the controlling employer knows both about the safety history and safety practices of the employer it controls and about that employer's level of expertise;

   d. More frequent inspections are normally needed if the controlling employer knows that the other employer has a history of non-compliance. Greater inspection frequency may also be needed, especially at the beginning of the project, if the controlling employer had never before worked with this other employer and does not know its compliance history; and

   e. Less frequent inspections may be appropriate where the controlling employer sees strong indications that the other employer has implemented effective safety and health efforts. The most important indicator of an effective safety and health effort by the other employer is a consistently high level of compliance. Other indicators include the use of an effective, graduated system of enforcement for non-compliance with safety and health requirements coupled with regular jobsite safety meetings and safety training.

4. **Evaluating Reasonable Care**. In evaluating whether a controlling employer has exercised reasonable care in preventing and discovering violations, consider questions such as whether the controlling employer:

   a. **Control Established by Contract**. In this case, the Employer Has a Specific Contract Right to Control Safety: To be a controlling employer, the employer must itself be able to prevent or correct a violation or to require another employer to prevent or correct the violation. One source of this ability is explicit contract authority. This can take the form of a specific contract right to require another employer to adhere to safety and health requirements and to correct violations the controlling employer discovers.

(1) Example 6: Employer GH contracts with Employer S to do sandblasting at GH's plant. Some of the work is regularly scheduled maintenance and so is general industry work; other parts of the project involve new work and are considered construction. Respiratory protection is required. Further, the contract explicitly requires S to comply with safety and health requirements. Under the contract GH has the right to take various actions against S for failing to meet contract requirements, including the right to have non-compliance corrected by using other workers and back-charging for that work. S is one of two employers under contract with GH at the work site, where a total of five employees work. All work is done within an existing building. The number and types of hazards involved in S's work do not significantly change as the work progresses. Further, GH has worked with S over the course of several years. S provides periodic and other safety and health training and uses a graduated system of enforcement of safety and health rules. S has consistently had a high level of compliance at its previous jobs and at this site. GH monitors S by a combination of weekly inspections, telephone discussions and a weekly review of S's own inspection reports. GH has a system of graduated enforcement that it has applied to S for the few safety and health violations that had been committed by S in the past few years. Further, due to respirator equipment problems S violates respiratory protection requirements two days before GH's next scheduled inspection of S. The next day there is an OSHA inspection. There is no notation of the equipment problems in S's inspection reports to GH and S made no mention of it in its telephone discussions.

Analysis: **Step 1**: GH is a controlling employer because it has general supervisory authority over the worksite, including contractual authority to correct safety and health violations. **Step 2**: GH has taken reasonable steps to try to make sure that S meets safety and health requirements. Its inspection frequency is appropriate in light of the low number of workers at the site, lack of significant changes in the nature of the work and types of hazards involved, GH's knowledge of S's history of compliance and its effective safety and health efforts on this job. GH has exercised reasonable care and is not citable for this condition.

(2) Example 7: Employer GC contracts with Employer P to do painting work. GC has the same contract authority over P as Employer GH had in Example 6. GC has never before worked with P. GC conducts inspections that are sufficiently frequent in light of the factors listed above in (G)(3). Further, during a number of its inspections, GC finds that P has violated fall protection requirements. It points the violations out to P during each inspection but takes no further actions.

Analysis: **Step 1**: GC is a controlling employer since it has general supervisory authority over the site, including a contractual right of control over P. **Step 2**: GC took adequate steps to meet its obligation to discover violations. However, it failed to take reasonable steps to require P to correct hazards since it lacked a graduated system of enforcement. A citation to GC for the fall protection violations is appropriate.

(3) Example 8: Employer GC contracts with Sub E, an electrical subcontractor. GC has full contract authority over Sub E, as in Example 6. Sub E installs an electric panel box exposed to the weather and implements an assured equipment grounding conductor program, as required under the contract. It fails to connect a grounding wire inside the box to one of the outlets. This incomplete ground is not apparent from a visual inspection. Further, GC inspects the site with a frequency appropriate for the site in light of the factors discussed above in (G)(3). It saw the panel box but did not test the outlets to determine if they were all grounded because Sub E represents that it is doing all of the required tests on all receptacles. GC knows that Sub E has implemented an effective safety and health program. From previous experience it also knows Sub E is familiar with the applicable safety requirements and is technically competent. GC had asked Sub E if the electrical equipment is OK for use and was assured that it is.

Analysis: **Step 1**: GC is a controlling employer since it has general supervisory authority over the site, including a contractual right of control over Sub E. **Step 2**: GC exercised reasonable care. It had determined that Sub E had technical expertise, safety knowledge and had implemented safe work practices. It conducted inspections with appropriate frequency. It also made some basic inquiries into the safety of the electrical equipment. Under these circumstances GC was not obligated to test the outlets itself to determine if they were all grounded. It is not citable for the grounding violation.

b. **Control Established by a Combination of Other Contract Rights**: Where there is no explicit contract provision granting the right to control safety, or where the contract says the employer does not have such a right, an employer may still be a controlling employer. The ability of an employer to control safety in this circumstance can result from a combination of contractual rights that, together, give it broad responsibility at the site involving almost all aspects of the job. Its responsibility is broad enough so that its contractual authority necessarily involves safety. The authority to resolve disputes between subcontractors, set schedules and determine construction sequencing are particularly significant because they are likely to affect safety. (**NOTE:** citations should only be issued in this type of case after consulting with the Regional Solicitor's office).

(1) Example 9: Construction manager M is contractually obligated to: set schedules and construction sequencing, require subcontractors to meet contract specifications, negotiate with trades, resolve disputes between subcontractors, direct work and make purchasing decisions, which affect safety. However, the contract states that M does not have a right to require compliance with safety and health requirements. Further, Subcontractor S asks M to alter the schedule so that S would not have to start work until Subcontractor G has completed installing guardrails. M is contractually responsible for deciding whether to approve S's request.

Analysis: **Step 1**: Even though its contract states that M does not have authority over safety, the combination of rights actually given in the contract provides broad responsibility over the site and results in the ability of M to direct actions that necessarily affect safety. For example, M's contractual obligation to determine whether to approve S's request to alter the schedule has direct safety implications. M's decision relates directly to whether S's employees will be protected from a fall hazard. M is a controlling employer. **Step 2**: In this example, if M refused to alter the schedule, it would be citable for the fall hazard violation.

(2) Example 10: Employer ML's contractual authority is limited to reporting on subcontractors' contract compliance to owner/developer O and making contract payments. Although it reports on the extent to which the subcontractors are complying with safety and health infractions to O, ML does not exercise any control over safety at the site.

Analysis: **Step 1**: ML is not a controlling employer because these contractual rights are insufficient to confer control over the subcontractors and ML did not exercise control over safety. Reporting safety and health infractions to another entity does not, by itself (or in combination with these very limited contract rights), constitute an exercise of control over safety. **Step 2**: Since it is not a controlling employer it had no duty under the OSH Act to exercise reasonable care with respect to enforcing the subcontractors' compliance with safety; there is therefore no need to go to Step 2.

c. Architects and Engineers: Architects, engineers, and other entities are controlling employers only if the breadth of their involvement in a construction project is sufficient to bring them within the parameters discussed above.

(1) Example 11: Architect A contracts with owner O to prepare contract drawings and specifications, inspect the work, report to O on contract compliance, and to certify completion of work. A has no authority or means to enforce compliance, no authority to approve/reject work and does not exercise any other authority at the site, although it does call the general contractor's attention to observed hazards noted during its inspections.

Analysis: **Step 1**: A's responsibilities are very limited in light of the numerous other administrative responsibilities necessary to complete the project. It is little more than a supplier of architectural services and conduit of information to O. Its responsibilities are insufficient to confer control over the subcontractors and it did not exercise control over safety. The responsibilities it does have are insufficient to make it a controlling employer. Merely pointing out safety violations did not make it a controlling employer. **NOTE:** In a circumstance such as this it is likely that broad control over the project rests with another entity. **Step 2**: Since A is not a controlling employer it had no duty under the OSH Act to exercise reasonable care with respect to enforcing the subcontractors' compliance with safety; there is therefore no need to go to Step 2.

(2) Example 12: Engineering firm E has the same contract authority and functions as in Example 9.

Analysis: **Step 1**: Under the facts in Example 9, E would be considered a controlling employer. **Step 2**: The same type of analysis described in Example 9 for **Step 2** would apply here to determine if E should be cited.

d. **Control Without Explicit Contractual Authority**. Even where an employer has no explicit contract rights with respect to safety, an employer can still be a controlling employer if, in actual practice, it exercises broad control over subcontractors at the site (see Example 9). **NOTE:** Citations should only be issued in this type of case after consulting with the Regional Solicitor's office.

(1) Example 13: Construction manager MM does not have explicit contractual authority to require subcontractors to comply with safety requirements, nor does it explicitly have broad contractual authority at the site. However, it exercises control over most aspects of the subcontractors' work anyway, including aspects that relate to safety.

Analysis: **Step 1**: MM would be considered a controlling employer since it exercises control over most aspects of the subcontractor's work, including safety aspects. **Step 2**: The same type of analysis on reasonable care described in the examples in (G)(5)(a) would apply to determine if a citation should be issued to this type of controlling employer.

F. **Multiple Roles**

1. A creating, correcting or controlling employer will often also be an exposing employer. Consider whether the employer is an exposing employer before evaluating its status with respect to these other roles.

2. Exposing, creating and controlling employers can also be correcting employers if they are authorized to correct the hazard.

29 CFR PART 1903
Inspections, Citations and Proposed Penalties

Section Contents

1903—Inspections, Citations and Proposed Penalties

Authority: Secs. 8 and 9 of the Occupational Safety and Health Act of 1970 (29 U.S.C. 657, 658); 5 U.S.C. 553; 28 U.S.C. 2461 note (Federal Civil Penalties Inflation Adjustment Act of 1990), as amended by Section 701, Pub. L. 114–74; Secretary of Labor's Order No. 1–2012 (77 FR 3912, Jan. 25, 2012)

§1903.1 Purpose and scope

The Williams-Steiger Occupational Safety and Health Act of 1970 (84 Stat. 1590 et seq., 29 U.S.C. 651 et seq.) requires, in part, that every employer covered under the Act furnish to his employees employment and a place of employment which are free from recognized hazards that are causing or are likely to cause death or serious physical harm to his employees. The Act also requires that employers comply with occupational safety and health standards promulgated under the Act, and that employees comply with standards, rules, regulations and orders issued under the Act which are applicable to their own actions and conduct. The Act authorizes the Department of Labor to conduct inspections, and to issue citations and proposed penalties for alleged violations. The Act, under Section 20(b), also authorizes the Secretary of Health, Education, and Welfare to conduct inspections and to question employers and employees in connection with research and other related activities. The Act contains provisions for adjudication of violations, periods prescribed for the abatement of violations, and proposed penalties by the Occupational Safety and Health Review Commission, if contested by an employer or by an employee or authorized representative of employees, and for judicial review. The purpose of this Part §1903 is to prescribe rules and to set forth general policies for enforcement of the inspection, citation, and proposed penalty provisions of the Act. In situations where this Part §1903 sets forth general enforcement policies rather than substantive or procedural rules, such policies may be modified in specific circumstances where the Secretary or his designee determines that an alternative course of action would better serve the objectives of the Act.

§1903.2 Posting of notice; availability of the Act, regulations and applicable standards

(a)

(a)(1) Each employer shall post and keep posted a notice or notices, to be furnished by the Occupational Safety and Health Administration, U.S. Department of Labor, informing employees of the protections and obligations provided for in the Act, and that for assistance and information, including copies of the Act and of specific safety and health standards, employees should contact the employer or the nearest office of the Department of Labor. Such notice or notices shall be posted by the employer in each establishment in a conspicuous place or places where notices to employees are customarily posted. Each employer shall take steps to insure that such notices are not altered, defaced, or covered by other material.

(a)(2) Where a State has an approved poster informing employees of their protections and obligations as defined in §1902.9 of this chapter, such poster, when posted by employers covered by the State plan, shall constitute compliance with the posting requirements of Section 8(c)(1) of the Act. Employers whose operations are not within the issues covered by the State plan must comply with paragraph (a)(1) of this Section.

(a)(3) Reproductions or facsimiles of such Federal or State posters shall constitute compliance with the posting requirements of Section 8(c)(1) of the Act where such reproductions or facsimiles are at least 8 ½ inches by 14 inches, and the printing size is at least 10 pt. Whenever the size of the poster increases, the size of the print shall also increase accordingly. The caption or heading on the poster shall be in large type, generally not less than 36 pt.

(b) Establishment means a single physical location where business is conducted or where services or industrial operations are performed. (For example: A factory, mill, store, hotel, restaurant, movie theatre, farm, ranch, bank, sales office, warehouse, or central administrative office.) Where distinctly separate activities are performed at a single physical location (such as contract construction activities from the same physical location as a lumber yard), each activity shall be treated as a separate physical establishment, and a separate notice or notices shall be posted in each such establishment, to the extent that such notices have been furnished by the Occupational Safety and Health Administration, U.S. Department of Labor. Where employers are engaged in activities which are physically dispersed, such as agriculture, construction, transportation, communications, and electric, gas and sanitary services, the notice or notices required by this Section shall be posted at the location to which employees report each day. Where employees do not usually work at, or report to, a single establishment, such as longshoremen, traveling salesmen, technicians, engineers, etc., such notice or notices shall be posted at the location from which the employees operate to carry out their activities. In all cases, such notice or notices shall be posted in accordance with the requirements of paragraph (a) of this Section.

(c) Copies of the Act, all regulations published in this chapter and all applicable standards will be available at all Area Offices of the Occupational Safety and Health Administration, U.S. Department of Labor. If an employer has obtained copies of these materials, he shall make them available upon request to any employee or his authorized representative for review in the establishment where the employee is employed on the same day the request is made or at the earliest time mutually convenient to the employee or his authorized representative and the employer.

(d) Any employer failing to comply with the provisions of this Section shall be subject to citation and penalty in accordance with the provisions of §1903.15(d).

§1903.3 Authority for inspection

(a) Compliance Safety and Health Officers of the Department of Labor are authorized to enter without delay and at reasonable times any factory, plant, establishment, construction site, or other area, workplace or environment where work is performed by an employee of an employer; to inspect and investigate during regular working hours and at other reasonable times, and within reasonable limits and in a reasonable manner, any such place of employment, and all pertinent conditions, structures, machines, apparatus, devices, equipment and materials therein; to question privately any employer, owner, operator, agent or employee; and to review records required by the Act and regulations published in this chapter, and other records which are directly related to the purpose of the inspection. Representatives of the Secretary of Health, Education, and Welfare are authorized to make inspections and to question employers and employees in order to carry out the functions of the Secretary of Health, Education, and Welfare under the Act. Inspections conducted by Department of Labor Compliance Safety and Health Officers and representatives of the Secretary of Health, Education, and Welfare under Section 8 of the Act and pursuant to this part 1903 shall not affect the authority of any State to conduct inspections in accordance with agreements and plans under Section 18 of the Act.

(b) Prior to inspecting areas containing information which is classified by an agency of the United States Government in the interest of national security, Compliance Safety and Health Officers shall have obtained the appropriate security clearance.

§1903.4 Objection to inspection

(a) Upon a refusal to permit the Compliance Safety and Health Officer, in exercise of his official duties, to enter without delay and at reasonable times any place of employment or any place therein, to inspect, to review records, or to question any employer, owner, operator, agent, or employee, in accordance with §1903.3 or to permit a representative of employees to accompany the Compliance Safety and Health Officer during the physical inspection of any workplace in accordance with §1903.8, the Safety and Health Officer shall terminate the inspection or confine the inspection to other areas, conditions, structures, machines, apparatus, devices, equipment, materials, records, or interviews concerning which no objection is raised. The Compliance Safety and Health Officer shall endeavor to ascertain the reason for such refusal, and shall immediately report the refusal and the reason therefore to the Area Director. The Area Director shall consult with the Regional Solicitor, who shall take appropriate action, including compulsory process, if necessary.

(b) Compulsory process shall be sought in advance of an attempted inspection or investigation if, in the judgment of the Area Director and the Regional Solicitor, circumstances exist which make such preinspection process desirable or necessary. Some examples of circumstances in which it may be desirable or necessary to seek compulsory process in advance of an attempt to inspect or investigate include (but are not limited to):

(b)(1) When the employer's past practice either implicitly or explicitly puts the Secretary on notice that a warrantless inspection will not be allowed;

(b)(2) When an inspection is scheduled far from the local office and procuring a warrant prior to leaving to conduct the inspection would avoid, in case of refusal of entry, the expenditure of significant time and resources to return to the office, obtain a warrant and return to the worksite;

(b)(3) When an inspection includes the use of special equipment or when the presence of an expert or experts is needed in order to properly conduct the inspection, and procuring a warrant prior to an attempt to inspect would alleviate the difficulties or costs encountered in coordinating the availability of such equipment or expert.

(c) With the approval of the Regional Administrator and the Regional Solicitor, compulsory process may also be obtained by the Area Director or his designee.

(d) For purposes of this Section, the term compulsory process shall mean the institution of any appropriate action, including ex parte application for an inspection warrant or its equivalent. Ex parte inspection warrants shall be the preferred form of compulsory process in all circumstances where compulsory process is relied upon to seek entry to a workplace under this Section.

[45 FR 65923, Oct. 3, 1980]

§1903.5 Entry not a waiver

Any permission to enter, inspect, review records, or question any person, shall not imply or be conditioned upon a waiver of any cause of action, citation, or penalty under the Act. Compliance Safety and Health Officers are not authorized to grant any such waiver.

§1903.6 Advance notice of inspections

(a) Advance notice of inspections may not be given, except in the following situations:

(a)(1) In cases of apparent imminent danger, to enable the employer to abate the danger as quickly as possible;

(a)(2) In circumstances where the inspection can most effectively be conducted after regular business hours or where special preparations are necessary for an inspection;

(a)(3) Where necessary to assure the presence of representatives of the employer and employees or the appropriate personnel needed to aid in the inspection; and

(a)(4) In other circumstances where the Area Director determines that the giving of advance notice would enhance the probability of an effective and thorough inspection.

(b) In the situations described in paragraph (a) of this Section, advance notice of inspections may be given only if authorized by the Area Director, except that in cases of apparent imminent danger, advance notice may be given by the Compliance Safety and Health Officer without such authorization if the Area Director is not immediately available. When advance notice is given, it shall be the employer's responsibility promptly to notify the authorized representative of employees of the inspection, if the identity of such representative is known to the employer. (See §1903.8(b) as to situations where there is no authorized representative of employees.) Upon the request of the employer, the Compliance Safety and Health Officer will inform the authorized representative of employees of the inspection, provided that the employer furnishes the Compliance Safety and Health Officer with the identity of such representative and with such other information as is necessary to enable him promptly to inform such representative of the inspection. An employer who fails to comply with his obligation under this paragraph promptly to inform the authorized representative of employees of the inspection or to furnish such information as is necessary to enable the Compliance Safety and Health Officer promptly to inform such representative of the inspection, may be subject to citation and penalty in accordance with §1903.15(d)(4). Advance notice in any of the situations described in paragraph (a) of this Section shall not be given more than 24 hours before the inspection is scheduled to be conducted, except in apparent imminent danger situations and in other unusual circumstances.

(c) The Act provides in Section 17(f) that any person who gives advance notice of any inspection to be conducted under the Act, without authority from the Secretary or his designees, shall, upon conviction, be punished by fine of not more than $1,000 or by imprisonment for not more than 6 months, or by both.

§1903.7 Conduct of inspections

(a) Subject to the provisions of §1903.3, inspections shall take place at such times and in such places of employment as the Area Director or the Compliance Safety and Health Officer may direct. At the beginning of an inspection, Compliance Safety and Health Officers shall present their credentials to the owner, operator, or agent in charge at the establishment; explain the nature and purpose of the inspection; and indicate generally the scope of the inspection and the records specified in §1903.3 which they wish to review. However, such designation of records shall not preclude access to additional records specified in §1903.3.

(b) Compliance Safety and Health Officers shall have authority to take environmental samples and to take or obtain photographs related to the purpose of the inspection, employ other reasonable investigative techniques, and question privately any employer, owner, operator, agent or employee of an establishment. (See §1903.9 on trade secrets.) As used herein, the term employ other reasonable investigative techniques includes, but is not limited to, the use of devices to measure employee exposures and the attachment of personal sampling equipment such as dosimeters, pumps, badges and other similar devices to employees in order to monitor their exposures.

(c) In taking photographs and samples, Compliance Safety and Health Officers shall take reasonable precautions to insure that such actions with flash, spark-producing, or other equipment would not be hazardous. Compliance Safety and Health Officers shall comply with all employer safety and health rules and practices at the establishment being inspected, and they shall wear and use appropriate protective clothing and equipment.

(d) The conduct of inspections shall be such as to preclude unreasonable disruption of the operations of the employer's establishment.

(e) At the conclusion of an inspection, the Compliance Safety and Health Officer shall confer with the employer or his representative and informally advise him of any apparent safety or health violations disclosed by the inspection. During such conference, the employer shall be afforded an opportunity to bring to the attention of the Compliance Safety and Health Officer any pertinent information regarding conditions in the workplace.

(f) Inspections shall be conducted in accordance with the requirements of this part.

[36 FR 17850, Sept. 14, 1971, as amended at 47 FR 6533, Feb. 12, 1982; 47 FR 55481, Dec. 10, 1982]

§1903.8 Representatives of employers and employees

(a) Compliance Safety and Health Officers shall be in charge of inspections and questioning of persons. A representative of the employer and a representative authorized by his employees shall be given an opportunity to accompany the Compliance Safety and Health Officer during the physical inspection of any workplace for the purpose of aiding such inspection. A Compliance Safety and Health Officer may permit additional employer representatives and additional representatives authorized by employees to accompany him where he determines that such additional representatives will further aid the inspection. A different employer and employee representative may accompany the Compliance Safety and Health Officer during each different phase of an inspection if this will not interfere with the conduct of the inspection.

(b) Compliance Safety and Health Officers shall have authority to resolve all disputes as to who is the representative authorized by the employer and employees for the purpose of this Section. If there is no authorized representative of employees, or if the Compliance Safety and Health Officer is unable to determine with reasonable certainty who is such representative, he shall consult with a reasonable number of employees concerning matters of safety and health in the workplace.

(c) The representative(s) authorized by employees shall be an employee(s) of the employer. However, if in the judgment of the Compliance Safety and Health Officer, good cause has been shown why accompaniment by a third party who is not an employee of the employer (such as an industrial hygienist or a safety engineer) is reasonably necessary to the conduct of an effective and thorough physical inspection of the workplace, such third party may accompany the Compliance Safety and Health Officer during the inspection.

(d) Compliance Safety and Health Officers are authorized to deny the right of accompaniment under this Section to any person whose conduct interferes with a fair and orderly inspection. The right of accompaniment in areas containing trade secrets shall be subject to the provisions of §1903.9(d). With regard to information classified by an agency of the U.S. Government in the interest of national security, only persons authorized to have access to such information may accompany a Compliance Safety and Health Officer in areas containing such information.

§1903.9 Trade secrets

(a) Section 15 of the Act provides: "All information reported to or otherwise obtained by the Secretary or his representative in connection with any inspection or proceeding under this Act which contains or which might reveal a trade secret referred to in Section 1905 of title 18 of the United States Code shall be considered confidential for the purpose of that Section, except that such information may be disclosed to other officers or employees concerned with carrying out this Act or when relevant in any proceeding under this Act. In any such proceeding the Secretary, the Commission, or the court shall issue such orders as may be appropriate to protect the confidentiality of trade secrets." Section 15 of the Act is considered a statute within the meaning of Section 552(b)(3) of title 5 of the United States Code, which exempts from the disclosure requirements matters that are "specifically exempted from disclosure by statute."

(b) Section 1905 of title 18 of the United States Code provides: "Whoever, being an officer or employee of the United States or of any department or agency thereof, publishes, divulges, discloses, or makes known in any manner or to any extent not authorized by law any information coming to him in the course of his employment or official duties or by reason of any examination or investigation made by, or return, report or record made to or filed with, such department or agency or officer or employee thereof, which information concerns or relates to the trade secrets, processes, operations, style of work, or apparatus, or to the identity, confidential statistical data, amount or source of any income, profits, losses, or expenditures of any person, firm, partnership, corporation, or association; or permits any income return or copy thereof or any book containing any abstract or particulars thereof to be seen or examined by any person except as provided by law; shall be fined not more than $1,000, or imprisoned not more than 1 year, or both; and shall be removed from office or employment."

(c) At the commencement of an inspection, the employer may identify areas in the establishment which contain or which might reveal a trade secret. If the Compliance Safety and Health Officer has no clear reason to question such identification, information obtained in such areas, including all negatives and prints of photographs, and environmental samples, shall be labeled "confidential—trade secret" and shall not be disclosed except in accordance with the provisions of Section 15 of the Act.

(d) Upon the request of an employer, any authorized representative of employees under §1903.8 in an area containing trade secrets shall be an employee in that area or an employee authorized by the employer to enter that area. Where there is no such representative or employee, the Compliance Safety and Health Officer shall consult with a reasonable number of employees who work in that area concerning matters of safety and health.

§1903.10 [OI] Consultation with employees

Compliance Safety and Health Officers may consult with employees concerning matters of occupational safety and health to the extent they deem necessary for the conduct of an effective and thorough inspection. During the course of an inspection, any employee shall be afforded an opportunity to bring any violation of the Act which he has reason to believe exists in the workplace to the attention of the Compliance Safety and Health Officer.

§1903.11 [OI] Complaints by employees

(a) [OI] Any employee or representative of employees who believe that a violation of the Act exists in any workplace where such employee is employed may request an inspection of such workplace by giving notice of the alleged violation to the Area Director or to a Compliance Safety and Health Officer. Any such notice shall be reduced to writing, shall set forth with reasonable particularity the grounds for the notice, and shall be signed by the employee or representative of employees. A copy shall be provided the employer or his agent by the Area Director or Compliance Safety and Health Officer no later than at the time of inspection, except that, upon the request of the person giving such notice, his name and the names of individual employees referred to therein shall not appear in such copy or on any record published, released, or made available by the Department of Labor.

(b) If upon receipt of such notification the Area Director determines that the complaint meets the requirements set forth in paragraph (a) of this Section, and that there are reasonable grounds to believe that the alleged violation exists, he shall cause an inspection to be made as soon as practicable, to determine if such alleged violation exists. Inspections under this Section shall not be limited to matters referred to in the complaint.

(c) [OI] Prior to or during any inspection of a workplace, any employee or representative of employees employed in such workplace may notify the Compliance Safety and Health Officer, in writing, of any violation of the Act which they have reason to believe exists in such workplace. Any such notice shall comply with the requirements of paragraph (a) of this Section.

(d) Section 11(c)(1) of the Act provides: "No person shall discharge or in any manner discriminate against any employee because such employee has filed any complaint or instituted or caused to be instituted any proceeding under or related to this Act or has testified or is about to testify in any such proceeding or because of the exercise by such employee on behalf of himself or others of any right afforded by this Act."

(Approved by the Office of Management and Budget under control number 1218–0064)

[36 FR 17850, Sept. 4, 1973, as amended at 54 FR 24333, June 7, 1989]

§1903.12 Inspection not warranted; informal review

(a) If the Area Director determines that an inspection is not warranted because there are no reasonable grounds to believe that a violation or danger exists with respect to a complaint under §1903.11, he shall notify the complaining party in writing of such determination. The complaining party may obtain review of such determination by submitting a written statement of position with the Assistant Regional Director and, at the same time, providing the employer with a copy of such statement by certified mail. The employer may submit an opposing written statement of position with the Assistant Regional Director and, at the same time, provide the complaining party with a copy of such statement by certified mail. Upon the request of the complaining party or the employer, the Assistant Regional Director, at his discretion, may hold an informal conference in which the complaining party and the employer may orally present their views. After considering all written and oral views presented, the Assistant Regional Director shall affirm, modify, or reverse the determination of the Area Director and furnish the complaining party and the employer and written notification of this decision and the reasons therefore. The decision of the Assistant Regional Director shall be final and not subject to further review.

(b) If the Area Director determines that an inspection is not warranted because the requirements of §1903.11(a) have not been met, he shall notify the complaining party in writing of such determination. Such determination shall be without prejudice to the filing of a new complaint meeting the requirements of §1903.11(a).

§1903.13 Imminent danger

Whenever and as soon as a Compliance Safety and Health Officer concludes on the basis of an inspection that conditions or practices exist in any place of employment which could reasonably be expected to cause death or serious physical harm immediately or before the imminence of such danger can be eliminated through the enforcement procedures otherwise provided by the Act, he shall inform the affected employees and employers of the danger and that he is recommending a civil action to restrain such conditions or practices and for other appropriate relief in accordance with the provisions of Section 13(a) of the Act. Appropriate citations and notices of proposed penalties may be issued with respect to an imminent danger even though, after being informed of such danger by the Compliance Safety and Health Officer, the employer immediately eliminates the imminence of the danger and initiates steps to abate such danger.

§1903.14 Citations; notices of de minimis violations; policy regarding employee rescue activities

(a) The Area Director shall review the inspection report of the Compliance Safety and Health Officer. If, on the basis of the report the Area Director believes that the employer has violated a requirement of Section 5 of the Act, of any standard, rule or order promulgated pursuant to Section 6 of the Act, or of any substantive rule published in this chapter, he shall, if appropriate, consult with the Regional Solicitor, and he shall issue to the employer either a citation or a notice of de minimis violations which have no direct or immediate relationship to safety or health. An appropriate citation or notice of de minimis violations shall be issued even though after being informed of an alleged violation by the Compliance Safety and Health Officer, the employer immediately abates, or initiates steps to abate, such alleged violation. Any citation or notice of de minimis violations shall be issued with reasonable promptness after termination of the inspection. No citation may be issued under this Section after the expiration of 6 months following the occurrence of any alleged violation.

(b) Any citation shall describe with particularity the nature of the alleged violation, including a reference to the provision(s) of the Act, standard, rule, regulation, or order alleged to have been violated. Any citation shall also fix a reasonable time or times for the abatement of the alleged violation.

(c) If a citation or notice of de minimis violations is issued for a violation alleged in a request for inspection under §1903.11(a) or a notification of violation under §1903.11(c), a copy of the citation or notice of de minimis violations shall also be sent to the employee or representative of employees who made such request or notification.

(d) After an inspection, if the Area Director determines that a citation is not warranted with respect to a danger or violation alleged to exist in a request for inspection under §1903.11(a) or a notification of violation under §1903.11(c), the informal review procedures prescribed in §1903.12(a) shall be applicable. After considering all views presented, the Assistant Regional Director shall affirm the determination of the Area Director, order a reinspection, or issue a citation if he believes that the inspection disclosed a violation. The Assistant Regional Director shall furnish the complaining party and the employer with written notification of his determination and the reasons therefor. The determination of the Assistant Regional Director shall be final and not subject to review.

(e) Every citation shall state that the issuance of a citation does not constitute a finding that a violation of the Act has occurred unless there is a failure to contest as provided for in the Act or, if contested, unless the citation is affirmed by the Review Commission.

(f) No citation may be issued to an employer because of a rescue activity undertaken by an employee of that employer with respect to an individual in imminent danger unless:

(f)(1)(i) Such employee is designated or assigned by the employer to have responsibility to perform or assist in rescue operations; and

(f)(1)(ii) The employer fails to provide protection of the safety and health of such employee, including failing to provide appropriate training and rescue equipment; or

(f)(2)(i) Such employee is directed by the employer to perform rescue activities in the course of carrying out the employee's job duties, and

(f)(2)(ii) The employer fails to provide protection of the safety and health of such employee, including failing to provide appropriate training and rescue equipment; or

(f)(3)(i) Such employee is employed in a workplace that requires the employee to carry out duties that are directly related to a workplace operation where the likelihood of life-threatening accidents is foreseeable, such as a workplace operation where employees are located in confined spaces or trenches, handle hazardous waste, respond to emergency situations, perform excavations, or perform construction over water; and

(f)(3)(ii) Such employee has not been designated or assigned to perform or assist in rescue operations and voluntarily elects to rescue such an individual; and

(f)(3)(iii) The employer has failed to instruct employees not designated or assigned to perform or assist in rescue operations of the arrangements for rescue, not to attempt rescue, and of the hazards of attempting rescue without adequate training or equipment.

(f)(4) For purposes of this policy, the term "imminent danger" means the existence of any condition or practice that could reasonably be expected to cause death or serious physical harm before such condition or practice can be abated.

[36 FR 17850, Sept. 4, 1971, as amended at 59 FR 66613, Dec. 27, 1994]

§1903.14a Petitions for modification of abatement date

(a) An employer may file a petition for modification of abatement date when he has made a good faith effort to comply with the abatement requirements of a citation, but such abatement has not been completed because of factors beyond his reasonable control.

(b) A petition for modification of abatement date shall be in writing and shall include the following information:

(b)(1) All steps taken by the employer, and the dates of such action, in an effort to achieve compliance during the prescribed abatement period.

(b)(2) The specific additional abatement time necessary in order to achieve compliance.

(b)(3) The reasons such additional time is necessary, including the unavailability of professional or technical personnel or of materials and equipment, or because necessary construction or alteration of facilities cannot be completed by the original abatement date.

(b)(4) All available interim steps being taken to safeguard the employees against the cited hazard during the abatement period.

(b)(5) A certification that a copy of the petition has been posted and, if appropriate, served on the authorized representative of affected employees, in accordance with paragraph (c)(1) of this Section and a certification of the date upon which such posting and service was made.

(c) A petition for modification of abatement date shall be filed with the Area Director of the United States Department of Labor who issued the citation no later than the close of the next working day following the date on which abatement was originally required. A later-filed petition shall be accompanied by the employer's statement of exceptional circumstances explaining the delay.

(c)(1) A copy of such petition shall be posted in a conspicuous place where all affected employees will have notice thereof or near such location where the violation occurred. The petition shall remain posted for a period of ten (10) working days. Where affected employees are represented by an authorized representative, said representative shall be served with a copy of such petition.

(c)(2) Affected employees or their representatives may file an objection in writing to such petition with the aforesaid Area Director. Failure to file such objection within ten (10) working days of the date of posting of such petition or of service upon an authorized representative shall constitute a waiver of any further right to object to said petition.

(c)(3) The Secretary or his duly authorized agent shall have the authority to approve any petition for modification of abatement date filed pursuant to paragraphs (b) and (c) of this Section. Such uncontested petitions shall become final orders pursuant to Sections 10 (a) and (c) of the Act.

(c)(4) The Secretary or his authorized representative shall not exercise his approval power until the expiration of fifteen (15) working days from the date the petition was posted or served pursuant to paragraphs (c) (1) and (2) of this Section by the employer.

(d) Where any petition is objected to by the Secretary or affected employees, the petition, citation, and any objections shall be forwarded to the Commission within three (3) working days after the expiration of the fifteen (15) day period set out in paragraph (c)(4) of this Section.

[40 FR 6334, Feb. 11, 1975; 40 FR 11351, Mar. 11, 1975]

§1903.15 Proposed penalties

(a) After, or concurrent with, the issuance of a citation, and within a reasonable time after the termination of the inspection, the Area Director shall notify the employer by certified mail or by personal service by the Compliance Safety and Health Officer of the proposed penalty in accordance with paragraph (d) of this Section, or that no penalty is being proposed. Any notice of proposed penalty shall state that the proposed penalty shall be deemed to be the final order of the Review Commission and not subject to review by any court or agency unless, within 15 working days from the date of receipt of such notice, the employer notifies the Area Director in writing that he intends to contest the citation or the notification of proposed penalty before the Review Commission.

(b) The Area Director shall determine the amount of any proposed penalty, giving due consideration to the appropriateness of the penalty with respect to the size of the business of the employer being charged, the gravity of the violation, the good faith of the employer, and the history of previous violations, in accordance with the provisions of Section 17 of the Act and paragraph (d) of this Section.

(c) Appropriate penalties may be proposed with respect to an alleged violation even though after being informed of such alleged violation by the Compliance Safety and Health Officer, the employer immediately abates, or initiates steps to abate, such alleged violation. Penalties shall not be proposed for de minimis violations which have no direct or immediate relationship to safety or health.

(d) **Adjusted civil monetary penalties** The adjusted civil penalties for penalties proposed on or after August 1, 2016 are as follows:

(d)(1) **Willful violation** The penalty per willful violation under Section 17(a) of the Act, 29 U.S.C. 666(a), shall not be less than $8,908 and shall not exceed $124,709.

(d)(2) **Repeated violation** The penalty per repeated violation under Section 17(a) of the Act, 29 U.S.C. 666(a), shall not exceed $124,709.

(d)(3) **Serious violation** The penalty for a serious violation under Section 17(b) of the Act, 29 U.S.C. 666(b), shall not exceed $12,471.

(d)(4) **Other-than-serious violation** The penalty for an other-than-serious violation under Section 17(c) of the Act, 29 U.S.C. 666(c), shall not exceed $12,471.

(d)(5) **Failure to correct violation** The penalty for a failure to correct a violation under Section 17(d) of the Act, 29 U.S.C. 666(d), shall not exceed $12,471 per day.

(d)(6) **Posting requirement violation** The penalty for a posting requirement violation under Section 17(i) of the Act, 29 U.S.C. 666(i), shall not exceed $12,471.

§1903.16 Posting of citations

(a) Upon receipt of any citation under the Act, the employer shall immediately post such citation, or a copy thereof, unedited, at or near each place an alleged violation referred to in the citation occurred, except as provided below. Where, because of the nature of the employer's operations, it is not practicable to post the citation at or near each place of alleged violation, such citation shall be posted, unedited, in a prominent place where it will be readily observable by all affected employees. For example, where employers are engaged in activities which are physically dispersed (see §1903.2(b)), the citation may be posted at the location to which employees report each day. Where employees do not primarily work at or report to a single location (see §1903.2(b)), the citation may be posted at the location from which the employees operate to carry out their activities. The employer shall take steps to ensure that the citation is not altered, defaced, or covered by other material. Notices of de minimis violations need not be posted.

(b) Each citation, or a copy thereof, shall remain posted until the violation has been abated, or for 3 working days, whichever is later. The filing by the employer of a notice of intention to contest under §1903.17 shall not affect his posting responsibility under this Section unless and until the Review Commission issues a final order vacating the citation.

(c) An employer to whom a citation has been issued may post a notice in the same location where such citation is posted indicating that the citation is being contested before the Review Commission, and such notice may explain the reasons for such contest. The employer may also indicate that specified steps have been taken to abate the violation.

(d) Any employer failing to comply with the provisions of paragraphs (a) and (b) of this Section shall be subject to citation and penalty in accordance with §1903.15(d).

§1903.17 Employer and employee contests before the Review Commission

(a) [OI] Any employer to whom a citation or notice of proposed penalty has been issued may, under Section 10(a) of the Act, notify the Area Director in writing that he intends to contest such citation or proposed penalty before the Review Commission. Such notice of intention to contest shall be postmarked within 15 working days of the receipt by the employer of the notice of proposed penalty. Every notice of intention to contest shall specify whether it is directed to the citation or to the proposed penalty, or both. The Area Director shall immediately transmit such notice to the Review Commission in accordance with the rules of procedure prescribed by the Commission.

(b) Any employee or representative of employees of an employer to whom a citation has been issued may, under Section 10(c) of the Act, file a written notice with the Area Director alleging that the period of time fixed in the citation for the abatement of the violation is unreasonable. Such notice shall be postmarked within 15 working days of the receipt by the employer of the notice of proposed penalty or notice that no penalty is being proposed. The Area Director shall immediately transmit such notice to the Review Commission in accordance with the rules of procedure prescribed by the Commission.

§1903.18 Failure to correct a violation for which a citation has been issued

(a) If an inspection discloses that an employer has failed to correct an alleged violation for which a citation has been issued within the period permitted for its correction, the Area Director shall, if appropriate, consult with the Regional Solicitor, and he shall notify the employer by certified mail or by personal service by the Compliance Safety and Health Officer of such failure and of the additional penalty proposed under §1903.15(d)(5) by reason of such failure. The period for the correction of a violation for which a citation has been issued shall not begin to run until the entry of a final order of the Review Commission in the case of any review proceedings initiated by the employer in good faith and not solely for delay or avoidance of penalties.

(b) Any employer receiving a notification of failure to correct a violation and of proposed additional penalty may, under Section 10(b) of the Act, notify the Area Director in writing that he intends to contest such notification or proposed additional penalty before the Review Commission. Such notice of intention to contest shall be postmarked within 15 working days of the receipt by the employer of the notification of failure to correct a violation and of proposed additional penalty. The Area Director shall immediately transmit such notice to the Review Commission in accordance with the rules of procedure prescribed by the Commission.

(c) Each notification of failure to correct a violation and of proposed additional penalty shall state that it shall be deemed to be the final order of the Review Commission and not subject to review by any court or agency unless, within 15 working days from the date of receipt of such notification, the employer notifies the Area Director in writing that he intends to contest the notification or the proposed additional penalty before the Review Commission.

§1903.19 [OI] Abatement verification

Purpose OSHA's inspections are intended to result in the abatement of violations of the Occupational Safety and Health Act of 1970 (the OSH Act). This Section sets forth the procedures OSHA will use to ensure abatement. These procedures are tailored to the nature of the violation and the employer's abatement actions.

(a) **Scope and application** This Section applies to employers who receive a citation for a violation of the Occupational Safety and Health Act.

(b) **Definitions**

(b)(1) **Abatement** means action by an employer to comply with a cited standard or regulation or to eliminate a recognized hazard identified by OSHA during an inspection.

(b)(2) **Abatement date** means:

(b)(2)(i) For an uncontested citation item, the later of:

(b)(2)(i)(A) The date in the citation for abatement of the violation;

(b)(2)(i)(B) The date approved by OSHA or established in litigation as a result of a petition for modification of the abatement date (PMA); or

(b)(2)(i)(C) The date established in a citation by an informal settlement agreement.

(b)(2)(ii) For a contested citation item for which the Occupational Safety and Health Review Commission (OSHRC) has issued a final order affirming the violation, the later of:

(b)(2)(ii)(A) The date identified in the final order for abatement; or

(b)(2)(ii)(B) The date computed by adding the period allowed in the citation for abatement to the final order date;

(b)(2)(ii)(C) The date established by a formal settlement agreement.

(b)(3) **Affected employees** means those employees who are exposed to the hazard(s) identified as violation(s) in a citation.

(b)(4) **Final order date** means:

(b)(4)(i) For an uncontested citation item, the fifteenth working day after the employer's receipt of the citation;

(b)(4)(ii) For a contested citation item:

(b)(4)(ii)(A) The thirtieth day after the date on which a decision or order of a commission administrative law judge has been docketed with the commission, unless a member of the commission has directed review; or

(b)(4)(ii)(B) Where review has been directed, the thirtieth day after the date on which the Commission issues its decision or order disposing of all or pertinent part of a case; or

(b)(4)(ii)(C) The date on which a federal appeals court issues a decision affirming the violation in a case in which a final order of OSHRC has been stayed.

(b)(5) **Movable equipment** means a hand-held or non-hand-held machine or device, powered or unpowered, that is used to do work and is moved within or between worksites.

(c) **Abatement certification**

(c)(1) Within 10 calendar days after the abatement date, the employer must certify to OSHA (the Agency) that each cited violation has been abated, except as provided in paragraph (c)(2) of this Section.

(c)(2) The employer is not required to certify abatement if the OSHA Compliance Officer, during the on-site portion of the inspection:

(c)(2)(i) Observes, within 24 hours after a violation is identified, that abatement has occurred; and

(c)(2)(ii) Notes in the citation that abatement has occurred.

(c)(3) The employer's certification that abatement is complete must include, for each cited violation, in addition to the information required by paragraph (h) of this Section, the date and method of abatement and a statement that affected employees and their representatives have been informed of the abatement.

Note to paragraph (c): Appendix A contains a sample Abatement Certification Letter.

(d) **Abatement documentation**

(d)(1) The employer must submit to the Agency, along with the information on abatement certification required by paragraph (c)(3) of this Section, documents demonstrating that abatement is complete for each willful or repeat violation and for any serious violation for which the Agency indicates in the citation that such abatement documentation is required.

(d)(2) Documents demonstrating that abatement is complete may include, but are not limited to, evidence of the purchase or repair of equipment, photographic or video evidence of abatement, or other written records.

(e) **Abatement plans**

(e)(1) The Agency may require an employer to submit an abatement plan for each cited violation (except an other-than-serious violation) when the time permitted for abatement is more than 90 calendar days. If an abatement plan is required, the citation must so indicate.

(e)(2) The employer must submit an abatement plan for each cited violation within 25 calendar days from the final order date when the citation indicates that such a plan is required. The abatement plan must identify the violation and the steps to be taken to achieve abatement, including a schedule for completing abatement and, where necessary, how employees will be protected from exposure to the violative condition in the interim until abatement is complete.

Note to paragraph (e): Appendix B contains a Sample Abatement Plan form.

(f) **Progress reports**

(f)(1) An employer who is required to submit an abatement plan may also be required to submit periodic progress reports for each cited violation. The citation must indicate:

(f)(1)(i) That periodic progress reports are required and the citation items for which they are required;

(f)(1)(ii) The date on which an initial progress report must be submitted, which may be no sooner than 30 calendar days after submission of an abatement plan;

(f)(1)(iii) Whether additional progress reports are required; and

(f)(1)(iv) The date(s) on which additional progress reports must be submitted.

(f)(2) For each violation, the progress report must identify, in a single sentence if possible, the action taken to achieve abatement and the date the action was taken.

Note to paragraph (f): Appendix B contains a Sample Progress Report form.

(g) **Employee notification**

(g)(1) The employer must inform affected employees and their representative(s) about abatement activities covered by this Section by posting a copy of each document submitted to the Agency or a summary of the document near the place where the violation occurred.

(g)(2) Where such posting does not effectively inform employees and their representatives about abatement activities (for example, for employers who have mobile work operations), the employer must:

(g)(2)(i) Post each document or a summary of the document in a location where it will be readily observable by affected employees and their representatives; or

(g)(2)(ii) Take other steps to communicate fully to affected employees and their representatives about abatement activities.

(g)(3) The employer must inform employees and their representatives of their right to examine and copy all abatement documents submitted to the Agency.

(g)(3)(i) An employee or an employee representative must submit a request to examine and copy abatement documents within 3 working days of receiving notice that the documents have been submitted.

(g)(3)(ii) The employer must comply with an employee's or employee representative's request to examine and copy abatement documents within 5 working days of receiving the request.

(g)(4) The employer must ensure that notice to employees and employee representatives is provided at the same time or before the information is provided to the Agency and that abatement documents are:

(g)(4)(i) Not altered, defaced, or covered by other material; and

(g)(4)(ii) Remain posted for three working days after submission to the Agency.

(h) **Transmitting abatement documents**

(h)(1) The employer must include, in each submission required by this Section, the following information:

(h)(1)(i) The employer's name and address;

(h)(1)(ii) The inspection number to which the submission relates;

(h)(1)(iii) The citation and item numbers to which the submission relates;

(h)(1)(iv) A statement that the information submitted is accurate; and

(h)(1)(v) The signature of the employer or the employer's authorized representative.

(h)(2) The date of postmark is the date of submission for mailed documents. For documents transmitted by other means, the date the Agency receives the document is the date of submission.

(h)(2)(i) **Movable equipment**

(h)(2)(i)(1) For serious, repeat, and willful violations involving movable equipment, the employer must attach a warning tag or a copy of the citation to the operating controls or to the cited component of equipment that is moved within the worksite or between worksites.

Note to paragraph (i)(1): Attaching a copy of the citation to the equipment is deemed by OSHA to meet the tagging requirement of paragraph (i)(1) of this Section as well as the posting requirement of 29 CFR 1903.16.

(h)(2)(i)(2) The employer must use a warning tag that properly warns employees about the nature of the violation involving the equipment and identifies the location of the citation issued.

Note to paragraph (i)(2): Nonmandatory Appendix C contains a sample tag that employers may use to meet this requirement.

(h)(2)(i)(3) If the violation has not already been abated, a warning tag or copy of the citation must be attached to the equipment:

(h)(2)(i)(3)(i) For hand-held equipment, immediately after the employer receives the citation; or

(h)(2)(i)(3)(ii) For non-hand-held equipment, prior to moving the equipment within or between worksites.

(h)(2)(i)(4) For the construction industry, a tag that is designed and used in accordance with 29 CFR 1926.20(b)(3) and 29 CFR 1926.200(h) is deemed by OSHA to meet the requirements of this Section when the information required by paragraph (i)(2) is included on the tag.

(h)(2)(i)(5) The employer must assure that the tag or copy of the citation attached to movable equipment is not altered, defaced, or covered by other material.

(h)(2)(i)(6) The employer must assure that the tag or copy of the citation attached to movable equipment remains attached until:

(h)(2)(i)(6)(i) The violation has been abated and all abatement verification documents required by this regulation have been submitted to the Agency;

(h)(2)(i)(6)(ii) The cited equipment has been permanently removed from service or is no longer within the employer's control; or

(h)(2)(i)(6)(iii) The Commission issues a final order vacating the citation.

§1903.19 Appendices
Abatement verification

Note: Appendices A through C provide information and nonmandatory guidelines to assist employers and employees in complying with the appropriate requirements of this Section.

§1903.19 Appendix A
Sample Abatement-Certification letter
(Nonmandatory)

(Name), Area Director

U. S. Department of Labor—OSHA

Address of the Area Office (on the citation)

[Company's Name]

[Company's Address]

The hazard referenced in Inspection Number [insert 9-digit #] for violation identified as:

Citation [insert #] and item [insert #] was corrected on [insert date] by: ______________________________.

Citation [insert #] and item [insert #] was corrected on [insert date] by: ______________________________.

Citation [insert #] and item [insert #] was corrected on [insert date] by: ______________________________.

Citation [insert #] and item [insert #] was corrected on [insert date] by: ______________________________.

Citation [insert #] and item [insert #] was corrected on [insert date] by: ______________________________.

Citation [insert #] and item [insert #] was corrected on [insert date] by: ______________________________.

Citation [insert #] and item [insert #] was corrected on insert date by: ______________________________.

Citation [insert #] and item [insert #] was corrected on [insert date] by: ______________________________.

I attest that the information contained in this document is accurate.

____

Signature

____

Typed or Printed Name

§1903.19 Appendix B Sample Abatement Plan or Progress Report (Nonmandatory)

(Name), Area Director

U. S. Department of Labor—OSHA

Address of Area Office (on the citation)

[Company's Name]

[Company's Address]

Check one:

Abatement Plan [ ]

Progress Report [ ]

Inspection Number ____________________

Page ___ of _____

Citation Number(s)*____________________

Item Number(s)*____________________

Date required for final abatement:____________________

I attest that the information contained in this document is accurate.

____

Signature

____

Typed or Printed Name

Name of primary point of contact for questions: [optional]

Telephone number:____________________

§1903.19 Appendix C Sample Warning Tag (Nonmandatory)

WARNING:

EQUIPMENT HAZARD CITED BY OSHA

EQUIPMENT CITED:

____

____

____

HAZARD CITED:

____

____

____

FOR DETAILED INFORMATION
SEE OSHA CITATION POSTED AT:

____

____

BACKGROUND COLOR - ORANGE

MESSAGE COLOR - BLACK

[62 FR 15337, Mar. 31, 1997]

§1903.20 Informal conferences

At the request of an affected employer, employee, or representative of employees, the Assistant Regional Director may hold an informal conference for the purpose of discussing any issues raised by an inspection, citation, notice of proposed penalty, or notice of intention to contest. The settlement of any issue at such conference shall be subject to the rules of procedure prescribed by the Review Commission. If the conference is requested by the employer, an affected employee or his representative shall be afforded an opportunity to participate, at the discretion of the Assistant Regional Director. If the conference is requested by an employee or representative of employees, the employer shall be afforded an opportunity to participate, at the discretion of the Assistant Regional Director. Any party may be represented by counsel at such conference. No such conference or request for such conference shall operate as a stay of any 15-working-day period for filing a notice of intention to contest as prescribed in §1903.17.

[36 FR 17850, Sept. 4, 1971. Redesignated at 62 FR 15337, Mar. 31, 1997]

§1903.21 State administration

Nothing in this part 1903 shall preempt the authority of any State to conduct inspections, to initiate enforcement proceedings or otherwise to implement the applicable provisions of State law with respect to State occupational safety and health standards in accordance with agreements and plans under Section 18 of the Act and parts 1901 and 1902 of this chapter.

[36 FR 17850, Sept. 4, 1971. Redesignated at 62 FR 15337, Mar. 31, 1997]

§1903.22 Definitions

(a) **Act** means the Williams-Steiger Occupational Safety and Health Act of 1970. (84 Stat. 1590 et seq., 29 U.S.C. 651 et seq.)

(b) The definitions and interpretations contained in Section 3 of the Act shall be applicable to such terms when used in this part 1903.

(c) **Working days** means Mondays through Fridays but shall not include Saturdays, Sundays, or Federal holidays. In computing 15 working days, the day of receipt of any notice shall not be included, and the last day of the 15 working days shall be included.

(d) **Compliance Safety and Health Officer** means a person authorized by the Occupational Safety and Health Administration, U.S. Department of Labor, to conduct inspections.

(e) **Area Director** means the employee or officer regularly or temporarily in charge of an Area Office of the Occupational Safety and Health Administration, U.S. Department of Labor, or any other person or persons who are authorized to act for such employee or officer. The latter authorizations may include general delegations of the authority of an Area Director under this part to a Compliance Safety and Health Officer or delegations to such an officer for more limited purposes, such as the exercise of the Area Director's duties under §1903.14(a). The term also includes any employee or officer exercising supervisory responsibilities over an Area Director. A supervisory employee or officer is considered to exercise concurrent authority with the Area Director.

(f) **Assistant Regional Director** means the employee or officer regularly or temporarily in charge of a Region of the Occupational Safety and Health Administration, U.S. Department of Labor, or any other person or persons who are specifically designated to act for such employee or officer in his absence. The term also includes any employee or officer in the Occupational Safety and Health Administration exercising supervisory responsibilities over the Assistant Regional Director. Such supervisory employee or officer is considered to exercise concurrent authority with the Assistant Regional Director. No delegation of authority under this paragraph shall adversely affect the procedures for independent informal review of investigative determinations prescribed under §1903.12 of this part.

(g) **Inspection** means any inspection of an employer's factory, plant, establishment, construction site, or other area, workplace or environment where work is performed by an employee of an employer, and includes any inspection conducted pursuant to a complaint filed under §1903.11 (a) and (c), any reinspection, followup inspection, accident investigation or other inspection conducted under Section 8(a) of the Act.

[36 FR 17850, Sept. 4, 1971, as amended at 38 FR 22624, Aug. 23, 1973. Redesignated at 62 FR 15337, Mar. 31, 1997]

This page intentionally left blank.

29 CFR PART 1904
Recording and Reporting Occupational Injuries and Illnesses

Section Contents

1904—Recording and Reporting Occupational Injuries and Illnesses

Authority: 29 U.S.C. 657, 658, 660, 666, 669, 673, Secretary of Labor's Order No. 3–2000 (65 FR 50017), or 1–2012 (77 FR 3912), and 5 U.S.C. 55.

Source: 66 FR 6122, Jan. 19, 2001, unless otherwise noted.

Subpart A—Purpose

§1904.0 Purpose

The purpose of this rule (Part 1904) is to require employers to make and maintain accurate records of and report work-related fatalities, injuries, and illnesses, and to make such records available to the Government and to employees and their representatives so that they can be used to secure safe and healthful working conditions. For purposes of this Part, accurate records are records of each and every recordable injury and illness that are made and maintained in accordance with the requirements of this par.

Note to §1904.0: Recording or reporting a work-related injury, illness, or fatality does not mean that the employer or employee was at fault, that an OSHA rule has been violated, or that the employee is eligible for workers' compensation or other benefits

Subpart B—Scope

Note to Subpart B: All employers covered by the Occupational Safety and Health Act (OSH Act) are covered by these Part 1904 regulations. However, most employers do not have to keep OSHA injury and illness records unless OSHA or the Bureau of Labor Statistics (BLS) informs them in writing that they must keep records. For example, employers with 10 or fewer employees and business establishments in certain industry classifications are partially exempt from keeping OSHA injury and illness records.

§1904.1 Partial exemption for employers with 10 or fewer employees

(a) **Basic requirement**

(a)(1) If your company had ten (10) or fewer employees at all times during the last calendar year, you do not need to keep OSHA injury and illness records unless OSHA or the BLS informs you in writing that you must keep records under §1904.41 or §1904.42. However, as required by §1904.39, all employers covered by the OSH Act must report to OSHA any workplace incident that results in a fatality or the hospitalization of three or more employees.

(a)(2) If your company had more than ten (10) employees at any time during the last calendar year, you must keep OSHA injury and illness records unless your establishment is classified as a partially exempt industry under §1904.2.

(b) **Implementation**

(b)(1) *Is the partial exemption for size based on the size of my entire company or on the size of an individual business establishment?* The partial exemption for size is based on the number of employees in the entire company.

(b)(2) *How do I determine the size of my company to find out if I qualify for the partial exemption for size?* To determine if you are exempt because of size, you need to determine your company's peak employment during the last calendar year. If you had no more than 10 employees at any time in the last calendar year, your company qualifies for the partial exemption for size.

§1904.2 Partial exemption for establishments in certain industries

(a) **Basic requirement**

(a)(1) If your business establishment is classified in a specific industry group listed in Appendix A to this Subpart, you do not need to keep OSHA injury and illness records unless the government asks you to keep the records under §1904.41 or §1904.42. However, all employers must report to OSHA any workplace incident that results in an employee's fatality, in-patient hospitalization, amputation, or loss of an eye (see §1904.39).

(a)(2) If one or more of your company's establishments are classified in a non-exempt industry, you must keep OSHA injury and illness records for all of such establishments unless your company is partially exempted because of size under §1904.1.

(b) **Implementation**

(b)(1) *Is the partial industry classification exemption based on the industry classification of my entire company or on the classification of individual business establishments operated by my company?* The partial industry classification exemption applies to individual business establishments. If a company has several business establishments engaged in different classes of business activities, some of the company's establishments may be required to keep records, while others may be partially exempt

(b)(2) *How do I determine the correct NAICS code for my company or for individual establishments?* You can determine your NAICS code by using one of three methods, or you may contact your nearest OSHA office or State agency for help in determining your NAICS code:

(b)(2)(1) You can use the search feature at the U.S. Census Bureau NAICS main Web page: http://www.census.gov/eos/www/naics/. In the search box for the most recent NAICS, enter a keyword that describes your kind of business. A list of primary business activities containing that keyword and the corresponding NAICS codes will appear. Choose the one that most closely corresponds to your primary business activity, or refine your search to obtain other choices.

(b)(2)(ii) Rather than searching through a list of primary business activities, you may also view the most recent complete NAICS structure with codes and titles by clicking on the link for the most recent NAICS on the U.S. Census Bureau NAICS main Web page: http://www.census.gov/eos/www/naics/. Then click on the two-digit Sector code to see all the NAICS codes under that Sector. Then choose the six-digit code of your interest to see the corresponding definition, as well as cross-references and index items, when available.

(b)(2) (iii) If you know your old SIC code, you can also find the appropriate 2002 NAICS code by using the detailed conversion (concordance) between the 1987 SIC and 2002 NAICS available in Excel format for download at the "Concordances" link at the U.S. Census Bureau NAICS main Web page: http://www.census.gov/eos/www/naics/.

(b)(3) *How do I determine the Standard Industrial Classification code for my company or for individual establishments?* You determine your Standard Industrial Classification (SIC) code by using the Standard Industrial Classification Manual, Executive Office of the President, Office of Management and Budget. You may contact your nearest OSHA office or State agency for help in determining your SIC.

§1904.3 [OI]
Keeping records for more than one agency

If you create records to comply with another government agency's injury and illness recordkeeping requirements, OSHA will consider those records as meeting OSHA's Part 1904 recordkeeping requirements if OSHA accepts the other agency's records under a memorandum of understanding with that agency, or if the other agency's records contain the same information as this Part 1904 requires you to record. You may contact your nearest OSHA office or State agency for help in determining whether your records meet OSHA's requirements.

Subpart B Appendix A
Partially exempt industries
(Nonmandatory)

Employers are not required to keep OSHA injury and illness records for any establishment classified in the following North American Industry Classification System (NAICS) codes, unless they are asked in writing to do so by OSHA, the Bureau of Labor Statistics (BLS), or a state agency operating under the authority of OSHA or the BLS. All employers, including those partially exempted by reason of company size or industry classification, must report to OSHA any employee's fatality, in-patient hospitalization, amputation, or loss of an eye (see §1904.39).

NAICS code	Industry	NAICS code	Industry
4412	Other Motor Vehicle Dealers	5411	Legal Services.
4431	Electronics and Appliance Stores.	5412	Accounting, Tax Preparation, Bookkeeping, and Payroll Services
4461	Health and Personal Care Stores.	5413	Architectural, Engineering, and Related Services
4471	Gasoline Stations.	5414	Specialized Design Services.
4481	Clothing Stores.	5415	Computer Systems Design and Related Services
4482	Shoe Stores.	5416	Management, Scientific, and Technical Consulting Services
4483	Jewelry, Luggage, and Leather Goods Stores	5417	Scientific Research and Development Services
4511	Sporting Goods, Hobby, and Musical Instrument Stores	5418	Advertising and Related Services.
4512	Book, Periodical, and Music Stores.	5511	Management of Companies and Enterprises
4531	Florists.	5611	Office Administrative Services.
4532	Office Supplies, Stationery, and Gift Stores	5614	Business Support Services.

NAICS code	Industry	NAICS code	Industry
4812	Nonscheduled Air Transportation.	5615	Travel Arrangement and Reservation Services
4861	Pipeline Transportation of Crude Oil.	5616	Investigation and Security Services.
4862	Pipeline Transportation of Natural Gas.	6111	Elementary and Secondary Schools.
4869	Other Pipeline Transportation.	6112	Junior Colleges.
4879	Scenic and Sightseeing Transportation, Other	6113	Colleges, Universities, and Professional Schools
4885	Freight Transportation Arrangement.	6114	Business Schools and Computer and Management Training
5111	Newspaper, Periodical, Book, and Directory Publishers	6115	Technical and Trade Schools.
5112	Software Publishers.	6116	Other Schools and Instruction.
5121	Motion Picture and Video Industries.	6117	Educational Support Services.
5122	Sound Recording Industries.	6211	Offices of Physicians.
5151	Radio and Television Broadcasting.	6212	Offices of Dentists.
5172	Wireless Telecommunications Carriers (except Satellite)	6213	Offices of Other Health Practitioners.
5173	Telecommunications Resellers.	6214	Outpatient Care Centers.
5179	Other Telecommunications.	6215	Medical and Diagnostic Laboratories.
5181	Internet Service Providers and Web Search Portals	6244	Child Day Care Services.
5182	Data Processing, Hosting, and Related Services	7114	Agents and Managers for Artists, Athletes, Entertainers, and Other Public Figures
5191	Other Information Services.	7115	Independent Artists, Writers, and Performers
5211	Monetary Authorities_ Central Bank.	7213	Rooming and Boarding Houses.
5221	Depository Credit Intermediation.	7221	Full-Service Restaurants.
5222	Nondepository Credit Intermediation.	7222	Limited-Service Eating Places.
5223	Activities Related to Credit Intermediation	7224	Drinking Places (Alcoholic Beverages).
5231	Securities and Commodity Contracts Intermediation and Brokerage	8112	Electronic and Precision Equipment Repair and Maintenance
5232	Securities and Commodity Exchanges.	8114	Personal and Household Goods Repair and Maintenance
5239	Other Financial Investment Activities.	8121	Personal Care Services.
5241	Insurance Carriers.	8122	Death Care Services.
5242	Agencies, Brokerages, and Other Insurance Related Activities	8131	Religious Organizations.

NAICS code	Industry	NAICS code	Industry
5251	Insurance and Employee Benefit Funds.	8132	Grantmaking and Giving Services.
5259	Other Investment Pools and Funds.	8133	Social Advocacy Organizations.
5312	Offices of Real Estate Agents and Brokers	8134	Civic and Social Organizations.
5331	Lessors of Nonfinancial Intangible Assets (except Copyrighted Works	8139	Business, Professional, Labor, Political, and Similar Organizations

Subpart C—Recordkeeping Forms and Recording Criteria

Note to Subpart C: This Subpart describes the work-related injuries and illnesses that an employer must enter into the OSHA records and explains the OSHA forms that employers must use to record work-related fatalities, injuries, and illnesses.

§1904.4 Recording criteria

(a) **Basic requirement** Each employer required by this Part to keep records of fatalities, injuries, and illnesses must, in accordance with the requirements of this Part, make and maintain an accurate record of each and every fatality, injury, and illness that:

(a)(1) Is work-related; and

(a)(2) Is a new case; and

(a)(3) Meets one or more of the general recording criteria of §1904.7 or the application to specific cases of §1904.8 through §1904.12.

Note to §1904.4(a): This obligation to make and maintain an accurate record of each and every recordable fatality, injury, and illness continues throughout the entire record retention period described in §1904.3

(b) Implementation

(b)(1) *What Sections of this rule describe recording criteria for recording work-related injuries and illnesses?* The table below indicates which Sections of the rule address each topic.

(b)(1)(i) Determination of work-relatedness. See §1904.5.

(b)(1)(ii) Determination of a new case. See §1904.6.

(b)(1)(iii) General recording criteria. See §1904.7.

(b)(1)(iv) Additional criteria. (Needlestick and sharps injury cases, tuberculosis cases, hearing loss cases, medical removal cases, and musculoskeletal disorder cases). See §1904.8 through §1904.12.

(b)(2) *How do I decide whether a particular injury or illness is recordable?* The decision tree for recording work-related injuries and illnesses below shows the steps involved in making this determination.

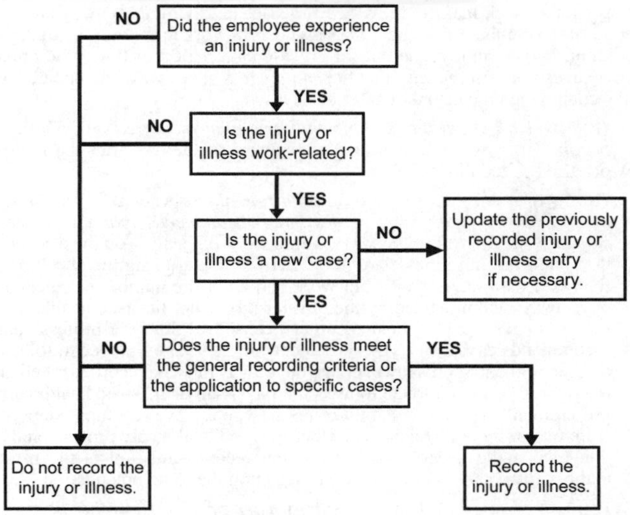

§1904.5 Determination of work–relatedness

(a) **Basic requirement** You must consider an injury or illness to be work-related if an event or exposure in the work environment either caused or contributed to the resulting condition or significantly aggravated a pre-existing injury or illness. Work-relatedness is presumed for injuries and illnesses resulting from events or exposures occurring in the work environment, unless an exception in §1904.5(b)(2) specifically applies.

(b) **Implementation**

(b)(1) *What is the "work environment"?* OSHA defines the work environment as "the establishment and other locations where one or more employees are working or are present as a condition of their employment. The work environment includes not only physical locations, but also the equipment or materials used by the employee during the course of his or her work."

(b)(2) *Are there situations where an injury or illness occurs in the work environment and is not considered work-related?* Yes, an injury or illness occurring in the work environment that falls under one of the following exceptions is not work-related, and therefore is not recordable.

1904.5(b)(2)	You are not required to record injuries and illnesses if . . .
(i)	At the time of the injury or illness, the employee was present in the work environment as a member of the general public rather than as an employee.
(ii)	The injury or illness involves signs or symptoms that surface at work but result solely from a non-work-related event or exposure that occurs outside the work environment.
(iii)	The injury or illness results solely from voluntary participation in a wellness program or in a medical, fitness, or recreational activity such as blood donation, physical examination, flu shot, exercise class, racquetball, or baseball.
(iv)	The injury or illness is solely the result of an employee eating, drinking, or preparing food or drink for personal consumption (whether bought on the employer's premises or brought in). For example, if the employee is injured by choking on a sandwich while in the employer's establishment, the case would not be considered work-related. **Note:** If the employee is made ill by ingesting food contaminated by workplace contaminants (such as lead), or gets food poisoning from food supplied by the employer, the case would be considered work-related.
(v)	The injury or illness is solely the result of an employee doing personal tasks (unrelated to their employment) at the establishment outside of the employee's assigned working hours.
(vi)	The injury or illness is solely the result of personal grooming, self medication for a non-work-related condition, or is intentionally self-inflicted.
(vii)	The injury or illness is caused by a motor vehicle accident and occurs on a company parking lot or company access road while the employee is commuting to or from work.
(viii)	The illness is the common cold or flu (**Note:** contagious diseases such as tuberculosis, brucellosis, hepatitis A, or plague are considered work-related if the employee is infected at work).
(ix)	The illness is a mental illness. Mental illness will not be considered work-related unless the employee voluntarily provides the employer with an opinion from a physician or other licensed health care professional with appropriate training and experience (psychiatrist, psychologist, psychiatric nurse practitioner, etc.) stating that the employee has a mental illness that is work-related.

(b)(3) *How do I handle a case if it is not obvious whether the precipitating event or exposure occurred in the work environment or occurred away from work?* In these situations, you must evaluate the employee's work duties and environment to decide whether or not one or more events or exposures in the work environment either caused or contributed to the resulting condition or significantly aggravated a pre-existing condition.

(b)(4) *How do I know if an event or exposure in the work environment "significantly aggravated" a preexisting injury or illness?* A preexisting injury or illness has been significantly aggravated, for purposes of OSHA injury and illness recordkeeping, when an event or exposure in the work environment results in any of the following:

(b)(4)(i) Death, provided that the preexisting injury or illness would likely not have resulted in death but for the occupational event or exposure;

(b)(4)(ii) Loss of consciousness, provided that the preexisting injury or illness would likely not have resulted in loss of consciousness but for the occupational event or exposure;

(b)(4)(iii) One or more days away from work, or days of restricted work, or days of job transfer that otherwise would not have occurred but for the occupational event or exposure. and

(b)(4)(iv) Medical treatment in a case where no medical treatment was needed for the injury or illness before the workplace event or exposure, or a change in medical treatment was necessitated by the workplace event or exposure.

(b)(5) *Which injuries and illnesses are considered pre-existing conditions?* An injury or illness is a preexisting condition if it resulted solely from a non-work-related event or exposure that occured outside the work environment.

(b)(6) *How do I decide whether an injury or illness is work-related if the employee is on travel status at the time the injury or illness occurs?* Injuries and illnesses that occur while an employee is on travel status are work-related if, at the time of the injury or illness, the employee was engaged in work activities "in the interest of the employer." Examples of such activities include travel to and from customer contacts, conducting job tasks, and entertaining or being entertained to transact, discuss, or promote business (work-related entertainment includes only entertainment activities being engaged in at the direction of the employer).

Injuries or illnesses that occur when the employee is on travel status do not have to be recorded if they meet one of the exceptions listed below.

1904.5 (b)(6)	If the employee has . . .	You may use the following to determine if an injury or illness is work-related
(i)	checked into a hotel or motel for one or more days	When a traveling employee checks into a hotel, motel, or into an other temporary residence, he or she establishes a "home away from home." You must evaluate the employee's activities after he or she checks into the hotel, motel, or other temporary residence for their work-relatedness in the same manner as you evaluate the activities of a non-traveling employee. When the employee checks into the temporary residence, he or she is considered to have left the work environment. When the employee begins work each day, he or she re-enters the work environment. If the employee has established a "home away from home" and is reporting to a fixed worksite each day, you also do not consider injuries or illnesses work-related if they occur while the employee is commuting between the temporary residence and the job location.
(ii)	taken a detour for personal reasons	Injuries or illnesses are not considered work-related if they occur while the employee is on a personal detour from a reasonably direct route of travel (e.g., has taken a side trip for personal reasons).

(b)(7) How do I decide if a case is work-related when the employee is working at home? Injuries and illnesses that occur while an employee is working at home, including work in a home office, will be considered work-related if the injury or illness occurs while the employee is performing work for pay or compensation in the home, and the injury or illness is directly related to the performance of work rather than to the general home environment or setting. For example, if an employee drops a box of work documents and injures his or her foot, the case is considered work-related. If an employee's fingernail is punctured by a needle from a sewing machine used to perform garment work at home, becomes infected and requires medical treatment, the injury is considered work-related. If an employee is injured because he or she trips on the family dog while rushing to answer a work phone call, the case is not considered work-related. If an employee working at home is electrocuted because of faulty home wiring, the injury is not considered work-related.

§1904.6
Determination of new cases

(a) **Basic requirement** You must consider an injury or illness to be a "new case" if:

(a)(1) The employee has not previously experienced a recorded injury or illness of the same type that affects the same part of the body, or

(a)(2) The employee previously experienced a recorded injury or illness of the same type that affected the same part of the body but had recovered completely (all signs and symptoms had disappeared) from the previous injury or illness and an event or exposure in the work environment caused the signs or symptoms to reappear.

(b) **Implementation**

(b)(1) *When an employee experiences the signs or symptoms of a chronic work-related illness, do I need to consider each recurrence of signs or symptoms to be a new case?* No, for occupational illnesses where the signs or symptoms may recur or continue in the absence of an exposure in the workplace, the case must only be recorded once. Examples may include occupational cancer, asbestosis, byssinosis and silicosis.

(b)(2) *When an employee experiences the signs or symptoms of an injury or illness as a result of an event or exposure in the workplace, such as an episode of occupational asthma, must I treat the episode as a new case?* Yes, because the episode or recurrence was caused by an event or exposure in the workplace, the incident must be treated as a new case.

(b)(3) *May I rely on a physician or other licensed health care professional to determine whether a case is a new case or a recurrence of an old case?* You are not required to seek the advice of a physician or other licensed health care professional. However, if you do seek such advice, you must follow the physician or other licensed health care professional's recommendation about whether the case is a new case or a recurrence. If you receive recommendations from two or more physicians or other licensed health care professionals, you must make a decision as to which recommendation is the most authoritative (best documented, best reasoned, or most authoritative), and record the case based upon that recommendation.

§1904.7
General recording criteria

(a) **Basic requirement** You must consider an injury or illness to meet the general recording criteria, and therefore to be recordable, if it results in any of the following: death, days away from work, restricted work or transfer to another job, medical treatment beyond first aid, or loss of consciousness. You must also consider a case to meet the general recording criteria if it involves a significant injury or illness diagnosed by a physician or other licensed health care professional, even if it does not result in death, days away from work, restricted work or job transfer, medical treatment beyond first aid, or loss of consciousness.

(b) **Implementation**

(b)(1) *How do I decide if a case meets one or more of the general recording criteria?* A work-related injury or illness must be recorded if it results in one or more of the following:

(b)(1)(i) Death. See §1904.7(b)(2).

(b)(1)(ii) Days away from work. See §1904.7(b)(3).

(b)(1)(iii) Restricted work or transfer to another job. See §1904.7(b)(4).

(b)(1)(iv) Medical treatment beyond first aid. See §1904.7(b)(5).

(b)(1)(v) Loss of consciousness. See §1904.7(b)(6).

(b)(1)(vi) A significant injury or illness diagnosed by a physician or other licensed health care professional. See §1904.7(b)(7).

(b)(2) *How do I record a work-related injury or illness that results in the employee's death?* You must record an injury or illness that results in death by entering a check mark on the OSHA 300 Log in the space for cases resulting in death. You must also report any work-related fatality to OSHA within eight (8) hours, as required by §1904.39.

(b)(3) *How do I record a work-related injury or illness that results in days away from work?* When an injury or illness involves one or more days away from work, you must record the injury or illness on the OSHA 300 Log with a check mark in the space for cases involving days away and an entry of the number of calendar days away from work in the number of days column. If the employee is out for an extended period of time, you must enter an estimate of the days that the employee will be away, and update the day count when the actual number of days is known.

(b)(3)(i) *Do I count the day on which the injury occurred or the illness began?* No, you begin counting days away on the day after the injury occurred or the illness began.

(b)(3)(ii) *How do I record an injury or illness when a physician or other licensed health care professional recommends that the worker stay at home but the employee comes to work anyway?* You must record these injuries and illnesses on the OSHA 300 Log using the check box for cases with days away from work and enter the number of calendar days away recommended by the physician or other licensed health care professional. If a physician or other licensed health care professional recommends days away, you should encourage your employee to follow that recommendation. However, the days away must be recorded whether the injured or ill employee follows the physician or licensed health care professional's recommendation or not. If you receive recommendations from two or more physicians or other licensed health care professionals, you may make a decision as to which recommendation is the most authoritative, and record the case based upon that recommendation.

(b)(3)(iii) *How do I handle a case when a physician or other licensed health care professional recommends that the worker return to work but the employee stays at home anyway?* In this situation, you must end the count of days away from work on the date the physician or other licensed health care professional recommends that the employee return to work.

(b)(3)(iv) *How do I count weekends, holidays, or other days the employee would not have worked anyway?* You must count the number of calendar days the employee was unable to work as a result of the injury or illness, regardless of whether or not the employee was scheduled to work on those day(s). Weekend days, holidays, vacation days or other days off are included in the total number of days recorded if the employee would not have been able to work on those days because of a work-related injury or illness.

(b)(3)(v) *How do I record a case in which a worker is injured or becomes ill on a Friday and reports to work on a Monday, and was not scheduled to work on the weekend?* You need to record this case only if you receive information from a physician or other licensed health care professional indicating that the employee should not have worked, or should have performed only restricted work, during the weekend. If so, you must record the injury or illness as a case with days away from work or restricted work, and enter the day counts, as appropriate.

(b)(3)(vi) *How do I record a case in which a worker is injured or becomes ill on the day before scheduled time off such as a holiday, a planned vacation, or a temporary plant closing?* You need to record a case of this type only if you receive information from a physician or other licensed health care professional indicating that the employee should not have worked, or should have performed only restricted work, during the scheduled time off. If so, you must record the injury or illness as a case with days away from work or restricted work, and enter the day counts, as appropriate.

(b)(3)(vii) *Is there a limit to the number of days away from work I must count?* Yes, you may "cap" the total days away at 180 calendar days. You are not required to keep track of the number of calendar days away from work if the injury or illness resulted in more than 180 calendar days away from work and/or days of job transfer or restriction. In such a case, entering 180 in the total days away column will be considered adequate.

(b)(3)(viii) *May I stop counting days if an employee who is away from work because of an injury or illness retires or leaves my company?* Yes, if the employee leaves your company for some reason unrelated to the injury or illness, such as retirement, a plant closing, or to take another job, you may stop counting days away from work or days of restriction/job transfer. If the employee leaves your company because of the injury or illness, you must estimate the total number of days away or days of restriction/job transfer and enter the day count on the 300 Log.

(b)(3)(ix) *If a case occurs in one year but results in days away during the next calendar year, do I record the case in both years?* No, you only record the injury or illness once. You must enter the number of calendar days away for the injury or illness on the OSHA 300 Log for the year in which the injury or illness occurred. If the employee is still away from work because of the injury or illness when you prepare the annual summary, estimate the total number of calendar days you expect the employee to be away from work, use this number to calculate the total for the annual summary, and then update the initial log entry later when the day count is known or reaches the 180-day cap.

(b)(4) *How do I record a work-related injury or illness that results in restricted work or job transfer?* When an injury or illness involves restricted work or job transfer but does not involve death or days away from work, you must record the injury or illness on the OSHA 300 Log by placing a check mark in the space for job transfer or restriction and an entry of the number of restricted or transferred days in the restricted workdays column.

(b)(4)(i) *How do I decide if the injury or illness resulted in restricted work?* Restricted work occurs when, as the result of a work-related injury or illness:

(b)(4)(i)(A) You keep the employee from performing one or more of the routine functions of his or her job, or from working the full workday that he or she would otherwise have been scheduled to work; or

(b)(4)(i)(B) A physician or other licensed health care professional recommends that the employee not perform one or more of the routine functions of his or her job, or not work the full workday that he or she would otherwise have been scheduled to work.

(b)(4)(ii) *What is meant by "routine functions"?* For recordkeeping purposes, an employee's routine functions are those work activities the employee regularly performs at least once per week.

(b)(4)(iii) *Do I have to record restricted work or job transfer if it applies only to the day on which the injury occurred or the illness began?* No, you do not have to record restricted work or job transfers if you, or the physician or other licensed health care professional, impose the restriction or transfer only for the day on which the injury occurred or the illness began.

(b)(4)(iv) *If you or a physician or other licensed health care professional recommends a work restriction, is the injury or illness automatically recordable as a "restricted work" case?* No, a recommended work restriction is recordable only if it affects one or more of the employee's routine job functions. To determine whether this is the case, you must evaluate the restriction in light of the routine functions of the injured or ill employee's job. If the restriction from you or the physician or other licensed health care professional keeps the employee from performing one or more of his or her routine job functions, or from working the full workday the injured or ill employee would otherwise have worked, the employee's work has been restricted and you must record the case.

(b)(4)(v) *How do I record a case where the worker works only for a partial work shift because of a work-related injury or illness?* A partial day of work is recorded as a day of job transfer or restriction for recordkeeping purposes, except for the day on which the injury occurred or the illness began.

(b)(4)(vi) *If the injured or ill worker produces fewer goods or services than he or she would have produced prior to the injury or illness but otherwise performs all of the routine functions of his or her work, is the case considered a restricted work case?* No, the case is considered restricted work only if the worker does not perform all of the routine functions of his or her job or does not work the full shift that he or she would otherwise have worked.

(b)(4)(vii) *How do I handle vague restrictions from a physician or other licensed health care professional, such as that the employee engage only in "light duty" or "take it easy for a week"?* If you are not clear about the physician or other licensed health care professional's recommendation, you may ask that person whether the employee can do all of his or her routine job functions and work all of his or her normally assigned work shift. If the answer to both of these questions is "Yes," then the case does not involve a work restriction and does not have to be recorded as such. If the answer to one or both of these questions is "No," the case involves restricted work and must be recorded as a restricted work case. If you are unable to obtain this additional information from the physician or other licensed health care professional who recommended the restriction, record the injury or illness as a case involving restricted work.

(b)(4)(viii) *What do I do if a physician or other licensed health care professional recommends a job restriction meeting OSHA's definition, but the employee does all of his or her routine job functions anyway?* You must record the injury or illness on the OSHA 300 Log as a restricted work case. If a physician or other licensed health care professional recommends a job restriction, you should ensure that the employee complies with that restriction. If you receive recommendations from two or more physicians or other licensed health care professionals, you may make a decision as to which recommendation is the most authoritative, and record the case based upon that recommendation.

(b)(4)(ix) *How do I decide if an injury or illness involved a transfer to another job?* If you assign an injured or ill employee to a job other than his or her regular job for part of the day, the case involves transfer to another job. **Note:** This does not include the day on which the injury or illness occurred.

(b)(4)(x) *Are transfers to another job recorded in the same way as restricted work cases?* Yes, both job transfer and restricted work cases are recorded in the same box on the OSHA 300 Log. For example, if you assign, or a physician or other licensed health care professional recommends that you assign, an injured or ill worker to his or her routine job duties for part of the day and to another job for the rest of the day, the injury or illness involves a job transfer. You must record an injury or illness that involves a job transfer by placing a check in the box for job transfer.

(b)(4)(xi) *How do I count days of job transfer or restriction?* You count days of job transfer or restriction in the same way you count days away from work, using §1904.7(b)(3)(i) to (viii), above. The only difference is that, if you permanently assign the injured or ill employee to a job that has been modified or permanently changed in a manner that eliminates the routine functions the employee was restricted from performing, you may stop the day count when the modification or change is made permanent. You must count at least one day of restricted work or job transfer for such cases.

(b)(5) *How do I record an injury or illness that involves medical treatment beyond first aid?* If a work-related injury or illness results in medical treatment beyond first aid, you must record it on the OSHA 300 Log. If the injury or illness did not involve death, one or more days away from work, one or more days of restricted work, or one or more days of job transfer, you enter a check mark in the box for cases where the employee received medical treatment but remained at work and was not transferred or restricted.

(b)(5)(i) *What is the definition of medical treatment?* "Medical treatment" means the management and care of a patient to combat disease or disorder. For the purposes of Part 1904, medical treatment does not include:

(b)(5)(i)(A) Visits to a physician or other licensed health care professional solely for observation or counseling;

(b)(5)(i)(B) The conduct of diagnostic procedures, such as x-rays and blood tests, including the administration of prescription medications used solely for diagnostic purposes (e.g., eye drops to dilate pupils); or

(b)(5)(i)(C) "First aid" as defined in paragraph (b)(5)(ii) of this Section.

(b)(5)(ii) *What is "first aid"?* For the purposes of Part 1904, "first aid" means the following:

(b)(5)(ii)(A) Using a non-prescription medication at nonprescription strength (for medications available in both prescription and non-prescription form, a recommendation by a physician or other licensed health care professional to use a non-prescription medication at prescription strength is considered medical treatment for recordkeeping purposes);

(b)(5)(ii)(B) Administering tetanus immunizations (other immunizations, such as Hepatitis B vaccine or rabies vaccine, are considered medical treatment);

(b)(5)(ii)(C) Cleaning, flushing or soaking wounds on the surface of the skin;

(b)(5)(ii)(D) Using wound coverings such as bandages, Band-Aids™, gauze pads, etc.; or using butterfly bandages or Steri-Strips™ (other wound closing devices such as sutures, staples, etc., are considered medical treatment);

(b)(5)(ii)(E) Using hot or cold therapy;

(b)(5)(ii)(F) Using any non-rigid means of support, such as elastic bandages, wraps, non-rigid back belts, etc. (devices with rigid stays or other systems designed to immobilize parts of the body are considered medical treatment for recordkeeping purposes);

(b)(5)(ii)(G) Using temporary immobilization devices while transporting an accident victim (e.g., splints, slings, neck collars, back boards, etc.).

(b)(5)(ii)(H) Drilling of a fingernail or toenail to relieve pressure, or draining fluid from a blister;

(b)(5)(ii)(I) Using eye patches;

(b)(5)(ii)(J) Removing foreign bodies from the eye using only irrigation or a cotton swab;

(b)(5)(ii)(K) Removing splinters or foreign material from areas other than the eye by irrigation, tweezers, cotton swabs or other simple means;

(b)(5)(ii)(L) Using finger guards;

(b)(5)(ii)(M) Using massages (physical therapy or chiropractic treatment are considered medical treatment for recordkeeping purposes); or

(b)(5)(ii)(N) Drinking fluids for relief of heat stress.

(b)(5)(iii) *Are any other procedures included in first aid?* No, this is a complete list of all treatments considered first aid for Part 1904 purposes.

(b)(5)(iv) *Does the professional status of the person providing the treatment have any effect on what is considered first aid or medical treatment?* No, OSHA considers the treatments listed in §1904.7(b)(5)(ii) of this Part to be first aid regardless of the professional status of the person providing the treatment. Even when these treatments are provided by a physician or other licensed health care professional, they are considered first aid for the purposes of Part 1904. Similarly, OSHA considers treatment beyond first aid to be medical treatment even when it is provided by someone other than a physician or other licensed health care professional.

(b)(5)(v) *What if a physician or other licensed health care professional recommends medical treatment but the employee does not follow the recommendation?* If a physician or other licensed health care professional recommends medical treatment, you should encourage the injured or ill employee to follow that recommendation. However, you must record the case even if the injured or ill employee does not follow the physician or other licensed health care professional's recommendation.

(b)(6) *Is every work-related injury or illness case involving a loss of consciousness recordable?* Yes, you must record a work-related injury or illness if the worker becomes unconscious, regardless of the length of time the employee remains unconscious.

(b)(7) *What is a "significant" diagnosed injury or illness that is recordable under the general criteria even if it does not result in death, days away from work, restricted work or job transfer, medical treatment beyond first aid, or loss of consciousness?* Work-related cases involving cancer, chronic irreversible disease, a fractured or cracked bone, or a punctured eardrum must always be recorded under the general criteria at the time of diagnosis by a physician or other licensed health care professional.

Note to §1904.7: OSHA believes that most significant injuries and illnesses will result in one of the criteria listed in §1904.7(a): death, days away from work, restricted work or job transfer, medical treatment beyond first aid, or loss of consciousness. However, there are some significant injuries, such as a punctured eardrum or a fractured toe or rib, for which neither medical treatment nor work restrictions may be recommended. In addition, there are some significant progressive diseases, such as byssinosis, silicosis, and some types of cancer, for which medical treatment or work restrictions may not be recommended at the time of diagnosis but are likely to be recommended as the disease progresses. OSHA believes that cancer, chronic irreversible diseases, fractured or cracked bones, and punctured eardrums are generally considered significant injuries and illnesses, and must be recorded at the initial diagnosis even if medical treatment or work restrictions are not recommended, or are postponed, in a particular case.

§1904.8
Recording criteria for needlestick and sharps injuries

(a) **Basic requirement** You must record all work-related needlestick injuries and cuts from sharp objects that are contaminated with another person's blood or other potentially infectious material (as defined by 29 CFR §1910.1030). You must enter the case on the OSHA 300 Log as an injury. To protect the employee's privacy, you may not enter the employee's name on the OSHA 300 Log (see the requirements for privacy cases in paragraphs §1904.29(b)(6) through §1904.29(b)(9)).

(b) **Implementation**

(b)(1) *What does "other potentially infectious material" mean?* The term "other potentially infectious materials" is defined in the OSHA Bloodborne Pathogens standard at §1910.1030(b). These materials include:

(b)(1)(i) Human bodily fluids, tissues and organs; and

(b)(1)(ii) Other materials infected with the HIV or hepatitis B (HBV) virus such as laboratory cultures or tissues from experimental animals.

(b)(2) *Does this mean that I must record all cuts, lacerations, punctures, and scratches?* No, you need to record cuts, lacerations, punctures, and scratches only if they are work-related and involve contamination with another person's blood or other potentially infectious material. If the cut, laceration, or scratch involves a clean object, or a contaminant other than blood or other potentially infectious material, you need to record the case only if it meets one or more of the recording criteria in §1904.7.

(b)(3) *If I record an injury and the employee is later diagnosed with an infectious bloodborne disease, do I need to update the OSHA 300 Log?* Yes, you must update the classification of the case on the OSHA 300 Log if the case results in death, days away from work, restricted work, or job transfer. You must also update the description to identify the infectious disease and change the classification of the case from an injury to an illness.

(b)(4) *What if one of my employees is splashed or exposed to blood or other potentially infectious material without being cut or scratched? Do I need to record this incident?* You need to record such an incident on the OSHA 300 Log as an illness if:

(b)(4)(i) It results in the diagnosis of a bloodborne illness, such as HIV, hepatitis B, or hepatitis C; or

(b)(4)(ii) It meets one or more of the recording criteria in §1904.7.

§1904.9
Recording criteria for cases involving medical removal under OSHA standards

(a) **Basic requirement** If an employee is medically removed under the medical surveillance requirements of an OSHA standard, you must record the case on the OSHA 300 Log.

(b) **Implementation**

(b)(1) *How do I classify medical removal cases on the OSHA 300 Log?* You must enter each medical removal case on the OSHA 300 Log as either a case involving days away from work or a case involving restricted work activity, depending on how you decide to comply with the medical removal requirement. If the medical removal is the result of a chemical exposure, you must enter the case on the OSHA 300 Log by checking the "poisoning" column.

(b)(2) *Do all of OSHA's standards have medical removal provisions?* No, some OSHA standards, such as the standards covering bloodborne pathogens and noise, do not have medical removal provisions. Many OSHA standards that cover specific chemical substances have medical removal provisions. These standards include, but are not limited to, lead, cadmium, methylene chloride, formaldehyde, and benzene.

(b)(3) *Do I have to record a case where I voluntarily removed the employee from exposure before the medical removal criteria in an OSHA standard are met?* No, if the case involves voluntary medical removal before the medical removal levels required by an OSHA standard, you do not need to record the case on the OSHA 300 Log.

§1904.10
Recording criteria for cases involving occupational hearing loss

(a) **Basic requirement** If an employee's hearing test (audiogram) reveals that the employee has experienced a work-related Standard Threshold Shift (STS) in hearing in one or both ears, and the employee's total hearing level is 25 decibels (dB) or more above audiometric zero (averaged at 2000, 3000, and 4000 Hz) in the same ear(s) as the STS, you must record the case on the OSHA 300 Log.

(b) **Implementation**

(b)(1) *What is a Standard Threshold Shift?* A Standard Threshold Shift, or STS, is defined in the occupational noise exposure standard at 29 CFR §1910.95(g)(10)(i) as a change in hearing threshold, relative to the baseline audiogram for that employee, of an average of 10 decibels (dB) or more at 2000, 3000, and 4000 hertz (Hz) in one or both ears.

(b)(2) *How do I evaluate the current audiogram to determine whether an employee has an STS and a 25–dB hearing level?*

(b)(2)(i) **STS** If the employee has never previously experienced a recordable hearing loss, you must compare the employee's current audiogram with that employee's baseline audiogram. If the employee has previously experienced a recordable hearing loss, you must compare the employee's current audiogram with the employee's revised baseline audiogram (the audiogram reflecting the employee's previous recordable hearing loss case).

(b)(2)(ii) **25–dB loss** Audiometric test results reflect the employee's overall hearing ability in comparison to audiometric zero. Therefore, using the employee's current audiogram, you must use the average hearing level at 2000, 3000, and 4000 Hz to determine whether or not the employee's total hearing level is 25 dB or more.

(b)(3) *May I adjust the current audiogram to reflect the effects of aging on hearing?* Yes. When you are determining whether an STS has occurred, you may age adjust the employee's current audiogram results by using Tables F–1 or F–2, as appropriate, in Appendix F of 29 CFR §1910.95. You may not use an age adjustment when determining whether the employee's total hearing level is 25 dB or more above audiometric zero.

(b)(4) *Do I have to record the hearing loss if I am going to retest the employee's hearing?* No, if you retest the employee's hearing within 30 days of the first test, and the retest does not confirm the recordable STS, you are not required to record the hearing loss case on the OSHA 300 Log. If the retest confirms the recordable STS, you must record the hearing loss illness within seven (7) calendar days of the retest. If subsequent audiometric testing performed under the testing requirements of the §1910.95 noise standard indicates that an STS is not persistent, you may erase or line-out the recorded entry.

(b)(5) *Are there any special rules for determining whether a hearing loss case is work-related?* No. You must use the rules in §1904.5 to determine if the hearing loss is work-related. If an event or exposure in the work environment either caused or contributed to the hearing loss, or significantly aggravated a pre-existing hearing loss, you must consider the case to be work related.

(b)(6) *If a physician or other licensed health care professional determines the hearing loss is not work-related, do I still need to record the case?* If a physician or other licensed health care professional determines that the hearing loss is not work-related or has not been significantly aggravated by occupational noise exposure, you are not required to consider the case work-related or to record the case on the OSHA 300 Log.

(b)(7) *How do I complete the 300 Log for a hearing loss case?* When you enter a recordable hearing loss case on the OSHA 300 Log, you must check the 300 Log column for hearing loss.

(**Note:** §1904.10(b)(7) is effective beginning January 1, 2004.)

[67 FR 44047, July 1, 2002, as amended at 67 FR 77170, Dec. 17, 2002]

§1904.11 Recording criteria for work–related tuberculosis cases

(a) **Basic requirement** If any of your employees has been occupationally exposed to anyone with a known case of active tuberculosis (TB), and that employee subsequently develops a tuberculosis infection, as evidenced by a positive skin test or diagnosis by a physician or other licensed health care professional, you must record the case on the OSHA 300 Log by checking the "respiratory condition" column.

(b) **Implementation**

(b)(1) *Do I have to record, on the Log, a positive TB skin test result obtained at a pre-employment physical?* No, you do not have to record it because the employee was not occupationally exposed to a known case of active tuberculosis in your workplace.

(b)(2) *May I line-out or erase a recorded TB case if I obtain evidence that the case was not caused by occupational exposure?* Yes, you may line-out or erase the case from the Log under the following circumstances:

(b)(2)(i) The worker is living in a household with a person who has been diagnosed with active TB;

(b)(2)(ii) The Public Health Department has identified the worker as a contact of an individual with a case of active TB unrelated to the workplace; or

(b)(2)(iii) A medical investigation shows that the employee's infection was caused by exposure to TB away from work, or proves that the case was not related to the workplace TB exposure.

§1904.13-§1904.28 [Reserved]

§1904.29 Forms

(a) **Basic requirement** You must use OSHA 300, 300–A, and 301 forms, or equivalent forms, for recordable injuries and illnesses. The OSHA 300 form is called the Log of Work-Related Injuries and Illnesses, the 300–A is the Summary of Work-Related Injuries and Illnesses, and the OSHA 301 form is called the Injury and Illness Incident Report.

(b) **Implementation**

(b)(1) *What do I need to do to complete the OSHA 300 Log?* You must enter information about your business at the top of the OSHA 300 Log, enter a one or two line description for each recordable injury or illness, and summarize this information on the OSHA 300–A at the end of the year.

(b)(2) *What do I need to do to complete the OSHA 301 Incident Report?* You must complete an OSHA 301 Incident Report form, or an equivalent form, for each recordable injury or illness entered on the OSHA 300 Log.

(b)(3) *How quickly must each injury or illness be recorded?* You must enter each and every recordable injury or illness on the OSHA 300 Log and on a 301 Incident Report within seven (7) calendar days of receiving information that the recordable injury or illness occurred. A failure to record within seven days does not extinguish your continuing obligation to make a record of the injury or illness and to maintain accurate records of all recordable injuries and illnesses in accordance with the requirements of this Part. This obligation continues throughout the entire record retention period described in §1904.33. See §1904.4(a); §1904.32(a)(1); §1904.33(b)(1); and §1904.40(a).

(b)(4) *What is an equivalent form?* An equivalent form is one that has the same information, is as readable and understandable, and is completed using the same instructions as the OSHA form it replaces. Many employers use an insurance form instead of the OSHA 301 Incident Report, or supplement an insurance form by adding any additional information required by OSHA.

(b)(5) *May I keep my records on a computer?* Yes, if the computer can produce equivalent forms when they are needed, as described under §1904.35 and §1904.40, you may keep your records using the computer system.

(b)(6) *Are there situations where I do not put the employee's name on the forms for privacy reasons?* Yes, if you have a "privacy concern case," you may not enter the employee's name on the OSHA 300 Log. Instead, enter "privacy case" in the space normally used for the employee's name. This will protect the privacy of the injured or ill employee when another employee, a former employee, or an authorized employee representative is provided access to the OSHA 300 Log under §1904.35(b)(2). You must keep a separate, confidential list of the case numbers and employee names for your privacy concern cases so you can update the cases and provide the information to the government if asked to do so.

(b)(7) *How do I determine if an injury or illness is a privacy concern case?* You must consider the following injuries or illnesses to be privacy concern cases:

(b)(7)(i) An injury or illness to an intimate body part or the reproductive system;

(b)(7)(ii) An injury or illness resulting from a sexual assault;

(b)(7)(iii) Mental illnesses;

(b)(7)(iv) HIV infection, hepatitis, or tuberculosis;

(b)(7)(v) Needlestick injuries and cuts from sharp objects that are contaminated with another person's blood or other potentially infectious material (see §1904.8 for definitions); and

(b)(7)(vi) Other illnesses, if the employee voluntarily requests that his or her name not be entered on the log.

(b)(8) *May I classify any other types of injuries and illnesses as privacy concern cases?* No, this is a complete list of all injuries and illnesses considered privacy concern cases for Part 1904 purposes.

(b)(9) If I have removed the employee's name, but still believe that the employee may be identified from the information on the forms, is there anything else that I can do to further protect the employee's privacy? Yes, if you have a reasonable basis to believe that information describing the privacy concern case may be personally identifiable even though the employee's name has been omitted, you may use discretion in describing the injury or illness on both the OSHA 300 and 301 forms. You must enter enough information to identify the cause of the incident and the general severity of the injury or illness, but you do not need to include details of an intimate or private nature. For example, a sexual assault case could be described as "injury from assault," or an injury to a reproductive organ could be described as "lower abdominal injury."

(b)(10) *What must I do to protect employee privacy if I wish to provide access to the OSHA Forms 300 and 301 to persons other than government representatives, employees, former employees or authorized representatives?* If you decide to voluntarily disclose the Forms to persons other than government representatives, employees, former employees or authorized representatives (as required by §1904.35 and §1904.40), you must remove or hide the employees' names and other personally identifying information, except for the following cases. You may disclose the Forms with personally identifying information only:

(b)(10)(i) to an auditor or consultant hired by the employer to evaluate the safety and health program;

(b)(10)(ii) to the extent necessary for processing a claim for workers' compensation or other insurance benefits; or

(b)(10)(iii) to a public health authority or law enforcement agency for uses and disclosures for which consent, an authorization, or opportunity to agree or object is not required under Department of Health and Human Services Standards for Privacy of Individually Identifiable Health Information, 45 CFR 164.512.

[66 FR 6122, Jan. 19, 2001, as amended at 66 FR 52034, Oct. 12, 2001; 67 FR 77170, Dec. 17, 2002; 68 FR 38607, June 30, 2003]

Subpart D—Other OSHA Injury and Illness Recordkeeping Requirements

§1904.30 Multiple business establishments

(a) **Basic requirement** You must keep a separate OSHA 300 Log for each establishment that is expected to be in operation for one year or longer.

(b) **Implementation**

(b)(1) *Do I need to keep OSHA injury and illness records for short-term establishments (i.e., establishments that will exist for less than a year)?* Yes, however, you do not have to keep a separate OSHA 300 Log for each such establishment. You may keep one OSHA 300 Log that covers all of your short-term establishments. You may also include the short-term establishments' recordable injuries and illnesses on an OSHA 300 Log that covers short-term establishments for individual company divisions or geographic regions.

(b)(2) *May I keep the records for all of my establishments at my headquarters location or at some other central location?* Yes, you may keep the records for an establishment at your headquarters or other central location if you can:

(b)(2)(i) Transmit information about the injuries and illnesses from the establishment to the central location within seven (7) calendar days of receiving information that a recordable injury or illness has occurred; and

(b)(2)(ii) Produce and send the records from the central location to the establishment within the time frames required by §1904.35 and §1904.40 when you are required to provide records to a government representative, employees, former employees or employee representatives.

(b)(3) *Some of my employees work at several different locations or do not work at any of my establishments at all. How do I record cases for these employees?* You must link each of your employees with one of your establishments, for recordkeeping purposes. You must record the injury and illness on the OSHA 300 Log of the injured or ill employee's establishment, or on an OSHA 300 Log that covers that employee's short-term establishment.

(b)(4) *How do I record an injury or illness when an employee of one of my establishments is injured or becomes ill while visiting or working at another of my establishments, or while working away from any of my establishments?* If the injury or illness occurs at one of your establishments, you must record the injury or illness on the OSHA 300 Log of the establishment at which the injury or illness occurred. If the employee is injured or becomes ill and is not at one of your establishments, you must record the case on the OSHA 300 Log at the establishment at which the employee normally works.

§1904.31 Covered employees

(a) **Basic requirement** You must record on the OSHA 300 Log the recordable injuries and illnesses of all employees on your payroll, whether they are labor, executive, hourly, salary, part-time, seasonal, or migrant workers. You also must record the recordable injuries and illnesses that occur to employees who are not on your payroll if you supervise these employees on a day-to-day basis. If your business is organized as a sole proprietorship or partnership, the owner or partners are not considered employees for recordkeeping purposes.

(b) **Implementation**

(b)(1) *If a self-employed person is injured or becomes ill while doing work at my business, do I need to record the injury or illness?* No, self-employed individuals are not covered by the OSH Act or this regulation.

(b)(2) *If I obtain employees from a temporary help service, employee leasing service, or personnel supply service, do I have to record an injury or illness occurring to one of those employees?* You must record these injuries and illnesses if you supervise these employees on a day-to-day basis.

(b)(3) *If an employee in my establishment is a contractor's employee, must I record an injury or illness occurring to that employee?* If the contractor's employee is under the day-to-day supervision of the contractor, the contractor is responsible for recording the injury or illness. If you supervise the contractor employee's work on a day-to-day basis, you must record the injury or illness.

(b)(4) *Must the personnel supply service, temporary help service, employee leasing service, or contractor also record the injuries or illnesses occurring to temporary, leased or contract employees that I supervise on a day-to-day basis?* No, you and the temporary help service, employee leasing service, personnel supply service, or contractor should coordinate your efforts to make sure that each injury and illness is recorded only once: either on your OSHA 300 Log (if you provide day-to-day supervision) or on the other employer's OSHA 300 Log (if that company provides day-to-day supervision).

§1904.32 Year-end review and annual summary

(a) **Basic requirement** At the end of each calendar year, you must:

(a)(1) Review that year's OSHA 300 Log to verify that it contains accurate entries for all recordable injuries and illnesses that occurred during the year, and make any additions or corrections necessary to ensure its accuracy;

(a)(2) Verify that each injury and illness recorded on the 300 Log, including any injuries and illnesses added to the Log following your year-end review pursuant to paragraph (a)(1) of this Section, is accurately recorded on a corresponding 301 Incident Report form;

(a)(3) After you have verified the accuracy of the Log, create an annual summary of injuries and illnesses recorded on the Log;

(a)(4) Certify the summary; and

(a)(5) Post the summary.

(b) **Implementation**

(b)(1) *How extensively do I have to review the OSHA 300 Log at the end of the year?* You must review the Log and its entries as extensively as necessary to verify that all recordable injuries and illnesses that occurred during the year are entered and that the Log and its entries are accurate.

(b)(2) *How do I complete the annual summary?* You must:

(b)(2)(i) Total the columns on the OSHA 300 Log (if you had no recordable cases, enter zeros for each column total); and

(b)(2)(ii) Enter the calendar year covered, the company's name, establishment name, establishment address, annual average number of employees covered by the OSHA 300 Log, and the total hours worked by all employees covered by the OSHA 300 Log.

(b)(2)(iii) If you are using an equivalent form other than the OSHA 300-A summary form, as permitted under §1904.6(b)(4), the summary you use must also include the employee access and employer penalty statements found on the OSHA 300-A Summary form.

(b)(3) *How do I certify the annual summary?* A company executive must certify that he or she has examined the OSHA 300 Log and that he or she reasonably believes, based on his or her knowledge of the process by which the information was recorded, that the annual summary is correct and complete.

(b)(4) *Who is considered a company executive?* The company executive who certifies the log must be one of the following persons:

(b)(4)(i) An owner of the company (only if the company is a sole proprietorship or partnership);

(b)(4)(ii) An officer of the corporation;

(b)(4)(iii) The highest ranking company official working at the establishment; or

(b)(4)(iv) The immediate supervisor of the highest ranking company official working at the establishment.

(b)(5) *How do I post the annual summary?* You must post a copy of the annual summary in each establishment in a conspicuous place or places where notices to employees are customarily posted. You must ensure that the posted annual summary is not altered, defaced or covered by other material.

(b)(6) *When do I have to post the annual summary?* You must post the summary no later than February 1 of the year following the year covered by the records and keep the posting in place until April 30.

§1904.33 Retention and maintenance of accurate records.

(a) **Basic requirement** You must save the OSHA 300 Log, the privacy case list (if one exists), the annual summary, and the OSHA 301 Incident Report forms for five (5) years following the end of the calendar year that these records cover.

OI indicates an OSHA Letter of Interpretation exists for this specific reference. Please see www.oshainterpretation.us for details.

(b) **Implementation**

(b)(1) *Other than the obligation identified in §1904.32, do I have further recording duties with respect to the OSHA 300 Logs and 301 Incident Reports during the five-year retention period?* You must make the following additions and corrections to the OSHA Log and Incident Reports during the five-year retention period:

(b)(1)(i) The OSHA Logs must contain entries for all recordable injuries and illnesses that occurred during the calendar year to which each Log relates. In addition, each and every recordable injury and illness must be recorded on an Incident Report. This means that if a recordable case occurred and you failed to record it on the Log for the year in which the injury or illness occurred, and/or on an Incident Report, you are under a continuing obligation to record the case on the Log and/or Incident Report during the five-year retention period for that Log and/or Incident Report;

(b)(1)(ii) You must also make any additions and corrections to the OSHA Log that are necessary to accurately reflect any changes that have occurred with respect to previously recorded injuries and illnesses. Thus, if the classification, description, or outcome of a previously recorded case changes, you must remove or line out the original entry and enter the new information; and

(b)(1)(iii) You must have an Incident Report for each and every recordable injury and illness; however, you are not required to make additions or corrections to Incident Reports during the five-year retention period.

(b)(2) *Do I have to make additions or corrections to the annual summary during the five-year retention period?* You are not required to make additions or corrections to the annual summaries during the five-year retention period.

§1904.34 Change in business ownership

If your business changes ownership, you are responsible for recording and reporting work-related injuries and illnesses only for that period of the year during which you owned the establishment. You must transfer the Part 1904 records to the new owner. The new owner must save all records of the establishment kept by the prior owner, as required by §1904.33, but need not update or correct the records of the prior owner. The new owner is not responsible for recording and reporting work-related injuries and illnesses that occurred before the new owner took ownership of the establishment.

§1904.35 Employee involvement

(a) **Basic requirement** Your employees and their representatives must be involved in the recordkeeping system in several ways.

(a)(1) You must inform each employee of how he or she is to report a work-related injury or illness to you.

(a)(2) You must provide employees with the information described in paragraph (b)(1)(iii) of this Section.

(a)(3) You must provide access to your injury and illness records for your employees and their representatives as described in paragraph (b)(2) of this Section.

(b) **Implementation**

(b)(1) *What must I do to make sure that employees report work-related injuries and illnesses to me?*

(b)(1)(i) You must establish a reasonable procedure for employees to report work-related injuries and illnesses promptly and accurately. A procedure is not reasonable if it would deter or discourage a reasonable employee from accurately reporting a workplace injury or illness;

(b)(1)(ii) You must inform each employee of your procedure for reporting work-related injuries and illnesses;

(b)(1)(iii) You must inform each employee that:

(b)(1)(iii)(A) Employees have the right to report work-related injuries and illnesses; and

(b)(1)(iii)(B) Employers are prohibited from discharging or in any manner discriminating against employees for reporting work-related injuries or illnesses; and

(b)(1)(iii)(iv) You must not discharge or in any manner discriminate against any employee for reporting a work-related injury or illness

(b)(2) *Do I have to give my employees and their representatives access to the OSHA injury and illness records?* Yes, your employees, former employees, their personal representatives, and their authorized employee representatives have the right to access accurate OSHA injury and illness records, with some limitations, as discussed below.

(b)(2)(i) *Who is an authorized employee representative?* An authorized employee representative is an authorized collective bargaining agent of employees.

(b)(2)(ii) *Who is a "personal representative" of an employee or former employee?* A personal representative is:

(b)(2)(ii)(A) Any person that the employee or former employee designates as such, in writing; or

(b)(2)(ii)(B) The legal representative of a deceased or legally incapacitated employee or former employee.

(b)(2)(iii) *If an employee or representative asks for access to the OSHA 300 Log, when do I have to provide it?* When an employee, former employee, personal representative, or authorized employee representative asks for copies of your current or stored OSHA 300 Log(s) for an establishment the employee or former employee has worked in, you must give the requester a copy of the relevant and accurate OSHA 300 Log(s) by the end of the next business day.

(b)(2)(iv) *May I remove the names of the employees or any other information from the OSHA 300 Log before I give copies to an employee, former employee, or employee representative?* No, you must leave the names on the 300 Log. However, to protect the privacy of injured and ill employees, you may not record the employee's name on the OSHA 300 Log for certain "privacy concern cases," as specified in paragraphs §1904.29(b)(6) through §1904.29(b)(9).

(b)(2)(v) *If an employee or representative asks for access to the OSHA 301 Incident Report, when do I have to provide it?*

(b)(2)(v)(A) When an employee, former employee, or personal representative asks for a copy of the OSHA 301 Incident Report describing an injury or illness to that employee or former employee, you must give the requester a copy of the OSHA 301 Incident Report containing that information by the end of the next business day.

(b)(2)(v)(B) When an authorized employee representative asks for copies of the OSHA 301 Incident Reports for an establishment where the agent represents employees under a collective bargaining agreement, you must give copies of those forms to the authorized employee representative within 7 calendar days. You are only required to give the authorized employee representative information from the OSHA 301 Incident Report section titled "Tell us about the case." You must remove all other information from the copy of the OSHA 301 Incident Report or the equivalent substitute form that you give to the authorized employee representative.

(b)(2)(vi) *May I charge for the copies?* No, you may not charge for these copies the first time they are provided. However, if one of the designated persons asks for additional copies, you may assess a reasonable charge for retrieving and copying the records.

§1904.36 Prohibition against discrimination

In addition to §1904.35, section 11(c) of the OSH Act also prohibits you from discriminating against an employee for reporting a work-related fatality, injury, or illness. That provision of the Act also protects the employee who files a safety and health complaint, asks for access to the Part 1904 records, or otherwise exercises any rights afforded by the OSH Act.

§1904.37 State recordkeeping regulations

(a) **Basic requirement** Some States operate their own OSHA programs, under the authority of a State plan as approved by OSHA. States operating OSHA-approved State plans must have occupational injury and illness recording and reporting requirements that are substantially identical to the requirements in this Part (see 29 CFR §1902.3(j), 29 CFR §1902.7, and 29 CFR §1956.10(i)).

(b) **Implementation**

(b)(1) State-Plan States must have the same requirements as Federal OSHA for determining which injuries and illnesses are recordable and how they are recorded.

(b)(2) For other Part 1904 provisions (for example, industry exemptions, reporting of fatalities and hospitalizations, record retention, or employee involvement), State-Plan State requirements may be more stringent than or supplemental to the Federal requirements, but because of the unique nature of the national recordkeeping program, States must consult with and obtain approval of any such requirements.

(b)(3) Although State and local government employees are not covered Federally, all State-Plan States must provide coverage, and must develop injury and illness statistics, for these workers. State Plan recording and reporting requirements for State and local government entities may differ from those for the private sector but must meet the requirements of paragraphs §1904.37(b)(1) and (b)(2).

(b)(4) A State-Plan State may not issue a variance to a private sector employer and must recognize all variances issued by Federal OSHA.

(b)(5) A State Plan State may only grant an injury and illness recording and reporting variance to a State or local government employer within the State after obtaining approval to grant the variance from Federal OSHA.

§1904.38 Variances from the recordkeeping rule

(a) **Basic requirement** If you wish to keep records in a different manner from the manner prescribed by the Part 1904 regulations, you may submit a variance petition to the Assistant Secretary of Labor for Occupational Safety and Health, U.S. Department of Labor, Washington, DC 20210. You can obtain a variance only if you can show that your alternative recordkeeping system:

(a)(1) Collects the same information as this Part requires;

(a)(2) Meets the purposes of the Act; and

(a)(3) Does not interfere with the administration of the Act.

(b) **Implementation**

(b)(1) *What do I need to include in my variance petition?* You must include the following items in your petition:

(b)(1)(i) Your name and address;

(b)(1)(ii) A list of the State(s) where the variance would be used;

(b)(1)(iii) The address(es) of the business establishment(s) involved;

(b)(1)(iv) A description of why you are seeking a variance;

(b)(1)(v) A description of the different recordkeeping procedures you propose to use;

(b)(1)(vi) A description of how your proposed procedures will collect the same information as would be collected by this Part and achieve the purpose of the Act; and

(b)(1)(vii) A statement that you have informed your employees of the petition by giving them or their authorized representative a copy of the petition and by posting a statement summarizing the petition in the same way as notices are posted under §1903.2(a).

(b)(2) *How will the Assistant Secretary handle my variance petition?* The Assistant Secretary will take the following steps to process your variance petition.

(b)(2)(i) The Assistant Secretary will offer your employees and their authorized representatives an opportunity to submit written data, views, and arguments about your variance petition.

(b)(2)(ii) The Assistant Secretary may allow the public to comment on your variance petition by publishing the petition in the Federal Register. If the petition is published, the notice will establish a public comment period and may include a schedule for a public meeting on the petition.

(b)(2)(iii) After reviewing your variance petition and any comments from your employees and the public, the Assistant Secretary will decide whether or not your proposed recordkeeping procedures will meet the purposes of the Act, will not otherwise interfere with the Act, and will provide the same information as the Part 1904 regulations provide. If your procedures meet these criteria, the Assistant Secretary may grant the variance subject to such conditions as he or she finds appropriate.

(b)(2)(iv) If the Assistant Secretary grants your variance petition, OSHA will publish a notice in the Federal Register to announce the variance. The notice will include the practices the variance allows you to use, any conditions that apply, and the reasons for allowing the variance.

(b)(3) *If I apply for a variance, may I use my proposed recordkeeping procedures while the Assistant Secretary is processing the variance petition?* No, alternative recordkeeping practices are only allowed after the variance is approved. You must comply with the Part 1904 regulations while the Assistant Secretary is reviewing your variance petition.

(b)(4) *If I have already been cited by OSHA for not following the Part 1904 regulations, will my variance petition have any effect on the citation and penalty?* No, in addition, the Assistant Secretary may elect not to review your variance petition if it includes an element for which you have been cited and the citation is still under review by a court, an Administrative Law Judge (ALJ), or the OSH Review Commission.

(b)(5) *If I receive a variance, may the Assistant Secretary revoke the variance at a later date?* Yes, the Assistant Secretary may revoke your variance if he or she has good cause. The procedures revoking a variance will follow the same process as OSHA uses for reviewing variance petitions, as outlined in paragraph §1904.38(b)(2). Except in cases of willfulness or where necessary for public safety, the Assistant Secretary will:

(b)(5)(i) Notify you in writing of the facts or conduct that may warrant revocation of your variance; and

(b)(5)(ii) Provide you, your employees, and authorized employee representatives with an opportunity to participate in the revocation procedures.

Subpart E—Reporting Accurate Fatality, Injury, and Illness Information to the Government

Authority: 29 U.S.C. 657, 673, 5 U.S.C. 553, and Secretary of Labor's Order 1-2012 (77 FR 3912, Jan. 25, 2012).

§1904.39 [OI] Reporting fatalities, hospitalizations, amputations, and losses of an eye as a result of work-related incidents to OSHA

(a) **Basic requirement**

(a)(1) Within eight (8) hours after the death of any employee as a result of a work-related incident, you must report the fatality to the Occupational Safety and Health Administration (OSHA), U.S. Department of Labor.

(a)(2) Within twenty-four (24) hours after the in-patient hospitalization of one or more employees or an employee's amputation or an employee's loss of an eye, as a result of a work-related incident, you must report the in-patient hospitalization, amputation, or loss of an eye to OSHA.

(a)(3) You must report the fatality, in-patient hospitalization, amputation, or loss of an eye using one of the following methods:

(a)(3)(i) By telephone or in person to the OSHA Area Office that is nearest to the site of the incident.

(a)(3)(ii) By telephone to the OSHA toll-free central telephone number, 1-800-321-OSHA (1-800-321-6742).

(a)(3)(iii) By electronic submission using the reporting application located on OSHA's public Web site at www.osha.gov.

(b) **Implementation**

(b)(1) *If the Area Office is closed, may I report the fatality, in-patient hospitalization, amputation, or loss of an eye by leaving a message on OSHA's answering machine, faxing the Area Office, or sending an email?* No, if the Area Office is closed, you must report the fatality, in-patient hospitalization, amputation, or loss of an eye using either the 800 number or the reporting application located on OSHA's public Web site at www.osha.gov.

(b)(2) *What information do I need to give to OSHA about the in-patient hospitalization, amputation, or loss of an eye?* You must give OSHA the following information for each fatality, in-patient hospitalization, amputation, or loss of an eye:

(b)(2)(i) The establishment name;

(b)(2)(ii) The location of the work-related incident;

(b)(2)(iii) The time of the work-related incident;

(b)(2)(iv) The type of reportable event (i.e., fatality, in-patient hospitalization, amputation, or loss of an eye);

(b)(2)(v) The number of employees who suffered a fatality, in-patient hospitalization, amputation, or loss of an eye;

(b)(2)(vi) The names of the employees who suffered a fatality, in-patient hospitalization, amputation, or loss of an eye;

(b)(2)(vii) Your contact person and his or her phone number; and

(b)(2)(viii) A brief description of the work-related incident.

(b)(3) *Do I have to report the fatality, in-patient hospitalization, amputation, or loss of an eye if it resulted from a motor vehicle accident on a public street or highway?* If the motor vehicle accident occurred in a construction work zone, you must report the fatality, in-patient hospitalization, amputation, or loss of an eye. If the motor vehicle accident occurred on a public street or highway, but not in a construction work zone, you do not have to report the fatality, in-patient hospitalization, amputation, or loss of an eye to OSHA. However, the fatality, in-patient hospitalization, amputation, or loss of an eye must be recorded on your OSHA injury and illness records, if you are required to keep such records.

(b)(4) *Do I have to report the fatality, in-patient hospitalization, amputation, or loss of an eye if it occurred on a commercial or public transportation system?* No, you do not have to report the fatality, in-patient hospitalization, amputation, or loss of an eye to OSHA if it occurred on a commercial or public transportation system (e.g., airplane, train, subway, or bus). However, the fatality, in-patient hospitalization, amputation, or loss of an eye must be recorded on your OSHA injury and illness records, if you are required to keep such records.

(b)(5) *Do I have to report a work-related fatality or in-patient hospitalization caused by a heart attack?* Yes, your local OSHA Area Office director will decide whether to investigate the event, depending on the circumstances of the heart attack.

(b)(6) *What if the fatality, in-patient hospitalization, amputation, or loss of an eye does not occur during or right after the work-related incident?* You must only report a fatality to OSHA if the fatality occurs within thirty (30) days of the work-related incident. For an in-patient hospitalization, amputation, or loss of an eye, you must only report the event to OSHA if it occurs within twenty-four (24) hours of the work-related incident. However, the fatality, in-patient hospitalization, amputation, or loss of an eye must be recorded on your OSHA injury and illness records, if you are required to keep such records.

(b)(7) *What if I don't learn about a reportable fatality, in-patient hospitalization, amputation, or loss of an eye right away?* If you do not learn about a reportable fatality, in-patient hospitalization, amputation, or loss of an eye at the time it takes place, you must make the report to OSHA within the following time period after the fatality, in-patient hospitalization, amputation, or loss of an eye is reported to you or to any of your agent(s): Eight (8) hours for a fatality, and twenty-four (24) hours for an in-patient hospitalization, an amputation, or a loss of an eye.

(b)(8) *What if I don't learn right away that the reportable fatality, in-patient hospitalization, amputation, or loss of an eye was the result of a work-related incident?* If you do not learn right away that the reportable fatality, in-patient hospitalization, amputation, or loss of an eye was the result of a work-related incident, you must make the report to OSHA within the following time period after you or any of your agent(s) learn that the reportable fatality, in-patient hospitalization, amputation, or loss of an eye was the result of a work-related incident: Eight (8) hours for a fatality, and twenty-four (24) hours for an in-patient hospitalization, an amputation, or a loss of an eye.

(b)(9) *How does OSHA define "in-patient hospitalization"?* OSHA defines in-patient hospitalization as a formal admission to the in-patient service of a hospital or clinic for care or treatment.

(b)(10) *Do I have to report an in-patient hospitalization that involves only observation or diagnostic testing?* No, you do not have to report an in-patient hospitalization that involves only observation or diagnostic testing. You must only report to OSHA each in-patient hospitalization that involves care or treatment.

(b)(11) *How does OSHA define "amputation"?* An amputation is the traumatic loss of a limb or other external body part. Amputations include a part, such as a limb or appendage, that has been severed, cut off, amputated (either completely or partially); fingertip amputations with or without bone loss; medical amputations resulting from irreparable damage; amputations of body parts that have since been reattached. Amputations do not include avulsions, enucleations, deglovings, scalpings, severed ears, or broken or chipped teeth.

§1904.40 OI
Providing accurate records to government representatives

(a) **Basic requirement** When an authorized government representative requests the records you keep under Part 1904, you must provide accurate records, or copies thereof, within four (4) business hours of the request.

(b) OI **Implementation**

(b)(1) *What government representatives have the right to get copies of my Part 1904 records?* The government representatives authorized to receive the records are:

(b)(1)(i) A representative of the Secretary of Labor conducting an inspection or investigation under the Act;

(b)(1)(ii) A representative of the Secretary of Health and Human Services (including the National Institute for Occupational Safety and Health—NIOSH) conducting an investigation under Section 20(b) of the Act, or

(b)(1)(iii) A representative of a State agency responsible for administering a State plan approved under Section 18 of the Act.

(b)(2) *Do I have to produce the records within four (4) hours if my records are kept at a location in a different time zone?* OSHA will consider your response to be timely if you give the records to the government representative within four (4) business hours of the request. If you maintain the records at a location in a different time zone, you may use the business hours of the establishment at which the records are located when calculating the deadline.

§1904.41 OI
Annual OSHA injury and illness survey of ten or more employers

(a) **Basic requirements**

(a)(1) **Annual electronic submission of Part 1904 records by establishments with 250 or more employees** If your establishment had 250 or more employees at any time during the previous calendar year, and this Part requires your establishment to keep records, then you must electronically submit information from the three recordkeeping forms that you keep under this Part (OSHA Form 300A Summary of Work-Related Injuries and Illnesses, OSHA Form 300 Log of Work-Related Injuries and Illnesses, and OSHA Form 301 Injury and Illness Incident Report) to OSHA or OSHA's designee. You must submit the information once a year, no later than the date listed in paragraph (c) of this section of the year after the calendar year covered by the forms.

(a)(2) **Annual electronic submission of OSHA Form 300A Summary of Work-Related Injuries and Illnesses by establishments with 20 or more employees but fewer than 250 employees in designated industries** If your establishment had 20 or more employees but fewer than 250 employees at any time during the previous calendar year, and your establishment is classified in an industry listed in Appendix A to Subpart E of this Part, then you must electronically submit information from OSHA Form 300A Summary of Work-Related Injuries and Illnesses to OSHA or OSHA's designee. You must submit the information once a year, no later than the date listed in paragraph (c) of this section of the year after the calendar year covered by the form.

(a)(3) **Electronic submission of Part 1904 records upon notification** Upon notification, you must electronically submit the requested information from your Part 1904 records to OSHA or OSHA's designee.

(b) **Implementation**

(b)(1) *Does every employer have to routinely submit information from the injury and illness records to OSHA?* No, only two categories of employers must routinely submit information from their injury and illness records. First, if your establishment had 250 or more employees at any time during the previous calendar year, and this Part requires your establishment to keep records, then you must submit the required Form 300A, 300, and 301 information to OSHA once a year. Second, if your establishment had 20 or more employees but fewer than 250 employees at any time during the previous calendar year, and your establishment is classified in an industry listed in Appendix A to Subpart E of this Part, then you must submit the required Form 300A information to OSHA once a year. Employers in these two categories must submit the required information by the date listed in paragraph (c) of this section of the year after the calendar year covered by the form or forms (for example, 2017 for the 2016 forms). If you are not in either of these two categories, then you must submit information from the injury and illness records to OSHA only if OSHA notifies you to do so for an individual data collection.

(b)(2) *If I have to submit information under paragraph (a)(1) of this Section, do I have to submit all of the information from the recordkeeping form?* No, you are required to submit all of the information from the form except the following:

(b)(2)(i) Log of Work-Related Injuries and Illnesses (OSHA Form 300): Employee name (column B).

(b)(2)(ii) Injury and Illness Incident Report (OSHA Form 301): Employee name (field 1), employee address (field 2), name of physician or other health care professional (field 6), facility name and address if treatment was given away from the worksite (field 7).

(b)(3) *Do part-time, seasonal, or temporary workers count as employees in the criteria for number of employees in paragraph (a) of this Section?* Yes, each individual employed in the establishment at any time during the calendar year counts as one employee, including full-time, part-time, seasonal, and temporary workers.

(b)(4) *How will OSHA notify me that I must submit information from the injury and illness records as part of an individual data collection under paragraph (a)(3) of this Section?* OSHA will notify you by mail if you will have to submit information as part of an individual data collection under paragraph (a)(3). OSHA will also announce individual data collections through publication in the Federal Register and the OSHA newsletter, and announcements on the OSHA Web site. If you are an employer who must routinely submit the information, then OSHA will not notify you about your routine submittal.

(b)(5) *How often do I have to submit the information from the injury and illness records?* If you are required to submit information under paragraph (a)(1) or (2) of this Section, then you must submit the information once a year, by the date listed in paragraph (c) of this Section of the year after the calendar year covered by the form or forms. If you are submitting information because OSHA notified you to submit information as part of an individual data collection under paragraph (a)(3) of this Section, then you must submit the information as often as specified in the notification.

(b)(6) *How do I submit the information?* You must submit the information electronically. OSHA will provide a secure Web site for the electronic submission of information. For individual data collections under paragraph (a)(3) of this Section, OSHA will include the Web site's location in the notification for the data collection.

(b)(7) *Do I have to submit information if my establishment is partially exempt from keeping OSHA injury and illness records?* If you are partially exempt from keeping injury and illness records under §1904.1 and/or §1904.2, then you do not have to routinely submit Part 1904 information under paragraphs (a)(1) and (2) of this Section. You will have to submit information under paragraph (a)(3) of this Section if OSHA informs you in writing that it will collect injury and illness information from you. If you receive such a notification, then you must keep the injury and illness records required by this Part and submit information as directed.

(b)(8) *Do I have to submit information if I am located in a State Plan State?* Yes, the requirements apply to employers located in State Plan States.

(b)(9) *May an enterprise or corporate office electronically submit Part 1904 records for its establishment(s)?* Yes, if your enterprise or corporate office had ownership of or control over one or more establishments required to submit information under paragraph (a)(1) or (2) of this Section, then the enterprise or corporate office may collect and electronically submit the information for the establishment(s).

(c) **Reporting dates**

(c)(1) In 2017 and 2018, establishments required to submit under paragraph (a)(1) or (2) of this Section must submit the required information according to the table in this paragraph (c)(1):

Submission year	Establishments submitting under paragraph (a)(1) of this Section must submit the required information from this form/these forms:	Establishments submitting under paragraph (a)(2) of this Section must submit the required information from this form:	Submission deadline
2017	300A	300A	July 1, 2017
2018	300A, 300, 301	300A	July 1, 2018

(2) Beginning in 2019, establishments that are required to submit under paragraph (a)(1) or (2) of this Section will have to submit all of the required information by March 2 of the year after the calendar year covered by the form or forms (for example, by March 2, 2019, for the forms covering 2018).

§1904.42 OI Requests from the Bureau of Labor Statistics for data

(a) **Basic requirement** If you receive a Survey of Occupational Injuries and Illnesses Form from the Bureau of Labor Statistics (BLS), or a BLS designee, you must promptly complete the form and return it following the instructions contained on the survey form.

(b) **Implementation**

(b)(1) *Does every employer have to send data to the BLS?* No, each year, the BLS sends injury and illness survey forms to randomly selected employers and uses the information to create the Nation's occupational injury and illness statistics. In any year, some employers will receive a BLS survey form and others will not. You do not have to send injury and illness data to the BLS unless you receive a survey form.

(b)(2) *If I get a survey form from the BLS, what do I have to do?* If you receive a Survey of Occupational Injuries and Illnesses Form from the Bureau of Labor Statistics (BLS), or a BLS designee, you must promptly complete the form and return it, following the instructions contained on the survey form.

(b)(3) *Do I have to respond to a BLS survey form if I am normally exempt from keeping OSHA injury and illness records?* Yes, even if you are exempt from keeping injury and illness records under §1904.1 to §1904.3, the BLS may inform you in writing that it will be collecting injury and illness information from you in the coming year. If you receive such a letter, you must keep the injury and illness records required by §1904.5 to §1904.15 and make a survey report for the year covered by the survey.

(b)(4) *Do I have to answer the BLS survey form if I am located in a State-Plan State?* Yes, all employers who receive a survey form must respond to the survey, even those in State-Plan States.

§1904 Subpart E Appendix A Designated Industries for §1904.41(a)(2) Annual Electronic Submission of OSHA Form 300A Summary of Work-Related Injuries and Illnesses by Establishments With 20 or More Employees but Fewer Than 250 Employees in Designated Industries

NAICS	Industry
11	Agriculture, forestry, fishing and hunting.
22	Utilities.
23	Construction.
31-33	Manufacturing.
42	Wholesale trade.
4413	Automotive parts, accessories, and tire stores.
4421	Furniture stores.
4422	Home furnishings stores.
4441	Building material and supplies dealers.
4442	Lawn and garden equipment and supplies stores.
4451	Grocery stores.
4452	Specialty food stores.
4521	Department stores.
4529	Other general merchandise stores.
4533	Used merchandise stores.
4542	Vending machine operators.
4543	Direct selling establishments.
4811	Scheduled air transportation.
4841	General freight trucking.
4842	Specialized freight trucking.
4851	Urban transit systems.
4852	Interurban and rural bus transportation.
4853	Taxi and limousine service.
4854	School and employee bus transportation.
4855	Charter bus industry.
4859	Other transit and ground passenger transportation.
4871	Scenic and sightseeing transportation, land.
4881	Support activities for air transportation.
4882	Support activities for rail transportation.
4883	Support activities for water transportation.
4884	Support activities for road transportation.
4889	Other support activities for transportation.
4911	Postal service.
4921	Couriers and express delivery services.
4922	Local messengers and local delivery.
4931	Warehousing and storage.
5152	Cable and other subscription programming.
5311	Lessors of real estate.
5321	Automotive equipment rental and leasing.
5322	Consumer goods rental.
5323	General rental centers.
5617	Services to buildings and dwellings.
5621	Waste collection.
5622	Waste treatment and disposal.
5629	Remediation and other waste management services.
6219	Other ambulatory health care services.
6221	General medical and surgical hospitals.
6222	Psychiatric and substance abuse hospitals.
6223	Specialty (except psychiatric and substance abuse) hospitals.
6231	Nursing care facilities.
6232	Residential mental retardation, mental health and substance abuse facilities.
6233	Community care facilities for the elderly.
6239	Other residential care facilities.
6242	Community food and housing, and emergency and other relief services.
6243	Vocational rehabilitation services.

NAICS	Industry
7111	Performing arts companies.
7112	Spectator sports.
7121	Museums, historical sites, and similar institutions.
7131	Amusement parks and arcades.
7132	Gambling industries.
7211	Traveler accommodation.
7212	RV (recreational vehicle) parks and recreational camps.
7213	Rooming and boarding houses.
7223	Special food services.
8113	Commercial and industrial machinery and equipment (except automotive and electronic) repair and maintenance.
8123	Dry-cleaning and laundry services.

Subpart F—Transition From the Former Rule

§1904.43 Summary and posting of the 2001 data

(a) **Basic requirement** If you were required to keep OSHA 200 Logs in 2001, you must post a 2000 annual summary from the OSHA 200 Log of occupational injuries and illnesses for each establishment.

(b) **Implementation**

(b)(1) *What do I have to include in the summary?*

(b)(1)(i) You must include a copy of the totals from the 2001 OSHA 200 Log and the following information from that form:

(b)(1)(i)(A) The calendar year covered;

(b)(1)(i)(B) Your company name;

(b)(1)(i)(C) The name and address of the establishment; and

(b)(1)(i)(D) The certification signature, title and date.

(b)(1)(ii) If no injuries or illnesses occurred at your establishment in 2001, you must enter zeros on the totals line and post the 2001 summary.

(b)(2) *When am I required to summarize and post the 2001 information?*

(b)(2)(i) You must complete the summary by February 1, 2002; and

(b)(2)(ii) You must post a copy of the summary in each establishment in a conspicuous place or places where notices to employees are customarily posted. You must ensure that the summary is not altered, defaced or covered by other material.

(b)(3) You must post the 2001 summary from February 1, 2002 to March 1, 2002.

§1904.44 Retention and updating of old forms

You must save your copies of the OSHA 200 and 101 forms for five years following the year to which they relate and continue to provide access to the data as though these forms were the OSHA 300 and 301 forms. You are not required to update your old 200 and 101 forms.

§1904.45 OMB control numbers under the Paperwork Reduction ACT

The following Sections each contain a collection of information requirement which has been approved by the Office of Management and Budget under the control number listed.

29 CFR citation	OMB Control No.
§1904.4–35	1218–0176
§1904.39–41	1218–0176
§1904.42	1220–0045
§1904.43–44	1218–0176

Subpart G—Definitions

§1904.46 [OI] Definitions

The Act. The Act means the Occupational Safety and Health Act of 1970 (29 U.S. 651 et seq.). The definitions contained in Section 3 of the Act (29 U.S.C. 652) and related interpretations apply to such terms when used in this Part 1904.

Establishment An establishment is a single physical location where business is conducted or where services or industrial operations are performed. For activities where employees do not work at a single physical location, such as construction; transportation; communications, electric, gas and sanitary services; and similar operations, the establishment is represented by main or branch offices, terminals, stations, etc. that either supervise such activities or are the base from which personnel carry out these activities.

(1) *Can one business location include two or more establishments?* Normally, one business location has only one establishment. Under limited conditions, the employer may consider two or more separate businesses that share a single location to be separate establishments. An employer may divide one location into two or more establishments only when:

(1)(i) Each of the establishments represents a distinctly separate business;

(1)(ii) Each business is engaged in a different economic activity;

(1)(iii) No one industry description in the Standard Industrial Classification Manual (1987) applies to the joint activities of the establishments; and

(1)(iv) Separate reports are routinely prepared for each establishment on the number of employees, their wages and salaries, sales or receipts, and other business information. For example, if an employer operates a construction company at the same location as a lumber yard, the employer may consider each business to be a separate establishment.

(2) *Can an establishment include more than one physical location?* Yes, but only under certain conditions. An employer may combine two or more physical locations into a single establishment only when:

(2)(i) The employer operates the locations as a single business operation under common management;

(2)(ii) The locations are all located in close proximity to each other; and

(2)(iii) The employer keeps one set of business records for the locations, such as records on the number of employees, their wages and salaries, sales or receipts, and other kinds of business information. For example, one manufacturing establishment might include the main plant, a warehouse a few blocks away, and an administrative services building across the street.

(3) [OI] *If an employee telecommutes from home, is his or her home considered a separate establishment?* No, for employees who telecommute from home, the employee's home is not a business establishment and a separate 300 Log is not required. Employees who telecommute must be linked to one of your establishments under §1904.30(b)(3).

Injury or illness An injury or illness is an abnormal condition or disorder. Injuries include cases such as, but not limited to, a cut, fracture, sprain, or amputation. Illnesses include both acute and chronic illnesses, such as, but not limited to, a skin disease, respiratory disorder, or poisoning. (**Note:** Injuries and illnesses are recordable only if they are new, work-related cases that meet one or more of the Part 1904 recording criteria.)

Physician or Other Licensed Health Care Professional A physician or other licensed health care professional is an individual whose legally permitted scope of practice (i.e., license, registration, or certification) allows him or her to independently perform, or be delegated the responsibility to perform, the activities described by this regulation.

You "You" means an employer as defined in Section 3 of the Occupational Safety and Health Act of 1970 (29 U.S.C. 652).

OSHA
Forms for Recording
Work-Related Injuries and Illnesses

Dear Employer:

This booklet includes the forms needed for maintaining occupational injury and illness records for 2004. These new forms have changed in several important ways from the 2003 recordkeeping forms.

In the December 17, 2002 Federal Register (67 FR 77165-77170), OSHA announced its decision to add an occupational hearing loss column to OSHA's Form 300, Log of Work-Related Injuries and Illnesses. This forms package contains modified Forms 300 and 300A which incorporate the additional column M(5) Hearing Loss. Employers required to complete the injury and illness forms must begin to use these forms on January 1, 2004.

In response to public suggestions, OSHA also has made several changes to the forms package to make the recordkeeping materials clearer and easier to use:

- On Form 300, we've switched the positions of the day count columns. The days "away from work" column now comes before the days "on job transfer or restriction."
- We've clarified the formulas for calculating incidence rates.
- We've added new recording criteria for occupational hearing loss to the "Overview" section.
- On Form 300, we've made the column heading "Classify the Case" more prominent to make it clear that employers should mark only one selection among the four columns offered.

The Occupational Safety and Health Administration shares with you the goal of preventing injuries and illnesses in our nation's workplaces. Accurate injury and illness records will help us achieve that goal.

Occupational Safety and Health Administration
U.S. Department of Labor

What's Inside...

In this package, you'll find everything you need to complete OSHA's *Log* and the *Summary of Work-Related Injuries and Illnesses* for the next several years. On the following pages, you'll find:

- ▼ **An Overview: Recording Work-Related Injuries and Illnesses** — General instructions for filling out the forms in this package and definitions of terms you should use when you classify your cases as injuries or illnesses.
- ▼ **How to Fill Out the Log** — An example to guide you in filling out the *Log* properly.
- ▼ **Log of Work-Related Injuries and Illnesses** — Several pages of the *Log* (but you may make as many copies of the *Log* as you need.) Notice that the *Log* is separate from the *Summary*.

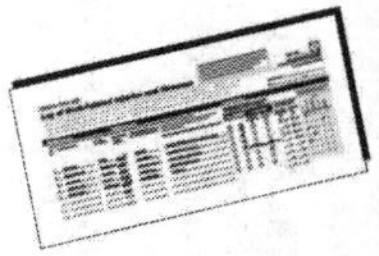

- ▼ **Summary of Work-Related Injuries and Illnesses** — Removable *Summary* pages for easy posting at the end of the year. Note that you post the *Summary* only, not the *Log*.

- ▼ **Worksheet to Help You Fill Out the Summary** — A worksheet for figuring the average number of employees who worked for your establishment and the total number of hours worked.
- ▼ **OSHA's 301: Injury and Illness Incident Report** — A copy of the OSHA 301 to provide details about the incident. You may make as many copies as you need or use an equivalent form.

Take a few minutes to review this package. If you have any questions, **visit us online at www.osha.gov or call your local OSHA office.** We'll be happy to help you.

U.S. Department of Labor
Occupational Safety and Health Administration

U.S. Department of Labor
Occupational Safety and Health Administration

An Overview: Recording Work-Related Injuries and Illnesses

The Occupational Safety and Health (OSH) Act of 1970 requires certain employers to prepare and maintain records of work-related injuries and illnesses. Use these definitions when you classify cases on the Log. OSHA's recordkeeping regulation (see 29 CFR Part 1904) provides more information about the definitions below.

The *Log of Work-Related Injuries and Illnesses* (Form 300) is used to classify work-related injuries and illnesses and to note the extent and severity of each case. When an incident occurs, use the *Log* to record specific details about what happened and how it happened. The *Summary* — a separate form (Form 300A) — shows the totals for the year in each category. At the end of the year, post the *Summary* in a visible location so that your employees are aware of the injuries and illnesses occurring in their workplace.

Employers must keep a *Log* for each establishment or site. If you have more than one establishment, you must keep a separate *Log* and *Summary* for each physical location that is expected to be in operation for one year or longer.

Note that your employees have the right to review your injury and illness records. For more information, see 29 Code of Federal Regulations Part 1904.35, *Employee Involvement.*

Cases listed on the *Log of Work-Related Injuries and Illnesses* are not necessarily eligible for workers' compensation or other insurance benefits. Listing a case on the *Log* does not mean that the employer or worker was at fault or that an OSHA standard was violated.

When is an injury or illness considered work-related?

An injury or illness is considered work-related if an event or exposure in the work environment caused or contributed to the condition or significantly aggravated a preexisting condition. Work-relatedness is presumed for injuries and illnesses resulting from events or exposures occurring in the workplace, unless an exception specifically applies. See 29 CFR Part 1904.5(b)(2) for the exceptions. The work environment includes the establishment and other locations where one or more employees are working or are present as a condition of their employment. See 29 CFR Part 1904.5(b)(1).

Which work-related injuries and illnesses should you record?

Record those work-related injuries and illnesses that result in:

- ▼ death,
- ▼ loss of consciousness,
- ▼ days away from work,
- ▼ restricted work activity or job transfer, or
- ▼ medical treatment beyond first aid.

You must also record work-related injuries and illnesses that are significant (as defined below) or meet any of the additional criteria listed below.

You must record any significant work-related injury or illness that is diagnosed by a physician or other licensed health care professional. You must record any work-related case involving cancer, chronic irreversible disease, a fractured or cracked bone, or a punctured eardrum. See 29 CFR 1904.7.

What are the additional criteria?

You must record the following conditions when they are work-related:

- ▼ any needlestick injury or cut from a sharp object that is contaminated with another person's blood or other potentially infectious material;
- ▼ any case requiring an employee to be medically removed under the requirements of an OSHA health standard;
- ▼ tuberculosis infection as evidenced by a positive skin test or diagnosis by a physician or other licensed health care professional after exposure to a known case of active tuberculosis.
- ▼ an employee's hearing test (audiogram) reveals 1) that the employee has experienced a Standard Threshold Shift (STS) in hearing in one or both ears (averaged at 2000, 3000, and 4000 Hz) and 2) the employee's total hearing level is 25 decibels (dB) or more above audiometric zero (also averaged at 2000, 3000, and 4000 Hz) in the same ear(s) as the STS.

What is medical treatment?

Medical treatment includes managing and caring for a patient for the purpose of combating disease or disorder. The following are not considered medical treatments and are NOT recordable:

- ▼ visits to a doctor or health care professional solely for observation or counseling;

What do you need to do?

1. Within 7 calendar days after you receive information about a case, decide if the case is recordable under the OSHA recordkeeping requirements.
2. Determine whether the incident is a new case or a recurrence of an existing one.
3. Establish whether the case was work-related.
4. If the case is recordable, decide which form you will fill out as the injury and illness incident report.

You may use *OSHA's 301: Injury and Illness Incident Report* or an equivalent form. Some state workers compensation, insurance, or other reports may be acceptable substitutes, as long as they provide the same information as the OSHA 301.

How to work with the Log

1. Identify the employee involved unless it is a privacy concern case as described below.
2. Identify when and where the case occurred.
3. Describe the case, as specifically as you can.
4. Classify the seriousness of the case by recording the **most serious outcome** associated with the case, with column G (Death) being the most serious and column J (Other recordable cases) being the least serious.
5. Identify whether the case is an injury or illness. If the case is an injury, check the injury category. If the case is an illness, check the appropriate illness category.

- diagnostic procedures, including administering prescription medications that are used solely for diagnostic purposes; and
- any procedure that can be labeled first aid. (*See below for more information about first aid.*)

What is first aid?

If the incident required only the following types of treatment, consider it first aid. Do NOT record the case if it involves only:

- using non-prescription medications at non-prescription strength;
- administering tetanus immunizations;
- cleaning, flushing, or soaking wounds on the skin surface;
- using wound coverings, such as bandages, BandAids™, gauze pads, etc., or using SteriStrips™ or butterfly bandages.
- using hot or cold therapy;
- using any totally non-rigid means of support, such as elastic bandages, wraps, non-rigid back belts, etc.;
- using temporary immobilization devices while transporting an accident victim (splints, slings, neck collars, or back boards).
- drilling a fingernail or toenail to relieve pressure, or draining fluids from blisters;
- using eye patches;
- using simple irrigation or a cotton swab to remove foreign bodies not embedded in or adhered to the eye;
- using irrigation, tweezers, cotton swab or other simple means to remove splinters or foreign material from areas other than the eye;
- using finger guards;
- using massages;
- drinking fluids to relieve heat stress

How do you decide if the case involved restricted work?

Restricted work activity occurs when, as the result of a work-related injury or illness, an employer or health care professional keeps, or recommends keeping, an employee from doing the routine functions of his or her job or from working the full workday that the employee would have been scheduled to work before the injury or illness occurred.

How do you count the number of days of restricted work activity or the number of days away from work?

Count the number of calendar days the employee was on restricted work activity or was away from work as a result of the recordable injury or illness. Do not count the day on which the injury or illness occurred in this number. Begin counting days from the day after the incident occurs. If a single injury or illness involved both days away from work and days of restricted work activity, enter the total number of days for each. You may stop counting days of restricted work activity or days away from work once the total of either or the combination of both reaches 180 days.

Under what circumstances should you NOT enter the employee's name on the OSHA Form 300?

You must consider the following types of injuries or illnesses to be privacy concern cases:

- an injury or illness to an intimate body part or to the reproductive system,
- an injury or illness resulting from a sexual assault,
- a mental illness,
- a case of HIV infection, hepatitis, or tuberculosis,
- a needlestick injury or cut from a sharp object that is contaminated with blood or other potentially infectious material (see 29 CFR Part 1904.8 for definition), and
- other illnesses, if the employee independently and voluntarily requests that his or her name not be entered on the log.

You must not enter the employee's name on the OSHA 300 *Log* for these cases. Instead, enter "privacy case" in the space normally used for the employee's name. You must keep a separate, confidential list of the case numbers and employee names for the establishment's privacy concern cases so that you can update the cases and provide information to the government if asked to do so.

If you have a reasonable basis to believe that information describing the privacy concern case may be personally identifiable even though the employee's name has been omitted, you may use discretion in describing the injury or illness on both the OSHA 300 and 301 forms. You must enter enough information to identify the cause of the incident and the general severity of the injury or illness, but you do not need to include details of an intimate or private nature.

What if the outcome changes after you record the case?

If the outcome or extent of an injury or illness changes after you have recorded the case, simply draw a line through the original entry or, if you wish, delete or white-out the original entry. Then write the new entry where it belongs. Remember, you need to record the most serious outcome for each case.

Classifying injuries

An injury is any wound or damage to the body resulting from an event in the work environment.

Examples: Cut, puncture, laceration, abrasion, fracture, bruise, contusion, chipped tooth, amputation, insect bite, electrocution, or a thermal, chemical, electrical, or radiation burn. Sprain and strain injuries to muscles, joints, and connective tissues are classified as injuries when they result from a slip, trip, fall or other similar accidents.

U.S. Department of Labor
Occupational Safety and Health Administration

Classifying illnesses

Skin diseases or disorders
Skin diseases or disorders are illnesses involving the worker's skin that are caused by work exposure to chemicals, plants, or other substances.

Examples: Contact dermatitis, eczema, or rash caused by primary irritants and sensitizers or poisonous plants; oil acne; friction blisters, chrome ulcers; inflammation of the skin.

Respiratory conditions
Respiratory conditions are illnesses associated with breathing hazardous biological agents, chemicals, dust, gases, vapors, or fumes at work.

Examples: Silicosis, asbestosis, pneumonitis, pharyngitis, rhinitis or acute congestion; farmer's lung, beryllium disease, tuberculosis, occupational asthma, reactive airways dysfunction syndrome (RADS), chronic obstructive pulmonary disease (COPD), hypersensitivity pneumonitis, toxic inhalation injury, such as metal fume fever, chronic obstructive bronchitis, and other pneumoconioses.

Poisoning
Poisoning includes disorders evidenced by abnormal concentrations of toxic substances in blood, other tissues, other bodily fluids, or the breath that are caused by the ingestion or absorption of toxic substances into the body.

Examples: Poisoning by lead, mercury, cadmium, arsenic, or other metals; poisoning by carbon monoxide, hydrogen sulfide, or other gases; poisoning by benzene, benzol, carbon tetrachloride, or other organic solvents; poisoning by insecticide sprays, such as parathion or lead arsenate; poisoning by other chemicals, such as formaldehyde.

Hearing Loss
Noise-induced hearing loss is defined for recordkeeping purposes as a change in hearing threshold relative to the baseline audiogram of an average of 10 dB or more in either ear at 2000, 3000 and 4000 hertz, and the employee's total hearing level is 25 decibels (dB) or more above audiometric zero (also averaged at 2000, 3000, and 4000 hertz) in the same ear(s).

All other illnesses
All other occupational illnesses.

Examples: Heatstroke, sunstroke, heat exhaustion, heat stress and other effects of environmental heat; freezing, frostbite, and other effects of exposure to low temperatures; decompression sickness; effects of ionizing radiation (isotopes, x-rays, radium); effects of nonionizing radiation (welding flash, ultra-violet rays, lasers); anthrax; bloodborne pathogenic diseases, such as AIDS, HIV, hepatitis B or hepatitis C; brucellosis; malignant or benign tumors; histoplasmosis; coccidioidomycosis.

When must you post the Summary?

You must post the *Summary* only — not the *Log* — by February 1 of the year following the year covered by the form and keep it posted until April 30 of that year.

How long must you keep the Log and Summary on file?

You must keep the *Log* and *Summary* for 5 years following the year to which they pertain.

Do you have to send these forms to OSHA at the end of the year?

No. You do not have to send the completed forms to OSHA unless specifically asked to do so.

How can we help you?

If you have a question about how to fill out the *Log*,

- ❑ **visit us online at www.osha.gov** or
- ❑ **call your local OSHA office.**

U.S. Department of Labor
Occupational Safety and Health Administration

Optional

Calculating Injury and Illness Incidence Rates

What is an incidence rate?

An incidence rate is the number of recordable injuries and illnesses occurring among a given number of full-time workers (usually 100 full-time workers) over a given period of time (usually one year). To evaluate your firm's injury and illness experience over time or to compare your firm's experience with that of your industry as a whole, you need to compute your incidence rate. Because a specific number of workers and a specific period of time are involved, these rates can help you identify problems in your workplace and/or progress you may have made in preventing work-related injuries and illnesses.

How do you calculate an incidence rate?

You can compute an occupational injury and illness incidence rate for all recordable cases or for cases that involved days away from work for your firm quickly and easily. The formula requires that you follow instructions in paragraph (a) below for the total recordable cases or those in paragraph (b) for cases that involved days away from work, *and* for both rates the instructions in paragraph (c).

(a) *To find out the total number of recordable injuries and illnesses that occurred during the year,* count the number of line entries on your OSHA Form 300, or refer to the OSHA Form 300A and sum the entries for columns (G), (H), (I), and (J).

(b) *To find out the number of injuries and illnesses that involved days away from work,* count the number of line entries on your OSHA Form 300 that received a check mark in column (H), or refer to the entry for column (H) on the OSHA Form 300A.

(c) *The number of hours all employees actually worked during the year.* Refer to OSHA Form 300A and optional worksheet to calculate this number.

You can compute the incidence rate for all recordable cases of injuries and illnesses using the following formula:

Total number of injuries and illnesses X *200,000 ÷ Number of hours worked by all employees = Total recordable case rate*

(The 200,000 figure in the formula represents the number of hours 100 employees working 40 hours per week, 50 weeks per year would work, and provides the standard base for calculating incidence rates.)

You can compute the incidence rate for recordable cases involving days away from work, days of restricted work activity or job transfer (DART) using the following formula:

(Number of entries in column H + Number of entries in column I) X *200,000 ÷ Number of hours worked by all employees = DART incidence rate*

You can use the same formula to calculate incidence rates for other variables such as cases involving restricted work activity (column (I) on Form 300A), cases involving skin disorders (column (M-2) on Form 300A), etc. Just substitute the appropriate total for these cases, from Form 300A, into the formula in place of the total number of injuries and illnesses.

What can I compare my incidence rate to?

The Bureau of Labor Statistics (BLS) conducts a survey of occupational injuries and illnesses each year and publishes incidence rate data by various classifications (e.g., by industry, by employer size, etc.). You can obtain these published data at www.bls.gov/iif or by calling a BLS Regional Office.

Worksheet

Total number of injuries and illnesses				Number of hours worked by all employees		Total recordable case rate
[ ]	X	200,000	÷	[ ]	=	[ ]

Number of entries in Column H + Column I				Number of hours worked by all employees		DART incidence rate
[ ]	X	200,000	÷	[ ]	=	[ ]

U.S. Department of Labor
Occupational Safety and Health Administration

How to Fill Out the Log

The *Log of Work-Related Injuries and Illnesses* is used to classify work-related injuries and illnesses and to note the extent and severity of each case. When an incident occurs, use the *Log* to record specific details about what happened and how it happened.

If your company has more than one establishment or site, you must keep separate records for each physical location that is expected to remain in operation for one year or longer.

We have given you several copies of the *Log* in this package. If you need more than we provided, you may photocopy and use as many as you need.

The *Summary* — a separate form — shows the work-related injury and illness totals for the year in each category. At the end of the year, count the number of incidents in each category and transfer the totals from the *Log* to the *Summary*. Then post the *Summary* in a visible location so that your employees are aware of injuries and illnesses occurring in their workplace.

You don't post the Log. You post only the Summary at the end of the year.

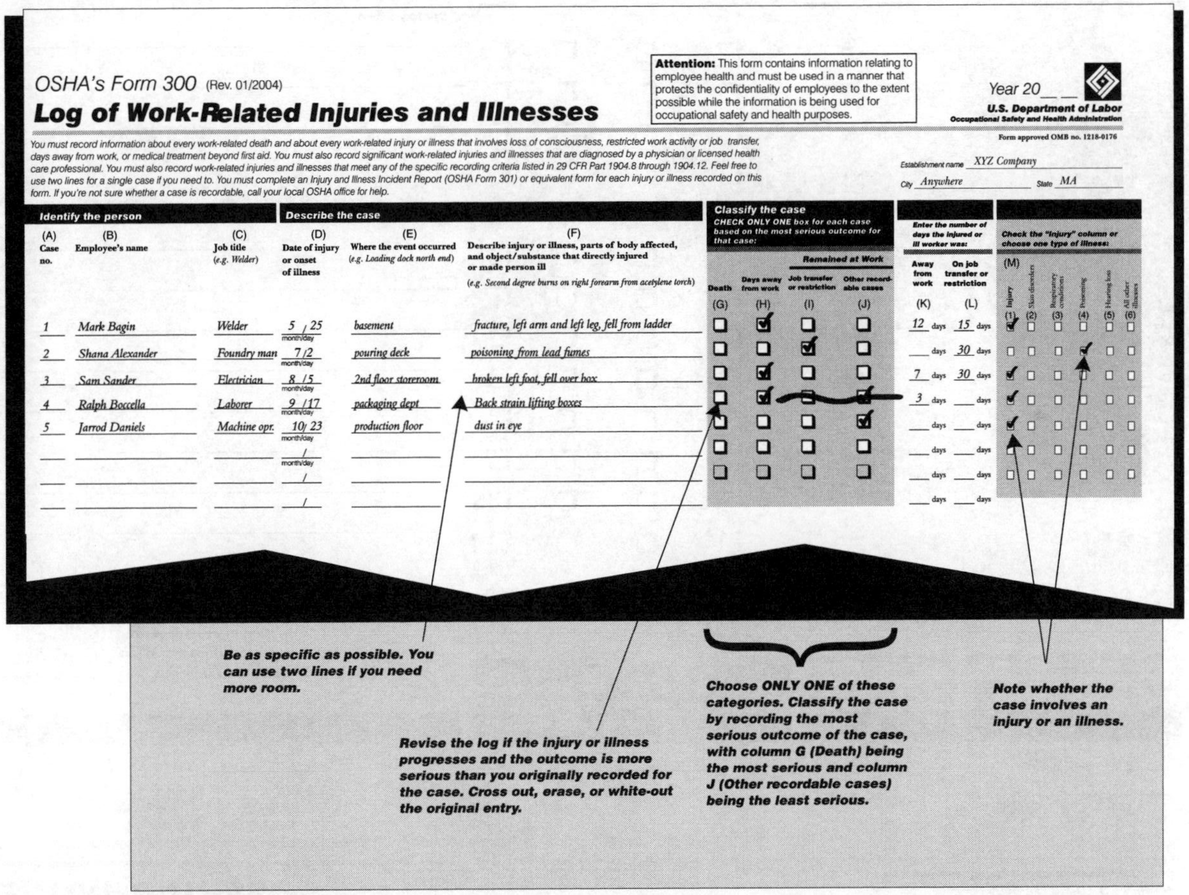

OSHA's Form 300 (Rev. 01/2004)

Log of Work-Related Injuries and Illnesses

Attention: This form contains information relating to employee health and must be used in a manner that protects the confidentiality of employees to the extent possible while the information is being used for occupational safety and health purposes.

Year 20__ __

U.S. Department of Labor
Occupational Safety and Health Administration

Form approved OMB no. 1218-0176

You must record information about every work-related death and about every work-related injury or illness that involves loss of consciousness, restricted work activity or job transfer, days away from work, or medical treatment beyond first aid. You must also record significant work-related injuries and illnesses that are diagnosed by a physician or licensed health care professional. You must also record work-related injuries and illnesses that meet any of the specific recording criteria listed in 29 CFR Part 1904.8 through 1904.12. Feel free to use two lines for a single case if you need to. You must complete an Injury and Illness Incident Report (OSHA Form 301) or equivalent form for each injury or illness recorded on this form. If you're not sure whether a case is recordable, call your local OSHA office for help.

Establishment name ________________

City __________ State ______

Identify the person			Describe the case			Classify the case CHECK ONLY ONE box for each case based on the most serious outcome for that case:				Enter the number of days the injured or ill worker was:		Check the "Injury" column or choose one type of illness:					
								Remained at Work				(M)					
(A) Case no.	(B) Employee's name	(C) Job title (*e.g., Welder*)	(D) Date of injury or onset of illness	(E) Where the event occurred (*e.g., Loading dock north end*)	(F) Describe injury or illness, parts of body affected, and object/substance that directly injured or made person ill (*e.g., Second degree burns on right forearm from acetylene torch*)	Death (G)	Days away from work (H)	Job transfer or restriction (I)	Other record-able cases (J)	Away from work (K)	On job transfer or restriction (L)	Injury (1)	Skin disorder (2)	Respiratory condition (3)	Poisoning (4)	Hearing loss (5)	All other illnesses (6)
___	___	___	__/__ month/day	___	___	☐	☐	☐	☐	___ days	___ days	☐	☐	☐	☐	☐	☐
___	___	___	__/__ month/day	___	___	☐	☐	☐	☐	___ days	___ days	☐	☐	☐	☐	☐	☐
___	___	___	__/__ month/day	___	___	☐	☐	☐	☐	___ days	___ days	☐	☐	☐	☐	☐	☐
___	___	___	__/__ month/day	___	___	☐	☐	☐	☐	___ days	___ days	☐	☐	☐	☐	☐	☐
___	___	___	__/__ month/day	___	___	☐	☐	☐	☐	___ days	___ days	☐	☐	☐	☐	☐	☐
___	___	___	__/__ month/day	___	___	☐	☐	☐	☐	___ days	___ days	☐	☐	☐	☐	☐	☐
___	___	___	__/__ month/day	___	___	☐	☐	☐	☐	___ days	___ days	☐	☐	☐	☐	☐	☐
___	___	___	__/__ month/day	___	___	☐	☐	☐	☐	___ days	___ days	☐	☐	☐	☐	☐	☐
___	___	___	__/__ month/day	___	___	☐	☐	☐	☐	___ days	___ days	☐	☐	☐	☐	☐	☐
___	___	___	__/__ month/day	___	___	☐	☐	☐	☐	___ days	___ days	☐	☐	☐	☐	☐	☐
___	___	___	__/__ month/day	___	___	☐	☐	☐	☐	___ days	___ days	☐	☐	☐	☐	☐	☐
___	___	___	__/__ month/day	___	___	☐	☐	☐	☐	___ days	___ days	☐	☐	☐	☐	☐	☐
___	___	___	__/__ month/day	___	___	☐	☐	☐	☐	___ days	___ days	☐	☐	☐	☐	☐	☐
					Page totals ➤	___	___	___	___	___	___	___ Injury (1)	___ Skin disorder (2)	___ Respiratory condition (3)	___ Poisoning (4)	___ Hearing loss (5)	___ All other illnesses (6)

Be sure to transfer these totals to the Summary page (Form 300A) before you post it.

Public reporting burden for this collection of information is estimated to average 14 minutes per response, including time to review the instructions, search and gather the data needed, and complete and review the collection of information. Persons are not required to respond to the collection of information unless it displays a currently valid OMB control number. If you have any comments about these estimates or any other aspects of this data collection, contact: US Department of Labor, OSHA Office of Statistical Analysis, Room N-3644, 200 Constitution Avenue, NW, Washington, DC 20210. Do not send the completed forms to this office.

Page ___ of ___

OSHA's Form 300A (Rev. 01/2004)

Summary of Work-Related Injuries and Illnesses

Year 20__ __

U.S. Department of Labor
Occupational Safety and Health Administration

Form approved OMB no. 1218-0176

All establishments covered by Part 1904 must complete this Summary page, even if no work-related injuries or illnesses occurred during the year. Remember to review the Log to verify that the entries are complete and accurate before completing this summary.

Using the Log, count the individual entries you made for each category. Then write the totals below, making sure you've added the entries from every page of the Log. If you had no cases, write "0."

Employees, former employees, and their representatives have the right to review the OSHA Form 300 in its entirety. They also have limited access to the OSHA Form 301 or its equivalent. See 29 CFR Part 1904.35, in OSHA's recordkeeping rule, for further details on the access provisions for these forms.

Number of Cases

Total number of deaths	Total number of cases with days away from work	Total number of cases with job transfer or restriction	Total number of other recordable cases
______	______	______	______
(G)	(H)	(I)	(J)

Number of Days

Total number of days away from work	Total number of days of job transfer or restriction
______	______
(K)	(L)

Injury and Illness Types

Total number of . . .
(M)

(1) Injuries ______

(2) Skin disorders ______

(3) Respiratory conditions ______

(4) Poisonings ______

(5) Hearing loss ______

(6) All other illnesses ______

Post this Summary page from February 1 to April 30 of the year following the year covered by the form.

Public reporting burden for this collection of information is estimated to average 58 minutes per response, including time to review the instructions, search and gather the data needed, and complete and review the collection of information. Persons are not required to respond to the collection of information unless it displays a currently valid OMB control number. If you have any comments about these estimates or any other aspects of this data collection, contact: US Department of Labor, OSHA Office of Statistical Analysis, Room N-3644, 200 Constitution Avenue, NW, Washington, DC 20210. Do not send the completed forms to this office.

Establishment information

Your establishment name ______________________

Street ______________________

City ______________ State ____ ZIP ______

Industry description (*e.g., Manufacture of motor truck trailers*)

____

Standard Industrial Classification (SIC), if known (*e.g., 3715*)

__ __ __ __

OR

North American Industrial Classification (NAICS), if known (e.g., 336212)

__ __ __ __ __ __

Employment information *(If you don't have these figures, see the Worksheet on the back of this page to estimate.)*

Annual average number of employees ______

Total hours worked by all employees last year ______

Sign here

Knowingly falsifying this document may result in a fine.

I certify that I have examined this document and that to the best of my knowledge the entries are true, accurate, and complete.

______________________ ______
Company executive Title

( ) - / /
Phone Date

U.S. Department of Labor
Occupational Safety and Health Administration

Optional

Worksheet to Help You Fill Out the Summary

At the end of the year, OSHA requires you to enter the average number of employees and the total hours worked by your employees on the summary. If you don't have these figures, you can use the information on this page to estimate the numbers you will need to enter on the Summary page at the end of the year.

How to figure the average number of employees who worked for your establishment during the year:

❶ **Add** the total number of employees your establishment paid in all pay periods during the year. Include all employees: full-time, part-time, temporary, seasonal, salaried, and hourly.

The number of employees paid in all pay periods = ❶ ________

❷ **Count** the number of pay periods your establishment had during the year. Be sure to include any pay periods when you had no employees.

The number of pay periods during the year = ❷ ________

❸ **Divide** the number of employees by the number of pay periods.

❶ / ❷ ________ = ❸ ________

❹ **Round the answer** to the next highest whole number. Write the rounded number in the blank marked *Annual average number of employees.*

The number rounded = ❹ ________

For example, Acme Construction figured its average employment this way:

For pay period...	Acme paid this number of employees...
1	10
2	0
3	15
4	30
5	40
▼	▼
24	20
25	15
26	+10
	830

Number of employees paid = 830 ❶

Number of pay periods = 26 ❷

$\frac{830}{26} = 31.92$ ❸

31.92 rounds to 32 ❹

32 is the annual average number of employees

How to figure the total hours worked by all employees:

Include hours worked by salaried, hourly, part-time and seasonal workers, as well as hours worked by other workers subject to day to day supervision by your establishment (e.g., temporary help services workers).

Do not include vacation, sick leave, holidays, or any other non-work time, even if employees were paid for it. If your establishment keeps records of only the hours paid or if you have employees who are not paid by the hour, please estimate the hours that the employees actually worked.

If this number isn't available, you can use this optional worksheet to estimate it.

Optional Worksheet

________ **Find** the number of full-time employees in your establishment for the year.

X ________ **Multiply** by the number of work hours for a full-time employee in a year.

________ This is the number of full-time hours worked.

\+ ________ **Add** the number of any overtime hours as well as the hours worked by other employees (part-time, temporary, seasonal)

________ **Round** the answer to the next highest whole number. Write the rounded number in the blank marked *Total hours worked by all employees last year.*

OSHA's Form 301
Injury and Illness Incident Report

Attention: This form contains information relating to employee health and must be used in a manner that protects the confidentiality of employees to the extent possible while the information is being used for occupational safety and health purposes.

U.S. Department of Labor
Occupational Safety and Health Administration

Form approved OMB no. 1218-0176

This *Injury and Illness Incident Report* is one of the first forms you must fill out when a recordable work-related injury or illness has occurred. Together with the *Log of Work-Related Injuries and Illnesses* and the accompanying *Summary*, these forms help the employer and OSHA develop a picture of the extent and severity of work-related incidents.

Within 7 calendar days after you receive information that a recordable work-related injury or illness has occurred, you must fill out this form or an equivalent. Some state workers' compensation, insurance, or other reports may be acceptable substitutes. To be considered an equivalent form, any substitute must contain all the information asked for on this form.

According to Public Law 91-596 and 29 CFR 1904, OSHA's recordkeeping rule, you must keep this form on file for 5 years following the year to which it pertains.

If you need additional copies of this form, you may photocopy and use as many as you need.

Completed by ______________________

Title ______________________

Phone (____)____-________ Date ____/____/____

Information about the employee

1) Full name ______________________

2) Street ______________________

City ____________ State ______ ZIP ______

3) Date of birth ____/____/____

4) Date hired ____/____/____

5) ☐ Male
☐ Female

Information about the physician or other health care professional

6) Name of physician or other health care professional ______________________

7) If treatment was given away from the worksite, where was it given?

Facility ______________________

Street ______________________

City ____________ State ______ ZIP ______

8) Was employee treated in an emergency room?
☐ Yes
☐ No

9) Was employee hospitalized overnight as an in-patient?
☐ Yes
☐ No

Information about the case

10) Case number from the *Log* ____________ *(Transfer the case number from the Log after you record the case.)*

11) Date of injury or illness ____/____/____

12) Time employee began work ____________ AM / PM

13) Time of event ____________ AM / PM ☐ Check if time cannot be determined

14) ***What was the employee doing just before the incident occurred?*** Describe the activity, as well as the tools, equipment, or material the employee was using. Be specific. *Examples:* "climbing a ladder while carrying roofing materials"; "spraying chlorine from hand sprayer"; "daily computer key-entry."

15) ***What happened?*** Tell us how the injury occurred. *Examples:* "When ladder slipped on wet floor, worker fell 20 feet"; "Worker was sprayed with chlorine when gasket broke during replacement"; "Worker developed soreness in wrist over time."

16) ***What was the injury or illness?*** Tell us the part of the body that was affected and how it was affected; be more specific than "hurt," "pain," or sore." *Examples:* "strained back"; "chemical burn, hand"; "carpal tunnel syndrome."

17) ***What object or substance directly harmed the employee?*** *Examples:* "concrete floor"; "chlorine"; "radial arm saw." *If this question does not apply to the incident, leave it blank.*

18) ***If the employee died, when did death occur?*** Date of death ____/____/____

Public reporting burden for this collection of information is estimated to average 22 minutes per response, including time for reviewing instructions, searching existing data sources, gathering and maintaining the data needed, and completing and reviewing the collection of information. Persons are not required to respond to the collection of information unless it displays a current valid OMB control number. If you have any comments about this estimate or any other aspects of this data collection, including suggestions for reducing this burden, contact: US Department of Labor, OSHA Office of Statistical Analysis, Room N-3644, 200 Constitution Avenue, NW, Washington, DC 20210. Do not send the completed forms to this office.

If You Need Help...

If you need help deciding whether a case is recordable, or if you have questions about the information in this package, feel free to contact us. We'll gladly answer any questions you have.

- **Visit us online at www.osha.gov**
- **Call your OSHA Regional office and ask for the recordkeeping coordinator**

or

- **Call your State Plan office**

Federal Jurisdiction

Region 1 - 617 / 565-9860
Connecticut; Massachusetts; Maine; New Hampshire; Rhode Island

Region 2 - 212 / 337-2378
New York; New Jersey

Region 3 - 215 / 861-4900
DC; Delaware; Pennsylvania; West Virginia

Region 4 - 404 / 562-2300
Alabama; Florida; Georgia; Mississippi

Region 5 - 312 / 353-2220
Illinois; Ohio; Wisconsin

Region 6 - 214 / 767-4731
Arkansas; Louisiana; Oklahoma; Texas

Region 7 - 816 / 426-5861
Kansas; Missouri; Nebraska

Region 8 - 303 / 844-1600
Colorado; Montana; North Dakota; South Dakota

Region 9 - 415 / 975-4310

Region 10 - 206 / 553-5930
Idaho

State Plan States

Alaska - 907 / 269-4957

Arizona - 602 / 542-5795

California - 415 / 703-5100

*Connecticut - 860 / 566-4380

Hawaii - 808 / 586-9100

Indiana - 317 / 232-2688

Iowa - 515 / 281-3661

Kentucky - 502 / 564-3070

Maryland - 410 / 767-2371

Michigan - 517 / 322-1848

Minnesota - 651 / 284-5050

Nevada - 702 / 486-9020

*New Jersey - 609 / 984-1389

New Mexico - 505 / 827-4230

*New York - 518 / 457-2574

North Carolina - 919 / 807-2875

Oregon - 503 / 378-3272

Puerto Rico - 787 / 754-2172

South Carolina - 803 / 734-9669

Tennessee - 615 / 741-2793

Utah - 801 / 530-6901

Vermont - 802 / 828-2765

Virginia - 804 / 786-6613

Virgin Islands - 340 / 772-1315

Washington - 360 / 902-5601

Wyoming - 307 / 777-7786

*Public Sector only

U.S. Department of Labor
Occupational Safety and Health Administration

29 CFR PART 1910
OCCUPATIONAL SAFETY AND HEALTH STANDARDS

Subpart A—General

Section Contents

Subpart A—General

Authority: 29 U.S.C. 653, 655, 657; Secretary of Labor's Order No. 12–71 (36 FR 8754), 8–76 (41 FR 25059), 9–83 (48 FR 35736), 1–90 (55 FR 9033), 6–96 (62 FR 111), 3–2000 (65 FR 50017), 5–2002 (67 FR 65008), 5–2007 (72 FR 31159), 4–2010 (75 FR 55355), or 1–2012 (77 FR 3912), as applicable.

Sections §1910.6, §1910.7, §1910.8 and §1910.9 also issued under 29 CFR 1911. Section §1910.7(f) also issued under 31 U.S.C. 9701, 29 U.S.C. 9a, 5 U.S.C. 553; Public Law 106–113 (113 Stat. 1501A–222); Pub. L. 11-8 and 111–317; and OMB Circular A–25 (dated July 8, 1993) (58 FR 38142, July 15, 1993).

§1910.1
Purpose and scope

(a) Section 6(a) of the Williams-Steiger Occupational Safety and Health Act of 1970 (84 Stat. 1593) provides that "without regard to chapter 5 of title 5, United States Code, or to the other subsections of this Section, the Secretary shall, as soon as practicable during the period beginning with the effective date of this Act and ending 2 years after such date, by rule promulgate as an occupational safety or health standard any national consensus standard, and any established Federal standard, unless he determines that the promulgation of such a standard would not result in improved safety or health for specifically designated employees." The legislative purpose of this provision is to establish, as rapidly as possible and without regard to the rule-making provisions of the Administrative Procedure Act, standards with which industries are generally familiar, and on whose adoption interested and affected persons have already had an opportunity to express their views. Such standards are either:

(a)(1) National consensus standards on whose adoption affected persons have reached substantial agreement, or

(a)(2) Federal standards already established by Federal statutes or regulations.

(b) This Part carries out the directive to the Secretary of Labor under Section 6(a) of the Act. It contains occupational safety and health standards which have been found to be national consensus standards or established Federal standards.

§1910.2
Definitions

As used in this Part, unless the context clearly requires otherwise:

(a) **Act** means the Williams-Steiger Occupational Safety and Health Act of 1970 (84 Stat. 1590).

(b) **Assistant Secretary of Labor** means the Assistant Secretary of Labor for Occupational Safety and Health;

(c) **Employer** means a person engaged in a business affecting commerce who has employees, but does not include the United States or any State or political subdivision of a State;

(d) **Employee** means an employee of an employer who is employed in a business of his employer which affects commerce;

(e) **Commerce** means trade, traffic, commerce, transportation, or communication among the several States, or between a State and any place outside thereof, or within the District of Columbia, or a possession of the United States (other than the Trust Territory of the Pacific Islands), or between points in the same State but through a point outside thereof;

(f) **Standard** means a standard which requires conditions, or the adoption or use of one or more practices, means, methods, operations, or processes, reasonably necessary or appropriate to provide safe or healthful employment and places of employment;

(g) **National consensus standard** means any standard or modification thereof which

(g)(1) has been adopted and promulgated by a nationally recognized standards-producing organization under procedures whereby it can be determined by the Secretary of Labor or by the Assistant Secretary of Labor that persons interested and affected by the scope or provisions of the standard have reached substantial agreement on its adoption,

(g)(2) was formulated in a manner which afforded an opportunity for diverse views to be considered, and

(g)(3) has been designated as such a standard by the Secretary or the Assistant Secretary, after consultation with other appropriate Federal agencies; and

(h) **Established Federal standard** means any operative standard established by any agency of the United States and in effect on April 28, 1971, or contained in any Act of Congress in force on the date of enactment of the Williams-Steiger Occupational Safety and Health Act.

§1910.3
Petitions for the issuance, amendment, or repeal of a standard

(a) Any interested person may petition in writing the Assistant Secretary of Labor to promulgate, modify, or revoke a standard. The petition should set forth the terms or the substance of the rule desired, the effects thereof if promulgated, and the reasons therefor.

(b)(1) The relevant legislative history of the Act indicates congressional recognition of the American National Standards Institute and the National Fire Protection Association as the major sources of national consensus standards. National consensus standards adopted on May 29, 1971, pursuant to Section 6(a) of the Act are from those two sources. However, any organization which deems itself a producer of national consensus standards, within the meaning of Section 3(9) of the Act, is invited to submit in writing to the Assistant Secretary of Labor at any time prior to February 1, 1973, all relevant information which may enable the Assistant Secretary to determine whether any of its standards satisfy the requirements of the definition of "national consensus standard" in Section 3(9) of the Act.

(b)(2) Within a reasonable time after the receipt of a submission pursuant to paragraph (b)(1) of this Section, the Assistant Secretary of Labor shall publish or cause to be published in the Federal Register a notice of such submission, and shall afford interested persons a reasonable opportunity to present written data, views, or arguments with regard to the question whether any standards of the organization making the submission are national consensus standards.

§1910.4
Amendments to this part

(a) The Assistant Secretary of Labor shall have all of the authority of the Secretary of Labor under Sections 3(9) and 6(a) of the Act.

(b) The Assistant Secretary of Labor may at any time before April 28, 1973, on his own motion or upon the written petition of any person, by rule promulgate as a standard any national consensus standard and any established Federal standard, pursuant to and in accordance with Section 6(a) of the Act, and, in addition, may modify or revoke any Standard in this Part §1910. In the event of conflict among any such Standards, the Assistant Secretary of Labor shall take the action necessary to eliminate the conflict, including the revocation or modification of a Standard in this Part, so as to assure the greatest protection of the safety or health of the affected employees.

§1910.5
Applicability of Standards

(a) Except as provided in paragraph (b) of this Section, the Standards contained in this Part shall apply with respect to employments performed in a workplace in a State, the District of Columbia, the Commonwealth of

Puerto Rico, the Virgin Islands, American Samoa, Guam, Trust Territory of the Pacific Islands, Wake Island, Outer Continental Shelf lands defined in the Outer Continental Shelf Lands Act, Johnston Island, and the Canal Zone.

(b) None of the Standards in this Part shall apply to working conditions of employees with respect to which Federal agencies other than the Department of Labor, or State agencies acting under Section 274 of the Atomic Energy Act of 1954, as amended (42 U.S.C. 2021), exercise statutory authority to prescribe or enforce standards or regulations affecting occupational safety or health.

(c)

(c)(1) If a particular Standard is specifically applicable to a condition, practice, means, method, operation, or process, it shall prevail over any different general standard which might otherwise be applicable to the same condition, practice, means, method, operation, or process. For example, §1915.23(c)(3) of this title prescribes personal protective equipment for certain ship repairmen working in specified areas. Such a standard shall apply, and shall not be deemed modified nor superseded by any different general standard whose provisions might otherwise be applicable, to the ship repairmen working in the areas specified in §1915.23(c)(3).

(c)(2) On the other hand, any standard shall apply according to its terms to any employment and place of employment in any industry, even though particular standards are also prescribed for the industry, as in Subpart B or Subpart R of this Part, to the extent that none of such particular standards applies. To illustrate, the general standard regarding noise exposure in §1910.95 applies to employments and places of employment in pulp, paper, and paperboard mills covered by §1910.261.

(d) In the event a standard protects on its face a class of persons larger than employees, the standard shall be applicable under this Part only to employees and their employment and places of employment.

(e) [Reserved]

(f) An employer who is in compliance with any Standard in this Part shall be deemed to be in compliance with the requirement of Section 5(a)(1) of the Act, but only to the extent of the condition, practice, means, method, operation, or process covered by the Standard.

[39 FR 23502, June 27, 1974, as amended at 58 FR 35308, June 30, 1993]

§1910.6 Incorporation by reference

(a)(1) The standards of agencies of the U.S. Government, and organizations which are not agencies of the U.S. Government which are incorporated by reference in this Part, have the same force and effect as other standards in this Part. Only the mandatory provisions (i.e., provisions containing the word "shall" or other mandatory language) of standards incorporated by reference are adopted as standards under the Occupational Safety and Health Act.

(a)(2) Any changes in the standards incorporated by reference in this Part and an official historic file of such changes are available for inspection in the Docket Office at the national office of the Occupational Safety and Health Administration, U.S. Department of Labor, Washington, DC 20910; telephone: 202–693–2350 (TTY number: 877–889–5627).

(a)(3) The materials listed in paragraphs (b) through (w) of this Section are incorporated by reference in the corresponding sections noted as they exist on the date of the approval, and a notice of any change in these materials will be published in the Federal Register. These incorporations by reference were approved by the Director of the Federal Register in accordance with 5 U.S.C. 552(a) and 1 CFR Part §51.

(a)(4) Copies of standards listed in this Section and issued by private standards organizations are available for purchase from the issuing organizations at the addresses or through the other contact information listed below for these private standards organizations. In addition, these standards are available for inspection at any Regional Office of the Occupational Safety and Health Administration (OSHA), or at the OSHA Docket Office, U.S. Department of Labor, 200 Constitution Avenue NW., Room N–2625, Washington, DC 20210; telephone: 202–693–2350 (TTY number: 877–889–5627). They are also available for inspection at the National Archives and Records Administration (NARA). For information on the availability of these standards at NARA, telephone: 202–741–6030, or go to http://www.archives.gov/federal_register/code_of_federal_regulations/ibr_locations.html.

(b) The following material is available for purchase from the American Conference of Governmental Industrial Hygienists (ACGIH), 1014 Broadway, Cincinnati OH 45202:
(b)(1) "Industrial Ventilation: A Manual of Recommended Practice" (22nd ed., 1995), incorporation by reference (IBR) approved for §1910.124(b)(4)(iii).
(b)(2) Threshold Limit Values and Biological Exposure Indices for 1986–87 (1986), IBR approved for §1910.120, PEL definition.

(c) The following material is available for purchase from the American Society of Agricultural Engineers (ASAE), 2950 Niles Road, Post Office Box 229, St. Joseph, MI 49085:
(c)(1) ASAE Emblem for Identifying Slow Moving Vehicles, ASAE S276.2 (1968), IBR approved for §1910.145(d)(10).
(c)(2) [Reserved]

(d) The following material is available for purchase from the Agriculture Ammonia Institute-Rubber Manufacturers (AAI-RMA) Association, 1400 K St. NW, Washington DC 20005:
(d)(1) AAI-RMA Specifications for Anhydrous Ammonia Hose, IBR approved for §1910.111(b)(8)(i).
(d)(2) [Reserved]

(e) Except as noted, copies of the standards listed below in this paragraph are available for purchase from the American National Standards Institute (ANSI), 25 West 43rd Street, 4th Floor, New York, NY 10036; telephone: 212–642–4900; fax: 212–398–0023; Web site: http://www.ansi.org .
(e)(1)–(2) [Reserved]
(e)(3) ANSI A11.1–65 (R 70) Practice for Industrial Lighting, IBR approved for §1910.219(c)(5)(iii); §1910.261(a)(3)(i), (c)(10), and (k)(21); and §1910.265(c)(2).
(e)(4) ANSI A11.1–65 Practice for Industrial Lighting, IBR approved for §1910.262(c)(6) and §1910.265(d)(2)(i)(A).
(e)(5) [Reserved]
(e)(6) ANSI A13.1–56 Scheme for the Identification of Piping Systems, IBR approved for §1910.253(d)(4)(ii); §1910.261(a)(3)(iii); §1910.262(c)(7).
(e)(7) ANSI A14.1–68 Safety Code for Portable Wood Ladders, Supplemented by ANSI A14.1a–77, IBR approved for §1910.261(a)(3)(iv) and (c)(3)(i).
(e)(8) ANSI A14.2–56 Safety Code for Portable Metal Ladders, Supplemented by ANSI A14.2a–77, IBR approved for §1910.261(a)(3)(v) and (c)(3)(i).
(e)(9) ANSI A14.3–56 Safety Code for Fixed Ladders, IBR approved for §1910.68(b) (4); and §1910.261(a)(3)(vi) and (c)(3)(i).
(e)(10) ANSI A17.1–65 Safety Code for Elevators, Dumbwaiters and Moving Walks, Including Supplements, A17.1a (1967); A17.1b (1968); A17.1c (1969); A17.1d (1970), IBR approved for §1910.261(a)(3)(vii), (g)(11)(i), and (l)(4).
(e)(11) ANSI A17.2–60 Practice for the Inspection of Elevators, Including Supplements, A17.2a (1965), A17.2b (1967), IBR approved for §1910.261(a)(3)(viii).
(e)(12) ANSI A90.1–69 Safety Standard for Manlifts, IBR approved for §1910.68(b)(3).
(e)(13) ANSI A92.2–69 Standard for Vehicle Mounted Elevating and Rotating Work Platforms, IBR approved for §1910.67(b)(1), (2), (c)(3), and (4) and §1910.268(s)(1)(v).
(e)(14) ANSI A120.1–70 Safety Code for Powered Platforms for Exterior Building Maintenance, IBR approved for §1910.66 App. D (b) through (d).
(e)(15) ANSI B7.1–70 Safety Code for the Use, Care and Protection of Abrasive Wheels, IBR approved for §1910.215(b)(12) and §1910.218(j).
(e)(16) ANSI B15.1–53 (R 58) Safety Code for Mechanical Power Transmission Apparatus, IBR approved for §1910.68(b)(4) and §1910.261(a)(3)(ix), (b)(1), (e)(3), (e)(9), (f)(4), (j)(5)(iv), (k)(12), and (l)(3).
(e)(17) ANSI B20.1–57 Safety Code for Conveyors, Cableways, and Related Equipment, IBR approved for §1910.218(j)(3); §1910.261(a)(3)(x), (b)(1), (c)(15)(iv), (f)(4), and (j)(2); §1910.265(c)(18)(i).
(e)(18) ANSI B30.2–43 (R 52) Safety Code for Cranes, Derricks, and Hoists, IBR approved for §1910.261(a)(3)(xi), (c)(2)(vi), and (c)(8) (i) and (iv).
(e)(19) ANSI B30.2.0–67 Safety Code for Overhead and Gantry Cranes, IBR approved for §1910.179(b)(2); §1910.261(a)(3)(xii), (c)(2)(v), and (c)(8) (i) and (iv).
(e)(20) ANSI B30.5–68 Safety Code for Crawler, Locomotive, and Truck Cranes, IBR approved for §1910.180(b)(2) and §1910.261(a)(3)(xiii).
(e)(21) ANSI B30.6–69 Safety Code for Derricks, IBR approved for §1910.181(b)(2) and §1910.268(j)(4)(iv)(E) and (H).
(e)(22) ANSI B31.1–55 Code for Pressure Piping, IBR approved for §1910.261(g)(18)(iii).
(e)(23) ANSI B31.1–67, IBR approved for §1910.253(d)(1)(i)(A)
(e)(24) ANSI B31.1a–63 Addenda to ANSI B31.1 (1955), IBR approved for §1910.261(g)(18)(iii).
(e)(25) ANSI B31.1–67 and Addenda B31.1 (1969) Code for Pressure Piping, IBR approved for §1910.103(b)(1)(iii)(B); §1910.104(b)(5)(ii); §1910.218(d)(4) and (e)(1)(iv); and §1910.261(a)(3)(xiv) and (g)(18)(iii).
(e)(26) ANSI B31.2–68 Fuel Gas Piping, IBR approved for §1910.261(g)(18)(iii).
(e)(27) ANSI B31.3–66 Petroleum Refinery Piping, IBR approved for §1910.103(b)(3)(v)(B).
(e)(28) ANSI B31.5–66 Addenda B31.5a (1968) Refrigeration Piping, IB approved for §1910.103(b)(3)(v)(B) and §1910.111(b)(7)(iii).
(e)(29) ANSI B56.1–69 Safety Standard for Powered Industrial Trucks, IBR approved for §1910.178(a) (2) and (3) and §1910.261(a)(3)(xv), (b)(6), (m)(2), and (m)(5)(iii).

(e)(30) ANSI B57.1–65 Compressed Gas Cylinder Valve Outlet and Inlet Connections, IBR approved for §1910.253(b)(1)(iii).
(e)(31) [Reserved]
(e)(32) ANSI B175.1–1991, Safety Requirements for Gasoline-Powered Chain Saws §1910.266(e)(2)(i).
(e)(33) [Reserved]
(e)(34) ANSI C33.2–56 Safety Standard for Transformer-Type Arc Welding Machines, IBR approved for §1910.254(b)(1).
(e)(35) [Reserved]
(e)(36) ANSI H23.1–70 Seamless Copper Water Tube Specification, IBR approved for §1910.110(b)(8)(ii) and (13)(ii)(B)(1).
(e)(37) ANSI H38.7–69 Specification for Aluminum Alloy Seamless Pipe and Seamless Extruded Tube, IBR approved for §1910.110(b)(8)(i).
(e)(38) ANSI J6.4–71 Standard Specification for Rubber Insulating Blankets, IBR approved for §1910.268(f)(1) and (n)(11)(v).
(e)(39) ANSI J6.6–71 Standard Specification for Rubber Insulating Gloves, IBR approved for §1910.268(f)(1) and (n)(11)(iv).
(e)(40) ANSI K13.1–67 Identification of Gas Mask Canisters, IBR approved for §1910.261(a)(3)(xvi) and (h)(2)(iii).
(e)(41) ANSI K61.1–60 Safety Requirements for the Storage and Handling of Anhydrous Ammonia, IBR approved for §1910.111(b)(11)(i).
(e)(42) ANSI K61.1–66 Safety Requirements for the Storage and Handling of Anhydrous Ammonia, IBR approved for §1910.111(b)(11)(i).
(e)(43) ANSI O1.1–54 (R 61) Safety Code for Woodworking Machinery, IBR approved for §1910.261(a)(3)(xvii), (e)(7), and (i)(2).
(e)(44) ANSI S1.4–71 (R 76) Specification for Sound Level Meters, IBR approved for §1910.95 Appendices D and I.
(e)(45) ANSI S1.11–71 (R 76) Specification for Octave, Half-Octave and Third-Octave Band Filter Sets, IBR approved for §1910.95 Appendix D.
(e)(46) ANSI S3.6–69 Specifications for Audiometers, IBR approved for §1910.95(h)(2) and (5)(ii) and Appendix D.
(e)(47) ANSI Z4.1–68 Requirements for Sanitation in Places of Employment, IBR approved for §1910.261(a)(3)(xviii) and (g)(15)(vi).
(e)(48) [Reserved]
(e)(49) ANSI Z9.1–51 Safety Code for Ventilation and Operation of Open Surface Tanks, IBR approved for §1910.261(a)(3)(xix), (g)(18)(v), and (h)(2)(i).
(e)(50) ANSI Z9.1–71 Practices for Ventilation and Operation of Open-Surface Tanks, IBR approved for §1910.124(b)(4)(iv).
(e)(51) ANSI Z9.2–60 Fundamentals Governing the Design and Operation of Local Exhaust Systems, IBR approved for §1910.94(a)(4)(i) introductory text, (a)(6) introductory text, (b)(3)(ix), (b)(4)(i) and (ii), (c)(3)(i) introductory text, (c)(5)(iii)(b), and (c)(7)(iv)(a); §1910.261(a)(3)(xx), (g)(1)(i) and (iii), and (h)(2)(ii).
(e)(52) ANSI Z9.2–79 Fundamentals Governing the Design and Operation of Local Exhaust Systems, IBR approved for §1910.124(b)(4)(i).
(e)(53) ANSI Z12.12–68 Standard for the Prevention of Sulfur Fires and Explosions, IBR approved for §1910.261(a)(3)(xxi), (d)(1)(i), (f)(2)(iv), and (g)(1)(i).
(e)(54) ANSI Z12.20–62 (R 69) Code for the Prevention of Dust Explosions in Woodworking and Wood Flour Manufacturing Plants, IBR approved for §1910.265(c)(20)(i).
(e)(55) ANSI Z21.30–64 Requirements for Gas Appliances and Gas Piping Installations, IBR approved for §1910.265(c)(15).
(e)(56) ANSI Z24.22–57 Method of Measurement of Real-Ear Attenuation of Ear Protectors at Threshold, IBR approved for §1910.261(a)(3)(xxii).
(e)(57) ANSI Z33.1–61 Installation of Blower and Exhaust Systems for Dust, Stock, and Vapor Removal or Conveying, IBR approved for §1910.94(a)(4)(i); §1910.261(a)(3)(xxiii) and (f)(5); and §1910.265(c)(20)(i).
(e)(58) ANSI Z33.1–66 Installation of Blower and Exhaust Systems for Dust, Stock, and Vapor Removal or Conveying, IBR approved for §1910.94(a)(2)(ii).
(e)(59) ANSI Z35.1–68 Specifications for Accident Prevention Signs; IBR approved for §1910.261(c). Copies available for purchase from the IHS Standards Store, 15 Inverness Way East, Englewood, CO 80112; telephone: 1– 877–413–5184; Web site: www.global.ihs.com.
(e)(60) ANSI Z41–1999, American National Standard for Personal Protection—Protective Footwear; IBR approved for §1910.136(b)(1)(ii). Copies of ANSI Z41–1999 are available for purchase only from the National Safety Council, P.O. Box 558, Itasca, IL 60143–0558; telephone: 1–800–621–7619; fax: 708–285–0797; Web site: http://www.nsc.org.
(e)(61) ANSI Z41–1991, American National Standard for Personal Protection—Protective Footwear; IBR approved for §1910.136(b)(1)(iii). Copies of ANSI Z41–1991 are available for purchase only from the National Safety Council, P.O. Box 558, Itasca, IL 60143–0558; telephone: 1–800–621–7619; fax: 708–285–0797; Web site: http://www.nsc.org.
(e)(62)–(63) [Reserved]
(e)(64) ANSI Z49.1–67 Safety in Welding and Cutting, IBR approved for §1910.252(c)(1)(iv)(A) and (B).
(e)(65) USAS Z53.1–1967 (also referred to as ANSI Z53.1–1967), Safety Color Code for Marking Physical Hazards, ANSI approved October 9, 1967; IBR approved for §1910.97(a) and §1910.145(d). Copies available for purchase from the IHS Standards Store, 15 Inverness Way East, Englewood, CO 80112; telephone: 1–877–413–5184; Web site: www.global.ihs.com.
(e)(66) ANSI Z535.1–2006 (R2011), Safety Colors, reaffirmed July 19, 2011; IBR approved for §1910.97(a) and §910.145(d). Copies available for purchase from the:
(e)(66)(i) ANSI's e-Standards Store, 25 W. 43rd Street, 4th Floor, New York, NY 10036; telephone: 212-642-4980; Web site: http:/webstore.ansi.org/;
(e)(66)(ii) IHS Standards Store, 15 Inverness Way East, Englewood, CO 80112; telephone: 877-413-5184; Web site: www.global.ihs.com; or
(e)(66)(iii) TechStreet Store, 3916 Ranchero Dr., Ann Arbor, MI 48108; telephone: 877-699-9277; Web site: www.techstreet.com.
(e)(67) ANSI Z535.2–2011, Environmental and Facility Safety Signs, published September 15, 2011; IBR approved for §1910.261(c). Copies available for purchase from the:
(e)(67)(i) ANSI's e-Standards Store, 25 W. 43rd Street, 4th Floor, New York, NY 10036; telephone: 212-642-4980; Web site: http:/webstore.ansi.org/;
(e)(67)(ii) IHS Standards Store, 15 Inverness Way East, Englewood, CO 80112; telephone: 877-413-5184; Web site: www.global.ihs.com; or
(e)(68)(iii) TechStreet Store, 3916 Ranchero Dr., Ann Arbor, MI 48108; telephone: 877-699-9277; Web site: www.techstreet.com.
(e)(68) ANSI Z54.1–63 Safety Standard for Non-Medical X-Ray and Sealed Gamma Ray Sources, IBR approved for §1910.252(d) (1)(vii) and (2)(ii).
(e)(69) ANSI/ISEA Z87.1-2010, Occupational and Educational Personal Eye and Face Protection Devices, Approved April 13, 2010; IBR approved for §1910.133(b). Copies are available for purchase from:
(e)(69)(i) American National Standards Institute's e-Standards Store, 25 W 43rd Street, 4th Floor, New York, NY 10036; telephone: (212) 642-4980; Web site: http://webstore.ansi.org/;
(e)(69)(ii) IHS Standards Store, 15 Inverness Way East, Englewood, CO 80112; telephone: (877) 413-5184; Web site: http://global.ihs.com; or
(e)(69)(iii) TechStreet Store, 3916 Ranchero Dr., Ann Arbor, MI 48108; telephone: (877) 699-9277; Web site: http://techstreet.com.
(e)(70) ANSI Z87.1-2003, Occupational and Educational Eye and Face Personal Protection Devices Approved June 19, 2003; IBR approved for §§1910.133(b). Copies available for purchase from the:
(e)(70)(i) American National Standards Institute's e-Standards Store, 25 W 43rd Street, 4th Floor, New York, NY 10036; telephone: (212) 642-4980; Web site: http://webstore.ansi.org/;
(e)(70)(ii) IHS Standards Store, 15 Inverness Way East, Englewood, CO 80112; telephone: (877) 413-5184; Web site: http://global.ihs.com; or
(e)(70)(iii) TechStreet Store, 3916 Ranchero Dr., Ann Arbor, MI 48108; telephone: (877) 699-9277; Web site: http://techstreet.com.
(e)(71) ANSI Z87.1-1989 (R-1998), Practice for Occupational and Educational Eye and Face Protection, Reaffirmation approved January 4, 1999; IBR approved for §1910.133(b). Copies are available for purchase from:
(e)(71)(i) American National Standards Institute's e-Standards Store, 25 W 43rd Street, 4th Floor, New York, NY 10036; telephone: (212) 642-4980; Web site: http://webstore.ansi.org/;
(e)(71)(ii) IHS Standards Store, 15 Inverness Way East, Englewood, CO 80112; telephone: (877) 413-5184; Web site: http://global.ihs.com; or
(e)(71)(iii) TechStreet Store, 3916 Ranchero Dr., Ann Arbor, MI 48108; telephone: (877) 699-9277; Web site: http://techstreet.com.
(e)(72) ANSI Z88.2–1969, Practices for Respiratory Protection; IBR approved for §1910.94(c)(6)(iii)(a), §1910.134(c); and §1910.261(a)(3)(xxvi), (b)(2), (f)(5), (g)(15)(v), (h)(2)(iii), (h)(2)(iv), and (i)(4).
(e)(73) American National Standards Institute (ANSI) Z89.1–2009, American National Standard for Industrial Head Protection, approved January 26, 2009; IBR approved for §1910.135(b)(1)(i). Copies of ANSI Z89.1–2009 are available for purchase only from the International Safety Equipment Association, 1901 North Moore Street, Arlington, VA 22209–1762; telephone: 703–525–1695; fax: 703–528–2148; Web site: www.safetyequipment.org.
(e)(74) American National Standards Institute (ANSI) Z89.1–2003, American National Standard for Industrial Head Protection; IBR approved for §1910.135(b)(1)(ii). Copies of ANSI Z89.1–2003 are available for purchase only from the International Safety Equipment Association, 1901 North Moore Street, Arlington, VA 22209–1762; telephone: 703–525–1695; fax: 703–528–2148; Web site: www.safetyequipment.org.
(e)(75) American National Standards Institute (ANSI) Z89.1–1997, American National Standard for Personnel Protection—Protective Headwear for Industrial Workers—Requirements; IBR approved for §1910.135(b)(1)(iii). Copies of ANSI Z89.1–1997 are available for purchase only from the International Safety Equipment Association, 1901 North Moore Street, Arlington, VA 22209–1762; telephone: 703–525–1695; fax: 703–528–2148; Web site: www.safetyequipment.org.
(e)(76) ANSI Z41.1–1967 Men's Safety Toe Footwear; IBR approved for §1910.261(i)(4).
(e)(77) ANSI Z87.1–1968 Practice of Occupational and Educational Eye and Face Protection; IBR approved for §1910.261(a)(3)(xxv), (d)(1)(ii), (f)(5), (g)(1), (g)(15)(v), (g)(18)(ii), and (i)(4).

(e)(78) ANSI Z89.1–1969 Safety Requirements for Industrial Head Protection; IBR approved for §1910.261(a)(3)(xxvii), (b)(2), (g)(15)(v), and (i)(4).
(e)(79) ANSI Z89.2–1971 Safety Requirements for Industrial Protective Helmets for Electrical Workers, Class B; IBR approved for §1910.268(i)(1).

(f) The following material is available for purchase from the American Petroleum Institute (API), 1220 L Street NW, Washington DC 20005:
(f)(1) [Reserved]
(f)(2) API 12B (May 1958) Specification for Bolted Production Tanks, 11th Ed., With Supplement No. 1, Mar. 1962, IBR approved for §1910.106(b)(1)(i)(a)(3).
(f)(3) API 12D (Aug. 1957) Specification for Large Welded Production Tanks, 7th Ed., IBR approved for §1910.106(b)(1)(i)(A)(3).
(f)(4) API 12F (Mar. 1961) Specification for Small Welded Production Tanks, 5th Ed., IBR approved for §1910.106(b)(1)(i)(A)(3).
(f)(5) API 620, Fourth Ed. (1970) Including Appendix R, Recommended Rules for Design and Construction of Large Welded Low Pressure Storage Tanks, IBR approved for §1910.103(c)(1)(i)(A); §1910.106(b)(1)(iv)(B)(1); and §1910.111(d)(1)(ii) and (iii).
(f)(6) API 650 (1966) Welded Steel Tanks for Oil Storage, 3rd Ed., IBR approved for §1910.106(b)(1)(iii)(A)(2).
(f)(7) API 1104 (1968) Standard for Welding Pipelines and Related Facilities, IBR approved for §1910.252(d)(1)(v).
(f)(8) API 2000 (1968) Venting Atmospheric and Low Pressure Storage Tanks, IBR approved for §1910.106(b)(2)(iv)(B)(1).
(f)(9) API 2201 (1963) Welding or Hot Tapping on Equipment Containing Flammables, IBR approved for §1910.252(d)(1)(vi).

(g) The following material is available for purchase from the American Society of Mechanical Engineers (ASME), United Engineering Center, 345 East 47th Street, New York, NY 10017:
(g)(1) ASME Boiler and Pressure Vessel Code, Sec. VIII, 1949, 1950, 1952, 1956, 1959, and 1962 Ed., IBR approved for §1910.110(b)(10)(iii) (Table H–26), (d)(2) (Table H–31); (e)(3)(i) (Table H–32), (h)(2) (Table H–34); and §1910.111(b)(2)(vi);
(g)(2) ASME Code for Pressure Vessels, 1968 Ed., IBR approved for §1910.106(i)(3)(i); §1910.110(g)(2)(iii)(B)(2); and §1910.217(b)(12);
(g)(3) ASME Boiler and Pressure Vessel Code, Sec. VIII, 1968, IBR approved for §1910.103; §1910.104(b)(4)(ii); §1910.106(b)(1)(iv)(B)(2) and (i)(3)(ii); §1910.107; §1910.110(b)(11)(i)(B) and (iii)(A)(1); §1910.111(b)(2)(i), (ii), and (iv); and §1910.169(a)(2)(i) and (ii);
(g)(4) ASME Boiler and Pressure Vessel Code, Sec. VIII, Paragraph UG–84, 1968, IBR approved for §1910.104(b)(4)(ii) and (b)(5)(iii);
(g)(5) ASME Boiler and Pressure Vessel Code, Sec. VIII, Unfired Pressure Vessels, Including Addenda (1969), IBR approved for §1910.261; §1910.262; §1910.263(i)(24)(ii);
(g)(6) Code for Unfired Pressure Vessels for Petroleum Liquids and Gases of the API and the ASME, 1951 Ed., IBR approved for §1910.110(b)(3)(iii); and
(g)(7) ASME B56.6–1992 (with addenda), Safety Standard for Rough Terrain Forklift Trucks, IBR approved for §1910.266(f)(4).

(h) Copies of the standards listed below in this paragraph (h) are available for purchase from ASTM International, 100 Barr Harbor Drive, P.O. Box C700, West Conshohocken, PA 19428–2959; Telephone: 610–832–9585; Fax: 610–832–9555; Email: seviceastm.org; Web site: http://www.astm.org. Copies of historical standards or standards that ASTM does not have may be purchased from Information Handling Services, Global Engineering Documents, 15 Inverness Way East, Englewood, CO 80112; Telephone: 1–800–854–7179; Email: global@ihs.com; Web sites: http://global.ihs.com or http://www.store.ihs.com.
(h)(1) ASTM A 47–68, Malleable Iron Castings, IBR approved for §1910.111.
(h)(2) ASTM A 53–69, Welded and Seamless Steel Pipe, IBR approved for §1910.110 and §1910.111.
(h)(3) ASTM A 126–66, Gray Iron Casting for Valves, Flanges and Pipe Fitting, IBR approved for §1910.111.
(h)(4) ASTM A 391–65 (ANSI G61.1–1968), Alloy Steel Chain, IBR approved for §1910.184.
(h)(5) ASTM A 395–68, Ductile Iron for Use at Elevated Temperatures, IBR approved for §1910.111.
(h)(6) ASTM B 88–66A, Seamless Copper Water Tube, IBR approved for §1910.252.
(h)(7) ASTM B 88–69, Seamless Copper Water Tube, IBR approved for §1910.110.
(h)(8) [Reserved]
(h)(9) ASTM B 210–68, Aluminum-Alloy Drawn Seamless Tubes, IBR approved for §1910.110.
(h)(10) ASTM B 241–69, Standard Specifications for Aluminum-Alloy Seamless Pipe and Seamless Extruded Tube, IBR approved for §1910.110.
(h)(11) ASTM D 5–65, Test for Penetration by Bituminous Materials, IBR approved for §1910.106.
(h)(12) ASTM D 56–70, Test for Flash Point by Tag Closed Tester, IBR approved for §1910.106.
(h)(13) ASTM D 56–05, Standard Test Method for Flash Point by Tag Closed Cup Tester, Approved May 1, 2005, IBR approved for Appendix B to §1910.1200.
(h)(14) ASTM D 86–62, Test for Distillation of Petroleum Products, IBR approved for §1910.106 and §1910.119.
(h)(15) ASTM D 86–07a, Standard Test Method for Distillation of Petroleum Products at Atmospheric Pressure, Approved April 1, 2007, IBR approved for Appendix B to §1910.1200.
(h)(16) ASTM D 88–56, Test for Saybolt Viscosity, IBR approved for §1910.106.
(h)(17) ASTM D 93–71, Test for Flash Point by Pensky Martens, IBR approved for §1910.106.
(h)(18) ASTM D 93–08, Standard Test Methods for Flash Point by Pensky-Martens Closed Cup Tester, Approved Oct. 15, 2008, IBR approved for Appendix B to §1910.1200.
(h)(19) ASTM D 240–02 (Reapproved 2007), Standard Test Method for Heat of Combustion of Liquid Hydrocarbon Fuels by Bomb Calorimeter, Approved May 1, 2007, IBR approved for Appendix B to §1910.1200.
(h)(20) ASTM D 323–68, Standard Test Method of Test for Vapor Pressure of Petroleum Products (Reid Method), IBR approved for §1910.106.
(h)(21) ASTM D 445–65, Test for Viscosity of Transparent and Opaque Liquids, IBR approved for §1910.106.
(h)(22) ASTM D 1078–05, Standard Test Method for Distillation Range of Volatile Organic Liquids, Approved May 15, 2005, IBR approved for Appendix B to §1910.1200.
(h)(23) ASTM D 1692–68, Test for Flammability of Plastic Sheeting and Cellular Plastics, IBR approved for §1910.103.
(h)(24) ASTM D 2161–66, Conversion Tables for SUS, IBR approved for §1910.106.
(h)(25) ASTM D 3278–96 (Reapproved 2004) E1, Standard Test Methods for Flash Point of Liquids by Small Scale Closed-Cup Apparatus, Approved November 1, 2004, IBR approved for Appendix B to §1910.1200.
(h)(26) ASTM D 3828–07a, Standard Test Methods for Flash Point by Small Scale Closed Cup Tester, Approved July 15, 2007, IBR approved for Appendix B to §1910.1200.
(h)(27) ASTM F–2412–2005, Standard Test Methods for Foot Protection, IBR approved for §1910.136.
(h)(28) ASTM F–2413–2005, Standard Specification for Performance Requirements for Protective Footwear, IBR approved for §1910.136.

(i) The following material is available for purchase from the American Welding Society (AWS), 550 NW, LeJeune Road, P.O. Box 351040, Miami FL 33135:
(i)(1)–(2) [Reserved]
(i)(3) AWS B3.0–41 Standard Qualification Procedure, IBR approved for §1910.67(c)(5)(i).
(i)(4) AWS D1.0–1966 Code for Welding in Building Construction, IBR approved for §1910.27(b)(6).
(i)(5) AWS D2.0–69 Specifications for Welding Highway and Railway Bridges, IBR approved for §1910.67(c)(5)(iv).
(i)(6) AWS D8.4–61 Recommended Practices for Automotive Welding Design, IBR approved for §1910.67(c)(5)(ii).
(i)(7) AWS D10.9–69 Standard Qualification of Welding Procedures and Welders for Piping and Tubing, IBR approved for §1910.67(c)(5)(iii).

(j) The following material is available for purchase from the Department of Commerce:
(j)(1) [Reserved]
(j)(2) Publication "Model Performance Criteria for Structural Fire Fighters' Helmets," IBR approved for §1910.156(e)(5)(i).

(k) The following material is available for purchase from the Compressed Gas Association (CGA), 1235 Jefferson Davis Highway, Arlington, VA 22202:
(k)(1) CGA C–6 (1968) Standards for Visual Inspection of Compressed Gas Cylinders, IBR approved for §1910.101(a).
(k)(2) CGA C–8 (1962) Standard for Requalification of ICC–3HT Cylinders, IBR approved for §1910.101(a).
(k)(3) CGA G–1–2009 Acetylene, Twelfth Edition, IBR approved for §1910.102(a). Copies of CGA Pamphlet G–1–2009 are available for purchase from the: Compressed Gas Association, Inc., 4221 Walney Road, 5th Floor, Chantilly, VA 20151; telephone: (703) 788–2700; fax: (703) 961–1831; email: cga@cganet.com.
(k)(4) CGA G–7.1 (1966) Commodity Specification, IBR approved for §1910.134(d)(1).
(k)(5) CGA G–8.1 (1964) Standard for the Installation of Nitrous Oxide Systems at Consumer Sites, IBR approved for §1910.105.
(k)(6) CGA P–1 (1965) Safe Handling of Compressed Gases, IBR approved for §1910.101(b).
(k)(7) CGA P–3 (1963) Specifications, Properties, and Recommendations for Packaging, Transportation, Storage and Use of Ammonium Nitrate, IBR approved for §1910.109(i)(1)(ii)(B).
(k)(8) CGA S–1.1 (1963) and 1965 Addenda. Safety Release Device Standards—Cylinders for Compressed Gases, IBR approved for §1910.101(c); §1910.103(c)(1)(iv)(A)(2).

(k)(9) CGA S–1.2 (1963) Safety Release Device Standards, Cargo and Portable Tanks for Compressed Gases, IBR approved for §1910.101(c); §1910.103(c)(1)(iv)(A)(2).
(k)(10) CGA S–1.3 (1959) Safety Release Device Standards-Compressed Gas Storage Containers, IBR approved for §1910.103(c)(1)(iv)(A)(2); §1910.104(b)(6)(iii); and §1910.111(d)(4)(ii)(B).
(k)(11) CGA 1957 Standard Hose Connection Standard, IBR approved for §1910.253(e)(4)(v) and (5)(iii).
(k)(12) CGA and RMA (Rubber Manufacturer's Association) Specification for Rubber Welding Hose (1958), IBR approved for §1910.253(e)(5)(i).
(k)(13) CGA 1958 Regulator Connection Standard, IBR approved for §1910.253(e)(4)(iv) and (6).

(l) The following material is available for purchase from the Crane Manufacturer's Association of America, Inc. (CMAA), 1 Thomas Circle NW, Washington DC 20005:
(l)(1) CMAA Specification 1B61, Specifications for Electric Overhead Traveling Cranes, IBR approved for §1910.179(b)(6)(i).
(l)(2) [Reserved]

(m) The following material is available for purchase from the General Services Administration:
(m)(1) GSA Pub. GG-B–0067b, Air Compressed for Breathing Purposes, or Interim Federal Specifications, Apr. 1965, IBR approved for §1910.134(d)(4).
(m)(2) [Reserved]

(n) The following material is available for purchase from the Department of Health and Human Services:
(n)(1) Publication No. 76–120 (1975), List of Personal Hearing Protectors and Attenuation Data, IBR approved for §1910.95 App. B.
(n)(2) [Reserved]

(o) The following material is available for purchase from the Institute of Makers of Explosives (IME), 420 Lexington Avenue, New York, NY 10017:
(o)(1) IME Pamphlet No. 17, 1960, Safety in the Handling and Use of Explosives, IBR approved for §1910.261(a)(4)(iii) and (c)(14)(ii).
(o)(2) [Reserved]

(p) The following material is available for purchase from the National Electrical Manufacturer's Association (NEMA):
(p)(1) NEMA EW–1 (1962) Requirements for Electric Arc Welding Apparatus, IBR approved for §1910.254(b)(1).
(p)(2) [Reserved]

(q) The following material is available for purchase from the National Fire Protection Association (NFPA), 1 Batterymarch Park, Quincy, MA 02269; Telephone: 800–344–3555 or 617–770–3000; Fax: 1–800–593–6372 or 1–508–895–8301; Email: custserv@nfpa.org; Web site: http://www.nfpa.org.
(q)(1) NFPA 30 (1969) Flammable and Combustible Liquids Code, IBR approved for §1910.178(f)(1).
(q)(2) NFPA 32–1970 Standard for Dry Cleaning Plants, IBR approved for §1910.106(j)(6)(i).
(q)(3) NFPA 33–1969 Standard for Spray Finishing Using Flammable and Combustible Material, IBR approved for §1910.94(c)(2).
(q)(4) NFPA 34–1966 Standard for Dip Tanks Containing Flammable or Combustible Liquids, IBR approved for §1910.124(b)(4)(iv).
(q)(5) NFPA 34–1995 Standard for Dip Tanks Containing Flammable or Combustible Liquids, IBR approved for §1910.124(b)(4)(ii).
(q)(6) NFPA 35–1970 Standard for the Manufacture of Organic Coatings, IBR approved for §1910.106(j)(6)(ii).
(q)(7) NFPA 36–1967 Standard for Solvent Extraction Plants, IBR approved for §1910.106(j)(6)(iii).
(q)(8) NFPA 37–1970 Standard for the Installation and Use of Stationary Combustion Engines and Gas Turbines, IBR approved for §1910.106(j)(6)(iv) and §1910.110(b)(20)(iv)(c) and (e)(11).
(q)(9) NFPA 51B–1962 Standard for Fire Protection in Use of Cutting and Welding Processes, IBR approved for §1910.252(a)(1) introductory text.
(q)(10) NFPA 54–1969 Standard for the Installation of Gas Appliances and Gas Piping, IBR approved for §1910.110(b)(20)(iv)(A).
(q)(11) NFPA 54A–1969 Standard for the Installation of Gas Piping and Gas Equipment on Industrial Premises and Certain Other Premises, IBR approved for §1910.110(b)(20)(iv)(B).
(q)(12) NFPA 58–1969 Standard for the Storage and Handling of Liquefied Petroleum Gases (ANSI Z106.1–1970), IBR approved for §1910.110(b)(3)(iv) and (i)(3)(i) and (ii); and §1910.178(f)(2).
(q)(13) NFPA 59–1968 Standard for the Storage and Handling of Liquefied Petroleum Gases at Utility Gas Plants, IBR approved for §1910.110(b)(3)(iv) and (i)(2)(iv).
(q)(14) NFPA 62–1967 Standard for the Prevention of Dust Explosions in the Production, Packaging, and Handling of Pulverized Sugar and Cocoa, IBR approved for §1910.263(k)(2)(i).
(q)(15) NFPA 68–1954 Guide for Explosion Venting, IBR approved for §1910.94(a)(2)(iii).
(q)(16) [Reserved]
(q)(17) NFPA 78–1968 Lightning Protection Code, IBR approved for §1910.109(i)(6)(ii).
(q)(18) NFPA 80–1968 Standard for Fire Doors and Windows, IBR approved for §1910.106(d)(4)(i).
(q)(19) NFPA 80–1970 Standard for the Installation of Fire Doors and Windows, IBR approved for §1910.253(f)(6)(i)(I).
(q)(20) NFPA 86A–1969 Standard for Oven and Furnaces Design, Location and Equipment, IBR approved for §1910.107(j)(1) and (l)(3) and §1910.108(b)(2) and (d)(2).
(q)(21) NFPA 91–1961 Standard for the Installation of Blower and Exhaust Systems for Dust, Stock, and Vapor Removal or Conveying (ANSI Z33.1–61), IBR approved for §1910.107(d)(1).
(q)(22) NFPA 91–1969 Standards for Blower and Exhaust Systems, IBR approved for §1910.108(b)(1).
(q)(23) NFPA 96–1970 Standard for the Installation of Equipment for the Removal of Smoke and Grease Laden Vapors from Commercial Cooking Equipment, IBR approved for §1910.110(b)(20)(iv)(D).
(q)(24) NFPA 101–1970 Code for Life Safety From Fire in Buildings and Structures, IBR approved for §1910.261(a)(4)(ii).
(q)(25) NFPA 101–2009, Life Safety Code, 2009 edition, IBR approved for §1910.34, §1910.35, §1910.36, and §1910.37.
(q)(26) NFPA 203M–1970 Manual on Roof Coverings, IBR approved for §1910.109(i)(1)(iii)(C).
(q)(27) NFPA 251–1969 Standard Methods of Fire Tests of Building Construction and Materials, IBR approved for §1910.106(d)(3)(ii) introductory text and (d)(4)(i).
(q)(28) NFPA 302–1968 Fire Protection Standard for Motor-Craft (Pleasure and Commercial), IBR approved for §1910.265(d)(2)(iv) introductory text.
(q)(29) NFPA 385–1966 Recommended Regulatory Standard for Tank Vehicles for Flammable and Combustible Liquids, IBR approved for §1910.106(g)(1)(i)(e)(1).
(q)(30) NFPA 496–1967 Standard for Purged Enclosures for Electrical Equipment in Hazardous Locations, IBR approved for §1910.103(c)(1)(ix)(e)(1).
(q)(31) NFPA 505–1969 Standard for Type Designations, Areas of Use, Maintenence, and Operation of Powered Industrial Trucks, IBR approved for §1910.110(e)(2)(iv).
(q)(32) NFPA 566–1965 Standard for the Installation of Bulk Oxygen Systems at Consumer Sites, IBR approved for §1910.253(b)(4)(iv) and (c)(2)(v).
(q)(33) NFPA 656–1959 Code for the Prevention of Dust Ignition in Spice Grinding Plants, IBR approved for §1910.263(k)(2)(i).
(q)(34) NFPA 1971–1975 Protective Clothing for Structural Fire Fighting, IBR approved for §1910.156(e)(3)(ii) introductory text.
(q)(35) NFPA 51A (2001) Standard for Acetylene Cylinder Charging Plants, IBR approved for §1910.102(b) and (c). Copies of NFPA 51A–2001 are available for purchase from the: National Fire Protection Association, 1 Batterymarch Park, Quincy, MA 02169–7471; telephone: 1–800–344–35557; e-mail: custserv@nfpa.org .
(q)(36) NFPA 51A (2006) Standard for Acetylene Cylinder Charging Plants, IBR approved for §1910.102(b) and (c). Copies of NFPA 51A–2006 are available for purchase from the: National Fire Protection Association, 1 Batterymarch Park, Quincy, MA 02169–7471; telephone: 1–800–344–35557; e-mail: custserv@nfpa.org .
(q)(37) NFPA 30B, Code for the Manufacture and Storage of Aerosol Products, 2007 Edition, Approved August 17, 2006, IBR approved for Appendix B to §1910.1200.

(r) The following material is available for purchase from the National Food Plant Institute, 1700 K St. NW., Washington, DC 20006:
(r)(1) Definition and Test Procedures for Ammonium Nitrate Fertilizer (Nov. 1964), IBR approved for §1910.109 Table H–22, ftn. 3.
(r)(2) [Reserved]

(s) The following material is available for purchase from the National Institute for Occupational Safety and Health (NIOSH):
(s)(1) Registry of Toxic Effects of Chemical Substances, 1978, IBR approved for §1910.20(c)(13)(i) and Appendix B.
(s)(2) Development of Criteria for Fire Fighters Gloves; Vol. II, Part II; Test Methods, 1976, IBR approved for §1910.156(e)(4)(i) introductory text.
(s)(3) NIOSH Recommendations for Occupational Safety and Health Standards (Sept. 1987), IBR approved for §1910.120 PEL definition.

(t) The following material is available for purchase from the Public Health Service:
(t)(1) U.S. Pharmacopeia, IBR approved for §1910.134(d)(1).
(t)(2) Publication No. 934 (1962), Food Service Sanitation Ordinance and Code, Part V of the Food Service Sanitation Manual, IBR approved for §1910.142(i)(1).

(u) The following material is available for purchase from the Society of Automotive Engineers (SAE), 485 Lexington Avenue, New York, NY 10017:
(u)(1) SAE J185, June 1988, Recommended Practice for Access Systems for Off-Road Machines, IBR approved for §1910.266(f)(5)(i).
(u)(2) SAE J231, January 1981, Minimum Performance Criteria for Falling Object Protective Structure (FOPS), IBR approved for §1910.266(f)(3)(ii).
(u)(3) SAE J386, June 1985, Operator Restraint Systems for Off-Road Work Machines, IBR approved for §1910.266(d)(3)(iv).

(u)(4) SAE J397, April 1988, Deflection Limiting Volume-ROPS/FOPS Laboratory Evaluation, IBR approved for §1910.266(f)(3)(iv).
(u)(5) SAE 765 (1961) SAE Recommended Practice: Crane Loading Stability Test Code, IBR approved for §1910.180(c)(1)(iii) and (e)(2)(iii)(a).
(u)(6) SAE J1040, April 1988, Performance Criteria for Rollover Protective Structures (ROPS) for Construction, Earthmoving, Forestry and Mining Machines, IBR approved for §1910.266(f)(3)(ii).

(v) The following material is available for purchase from the Fertilizer Institute, 1015 18th Street NW, Washington, DC 20036:
(v)(1) Standard M–1 (1953, 1955, 1957, 1960, 1961, 1963, 1965, 1966, 1967, 1968), Superseded by ANSI K61.1–1972, IBR approved for §1910.111(b)(1)(i) and (iii).
(v)(2) [Reserved]

(w) The following material is available for purchase from Underwriters Laboratories (UL), 207 East Ohio Street, Chicago, IL 60611:
(w)(1) UL 58–61 Steel Underground Tanks for Flammable and Combustible Liquids, 5th Ed., IBR approved for §1910.106(b)(1)(iii)(A)(1).
(w)(2) UL 80–63 Steel Inside Tanks for Oil-Burner Fuel, IBR approved for §1910.106(b)(1)(iii)(A)(1).
(w)(3) UL 142–68 Steel Above Ground Tanks for Flammable and Combustible Liquids, IBR approved for §1910.106(b)(1)(iii)(A)(1).

(x) The following material is available for purchase from the: International Code Council, Chicago District Office, 4051 W. Flossmoor Rd., Country Club Hills, IL 60478; telephone: 708–799–2300, x3–3801; facsimile: 001–708–799–4981; e-mail: order@iccsafe.org.
(x)(1) IFC–2009, International Fire Code, copyright 2009, IBR approved for §1910.34, §1910.35, §1910.36, and §1910.37.
(x)(2) [Reserved]

(y)(1) The following materials are available for purchase from the International Standards Organization (ISO) through ANSI, 25 West 43rd Street, Fourth Floor, New York, NY 10036–7417; Telephone: 212–642–4980; Fax: 212–302–1286; Email: info@ansi.org; Web site: http://www.ansi.org .
(y)(2) Documents not available in the ANSI store may be purchased from:
(y)(2)(i) Document Center Inc., 111 Industrial Road, Suite 9, Belmont, 94002; Telephone: 650–591–7600; Fax: 650–591–7617; Email: info@document-center.com; Web site: www.document-center.com.
(y)(2)(ii) DECO—Document Engineering Co., Inc., 15210 Stagg Street, Van Nuys, CA 91405; Telephone: 800–645–7732 or 818–782–1010; Fax: 818–782–2374; Email: doceng@doceng.com; Web site: www.doceng.com
(y)(2)(iii) Global Engineering Documents, 15 Inverness Way East, Englewood, CO 80112; Telephone: 1–800–854–7179 or 303–397–7956; Fax: 303–397–2740; Email: global@ihs.com; Web sites: http://global.ihs.com or http://www.store.ihs.com ;
(y)(2)(iv) ILI Infodisk, Inc., 610 Winters Avenue, Paramus, NJ 07652; Telephone: 201–986–1131; Fax: 201–986–7886; Email: sales@ili-info.com; Web site: www.ili-info.com .
(y)(2)(v) Techstreet, a business of Thomson Reuters, 3916 Ranchero Drive, Ann Arbor, MI 48108; Telephone: 800–699–9277 or 734–780–8000; Fax: 734–780–2046; Email: techstreet.service@thomsonreuters.com; Web site: www.Techstreet.com.
(y)(3) ISO 10156:1996 (E), Gases and Gas Mixtures—Determination of Fire Potential and Oxidizing Ability for the Selection of Cylinder Valve Outlets, Second Edition, Feb. 15, 1996, IBR approved for Appendix B to §1910.1200.
(y)(4) ISO 10156–2:2005 (E), Gas cylinders—Gases and Gas Mixtures—Part 2: Determination of Oxidizing Ability of Toxic and Corrosive Gases and Gas Mixtures, First Edition, Aug. 1, 2005, IBR approved for Appendix B to §1910.1200.
(y)(5) ISO 13943:2000 (E/F), Fire Safety—Vocabulary, First Edition, April, 15, 2000, IBR approved for Appendix B to §1910.1200.

(z)(1) The following document is available for purchase from United Nations Publications, Customer Service, c/o National Book Network, 15200 NBN Way, PO Box 190, Blue Ridge Summit, PA 17214; telephone: 1–888–254–4286; fax: 1–800–338–4550; email: unpublications@nbnbooks.com . Other distributors of United Nations Publications include:
(z)(1)(i) Bernan, 15200 NBN Way, Blue Ridge Summit, PA 17214; telephone: 1–800–865–3457; fax: 1–800–865–3450; email: customercare@bernan; Web site: http://www.bernan.com; and
(z)(1)(ii) Renouf Publishing Co. Ltd., 812 Proctor Avenue, Ogdensburg, NY 13669–2205; telephone: 1–888–551–7470; Fax: 1–888–551–7471; email: orders@renoufbooks.com; Web site: http://www.renoufbooks.com.
(z)(2) UN ST/SG/AC.10/Rev.4, The UN Recommendations on the Transport of Dangerous Goods, Manual of Tests and Criteria, Fourth Revised Edition, 2003, IBR approved for Appendix B to §1910.1200.

[39 FR 23502, June 27, 1974, as amended at 49 FR 5321, Feb. 10, 1984; 61 FR 9231, Mar. 7, 1996; 64 FR 13908, Mar. 23, 1999; 69 FR 18803, Apr. 9, 2004; 70 FR 53929, Sept. 13, 2005; 72 FR 7190, Feb. 14, 2007; 72 FR 71068, Dec. 14, 2007; 74 FR 46355, Sept. 9, 2009; 74 FR 40447, Aug. 11, 2009; 76 FR 33606, June 8, 2011; 76 FR 75786, Dec. 5, 2011; 77 FR 17764, Mar. 26, 2012; 77 FR 37598, June 22, 2012]

§1910.7 Definition and requirements for a nationally recognized testing laboratory

(a) **Application** This Section shall apply only when the term nationally recognized testing laboratory is used in other Sections of this Part.

(b) **Laboratory requirements** The term nationally recognized testing laboratory (NRTL) means an organization which is recognized by OSHA in accordance with Appendix A of this Section and which tests for safety, and lists or labels or accepts, equipment or materials and which meets all of the following criteria:
(b)(1) For each specified item of equipment or material to be listed, labeled or accepted, the NRTL has the capability (including proper testing equipment and facilities, trained staff, written testing procedures, and calibration and quality control programs) to perform:
(b)(1)(i) Testing and examining of equipment and materials for workplace safety purposes to determine conformance with appropriate test standards; or
(b)(1)(ii) Experimental testing and examining of equipment and materials for workplace safety purposes to determine conformance with appropriate test standards or performance in a specified manner.
(b)(2) The NRTL shall provide, to the extent needed for the particular equipment or materials listed, labeled, or accepted, the following controls or services:
(b)(2)(i) Implements control procedures for identifying the listed and labeled equipment or materials;
(b)(2)(ii) Inspects the run of production of such items at factories for product evaluation purposes to assure conformance with the test standards; and
(b)(2)(iii) Conducts field inspections to monitor and to assure the proper use of its identifying mark or labels on products;
(b)(3) The NRTL is completely independent of employers subject to the tested equipment requirements, and of any manufacturers or vendors of equipment or materials being tested for these purposes; and,
(b)(4) The NRTL maintains effective procedures for:
(b)(4)(i) Producing creditable findings or reports that are objective and without bias; and
(b)(4)(ii) Handling complaints and disputes under a fair and reasonable system.

(c) **Test standards** An appropriate test standard referred to in §1910.7(b)(1)(i) and (ii) is a document which specifies the safety requirements for specific equipment or class of equipment and is:
(c)(1) Recognized in the United States as a safety standard providing an adequate level of safety, and
(c)(2) Compatible with and maintained current with periodic revisions of applicable national codes and installation standards, and
(c)(3) Developed by a standards developing organization under a method providing for input and consideration of views of industry groups, experts, users, consumers, governmental authorities, and others having broad experience in the safety field involved, or
(c)(4) In lieu of paragraphs (c)(1), (2), and (3), the standard is currently designated as an American National Standards Institute (ANSI) safety-designated product standard or an American Society for Testing and Materials (ASTM) test standard used for evaluation of products or materials.

(d) **Alternative test standard** If a testing laboratory desires to use a test standard other than one allowed under paragraph (c) of this Section, then the Assistant Secretary of Labor shall evaluate the proposed standard to determine that it provides an adequate level of safety before it is used.

(e) **Implementation** A testing organization desiring recognition by OSHA as an NRTL shall request that OSHA evaluate its testing and control programs against the requirements in this Section for any equipment or material it may specify. The recognition procedure shall be conducted in accordance with Appendix A to this Section.

(f) **Fees**

(f)(1) Each applicant for NRTL recognition and each NRTL must pay fees for services provided by OSHA in advance of the provision of those services. OSHA will assess fees for the following services:
(f)(1)(i) Processing of applications for initial recognition, expansion of recognition, or renewal of recognition, including on-site reviews; review and evaluation of the applications; and preparation of reports, evaluations and Federal Register notices; and
(f)(1)(ii) Audits of sites.

(f)(2) The fee schedule established by OSHA reflects the full cost of performing the activities for each service listed in paragraph (f)(1) of this Section. OSHA calculates the fees based on either the average or actual time required to perform the work necessary; the staff costs per hour (which include wages, fringe benefits, and expenses other than travel for personnel that perform or administer the activities covered by the fees); and the

Milestones/Dates	Action required
I. Periodic Review of Fee Schedule	
When review completed	OSHA will publish any proposed new fee schedule in the Federal Register if OSHA determines that costs warrant changes in the fee schedule.
Fifteen days after publication	Comments due on the proposed new fee schedule.
When OSHA approves the fee schedule	OSHA will publish the final fee schedule in the Federal Register, making the fee schedule effective on a specific date.
II. Application Processing Fees	
Time of application	Applicant must pay the applicable fees in the fee schedule that are due when submitting an application; OSHA will not begin processing the application until it receives the fees.
Before assessment performed	Applicant must pay the estimated staff time and travel costs for its assessment based on the fees in effect at the time of the assessment. Applicant also must pay the fees for the final report and Federal Register notice, and other applicable fees, as specified in the fee schedule. OSHA may cancel an application if the applicant does not pay these fees, or any balance of these fees, when due.
III. Audit Fees	
Before audit performed	NRTL must pay the estimated staff time and travel costs for its audit based on the fees in effect at the time of the audit. NRTL also must pay other applicable fees, as specified in the fee schedule. After the audit, OSHA adjusts the audit fees to account for the actual costs for travel and staff time.
On due date	NRTL must pay the estimated audit fees, or any balance due, by the due date established by OSHA; OSHA will assess a late fee if NRTL does not pay audit fees (or any balance of fees due) by the due date. OSHA may still perform the audit when an NRTL does not pay the fees or does not pay them on time.
Thirty days after due date or, if earlier, date NRTL refuses to pay	OSHA will begin processing a notice for publication in the Federal Register announcing its plan to revoke recognition for NRTLs that do not pay the estimated audit fees and any balance of audit fees due.

Note: For the purposes of 29 CFR §1910.7(f)(4), "days" means "calendar days," and "applicant" means "the NRTL" or "an applicant for NRTL recognition."

average or actual costs for travel when on-site reviews are involved. The formula for the fee calculation is as follows:

Activity Fee = [Average (or Actual) Hours to Complete the Activity × Staff Costs per Hour] + Average (or Actual) Travel Costs

(f)(3)(i) OSHA will review the full costs periodically and will propose a revised fee schedule, if warranted. In its review, OSHA will apply the formula established in paragraph (f)(2) of this Section to the current estimated full costs for the NRTL Program. If a change is warranted, OSHA will follow the implementation shown in paragraph (f)(4) of this Section.

(f)(3)(ii) OSHA will publish all fee schedules in the Federal Register. Once published, a fee schedule remains in effect until it is superseded by a new fee schedule. Any member of the public may request a change to the fees included in the current fee schedule. Such a request must include appropriate documentation in support of the suggested change. OSHA will consider such requests during its annual review of the fee schedule.

(f)(4) OSHA will implement periodic review, and fee assessment, collection, and payment, as follows:

(f)(5) OSHA will provide details about how to pay the fees through appropriate OSHA Program Directives, which will be available on the OSHA web site.

§1910.7 Appendix A OSHA recognition process for nationally recognized testing laboratories

Introduction

This Appendix provides requirements and criteria which OSHA will use to evaluate and recognize a Nationally Recognized Testing Laboratory (NRTL). This process will include the evaluation of the product evaluation and control programs being operated by the NRTL, as well as the NRTL's testing facilities being used in its program. In the evaluation of the NRTLs, OSHA will use either consensus-based standards currently in use nationally, or other standards or criteria which may be considered appropriate. This Appendix implements the definition of NRTL in 29 CFR §1910.7 which sets out the criteria that a laboratory must meet to be recognized by OSHA (initially and on a continuing basis). The Appendix is broader in scope, providing procedures for renewal, expansion and revocation of OSHA recognition. Except as otherwise provided, the burden is on the applicant to establish by a preponderance of the evidence that it is entitled to recognition as an NRTL. If further detailing of these requirements and criteria will assist the NRTLs or OSHA in this activity, this detailing will be done through appropriate OSHA Program Directives.

I. Procedures for Initial OSHA Recognition

A. Applications

1. Eligibility

a. Any testing agency or organization considering itself to meet the definition of nationally recognized testing laboratory as specified in §1910.7 may apply for OSHA recognition as an NRTL.

b. However, in determining eligibility for a foreign-based testing agency or organization, OSHA shall take into consideration the policy of the foreign government regarding both the acceptance in that country of testing data, equipment acceptances, and listings, and labeling, which are provided through nationally recognized testing laboratories recognized by the Assistant Secretary, and the accessibility to government recognition or a similar system in that country by U.S.-based safety-related testing agencies, whether recognized by the Assistant Secretary or not, if such recognition or a similar system is required by that country.

2. Content of application

a. The applicant shall provide sufficient information and detail demonstrating that it meets the requirements set forth in §1910.7, in order for an informed decision concerning recognition to be made by the Assistant Secretary.

b. The applicant also shall identify the scope of the NRTL-related activity for which the applicant wishes to be recognized. This will include identifying the testing methods it will use to test or judge the specific equipment and materials for which recognition is being requested, unless such test methods are already specified in the test standard. If requested to do so by OSHA, the applicant shall provide documentation of the efficacy of these testing methods.

c. The applicant may include whatever enclosures, attachments, or exhibits the applicant deems appropriate. The application need not be submitted on a Federal form.

3. Filing office location The application shall be filed with: NRTL Recognition Program, Occupational Safety and Health Administration, U.S. Department of Labor, 200 Constitution Avenue, NW., Washington, DC 20210.

4. Amendments and withdrawals

a. An application may be revised by an applicant at any time prior to the completion of activity under paragraph I.B.4. of this Appendix.

b. An application may be withdrawn by an applicant, without prejudice, at any time prior to the final decision by the Assistant Secretary in paragraph I.B.7.c. of this Appendix.

B. Review and Decision Process; Issuance or Renewal

1. Acceptance and on-site review

a. Applications submitted by eligible testing agencies will be accepted by OSHA, and their receipt acknowledged in writing. After receipt of an application, OSHA may request additional information if it believes information relevant to the requirements for recognition has been omitted.

b. OSHA shall, as necessary, conduct an on-site review of the testing facilities of the applicant, as well as the applicant's administrative and technical practices, and, if necessary, review any additional documentation underlying the application.

c. These on-site reviews will be conducted by qualified individuals technically expert in these matters, including, as appropriate, non-Federal consultants/contractors acceptable to OSHA. The protocol for each review will be based on appropriate national consensus standards or international guides, with such additions, changes, or deletions as may be considered necessary and appropriate in each case by OSHA. A written report shall be made of each on-site review and a copy shall be provided to the applicant.

2. **Positive finding by staff** If, after review of the application, and additional information, and the on-site review report, the applicant appears to have met the requirements for recognition, a written recommendation shall be submitted by the responsible OSHA personnel to the Assistant Secretary that the application be approved, accompanied by a supporting explanation.

3. **Negative finding by staff**

a. Notification to applicant If, after review of the application, any additional information and the on-site review report, the applicant does not appear to have met the requirements for recognition, the responsible OSHA personnel shall notify the applicant in writing, listing the specific requirements of §1910.7 and this Appendix which the applicant has not met, and allow a reasonable period for response.

b. Revision of application

(i) After receipt of a notification of negative finding (i.e., for intended disapproval of the application), and within the response period provided, the applicant may:

(a) Submit a revised application for further review, which could result in a positive finding by the responsible OSHA personnel pursuant to subsection I.B.2. of this Appendix; or

(b) Request that the original application be submitted to the Assistant Secretary with an attached statement of reasons, supplied by the applicant of why the application should be approved.

(ii) This procedure for applicant notification and potential revision shall be used only once during each recognition process.

4. **Preliminary finding by Assistant Secretary**

a. The Assistant Secretary, or a special designee for this purpose, will make a preliminary finding as to whether the applicant has or has not met the requirements for recognition, based on the completed application file, the written staff recommendation, and the statement of reasons supplied by the applicant if there remains a staff recommendation of disapproval.

b. Notification of this preliminary finding will be sent to the applicant and subsequently published in the Federal Register.

c. This preliminary finding shall not be considered an official decision by the Assistant Secretary or OSHA, and does not confer any change in status or any interim or temporary recognition for the applicant.

5. **Public review and comment period**

a. The Federal Register notice of preliminary finding will provide a period of not less than 30 calendar days for written comments on the applicant's fulfillment of the requirements for recognition. The application, supporting documents, staff recommendation, statement of applicant's reasons, and any comments received, will be available for public inspection in the OSHA Docket Office.

b. Any member of the public, including the applicant, may supply detailed reasons and evidence supporting or challenging the sufficiency of the applicant's having met the requirements of the definition in 29 CFR §1910.7 and this Appendix. Submission of pertinent documents and exhibits shall be made in writing by the close of the comment period.

6. **Action after public comment**

a. **Final decision by Assistant Secretary** Where the public review and comment record supports the Assistant Secretary's preliminary finding concerning the application, i.e., absent any serious objections or substantive claims contrary to the preliminary finding having been received in writing from the public during the comment period, the Assistant Secretary will proceed to final written decision on the application. The reasons supporting this decision shall be derived from the evidence available as a result of the full application, the supporting documentation, the staff finding, and the written comments and evidence presented during the public review and comment period.

b. **Public announcement** A copy of the Assistant Secretary's final decision will be provided to the applicant. Subsequently, a notification of the final decision shall be published in the Federal Register. The publication date will be the effective date of the recognition.

c. **Review of final decision** There will be no further review activity available within the Department of Labor from the final decision of the Assistant Secretary.

7. **Action after public objection**

a. **Review of negative information** At the discretion of the Assistant Secretary or his designee, OSHA may authorize Federal or contract personnel to initiate a special review of any information provided in the public comment record which appears to require resolution, before a final decision can be made.

b. **Supplementation of record** The contents and results of special reviews will be made part of this record by the Assistant Secretary by either:

(i) Reopening the written comment period for public comments on these reviews; or

(ii) Convening an informal hearing to accept public comments on these reviews, conducted under applicable OSHA procedures for similar hearings.

c. **Final decision by the Assistant Secretary** The Assistant Secretary shall issue a decision as to whether it has been demonstrated, based on a preponderance of the evidence, that the applicant meets the requirements for recognition. The reasons supporting this decision shall be derived from the evidence available as a result of the full application, the supporting documentation, the staff finding, the comments and evidence presented during the public review and comment period, and written to transcribed evidence received during any subsequent reopening of the written comment period or informal public hearing held.

d. **Public announcement** A copy of the Assistant Secretary's final decision will be provided to the applicant, and a notification will be published in the Federal Register subsequently announcing the decision.

e. **Review of final decision** There will be no further review activity available within the Department of Labor from the final decision of the Assistant Secretary.

C. **Terms and conditions of recognition** The following terms and conditions shall be part of every recognition:

1. **Letter of recognition** The recognition by OSHA of any NRTL will be evidenced by a letter of recognition from OSHA. The letter will provide the specific details of the scope of the OSHA recognition, including the specific equipment or materials for which OSHA recognition has been granted, as well as any specific conditions imposed by OSHA.

2. **Period of recognition** The recognition by OSHA of each NRTL will be valid for five years, unless terminated before the expiration of the period. The dates of the period of recognition will be stated in the recognition letter.

3. **Constancy in operations** The recognized NRTL shall continue to satisfy all the requirements or limitations in the letter of recognition during the period of recognition.

4. **Accurate publicity** The OSHA-recognized NRTL shall not engage in or permit others to engage in misrepresentation of the scope or conditions of its recognition.

5. **Temporary Recognition of Certain NRTLs**

a. Notwithstanding all other requirements and provisions of §1910.7 and this Appendix, the following two organizations are recognized temporarily as nationally recognized testing laboratories by the Assistant Secretary for a period of five years beginning June 13, 1988 and ending on July 13, 1993:

(i) Underwriters Laboratories, Inc., 333 Pfingsten Road, Northbrook, Illinois 60062.

(ii) Factory Mutual Research Corporation, 1151 Boston-Providence Turnpike, Norwood, Massachusetts 02062.

b. At the end of the five-year period, the two temporarily recognized laboratories shall apply for renewal of OSHA recognition utilizing the following procedures established for renewal of OSHA recognition.

II. Supplementary Procedures

A. Test standard changes

A recognized NRTL may change a testing standard or elements incorporated in the standard such as testing methods or pass-fail criteria by notifying the Assistant Secretary of the change, certifying that the revised standard will be at least as effective as the prior standard, and providing the supporting data upon which its conclusions are based. The NRTL need not inform the Assistant Secretary of minor deviations from a test standard such as the use of new instrumentation that is more accurate or sensitive than originally called for in the standard. The NRTL also need not inform the Assistant Secretary of its adoption of revisions to third-party testing standards meeting the requirements of §1910.7(c)(4), if such revisions have been developed by the standards developing organization, or of its adoption of revisions to other third-party test standards which the developing organization has submitted to OSHA. If, upon review, the Assistant Secretary or his designee determines that the proposed revised standard is not "substantially equivalent" to the previous version with regard to the level of safety obtained, OSHA will not accept the proposed testing standard by the recognized NRTL, and will initiate discontinuance of that aspect of OSHA-recognized activity by the NRTL by modification of the official letter of recognition. OSHA will publicly announce this action and the NRTL will be required to communicate this OSHA decision directly to affected manufacturers.

B. Expansion of current recognition

1. **Eligibility** A recognized NRTL may apply to OSHA for an expansion of its current recognition to cover other categories of NRTL testing in addition to those included in the current recognition.

2. **Procedure**

a. OSHA will act upon and process the application for expansion in accordance with subsection I.B. of this Appendix, except that the period for written comments, specified in paragraph 5.a of subsection I.B. of this Appendix, will be not less than 15 calendar days.

b. In that process, OSHA may decide not to conduct an on-site review, where the substantive scope of the request to expand recognition is closely related to the current area of recognition.

c. The expiration date for each expansion of recognition shall coincide with the expiration date of the current basic recognition period.

C. Renewal of OSHA recognition

1. **Eligibility** A recognized NRTL may renew its recognition by filing a renewal request at the address in paragraph I.A.3. of this Appendix not less than nine months, nor more than one year, before the expiration date of its current recognition.

2. **Procedure**

a. OSHA will process the renewal request in accordance with subsection I.B. of this Appendix, except that the period for written comments, specified in paragraph 5.a of subsection I.B. of this Appendix, will be not less than 15 calendar days.

b. In that process, OSHA may determine not to conduct the on-site reviews in I.B.1.a. where appropriate.

c. When a recognized NRTL has filed a timely and sufficient renewal request, its current recognition will not expire until a final decision has been made by OSHA on the request.

d. After the first renewal has been granted to the NRTL, the NRTL shall apply for a continuation of its recognition status every five years by submitting a renewal request. In lieu of submitting a renewal request after the initial renewal, the NRTL may certify its continuing compliance with the terms of its letter of recognition and 29 CFR §1910.7.

3. **Alternative procedure** After the initial recognition and before the expiration thereof, OSHA may (for good cause) determine that there is a sufficient basis to dispense with the renewal requirement for a given laboratory and will so notify the laboratory of such a determination in writing. In lieu of submitting a renewal request, any laboratory so notified shall certify its continuing compliance with the terms of its letter of recognition and 29 CFR §1910.7.

D. Voluntary termination of recognition.

At any time, a recognized NRTL may voluntarily terminate its recognition, either in its entirety or with respect to any area covered in its recognition, by giving written notice to OSHA. The written notice shall state the date as of which the termination is to take effect. The Assistant Secretary shall inform the public of any voluntary termination by Federal Register notice.

E. Revocation of recognition by OSHA

1. **Potential causes** If an NRTL either has failed to continue to substantially satisfy the requirements of §1910.7 or this Appendix, or has not been reasonably performing the NRTL testing requirements encompassed within its letter of recognition, or has materially misrepresented itself in its applications or misrepresented the scope or conditions of its recognition, the Assistant Secretary may revoke the recognition of a recognized NRTL, in whole or in part. OSHA may initiate revocation procedures on the basis of information provided by any interested person.

2. **Procedure**

a. Before proposing to revoke recognition, the Agency will notify the recognized NRTL in writing, giving it the opportunity to rebut or correct the alleged deficiencies which would form the basis of the proposed revocation, within a reasonable period.

b. If the alleged deficiencies are not corrected or reconciled within a reasonable period, OSHA will propose, in writing to the recognized NRTL, to revoke recognition. If deemed appropriate, no other announcement need be made by OSHA.

c. The revocation shall be effective in 60 days unless within that period the recognized NRTL corrects the deficiencies or requests a hearing in writing.

d. If a hearing is requested, it shall be held before an administrative law judge of the Department of Labor pursuant to the rules specified in 29 CFR Part §1905, Subpart C.

e. The parties shall be OSHA and the recognized NRTL. The Assistant Secretary may allow other interested persons to participate in these hearings if such participation would contribute to the resolution of issues germane to the proceeding and not cause undue delay.

f. The burden of proof shall be on OSHA to demonstrate by a preponderance of the evidence that the recognition should be revoked because the NRTL is not meeting the requirements for recognition, has not been reasonably performing the product testing functions as required by §1910.7, this Appendix A, or the letter of recognition, or has materially misrepresented itself in its applications or publicity.

3. **Final decision**

a. After the hearing, the Administrative Law Judge shall issue a decision stating the reasons based on the record as to whether it has been demonstrated, based on a preponderance of evidence, that the applicant does not continue to meet the requirements for its current recognition.

b. Upon issuance of the decision, any party to the hearing may file exceptions within 20 days pursuant to 29 CFR 1905.28. If no exceptions are filed, this decision is the final decision of the Assistant Secretary. If objections are filed, the Administrative Law Judge shall forward the decision, exceptions and record to the Assistant Secretary for the final decision on the proposed revocation.

c. The Assistant Secretary will review the record, the decision by the Administrative Law Judge, and the exceptions filed. Based on this, the Assistant Secretary shall issue the final decision as to whether it has been demonstrated, by a preponderance of evidence, that the recognized NRTL has not continued to meet the requirements for OSHA recognition. If the Assistant Secretary finds that the NRTL does not meet the NRTL recognition requirements, the recognition will be revoked.

4. **Public announcement** A copy of the Assistant Secretary's final decision will be provided to the applicant, and a notification will be published in the Federal Register announcing the decision, and the availability of the complete record of this proceeding at OSHA. The effective date of any revocation will be the date the final decision copy is sent to the NRTL.

5. **Review of final decision** There will be no further review activity available within the Department of Labor from the final decision of the Assistant Secretary.

[53 FR 12120, Apr. 12, 1988; 53 FR 16838, May 11, 1988, as amended at 54 FR 24333, June 7, 1989; 65 FR 46818, 46819, July 31, 2000; 76 FR 10515, Feb. 25, 2011]

§1910.8 OMB control numbers under the Paperwork Reduction Act

The following sections or paragraphs each contain a collection of information requirement which has been approved by the Office of Management and Budget under the control number listed.

29 CFR citation	OMB control No.	29 CFR citation	OMB control No.
1910.7	1218-0147	1910.308	1218-0256
1910.23	1218-0199	1910.420	1218-0069
1910.66	1218-0121	1910.421	1218-0069
1910.67(b)	1218-0230	1910.423	1218-0069
1910.68	1218-0226	1910.430	1218-0069
1910.95	1218-0048	1910.440	1218-0069
1910.111	1218-0208	1910.1001	1218-0133
1910.119	1218-0200	1910.1003	1218-0085
1910.120	1218-0202	1910.1004	1218-0084
1910.132	1218-0205	1910.1006	1218-0086

Note: Table data continues on next page.

29 CFR citation	OMB control No.
1910.134	1218-0099
1910.137	1218-0190
1910.142	1218-0096
1910.145	1218-0132
1910.146	1218-0203
1910.147	1218-0150
1910.156	1218-0075
1910.157(e)(3)	1218-0210
1910.157(f)(16)	1218-0218
1910.177(d)(3)(iv)	1218-0219
1910.179(j)(2)(iii) and (iv)	1218-0224
1910.179(m)(1) and (m)(2)	1218-0224
1910.180(d)(6)	1218-0221
1910.180(g)(1) and (g)(2)(ii)	1218-0221
1910.181(g)(1) and (g)(3)	1218-0222
1910.184(e)(4), (f)(4) and (i)(8)(ii)	1218-0223
1910.217(e)(1)(i) and (ii)	1218-0229
1910.217(g)	1218-0070
1910.217(h)	1218-0143
1910.218(a)(2)(i) and (ii)	1218-0228
1910.252(a)(2)(xiii)(c)	1218-0207
1910.255(e)	1218-0207
1910.266	1218-0198
1910.268	1218-0225
1910.269	1218-0190
1910.272	1218-0206
1910.302	1218-0256
1910.303	1218-0256
1910.304	1218-0256
1910.305	1218-0256
1910.306	1218-0256
1910.307	1218-0256
1910.1007	1218-0083
1910.1008	1218-0087
1910.1009	1218-0089
1910.1010	1218-0082
1910.1011	1218-0090
1910.1012	1218-0080
1910.1013	1218-0079
1910.1014	1218-0088
1910.1015	1218-0044
1910.1016	1218-0081
1910.1017	1218-0010
1910.1018	1218-0104
1910.1020	1218-0065
1910.1025	1218-0092
1910.1026	1218-0252
1910.1027	1218-0185
1910.1028	1218-0129
1910.1029	1218-0128
1910.1030	1218-0180
1910.1043	1218-0061
1910.1044	1218-0101
1910.1045	1218-0126
1910.1047	1218-0108
1910.1048	1218-0145
1910.1050	1218-0184
1910.1051	1218-0170
1910.1052	1218-0179
1910.1053	1218-0266
1910.1096	1218-0103
1910.1200	1218-0072
1910.1450	1218-0131

[61 FR 5508, Feb. 13, 1996, as amended at 62 FR 29668, June 2, 1997; 62 FR 42666, Aug. 8, 1997; 62 FR 43581, Aug. 14, 1997; 62 FR 65203, Dec. 11, 1997; 63 FR 13340, Mar. 19, 1998; 63 FR 17093, Apr. 8, 1998; 71 FR 38086, July 5, 2006; 72 FR 40075, July 23, 2007]

§1910.9 Compliance duties owed to each employee

(a) **Personal protective equipment** Standards in this Part requiring the employer to provide personal protective equipment (PPE), including respirators and other types of PPE, because of hazards to employees impose a separate compliance duty with respect to each employee covered by the requirement. The employer must provide PPE to each employee required to use the PPE, and each failure to provide PPE to an employee may be considered a separate violation.

(b) **Training** Standards in this Part requiring training on hazards and related matters, such as standards requiring that employees receive training or that the employer train employees, provide training to employees, or institute or implement a training program, impose a separate compliance duty with respect to each employee covered by the requirement. The employer must train each affected employee in the manner required by the standard, and each failure to train an employee may be considered a separate violation.

[73 FR 75583, Dec. 12, 2008]

29 CFR PART 1910 Subpart B
Adoption and Extension of Established Federal Standards

Section Contents

Subpart B—Adoption and Extension of Established Federal Standards

Authority: Secs. 4, 6, and 8 of the Occupational Safety and Health Act, 29 U.S.C. 653, 655, 657; Walsh-Healey Act, 41 U.S.C. 35 et seq. ; Service Contract Act of 1965, 41 U.S.C. 351 et seq. ; Sec.107, Contract Work Hours and Safety Standards Act (Construction Safety Act), 40 U.S.C. 333; Sec. 41, Longshore and Harbor Workers' Compensation Act, 33 U.S.C. 941; National Foundation of Arts and Humanities Act, 20 U.S.C. 951 et seq. ; Secretary of Labor's Order No. 12–71 (36 FR 8754), 8–76 (41 FR 1911), 9–83 (48 FR 35736), 1–90 (55 FR 9033), or 6-96 (62 FR 111), as applicable.

§1910.11
Scope and purpose

(a) The provisions of this Subpart B adopt and extend the applicability of, established Federal standards in effect on April 28, 1971, with respect to every employer, employee, and employment covered by the Act.

(b) It bears emphasis that only standards (i.e., substantive rules) relating to safety or health are adopted by any incorporations by reference of standards prescribed elsewhere in this chapter or this title. Other materials contained in the referenced parties are not adopted. Illustrations of the types of materials which are not adopted are these. The incorporations by reference of parts §1915, §1916, §1917, §1918 in §1910.13, §1910.14, §1910.15, and §1910.16 are not intended to include the discussion in those parts of the coverage of the Longshoremen's and Harbor Workers' Compensation Act or the penalty provisions of the Act. Similarly, the incorporation by reference of part §1926 in §1910.12 is not intended to include references to interpretative rules having relevance to the application of the Construction Safety Act, but having no relevance to the application to the Occupational Safety and Health Act.

§1910.12
Construction work

(a) **Standards** The standards prescribed in Part 1926 of this chapter are adopted as occupational safety and health standards under section 6 of the Act and shall apply, according to the provisions thereof, to every employment and place of employment of every employee engaged in construction work. Each employer shall protect the employment and places of employment of each of his employees engaged in construction work by complying with the appropriate standards prescribed in this paragraph.

(b) **Definition** For purposes of this section, Construction work means work for construction, alteration and/or repair, including painting and decorating. See discussion of these terms in §1926.13 of this title.

(c) **Construction Safety Act distinguished** This section adopts as occupational safety and health standards under section 6 of the Act the standards which are prescribed in Part 1926 of this chapter. Thus, the standards (substantive rules) published in Subpart C and the following subparts of Part 1926 of this chapter are applied. This section does not incorporate Subparts A and B of Part 1926 of this chapter. Subparts A and B have pertinence only to the application of section 107 of the Contract Work Hours and Safety Standards Act (the Construction Safety Act). For example, the interpretation of the term "subcontractor" in paragraph (c) of §1926.13 of this chapter is significant in discerning the coverage of the Construction Safety Act and duties thereunder. However, the term "subcontractor" has no significance in the application of the Act, which was enacted under the Commerce Clause and which establishes duties for "employers" which are not dependent for their application upon any contractual relationship with the Federal Government or upon any form of Federal financial assistance.

(d) For the purposes of this part, to the extent that it may not already be included in paragraph (b) of this section, "construction work" includes the erection of new electric transmission and distribution lines and equipment, and the alteration, conversion, and improvement of the existing transmission and distribution lines and equipment.

§1910.15
Shipyard employment

(a) Adoption and extension of established safety and health standards for shipyard employment. The standards prescribed by part 1915 (formerly parts 1501–1503) of this title and in effect on April 28, 1971 (as revised), are adopted as occupational safety or health standards under section 6(a) of the Act and shall apply, according to the provisions thereof, to every employment and place of employment of every employee engaged in ship repair, shipbreaking, and shipbuilding, or a related employment. Each employer shall protect the employment and places of employment of each of his employees engaged in ship repair, shipbreaking, and shipbuilding, or a related employment, by complying with the appropriate standards prescribed by this paragraph.

(b) **Definitions** For purposes of this section:

(b)(1) **Ship repair** means any repair of a vessel, including, but not restricted to, alterations, conversions, installations, cleaning, painting, and maintenance work;

(b)(2) **Shipbreaking** means any breaking down of a vessel's structure for the purpose of scrapping the vessel, including the removal of gear, equipment, or any component of a vessel;

(b)(3) **Shipbuilding** means the construction of a vessel, including the installation of machinery and equipment;

(b)(4) **Related employment** means any employment performed as an incident to, or in conjunction with, ship repair, shipbreaking, and shipbuilding work, including, but not restricted to, inspection, testing, and employment as a watchman; and

(b)(5) **Vessel** includes every description of watercraft or other artificial contrivance used, or capable of being used, as a means of transportation on water, including special purpose floating structures not primarily designed for, or used as a means of, transportation on water.

[58 FR 35308, June 30, 1993]

§1910.16
Longshoring and marine terminals

(a) **Safety and health standards for longshoring**

(a)(1) Part 1918 of this chapter shall apply exclusively, according to the provisions thereof, to all employment of every employee engaged in longshoring operations or related employment aboard any vessel. All cargo transfer accomplished with the use of shore-based material handling devices shall be governed by part 1917 of this chapter.

(a)(2) Part 1910 does not apply to longshoring operations except for the following provisions:

- (a)(2)(i) Access to employee exposure and medical records. Subpart Z, §1910.1020;
- (a)(2)(ii) Commercial diving operations. Subpart T;
- (a)(2)(iii) Electrical. Subpart S when shore-based electrical installations provide power for use aboard vessels;
- (a)(2)(iv) Hazard communication. Subpart Z, §1910.1200;
- (a)(2)(v) Ionizing radiation. Subpart Z, §1910.1096;
- (a)(2)(vi) Noise. Subpart G, §1910.95;
- (a)(2)(vii) Nonionizing radiation. Subpart G, §1910.97;

Note to paragraph (a)(2)(vii): Exposures to nonionizing radiation emissions from commercial vessel transmitters are considered hazardous under the following conditions: (1) where the radar is transmitting, the scanner is stationary, and the exposure distance is 18.7 feet (6 m.) or less; or (2) where the radar is transmitting, the scanner is rotating, and the exposure distance is 5.2 feet (1.8 m.) or less.

- (a)(2)(viii) Respiratory protection. Subpart I, §1910.134;
- (a)(2)(ix) Toxic and hazardous substances. Subpart Z applies to marine cargo handling activities except for the following:
  - (a)(2)(ix)(A) When a substance or cargo is contained within a sealed, intact means of packaging or containment complying with Department of Transportation or International Maritime Organization requirements;[1]
  - (a)(2)(ix)(B) Bloodborne pathogens, §1910.1030;

[1] The International Maritime Organization publishes the International Maritime Dangerous Goods Code to aid compliance with the international legal requirements of the International Convention for the Safety of Life at Sea, 1960.

(a)(2)(ix)(C) Carbon monoxide, §1910.1000 (See §1918.94 (a)); and
(a)(2)(ix)(D) Hydrogen sulfide, §1910.1000 (See §1918.94 (f)).
(a)(2)(x) Powered industrial truck operator training, Subpart N, §1910.178(l).

(b) Safety and health standards for marine terminals Part 1917 of this chapter shall apply exclusively, according to the provisions thereof, to employment within a marine terminal, except as follows:

(b)(1) The provisions of part 1917 of this chapter do not apply to the following:
(b)(1)(i) Facilities used solely for the bulk storage, handling, and transfer of flammable and combustible liquids and gases.
(b)(1)(ii) Facilities subject to the regulations of the Office of Pipeline Safety of the Research and Special Programs Administration, Department of Transportation (49 CFR chapter I, subchapter D), to the extent such regulations apply to specific working conditions.
(b)(1)(iii) Fully automated bulk coal handling facilities contiguous to electrical power generating plants.

(b)(2) Part 1910 does not apply to marine terminals except for the following:
(b)(2)(i) Abrasive blasting. Subpart G, §1910.94(a);
(b)(2)(ii) Access to employee exposure and medical records. Subpart Z, §1910.1020;
(b)(2)(iii) Commercial diving operations. Subpart T;
(b)(2)(iv) Electrical. Subpart S;
(b)(2)(v) Grain handling facilities. Subpart R, §1910.272;
(b)(2)(vi) Hazard communication. Subpart Z, §1910.1200;
(b)(2)(vii) Ionizing radiation. Subpart Z, §1910.1096;
(b)(2)(viii) Noise. Subpart G, §1910.95;
(b)(2)(ix) Nonionizing radiation. Subpart G, §1910.97;
(b)(2)(x) Respiratory protection. Subpart I, §1910.134;
(b)(2)(xi) Safety requirements for scaffolding. Subpart D, §1910.28;
(b)(2)(xii) Servicing multi-piece and single piece rim wheels. Subpart N, §1910.177;
(b)(2)(xiii) Toxic and hazardous substances. Subpart Z applies to marine cargo handling activities except for the following:
(b)(2)(xiii)(A) When a substance or cargo is contained within a sealed, intact means of packaging or containment complying with Department of Transportation or International Maritime Organization requirements;[1]
(b)(2)(xiii)(B) Bloodborne pathogens, §1910.1030;
(b)(2)(xiii)(C) Carbon monoxide, §1910.1000 (See §1917.24(a)); and
(b)(2)(xiii)(D) Hydrogen sulfide, §1910.1000 (See §1917.73(a)(2)); and
(b)(2)(xiv) Powered industrial truck operator training, Subpart N, §1910.178(l).

(c) **Definitions** For purposes of this section:
(c)(1) **Longshoring operation** means the loading, unloading, moving, or handling of, cargo, ship's stores, gear, etc., into, in, on, or out of any vessel;
(c)(2) **Related employment** means any employment performed as an incident to or in conjunction with, longshoring operations including, but not restricted to, securing cargo, rigging, and employment as a porter, checker, or watchman; and
(c)(3) **Vessel** includes every description of watercraft or other artificial contrivance used, or capable of being used, as a means of transportation on water, including special purpose floating structures not primarily designed for, or used as a means of, transportation on water.
(c)(4) **Marine terminal** means wharves, bulkheads, quays, piers, docks and other berthing locations and adjacent storage or adjacent areas and structures associated with the primary movement of cargo or materials from vessel to shore or shore to vessel including structures which are devoted to receiving, handling, holding, consolidation and loading or delivery of waterborne shipments or passengers, including areas devoted to the maintenance of the terminal or equipment. The term does not include production or manufacturing areas having their own docking facilities and located at a marine terminal nor does the term include storage facilities directly associated with those production or manufacturing areas.

[39 FR 23502, June 27, 1974, as amended at 48 FR 30908, July 5, 1983; 52 FR 36026, Sept. 25, 1987; 62 FR 40195, July 25, 1997; 63 FR 66270, Dec. 1, 1998]

§1910.17 Effective dates

(a)–(b) [Reserved]

(c) Except whenever any employment or place of employment is, or becomes, subject to any safety and health standard prescribed in Part 1915, 1916, 1917, 1918, or 1926 of this title on a date before August 27, 1971, by virtue of the Construction Safety Act or the Longshoremen's and Harbor Workers' Compensation Act, that occupational safety and health standard as incorporated by reference in this Subpart shall also become effective under the Williams-Steiger Occupational Safety and Health Act of 1970 on that date.

[39 FR 23502, June 27, 1974, as amended at 61 FR 9235, Mar. 7, 1996]

§1910.18 Changes in established Federal standards.

Whenever an occupational safety and health standard adopted and incorporated by reference in this Subpart B is changed pursuant to section 6(b) of the Act and the statute under which the standard was originally promulgated, and in accordance with part 1911 of this chapter, the standard shall be deemed changed for purposes of that statute and this Subpart B, and shall apply under this Subpart B. For the purposes of this section, a change in a standard includes any amendment, addition, or repeal, in whole or in part, of any standard.

§1910.19 Special provisions for air contaminants

(a) **Asbestos, tremolite, anthophyllite, and actinolite dust**. Section §1910.1001 shall apply to the exposure of every employee to asbestos, tremolite, anthophyllite, and actinolite dust in every employment and place of employment covered by §1910.16, in lieu of any different standard on exposure to asbestos, tremolite, anthophyllite, and actinolite dust which would otherwise be applicable by virtue of any of those sections.

(b) **Vinyl chloride** Section §1910.1017 shall apply to the exposure of every employee to vinyl chloride in every employment and place of employment covered by §1910.12, §1910.13, §1910.14, §1910.15, or §1910.16, in lieu of any different standard on exposure to vinyl chloride which would otherwise be applicable by virtue of any of those sections.

(c) **Acrylonitrile** Section §1910.1045 shall apply to the exposure of every employee to acrylonitrile in every employment and place of employment covered by §1910.12, §1910.13, §1910.14, §1910.15, or §1910.16, in lieu of any different standard on exposure to acrylonitrile which would otherwise be applicable by virtue of any of those sections.

(d) [Reserved]

(e) **Inorganic arsenic** Section §1910.1018 shall apply to the exposure of every employee to inorganic arsenic in every employment covered by §1910.12, §1910.13, §1910.14, §1910.15, or §1910.16, in lieu of any different standard on exposure to inorganic arsenic which would otherwise be applicable by virtue of any of those sections.

(f) [Reserved]

(g) **Lead** Section §1910.1025 shall apply to the exposure of every employee to lead in every employment and place of employment covered by §1910.13, §1910.14, §1910.15, and §1910.16, in lieu of any different standard on exposure to lead which would otherwise be applicable by virtue of those sections.

(h) **Ethylene oxide** §1910.1047 shall apply to the exposure of every employee to ethylene oxide in every employment and place of employment covered by §1910.12, §1910.13, §1910.14, §1910.15, or §1910.16, in lieu of any different standard on exposure to ethylene oxide which would otherwise be applicable by virtue of those sections.

(i) **4,4′-Methylenedianiline (MDA)** Section §1910.1050 shall apply to the exposure of every employee to MDA in every employment and place of employment covered by §1910.13, §1910.14, §1910.15, or §1910.16, in lieu of any different standard on exposure to MDA which would otherwise be applicable by virtue of those sections.

(j) **Formaldehyde** Section §1910.1048 shall apply to the exposure of every employee to formaldehyde in every employment and place of employment covered by §1910.12, §1910.13, §1910.14, §1910.15 or §1910.16 in lieu of any different standard on exposure to formaldehyde which would otherwise be applicable by virtue of those sections.

(k) **Cadmium** Section §1910.1027 shall apply to the exposure of every employee to cadmium in every employment and place of employment covered by §1910.16 in lieu of any different standard on exposures to cadmium that would otherwise be applicable by virtue of those sections.

(l) **1,3-Butadiene (BD)** §1910.1051 shall apply to the exposure of every employee to BD in every employment and place of employment covered by §1910.12, §1910.13, §1910.14, §1910.15, or §1910.16, in lieu of any different standard on exposure to BD which would otherwise be applicable by virtue of those sections.

(m) **Methylene chloride (MC)** Section §1910.1052 shall apply to the exposure of every employee to MC in every employment and place of employment covered by §1910.16 in lieu of any different standard on exposure to MC which would otherwise be applicable by virtue of that section when it is not present in sealed, intact containers.

[43 FR 28473, June 30, 1978, as amended at 43 FR 45809, Oct. 3, 1978; 43 FR 53007, Nov. 14, 1978; 44 FR 5447, Jan. 26, 1979; 46 FR 32022, June 19, 1981; 49 FR 25796, June 22, 1984; 50 FR 51173, Dec. 13, 1985; 52 FR 46291, Dec. 4, 1987; 57 FR 35666, Aug. 10, 1992; 57 FR 42388, Sept. 14, 1992; 59 FR 41057, Aug. 10, 1994; 61 FR 56831, Nov. 4, 1996; 62 FR 1600, Jan. 10, 1997]

29 CFR PART 1910 Subpart C [Reserved]

This page intentionally left blank.

29 CFR PART 1910 Subpart D
Walking-Working Surfaces

Section Contents

Subpart D—Walking-Working Surfaces

Authority: 29 U.S.C. 653, 655, and 657; Secretary of Labor's Order No. 12-71 (36 FR 8754), 8-76 (41 FR 25059), 9-83 (48 FR 35736), 1-90 (55 FR 9033), and 1-2012 (77 FR 3912), as applicable; and 29 CFR Part 1911.

§1910.21
Scope and definitions

(a) **Scope** This Subpart applies to all general industry workplaces. It covers all walking-working surfaces unless specifically excluded by an individual Section of this Subpart.

(b) **Definition**. The following definitions apply in this Subpart.

Alternating tread-type stair means a type of stairway consisting of a series of treads that usually are attached to a center support in an alternating manner such that an employee typically does not have both feet on the same level while using the stairway.

Anchorage means a secure point of attachment for equipment such as lifelines, lanyards, deceleration devices, and rope descent systems.

Authorized means an employee who the employer assigns to perform a specific type of duty, or allows in a specific location or area.

Cage means an enclosure mounted on the side rails of a fixed ladder or fastened to a structure behind the fixed ladder that is designed to surround the climbing space of the ladder. A cage also is called a "cage guard" or "basket guard."

Carrier means the track of a ladder safety system that consists of a flexible cable or rigid rail attached to the fixed ladder or immediately adjacent to it.

Combination ladder means a portable ladder that can be used as a stepladder, extension ladder, trestle ladder, or stairway ladder. The components of a combination ladder also may be used separately as a single ladder.

Dangerous equipment means equipment, such as vats, tanks, electrical equipment, machinery, equipment or machinery with protruding parts, or other similar units, that, because of their function or form, may harm an employee who falls into or onto the equipment.

Designated area means a distinct portion of a walking-working surface delineated by a warning line in which employees may perform work without additional fall protection.

Dockboard means a portable or fixed device that spans a gap or compensates for a difference in elevation between a loading platform and a transport vehicle. Dockboards include, but are not limited to, bridge plates, dock plates, and dock levelers.

Equivalent means alternative designs, equipment, materials, or methods, that the employer can demonstrate will provide an equal or greater degree of safety for employees compared to the designs, equipment, materials, or methods specified in this Subpart.

Extension ladder means a non-self-supporting portable ladder that is adjustable in length.

Failure means a load refusal, breakage, or separation of component parts. A load refusal is the point at which the ultimate strength of a component or object is exceeded.

Fall hazard means any condition on a walking-working surface that exposes an employee to a risk of harm from a fall on the same level or to a lower level.

Fall protection means any equipment, device, or system that prevents an employee from falling from an elevation or mitigates the effect of such a fall.

Fixed ladder means a ladder with rails or individual rungs that is permanently attached to a structure, building, or equipment. Fixed ladders include individual-rung ladders, but not ship stairs, step bolts, or manhole steps.

Grab bar means an individual horizontal or vertical handhold installed to provide access above the height of the ladder.

Guardrail system means a barrier erected along an unprotected or exposed side, edge, or other area of a walking-working surface to prevent employees from falling to a lower level.

Handrail means a rail used to provide employees with a handhold for support.

Hoist area means any elevated access opening to a walking-working surface through which equipment or materials are loaded or received.

Hole means a gap or open space in a floor, roof, horizontal walking-working surface, or similar surface that is at least 2 inches (5 cm) in its least dimension.

Individual-rung ladder means a ladder that has rungs individually attached to a building or structure. An individual-rung ladder does not include manhole steps.

Ladder means a device with rungs, steps, or cleats used to gain access to a different elevation.

Ladder safety system means a system designed to eliminate or reduce the possibility of falling from a ladder. A ladder safety system usually consists of a carrier, safety sleeve, lanyard, connectors, and body harness. Cages and wells are not ladder safety systems.

Low-slope roof means a roof that has a slope less than or equal to a ratio of 4 in 12 (vertical to horizontal).

Lower level means a surface or area to which an employee could fall. Such surfaces or areas include, but are not limited to, ground levels, floors, roofs, ramps, runways, excavations, pits, tanks, materials, water, equipment, and similar surfaces and structures, or portions thereof.

Manhole steps means steps that are individually attached to, or set into, the wall of a manhole structure.

Maximum intended load means the total load (weight and force) of all employees, equipment, vehicles, tools, materials, and other loads the employer reasonably anticipates to be applied to a walking-working surface at any one time.

Mobile means manually propelled or moveable.

Mobile ladder stand (ladder stand) means a mobile, fixed-height, self-supporting ladder that usually consists of wheels or casters on a rigid base and steps leading to a top step. A mobile ladder stand also may have handrails and is designed for use by one employee at a time.

Mobile ladder stand platform means a mobile, fixed-height, self-supporting unit having one or more standing platforms that are provided with means of access or egress.

Open riser means the gap or space between treads of stairways that do not have upright or inclined members (risers).

Opening means a gap or open space in a wall, partition, vertical walking-working surface, or similar surface that is at least 30 inches (76 cm) high and at least 18 inches (46 cm) wide, through which an employee can fall to a lower level.

Personal fall arrest system means a system used to arrest an employee in a fall from a walking-working surface. It consists of a body harness, anchorage, and connector. The means of connection may include a lanyard, deceleration device, lifeline, or a suitable combination of these.

Personal fall protection system means a system (including all components) an employer uses to provide protection from falling or to safely arrest an employee's fall if one occurs. Examples of personal fall protection systems include personal fall arrest systems, positioning systems, and travel restraint systems.

Platform means a walking-working surface that is elevated above the surrounding area.

Portable ladder means a ladder that can readily be moved or carried, and usually consists of side rails joined at intervals by steps, rungs, or cleats.

Positioning system (work-positioning system) means a system of equipment and connectors that, when used with a body harness or body belt, allows an employee to be supported on an elevated vertical surface, such as a wall or window sill, and work with both hands free. Positioning systems also are called "positioning system devices" and "work-positioning equipment."

Qualified describes a person who, by possession of a recognized degree, certificate, or professional standing, or who by extensive knowledge, training, and experience has successfully demonstrated the ability to solve or resolve problems relating to the subject matter, the work, or the project.

Ramp means an inclined walking-working surface used to access another level.

Riser means the upright (vertical) or inclined member of a stair that is located at the back of a stair tread or platform and connects close to the front edge of the next higher tread, platform, or landing.

Rope descent system means a suspension system that allows an employee to descend in a controlled manner and, as needed, stop at any point during the descent. A rope descent system usually consists of a roof anchorage, support rope, a descent device, carabiner(s) or shackle(s), and a chair (seatboard). A rope descent system also is called controlled descent equipment or apparatus. Rope descent systems do not include industrial rope access systems.

Rung, step, or cleat means the cross-piece of a ladder on which an employee steps to climb up and down.

Runway means an elevated walking-working surface, such as a catwalk, a foot walk along shafting, or an elevated walkway between buildings.

Scaffold means any temporary elevated or suspended platform and its supporting structure, including anchorage points, used to support employees, equipment, materials, and other items. For purposes of this Subpart, a scaffold does not include a crane-suspended or derrick-suspended personnel platform or a rope descent system.

Ship stair (ship ladder) means a stairway that is equipped with treads, stair rails, and open risers, and has a slope that is between 50 and 70 degrees from the horizontal.

Side-step ladder means a type of fixed ladder that requires an employee to step sideways from it in order to reach a walking-working surface, such as a landing.

Spiral stairs means a series of treads attached to a vertical pole in a winding fashion, usually within a cylindrical space.

Stair rail or stair rail system means a barrier erected along the exposed or open side of stairways to prevent employees from falling to a lower level.

Stairway (stairs) means risers and treads that connect one level with another, and includes any landings and platforms in between those levels. Stairways include standard, spiral, alternating tread-type, and ship stairs.

Standard stairs means a fixed or permanently installed stairway. Ship, spiral, and alternating tread-type stairs are not considered standard stairs.

Step bolt (pole step) means a bolt or rung attached at intervals along a structural member used for foot placement and as a handhold when climbing or standing.

Stepladder means a self-supporting, portable ladder that has a fixed height, flat steps, and a hinged back.

Stepstool means a self-supporting, portable ladder that has flat steps and side rails. For purposes of the final rule, stepstool includes only those ladders that have a fixed height, do not have a pail shelf, and do not exceed 32 inches (81 cm) in overall height to the top cap, although side rails may extend above the top cap. A stepstool is designed so an employee can climb and stand on all of the steps and the top cap.

Through ladder means a type of fixed ladder that allows the employee to step through the side rails at the top of the ladder to reach a walking-working surface, such as a landing.

Tieback means an attachment between an anchorage (e.g., structural member) and a supporting device (e.g., parapet clamp or cornice hook).

Toeboard means a low protective barrier that is designed to prevent materials, tools, and equipment from falling to a lower level, and protect employees from falling.

Travel restraint system means a combination of an anchorage, anchorage connector, lanyard (or other means of connection), and body support that an employer uses to eliminate the possibility of an employee going over the edge of a walking-working surface.

Tread means a horizontal member of a stair or stairway, but does not include landings or platforms.

Unprotected sides and edges mean any side or edge of a walking-working surface (except at entrances and other points of access) where there is no wall, guardrail system, or stair rail system to protect an employee from falling to a lower level.

Walking-working surface means any horizontal or vertical surface on or through which an employee walks, works, or gains access to a work area or workplace location.

Warning line means a barrier erected to warn employees that they are approaching an unprotected side or edge, and which designates an area in which work may take place without the use of other means of fall protection.

Well means a permanent, complete enclosure around a fixed ladder.

§1910.22 General requirements

(a) **Surface conditions** The employer must ensure:

(a)(1) All places of employment, passageways, storerooms, service rooms, and walking-working surfaces are kept in a clean, orderly, and sanitary condition.

(a)(2) The floor of each workroom is maintained in a clean and, to the extent feasible, in a dry condition. When wet processes are used, drainage must be maintained and, to the extent feasible, dry standing places, such as false floors, platforms, and mats must be provided.

(a)(3) Walking-working surfaces are maintained free of hazards such as sharp or protruding objects, loose boards, corrosion, leaks, spills, snow, and ice.

(b) **Loads** The employer must ensure that each walking-working surface can support the maximum intended load for that surface.

(c) **Access and egress** The employer must provide, and ensure each employee uses, a safe means of access and egress to and from walking-working surfaces.

(d) **Inspection, maintenance, and repair** The employer must ensure:

(d)(1) Walking-working surfaces are inspected, regularly and as necessary, and maintained in a safe condition;

(d)(2) Hazardous conditions on walking-working surfaces are corrected or repaired before an employee uses the walking-working surface again. If the correction or repair cannot be made immediately, the hazard must be guarded to prevent employees from using the walking-working surface until the hazard is corrected or repaired; and

(d)(3) When any correction or repair involves the structural integrity of the walking-working surface, a qualified person performs or supervises the correction or repair.

§1910.23 Ladders

(a) **Application** The employer must ensure that each ladder used meets the requirements of this Section. This Section covers all ladders, except when the ladder is:

(a)(1) Used in emergency operations such as firefighting, rescue, and tactical law enforcement operations, or training for these operations; or

(a)(2) Designed into or is an integral part of machines or equipment.

(b) **General requirements for all ladders** The employer must ensure:

(b)(1) Ladder rungs, steps, and cleats are parallel, level, and uniformly spaced when the ladder is in position for use;

(b)(2) Ladder rungs, steps, and cleats are spaced not less than 10 inches (25 cm) and not more than 14 inches (36 cm) apart, as measured between the centerlines of the rungs, cleats, and steps, except that:

(b)(2)(i) Ladder rungs and steps in elevator shafts must be spaced not less than 6 inches (15 cm) apart and not more than 16.5 inches (42 cm) apart, as measured along the ladder side rails; and

(b)(2)(ii) Fixed ladder rungs and steps on telecommunication towers must be spaced not more than 18 inches (46 cm) apart, measured between the centerlines of the rungs or steps;

(b)(3) Steps on stepstools are spaced not less than 8 inches (20 cm) apart and not more than 12 inches (30 cm) apart, as measured between the centerlines of the steps;

(b)(4) Ladder rungs, steps, and cleats have a minimum clear width of 11.5 inches (29 cm) on portable ladders and 16 inches (41 cm) (measured before installation of ladder safety systems) for fixed ladders, except that:

(b)(4)(i) The minimum clear width does not apply to ladders with narrow rungs that are not designed to be stepped on, such as those located on the tapered end of orchard ladders and similar ladders;

(b)(4)(ii) Rungs and steps of manhole entry ladders that are supported by the manhole opening must have a minimum clear width of 9 inches (23 cm);

(b)(4)(iii) Rungs and steps on rolling ladders used in telecommunication centers must have a minimum clear width of 8 inches (20 cm); and

(b)(4)(iv) Stepstools have a minimum clear width of 10.5 inches (26.7 cm);

(b)(5) Wooden ladders are not coated with any material that may obscure structural defects;

(b)(6) Metal ladders are made with corrosion-resistant material or protected against corrosion;

(b)(7) Ladder surfaces are free of puncture and laceration hazards;

(b)(8) Ladders are used only for the purposes for which they were designed;

(b)(9) Ladders are inspected before initial use in each work shift, and more frequently as necessary, to identify any visible defects that could cause employee injury;

(b)(10) Any ladder with structural or other defects is immediately tagged "Dangerous: Do Not Use" or with similar language in accordance with §1910.145 and removed from service until repaired in accordance with §1910.22(d), or replaced;

(b)(11) Each employee faces the ladder when climbing up or down it;

(b)(12) Each employee uses at least one hand to grasp the ladder when climbing up and down it; and

(b)(13) No employee carries any object or load that could cause the employee to lose balance and fall while climbing up or down the ladder.

(c) **Portable ladders** The employer must ensure:

(c)(1) Rungs and steps of portable metal ladders are corrugated, knurled, dimpled, coated with skid-resistant material, or otherwise treated to minimize the possibility of slipping;

(c)(2) Each stepladder or combination ladder used in a stepladder mode is equipped with a metal spreader or locking device that securely holds the front and back sections in an open position while the ladder is in use;

(c)(3) Ladders are not loaded beyond the maximum intended load;

Note: The maximum intended load, as defined in §1910.21(b), includes the total load (weight and force) of the employee and all tools, equipment, and materials being carried.

(c)(4) Ladders are used only on stable and level surfaces unless they are secured or stabilized to prevent accidental displacement;

(c)(5) No portable single rail ladders are used;

(c)(6) No ladder is moved, shifted, or extended while an employee is on it;

(c)(7) Ladders placed in locations such as passageways, doorways, or driveways where they can be displaced by other activities or traffic:

(c)(7)(i) Are secured to prevent accidental displacement; or

(c)(7)(ii) Are guarded by a temporary barricade, such as a row of traffic cones or caution tape, to keep the activities or traffic away from the ladder;

(c)(8) The cap (if equipped) and top step of a stepladder are not used as steps;

(c)(9) Portable ladders used on slippery surfaces are secured and stabilized;

(c)(10) The top of a non-self-supporting ladder is placed so that both side rails are supported, unless the ladder is equipped with a single support attachment;

(c)(11) Portable ladders used to gain access to an upper landing surface have side rails that extend at least 3 feet (0.9 m) above the upper landing surface (see Figure D-1 of this Section);

(c)(12) Ladders and ladder sections are not tied or fastened together to provide added length unless they are specifically designed for such use;

(c)(13) Ladders are not placed on boxes, barrels, or other unstable bases to obtain additional height.

(c)(13) Ladders are not placed on boxes, barrels, or other unstable bases to obtain additional height.

Figure D-1—Portable Ladder Setup

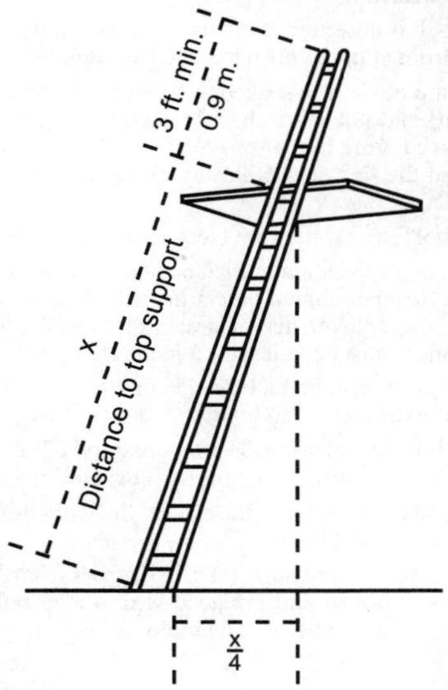

(d) **Fixed ladders** The employer must ensure:

(d)(1) Fixed ladders are capable of supporting their maximum intended load;

(d)(2) The minimum perpendicular distance from the centerline of the steps or rungs, or grab bars, or both, to the nearest permanent object in back of the ladder is 7 inches (18 cm), except for elevator pit ladders, which have a minimum perpendicular distance of 4.5 inches (11 cm);

(d)(3) Grab bars do not protrude on the climbing side beyond the rungs of the ladder that they serve;

(d)(4) The side rails of through or side-step ladders extend 42 inches (1.1 m) above the top of the access level or landing platform served by the ladder. For parapet ladders, the access level is:

(d)(4)(i) The roof, if the parapet is cut to permit passage through the parapet; or

(d)(4)(ii) The top of the parapet, if the parapet is continuous;

(d)(5) For through ladders, the steps or rungs are omitted from the extensions, and the side rails are flared to provide not less than 24 inches (61cm) and not more than 30 inches (76 cm) of clearance. When a ladder safety system is provided, the maximum clearance between side rails of the extension must not exceed 36 inches (91 cm);

(d)(6) For side-step ladders, the side rails, rungs, and steps must be continuous in the extension (see Figure D-2 of this Section);

(d)(7) Grab bars extend 42 inches (1.1 m) above the access level or landing platforms served by the ladder;

(d)(8) The minimum size (cross-section) of grab bars is the same size as the rungs of the ladder.

(d)(9) When a fixed ladder terminates at a hatch (see Figure D-3 of this Section), the hatch cover:

(d)(9)(i) Opens with sufficient clearance to provide easy access to or from the ladder; and

(d)(ii) Opens at least 70 degrees from horizontal if the hatch is counterbalanced;

(d)(10) Individual-rung ladders are constructed to prevent the employee's feet from sliding off the ends of the rungs (see Figure D-4 of this Section);

(d)(11) Fixed ladders having a pitch greater than 90 degrees from the horizontal are not used;

(d)(12) The step-across distance from the centerline of the rungs or steps is:

(d)(12)(i) For through ladders, not less than 7 inches (18 cm) and not more than 12 inches (30 cm) to the nearest edge of the structure, building, or equipment accessed from the ladders;

(d)(12)(ii) For side-step ladders, not less than 15 inches (38 cm) and not more than 20 inches (51 cm) to the access points of the platform edge;

(d)(13) Fixed ladders that do not have cages or wells have:

(d)(13)(i) A clear width of at least 15 inches (38 cm) on each side of the ladder centerline to the nearest permanent object; and

(d)(13)(ii) A minimum perpendicular distance of 30 inches (76 cm) from the centerline of the steps or rungs to the nearest object on the climbing side. When unavoidable obstructions are encountered, the minimum clearance at the obstruction may be reduced to 24 inches (61 cm), provided deflector plates are installed (see Figure D-5 of this Section).

Note: §1910.28 establishes the employer's duty to provide fall protection for employees on fixed ladders, and §1910.29 specifies the criteria for fall protection systems for fixed ladders.

Figure D-2—Side-Step Fixed Ladder Sections

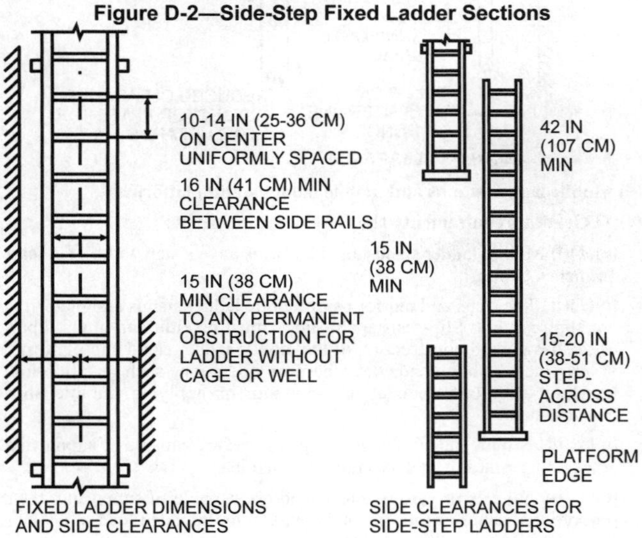

Figure D-3—Example of Counterbalanced Hatch Cover at Roof

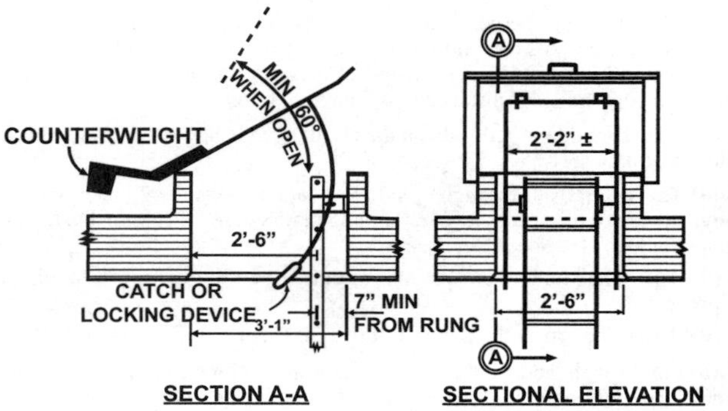

Figure D-4—Individual Rung Ladder

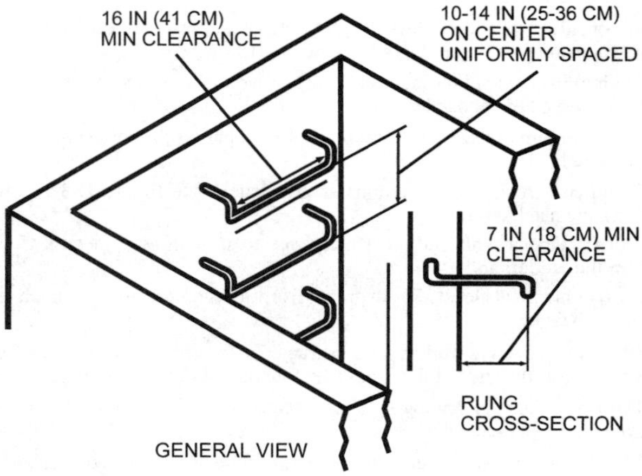

Figure D-5—Fixed Ladder Clearances

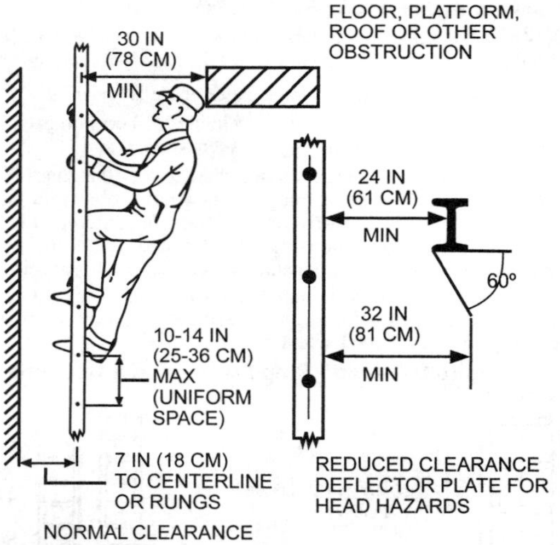

(e) **Mobile ladder stands and mobile ladder stand platforms**

(e)(1) **General requirements** The employer must ensure:

(e)(1)(i) Mobile ladder stands and platforms have a step width of at least 16 inches (41 cm);

(e)(1)(ii) The steps and platforms of mobile ladder stands and platforms are slip resistant. Slip-resistant surfaces must be either an integral part of the design and construction of the mobile ladder stand and platform, or provided as a secondary process or operation, such as dimpling, knurling, shotblasting, coating, spraying, or applying durable slip-resistant tapes;

(e)(1)(iii) Mobile ladder stands and platforms are capable of supporting at least four times their maximum intended load;

(e)(1)(iv) Wheels or casters under load are capable of supporting their proportional share of four times the maximum intended load, plus their proportional share of the unit's weight;

(e)(1)(v) Unless otherwise specified in this Section, mobile ladder stands and platforms with a top step height of 4 feet (1.2 m) or above have handrails with a vertical height of 29.5 inches (75 cm) to 37 inches (94 cm), measured from the front edge of a step. Removable gates or non-rigid members, such as chains, may be used instead of handrails in special-use applications;

(e)(1)(vi) The maximum work-surface height of mobile ladder stands and platforms does not exceed four times the shortest base dimension, without additional support. For greater heights, outriggers, counterweights, or comparable means that stabilize the mobile ladder stands and platforms and prevent overturning must be used;

(e)(1)(vii) Mobile ladder stands and platforms that have wheels or casters are equipped with a system to impede horizontal movement when an employee is on the stand or platform; and

(e)(1)(viii) No mobile ladder stand or platform moves when an employee is on it.

(e)(2) **Design requirements for mobile ladder stands** The employer must ensure:

(e)(2)(i) Steps are uniformly spaced and arranged, with a rise of not more than 10 inches (25 cm) and a depth of not less than 7 inches (18 cm). The slope of the step stringer to which the steps are attached must not be more than 60 degrees, measured from the horizontal;

(e)(2)(ii) Mobile ladder stands with a top step height above 10 feet (3 m) have the top step protected on three sides by a handrail with a vertical height of at least 36 inches (91 cm); and top steps that are 20 inches (51 cm) or more, front to back, have a midrail and toeboard. Removable gates or non-rigid members, such as chains, may be used instead of handrails in special-use applications; and

(e)(2)(iii) The standing area of mobile ladder stands is within the base frame.

(e)(3) **Design requirements for mobile ladder stand platforms** The employer must ensure:

(e)(3)(i) Steps of mobile ladder stand platforms meet the requirements of paragraph (e)(2)(i) of this Section. When the employer demonstrates that the requirement is not feasible, steeper slopes or vertical rung ladders may be used, provided the units are stabilized to prevent overturning;

(e)(3)(ii) Mobile ladder stand platforms with a platform height of 4 to 10 feet (1.2 m to 3 m) have, in the platform area, handrails with a vertical height of at least 36 inches (91 cm) and midrails; and

(e)(3)(iii) All ladder stand platforms with a platform height above 10 feet (3 m) have guardrails and toeboards on the exposed sides and ends of the platform.

(e)(3)(iv) Removable gates or non-rigid members, such as chains, may be used on mobile ladder stand platforms instead of handrails and guardrails in special-use applications.

§1910.24
Step bolts and manhole steps

(a) **Step bolts** The employer must ensure:

(a)(1) Each step bolt installed on or after January 17, 2017 in an environment where corrosion may occur is constructed of, or coated with, material that protects against corrosion;

(a)(2) Each step bolt is designed, constructed, and maintained to prevent the employee's foot from slipping off the end of the step bolt;

(a)(3) Step bolts are uniformly spaced at a vertical distance of not less than 12 inches (30 cm) and not more than 18 inches (46 cm) apart, measured center to center (see Figure D-6 of this Section). The spacing from the entry and exit surface to the first step bolt may differ from the spacing between the other step bolts;

(a)(4) Each step bolt has a minimum clear width of 4.5 inches (11 cm);

(a)(5) The minimum perpendicular distance between the centerline of each step bolt to the nearest permanent object in back of the step bolt is 7 inches (18 cm). When the employer demonstrates that an obstruction cannot be avoided, the distance must be at least 4.5 inches (11 cm);

(a)(6) Each step bolt installed before January 17, 2017 is capable of supporting its maximum intended load;

(a)(7) Each step bolt installed on or after January 17, 2017 is capable of supporting at least four times its maximum intended load;

(a)(8) Each step bolt is inspected at the start of the workshift and maintained in accordance with §1910.22; and

(a)(9) Any step bolt that is bent more than 15 degrees from the perpendicular in any direction is removed and replaced with a step bolt that meets the requirements of this Section before an employee uses it.

Figure D-6—Step Bolt Spacing

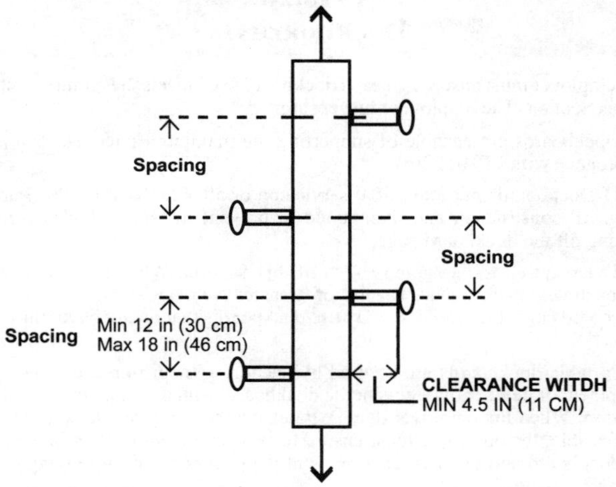

(b) **Manhole steps**

(b)(1) The employer must ensure that each manhole step is capable of supporting its maximum intended load.

(b)(2) The employer must ensure that each manhole step installed on or after January 17, 2017:

(b)(2)(i) Has a corrugated, knurled, dimpled, or other surface that minimizes the possibility of an employee slipping;

(b)(2)(ii) Is constructed of, or coated with, material that protects against corrosion if the manhole step is located in an environment where corrosion may occur;

(b)(2)(iii) Has a minimum clear step width of 10 inches (25 cm);

(b)(2)(iv) Is uniformly spaced at a vertical distance not more than 16 inches (41 cm) apart, measured center to center between steps. The spacing from the entry and exit surface to the first manhole step may differ from the spacing between the other steps.

(b)(2)(v) Has a minimum perpendicular distance between the centerline of the manhole step to the nearest permanent object in back of the step of at least 4.5 inches (11 cm); and

(b)(2)(vi) Is designed, constructed, and maintained to prevent the employee's foot from slipping or sliding off the end.

(b)(3) The employer must ensure that each manhole step is inspected at the start of the work shift and maintained in accordance with §1910.22.

§1910.25 Stairways

(a) **Application** This Section covers all stairways (including standard, spiral, ship, and alternating tread-type stairs), except for stairs serving floating roof tanks, stairs on scaffolds, stairs designed into machines or equipment, and stairs on self-propelled motorized equipment.

(b) **General requirements** The employer must ensure:

(b)(1) Handrails, stair rail systems, and guardrail systems are provided in accordance with §1910.28;

(b)(2) Vertical clearance above any stair tread to any overhead obstruction is at least 6 feet, 8 inches (203 cm), as measured from the leading edge of the tread. Spiral stairs must meet the vertical clearance requirements in paragraph (d)(3) of this Section.

(b)(3) Stairs have uniform riser heights and tread depths between landings;

(b)(4) Stairway landings and platforms are at least the width of the stair and at least 30 inches (76 cm) in depth, as measured in the direction of travel;

(b)(5) When a door or a gate opens directly on a stairway, a platform is provided, and the swing of the door or gate does not reduce the platform's effective usable depth to:

(b)(5)(i) Less than 20 inches (51 cm) for platforms installed before January 17, 2017; and

(b)(5)(ii) Less than 22 inches (56 cm) for platforms installed on or after January 17, 2017 (see Figure D-7 of this Section);

(b)(6) Each stair can support at least five times the normal anticipated live load, but never less than a concentrated load of 1,000 pounds (454 kg) applied at any point;

(b)(7) Standard stairs are used to provide access from one walking-working surface to another when operations necessitate regular and routine travel between levels, including access to operating platforms for equipment. Winding stairways may be used on tanks and similar round structures when the diameter of the tank or structure is at least 5 feet (1.5 m).

(b)(8) Spiral, ship, or alternating tread-type stairs are used only when the employer can demonstrate that it is not feasible to provide standard stairs.

(b)(9) When paragraph (b)(8) of this Section allows the use of spiral, ship, or alternating tread-type stairs, they are installed, used, and maintained in accordance with manufacturer's instructions.

Figure D-7—Door or Gate Opening on Stairway

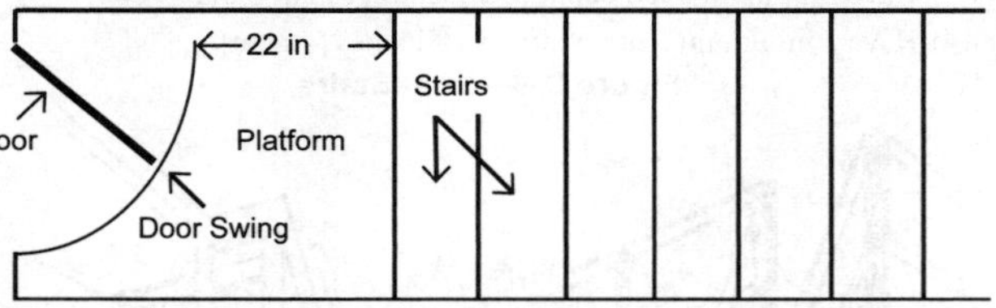

(c) **Standard stairs** In addition to paragraph (b) of this Section, the employer must ensure standard stairs:

(c)(1) Are installed at angles between 30 to 50 degrees from the horizontal;

(c)(2) Have a maximum riser height of 9.5 inches (24 cm);

(c)(3) Have a minimum tread depth of 9.5 inches (24 cm); and

(c)(4) Have a minimum width of 22 inches (56 cm) between vertical barriers (see Figure D-8 of this Section).

(c)(5) Exception to paragraphs (c)(2) and (3) of this Section. The requirements of paragraphs (c)(2) and (3) do not apply to standard stairs installed prior to January 17, 2017. OSHA will deem those stairs in compliance if they meet the dimension requirements specified in Table D-1 of this Section or they use a combination that achieves the angle requirements of paragraph (c)(1) of this Section.

Table D-1—Stairway Rise and Tread Dimensions

Angle to horizontal	Rise (in inches)	Tread run (in inches)
30° 35'	6 ½	11
32° 08'	6 ¾	10 3/4
33° 41'	7	10 1/2
35° 16'	7 ¼	10 1/4
36° 52'	7 ½	10
38° 29'	7 ¾	9 3/4
40° 08'	8	9 1/2
41° 44'	8 ¼	9 1/4
43° 22'	8 ½	9
45° 00'	8 ¾	8 3/4
46° 38'	9	8 1/2
48° 16'	9 ¼	8 1/4
49° 54'	9 ½	8

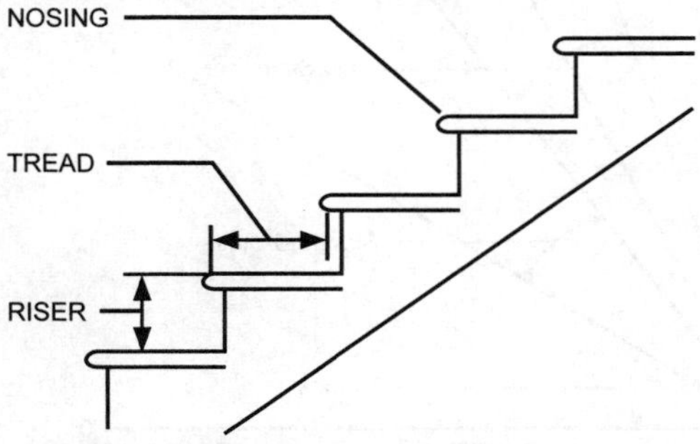

MINIMUM TREAD WIDTH 22 IN (56 CM)
MINIMUM TREAD DEPTH 9.5 IN (24 CM)
MAXIMUM RISER HEIGHT 9.5 IN (24 CM)

(d) **Spiral stairs** In addition to paragraph (b) of this Section, the employer must ensure spiral stairs:

(d)(1) Have a minimum clear width of 26 inches (66 cm);

(d)(2) Have a maximum riser height of 9.5 inches (24 cm);

(d)(3) Have a minimum headroom above spiral stair treads of at least 6 feet, 6 inches (2 m), measured from the leading edge of the tread;

(d)(4) Have a minimum tread depth of 7.5 inches (19 cm), measured at a point 12 inches (30 cm) from the narrower edge;

(d)(5) Have a uniform tread size;

(e) **Ship stairs** In addition to paragraph (b) of this Section, the employer must ensure ship stairs (see Figure D-9 of this Section):

(e)(1) Are installed at a slope of 50 to 70 degrees from the horizontal;

(e)(2) Have open risers with a vertical rise between tread surfaces of 6.5 to 12 inches (17 to 30 cm);

(e)(3) Have minimum tread depth of 4 inches (10 cm); and

(e)(4) Have a minimum tread width of 18 inches (46 cm).

Figure D-9—Ship Stairs

(f) Alternating tread-type stairs. In addition to paragraph (b) of this Section, the employer must ensure alternating tread-type stairs:

(f)(1) Have a series of treads installed at a slope of 50 to 70 degrees from the horizontal;

(f)(2) Have a distance between handrails of 17 to 24 inches (51 to 61 cm);

(f)(3) Have a minimum tread depth of 8.5 inches (22 cm); and

(f)(4) Have open risers if the tread depth is less than 9.5 inches (24 cm);

(f)(5) Have a minimum tread width of 7 inches (18 cm), measured at the leading edge of the tread (i.e., nosing).

Figure #-10—Angles for Stairs, Ramps, and Ladders

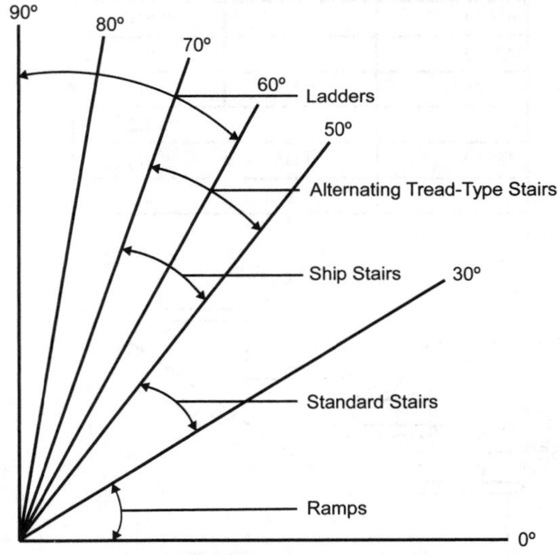

Angle	Type
≤ 30°	Ramps
30° - 50°	Standard Stairs
50° -70°	Ship Stairs
50° - 70°	Alternating Tred-Type Stairs
60° - 90°	Ladders

§1910.26 Dockboards

The employer must ensure that each dockboard used meets the requirements of this Section. The employer must ensure:

(a) Dockboards are capable of supporting the maximum intended load in accordance with §1910.22(b);

(b)(1) Dockboards put into initial service on or after January 17, 2017 are designed, constructed, and maintained to prevent transfer vehicles from running off the dockboard edge;

(b)(2) Exception to paragraph (b)(1) of this Section. When the employer demonstrates there is no hazard of transfer vehicles running off the dockboard edge, the employer may use dockboards that do not have run-off protection.

(c) Portable dockboards are secured by anchoring them in place or using equipment or devices that prevent the dockboard from moving out of a safe position. When the employer demonstrates that securing the dockboard is not feasible, the employer must ensure there is sufficient contact between the dockboard and the surface to prevent the dockboard from moving out of a safe position;

(d) Measures, such as wheel chocks or sand shoes, are used to prevent the transport vehicle (e.g. a truck, semi-trailer, trailer, or rail car) on which a dockboard is placed, from moving while employees are on the dockboard; and

(e) Portable dockboards are equipped with handholds or other means to permit safe handling of dockboards.

§1910.27 Scaffolds and rope descent systems

(a) **Scaffolds** Scaffolds used in general industry must meet the requirements in 29 CFR Part §1926, Subpart L (Scaffolds).

(b) **Rope descent systems**

(b)(1) **Anchorages**

(b)(1)(i) Before any rope descent system is used, the building owner must inform the employer, in writing that the building owner has identified, tested, certified, and maintained each anchorage so it is capable of supporting at least 5,000 pounds (268 kg), in any direction, for each employee attached. The information must be based on an annual inspection by a qualified person and certification of each anchorage by a qualified person, as necessary, and at least every 10 years.

(b)(1)(ii) The employer must ensure that no employee uses any anchorage before the employer has obtained written information from the building owner that each anchorage meets the requirements of paragraph (b)(1)(i) of this Section. The employer must keep the information for the duration of the job.

(b)(1)(iii) The requirements in paragraphs (b)(1)(i) and (ii) of this Section must be implemented no later than November 20, 2017.

(b)(2) **Use of rope descent systems** The employer must ensure:

(b)(2)(i) No rope descent system is used for heights greater than 300 feet (91 m) above grade unless the employer demonstrates that it is not feasible to access such heights by any other means or that those means pose a greater hazard than using a rope descent system;

(b)(2)(ii) The rope descent system is used in accordance with instructions, warnings, and design limitations set by the manufacturer or under the direction of a qualified person;

(b)(2)(iii) Each employee who uses the rope descent system is trained in accordance with §1910.30;

(b)(2)(iv) The rope descent system is inspected at the start of each workshift that it is to be used. The employer must ensure damaged or defective equipment is removed from service immediately and replaced;

(b)(2)(v) The rope descent system has proper rigging, including anchorages and tiebacks, with particular emphasis on providing tiebacks when counterweights, cornice hooks, or similar non-permanent anchorages are used;

(b)(2)(vi) Each employee uses a separate, independent personal fall arrest system that meets the requirements of Subpart I of this Part;

(b)(2)(vii) All components of each rope descent system, except seat boards, are capable of sustaining a minimum rated load of 5,000 pounds (22.2 kN). Seat boards must be capable of supporting a live load of 300 pounds (136 kg);

(b)(2)(viii) Prompt rescue of each employee is provided in the event of a fall;

(b)(2)(ix) The ropes of each rope descent system are effectively padded or otherwise protected, where they can contact edges of the building, anchorage, obstructions, or other surfaces, to prevent them from being cut or weakened;

(b)(2)(x) Stabilization is provided at the specific work location when descents are greater than 130 feet (39.6 m);

(b)(2)(xi) No employee uses a rope descent system when hazardous weather conditions, such as storms or gusty or excessive wind, are present;

(b)(2)(xii) Equipment, such as tools, squeegees, or buckets, is secured by a tool lanyard or similar method to prevent it from falling; and

(b)(2)(xiii) The ropes of each rope descent system are protected from exposure to open flames, hot work, corrosive chemicals, and other destructive conditions.

§1910.28 Duty to have fall protection and falling object protection

(a) **General**

(a)(1) This Section requires employers to provide protection for each employee exposed to fall and falling object hazards. Unless stated otherwise, the employer must ensure that all fall protection and falling object protection required by this Section meet the criteria in §1910.29, except that personal fall protection systems required by this Section meet the criteria of §1910.140.

(a)(2) This Section does not apply:

(a)(2)(i) To portable ladders;

(a)(2)(ii) When employers are inspecting, investigating, or assessing workplace conditions or work to be performed prior to the start of work or after all work has been completed. This exemption does not apply when fall protection systems or equipment meeting the requirements of §1910.29 have been installed and are available for workers to use for pre-work and post-work inspections, investigations, or assessments;

(a)(2)(iii) To fall hazards presented by the exposed perimeters of entertainment stages and the exposed perimeters of rail-station platforms;

(a)(2)(iv) To powered platforms covered by §1910.66(j);

(a)(2)(v) To aerial lifts covered by §1910.67(c)(2)(v);

(a)(2)(vi) To telecommunications work covered by §1910.268(n)(7) and (8); and

(a)(2)(vii) To electric power generation, transmission, and distribution work covered by §1910.269(g)(2)(i).

(b) **Protection from fall hazards**

(b)(1) **Unprotected sides and edges**

(b)(1)(i) Except as provided elsewhere in this Section, the employer must ensure that each employee on a walking-working surface with an unprotected side or edge that is 4 feet (1.2 m) or more above a lower level is protected from falling by one or more of the following:

(b)(1)(i)(A) Guardrail systems;

(b)(1)(i)(B) Safety net systems; or

(b)(1)(i)(C) Personal fall protection systems, such as personal fall arrest, travel restraint, or positioning systems.

(b)(1)(ii) When the employer can demonstrate that it is not feasible or creates a greater hazard to use guardrail, safety net, or personal fall protection systems on residential roofs, the employer must develop and implement a fall protection plan that meets the requirements of 29 CFR 1926.502(k) and training that meets the requirements of 29 CFR 1926.503(a) and (c).

Note: There is a presumption that it is feasible and will not create a greater hazard to use at least one of the above-listed fall protection systems specified in paragraph (b)(1)(i) of this Section. Accordingly, the employer has the burden of establishing that it is not feasible or creates a greater hazard to provide the fall protection systems specified in paragraph (b)(1)(i) and that it is necessary to implement a fall protection plan that complies with §1926.502(k) in the particular work operation, in lieu of implementing any of those systems.

(b)(1)(iii) When the employer can demonstrate that the use of fall protection systems is not feasible on the working side of a platform used at a loading rack, loading dock, or teeming platform, the work may be done without a fall protection system, provided:

(b)(1)(iii)(A) The work operation for which fall protection is infeasible is in process;

(b)(1)(iii)(B) Access to the platform is limited to authorized employees; and,

(b)(1)(iii)(C) The authorized employees are trained in accordance with §1910.30.

(b)(2) **Hoist areas** The employer must ensure:

(b)(2)(i) Each employee in a hoist area is protected from falling 4 feet (1.2 m) or more to a lower level by:

(b)(2)(i)(A) A guardrail system;

(b)(2)(i)(B) A personal fall arrest system; or

(b)(2)(i)(C) A travel restraint system.

(b)(2)(ii) When any portion of a guardrail system, gate, or chains is removed, and an employee must lean through or over the edge of the access opening to facilitate hoisting, the employee is protected from falling by a personal fall arrest system.

(b)(2)(i)(iii) If grab handles are installed at hoist areas, they meet the requirements of §1910.29(l).

(b)(3) **Holes** The employer must ensure:

(b)(3)(i) Each employee is protected from falling through any hole (including skylights) that is 4 feet (1.2 m) or more above a lower level by one or more of the following:

(b)(3)(i)(A) Covers;

(b)(3)(i)(B) Guardrail systems;

(b)(3)(i)(C) Travel restraint systems; or

(b)(3)(i)(D) Personal fall arrest systems.

(b)(3)(ii) Each employee is protected from tripping into or stepping into or through any hole that is less than 4 feet (1.2 m) above a lower level by covers or guardrail systems.

(b)(3)(iii) Each employee is protected from falling into a stairway floor hole by a fixed guardrail system on all exposed sides, except at the stairway entrance. However, for any stairway used less than once per day where traffic across the stairway floor hole prevents the use of a fixed guardrail system (e.g., holes located in aisle spaces), the employer may protect employees from falling into the hole by using a hinged floor hole cover that meets the criteria in §1910.29 and a removable guardrail system on all exposed sides, except at the entrance to the stairway.

(b)(3)(iv) Each employee is protected from falling into a ladderway floor hole or ladderway platform hole by a guardrail system and toeboards erected on all exposed sides, except at the entrance to the hole, where a self-closing gate or an offset must be used.

(b)(3)(v) Each employee is protected from falling through a hatchway and chute-floor hole by:

(b)(3)(v)(A) A hinged floor-hole cover that meets the criteria in §1910.29 and a fixed guardrail system that leaves only one exposed side. When the hole is not in use, the employer must ensure the cover is closed or a removable guardrail system is provided on the exposed sides;

(b)(3)(v)(B) A removable guardrail system and toeboards on not more than two sides of the hole and a fixed guardrail system on all other exposed sides. The employer must ensure the removable guardrail system is kept in place when the hole is not in use; or

(b)(3)(v)(C) A guardrail system or a travel restraint system when a work operation necessitates passing material through a hatchway or chute floor hole.

(b)(4) **Dockboards**

(b)(4)(i) The employer must ensure that each employee on a dockboard is protected from falling 4 feet (1.2 m) or more to a lower level by a guardrail system or handrails.

(b)(4)(ii) A guardrail system or handrails are not required when:

(b)(4)(A) Dockboards are being used solely for materials-handling operations using motorized equipment;

(b)(4)(B) Employees engaged in these operations are not exposed to fall hazards greater than 10 feet (3 m); and

(b)(4)(C) Those employees have been trained in accordance with §1910.30.

(b)(5) **Runways and similar walkways**

(b)(5)(i) The employer must ensure each employee on a runway or similar walkway is protected from falling 4 feet (1.2 m) or more to a lower level by a guardrail system.

(b)(5)(ii) When the employer can demonstrate that it is not feasible to have guardrails on both sides of a runway used exclusively for a special purpose, the employer may omit the guardrail on one side of the runway, provided the employer ensures:

(b)(5)(ii)(A) The runway is at least 18 inches (46 cm) wide; and

(b)(5)(ii)(B) Each employee is provided with and uses a personal fall arrest system or travel restraint system.

(b)(6) **Dangerous equipment** The employer must ensure:

(b)(6)(i) Each employee less than 4 feet (1.2 m) above dangerous equipment is protected from falling into or onto the dangerous equipment by a guardrail system or a travel restraint system, unless the equipment is covered or guarded to eliminate the hazard.

(b)(6)(ii) Each employee 4 feet (1.2 m) or more above dangerous equipment must be protected from falling by:

(b)(6)(ii)(A) Guardrail systems;

(b)(6)(ii)(B) Safety net systems;

(b)(6)(ii)(C) Travel restraint systems; or

(b)(6)(ii)(D) Personal fall arrest systems.

(b)(7) **Openings** The employer must ensure that each employee on a walking-working surface near an opening, including one with a chute attached, where the inside bottom edge of the opening is less than 39 inches (99 cm) above that walking-working surface and the outside bottom edge of the opening is 4 feet (1.2 m) or more above a lower level is protected from falling by the use of:

(b)(7)(i) Guardrail systems;

(b)(7)(ii) Safety net systems;

(b)(7)(iii) Travel restraint systems; or,

(b)(7)(iv) Personal fall arrest systems.

(b)(8) **Repair pits, service pits, and assembly pits less than 10 feet in depth** The use of a fall protection system is not required for a repair pit, service pit, or assembly pit that is less than 10 feet (3 m) deep, provided the employer:

(b)(8)(i) Limits access within 6 feet (1.8 m) of the edge of the pit to authorized employees trained in accordance with §1910.30;

(b)(8)(ii) Applies floor markings at least 6 feet (1.8 m) from the edge of the pit in colors that contrast with the surrounding area; or places a warning line at least 6 feet (1.8 m) from the edge of the pit as well as stanchions that are capable of resisting, without tipping over, a force of at least 16 pounds (71 N) applied horizontally against the stanchion at a height of 30 inches (76 cm); or places a combination of floor markings and warning lines at least 6 feet (1.8 m) from the edge of the pit. When two or more pits in a common area are not more than 15 feet (4.5m) apart, the employer may comply by placing contrasting floor markings at least 6 feet (1.8 m) from the pit edge around the entire area of the pits; and

(b)(8)(iii) Posts readily visible caution signs that meet the requirements of §1910.145 and state "Caution—Open Pit."

(b)(9) **Fixed ladders (that extend more than 24 feet (7.3 m) above a lower level)**

(b)(9)(i) For fixed ladders that extend more than 24 feet (7.3 m) above a lower level, the employer must ensure:

(b)(9)(i)(A) **Existing fixed ladders** Each fixed ladder installed before November 19, 2018 is equipped with a personal fall arrest system, ladder safety system, cage, or well;

(b)(9)(i)(B) **New fixed ladders** Each fixed ladder installed on and after November 19, 2018, is equipped with a personal fall arrest system or a ladder safety system;

(b)(9)(i)(C) **Replacement** When a fixed ladder, cage, or well, or any portion of a section thereof, is replaced, a personal fall arrest system or ladder safety system is installed in at least that section of the fixed ladder, cage, or well where the replacement is located; and

(b)(9)(i)(D) **Final deadline** On and after November 18, 2036, all fixed ladders are equipped with a personal fall arrest system or a ladder safety system.

(b)(9)(ii) When a one-section fixed ladder is equipped with a personal fall protection or a ladder safety system or a fixed ladder is equipped with a personal fall arrest or ladder safety system on more than one section, the employer must ensure:

(b)(9)(ii)(A) The personal fall arrest system or ladder safety system provides protection throughout the entire vertical distance of the ladder, including all ladder sections; and

(b)(9)(ii)(B) The ladder has rest platforms provided at maximum intervals of 150 feet (45.7 m).

(b)(9)(iii) The employer must ensure ladder sections having a cage or well:

(b)(9)(iii)(A) Are offset from adjacent sections; and

(b)(9)(iii)(B) Have landing platforms provided at maximum intervals of 50 feet (15.2 m).

(b)(9)(iv) The employer may use a cage or well in combination with a personal fall arrest system or ladder safety system provided that the cage or well does not interfere with the operation of the system.

(b)(10) **Outdoor advertising (billboards)**

(b)(10)(i) The requirements in paragraph (b)(9) of this Section, and other requirements in Subparts D and I of this Part, apply to fixed ladders used in outdoor advertising activities.

(b)(10)(ii) When an employee engaged in outdoor advertising climbs a fixed ladder before November 19, 2018 that is not equipped with a cage, well, personal fall arrest system, or a ladder safety system the employer must ensure the employee:

(b)(10)(ii)(A) Receives training and demonstrates the physical capability to perform the necessary climbs in accordance with §1910.29(h);

(b)(10)(ii)(B) Wears a body harness equipped with an 18-inch (46 cm) rest lanyard;

(b)(10)(ii)(C) Keeps both hands free of tools or material when climbing on the ladder; and

(b)(10)(ii)(D) Is protected by a fall protection system upon reaching the work position.

(b)(11) **Stairways** The employer must ensure:

(b)(11)(i) Each employee exposed to an unprotected side or edge of a stairway landing that is 4 feet (1.2 m) or more above a lower level is protected by a guardrail or stair rail system;

(b)(11)(ii) Each flight of stairs having at least 3 treads and at least 4 risers is equipped with stair rail systems and handrails as follows:

Table D-2—Stairway Handrail Requirements

Stair width	Enclosed	One open side	Two open sides	With earth built up on both sides
Less than 4 inches (1.1m)	At least one handrail.	One stair rail system with handrail on open side.	One stair rail system each open side.	
44 inches (1.1m) to 88 inches (2.2m)	One handrail on each enclosed side.	One stair rail system with handrail on open side and one handrail on enclosed side.	One stair rail system with handrail on each open side.	
Greater than 88 inches (2.2m)	One handrail on each enclosed side and one intermediate handrail located in the middle of the stair.	One stair rail system with handrail on open side, one handrail on enclosed side, and one intermediate handraol located in the middle of the stair.	Open stair rail system with handrail on each open side and one intermediate handrail located in themiddle of the stair.	
Exterior staris less than 44 inches (1.1m)				One handrail on at least one side.

Note: The width of the stair must be clear of all obstructions except handrails.

(b)(11)(iii) Each ship stairs and alternating tread type stairs is equipped with handrails on both sides.

(b)(12) **Scaffolds and rope descent systems** The employer must ensure:

(b)(12)(i) Each employee on a scaffold is protected from falling in accordance 29 CFR Part §1926, Subpart L; and

(b)(12)(ii) Each employee using a rope descent system 4 feet (1.2 m) or more above a lower level is protected from falling by a personal fall arrest system.

(b)(13) **Work on low-slope roofs**

(b)(13)(i) When work is performed less than 6 feet (1.6 m) from the roof edge, the employer must ensure each employee is protected from falling by a guardrail system, safety net system, travel restraint system, or personal fall arrest system.

(b)(13)(ii) When work is performed at least 6 feet (1.6 m) but less than 15 feet (4.6 m) from the roof edge, the employer must ensure each employee is protected from falling by using a guardrail system, safety net system, travel restraint system, or personal fall arrest system. The employer may use a designated area when performing work that is both infrequent and temporary.

(b)(13)(iii) When work is performed 15 feet (4.6 m) or more from the roof edge, the employer must:

(b)(13)(iii)(A) Protect each employee from falling by a guardrail system, safety net system, travel restraint system, or personal fall arrest system or a designated area. The employer is not required to provide any fall protection, provided the work is both infrequent and temporary; and

(b)(13)(iii)(B) Implement and enforce a work rule prohibiting employees from going within 15 feet (4.6 m) of the roof edge without using fall protection in accordance with paragraphs (b)(13)(i) and (ii) of this Section.

(b)(14) **Slaughtering facility platforms**

(b)(14)(i) The employer must protect each employee on the unprotected working side of a slaughtering facility platform that is 4 feet (1.2 m) or more above a lower level from falling by using:

(b)(14)(i)(A) Guardrail systems; or

(b)(14)(i)(B) Travel restraint systems.

(b)(14)(ii) When the employer can demonstrate the use of a guardrail or travel restraint system is not feasible, the work may be done without those systems provided:

(b)(14)(ii)(A) The work operation for which fall protection is infeasible is in process;

(b)(14)(ii)(B) Access to the platform is limited to authorized employees; and

(b)(14)(ii)(C) The authorized employees are trained in accordance with §1910.30.

(b)(15) **Walking-working surfaces not otherwise addressed** Except as provided elsewhere in this Section or by other Subparts of this Part, the employer must ensure each employee on a walking-working surface 4 feet (1.2 m) or more above a lower level is protected from falling by:

(b)(15)(i) Guardrail systems;

(b)(15)(ii) Safety net systems; or

(b)(15)(iii) Personal fall protection systems, such as personal fall arrest, travel restraint, or positioning systems.

(c) **Protection from falling objects** When an employee is exposed to falling objects, the employer must ensure that each employee wears head protection that meets the requirements of Subpart I of this Part. In addition, the employer must protect employees from falling objects by implementing one or more of the following:

(c)(1) Erecting toeboards, screens, or guardrail systems to prevent objects from falling to a lower level;

(c)(2) Erecting canopy structures and keeping potential falling objects far enough from an edge, hole, or opening to prevent them from falling to a lower level; or

(c)(3) Barricading the area into which objects could fall, prohibiting employees from entering the barricaded area, and keeping objects far enough from an edge or opening to prevent them from falling to a lower level.

§1910.29 Fall protection systems and falling object protection—criteria and practices

(a) **General requirements** The employer must:

(a)(1) Ensure each fall protection system and falling object protection, other than personal fall protection systems, that this Part requires meets the requirements in this Section. The employer must ensure each personal fall protection system meets the requirements in Subpart I of this Part; and

(a)(2) Provide and install all fall protection systems and falling object protection this Subpart requires, and comply with the other requirements in this Subpart before any employee begins work that necessitates fall or falling object protection.

(b) **Guardrail systems** The employer must ensure guardrail systems meet the following requirements:

(b)(1) The top edge height of top rails, or equivalent guardrail system members, are 42 inches (107 cm), plus or minus 3 inches (8 cm), above the walking-working surface. The top edge height may exceed 45 inches (114 cm), provided the guardrail system meets all other criteria of paragraph (b) of this Section (see Figure D-11 of this Section).

(b)(2) Midrails, screens, mesh, intermediate vertical members, solid panels, or equivalent intermediate members are installed between the walking-working surface and the top edge of the guardrail system as follows when there is not a wall or parapet that is at least 21 inches (53 cm) high:

(b)(2)(i) Midrails are installed at a height midway between the top edge of the guardrail system and the walking-working surface;

(b)(2)(ii) Screens and mesh extend from the walking-working surface to the top rail and along the entire opening between top rail supports;

(b)(2)(iii) Intermediate vertical members (such as balusters) are installed no more than 19 inches (48 cm) apart; and

(b)(2)(iv) Other equivalent intermediate members (such as additional midrails and architectural panels) are installed so that the openings are not more than 19 inches (48 cm) wide.

(b)(3) Guardrail systems are capable of withstanding, without failure, a force of at least 200 pounds (890 N) applied in a downward or outward direction within 2 inches (5 cm) of the top edge, at any point along the top rail.

(b)(4) When the 200-pound (890-N) test load is applied in a downward direction, the top rail of the guardrail system must not deflect to a height of less than 39 inches (99 cm) above the walking-working surface.

(b)(5) Midrails, screens, mesh, intermediate vertical members, solid panels, and other equivalent intermediate members are capable of withstanding, without failure, a force of at least 150 pounds (667 N) applied in any downward or outward direction at any point along the intermediate member.

(b)(6) Guardrail systems are smooth-surfaced to protect employees from injury, such as punctures or lacerations, and to prevent catching or snagging of clothing.

(b)(7) The ends of top rails and midrails do not overhang the terminal posts, except where the overhang does not pose a projection hazard for employees.

(b)(8) Steel banding and plastic banding are not used for top rails or midrails.

(b)(9) Top rails and midrails are at least 0.25-inches (0.6 cm) in diameter or in thickness.

(b)(10) When guardrail systems are used at hoist areas, a removable guardrail section, consisting of a top rail and midrail, are placed across the access opening between guardrail sections when employees are not performing hoisting operations. The employer may use chains or gates instead of a removable guardrail section at hoist areas if the employer demonstrates the chains or gates provide a level of safety equivalent to guardrails.

(b)(11) When guardrail systems are used around holes, they are installed on all unprotected sides or edges of the hole.

(b)(12) For guardrail systems used around holes through which materials may be passed:

(b)(12)(i) When materials are being passed through the hole, not more than two sides of the guardrail system are removed; and

(b)(12)(ii) When materials are not being passed through the hole, the hole must be guarded by a guardrail system along all unprotected sides or edges or closed over with a cover.

(b)(13) When guardrail systems are used around holes that serve as points of access (such as ladderways), the guardrail system opening:

(b)(13)(i) Has a self-closing gate that slides or swings away from the hole, and is equipped with a top rail and midrail or equivalent intermediate member that meets the requirements in paragraph (b) of this Section; or

(b)(13)(ii) Is offset to prevent an employee from walking or falling into the hole;

(b)(14) Guardrail systems on ramps and runways are installed along each unprotected side or edge.

(b)(15) Manila or synthetic rope used for top rails or midrails are inspected as necessary to ensure that the rope continues to meet the strength requirements in paragraphs (b)(3) and (5) of this Section.

Note: The criteria and practices requirements for guardrail systems on scaffolds are contained in 29 CFR Part §1926, Subpart L.

Figure D-11—Guard Rail Systems

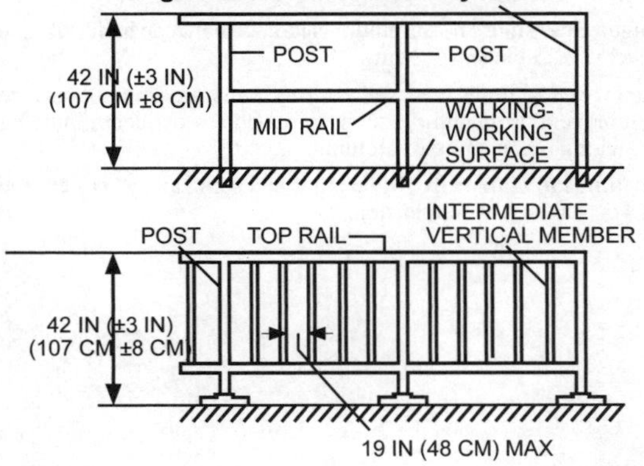

(c) Safety net systems The employer must ensure each safety net system meets the requirements in 29 CFR Part 1926, Subpart M.

(d) Designated areas

(d)(1) When the employer uses a designated area, the employer must ensure:

(d)(1)(i) Employees remain within the designated area while work operations are underway; and

(d)(1)(ii) The perimeter of the designated area is delineated with a warning line consisting of a rope, wire, tape, or chain that meets the requirements of paragraphs (d)(2) and (3) of this Section.

(d)(2) The employer must ensure each warning line:

(d)(2)(i) Has a minimum breaking strength of 200 pounds (0.89 kN);

(d)(2)(ii) Is installed so its lowest point, including sag, is not less than 34 inches (86 cm) and not more than 39 inches (99 cm) above the walking-working surface;

(d)(2)(iii) Is supported in such a manner that pulling on one section of the line will not result in slack being taken up in adjacent sections causing the line to fall below the limits specified in paragraph (d)(2)(ii) of this Section;

(d)(2)(iv) Is clearly visible from a distance of 25 feet (7.6 m) away, and anywhere within the designated area;

(d)(2)(v) Is erected as close to the work area as the task permits; and

(d)(2)(vi) Is erected not less than 6 feet (1.8 m) from the roof edge for work that is both temporary and infrequent, or not less than 15 feet (4.6 m) for other work.

(d)(3) When mobile mechanical equipment is used to perform work that is both temporary and infrequent in a designated area, the employer must ensure the warning line is erected not less than 6 feet (1.8 m) from the unprotected side or edge that is parallel to the direction in which the mechanical equipment is operated, and not less than 10 feet (3 m) from the unprotected side or edge that is perpendicular to the direction in which the mechanical equipment is operated.

(e) Covers The employer must ensure each cover for a hole in a walking-working surface:

(e)(1) Is capable of supporting without failure, at least twice the maximum intended load that may be imposed on the cover at any one time; and

(e)(2) Is secured to prevent accidental displacement.

(f) Handrails and stair rail systems The employer must ensure:

(f)(1) Height criteria

(f)(1)(i) Handrails are not less than 30 inches (76 cm) and not more than 38 inches (97 cm), as measured from the leading edge of the stair tread to the top surface of the handrail (see Figure D-12 of this Section).

(f)(1)(ii) The height of stair rail systems meets the following:

(f)(1)(ii)(A) The height of stair rail systems installed before January 17, 2017 is not less than 30 inches (76 cm) from the leading edge of the stair tread to the top surface of the top rail; and

(f)(1)(ii)(B) The height of stair rail systems installed on or after January 17, 2017 is not less than 42 inches (107 cm) from the leading edge of the stair tread to the top surface of the top rail.

(f)(1)(iii) The top rail of a stair rail system may serve as a handrail only when:

(f)(1)(iii)(A) The height of the stair rail system is not less than 36 inches (91 cm) and not more than 38 inches (97 cm) as measured at the leading edge of the stair tread to the top surface of the top rail (see Figure D-13 of this Section); and

(f)(1)(iii)(B) The top rail of the stair rail system meets the other handrail requirements in paragraph (f) of this Section.

(f)(2) Finger clearance The minimum clearance between handrails and any other object is 2.25 inches (5.7 cm).

(f)(3) Surfaces Handrails and stair rail systems are smooth-surfaced to protect employees from injury, such as punctures or lacerations, and to prevent catching or snagging of clothing.

(f)(4) Openings in stair rails No opening in a stair rail system exceeds 19 inches (48 cm) at its least dimension.

(f)(5) Handhold Handrails have the shape and dimension necessary so that employees can grasp the handrail firmly.

(f)(6) Projection hazards The ends of handrails and stair rail systems do not present any projection hazards.

(f)(7) Strength criteria Handrails and the top rails of stair rail systems are capable of withstanding, without failure, a force of at least 200 pounds (890 N) applied in any downward or outward direction within 2 inches (5 cm) of any point along the top edge of the rail.

Figure D-12—Handrail Measurement

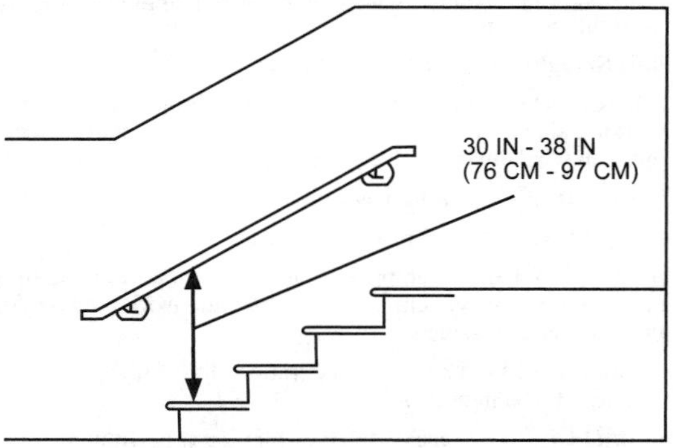

Figure D-13—Combinations Handrail and Stair Rail

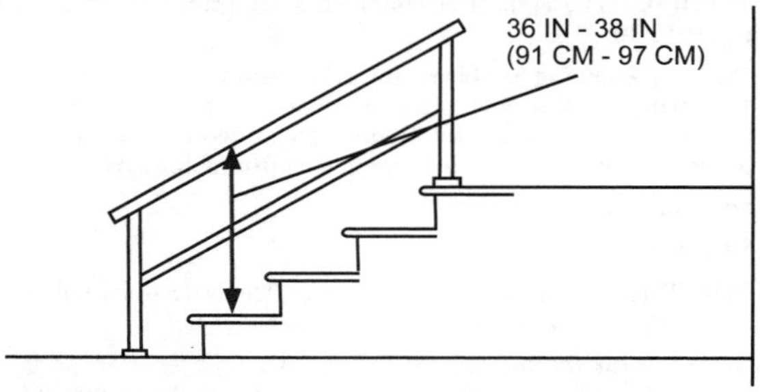

(g) Cages, wells, and platforms used with fixed ladders The employer must ensure:

(g)(1) Cages and wells installed on fixed ladders are designed, constructed, and maintained to permit easy access to, and egress from, the ladder that they enclose (see Figures D-14 and D-15 of this Section);

(g)(2) Cages and wells are continuous throughout the length of the fixed ladder, except for access, egress, and other transfer points;

(g)(3) Cages and wells are designed, constructed, and maintained to contain employees in the event of a fall, and to direct them to a lower landing; and

(g)(4) Platforms used with fixed ladders provide a horizontal surface of at least 24 inches by 30 inches (61 cm by 76 cm).

Note: Section §1910.28 establishes the requirements that employers must follow on the use of cages and wells as a means of fall protection.

Figure D-14—Clearances for Fixed Ladders in Wells

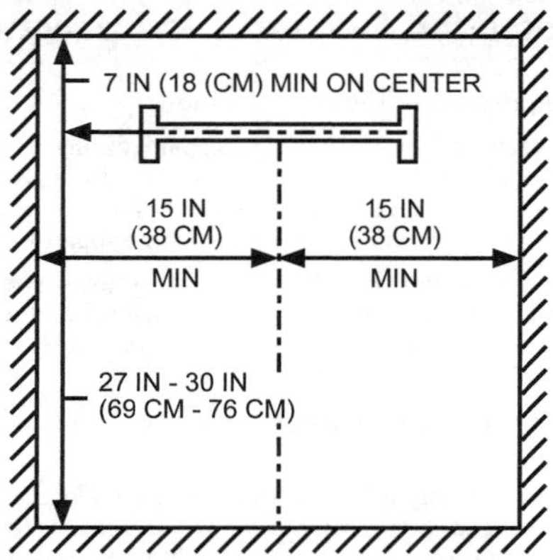

Figure D-15—Example of General Construction of Cages

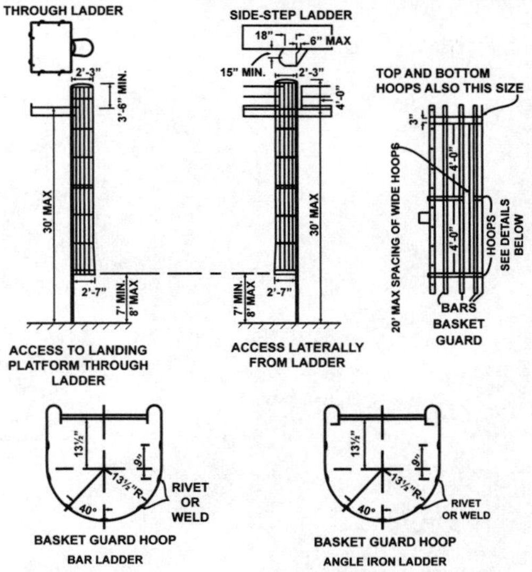

(h) **Outdoor advertising** This paragraph (h) applies only to employers engaged in outdoor advertising operations (see §1910.28(b)(10)). Employers must ensure that each employee who climbs a fixed ladder without fall protection:

(h)(1) Is physically capable, as demonstrated through observations of actual climbing activities or by a physical examination, to perform the duties that may be assigned, including climbing fixed ladders without fall protection;

(h)(2) Has successfully completed a training or apprenticeship program that includes hands-on training on the safe climbing of ladders and is retrained as necessary to maintain the necessary skills;

(h)(3) Has the skill to climb ladders safely, as demonstrated through formal classroom training or on-the-job training, and performance observation; and

(h)(4) Performs climbing duties as a part of routine work activity.

(i) **Ladder safety systems** The employer must ensure:

(i)(1) Each ladder safety system allows the employee to climb up and down using both hands and does not require that the employee continuously hold, push, or pull any part of the system while climbing;

(i)(2) The connection between the carrier or lifeline and the point of attachment to the body harness or belt does not exceed 9 inches (23 cm);

(i)(3) Mountings for rigid carriers are attached at each end of the carrier, with intermediate mountings spaced, as necessary, along the entire length of the carrier so the system has the strength to stop employee falls;

(i)(4) Mountings for flexible carriers are attached at each end of the carrier and cable guides for flexible carriers are installed at least 25 feet (7.6 m) apart but not more than 40 feet (12.2 m) apart along the entire length of the carrier;

(i)(5) The design and installation of mountings and cable guides does not reduce the design strength of the ladder; and

(i)(6) Ladder safety systems and their support systems are capable of withstanding, without failure, a drop test consisting of an 18-inch (41-cm) drop of a 500-pound (227-kg) weight.

(j) **Personal fall protection systems** Body belts, harnesses, and other components used in personal fall arrest systems, work positioning systems, and travel restraint systems must meet the requirements of §1910.140.

(k) **Protection from falling objects**

(k)(1) The employers must ensure toeboards used for falling object protection:

(k)(1)(i) Are erected along the exposed edge of the overhead walking-working surface for a length that is sufficient to protect employees below.

(k)(1)(ii) Have a minimum vertical height of 3.5 inches (9 cm) as measured from the top edge of the toeboard to the level of the walking-working surface.

(k)(1)(iii) Do not have more than a 0.25-inch (0.5-cm) clearance or opening above the walking-working surface.

(k)(1)(iv) Are solid or do not have any opening that exceeds 1 inch (3 cm) at its greatest dimension.

(k)(1)(v) Have a minimum height of 2.5 inches (6 cm) when used around vehicle repair, service, or assembly pits. Toeboards may be omitted around vehicle repair, service, or assembly pits when the employer can demonstrate that a toeboard would prevent access to a vehicle that is over the pit.

(k)(1)(vi) Are capable of withstanding, without failure, a force of at least 50 pounds (222 N) applied in any downward or outward direction at any point along the toeboard.

(k)(2) The employer must ensure:

(k)(2)(i) Where tools, equipment, or materials are piled higher than the top of the toeboard, paneling or screening is installed from the toeboard to the midrail of the guardrail system and for a length that is sufficient to protect employees below. If the items are piled higher than the midrail, the employer also must install paneling or screening to the top rail and for a length that is sufficient to protect employees below; and

(k)(2)(ii) All openings in guardrail systems are small enough to prevent objects from falling through the opening.

(k)(3) The employer must ensure canopies used for falling object protection are strong enough to prevent collapse and to prevent penetration by falling objects.

(l) **Grab handles** The employer must ensure each grab handle:

(l)(1) Is not less than 12 inches (30 cm) long;

(l)(2) Is mounted to provide at least 3 inches (8 cm) of clearance from the framing or opening; and

(l)(3) Is capable of withstanding a maximum horizontal pull-out force equal to two times the maximum intended load or 200 pounds (890 N), whichever is greater

§1910.30
Training requirements

(a) **Fall hazards**

(a)(1) Before any employee is exposed to a fall hazard, the employer must provide training for each employee who uses personal fall protection systems or who is required to be trained as specified elsewhere in this Subpart. Employers must ensure employees are trained in the requirements of this paragraph on or before May 17, 2017.

(a)(2) The employer must ensure that each employee is trained by a qualified person.

(a)(3) The employer must train each employee in at least the following topics:

(a)(3)(i) The nature of the fall hazards in the work area and how to recognize them;

(a)(3)(ii) The procedures to be followed to minimize those hazards;

(a)(3)(iii) The correct procedures for installing, inspecting, operating, maintaining, and disassembling the personal fall protection systems that the employee uses; and

(a)(3)(iv) The correct use of personal fall protection systems and equipment specified in paragraph (a)(1) of this Section, including, but not limited to, proper hook-up, anchoring, and tie-off techniques, and methods of equipment inspection and storage, as specified by the manufacturer.

(b) **Equipment hazards**

(b)(1) The employer must train each employee on or before May 17, 2017 in the proper care, inspection, storage, and use of equipment covered by this Subpart before an employee uses the equipment.

(b)(2) The employer must train each employee who uses a dockboard to properly place and secure it to prevent unintentional movement.

(b)(3) The employer must train each employee who uses a rope descent system in proper rigging and use of the equipment in accordance with §1910.27.

(b)(4) The employer must train each employee who uses a designated area in the proper set-up and use of the area.

(c) **Retraining** The employer must retrain an employee when the employer has reason to believe the employee does not have the understanding and skill required by paragraphs (a) and (b) of this Section. Situations requiring retraining include, but are not limited to, the following:

(c)(1) When changes in the workplace render previous training obsolete or inadequate;

(c)(2) When changes in the types of fall protection systems or equipment to be used render previous training obsolete or inadequate; or

(c)(3) When inadequacies in an affected employee's knowledge or use of fall protection systems or equipment indicate that the employee no longer has the requisite understanding or skill necessary to use equipment or perform the job safely.

(d) **Training must be understandable** The employer must provide information and training to each employee in a manner that the employee understands.

This page intentionally left blank.

29 CFR PART 1910 Subpart E
Exit Routes and Emergency Planning

Section Contents

Subpart E—Exit Routes and Emergency Planning

Authority: 29 U.S.C. 653, 655, 657; Secretary of Labor's Order No. 12–71 (36 FR 8754), 8–76 (41 FR 25059), 9–83 (48 FR 35736), 1–90 (55 FR 9033), 6–96 (62 FR 111), 3–2000 (65 FR 50017), 5–2002 (67 FR 65008), 5–2007 (72 FR 31160), or 4–2010 (75 FR 55355), as applicable; and 29 CFR 1911.

§1910.33
Table of contents

This Section lists the sections and paragraph headings contained in §1910.34 through §1910.39

§1910.34 Coverage and definitions;
- (a) Every employer is covered;
- (b) Exit routes are covered;
- (c) Definitions.

§1910.35 Compliance with Alternate Exit Route Codes.

§1910.36 Design and construction requirements for exit routes.
- (a) Basic requirements;
- (b) The number of exit routes must be adequate;
- (c) Exit discharge;
- (d) An exit door must be unlocked;
- (e) A side-hinged exit door must be used;
- (f) The capacity of an exit route must be adequate;
- (g) An exit route must meet minimum height and width requirements;
- (h) An outdoor exit route is permitted.

§1910.37 Maintenance, safeguards, and operational features for exit routes.
- (a) The danger to employees must be minimized;
- (b) Lighting and marking must be adequate and appropriate;
- (c) The fire retardant properties of paints or solutions must be maintained;
- (d) Exit routes must be maintained during construction, repairs, or alterations;
- (e) An employee alarm system must be operable.

§1910.38 Emergency action plans.
- (a) Application;
- (b) Written and oral emergency action plans;
- (c) Minimum elements of an emergency action plan;
- (d) Employee alarm system;
- (e) Training;
- (f) Review of emergency action plan.

§1910.39 Fire prevention plans.
- (a) Application;
- (b) Written and oral fire prevention plans;
- (c) Minimum elements of a fire prevention plan;
- (d) Employee information.

[67 FR 67961, Nov. 7, 2002, as amended at 76 FR 33606, June 8, 2011]

§1910.34 O/I
Coverage and definitions

(a) **Every employer is covered** Sections §1910.34 through §1910.39 apply to workplaces in general industry except mobile workplaces such as vehicles or vessels.

(b) **Exits routes are covered** The rules in §1910.34 through §1910.39 cover the minimum requirements for exit routes that employers must provide in their workplace so that employees may evacuate the workplace safely during an emergency. Sections §1910.34 through §1910.39 also cover the minimum requirements for emergency action plans and fire prevention plans.

(c) **Definitions**

Electroluminescent means a light-emitting capacitor. Alternating current excites phosphor atoms when placed between the electrically conductive surfaces to produce light. This light source is typically contained inside the device.

Exit means that portion of an exit route that is generally separated from other areas to provide a protected way of travel to the exit discharge. An example of an exit is a two-hour fire resistance-rated enclosed stairway that leads from the fifth floor of an office building to the outside of the building.

Exit access means that portion of an exit route that leads to an exit. An example of an exit access is a corridor on the fifth floor of an office building that leads to a two-hour fire resistance-rated enclosed stairway (the Exit).

Exit discharge means the part of the exit route that leads directly outside or to a street, walkway, refuge area, public way, or open space with access to the outside. An example of an exit discharge is a door at the bottom of a two-hour fire resistance-rated enclosed stairway that discharges to a place of safety outside the building.

Exit route means a continuous and unobstructed path of exit travel from any point within a workplace to a place of safety (including refuge areas). An exit route consists of three parts: The exit access; the exit; and, the exit discharge. (An exit route includes all vertical and horizontal areas along the route.)

High hazard area means an area inside a workplace in which operations include high hazard materials, processes, or contents.

Occupant load means the total number of persons that may occupy a workplace or portion of a workplace at any one time. The occupant load of a workplace is calculated by dividing the gross floor area of the workplace or portion of the workplace by the occupant load factor for that particular type of workplace occupancy. Information regarding the "Occupant load" is located in NFPA 101–2009, Life Safety Code, and in IFC–2009, International Fire Code (incorporated by reference, see §1910.6).

Refuge area means either:
- (1) A space along an exit route that is protected from the effects of fire by separation from other spaces within the building by a barrier with at least a one-hour fire resistance-rating; or
- (2) A floor with at least two spaces, separated from each other by smoke-resistant partitions, in a building protected throughout by an automatic sprinkler system that complies with §1910.159 of this part.

Self-luminous means a light source that is illuminated by a self-contained power source (e.g., tritium) and that operates independently from external power sources. Batteries are not acceptable self-contained power sources. The light source is typically contained inside the device.

[67 FR 67961, Nov. 7, 2002, as amended at 76 FR 33606, June 8, 2011]

§1910.35 O/I
Compliance with alternate exit-route codes

OSHA will deem an employer demonstrating compliance with the exit-route provisions of NFPA 101, Life Safety Code, 2009 edition, or the exit-route provisions of the International Fire Code, 2009 edition, to be in compliance with the corresponding requirements in §1910.34, §1910.36, and §1910.37 (incorporated by reference, see section §1910.6).

[76 FR 33606, June 8, 2011]

§1910.36 O/I
Design and construction requirements for exit routes

(a) **Basic requirements** Exit routes must meet the following design and construction requirements:

(a)(1) An exit route must be permanent. Each exit route must be a permanent part of the workplace.

(a)(2) An exit must be separated by fire resistant materials. Construction materials used to separate an exit from other parts of the workplace must have a one-hour fire resistance-rating if the exit connects three or fewer stories and a two-hour fire resistance-rating if the exit connects four or more stories.

(a)(3) Openings into an exit must be limited. An exit is permitted to have only those openings necessary to allow access to the exit from occupied areas of the workplace, or to the exit discharge. An opening into an exit must be protected by a self-closing fire door that remains closed or automatically closes in an emergency upon the sounding of a fire alarm or employee alarm system. Each fire door, including its frame and hardware, must be listed or approved by a nationally recognized testing laboratory. Section §1910.155(c)(3)(iv)(A) of this part defines "listed" and §1910.7 of this part defines a "nationally recognized testing laboratory."

(b) OI **The number of exit routes must be adequate**

(b)(1) **Two exit routes** At least two exit routes must be available in a workplace to permit prompt evacuation of employees and other building occupants during an emergency, except as allowed in paragraph (b)(3) of this section. The exit routes must be located as far away as practical from each other so that if one exit route is blocked by fire or smoke, employees can evacuate using the second exit route.

(b)(2) **More than two exit routes** More than two exit routes must be available in a workplace if the number of employees, the size of the building, its occupancy, or the arrangement of the workplace is such that all employees would not be able to evacuate safely during an emergency.

(b)(3) **A single exit route** A single exit route is permitted where the number of employees, the size of the building, its occupancy, or the arrangement of the workplace is such that all employees would be able to evacuate safely during an emergency.

Note to paragraph §1910.36(b): For assistance in determining the number of exit routes necessary for your workplace, consult NFPA 101-2009, Life Safety Code, or IFC-2009, International Fire Code (incorporated by reference, See: §1910.6).

(c) **Exit discharge**

(c)(1) OI Each exit discharge must lead directly outside or to a street, walkway, refuge area, public way, or open space with access to the outside.

(c)(2) OI The street, walkway, refuge area, public way, or open space to which an exit discharge leads must be large enough to accommodate the building occupants likely to use the exit route.

(c)(3) Exit stairs that continue beyond the level on which the exit discharge is located must be interrupted at that level by doors, partitions, or other effective means that clearly indicate the direction of travel leading to the exit discharge.

(d) OI **An exit door must be unlocked**

(d)(1) OI Employees must be able to open an exit route door from the inside at all times without keys, tools, or special knowledge. A device such as a panic bar that locks only from the outside is permitted on exit discharge doors.

(d)(2) OI Exit route doors must be free of any device or alarm that could restrict emergency use of the exit route if the device or alarm fails.

(d)(3) An exit route door may be locked from the inside only in mental, penal, or correctional facilities and then only if supervisory personnel are continuously on duty and the employer has a plan to remove occupants from the facility during an emergency.

(e) **A side-hinged exit door must be used**

(e)(1) A side-hinged door must be used to connect any room to an exit route.

(e)(2) The door that connects any room to an exit route must swing out in the direction of exit travel if the room is designed to be occupied by more than 50 people or if the room is a high hazard area (i.e., contains contents that are likely to burn with extreme rapidity or explode).

(f) **The capacity of an exit route must be adequate**

(f)(1) Exit routes must support the maximum permitted occupant load for each floor served.

(f)(2) The capacity of an exit route may not decrease in the direction of exit route travel to the exit discharge.

Note to paragraph §1910.36(f): Information regarding the "Occupant load" is located in NFPA 101-2009, Life Safety Code, and in IFC-2009, International Fire Code (incorporated by reference, see §1910.6).

(g) **An exit route must meet minimum height and width requirements.**

(g)(1) OI The ceiling of an exit route must be at least seven feet six inches (2.3 m) high. Any projection from the ceiling must not reach a point less than six feet eight inches (2.0 m) from the floor.

(g)(2) OI An exit access must be at least 28 inches (71.1 cm) wide at all points. Where there is only one exit access leading to an exit or exit discharge, the width of the exit and exit discharge must be at least equal to the width of the exit access.

(g)(3) The width of an exit route must be sufficient to accommodate the maximum permitted occupant load of each floor served by the exit route.

(g)(4) Objects that project into the exit route must not reduce the width of the exit route to less than the minimum width requirements for exit routes.

(h) **An outdoor exit route is permitted.** Each outdoor exit route must meet the minimum height and width requirements for indoor exit routes and must also meet the following requirements:

(h)(1) The outdoor exit route must have guardrails to protect unenclosed sides if a fall hazard exists;

(h)(2) The outdoor exit route must be covered if snow or ice is likely to accumulate along the route, unless the employer can demonstrate that any snow or ice accumulation will be removed before it presents a slipping hazard;

(h)(3) The outdoor exit route must be reasonably straight and have smooth, solid, substantially level walkways; and

(h)(4) The outdoor exit route must not have a dead-end that is longer than 20 feet (6.2 m).

[67 FR 67961, Nov. 7, 2002, as amended at 76 FR 33606, June 8, 2011]

§1910.37 OI
Maintenance, safeguards, and operational features for exit routes

(a) **The danger to employees must be minimized**

(a)(1) Exit routes must be kept free of explosive or highly flammable furnishings or other decorations.

(a)(2) Exit routes must be arranged so that employees will not have to travel toward a high hazard area, unless the path of travel is effectively shielded from the high hazard area by suitable partitions or other physical barriers.

(a)(3) OI Exit routes must be free and unobstructed. No materials or equipment may be placed, either permanently or temporarily, within the exit route. The exit access must not go through a room that can be locked, such as a bathroom, to reach an exit or exit discharge, nor may it lead into a dead-end corridor. Stairs or a ramp must be provided where the exit route is not substantially level.

(a)(4) Safeguards designed to protect employees during an emergency (e.g., sprinkler systems, alarm systems, fire doors, exit lighting) must be in proper working order at all times.

(b) OI **Lighting and marking must be adequate and appropriate**

(b)(1) Each exit route must be adequately lighted so that an employee with normal vision can see along the exit route.

(b)(2) Each exit must be clearly visible and marked by a sign reading "Exit."

(b)(3) Each exit route door must be free of decorations or signs that obscure the visibility of the exit route door.

(b)(4) OI If the direction of travel to the exit or exit discharge is not immediately apparent, signs must be posted along the exit access indicating the direction of travel to the nearest exit and exit discharge. Additionally, the line-of-sight to an exit sign must clearly be visible at all times.

(b)(5) Each doorway or passage along an exit access that could be mistaken for an exit must be marked "Not an Exit" or similar designation, or be identified by a sign indicating its actual use (e.g., closet).

(b)(6) OI Each exit sign must be illuminated to a surface value of at least five foot-candles (54 lux) by a reliable light source and be distinctive in color. Self-luminous or electroluminescent signs that have a minimum luminance surface value of at least .06 footlamberts (0.21 cd/m^2) are permitted.

(b)(7) OI Each exit sign must have the word "Exit" in plainly legible letters not less than six inches (15.2 cm) high, with the principal strokes of the letters in the word "Exit" not less than three-fourths of an inch (1.9 cm) wide.

(c) **The fire retardant properties of paints or solutions must be maintained.** Fire retardant paints or solutions must be renewed as often as necessary to maintain their fire retardant properties.

(d) **Exit routes must be maintained during construction, repairs, or alterations.**

(d)(1) During new construction, employees must not occupy a workplace until the exit routes required by this Subpart are completed and ready for employee use for the portion of the workplace they occupy.

(d)(2) During repairs or alterations, employees must not occupy a workplace unless the exit routes required by this Subpart are available and existing fire protections are maintained, or until alternate fire protection is furnished that provides an equivalent level of safety.

(d)(3) Employees must not be exposed to hazards of flammable or explosive substances or equipment used during construction, repairs, or alterations, that are beyond the normal permissible conditions in the workplace, or that would impede exiting the workplace.

(e) [OI] **An employee alarm system must be operable** Employers must install and maintain an operable employee alarm system that has a distinctive signal to warn employees of fire or other emergencies, unless employees can promptly see or smell a fire or other hazard in time to provide adequate warning to them. The employee alarm system must comply with §1910.165.

[67 FR 67961, Nov. 7, 2002]

§1910.38 [OI] Emergency action plans

(a) [OI] **Application** An employer must have an emergency action plan whenever an OSHA standard in this part requires one. The requirements in this section apply to each such emergency action plan.

(b) [OI] **Written and oral emergency action plans** An emergency action plan must be in writing, kept in the workplace, and available to employees for review. However, an employer with 10 or fewer employees may communicate the plan orally to employees.

(c) **Minimum elements of an emergency action plan** An emergency action plan must include at a minimum:

(c)(1) Procedures for reporting a fire or other emergency;

(c)(2) Procedures for emergency evacuation, including type of evacuation and exit route assignments;

(c)(3) [OI] Procedures to be followed by employees who remain to operate critical plant operations before they evacuate;

(c)(4) Procedures to account for all employees after evacuation;

(c)(5) Procedures to be followed by employees performing rescue or medical duties; and

(c)(6) The name or job title of every employee who may be contacted by employees who need more information about the plan or an explanation of their duties under the plan.

(d) [OI] **Employee alarm system** An employer must have and maintain an employee alarm system. The employee alarm system must use a distinctive signal for each purpose and comply with the requirements in §1910.165.

(e) [OI] **Training** An employer must designate and train employees to assist in a safe and orderly evacuation of other employees.

(f) **Review of emergency action plan** An employer must review the emergency action plan with each employee covered by the plan:

(f)(1) When the plan is developed or the employee is assigned initially to a job;

(f)(2) When the employee's responsibilities under the plan change; and

(f)(3) When the plan is changed.

[67 FR 67961, Nov. 7, 2002].

§1910.39 [OI] Fire prevention plans

(a) **Application** An employer must have a fire prevention plan when an OSHA standard in this part requires one. The requirements in this section apply to each such fire prevention plan.

(b) [OI] **Written and oral fire prevention plans** A fire prevention plan must be in writing, be kept in the workplace, and be made available to employees for review. However, an employer with 10 or fewer employees may communicate the plan orally to employees.

(c) **Minimum elements of a fire prevention plan** A fire prevention plan must include:

(c)(1) A list of all major fire hazards, proper handling and storage procedures for hazardous materials, potential ignition sources and their control, and the type of fire protection equipment necessary to control each major hazard;

(c)(2) Procedures to control accumulations of flammable and combustible waste materials;

(c)(3) Procedures for regular maintenance of safeguards installed on heat-producing equipment to prevent the accidental ignition of combustible materials;

(c)(4) The name or job title of employees responsible for maintaining equipment to prevent or control sources of ignition or fires; and

(c)(5) The name or job title of employees responsible for the control of fuel source hazards.

(d) **Employee information** An employer must inform employees upon initial assignment to a job of the fire hazards to which they are exposed. An employer must also review with each employee those parts of the fire prevention plan necessary for self-protection.

[67 FR 67961, Nov. 7, 2002]

Subpart E of Part 1910 Appendix Exit routes, emergency action plans, and fire prevention plans

This Appendix serves as a nonmandatory guideline to assist employers in complying with the appropriate requirements of Subpart E.

§1910.38 Employee emergency plans.

1. Emergency action plan elements. The emergency action plan should address emergencies that the employer may reasonably expect in the workplace. Examples are: fire; toxic chemical releases; hurricanes; tornadoes; blizzards; floods; and others. The elements of the emergency action plan presented in paragraph §1910.38(c) can be supplemented by the following to more effectively achieve employee safety and health in an emergency. The employer should list in detail the procedures to be taken by those employees who have been selected to remain behind to care for essential plant operations until their evacuation becomes absolutely necessary. Essential plant operations may include the monitoring of plant power supplies, water supplies, and other essential services which cannot be shut down for every emergency alarm. Essential plant operations may also include chemical or manufacturing processes which must be shut down in stages or steps where certain employees must be present to assure that safe shut down procedures are completed.

The use of floor plans or workplace maps which clearly show the emergency escape routes should be included in the emergency action plan. Color coding will aid employees in determining their route assignments.

The employer should also develop and explain in detail what rescue and medical first aid duties are to be performed and by whom. All employees are to be told what actions they are to take in these emergency situations that the employer anticipates may occur in the workplace.

2. Emergency evacuation. At the time of an emergency, employees should know what type of evacuation is necessary and what their role is in carrying out the plan. In some cases where the emergency is very grave, total and immediate evacuation of all employees is necessary. In other emergencies, a partial evacuation of nonessential employees with a delayed evacuation of others may be necessary for continued plant operation. In some cases, only those employees in the immediate area of the fire may be expected to evacuate or move to a safe area such as when a local application fire suppression system discharge employee alarm is sounded. Employees must be sure that they know what is expected of them in all such emergency possibilities which have been planned in order to provide assurance of their safety from fire or other emergency.

The designation of refuge or safe areas for evacuation should be determined and identified in the plan. In a building divided into fire zones by fire walls, the refuge area may still be within the same building but in a different zone from where the emergency occurs.

Exterior refuge or safe areas may include parking lots, open fields or streets which are located away from the site of the emergency and which provide sufficient space to accommodate the employees. Employees should be instructed to move away from the exit discharge doors of the building, and to avoid congregating close to the building where they may hamper emergency operations.

3. Emergency action plan training. The employer should assure that an adequate number of employees are available at all times during working hours to act as evacuation wardens so that employees can be swiftly moved from the danger location to the safe areas. Generally, one warden for each twenty employees in the workplace should be able to provide adequate guidance and instruction at the time of a fire emergency. The employees selected or who volunteer to serve as wardens should be trained in the complete workplace layout and the various alternative escape routes from the workplace. All wardens and fellow employees should be made aware of handicapped employees who may need extra assistance, such as using the buddy system, and of hazardous areas to be avoided during emergencies. Before leaving, wardens should check rooms and other enclosed spaces in the workplace for employees who may be trapped or otherwise unable to evacuate the area.

After the desired degree of evacuation is completed, the wardens should be able to account for or otherwise verify that all employees are in the safe areas.

In buildings with several places of employment, employers are encouraged to coordinate their plans with the other employers in the building. A building-wide or standardized plan for the whole building is acceptable provided that the employers inform their respective employees of their duties and responsibilities under the plan. The standardized plan need not be kept by each employer in the multi-employer building, provided there is an accessible location within the building where the plan can be reviewed by affected employees. When multi-employer building-wide plans are not feasible, employers should coordinate their plans with the other employers within the building to assure that conflicts and confusion are avoided during times of emergencies. In multi-story buildings where more than one employer is on a single floor, it is essential that these employers coordinate their plans with each other to avoid conflicts and confusion.

4. Fire prevention housekeeping. The standard calls for the control of accumulations of flammable and combustible waste materials.

It is the intent of this standard to assure that hazardous accumulations of combustible waste materials are controlled so that a fast developing fire, rapid spread of toxic smoke, or an explosion will not occur. This does not necessarily mean that each room has to be swept each day. Employers and employees should be aware of the hazardous properties of materials in their workplaces, and the degree of hazard each poses. Certainly oil soaked rags have to be treated differently than general paper trash in office areas. However, large accumulations of waste paper or corrugated boxes, etc., can pose a significant fire hazard. Accumulations of materials which can cause large fires or generate dense smoke that are easily ignited or may start from spontaneous combustion, are the types of materials with which this standard is concerned. Such combustible materials may be easily ignited by matches, welder's sparks, cigarettes and similar low level energy ignition sources.

5. Maintenance of equipment under the fire prevention plan. Certain equipment is often installed in workplaces to control heat sources or to detect fuel leaks. An example is a temperature limit switch often found on deep-fat food fryers found in restaurants. There may be similar switches for high temperature dip tanks, or flame failure and flashback arrester devices on furnaces and similar heat producing equipment. If these devices are not properly maintained or if they become inoperative, a definite fire hazard exists. Again employees and supervisors should be aware of the specific type of control devices on equipment involved with combustible materials in the workplace and should make sure, through periodic inspection or testing, that these controls are operable. Manufacturers' recommendations should be followed to assure proper maintenance procedures.

[45 FR 60714, Sept. 12, 1980]

29 CFR PART 1910 Subpart F
Powered Platforms, Manlifts, and Vehicle–Mounted Work Platforms

Section Contents

Subpart F—Powered Platforms, Manlifts, and Vehicle–Mounted Work Platforms

Authority: 29 U.S.C. 653, 655, and 657; Secretary of Labor's Order No. 12-71 (36 FR 8754), 8-76 (41 FR 25059), 9-83 (48 FR 35736), 1-90 (55 FR 9033), 5-2007 (72 FR 31159), or 1-2012 (77 FR 3912), as applicable; and 29 CFR part 1911.

§1910.66 [OI] Powered platforms for building maintenance

(a) **Scope** This Section covers powered platform installations permanently dedicated to interior or exterior building maintenance of a specific structure or group of structures. This Section does not apply to suspended scaffolds (swinging scaffolds) used to service buildings on a temporary basis and covered under Subpart D of this part, nor to suspended scaffolds used for construction work and covered under Subpart L of 29 CFR Part 1926. Building maintenance includes, but is not limited to, such tasks as window cleaning, caulking, metal polishing and reglazing.

(b) **Application**

(b)(1) [OI] **New installations** This Section applies to all permanent installations completed after July 23, 1990. Major modifications to existing installations completed after that date are also considered new installations under this Section.

(b)(2) [OI] **Existing installations**

(b)(2)(i) [OI] Permanent installations in existence and/or completed before July 23, 1990 shall comply with paragraphs (g), (h), (i), (j) and Appendix C to Subpart I of this Part.

(b)(2)(ii) [OI] In addition, permanent installations completed after August 27, 1971, and in existence and/or completed before July 23, 1990, shall comply with Appendix D of this Section.

(c) [OI] **Assurance**

(c)(1) Building owners of new installations shall inform the employer before each use in writing that the installation meets the requirements of paragraphs (e)(1) and (f)(1) of this Section and the additional design criteria contained in other provisions of paragraphs (e) and (f) of this Section relating to: required load sustaining capabilities of platforms, building components, hoisting and supporting equipment; stability factors for carriages, platforms and supporting equipment; maximum horizontal force for movement of carriages and davits; design of carriages, hoisting machines, wire rope and stabilization systems; and design criteria for electrical wiring and equipment.

(c)(2) Building owners shall base the information required in paragraph (c)(1) of this Section on the results of a field test of the installation before being placed into service and following any major alteration to an existing installation, as required in paragraph (g)(1) of this Section. The assurance shall also be based on all other relevant available information, including, but not limited to, test data, equipment specifications and verification by a registered professional engineer.

(c)(3) Building owners of all installations, new and existing, shall inform the employer in writing that the installation has been inspected, tested, and maintained in compliance with the requirements of paragraphs (g) and (h) of this Section and that all anchorages meet the requirements of §1910.140(c)(13).

(c)(4) The employer shall not permit employees to use the installation prior to receiving assurance from the building owner that the installation meets the requirements contained in paragraphs (c)(1) and (c)(3) of this Section.

(d) **Definitions**

Anemometer means an instrument for measuring wind velocity.

Angulated roping means a suspension method where the upper point of suspension is inboard from the attachments on the suspended unit, thus causing the suspended unit to bear against the face of the building.

Building face roller means a rotating cylindrical member designed to ride on the face of the building wall to prevent the platform from abrading the face of the building and to assist in stabilizing the platform.

Building maintenance means operations such as window cleaning, caulking, metal polishing, reglazing, and general maintenance on building surfaces.

Cable means a conductor, or group of conductors, enclosed in a weatherproof sheath, that may be used to supply electrical power and/or control current for equipment or to provide voice communication circuits.

Carriage means a wheeled vehicle used for the horizontal movement and support of other equipment.

Certification means a written, signed and dated statement confirming the performance of a requirement of this Section.

Combination cable means a cable having both steel structural members capable of supporting the platform, and copper or other electrical conductors insulated from each other and the structural members by nonconductive barriers.

Competent person means a person who, because of training and experience, is capable of identifying hazardous or dangerous conditions in powered platform installations and of training employees to identify such conditions.

Continuous pressure means the need for constant manual actuation for a control to function.

Control means a mechanism used to regulate or guide the operation of the equipment.

Davit means a device, used singly or in pairs, for suspending a powered platform from work, storage and rigging locations on the building being serviced. Unlike outriggers, a davit reacts its operating load into a single roof socket or carriage attachment.

Equivalent means alternative designs, materials or methods which the employer can demonstrate will provide an equal or greater degree of safety for employees than the methods, materials or designs specified in the standard.

Ground rigging means a method of suspending a working platform starting from a safe surface to a point of suspension above the safe surface.

Ground rigged davit means a davit which cannot be used to raise a suspended working platform above the building face being serviced.

Guide button means a building face anchor designed to engage a guide track mounted on a platform.

Guide roller means a rotating cylindrical member, operating separately or as part of a guide assembly, designed to provide continuous engagement between the platform and the building guides or guideways.

Guide shoe means a device attached to the platform designed to provide a sliding contact between the platform and the building guides.

Hoisting machine means a device intended to raise and lower a suspended or supported unit.

Hoist rated load means the hoist manufacturer's maximum allowable operating load.

Installation means all the equipment and all affected parts of a building which are associated with the performance of building maintenance using powered platforms.

Interlock means a device designed to ensure that operations or motions occur in proper sequence.

Intermittent stabilization means a method of platform stabilization in which the angulated suspension wire rope(s) are secured to regularly spaced building anchors.

Lanyard means a flexible line of rope, wire rope or strap which is used to secure the body belt or body harness to a deceleration device, lifeline or anchorage.

Lifeline means a component consisting of a flexible line for connection to an anchorage at one end to hang vertically (vertical lifeline), or for connection to anchorages at both ends to stretch horizontally (horizontal lifeline), and which serves as a means for connecting other components of a personal fall arrest system to the anchorage.

Live load means the total static weight of workers, tools, parts, and supplies that the equipment is designed to support.

Obstruction detector means a control that will stop the suspended or supported unit in the direction of travel if an obstruction is encountered, and will allow the unit to move only in a direction away from the obstruction.

Operating control means a mechanism regulating or guiding the operation of equipment that ensures a specific operating mode.

Operating device means a device actuated manually to activate a control.

Outrigger means a device, used singly or in pairs, for suspending a working platform from work, storage, and rigging locations on the building being serviced. Unlike davits, an outrigger reacts its operating moment load as at least two opposing vertical components acting into two or more distinct roof points and/or attachments.

Platform rated load means the combined weight of workers, tools, equipment and other material which is permitted to be carried by the working platform at the installation, as stated on the load rating plate.

Poured socket means the method of providing wire rope terminations in which the ends of the rope are held in a tapered socket by means of poured spelter or resins.

Primary brake means a brake designed to be applied automatically whenever power to the prime mover is interrupted or discontinued.

Prime mover means the source of mechanical power for a machine.

Rated load means the manufacturer's recommended maximum load.

Rated strength means the strength of wire rope, as designated by its manufacturer or vendor, based on standard testing procedures or acceptable engineering design practices.

Rated working load means the combined static weight of men, materials, and suspended or supported equipment.

Registered professional engineer means a person who has been duly and currently registered and licensed by an authority within the United States or its territories to practice the profession of engineering.

Roof powered platform means a working platform where the hoist(s) used to raise or lower the platform is located on the roof.

Roof rigged davit means a davit used to raise the suspended working platform above the building face being serviced. This type of davit can also be used to raise a suspended working platform which has been ground-rigged.

Rope means the equipment used to suspend a component of an equipment installation, i.e., wire rope.

Safe surface means a horizontal surface intended to be occupied by personnel, which is so protected by a fall protection system that it can be reasonably assured that said occupants will be protected against falls.

Secondary brake means a brake designed to arrest the descent of the suspended or supported equipment in the event of an overspeed condition.

Self powered platform means a working platform where the hoist(s) used to raise or lower the platform is mounted on the platform.

Speed reducer means a positive type speed reducing machine.

Stability factor means the ratio of the stabilizing moment to the overturning moment.

Stabilizer tie means a flexible line connecting the building anchor and the suspension wire rope supporting the platform.

Supported equipment means building maintenance equipment that is held or moved to its working position by means of attachment directly to the building or extensions of the building being maintained.

Suspended equipment means building maintenance equipment that is suspended and raised or lowered to its working position by means of ropes or combination cables attached to some anchorage above the equipment.

Suspended scaffold (swinging scaffold) means a scaffold supported on wire or other ropes, used for work on, or for providing access to, vertical sides of structures on a temporary basis. Such scaffold is not designed for use on a specific structure or group of structures.

Tail line means the nonsupporting end of the wire rope used to suspend the platform.

Tie-in guides means the portion of a building that provides continuous positive engagement between the building and a suspended or supported unit during its vertical travel on the face of the building.

Traction hoist means a type of hoisting machine that does not accumulate the suspension wire rope on the hoisting drum or sheave, and is designed to raise and lower a suspended load by the application of friction forces between the suspension wire rope and the drum or sheave.

Transportable outriggers means outriggers designed to be moved from one work location to another.

Trolley carriage means a carriage suspended from an overhead track structure.

Verified means accepted by design, evaluation, or inspection by a registered professional engineer.

Weatherproof means so constructed that exposure to adverse weather conditions will not affect or interfere with the proper use or functions of the equipment or component.

Winding drum hoist means a type of hoisting machine that accumulates the suspension wire rope on the hoisting drum.

Working platform means suspended or supported equipment intended to provide access to the face of a building and manned by persons engaged in building maintenance.

Wrap means one complete turn of the suspension wire rope around the surface of a hoist drum.

(e) **Powered platform installations—Affected parts of buildings**

(e)(1) **General requirements** The following requirements apply to affected parts of buildings which utilize working platforms for building maintenance.

(e)(1)(i) Structural supports, tie-downs, tie-in guides, anchoring devices and any affected parts of the building included in the installation shall be designed by or under the direction of a registered professional engineer experienced in such design;

(e)(1)(ii) Exterior installations shall be capable of withstanding prevailing climatic conditions;

(e)(1)(iii) The building installation shall provide safe access to, and egress from, the equipment and sufficient space to conduct necessary maintenance of the equipment;

(e)(1)(iv) The affected parts of the building shall have the capability of sustaining all the loads imposed by the equipment; and

(e)(1)(v) The affected parts of the building shall be designed so as to allow the equipment to be used without exposing employees to a hazardous condition.

(e)(2) OI **Tie-in guides**

(e)(2)(i) OI The exterior of each building shall be provided with tie-in guides unless the conditions in paragraph (e)(2)(ii) or (e)(2)(iii) of this Section are met.

Note: See Figure 1 in Appendix B of this Section for a description of a typical continuous stabilization system utilizing tie-in guides.

(e)(2)(ii) If angulated roping is employed, tie-in guides required in paragraph (e)(2)(i) of this Section may be eliminated for not more than 75 feet (22.9 m) of the uppermost elevation of the building, if infeasible due to exterior building design, provided an angulation force of at least 10 pounds (44.4 n) is maintained under all conditions of loading.

(e)(2)(iii) OI Tie-in guides required in paragraph (e)(2)(i) of this Section may be eliminated if one of the guide systems in paragraph (e)(2)(iii)(A), (e)(2)(iii)(B) or (e)(2)(iii)(C) of this Section is provided, or an equivalent.

(e)(2)(iii)(A) **Intermittent stabilization system** The system shall keep the equipment in continuous contact with the building facade, and shall prevent sudden horizontal movement of the platform. The system may be used together with continuous positive building guide systems using tie-in guides on the same building, provided the requirements for each system are met.

(e)(2)(iii)(A)(1) The maximum vertical interval between building anchors shall be three floors or 50 feet (15.3 m), whichever is less.

(e)(2)(iii)(A)(2) Building anchors shall be located vertically so that attachment of the stabilizer ties will not cause the platform suspension ropes to angulate the platform horizontally across the face of the building. The anchors shall be positioned horizontally on the building face so as to be symmetrical about the platform suspension ropes.

(e)(2)(iii)(A)(3) Building anchors shall be easily visible to employees and shall allow a stabilizer tie attachment for each of the platform suspension ropes at each vertical interval. If more than two suspension ropes are used on a platform, only the two building-side suspension ropes at the platform ends shall require a stabilizer attachment.

(e)(2)(iii)(A)(4) Building anchors which extend beyond the face of the building shall be free of sharp edges or points. Where cables, suspension wire ropes and lifelines may be in contact with the building face, external building anchors shall not interfere with their handling or operation.

(e)(2)(iii)(A)(5) The intermittent stabilization system building anchors and components shall be capable of sustaining without failure at least four times the maximum anticipated load applied or transmitted to the components and anchors. The minimum design wind load for each anchor shall be 300 (1334 n) pounds, if two anchors share the wind load.

(e)(2)(iii)(A)(6) The building anchors and stabilizer ties shall be capable of sustaining anticipated horizontal and vertical loads from winds specified for roof storage design which may act on the platform and wire ropes if the platform is stranded on a building face. If the building anchors have different spacing than the suspension wire rope or if the building requires different suspension spacings on one platform, one building anchor and stabilizer tie shall be capable of sustaining the wind loads.

Note: See Figure 2 in Appendix B of this Section for a description of a typical intermittent stabilization system.

(e)(2)(iii)(B) **Button guide stabilization system**

(e)(2)(iii)(B)(1) Guide buttons shall be coordinated with platform mounted equipment of paragraph (f)(5)(vi) of this Section.

(e)(2)(iii)(B)(2) Guide buttons shall be located horizontally on the building face so as to allow engagement of each of the guide tracks mounted on the platform.

(e)(2)(iii)(B)(3) Guide buttons shall be located in vertical rows on the building face for proper engagement of the guide tracks mounted on the platform.

(e)(2)(iii)(B)(4) Two guide buttons shall engage each guide track at all times except for the initial engagement.

(e)(2)(iii)(B)(5) Guide buttons which extend beyond the face of the building shall be free of sharp edges or points. Where cables, ropes and lifelines may be in contact with the building face, guide buttons shall not interfere with their handling or operation.

(e)(2)(iii)(B)(6) Guide buttons, connections and seals shall be capable of sustaining without damage at least the weight of the platform, or provision shall be made in the guide tracks or guide track connectors to prevent the platform and its attachments from transmitting the weight of the platform to the guide buttons, connections and seals. In either case, the minimum design load shall be 300 pounds (1334 n) per building anchor.

Note: See paragraph (f)(5)(vi) of this Section for relevant equipment provisions.

Note: See Figure 3 in Appendix B of this Section for a description of a typical button guide stabilization system.

(e)(2)(iii)(C) **System utilizing angulated roping and building face rollers** The system shall keep the equipment in continuous contact with the building facade, and shall prevent sudden horizontal movement of the platform. This system is acceptable only where the suspended portion of the equipment in use does not exceed 130 feet (39.6 m) above a safe surface or ground level, and where the platform maintains no less than 10 pounds (44.4 n) angulation force on the building facade.

(e)(2)(iv) Tie-in guides for building interiors (atriums) may be eliminated when a registered professional engineer determines that an alternative stabilization system, including systems in paragraphs (e)(2)(iii) (A), (B) and (C), or a platform tie-off at each work station will provide equivalent safety.

(e)(3) **Roof guarding**

(e)(3)(i) Employees working on roofs while performing building maintenance shall be protected by a perimeter guarding system which meets the requirements of paragraph (c)(1) of §1910.23 of this part.

(e)(3)(ii) The perimeter guard shall not be more than six inches (152 mm) inboard of the inside face of a barrier, i.e. the parapet wall, or roof edge curb of the building being serviced; however, the perimeter guard location shall not exceed an 18 inch (457 mm) setback from the exterior building face.

(e)(4) Equipment stops. Operational areas for trackless type equipment shall be provided with structural stops, such as curbs, to prevent equipment from traveling outside its intended travel areas and to prevent a crushing or shearing hazard.

(e)(5) Maintenance access. Means shall be provided to traverse all carriages and their suspended equipment to a safe area for maintenance and storage.

(e)(6) **Elevated track**

(e)(6)(i) An elevated track system which is located four feet (1.2 m) or more above a safe surface, and traversed by carriage supported equipment, shall be provided with a walkway and guardrail system; or

(e)(6)(ii) The working platform shall be capable of being lowered, as part of its normal operation, to the lower safe surface for access and egress of the personnel and shall be provided with a safe means of access and egress to the lower safe surface.

(e)(7) **Tie-down anchors** Imbedded tie-down anchors, fasteners, and affected structures shall be resistant to corrosion.

(e)(8) **Cable stabilization**

(e)(8)(i) Hanging lifelines and all cables not in tension shall be stabilized at each 200 foot (61 m) interval of vertical travel of the working platform beyond an initial 200 foot (61 m) distance.

(e)(8)(ii) Hanging cables, other than suspended wire ropes, which are in constant tension shall be stabilized when the vertical travel exceeds an initial 600 foot (183 m) distance, and at further intervals of 600 feet (183 m) or less.

(e)(9) **Emergency planning** A written emergency action plan shall be developed and implemented for each kind of working platform operation. This plan shall explain the emergency procedures which are to be followed in the event of a power failure, equipment failure or other emergencies which may be encountered. The plan shall also explain that employees inform themselves about the building emergency escape routes, procedures and alarm systems before operating a platform. Upon initial assignment and whenever the plan is changed the employer shall review with each employee those parts of the plan which the employee must know to protect himself or herself in the event of an emergency.

(e)(10) **Building maintenance** Repairs or major maintenance of those building portions that provide primary support for the suspended equipment shall not affect the capability of the building to meet the requirements of this standard.

(e)(11) **Electrical requirements** The following electrical requirements apply to buildings which utilize working platforms for building maintenance.

(e)(11)(i) General building electrical installations shall comply with §1910.302 through §1910.308 of this part, unless otherwise specified in this Section;

(e)(11)(ii) Building electrical wiring shall be of such capacity that when full load is applied to the equipment power circuit not more than a five percent drop from building service-vault voltage shall occur at any power circuit outlet used by equipment regulated by this Section;

(e)(11)(iii) The equipment power circuit shall be an independent electrical circuit that shall remain separate from all other equipment within or on the building, other than power circuits used for hand tools that will be used in conjunction with the equipment. If the building is provided with an emergency power system, the equipment power circuit may also be connected to this system;

(e)(11)(iv) The power circuit shall be provided with a disconnect switch that can be locked in the "OFF" and "ON" positions. The switch shall be conveniently located with respect to the primary operating area of the equipment to allow the operators of the equipment access to the switch;

(e)(11)(v) The disconnect switch for the power circuit shall be locked in the "ON" position when the equipment is in use; and

(e)(11)(vi) An effective two-way voice communication system shall be provided between the equipment operators and persons stationed within the building being serviced. The communications facility shall be operable and shall be manned at all times by persons stationed within the building whenever the platform is being used.

(f) **Powered platform installations—Equipment**

(f)(1) **General requirements** The following requirements apply to equipment which are part of a powered platform installation, such as platforms, stabilizing components, carriages, outriggers, davits, hoisting machines, wire ropes and electrical components.

(f)(1)(i) Equipment installations shall be designed by or under the direction of a registered professional engineer experienced in such design;

(f)(1)(ii) The design shall provide for a minimum live load of 250 pounds (113.6 kg) for each occupant of a suspended or supported platform;

(f)(1)(iii) Equipment that is exposed to wind when not in service shall be designed to withstand forces generated by winds of at least 100 miles per hour (44.7 m/s) at 30 feet (9.2 m) above grade; and

(f)(1)(iv) Equipment that is exposed to wind when in service shall be designed to withstand forces generated by winds of at least 50 miles per hour (22.4 m/s) for all elevations.

(f)(2) **Construction requirements** Bolted connections shall be self-locking or shall otherwise be secured to prevent loss of the connections by vibration.

(f)(3) **Suspension methods** Elevated building maintenance equipment shall be suspended by a carriage, outriggers, davits or an equivalent method.

(f)(3)(i) **Carriages** Carriages used for suspension of elevated building maintenance equipment shall comply with the following:

(f)(3)(i)(A) The horizontal movement of a carriage shall be controlled so as to ensure its safe movement and allow accurate positioning of the platform for vertical travel or storage;

(f)(3)(i)(B) Powered carriages shall not exceed a traversing speed of 50 feet per minute (0.3 m/s);

(f)(3)(i)(C) The initiation of a traversing movement for a manually propelled carriage on a smooth level surface shall not require a person to exert a horizontal force greater than 40 pounds (444.8 n);

(f)(3)(i)(D) Structural stops and curbs shall be provided to prevent the traversing of the carriage beyond its designed limits of travel;

(f)(3)(i)(E) Traversing controls for a powered carriage shall be of a continuous pressure weatherproof type. Multiple controls when provided shall be arranged to permit operation from only one control station at a time. An emergency stop device shall be provided on each end of a powered carriage for interrupting power to the carriage drive motors;

(f)(3)(i)(F) The operating controls(s) shall be so connected that in the case of suspended equipment, traversing of a carriage is not possible until the suspended portion of the equipment is located at its uppermost designed position for traversing; and is free of contact with the face of the building or building guides. In addition, all protective devices and interlocks are to be in the proper position to allow traversing of the carriage;

(f)(3)(i)(G) Stability for underfoot supported carriages shall be obtained by gravity, by an attachment to a structural support, or by a combination of gravity and a structural support. The use of flowing counterweights to achieve stability is prohibited.

(f)(3)(i)(G)(1) The stability factor against overturning shall not be less than two for horizontal traversing of the carriage, including the effects of impact and wind.

(f)(3)(i)(G)(2) The carriages and their anchorages shall be capable of resisting accidental over-tensioning of the wire ropes suspending the working platform, and this calculated value shall include the effect of one and one-half times the stall capacity of the hoist motor. All parts of the installation shall be capable of withstanding without damage to any part of the installation the forces resulting from the stall load of the hoist and one half the wind load.

(f)(3)(i)(G)(3) Roof carriages which rely on having tie-down devices secured to the building to develop the required stability against overturning shall be provided with an interlock which will prevent vertical platform movement unless the tie-down is engaged;

(f)(3)(i)(H) An automatically applied braking or locking system, or equivalent, shall be provided that will prevent unintentional traversing of power traversed or power assisted carriages;

(f)(3)(i)(I) A manual or automatic braking or locking system or equivalent, shall be provided that will prevent unintentional traversing of manually propelled carriages;

(f)(3)(i)(J) A means to lock out the power supply for the carriage shall be provided;

(f)(3)(i)(K) Safe access to and egress from the carriage shall be provided from a safe surface. If the carriage traverses an elevated area, any operating area on the carriage shall be protected by a guardrail system in compliance with the provisions of paragraph (f)(5)(i)(F) of this Section. Any access gate shall be self-closing and self-latching, or provided with an interlock;

(f)(3)(i)(L) Each carriage work station position shall be identified by location markings and/or position indicators; and

(f)(3)(i)(M) The motors shall stall if the load on the hoist motors is at any time in excess of three times that necessary for lifting the working platform with its rated load.

(f)(3)(ii) [OI] **Transportable outriggers**

(f)(3)(ii)(A) Transportable outriggers may be used as a method of suspension for ground rigged working platforms where the point of suspension does not exceed 300 feet (91.5 m) above a safe surface. Tie-in guide system(s) shall be provided which meet the requirements of paragraph (e)(2) of this Section.

(f)(3)(ii)(B) Transportable outriggers shall be used only with self-powered, ground rigged working platforms.

(f)(3)(ii)(C) Each transportable outrigger shall be secured with a tie-down to a verified anchorage on the building during the entire period of its use. The anchorage shall be designed to have a stability factor of not less than four against overturning or upsetting of the outrigger.

(f)(3)(ii)(D) Access to and egress from the working platform shall be from and to a safe surface below the point of suspension.

(f)(3)(ii)(E) Each transportable outrigger shall be designed for lateral stability to prevent roll-over in the event an accidental lateral load is applied to the outrigger. The accidental lateral load to be considered in this design shall be not less than 70 percent of the rated load of the hoist.

(f)(3)(ii)(F) Each transportable outrigger shall be designed to support an ultimate load of not less than four times the rated load of the hoist.

(f)(3)(ii)(G) Each transportable outrigger shall be so located that the suspension wire ropes for two point suspended working platforms are hung parallel.

(f)(3)(ii)(H) A transportable outrigger shall be tied-back to a verified anchorage on the building with a rope equivalent in strength to the suspension rope.

(f)(3)(ii)(I) The tie-back rope shall be installed parallel to the centerline of the outrigger.

(f)(3)(iii) **Davits**

(f)(3)(iii)(A) Every davit installation, fixed or transportable, rotatable or non-rotatable shall be designed and installed to insure that it has a stability factor against overturning of not less than four.

(f)(3)(iii)(B) The following requirements apply to roof rigged davit systems:

(f)(3)(iii)(B)(1) Access to and egress from the working platform shall be from a safe surface. Access or egress shall not require persons to climb over a building's parapet or guard railing; and

(f)(3)(iii)(B)(2) The working platform shall be provided with wheels, casters or a carriage for traversing horizontally.

(f)(3)(iii)(C) The following requirements apply to ground rigged davit systems:

(f)(3)(iii)(C)(1) The point of suspension shall not exceed 300 feet (91.5 m) above a safe surface. Guide system(s) shall be provided which meet the requirements of paragraph (e)(2) of this Section;

(f)(3)(iii)(C)(2) Access and egress to and from the working platform shall only be from a safe surface below the point of suspension.

(f)(3)(iii)(D) A rotating davit shall not require a horizontal force in excess of 40 pounds (177.9 n) per person to initiate a rotating movement.

(f)(3)(iii)(E) The following requirements shall apply to transportable davits:

(f)(3)(iii)(E)(1) A davit or part of a davit weighing more than 80 pounds (36 kg) shall be provided with a means for its transport, which shall keep the center of gravity of the davit at or below 36 inches (914 mm) above the safe surface during transport;

(f)(3)(iii)(E)(2) A davit shall be provided with a pivoting socket or with a base that will allow the insertion or removal of a davit at a position of not more than 35 degrees above the horizontal, with the complete davit inboard of the building face being serviced; and

(f)(3)(iii)(E)(3) Means shall be provided to lock the davit to its socket or base before it is used to suspend the platform.

(f)(4) **Hoisting machines**

(f)(4)(i) Raising and lowering of suspended or supported equipment shall be performed only by a hoisting machine.

(f)(4)(ii) Each hoisting machine shall be capable of arresting any overspeed descent of the load.

(f)(4)(iii) Each hoisting machine shall be powered only by air, electric or hydraulic sources.

(f)(4)(iv) Flammable liquids shall not be carried on the working platform.

(f)(4)(v) Each hoisting machine shall be capable of raising or lowering 125 percent of the rated load of the hoist.

(f)(4)(vi) Moving parts of a hoisting machine shall be enclosed or guarded in compliance with paragraphs (a)(1) and (2) of §1910.212 of this part.

(f)(4)(vii) Winding drums, traction drums and sheaves and directional sheaves used in conjunction with hoisting machines shall be compatible with, and sized for, the wire rope used.

(f)(4)(viii) Each winding drum shall be provided with a positive means of attaching the wire rope to the drum. The attachment shall be capable of developing at least four times the rated load of the hoist.

(f)(4)(ix) Each hoisting machine shall be provided with a primary brake and at least one independent secondary brake, each capable of stopping and holding not less than 125 percent of the lifting capacity of the hoist.

(f)(4)(ix)(A) The primary brake shall be directly connected to the drive train of the hoisting machine, and shall not be connected through belts, chains, clutches, or set screw type devices. The brake shall automatically set when power to the prime mover is interrupted.

(f)(4)(ix)(B)(1) The secondary brake shall be an automatic emergency type of brake that, if actuated during each stopping cycle, shall not engage before the hoist is stopped by the primary brake.

(f)(4)(ix)(B)(2) When a secondary brake is actuated, it shall stop and hold the platform within a vertical distance of 24 inches (609.6 mm).

(f)(4)(x) Any component of a hoisting machine which requires lubrication for its protection and proper functioning shall be provided with a means for that lubrication to be applied.

(f)(5) **Suspended equipment**

(f)(5)(i) **General requirements**

(f)(5)(i)(A) Each suspended unit component, except suspension ropes and guardrail systems, shall be capable of supporting, without failure, at least four times the maximum intended live load applied or transmitted to that component.

(f)(5)(i)(B) Each suspended unit component shall be constructed of materials that will withstand anticipated weather conditions.

(f)(5)(i)(C) Each suspended unit shall be provided with a load rating plate, conspicuously located, stating the unit weight and rated load of the suspended unit.

(f)(5)(i)(D) When the suspension points on a suspended unit are not at the unit ends, the unit shall be capable of remaining continuously stable under all conditions of use and position of the live load, and shall maintain at least a 1.5 to 1 stability factor against unit upset.

(f)(5)(i)(E) Guide rollers, guide shoes or building face rollers shall be provided, and shall compensate for variations in building dimensions and for minor horizontal out-of-level variations of each suspended unit.

(f)(5)(i)(F) Each working platform of a suspended unit shall be secured to the building facade by one or more of the following methods, or by an equivalent method:

(f)(5)(i)(F)(1) Continuous engagement to building anchors as provided in paragraph (e)(2)(i) of this Section;

(f)(5)(i)(F)(2) Intermittent engagement to building anchors as provided in paragraph (e)(2)(iii)(A) of this Section;

(f)(5)(i)(F)(3) Button guide engagement as provided in paragraph (e)(2)(iii)(B) of this Section; or

(f)(5)(i)(F)(4) Angulated roping and building face rollers as provided in paragraph (e)(2)(iii)(C) of this Section.

(f)(5)(i)(G) Each working platform of a suspended unit shall be provided with a guardrail system on all sides which shall meet the following requirements:

(f)(5)(i)(G)(1) The system shall consist of a top guardrail, midrail, and a toeboard;

(f)(5)(i)(G)(2) The top guardrail shall not be less than 36 inches (914 mm) high and shall be able to withstand at least a 100-pound (444 n) force in any downward or outward direction;

(f)(5)(i)(G)(3) The midrail shall be able to withstand at least a 75-pound (333 n) force in any downward or outward direction; and

(f)(5)(i)(G)(4) The areas between the guardrail and toeboard on the ends and outboard side, and the area between the midrail and toeboard on the inboard side, shall be closed with a material that is capable of withstanding a load of 100 pounds (45.4 KG.) applied horizontally over any area of one square foot (.09 m2). The material shall have all openings small enough to reject passage of life lines and potential falling objects which may be hazardous to persons below.

(f)(5)(i)(G)(5) Toeboards shall be capable of withstanding, without failure, a force of at least 50 pounds (222 n) applied in any downward or horizontal direction at any point along the toeboard.

(f)(5)(i)(G)(6) Toeboards shall be three and one-half inches (9 cm) minimum in length from their top edge to the level of the platform floor.

(f)(5)(i)(G)(7) Toeboards shall be securely fastened in place at the outermost edge of the platform and have no more than one-half inch (1.3 cm) clearance above the platform floor.

(f)(5)(i)(G)(8) Toeboards shall be solid or with an opening not over one inch (2.5 cm) in the greatest dimension.

(f)(5)(ii) **Two and four-point suspended working platforms**

(f)(5)(ii)(A) The working platform shall be not less than 24 inches (610 mm) wide and shall be provided with a minimum of a 12 inch (305 mm) wide passage at or past any obstruction on the platform.

(f)(5)(ii)(B) The flooring shall be of a slip-resistant type and shall contain no opening that would allow the passage of life lines, cables and other potential falling objects. If a larger opening is provided, it shall be protected by placing a material under the opening which shall prevent the passage of life lines, cables and potential falling objects.

(f)(5)(ii)(C) The working platfrom shall be provided with a means of suspension that will restrict the platform's inboard to outboard roll about its longitudinal axis to a maximum of 15 degrees from a horizontal plane when moving the live load from the inboard to the outboard side of the platform.

(f)(5)(ii)(D) Any cable suspended from above the platform shall be provided with a means for storage to prevent accumulation of the cable on the floor of the platform.

(f)(5)(ii)(E) All operating controls for the vertical travel of the platform shall be of the continuous-pressure type, and shall be located on the platform.

(f)(5)(ii)(F) Each operating station of every working platform shall be provided with a means of interrupting the power supply to all hoist motors to stop any further powered ascent or descent of the platform.

(f)(5)(ii)(G) The maximum rated speed of the platform shall not exceed 50 feet per minute (0.3 ms) with single speed hoists, nor 75 feet per minute (0.4 ms) with multi-speed hoists.

(f)(5)(ii)(H) Provisions shall be made for securing all tools, water tanks, and other accessories to prevent their movement or accumulation on the floor of the platform.

(f)(5)(ii)(I) Portable fire extinguishers conforming to the provisions of §1910.155 and §1910.157 of this part shall be provided and securely attached on all working platforms.

(f)(5)(ii)(J) Access to and egress from a working platfrom, except for those that land directly on a safe surface, shall be provided by stairs, ladders, platforms and runways conforming to the provisions of Subpart D of this part. Access gates shall be self-closing and self-latching.

(f)(5)(ii)(K) Means of access to or egress from a working platform which is 48 inches (1.2 m) or more above a safe surface shall be provided with a guardrail system or ladder handrails that conform to the provisions of Subpart D of this part.

(f)(5)(ii)(L) The platform shall be provided with a secondary wire rope suspension system if the platform contains overhead structures which restrict the emergency egress of employees. A horizontal lifeline or a direct connection anchorage shall be provided as part of a personal fall arrest system that meets the requirements of Subpart I of this Part for each employee on such a platform.

(f)(5)(ii)(M) A vertical lifeline shall be provided as part of a personal fall arrest system that meets the requirements of Subpart I of this Part for each employee on a working platform suspended by two or more wire ropes, if the failure of one wire rope or suspension attachment will cause the platform to upset. If a secondary wire rope suspension is used, vertical lifelines are not required for the personal fall arrest system, provided that each employee is attached to a horizontal lifeline anchored to the platform.

(f)(5)(ii)(N) An emergency electric operating device shall be provided on roof powered platforms near the hoisting machine for use in the event of failure of the normal operating device located on the working platform, or failure of the cable connected to the platform. The emergency electric operating device shall be mounted in a secured compartment, and the compartment shall be labeled with instructions for use. A means for opening the compartment shall be mounted in a break-glass receptable located near the emergency electric operating device or in an equivalent secure and accessible location.

(f)(5)(iii) **Single point suspended working platforms**

(f)(5)(iii)(A) The requirements of paragraphs (f)(5)(ii)(A) through (K) of this Section shall also apply to a single point working platform.

(f)(5)(iii)(B) Each single point suspended working platform shall be provided with a secondary wire rope suspension system which will prevent the working platform from falling should there be a failure of the primary means of support, or if the platform contains overhead structures which restrict the egress of the employees. A horizontal life line or a direct connection anchorage shall be provided as part of a personal fall arrest system that meets the requirements of Subpart I of this Part for each employee on the platform.

(f)(5)(iv) **Ground-rigged working platforms**

(f)(5)(iv)(A) Groundrigged working platforms shall comply with all the requirements of paragraphs (f)(5)(ii)(A) through (M) of this Section.

(f)(5)(iv)(B) After each day's use, the power supply within the building shall be disconnected from a ground-rigged working platform, and the platform shall be either disengaged from its suspension points or secured and stored at grade.

(f)(5)(v) **Intermittently stabilized platforms**

(f)(5)(v)(A) The platform shall comply with paragraphs (F)(5)(ii)(A) through (M) of this Section.

(f)(5)(v)(B) Each stabilizer tie shall be equipped with a "quick connect-quick disconnect" device which cannot be accidently disengaged, for attachment to the building anchor, and shall be resistant to adverse environmental conditions.

(f)(5)(v)(C) The platform shall be provided with a stopping device that will interrupt the hoist power supply in the event the platform contacts a stabilizer tie during its ascent.

(f)(5)(v)(D) Building face rollers shall not be placed at the anchor setting if exterior anchors are used on the building face.

(f)(5)(v)(E) Stabilizer ties used on intermittently stabilized platforms shall allow for the specific attachment length needed to effect the predetermined angulation of the suspended wire rope. The specific attachment length shall be maintained at all building anchor locations.

(f)(5)(v)(F) The platform shall be in continuous contact with the face of the building during ascent and descent.

(f)(5)(v)(G) The attachment and removal of stabilizer ties shall not require the horizontal movement of the platform.

(f)(5)(v)(H) The platform-mounted equipment and its suspension wire ropes shall not be physically damaged by the loads from the stabilizer tie or its building anchor. The platform, platform mounted equipment and wire ropes shall be able to withstand a load that is at least twice the ultimate strength of the stabilizer tie.

Note: See Figure II in Appendix B of this Section for a description of a typical intermittent stabilization system.

(f)(5)(vi) **Button-guide stabilized platforms**

(f)(5)(vi)(A) The platform shall comply with paragraphs (f)(5)(ii) (A) through (M) of this Section.

(f)(5)(vi)(B) Each guide track on the platform shall engage a minimum of two guide buttons during any vertical travel of the platform following the initial button engagement.

(f)(5)(vi)(C) Each guide track on a platform that is part of a roof rigged system shall be provided with a storage position on the platform.

(f)(5)(vi)(D) Each guide track on the platform shall be sufficiently maneuverable by platform occupants to permit easy engagement of the guide buttons, and easy movement into and out of its storage position on the platform.

(f)(5)(vi)(E) Two guide tracks shall be mounted on the platform and shall provide continuous contact with the building face.

(f)(5)(vi)(F) The load carrying components of the button guide stabilization system which transmit the load into the platform shall be capable of supporting the weight of the platform, or provision shall be made in the guide track connectors or platform attachments to prevent the weight of the platform from being transmitted to the platform attachments.

Note: See Figure III in Appendix B of this Section for a description of a typical button guide stabilization system.

(f)(6) **Supported equipment**

(f)(6)(i) Supported equipment shall maintain a vertical position in respect to the face of the building by means other than friction.

(f)(6)(ii) Cog wheels or equivalent means shall be incorporated to provide climbing traction between the supported equipment and the building guides. Additional guide wheels or shoes shall be incorporated as may be necessary to ensure that the drive wheels are continuously held in positive engagement with the building guides.

(f)(6)(iii) Launch guide mullions indexed to the building guides and retained in alignment with the building guides shall be used to align drive wheels entering the building guides.

(f)(6)(iv) Manned platforms used on supported equipment shall comply with the requirements of paragraphs (f)(5)(ii)(A), (f)(5)(ii)(B), and (f)(5)(ii)(D) through (K) of this Section covering suspended equipment.

(f)(7) **Suspension wire ropes and rope connections**

(f)(7)(i) Each specific installation shall use suspension wire ropes or combination cable and connections meeting the specification recommended by the manufacturer of the hoisting machine used. Connections shall be capable of developing at least 80 percent of the rated breaking strength of the wire rope.

(f)(7)(ii) Each suspension rope shall have a "Design Factor" of at least 10. The "Design Factor" is the ratio of the rated strength of the suspension wire rope to the rated working load, and shall be calculated using the following formula:

$$F = \frac{S(N)}{W}$$

Where:

F = Design factor

S = Manufacturer's rated strength of one suspension rope

N = Number of suspension ropes under load

W = Rated working load on all ropes at any point of travel

(f)(7)(iii) Suspension wire rope grade shall be at least improved plow steel or equivalent.

(f)(7)(iv) Suspension wire ropes shall be sized to conform with the required design factor, but shall not be less than $\frac{5}{16}$ inch (7.94 mm) in diameter.

(f)(7)(v) No more than one reverse bend in six wire rope lays shall be permitted.

(f)(7)(vi) A corrosiown-resistant tag shall be securely attached to one of the wire rope fastenings when a suspension wire rope is to be used at a specific location and will remain in that location. This tag shall bear the following wire rope data:

(f)(7)(vi)(A) The diameter (inches and/or mm);

(f)(7)(vi)(B) Construction classification;

(f)(7)(vi)(C) Whether non-preformed or preformed;

(f)(7)(vi)(D) The grade of material;

(f)(7)(vi)(E) The manufacturer's rated strength;

(f)(7)(vi)(F) The manufacturer's name;

(f)(7)(vi)(G) The month and year the ropes were installed; and

(f)(7)(vi)(H) The name of the person or company which installed the ropes.

(f)(7)(vii) A new tag shall be installed at each rope renewal.

(f)(7)(viii) The original tag shall be stamped with the date of the resocketing, or the original tag shall be retained and a supplemental tag shall be provided when ropes are resocketed. The supplemental tag shall show the date of resocketing and the name of the person or company that resocketed the rope.

(f)(7)(ix) Winding drum type hoists shall contain at least three wraps of the suspension wire rope on the drum when the suspended unit has reached the lowest possible point of its vertical travel.

(f)(7)(x) Traction drum and sheave type hoists shall be provided with a wire rope of sufficient length to reach the lowest possible point of vertical travel of the suspended unit, and an additional length of the wire rope of at least four feet (1.2 m).

(f)(7)(xi) The lengthening or repairing of suspension wire ropes is prohibited.

(f)(7)(xii) Babbitted fastenings for suspension wire rope are prohibited.

(f)(8) **Control circuits, power circuits and their components**

(f)(8)(i) Electrical wiring and equipment shall comply with Subpart S of this part, except as otherwise required by this Section.

(f)(8)(ii) Electrical runway conductor systems shall be of a type designed for use in exterior locations, and shall be located so that they do not come into contact with accumulated snow or water.

(f)(8)(iii) Cables shall be protected against damage resulting from overtensioning or from other causes.

(f)(8)(iv) Devices shall be included in the control system for the equipment which will provide protection against electrical overloads, three phase reversal and phase failure. The control system shall have a separate method, independent of the direction control circuit, for breaking the power circuit in case of an emergency or malfunction.

(f)(8)(v) Suspended or supported equipment shall have a control system which will require the operator of the equipment to follow predetermined procedures.

(f)(8)(vi) The following requirements shall apply to electrical protection devices:

(f)(8)(vi)(A) On installations where the carriage does not have a stability factor of at least four against overturning, electrical contact(s) shall be provided and so connected that the operating devices for the suspended or supported equipment shall be operative only when the carriage is located and mechanically retained at an established operating point;

(f)(8)(vi)(B) Overload protection shall be provided in the hoisting or suspension system to protect against the equipment operating in the "up" direction with a load in excess of 125 percent of the rated load of the platform; and

(f)(8)(vi)(C) An automatic detector shall be provided for each suspension point that will interrupt power to all hoisting motors for travel in the "down" direction, and apply the primary brakes if any suspension wire rope becomes slack. A continuous-pressure rigging-bypass switch designed for use during rigging is permitted. This switch shall only be used during rigging.

(f)(8)(vii) Upper and lower directional switches designed to prevent the travel of suspended units beyond safe upward and downward levels shall be provided.

(f)(8)(viii) Emergency stop switches shall be provided on remote controlled, roof-powered manned platforms adjacent to each control station on the platform.

(f)(8)(ix) Cables which are in constant tension shall have overload devices which will prevent the tension in the cable from interfering with the load limiting device required in paragraph (f)(8)(vi)(B) of this Section, or with the platform roll limiting device required in paragraph (f)(5)(ii)(C) of this Section. The setting of these devices shall be coordinated with other overload settings at the time of design of the system, and shall be clearly indicated on or near the device. The device shall interrupt the equipment travel in the "down" direction.

(g) **Inspection and tests**

(g)(1) **Installations and alterations** All completed building maintenance equipment installations shall be inspected and tested in the field before being placed in initial service to determine that all parts of the installation conform to applicable requirements of this standard, and that all safety and operating equipment is functioning as required. A similar inspection and test shall be made following any major alteration to an existing installation. No hoist in an installation shall be subjected to a load in excess of 125 percent of its rated load.

(g)(2) **Periodic inspections and tests**

(g)(2)(i) Related building supporting structures shall undergo periodic inspection by a competent person at intervals not exceeding 12 months.

(g)(2)(ii) All parts of the equipment including control systems shall be inspected, and, where necessary, tested by a competent person at intervals specified by the manufacturer/supplier, but not to exceed 12 months, to determine that they are in safe operating condition. Parts subject to wear, such as wire ropes, bearings, gears, and governors shall be inspected and/or tested to determine that they have not worn to such an extent as to affect the safe operation of the installation.

(g)(2)(iii) The building owner shall keep a certification record of each inspection and test required under paragraphs (g)(2)(i) and (ii) of this Section. The certification record shall include the date of the inspection, the signature of the person who performed the inspection, and the number, or other identifier, of the building support structure and equipment which was inspected. This certification record shall be kept readily available for review by the Assistant Secretary of Labor or the Assistant Secretary's representative and by the employer.

(g)(2)(iv) Working platforms and their components shall be inspected by the employer for visible defects before every use and after each occurrence which could affect the platform's structural integrity.

(g)(3) **Maintenance inspections and tests**

(g)(3)(i) A maintenance inspection and, where necessary, a test shall be made of each platform installation every 30 days, or where the work cycle is less than 30 days such inspection and/or test shall be made prior to each work cycle. This inspection and test shall follow procedures recommended by the manufacturer, and shall be made by a competent person.

(g)(3)(ii) The building owner shall keep a certification record of each inspection and test performed under paragraph (g)(3)(i) of this Section. The certification record shall include the date of the inspection and test, the signature of the person who performed the inspection and/or test, and an identifier for the platform installation which was inspected. The certification record shall be kept readily available for review by the Assistant Secretary of Labor or the Assistant Secretary's representative and by the employer.

(g)(4) **Special inspection of governors and secondary brakes**

(g)(4)(i) Governors and secondary brakes shall be inspected and tested at intervals specified by the manufacturer/supplier but not to exceed every 12 months.

(g)(4)(ii) The results of the inspection and test shall confirm that the initiating device for the secondary braking system operates at the proper overspeed.

(g)(4)(iii) The results of the inspection and test shall confirm that the secondary brake is functioning properly.

(g)(4)(iv) If any hoisting machine or initiating device for the secondary brake system is removed from the equipment for testing, all reinstalled and directly related components shall be reinspected prior to returning the equipment installation to service.

(g)(4)(v) Inspection of governors and secondary brakes shall be performed by a competent person.

(g)(4)(vi) The secondary brake governor and actuation device shall be tested before each day's use. Where testing is not feasible, a visual inspection of the brake shall be made instead to ensure that it is free to operate.

(g)(5) **Suspension wire rope maintenance, inspection and replacement**

(g)(5)(i) Suspension wire rope shall be maintained and used in accordance with procedures recommended by the wire rope manufacturer.

(g)(5)(ii) Suspension wire rope shall be inspected by a competent person for visible defects and gross damage to the rope before every use and after each occurrence which might affect the wire rope's integrity.

(g)(5)(iii) A thorough inspection of suspension wire ropes in service shall be made once a month. Suspension wire ropes that have been inactive for 30 days or longer shall have a thorough inspection before they are placed into service. These thorough inspections of suspension wire ropes shall be performed by a competent person.

(g)(5)(iv) The need for replacement of a suspension wire rope shall be determined by inspection and shall be based on the condition of the wire rope. Any of the following conditions or combination of conditions will be cause for removal of the wire rope:

(g)(5)(iv)(A) Broken wires exceeding three wires in one strand or six wires in one rope lay;

(g)(5)(iv)(B) Distortion of rope structure such as would result from crushing or kinking;

(g)(5)(iv)(C) Evidence of heat damage;

(g)(5)(iv)(D) Evidence of rope deterioration from corrosion;

(g)(5)(iv)(E) A broken wire within 18 inches (460.8 mm) of the end attachments;

(g)(5)(iv)(F) Noticeable rusting and pitting;

(g)(5)(iv)(G) Evidence of core failure (a lengthening of rope lay, protrusion of the rope core and a reduction in rope diameter suggests core failure); or

(g)(5)(iv)(H) More than one valley break (broken wire);

(g)(5)(iv)(I) Outer wire wear exceeds one-third of the original outer wire diameter; and

(g)(5)(iv)(J) Any other condition which the competent person determines has significantly affected the integrity of the rope.

(g)(5)(v) The building owner shall keep a certification record of each monthly inspection of a suspension wire rope as required in paragraph (g)(5)(iii) of this Section. The record shall include the date of the inspection, the signature of the person who performed the inspection, and a number, or other identifier, of the wire rope which was inspected. This record of inspection shall be made available for review by the Assistant Secretary of Labor or the Assistant Secretary's representative and by the employer.

(g)(6) **Hoist inspection** Before lowering personnel below the top elevation of the building, the hoist shall be tested each day in the lifting direction with the intended load to make certain it has sufficient capacity to raise the personnel back to the boarding level.

(h) **Maintenance**

(h)(1) **General maintenance** All parts of the equipment affecting safe operation shall be maintained in proper working order so that they may perform the functions for which they were intended. The equipment shall be taken out of service when it is not in proper working order.

(h)(2) **Cleaning**

(h)(2)(i) Control or power contactors and relays shall be kept clean.

(h)(2)(ii) All other parts shall be kept clean if their proper functioning would be affected by the presence of dirt or other contaminants.

(h)(3) **Periodic resocketing of wire rope fastenings**

(h)(3)(i) Hoisting ropes utilizing poured socket fastenings shall be resocketed at the non-drum ends at intervals not exceeding 24 months. In resocketing the ropes, a sufficient length shall be cut from the end of the rope to remove damaged or fatigued portions.

(h)(3)(ii) Resocketed ropes shall conform to the requirements of paragraph (f)(7) of this Section.

(h)(3)(iii) Limit switches affected by the resocketed ropes shall be reset, if necessary.

(h)(4) **Periodic reshackling of suspension wire ropes** The hoisting ropes shall be reshackled at the nondrum ends at intervals not exceeding 24 months. When reshackling the ropes, a sufficient length shall be cut from the end of the rope to remove damaged or fatigued portions.

(h)(5) **Roof systems** Roof track systems, tie-downs, or similar equipment shall be maintained in proper working order so that they perform the function for which they were intended.

(h)(6) **Building face guiding members** T-rails, indented mullions, or equivalent guides located in the face of a building shall be maintained in proper working order so that they perform the functions for which they were intended. Brackets for cable stabilizers shall similarly be maintained in proper working order.

(h)(7) **Inoperative safety devices** No person shall render a required safety device or electrical protective device inoperative, except as necessary for tests, inspections, and maintenance. Immediately upon completion of such tests, inspections and maintenance, the device shall be restored to its normal operating condition.

(i) **Operations**

(i)(1) **Training**

(i)(1)(i) Working platforms shall be operated only by persons who are proficient in the operation, safe use and inspection of the particular working platform to be operated.

(i)(1)(ii) All employees who operate working platforms shall be trained in the following:

(i)(1)(ii)(A) Recognition of, and preventive measures for, the safety hazards associated with their individual work tasks;

(i)(1)(ii)(B) General recognition and prevention of safety hazards associated with the use of working platforms, including the provisions in the Section relating to the particular working platform to be operated;

(i)(1)(ii)(C) Emergency action plan procedures required in paragraph (e)(9) of this Section;

(i)(1)(ii)(D) Work procedures required in paragraph (i)(1)(iv) of this Section; and

(i)(1)(ii)(E) Personal fall arrest system inspection, care, use and system performance.

(i)(1)(iii) Training of employees in the operation and inspection of working platforms shall be done by a competent person.

(i)(1)(iv) Written work procedures for the operation, safe use and inspection of working platforms shall be provided for employee training. Pictorial methods of instruction, may be used, in lieu of written work procedures, if employee communication is improved using this method. The operating manuals supplied by manufacturers for platform system components can serve as the basis for these procedures.

(i)(1)(v) The employer shall certify that employees have been trained in operating and inspecting a working platform by preparing a certification record which includes the identity of the person trained, the signature of the employer or the person who conducted the training and the date that training was completed. The certification record shall be prepared at the completion of the training required in paragraph (i)(1)(ii) of this Section, and shall be maintained in a file for the duration of the employee's employment. The certification record shall be kept readily available for review by the Assistant Secretary of Labor or the Assistant Secretary's representative.

(i)(2) **Use**

(i)(2)(i) Working platforms shall not be loaded in excess of the rated load, as stated on the platform load rating plate.

(i)(2)(ii) Employees shall be prohibited from working on snow, ice, or other slippery material covering platforms, except for the removal of such materials.

(i)(2)(iii) Adequate precautions shall be taken to protect the platform, wire ropes and life lines from damage due to acids or other corrosive substances, in accordance with the recommendations of the corrosive substance producer, supplier, platform manufacturer or other equivalent information sources. Platform members which have been exposed to acids or other corrosive substances shall be washed down with a neutralizing solution, at a frequency recommended by the corrosive substance producer or supplier.

(i)(2)(iv) Platform members, wire ropes and life lines shall be protected when using a heat producing process. Wire ropes and life lines which have been contacted by the heat producing process shall be considered to be permanently damaged and shall not be used.

(i)(2)(v) The platform shall not be operated in winds in excess of 25 miles per hour (40.2 km/hr) except to move it from an operating to a storage position. Wind speed shall be determined based on the best available information, which includes on-site anemometer readings and local weather forecasts which predict wind velocities for the area.

(i)(2)(vi) On exterior installations, an anemometer shall be mounted on the platform to provide information of on-site wind velocities prior to and during the use of the platform. The anemometer may be a portable (hand held) unit which is temporarily mounted during platform use.

(i)(2)(vii) Tools, materials and debris not related to the work in progress shall not be allowed to accumulate on platforms. Stabilizer ties shall be located so as to allow unencumbered passage along the full length of the platform and shall be of such length so as not to become entangled in rollers, hoists or other machinery.

(j) **Personal fall protection** Employees on working platforms shall be protected by a personal fall arrest system meeting the requirements of Subpart I of this Part and as otherwise provided by this Standard.

§1910.66 Appendix A Guidelines (Advisory)

1. Use of the Appendix Appendix A provides examples of equipment and methods to assist the employer in meeting the requirements of the indicated provision of the standard. Employers may use other equipment or procedures which conform to the requirements of the standard. This Appendix neither adds to nor detracts from the mandatory requirements set forth in §1910.66.

2. Assurance Paragraph (c) of the standard requires the building owner to inform the employer in writing that the powered platform installation complies with certain requirements of the standard, since the employer may not have the necessary information to make these determinations. The employer, however, remains responsible for meeting these requirements which have not been set off in paragraph (c)(1).

3. Design Requirements The design requirements for each installation should be based on the limitations (stresses, deflections, etc.), established by nationally recognized standards as promulgated by the following organizations, or to equivalent standards:

- AA—The Aluminum Association, 818 Connecticut Avenue, NW., Washington, DC, 20006
- Aluminum Construction Manual
- Specifications For Aluminum Structures
- Aluminum Standards and Data
- AGMA—American Gear Manufacturers Association, 101 North Fort Meyer Dr., Suite 1000, Arlington, VA 22209
- AISC—American Institute of Steel Construction, 400 North Michigan Avenue, Chicago, IL 60611
- ANSI—American National Standards Institute, Inc., 1430 Broadway, New York, NY 10018
- ASCE—American Society of Civil Engineers, 345 East 47th Street, New York, NY 10017
- ASME—American Society of Mechanical Engineers, 345 East 47th Street, New York, NY 10017
- ASTM—American Society for Testing and Materials, 1916 Race Street, Philadelphia, PA 19103
- AWS—American Welding Society, Inc., Box 351040, 550 NW. LeJeunne Road, Miami, FL 33126
- JIC—Joint Industrial Council, 2139 Wisconsin Avenue NW., Washington, DC 20007
- NEMA—National Electric Manufacturers Association, 2101 L Street, NW., Washington, DC 20037

4. Tie-in-guides Indented mullions T-rails or other equivalent guides are acceptable as tie-in guides in a building face for a continuous stabilization system. Internal guides are embedded in other building members with only the opening exposed (see Figure 1 of Appendix B). External guides, however, are installed external to the other building members and so are fully exposed. The minimum opening for tie-in guides is three-quarters of an inch (19 mm), and the minimum inside dimensions are one-inch (25 mm) deep and two inches (50 mm) wide.

Employers should be aware of the hazards associated with tie-in guides in a continuous stabilization system which was not designed properly. For example, joints in these track systems may become extended or discontinuous due to installation or building settlement. If this alignment problem is not corrected, the system could jam when a guide roller or guide shoe strikes a joint and this would cause a hazardous situation for employees. In another instance, faulty design will result in guide rollers being mounted in a line so they will jam in the track at the slightest misalignment.

5. Building anchors (intermittent stabilization system) In the selection of the vertical distance between building anchors, certain factors should be given consideration. These factors include building height and architectural design, platform length and weight, wire rope angulation, and the wind velocities in the building area. Another factor to consider is the material of the building face, since this material may be adversely affected by the building rollers.

External or indented type building anchors are acceptable. Receptacles in the building facade used for the indented type should be kept clear of extraneous materials which will hinder their use. During the inspection of the platform installation, evidence of a failure or abuse of the anchors should be brought to the attention of the employer.

6. Stabilizer tie length A stabilizer tie should be long enough to provide for the planned angulation of the suspension cables. However, the length of the tie should not be excessive and become a problem by possibly becoming entangled in the building face rollers or parts of the platform machinery.

The attachment length may vary due to material elongation and this should be considered when selecting the material to be used. Consideration should also be given to the use of ties which are easily installed by employees, since this will encourage their use.

7. Intermittent stabilization system Intermittent stabilization systems may use different equipment, tie-in devices and methods to restrict the horizontal movement of a powered platform with respect to the face of the building. One acceptable method employs corrosion-resistant building anchors secured in the face of the building in vertical rows every third floor or 50 feet (15.3 m), whichever is less. The anchors are spaced horizontally to allow a stabilization attachment (stabilizer tie) for each of the two platform suspension wire ropes. The stabilizer tie consists of two parts. One part is a quick connect-quick disconnect device which utilizes a corrosion-resistant yoke and retainer spring that is designed to fit over the building anchors. The second part of the stabilizer tie is a lanyard which is used to maintain a fixed distance between the suspension wire rope and the face of the building.

In this method, as the suspended powered platform descends past the elevation of each anchor, the descent is halted and each of the platform occupants secures a stabilizer tie between a suspension wire rope and a building anchor. The procedure is repeated as each elevation of a building anchor is reached during the descent of the powered platform.

As the platform ascends, the procedure is reversed; that is, the stabilizer ties are removed as each elevation of a building anchor is reached. The removal of each stabilizer tie is assured since the platform is provided with stopping devices which will interrupt power to its hoist(s) in the event either stopping device contacts a stabilizer during the ascent of the platform.

Figure 2 of Appendix B illustrates another type of acceptable intermittent stabilization system which utilizes retaining pins as the quick connect-quick disconnect device in the stabilizer tie.

8. Wire Rope Inspection The inspection of the suspension wire rope is important since the rope gradually loses strength during its useful life. The purpose of the inspection is to determine whether the wire rope has sufficient integrity to support a platform with the required design factor.

If there is any doubt concerning the condition of a wire rope or its ability to perform the required work, the rope should be replaced. The cost of wire rope replacement is quite small if compared to the cost in terms of human injuries, equipment down time and replacement.

No listing of critical inspection factors, which serve as a basis for wire rope replacement in the standard, can be a substitute for an experienced inspector of wire rope. The listing serves as a user's guide to the accepted standards by which ropes must be judged.

Rope life can be prolonged if preventive maintenance is performed regularly. Cutting off an appropriate length of rope at the end termination before the core degrades and valley breaks appear minimizes degradation at these sections.

9. General Maintenance In meeting the general maintenance requirement in paragraph (h)(1) of the standard, the employer should undertake the prompt replacement of broken, worn and damaged parts, switch contacts, brushes, and short flexible conductors of electrical devices. The components of the electrical service system and traveling cables should be replaced when damaged or significantly abraded. In addition, gears, shafts, bearings, brakes and hoisting drums should be kept in proper alignment.

10. Training In meeting the training requirement of paragraph (i)(1) of the standard, employers should use both on the job training and formal classroom training. The written work procedures used for this training should be obtained from the manufacturer, if possible, or prepared as necessary for the employee's information and use.

Employees who will operate powered platforms with intermittent stabilization systems should receive instruction in the specific ascent and descent procedures involving the assembly and disassembly of the stabilizer ties.

An acceptable training program should also include employee instruction in basic inspection procedures for the purpose of determining the need for repair and replacement of platform equipment. In addition, the program should cover the inspection, care and use of the personal fall protection equipment required in paragraph (j)(1) of the standard.

In addition, the training program should also include emergency action plan elements. OSHA brochure #1B3088 (Rev.) 1985, "How to Prepare for Workplace Emergencies," details the basic steps needed to prepare to handle emergencies in the workplace.

Following the completion of a training program, the employee should be required to demonstrate competency in operating the equipment safely. Supplemental training of the employee should be provided by the employer, as necessary, if the equipment used or other working conditions should change.

An employee who is required to work with chemical products on a platform should receive training in proper cleaning procedures, and in the hazards, care and handling of these products. In addition, the employee should be supplied with the appropriate personal protective equipment, such as gloves and eye and face protection.

11. Suspension and Securing of Powered Platforms (Equivalency) One acceptable method of demonstrating the equivalency of a method of suspending or securing a powered platform, as required in paragraphs (e)(2)(iii), (f)(3) and (f)(5)(i)(F), is to provide an engineering analysis by a registered professional engineer. The analysis should demonstrate that the proposed method will provide an equal or greater degree of safety for employees than any one of the methods specified in the standard.

§1910.66 Appendix B Exhibits (Advisory)

The three drawings in Appendix B illustrate typical platform stabilization systems which are addressed in the standard. The drawings are to be used for reference purposes only, and do not illustrate all the mandatory requirements for each system.

Figure 1. Typical Self-Powered Platform--Continuous External or Indented Mullion Guide System

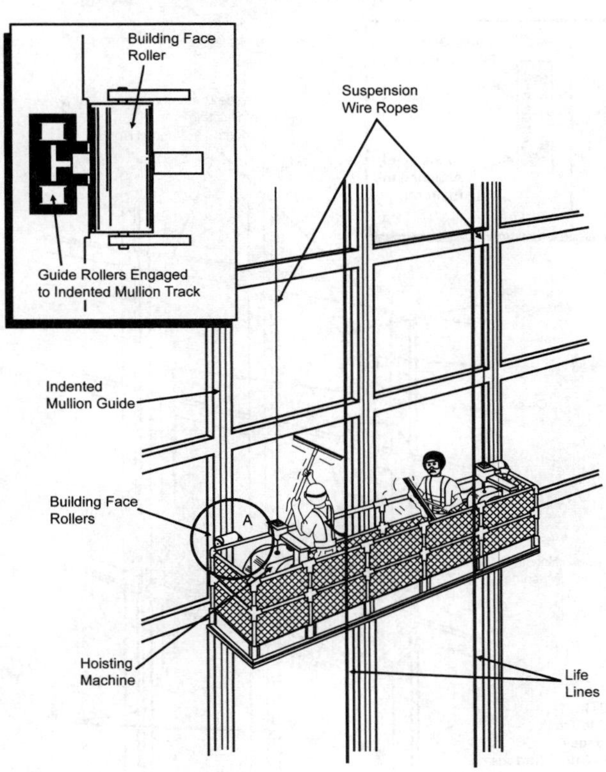

Figure 2. Typical Self-Powered Platform--Intermittent Tie-In System

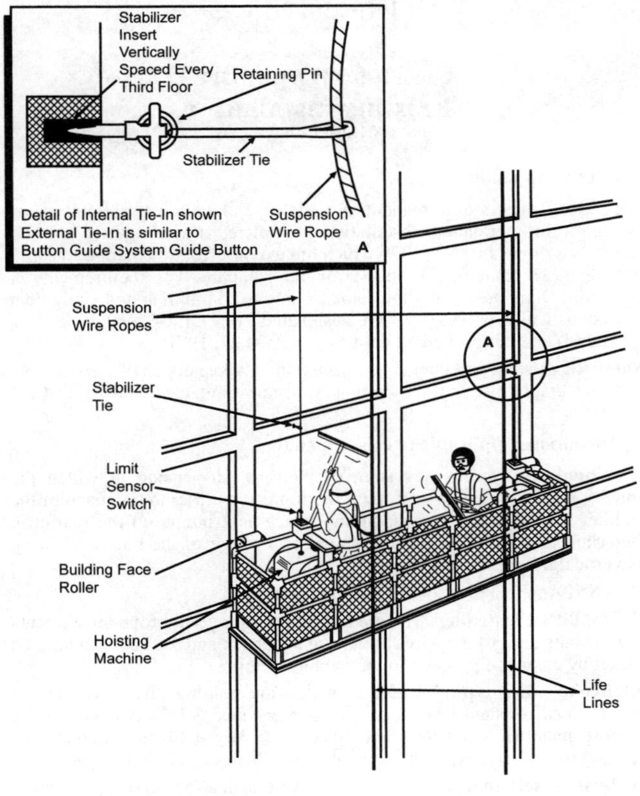

Figure 3. Typical Self-Powered Platform-- Button Guide System

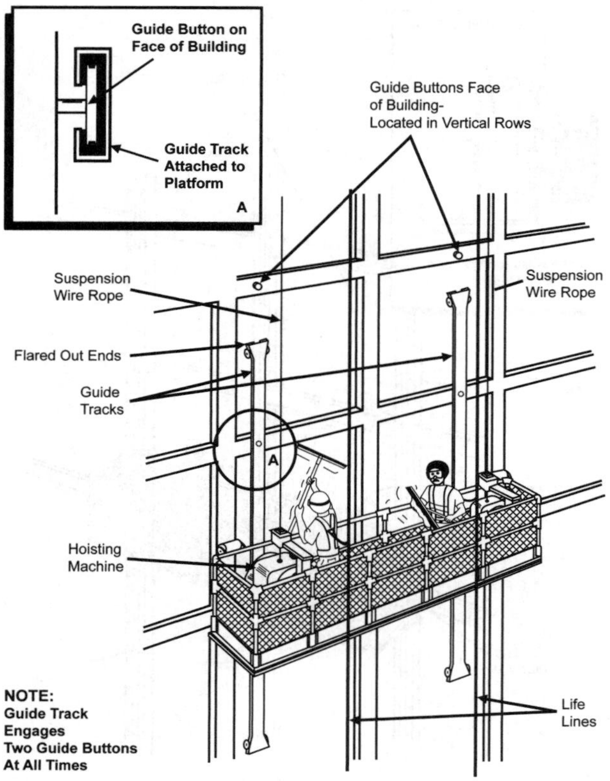

§1910.66 Appendix C [Reserved]

§1910.66 Appendix D Existing installations
(Mandatory)

Use of the Appendix

Appendix D sets out the mandatory building and equipment requirements for applicable permanent installations completed after August 27, 1971, and no later than July 23, 1990 which are exempt from the paragraphs (a), (b)(1), (b)(2), (c), (d), (e), and (f) of this standard. The requirements in Appendix D are essentially the same as unrevised building and equipment provisions which previously were designated as 29 CFR §1910.66 (a), (b), (c) and (d) and which were effective on August 27, 1971.

Note: All existing installations subject to this Appendix shall also comply with paragraphs (g), (h), (i), (j) and Appendix C of the standard 29 CFR §1910.66.

(a) Definitions applicable to this Appendix

(1) **Angulated roping** A system of platform suspension in which the upper wire rope sheaves or suspension points are closer to the plane of the building face than the corresponding attachment points on the platform, thus causing the platform to press against the face of the building during its vertical travel.

(2) **ANSI** American National Standards Institute.

(3) **Babbitted fastenings** The method of providing wire rope attachments in which the ends of the wire strands are bent back and are held in a tapered socket by means of poured molten babbitt metal.

(4) **Brake—disc type** A brake in which the holding effect is obtained by frictional resistance between one or more faces of discs keyed to the rotating member to be held and fixed discs keyed to the stationary or housing member (pressure between the discs being applied axially).

(5) **Brake—self-energizing band type** An essentially undirectional brake in which the holding effect is obtained by the snubbing action of a flexible band wrapped about a cylindrical wheel or drum affixed to the rotating member to be held, the connections and linkages being so arranged that the motion of the brake wheel or drum will act to increase the tension or holding force of the band.

(6) **Brake—shoe type** A brake in which the holding effect is obtained by applying the direct pressure of two or more segmental friction elements held to a stationary member against a cylindrical wheel or drum affixed to the rotating member to be held.

(7) **Building face rollers** A specialized form of guide roller designed to contact a portion of the outer face or wall structure of the building, and to assist in stabilizing the operators' platform during vertical travel.

(8) **Continuous pressure** Operation by means of buttons or switches, any one of which may be used to control the movement of the working platform or roof car, only as long as the button or switch is manually maintained in the actuating position.

(9) **Control** A system governing starting, stopping, direction, acceleration, speed, and retardation of moving members.

(10) **Controller** A device or group of devices, usually contained in a single enclosure, which serves to control in some predetermined manner the apparatus to which it is connected.

(11) **Electrical ground** A conducting connection between an electrical circuit or equipment and the earth, or some conducting body which serves in place of the earth.

(12) **Guide roller** A rotating, bearing-mounted, generally cylindrical member, operating separately or as part of a guide shoe assembly, attached to the platform, and providing rolling contact with building guideways, or other building contact members.

(13) **Guide shoe** An assembly of rollers, slide members, or the equivalent, attached as a unit to the operators' platform, and designed to engage with the building members provided for the vertical guidance of the operators' platform.

(14) **Interlock** A device actuated by the operation of some other device with which it is directly associated, to govern succeeding operations of the same or allied devices.

(15) **Operating device** A pushbutton, lever, or other manual device used to actuate a control.

(16) **Powered platform** Equipment to provide access to the exterior of a building for maintenance, consisting of a suspended power-operated working platform, a roof car, or other suspension means, and the requisite operating and control devices.

(17) **Rated load** The combined weight of employees, tools, equipment, and other material which the working platform is designed and installed to lift.

(18) **Relay, direction** An electrically energized contactor responsive to an initiating control circuit, which in turn causes a moving member to travel in a particular direction.

(19) **Relay, potential for vertical travel** An electrically energized contactor responsive to initiating control circuit, which in turn controls the operation of a moving member in both directions. This relay usually operates in conjunction with direction relays, as covered under the definition, "relay, direction."

(20) **Roof car** A structure for the suspension of a working platform, providing for its horizontal movement to working positions.

(21) **Roof-powered platform** A powered platform having the raising and lowering mechanism located on a roof car.

(22) **Self-powered platform** A powered platform having the raising and lowering mechanism located on the working platform.

(23) **Traveling cable** A cable made up of electrical or communication conductors or both, and providing electrical connection between the working platform and the roof car or other fixed point.

(24) **Weatherproof** Equipment so constructed or protected that exposure to the weather will not interfere with its proper operation.

(25) **Working platform** The suspended structure arranged for vertical travel which provides access to the exterior of the building or structure.

(26) **Yield point** The stress at which the material exhibits a permanent set of 0.2 percent.

(27) **Zinced fastenings** The method of providing wire rope attachments in which the splayed or fanned wire ends are held in a tapered socket by means of poured molten zinc.

(b) General requirements

(1) Design requirements All powered platform installations for exterior building maintenance completed as of August 27, 1971, but no later than [insert date, 180 days after the effective date], shall meet all of the design, construction and installation requirements of part II and III of the "American National Standard Safety Requirements for Powered Platforms for Exterior Building Maintenance ANSI A120.1–1970" and of this Appendix. References shall be made to appropriate parts of ANSI A120.1–1970 for detail specifications for equipment and special installations.

(2) Limitation The requirements of this Appendix apply only to electric powered platforms. It is not the intent of this Appendix to prohibit the use of other types of power. Installation of powered platforms using other types of power is permitted, provided such platforms have adequate protective devices for the type of power used, and otherwise provide for reasonable safety of life and limb to users of equipment and to others who may be exposed.

OI indicates an OSHA Letter of Interpretation exists for this specific reference. Please see www.oshainterpretation.us for details.

(3) Types of powered platforms

(i) For the purpose of applying this Appendix, powered platforms are divided into two basic types, Type F and Type T.

(ii) Powered platforms designated as Type F shall meet all the requirements in part II of ANSI A 120.1–1970, American National Standard Safety Requirements for Powered Platforms for Exterior Building Maintenance. A basic requirement of Type F equipment is that the work platform is suspended by at least four wire ropes and designed so that failure of any one wire rope will not substantially alter the normal position of the working platform. Another basic requirement of Type F equipment is that only one layer of hoisting rope is permitted on winding drums. Type F powered platforms may be either roof-powered or self-powered.

(iii)Powered platforms designated as Type T shall meet all the requirements in part III of ANSI A120.1–1970 American National Standard Safety Requirements for Powered Platforms for Exterior Building Maintenance, except for section 28, Safety Belts and Life Lines. A basic requirement of Type T equipment is that the working platform is suspended by at least two wire ropes. Failure of one wire rope would not permit the working platform to fall to the ground, but would upset its normal position. Type T powered platforms may be either roof-powered or self-powered.

(iv)The requirements of this section apply to powered platforms with winding drum type hoisting machines. It is not the intent of this section to prohibit powered platforms using other types of hoisting machines such as, but not limited to, traction drum hoisting machines, air powered machines, hydraulic powered machines, and internal combustion machines. Installation of powered platforms with other types of hoisting machines is permitted, provided adequate protective devices are used, and provided reasonable safety of life and limb to users of the equipment and to others who may be exposed is assured.

(v) Both Type F and Type T powered platforms shall comply with the requirements of Appendix C of this standard.

(c) Type F powered platforms

(1) Roof car, general

(i) A roof car shall be provided whenever it is necessary to move the working platform horizontally to working or storage positions.

(ii) The maximum rated speed at which a power traversed roof car may be moved in a horizontal direction shall be 50 feet per minute.

(2) Movement and positioning of roof car

(i) Provision shall be made to protect against having the roof car leave the roof or enter roof areas not designed for travel.

(ii) The horizontal motion of the roof cars shall be positively controlled so as to insure proper movement and positioning of the roof car.

(iii) Roof car positioning devices shall be provided to insure that the working platform is placed and retained in proper position for vertical travel and during storage.

(iv) Mechanical stops shall be provided to prevent the traversing of the roof car beyond its normal limits of travel. Such stops shall be capable of withstanding a force equal to 100 percent of the inertial effect of the roof car in motion with traversing power applied.

(v)(a) The operating device of a power-operated roof car for traversing shall be located on the roof car, the working platform, or both, and shall be of the continuous pressure weather-proof electric type. If more than one operating device is provided, they shall be so arranged that traversing is possible only from one operating device at a time.

(b) The operating device shall be so connected that it is not operable until:

(1) The working platform is located at its uppermost position of travel and is not in contact with the building face or fixed vertical guides in the face of the building; and

(2) All protective devices and interlocks are in a position for traversing.

(3) Roof car stability Roof car stability shall be determined by either paragraph (c)(3)(i) or (ii) of this Appendix, whichever is greater.

(i) The roof car shall be continuously stable, considering overturning moment as determined by 125 percent rated load, plus maximum dead load and the prescribed wind loading.

(ii) The roof car and its anchorages shall be capable of resisting accidental over-tensioning of the wire ropes suspending the working platform and this calculated value shall include the effect of one and one-half times the value. For this calculation, the simultaneous effect of one-half wind load shall be included, and the design stresses shall not exceed those referred to in paragraph (b)(1) of this Appendix.

(iii) If the load on the motors is at any time in excess of three times that required for lifting the working platform with its rated load the motor shall stall.

(4) Access to the roof car Safe access to the roof car and from the roof car to the working platform shall be provided. If the access to the roof car at any point of its travel is not over the roof area or where otherwise necessary for safety, then self-closing, self-locking gates shall be provided. Access to and from roof cars must comply with the requirements of Subpart D of this Part.

(5) Means for maintenance, repair, and storage Means shall be provided to run the roof car away from the roof perimeter, where necessary, and to provide a safe area for maintenance, repairs, and storage. Provisions shall be made to secure the machine in the stored position. For stored machines subject to wind forces, see special design and anchorage requirements for "wind forces" in part II, section 10.5.1.1 of ANSI A120.1–1970 American National Standard Safety Requirements for Powered Platforms for Exterior Building Maintenance.

(6) General requirements for working platforms The working platform shall be of girder or truss construction and shall be adequate to support its rated load under any position of loading, and comply with the provisions set forth in section 10 of ANSI A120.1–1970, American National Standard Safety Requirements for Powered Platforms for Exterior Building Maintenance.

(7) Load rating plate Each working platform shall bear a manufacturer's load rating plate, conspicuously posted; stating the maximum permissible rated load. Load rating plates shall be made of noncorrosive material and shall have letters and figures stamped, etched, or cast on the surface. The minimum height of the letters and figures shall be one-fourth inch.

(8) Minimum size The working platform shall have a minimum net width of 24 inches.

(9) Guardrails Working platforms shall be furnished with permanent guard rails not less than 36 inches high, and not more than 42 inches high at the front (building side). At the rear, and on the sides, the rail shall not be less than 42 inches high. An intermediate guardrail shall be provided around the entire platform between the top guardrail and the toeboard.

(10) Toeboards A four-inch toeboard shall be provided along all sides of the working platform.

(11) Open spaces between guardrails and toeboards The spaces between the intermediate guardrail and platform toeboard on the building side of the working platform, and between the top guardrail and the toeboard on other sides of the platform, shall be filled with metalic mesh or similar material that will reject a ball one inch in diameter. The installed mesh shall be capable of withstanding a load of 100 pounds applied horizontally over any area of 144 square inches. If the space between the platform and the building face does not exceed eight inches, and the platform is restrained by guides, the mesh may be omitted on the front side.

(12) Flooring The platform flooring shall be of the nonskid type, and if of open construction, shall reject a 9/16 inch diameter ball, or be provided with a screen below the floor to reject a9/16 inch diameter ball.

(13) Access gates Where access gates are provided, they shall be self-closing and self-locking.

(14) Operating device for vertical movement of the working platform

(i) The normal operating device for the working platform shall be located on the working platform and shall be of the continuous pressure weatherproof electric type.

(ii) The operating device shall be operable only when all electrical protective devices and interlocks on the working platform are in position for normal service and, the roof car, if provided, is at an established operating point.

(15) Emergency electric operative device

(i) In addition, on roof-powered platforms, an emergency electric operating device shall be provided near the hoisting machine for use in the event of failure of the normal operating device for the working platform, or failure of the traveling cable system. The emergency operating device shall be mounted in a locked compartment and shall have a legend mounted thereon reading: "For Emergency Operation Only. Establish Communication With Personnel on Working Platform Before Use."

(ii) A key for unlocking the compartment housing the emergency operating device shall be mounted in a break-glass receptacle located near the emergency operating device.

(16) Manual cranking for emergency operation Emergency operation of the main drive machine may be provided to allow manual cranking. This provision for manual operation shall be designed so that not more than two persons will be required to perform this operation. The access to this provision shall include a means to automatically make the machine inoperative electrically while under the emergency manual operation. The design shall be such that the emergency brake is operative at or below governor tripping speed during manual operation.

(17) Arrangement and guarding of hoisting equipment

(i) Hoisting equipment shall consist of a power-driven drum or drum contained in the roof car (roof-powered platforms) or contained on the working platform (self-powered platform).

(ii) The hoisting equipment shall be power-operated in both up and down directions.

(iii) Guard or other protective devices shall be installed wherever rotating shafts or other mechanisms or gears may expose personnel to a hazard.

(iv) Friction devices or clutches shall not be used for connecting the main driving mechanism to the drum or drums. Belt or chain-driven machines are prohibited.

(18) Hoisting motors

(i) Hoisting motors shall be electric and of weather-proof construction.

(ii) Hoisting motors shall be in conformance with applicable provisions of paragraph (c)(22) of this Appendix, Electric Wiring and Equipment.

(iii) Hoisting motors shall be directly connected to the hoisting machinery. Motor couplings, if used, shall be of steel construction.

(19) Brakes The hoisting machine(s) shall have two independent braking means, each designed to stop and hold the working platform with 125 percent of rated load.

(20) Hoisting ropes and rope connections

(i) Working platforms shall be suspended by wire ropes of either 6 x19 or 6 x 37 classification, preformed or nonpreformed.

(ii) [Reserved]

(iii) The minimum factor of safety shall be 10, and shall be calculated by the following formula:

$$F= \frac{SxN}{W}$$

Where

S = Manufacturer's rated breaking strength of one rope.

N = Number of ropes under load.

W = Maximum static load on all ropes with the platform and its rated load at any point of its travel.

(iv) Hoisting ropes shall be sized to conform with the required factor of safety, but in no case shall the size be less than 5/16 inch diameter.

(v) Winding drums shall have at least three turns of rope remaining when the platform has landed at the lowest possible point of its travel.

(vi) The lengthening or repairing of wire rope by the joining of two or more lengths is prohibited.

(vii) The nondrum ends of the hoisting ropes shall be provided with individual shackle rods which will permit individual adjustment of rope lengths, if required.

(viii) More than two reverse bends in each rope is prohibited.

(21) Rope tag data

(i) A metal data tag shall be securely attached to one of the wire rope fastenings. This data tag shall bear the following wire rope data:

(a) The diameter in inches;

(b) Construction classification;

(c) Whether nonpreformed or preformed;

(d The grade of material used;

(e) The manufacturer's rated breaking strength;

(f) Name of the manufacturer of the rope;

(g) The month and year the ropes were installed.

(22) Electrical wiring and equipment

(i) All electrical equipment and wiring shall conform to the requirements of Subpart S of this Part, except as modified by ANSI A120.1—1970 "American National Standard Safety Requirements for Powered Platforms for Exterior Building Maintenance" (see §1910.6). For detail design specifications for electrical equipment, see part 2, ANSI A120.1–1970.

(ii) All motors and operation and control equipment shall be supplied from a single power source.

(iii) The power supply for the powered platform shall be an independent circuit supplied through a fused disconnect switch.

(iv) Electrical conductor parts of the power supply system shall be protected against accidental contact.

(v) Electrical grounding shall be provided.

(a) Provisions for electrical grounding shall be included with the power-supply system.

(b) Controller cabinets, motor frames, hoisting machines, the working platform, roof car and roof car track system, and noncurrent carrying parts of electrical equipment, where provided, shall be grounded.

(c) The controller, where used, shall be so designed and installed that a single ground or short circuit will not prevent both the normal and final stopping device from stopping the working platform.

(d) Means shall be provided on the roof car and working platform for grounding portable electric tools.

(e) The working platform shall be grounded through a grounding connection in a traveling cable. Electrically powered tools utilized on the working platform shall be grounded.

(vi) Electrical receptacles located on the roof or other exterior location shall be of a weatherproof type and shall be located so as not to be subject to contact with water or accumulated snow. The receptacles shall be grounded and the electric cable shall include a grounding conductor. The receptacle and plug shall be a type designed to avoid hazard to persons inserting or withdrawing the plug. Provision shall be made to prevent application of cable strain directly to the plug and receptacle.

(vii) Electric runway conductor systems shall be of the type designed for use in exterior locations and shall be located so as not to be subject to contact with water or accumulated snow. The conductors, collectors, and disconnecting means shall conform to the same requirements as those for cranes and hoists in Subpart S of this Part. A grounded conductor shall parallel the power conductors and be so connected that it cannot be opened by the disconnecting means. The system shall be designed to avoid hazard to persons in the area.

(viii) Electrical protective devices and interlocks of the weatherproof type shall be provided.

(ix) Where the installation includes a roof car, electric contact(s) shall be provided and so connected that the operating devices for the working platform shall be operative only when the roof car is located and mechanically retained at an established operating point.

(x) Where the powered platform includes a powered-operated roof car, the operating device for the roof car shall be inoperative when the roof car is mechanically retained at an established operating point.

(xi) An electric contact shall be provided and so connected that it will cause the down direction relay for vertical travel to open if the tension in the traveling cable exceeds safe limits.

(xii) An automatic overload device shall be provided to cut off the electrical power to the circuit in all hoisting motors for travel in the up direction, should the load applied to the hoisting ropes at either end of the working platform exceed 125 percent of its normal tension with rated load, as shown on the manufacturer's data plate on the working platform.

(xiii) An automatic device shall be provided for each hoisting rope which will cut off the electrical power to the hoisting motor or motors in the down direction and apply the brakes if any hoisting rope becomes slack.

(xiv) Upper and lower directional limit devices shall be provided to prevent the travel of the working platform beyond the normal upper and lower limits of travel.

(xv) Operation of a directional limit device shall prevent further motion in the appropriate direction, if the normal limit of travel has been reached.

(xvi) Directional limit devices, if driven from the hoisting machine by chains, tapes, or cables, shall incorporate a device to disconnect the electric power from the hoisting machine and apply both the primary and secondary brakes in the event of failure of the driving means.

(xvii) Final terminal stopping devices of the working platform:

(a) Final terminal stopping devices for the working platform shall be provided as a secondary means of preventing the working platform from over-traveling at the terminals.

(b) The device shall be set to function as close to each terminal landing as practical, but in such a way that under normal operating conditions it will not function when the working platform is stopped by the normal terminal stopping device.

(c) Operation of the final terminal stopping device shall open the potential relay for vertical travel, thereby disconnecting the electric power from the hoisting machine, and applying both the primary and secondary brakes.

(d) The final terminal stopping device for the upper limit of travel shall be mounted so that it is operated directly by the motion of the working platform itself.

(xviii) Emergency stop switches shall be provided in or adjacent to each operating device.

(xix) Emergency stop switches shall:

(a) Have red operating buttons or handles;

(b) Be conspicuously and permanently marked "Stop";

(c) Be the manually opened and manually closed type;

(d) Be positively opened with the opening not solely dependent on springs.

(xx) The manual operation of an emergency stop switch associated with an operating device for the working platform shall open the potential relay for vertical travel, thereby disconnecting the electric power from the hoisting machine and applying both the primary and secondary brakes.

(xxi) The manual operation of the emergency stop switch associated with the operating device for a power-driven roof car shall cause the electrical power to the traverse machine to be interrupted, and the traverse machine brake to apply.

(23) Requirements for emergency communications

(i) Communication equipment shall be provided for each powered platform for use in an emergency.

(ii) Two-way communication shall be established between personnel on the roof and personnel on the stalled working platform before any emergency operation of the working platform is undertaken by personnel on the roof.

(iii) The equipment shall permit two-way voice communication between the working platform and

(a) Designated personnel continuously available while the powered platform is in use; and

(b) Designated personnel on roof-powered platforms, undertaking emergency operation of the working platform by means of the emergency operating device located near the hoisting machine.

(iv) The emergency communication equipment shall be one of the following types:

(a) Telephone connected to the central telephone exchange system; or

(b) Telephones on a limited system or an approved two-way radio system, provided designated personnel are available to receive a message during the time the powered platform is in use.

(d) Type T powered platforms

(1) Roof car The requirements of paragraphs (c)(1) through (c)(5) of this Appendix shall apply to Type T powered platforms.

(2) Working platform The requirements of paragraphs (c)(6) through (c)(16) of this Appendix apply to Type T powered platforms.

(i) The working platform shall be suspended by at least two wire ropes.

(ii) The maximum rated speed at which the working platform of self-powered platforms may be moved in a vertical direction shall not exceed 35 feet per minute.

(3) Hoisting equipment The requirements of paragraphs (c)(17) and (18) of this Appendix shall apply to Type T powered platforms.

(4) Brakes Brakes requirements of paragraph (c)(19) of this Appendix shall apply.

(5) Hoisting ropes and rope connections

(i) Paragraphs (c)(20)(i) through (vi) and (viii) of this Appendix shall apply to Type T powered platforms.

(ii) Adjustable shackle rods in subparagraph (c)(20)(vii) of this Appendix shall apply to Type T powered platforms, if the working platform is suspended by more than two wire ropes.

(6) Electrical wiring and equipment

(i) The requirements of paragraphs (c)(22)(i) through (vi) of this Appendix shall apply to Type T powered platforms. "Circuit protection limitation," "powered platform electrical service system," all operating services and control equipment shall comply with the specifications contained in part 2, section 26, ANSI A120.1–1970.

(ii) For electrical protective devices the requirements of paragraphs (c)(22) (i) through (viii) of this Appendix shall apply to Type T powered platforms. Requirements for the "circuit potential limitation" shall be in accordance with specifications contained in part 2, section 26, of ANSI A120.1–1970.

(7) Emergency communications All the requirements of paragraph (c)(23) of this Appendix shall apply to Type T powered platforms.

[54 FR 31456, July 28, 1989, as amended at 61 FR 9235, Mar. 7, 1996; 72 FR 7190, Feb. 14, 2007]

§1910.67 Vehicle–mounted elevating and rotating work platforms

(a) Definitions applicable to this section

(a)(1) **Aerial device** Any vehicle—mounted device, telescoping or articulating, or both, which is used to position personnel.

(a)(2) **Aerial ladder** An aerial device consisting of a single- or multiple-section extensible ladder.

(a)(3) **Articulating boom platform** An aerial device with two or more hinged boom sections.

(a)(4) **Extensible boom platform** An aerial device (except ladders) with a telescopic or extensible boom. Telescopic derricks with personnel platform attachments shall be considered to be extensible boom platforms when used with a personnel platform.

(a)(5) **Insulated aerial device** An aerial device designed for work on energized lines and apparatus.

(a)(6) **Mobile unit** A combination of an aerial device, its vehicle, and related equipment.

(a)(7) **Platform** Any personnel-carrying device (basket or bucket) which is a component of an aerial device.

(a)(8) **Vehicle** Any carrier that is not manually propelled.

(a)(9) **Vertical tower** An aerial device designed to elevate a platform in a substantially vertical axis.

(b) General requirements

(b)(1) Unless otherwise provided in this section, aerial devices (aerial lifts) acquired on or after July 1, 1975, shall be designed and constructed in conformance with the applicable requirements of the American National Standard for "Vehicle Mounted Elevating and Rotating Work Platforms," ANSI A92.2—1969, including Appendix, which is incorporated by reference as specified in §1910.6. Aerial lifts acquired for use before July 1, 1975 which do not meet the requirements of ANSI A92.2—1969, may not be used after July 1, 1976, unless they shall have been modified so as to conform with the applicable design and construction requirements of ANSI A92.2—1969. Aerial devices include the following types of vehicle-mounted aerial devices used to elevate personnel to jobsites above ground: (i) Extensible boom platforms, (ii) aerial ladders, (iii) articulating boom platforms, (iv) vertical towers, and (v) a combination of any of the above. Aerial equipment may be made of metal, wood, fiberglass reinforced plastic (FRP), or other material; may be powered or manually operated; and are deemed to be aerial lifts whether or not they are capable of rotating about a substantially vertical axis.

(b)(2) Aerial lifts may be "field modified" for uses other than those intended by the manufacturer, provided the modification has been certified in writing by the manufacturer or by any other equivalent entity, such as a nationally recognized testing laboratory, to be in conformity with all applicable provisions of ANSI A92.2—1969 and this section, and to be at least as safe as the equipment was before modification.

(b)(3) The requirements of this section do not apply to firefighting equipment or to the vehicles upon which aerial devices are mounted, except with respect to the requirement that a vehicle be a stable support for the aerial device.

(b)(4) For operations near overhead electric lines, see §1910.333(c)(3).

(c) Specific requirements

(c)(1) **Ladder trucks and tower trucks** Before the truck is moved for highway travel, aerial ladders shall be secured in the lower traveling position by the locking device above the truck cab, and the manually operated device at the base of the ladder, or by other equally effective means (e.g., cradles which prevent rotation of the ladder in combination with positive acting linear actuators).

(c)(2) Extensible and articulating boom platforms

(c)(2)(i) Lift controls shall be tested each day prior to use to determine that such controls are in safe working condition.

(c)(2)(ii) Only trained persons shall operate an aerial lift.

(c)(2)(iii) Belting off to an adjacent pole, structure, or equipment while working from an aerial lift shall not be permitted.

(c)(2)(iv) Employees shall always stand firmly on the floor of the basket, and shall not sit or climb on the edge of the basket or use planks, ladders, or other devices for a work position.

(c)(2)(v) A personal fall arrest or travel restraint system that meets the requirements in subpart I of this part shall be worn and attached to the boom or basket when working from an aerial lift.

(c)(2)(vi) Boom and basket load limits specified by the manufacturer shall not be exceeded.

(c)(2)(vii) The brakes shall be set and outriggers, when used, shall be positioned on pads or a solid surface. Wheel chocks shall be installed before using an aerial lift on an incline.

(c)(2)(viii) An aerial lift truck may not be moved when the boom is elevated in a working position with men in the basket, except for equipment which is specifically designed for this type of operation in accordance with the provisions of paragraphs (b)(1) and (b)(2) of this Section.

(c)(2)(ix) Articulating boom and extensible boom platforms, primarily designed as personnel carriers, shall have both platform (upper) and lower controls. Upper controls shall be in or beside the platform within easy reach of the operator. Lower controls shall provide for overriding the upper controls. Controls shall be plainly marked as to their function. Lower level controls shall not be operated unless permission has been obtained from the employee in the lift, except in case of emergency.

(c)(2)(x) Climbers shall not be worn while performing work from an aerial lift.

(c)(2)(xi) The insulated portion of an aerial lift shall not be altered in any manner that might reduce its insulating value.

(c)(2)(xii) Before moving an aerial lift for travel, the boom(s) shall be inspected to see that it is properly cradled and outriggers are in stowed position, except as provided in paragraph (c)(2)(viii) of this section.

(c)(3) **Electrical tests** Electrical tests shall be made in conformance with the requirements of ANSI A92.2—1969, Section 5. However, equivalent DC voltage tests may be used in lieu of the AC voltage test specified in A92.2—1969. DC voltage tests which are approved by the equipment manufacturer or equivalent entity shall be considered an equivalent test for the purpose of this paragraph (c)(3).

(c)(4) **Bursting safety factor** All critical hydraulic and pneumatic components shall comply with the provisions of the American National Standards Institute standard, ANSI A92.2—1969, Section 4.9 Bursting Safety Factor. Critical components are those in which a failure would result in a free fall or free rotation of the boom. All noncritical components shall have a bursting safety factor of at least two to one.

(c)(5) **Welding standards** All welding shall conform to the following American Welding Society (AWS) Standards, which are incorporated by reference as specified in §1910.6, as applicable:

(c)(5)(i) Standard Qualification Procedure, AWS B3.0—41;

(c)(5)(ii) Recommended Practices for Automotive Welding Design, AWS D8.4–61;

(c)(5)(iii) Standard Qualification of Welding Procedures and Welders for Piping and Tubing, AWS D10.9–69;

(c)(5)(iv) Specifications for Welding Highway and Railway Bridges, AWS D2.0–69.

[39 FR 23502, June 27, 1974, as amended at 40 FR 13439, Mar. 26, 1975; 55 FR 32014, Aug. 6, 1990; 61 FR 9235, Mar. 7, 1996]

§1910.68 Manlifts

(a) **Definitions applicable to this section**

(a)(1) **Handhold (Handgrip)** A handhold is a device attached to the belt which can be grasped by the passenger to provide a means of maintaining balance.

(a)(2) **Open type** One which has a handgrip surface fully exposed and capable of being encircled by the passenger's fingers.

(a)(3) **Closed type** A cup-shaped device, open at the top in the direction of travel of the step for which it is to be used, and closed at the bottom, into which the passenger may place his fingers.

(a)(4) **Limit switch** A device, the purpose of which is to cut off the power to the motor and apply the brake to stop the carrier in the event that a loaded step passes the terminal landing.

(a)(5) **Manlift** A device consisting of a power-driven endless belt moving in one direction only, and provided with steps or platforms and handholds attached to it for the transportation of personnel from floor to floor.

(a)(6) **Rated speed** Rated speed is the speed for which the device is designed and installed.

(a)(7) **Split-rail switch** An electric limit switch operated mechanically by the rollers on the manlift steps. It consists of an additional hinged or "split" rail, mounted on the regular guide rail, over which the step rollers pass. It is springloaded in the "split" position. If the step supports no load, the rollers will "bump" over the switch; if a loaded step should pass over the section, the split rail will be forced straight, tripping the switch and opening the electrical circuit.

(a)(8) **Step (platform)** A step is a passenger carrying unit.

(a)(9) **Travel** The travel is the distance between the centers of the top and bottom pulleys.

(b) **General requirements**

(b)(1) **Application** This section applies to the construction, maintenance, inspection, and operation of manlifts in relation to accident hazards. Manlifts covered by this section consist of platforms or brackets and accompanying handholds mounted on, or attached to an endless belt, operating vertically in one direction only and being supported by, and driven through pulleys, at the top and bottom. These manlifts are intended for conveyance of persons only. It is not intended that this section cover moving stairways, elevators with enclosed platforms ("Paternoster" elevators), gravity lifts, nor conveyors used only for conveying material. This section applies to manlifts used to carry only personnel trained and authorized by the employer in their use.

(b)(2) **Purpose** The purpose of this section is to provide reasonable safety for life and limb.

(b)(3) **Design requirements** All new manlift installations and equipment installed after the effective date of these regulations shall meet the design requirements of the "American National Safety Standard for Manlifts ANSI A90.1–1969", which is incorporated by reference as specified in §1910.6, and the requirements of this section.

(b)(4) **Reference to other codes and subparts** The following codes and subparts of this part are applicable to this section: Safety Code for Mechanical Power Transmission Apparatus, ANSI B15.1–1953 (R 1958); Safety Code for Fixed Ladders, ANSI A14.3–1956; and Subparts D, O, and S. The preceding ANSI standards are incorporated by reference as specified in §1910.6.

(b)(5) **Floor openings**

(b)(5)(i) **Allowable size** Floor openings for both the "up" and "down" runs shall be not less than 28 inches nor more than 36 inches in width for a 12 inch belt; not less than 34 inches nor more than 38 inches for a 14 inch belt; and not less than 36 inches nor more than 40 inches for a 16 inch belt and shall extend not less than 24 inches, nor more than 28 inches from the face of the belt.

(b)(5)(ii) **Uniformity** All floor openings for a given manlift shall be uniform in size and shall be approximately circular, and each shall be located vertically above the opening below it.

(b)(6) **Landing**

(b)(6)(i) **Vertical clearance** The clearanace between the floor or mounting platform and the lower edge for the conical guard above it required by subparagraph (7) of this paragraph shall not be less than 7 feet 6 inches. Where this clearance cannot be obtained no access to the manlift shall be provided and the manlift runway shall be enclosed where it passes through such floor.

(b)(6)(ii) **Clear landing space** The landing space adjacent to the floor openings shall be free from obstruction and kept clear at all times. This landing space shall be at least 2 feet in width from the edge of the floor opening used for mounting and dismounting.

(b)(6)(iii) **Lighting and landing** Adequate lighting, not less than 5-foot candles, shall be provided at each floor landing at all times when the lift is in operation.

(b)(6)(iv) **Landing surface** The landing surfaces at the entrances and exits to the manlift shall be constructed and maintained as to provide safe footing at all times.

(b)(6)(v) **Emergency landings** Where there is a travel of 50 feet or more between floor landings, one or more emergency landings shall be provided so that there will be a landing (either floor or emergency) for every 25 feet or less of manlift travel.

(b)(6)(v)(A) Emergency landings shall be accessible from both the "up" and "down" rungs of the manlift and shall give access to the ladder required in subparagraph (12) of this paragraph.

(b)(6)(v)(B) Emergency landings shall be completely enclosed with a standard railing and toeboard.

(b)(6)(v)(C) Platforms constructed to give access to bucket elevators or other equipment for the purpose of inspection, lubrication, and repair may also serve as emergency landings under this rule. All such platforms will then be considered part of the emergency landing and shall be provided with standard railings and toeboards.

(b)(7) **Guards on underside of floor openings**

(b)(7)(i) **Fixed type** On the ascending side of the manlift floor openings shall be provided with a bevel guard or cone meeting the following requirements:

(b)(7)(i)(A) The cone shall make an angle of not less than 45° with the horizontal. An angle of 60° or greater shall be used where ceiling heights permit.

(b)(7)(i)(B) The lower edge of this guard shall extend at least 42 inches outward from any handhold on the belt. It shall not extend beyond the upper surface of the floor above.

(b)(7)(i)(C) The cone shall be made of not less than No. 18 U.S. gauge sheet steel or material of equivalent strength or stiffness. The lower edge shall be rolled to a minimum diameter of one-half inch and the interior shall be smooth with no rivets, bolts or screws protruding.

(b)(7)(ii) **Floating type** In lieu of the fixed guards specified in subdivision (i) of this subparagraph a floating type safety cone may be used, such floating cones to be mounted on hinges at least 6 inches below the underside of the floor and so constructed as to actuate a limit switch should a force of 2 pounds be applied on the edge of the cone closest to the hinge. The depth of this floating cone need not exceed 12 inches.

(b)(8) Protection of entrances and exits

(b)(8)(i) Guard rail requirement The entrances and exits at all floor landings affording access to the manlift shall be guarded by a maze (staggered railing) or a handrail equipped with self-closing gates.

(b)(8)(ii) Construction The rails shall be standard guardrails with toeboards that meet the requirements in Subpart D of this Part.

(b)(8)(iii) Gates Gates, if used, shall open outward and shall be self-closing. Corners of gates shall be rounded.

(b)(8)(iv) Maze Maze or staggered openings shall offer no direct passage between enclosure and outer floor space.

(b)(8)(v) Except where building layout prevents, entrances at all landings shall be in the same relative position.

(b)(9) Guards for openings

(b)(9)(i) Construction The floor opening at each landing shall be guarded on sides not used for entrance or exit by a wall, a railing and toeboard or by panels of wire mesh of suitable strength.

(b)(9)(ii) Height and location Such rails or guards shall be at least 42 inches in height on the up-running side and 66 inches on the down-running side.

(b)(10) Bottom arrangement

(b)(10)(i) Bottom landing At the bottom landing the clear area shall be not smaller than the area enclosed by the guardrails on the floors above, and any wall in front of the down-running side of the belt shall be not less than 48 inches from the face of the belt. This space shall not be encroached upon by stairs or ladders.

(b)(10)(ii) Location of lower pulley The lower (boot) pulley shall be installed so that it is supported by the lowest landing served. The sides of the pulley support shall be guarded to prevent contact with the pulley or the steps.

(b)(10)(iii) Mounting platform A mounting platform shall be provided in front or to one side of the uprun at the lowest landing, unless the floor level is such that the following requirement can be met: The floor or platform shall be at or above the point at which the upper surface of the ascending step completes its turn and assumes a horizontal position.

(b)(10)(iv) Guardrails To guard against persons walking under a descending step, the area on the downside of the manlift shall be guarded in accordance with subparagraph (8) of this paragraph. To guard against a person getting between the mounting platform and an ascending step, the area between the belt and the platform shall be protected by a guardrail.

(b)(11) Top arrangements

(b)(11)(i) Clearance from floor A top clearance shall be provided of at least 11 feet above the top terminal landing. This clearance shall be maintained from a plane through each face of the belt to a vertical cylindrical plane having a diameter 2 feet greater than the diameter of the floor opening, extending upward from the top floor to the ceiling on the up-running side of the belt. No encroachment of structural or machine supporting members within this space will be permitted.

(b)(11)(ii) Pulley clearance

(b)(11)(ii)(A) There shall be a clearance of at least 5 feet between the center of the head pulley shaft and any ceiling obstruction.

(b)(11)(ii)(B) The center of the head pulley shaft shall be not less than 6 feet above the top terminal landing.

(b)(11)(iii) Emergency grab rail An emergency grab bar or rail and platform shall be provided at the head pulley when the distance to the head pulley is over 6 feet above the top landing, otherwise only a grab bar or rail is to be provided to permit the rider to swing free should the emergency stops become inoperative.

(b)(12) Emergency exit ladder A fixed metal ladder accessible from both the "up" and "down" run of the manlift shall be provided for the entire travel of the manlift. Such ladders shall meet the requirements in Subpart D of this Part.

(b)(13) Superstructure bracing Manlift rails shall be secured in such a manner as to avoid spreading, vibration, and misalignment.

(b)(14) Illumination

(b)(14)(i) General Both runs of the manlift shall be illuminated at all times when the lift is in operation. An intensity of not less than 1-foot candle shall be maintained at all points. (However, see subparagraph (6)(iii) of this paragraph for illumination requirements at landings.)

(b)(14)(ii) Control of illumination Lighting of manlift runways shall be by means of circuits permanently tied in to the building circuits (no switches), or shall be controlled by switches at each landing. Where separate switches are provided at each landing, any switch shall turn on all lights necessary to illuminate the entire runway.

(b)(15) Weather protection The entire manlift and its driving mechanism shall be protected from the weather at all times.

(c) Mechanical requirements

(c)(1) Machines, general

(c)(1)(i) Brakes Brakes provided for stopping and holding a manlift shall be inherently self-engaging, by requiring power or force from an external source to cause disengagement. The brake shall be electrically released, and shall be applied to the motor shaft for direct-connected units or to the input shaft for belt-driven units. The brake shall be capable of stopping and holding the manlift when the descending side is loaded with 250 lb on each step.

(c)(1)(ii) Belt

(c)(1)(ii)(A) The belts shall be of hard-woven canvas, rubber-coated canvas, leather, or other material meeting the strength requirements of paragraph (b)(3) of this section and having a coefficient of friction such that when used in conjunction with an adequate tension device it will meet the brake test specified in subdivision (i) of this subparagraph.

(c)(1)(ii)(B) The width of the belt shall be not less than 12 inches for a travel not exceeding 100 feet, not less than 14 inches for a travel greater than 100 feet but not exceeding 150 feet and 16 inches for a travel exceeding 150 feet.

(c)(1)(ii)(C) A belt that has become torn while in use on a manlift shall not be spliced and put back in service.

(c)(2) Speed

(c)(2)(i) Maximum speed No manlift designed for a speed in excess of 80 feet per minute shall be installed.

(c)(2)(ii) [Reserved]

(c)(3) Platforms or steps

(c)(3)(i) Minimum depth Steps or platforms shall be not less than 12 inches nor more than 14 inches deep, measured from the belt to the edge of the step or platform.

(c)(3)(ii) Width The width of the step or platform shall be not less than the width of the belt to which it is attached.

(c)(3)(iii) Distance between steps The distance between steps shall be equally spaced and not less than 16 feet measured from the upper surface of one step to the upper surface of the next step above it.

(c)(3)(iv) Angle of step The surface of the step shall make approximately a right angle with the "up" and "down" run of the belt, and shall travel in the approximate horizontal position with the "up" and "down" run of the belt.

(c)(3)(v) Surfaces The upper or working surfaces of the step shall be of a material having inherent nonslip characteristics (coefficient of friction not less than 0.5) or shall be covered completely by a nonslip tread securely fastened to it.

(c)(3)(vi) Strength of step supports When subjected to a load of 400 pounds applied at the approximate center of the step, step frames, or supports and their guides shall be of adequate strength to:

(c)(3)(vi)(A) Prevent the disengagement of any step roller;

(c)(3)(vi)(B) Prevent any appreciable misalignment;

(c)(3)(vi)(C) Prevent any visible deformation of the steps or its support.

(c)(3)(vii) Prohibition of steps without handholds No steps shall be provided unless there is a corresponding handhold above or below it meeting the requirements of paragraph (c)(4) of this section. If a step is removed for repairs or permanently, the handholds immediately above and below it shall be removed before the lift is again placed in service.

(c)(4) Handholds

(c)(4)(i) Location Handholds attached to the belt shall be provided and installed so that they are not less than 4 feet nor more than 4 feet 8 inches above the step tread. These shall be so located as to be available on the both "up" and "down" run of the belt.

(c)(4)(ii) Size The grab surface of the handhold shall be not less than 4½ inches in width, not less than 3 inches in depth, and shall provide 2 inches of clearance from the belt. Fastenings for handholds shall be located not less than 1 inch from the edge of the belt.

(c)(4)(iii) Strength The handhold shall be capable of withstanding, without damage, a load of 300 pounds applied parallel to the run of the belt.

(c)(4)(iv) Prohibition of handhold without steps No handhold shall be provided without a corresponding step. If a handhold is removed permanently or temporarily, the corresponding step and handhold for the opposite direction of travel shall also be removed before the lift is again placed in service.

(c)(4)(v) Type All handholds shall be of the closed type.

(c)(5) Up limit stops

(c)(5)(i) **Requirements** Two separate automatic stop devices shall be provided to cut off the power and apply the brake when a loaded step passes the upper terminal landing. One of these shall consist of a split-rail switch mechanically operated by the step roller and located not more than 6 inches above the top terminal landing. The second automatic stop device may consist of any of the following:

(c)(5)(i)(A) Any split-rail switch placed 6 inches above and on the side opposite the first limit switch;

(c)(5)(i)(B) An electronic device;

(c)(5)(i)(C) A switch actuated by a lever, rod, or plate, the latter to be placed on the "up" side of the head pulley so as to just clear a passing step.

(c)(5)(ii) **Manual reset location** After the manlift has been stopped by a stop device it shall be necessary to reset the automatic stop manually. The device shall be so located that a person resetting it shall have a clear view of both the "up" and "down" runs of the manlift. It shall not be possible to reset the device from any step or platform.

(c)(5)(iii) **Cut-off point** The initial limit stop device shall function so that the manlift will be stopped before the loaded step has reached a point 24 inches above the top terminal landing.

(c)(5)(iv) **Electrical requirements**

(c)(5)(iv)(A) Where such switches open the main motor circuit directly they shall be of the multipole type.

(c)(5)(iv)(B) Where electronic devices are used they shall be so designed and installed that failure will result in shutting off the power to the driving motor.

(c)(5)(iv)(C) Where flammable vapors or combustible dusts may be present, electrical installations shall be in accordance with the requirements of Subpart S of this part for such locations.

(c)(5)(iv)(D) Unless of the oil-immersed type controller contacts carrying the main motor current shall be copper to carbon or equal, except where the circuit is broken at two or more points simultaneously.

(c)(6) Emergency stop

(c)(6)(i) **General** An emergency stop means shall be provided.

(c)(6)(ii) **Location** This stop means shall be within easy reach of the ascending and descending runs of the belt.

(c)(6)(iii) **Operation** This stop means shall be so connected with the control lever or operating mechanism that it will cut off the power and apply the brake when pulled in the direction of travel.

(c)(6)(iv) **Rope** If rope is used, it shall be not less than three-eights inch in diameter. Wire rope, unless marlin-covered, shall not be used.

(c)(7) Instruction and warning signs

(c)(7)(i) **Instruction signs at landings or belts** Signs of conspicuous and easily read style giving instructions for the use of the manlift shall be posted at each landing or stenciled on the belt.

(c)(7)(i)(A) [Reserved]

(c)(7)(i)(B) The instructions shall read approximately as follows:

Face the Belt
Use the Handholds
To Stop—Pull Rope

(c)(7)(ii) Top floor warning sign and light

(c)(7)(ii)(A) At the top floor an illuminated sign shall be displayed bearing the following wording:

"TOP FLOOR—GET OFF"

Signs shall be in block letters not less than 2 inches in height. This sign shall be located within easy view of an ascending passenger and not more than 2 feet above the top terminal landing.

(c)(7)(ii)(B) In addition to the sign required by paragraph (c)(7)(ii)(a) of this section, a red warning light of not less than 40- watt rating shall be provided immediately below the upper landing terminal and so located as to shine in the passenger's face.

(c)(7)(iii) **Visitor warning** A conspicuous sign having the following legend—

AUTHORIZED PERSONNEL ONLY

—shall be displayed at each landing.

(d) Operating rules

(d)(1) **Proper use of manlifts** No freight, packaged goods, pipe, lumber, or construction materials of any kind shall be handled on any manlift.

(d)(2) [Reserved]

(e) Periodic inspection

(e)(1) **Frequency** All manlifts shall be inspected by a competent designated person at intervals of not more than 30 days. Limit switches shall be checked weekly. Manlifts found to be unsafe shall not be operated until properly repaired.

(e)(2) **Items covered** This periodic inspection shall cover but is not limited to the following items:

- Steps;
- Step Fastenings;
- Rails;
- Rail Supports and Fastenings;
- Rollers and Slides;
- Belt and Belt Tension;
- Handholds and Fastenings;
- Floor Landings;
- Guardrails;
- Lubrication;
- Limit Switches;
- Warning Signs and Lights;
- Illumination;
- Drive Pulley;
- Bottom (boot) Pulley and Clearance;
- Pulley Supports;
- Motor;
- Driving Mechanism;
- Brake;
- Electrical Switches;
- Vibration and Misalignment;
- "Skip" on up or down run when mounting step (indicating worn gears).

(e)(3) **Inspection record** A certification record shall be kept of each inspection which includes the date of the inspection, the signature of the person who performed the inspection and the serial number, or other identifier, of the manlift which was inspected. This record of inspection shall be made available to the Assistant Secretary of Labor or a duly authorized representative.

[39 FR 23502, June 27, 1974, as amended at 43 FR 49746, Oct. 24, 1978; 51 FR 34560, Sept. 29, 1986; 54 FR 24334, June 7, 1989; 55 FR 32014, Aug. 6, 1990; 61 FR 9235, Mar. 7, 1996; 72 FR 71068, Dec. 14, 2007]

29 CFR PART 1910 Subpart G
Occupational Health and Environmental Control

Section Contents

Subpart G—Occupational Health and Environmental Control

Authority: 29 U.S.C. 653, 655, 657; Secretary of Labor's Order No. 12–71 (36 FR 8754), 8–76 (41 FR 25059), 9–83 (48 FR 35736), 1–90 (55 FR 9033), 6–96 (62 FR 111), 3–2000 (65 FR 50017), 5–2002 (67 FR 50017), 5–2007 (72 FR 31159), 4–2010 (75 FR 55355), or 1–2012 (77 FR 3912), as applicable; and 29 CFR part 1911.

§1910.94
Ventilation

(a) **Abrasive blasting**

(a)(1) **Definitions applicable to this paragraph**

(a)(1)(i) **Abrasive** A solid substance used in an abrasive blasting operation.

(a)(1)(ii) **Abrasive-blasting respirator** A respirator constructed so that it covers the wearer's head, neck, and shoulders to protect the wearer from rebounding abrasive.

(a)(1)(iii) **Blast cleaning barrel** A complete enclosure which rotates on an axis, or which has an internal moving tread to tumble the parts, in order to expose various surfaces of the parts to the action of an automatic blast spray.

(a)(1)(iv) **Blast cleaning room** A complete enclosure in which blasting operations are performed and where the operator works inside of the room to operate the blasting nozzle and direct the flow of the abrasive material.

(a)(1)(v) **Blasting cabinet** An enclosure where the operator stands outside and operates the blasting nozzle through an opening or openings in the enclosure.

(a)(1)(vi) **Clean air** Air of such purity that it will not cause harm or discomfort to an individual if it is inhaled for extended periods of time.

(a)(1)(vii) **Dust collector** A device or combination of devices for separating dust from the air handled by an exhaust ventilation system.

(a)(1)(viii) **Exhaust ventilation system** A system for removing contaminated air from a space, comprising two or more of the following elements (a) enclosure or hood, (b) duct work, (c) dust collecting equipment, (d) exhauster, and (e) discharge stack.

(a)(1)(ix) **Particulate-filter respirator** An air purifying respirator, commonly referred to as a dust or a fume respirator, which removes most of the dust or fume from the air passing through the device.

(a)(1)(x) **Respirable dust** Airborne dust in sizes capable of passing through the upper respiratory system to reach the lower lung passages.

(a)(1)(xi) **Rotary blast cleaning table** An enclosure where the pieces to be cleaned are positioned on a rotating table and are passed automatically through a series of blast sprays.

(a)(1)(xii) **Abrasive blasting** The forcible application of an abrasive to a surface by pneumatic pressure, hydraulic pressure, or centrifugal force.

(a)(2) **Dust hazards from abrasive blasting**

(a)(2)(i) Abrasives and the surface coatings on the materials blasted are shattered and pulverized during blasting operations and the dust formed will contain particles of respirable size. The composition and toxicity of the dust from these sources shall be considered in making an evaluation of the potential health hazards.

(a)(2)(ii) The concentration of respirable dust or fume in the breathing zone of the abrasive-blasting operator or any other worker shall be kept below the levels specified in §1910.1000.

(a)(2)(iii) Organic abrasives which are combustible shall be used only in automatic systems. Where flammable or explosive dust mixtures may be present, the construction of the equipment, including the exhaust system and all electric wiring, shall conform to the requirements of American National Standard Installation of Blower and Exhaust Systems for Dust, Stock, and Vapor Removal or Conveying, Z33.1–1961 (NFPA 91–1961), which is incorporated by reference as specified in §1910.6, and Subpart S of this part. The blast nozzle shall be bonded and grounded to prevent the build up of static charges. Where flammable or explosive dust mixtures may be present, the abrasive blasting enclosure, the ducts, and the dust collector shall be constructed with loose panels or explosion venting areas, located on sides away from any occupied area, to provide for pressure relief in case of explosion, following the principles set forth in the National Fire Protection Association Explosion Venting Guide, NFPA 68–1954, which is incorporated by reference as specified in §1910.6.

(a)(3) **Blast-cleaning enclosures**

(a)(3)(i) Blast-cleaning enclosures shall be exhaust ventilated in such a way that a continuous inward flow of air will be maintained at all openings in the enclosure during the blasting operation.

(a)(3)(i)(A) All air inlets and access openings shall be baffled or so arranged that by the combination of inward air flow and baffling the escape of abrasive or dust particules into an adjacent work area will be minimized and visible spurts of dust will not be observed.

(a)(3)(i)(B) The rate of exhaust shall be sufficient to provide prompt clearance of the dust-laden air within the enclosure after the cessation of blasting.

(a)(3)(i)(C) Before the enclosure is opened, the blast shall be turned off and the exhaust system shall be run for a sufficient period of time to remove the dusty air within the enclosure.

(a)(3)(i)(D) Safety glass protected by screening shall be used in observation windows, where hard deep-cutting abrasives are used.

(a)(3)(i)(E) Slit abrasive-resistant baffles shall be installed in multiple sets at all small access openings where dust might escape, and shall be inspected regularly and replaced when needed.

(a)(3)(i)(E)(1) Doors shall be flanged and tight when closed.

(a)(3)(i)(E)(2) Doors on blast-cleaning rooms shall be operable from both inside and outside, except that where there is a small operator access door, the large work access door may be closed or opened from the outside only.

(a)(3)(i)(E)(2)(ii) [Reserved]

(a)(4) **Exhaust ventilation systems**

(a)(4)(i) The construction, installation, inspection, and maintenance of exhaust systems shall conform to the principles and requirements set forth in American National Standard Fundamentals Governing the Design and Operation of Local Exhaust Systems, Z9.2–1960, and ANSI Z33.1–1961, which is incorporated by reference as specified in §1910.6.

(a)(4)(i)(A) When dust leaks are noted, repairs shall be made as soon as possible.

(a)(4)(i)(B) The static pressure drop at the exhaust ducts leading from the equipment shall be checked when the installation is completed and periodically thereafter to assure continued satisfactory operation. Whenever an appreciable change in the pressure drop indicates a partial blockage, the system shall be cleaned and returned to normal operating condition.

(a)(4)(ii) In installations where the abrasive is recirculated, the exhaust ventilation system for the blasting enclosure shall not be relied upon for the removal of fines from the spent abrasive instead of an abrasive separator. An abrasive separator shall be provided for the purpose.

(a)(4)(iii) The air exhausted from blast-cleaning equipment shall be discharged through dust collecting equipment. Dust collectors shall be set up so that the accumulated dust can be emptied and removed without contaminating other working areas.

(a)(5) **Personal protective equipment**

(a)(5)(i) Employers must use only respirators approved by the National Institute for Occupational Safety and Health (NIOSH) under 42 CFR part 84 to protect employees from dusts produced during abrasive-blasting operations.

(a)(5)(ii) Abrasive-blasting respirators shall be worn by all abrasive-blasting operators:

(a)(5)(ii)(A) When working inside of blast-cleaning rooms; or

(a)(5)(ii)(B) When using silica sand in manual blasting operations where the nozzle and blast are not physically separated from the operator in an exhaust ventilated enclosure, or (a)(5)(ii)(C) Where concentrations of toxic dust dispersed by the abrasive blasting may exceed the limits set in §1910.1000 and the nozzle and blast are not physically separated from the operator in an exhaust-ventilated enclosure.

(a)(5)(iii) Properly fitted particulate-filter respirators, commonly referred to as dust-filter respirators, may be used for short, intermittent, or occasional dust exposures such as cleanup, dumping of dust collectors, or unloading shipments of sand at a receiving point when it is not feasible to control the dust by enclosure, exhaust ventilation, or other means. The respirators used must be approved by NIOSH under 42 CFR part 84 for protection against the specific type of dust encountered.

(a)(5)(iii)(A) Dust-filter respirators may be used to protect the operator of outside abrasive-blasting operations where nonsilica abrasives are used on materials having low toxicities.

(a)(5)(iii)(B) Dust-filter respirators shall not be used for continuous protection where silica sand is used as the blasting abrasive, or toxic materials are blasted.

(a)(5)(iv) For employees who use respirators required by this section, the employer must implement a respiratory protection program in accordance with 29 CFR §1910.134.

(a)(5)(v) Operators shall be equipped with heavy canvas or leather gloves and aprons or equivalent protection to protect them from the impact of abrasives. Safety shoes shall be worn to protect against foot injury where heavy pieces of work are handled.

(a)(5)(v)(A) Protective footwear must comply with the requirements specified by 29 CFR §1910.136(b)(1).

(a)(5)(v)(B) Equipment for protection of the eyes and face shall be supplied to the operator when the respirator design does not provide such protection and to any other personnel working in the vicinity of abrasive blasting operations. This equipment shall conform to the requirements of §1910.133.

(a)(6) **Air supply and air compressors** Air for abrasive-blasting respirators must be free of harmful quantities of dusts, mists, or noxious gases, and must meet the requirements for supplied-air quality and use specified in 29 CFR §1910.134(i).

(a)(7) **Operational procedures and general safety** Dust shall not be permitted to accumulate on the floor or on ledges outside of an abrasive-blasting enclosure, and dust spills shall be cleaned up promptly. Aisles and walkways shall be kept clear of steel shot or similar abrasive which may create a slipping hazard.

(a)(8) **Scope** This paragraph (a) applies to all operations where an abrasive is forcibly applied to a surface by pneumatic or hydraulic pressure, or by centrifugal force. It does not apply to steam blasting, or steam cleaning, or hydraulic cleaning methods where work is done without the aid of abrasives.

(b) [OI] Grinding, polishing, and buffing operations

(b)(1) Definitions applicable to this paragraph

(b)(1)(i) **Abrasive cutting-off wheels** Organic-bonded wheels, the thickness of which is not more than one forty-eighth of their diameter for those up to, and including, 20 inches in diameter, and not more than one-sixtieth of their diameter for those larger than 20 inches in diameter, used for a multitude of operations variously known as cutting, cutting off, grooving, slotting, coping, and jointing, and the like. The wheels may be "solid" consisting of organic-bonded abrasive material throughout, "steel centered" consisting of a steel disc with a rim of organic-bonded material moulded around the periphery, or of the "inserted tooth" type consisting of a steel disc with organic-bonded abrasive teeth or inserts mechanically secured around the periphery.

(b)(1)(ii) **Belts** All power-driven, flexible, coated bands used for grinding, polishing, or buffing purposes.

(b)(1)(iii) **Branch pipe** The part of an exhaust system piping that is connected directly to the hood or enclosure.

(b)(1)(iv) **Cradle** A movable fixture, upon which the part to be ground or polished is placed.

(b)(1)(v) **Disc wheels** All power-driven rotatable discs faced with abrasive materials, artificial or natural, and used for grinding or polishing on the side of the assembled disc.

(b)(1)(vi) **Entry loss** The loss in static pressure caused by air flowing into a duct or hood. It is usually expressed in inches of water gauge.

(b)(1)(vii) **Exhaust system** A system consisting of branch pipes connected to hoods or enclosures, one or more header pipes, an exhaust fan, means for separating solid contaminants from the air flowing in the system, and a discharge stack to outside.

(b)(1)(viii) **Grinding wheels** All power-driven rotatable grinding or abrasive wheels, except disc wheels as defined in this standard, consisting of abrasive particles held together by artificial or natural bonds and used for peripheral grinding.

(b)(1)(ix) **Header pipe (main pipe)** A pipe into which one or more branch pipes enter and which connects such branch pipes to the remainder of the exhaust system.

(b)(1)(x) **Hoods and enclosures** The partial or complete enclosure around the wheel or disc through which air enters an exhaust system during operation.

(b)(1)(xi) **Horizontal double-spindle disc grinder** A grinding machine carrying two power-driven, rotatable, coaxial, horizontal spindles upon the inside ends of which are mounted abrasive disc wheels used for grinding two surfaces simultaneously.

(b)(1)(xii) **Horizontal single-spindle disc grinder** A grinding machine carrying an abrasive disc wheel upon one or both ends of a power-driven, rotatable single horizontal spindle.

(b)(1)(xiii) **Polishing and buffing wheels** All power-driven rotatable wheels composed all or in part of textile fabrics, wood, felt, leather, paper, and may be coated with abrasives on the periphery of the wheel for purposes of polishing, buffing, and light grinding.

(b)(1)(xiv) **Portable grinder** Any power-driven rotatable grinding, polishing, or buffing wheel mounted in such manner that it may be manually manipulated.

(b)(1)(xv) **Scratch brush wheels** All power-driven rotatable wheels made from wire or bristles, and used for scratch cleaning and brushing purposes.

(b)(1)(xvi) **Swing-frame grinder** Any power-driven rotatable grinding, polishing, or buffing wheel mounted in such a manner that the wheel with its supporting framework can be manipulated over stationary objects.

(b)(1)(xvii) **Velocity pressure (vp)** The kinetic pressure in the direction of flow necessary to cause a fluid at rest to flow at a given velocity. It is usually expressed in inches of water gauge.

(b)(1)(xviii) **Vertical spindle disc grinder** A grinding machine having a vertical, rotatable power-driven spindle carrying a horizontal abrasive disc wheel.

(b)(2) **Application** Wherever dry grinding, dry polishing or buffing is performed, and employee exposure, without regard to the use of respirators, exceeds the permissible exposure limits prescribed in §1910.1000 or other sections of this part, a local exhaust ventilation system shall be provided and used to maintain employee exposures within the prescribed limits.

(b)(3) Hood and branch pipe requirements

(b)(3)(i) Hoods connected to exhaust systems shall be used, and such hoods shall be designed, located, and placed so that the dust or dirt particles shall fall or be projected into the hoods in the direction of the air flow. No wheels, discs, straps, or belts shall be operated in such manner and in such direction as to cause the dust and dirt particles to be thrown into the operator's breathing zone.

(b)(3)(ii) Grinding wheels on floor stands, pedestals, benches, and special-purpose grinding machines and abrasive cutting-off wheels shall have not less than the minimum exhaust volumes shown in Table G–4 with a recommended minimum duct velocity of 4,500 feet per minute in the branch and 3,500 feet per minute in the main. The entry losses from all hoods except the vertical-spindle disc grinder hood, shall equal 0.65 velocity pressure for a straight takeoff and 0.45 velocity pressure for a tapered takeoff. The entry loss for the vertical-spindle disc grinder hood is shown in figure G–1 (following §1910.94(b)).

Table G–4—Grinding and Abrasive Cutting-Off Wheels

Wheel diameter (inches)	Wheel width (inches)	Minimum exhaust volume (feet^3/min.)
To 9	1 ½	220
Over 9 to 16	2	390
Over 16 to 19	3	500
Over 19 to 24	4	610
Over 24 to 30	5	880
Over 30 to 36	6	1,200

For any wheel wider than wheel diameters shown in Table G–4, increase the exhaust volume by the ratio of the new width to the width shown.

Example: If wheel width = 4 ½ inches,
then 4.5 ÷ 4 × 610 = 686 (rounded to 690).

(b)(3)(iii) Scratch-brush wheels and all buffing and polishing wheels mounted on floor stands, pedestals, benches, or special-purpose machines shall have not less than the minimum exhaust volume shown in Table G–5.

Table G–5—Buffing and Polishing Wheels

Wheel diameter (inches)	Wheel width (inches)	Minimum exhaust volume (feet³/min.)
To 9	2	300
Over 9 to 16	3	500
Over 16 to 19	4	610
Over 19 to 24	5	740
Over 24 to 30	6	1,040
Over 30 to 36	6	1,200

(b)(3)(iv) Grinding wheels or discs for horizontal single-spindle disc grinders shall be hooded to collect the dust or dirt generated by the grinding operation and the hoods shall be connected to branch pipes having exhaust volumes as shown in Table G–6.

Table G–6—Horizontal Single-Spindle Disc Grinder

Disc diameter (inches)	Exhaust volume (feet³/min.)
Up to 12	220
Over 12 to 19	390
Over 19 to 30	610
Over 30 to 36	880

(b)(3)(v) Grinding wheels or discs for horizontal double-spindle disc grinders shall have a hood enclosing the grinding chamber and the hood shall be connected to one or more branch pipes having exhaust volumes as shown in Table G–7.

Table G–7—Horizontal Double-Spindle Disc Grinder

Disc diameter (inches)	Exhaust volume (feet³/min.)
Up to 19	610
Over 19 to 25	880
Over 25 to 30	1,200
Over 30 to 53	1,770
Over 53 to 72	6,280

(b)(3)(vi) Grinding wheels or discs for vertical single-spindle disc grinders shall be encircled with hoods to remove the dust generated in the operation. The hoods shall be connected to one or more branch pipes having exhaust volumes as shown in Table G–8.

Table G–8—Vertical Spindle Disc Grinder

Disc diameter (inches)	One-half or more of disc covered		Disc not covered	
	Number[1]	Exhaust (feet³/min.)	Number[1]	Exhaust (feet³/min.)
Up to 20	1	500	2	780
Over 20 to 30	2	780	2	1,480
Over 30 to 53	2	1,770	4	3,530
Over 53 to 72	2	3,140	5	6,010

[1] *Number of exhaust outlets around periphery of hood, or equal distribution provided by other means.*

(b)(3)(vii) Grinding and polishing belts shall be provided with hoods to remove dust and dirt generated in the operations and the hoods shall be connected to branch pipes having exhaust volumes as shown in Table G–9.

Table G–9—Grinding and Polishing Belts

Belts width (inches)	Exhaust volume (feet³/min.)
Up to 3	220
Over 3 to 5	300
Over 5 to 7	390
Over 7 to 9	500
Over 9 to 11	610
Over 11 to 13	740

(b)(3)(viii) Cradles and swing-frame grinders. Where cradles are used for handling the parts to be ground, polished, or buffed, requiring large partial enclosures to house the complete operation, a minimum average air velocity of 150 feet per minute shall be maintained over the entire opening of the enclosure. Swing-frame grinders shall also be exhausted in the same manner as provided for cradles. (See fig. G–3)

(b)(3)(ix) Where the work is outside the hood, air volumes must be increased as shown in American Standard Fundamentals Governing the Design and Operation of Local Exhaust Systems, Z9.2–1960 (section 4, exhaust hoods).

(b)(4) **Exhaust systems**

(b)(4)(i) Exhaust systems for grinding, polishing, and buffing operations should be designed in accordance with American Standard Fundamentals Governing the Design and Operation of Local Exhaust Systems, Z9.2–1960.

(b)(4)(ii) Exhaust systems for grinding, polishing, and buffing operations shall be tested in the manner described in American Standard Fundamentals Governing the Design and Operation of Local Exhaust Systems, Z9.2–1960.

(b)(4)(iii) All exhaust systems shall be provided with suitable dust collectors.

(b)(5) **Hood and enclosure design**

(b)(5)(i)(A) It is the dual function of grinding and abrasive cutting-off wheel hoods to protect the operator from the hazards of bursting wheels, as well as to provide a means for the removal of dust and dirt generated. All hoods shall be not less in structural strength than specified in Tables O–1 and O–9 of §1910.215.

(b)(5)(i)(B) Due to the variety of work and types of grinding machines employed, it is necessary to develop hoods adaptable to the particular machine in question, and such hoods shall be located as close as possible to the operation.

(b)(5)(ii) Exhaust hoods for floor stands, pedestals, and bench grinders shall be designed in accordance with figure G–2. The adjustable tongue shown in the figure shall be kept in working order and shall be adjusted within one-fourth inch of the wheel periphery at all times.

(b)(5)(iii) Swing-frame grinders shall be provided with exhaust booths as indicated in figure G–3.

(b)(5)(iv) Portable grinding operations, whenever the nature of the work permits, shall be conducted within a partial enclosure. The opening in the enclosure shall be no larger than is actually required in the operation and an average face air velocity of not less than 200 feet per minute shall be maintained.

(b)(5)(v) Hoods for polishing and buffing and scratch-brush wheels shall be constructed to conform as closely to figure G–4 as the nature of the work will permit.

(b)(5)(vi) Cradle grinding and polishing operations shall be performed within a partial enclosure similar to figure G–5. The operator shall be positioned outside the working face of the opening of the enclosure. The face opening of the enclosure should not be any greater in area than that actually required for the performance of the operation and the average air velocity into the working face of the enclosure shall not be less than 150 feet per minute.

(b)(5)(vii) Hoods for horizontal single-spindle disc grinders shall be constructed to conform as closely as possible to the hood shown in figure G–6. It is essential that there be a space between the back of the wheel and the hood, and a space around the periphery of the wheel of at least 1 inch in order to permit the suction to act around the wheel periphery. The opening on the side of the disc shall be no larger than is required for the grinding operation, but must never be less than twice the area of the branch outlet.

(b)(5)(viii) Horizontal double-spindle disc grinders shall have a hood encircling the wheels and grinding chamber similar to that illustrated in figure G–7. The openings for passing the work into the grinding chamber should be kept as small as possible, but must never be less than twice the area of the branch outlets.

(b)(5)(ix) Vertical-spindle disc grinders shall be encircled with a hood so constructed that the heavy dust is drawn off a surface of the disc and the lighter dust exhausted through a continuous slot at the top of the hood as shown in figure G–1.

(b)(5)(x) Grinding and polishing belt hoods shall be constructed as close to the operation as possible. The hood should extend almost to the belt, and 1-inch wide openings should be provided on either side. Figure G–8 shows a typical hood for a belt operation.

Figure G–1
Verticle Spindle Disc Grinder Exhaust Hood and Brand Pipe Connections

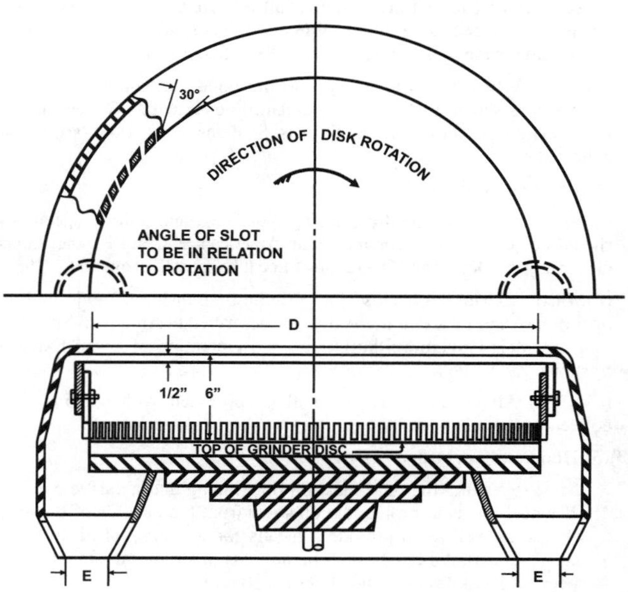

Dia *D.* inches		Exhaust *E*		Volume Exhausted at 4,500 ft/min ft³/min	Note
Min.	Max.	No Pipes	Dia.		
	20	1	4 ¼	500	When one-half or more of the disc can be hooded, use exhaust ducts as shown at the left.
Over 20	30	2	4	780	
Over 30	72	2	6	1,770	
Over 53	72	2	8	3,140	
	20	2	4	780	When no hood can be used over disc, use exhaust ducts as shown at left.
Over 20	20	2	4	780	
Over 30	30	2	5 ½	1,480	
Over 53	53	4	6	3,530	
	72	5	7	6,010	

Figure G–2
Standard Grinder Hood

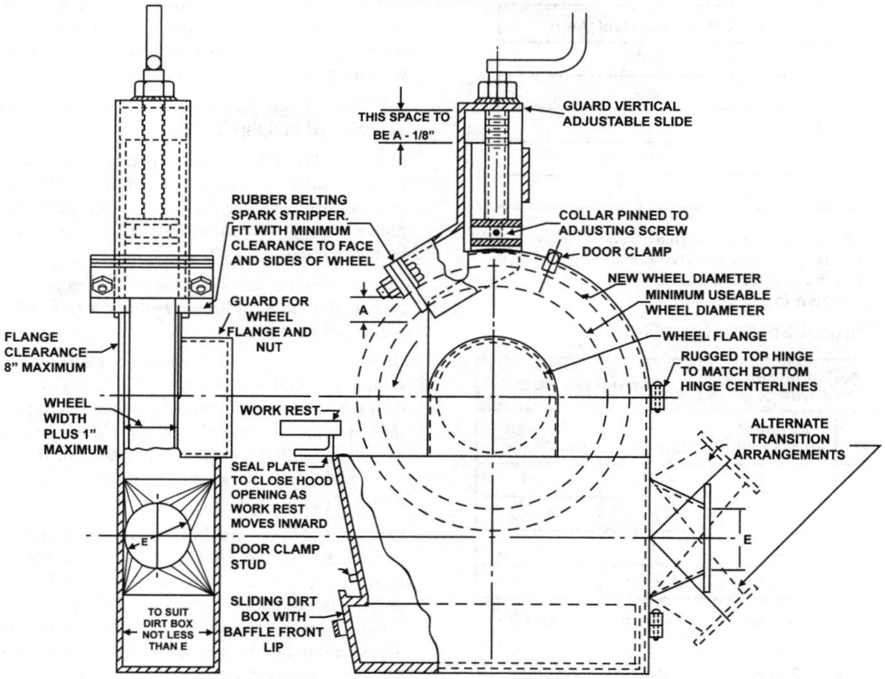

Wheel dimension, inches			Exhaust outlet, inches E	Volume of air at 4,500 ft/min
Diameter				
Min= *d*	Max= *D*	Width, Max		
	9	1 ½	3	220
Over 9	16	2	4	390
Over 16	19	3	4 ½	500
Over 19	24	4	5	610
Over 24	30	5	6	880
Over 30	36	6	7	1,200

Figure G–3
A Method of Applying an Exhaust Enclosure to Swing-Frame Grinders
(**Note:** Baffle to reduce front opening as much as possible

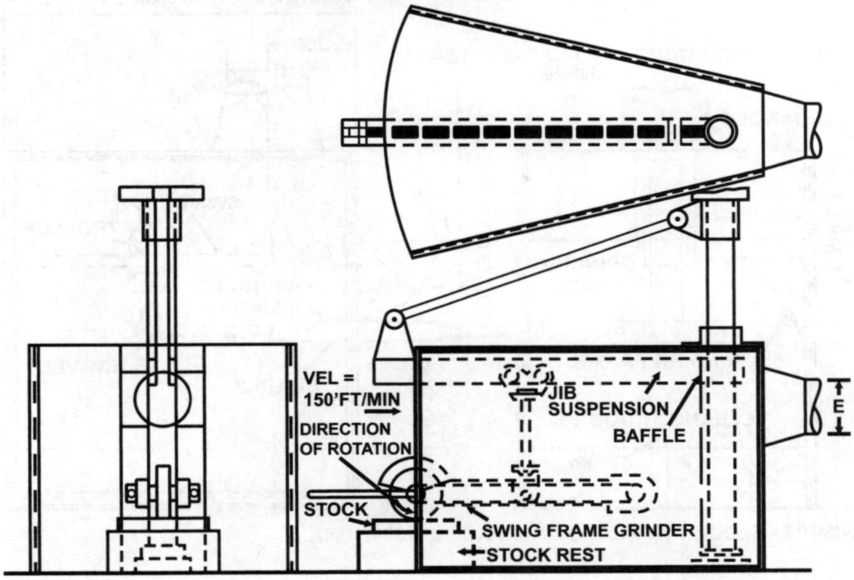

Figure G–4
Standard Buffering and Polishing Hood

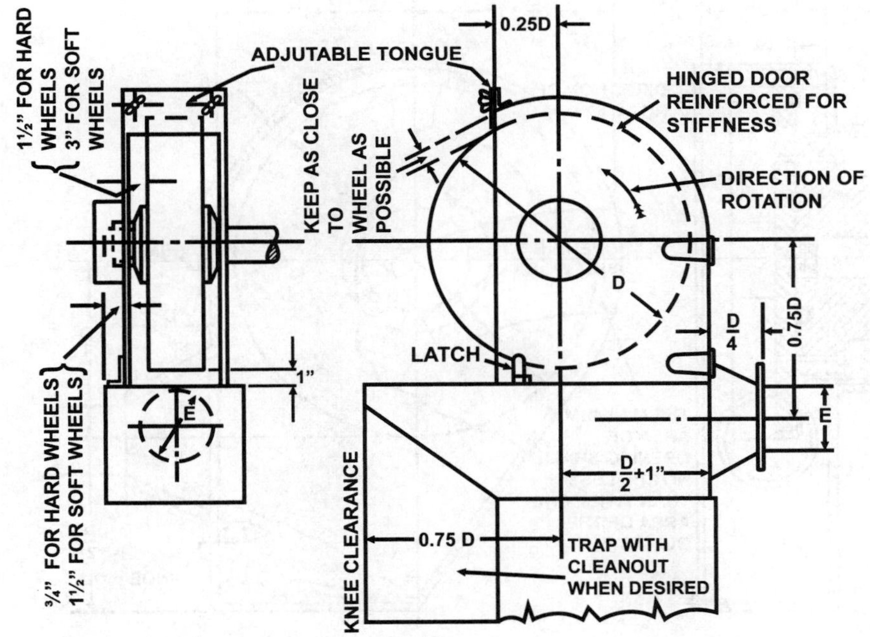

Wheel dimension, inches			Exhaust outlet, inches E	Volume of air at 4,500 ft/min
Diameter				
Min = *d*	Max = *D*	Width, Max		
	9	2	3 ½	300
Over 9	16	3	4	500
Over 16	19	4	5	610
Over 19	24	5	5 ½	740
Over 24	30	6	6 ½	1,040
Over 30	36	6	7	1,200

Entry loss = 0.15 velocity pressure for tapered takeoff; 0.65 velocity pressure for straight takeoff

Figure G–5
Cradle Polishing or Grinding Enclosure
Entry loss = 0.45 velocity pressure for tapered takeoff

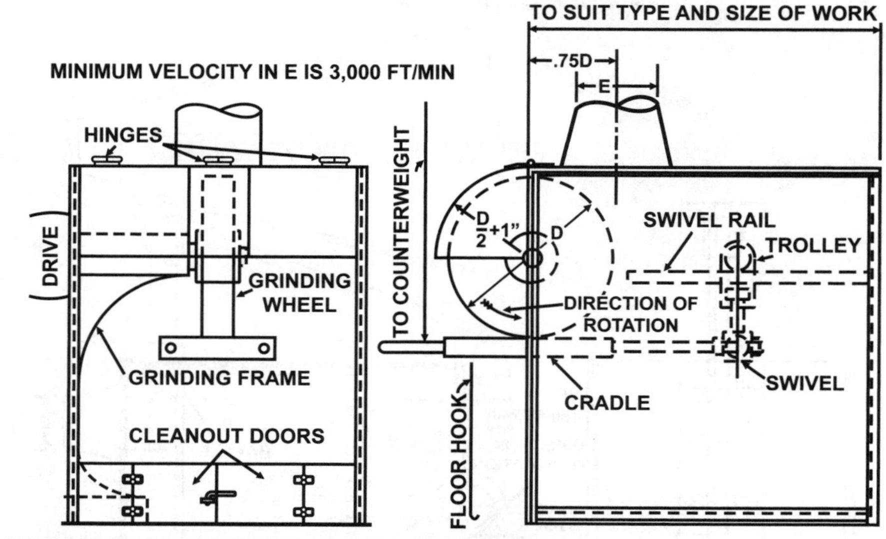

Figure G–6
Horizontal Single–Spindle Disc Grinder Exhaust Hood and Branch Pipe Connections

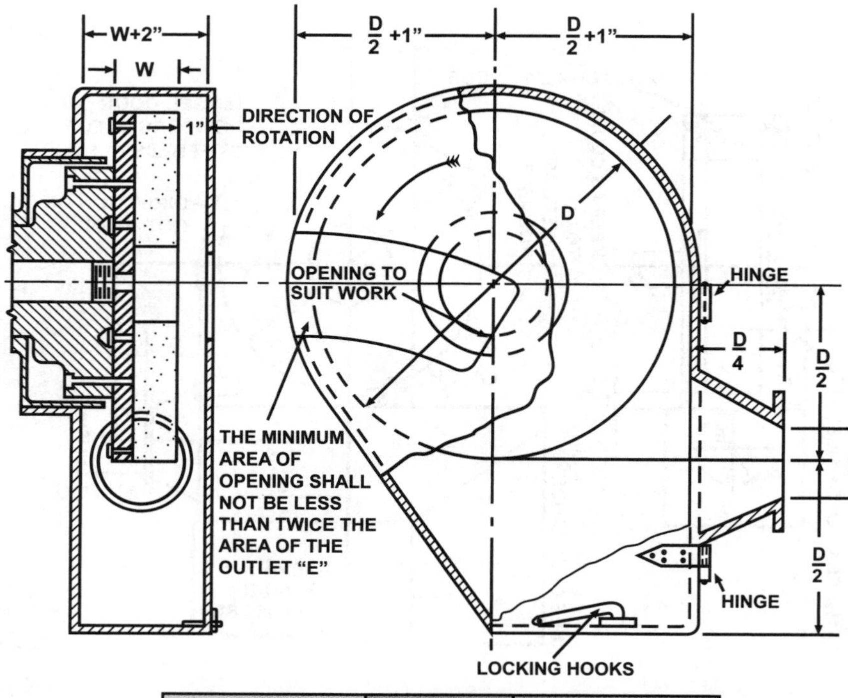

Dia D, inches		Exhaust E, dia. inches	Volume exhausted at 4,500 ft/min ft³/min
Min.	Max.		
	12	3	220
Over 12	19	4	390
Over 19	30	5	610
Over 30	36	6	880

Note: *If grinding wheels are used for disc grinding purposes, hoods must conform to structural strength and materials as described in 9.1.*

Entry loss = 0.45 velocity pressure for tapered takeoff.

Figure G–7
Horizontal Double–Spindle Disc Grinder Exhaust Hood and Branch Pipe Connections

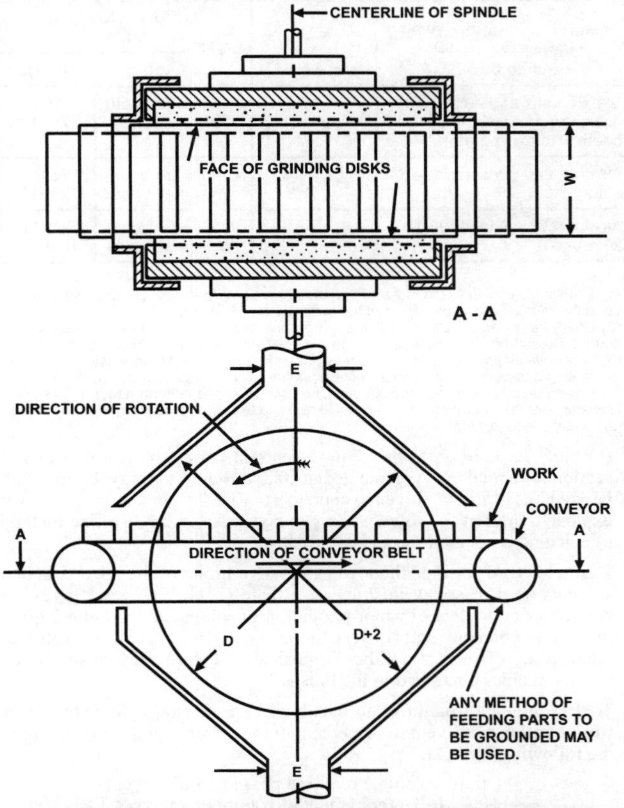

Disc dia. inches		Exhaust E		Volume exhaust at 4,500 ft/min. ft^3/min	Note
Min.	Max.	No Pipes	Dia		
	19	1	5	610	
Over 19	25	1	6	880	When width "W" permits, exhaust ducts should be as near heaviest grinding as possible.
Over 25	30	1	7	1,200	
Over 30	53	2	6	1,770	
Over 53	72	4	8	6,280	

Entry loss = 0.45 velocity pressure for tapered takeoff.

Figure G–8
A Typical Hood for a Belt Operation

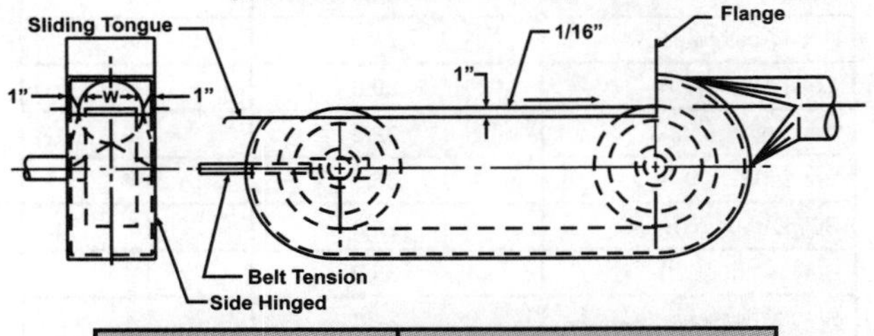

Belt width W. Inches	Exhaust volume. ft./min
Up to 3	220
3 to 5	300
5 to 7	390
7 to 9	500
9 to 11	610
11 to 13	740

(b)(6) **Scope** This paragraph (b), prescribes the use of exhaust hood enclosures and systems in removing dust, dirt, fumes, and gases generated through the grinding, polishing, or buffing of ferrous and nonferrous metals.

(c) Spray finishing operations

(c)(1) Definitions applicable to this paragraph

(c)(1)(i) **Spray-finishing operations** Spray-finishing operations are employment of methods wherein organic or inorganic materials are utilized in dispersed form for deposit on surfaces to be coated, treated, or cleaned. Such methods of deposit may involve either automatic, manual, or electrostatic deposition but do not include metal spraying or metallizing, dipping, flow coating, roller coating, tumbling, centrifuging, or spray washing and degreasing as conducted in self-contained washing and degreasing machines or systems.

(c)(1)(ii) **Spray booth** Spray booths are defined and described in §1910.107(a).

(c)(1)(iii) **Spray room** A spray room is a room in which spray-finishing operations not conducted in a spray booth are performed separately from other areas.

(c)(1)(iv) **Minimum maintained velocity** Minimum maintained velocity is the velocity of air movement which must be maintained in order to meet minimum specified requirements for health and safety.

(c)(2) **Location and application** Spray booths or spray rooms are to be used to enclose or confine all operations. Spray-finishing operations shall be located as provided in sections 201 through 206 of the Standard for Spray Finishing Using Flammable and Combustible Materials, NFPA No. 33–1969.

(c)(3) Design and construction of spray booths

(c)(3)(i) Spray booths shall be designed and constructed in accordance with §1910.107(b)(1) through (b)(4) and (b)(6) through (b)(10). For a more detailed discussion of fundamentals relating to this subject, see ANSI Z9.2–1960, which is incorporated by reference as specified in §1910.6.

(c)(3)(i)(A) Lights, motors, electrical equipment, and other sources of ignition shall conform to the requirements of §1910.107(b)(10) and (c).

(c)(3)(i)(B) In no case shall combustible material be used in the construction of a spray booth and supply or exhaust duct connected to it.

(c)(3)(ii) Unobstructed walkways shall not be less than 6 ½ feet high and shall be maintained clear of obstruction from any work location in the booth to a booth exit or open booth front. In booths where the open front is the only exit, such exits shall be not less than 3 feet wide. In booths having multiple exits, such exits shall not be less than 2 feet wide, provided that the maximum distance from the work location to the exit is 25 feet or less. Where booth exits are provided with doors, such doors shall open outward from the booth.

(c)(3)(iii) Baffles, distribution plates, and dry-type overspray collectors shall conform to the requirements of §1910.107(b)(4) and (b)(5).

(c)(3)(iii)(A) Overspray filters shall be installed and maintained in accordance with the requirements of §1910.107(b)(5), and shall only be in a location easily accessible for inspection, cleaning, or replacement.

(c)(3)(iii)(B) Where effective means, independent of the overspray filters, are installed which will result in design air distribution across the booth cross section, it is permissible to operate the booth without the filters in place.

(c)(3)(iv)(A) For wet or water-wash spray booths, the water-chamber enclosure, within which intimate contact of contaminated air and cleaning water or other cleaning medium is maintained, if made of steel, shall be 18 gage or heavier and adequately protected against corrosion.

(c)(3)(iv)(B) Chambers may include scrubber spray nozzles, headers, troughs, or other devices. Chambers shall be provided with adequate means for creating and maintaining scrubbing action for removal of particulate matter from the exhaust air stream.

(c)(3)(v) Collecting tanks shall be of welded steel construction or other suitable non-combustible material. If pits are used as collecting tanks, they shall be concrete, masonry, or other material having similar properties.

(c)(3)(v)(A) Tanks shall be provided with weirs, skimmer plates, or screens to prevent sludge and floating paint from entering the pump suction box. Means for automatically maintaining the proper water level shall also be provided. Fresh water inlets shall not be submerged. They shall terminate at least one pipe diameter above the safety overflow level of the tank.

(c)(3)(v)(B) Tanks shall be so constructed as to discourage accumulation of hazardous deposits.

(c)(3)(vi) Pump manifolds, risers, and headers shall be adequately sized to insure sufficient water flow to provide efficient operation of the water chamber.

(c)(4) Design and construction of spray rooms

(c)(4)(i) Spray rooms, including floors, shall be constructed of masonry, concrete, or other noncombustible material.

(c)(4)(ii) Spray rooms shall have noncombustible fire doors and shutters.

(c)(4)(iii) Spray rooms shall be adequately ventilated so that the atmosphere in the breathing zone of the operator shall be maintained in accordance with the requirements of paragraph (c)(6)(ii) of this section.

(c)(4)(iv) Spray rooms used for production spray-finishing operations shall conform to the requirements for spray booths.

(c)(5) Ventilation

(c)(5)(i) Ventilation shall be provided in accordance with provisions of §1910.107(d), and in accordance with the following:

(c)(5)(i)(A) Where a fan plenum is used to equalize or control the distribution of exhaust air movement through the booth, it shall be of sufficient strength or rigidity to withstand the differential air pressure or other superficially imposed loads for which the equipment is designed and also to facilitate cleaning. Construction specifications shall be at least equivalent to those of paragraph (c)(5)(iii) of this section.

(c)(5)(i)(B) [Reserved]

(c)(5)(ii) Inlet or supply ductwork used to transport makeup air to spray booths or surrounding areas shall be constructed of noncombustible materials.

(c)(5)(ii)(A) If negative pressure exists within inlet ductwork, all seams and joints shall be sealed if there is a possibility of infiltration of harmful quantities of noxious gases, fumes, or mists from areas through which ductwork passes.

(c)(5)(ii)(B) Inlet ductwork shall be sized in accordance with volume flow requirements and provide design air requirements at the spray booth.

(c)(5)(ii)(C) Inlet ductwork shall be adequately supported throughout its length to sustain at least its own weight plus any negative pressure which is exerted upon it under normal operating conditions.

(c)(5)(iii)(A) Exhaust ductwork shall be adequately supported throughout its length to sustain its weight plus any normal accumulation in interior during normal operating conditions and any negative pressure exerted upon it.

(c)(5)(iii)(B) Exhaust ductwork shall be sized in accordance with good design practice which shall include consideration of fan capacity, length of duct, number of turns and elbows, variation in size, volume, and character of materials being exhausted. See American National Standard Z9.2–1960 for further details and explanation concerning elements of design.

(c)(5)(iii)(C) Longitudinal joints in sheet steel ductwork shall be either lock-seamed, riveted, or welded. For other than steel construction, equivalent securing of joints shall be provided.

(c)(5)(iii)(D) Circumferential joints in ductwork shall be substantially fastened together and lapped in the direction of airflow. At least every fourth joint shall be provided with connecting flanges, bolted together, or of equivalent fastening security.

(c)(5)(iii)(E) Inspection or clean-out doors shall be provided for every 9 to 12 feet of running length for ducts up to 12 inches in diameter, but the distance between cleanout doors may be greater for larger pipes. A clean-out door or doors shall be provided for servicing the fan, and where necessary, a drain shall be provided.

(c)(5)(iii)(F) Where ductwork passes through a combustible roof or wall, the roof or wall shall be protected at the point of penetration by open space or fire-resistive material between the duct and the roof or wall. When ducts pass through firewalls, they shall be provided with automatic fire dampers on both sides of the wall, except that three-eighth-inch steel plates may be used in lieu of automatic fire dampers for ducts not exceeding 18 inches in diameter.

(c)(5)(iii)(G) Ductwork used for ventilating any process covered in this standard shall not be connected to ducts ventilating any other process or any chimney or flue used for conveying any products of combustion.

(c)(6) Velocity and air flow requirements

(c)(6)(i) [OI] Except where a spray booth has an adequate air replacement system, the velocity of air into all openings of a spray booth shall be not less than that specified in Table G–10 for the operating conditions specified. An adequate air replacement system is one which introduces replacement air upstream or above the object being sprayed and is so designed that the velocity of air in the booth cross section is not less than that specified in Table G–10 when measured upstream or above the object being sprayed.

Table G–10
Minimum Maintained Velocities Into Spray Booths

Operating conditions for objects completely inside booth	Crossdraft, f.p.m.	Airflow velocities, f.p.m.	
		Design	Range
Electrostatic and automatic airless operation contained in booth without operator	Negligible	50 large booth 100 small booth	50–75 75–125
Air-operated guns, manual or automatic	Up to 50	100 large booth 150 small booth	75–125 125–175
Air-operated guns, manual or automatic	Up to 100	150 large booth 200 small booth	125–175 150–250

Notes:
(1) Attention is invited to the fact that the effectiveness of the spray booth is dependent upon the relationship of the depth of the booth to its height and width.
(2) Crossdrafts can be eliminated through proper design and such design should be sought. Crossdrafts in excess of 100 fpm (feet per minute) should not be permitted.
(3) Excessive air pressures result in loss of both efficiency and material waste in addition to creating a backlash that may carry overspray and fumes into adjacent work areas.
(4) Booths should be designed with velocities shown in the column headed "Design." However, booths operating with velocities shown in the column headed "Range" are in compliance with this standard.

(c)(6)(ii) In addition to the requirements in paragraph (c)(6)(i) of this section the total air volume exhausted through a spray booth shall be such as to dilute solvent vapor to at least 25 percent of the lower explosive limit of the solvent being sprayed. An example of the method of calculating this volume is given below.

Example: To determine the lower explosive limits of the most common solvents used in spray finishing, see Table G–11. Column 1 gives the number of cubic feet of vapor per gallon of solvent and column 2 gives the lower explosive limit (LEL) in percentage by volume of air. Note that the quantity of solvent will be diminished by the quantity of solids and nonflammables contained in the finish.

To determine the volume of air in cubic feet necessary to dilute the vapor from 1 gallon of solvent to 25 percent of the lower explosive limit, apply the following formula:

Dilution volume required per gallon of solvent =
4 (100 − LEL) (cubic feet of vapor per gallon) ÷ LEL

Using toluene as the solvent:

(1) LEL of toluene from Table G–11, column 2, is 1.4 percent.
(2) Cubic feet of vapor per gallon from Table G–11, column 1, is 30.4 cubic feet per gallon.
(3) Dilution volume required = 4 (100 − 1.4) 30.4 ÷ 1.4 = 8,564 cubic feet.
(4) To convert to cubic feet per minute of required ventilation, multiply the dilution volume required per gallon of solvent by the number of gallons of solvent evaporated per minute.

Table G–11
Lower Explosive Limit of Some Commonly Used Solvents

Solvent	Cubic feet per gallon of vapor of liquid at 70 °F.	Lower explosive limit in percent by volume of air at 70 °F
	Column 1	Column 2
Acetone	44.0	2.6
Amyl Acetate (iso)	21.6	[1]1.0
Amyl Alcohol (n)	29.6	1.2
Amyl Alcohol (iso)	29.6	1.2
Benzene	36.8	[1]1.4
Butyl Acetate (n)	24.8	1.7
Butyl Alcohol (n)	35.2	1.4
Butyl Cellosolve	24.8	1.1
Cellosolve	33.6	1.8
Cellosolve Acetate	23.2	1.7
Cyclohexanone	31.2	[1]1.1
1,1 Dichloroethylene	42.4	5.9
1,2 Dichloroethylene	42.4	9.7
Ethyl Acetate	32.8	2.5
Ethyl Alcohol	55.2	4.3
Ethyl Lactate	28.0	[1]1.5

Solvent	Cubic feet per gallon of vapor of liquid at 70 °F.	Lower explosive limit in percent by volume of air at 70 °F
Methyl Acetate	40.0	3.1
Methyl Alcohol	80.8	7.3
Methyl Cellosolve	40.8	2.5
Methyl Ethyl Ketone	36.0	1.8
Methyl n-Propyl Ketone	30.4	1.5
Naphtha (VM&P) (76° Naphtha)	22.4	0.9
Naphtha (100 °Flash) Safety Solvent–Stoddard Solvent	23.2	1.0
Propyl Acetate (n)	27.2	2.8
Propyl Acetate (iso)	28.0	1.1
Propyl Alcohol (n)	44.8	2.1
Propyl Alcohol (iso)	44.0	2.0
Toluene	30.4	1.4
Turpentine	20.8	0.8
Xylene (o)	26.4	1.0

[1] At 212 °F.

(c)(6)(iii)(A) When an operator is in a booth downstream from the object being sprayed, an air-supplied respirator or other type of respirator must be used by employees that has been approved by NIOSH under 42 CFR part 84 for the material being sprayed.

(c)(6)(iii)(B) Where downdraft booths are provided with doors, such doors shall be closed when spray painting.

(c)(7) **Make-up air**

(c)(7)(i) Clean fresh air, free of contamination from adjacent industrial exhaust systems, chimneys, stacks, or vents, shall be supplied to a spray booth or room in quantities equal to the volume of air exhausted through the spray booth.

(c)(7)(ii) Where a spray booth or room receives make-up air through self-closing doors, dampers, or louvers, they shall be fully open at all times when the booth or room is in use for spraying. The velocity of air through such doors, dampers, or louvers shall not exceed 200 feet per minute. If the fan characteristics are such that the required air flow through the booth will be provided, higher velocities through the doors, dampers, or louvers may be used.

(c)(7)(iii)(A) Where the air supply to a spray booth or room is filtered, the fan static pressure shall be calculated on the assumption that the filters are dirty to the extent that they require cleaning or replacement.

(c)(7)(iii)(B) The rating of filters shall be governed by test data supplied by the manufacturer of the filter. A pressure gage shall be installed to show the pressure drop across the filters. This gage shall be marked to show the pressure drop at which the filters require cleaning or replacement. Filters shall be replaced or cleaned whenever the pressure drop across them becomes excessive or whenever the air flow through the face of the booth falls below that specified in Table G–10.

(c)(7)(iv)(A) Means for heating make-up air to any spray booth or room, before or at the time spraying is normally performed, shall be provided in all places where the outdoor temperature may be expected to remain below 55 °F for appreciable periods of time during the operation of the booth except where adequate and safe means of radiant heating for all operating personnel affected is provided. The replacement air during the heating seasons shall be maintained at not less than 65 °F at the point of entry into the spray booth or spray room. When otherwise unheated make-up air would be at a temperature of more than 10 °F below room temperature, its temperature shall be regulated as provided in section 3.6.3 of ANSI Z9.2–1960.

(c)(7)(iv)(B) As an alternative to an air replacement system complying with the preceding section, general heating of the building in which the spray room or booth is located may be employed provided that all occupied parts of the building are maintained at not less than 65 °F. when the exhaust system is in operation or the general heating system supplemented by other sources of heat may be employed to meet this requirement.

(c)(7)(iv)(C) No means of heating make-up air shall be located in a spray booth.

(c)(7)(iv)(D) Where make-up air is heated by coal or oil, the products of combustion shall not be allowed to mix with the make-up air, and the products of combustion shall be conducted outside the building through a flue terminating at a point remote from all points where make-up air enters the building.

(c)(7)(iv)(E) Where make-up air is heated by gas, and the products of combustion are not mixed with the make-up air but are conducted through an independent flue to a point outside the building remote from all points where make-up air enters the building, it is not necessary to comply with paragraph (c)(7)(iv)(f) of this section.

(c)(7)(iv)(F) Where make-up air to any manually operated spray booth or room is heated by gas and the products of combustion are allowed to mix with the supply air, the following precautions must be taken:

(c)(7)(iv)(F)(1) The gas must have a distinctive and strong enough odor to warn workmen in a spray booth or room of its presence if in an unburned state in the make-up air.

(c)(7)(iv)(F)(2) The maximum rate of gas supply to the make-up air heater burners must not exceed that which would yield in excess of 200 p.p.m. (parts per million) of carbon monoxide or 2,000 p.p.m. of total combustible gases in the mixture if the unburned gas upon the occurrence of flame failure were mixed with all of the make-up air supplied.

(c)(7)(iv)(F)(3) A fan must be provided to deliver the mixture of heated air and products of combustion from the plenum chamber housing the gas burners to the spray booth or room.

(c)(8) **Scope** Spray booths or spray rooms are to be used to enclose or confine all spray finishing operations covered by this paragraph (c). This paragraph does not apply to the spraying of the exteriors of buildings, fixed tanks, or similar structures, nor to small portable spraying apparatus not used repeatedly in the same location.

[39 FR 23502, June 27, 1974, as amended at 40 FR 23073, May 28, 1975; 40 FR 24522, June 9, 1975; 43 FR 49746, Oct. 24, 1978; 49 FR 5322, Feb. 10, 1984; 55 FR 32015, Aug. 6, 1990; 58 FR 35308, June 30, 1993; 61 FR 9236, Mar. 7, 1996; 63 FR 1269, Jan. 8, 1998; 64 FR 13909, Mar. 23, 1999; 72 FR 71069, Dec. 14, 2007; 74 FR 46356, Sept. 9, 2009]

§1910.95 Occupational noise exposure

(a) Protection against the effects of noise exposure shall be provided when the sound levels exceed those shown in Table G–16 when measured on the A scale of a standard sound level meter at slow response. When noise levels are determined by octave band analysis, the equivalent A-weighted sound level may be determined as follows:

Figure G–9

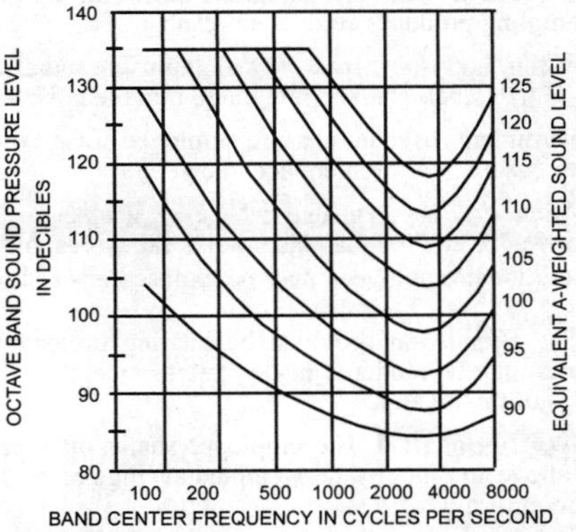

Equivalent sound level contours. Octave band sound pressure levels may be converted to the equivalent A-weighted sound level by plotting them on this graph and noting the A-weighted sound level corresponding to the point of highest penetration into the sound level contours. This equivalent A-weighted sound level, which may differ from the actual A-weighted sound level of the noise, is used to determine exposure limits from Table G–16.

(b)(1) When employees are subjected to sound exceeding those listed in Table G–16, feasible administrative or engineering controls shall be utilized. If such controls fail to reduce sound levels within the levels of Table G–16, personal protective equipment shall be provided and used to reduce sound levels within the levels of the table.

(b)(2) If the variations in noise level involve maxima at intervals of 1 second or less, it is to be considered continuous.

Table G–16—Permissible Noise Exposures[1]

Duration per day, hours	Sound level dBA slow response
8	90
6	92
4	95
3	97
2	100
1 ½	102
1	105
½	110
¼ or less	115

[1] When the daily noise exposure is composed of two or more periods of noise exposure of different levels, their combined effect should be considered, rather than the individual effect of each. If the sum of the following fractions: $C_1 / T_1 + C_2 / T_2 C_n / T_n$ exceeds unity, then, the mixed exposure should be considered to exceed the limit value. C_n indicates the total time of exposure at a specified noise level, and T_n indicates the total time of exposure permitted at that level.

Exposure to impulsive or impact noise should not exceed 140 dB peak sound pressure level.

(c) **Hearing conservation program**

(c)(1) The employer shall administer a continuing, effective hearing conservation program, as described in paragraphs (c) through (o) of this section, whenever employee noise exposures equal or exceed an 8-hour time-weighted average sound level (TWA) of 85 decibels measured on the A scale (slow response) or, equivalently, a dose of fifty percent. For purposes of the hearing conservation program, employee noise exposures shall be computed in accordance with Appendix A and Table G–16a, and without regard to any attenuation provided by the use of personal protective equipment.

(c)(2) For purposes of paragraphs (c) through (n) of this section, an 8-hour time-weighted average of 85 decibels or a dose of fifty percent shall also be referred to as the action level.

(d) **Monitoring**

(d)(1) When information indicates that any employee's exposure may equal or exceed an 8-hour time-weighted average of 85 decibels, the employer shall develop and implement a monitoring program.

(d)(1)(i) The sampling strategy shall be designed to identify employees for inclusion in the hearing conservation program and to enable the proper selection of hearing protectors.

(d)(1)(ii) Where circumstances such as high worker mobility, significant variations in sound level, or a significant component of impulse noise make area monitoring generally inappropriate, the employer shall use representative personal sampling to comply with the monitoring requirements of this paragraph unless the employer can show that area sampling produces equivalent results.

(d)(2)(i) All continuous, intermittent and impulsive sound levels from 80 decibels to 130 decibels shall be integrated into the noise measurements.

(d)(2)(ii) Instruments used to measure employee noise exposure shall be calibrated to ensure measurement accuracy.

(d)(3) Monitoring shall be repeated whenever a change in production, process, equipment or controls increases noise exposures to the extent that:

(d)(3)(i) Additional employees may be exposed at or above the action level; or

(d)(3)(ii) The attenuation provided by hearing protectors being used by employees may be rendered inadequate to meet the requirements of paragraph (j) of this section.

(e) **Employee notification** The employer shall notify each employee exposed at or above an 8-hour time-weighted average of 85 decibels of the results of the monitoring.

(f) **Observation of monitoring** The employer shall provide affected employees or their representatives with an opportunity to observe any noise measurements conducted pursuant to this section.

(g) **Audiometric testing program**

(g)(1) The employer shall establish and maintain an audiometric testing program as provided in this paragraph by making audiometric testing available to all employees whose exposures equal or exceed an 8-hour time-weighted average of 85 decibels.

(g)(2) The program shall be provided at no cost to employees.

(g)(3) Audiometric tests shall be performed by a licensed or certified audiologist, otolaryngologist, or other physician, or by a technician who is certified by the Council of Accreditation in Occupational Hearing Conservation, or who has satisfactorily demonstrated competence in administering audiometric examinations, obtaining valid audiograms, and properly using, maintaining and checking calibration and proper functioning of the audiometers being used. A technician who operates microprocessor audiometers does not need to be certified. A technician who performs audiometric tests must be responsible to an audiologist, otolaryngologist or physician.

(g)(4) All audiograms obtained pursuant to this section shall meet the requirements of Appendix C: Audiometric Measuring Instruments.

(g)(5) **Baseline audiogram**

(g)(5)(i) Within 6 months of an employee's first exposure at or above the action level, the employer shall establish a valid baseline audiogram against which subsequent audiograms can be compared.

(g)(5)(ii) Mobile test van exception. Where mobile test vans are used to meet the audiometric testing obligation, the employer shall obtain a valid baseline audiogram within 1 year of an employee's first exposure at or above the action level. Where baseline audiograms are obtained more than 6 months after the employee's first exposure at or above the action level, employees shall wearing hearing protectors for any period exceeding 6 months after first exposure until the baseline audiogram is obtained.

(g)(5)(iii) Testing to establish a baseline audiogram shall be preceded by at least 14 hours without exposure to workplace noise. Hearing protectors may be used as a substitute for the requirement that baseline audiograms be preceded by 14 hours without exposure to workplace noise.

(g)(5)(iv) The employer shall notify employees of the need to avoid high levels of non-occupational noise exposure during the 14-hour period immediately preceding the audiometric examination.

(g)(6) **Annual audiogram** At least annually after obtaining the baseline audiogram, the employer shall obtain a new audiogram for each employee exposed at or above an 8-hour time-weighted average of 85 decibels.

(g)(7) **Evaluation of audiogram**

(g)(7)(i) Each employee's annual audiogram shall be compared to that employee's baseline audiogram to determine if the audiogram is valid and if a standard threshold shift as defined in paragraph (g)(10) of this section has occurred. This comparison may be done by a technician.

(g)(7)(ii) If the annual audiogram shows that an employee has suffered a standard threshold shift, the employer may obtain a retest within 30 days and consider the results of the retest as the annual audiogram.

(g)(7)(iii) The audiologist, otolaryngologist, or physician shall review problem audiograms and shall determine whether there is a need for further evaluation. The employer shall provide to the person performing this evaluation the following information:

(g)(7)(iii)(A) A copy of the requirements for hearing conservation as set forth in paragraphs (c) through (n) of this section;

(g)(7)(iii)(B) The baseline audiogram and most recent audiogram of the employee to be evaluated;

(g)(7)(iii)(C) Measurements of background sound pressure levels in the audiometric test room as required in Appendix D: Audiometric Test Rooms.

(g)(7)(iii)(D) Records of audiometer calibrations required by paragraph (h)(5) of this section.

(g)(8) **Follow-up procedures**

(g)(8)(i) If a comparison of the annual audiogram to the baseline audiogram indicates a standard threshold shift as defined in paragraph (g)(10) of this section has occurred, the employee shall be informed of this fact in writing, within 21 days of the determination.

(g)(8)(ii) Unless a physician determines that the standard threshold shift is not work related or aggravated by occupational noise exposure, the employer shall ensure that the following steps are taken when a standard threshold shift occurs:

(g)(8)(ii)(A) Employees not using hearing protectors shall be fitted with hearing protectors, trained in their use and care, and required to use them;

(g)(8)(ii)(B) Employees already using hearing protectors shall be refitted and retrained in the use of hearing protectors and provided with hearing protectors offering greater attenuation if necessary;

(g)(8)(ii)(C) The employee shall be referred for a clinical audiological evaluation or an otological examination, as appropriate, if additional testing is necessary or if the employer suspects that a medical pathology of the ear is caused or aggravated by the wearing of hearing protectors;

(g)(8)(ii)(D) The employee is informed of the need for an otological examination if a medical pathology of the ear that is unrelated to the use of hearing protectors is suspected.

(g)(8)(iii) If subsequent audiometric testing of an employee whose exposure to noise is less than an 8-hour TWA of 90 decibels indicates that a standard threshold shift is not persistent, the employer:

(g)(8)(iii)(A) Shall inform the employee of the new audiometric interpretation; and (g)(8)(iii)(B) May discontinue the required use of hearing protectors for that employee.

(g)(9) **Revised baseline** An annual audiogram may be substituted for the baseline audiogram when, in the judgment of the audiologist, otolaryngologist or physician who is evaluating the audiogram:

(g)(9)(i) The standard threshold shift revealed by the audiogram is persistent; or

(g)(9)(ii) The hearing threshold shown in the annual audiogram indicates significant improvement over the baseline audiogram.

(g)(10) **Standard threshold shift**

(g)(10)(i) As used in this section, a standard threshold shift is a change in hearing threshold relative to the baseline audiogram of an average of 10 dB or more at 2000, 3000, and 4000 Hz in either ear.

(g)(10)(ii) In determining whether a standard threshold shift has occurred, allowance may be made for the contribution of aging (presbycusis) to the change in hearing level by correcting the annual audiogram according to the procedure described in Appendix F: Calculation and Application of Age Correction to Audiograms.

(h) **Audiometric test requirements**

(h)(1) Audiometric tests shall be pure tone, air conduction, hearing threshold examinations, with test frequencies including as a minimum 500, 1000, 2000, 3000, 4000, and 6000 Hz. Tests at each frequency shall be taken separately for each ear.

(h)(2) Audiometric tests shall be conducted with audiometers (including microprocessor audiometers) that meet the specifications of, and are maintained and used in accordance with, American National Standard Specification for Audiometers, S3.6–1969, which is incorporated by reference as specified in §1910.6.

(h)(3) Pulsed-tone and self-recording audiometers, if used, shall meet the requirements specified in Appendix C: Audiometric Measuring Instruments.

(h)(4) Audiometric examinations shall be administered in a room meeting the requirements listed in Appendix D: Audiometric Test Rooms.

(h)(5) **Audiometer calibration**

(h)(5)(i) The functional operation of the audiometer shall be checked before each day's use by testing a person with known, stable hearing thresholds, and by listening to the audiometer's output to make sure that the output is free from distorted or unwanted sounds. Deviations of 10 decibels or greater require an acoustic calibration.

(h)(5)(ii) Audiometer calibration shall be checked acoustically at least annually in accordance with Appendix E: Acoustic Calibration of Audiometers. Test frequencies below 500 Hz and above 6000 Hz may be omitted from this check. Deviations of 15 decibels or greater require an exhaustive calibration.

(h)(5)(iii) An exhaustive calibration shall be performed at least every two years in accordance with sections 4.1.2; 4.1.3.; 4.1.4.3; 4.2; 4.4.1; 4.4.2; 4.4.3; and 4.5 of the American National Standard Specification for Audiometers, S3.6–1969. Test frequencies below 500 Hz and above 6000 Hz may be omitted from this calibration.

(i) **Hearing protectors**

(i)(1) Employers shall make hearing protectors available to all employees exposed to an 8-hour time-weighted average of 85 decibels or greater at no cost to the employees. Hearing protectors shall be replaced as necessary.

(i)(2) Employers shall ensure that hearing protectors are worn:

(i)(2)(i) By an employee who is required by paragraph (b)(1) of this section to wear personal protective equipment; and

(i)(2)(ii) By any employee who is exposed to an 8-hour time-weighted average of 85 decibels or greater, and who:

(i)(2)(ii)(A) Has not yet had a baseline audiogram established pursuant to paragraph (g)(5)(ii); or

(i)(2)(ii)(B) Has experienced a standard threshold shift.

(i)(3) Employees shall be given the opportunity to select their hearing protectors from a variety of suitable hearing protectors provided by the employer.

(i)(4) The employer shall provide training in the use and care of all hearing protectors provided to employees.

(i)(5) The employer shall ensure proper initial fitting and supervise the correct use of all hearing protectors.

(j) **Hearing protector attenuation**

(j)(1) The employer shall evaluate hearing protector attenuation for the specific noise environments in which the protector will be used. The employer shall use one of the evaluation methods described in Appendix B: Methods for Estimating the Adequacy of Hearing Protection Attenuation.

(j)(2) Hearing protectors must attenuate employee exposure at least to an 8-hour time-weighted average of 90 decibels as required by paragraph (b) of this section.

(j)(3) For employees who have experienced a standard threshold shift, hearing protectors must attenuate employee exposure to an 8-hour time-weighted average of 85 decibels or below.

(j)(4) The adequacy of hearing protector attenuation shall be re-evaluated whenever employee noise exposures increase to the extent that the hearing protectors provided may no longer provide adequate attenuation. The employer shall provide more effective hearing protectors where necessary.

(k) **Training program**

(k)(1) The employer shall train each employee who is exposed to noise at or above an 8-hour time weighted average of 85 decibels in accordance with the requirements of this section. The employer shall institute a training program and ensure employee participation in the program.

(k)(2) The training program shall be repeated annually for each employee included in the hearing conservation program. Information provided in the training program shall be updated to be consistent with changes in protective equipment and work processes.

(k)(3) The employer shall ensure that each employee is informed of the following:

(k)(3)(i) The effects of noise on hearing;

(k)(3)(ii) The purpose of hearing protectors, the advantages, disadvantages, and attenuation of various types, and instructions on selection, fitting, use, and care; and

(k)(3)(iii) The purpose of audiometric testing, and an explanation of the test procedures.

(l) **Access to information and training materials**

(l)(1) The employer shall make available to affected employees or their representatives copies of this standard and shall also post a copy in the workplace.

(l)(2) The employer shall provide to affected employees any informational materials pertaining to the standard that are supplied to the employer by the Assistant Secretary.

(l)(3) The employer shall provide, upon request, all materials related to the employer's training and education program pertaining to this standard to the Assistant Secretary and the Director.

(m) **Recordkeeping**

(m)(1) **Exposure measurements** The employer shall maintain an accurate record of all employee exposure measurements required by paragraph (d) of this section.

(m)(2) **Audiometric tests**

(m)(2)(i) The employer shall retain all employee audiometric test records obtained pursuant to paragraph (g) of this section.

(m)(2)(ii) This record shall include:

(m)(2)(ii)(A) Name and job classification of the employee;

(m)(2)(ii)(B) Date of the audiogram;

(m)(2)(ii)(C) The examiner's name;

(m)(2)(ii)(D) Date of the last acoustic or exhaustive calibration of the audiometer;

(m)(2)(ii)(E) Employee's most recent noise exposure assessment; and

(m)(2)(ii)(F) The employer shall maintain accurate records of the measurements of the background sound pressure levels in audiometric test rooms.

(m)(3) **Record retention** The employer shall retain records required in this paragraph (m) for at least the following periods.

(m)(3)(i) Noise exposure measurement records shall be retained for two years.

(m)(3)(ii) Audiometric test records shall be retained for the duration of the affected employee's employment.

(m)(4) **Access to records** All records required by this section shall be provided upon request to employees, former employees, representatives designated by the individual employee, and the Assistant Secretary. The provisions of 29 CFR §1910.1020 (a)–(e) and (g)–(i) apply to access to records under this section.

(m)(5) **Transfer of records** If the employer ceases to do business, the employer shall transfer to the successor employer all records required to be maintained by this section, and the successor employer shall retain them for the remainder of the period prescribed in paragraph (m)(3) of this section.

(n) **Appendices**

(n)(1) Appendices A, B, C, D, and E to this section are incorporated as part of this section and the contents of these Appendices are mandatory.

(n)(2) Appendices F and G to this section are informational and are not intended to create any additional obligations not otherwise imposed or to detract from any existing obligations.

(o) **Exemptions** Paragraphs (c) through (n) of this section shall not apply to employers engaged in oil and gas well drilling and servicing operations.

§1910.95 Appendix A Noise exposure computation

This Appendix is Mandatory

I. Computation of Employee Noise Exposure

(1) Noise dose is computed using Table G–16a as follows:

(i) When the sound level, L, is constant over the entire work shift, the noise dose, D, in percent, is given by: D=100 C/T where C is the total length of the work day, in hours, and T is the reference duration corresponding to the measured sound level, L, as given in Table G–16a or by the formula shown as a footnote to that table.

(ii) When the workshift noise exposure is composed of two or more periods of noise at different levels, the total noise dose over the work day is given by:

$$D = 100(C_1/T_1 + C_2/T_2 + C_n/T_n),$$

where C_n indicates the total time of exposure at a specific noise level, and T_n indicates the reference duration for that level as given by Table G–16a.

(2) The eight-hour time-weighted average sound level (TWA), in decibels, may be computed from the dose, in percent, by means of the formula:

$$TWA = 16.61 \log_{10}(D/100) + 90$$

For an eight-hour workshift with the noise level constant over the entire shift, the TWA is equal to the measured sound level.

(3) A table relating dose and TWA is given in Section II.

Table G–16a

A-weighted sound level, L (decibel)	Reference duration, T (hour)
80	32
81	27.9
82	24.3
83	21.1
84	18.4
85	16
86	13.9
87	12.1
88	10.6
89	9.2
90	8
91	7.0
92	6.1
93	5.3
94	4.6
95	4
96	3.5
97	3.0
98	2.6
99	2.3
100	2
101	1.7
102	1.5
103	1.3
104	1.1
105	1
106	0.87
107	0.76
108	0.66
109	0.57
110	0.5
111	0.44
112	0.38
113	0.33
114	0.29
115	0.25
116	0.22
117	0.19
118	0.16
119	0.14
120	0.125
121	0.11
122	0.095
123	0.082
124	0.072
125	0.063
126	0.054
127	0.047
128	0.041
129	0.036
130	0.031

In the above table the reference duration, T is computed by

$$T = \frac{8}{2^{(L-90)/5}}$$

where L is the measured A-weighted sound level.

II. Conversion Between "Dose" and "8-Hour Time-Weighted Average" Sound Level

Compliance with paragraphs (c)–(r) of this regulation is determined by the amount of exposure to noise in the workplace. The amount of such exposure is usually measured with an audiodosimeter which gives a readout in terms of "dose." In order to better understand the requirements of the amendment, dosimeter readings can be converted to an "8-hour time-weighted average sound level." (TWA).

In order to convert the reading of a dosimeter into TWA, see Table A–1, below. This table applies to dosimeters that are set by the manufacturer to calculate dose or percent exposure according to the relationships in Table G–16a. So, for example, a dose of 91 percent over an eight hour day results in a TWA of 89.3 dB, and, a dose of 50 percent corresponds to a TWA of 85 dB.

If the dose as read on the dosimeter is less than or greater than the values found in Table A–1, the TWA may be calculated by using the formula:

$$TWA = 16.61 \log_{10}(D/100) + 90$$

where TWA=8-hour time-weighted average sound level and D = accumulated dose in percent exposure.

Table A–1
Conversion From "Percent Noise Exposure" or "Dose" to "8-Hour Time-Weighted Average Sound Level" (TWA)

Dose or percent noise exposure	TWA
10	73.4
15	76.3
20	78.4
25	80.0
30	81.3
35	82.4
40	83.4
45	84.2

Dose or percent noise exposure	TWA
50	85.0
55	85.7
60	86.3
65	86.9
70	87.4
75	87.9
80	88.4
81	88.5
82	88.6
83	88.7
84	88.7
85	88.8
86	88.9
87	89.0
88	89.1
89	89.2
90	89.2
91	89.3
92	89.4
93	89.5
94	89.6
95	89.6
96	89.7
97	89.8
98	89.9
99	89.9
100	90.0
101	90.1
102	90.1
103	90.2
104	90.3
105	90.4
106	90.4
107	90.5
108	90.6
109	90.6
110	90.7
111	90.8
112	90.8
113	90.9
114	90.9
115	91.1
116	91.1
117	91.1
118	91.2
119	91.3
120	91.3
125	91.6
130	91.9
135	92.2
140	92.4
145	92.7
150	92.9
155	93.2
160	93.4
165	93.6
170	93.8
175	94.0
180	94.2
185	94.4
190	94.6
195	94.8
200	95.0
210	95.4
220	95.7
230	96.0
240	96.3
250	96.6
260	96.9
270	97.2
280	97.4
290	97.7
300	97.9
310	98.2
320	98.4
330	98.6
340	98.8
350	99.0
360	99.2
370	99.4
380	99.6
390	99.8
400	100.0
410	100.2
420	100.4
430	100.5
440	100.7
450	100.8
460	101.0
470	101.2
480	101.3
490	101.5
500	101.6
510	101.8
520	101.9
530	102.0
540	102.2
550	102.3
560	102.4
570	102.6
580	102.7
590	102.8
600	102.9

Note: Table data continues on next page.

Dose or percent noise exposure	TWA
610	103.0
620	103.2
630	103.3
640	103.4
650	103.5
660	103.6
670	103.7
680	103.8
690	103.9
700	104.0
710	104.1
720	104.2
730	104.3
740	104.4
750	104.5
760	104.6
770	104.7
780	104.8
790	104.9
800	105.0
810	105.1
820	105.2
830	105.3
840	105.4
850	105.4
860	105.5
870	105.6
880	105.7
890	105.8
900	105.8
910	105.9
920	106.0
930	106.1
940	106.2
950	106.2
960	106.3
970	106.4
980	106.5
990	106.5
999	106.6

§1910.95 Appendix B
Methods for estimating the adequacy of hearing protector attenuation

This Appendix is Mandatory

For employees who have experienced a significant threshold shift, hearing protector attenuation must be sufficient to reduce employee exposure to a TWA of 85 dB. Employers must select one of the following methods by which to estimate the adequacy of hearing protector attenuation.

The most convenient method is the Noise Reduction Rating (NRR) developed by the Environmental Protection Agency (EPA). According to EPA regulation, the NRR must be shown on the hearing protector package. The NRR is then related to an individual worker's noise environment in order to assess the adequacy of the attenuation of a given hearing protector. This Appendix describes four methods of using the NRR to determine whether a particular hearing protector provides adequate protection within a given exposure environment. Selection among the four procedures is dependent upon the employer's noise measuring instruments.

Instead of using the NRR, employers may evaluate the adequacy of hearing protector attenuation by using one of the three methods developed by the National Institute for Occupational Safety and Health (NIOSH), which are described in the "List of Personal Hearing Protectors and Attenuation Data," HEW Publication No. 76–120, 1975, pages 21–37. These methods are known as NIOSH methods #1B1, #1B2 and #1B3. The NRR described below is a simplification of NIOSH method #1B2. The most complex method is NIOSH method #1B1, which is probably the most accurate method since it uses the largest amount of spectral information from the individual employee's noise environment. As in the case of the NRR method described below, if one of the NIOSH methods is used, the selected method must be applied to an individual's noise environment to assess the adequacy of the attenuation. Employers should be careful to take a sufficient number of measurements in order to achieve a representative sample for each time segment.

Note: The employer must remember that calculated attenuation values reflect realistic values only to the extent that the protectors are properly fitted and worn.

When using the NRR to assess hearing protector adequacy, one of the following methods must be used:

(i) When using a dosimeter that is capable of C-weighted measurements:
(A) Obtain the employee's C-weighted dose for the entire workshift, and convert to TWA (see Appendix A, II);
(B) Subtract the NRR from the C-weighted TWA to obtain the estimated A-weighted TWA under the ear protector.

(ii) When using a dosimeter that is not capable of C-weighted measurements, the following method may be used:
(A) Convert the A-weighted dose to TWA (see Appendix A);
(B) Subtract 7 dB from the NRR;
(C) Subtract the remainder from the A-weighted TWA to obtain the estimated A-weighted TWA under the ear protector.

(iii) When using a sound level meter set to the A-weighting network:
(A) Obtain the employee's A-weighted TWA;
(B) Subtract 7 dB from the NRR, and subtract the remainder from the A-weighted TWA to obtain the estimated A-weighted TWA under the ear protector.

(iv) When using a sound level meter set on the C-weighting network:
(A) Obtain a representative sample of the C-weighted sound levels in the employee's environment;
(B) Subtract the NRR from the C-weighted average sound level to obtain the estimated A-weighted TWA under the ear protector.

(v) When using area monitoring procedures and a sound level meter set to the A-weighing network:
(A) Obtain a representative sound level for the area in question;
(B) Subtract 7 dB from the NRR and subtract the remainder from the A-weighted sound level for that area.

(vi) When using area monitoring procedures and a sound level meter set to the C-weighting network:
(A) Obtain a representative sound level for the area in question;
(B) Subtract the NRR from the C-weighted sound level for that area.

§1910.95 Appendix C OI
Audiometric measuring instruments

This Appendix is Mandatory

1. In the event that pulsed-tone audiometers are used, they shall have a tone on-time of at least 200 milliseconds.

2. Self-recording audiometers shall comply with the following requirements:
(A) The chart upon which the audiogram is traced shall have lines at positions corresponding to all multiples of 10 dB hearing level within the intensity range spanned by the audiometer. The lines shall be equally spaced and shall be separated by at least1/4inch. Additional increments are optional. The audiogram pen tracings shall not exceed 2 dB in width.
(B) It shall be possible to set the stylus manually at the 10-dB increment lines for calibration purposes.
(C) The slewing rate for the audiometer attenuator shall not be more than 6 dB/sec except that an initial slewing rate greater than 6 dB/sec is permitted at the beginning of each new test frequency, but only until the second subject response.
(D) The audiometer shall remain at each required test frequency for 30 seconds (± 3 seconds). The audiogram shall be clearly marked at each change of frequency and the actual frequency change of the audiometer shall not deviate from the frequency boundaries marked on the audiogram by more than ± 3 seconds.
(E) It must be possible at each test frequency to place a horizontal line segment parallel to the time axis on the audiogram, such that the audiometric tracing crosses the line segment at least six times at that test frequency. At each test frequency the threshold shall be the average of the midpoints of the tracing excursions.

§1910.95 Appendix D
Audiometric test rooms

This Appendix is Mandatory

Rooms used for audiometric testing shall not have background sound pressure levels exceeding those in Table D–1 when measured by equipment conforming at least to the Type 2 requirements of American National Standard Specification for Sound Level Meters, S1.4–1971 (R1976), and to the Class II requirements of American National Standard Specification for Octave, Half-Octave, and Third-Octave Band Filter Sets, S1.11–1971 (R1976).

Table D–1
Maximum Allowable Octave-Band Sound Pressure Levels for Audiometric Test Rooms

Octave-band center frequency (Hz)	500	1000	2000	4000	8000
Sound pressure level (dB)	40	40	47	57	62

§1910.95 Appendix E
Acoustic calibration of audiometers

This Appendix is Mandatory

Audiometer calibration shall be checked acoustically, at least annually, according to the procedures described in this Appendix. The equipment necessary to perform these measurements is a sound level meter, octave-band filter set, and a National Bureau of Standards 9A coupler. In making these measurements, the accuracy of the calibrating equipment shall be sufficient to determine that the audiometer is within the tolerances permitted by American Standard Specification for Audiometers, S3.6–1969.

(1) Sound Pressure Output Check

A. Place the earphone coupler over the microphone of the sound level meter and place the earphone on the coupler.

B. Set the audiometer's hearing threshold level (HTL) dial to 70 dB.

C. Measure the sound pressure level of the tones at each test frequency from 500 Hz through 6000 Hz for each earphone.

D. At each frequency the readout on the sound level meter should correspond to the levels in Table E–1 or Table E–2, as appropriate, for the type of earphone, in the column entitled "sound level meter reading."

(2) Linearity Check

A. With the earphone in place, set the frequency to 1000 Hz and the HTL dial on the audiometer to 70 dB.

B. Measure the sound levels in the coupler at each 10-dB decrement from 70 dB to 10 dB, noting the sound level meter reading at each setting.

C. For each 10-dB decrement on the audiometer the sound level meter should indicate a corresponding 10 dB decrease.

D. This measurement may be made electrically with a voltmeter connected to the earphone terminals.

(3) Tolerances

When any of the measured sound levels deviate from the levels in Table E–1 or Table E–2 by ± 3 dB at any test frequency between 500 and 3000 Hz, 4 dB at 4000 Hz, or 5 dB at 6000 Hz, an exhaustive calibration is advised. An exhaustive calibration is required if the deviations are greater than 15 dB or greater at any test frequency.

Table E–1
Reference Threshold Levels for Telephonics—TDH–39 Earphones

Frequency, Hz	Reference threshold level for TDH–39 earphones, dB	Sound level meter reading, dB
500	11.5	81.5
1000	7	77
2000	9	79
3000	10	80
4000	9.5	79.5
6000	15.5	85.5

Table E–2
Reference Threshold Levels for Telephonics—TDH–49 Earphones

Frequency, Hz	Reference threshold level for TDH–49 earphones, dB	Sound level meter reading, dB
500	13.5	83.5
1000	7.5	77.5
2000	11	81.0
3000	9.5	79.5
4000	10.5	80.5
6000	13.5	83.5

§1910.95 Appendix F
Calculations and application of age corrections to audiograms

This Appendix Is Non-Mandatory

In determining whether a standard threshold shift has occurred, allowance may be made for the contribution of aging to the change in hearing level by adjusting the most recent audiogram. If the employer chooses to adjust the audiogram, the employer shall follow the procedure described below. This procedure and the age correction tables were developed by the National Institute for Occupational Safety and Health in the criteria document entitled "Criteria for a Recommended Standard . . . Occupational Exposure to Noise," ((HSM)–11001).

For each audiometric test frequency;

(i) Determine from Tables F–1 or F–2 the age correction values for the employee by:

(A) Finding the age at which the most recent audiogram was taken and recording the corresponding values of age corrections at 1000 Hz through 6000 Hz;

(B) Finding the age at which the baseline audiogram was taken and recording the corresponding values of age corrections at 1000 Hz through 6000 Hz.

(ii) Subtract the values found in step (i)(B) from the value found in step (i)(A).

(iii) The differences calculated in step (ii) represented that portion of the change in hearing that may be due to aging.

Example: Employee is a 32-year-old male. The audiometric history for his right ear is shown in decibels below.

Employee's age	Audiometric test frequency (Hz)				
	1000	2000	3000	4000	6000
26	10	5	5	10	5
*27	0	0	0	5	5
28	0	0	0	10	5
29	5	0	5	15	5
30	0	5	10	20	10
31	5	10	20	15	15
*32	5	10	10	25	20

The audiogram at age 27 is considered the baseline since it shows the best hearing threshold levels. Asterisks have been used to identify the baseline and most recent audiogram. A threshold shift of 20 dB exists at 4000 Hz between the audiograms taken at ages 27 and 32.

(The threshold shift is computed by subtracting the hearing threshold at age 27, which was 5, from the hearing threshold at age 32, which is 25). A retest audiogram has confirmed this shift. The contribution of aging to this change in hearing may be estimated in the following manner:

Go to Table F–1 and find the age correction values (in dB) for 4000 Hz at age 27 and age 32.

	Frequency (Hz)				
	1000	2000	3000	4000	6000
Age 32	6	5	7	10	14
Age 27	5	4	6	7	11
Difference	1	1	1	3	3

The difference represents the amount of hearing loss that may be attributed to aging in the time period between the baseline audiogram and the most recent audiogram. In this example, the difference at 4000 Hz is 3 dB. This value is subtracted from the hearing level at 4000 Hz, which in the most recent audiogram is 25, yielding 22 after adjustment. Then the hearing threshold in the baseline audiogram at 4000 Hz (5) is subtracted from the adjusted annual audiogram hearing threshold at 4000 Hz (22). Thus the age-corrected threshold shift would be 17 dB (as opposed to a threshold shift of 20 dB without age correction).

Table F–1

Age Correction Values in Decibels for Males

Years	Audiometric Test Frequencies (Hz)				
	1000	2000	3000	4000	6000
20 or younger	5	3	4	5	8
21	5	3	4	5	8
22	5	3	4	5	8
23	5	3	4	6	9
24	5	3	5	6	9
25	5	3	5	7	10
26	5	4	5	7	10
27	5	4	6	7	11
28	6	4	6	8	11
29	6	4	6	8	12
30	6	4	6	9	12
31	6	4	7	9	13
32	6	5	7	10	14
33	6	5	7	10	14
34	6	5	8	11	15
35	7	5	8	11	15
36	7	5	9	12	16
37	7	6	9	12	17
38	7	6	9	13	17
39	7	6	10	14	18
40	7	6	10	14	19
41	7	6	10	14	20
42	8	7	11	16	20
43	8	7	12	16	21
44	8	7	12	17	22
45	8	7	13	18	23
46	8	8	13	19	24
47	8	8	14	19	24
48	9	8	14	20	25
49	9	9	15	21	26
50	9	9	16	22	27
51	9	9	16	23	28
52	9	10	17	24	29
53	9	10	18	25	30
54	10	10	18	26	31
55	10	11	19	27	32
56	10	11	20	28	34
57	10	11	21	29	35
58	10	12	22	31	36
59	11	12	22	32	37
60 or older	11	13	23	33	38

Table F–2

Age Correction Values in Decibels for Females

Years	Audiometric Test Frequencies (Hz)				
	1000	2000	3000	4000	6000
20 or younger	7	4	3	3	6
21	7	4	4	3	6
22	7	4	4	4	6
23	7	5	4	4	7
24	7	5	4	4	7
25	8	5	4	4	7
26	8	5	5	4	8
27	8	5	5	5	8
28	8	5	5	5	8
29	8	5	5	5	9
30	8	6	5	5	9
31	8	6	6	5	9
32	9	6	6	6	10
33	9	6	6	6	10
34	9	6	6	6	10
35	9	6	7	7	11
36	9	7	7	7	11
37	9	7	7	7	12
38	10	7	7	7	12
39	10	7	8	8	12
40	10	7	8	8	13
41	10	8	8	8	13
42	10	8	9	9	13
43	11	8	9	9	14
44	11	8	9	9	14
45	11	8	10	10	15
46	11	9	10	10	15
47	11	9	10	11	16
48	12	9	11	11	16
49	12	9	11	11	16
50	12	10	11	12	17
51	12	10	12	12	17
52	12	10	12	13	18
53	13	10	13	13	18
54	13	11	13	14	19
55	13	11	14	14	19
56	13	11	14	15	20
57	13	11	15	15	20
58	14	12	15	16	21
59	14	12	16	16	21
60 or older	14	12	16	17	22

§1910.95 Appendix G
Monitoring noise levels
Nonmandatory Informational Appendix

This Appendix provides information to help employers comply with the noise monitoring obligations that are part of the hearing conservation amendment.

What is the purpose of noise monitoring?

This revised amendment requires that employees be placed in a hearing conservation program if they are exposed to average noise levels of 85 dB or greater during an 8 hour workday. In order to determine if exposures are at or above this level, it may be necessary to measure or monitor the actual noise levels in the workplace and to estimate the noise exposure or "dose" received by employees during the workday.

When is it necessary to implement a noise monitoring program?

It is not necessary for every employer to measure workplace noise. Noise monitoring or measuring must be conducted only when exposures are at or above 85 dB. Factors which suggest that noise exposures in the workplace may be at this level include employee complaints about the loudness of noise, indications that employees are losing their hearing, or noisy conditions which make normal conversation difficult. The employer should also consider any information available regarding noise emitted from specific machines. In addition, actual workplace noise measurements can suggest whether or not a monitoring program should be initiated.

How is noise measured?

Basically, there are two different instruments to measure noise exposures: the sound level meter and the dosimeter. A sound level meter is a device that measures the intensity of sound at a given moment. Since sound level meters provide a measure of sound intensity at only one point in time, it is generally necessary to take a number of measurements at different times during the day to estimate noise exposure over a workday. If noise levels fluctuate, the amount of time noise remains at each of the various measured levels must be determined.

To estimate employee noise exposures with a sound level meter it is also generally necessary to take several measurements at different locations within the workplace. After appropriate sound level meter readings are obtained, people sometimes draw "maps" of the sound levels within different areas of the workplace. By using a sound level "map" and information on employee locations throughout the day, estimates of individual exposure levels can be developed. This measurement method is generally referred to as area noise monitoring.

A dosimeter is like a sound level meter except that it stores sound level measurements and integrates these measurements over time, providing an average noise exposure reading for a given period of time, such as an 8-hour workday. With a dosimeter, a microphone is attached to the employee's clothing and the exposure measurement is simply read at the end of the desired time period. A reader may be used to read-out the dosimeter's measurements. Since the dosimeter is worn by the employee, it measures noise levels in those locations in which the employee travels. A sound level meter can also be positioned within the immediate vicinity of the exposed worker to obtain an individual exposure estimate. Such procedures are generally referred to as personal noise monitoring.

Area monitoring can be used to estimate noise exposure when the noise levels are relatively constant and employees are not mobile. In workplaces where employees move about in different areas or where the noise intensity tends to fluctuate over time, noise exposure is generally more accurately estimated by the personal monitoring approach.

In situations where personal monitoring is appropriate, proper positioning of the microphone is necessary to obtain accurate measurements. With a dosimeter, the microphone is generally located on the shoulder and remains in that position for the entire workday. With a sound level meter, the microphone is stationed near the employee's head, and the instrument is usually held by an individual who follows the employee as he or she moves about.

Manufacturer's instructions, contained in dosimeter and sound level meter operating manuals, should be followed for calibration and maintenance. To ensure accurate results, it is considered good professional practice to calibrate instruments before and after each use.

How often is it necessary to monitor noise levels?

The amendment requires that when there are significant changes in machinery or production processes that may result in increased noise levels, remonitoring must be conducted to determine whether additional employees need to be included in the hearing conservation program. Many companies choose to remonitor periodically (once every year or two) to ensure that all exposed employees are included in their hearing conservation programs.

Where can equipment and technical advice be obtained?

Noise monitoring equipment may be either purchased or rented. Sound level meters cost about $500 to $1,000, while dosimeters range in price from about $750 to $1,500. Smaller companies may find it more economical to rent equipment rather than to purchase it. Names of equipment suppliers may be found in the telephone book (Yellow Pages) under headings such as: "Safety Equipment," "Industrial Hygiene," or "Engineers-Acoustical." In addition to providing information on obtaining noise monitoring equipment, many companies and individuals included under such listings can provide professional advice on how to conduct a valid noise monitoring program. Some audiological testing firms and industrial hygiene firms also provide noise monitoring services. Universities with audiology, industrial hygiene, or acoustical engineering departments may also provide information or may be able to help employers meet their obligations under this amendment.

Free, on-site assistance may be obtained from OSHA-supported state and private consultation organizations. These safety and health consultative entities generally give priority to the needs of small businesses.

§1910.95 Appendix H
Availability of referenced documents

Paragraphs (c) through (o) of 29 CFR §1910.95 and the accompanying Appendices contain provisions which incorporate publications by reference. Generally, the publications provide criteria for instruments to be used in monitoring and audiometric testing. These criteria are intended to be mandatory when so indicated in the applicable paragraphs of §1910.95 and Appendices.

It should be noted that OSHA does not require that employers purchase a copy of the referenced publications. Employers, however, may desire to obtain a copy of the referenced publications for their own information.

The designation of the paragraph of the standard in which the referenced publications appear, the titles of the publications, and the availability of the publications are as follows:

Paragraph designation	Referenced publication	Available from—
Appendix B	"List of Personal Hearing Protectors and Attenuation Data," HEW Pub. No. 76–120, 1975. NTIS-PB267461	National Technical Information Service, Port Royal Road, Springfield, VA 22161.
Appendix D	"Specification for Sound Level Meters," S1.4–1971 (R1976)	American National Standards Institute, Inc., 1430 Broadway, New York, NY 10018.
§1910.95(k)(2), Appendix E	"Specifications for Audiometers," S3.6–1969	American National Standards Institute, Inc., 1430 Broadway, New York, NY 10018.
Appendix D	"Specification for Octave, Half-Octave and Third-Octave Band Filter Sets," S1.11–1971 (R1976)	Back Numbers Department, Dept. STD, American Institute of Physics, 333 E. 45th St., New York, NY 10017; American National Standards Institute, Inc., 1430 Broadway, New York, NY 10018.

The referenced publications (or a microfiche of the publications) are available for review at many universities and public libraries throughout the country. These publications may also be examined at the OSHA Technical Data Center, Room N2439, United States Department of Labor, 200 Constitution Avenue, NW., Washington, DC 20210, (202) 219–7500 or at any OSHA Regional Office (see telephone directories under United States Government—Labor Department).

§1910.95 Appendix I
Definitions

These definitions apply to the following terms as used in paragraphs (c) through (n) of 29 CFR §1910.95.

Action level An 8-hour time-weighted average of 85 decibels measured on the A-scale, slow response, or equivalently, a dose of fifty percent.

Audiogram A chart, graph, or table resulting from an audiometric test showing an individual's hearing threshold levels as a function of frequency.

Audiologist A professional, specializing in the study and rehabilitation of hearing, who is certified by the American Speech-Language-Hearing Association or licensed by a state board of examiners.

Baseline audiogram The audiogram against which future audiograms are compared.

Criterion sound level A sound level of 90 decibels.

Decibel (dB) Unit of measurement of sound level.

Hertz (Hz) Unit of measurement of frequency, numerically equal to cycles per second.

Medical pathology A disorder or disease. For purposes of this regulation, a condition or disease affecting the ear, which should be treated by a physician specialist.

Noise dose The ratio, expressed as a percentage, of (1) the time integral, over a stated time or event, of the 0.6 power of the measured SLOW exponential time-averaged, squared A-weighted sound pressure and (2) the product of the criterion duration (8 hours) and the 0.6 power of the squared sound pressure corresponding to the criterion sound level (90 dB).

Noise dosimeter An instrument that integrates a function of sound pressure over a period of time in such a manner that it directly indicates a noise dose.

Otolaryngologist A physician specializing in diagnosis and treatment of disorders of the ear, nose and throat.

Representative exposure Measurements of an employee's noise dose or 8-hour time-weighted average sound level that the employers deem to be representative of the exposures of other employees in the workplace.

Sound level Ten times the common logarithm of the ratio of the square of the measured A-weighted sound pressure to the square of the standard reference pressure of 20 micropascals. Unit: decibels (dB). For use with this regulation, SLOW time response, in accordance with ANSI S1.4–1971 (R1976), is required.

Sound level meter An instrument for the measurement of sound level.

Time-weighted average sound level That sound level, which if constant over an 8-hour exposure, would result in the same noise dose as is measured.

[39 FR 23502, June 27, 1974, as amended at 46 FR 4161, Jan. 16, 1981; 46 FR 62845, Dec. 29, 1981; 48 FR 9776, Mar. 8, 1983; 48 FR 29687, June 28, 1983; 54 FR 24333, June 7, 1989; 61 FR 9236, Mar. 7, 1996; 71 FR 16672, Apr. 3, 2006; 73 FR 75584, Dec. 12, 2008]

§1910.97 OI Nonionizing radiation

(a) **Electromagnetic radiation**

(a)(1) **Definitions applicable to this paragraph**

(a)(1)(i) The term **electromagnetic radiation** is restricted to that portion of the spectrum commonly defined as the radio frequency region, which for the purpose of this specification shall include the microwave frequency region.

(a)(1)(ii) **Partial body irradiation** Pertains to the case in which part of the body is exposed to the incident electromagnetic energy.

(a)(1)(iii) **Radiation protection guide** Radiation level which should not be exceeded without careful consideration of the reasons for doing so.

(a)(1)(iv) The word **"symbol"** as used in this specification refers to the overall design, shape, and coloring of the rf radiation sign shown in figure G–11.

(a)(1)(v) **Whole body irradiation** Pertains to the case in which the entire body is exposed to the incident electromagnetic energy or in which the cross section of the body is smaller than the cross section of the incident radiation beam.

(a)(2) **Radiation protection guide**

(a)(2)(i) For normal environmental conditions and for incident electromagnetic energy of frequencies from 10 MHz to 100 GHz, the radiation protection guide is 10 mW/cm.2 (milliwatt per square centimeter) as averaged over any possible 0.1-hour period. This means the following:

- Power density: 10 mW./cm.2 for periods of 0.1-hour or more;
- Energy density: 1 mW.-hr./cm.2 (milliwatt hour per square centimeter) during any 0.1-hour period;
- This guide applies whether the radiation is continuous or intermittent.

(a)(2)(ii) These formulated recommendations pertain to both whole body irradiation and partial body irradiation. Partial body irradiation must be included since it has been shown that some parts of the human body (e.g., eyes, testicles) may be harmed if exposed to incident radiation levels significantly in excess of the recommended levels.

(a)(3) **Warning symbol**

(a)(3)(i) The warning symbol for radio frequency radiation hazards shall consist of a red isosceles triangle above an inverted black isosceles triangle, separated and outlined by an aluminum color border. The words "Warning—Radio-Frequency Radiation Hazard" shall appear in the upper triangle. See figure G–11.

(a)(3)(ii) ANSI Z53.1–1967 or ANSI Z535.1–2006(R2011), incorporated by reference in §1910.6, is for use for color specification. All lettering and the border shall be of aluminum color.

(a)(3)(iii) The inclusion and choice of warning information or precautionary instructions is at the discretion of the user. If such information is included it shall appear in the lower triangle of the warning symbol.

Figure G–11
Radio–Frequency Radiation Hazard Warning Symbol

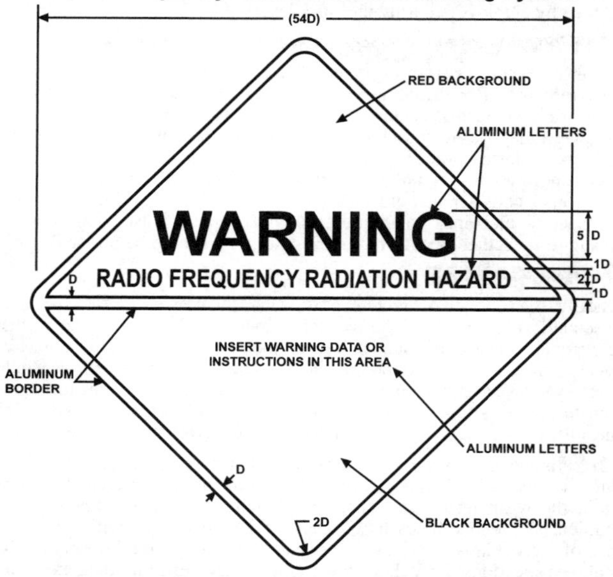

1.Place handing and mounting instructions on reverse side.

2. D = Scaling unit.

3. Lettering: Ratio of letter height to thickness of letter lines.

Upper triangle:	5 to 1 Large
	6 to 1 Medium
Lower triangle:	4 to 1 Small
	6 to 1 Medium

4. Symbol is square, triangles are right-angle isosceles.

(a)(4) **Scope** This section applies to all radiations originating from radio stations, radar equipment, and other possible sources of electromagnetic radiation such as used for communication, radio navigation, and industrial and scientific purposes. This section does not apply to the deliberate exposure of patients by, or under the direction of, practitioners of the healing arts.

(b) [Reserved]

[39 FR 23502, June 27, 1974, as amended at 61 FR 9236, Mar. 7, 1996]

§1910.98 Effective dates

(a) The provisions of this Subpart G shall become effective on August 27, 1971, except as provided in the remaining paragraphs of this section.

(b) The following provisions shall become effective on February 15, 1972:

§1910.94 (a)(2)(iii), (a)(3), (a)(4), (b), (c)(2), (c)(3), (c)(4), (c)(5), (c)(6)(i), (c)(6)(ii), (d)(1)(ii), (d)(3), (d)(4), (d)(5), and (d)(7).

(c) Notwithstanding anything in paragraph (a), (b), or (d) of this section, any provision in any other section of this Subpart which contains in itself a specific effective date or time limitation shall become effective on such date or shall apply in accordance with such limitation.

(d) Notwithstanding anything in paragraph (a) of this section, if any standard in 41 CFR part 50–204, other than a national consensus standard incorporated by reference in §50–204.2(a)(1), is or becomes applicable at any time to any employment and place of employment, by virtue of the Walsh-Healey Public Contracts Act, or the Service Contract Act of 1965, or the National Foundation on Arts and Humanities Act of 1965, any corresponding established Federal standard in this Subpart G which is derived from 41 CFR part 50–204 shall also become effective, and shall be applicable to such employment and place of employment, on the same date.

29 CFR PART 1910 Subpart H
Hazardous Materials

Section Contents

Subpart H—Hazardous Materials

Authority: Sections 4, 6, and 8 of the Occupational Safety and Health Act of 1970 (29 U.S.C. 653, 655, 657); Secretary of Labor's Order No. 12-71 (36 FR 8754), 8-76 (41 FR 25059), 9-83 (48 FR 35736), 1-90 (55 FR 9033), 6-96 (62 FR 111), 3-2000 (65 FR 50017), or 5-2007 (72 FR 31159), 4-2010 (75 FR 55355) or 1-2012 (77 FR 3912), as applicable; and 29 CFR part 1911.

Sections 1910.103, 1910.106 through 1910.111, and 1910.119, 1910.120, and 1910.122 through 1910.126 also issued under 29 CFR part 1911.

Section 1910.119 also issued under Section 304, Clean Air Act Amendments of 1990 (Pub. L. 101-549), reprinted at 29 U.S.C.A. 655 Note.

Section 1910.120 also issued under Section 126, Superfund Amendments and Reauthorization Act of 1986 as amended (29 U.S.C.A. 655 Note), and 5 U.S.C. 553.

§1910.101
Compressed gases (general requirements)

(a) **Inspection of compressed gas cylinders** Each employer shall determine that compressed gas cylinders under his control are in a safe condition to the extent that this can be determined by visual inspection. Visual and other inspections shall be conducted as prescribed in the Hazardous Materials Regulations of the Department of Transportation (49 CFR parts 171–179 and 14 CFR part 103). Where those regulations are not applicable, visual and other inspections shall be conducted in accordance with Compressed Gas Association Pamphlets C–6–1968 and C–8–1962, which is incorporated by reference as specified in §1910.6.

(b) **Compressed gases** The in-plant handling, storage, and utilization of all compressed gases in cylinders, portable tanks, rail tankcars, or motor vehicle cargo tanks shall be in accordance with Compressed Gas Association Pamphlet P–1–1965, which is incorporated by reference as specified in §1910.6.

(c) **Safety relief devices for compressed gas containers** Compressed gas cylinders, portable tanks, and cargo tanks shall have pressure relief devices installed and maintained in accordance with Compressed Gas Association Pamphlets S–1.1–1963 and 1965 addenda and S–1.2–1963, which is incorporated by reference as specified in §1910.6.

[39 FR 23502, June 27, 1974, as amended at 61 FR 9236, Mar. 7, 1996]

§1910.102
Acetylene

(a) **Cylinders** Employers must ensure that the in-plant transfer, handling, storage, and use of acetylene in cylinders comply with the provisions of CGA Pamphlet G–1–2009 ("Acetylene") (incorporated by reference, see §1910.6).

(b) **Piped systems**

(b)(1) Employers must comply with Chapter 9 ("Acetylene Piping") of NFPA 51A–2006 ("Standard for Acetylene Charging Plants") (National Fire Protection Association, 2006 ed., 2006).

(b)(2) When employers can demonstrate that the facilities, equipment, structures, or installations used to generate acetylene or to charge (fill) acetylene cylinders were installed prior to February 16, 2006, these employers may comply with the provisions of Chapter 7 ("Acetylene Piping") of NFPA 51A–2001 ("Standard for Acetylene Charging Plants") (National Fire Protection Association, 2001 ed., 2001).

(b)(3) The provisions of §1910.102(b)(2) also apply when the facilities, equipment, structures, or installations used to generate acetylene or to charge (fill) acetylene cylinders were approved for construction or installation prior to February 16, 2006, but constructed and installed on or after that date.

(b)(4) For additional information on acetylene piping systems, see CGA G–1.2–2006, part 3 ("Acetylene piping") (Compressed Gas Association, Inc., 3rd ed., 2006).

(c) **Generators and filling cylinders**

(c)(1) Employers must ensure that facilities, equipment, structures, or installations used to generate acetylene or to charge (fill) acetylene cylinders comply with the provisions of NFPA 51A–2006 ("Standard for Acetylene Charging Plants") (National Fire Protection Association, 2006 ed., 2006).

(c)(2) When employers can demonstrate that the facilities, equipment, structures, or installations used to generate acetylene or to charge (fill) of acetylene cylinders were constructed or installed prior to February 16, 2006, these employers may comply with the provisions of NFPA 51A–2001 ("Standard for Acetylene Charging Plants") (National Fire Protection Association, 2001 ed., 2001).

(c)(3) The provisions of §1910.102(c)(2) also apply when the facilities, equipment, structures, or installations were approved for construction or installation prior to February 16, 2006, but constructed and installed on or after that date.

[74 FR 40447, Aug. 11, 2009]

§1910.103
Hydrogen

(a) **General**

(a)(1) **Definitions** As used in this section

(a)(1)(i) **Gaseous hydrogen system** is one in which the hydrogen is delivered, stored and discharged in the gaseous form to consumer's piping. The system includes stationary or movable containers, pressure regulators, safety relief devices, manifolds, interconnecting piping and controls. The system terminates at the point where hydrogen at service pressure first enters the consumer's distribution piping.

(a)(1)(ii) **Approved**—Means, unless otherwise indicated, listed or approved by a nationally recognized testing laboratory. Refer to §1910.7 for definition of nationally recognized testing laboratory.

(a)(1)(iii) **Listed**—See "approved"

(a)(1)(iv) **ASME**—American Society of Mechanical Engineers

(a)(1)(v) **DOT Specifications**—Regulations of the Department of Transportation published in 49 CFR Chapter I

(a)(1)(vi) **DOT regulations**—See §1910.103(a)(1)(v)

(a)(2) **Scope**

(a)(2)(i) **Gaseous hydrogen systems**

(a)(2)(i)(A) Paragraph (b) of this section applies to the installation of gaseous hydrogen systems on consumer premises where the hydrogen supply to the consumer premises originates outside the consumer premises and is delivered by mobile equipment.

(a)(2)(i)(B) Paragraph (b) of this section does not apply to gaseous hydrogen systems having a total hydrogen content of less than 400 cubic feet, nor to hydrogen manufacturing plants or other establishments operated by the hydrogen supplier or his agent for the purpose of storing hydrogen and refilling portable containers, trailers, mobile supply trucks, or tank cars.

(a)(2)(ii) **Liquefied hydrogen systems**

(a)(2)(ii)(A) Paragraph (c) of this section applies to the installation of liquefied hydrogen systems on consumer premises.

(a)(2)(ii)(B) Paragraph (c) of this section does not apply to liquefied hydrogen portable containers of less than 150 liters (39.63 gallons) capacity; nor to liquefied hydrogen manufacturing plants or other establishments operated by the hydrogen supplier or his agent for the sole purpose of storing liquefied hydrogen and refilling portable containers, trailers, mobile supply trucks, or tank cars.

(b) **Gaseous hydrogen systems**

(b)(1) **Design**

(b)(1)(i) **Containers**

(b)(1)(i)(A) Hydrogen containers shall comply with one of the following:

(b)(1)(i)(A)(1) Designed, constructed, and tested in accordance with appropriate requirements of ASME Boiler and Pressure Vessel Code, section VIII—Unfired Pressure Vessels—1968, which is incorporated by reference as specified in §1910.6;

(b)(1)(i)(A)(2) Designed, constructed, tested and maintained in accordance with U.S. Department of Transportation Specifications and Regulations.

(b)(1)(i)(B) Permanently installed containers shall be provided with substantial noncombustible supports on firm noncombustible foundations.

(b)(1)(i)(C) Each portable container shall be legibly marked with the name "Hydrogen" in accordance with the marking requirements set forth in §1910.253(b)(1)(ii). Each manifolded hydrogen supply unit shall be legibly marked with the name "Hydrogen" or a legend such as "This unit contains hydrogen."

(b)(1)(ii) **Safety relief devices**

(b)(1)(ii)(A) Hydrogen containers shall be equipped with safety relief devices as required by the ASME Boiler and Pressure Vessel Code, section VIII Unfired Pressure Vessels, 1968 or the DOT Specifications and Regulations under which the container is fabricated.

(b)(1)(ii)(B) Safety relief devices shall be arranged to discharge upward and unobstructed to the open air in such a manner as to prevent any impingement of escaping gas upon the container, adjacent structure or personnel. This requirement does not apply to DOT Specification containers having an internal volume of 2 cubic feet or less.

(b)(1)(ii)(C) Safety relief devices or vent piping shall be designed or located so that moisture cannot collect and freeze in a manner which would interfere with proper operation of the device.

(b)(1)(iii) **Piping, tubing, and fittings**

(b)(1)(iii)(A) Piping, tubing, and fittings shall be suitable for hydrogen service and for the pressures and temperatures involved. Cast iron pipe and fittings shall not be used.

(b)(1)(iii)(B) Piping and tubing shall conform to section 2—"Industrial Gas and Air Piping"—Code for Pressure Piping, ANSI B31.1–1967 with addenda B31.1–1969, which is incorporated by reference as specified in §1910.6.

(b)(1)(iii)(C) Joints in piping and tubing may be made by welding or brazing or by use of flanged, threaded, socket, or compression fittings. Gaskets and thread sealants shall be suitable for hydrogen service.

(b)(1)(iv) **Equipment assembly**

(b)(1)(iv)(A) Valves, gauges, regulators, and other accessories shall be suitable for hydrogen service.

(b)(1)(iv)(B) Installation of hydrogen systems shall be supervised by personnel familiar with proper practices with reference to their construction and use.

(b)(1)(iv)(C) Storage containers, piping, valves, regulating equipment, and other accessories shall be readily accessible, and shall be protected against physical damage and against tampering.

(b)(1)(iv)(D) Cabinets or housings containing hydrogen control or operating equipment shall be adequately ventilated.

(b)(1)(iv)(E) Each mobile hydrogen supply unit used as part of a hydrogen system shall be adequately secured to prevent movement.

(b)(1)(iv)(F) Mobile hydrogen supply units shall be electrically bonded to the system before discharging hydrogen.

(b)(1)(v) **Marking** The hydrogen storage location shall be permanently placarded as follows:

**"HYDROGEN—FLAMMABLE GAS—NO SMOKING–
NO OPEN FLAMES,"**

or equivalent.

(b)(1)(vi) **Testing** After installations, all piping, tubing, and fittings shall be tested and proved hydrogen gas tight at maximum operating pressure.

(b)(2) **Location**

(b)(2)(i) **General**

(b)(2)(i)(A) The system shall be located so that it is readily accessible to delivery equipment and to authorized personnel.

(b)(2)(i)(B) Systems shall be located above ground.

(b)(2)(i)(C) Systems shall not be located beneath electric power lines.

(b)(2)(i)(D) Systems shall not be located close to flammable liquid piping or piping of other flammable gases.

(b)(2)(i)(E) Systems near aboveground flammable liquid storage shall be located on ground higher than the flammable liquid storage except when dikes, diversion curbs, grading, or separating solid walls are used to prevent accumulation of flammable liquids under the system.

(b)(2)(ii) **Specific requirements**

(b)(2)(ii)(A) The location of a system, as determined by the maximum total contained volume of hydrogen, shall be in the order of preference as indicated by Roman numerals in Table H–1.

Table H–1

Nature of location	Size of hydrogen system		
	Less than 3,000 CF	3,000 CF to 15,000 CF	In excess of 15,000 CF
Outdoors	I	IDI	
In a separate building	II	II	II
In a special room	III	III	Not permitted.
Inside buildings not in a special room and exposed to other occupancies	IV	Not permitted.	Not permitted.

(b)(2)(ii)(B) The minimum distance in feet from a hydrogen system of indicated capacity located outdoors, in separate buildings or in special rooms to any specified outdoor exposure shall be in accordance with Table H–2.

(b)(2)(ii)(C) The distances in Table H–2 Items 1 and 3 to 10 inclusive do not apply where protective structures such as adequate fire walls are located between the system and the exposure.

Table H–2

Type of outdoor exposure		Size of hydrogen system		
		Less than 3,000 CF	3,000 CF to 15,000 CF	In excess of 15,000 CF
1. Building or structure	Wood frame construction[1]	10	25	50
	Heavy timber, noncombustible or ordinary construction[1]	0	10	[2]25
	Fire-resistive construction[1]	0	0	0
2. Wall openings	Not above any part of a system	10	10	10
	Above any part of a system	25	25	25
3. Flammable liquids above groun	0 to 1,000 gallons	10	25	25
	In excess of 1,000 gallons	25	50	50
4. Flammable liquids below ground—0 to 1,000 gallons	Tank	10	10	10
	Vent or fill opening of tank	25	25	25
5. Flammable liquids below ground—in excess of 1,000 gallons.	Tank	20	20	20
	Vent or fill opening of tank	25	25	25
6. Flammable gas storage, either high pressure or low pressure	0 to 15,000 CF capacity	10	25	25
	In excess of 15,000 CF capacity	25	50	50

H

Hazardous Materials

Hydrogen

Type of outdoor exposure		Size of hydrogen system		
		Less than 3,000 CF	3,000 CF to 15,000 CF	In excess of 15,000 CF
7. Oxygen storage	12,000 CF or less[4]			
	More than 12,000 CF[5]			
8. Fast burning solids such as ordinary lumber, excelsior or paper		50	50	50
9. Slow burning solids such as heavy timber or coal		25	25	25
10. Open flames and other sources of ignition		25	25	25
11. Air compressor intakes or inlets to ventilating or air-conditioning equipment		50	50	50
12. Concentration of people[3]		50	50	50

[1] Refer to NFPA No. 220 Standard Types of Building Construction for definitions of various types of construction. (1969 Ed.)
[2] But not less than one-half the height of adjacent side wall of the structure.
[3] In congested areas such as offices, lunchrooms, locker rooms, time-clock areas.
[4] Refer to NFPA No. 51, gas systems for welding and cutting (1969).
[5] Refer to NFPA No. 566, bulk oxygen systems at consumer sites (1969).

(b)(2)(ii)(D) Hydrogen systems of less than 3,000 CF when located inside buildings and exposed to other occupancies shall be situated in the building so that the system will be as follows:

(b)(2)(ii)(D)(1) In an adequately ventilated area as in paragraph (b)(3)(ii)(B) of this section.

(b)(2)(ii)(D)(2) Twenty;feet from stored flammable materials or oxidizing gases;

(b)(2)(ii)(D)(3) Twenty-five feet from open flames, ordinary electrical equipment or other sources of ignition;

(b)(2)(ii)(D)(4) Twenty-five feet from concentrations of people;

(b)(2)(ii)(D)(5) Fifty feet from intakes of ventilation or air-conditioning equipment and air compressors;

(b)(2)(ii)(D)(6) Fifty feet from other flammable gas storage;

(b)(2)(ii)(D)(7) Protected against damage or injury due to falling objects or working activity in the area; and

(b)(2)(ii)(D)(8) More than one system of 3,000 CF or less may be installed in the same room, provided the systems are separated by at least 50 feet. Each such system shall meet all of the requirements of this paragraph.

(b)(3) Design consideration at specific locations

(b)(3)(i) Outdoor locations

(b)(3)(i)(A) Where protective walls or roofs are provided, they shall be constructed of noncombustible materials.

(b)(3)(i)(B) Where the enclosing sides adjoin each other, the area shall be properly ventilated.

(b)(3)(i)(C) Electrical equipment within 15 feet shall be in accordance with Subpart S of this part.

(b)(3)(ii) Separate buildings

(b)(3)(ii)(A) Separate buildings shall be built of at least noncombustible construction. Windows and doors shall be located so as to be readily accessible in case of emergency. Windows shall be of glass or plastic in metal frames.

(b)(3)(ii)(B) Adequate ventilation to the outdoors shall be provided. Inlet openings shall be located near the floor in exterior walls only. Outlet openings shall be located at the high point of the room in exterior walls or roof. Inlet and outlet openings shall each have minimum total area of one (1) square foot per 1,000 cubic feet of room volume. Discharge from outlet openings shall be directed or conducted to a safe location.

(b)(3)(ii)(C) Explosion venting shall be provided in exterior walls or roof only. The venting area shall be equal to not less than 1 square foot per 30 cubic feet of room volume and may consist of any one or any combination of the following: Walls of light, noncombustible material, preferably single thickness, single strength glass; lightly fastened hatch covers; lightly fastened swinging doors in exterior walls opening outward; lightly fastened walls or roof designed to relieve at a maximum pressure of 25 pounds per square foot.

(b)(3)(ii)(D) There shall be no sources of ignition from open flames, electrical equipment, or heating equipment.

(b)(3)(ii)(E) Electrical equipment shall be in accordance with Subpart S of this part for Class I, Division 2 locations.

(b)(3)(ii)(F) Heating, if provided, shall be by steam, hot water, or other indirect means.

(b)(3)(iii) Special rooms

(b)(3)(iii)(A) Floor, walls, and ceiling shall have a fire-resistance rating of at least 2 hours. Walls or partitions shall be continuous from floor to ceiling and shall be securely anchored. At least one wall shall be an exterior wall. Openings to other parts of the building shall not be permitted. Windows and doors shall be in exterior walls and shall be located so as to be readily accessible in case of emergency. Windows shall be of glass or plastic in metal frames.

(b)(3)(iii)(B) Ventilation shall be as provided in paragraph (b)(3)(ii)(B) of this section.

(b)(3)(iii)(C) Explosion venting shall be as provided in paragraph (b)(3)(ii)(C) of this section.

(b)(3)(iii)(D) There shall be no sources of ignition from open flames, electrical equipment, or heating equipment.

(b)(3)(iii)(E) Electric equipment shall be in accordance with the requirements of Subpart S of this part for Class I, Division 2 locations.

(b)(3)(iii)(F) Heating, if provided, shall be by steam, hot water, or indirect means.

(b)(4) **Operating instructions** For installations which require any operation of equipment by the user, legible instructions shall be maintained at operating locations.

(b)(5) **Maintenance** The equipment and functioning of each charged gaseous hydrogen system shall be maintained in a safe operating condition in accordance with the requirements of this section. The area within 15 feet of any hydrogen container shall be kept free of dry vegetation and combustible material.

(c) Liquefied hydrogen systems

(c)(1) Design

(c)(1)(i) Containers

(c)(1)(i)(A) Hydrogen containers shall comply with the following: Storage containers shall be designed, constructed, and tested in accordance with appropriate requirements of the ASME Boiler and Pressure Vessel Code, section VIII—Unfired Pressure Vessels (1968) or applicable provisions of API Standard 620, Recommended Rules for Design and Construction of Large, Welded, Low-Pressure Storage Tanks, Second Edition (June 1963) and Appendix R (April 1965), which is incorporated by reference as specified in §1910.6.

(c)(1)(i)(B) Portable containers shall be designed, constructed and tested in accordance with DOT Specifications and Regulations.

(c)(1)(ii) **Supports** Permanently installed containers shall be provided with substantial noncombustible supports securely anchored on firm noncombustible foundations. Steel supports in excess of 18 inches in height shall be protected with a protective coating having a 2-hour fire-resistance rating.

(c)(1)(iii) Marking. Each container shall be legibly marked to indicate **"LIQUEFIED HYDROGEN—FLAMMABLE GAS."**

(c)(1)(iv) Safety relief devices

(c)(1)(iv)(A)(1) Stationary liquefied hydrogen containers shall be equipped with safety relief devices sized in accordance with CGA Pamphlet S–1, part 3, Safety Relief Device Standards for Compressed Gas Storage Containers, which is incorporated by reference as specified in §1910.6.

(c)(1)(iv)(A)(2) Portable liquefied hydrogen containers complying with the U.S. Department of Transportation Regulations shall be equipped with safety relief devices as required in the U.S. Department of Transportation Specifications and Regulations. Safety relief devices shall be sized in accordance with the requirements of CGA Pamphlet S–1, Safety Relief Device Standards, part 1, Compressed Gas Cylinders and part 2, Cargo and Portable Tank Containers.

(c)(1)(iv)(B) Safety relief devices shall be arranged to discharge unobstructed to the outdoors and in such a manner as to prevent impingement of escaping liquid or gas upon the container, adjacent structures or personnel. See paragraph (c)(2)(i)(f) of this section for venting of safety relief devices in special locations.

(c)(1)(iv)(C) Safety relief devices or vent piping shall be designed or located so that moisture cannot collect and freeze in a manner which would interfere with proper operation of the device.

(c)(1)(iv)(D) Safety relief devices shall be provided in piping wherever liquefied hydrogen could be trapped between closures.

(c)(1)(v) **Piping, tubing, and fittings**

(c)(1)(v)(A) Piping, tubing, and fittings and gasket and thread sealants shall be suitable for hydrogen service at the pressures and temperatures involved. Consideration shall be given to the thermal expansion and contraction of piping systems when exposed to temperature fluctuations of ambient to liquefied hydrogen temperatures.

(c)(1)(v)(B) Gaseous hydrogen piping and tubing (above −20 °F.) shall conform to the applicable sections of Pressure Piping section 2—Industrial Gas and Air Piping, ANSI B31.1–1967 with addenda B31.1–1969. Design of liquefied hydrogen or cold (−20 °F. or below) gas piping shall use Petroleum Refinery Piping ANSI B31.3–1966 or Refrigeration Piping ANSI B31.5–1966 with addenda B31.5a–1968 as a guide, which are incorporated by reference as specified in §1910.6.

(c)(1)(v)(C) Joints in piping and tubing shall preferably be made by welding or brazing; flanged, threaded, socket, or suitable compression fittings may be used.

(c)(1)(v)(D) Means shall be provided to minimize exposure of personnel to piping operating at low temperatures and to prevent air condensate from contacting piping, structural members, and surfaces not suitable for cryogenic temperatures. Only those insulating materials which are rated nonburning in accordance with ASTM Procedures D1692–68, which is incorporated by reference as specified in §1910.6, may be used. Other protective means may be used to protect personnel. The insulation shall be designed to have a vapor-tight seal in the outer covering to prevent the condensation of air and subsequent oxygen enrichment within the insulation. The insulation material and outside shield shall also be of adequate design to prevent attrition of the insulation due to normal operating conditions.

(c)(1)(v)(E) Uninsulated piping and equipment which operate at liquefied-hydrogen temperature shall not be installed above asphalt surfaces or other combustible materials in order to prevent contact of liquid air with such materials. Drip pans may be installed under uninsulated piping and equipment to retain and vaporize condensed liquid air.

(c)(1)(vi) **Equipment assembly**

(c)(1)(vi)(A) Valves, gauges, regulators, and other accessories shall be suitable for liquefied hydrogen service and for the pressures and temperatures involved.

(c)(1)(vi)(B) Installation of liquefied hydrogen systems shall be supervised by personnel familiar with proper practices and with reference to their construction and use.

(c)(1)(vi)(C) Storage containers, piping, valves, regulating equipment, and other accessories shall be readily accessible and shall be protected against physical damage and against tampering. A shutoff valve shall be located in liquid product withdrawal lines as close to the container as practical. On containers of over 2,000 gallons capacity, this shutoff valve shall be of the remote control type with no connections, flanges, or other appurtenances (other than a welded manual shutoff valve) allowed in the piping between the shutoff valve and its connection to the inner container.

(c)(1)(vi)(D) Cabinets or housings containing hydrogen control equipment shall be ventilated to prevent any accumulation of hydrogen gas.

(c)(1)(vii) **Testing**

(c)(1)(vii)(A) After installation, all field-erected piping shall be tested and proved hydrogen gas-tight at operating pressure and temperature.

(c)(1)(vii)(B) Containers if out of service in excess of 1 year shall be inspected and tested as outlined in (a) of this subdivision. The safety relief devices shall be checked to determine if they are operable and properly set.

(c)(1)(viii) **Liquefied hydrogen vaporizers**

(c)(1)(viii)(A) The vaporizer shall be anchored and its connecting piping shall be sufficiently flexible to provide for the effect of expansion and contraction due to temperature changes.

(c)(1)(viii)(B) The vaporizer and its piping shall be adequately protected on the hydrogen and heating media sections with safety relief devices.

(c)(1)(viii)(C) Heat used in a liquefied hydrogen vaporizer shall be indirectly supplied utilizing media such as air, steam, water, or water solutions.

(c)(1)(viii)(D) A low temperature shutoff switch shall be provided in the vaporizer discharge piping to prevent flow of liquefied hydrogen in the event of the loss of the heat source.

(c)(1)(ix) **Electrical systems**

(c)(1)(ix)(A) Electrical wiring and equipment located within 3 feet of a point where connections are regularly made and disconnected, shall be in accordance with Subpart S of this part, for Class I, Group B, Division 1 locations.

(c)(1)(ix)(B) Except as provided in (a) of this subdivision, electrical wiring, and equipment located within 25 feet of a point where connections are regularly made and disconnected or within 25 feet of a liquid hydrogen storage container, shall be in accordance with Subpart S of this part, for Class I, Group B, Division 2 locations. When equipment approved for class I, group B atmospheres is not commercially available, the equipment may be—

(c)(1)(ix)(B)(1) Purged or ventilated in accordance with NFPA No. 496–1967, Standard for Purged Enclosures for Electrical Equipment in Hazardous Locations;

(c)(1)(ix)(B)(2) Intrinsically safe; or

(c)(1)(ix)(B)(3) Approved for Class I, Group C atmospheres. This requirement does not apply to electrical equipment which is installed on mobile supply trucks or tank cars from which the storage container is filled.

(c)(1)(x) **Bonding and grounding** The liquefied hydrogen container and associated piping shall be electrically bonded and grounded.

(c)(2) **Location of liquefied hydrogen storage**

(c)(2)(i) **General requirements**

(c)(2)(i)(A) The storage containers shall be located so that they are readily accessible to mobile supply equipment at ground level and to authorized personnel.

(c)(2)(i)(B) The containers shall not be exposed by electric power lines, flammable liquid lines, flammable gas lines, or lines carrying oxidizing materials.

(c)(2)(i)(C) When locating liquefied hydrogen storage containers near above-ground flammable liquid storage or liquid oxygen storage, it is advisable to locate the liquefied hydrogen container on ground higher than flammable liquid storage or liquid oxygen storage.

(c)(2)(i)(D) Where it is necessary to locate the liquefied hydrogen container on ground that is level with or lower than adjacent flammable liquid storage or liquid oxygen storage, suitable protective means shall be taken (such as by diking, diversion curbs, grading), with respect to the adjacent flammable liquid storage or liquid oxygen storage, to prevent accumulation of liquids within 50 feet of the liquefied hydrogen container.

(c)(2)(i)(E) Storage sites shall be fenced and posted to prevent entrance by unauthorized personnel. Sites shall also be placarded as follows:

"LIQUEFIED HYDROGEN—FLAMMABLE GAS–NO SMOKING—NO OPEN FLAMES."

(c)(2)(i)(F) If liquefied hydrogen is located in (as specified in Table H–3) a separate building, in a special room, or inside buildings when not in a special room and exposed to other occupancies, containers shall have the safety relief devices vented unobstructed to the outdoors at a minimum elevation of 25 feet above grade to a safe location as required in paragraph (c)(1)(iv)(B) of this section.

(c)(2)(ii) **Specific requirements**

(c)(2)(ii)(A) The location of liquefied hydrogen storage, as determined by the maximum total quantity of liquefied hydrogen, shall be in the order of preference as indicated by Roman numerals in the following Table H–3.

Table H–3

Maximum Total Quantity of Liquefied Hydrogen Storage Permitted

Nature of location	Size of hydrogen storage (capacity in gallons)			
	39.63 (150 liters) to 50	51 to 300	301 to 600	In excess of 600
Outdoors	I	I	I	I
In a separate building	II	II	II	Not permitted
In a special room	III	III	Not permitted	Do
Inside buildings not in a special room and exposed to other occupancies	IV	Not permitted	Do	Do

***Note:** This table does not apply to the storage in dewars of the type generally used in laboratories for experimental purposes.*

(c)(2)(ii)(B) The minimum distance in feet from liquefied hydrogen systems of indicated storage capacity located outdoors, in a separate building, or in a special room to any specified exposure shall be in accordance with Table H–4.

Table H–4
Minimum Distance (Feet) From Liquefied Hydrogen Systems to Exposure[1,2]

Type of exposure	Liquefied hydrogen storage (capacity in gallons)		
	39.63 (150 liters) to 3,500	3,501 to 15,000	15,001 to 30,000
1. Fire-resistive building and fire walls[3]	5	5	5
2. Noncombustible building[3]	25	50	75
3. Other buildings[3]	50	75	100
4. Wall openings, air-compressor intakes, inlets for air-conditioning or ventilating equipment	75	75	75
5. Flammable liquids (above ground and vent or fill openings if below ground) (see 513 and 514)	50	75	100
6. Between stationary liquefied hydrogen containers	5	5	5
7. Flammable gas storage	50	75	100
8. Liquid oxygen storage and other oxidizers (see 513 and 514)	100	100	100
9. Combustible solids	50	75	100
10. Open flames, smoking and welding	50	50	50
11. Concentrations of people	75	75	75

1 The distance in Nos. 2, 3, 5, 7, 9, and 12 in Table H–4 may be reduced where protective structures, such as firewalls equal to height of top of the container, to safeguard the liquefied hydrogen storage system, are located between the liquefied hydrogen storage installation and the exposure.
2 Where protective structures are provided, ventilation and confinement of product should be considered. The 5-foot distance in Nos. 1 and 6 facilitates maintenance and enhances ventilation.
3 Refer to Standard Types of Building Construction, NFPA No. 220–1969 for definitions of various types of construction. In congested areas such as offices, lunchrooms, locker rooms, time-clock areas.

(c)(2)(iii) Handling of liquefied hydrogen inside buildings other than separate buildings and special rooms. Portable liquefied hydrogen containers of 50 gallons or less capacity as permitted in Table H–3 and in compliance with subdivision (i)(f) of this subparagraph when housed inside buildings not located in a special room and exposed to other occupancies shall comply with the following minimum requirements:

(c)(2)(iii)(A) Be located 20 feet from flammable liquids and readily combustible materials such as excelsior or paper;

(c)(2)(iii)(B) Be located 25 feet from ordinary electrical equipment and other sources of ignition including process or analytical equipment;

(c)(2)(iii)(C) Be located 25 feet from concentrations of people;

(c)(2)(iii)(D) Be located 50 feet from intakes of ventilation and air-conditioning equipment or intakes of compressors;

(c)(2)(iii)(E) Be located 50 feet from storage of other flammable-gases or storage of oxidizing gases;

(c)(2)(iii)(F) Containers shall be protected against damage or injury due to falling objects or work activity in the area;

(c)(2)(iii)(G) Containers shall be firmly secured and stored in an upright position;

(c)(2)(iii)(H) Welding or cutting operations, and smoking shall be prohibited while hydrogen is in the room;

(c)(2)(iii)(I) The area shall be adequately ventilated. Safety relief devices on the containers shall be vented directly outdoors or to a suitable hood. See paragraphs (c)(1)(iv)(b) and (c)(2)(i)(F) of this section.

(c)(3) Design considerations at specific locations

(c)(3)(i) Outdoor locations

(c)(3)(i)(A) Outdoor location shall mean outside of any building or structure, and includes locations under a weather shelter or canopy provided such locations are not enclosed by more than two walls set at right angles and are provided with vent-space between the walls and vented roof or canopy.

(c)(3)(i)(B) Roadways and yard surfaces located below liquefied hydrogen piping, from which liquid air may drip, shall be constructed of noncombustible materials.

(c)(3)(i)(C) If protective walls are provided, they shall be constructed of noncombustible materials and in accordance with the provisions of paragraph (c)(3)(i)(A) of this section.

(c)(3)(i)(D) Electrical wiring and equipment shall comply with paragraph (c)(1)(ix)(a) and (b) of this section.

(c)(3)(i)(E) Adequate lighting shall be provided for nighttime transfer operation.

(c)(3)(ii) Separate buildings

(c)(3)(ii)(A) Separate buildings shall be of light noncombustible construction on a substantial frame. Walls and roofs shall be lightly fastened and designed to relieve at a maximum internal pressure of 25 pounds per square foot. Windows shall be of shatterproof glass or plastic in metal frames. Doors shall be located in such a manner that they will be readily accessible to personnel in an emergency.

(c)(3)(ii)(B) Adequate ventilation to the outdoors shall be provided. Inlet openings shall be located near the floor level in exterior walls only. Outlet openings shall be located at the high point of the room in exterior walls or roof. Both the inlet and outlet vent openings shall have a minimum total area of 1 square foot per 1,000 cubic feet of room volume. Discharge from outlet openings shall be directed or conducted to a safe location.

(c)(3)(ii)(C) There shall be no sources of ignition.

(c)(3)(ii)(D) Electrical wiring and equipment shall comply with paragraphs (c)(1)(ix)(A) and (B) of this section except that the provisions of paragraph (c)(1)(ix)(B) of this section shall apply to all electrical wiring and equipment in the separate building.

(c)(3)(ii)(E) Heating, if provided, shall be by steam, hot water, or other indirect means.

(c)(3)(iii) Special rooms

(c)(3)(iii)(A) Floors, walls, and ceilings shall have a fire resistance rating of at least 2 hours. Walls or partitions shall be continuous from floor to ceiling and shall be securely anchored. At least one wall shall be an exterior wall. Openings to other parts of the building shall not be permitted. Windows and doors shall be in exterior walls and doors shall be located in such a manner that they will be accessible in an emergency. Windows shall be of shatterproof glass or plastic in metal frames.

(c)(3)(iii)(B) Ventilation shall be as provided in paragraph (c)(3)(ii)(B) of this section.

(c)(3)(iii)(C) Explosion venting shall be provided in exterior walls or roof only. The venting area shall be equal to not less than 1 square foot per 30 cubic feet of room volume and may consist of any one or any combination of the following: Walls of light noncombustible material; lightly fastened hatch covers; lightly fastened swinging doors opening outward in exterior walls; lightly fastened walls or roofs designed to relieve at a maximum pressure of 25 pounds per square foot.

(c)(3)(iii)(D) There shall be no sources of ignition.

(c)(3)(iii)(E) Electrical wiring and equipment shall comply with paragraph (c)(1)(ix)(a) and (b) of this section except that the provision of paragraph (c)(1)(ix)(b) of this section shall apply to all electrical wiring and equipment in the special room.

(c)(3)(iii)(F) Heating, if provided, shall be steam, hot water, or by other indirect means.

(c)(4) Operating instructions

(c)(4)(i) **Written instructions** For installations which require any operation of equipment by the user, legible instructions shall be maintained at operating locations.

(c)(4)(ii) **Attendant** A qualified person shall be in attendance at all times while the mobile hydrogen supply unit is being unloaded.

(c)(4)(iii) **Security** Each mobile liquefied hydrogen supply unit used as part of a hydrogen system shall be adequately secured to prevent movement.

(c)(4)(iv) **Grounding** The mobile liquefied hydrogen supply unit shall be grounded for static electricity.

(c)(5) **Maintenance** The equipment and functioning of each charged liquefied hydrogen system shall be maintained in a safe operating condition in accordance with the requirements of this section. Weeds or similar combustibles shall not be permitted within 25 feet of any liquefied hydrogen equipment.

[39 FR 23502, June 27, 1974, as amended at 43 FR 49746, Oct. 24, 1978; 53 FR 12121, Apr. 12, 1988; 55 FR 32015, Aug. 6, 1990; 58 FR 35309, June 30, 1993; 61 FR 9236, 9237, Mar. 7, 1996; 69 FR 31881, June 8, 2004; 72 FR 71069, Dec. 14, 2007]

H

Hazardous Materials

Oxygen

§1910.104 Oxygen

(a) **Scope** This section applies to the installation of bulk oxygen systems on industrial and institutional consumer premises. This section does not apply to oxygen manufacturing plants or other establishments operated by the oxygen supplier or his agent for the purpose of storing oxygen and refilling portable containers, trailers, mobile supply trucks, or tank cars, nor to systems having capacities less than those stated in paragraph (b)(1) of this section.

(b) **Bulk oxygen systems**

(b)(1) **Definition** As used in this section: A **bulk oxygen system** is an assembly of equipment, such as oxygen storage containers, pressure regulators, safety devices, vaporizers, manifolds, and interconnecting piping, which has storage capacity of more than 13,000 cubic feet of oxygen, Normal Temperature and Pressure (NTP), connected in service or ready for service, or more than 25,000 cubic feet of oxygen (NTP) including unconnected reserves on hand at the site. The bulk oxygen system terminates at the point where oxygen at service pressure first enters the supply line. The oxygen containers may be stationary or movable, and the oxygen may be stored as gas or liquid.

(b)(2) **Location**

(b)(2)(i) **General** Bulk oxygen storage systems shall be located above ground out of doors, or shall be installed in a building of noncombustible construction, adequately vented, and used for that purpose exclusively. The location selected shall be such that containers and associated equipment shall not be exposed by electric power lines, flammable or combustible liquid lines, or flammable gas lines.

(b)(2)(ii) **Accessibility** The system shall be located so that it is readily accessible to mobile supply equipment at ground level and to authorized personnel.

(b)(2)(iii) **Leakage** Where oxygen is stored as a liquid, noncombustible surfacing shall be provided in an area in which any leakage of liquid oxygen might fall during operation of the system and filling of a storage container. For purposes of this paragraph, asphaltic or bituminous paving is considered to be combustible.

(b)(2)(iv) **Elevation** When locating bulk oxygen systems near above-ground flammable or combustible liquid storage which may be either indoors or outdoors, it is advisable to locate the system on ground higher than the flammable or combustible liquid storage.

(b)(2)(v) **Dikes** Where it is necessary to locate a bulk oxygen system on ground lower than adjacent flammable or combustible liquid storage suitable means shall be taken (such as by diking, diversion curbs, or grading) with respect to the adjacent flammable or combustible liquid storage to prevent accumulation of liquids under the bulk oxygen system.

(b)(3) **Distance between systems and exposures**

(b)(3)(i) **General** The minimum distance from any bulk oxygen storage container to exposures, measured in the most direct line except as indicated in paragraphs (b)(3)(vi) and (viii) of this section, shall be as indicated in paragraphs (b)(3)(ii) to (xviii) of this section inclusive.

(b)(3)(ii) **Combustible structures** Fifty feet from any combustible structures.

(b)(3)(iii) **Fire resistive structures** Twenty-five feet from any structures with fire-resistive exterior walls or sprinklered buildings of other construction, but not less than one-half the height of adjacent side wall of the structure.

(b)(3)(iv) **Openings** At least 10 feet from any opening in adjacent walls of fire resistive structures. Spacing from such structures shall be adequate to permit maintenance, but shall not be less than 1 foot.

(b)(3)(v) **Flammable liquid storage above-ground**

Distance (feet)	Capacity (gallons)
50	0 to 1000
90	1001 or more

(b)(3)(vi) **Flammable liquid storage below-ground**

Distance measured horizontally from oxygen storage container to flammable liquid tank (feet)	Distance from oxygen storage container to filling and vent connections or openings to flammable liquid tank (feet)	Capacity gallons
15	50	0 to 1000
30	50	1001 or more

(b)(3)(vii) **Combustible liquid storage above-ground**

Distance (feet)	Capacity (gallons)
25	0 to 1000
50	1001 or more

(b)(3)(viii) **Combustible liquid storage belowground**

Distance measured horizontally from oxygen storage container to combustible liquid tank (feet)	Distance from oxygen storage container to filling and vent connections or openings to combustible liquid tank (feet)
15	40

(b)(3)(ix) **Flammable gas storage** (Such as compressed flammable gases, liquefied flammable gases and flammable gases in low pressure gas holders):

Distance (feet)	Capacity (cu. ft. NTP)
50	Less than 5000
90	5000 or more

(b)(3)(x) **Highly combustible materials** Fifty feet from solid materials which burn rapidly, such as excelsior or paper.

(b)(3)(xi) Slow-burning materials. Twenty-five feet from solid materials which burn slowly, such as coal and heavy timber.

(b)(3)(xii) **Ventilation** Seventy-five feet in one direction and 35 feet in approximately 90° direction from confining walls (not including firewalls less than 20 feet high) to provide adequate ventilation in courtyards and similar confining areas.

(b)(3)(xiii) **Congested areas** Twenty-five feet from congested areas such as offices, lunchrooms, locker rooms, time clock areas, and similar locations where people may congregate.

(b)(3)(xiv)–(xvii) [Reserved]

(b)(3)(xviii) **Exceptions** The distances in paragraphs (b)(3)(ii), (iii), (v) to (xi) inclusive, of this section do not apply where protective structures such as firewalls of adequate height to safeguard the oxygen storage systems are located between the bulk oxygen storage installation and the exposure. In such cases, the bulk oxygen storage installation may be a minimum distance of 1 foot from the firewall.

(b)(4) **Storage containers**

(b)(4)(i) **Foundations and supports** Permanently installed containers shall be provided with substantial noncombustible supports on firm noncombustible foundations.

(b)(4)(ii) **Construction–liquid** Liquid oxygen storage containers shall be fabricated from materials meeting the impact test requirements of paragraph UG–84 of ASME Boiler and Pressure Vessel Code, section VIII—Unfired Pressure Vessels—1968, which is incorporated by reference as specified in §1910.6. Containers operating at pressures above 15 pounds per square inch gage (p.s.i.g.) shall be designed, constructed, and tested in accordance with appropriate requirements of ASME Boiler and Pressure Vessel Code, Section VII—Unfired Pressure Vessels—1968. Insulation surrounding the liquid oxygen container shall be noncombustible.

(b)(4)(iii) **Construction–gaseous** High- pressure gaseous oxygen containers shall comply with one of the following:

(b)(4)(iii)(A) Designed, constructed, and tested in accordance with appropriate requirements of ASME Boiler and Pressure Vessel Code, Section VIII—Unfired Pressure Vessels—1968.

(b)(4)(iii)(B) Designed, constructed, tested, and maintained in accordance with DOT Specifications and Regulations.

(b)(5) **Piping, tubing, and fittings**

(b)(5)(i) **Selection** Piping, tubing, and fittings shall be suitable for oxygen service and for the pressures and temperatures involved.

(b)(5)(ii) **Specification** Piping and tubing shall conform to Section 2—Gas and Air Piping Systems of Code for Pressure Piping, ANSI, B31.1-1967 with addenda B31.10a–1969, which is incorporated by reference as specified in §1910.6.

(b)(5)(iii) **Fabrication** Piping or tubing for operating temperatures below −20 °F. shall be fabricated from materials meeting the impact test requirements of paragraph UG–84 of ASME Boiler and Pressure Vessel Code, Section VIII—Unfired Pressure Vessels—1968, when tested at the minimum operating temperature to which the piping may be subjected in service.

(b)(6) **Safety relief devices**

(b)(6)(i) **General** Bulk oxygen storage containers, regardless of design pressure shall be equipped with safety relief devices as required by the ASME code or the DOT specifications and regulations.

(b)(6)(ii) **DOT containers** Bulk oxygen storage containers designed and constructed in accordance with DOT specification shall be equipped with safety relief devices as required thereby.

(b)(6)(iii) **ASME containers** Bulk oxygen storage containers designed and constructed in accordance with the ASME Boiler and Pressure Vessel Code, section VIII—Unfired Pressure Vessel—1968 shall be equipped with safety relief devices meeting the provisions of the Compressed Gas Association Pamphlet "Safety Relief Device Standards for Compressed Gas Storage Containers," S–1, Part 3, which is incorporated by reference as specified in §1910.6.

(b)(6)(iv) Insulation. Insulation casings on liquid oxygen containers shall be equipped with suitable safety relief devices.

(b)(6)(v) **Reliability** All safety relief devices shall be so designed or located that moisture cannot collect and freeze in a manner which would interfere with proper operation of the device.

(b)(7) **Liquid oxygen vaporizers**

(b)(7)(i) **Mounts and couplings** The vaporizer shall be anchored and its connecting piping be sufficiently flexible to provide for the effect of expansion and contraction due to temperature changes.

(b)(7)(ii) **Relief devices** The vaporizer and its piping shall be adequately protected on the oxygen and heating medium sections with safety relief devices.

(b)(7)(iii) **Heating** Heat used in an oxygen vaporizer shall be indirectly supplied only through media such as steam, air, water, or water solutions which do not react with oxygen.

(b)(7)(iv) **Grounding** If electric heaters are used to provide the primary source of heat, the vaporizing system shall be electrically grounded.

(b)(8) **Equipment assembly and installation**

(b)(8)(i) **Cleaning** Equipment making up a bulk oxygen system shall be cleaned in order to remove oil, grease or other readily oxidizable materials before placing the system in service.

(b)(8)(ii) **Joints** Joints in piping and tubing may be made by welding or by use of flanged, threaded, slip, or compression fittings. Gaskets or thread sealants shall be suitable for oxygen service.

(b)(8)(iii) **Accessories** Valves, gages, regulators, and other accessories shall be suitable for oxygen service.

(b)(8)(iv) **Installation** Installation of bulk oxygen systems shall be supervised by personnel familiar with proper practices with reference to their construction and use.

(b)(8)(v) **Testing** After installation all field erected piping shall be tested and proved gas tight at maximum operating pressure. Any medium used for testing shall be oil free and nonflammable.

(b)(8)(vi) **Security** Storage containers, piping, valves, regulating equipment, and other accessories shall be protected against physical damage and against tampering.

(b)(8)(vii) **Venting** Any enclosure containing oxygen control or operating equipment shall be adequately vented.

(b)(8)(viii) **Placarding** The bulk oxygen storage location shall be permanently placarded to indicate:

"OXYGEN—NO SMOKING—NO OPEN FLAMES",

or an equivalent warning.

(b)(8)(ix) **Electrical wiring** Bulk oxygen installations are not hazardous locations as defined and covered in Subpart S of this part. Therefore, general purpose or weatherproof types of electrical wiring and equipment are acceptable depending upon whether the installation is indoors or outdoors. Such equipment shall be installed in accordance with the applicable provisions of Subpart S of this part.

(b)(9) **Operating instructions** For installations which require any operation of equipment by the user, legible instructions shall be maintained at operating locations.

(b)(10) **Maintenance** The equipment and functioning of each charged bulk oxygen system shall be maintained in a safe operating condition in accordance with the requirements of this section. Wood and long dry grass shall be cut back within 15 feet of any bulk oxygen storage container.

[39 FR 23502, June 27, 1974, as amended at 43 FR 49746, Oct. 24, 1978; 61 FR 9237, Mar. 7, 1996]

§1910.105 Nitrous oxide

The piped systems for the in-plant transfer and distribution of nitrous oxide shall be designed, installed, maintained, and operated in accordance with Compressed Gas Association Pamphlet G–8.1–1964, which is incorporated by reference as specified in §1910.6.

[39 FR 23502, June 27, 1974, as amended at 61 FR 9237, Mar. 7, 1996]

§1910.106 Flammable liquids

(a) **Definitions** As used in this Section:

(a)(1) **Aerosol** shall mean a material which is dispensed from its container as a mist, spray, or foam by a propellant under pressure.

(a)(2) **Atmospheric tank** shall mean a storage tank which has been designed to operate at pressures from atmospheric through 0.5 p.s.i.g.

(a)(3) **Automotive service station** shall mean that portion of property where flammable liquids used as motor fuels are stored and dispensed from fixed equipment into the fuel tanks of motor vehicles and shall include any facilities available for the sale and service of tires, batteries, and accessories, and for minor automotive maintenance work. Major automotive repairs, painting, body and fender work are excluded.

(a)(4) **Basement** shall mean a story of a building or structure having one-half or more of its height below ground level and to which access for fire fighting purposes is unduly restricted.

(a)(5) **Boiling point** shall mean the boiling point of a liquid at a pressure of 14.7 pounds per square inch absolute (p.s.i.a.) (760 mm.). Where an accurate boiling point is unavailable for the material in question, or for mixtures which do not have a constant boiling point, for purposes of this section the 10 percent point of a distillation performed in accordance with the Standard Method of Test for Distillation of Petroleum Products, ASTM D–86–62, which is incorporated by reference as specified in §1910.6, may be used as the boiling point of the liquid.

(a)(6) **Boilover** shall mean the expulsion of crude oil (or certain other liquids) from a burning tank. The light fractions of the crude oil burnoff producing a heat wave in the residue, which on reaching a water strata may result in the expulsion of a portion of the contents of the tank in the form of froth.

(a)(7) **Bulk plant** shall mean that portion of a property where flammable liquids are received by tank vessel, pipelines, tank car, or tank vehicle, and are stored or blended in bulk for the purpose of distributing such liquids by tank vessel, pipeline, tank car, tank vehicle, or container.

(a)(8) **Chemical plant** shall mean a large integrated plant or that portion of such a plant other than a refinery or distillery where flammable liquids are produced by chemical reactions or used in chemical reactions.

(a)(9) **Closed container** shall mean a container as herein defined, so sealed by means of a lid or other device that neither liquid nor vapor will escape from it at ordinary temperatures.

(a)(10) **Crude petroleum** shall mean hydrocarbon mixtures that have a flash point below 150 °F. and which have not been processed in a refinery.

(a)(11) **Distillery** shall mean a plant or that portion of a plant where flammable or liquids produced by fermentation are concentrated, and where the concentrated products may also be mixed, stored, or packaged.

(a)(12) **Fire area** shall mean an area of a building separated from the remainder of the building by construction having a fire resistance of at least 1 hour and having all communicating openings properly protected by an assembly having a fire resistance rating of at least 1 hour.

(a)(13) **Flammable aerosol** shall mean a flammable aerosol as defined by Appendix B to §1910.1200—Physical Hazard Criteria. For the purposes of paragraph (d) of this section, such aerosols are considered Category 1 flammable liquids.

(a)(14) **Flashpoint** means the minimum temperature at which a liquid gives off vapor within a test vessel in sufficient concentration to form an ignitable mixture with air near the surface of the liquid, and shall be determined as follows:

(a)(14)(i) For a liquid which has a viscosity of less than 45 SUS at 100 °F (37.8 °C), does not contain suspended solids, and does not have a tendency to form a surface film while under test, the procedure specified in the Standard Method of Test for Flashpoint by Tag Closed Tester (ASTM D–56–70), which is incorporated by reference as specified in §1910.6, or an equivalent test method as defined in Appendix B to §1910.1200—Physical Hazard Criteria, shall be used.

(a)(14)(ii) For a liquid which has a viscosity of 45 SUS or more at 100 °F (37.8 °C), or contains suspended solids, or has a tendency to form a surface film while under test, the Standard Method of Test for Flashpoint

H

Hazardous Materials

Flammable liquids

by Pensky-Martens Closed Tester (ASTM D–93–71) or an equivalent method as defined by Appendix B to §1910.1200—Physical Hazard Criteria, shall be used except that the methods specified in Note 1 to section 1.1 of ASTM D–93–71 may be used for the respective materials specified in the Note. The preceding ASTM standard is incorporated by reference as specified in §1910.6.

(a)(14)(iii) For a liquid that is a mixture of compounds that have different volatilities and flashpoints, its flashpoint shall be determined by using the procedure specified in paragraph (a)(14)(i) or (ii) of this section on the liquid in the form it is shipped.

(a)(14)(iv) Organic peroxides, which undergo autoaccelerating thermal decomposition, are excluded from any of the flashpoint determination methods specified in this subparagraph.

(a)(15) **Hotel** shall mean buildings or groups of buildings under the same management in which there are sleeping accommodations for hire, primarily used by transients who are lodged with or without meals including but not limited to inns, clubs, motels, and apartment hotels.

(a)(16) **Institutional occupancy** shall mean the occupancy or use of a building or structure or any portion thereof by persons harbored or detained to receive medical, charitable or other care or treatment, or by persons involuntarily detained.

(a)(17) **Liquid** shall mean, for the purpose of this section, any material which has a fluidity greater than that of 300 penetration asphalt when tested in accordance with ASTM Test for Penetration for Bituminous Materials, D–5–65, which is incorporated by reference as specified in §1910.6.

(a)(18) [OI] **[Reserved]**

(a)(19) [OI] **Flammable liquid** means any liquid having a flashpoint at or below 199.4 °F (93 °C). Flammable liquids are divided into four categories as follows:

(a)(19)(i) **Category 1** shall include liquids having flashpoints below 73.4 °F (23 °C) and having a boiling point at or below 95 °F (35 °C);

(a)(19)(ii) **Category 2** shall include liquids having flashpoints below 73.4 °F (23 °C) and having a boiling point above 95 °F (35 °C);

(a)(19)(iii) **Category 3** shall include liquids having flashpoints at or above 73.4 °F (23 °C) and at or below 140 °F (60 °C). When a Category 3 liquid with a flashpoint at or above 100 °F (37.8 °C) is heated for use to within 30 °F (16.7 °C) of its flashpoint, it shall be handled in accordance with the requirements for a Category 3 liquid with a flashpoint below 100 °F (37.8 °C);

(a)(19)(iv) **Category 4** shall include liquids having flashpoints above 140 °F (60 °C) and at or below 199.4 °F (93 °C). When a Category 4 flammable liquid is heated for use to within 30 °F (16.7 °C) of its flashpoint, it shall be handled in accordance with the requirements for a Category 3 liquid with a flashpoint at or above 100 °F (37.8 °C); and

(a)(19)(v) When liquid with a flashpoint greater than 199.4 °F (93 °C) is heated for use to within 30 °F (16.7 °C) of its flashpoint, it shall be handled in accordance with the requirements for a Category 4 flammable liquid.

(a)(20) **Unstable (reactive) liquid** shall mean a liquid which in the pure state or as commercially produced or transported will vigorously polymerize, decompose, condense, or will become self-reactive under conditions of shocks, pressure, or temperature.

(a)(21) **Low-pressure tank** shall mean a storage tank which has been designed to operate at pressures above 0.5 p.s.i.g. but not more than 15 p.s.i.g.

(a)(22) **Marine service station** shall mean that portion of a property where flammable or liquids used as fuels are stored and dispensed from fixed equipment on shore, piers, wharves, or floating docks into the fuel tanks of self-propelled craft, and shall include all facilities used in connection therewith.

(a)(23) **Mercantile occupancy** shall mean the occupancy or use of a building or structure or any portion thereof for the displaying, selling, or buying of goods, wares, or merchandise.

(a)(24) **Office occupancy** shall mean the occupancy or use of a building or structure or any portion thereof for the transaction of business, or the rendering or receiving of professional services.

(a)(25) **Portable tank** shall mean a closed container having a liquid capacity over 60 U.S. gallons and not intended for fixed installation.

(a)(26) **Pressure vessel** shall mean a storage tank or vessel which has been designed to operate at pressures above 15 p.s.i.g.

(a)(27) **Protection for exposure** shall mean adequate fire protection for structures on property adjacent to tanks, where there are employees of the establishment.

(a)(28) **Refinery** shall mean a plant in which flammable liquids are produced on a commercial scale from crude petroleum, natural gasoline, or other hydrocarbon sources.

(a)(29) **Safety can** shall mean an approved container, of not more than 5 gallons capacity, having a spring-closing lid and spout cover and so designed that it will safely relieve internal pressure when subjected to fire exposure.

(a)(30) **Vapor pressure** shall mean the pressure, measured in pounds per square inch (absolute) exerted by a volatile liquid as determined by the "Standard Method of Test for Vapor Pressure of Petroleum Products (Reid Method)," American Society for Testing and Materials ASTM D323–68, which is incorporated by reference as specified in §1910.6.

(a)(31) **Ventilation** as specified in this section is for the prevention of fire and explosion. It is considered adequate if it is sufficient to prevent accumulation of significant quantities of vapor-air mixtures in concentration over one-fourth of the lower flammable limit.

(a)(32) **Storage**: Flammable liquids shall be stored in a tank or in a container that complies with paragraph (d)(2) of this section.

(a)(33) **Barrel** shall mean a volume of 42 U.S. gallons.

(a)(34) **Container** shall mean any can, barrel, or drum.

(a)(35) **Approved** unless otherwise indicated, approved, or listed by a nationally recognized testing laboratory. Refer to §1910.7 for definition of nationally recognized testing laboratory.

(a)(36) **Listed** see "approved" in §1910.106(a)(35).

(a)(37) **SUS** means Saybolt Universal Seconds as determined by the Standard Method of Test for Saybolt Viscosity (ASTM D–88–56), and may be determined by use of the SUS conversion tables specified in ASTM Method D2161–66 following determination of viscosity in accordance with the procedures specified in the Standard Method of Test for Viscosity of Transparent and Opaque Liquids (ASTM D445–65).

(a)(38) **Viscous** means a viscosity of 45 SUS or more.

(b) [OI] **Tank storage**

(b)(1) **Design and construction of tanks**

(b)(1)(i) [OI] **Materials**

(b)(1)(i)(A) Tanks shall be built of steel except as provided in paragraphs (b)(1)(i)(b) through (e) of this section.

(b)(1)(i)(B) Tanks may be built of materials other than steel for installation underground or if required by the properties of the liquid stored. Tanks located above ground or inside buildings shall be of noncombustible construction.

(b)(1)(i)(C) Tanks built of materials other than steel shall be designed to specifications embodying principles recognized as good engineering design for the material used.

(b)(1)(i)(D) Unlined concrete tanks may be used for storing flammable liquids having a gravity of 40° API or heavier. Concrete tanks with special lining may be used for other services provided the design is in accordance with sound engineering practice.

(b)(1)(i)(E) [Reserved]

(b)(1)(i)(F) Special engineering consideration shall be required if the specific gravity of the liquid to be stored exceeds that of water or if the tanks are designed to contain flammable liquids at a liquid temperature below 0 °F.

(b)(1)(ii) **Fabrication**

(b)(1)(ii)(A) [Reserved]

(b)(1)(ii)(B) Metal tanks shall be welded, riveted, and caulked, brazed, or bolted, or constructed by use of a combination of these methods. Filler metal used in brazing shall be nonferrous metal or an alloy having a melting point above 1000 °F. and below that of the metal joined.

(b)(1)(iii) **Atmospheric tanks**

(b)(1)(iii)(A) Atmospheric tanks shall be built in accordance with acceptable good standards of design. Atmospheric tanks may be built in accordance with the following consensus standards that are incorporated by reference as specified in §1910.6:

(b)(1)(iii)(A)(1) Underwriters' Laboratories, Inc., Subjects No. 142, Standard for Steel Aboveground Tanks for Flammable and Combustible Liquids, 1968; No. 58, Standard for Steel Underground Tanks for Flammable and Combustible Liquids, Fifth Edition, December 1961; or No. 80, Standard for Steel Inside Tanks for Oil-Burner Fuel, September 1963;

(b)(1)(iii)(A)(2) American Petroleum Institute Standards No. 650, Welded Steel Tanks for Oil Storage, Third Edition, 1966; and

(b)(1)(iii)(A)(3) American Petroleum Institute Standards No. 12B, Specification for Bolted Production Tanks, Eleventh Edition, May 1958, and Supplement 1, March 1962; No. 12D, Specification for Large Welded Production Tanks, Seventh Edition, August 1957; or No. 12F, Specification for Small Welded Production Tanks, Fifth Edition, March 1961. Tanks built in accordance with these standards shall be used only as production tanks for storage of crude petroleum in oil-producing areas.

(b)(1)(iii)(B) Tanks designed for underground service not exceeding 2,500 gallons capacity may be used aboveground.

(b)(1)(iii)(C) Low-pressure tanks and pressure vessels may be used as atmospheric tanks.

(b)(1)(iii)(D) Atmospheric tanks shall not be used for the storage of a flammable liquid at a temperature at or above its boiling point.

(b)(1)(iv) **Low pressure tanks**

(b)(1)(iv)(A) The normal operating pressure of the tank shall not exceed the design pressure of the tank.

(b)(1)(iv)(B) Low-pressure tanks shall be built in accordance with acceptable standards of design. Low-pressure tanks may be built in accordance with the following consensus standards that are incorporated by reference as specified in §1910.6:

(b)(1)(iv)(B)(1) American Petroleum Institute Standard No. 620. Recommended Rules for the Design and Construction of Large, Welded, Low-Pressure Storage Tanks, Third Edition, 1966;

(b)(1)(iv)(B)(2) The principles of the Code for Unfired Pressure Vessels, Section VIII of the ASME Boiler and Pressure Vessels Code, 1968.

(b)(1)(iv)(C) Atmospheric tanks built according to Underwriters' Laboratories, Inc., requirements in subdivision (iii)(a) of and shall be limited to 2.5 p.s.i.g. under emergency venting conditions.

This paragraph may be used for operating pressures not exceeding 1 p.s.i.g.

(b)(1)(iv)(D) **Pressure vessels may be used as low-pressure tanks**

(b)(1)(v) OI **Pressure vessels**

(b)(1)(v)(A) The normal operating pressure of the vessel shall not exceed the design pressure of the vessel.

(b)(1)(v)(B) OI Pressure vessels shall be built in accordance with the Code for Unfired Pressure Vessels, Section VIII of the ASME Boiler and Pressure Vessel Code 1968.

(b)(1)(vi) **Provisions for internal corrosion** When tanks are not designed in accordance with the American Petroleum Institute, American Society of Mechanical Engineers, or the Underwriters' Laboratories, Inc.'s, standards, or if corrosion is anticipated beyond that provided for in the design formulas used, additional metal thickness or suitable protective coatings or linings shall be provided to compensate for the corrosion loss expected during the design life of the tank.

(b)(2) **Installation of outside aboveground tanks**

(b)(2)(i) [Reserved]

(b)(2)(ii) **Spacing (shell-to-shell) between aboveground tanks**

(b)(2)(ii)(A) The distance between any two flammable liquid storage tanks shall not be less than 3 feet.

(b)(2)(ii)(B) Except as provided in paragraph (b)(2)(ii)(C) of this section, the distance between any two adjacent tanks shall not be less than one-sixth the sum of their diameters. When the diameter of one tank is less than one-half the diameter of the adjacent tank, the distance between the two tanks shall not be less than one-half the diameter of the smaller tank.

(b)(2)(ii)(C) Where crude petroleum in conjunction with production facilities are located in noncongested areas and have capacities not exceeding 126,000 gallons (3,000 barrels), the distance between such tanks shall not be less than 3 feet.

(b)(2)(ii)(D) Where unstable flammable liquids are stored, the distance between such tanks shall not be less than one-half the sum of their diameters.

(b)(2)(ii)(E) When tanks are compacted in three or more rows or in an irregular pattern, greater spacing or other means shall be provided so that inside tanks are accessible for firefighting purposes.

(b)(2)(ii)(F) The minimum separation between a liquefied petroleum gas container and a flammable liquid storage tank shall be 20 feet, except in the case of flammable liquid tanks operating at pressures exceeding 2.5 p.s.i.g. or equipped with emergency venting which will permit pressures to exceed 2.5 p.s.i.g. in which case the provisions of subdivisions (a) and (b) of this subdivision shall apply. Suitable means shall be taken to prevent the accumulation of flammable liquids under adjacent liquefied petroleum gas containers such as by diversion curbs or grading. When flammable liquid storage tanks are within a diked area, the liquefied petroleum gas containers shall be outside the diked area and at least 10 feet away from the centerline of the wall of the diked area. The foregoing provisions shall not apply when liquefied petroleum gas containers of 125 gallons or less capacity are installed adjacent to fuel oil supply tanks of 550 gallons or less capacity.

(b)(2)(iii) [Reserved]

(b)(2)(iv) **Normal venting for aboveground tanks**

(b)(2)(iv)(A) Atmospheric storage tanks shall be adequately vented to prevent the development of vacuum or pressure sufficient to distort the roof of a cone roof tank or exceeding the design pressure in the case of other atmospheric tanks, as a result of filling or emptying, and atmospheric temperature changes.

(b)(2)(iv)(B) Normal vents shall be sized either in accordance with: (1) The American Petroleum Institute Standard 2000 (1968), Venting Atmospheric and Low-Pressure Storage Tanks, which is incorporated by reference as specified in §1910.6; or (2) other accepted standard; or (3) shall be at least as large as the filling or withdrawal connection, whichever is larger but in no case less than 1¼ inch nominal inside diameter.

(b)(2)(iv)(C) Low-pressure tanks and pressure vessels shall be adequately vented to prevent development of pressure or vacuum, as a result of filling or emptying and atmospheric temperature changes, from exceeding the design pressure of the tank or vessel. Protection shall also be provided to prevent overpressure from any pump discharging into the tank or vessel when the pump discharge pressure can exceed the design pressure of the tank or vessel.

(b)(2)(iv)(D) If any tank or pressure vessel has more than one fill or withdrawal connection and simultaneous filling or withdrawal can be made, the vent size shall be based on the maximum anticipated simultaneous flow.

(b)(2)(iv)(E) Unless the vent is designed to limit the internal pressure 2.5 p.s.i. or less, the outlet of vents and vent drains shall be arranged to discharge in such a manner as to prevent localized overheating of any part of the tank in the event vapors from such vents are ignited.

(b)(2)(iv)(F)(1) Tanks and pressure vessels storing Category 1 flammable liquids shall be equipped with venting devices which shall be normally closed except when venting to pressure or vacuum conditions. Tanks and pressure vessels storing Category 2 flammable liquids and Category 3 flammable liquids with a flashpoint below 100 °F (37.8 °C) shall be equipped with venting devices which shall be normally closed except when venting under pressure or vacuum conditions, or with approved flame arresters.

(b)(2)(iv)(F)(2) Exemption: Tanks of 3,000 bbls (barrels). capacity or less containing crude petroleum in crude-producing areas and outside aboveground atmospheric tanks under 1,000 gallons capacity containing other than Category 1 flammable liquids may have open vents. (See paragraph (b)(2)(vi)(b) of this section.)

(b)(2)(iv)(G) Flame arresters or venting devices required in paragraph (b)(2)(iv)(f) of this section may be omitted for Category 2 flammable liquids and Category 3 flammable liquids with a flashpoint below 100 °F (37.8 °C) where conditions are such that their use may, in case of obstruction, result in tank damage.

(b)(2)(v) Emergency relief venting for fire exposure for aboveground tanks.

(b)(2)(v)(A) Every aboveground storage tank shall have some form of construction or device that will relieve excessive internal pressure caused by exposure fires.

(b)(2)(v)(B) In a vertical tank the construction referred to in subdivision (a) of this subdivision may take the form of a floating roof, lifter roof, a weak roof-to-shell seam, or other approved pressure relieving construction. The weak roof-to-shell seam shall be constructed to fail preferential to any other seam.

(b)(2)(v)(C) Where entire dependence for emergency relief is placed upon pressure relieving devices, the total venting capacity of both normal and emergency vents shall be enough to prevent rupture of the shell or bottom of the tank if vertical, or of the shell or heads if horizontal. If unstable liquids are stored, the effects of heat or gas resulting from polymerization, decomposition, condensation, or self-reactivity shall be taken into account. The total capacity of both normal and emergency venting devices shall be not less than that derived from Table H–10 except as provided in subdivision (e) or (f) of this subdivision. Such device may be a self-closing manhole cover, or one using long bolts that permit the cover to lift under internal pressure, or an additional or larger relief valve or valves. The wetted area of the tank shall be calculated on the basis of 55 percent of the total exposed area of a sphere or spheroid, 75 percent of the total exposed area of a horizontal tank and the first 30 feet above grade of the exposed shell area of a vertical tank.

Table H–10

Wetted Area Versus Cubic Feet Free Air Per Hour

[14.7 psia and 60 °F]

Square feet	CFH	Square feet	CFH	Square feet	CFH
20	21,100	200	211,000	1,000	524,000
30	31,600	250	239,000	1,200	557,000
40	42,100	300	265,000	1,400	587,000
50	52,700	350	288,000	1,600	614,000
60	63,200	400	312,000	1,800	639,000
70	73,700	500	354,000	2,000	662,000
80	84,200	600	392,000	2,400	704,000
90	94,800	700	428,000	2,800 and over	742,000
100	105,000	800	462,000		
120	126,000	900	493,000		
140	147,000				
160	168,000				
180	190,000				

(b)(2)(v)(D) For tanks and storage vessels designed for pressure over 1 p.s.i.g., the total rate of venting shall be determined in accordance with Table H–10, except that when the exposed wetted area of the surface is greater than 2,800 square feet, the total rate of venting shall be calculated by the following formula:

$$\mathrm{CFH} = 1{,}107A^{0.82}$$

Where:
CFH = Venting requirement, in cubic feet of free air per hour.
A = Exposed wetted surface, in square feet.
Note: *The foregoing formula is based on* $Q = 21{,}000A^{0.82}$.

(b)(2)(v)(E) The total emergency relief venting capacity for any specific stable liquid may be determined by the following formula:

$$V = 1337 \div L\sqrt{M}$$

Where:
V = Cubic feet of free air per hour from Table H–10;
L = Latent heat of vaporization of specific liquid in B.t.u. per pound;
M = Molecular weight of specific liquids.

(b)(2)(v)(F) The required airflow rate of subdivision (c) or (e) of this subdivision may be multiplied by the appropriate factor listed in the following schedule when protection is provided as indicated. Only one factor may be used for any one tank.

0.5 for drainage in accordance with subdivision (vii)(b) of this subparagraph for tanks over 200 square feet of wetted area;
0.3 for approved water spray;
0.3 for approved insulation;
0.15 for approved water spray with approved insulation.

(b)(2)(v)(G) The outlet of all vents and vent drains on tanks equipped with emergency venting to permit pressures exceeding 2.5 p.s.i.g. shall be arranged to discharge in such a way as to prevent localized overheating of any part of the tank, in the event vapors from such vents are ignited.

(b)(2)(v)(H) Each commercial tank venting device shall have stamped on it the opening pressure, the pressure at which the valve reaches the full open position, and the flow capacity at the latter pressure, expressed in cubic feet per hour of air at 60 °F. and at a pressure of 14.7 p.s.i.a.

(b)(2)(v)(I) The flow capacity of tank venting devices 12 inches and smaller in nominal pipe size shall be determined by actual test of each type and size of vent. These flow tests may be conducted by the manufacturer if certified by a qualified impartial observer, or may be conducted by an outside agency. The flow capacity of tank venting devices larger than 12 inches nominal pipe size, including manhole covers with long bolts or equivalent, may be calculated provided that the opening pressure is actually measured, the rating pressure and corresponding free orifice area are stated, the word "calculated" appears on the nameplate, and the computation is based on a flow coefficient of 0.5 applied to the rated orifice area.

(b)(2)(vi) **Vent piping for aboveground tanks**

(b)(2)(vi)(A) Vent piping shall be constructed in accordance with paragraph (c) of this section.

(b)(2)(vi)(B) Where vent pipe outlets for tanks storing Category 1 or 2 flammable liquids, or Category 3 flammable liquids with a flashpoint below 100 °F (37.8 °C), are adjacent to buildings or public ways, they shall be located so that the vapors are released at a safe point outside of buildings and not less than 12 feet above the adjacent ground level. In order to aid their dispersion, vapors shall be discharged upward or horizontally away from closely adjacent walls. Vent outlets shall be located so that flammable vapors will not be trapped by eaves or other obstructions and shall be at least five feet from building openings.

(b)(2)(vi)(C) When tank vent piping is manifolded, pipe sizes shall be such as to discharge, within the pressure limitations of the system, the vapors they may be required to handle when manifolded tanks are subject to the same fire exposure.

(b)(2)(vii) **Drainage, dikes, and walls for aboveground tanks**

(b)(2)(vii)(A) **Drainage and diked areas** The area surrounding a tank or a group of tanks shall be provided with drainage as in subdivision (b) of this subdivision, or shall be diked as provided in subdivision (c) of this subdivision, to prevent accidental discharge of liquid from endangering adjoining property or reaching waterways.

(b)(2)(vii)(B) **Drainage** Where protection of adjoining property or waterways is by means of a natural or manmade drainage system, such systems shall comply with the following:

(b)(2)(vii)(B)(1) [Reserved]

(b)(2)(vii)(B)(2) The drainage system shall terminate in vacant land or other area or in an impounding basin having a capacity not smaller than that of the largest tank served. This termination area and the route of the drainage system shall be so located that, if the flammable liquids in the drainage system are ignited, the fire will not seriously expose tanks or adjoining property.

(b)(2)(vii)(C) **Diked areas** Where protection of adjoining property or waterways is accomplished by retaining the liquid around the tank by means of a dike, the volume of the diked area shall comply with the following requirements:

(b)(2)(vii)(C)(1) Except as provided in subdivision (2) of this subdivision, the volumetric capacity of the diked area shall not be less than the greatest amount of liquid that can be released from the largest tank within the diked area, assuming a full tank. The capacity of the diked area enclosing more than one tank shall be calculated by deducting the volume of the tanks other than the largest tank below the height of the dike;

(b)(2)(vii)(C)(2) For a tank or group of tanks with fixed roofs containing crude petroleum with boilover characteristics, the volumetric capacity of the diked area shall be not less than the capacity of the largest tank served by the enclosure, assuming a full tank. The capacity of the diked enclosure shall be calculated by deducting the volume below the height of the dike of all tanks within the enclosure;

(b)(2)(vii)(C)(3) Walls of the diked area shall be of earth, steel, concrete or solid masonry designed to be liquidtight and to withstand a full hydrostatic head. Earthen walls 3 feet or more in height shall have a flat section at the top not less than 2 feet wide. The slope of an earthen wall shall be consistent with the angle of repose of the material of which the wall is constructed;

(b)(2)(vii)(C)(4) The walls of the diked area shall be restricted to an average height of 6 feet above interior grade;

(b)(2)(vii)(C)(5) [Reserved]

(b)(2)(vii)(C)(6) No loose combustible material, empty or full drum or barrel, shall be permitted within the diked area.

(b)(2)(viii) **Tank openings other than vents for aboveground tanks**

(b)(2)(viii)(A)–(C) [Reserved]

(b)(2)(viii)(D) Openings for gaging shall be provided with a vaportight cap or cover.

(b)(2)(viii)(E) For Category 2 flammable liquids and Category 3 flammable liquids with a flashpoint below 100 °F (37.8 °C), other than crude oils, gasolines, and asphalts, the fill pipe shall be so designed and installed as to minimize the possibility of generating static electricity. A fill pipe entering the top of a tank shall terminate within 6 inches of the bottom of the tank and shall be installed to avoid excessive vibration.

(b)(2)(viii)(F) Filling and emptying connections which are made and broken shall be located outside of buildings at a location free from any source of ignition and not less than 5 feet away from any building opening. Such connection shall be closed and liquidtight when not in use. The connection shall be properly identified.

(b)(3) **Installation of underground tanks**

(b)(3)(i) **Location** Excavation for underground storage tanks shall be made with due care to avoid undermining of foundations of existing structures. Underground tanks or tanks under buildings shall be so located with respect to existing building foundations and supports that the loads carried by the latter cannot be transmitted to the tank. The distance from any part of a tank storing Category 1 or 2 flammable liquids, or Category 3 flammable liquids with a flashpoint below 100 °F (37.8 °C), to the nearest wall of any basement or pit shall be not less than 1 foot, and to any property line that may be built upon, not less than 3 feet. The distance from any part of a tank storing Category 3 flammable liquids with a flashpoint at or above 100 °F (37.8 °C) or Category 4 flammable liquids to the nearest wall of any basement, pit or property line shall be not less than 1 foot.

(b)(3)(ii) **Depth and cover** Underground tanks shall be set on firm foundations and surrounded with at least 6 inches of noncorrosive, inert materials such as clean sand, earth, or gravel well tamped in place. The tank shall be placed in the hole with care since dropping or rolling the tank into the hole can break a weld, puncture or damage the tank, or scrape off the protective coating of coated tanks. Tanks shall be covered with a minimum of 2 feet of earth, or shall be covered with not less than 1 foot of earth, on top of which shall be placed a slab of reinforced concrete not less than 4 inches thick. When underground tanks are, or are likely to be, subject to traffic, they shall be protected against damage from vehicles passing over them by at least 3 feet of earth cover, or 18 inches of well-tamped earth, plus 6 inches of reinforced concrete or 8 inches of asphaltic concrete. When asphaltic or reinforced concrete paving is used as part of the protection, it shall extend at least 1 foot horizontally beyond the outline of the tank in all directions.

(b)(3)(iii) **Corrosion protection** Corrosion protection for the tank and its piping shall be provided by one or more of the following methods:

(b)(3)(iii)(A) Use of protective coatings or wrappings;

(b)(3)(iii)(B) Cathodic protection; or

(b)(3)(iii)(C) Corrosion resistant materials of construction.

(b)(3)(iv) **Vents**

(b)(3)(iv)(A) Location and arrangement of vents for Category 1 or 2 flammable liquids, or Category 3 flammable liquids with a flashpoint below 100 °F (37.8 °C). Vent pipes from tanks storing Category 1 or 2 flammable liquids, or Category 3 flammable liquids with a flashpoint below 100 °F (37.8 °C), shall be so located that the discharge point is outside of buildings, higher than the fill pipe opening, and not less than 12 feet above the adjacent ground level. Vent pipes shall discharge only upward in order to disperse vapors. Vent pipes 2 inches or less in nominal inside diameter shall not be obstructed by devices that will cause excessive back pressure. Vent pipe outlets shall be so located that flammable vapors will not enter building openings, or be trapped under eaves or other obstructions. If the vent pipe is less than 10 feet in length, or greater than 2 inches in nominal inside diameter, the outlet shall be provided with a vacuum and pressure relief device or there shall be an approved flame arrester located in the vent line at the outlet or within the approved distance from the outlet.

(b)(3)(iv)(B) Size of vents. Each tank shall be vented through piping adequate in size to prevent blow-back of vapor or liquid at the fill opening while the tank is being filled. Vent pipes shall be not less than 1¼ inch nominal inside diameter.

Table H–11
Vent Line Diameters

Maximum flow GPM	Pipe length[1]		
	50 feet	100 feet	200 feet
	Inches	Inches	Inches
100	1¼	1¼	1¼
200	1¼	1¼	1¼
300	1¼	1¼	1½
400	1¼	1½	2
500	1½	1½	2
600	1½	2	2
700	2	2	2
800	2	2	3
900	2	2	3
1,000	2	2	3

[1]Vent lines of 50 ft., 100 ft., and 200 ft. of pipe plus 7 ells.

(b)(3)(iv)(C) Location and arrangement of vents for Category 3 flammable liquids with a flashpoint at or above 100 °F (37.8 °C) or Category 4 flammable liquids. Vent pipes from tanks storing Category 3 flammable liquids with a flashpoint at or above 100 °F (37.8 °C) or Category 4 flammable liquids shall terminate outside of the building and higher than the fill pipe opening. Vent outlets shall be above normal snow level. They may be fitted with return bends, coarse screens or other devices to minimize ingress of foreign material.

(b)(3)(iv)(D) Vent piping shall be constructed in accordance with paragraph (c) of this section. Vent pipes shall be so laid as to drain toward the tank without sags or traps in which liquid can collect. They shall be located so that they will not be subjected to physical damage. The tank end of the vent pipe shall enter the tank through the top.

(b)(3)(iv)(E) When tank vent piping is manifolded, pipe sizes shall be such as to discharge, within the pressure limitations of the system, the vapors they may be required to handle when manifolded tanks are filled simultaneously.

(b)(3)(v) **Tank openings other than vents**

(b)(3)(v)(A) Connections for all tank openings shall be vapor or liquid tight.

(b)(3)(v)(B) Openings for manual gaging, if independent of the fill pipe, shall be provided with a liquid-tight cap or cover. If inside a building, each such opening shall be protected against liquid overflow and possible vapor release by means of a spring loaded check valve or other approved device.

(b)(3)(v)(C) Fill and discharge lines shall enter tanks only through the top. Fill lines shall be sloped toward the tank.

(b)(3)(v)(D) For Category 2 flammable liquids and Category 3 flammable liquids with a flashpoint below 100 °F (37.8 °C), other than crude oils, gasolines, and asphalts, the fill pipe shall be so designed and installed as to minimize the possibility of generating static electricity by terminating within 6 inches of the bottom of the tank.

(b)(3)(v)(E) Filling and emptying connections which are made and broken shall be located outside of buildings at a location free from any source of ignition and not less than 5 feet away from any building opening. Such connection shall be closed and liquidtight when not in use. The connection shall be properly identified.

(b)(4) **Installation of tanks inside of buildings**

(b)(4)(i) **Location** Tanks shall not be permitted inside of buildings except as provided in paragraphs (e), (g), (h), or (i) of this section.

(b)(4)(ii) [OI] **Vents** Vents for tanks inside of buildings shall be as provided in subparagraphs (2)(iv), (v), (vi)(b), and (3)(iv) of this paragraph, except that emergency venting by the use of weak roof seams on tanks shall not be permitted. Vents shall discharge vapors outside the buildings.

(b)(4)(iii) **Vent piping** Vent piping shall be constructed in accordance with paragraph (c) of this section.

(b)(4)(iv) **Tank openings other than vents**

(b)(4)(iv)(A) Connections for all tank openings shall be vapor or liquidtight. Vents are covered in subdivision (ii) of this subparagraph.

(b)(4)(iv)(B) Each connection to a tank inside of buildings through which liquid can normally flow shall be provided with an internal or an external valve located as close as practical to the shell of the tank. Such valves, when external, and their connections to the tank shall be of steel except when the chemical characteristics of the liquid stored are incompatible with steel. When materials other than steel are necessary, they shall be suitable for the pressures, structural stresses, and temperatures involved, including fire exposures.

(b)(4)(iv)(C) Flammable liquid tanks located inside of buildings, except in one-story buildings designed and protected for flammable liquid storage, shall be provided with an automatic-closing heat-actuated valve on each withdrawal connection below the liquid level, except for connections used for emergency disposal, to prevent continued flow in the event of fire in the vicinity of the tank. This function may be incorporated in the valve required in (b) of this subdivision, and if a separate valve, shall be located adjacent to the valve required in (b) of this subdivision.

(b)(4)(iv)(D) Openings for manual gaging, if independent of the fill pipe (see (f) of this subdivision), shall be provided with a vaportight cap or cover. Each such opening shall be protected against liquid overflow and possible vapor release by means of a spring loaded check valve or other approved device.

(b)(4)(iv)(E) [OI] For Category 2 flammable liquids and Category 3 flammable liquids with a flashpoint below 100 °F (37.8 °C), other than crude oils, gasoline, and asphalts, the fill pipe shall be so designed and installed as to minimize the possibility of generating static electricity by terminating within 6 inches of the bottom of the tank.

(b)(4)(iv)(F) The fill pipe inside of the tank shall be installed to avoid excessive vibration of the pipe.

(b)(4)(iv)(G) The inlet of the fill pipe shall be located outside of buildings at a location free from any source of ignition and not less than 5 feet away from any building opening. The inlet of the fill pipe shall be closed and liquidtight when not in use. The fill connection shall be properly identified.

(b)(4)(iv)(H) Tanks inside buildings shall be equipped with a device, or other means shall be provided, to prevent overflow into the building.

(b)(5) **Supports, foundations, and anchorage for all tank locations**

(b)(5)(i) **General** Tank supports shall be installed on firm foundations. Tank supports shall be of concrete, masonry, or protected steel. Single wood timber supports (not cribbing) laid horizontally may be used for outside aboveground tanks if not more than 12 inches high at their lowest point.

(b)(5)(ii) **Fire resistance** Steel supports or exposed piling shall be protected by materials having a fire resistance rating of not less than 2 hours, except that steel saddles need not be protected if less than 12 inches high at their lowest point. Water spray protection or its equivalent may be used in lieu of fire-resistive materials to protect supports.

(b)(5)(iii) **Spheres** The design of the supporting structure for tanks such as spheres shall receive special engineering consideration.

(b)(5)(iv) **Load distribution** Every tank shall be so supported as to prevent the excessive concentration of loads on the supporting portion of the shell.

(b)(5)(v) **Foundations** Tanks shall rest on the ground or on foundations made of concrete, masonry, piling, or steel. Tank foundations shall be designed to minimize the possibility of uneven settling of the tank and to minimize corrosion in any part of the tank resting on the foundation.

(b)(5)(vi) **Flood areas** Where a tank is located in an area that may be subjected to flooding, the applicable precautions outlined in this subdivision shall be observed.

(b)(5)(vi)(A) No aboveground vertical storage tank containing a flammable liquid shall be located so that the allowable liquid level within the tank is below the established maximum flood stage, unless the tank is provided with a guiding structure such as described in (M), (N), and (O) of this subdivision.

(b)(5)(vi)(B) Independent water supply facilities shall be provided at locations where there is no ample and dependable public water supply available for loading partially empty tanks with water.

(b)(5)(vi)(C) In addition to the preceding requirements, each tank so located that more than 70 percent, but less than 100 percent, of its allowable liquid storage capacity will be submerged at the established maximum flood stage, shall be safeguarded by one of the following methods: Tank shall be raised, or its height shall be increased, until its top extends above the maximum flood stage a distance equivalent to 30 percent or more of its allowable liquid storage capacity: Provided, however, that the submerged part of the tank shall not exceed two and one-half times the diameter. Or, as an alternative to the foregoing, adequate noncombustible structural guides, designed to permit the tank to float vertically without loss of product, shall be provided.

(b)(5)(vi)(D) Each horizontal tank so located that more than 70 percent of its storage capacity will be submerged at the established flood stage, shall be anchored, attached to a foundation of concrete or of steel and concrete, of sufficient weight to provide adequate load for the tank when filled with flammable liquid and submerged by flood waters to the established flood stage, or adequately secured by other means.

(b)(5)(vi)(E) [Reserved]

(b)(5)(vi)(F) At locations where there is no ample and dependable water supply, or where filling of underground tanks with liquids is impracticable because of the character of their contents, their use, or for other reasons, each tank shall be safeguarded against movement when empty and submerged by high ground water or flood waters by anchoring, weighting with concrete or other approved solid loading material, or securing by other means. Each such tank shall be so constructed and installed that it will safely resist external pressures due to high ground water or flood waters.

(b)(5)(vi)(G) At locations where there is an ample and dependable water supply available, underground tanks containing flammable liquids, so installed that more than 70 percent of their storage capacity will be submerged at the maximum flood stage, shall be so anchored, weighted, or secured by other means, as to prevent movement of such tanks when filled with flammable liquids, and submerged by flood waters to the established flood stage.

(b)(5)(vi)(H) Pipe connections below the allowable liquid level in a tank shall be provided with valves or cocks located as closely as practicable to the tank shell. Such valves and their connections to tanks shall be of steel or other material suitable for use with the liquid being stored. Cast iron shall not be permitted.

(b)(5)(vi)(I) At locations where an independent water supply is required, it shall be entirely independent of public power and water supply. Independent source of water shall be available when flood waters reach a level not less than 10 feet below the bottom of the lowest tank on a property.

(b)(5)(vi)(J) The self-contained power and pumping unit shall be so located or so designed that pumping into tanks may be carried on continuously throughout the rise in flood waters from a level 10 feet below the lowest tank to the level of the potential flood stage.

(b)(5)(vi)(K) Capacity of the pumping unit shall be such that the rate of rise of water in all tanks shall be equivalent to the established potential average rate of rise of flood waters at any stage.

(b)(5)(vi)(L) Each independent pumping unit shall be tested periodically to insure that it is in satisfactory operating condition.

(b)(5)(vi)(M) Structural guides for holding floating tanks above their foundations shall be so designed that there will be no resistance to the free rise of a tank, and shall be constructed of noncombustible material.

(b)(5)(vi)(N) The strength of the structure shall be adequate to resist lateral movement of a tank subject to a horizontal force in any direction equivalent to not less than 25 pounds per square foot acting on the projected vertical cross-sectional area of the tank.

(b)(5)(vi)(O) Where tanks are situated on exposed points or bends in a shoreline where swift currents in flood waters will be present, the structures shall be designed to withstand a unit force of not less than 50 pounds per square foot.

(b)(5)(vi)(P) The filling of a tank to be protected by water loading shall be started as soon as flood waters reach a dangerous flood stage. The rate of filling shall be at least equal to the rate of rise of the floodwaters (or the established average potential rate of rise).

(b)(5)(vi)(Q) Sufficient fuel to operate the water pumps shall be available at all times to insure adequate power to fill all tankage with water.

(b)(5)(vi)(R) All valves on connecting pipelines shall be closed and locked in closed position when water loading has been completed.

(b)(5)(vi)(S) Where structural guides are provided for the protection of floating tanks, all rigid connections between tanks and pipelines shall be disconnected and blanked off or blinded before the floodwaters reach the bottom of the tank, unless control valves and their connections to the tank are of a type designed to prevent breakage between the valve and the tank shell.

(b)(5)(vi)(T) All valves attached to tanks other than those used in connection with water loading operations shall be closed and locked.

(b)(5)(vi)(U) If a tank is equipped with a swing line, the swing pipe shall be raised to and secured at its highest position.

(b)(5)(vi)(V) **Inspections** The Assistant Secretary or his designated representative shall make periodic inspections of all plants where the storage of flammable liquids is such as to require compliance with the foregoing requirements, in order to assure the following:

(b)(5)(vi)(V)(1) That all flammable liquid storage tanks are in compliance with these requirements and so maintained;

(b)(5)(vi)(V)(2) That detailed printed instructions of what to do in flood emergencies are properly posted; and

(b)(5)(vi)(V)(3) That station operators and other employees depended upon to carry out such instructions are thoroughly informed as to the location and operation of such valves and other equipment necessary to effect these requirements.

(b)(5)(vii) **Earthquake areas** In areas subject to earthquakes, the tank supports and connections shall be designed to resist damage as a result of such shocks.

(b)(6) **Sources of ignition** In locations where flammable vapors may be present, precautions shall be taken to prevent ignition by eliminating or controlling sources of ignition. Sources of ignition may include open flames, lightning, smoking, cutting and welding, hot surfaces, frictional heat, sparks (static, electrical, and mechanical), spontaneous ignition, chemical and physical-chemical reactions, and radiant heat.

(b)(7) **Testing**

(b)(7)(i) **General** All tanks, whether shop built or field erected, shall be strength tested before they are placed in service in accordance with the applicable paragraphs of the code under which they were built. The American Society of Mechanical Engineers (ASME) code stamp, American Petroleum Institute (API) monogram, or the label of the Underwriters' Laboratories, Inc., on a tank shall be evidence of compliance with this strength test. Tanks not marked in accordance with the above codes shall be strength tested before they are placed in service in accordance with good engineering principles and reference shall be made to the sections on testing in the codes listed in subparagraphs (1)(iii)(A), (iv)(B), or (v)(B) of this paragraph.

(b)(7)(ii) **Strength** When the vertical length of the fill and vent pipes is such that when filled with liquid the static head imposed upon the bottom of the tank exceeds 10 pounds per square inch, the tank and related piping shall be tested hydrostatically to a pressure equal to the static head thus imposed.

(b)(7)(iii) **Tightness** In addition to the strength test called for in subdivisions (i) and (ii) of this subparagraph, all tanks and connections shall be tested for tightness. Except for underground tanks, this tightness test shall be made at operating pressure with air, inert gas, or water prior to placing the tank in service. In the case of field-erected tanks the strength test may be considered to be the test for tank tightness. Underground tanks and piping, before being covered, enclosed, or placed in use, shall be tested for tightness hydrostatically, or with air pressure at not less than 3 pounds per square inch and not more than 5 pounds per square inch.

(b)(7)(iv) **Repairs** All leaks or deformations shall be corrected in an acceptable manner before the tank is placed in service. Mechanical caulking is not permitted for correcting leaks in welded tanks except pinhole leaks in the roof.

(b)(7)(v) **Derated operations** Tanks to be operated at pressures below their design pressure may be tested by the applicable provisions of subdivision (i) or (ii) of this subparagraph, based upon the pressure developed under full emergency venting of the tank.

(c) Piping, valves, and fittings

(c)(1) General

(c)(1)(i) **Design** The design (including selection of materials) fabrication, assembly, test, and inspection of piping systems containing flammable liquids shall be suitable for the expected working pressures and structural stresses. Conformity with the applicable provisions of Pressure Piping, ANSI B31 series and the provisions of this paragraph, shall be considered prima facie evidence of compliance with the foregoing provisions.

(c)(1)(ii) **Exceptions** This paragraph does not apply to any of the following:

(c)(1)(ii)(A) Tubing or casing on any oil or gas wells and any piping connected directly thereto;

(c)(1)(ii)(B) Motor vehicle, aircraft, boat, or portable or stationary engines;

(c)(1)(ii)(C) Piping within the scope of any applicable boiler and pressures vessel code.

(c)(1)(iii) **Definitions** As used in this paragraph, piping systems consist of pipe, tubing, flanges, bolting, gaskets, valves, fittings, the pressure containing parts of other components such as expansion joints and strainers, and devices which serve such purposes as mixing, separating, snubbing, distributing, metering, or controlling flow.

(c)(2) Materials for piping, valves, and fittings

(c)(2)(i) **Required materials** Materials for piping, valves, or fittings shall be steel, nodular iron, or malleable iron, except as provided in paragraph (c)(2)(ii), (iii) and (iv) of this section.

(c)(2)(ii) **Exceptions** Materials other than steel, nodular iron, or malleable iron may be used underground, or if required by the properties of the flammable liquid handled. Material other than steel, nodular iron, or malleable iron shall be designed to specifications embodying principles recognized as good engineering practices for the material used.

(c)(2)(iii) **Linings** Piping, valves, and fittings may have combustible or noncombustible linings.

(c)(2)(iv) **Low-melting materials** When low-melting point materials such as aluminum and brass or materials that soften on fire exposure such as plastics, or non-ductile materials such as cast iron, are necessary, special consideration shall be given to their behavior on fire exposure. If such materials are used in above ground piping systems or inside buildings, they shall be suitably protected against fire exposure or so located that any spill resulting from the failure of these materials could not unduly expose persons, important buildings or structures or can be readily controlled by remote valves.

(c)(3) **Pipe joints** Joints shall be made liquid tight. Welded or screwed joints or approved connectors shall be used. Threaded joints and connections shall be made up tight with a suitable lubricant or piping compound. Pipe joints dependent upon the friction characteristics of combustible materials for mechanical continuity of piping shall not be used inside buildings. They may be used outside of buildings above or below ground. If used above ground, the piping shall either be secured to prevent disengagement at the fitting or the piping system shall be so designed that any spill resulting from such disengagement could not unduly expose persons, important buildings or structures, and could be readily controlled by remote valves.

(c)(4) **Supports** Piping systems shall be substantially supported and protected against physical damage and excessive stresses arising from settlement, vibration, expansion, or contraction.

(c)(5) **Protection against corrosion** All piping for flammable liquids, both aboveground and underground, where subject to external corrosion, shall be painted or otherwise protected.

(c)(6) **Valves** Piping systems shall contain a sufficient number of valves to operate the system properly and to protect the plant. Piping systems in connection with pumps shall contain a sufficient number of valves to control properly the flow of liquid in normal operation and in the event of physical damage. Each connection to pipelines, by which equipment such as tankcars or tank vehicles discharge liquids by means of pumps into storage tanks, shall be provided with a check valve for automatic protection against backflow if the piping arrangement is such that backflow from the system is possible.

(c)(7) **Testing** All piping before being covered, enclosed, or placed in use shall be hydrostatically tested to 150 percent of the maximum anticipated pressure of the system, or pneumatically tested to 110 percent of the maximum anticipated pressure of the system, but not less than 5 pounds per square inch gage at the highest point of the system. This test shall be maintained for a sufficient time to complete visual inspection of all joints and connections, but for at least 10 minutes.

(d) Container and portable tank storage

(d)(1) Scope

(d)(1)(i) **General** This paragraph shall apply only to the storage of flammable liquids in drums or other containers (including flammable aerosols) not exceeding 60 gallons individual capacity and those portable tanks not exceeding 660 gallons individual capacity.

(d)(1)(ii) **Exceptions** This paragraph shall not apply to the following:

(d)(1)(ii)(A) Storage of containers in bulk plants, service stations, refineries, chemical plants, and distilleries;

(d)(1)(ii)(B) Class I or Class II liquids in the fuel tanks of a motor vehicle, aircraft, boat, or portable or stationary engine;

(d)(1)(ii)(C) Flammable paints, oils, varnishes, and similar mixtures used for painting or maintenance when not kept for a period in excess of 30 days;

(d)(1)(ii)(D) Beverages when packaged in individual containers not exceeding 1 gallon in size.

(d)(2) Design, construction, and capacity of containers

(d)(2)(i) **General** Only approved containers and portable tanks shall be used. Metal containers and portable tanks meeting the requirements of and containing products authorized by chapter I, title 49 of the Code of Federal Regulations (regulations issued by the Hazardous Materials Regulations Board, Department of Transportation), shall be deemed to be acceptable.

(d)(2)(ii) **Emergency venting** Each portable tank shall be provided with one or more devices installed in the top with sufficient emergency venting capacity to limit internal pressure under fire exposure conditions to 10 p.s.i.g., or 30 percent of the bursting pressure of the tank, whichever is greater. The total venting capacity shall be not less than that specified in paragraphs (b)(2)(v)(C) or (E) of this section. At least one pressure-activated vent having a minimum capacity of 6,000 cubic feet of free air (14.7 p.s.i.a. and 60 °F.) shall be used. It shall be set to open at not less than 5 p.s.i.g. If fusible vents are used, they shall be actuated by elements that operate at a temperature not exceeding 300 °F.

(d)(2)(iii) **Size** Flammable liquid containers shall be in accordance with Table H–12, except that glass or plastic containers of no more than 1-gallon capacity may be used for a Class IA or IB flammable liquid if:

(d)(2)(iii)(A)

(d)(2)(iii)(A)(1) Such liquid either would be rendered unfit for its intended use by contact with metal or would excessively corrode a metal container so as to create a leakage hazard; and

(d)(2)(iii)(A)(2) The user's process either would require more than 1 pint of a Category 1 flammable liquid or more than 1 quart of a Category 2 flammable liquid of a single assay lot to be used at one time, or would require the maintenance of an analytical standard liquid of a quality which is not met by the specified standards of liquids available, and the quantity of the analytical standard liquid required to be used in any one control process exceeds one-sixteenth the capacity of the container allowed under Table H–12 for the category of liquid; or

(d)(2)(iii)(B) The containers are intended for direct export outside the United States.

Table H–12
Maximum Allowable Size of Containers and Portable Tanks for Flammable Liquids

Container type	Category 1	Category 2	Category 3	Category 4
Glass or approved plastic	1 pt	1 qt	1 gal	1 gal
Metal (other than DOT drums)	1 gal	5 gal	5 gal	5 gal
Safety cans	2 gal	5 gal	5 gal	5 gal
Note: Table data continues on next page.				

Container type	Category 1	Category 2	Category 3	Category 4
Metal drums (DOT specifications)	60 gal	60 gal	60 gal	60 gal
Approved portable tanks	660 gal	660 gal	660 gal	660 gal

Note: Container exemptions: (a) Medicines, beverages, foodstuffs, cosmetics, and other common consumer items, when packaged according to commonly accepted practices, shall be exempt from the requirements of §1910.106(d)(2)(i) and (ii).

(d)(3) Design, construction, and capacity of storage cabinets

(d)(3)(i) **Maximum capacity** Not more than 60 gallons of Category 1, 2, or 3 flammable liquids, nor more than 120 gallons of Category 4 flammable liquids may be stored in a storage cabinet.

(d)(3)(ii) Fire resistance Storage cabinets shall be designed and constructed to limit the internal temperature to not more than 325 °F. when subjected to a 10-minute fire test using the standard time-temperature curve as set forth in Standard Methods of Fire Tests of Building Construction and Materials, NFPA 251–1969, which is incorporated by reference as specified in §1910.6. All joints and seams shall remain tight and the door shall remain securely closed during the fire test. Cabinets shall be labeled in conspicuous lettering,

"Flammable—Keep Fire Away."

(d)(3)(ii)(A) Metal cabinets constructed in the following manner shall be deemed to be in compliance. The bottom, top, door, and sides of cabinet shall be at least No. 18 gage sheet iron and double walled with 1½ inch air space. Joints shall be riveted, welded or made tight by some equally effective means. The door shall be provided with a three-point lock, and the door sill shall be raised at least 2 inches above the bottom of the cabinet.

(d)(3)(ii)(B) Wooden cabinets constructed in the following manner shall be deemed in compliance. The bottom, sides, and top shall be constructed of an approved grade of plywood at least 1 inch in thickness, which shall not break down or delaminate under fire conditions. All joints shall be rabbetted and shall be fastened in two directions with flathead woodscrews. When more than one door is used, there shall be a rabbetted overlap of not less than 1 inch. Hinges shall be mounted in such a manner as not to lose their holding capacity due to loosening or burning out of the screws when subjected to the fire test.

(d)(4) **Design and construction of inside storage rooms**

(d)(4)(i) Construction Inside storage rooms shall be constructed to meet the required fire-resistive rating for their use. Such construction shall comply with the test specifications set forth in Standard Methods of Fire Tests of Building Construction and Materials, NFPA 251–1969. Where an automatic sprinkler system is provided, the system shall be designed and installed in an acceptable manner. Openings to other rooms or buildings shall be provided with noncombustible liquid-tight raised sills or ramps at least 4 inches in height, or the floor in the storage area shall be at least 4 inches below the surrounding floor. Openings shall be provided with approved self-closing fire doors. The room shall be liquid-tight where the walls join the floor. A permissible alternate to the sill or ramp is an open-grated trench inside of the room which drains to a safe location. Where other portions of the building or other properties are exposed, windows shall be protected as set forth in the Standard for Fire Doors and Windows, NFPA No. 80–1968, which is incorporated by reference as specified in §1910.6, for Class E or F openings. Wood at least 1 inch nominal thickness may be used for shelving, racks, dunnage, scuffboards, floor overlay, and similar installations.

(d)(4)(ii) Rating and capacity Storage in inside storage rooms shall comply with Table H–13.

Table H–13
Storage in Inside Rooms

Fire protection[1] provided	Fire resistance	Maximum size	Total allowable quantities (gals./sq. ft./floor area)
Yes	2 hours	500 sq. ft	10
No	2 hours	500 sq. ft	5
Yes	1 hour	150 sq. ft	4
No	1 hour	150 sq. ft	2

[1] Fire protection system shall be sprinkler, water spray, carbon dioxide, or other system.

(d)(4)(iii) Wiring Electrical wiring and equipment located in inside storage rooms used for Category 1 or 2 flammable liquids, or Category 3 flammable liquids with a flashpoint below 100 °F (37.8 °C), shall be approved under Subpart S of this part for Class I, Division 2 Hazardous Locations; for Category 3 flammable liquids with a flashpoint at or above 100 °F (37.8 °C) and Category 4 flammable liquids, shall be approved for general use.

(d)(4)(iv) Ventilation Every inside storage room shall be provided with either a gravity or a mechanical exhaust ventilation system. Such system shall be designed to provide for a complete change of air within the room at least six times per hour. If a mechanical exhaust system is used, it shall be controlled by a switch located outside of the door. The ventilating equipment and any lighting fixtures shall be operated by the same switch. A pilot light shall be installed adjacent to the switch if Category 1 or 2 flammable liquids, or Category 3 flammable liquids with a flashpoint below 100 °F (37.8 °C), are dispensed within the room. Where gravity ventilation is provided, the fresh air intake, as well as the exhaust outlet from the room, shall be on the exterior of the building in which the room is located.

(d)(4)(v) Storage in inside storage rooms In every inside storage room there shall be maintained one clear aisle at least 3 feet wide. Containers over 30 gallons capacity shall not be stacked one upon the other. Dispensing shall be by approved pump or self-closing faucet only.

(d)(5) Storage inside building

(d)(5)(i) **Egress** Flammable liquids, including stock for sale, shall not be stored so as to limit use of exits, stairways, or areas normally used for the safe egress of people.

(d)(5)(ii) Containers The storage of flammable liquids in containers or portable tanks shall comply with subdivisions (iii) through (v) of this subparagraph.

(d)(5)(iii) Office occupancies Storage shall be prohibited except that which is required for maintenance and operation of building and operation of equipment. Such storage shall be kept in closed metal containers stored in a storage cabinet or in safety cans or in an inside storage room not having a door that opens into that portion of the building used by the public.

(d)(5)(iv) Mercantile occupancies and other retail stores

(d)(5)(iv)(A)–(D) [Reserved]

(d)(5)(iv)(E) Leaking containers shall be removed to a storage room or taken to a safe location outside the building and the contents transferred to an undamaged container.

(d)(5)(v) **General purpose public warehouses** Storage shall be in accordance with Table H–14 or H–15 and in buildings or in portions of such buildings cut off by standard firewalls. Material creating no fire exposure hazard to the flammable liquids may be stored in the same area.

Table H–14
Indoor Container Storage

Category liquid	Storage level	Gallons: Protected storage maximum per pile	Gallons: Unprotected storage maximum per pile
1	Ground and upper floors Basement	2,750 (50) Not permitted	660 (12) Not permitted
2	Ground and upper floors Basement	5,500 (100) Not permitted	1,375 (25) Not permitted
3 FP<100F	Ground and upper floors Basement	16,500 (300) Not permitted	4,125 (75) Not permitted
3 FP≥100F	Ground and upper floors Basement	16,500 (300) 5,500 (100)	4,125 (75) Not permitted
4	Ground and upper floors Basement	55,000 (1000) 8,250 (450)	13,750 (250) Not permitted

Note 1: When 2 or more categories of materials are stored in a single pile, the maximum gallonage permitted in that pile shall be the smallest of the 2 or more separate maximum gallonages.
Note 2: Aisles shall be provided so that no container is more than 12 ft. from an aisle. Main aisles shall be at least 3 ft. wide and side aisles at least 4 ft. wide.
Note 3: Each pile shall be separated from each other by at least 4 ft.
Note 4: FP means Flashpoint.
(Numbers in parentheses indicate corresponding number of 55-gal. drums.)

Table H–15
Indoor Portable Tank Storage

Category	Storage level	Gallons: Protected storage maximum per pile	Gallons: Unprotected storage maximum per pile
1	Ground and upper floors Basement	Not permitted Not permitted	Not permitted Not permitted
2	Ground and upper floors Basement	20,000 Not permitted	2,000 Not permitted

Category	Storage level	Gallons	
		Protected storage maximum per pile	Unprotected storage maximum per pile
3 FP<100F	Ground and upper floors Basement	40,000 Not permitted	5,500 Not permitted
3 FP≥100F	Ground and upper floors Basement	40,000 20,000	5,500 Not permitted
4	Ground and upper floors Basement	60,000 20,000	22,000 Not permitted

Note 1: When 1 or more categories of materials are stored in a single pile, the maximum gallonage permitted in that pile shall be the smallest of the 2 or more separate maximum gallonages.
Note 2: Aisles shall be provided so that no portable tank is more than 12 ft. from an aisle. Main aisles shall be at least 8 ft. wide and side aisles at least 4 ft. wide.
Note 3: Each pile shall be separated from each other by at least 4 ft.
Note 4: FP means Flashpoint.

(d)(5)(vi) **Flammable liquid warehouses or storage buildings**

(d)(5)(vi)(A) If the storage building is located 50 feet or less from a building or line of adjoining property that may be built upon, the exposing wall shall be a blank wall having a fire-resistance rating of at least 2 hours.

(d)(5)(vi)(B) The total quantity of liquids within a building shall not be restricted, but the arrangement of storage shall comply with Table H–14 or H–15.

(d)(5)(vi)(C) Containers in piles shall be separated by pallets or dunnage where necessary to provide stability and to prevent excessive stress on container walls.

(d)(5)(vi)(D) Portable tanks stored over one tier high shall be designed to nest securely, without dunnage, and adequate materials handing equipment shall be available to handle tanks safely at the upper tier level.

(d)(5)(vi)(E) No pile shall be closer than 3 feet to the nearest beam, chord, girder, or other obstruction, and shall be 3 feet below sprinkler deflectors or discharge orifices of water spray, or other overhead fire protection systems.

(d)(5)(vi)(F) Aisles of at least 3 feet wide shall be provided where necessary for reasons of access to doors, windows or standpipe connections.

(d)(6) **Storage outside buildings**

(d)(6)(i) **General** Storage outside buildings shall be in accordance with Table H–16 or H–17, and subdivisions (ii) and (iv) of this subparagraph.

Table H–16
Outdoor Container Storage

1- Category	2- Maximum per pile	3- Distance between piles	4- Distance to property line that can be built upon	5- Distance to street, alley, public way
	gallons	feet	feet	feet
1	1,100	5	20	10
2	2,200	5	20	10
3 FP<100F	4,400	5	20	10
3 FP≥100F	8,800	5	10	5
4	22,000	5	10	5

Note 1: When 2 or more categories of materials are stored in a single pile, the maximum gallonage in that pile shall be the smallest of the 2 or more separate gallonages.
Note 2: Within 200 ft. of each container, there shall be a 12-ft. wide access way to permit approach of fire control apparatus.
Note 3: The distances listed apply to properties that have protection for exposures as defined. If there are exposures, and such protection for exposures does not exist, the distances in column 4 shall be doubled.
Note 4: When total quantity stored does not exceed 50 percent of maximum per pile, the distances in columns 4 and 5 may be reduced 50 percent, but not less than 3 ft.
Note 5: FP means Flashpoint.

(d)(6)(ii) **Maximum storage** A maximum of 1,100 gallons of flammable liquids may be located adjacent to buildings located on the same premises and under the same management provided the provisions of subdivisions (A) and (B) of this subdivision are complied with.

(d)(6)(ii)(A) [Reserved]

(d)(6)(ii)(B) Where quantity stored exceeds 1,100 gallons, or provisions of subdivision (a) of this subdivision cannot be met, a minimum distance of 10 feet between buildings and nearest container of flammable liquid shall be maintained.

(d)(6)(iii) **Spill containment** The storage area shall be graded in a manner to divert possible spills away from buildings or other exposures or shall be surrounded by a curb at least 6 inches high. When curbs are used, provisions shall be made for draining of accumulations of ground or rain water or spills of flammable liquids. Drains shall terminate at a safe location and shall be accessible to operation under fire conditions.

(d)(6)(iv) **Security** The storage area shall be protected against tampering or trespassers where necessary and shall be kept free of weeds, debris and other combustible material not necessary to the storage.

(d)(7) **Fire control**

(d)(7)(i) **Extinguishers** Suitable fire control devices, such as small hose or portable fire extinguishers, shall be available at locations where flammable liquids are stored.

Table H–17
Outdoor Portable Tank Storage

1- Category	2- Maximum per pile	3- Distance between piles	4- Distance to property line that can be built upon	5- Distance to street, alley, public way
	gallons	feet	feet	feet
1	2,200	5	20	10
2	4,400	5	20	10
3 <100F	8,800	5	20	10
3 ≥100F	17,600	5	10	5
4	44,000	5	10	5

Note 1: When 2 or more categories of materials are stored in a single pile, the maximum gallonage in that pile shall be the smallest of the 2 or more separate gallonages.
Note 2: Within 200 ft. of each portable tank, there shall be a 12-ft. wide access way to permit approach of fire control apparatus.
Note 3: The distances listed apply to properties that have protection for exposures as defined. If there are exposures, and such protection for exposures does not exist, the distances in column 4 shall be doubled.
Note 4: When total quantity stored does not exceed 50 percent of maximum per pile, the distances in columns 4 and 5 may be reduced 50 percent, but not less than 3 ft.
Note 5: FP means Flashpoint.

(d)(7)(i)(A) At least one portable fire extinguisher having a rating of not less than 12–B units shall be located outside of, but not more than 10 feet from, the door opening into any room used for storage.

(d)(7)(i)(B) At least one portable fire extinguisher having a rating of not less than 12–B units must be located not less than 10 feet, nor more than 25 feet, from any Category 1, 2, or 3 flammable liquid storage area located outside of a storage room but inside a building.

(d)(7)(ii) **Sprinklers** When sprinklers are provided, they shall be installed in accordance with §1910.159.

(d)(7)(iii) **Open flames and smoking** Open flames and smoking shall not be permitted in flammable liquid storage areas.

(d)(7)(iv) **Water reactive materials** Materials which will react with water shall not be stored in the same room with flammable liquids.

(e) **Industrial plants**

(e)(1) **Scope**

(e)(1)(i) **Application** This paragraph shall apply to those industrial plants where:

(e)(1)(i)(A) The use of flammable liquids is incidental to the principal business, or

(e)(1)(i)(B) Where flammable liquids are handled or used only in unit physical operations such as mixing, drying, evaporating, filtering, distillation, and similar operations which do not involve chemical reaction. This paragraph shall not apply to chemical plants, refineries or distilleries.

(e)(1)(ii) **Exceptions** Where portions of such plants involve chemical reactions such as oxidation, reduction, halogenation, hydrogenation, alkylation, polymerization, and other chemical processes, those portions of the plant shall be in accordance with paragraph (h) of this section.

(e)(2) **Incidental storage or use of flammable liquids**

(e)(2)(i) **Application** This subparagraph shall be applicable to those portions of an industrial plant where the use and handling of flammable liquids is only incidental to the principal business, such as automobile assembly, construction of electronic equipment, furniture manufacturing, or other similar activities.

(e)(2)(ii) **Containers** Flammable liquids shall be stored in tanks or closed containers.

(e)(2)(ii)(A) Except as provided in subdivisions (B) and (C) of this subdivision, all storage shall comply with paragraph (d)(3) or (4) of this section.

(e)(2)(ii)(B) The quantity of liquid that may be located outside of an inside storage room or storage cabinet in a building or in any one fire area of a building shall not exceed:

(e)(2)(ii)(B)(1) 25 gallons of Category 1 flammable liquids in containers;

(e)(2)(ii)(B)(2) 120 gallons of Category 2, 3 or 4 flammable liquids in containers;

(e)(2)(ii)(B)(3) 660 gallons of Category 2, 3 or 4 flammable liquids in a single portable tank.

(e)(2)(ii)(C) Where large quantities of flammable liquids are necessary, storage may be in tanks which shall comply with the applicable requirements of paragraph (b) of this section.

(e)(2)(iii) **Separation and protection** Areas in which flammable liquids are transferred from one tank or container to another container shall be separated from other operations in the building by adequate distance or by construction having adequate fire resistance. Drainage or other means shall be provided to control spills. Adequate natural or mechanical ventilation shall be provided.

(e)(2)(iv) **Handling liquids at point of final use**

(e)(2)(iv)(A) Category 1 or 2 flammable liquids, or Category 3 flammable liquids with a flashpoint below 100 °F (37.8 °C), shall be kept in covered containers when not actually in use.

(e)(2)(iv)(B) Where flammable liquids are used or handled, except in closed containers, means shall be provided to dispose promptly and safely of leakage or spills.

(e)(2)(iv)(C) Category 1 or 2 flammable liquids, or Category 3 flammable liquids with a flashpoint below 100 °F (37.8 °C), may be used only where there are no open flames or other sources of ignition within the possible path of vapor travel.

(e)(2)(iv)(D) Flammable liquids shall be drawn from or transferred into vessels, containers, or portable tanks within a building only through a closed piping system, from safety cans, by means of a device drawing through the top, or from a container or portable tanks by gravity through an approved self-closing valve. Transferring by means of air pressure on the container or portable tanks shall be prohibited.

(e)(3) **Unit physical operations**

(e)(3)(i) **Application** This subparagraph shall be applicable in those portions of industrial plants where flammable liquids are handled or used in unit physical operations such as mixing, drying, evaporating, filtering, distillation, and similar operations which do not involve chemical change. Examples are plants compounding cosmetics, pharmaceuticals, solvents, cleaning fluids, insecticides, and similar types of activities.

(e)(3)(ii) **Location** Industrial plants shall be located so that each building or unit of equipment is accessible from at least one side for firefighting and fire control purposes. Buildings shall be located with respect to lines of adjoining property which may be built upon as set forth in paragraph (h)(2)(i) and (ii) of this section except that the blank wall referred to in paragraph (h)(2)(ii) of this section shall have a fire resistance rating of at least 2 hours.

(e)(3)(iii) **Chemical processes** Areas where unstable liquids are handled or small scale unit chemical processes are carried on shall be separated from the remainder of the plant by a fire wall of 2-hour minimum fire resistance rating.

(e)(3)(iv) **Drainage**

(e)(3)(iv)(A) Emergency drainage systems shall be provided to direct flammable liquid leakage and fire protection water to a safe location. This may require curbs, scuppers, or special drainage systems to control the spread of fire; see paragraph (b)(2)(vii)(B) of this section.

(e)(3)(iv)(B) Emergency drainage systems, if connected to public sewers or discharged into public waterways, shall be equipped with traps or separator.

(e)(3)(v) **Ventilation**

(e)(3)(v)(A) Areas as defined in paragraph (e)(3)(i) of this section using Category 1 or 2 flammable liquids, or Category 3 flammable liquids with a flashpoint below 100 °F (37.8 °C), shall be ventilated at a rate of not less than 1 cubic foot per minute per square foot of solid floor area. This shall be accomplished by natural or mechanical ventilation with discharge or exhaust to a safe location outside of the building. Provision shall be made for introduction of makeup air in such a manner as not to short circuit the ventilation. Ventilation shall be arranged to include all floor areas or pits where flammable vapors may collect.

(e)(3)(v)(B) Equipment used in a building and the ventilation of the building shall be designed so as to limit flammable vapor-air mixtures under normal operating conditions to the interior of equipment, and to not more than 5 feet from equipment which exposes Category 1 or 2 flammable liquids, or Category 3 flammable liquids with a flashpoint below 100 °F (37.8 °C), to the air. Examples of such equipment are dispensing stations, open centrifuges, plate and frame filters, open vacuum filters, and surfaces of open equipment.

(e)(3)(vi) **Storage and handling** The storage, transfer, and handling of liquid shall comply with paragraph (h)(4) of this section.

(e)(4) **Tank vehicle and tank car loading and unloading**

(e)(4)(i) Tank vehicle and tank car loading or unloading facilities shall be separated from aboveground tanks, warehouses, other plant buildings or nearest line of adjoining property which may be built upon by a distance of 25 feet for Category 1 or 2 flammable liquids, or Category 3 flammable liquids with a flashpoint below 100 °F (37.8 °C), and 15 feet for Category 3 flammable liquids with a flashpoint at or above 100 °F (37.8 °C) and Category 4 flammable liquids, measured from the nearest position of any fill stem. Buildings for pumps or shelters for personnel may be a part of the facility. Operations of the facility shall comply with the appropriate portions of paragraph (f)(3) of this section.

(e)(4)(ii) [Reserved]

(e)(5) **Fire control**

(e)(5)(i) **Portable and special equipment** Portable fire extinguishment and control equipment shall be provided in such quantities and types as are needed for the special hazards of operation and storage.

(e)(5)(ii) **Water supply** Water shall be available in volume and at adequate pressure to supply water hose streams, foam-producing equipment, automatic sprinklers, or water spray systems as the need is indicated by the special hazards of operation, dispensing and storage.

(e)(5)(iii) **Special extinguishers** Special extinguishing equipment such as that utilizing foam, inert gas, or dry chemical shall be provided as the need is indicated by the special hazards of operation dispensing and storage.

(e)(5)(iv) **Special hazards** Where the need is indicated by special hazards of operation, flammable liquid processing equipment, major piping, and supporting steel shall be protected by approved water spray systems, deluge systems, approved fire-resistant coatings, insulation, or any combination of these.

(e)(5)(v) **Maintenance** All plant fire protection facilities shall be adequately maintained and periodically inspected and tested to make sure they are always in satisfactory operating condition, and they will serve their purpose in time of emergency.

(e)(6) **Sources of ignition**

(e)(6)(i) **General** Adequate precautions shall be taken to prevent the ignition of flammable vapors. Sources of ignition include but are not limited to open flames; lightning; smoking; cutting and welding; hot surfaces; frictional heat; static, electrical, and mechanical sparks; spontaneous ignition, including heat-producing chemical reactions; and radiant heat.

(e)(6)(ii) **Grounding** Category 1 or 2 flammable liquids, or Category 3 flammable liquids with a flashpoint below 100 °F (37.8 °C), shall not be dispensed into containers unless the nozzle and container are electrically interconnected. Where the metallic floorplate on which the container stands while filling is electrically connected to the fill stem or where the fill stem is bonded to the container during filling operations by means of a bond wire, the provisions of this section shall be deemed to have been complied with.

(e)(7) **Electrical**

(e)(7)(i) **Equipment**

(e)(7)(i)(A) All electrical wiring and equipment shall be installed according to the requirements of Subpart S of this part.

(e)(7)(i)(B) Locations where flammable vapor-air mixtures may exist under normal operations shall be classified Class I, Division 1 according to the requirements of Subpart S of this part. For those pieces of equipment installed in accordance with subparagraph (3)(v)(B) of this paragraph, the Division 1 area shall extend 5 feet in all directions from all points of vapor liberation. All areas within pits shall be classified Division 1 if any part of the pit is within a Division 1 or 2 classified area, unless the pit is provided with mechanical ventilation.

(e)(7)(i)(C) Locations where flammable vapor-air mixtures may exist under abnormal conditions and for a distance beyond Division 1 locations shall be classified Division 2 according to the requirements of Subpart S of this part. These locations include an area within 20 feet horizontally, 3 feet vertically beyond a Division 1 area, and up to 3 feet above floor or grade level within 25 feet, if indoors, or 10 feet if outdoors, from any pump, bleeder, withdrawal fitting, meter, or similar device handling Category 1 or 2 flammable liquids, or Category 3 flammable liquids with a flashpoint below 100 °F (37.8 °C). Pits provided with adequate mechanical ventilation within a Division 1 or 2 area shall be classified Division 2. If only Category 3 flammable liquids with a flashpoint at or above 100 °F (37.8 °C) or Category 4 flammable liquids are handled, then ordinary electrical equipment is satisfactory though care shall be used in locating electrical apparatus to prevent hot metal from falling into open equipment.

(e)(7)(i)(D) Where the provisions of subdivisions (A), (B), and (C), of this subdivision require the installation of electrical equipment suitable for Class I, Division 1 or Division 2 locations, ordinary electrical equipment including switchgear may be used if installed in a room or enclosure which is maintained under positive pressure with respect to the hazardous area. Ventilation makeup air shall be uncontaminated by flammable vapors.

(e)(8) **Repairs to equipment** Hot work, such as welding or cutting operations, use of spark-producing power tools, and chipping operations shall be permitted only under supervision of an individual in responsible charge. The individual in responsible charge shall make an inspection of the area to be sure that it is safe for the work to be done and that safe procedures will be followed for the work specified.

(e)(9) **Housekeeping**

(e)(9)(i) **General** Maintenance and operating practices shall be in accordance with established procedures which will tend to control leakage and prevent the accidental escape of flammable liquids. Spills shall be cleaned up promptly.

(e)(9)(ii) **Access** Adequate aisles shall be maintained for unobstructed movement of personnel and so that fire protection equipment can be brought to bear on any part of flammable liquid storage, use, or any unit physical operation.

(e)(9)(iii) [OI] **Waste and residue** Combustible waste material and residues in a building or unit operating area shall be kept to a minimum, stored in covered metal receptacles and disposed of daily.

(e)(9)(iv) **Clear zone** Ground area around buildings and unit operating areas shall be kept free of weeds, trash, or other unnecessary combustible materials.

(f) **Bulk plants**

(f)(1) **Storage**

(f)(1)(i) **Category 1 or 2 flammable liquids, or Category 3 flammable liquids with a flashpoint below 100 °F (37.8 °C)** Category 1 or 2 flammable liquids, or Category 3 flammable liquids with a flashpoint below 100 °F (37.8 °C), shall be stored in closed containers, or in storage tanks above ground outside of buildings, or underground in accordance with paragraph (b) of this section.

(f)(1)(ii) **Category 3 flammable liquids with a flashpoint at or above 100 °F (37.8 °C) and Category 4 flammable liquids** Category 3 flammable liquids with a flashpoint at or above 100 °F (37.8 °C) and Category 4 flammable liquids shall be stored in containers, or in tanks within buildings or above ground outside of buildings, or underground in accordance with paragraph (b) of this section.

(f)(1)(iii) **Piling containers** Containers of flammable liquids when piled one upon the other shall be separated by dunnage sufficient to provide stability and to prevent excessive stress on container walls. The height of the pile shall be consistent with the stability and strength of containers.

(f)(2) **Buildings**

(f)(2)(i) **Exits** Rooms in which flammable liquids are stored or handled by pumps shall have exit facilities arranged to prevent occupants from being trapped in the event of fire.

(f)(2)(ii) **Heating** Rooms in which Category 1 or 2 flammable liquids, or Category 3 flammable liquids with a flashpoint below 100 °F (37.8 °C), are stored or handled shall be heated only by means not constituting a source of ignition, such as steam or hot water. Rooms containing heating appliances involving sources of ignition shall be located and arranged to prevent entry of flammable vapors.

(f)(2)(iii) **Ventilation**

(f)(2)(iii)(A) Ventilation shall be provided for all rooms, buildings, or enclosures in which Category 1 or 2 flammable liquids, or Category 3 flammable liquids with a flashpoint below 100 °F (37.8 °C), are pumped or dispensed. Design of ventilation systems shall take into account the relatively high specific gravity of the vapors. Ventilation may be provided by adequate openings in outside walls at floor level unobstructed except by louvers or coarse screens. Where natural ventilation is inadequate, mechanical ventilation shall be provided.

(f)(2)(iii)(B) Category 1 or 2 flammable liquids, or Category 3 flammable liquids with a flashpoint below 100 °F (37.8 °C), shall not be stored or handled within a building having a basement or pit into which flammable vapors may travel, unless such area is provided with ventilation designed to prevent the accumulation of flammable vapors therein.

(f)(2)(iii)(C) Containers of Category 1 or 2 flammable liquids, or Category 3 flammable liquids with a flashpoint below 100 °F (37.8 °C), shall not be drawn from or filled within buildings unless provision is made to prevent the accumulation of flammable vapors in hazardous concentrations. Where mechanical ventilation is required, it shall be kept in operation while flammable liquids with a flashpoint below 100 °F (37.8 °C) are being handled.

(f)(3) **Loading and unloading facilities**

(f)(3)(i) [OI] **Separation** Tank vehicle and tank car loading or unloading facilities shall be separated from aboveground tanks, warehouses, other plant buildings or nearest line of adjoining property that may be built upon by a distance of 25 feet for Category 1 or 2 flammable liquids, or Category 3 flammable liquids with a flashpoint below 100 °F (37.8 °C), and 15 feet for Category 3 flammable liquids with a flashpoint at or above 100 °F (37.8 °C) and Category 4 flammable liquids measured from the nearest position of any fill spout. Buildings for pumps or shelters for personnel may be a part of the facility.

(f)(3)(ii) **Class restriction** Equipment such as piping, pumps, and meters used for the transfer of Category 1 or 2 flammable liquids, or Category 3 flammable liquids with a flashpoint below 100 °F (37.8 °C), between storage tanks and the fill stem of the loading rack shall not be used for the transfer of Category 3 flammable liquids with a flashpoint at or above 100 °F (37.8 °C) or Category 4 flammable liquids.

(f)(3)(iii) [OI] **Valves** Valves used for the final control for filling tank vehicles shall be of the self-closing type and manually held open except where automatic means are provided for shutting off the flow when the vehicle is full or after filling of a preset amount.

(f)(3)(iv) **Static protection**

(f)(3)(iv)(A) Bonding facilities for protection against static sparks during the loading of tank vehicles through open domes shall be provided:

(f)(3)(iv)(A)(*1*) Where Category 1 or 2 flammable liquids, or Category 3 flammable liquids with a flashpoint below 100 °F (37.8 °C), are loaded, or

(f)(3)(iv)(A)(*2*) Where Category 3 flammable liquids with a flashpoint at or above 100 °F (37.8 °C) or Category 4 flammable liquids are loaded into vehicles which may contain vapors from previous cargoes of Category 1 or 2 flammable liquids, or Category 3 flammable liquids with a flashpoint below 100 °F (37.8 °C).

(f)(3)(iv)(B) Protection as required in (A) of this subdivision (iv) shall consist of a metallic bond wire permanently electrically connected to the fill stem or to some part of the rack structure in electrical contact with the fill stem. The free end of such wire shall be provided with a clamp or equivalent device for convenient attachment to some metallic part in electrical contact with the cargo tank of the tank vehicle.

(f)(3)(iv)(C) Such bonding connection shall be made fast to the vehicle or tank before dome covers are raised and shall remain in place until filling is completed and all dome covers have been closed and secured.

(f)(3)(iv)(D) Bonding as specified in (A), (B), and (C) of this subdivision is not required:

(f)(3)(iv)(D)(*1*) Where vehicles are loaded exclusively with products not having a static accumulating tendency, such as asphalt, most crude oils, residual oils, and water soluble liquids;

(f)(3)(iv)(D)(*2*) Where no Category 1 or 2 flammable liquids, or Category 3 flammable liquids with a flashpoint below 100 °F (37.8 °C), are handled at the loading facility and the tank vehicles loaded are used exclusively for Category 3 flammable liquids with a flashpoint at or above 100 °F (37.8 °C) and Category 4 flammable liquids; and

(f)(3)(iv)(D)(*3*) Where vehicles are loaded or unloaded through closed bottom or top connections.

(f)(3)(iv)(E) Filling through open domes into the tanks of tank vehicles or tank cars, that contain vapor-air mixtures within the flammable range or where the liquid being filled can form such a mixture, shall be by means of a downspout which extends near the bottom of the tank. This precaution is not required when loading liquids which are nonaccumulators of static charges.

(f)(3)(v) **Stray currents** Tank car loading facilities where Category 1 or 2 flammable liquids, or Category 3 flammable liquids with a flashpoint below 100 °F (37.8 °C), are loaded through open domes shall be protected against stray currents by bonding the pipe to at least one rail and to the rack structure if of metal. Multiple lines entering the rack area shall be electrically bonded together. In addition, in areas where excessive stray currents are known to exist, all pipe entering the rack area shall be provided with insulating sections to electrically isolate the rack piping from the pipelines. No bonding between the tank car and the rack or piping is required during either loading or unloading of Category 3 flammable liquids with a flashpoint at or above 100 °F (37.8 °C) or Category 4 flammable liquids.

(f)(3)(vi) **Container filling facilities** Category 1 or 2 flammable liquids, or Category 3 flammable liquids with a flashpoint below 100 °F (37.8 °C), shall not be dispensed into containers unless the nozzle and container are electrically interconnected. Where the metallic floorplate on which the container stands while filling is electrically connected to the fill stem or where the fill stem is bonded to the container during filling operations by means of a bond wire, the provisions of this section shall be deemed to have been complied with.

(f)(4) **Wharves**

(f)(4)(i) **Definition, application** The term **wharf** shall mean any wharf, pier, bulkhead, or other structure over or contiguous to navigable water used in conjunction with a bulk plant, the primary function of which is the transfer of flammable liquid cargo in bulk between the bulk plant and any tank vessel, ship, barge, lighter boat, or other mobile floating craft; and this subparagraph shall apply to all such installations except Marine Service Stations as covered in paragraph (g) of this section.

(f)(4)(ii)–(iii) [Reserved]

(f)(4)(iv) **Design and construction** Substructure and deck shall be substantially designed for the use intended. Deck may employ any material which will afford the desired combination of flexibility, resistance to shock, durability, strength, and fire resistance. Heavy timber construction is acceptable.

(f)(4)(v) [Reserved]

(f)(4)(vi) **Pumps** Loading pumps capable of building up pressures in excess of the safe working pressure of cargo hose or loading arms shall be provided with bypasses, relief valves, or other arrangement to protect the loading facilities against excessive pressure. Relief devices shall be tested at not more than yearly intervals to determine that they function satisfactorily at the pressure at which they are set.

(f)(4)(vii) Hoses and couplings. All pressure hoses and couplings shall be inspected at intervals appropriate to the service. The hose and couplings shall be tested with the hose extended and using the "inservice maximum operating pressures." Any hose showing material deteriorations, signs of leakage, or weakness in its carcass or at the couplings shall be withdrawn from service and repaired or discarded.

(f)(4)(viii) **Piping and fittings** Piping, valves, and fittings shall be in accordance with paragraph (c) of this section, with the following exceptions and additions:

(f)(4)(viii)(A) Flexibility of piping shall be assured by appropriate layout and arrangement of piping supports so that motion of the wharf structure resulting from wave action, currents, tides, or the mooring of vessels will not subject the pipe to repeated strain beyond the elastic limit;

(f)(4)(viii)(B) Pipe joints depending upon the friction characteristics of combustible materials or grooving of pipe ends for mechanical continuity of piping shall not be used;

(f)(4)(viii)(C) Swivel joints may be used in piping to which hoses are connected, and for articulated swivel-joint transfer systems, provided that the design is such that the mechanical strength of the joint will not be impaired if the packing material should fail, as by exposure to fire;

(f)(4)(viii)(D) Piping systems shall contain a sufficient number of valves to operate the system properly and to control the flow of liquid in normal operation and in the event of physical damage;

(f)(4)(viii)(E) In addition to the requirements of paragraph (f)(4)(viii)(d) of this section, each line conveying Category 1 or 2 flammable liquids, or Category 3 flammable liquids with a flashpoint below 100 °F (37.8 °C), leading to a wharf shall be provided with a readily accessible block valve located on shore near the approach to the wharf and outside of any diked area. Where more than one line is involved, the valves shall be grouped in one location;

(f)(4)(viii)(F) Means of easy access shall be provided for cargo line valves located below the wharf deck;

(f)(4)(viii)(G) Pipelines on flammable liquids wharves shall be adequately bonded and grounded. If excessive stray currents are encountered, insulating joints shall be installed. Bonding and grounding connections on all pipelines shall be located on wharfside of hose-riser insulating flanges, if used, and shall be accessible for inspection;

(f)(4)(viii)(H) Hose or articulated swivel-joint pipe connections used for cargo transfer shall be capable of accommodating the combined effects of change in draft and maximum tidal range, and mooring lines shall be kept adjusted to prevent the surge of the vessel from placing stress on the cargo transfer system;

(f)(4)(viii)(I) Hose shall be supported so as to avoid kinking and damage from chafing.

(f)(4)(ix) **Fire protection** Suitable portable fire extinguishers with a rating of not less than 12–BC shall be located within 75 feet of those portions of the facility where fires are likely to occur, such as hose connections, pumps, and separator tanks.

(f)(4)(ix)(A) Where piped water is available, ready-connected fire hose in size appropriate for the water supply shall be provided so that manifolds where connections are made and broken can be reached by at least one hose stream.

(f)(4)(ix)(B) Material shall not be placed on wharves in such a manner as to obstruct access to firefighting equipment, or important pipeline control valves.

(f)(4)(ix)(C) Where the wharf is accessible to vehicle traffic, an unobstructed roadway to the shore end of the wharf shall be maintained for access of firefighting apparatus.

(f)(4)(x) **Operations control** Loading or discharging shall not commence until the wharf superintendent and officer in charge of the tank vessel agree that the tank vessel is properly moored and all connections are properly made. Mechanical work shall not be performed on the wharf during cargo transfer, except under special authorization based on a review of the area involved, methods to be employed, and precautions necessary.

(f)(5) **Electrical equipment**

(f)(5)(i) **Application** This paragraph (f)(5)(i) shall apply to areas where Category 1 or 2 flammable liquids, or Category 3 flammable liquids with a flashpoint below 100 °F (37.8 °C), are stored or handled. For areas where only Category 3 flammable liquids with a flashpoint at or above 100 °F (37.8 °C) or Category 4 flammable liquids are stored or handled, the electrical equipment may be installed in accordance with the provisions of Subpart S of this part, for ordinary locations.

(f)(5)(ii) **Conformance** All electrical equipment and wiring shall be of a type specified by and shall be installed in accordance with Subpart S of this part.

(f)(5)(iii) **Classification** So far as it applies Table H–18 shall be used to delineate and classify hazardous areas for the purpose of installation of electrical equipment under normal circumstances. In Table H–18 a classified area shall not extend beyond an unpierced wall, roof, or other solid partition. The area classifications listed shall be based on the premise that the installation meets the applicable requirements of this section in all respects.

(f)(6) **Sources of ignition** Category 1 or 2 flammable liquids, or Category 3 flammable liquids with a flashpoint below 100 °F (37.8 °C), shall not be handled, drawn, or dispensed where flammable vapors may reach a source of ignition. Smoking shall be prohibited except in designated localities. "No Smoking" signs shall be conspicuously posted where hazard from flammable liquid vapors is normally present.

(f)(7) **Drainage and waste disposal** Provision shall be made to prevent flammable liquids which may be spilled at loading or unloading points from entering public sewers and drainage systems, or natural waterways. Connection to such sewers, drains, or waterways by which flammable liquids might enter shall be provided with separator boxes or other approved means whereby such entry is precluded. Crankcase drainings and flammable liquids shall not be dumped into sewers, but shall be stored in tanks or tight drums outside of any building until removed from the premises.

(f)(8) **Fire control** Suitable fire-control devices, such as small hose or portable fire extinguishers, shall be available to locations where fires are likely to occur. Additional fire-control equipment may be required where a tank of more than 50,000 gallons individual capacity contains Category 1 or 2 flammable liquids, or Category 3 flammable liquids with a flashpoint below 100 °F (37.8 °C), and where an unusual exposure hazard exists from surrounding property. Such additional fire-control equipment shall be sufficient to extinguish a fire in the largest tank. The design and amount of such equipment shall be in accordance with approved engineering standards.

(g) **Service stations**

(g)(1) **Storage and handling**

(g)(1)(i) **General provisions**

(g)(1)(i)(A) Liquids shall be stored in approved closed containers not exceeding 60 gallons capacity, in tanks located underground, in tanks in special enclosures as described in paragraph (g)(i) of this section, or in aboveground tanks as provided for in paragraphs (g)(4)(ii), (B), (C) and (D) of this section.

(g)(1)(i)(B) Aboveground tanks, located in an adjoining bulk plant, may be connected by piping to service station underground tanks if, in addition to valves at aboveground tanks, a valve is also installed within control of service station personnel.

(g)(1)(i)(C) Apparatus dispensing Category 1 or 2 flammable liquids, or Category 3 flammable liquids with a flashpoint below 100 °F (37.8 °C), into the fuel tanks of motor vehicles of the public shall not be located at a bulk plant unless separated by a fence or similar barrier from the area in which bulk operations are conducted.

(g)(1)(i)(D) [Reserved]

(g)(1)(i)(E) The provisions of paragraph (g)(1)(i)(a) of this section shall not prohibit the dispensing of flammable liquids with a flashpoint below 100 °F (37.8 °C) in the open from a tank vehicle to a motor vehicle. Such dispensing shall be permitted provided:

(g)(1)(i)(E)(1) The tank vehicle complies with the requirements covered in the Standard on Tank Vehicles for Flammable Liquids, NFPA 385–1966.

(g)(1)(i)(E)(2) The dispensing is done on premises not open to the public.

(g)(1)(i)(E)(3) [Reserved]

(g)(1)(i)(E)(4) The dispensing hose does not exceed 50 feet in length.

(g)(1)(i)(E)(5) The dispensing nozzle is a listed automatic-closing type without a latchopen device.

(g)(1)(i)(F) Category 1 or 2 flammable liquids, or Category 3 flammable liquids with a flashpoint below 100 °F (37.8 °C), shall not be stored or handled within a building having a basement or pit into which flammable vapors may travel, unless such area is provided with ventilation designed to prevent the accumulation of flammable vapors therein.

(g)(1)(i)(G) [Reserved]

Table H–18
Electrical Equipment Hazardous Areas—Bulk Plants

Location	Class I Group D division	Extent of classified area
Tank vehicle and tank car:[1]		
Loading through open dome	1	Within 3 feet of edge of dome, extending in all directions.
	2	Area between 3 feet and 5 feet from edge of dome, extending in all directions.
Loading through bottom connections with atmospheric venting	1	Within 3 feet of point of venting to atmosphere extending in all directions.
	2	Area between 3 feet and 5 feet from point of venting to atmosphere, extending in all directions. Also up to 18 inches above grade within a horizontal radius of 10 feet from point of loading connection.
Loading through closed dome with atmospheric venting	1	Within 3 feet of open end of vent, extending in all directions.
	2	Area between 3 feet and 5 feet from open end of vent, extending in all directions. Also within 3 feet of edge of dome, extending in all directions.
Loading through closed dome with vapor recovery	2	Within 3 feet of point of connection of both fill and vapor lines, extending in all directions.
Bottom loading with vapor recovery or any bottom unloading	2	Within 3 feet of point of connections extending in all directions. Also up to 18 inches above grade within a horizontal radius of 10 feet from point of connection.
Drum and container filling:		
Outdoors, or indoors with adequate ventilation	1	Within 3 feet of vent and fill opening, extending in all directions.
	2	Area between 3 feet and 5 feet from vent or fill opening, extending in all directions. Also up to 18 inches above floor or grade level within a horizontal radius of 10 feet from vent or fill opening.
Outdoors, or indoors with adequate ventilation	1	Within 3 feet of vent and fill opening, extending in all directions.
	2	Area between 3 feet and 5 feet from vent or fill opening, extending in all directions. Also up to 18 inches above floor or grade level within a horizontal radius of 10 feet from vent or fill opening.
Tank—Aboveground:		
Shell, ends, or roof and dike area	2	Within 10 feet from shell, ends, or roof of tank, Area inside dikes to level of top of dike.
Vent	1	Within 5 feet of open end of vent, extending in all directions.
	2	Area between 5 feet and 10 feet from open end of vent, extending in all directions.
Floating roof	1	Area above the roof and within the shell.
Pits:		
Without mechanical ventilation	1	Entire area within pit if any part is within a Division 1 or 2 classified area.
With mechanical ventilation	2	Entire area within pit if any part is within a Division 1 or 2 classified area.
Containing valves, fittings or piping, and not within a Division 1 or 2 classified area	2	Entire pit.
Pumps, bleeders, withdrawal fittings, meters and similar devices:		
Indoors	2	Within 5 feet of any edge of such devices, extending in all directions. Also up to 3 feet above floor or grade level within 25 feet horizontally from any edge of such devices.
Outdoors	2	Within 3 feet of any edge of such devices, extending in all directions. Also up to 18 inches above grade level within 10 feet horizontally from any edge of such devices.
Storage and repair garage for tank vehicles	1	All pits or spaces below floor level.
	2	Area up to 18 inches above floor or grade level for entire storage or repair garage.
Drainage ditches, separators, impounding basins	2	Area up to 18 inches above ditch, separator or basin. Also up to 18 inches above grade within 15 feet horizontally from any edge.
Garages for other than tank vehicles	([2])	If there is any opening to these rooms within the extent of an outdoor classified area, the entire room shall be classified the same as the area classification at the point of the opening.
Note: Table data continues on next page.		

Location	Class I Group D division	Extent of classified area
Outdoor drum storage	(2)	
Indoor warehousing where there is no flammable liquid transfer	(2)	If there is any opening to these rooms within the extent of an indoor classified area, the room shall be classified the same as if the wall, curb or partition did not exist.
Office and rest rooms	(2)	

1 When classifying the extent of the area, consideration shall be given to the fact that tank cars or tank vehicles may be spotted at varying points. Therefore, the extremities of the loading or unloading positions shall be used.
2 Ordinary.

(g)(1)(ii) Special enclosures

(g)(1)(ii)(A) When installation of tanks in accordance with paragraph (b)(3) of this section is impractical because of property or building limitations, tanks for flammable liquids may be installed in buildings if properly enclosed.

(g)(1)(ii)(B) The enclosure shall be substantially liquid and vaportight without backfill. Sides, top, and bottom of the enclosure shall be of reinforced concrete at least 6 inches thick, with openings for inspection through the top only. Tank connections shall be so piped or closed that neither vapors nor liquid can escape into the enclosed space. Means shall be provided whereby portable equipment may be employed to discharge to the outside any liquid or vapors which might accumulate should leakage occur.

(g)(1)(iii) Inside buildings

(g)(1)(iii)(A) Except where stored in tanks as provided in paragraph (g)(1)(ii) of this section, no Category 1 or 2 flammable liquids, or Category 3 flammable liquids with a flashpoint below 100 °F (37.8 °C), shall be stored within any service station building except in closed containers of aggregate capacity not exceeding 60 gallons. One container not exceeding 60 gallons capacity equipped with an approved pump is permitted.

(g)(1)(iii)(B) Category 1 or 2 flammable liquids, or Category 3 flammable liquids with a flashpoint below 100 °F (37.8 °C), may be transferred from one container to another in lubrication or service rooms of a service station building provided the electrical installation complies with Table H–19 and provided that any heating equipment complies with paragraph (g)(6) of this section.

(g)(1)(iii)(C) Category 3 flammable liquids with a flashpoint at or above 100 °F (37.8 °C) and Category 4 flammable liquids may be stored and dispensed inside service station buildings from tanks of not more than 120 gallons capacity each.

(g)(1)(iv) [Reserved]

(g)(1)(v) Dispensing into portable containers No delivery of any Category 1 or 2 flammable liquids, or Category 3 flammable liquids with a flashpoint below 100 °F (37.8 °C), shall be made into portable containers unless the container is constructed of metal, has a tight closure with screwed or spring cover, and is fitted with a spout or so designed so the contents can be poured without spilling.

(g)(2) [Reserved]

(g)(3) Dispensing systems

(g)(3)(i) Location Dispensing devices at automotive service stations shall be so located that all parts of the vehicle being served will be on the premises of the service station.

(g)(3)(ii) Inside location Approved dispensing units may be located inside of buildings. The dispensing area shall be separated from other areas in an approved manner. The dispensing unit and its piping shall be mounted either on a concrete island or protected against collision damage by suitable means and shall be located in a position where it cannot be struck by a vehicle descending a ramp or other slope out of control. The dispensing area shall be provided with an approved mechanical or gravity ventilation system. When dispensing units are located below grade, only approved mechanical ventilation shall be used and the entire dispensing area shall be protected by an approved automatic sprinkler system. Ventilating systems shall be electrically interlocked with gasoline dispensing units so that the dispensing units cannot be operated unless the ventilating fan motors are energized.

(g)(3)(iii) Emergency power cutoff A clearly identified and easily accessible switch(es) or a circuit breaker(s) shall be provided at a location remote from dispensing devices, including remote pumping systems, to shut off the power to all dispensing devices in the event of an emergency.

(g)(3)(iv) Dispensing units

(g)(3)(iv)(A) Category 1 or 2 flammable liquids, or Category 3 flammable liquids with a flashpoint below 100 °F (37.8 °C), shall be transferred from tanks by means of fixed pumps so designed and equipped as to allow control of the flow and to prevent leakage or accidental discharge.

(g)(3)(iv)(B)(1) Only listed devices may be used for dispensing Category 1 or 2 flammable liquids, or Category 3 flammable liquids with a flashpoint below 100 °F (37.8 °C). No such device may be used if it shows evidence of having been dismantled1

(g)(3)(iv)(B)(2) Every dispensing device for Category 1 or 2 flammable liquids, or Category 3 flammable liquids with a flashpoint below 100 °F (37.8 °C), installed after December 31, 1978, shall contain evidence of listing so placed that any attempt to dismantle the device will result in damage to such evidence, visible without disassembly or dismounting of the nozzle.

(g)(3)(iv)(C) Category 1 or 2 flammable liquids, or Category 3 flammable liquids with a flashpoint below 100 °F (37.8 °C), shall not be dispensed by pressure from drums, barrels, and similar containers. Approved pumps taking suction through the top of the container or approved self-closing faucets shall be used.

(g)(3)(iv)(D) The dispensing units, except those attached to containers, shall be mounted either on a concrete island or protected against collision damage by suitable means.

(g)(3)(v) Remote pumping systems

(g)(3)(v)(A) This paragraph (g)(3)(v) shall apply to systems for dispensing Category 1 or 2 flammable liquids, or Category 3 flammable liquids with a flashpoint below 100 °F (37.8 °C), where such liquids are transferred from storage to individual or multiple dispensing units by pumps located elsewhere than at the dispensing units.

(g)(3)(v)(B) Pumps shall be designed or equipped so that no part of the system will be subjected to pressures above its allowable working pressure. Pumps installed above grade, outside of buildings, shall be located not less than 10 feet from lines of adjoining property which may be built upon, and not less than 5 feet from any building opening. When an outside pump location is impractical, pumps may be installed inside of buildings, as provided for dispensers in subdivision (ii) of this subparagraph, or in pits as provided in subdivision (c) of this subdivision. Pumps shall be substantially anchored and protected against physical damage by vehicles.

(g)(3)(v)(C) Pits for subsurface pumps or piping manifolds of submersible pumps shall withstand the external forces to which they may be subjected without damage to the pump, tank, or piping. The pit shall be no larger than necessary for inspection and maintenance and shall be provided with a fitted cover.

(g)(3)(v)(D) A control shall be provided that will permit the pump to operate only when a dispensing nozzle is removed from its bracket on the dispensing unit and the switch on this dispensing unit is manually actuated. This control shall also stop the pump when all nozzles have been returned to their brackets.

(g)(3)(v)(E) An approved impact valve, incorporating a fusible link, designed to close automatically in the event of severe impact or fire exposure shall be properly installed in the dispensing supply line at the base of each individual dispensing device.

(g)(3)(v)(F) Testing. After the completion of the installation, including any paving, that section of the pressure piping system between the pump discharge and the connection for the dispensing facility shall be tested for at least 30 minutes at the maximum operating pressure of the system. Such tests shall be repeated at 5-year intervals thereafter.

(g)(3)(vi) Delivery nozzles

(g)(3)(vi)(A) A listed manual or automatic-closing type hose nozzle valve shall be provided on dispensers used for the dispensing of Category 1 or 2 flammable liquids, or Category 3 flammable liquids with a flashpoint below 100 °F (37.8 °C).

(g)(3)(vi)(B) Manual-closing type valves shall be held open manually during dispensing. Automatic-closing type valves may be used in conjunction with an approved latch-open device.

(g)(4) **Marine service stations**

(g)(4)(i) **Dispensing**

(g)(4)(i)(A) The dispensing area shall be located away from other structures so as to provide room for safe ingress and egress of craft to be fueled. Dispensing units shall in all cases be at least 20 feet from any activity involving fixed sources of ignition.

(g)(4)(i)(B) Dispensing shall be by approved dispensing units with or without integral pumps and may be located on open piers, wharves, or floating docks or on shore or on piers of the solid fill type.

(g)(4)(i)(C) Dispensing nozzles shall be automatic-closing without a hold-open latch.

(g)(4)(ii) **Tanks and pumps**

(g)(4)(ii)(A) Tanks, and pumps not integral with the dispensing unit, shall be on shore or on a pier of the solid fill type, except as provided in paragraphs (g)(4)(ii)(B) and (C) of this section.

(g)(4)(ii)(B) Where shore location would require excessively long supply lines to dispensers, tanks may be installed on a pier provided that applicable portions of paragraph (b) of this section relative to spacing, diking, and piping are complied with and the quantity so stored does not exceed 1,100 gallons aggregate capacity.

(g)(4)(ii)(C) Shore tanks supplying marine service stations may be located above ground, where rock ledges or high water table make underground tanks impractical.

(g)(4)(ii)(D) Where tanks are at an elevation which would produce gravity head on the dispensing unit, the tank outlet shall be equipped with a pressure control valve positioned adjacent to and outside the tank block valve specified in paragraph (b)(2)(ix)(B) of this section, so adjusted that liquid cannot flow by gravity from the tank in case of piping or hose failure.

(g)(4)(iii) **Piping**

(g)(4)(iii)(A) Piping between shore tanks and dispensing units shall be as described in paragraph (c) of this section, except that, where dispensing is from a floating structure, suitable lengths of oil-resistant flexible hose may be employed between the shore piping and the piping on the floating structure as made necessary by change in water level or shoreline.

Table H–19
Electrical Equipment Hazardous Areas–Service Stations

Location	Class I Group D division	Extent of classified area
Underground tank:		
Fill opening	1	Any pit, box or space below grade level, any part of which is within the Division 1 or 2 classified area.
	2	Up to 18 inches above grade level within a horizontal radius of 10 feet from a loose fill connection and within a horizontal radius of 5 feet from a tight fill connection.
Vent—Discharging upward	1	Within 3 feet of open end of vent, extending in all directions.
	2	Area between 3 feet and 5 feet of open end of vent, extending in all directions.
Dispenser:		
Pits	1	Any pit, box or space below grade level, any part of which is within the Division 1 or 2 classified area.
Dispenser enclosure	1	The area 4 feet vertically above base within the enclosure and 18 inches horizontally in all directions.
Outdoor	2	Up to 18 inches above grade level within 20 feet horizontally of any edge of enclosure.
Indoor:		
With mechanical ventilation	2	Up to 18 inches above grade or floor level within 20 feet horizontally of any edge of enclosure.
With gravity ventilation	2	Up to 18 inches above grade or floor level within 25 feet horizontally of any edge of enclosure.
Remote pump—Outdoor	1	Any pit, box or space below grade level if any part is within a horizontal distance of 10 feet from any edge of pump.
	2	Within 3 feet of any edge of pump, extending in all directions. Also up to 18 inches above grade level within 10 feet horizontally from any edge of pump.
Remote pump—Indoor	1	Entire area within any pit.
	2	Within 5 feet of any edge of pump, extending in all directions. Also up to 3 feet above floor or grade level within 25 feet horizontally from any edge of pump.
Lubrication or service room	1	Entire area within any pit.
	2	Area up to 18 inches above floor or grade level within entire lubrication room.
Dispenser for Liquids with a flashpoint below 100 °F (37.8 °C) (1)	2	Within 3 feet of any fill or dispensing point, extending in all directions.
Special enclosure inside building per §1910.–106(f)(1)(ii)	1	Entire enclosure.
Sales, storage and rest rooms	(2)	If there is any opening to these rooms within the extent of a Division 1 area, the entire room shall be classified as Division 1.

Footnote 1 Category 1 or 2 flammable liquids, or for Category 3 flammable liquids with a flashpoint below 100 °F (37.8 °C).
Footnote 2 Ordinary.

(g)(4)(iii)(B) A readily accessible valve to shut off the supply from shore shall be provided in each pipeline at or near the approach to the pier and at the shore end of each pipeline adjacent to the point where flexible hose is attached.

(g)(4)(iii)(C) Piping shall be located so as to be protected from physical damage.

(g)(4)(iii)(D) Piping handling Category 1 or 2 flammable liquids, or Category 3 flammable liquids with a flashpoint below 100 °F (37.8 °C), shall be grounded to control stray currents.

(g)(5) **Electrical equipment**

(g)(5)(i) **Application** This paragraph (g)(5) shall apply to areas where Category 1 or 2 flammable liquids, or Category 3 flammable liquids with a flashpoint below 100 °F (37.8 °C), are stored or handled. For areas where Category 3 flammable liquids with a flashpoint at or above 100 °F (37.8 °C) or Category 4 flammable liquids are stored or handled the electrical equipment may be installed in accordance with the provisions of Subpart S of this part, for ordinary locations.

(g)(5)(ii) All electrical equipment and wiring shall be of a type specified by and shall be installed in accordance with Subpart S of this part.

(g)(5)(iii) So far as it applies. Table H–19 shall be used to delineate and classify hazardous areas for the purpose of installation of electrical equipment under normal circumstances. A classified area shall not extend beyond an unpierced wall, roof, or other solid partition.

(g)(5)(iv) The area classifications listed shall be based on the assumption that the installation meets the applicable requirements of this section in all respects.

(g)(6) **Heating equipment**

(g)(6)(i) **Conformance** Heating equipment shall be installed as provided in paragraphs (g)(6)(ii) through (v) of this section.

(g)(6)(ii) **Application** Heating equipment may be installed in the conventional manner in an area except as provided in paragraph (g)(6)(iii), (iv), or (v) of this section.

(g)(6)(iii) **Special room** Heating equipment may be installed in a special room separated from an area classified by Table H–19 by walls having a fire resistance rating of at least 1 hour and without any openings in the walls within 8 feet of the floor into an area classified in Table H–19. This room shall not be used f storage and all air for combustion purposes shall come from outside the building.

(g)(6)(iv) **Work areas** Heating equipment using gas or oil fuel may be installed in the lubrication, sales, or service room where there is no dispensing or transferring of Category 1 or 2 flammable liquids or 3 flammable liquids with a flashpoint below 100 °F (37.8 °C), provided the bottom of the combustion chamber is at least 18 inches above the floor and the heating equipment is protected from physical damage by vehicles. Heating equipment using gas or oil fuel listed for use in garages may be installed in the lubrication or service room where Category 1 or 2 flammable liquids, or Category 3 flammable liquids with a flashpoint below 100 °F (37.8 °C), are dispensed provided the equipment is installed at least 8 feet above the floor.

(g)(6)(v) **Electric heat** Electrical heating equipment shall conform to paragraph (g)(5) of this section.

(g)(7) **Drainage and waste disposal** Provision shall be made in the area where Category 1 or 2 flammable liquids, or Category 3 flammable liquids with a flashpoint below 100 °F (37.8 °C), are dispensed to prevent spilled liquids from flowing into the interior of service station buildings. Such provision may be by grading driveways, raising door sills, or other equally effective means. Crankcase drainings and flammable liquids shall not be dumped into sewers but shall be stored in tanks or drums outside of any building until removed from the premises.

(g)(8) **Sources of ignition** In addition to the previous restrictions of this paragraph, the following shall apply: There shall be no smoking or open flames in the areas used for fueling, servicing fuel systems for internal combustion engines, receiving or dispensing of flammable liquids. Conspicuous and legible signs prohibiting smoking shall be posted within sight of the customer being served. The motors of all equipment being fueled shall be shut off during the fueling operation.

(g)(9) **Fire control** Each service station shall be provided with at least one fire extinguisher having a minimum approved classification of 6 B, C, located so that an extinguisher, will be within 75 feet of each pump, dispenser, underground fill pipe opening, and lubrication or service room.

(h) **Processing plants**

(h)(1) **Scope** This paragraph shall apply to those plants or buildings which contain chemical operations such as oxidation, reduction, halogenation, hydrogenation, alkylation, polymerization, and other chemical processes but shall not apply to chemical plants, refineries or distilleries.

(h)(2) **Location**

(h)(2)(i) **Classification** The location of each processing vessel shall be based upon its flammable liquid capacity.

(h)(2)(ii) [Reserved]

(h)(3) **Processing building**

(h)(3)(i) **Construction**

(h)(3)(i)(A) Processing buildings shall be of fire-resistance or noncombustible construction, except heavy timber construction with load-bearing walls may be permitted for plants utilizing only stable Category 3 flammable liquids with a flashpoint at or above 100 °F (37.8 °C) or Category 4 flammable liquids. Except as provided in paragraph (h)(2)(ii) of this section or in the case of explosion resistant walls used in conjunction with explosion relieving facilities, see paragraph (h)(3)(iv) of this section, load-bearing walls are prohibited. Buildings shall be without basements or covered pits.

(h)(3)(i)(B) Areas shall have adequate exit facilities arranged to prevent occupants from being trapped in the event of fire. Exits shall not be exposed by the drainage facilities described in paragraph (h)(ii) of this section.

(h)(3)(ii) **Drainage**

(h)(3)(ii)(A) Emergency drainage systems shall be provided to direct flammable liquid leakage and fire protection water to a safe location. This may require curbs, scuppers, or special drainage systems to control the spread of fire, see paragraph (b)(2)(vii)(B) of this section.

(h)(3)(ii)(B) Emergency drainage systems, if connected to public sewers or discharged into public waterways, shall be equipped with traps or separators.

(h)(3)(iii) **Ventilation**

(h)(3)(iii)(A) Enclosed processing buildings shall be ventilated at a rate of not less than 1 cubic foot per minute per square foot of solid floor area. This shall be accomplished by natural or mechanical ventilation with discharge or exhaust to a safe location outside of the building. Provisions shall be made for introduction of makeup air in such a manner as not to short circuit the ventilation. Ventilation shall be arranged to include all floor areas or pits where flammable vapors may collect.

(h)(3)(iii)(B) Equipment used in a building and the ventilation of the building shall be designed so as to limit flammable vapor-air mixtures under normal operating conditions to the interior of equipment, and to not more than 5 feet from equipment which exposes Category 1 or 2 flammable liquids, or Category 3 flammable liquids with a flashpoint below 100 °F (37.8 °C), to the air. Examples of such equipment are dispensing stations, open centrifuges, plate and frame filters, open vacuum filters, and surfaces of open equipment.

(h)(3)(iv) **Explosion relief** Areas where Category 1 or unstable liquids are processed shall have explosion venting through one or more of the following methods:

(h)(3)(iv)(A) Open air construction;
(h)(3)(iv)(B) Lightweight walls and roof;
(h)(3)(iv)(C) Lightweight wall panels and roof hatches;
(h)(3)(iv)(D) Windows of explosion venting type.

(h)(4) **Liquid handling**

(h)(4)(i) **Storage**

(h)(4)(i)(A) The storage of flammable liquids in tanks shall be in accordance with the applicable provisions of paragraph (b) of this section.

(h)(4)(i)(B) If the storage of flammable liquids in outside aboveground or underground tanks is not practical because of temperature or production considerations, tanks may be permitted inside of buildings or structures in accordance with the applicable provisions of paragraph (b) of this section.

(h)(4)(i)(C) Storage tanks inside of buildings shall be permitted only in areas at or above grade which have adequate drainage and are separated from the processing area by construction having a fire resistance rating of at least 2 hours.

(h)(4)(i)(D) The storage of flammable liquids in containers shall be in accordance with the applicable provisions of paragraph (d) of this section.

(h)(4)(ii) **Piping, valves, and fittings**

(h)(4)(ii)(A) Piping, valves, and fittings shall be in accordance with paragraph (c) of this section.

(h)(4)(ii)(B) Approved flexible connectors may be used where vibration exists or where frequent movement is necessary. Approved hose may be used at transfer stations.

(h)(4)(ii)(C) Piping containing flammable liquids shall be identified.

(h)(4)(iii) **Transfer**

(h)(4)(iii)(A) [OI] The transfer of large quantities of flammable liquids shall be through piping by means of pumps or water displacement. Except as required in process equipment, gravity flow shall not be used. The use of compressed air as a transferring medium is prohibited.

(h)(4)(iii)(B) Positive displacement pumps shall be provided with pressure relief discharging back to the tank or to pump suction.

(h)(4)(iv) **Equipment**

(h)(4)(iv)(A) Equipment shall be designed and arranged to prevent the unintentional escape of liquids and vapors and to minimize the quantity escaping in the event of accidental release.

(h)(4)(iv)(B) Where the vapor space of equipment is usually within the flammable range, the probability of explosion damage to the equipment can be limited by inerting, by providing an explosion suppression system, or by designing the equipment to contain the peak explosion pressure which may be modified by explosion relief. Where the special hazards of operation, sources of ignition, or exposures indicate a need, consideration shall be given to providing protection by one or more of the above means.

(h)(5) **Tank vehicle and tank car loading and unloading** Tank vehicle and tank car loading or unloading facilities shall be separated from aboveground tanks, warehouses, other plant buildings, or nearest line of adjoining property which may be built upon by a distance of 25 feet for Category 1 or 2 flammable liquids, or Category 3 flammable liquids with a flashpoint below 100 °F (37.8 °C), and 15 feet for Category 3 flammable liquids with a flashpoint at or above 100 °F (37.8 °C) and Category 4 flammable liquids measured from the nearest position of any fill stem. Buildings for pumps or shelters for personnel may be a part of the facility. Operations of the facility shall comply with the appropriate portions of paragraph (f)(3) of this section.

(h)(6) **Fire control**

(h)(6)(i) **Portable extinguishers** Approved portable fire extinguishers of appropriate size, type, and number shall be provided.

(h)(6)(ii) **Other controls** Where the special hazards of operation or exposure indicate a need, the following fire control provision shall be provided.

(h)(6)(ii)(A) A reliable water supply shall be available in pressure and quantity adequate to meet the probable fire demands.

(h)(6)(ii)(B) Hydrants shall be provided in accordance with accepted good practice.

(h)(6)(ii)(C) Hose connected to a source of water shall be installed so that all vessels, pumps, and other equipment containing flammable liquids can be reached with at least one hose stream. Nozzles that are capable of discharging a water spray shall be provided.

(h)(6)(ii)(D) Processing plants shall be protected by an approved automatic sprinkler system or equivalent extinguishing system. If special extinguishing systems including but not limited to those employing foam, carbon dioxide, or dry chemical are provided, approved equipment shall be used and installed in an approved manner.

(h)(6)(iii) **Alarm systems** An approved means for prompt notification of fire to those within the plant and any public fire department available shall be provided. It may be advisable to connect the plant system with the public system where public fire alarm system is available.

(h)(6)(iv) **Maintenance** All plant fire protection facilities shall be adequately maintained and periodically inspected and tested to make sure they are always in satisfactory operating condition and that they will serve their purpose in time of emergency.

(h)(7) **Sources of ignition**

(h)(7)(i) **General**

(h)(7)(i)(A) Precautions shall be taken to prevent the ignition of flammable vapors. Sources of ignition include but are not limited to open flames; lightning; smoking; cutting and welding; hot surfaces; frictional heat; static, electrical, and mechanical sparks; spontaneous ignition, including heat-producing chemical reactions; and radiant heat.

(h)(7)(i)(B) OI Category 1 or 2 flammable liquids, or Category 3 flammable liquids with a flashpoint below 100 °F (37.8 °C), shall not be dispensed into containers unless the nozzle and container are electrically interconnected. Where the metallic floorplate on which the container stands while filling is electrically connected to the fill stem or where the fill stem is bonded to the container during filling operations by means of a bond wire, the provisions of this section shall be deemed to have been complied with.

(h)(7)(ii) **Maintenance and repair**

(h)(7)(ii)(A) When necessary to do maintenance work in a flammable liquid processing area, the work shall be authorized by a responsible representative of the employer.

(h)(7)(ii)(B) Hot work, such as welding or cutting operations, use of spark-producing power tools, and chipping operations shall be permitted only under supervision of an individual in responsible charge who shall make an inspection of the area to be sure that it is safe for the work to be done and that safe procedures will be followed for the work specified.

(h)(7)(iii) **Electrical**

(h)(7)(iii)(A) All electric wiring and equipment shall be installed in accordance with Subpart S of this part.

(h)(7)(iii)(B) Locations where flammable vapor-air mixtures may exist under normal operations shall be classified Class I, Division 1 according to the requirements of Subpart S of this part. For those pieces of equipment installed in accordance with paragraph (h)(3)(iii)(B) of this section, the Division 1 area shall extend 5 feet in all directions from all points of vapor liberation. All areas within pits shall be classified Division 1 if any part of the pit is within a Division 1 or 2 classified area, unless the pit is provided with mechanical ventilation.

(h)(7)(iii)(C) Locations where flammable vapor-air mixtures may exist under abnormal conditions and for a distance beyond Division 1 locations shall be classified Division 2 according to the requirements of Subpart S of this part. These locations include an area within 20 feet horizontally, 3 feet vertically beyond a Division 1 area, and up to 3 feet above floor or grade level within 25 feet, if indoors, or 10 feet if outdoors, from any pump, bleeder, withdrawal fitting, meter, or similar device handling Category 1 or 2 flammable liquids, or Category 3 flammable liquids with a flashpoint below 100 °F (37.8 °C). Pits provided with adequate mechanical ventilation within a Division 1 or 2 area shall be classified Division 2. If Category 3 flammable liquids with a flashpoint at or above 100 °F (37.8 °C) or Category 4 flammable liquids only are handled, then ordinary electrical equipment is satisfactory though care shall be used in locating electrical apparatus to prevent hot metal from falling into open equipment.

(h)(7)(iii)(D) Where the provisions of paragraphs (h)(7)(iii)(A), (B), and (C) of this section require the installation of explosion-proof equipment, ordinary electrical equipment including switchgear may be used if installed in a room or enclosure which is maintained under positive pressure with respect to the hazardous area. Ventilation makeup air shall be uncontaminated by flammable vapors.

(h)(8) **Housekeeping**

(h)(8)(i) **General** Maintenance and operating practices shall be in accordance with established procedures which will tend to control leakage and prevent the accidental escape of flammable liquids. Spills shall be cleaned up promptly.

(h)(8)(ii) **Access** Adequate aisles shall be maintained for unobstructed movement of personnel and so that fire protection equipment can be brought to bear on any part of the processing equipment.

(h)(8)(iii) **Waste and residues** Combustible waste material and residues in a building or operating area shall be kept to a minimum, stored in closed metal waste cans, and disposed of daily.

(h)(8)(iv) **Clear zone** Ground area around buildings and operating areas shall be kept free of tall grass, weeds, trash, or other combustible materials.

(i) OI **Refineries, chemical plants, and distilleries**

(i)(1) **Storage tanks** F8lammable liquids shall be stored in tanks, in containers, or in portable tanks. Tanks shall be installed in accordance with paragraph (b) of this section. Tanks for the storage of flammable liquids in tank farms and in locations other than process areas shall be located in accordance with paragraph (b)(2)(i) and (ii) of this section.

(i)(2) **Wharves** Wharves handling flammable liquids shall be in accordance with paragraph (f)(4) of this section.

(i)(3) **Fired and unfired pressure vessels**

(i)(3)(i) OI **Fired vessels** Fired pressure vessels shall be constructed in accordance with the Code for Fired Pressure Vessels, Section I of the ASME Boiler and Pressure Vessel Code—1968.

(i)(3)(ii) OI Unfired vessels shall be constructed in accordance with the Code for Unfired Pressure Vessels, Section VIII of the ASME Boiler and Pressure Vessel Code—1968.

(i)(4) **Location of process units** Process units shall be located so that they are accessible from at least one side for the purpose of fire control.

(i)(5) **Fire control**

(i)(5)(i) **Portable equipment** Portable fire extinguishment and control equipment shall be provided in such quantities and types as are needed for the special hazards of operation and storage.

(i)(5)(ii) **Water supply** Water shall be available in volume and at adequate pressure to supply water hose streams, foam producing equipment, automatic sprinklers, or water spray systems as the need is indicated by the special hazards of operation and storage.

(i)(5)(iii) **Special equipment** Special extinguishing equipment such as that utilizing foam, inert gas, or dry chemical shall be provided as the need is indicated by the special hazards of operation and storage.

(j) **Scope** This section applies to the handling, storage, and use of flammable liquids with a flashpoint at or below 199.4 °F (93 °C) unless otherwise noted. This section does not apply to:

(j)(1) Bulk transportation of flammable liquids;

(j)(2) Storage, handling, and use of fuel oil tanks and containers connected with oil burning equipment;

(j)(3) Storage of flammable liquids on farms;

(j)(4) Liquids without flashpoints that may be flammable under some conditions, such as certain halogenated hydrocarbons and mixtures containing halogenated hydrocarbons;

(j)(5) OI Mists, sprays, or foams, except flammable aerosols covered in paragraph (d) of this section; or

(j)(6) Installations made in accordance with requirements of the following standards that are incorporated by reference as specified in §1910.6:

(j)(6)(i) National Fire Protection Association Standard for Drycleaning Plants, NFPA No. 32–1970;

(j)(6)(ii) National Fire Protection Association Standard for the Manufacture of Organic Coatings, NFPA No. 35–1970;

(j)(6)(iii) National Fire Protection Association Standard for Solvent Extraction Plants, NFPA No. 36–1967; or

(j)(6)(iv) National Fire Protection Association Standard for the Installation and Use of Stationary Combustion Engines and Gas Turbines, NFPA No. 37–1970.

[39 FR 23502, June 27, 1974, as amended at 40 FR 3982, Jan. 27, 1975; 40 FR 23743, June 2, 1975; 43 FR 49746, Oct. 24, 1978; 43 FR 51759, Nov. 7, 1978; 47 FR 39164, Sept. 7, 1982; 51 FR 34560, Sept. 29, 1986; 53 FR 12121, Apr. 12, 1988; 55 FR 32015, Aug. 6, 1990; 61 FR 9237, Mar. 7, 1996; 70 FR 53929, Sept. 13, 2005]

§1910.107 Spray finishing using flammable and combustible materials

(a) Definitions applicable to this section

(a)(1) Aerated solid powders Aerated powders shall mean any powdered material used as a coating material which shall be fluidized within a container by passing air uniformly from below. It is common practice to fluidize such materials to form a fluidized powder bed and then dip the part to be coated into the bed in a manner similar to that used in liquid dipping. Such beds are also used as sources for powder spray operations.

(a)(2) Spraying area Any area in which dangerous quantities of flammable vapors or mists, residues, dusts, or deposits are present due to the operation of spraying processes.

(a)(3) Spray booth A power-ventilated structure provided to enclose or accommodate a spraying operation to confine and limit the escape of spray, vapor, and residue, and to safely conduct or direct them to an exhaust system.

(a)(4) Waterwash spray booth A spray booth equipped with a water washing system designed to minimize dusts or residues entering exhaust ducts and to permit the recovery of overspray finishing material.

(a)(5) Dry spray booth A spray booth not equipped with a water washing system as described in subparagraph (4) of this paragraph. A dry spray booth may be equipped with (i) distribution or baffle plates to promote an even flow of air through the booth or cause the deposit of overspray before it enters the exhaust duct; or (ii) overspray dry filters to minimize dusts; or (iii) overspray dry filters to minimize dusts or residues entering exhaust ducts; or (iv) overspray dry filter rolls designed to minimize dusts or residues entering exhaust ducts; or (v) where dry powders are being sprayed, with powder collection systems so arranged in the exhaust to capture oversprayed material.

(a)(6) Fluidized bed A container holding powder coating material which is aerated from below so as to form an air-supported expanded cloud of such material through which the preheated object to be coated is immersed and transported.

(a)(7) Electrostatic fluidized bed A container holding powder coating material which is aerated from below so as to form an air-supported expanded cloud of such material which is electrically charged with a charge opposite to the charge of the object to be coated; such object is transported, through the container immediately above the charged and aerated materials in order to be coated.

(a)(8) Approved Shall mean approved and listed by a nationally recognized testing laboratory. Refer to §1910.7 for definition of nationally recognized testing laboratory.

(a)(9) Listed See "approved" in §1910.107(a)(8).

(b) Spray booths

(b)(1) Construction Spray booths shall be substantially constructed of steel, securely and rigidly supported, or of concrete or masonry except that aluminum or other substantial noncombustible material may be used for intermittent or low volume spraying. Spray booths shall be designed to sweep air currents toward the exhaust outlet.

(b)(2) Interiors The interior surfaces of spray booths shall be smooth and continuous without edges and otherwise designed to prevent pocketing of residues and facilitate cleaning and washing without injury.

(b)(3) Floors The floor surface of a spray booth and operator's working area, if combustible, shall be covered with noncombustible material of such character as to facilitate the safe cleaning and removal of residues.

(b)(4) Distribution or baffle plates Distribution or baffle plates, if installed to promote an even flow of air through the booth or cause the deposit of overspray before it enters the exhaust duct, shall be of noncombustible material and readily removable or accessible on both sides for cleaning. Such plates shall not be located in exhaust ducts.

(b)(5) Dry type overspray collectors—(exhaust air filters) In conventional dry type spray booths, overspray dry filters or filter rolls, if installed, shall conform to the following:

(b)(5)(i) The spraying operations except electrostatic spraying operations shall be so designed, installed and maintained that the average air velocity over the open face of the booth (or booth cross section during spraying operations) shall be not less than 100 linear feet per minute. Electrostatic spraying operations may be conducted with an air velocity over the open face of the booth of not less than 60 linear feet per minute, or more, depending on the volume of the finishing material being applied and its flammability and explosion characteristics. Visible gauges or audible alarm or pressure activated devices shall be installed to indicate or insure that the required air velocity is maintained. Filter rolls shall be inspected to insure proper replacement of filter media;

(b)(5)(ii) All discarded filter pads and filter rolls shall be immediately removed to a safe, well-detached location or placed in a water-filled metal container and disposed of at the close of the day's operation unless maintained completely in water;

(b)(5)(iii) The location of filters in a spray booth shall be so as to not reduce the effective booth enclosure of the articles being sprayed;

(b)(5)(iv) Space within the spray booth on the downstream and upstream sides of filters shall be protected with approved automatic sprinklers;

(b)(5)(v) Filters or filter rolls shall not be used when applying a spray material known to be highly susceptible to spontaneous heating and ignition;

(b)(5)(vi) Clean filters or filter rolls shall be noncombustible or of a type having a combustibility not in excess of class 2 filters as listed by Underwriters' Laboratories, Inc. Filters and filter rolls shall not be alternately used for different types of coating materials, where the combination of materials may be conducive to spontaneous ignition. See also paragraph (g)(6) of this section.

(b)(6) Frontal area Each spray booth having a frontal area larger than 9 square feet shall have a metal deflector or curtain not less than 2½ inches deep installed at the upper outer edge of the booth over the opening.

(b)(7) Conveyors Where conveyors are arranged to carry work into or out of spray booths, the openings therefor shall be as small as practical.

(b)(8) Separation of operations Each spray booth shall be separated from other operations by not less than 3 feet, or by a greater distance, or by such partition or wall as to reduce the danger from juxtaposition of hazardous operations. See also paragraph (c)(1) of this section.

(b)(9) Cleaning Spray booths shall be so installed that all portions are readily accessible for cleaning. A clear space of not less than 3 feet on all sides shall be kept free from storage construction.

(b)(10) Illumination When spraying areas are illuminated through glass panels or other transparent materials, only fixed lighting units shall be used as a source of illumination. Panels shall effectively isolate the spraying area from the area in which the lighting unit is located, and shall be of a noncombustible material of such a nature or so protected that breakage will be unlikely. Panels shall be so arranged that normal accumulations of residue on the exposed surface of the panel will not be raised to a dangerous temperature by radiation or conduction from the source of illumination.

(c) Electrical and other sources of ignition

(c)(1) Conformance All electrical equipment, open flames and other sources of ignition shall conform to the requirements of this paragraph, except as follows:

(c)(1)(i) Electrostatic apparatus shall conform to the requirements of paragraphs (h) and (i) of this section;

(c)(1)(ii) Drying, curing, and fusion apparatus shall conform to the requirements of paragraph (j) of this section;

(c)(1)(iii) Automobile undercoating spray operations in garages shall conform to the requirements of paragraph (k) of this section;

(c)(1)(iv) Powder-coating equipment shall conform to the requirements of paragraph (l)(1) of this section.

(c)(2) Minimum separation There shall be no open flame or spark producing equipment in any spraying area nor within 20 feet thereof, unless separated by a partition.

(c)(3) Hot surfaces Space-heating appliances, steampipes, or hot surfaces shall not be located in a spraying area where deposits of combustible residues may readily accumulate.

(c)(4) Wiring conformance Electrical wiring and equipment shall conform to the provisions of this paragraph and shall otherwise be in accordance with Subpart S of this part.

(c)(5) Combustible residues, areas Unless specifically approved for locations containing both deposits of readily ignitable residue and explosive vapors, there shall be no electrical equipment in any spraying area, whereon deposits of combustible residues may readily accumulate, except wiring in rigid conduit or in boxes or fittings containing no taps, splices, or terminal connections.

(c)(6) Wiring type approved Electrical wiring and equipment not subject to deposits of combustible residues but located in a spraying area as herein

H Hazardous Materials Flammable liquids

defined shall be of explosion-proof type approved for Class I, group D locations and shall otherwise conform to the provisions of Subpart S of this part, for Class I, Division 1, Hazardous Locations. Electrical wiring, motors, and other equipment outside of but within twenty (20) feet of any spraying area, and not separated therefrom by partitions, shall not produce sparks under normal operating conditions and shall otherwise conform to the provisions of Subpart S of this part for Class I, Division 2 Hazardous Locations.

(c)(7) **Lamps** Electric lamps outside of, but within twenty (20) feet of any spraying area, and not separated therefrom by a partition, shall be totally enclosed to prevent the falling of hot particles and shall be protected from mechanical injury by suitable guards or by location.

(c)(8) **Portable lamps** Portable electric lamps shall not be used in any spraying area during spraying operations. Portable electric lamps, if used during cleaning or repairing operations, shall be of the type approved for hazardous Class I locations.

(c)(9) **Grounding**

(c)(9)(i) All metal parts of spray booths, exhaust ducts, and piping systems conveying flammable liquids or liquids with a flashpoint greater than 199.4 °F (93 °C) or or aerated solids shall be properly electrically grounded in an effective and permanent manner.

(c)(9)(ii) [Reserved]

(d) **Ventilation**

(d)(1) **Conformance** Ventilating and exhaust systems shall be in accordance with the Standard for Blower and Exhaust Systems for Vapor Removal, NFPA No. 91–1961, which is incorporated by reference as specified in §1910.6, where applicable and shall also conform to the provisions of this section.

(d)(2) **General** All spraying areas shall be provided with mechanical ventilation adequate to remove flammable vapors, mists, or powders to a safe location and to confine and control combustible residues so that life is not endangered. Mechanical ventilation shall be kept in operation at all times while spraying operations are being conducted and for a sufficient time thereafter to allow vapors from drying coated articles and drying finishing material residue to be exhausted.

(d)(3) **Independent exhaust** Each spray booth shall have an independent exhaust duct system discharging to the exterior of the building, except that multiple cabinet spray booths in which identical spray finishing material is used with a combined frontal area of not more than 18 square feet may have a common exhaust. If more than one fan serves one booth, all fans shall be so interconnected that one fan cannot operate without all fans being operated.

(d)(4) **Fan-rotating element** The fan-rotating element shall be nonferrous or nonsparking or the casing shall consist of or be lined with such material. There shall be ample clearance between the fan-rotating element and the fan casing to avoid a fire by friction, necessary allowance being made for ordinary expansion and loading to prevent contact between moving parts and the duct or fan housing. Fan blades shall be mounted on a shaft sufficiently heavy to maintain perfect alignment even when the blades of the fan are heavily loaded, the shaft preferably to have bearings outside the duct and booth. All bearings shall be of the self-lubricating type, or lubricated from the outside duct.

(d)(5) **Electric motors** Electric motors driving exhaust fans shall not be placed inside booths or ducts. See also paragraph (c) of this section.

(d)(6) **Belts** Belts shall not enter the duct or booth unless the belt and pulley within the duct or booth are thoroughly enclosed.

(d)(7) **Exhaust ducts** Exhaust ducts shall be constructed of steel and shall be substantially supported. Exhaust ducts without dampers are preferred; however, if dampers are installed, they shall be maintained so that they will be in a full open position at all times the ventilating system is in operation.

(d)(7)(i) Exhaust ducts shall be protected against mechanical damage and have a clearance from unprotected combustible construction or other combustible material of not less than 18 inches.

(d)(7)(ii) If combustible construction is provided with the following protection applied to all surfaces within 18 inches, clearances may be reduced to the distances indicated

(a) 28-gage sheet metal on 1/4-inch asbestos mill board.	12 inches.
(b) 28-gage sheet metal on 1/8-inch asbestos mill board spaced out 1 inch on noncombustible spacers.	9 inches.
(c) 22-gage sheet metal on 1-inch rockwool batts reinforced with wire mesh or the equivalent.	3 inches.
(d)Where ducts are protected with an approved automatic sprinkler system, properly maintained, the clearance required in subdivision (i) of this subparagraph may be reduced to 6 inches.	

(d)(8) **Discharge clearance** Unless the spray booth exhaust duct terminal is from a water-wash spray booth, the terminal discharge point shall be not less than 6 feet from any combustible exterior wall or roof nor discharge in the direction of any combustible construction or unprotected opening in any noncombustible exterior wall within 25 feet.

(d)(9) **Air exhaust** Air exhaust from spray operations shall not be directed so that it will contaminate makeup air being introduced into the spraying area or other ventilating intakes, nor directed so as to create a nuisance. Air exhausted from spray operations shall not be recirculated.

(d)(10) **Access doors** When necessary to facilitate cleaning, exhaust ducts shall be provided with an ample number of access doors.

(d)(11) **Room intakes** Air intake openings to rooms containing spray finishing operations shall be adequate for the efficient operation of exhaust fans and shall be so located as to minimize the creation of dead air pockets.

(d)(12) **Drying spaces** Freshly sprayed articles shall be dried only in spaces provided with adequate ventilation to prevent the formation of explosive vapors. In the event adequate and reliable ventilation is not provided such drying spaces shall be considered a spraying area. See also paragraph (j) of this section.

(e) **Flammable liquids or liquids with a flashpoint greater than 199.4 °F (93 °C)**

(e)(1) **Conformance** The storage of flammable liquids or liquids with a flashpoint greater than 199.4 °F (93 °C) in connection with spraying operations shall conform to the requirements of §1910.106, where applicable.

(e)(2) **Quantity** The quantity of flammable liquids or liquids with a flashpoint greater than 199.4 °F (93 °C) kept in the vicinity of spraying operations shall be the minimum required for operations and should ordinarily not exceed a supply for 1 day or one shift. Bulk storage of portable containers of flammable liquids or liquids with a flashpoint greater than 199.4 °F (93 °C) shall be in a separate, constructed building detached from other important buildings or cut off in a standard manner.

(e)(3) **Containers** Original closed containers, approved portable tanks, approved safety cans or a properly arranged system of piping shall be used for bringing flammable liquids or liquids with a flashpoint greater than 199.4 °F (93 °C) into spray finishing room. Open or glass containers shall not be used.

(e)(4) **Transferring liquids** Except as provided in paragraph (e)(5) of this section the withdrawal of flammable liquids and liquids with a flashpoint greater than 199.4 °F (93 °C) from containers having a capacity of greater than 60 gallons shall be by approved pumps. The withdrawal of flammable liquids or liquids with a flashpoint greater than 199.4 °F (93 °C) from containers and the filling of containers, including portable mixing tanks, shall be done only in a suitable mixing room or in a spraying area when the ventilating system is in operation. Adequate precautions shall be taken to protect against liquid spillage and sources of ignition.

(e)(5) **Spraying containers** Containers supplying spray nozzles shall be of closed type or provided with metal covers kept closed. Containers not resting on floors shall be on metal supports or suspended by wire cables. Containers supplying spray nozzles by gravity flow shall not exceed 10 gallons capacity. Original shipping containers shall not be subject to air pressure for supplying spray nozzles. Containers under air pressure supplying spray nozzles shall be of limited capacity, not exceeding that necessary for 1 day's operation; shall be designed and approved for such use; shall be provided with a visible pressure gage; and shall be provided with a relief valve set to operate in conformance with the requirements of the Code for Unfired Pressure Vessels, Section VIII of the ASME Boiler and Pressure Vessel Code—1968, which is incorporated by reference as specified in §1910.6. Containers under air pressure supplying spray nozzles, air-storage tanks and coolers shall conform to the standards of the Code for Unfired Pressure Vessels, Section VIII of the ASME Boiler and Pressure Vessel Code—1968 for construction, tests, and maintenance.

(e)(6) **Pipes and hoses**

(e)(6)(i) All containers or piping to which is attached a hose or flexible connection shall be provided with a shutoff valve at the connection. Such valves shall be kept shut when spraying operations are not being conducted.

(e)(6)(ii) When a pump is used to deliver products, automatic means shall be provided to prevent pressure in excess of the design working pressure of accessories, piping, and hose.

(e)(6)(iii) All pressure hose and couplings shall be inspected at regular intervals appropriate to this service. The hose and couplings shall be tested with the hose extended, and using the "inservice maximum operating pressures." Any hose showing material deteriorations, signs of leakage, or weakness in its carcass or at the couplings, shall be withdrawn from service and repaired or discarded.

(e)(6)(iv) Piping systems conveying flammable liquids or liquids with a flashpoint greater than 199.4 °F (93 °C) shall be of steel or other material having comparable properties of resistance to heat and physical damage. Piping systems shall be properly bonded and grounded.

(e)(7) Spray liquid heaters Electrically powered spray liquid heaters shall be approved and listed for the specific location in which used (see paragraph (c) of this section). Heaters shall not be located in spray booths nor other locations subject to the accumulation of deposits or combustible residue. If an electric motor is used, see paragraph (c) of this section.

(e)(8) Pump relief If flammable liquids or liquids with a flashpoint greater than 199.4 °F (93 °C) are supplied to spray nozzles by positive displacement pumps, the pump discharge line shall be provided with an approved relief valve discharging to a pump suction or a safe detached location, or a device provided to stop the prime mover if the discharge pressure exceeds the safe operating pressure of the system.

(e)(9) Grounding Whenever flammable liquids or liquids with a flashpoint greater than 199.4 °F (93 °C) are transferred from one container to another, both containers shall be effectively bonded and grounded to prevent discharge sparks of static electricity.

(f) Protection

(f)(1) Conformance In sprinklered buildings, the automatic sprinkler system in rooms containing spray finishing operations shall conform to the requirements of §1910.159. In unsprinklered buildings where sprinklers are installed only to protect spraying areas, the installation shall conform to such standards insofar as they are applicable. Sprinkler heads shall be located so as to provide water distribution throughout the entire booth.

(f)(2) Valve access Automatic sprinklers protecting each spray booth (together with its connecting exhaust) shall be under an accessibly located separate outside stem and yoke (OS&Y) subcontrol valve.

(f)(3) Cleaning of heads Sprinklers protecting spraying areas shall be kept as free from deposits as practical by cleaning daily if necessary. (See also paragraph (g) of this section.)

(f)(4) Portable extinguishers An adequate supply of suitable portable fire extinguishers shall be installed near all spraying areas.

(g) Operations and maintenance

(g)(1) Spraying Spraying shall not be conducted outside of predetermined spraying areas.

(g)(2) Cleaning All spraying areas shall be kept as free from the accumulation of deposits of combustible residues as practical, with cleaning conducted daily if necessary. Scrapers, spuds, or other such tools used for cleaning purposes shall be of nonsparking material.

(g)(3) Residue disposal Residue scrapings and debris contaminated with residue shall be immediately removed from the premises and properly disposed of. Approved metal waste cans shall be provided wherever rags or waste are impregnated with finishing material and all such rags or waste deposited therein immediately after use. The contents of waste cans shall be properly disposed of at least once daily or at the end of each shift.

(g)(4) Clothing storage Spray finishing employees' clothing shall not be left on the premises overnight unless kept in metal lockers.

(g)(5) Cleaning solvents The use of solvents for cleaning operations shall be restricted to those having flashpoints not less than 100 °F.; however, for cleaning spray nozzles and auxiliary equipment, solvents having flashpoints not less than those normally used in spray operations may be used. Such cleaning shall be conducted inside spray booths and ventilating equipment operated during cleaning.

(g)(6) Hazardous materials combinations Spray booths shall not be alternately used for different types of coating materials, where the combination of the materials may be conducive to spontaneous ignition, unless all deposits of the first used material are removed from the booth and exhaust ducts prior to spraying with the second used material.

(g)(7) "No Smoking" signs "No smoking" signs in large letters on contrasting color background shall be conspicuously posted at all spraying areas and paint storage rooms.

(h) Fixed electrostatic apparatus

(h)(1) Conformance Where installation and use of electrostatic spraying equipment is used, such installation and use shall conform to all other paragraphs of this section, and shall also conform to the requirements of this paragraph.

(h)(2) Type approval Electrostatic apparatus and devices used in connection with coating operations shall be of approved types.

(h)(3) Location Transformers, power packs, control apparatus, and all other electrical portions of the equipment, with the exception of high-voltage grids, electrodes, and electrostatic atomizing heads and their connections, shall be located outside of the spraying area, or shall otherwise conform to the requirements of paragraph (c) of this section.

(h)(4) Support Electrodes and electrostatic atomizing heads shall be adequately supported in permanent locations and shall be effectively insulated from the ground. Electrodes and electrostatic atomizing heads which are permanently attached to their bases, supports, or reciprocators, shall be deemed to comply with this section. Insulators shall be nonporous and noncombustible.

(h)(5) Insulators, grounding High-voltage leads to electrodes shall be properly insulated and protected from mechanical injury or exposure to destructive chemicals. Electrostatic atomizing heads shall be effectively and permanently supported on suitable insulators and shall be effectively guarded against accidental contact or grounding. An automatic means shall be provided for grounding the electrode system when it is electrically deenergized for any reason. All insulators shall be kept clean and dry.

(h)(6) Safe distance A safe distance shall be maintained between goods being painted and electrodes or electrostatic atomizing heads or conductors of at least twice the sparking distance. A suitable sign indicating this safe distance shall be conspicuously posted near the assembly.

(h)(7) Conveyors required Goods being painted using this process are to be supported on conveyors. The conveyors shall be so arranged as to maintain safe distances between the goods and the electrodes or electrostatic atomizing heads at all times. Any irregularly shaped or other goods subject to possible swinging or movement shall be rigidly supported to prevent such swinging or movement which would reduce the clearance to less than that specified in paragraph (h)(6) of this section.

(h)(8) Prohibition This process is not acceptable where goods being coated are manipulated by hand. When finishing materials are applied by electrostatic equipment which is manipulated by hand, see paragraph (i) of this section for applicable requirements.

(h)(9) Fail-safe controls Electrostatic apparatus shall be equipped with automatic controls which will operate without time delay to disconnect the power supply to the high voltage transformer and to signal the operator under any of the following conditions:

- **(h)(9)(i)** Stoppage of ventilating fans or failure of ventilating equipment from any cause.
- **(h)(9)(ii)** Stoppage of the conveyor carrying goods through the high voltage field.
- **(h)(9)(iii)** Occurrence of a ground or of an imminent ground at any point on the high voltage system.
- **(h)(9)(iv)** Reduction of clearance below that specified in paragraph (h)(6) of this section.

(h)(10) Guarding Adequate booths, fencing, railings, or guards shall be so placed about the equipment that they, either by their location or character or both, assure that a safe isolation of the process is maintained from plant storage or personnel. Such railings, fencing, and guards shall be of conducting material, adequately grounded.

(h)(11) Ventilation Where electrostatic atomization is used the spraying area shall be so ventilated as to insure safe conditions from a fire and health standpoint.

(h)(12) Fire protection All areas used for spraying, including the interior of the booth, shall be protected by automatic sprinklers where this protection is available. Where this protection is not available, other approved automatic extinguishing equipment shall be provided.

(i) Electrostatic hand spraying equipment

(i)(1) Application This paragraph shall apply to any equipment using electrostatically charged elements for the atomization and/or, precipitation of materials for coatings on articles, or for other similar purposes in which the atomizing device is hand held and manipulated during the spraying operation.

(i)(2) Conformance Electrostatic hand spraying equipment shall conform with the other provisions of this section.

(i)(3) Equipment approval and specifications Electrostatic hand spray apparatus and devices used in connection with coating operations shall be of approved types. The high voltage circuits shall be designed so as to not produce a spark of sufficient intensity to ignite any vapor-air mixtures nor result in appreciable shock hazard upon coming in contact with a grounded object under all normal operating conditions. The electrostatically charged exposed elements of the handgun shall be capable of being energized only by a switch which also controls the coating material supply.

(i)(4) Electrical support equipment Transformers, powerpacks, control apparatus, and all other electrical portions of the equipment, with the exception of the handgun itself and its connections to the power supply shall be located outside of the spraying area or shall otherwise conform to the requirements of paragraph (c) of this section.

(i)(5) Spray gun ground The handle of the spraying gun shall be electrically connected to ground by a metallic connection and to be so constructed that the operator in normal operating position is in intimate electrical contact with the grounded handle.

(i)(6) Grounding—general All electrically conductive objects in the spraying area shall be adequately grounded. This requirement shall apply to paint containers, wash cans, and any other objects or devices in the area. The equipment shall carry a prominent permanently installed warning regarding the necessity for this grounding feature.

(i)(7) Maintenance of grounds Objects being painted or coated shall be maintained in metallic contact with the conveyor or other grounded support. Hooks shall be regularly cleaned to insure this contact and areas of contact shall be sharp points or knife edges where possible. Points of support of the object shall be concealed from random spray where feasible and where the objects being sprayed are supported from a conveyor, the point of attachment to the conveyor shall be so located as to not collect spray material during normal operation.

(i)(8) **Interlocks** The electrical equipment shall be so interlocked with the ventilation of the spraying area that the equipment cannot be operated unless the ventilation fans are in operation.

(i)(9) **Ventilation** The spraying operation shall take place within a spray area which is adequately ventilated to remove solvent vapors released from the operation.

(j) **Drying, curing, or fusion apparatus**

(j)(1) **Conformance** Drying, curing, or fusion apparatus in connection with spray application of flammable and combustible finishes shall conform to the Standard for Ovens and Furnaces, NFPA 86A–1969, which is incorporated by reference as specified in §1910.6, where applicable and shall also conform with the following requirements of this paragraph.

(j)(2) **Alternate use prohibited** Spray booths, rooms, or other enclosures used for spraying operations shall not alternately be used for the purpose of drying by any arrangement which will cause a material increase in the surface temperature of the spray booth, room, or enclosure.

(j)(3) **Adjacent system interlocked** Except as specifically provided in paragraph (j)(4) of this section, drying, curing, or fusion units utilizing a heating system having open flames or which may produce sparks shall not be installed in a spraying area, but may be installed adjacent thereto when equipped with an interlocked ventilating system arranged to:

(j)(3)(i) Thoroughly ventilate the drying space before the heating system can be started;

(j)(3)(ii) Maintain a safe atmosphere at any source of ignition;

(j)(3)(iii) Automatically shut down the heating system in the event of failure of the ventilating system.

(j)(4) **Alternate use permitted** Automobile refinishing spray booths or enclosures, otherwise installed and maintained in full conformity with this section, may alternately be used for drying with portable electrical infrared drying apparatus when conforming with the following:

(j)(4)(i) Interior (especially floors) of spray enclosures shall be kept free of overspray deposits;

(j)(4)(ii) During spray operations, the drying apparatus and electrical connections and wiring thereto shall not be located within spray enclosure nor in any other location where spray residues may be deposited thereon;

(j)(4)(iii) The spraying apparatus, the drying apparatus, and the ventilating system of the spray enclosure shall be equipped with suitable interlocks so arranged that:

(j)(4)(iii)(A) The spraying apparatus cannot be operated while the drying apparatus is inside the spray enclosure;

(j)(4)(iii)(B) The spray enclosure will be purged of spray vapors for a period of not less than 3 minutes before the drying apparatus can be energized;

(j)(4)(iii)(C) The ventilating system will maintain a safe atmosphere within the enclosure during the drying process and the drying apparatus will automatically shut off in the event of failure of the ventilating system.

(j)(4)(iv) All electrical wiring and equipment of the drying apparatus shall conform with the applicable sections of Subpart S of this part. Only equipment of a type approved for Class I, Division 2 hazardous locations shall be located within 18 inches of floor level. All metallic parts of the drying apparatus shall be properly electrically bonded and grounded.

(j)(4)(v) The drying apparatus shall contain a prominently located, permanently attached warning sign indicating that ventilation should be maintained during the drying period and that spraying should not be conducted in the vicinity that spray will deposit on apparatus.

(k) **Automobile undercoating in garages** Automobile undercoating spray operations in garages, conducted in areas having adequate natural or mechanical ventilation, are exempt from the requirements pertaining to spray finishing operations, when using undercoating materials not more hazardous than kerosene (as listed by Underwriters' Laboratories in respect to fire hazard rating 30–40) or undercoating materials using only solvents listed as having a flash point in excess of 100 °F. Undercoating spray operations not conforming to these provisions are subject to all requirements of this section pertaining to spray finishing operations.

(l) **Powder coating**

(l)(1) **Electrical and other sources of ignition** Electrical equipment and other sources of ignition shall conform to the requirements of paragraphs (c)(1)(i)–(iv), (8) and (9)(i) of this section and Subpart S of this part.

(l)(2) **Ventilation**

(l)(2)(i) In addition to the provisions of paragraph (d) of this section, where applicable, exhaust ventilation shall be sufficient to maintain the atmosphere below the lowest explosive limits for the materials being applied. All nondeposited air-suspended powders shall be safely removed via exhaust ducts to the powder recovery cyclone or receptacle. Each installation shall be designed and operated to meet the foregoing performance specification.

(l)(2)(ii) Powders shall not be released to the outside atmosphere.

(l)(3) **Drying, curing, or fusion equipment** The provisions of the Standard for ovens and furnaces, NFPA No. 86A–1969 shall apply where applicable.

(l)(4) **Operation and maintenance**

(l)(4)(i) All areas shall be kept free of the accumulation of powder coating dusts, particularly such horizontal surfaces as ledges, beams, pipes, hoods, booths, and floors.

(l)(4)(ii) Surfaces shall be cleaned in such manner as to avoid scattering dust to other places or creating dust clouds.

(l)(4)(iii) "No Smoking" signs in large letters on contrasting color background shall be conspicuously posted at all powder coating areas and powder storage rooms.

(l)(5) **Fixed electrostatic spraying equipment** The provisions of paragraph (h) of this section and other subparagraphs of this paragraph shall apply to fixed electrostatic equipment, except that electrical equipment not covered therein shall conform to paragraph (l)(1) of this section.

(l)(6) **Electrostatic hand spraying equipment** The provisions of paragraph (i) of this section and other subparagraphs of this paragraph, shall apply to electrostatic handguns when used in powder coating, except that electrical equipment not covered therein shall conform to paragraph (l)(1) of this section.

(l)(7) **Electrostatic fluidized beds**

(l)(7)(i) Electrostatic fluidized beds and associated equipment shall be of approved types. The maximum surface temperature of this equipment in the coating area shall not exceed 150 °F. The high voltage circuits shall be so designed as to not produce a spark of sufficient intensity to ignite any powder-air mixtures nor result in appreciable shock hazard upon coming in contact with a grounded object under normal operating conditions.

(l)(7)(ii) Transformers, powerpacks, control apparatus, and all other electrical portions of the equipment, with the exception of the charging electrodes and their connections to the power supply shall be located outside of the powder coating area or shall otherwise conform to the requirements of paragraph (l)(1) of this section.

(l)(7)(iii) All electrically conductive objects within the charging influence of the electrodes shall be adequately grounded. The powder coating equipment shall carry a prominent, permanently installed warning regarding the necessity for grounding these objects.

(l)(7)(iv) Objects being coated shall be maintained in contact with the conveyor or other support in order to insure proper grounding. Hangers shall be regularly cleaned to insure effective contact and areas of contact shall be sharp points or knife edges where possible.

(l)(7)(v) The electrical equipment shall be so interlocked with the ventilation system that the equipment cannot be operated unless the ventilation fans are in operation.

(m) OI **Organic peroxides and dual component coatings**

(m)(1) **Conformance** All spraying operations involving the use of organic peroxides and other dual component coatings shall be conducted in approved sprinklered spray booths meeting the requirements of this section.

(m)(2) **Smoking** Smoking shall be prohibited and "No Smoking" signs shall be prominently displayed and only nonsparking tools shall be used in any area where organic peroxides are stored, mixed or applied.

(n) **Scope** This section applies to flammable and combustible finishing materials when applied as a spray by compressed air, "airless" or "hydraulic atomization," steam, electrostatic methods, or by any other means in continuous or intermittent processes. The section also covers the application of combustible powders by powder spray guns, electrostatic powder spray guns, fluidized beds, or electrostatic fluidized beds. The section does not apply to outdoor spray application of buildings, tanks, or other similar structures, nor to small portable spraying apparatus not used repeatedly in the same location.

[39 FR 23502, June 27, 1974, as amended at 45 FR 60704, Sept. 12, 1980; 49 FR 5322, Feb. 10, 1984; 53 FR 12121, Apr. 12, 1988; 61 FR 9237, Mar. 7, 1996; 72 FR 71069, Dec. 14, 2007]

§1910.108 OI
[Reserved]

§1910.109
Explosives and blasting agents

(a) **Definitions applicable to this section**

(a)(1) **Blasting agent** Any material or mixture, consisting of a fuel and oxidizer, intended for blasting, not otherwise classified as an explosive and in which none of the ingredients are classified as an explosive, provided that the finished product, as mixed and packaged for use or shipment, cannot be detonated by means of a No. 8 test blasting cap when unconfined.

(a)(2) **Explosive-actuated power devices** Explosive-actuated power device—any tool or special mechanized device which is actuated by explosives, but not including propellant-actuated power devices. Examples of explosive-actuated power devices are jet tappers and jet perforators.

(a)(3) **Explosive** Any chemical compound, mixture, or device, the primary or common purpose of which is to function by explosion, i.e., with substantially instantaneous release of gas and heat, unless such compound, mixture, or device is otherwise specifically classified by the U.S. Department of Transportation; see 49 CFR chapter I. The term "explosives" shall include all material which is classified as Class A, Class B, and Class C explosives by the U.S. Department of Transportation, and includes, but is not limited to dynamite, black powder, pellet powders, initiating explosives, blasting caps, electric blasting caps, safety fuse, fuse lighters, fuse igniters, squibs, cordeau detonant fuse, instantaneous fuse, igniter cord, igniters, small arms ammunition, small arms ammunition primers, smokeless propellant, cartridges for propellant-actuated power devices, and cartridges for industrial guns. Commercial explosives are those explosives which are intended to be used in commercial or industrial operations.

Note 1: *Classification of explosives is described by the U.S. Department of Transportation as follows (see 49 CFR chapter I):*

(a)(3)(i) **Class A explosives** Possessing, detonating, or otherwise maximum hazard; such as dynamite, nitroglycerin, picric acid, lead azide, fulminate of mercury, black powder, blasting caps, and detonating primers.

(a)(3)(ii) **Class B explosives** Possessing flammable hazard, such as propellant explosives (including some smokeless propellants), photographic flash powders, and some special fireworks.

(a)(3)(iii) **Class C explosives** Includes certain types of manufactured articles which contain Class A or Class B explosives, or both, as components but in restricted quantities.

(a)(3)(iv) **Forbidden or not acceptable explosives** Explosives which are forbidden or not acceptable for transportation by common carriers by rail freight, rail express, highway, or water in accordance with the regulations of the U.S. Department of Transportation, 49 CFR chapter I.

(a)(4) **Highway** Any public street, public alley, or public road.

(a)(5) [Reserved]

(a)(6) **Magazine** Any building or structure, other than an explosives manufacturing building, used for the storage of explosives.

(a)(7) **Motor vehicle** Any self-propelled vehicle, truck, tractor, semitrailer, or truck-full trailers used for the transportation of freight over public highways.

(a)(8) **Propellant-actuated power devices** Any tool or special mechanized device or gas generator system which is actuated by a smokeless propellant or which releases and directs work through a smokeless propellant charge.

(a)(9) [Reserved]

(a)(10) **Pyrotechnics** Any combustible or explosive compositions or manufactured articles designed and prepared for the purpose of producing audible or visible effects which are commonly referred to as fireworks.

(a)(11) [Reserved]

(a)(12) **Semiconductive hose** A hose with an electrical resistance high enough to limit flow of stray electric currents to safe levels, yet not so high as to prevent drainage of static electric charges to ground; hose of not more than 2 megohms resistance over its entire length and of not less than 5,000 ohms per foot meets the requirement.

(a)(13) **Small arms ammunition** Any shotgun, rifle, pistol, or revolver cartridge, and cartridges for propellant-actuated power devices and industrial guns. Military-type ammunition containing explosive-bursting charges, incendiary, tracer, spotting, or pyrotechnic projectiles is excluded from this definition.

(a)(14) **Small arms ammunition primers** Small percussion-sensitive explosive charges, encased in a cup, used to ignite propellant powder.

(a)(15) **Smokeless propellants** Solid propellants, commonly called smokeless powders in the trade, used in small arms ammunition, cannon, rockets, propellant-actuated power devices, etc.

(a)(16) **Special industrial explosives devices** Explosive-actuated power devices and propellant-actuated power devices.

(a)(17) **Special industrial explosives materials** Shaped materials and sheet forms and various other extrusions, pellets, and packages of high explosives, which include dynamite, trinitrotoluene (TNT), pentaerythritol tetranitrate (PETN), hexahydro-1,3,5-trinitro-s-triazine (RDX), and other similar compounds used for high-energy-rate forming, expanding, and shaping in metal fabrication, and for dismemberment and quick reduction of scrap metal.

(a)(18) **Water gels or slurry explosives** These comprise a wide variety of materials used for blasting. They all contain substantial proportions of water and high proportions of ammonium nitrate, some of which is in solution in the water. Two broad classes of water gels are (i) those which are sensitized by a material classed as an explosive, such as TNT or smokeless powder, (ii) those which contain no ingredient classified as an explosive; these are sensitized with metals such as aluminum or with other fuels. Water gels may be premixed at an explosives plant or mixed at the site immediately before delivery into the borehole.

(a)(19) **DOT specifications** Regulations of the Department of Transportation published in 49 CFR chapter I.

(b) **Miscellaneous provisions**

(b)(1) **General hazard** No person shall store, handle, or transport explosives or blasting agents when such storage, handling, and transportation of explosives or blasting agents constitutes an undue hazard to life.

(b)(2) [Reserved]

(c) **Storage of explosives**

(c)(1) **General provisions**

(c)(1)(i) All Class A, Class B, Class C explosives, and special industrial explosives, and any newly developed and unclassified explosives, shall be kept in magazines which meet the requirements of this paragraph.

(c)(1)(ii) Blasting caps, electric blasting caps, detonating primers, and primed cartridges shall not be stored in the same magazine with other explosives.

(c)(1)(iii) Ground around magazines shall slope away for drainage. The land surrounding magazines shall be kept clear of brush, dried grass, leaves, and other materials for a distance of at least 25 feet.

(c)(1)(iv) Magazines as required by this paragraph shall be of two classes; namely, Class I magazines, and Class II magazines.

(c)(1)(v) Class I magazines shall be required where the quantity of explosives stored is more than 50 pounds. Class II magazines may be used where the quantity of explosives stored is 50 pounds or less.

(c)(1)(vi) Class I magazines shall be located away from other magazines in conformity with Table H–21.

Table H–21
American Table of Distances for Storage of Explosives[1-5]

[As revised and approved by the Institute of Makers of Explosives, June 5, 1964]

Explosives		Distances in feet when storage is barricaded: Separation of magazines
Pounds over	Pounds not over	
2	5	6
5	10	8
10	20	10
20	30	11
30	40	12
40	50	14
50	75	15
75	100	16
100	125	18
125	150	19
150	200	21
200	250	23
250	300	24
300	400	27
400	500	29
500	600	31
600	700	32
700	800	33
800	900	35

Explosives		Distances in feet when storage is barricaded: Separation of magazines
Pounds over	Pounds not over	
900	1,000	36
1,000	1,200	39
1,200	1,400	41
1,400	1,600	43
1,600	1,800	44
1,800	2,000	45
2,000	2,500	49
2,500	3,000	52
3,000	4,000	58
4,000	5,000	61
5,000	6,000	65
6,000	7,000	68
7,000	8,000	72
8,000	9,000	75
9,000	10,000	78
10,000	12,000	82
12,000	14,000	87
14,000	16,000	90
16,000	18,000	94
18,000	20,000	98
20,000	25,000	105
25,000	30,000	112
30,000	35,000	119
35,000	40,000	124
40,000	45,000	129
45,000	50,000	135
50,000	55,000	140
55,000	60,000	145
60,000	65,000	150
65,000	70,000	155
70,000	75,000	160
75,000	80,000	165
80,000	85,000	170
85,000	90,000	175
90,000	95,000	180
95,000	100,000	185
100,000	110,000	195
110,000	120,000	205
120,000	130,000	215
130,000	140,000	225
140,000	150,000	235
150,000	160,000	245
160,000	170,000	255
170,000	180,000	265
180,000	190,000	275
190,000	200,000	285
200,000	210,000	295
210,000	230,000	315
230,000	250,000	335
250,000	275,000	360
275,500	300,000	385

[1] "Natural barricade" means natural features of the ground, such as hills, or timber of sufficient density that the surrounding exposures which require protection cannot be seen from the magazine when the trees are bare of leaves.

[2] "Artificial barricade" means an artificial mound or revetted wall of earth of a minimum thickness of three feet.

[3] "Barricaded" means that a building containing explosives is effectually screened from a magazine, building, railway, or highway, either by a natural barricade, or by an artificial barricade of such height that a straight line from the top of any sidewall of the building containing explosives to the eave line of any magazine, or building, or to a point 12 feet above the center of a railway or highway, will pass through such intervening natural or artificial barricade.

[4] When two or more storage magazines are located on the same property, each magazine must comply with the minimum distances specified from inhabited buildings, railways, and highways, and in addition, they should be separated from each other by not less than the distances shown for "Separation of Magazines," except that the quantity of explosives contained in cap magazines shall govern in regard to the spacing of said cap magazines from magazines containing other explosives. If any two or more magazines are separated from each other by less than the specified "Separation of Magazines" distances, then such two or more magazines, as a group, must be considered as one magazine, and the total quantity of explosives stored in such group must be treated as if stored in a single magazine located on the site of any magazine of the group, and must comply with the minimum of distances specified from other magazines, inhabited buildings, railways, and highways.

[5] This table applies only to the permanent storage of commercial explosives. It is not applicable to transportation of explosives, or any handling or temporary storage necessary or incident thereto. It is not intended to apply to bombs, projectiles, or other heavily encased explosives.

(c)(1)(vii) Except as provided in subdivision (viii) of this subparagraph, class II magazines shall be located in conformity with Table H–21, but may be permitted in warehouses and in wholesale and retail establishments when located on a floor which has an entrance at outside grade level and the magazine is located not more than 10 feet from such an entrance. Two class II magazines may be located in the same building when one is used only for blasting caps in quantities not in excess of 5,000 caps and a distance of 10 feet is maintained between magazines.

(c)(1)(viii) When used for temporary storage at a site for blasting operations, class II magazines shall be located away from other magazines. A distance of at least one hundred and fifty (150) feet shall be maintained between class II magazines and the work in progress when the quantity of explosives kept therein is in excess of 25 pounds, and at least 50 feet when the quantity of explosives is 25 pounds, or less.

(c)(1)(ix) This paragraph (c) does not apply to:

(c)(1)(ix)(A) Stocks of small arms ammunition, propellant-actuated power cartridges, small arms ammunition primers in quantities of less than 750,000, or of smokeless propellants in quantities less than 750 pounds;

(c)(1)(ix)(B) Explosive-actuated power devices when in quantities less than 50 pounds net weight of explosives;

(c)(1)(ix)(C) Fuse lighters and fuse igniters;

(c)(1)(ix)(D) Safety fuses other than cordeau detonant fuses.

(c)(2) **Construction of magazines—general**

(c)(2)(i) Magazines shall be constructed in conformity with the provisions of this paragraph.

(c)(2)(ii) Magazines for the storage of explosives, other than black powder, Class B and Class C explosives shall be bullet resistant, weather resistant, fire resistant, and ventilated sufficiently to protect the explosive in the specific locality. Magazines used only for storage of black powder, Class B and Class C explosives shall be weather resistant, fire-resistant, and have ventilation. Magazines for storage of blasting and electric blasting caps shall be weather resistant, fire-resistant, and ventilated.

(c)(2)(iii) Property upon which Class I magazines are located and property where Class II magazines are located outside of buildings shall be posted with signs reading:

"Explosives—Keep Off"

(c)(2)(iv) Magazines requiring heat shall be heated by either hot-water radiant heating with the magazine building; or air directed into the magazine building over either hot water or low pressure steam (15 p.s.i.g.) coils located outside the magazine building.

(c)(2)(v) The magazine heating systems shall meet the following requirements:

(c)(2)(v)(A) The radiant heating coils within the building shall be installed in such a manner that the explosives or explosives containers cannot contact the coils and air is free to circulate between the coils and the explosives or explosives containers;

(c)(2)(v)(B) The heating ducts shall be installed in such a manner that the hot-air discharge from the duct is not directed against the explosives or explosives containers.\;

(c)(2)(v)(C) The heating device used in connection with a magazine shall have controls which prevent the ambient building temperature from exceeding 130 °F;

(c)(2)(v)(D) The electric fan or pump used in the heating system for a magazine shall be mounted outside and separate from the wall of the magazine and shall be grounded;

(c)(2)(v)(E) The electric fan motor and the controls for electrical heating devices used in heating water or steam shall have overloads and disconnects, which comply with Subpart S of this part. All electrical switch gear shall be located a minimum distance of 25 feet from the magazine;

(c)(2)(v)(F) The heating source for water or steam shall be separated from the magazine by a distance of not less than 25 feet when electrical and 50 feet when fuel fired. The area between the heating unit and the magazine shall be cleared of all combustible materials;

(c)(2)(v)(G) The storage of explosives and explosives containers in the magazine shall allow uniform air circulation so product temperature uniformity can be maintained.

(c)(2)(vi) When lights are necessary inside the magazine, electric safety flashlight, or electric safety lanterns shall be used.

(c)(3) Construction of Class I magazines

(c)(3)(i) Class I magazines shall be of masonry construction or of wood or of metal construction, or a combination of these types. Thickness of masonry units shall not be less than 8 inches. Hollow masonry units used in construction required to be bullet resistant shall have all hollow spaces filled with weak cement or well-tamped sand. Wood constructed walls, required to be bullet resistant, shall have at least a 6-inch space between interior and exterior sheathing and the space between sheathing shall be filled with well-tamped sand. Metal wall construction, when required to be bullet resistant, shall be lined with brick at least 4 inches in thickness or shall have at least a 6-inch sandfill between interior and exterior walls.

(c)(3)(ii) Floors and roofs of masonry magazines may be of wood construction. Wood floors shall be tongue and grooved lumber having a nominal thickness of 1 inch.

(c)(3)(iii) Roofs required to be bullet resistant shall be protected by a sand tray located at the line of eaves and covering the entire area except that necessary for ventilation. Sand in the sand tray shall be maintained at a depth of not less than 4 inches.

(c)(3)(iv) All wood at the exterior of magazines, including eaves, shall be protected by being covered with black or galvanized steel or aluminum metal of thickness of not less than No. 26 gage. All nails exposed to the interior of magazines shall be well countersunk.

(c)(3)(v) Foundations for magazines shall be of substantial construction and arranged to provide good cross ventilation.

(c)(3)(vi) Magazines shall be ventilated sufficiently to prevent dampness and heating of stored explosives. Ventilating openings shall be screened to prevent the entrance of sparks.

(c)(3)(vii) Openings to magazines shall be restricted to that necessary for the placement and removal of stocks of explosives. Doors for openings in magazines for Class A explosives shall be bullet resistant. Doors for magazines not required to be bullet resistant shall be designed to prevent unauthorized entrance to the magazine.

(c)(3)(viii) [Reserved]

(c)(3)(ix) Provisions shall be made to prevent the piling of stocks of explosives directly against masonry walls, brick-lined or sand-filled metal walls and single-thickness metal walls; such protection, however, shall not interfere with proper ventilation at the interior of side and end walls.

(c)(4) Construction of Class II magazines

(c)(4)(i) Class II magazines shall be of wood or metal construction, or a combination thereof.

(c)(4)(ii) Wood magazines of this class shall have sides, bottom, and cover constructed of 2-inch hardwood boards well braced at corners and protected by being entirely covered with sheet metal of not less than No. 20 gage. All nails exposed to the interior of the magazine shall be well countersunk. All metal magazines of this class shall have sides, bottom, and cover constructed of sheet metal, and shall be lined with three-eighths-inch plywood or equivalent. Edges of metal covers shall overlap sides at least 1 inch.

(c)(4)(iii) Covers for both wood- and metal-constructed magazines of this class shall be provided with substantial strap hinges and shall be provided with substantial means for locking.

(c)(4)(iv) Magazines of this class shall be painted red and shall bear lettering in white, on all sides and top, at least 3 inches high, "Explosives—Keep Fire Away." Class II magazines when located in warehouses, and in wholesale and retail establishments shall be provided with substantial wheels or casters to facilitate easy removal in the case of fire. Where necessary due to climatic conditions, Class II magazines shall be ventilated.

(c)(5) Storage within magazines

(c)(5)(i) Packages of explosives shall be laid flat with top side up. Black powder when stored in magazines with other explosives shall be stored separately. Black powder stored in kegs shall be stored on ends, bungs down, or on side, seams down. Corresponding grades and brands shall be stored together in such a manner that brands and grade marks show. All stocks shall be stored so as to be easily counted and checked. Packages of explosives shall be piled in a stable manner. When any kind of explosive is removed from a magazine for use, the oldest explosive of that particular kind shall always be taken first.

(c)(5)(ii) Packages of explosives shall not be unpacked or repacked in a magazine nor within 50 feet of a magazine or in close proximity to other explosives. Tools used for opening packages of explosives shall be constructed of nonsparking materials, except that metal slitters may be used for opening fiberboard boxes. A wood wedge and a fiber, rubber, or wood mallet shall be used for opening or closing wood packages of explosives. Opened packages of explosives shall be securely closed before being returned to a magazine.

(c)(5)(iii) Magazines shall not be used for the storage of any metal tools nor any commodity except explosives, but this restriction shall not apply to the storage of blasting agents and blasting supplies.

(c)(5)(iv) Magazine floors shall be regularly swept, kept clean, dry, free of grit, paper, empty used packages, and rubbish. Brooms and other cleaning utensils shall not have any spark-producing metal parts. Sweepings from floors of magazines shall be properly disposed of. Magazine floors stained with nitroglycerin shall be cleaned according to instructions by the manufacturer.

(c)(5)(v) When any explosive has deteriorated to an extent that it is in an unstable or dangerous condition, or if nitroglycerin leaks from any explosives, then the person in possession of such explosive shall immediately proceed to destroy such explosive in accordance with the instructions of the manufacturer. Only experienced persons shall be allowed to do the work of destroying explosives.

(c)(5)(vi) When magazines need inside repairs, all explosives shall be removed therefrom and the floors cleaned. In making outside repairs, if there is a possibility of causing sparks or fire the explosives shall be removed from the magazine. Explosives removed from a magazine under repair shall either be placed in another magazine or placed a safe distance from the magazine where they shall be properly guarded and protected until repairs have been completed, when they shall be returned to the magazine.

(c)(5)(vii) Smoking, matches, open flames, spark-producing devices, and firearms (except firearms carried by guards) shall not be permitted inside of or within 50 feet of magazines. The land surrounding a magazine shall be kept clear of all combustible materials for a distance of at least 25 feet. Combustible materials shall not be stored within 50 feet of magazines.

(c)(5)(viii) Magazines shall be in the charge of a competent person at all times and who shall be held responsible for the enforcement of all safety precautions.

(c)(5)(ix) Explosives recovered from blasting misfires shall be placed in a separate magazine until competent personnel has determined from the manufacturer the method of disposal. Caps recovered from blasting misfires shall not be reused. Such explosives and caps shall then be disposed of in the manner recommended by the manufacturer.

(d) Transportation of explosives

(d)(1) General provisions

(d)(1)(i) No employee shall be allowed to smoke, carry matches or any other flame-producing device, or carry any firearms or loaded cartridges while in or near a motor vehicle transporting explosives; or drive, load, or unload such vehicle in a careless or reckless manner.

(d)(1)(ii) [Reserved]

(d)(1)(iii) Explosives shall not be transferred from one vehicle to another within the confines of any jurisdiction (city, county, State, or other area) without informing the fire and police departments thereof. In the event of breakdown or collision the local fire and police departments shall be promptly notified to help safeguard such emergencies. Explosives shall be transferred from the disabled vehicle to another only, when proper and qualified supervision is provided.

(d)(1)(iv) Blasting caps or electric blasting caps shall not be transported over the highways on the same vehicles with other explosives, unless packaged, segregated, and transported in accordance with the Department of Transportation's Hazardous Materials Regulations (49 CFR parts 177–180).

(d)(2) Transportation vehicles

(d)(2)(i) Vehicles used for transporting explosives shall be strong enough to carry the load without difficulty and be in good mechanical condition. If vehicles do not have a closed body, the body shall be covered with a flameproof and moistureproof tarpaulin or other effective protection against moisture and sparks. All vehicles used for the transportation of explosives shall have tight floors and any exposed spark-producing metal on the inside of the body shall be covered with wood or other nonsparking materials to prevent contact with packages of explosives. Packages of explosives shall not be loaded above the sides of an open-body vehicle.

(d)(2)(ii) Every vehicle used for transporting explosives and oxidizing materials listed in paragraph (d)(2)(ii)(A) of this section shall be marked as follows:

(d)(2)(ii)(A) Exterior markings or placards required on applicable vehicles shall be as follows for the various classes of commodities:

Commodity	Type of marking or placard
Explosives, Class A, any quantity or a combination of Class A and Class B explosives	Explosives A (Red letters on white background).
Explosives, Class B, and quantity	Explosives B (Red letters on white background).
Oxidizing material (blasting agents, ammonium nitrate, etc.), 1,000 pounds or more gross weight	Oxidizers (Yellow letters on black background).

(d)(2)(ii)(B) [Reserved]

(d)(2)(ii)(C) Such markings or placards shall be displayed at the front, rear, and on each side of the motor vehicle or trailer, or other cargo carrying body while it contains explosives or other dangerous articles of such type and in such quantity as specified in paragraph (d)(1)(ii)(A) of this subdivision. The front marking or placard may be displayed on the front of either the truck, truck body, truck tractor or the trailer.

(d)(2)(ii)(D) Any motor vehicle, trailer, or other cargo-carrying body containing more than one kind of explosive as well as an oxidizing material requiring a placard under the provisions of paragraph (d)(2)(ii)(A), the aggregate gross weight of which totals 1,000 pounds or more, shall be marked or placarded "Dangerous" as well as "Explosive A" or "Explosive B" as appropriate. If explosives Class A and explosives Class B are loaded on the same vehicle, the "Explosives B" marking need not be displayed.

(d)(2)(ii)(E) In any combination of two or more vehicles containing explosives or other dangerous articles each vehicle shall be marked or placarded as to its contents and in accordance with paragraphs (d)(2)(ii)(A) and (C) of this subdivision.

(d)(2)(iii) Each motor vehicle used for transporting explosives shall be equipped with a minimum of two extinguishers, each having a rating of at least 10–BC.

(d)(2)(iii)(A) Only extinguishers listed or approved by a nationally recognized testing laboratory shall be deemed suitable for use on explosives-carrying vehicles. Refer to §1910.155(c)(3)(iv)(A) for definition of listed, and §1910.7 for nationally recognized testing laboratory.

(d)(2)(iii)(B) Extinguishers shall be filled and ready for immediate use and located near the driver's seat. Extinguishers shall be examined periodically by a competent person.

(d)(2)(iv) A motor vehicle used for transporting explosives shall be given the following inspection to determine that it is in proper condition for safe transportation of explosives:

(d)(2)(iv)(A) Fire extinguishers shall be filled and in working order;

(d)(2)(iv)(B) All electrical wiring shall be completely protected and securely fastened to prevent short-circuiting;

(d)(2)(iv)(C) Chassis, motor, pan, and underside of body shall be reasonably clean and free of excess oil and grease;

(d)(2)(iv)(D) Fuel tank and feedline shall be secure and have no leaks;

(d)(2)(iv)(E) Brakes, lights, horn, windshield wipers, and steering apparatus shall function properly;

(d)(2)(iv)(F) Tires shall be checked for proper inflation and defects;

(d)(2)(iv)(G) The vehicle shall be in proper condition in every other respect and acceptable for handling explosives.

(d)(3) **Operation of transportation vehicles**

(d)(3)(i) Vehicles transporting explosives shall only be driven by and be in the charge of a driver who is familiar with the traffic regulations, State laws, and the provisions of this section.

(d)(3)(ii) Except under emergency conditions, no vehicle transporting explosives shall be parked before reaching its destination, even though attended, on any public street adjacent to or in proximity to any place where people work.

(d)(3)(iii) Every motor vehicle transporting any quantity of Class A or Class B explosives shall, at all times, be attended by a driver or other attendant of the motor carrier. This attendant shall have been made aware of the class of the explosive material in the vehicle and of its inherent dangers, and shall have been instructed in the measures and procedures to be followed in order to protect the public from those dangers. He shall have been made familiar with the vehicle he is assigned, and shall be trained, supplied with the necessary means, and authorized to move the vehicle when required.

(d)(3)(iii)(A) For the purpose of this subdivision, a motor vehicle shall be deemed "attended" only when the driver or other attendant is physically on or in the vehicle, or has the vehicle within his field of vision and can reach it quickly and without any kind of interference. "Attended" also means that the driver or attendant is awake, alert, and not engaged in other duties or activities which may divert his attention from the vehicle, except for necessary communication with public officers, or representatives of the carrier shipper, or consignee, or except for necessary absence from the vehicle to obtain food or to provide for his physical comfort.

(d)(3)(iii)(B) However, an explosive-laden vehicle may be left unattended if parked within a securely fenced or walled area with all gates or entrances locked where parking of such vehicle is otherwise permissible, or at a magazine site established solely for the purpose of storing explosives.

(d)(3)(iv) No spark-producing metal, spark-producing metal tools, oils, matches, firearms, electric storage batteries, flammable substances, acids, oxidizing materials, or corrosive compounds shall be carried in the body of any motor truck and/or vehicle transporting explosives, unless the loading of such dangerous articles and the explosives comply with U.S. Department of Transportation regulations.

(d)(3)(v) Vehicles transporting explosives shall avoid congested areas and heavy traffic. Where routes through congested areas have been designated by local authorities such routes shall be followed.

(d)(3)(vi) Delivery shall only be made to authorized persons and into authorized magazines or authorized temporary storage or handling areas.

(e) **Use of explosives and blasting agents**

(e)(1) **General provisions**

(e)(1)(i) While explosives are being handled or used, smoking shall not be permitted and no one near the explosives shall possess matches, open light or other fire or flame. No person shall be allowed to handle explosives while under the influence of intoxicating liquors, narcotics, or other dangerous drugs.

(e)(1)(ii) Original containers or Class II magazines shall be used for taking detonators and other explosives from storage magazines to the blasting area.

(e)(1)(iii) When blasting is done in congested areas or in close proximity to a structure, or any other installation that may be damaged, the blast shall be covered before firing with a mat constructed so that it is capable of preventing fragments from being thrown.

(e)(1)(iv) Persons authorized to prepare explosive charges or conduct blasting operations shall use every reasonable precaution, including but not limited to warning signals, flags, barricades, or woven wire mats to insure the safety of the general public and workmen.

(e)(1)(v) Blasting operations shall be conducted during daylight hours.

(e)(1)(vi) Whenever blasting is being conducted in the vicinity of gas, electric, water, fire alarm, telephone, telegraph, and steam utilities, the blaster shall notify the appropriate representatives of such utilities at least 24 hours in advance of blasting, specifying the location and intended time of such blasting. Verbal notice shall be confirmed with written notice.

(e)(1)(vii) Due precautions shall be taken to prevent accidental discharge of electric blasting caps from current induced by radar, radio transmitters, lightning, adjacent powerlines, dust storms, or other sources of extraneous electricity. These precautions shall include:

(e)(1)(vii)(A) The suspension of all blasting operations and removal of persons from the blasting area during the approach and progress of an electric storm;

(e)(1)(vii)(B) The posting of signs warning against the use of mobile radio transmitters on all roads within 350 feet of the blasting operations.

(e)(2) **Storage at use sites**

(e)(2)(i) Empty containers and paper and fiber packing materials which have previously contained explosive materials shall be disposed of in a safe manner, or reused in accordance with the Department of Transportation's Hazardous Materials Regulations (49 CFR parts 177–180).

(e)(2)(ii) Containers of explosives shall not be opened in any magazine or within 50 feet of any magazine. In opening kegs or wooden cases, no sparking metal tools shall be used; wooden wedges and either wood, fiber or rubber mallets shall be used. Nonsparking metallic slitters may be used for opening fiberboard cases.

(e)(2)(iii) Explosives or blasting equipment that are obviously deteriorated or damaged shall not be used.

(e)(2)(iv) No explosives shall be abandoned.

(e)(3) Loading of explosives in blast holes

(e)(3)(i) All drill holes shall be sufficiently large to admit freely the insertion of the cartridges of explosives.

(e)(3)(ii) Tamping shall be done only with wood rods without exposed metal parts, but nonsparking metal connectors may be used for jointed poles. Violent tamping shall be avoided. Primed cartridges shall not be tamped.

(e)(3)(iii) When loading blasting agents pneumatically over electric blasting caps, semiconductive delivery hose shall be used and the equipment shall be bonded and grounded.

(e)(3)(iv) No holes shall be loaded except those to be fired in the next round of blasting. After loading, all remaining explosives shall be immediately returned to an authorized magazine.

(e)(3)(v) Drilling shall not be started until all remaining butts of old holes are examined with a wooden stick for unexploded charges, and if any are found, they shall be refired before work proceeds.

(e)(3)(vi) No person shall be allowed to deepen drill holes which have contained explosives.

(e)(3)(vii) After loading for a blast is completed, all excess blasting caps or electric blasting caps and other explosives shall immediately be returned to their separate storage magazines.

(e)(4) Initiation of explosive charges

(e)(4)(i) [Reserved]

(e)(4)(ii) When fuse is used, the blasting cap shall be securely attached to the safety fuse with a standard-ring type cap crimper. All primers shall be assembled at least 50 feet from any magazine.

(e)(4)(iii) Primers shall be made up only as required for each round of blasting.

(e)(4)(iv) No blasting cap shall be inserted in the explosives without first making a hole in the cartridge for the cap with a wooden punch of proper size or standard cap crimper.

(e)(4)(v) Explosives shall not be extracted from a hole that has once been charged or has misfired unless it is impossible to detonate the unexploded charge by insertion of a fresh additional primer.

(e)(4)(vi) If there are any misfires while using cap and fuse, all persons shall be required to remain away from the charge for at least 1 hour. If electric blasting caps are used and a misfire occurs, this waiting period may be reduced to 30 minutes. Misfires shall be handled under the direction of the person in charge of the blasting and all wires shall be carefully traced and search made for unexploded charges.

(e)(4)(vii) Blasters, when testing circuits to charged holes, shall use only blasting galvanometers designed for this purpose.

(e)(4)(viii) Only the employee making leading wire connections in electrical firing shall be allowed to fire the shot. Leading wires shall remain shorted and not be connected to the blasting machine or other source of current until the charge is to be fired.

(e)(5) Warning required Before a blast is fired, the employer shall require that a loud warning signal be given by the person in charge, who has made certain that all surplus explosives are in a safe place, all persons and vehicles are at a safe distance or under sufficient cover, and that an adequate warning has been given.

(f) Explosives at piers, railway stations, and cars or vessels not otherwise specified in this standard

(f)(1) Railway cars Except in an emergency and with permission of the local authority, no person shall have or keep explosives in a railway car unless said car and contents and methods of loading are in accordance with the U.S. Department of Transportation Regulations for the Transportation of Explosives, 49 CFR chapter I.

(f)(2) Packing and marking No person shall deliver any explosive to any carrier unless such explosive conforms in all respects, including marking and packing, to the U.S. Department of Transportation Regulations for the Transportation of Explosives.

(f)(3) Marking cars Every railway car containing explosives which has reached its designation, or is stopped in transit so as no longer to be in interstate commerce, shall have attached to both sides and ends of the car, cards with the words "Explosives—Handle Carefully—Keep Fire Away" in red letters at least 1½ inches high on a white background.

(f)(4) Storage Any explosives at a railway facility, truck terminal, pier, wharf harbor facility, or airport terminal whether for delivery to a consignee, or forwarded to some other destination shall be kept in a safe place, isolated as far as practicable and in such manner that they can be easily and quickly removed.

(f)(5) Hours of transfer Explosives shall not be delivered to or received from any railway station, truck terminal, pier, wharf, harbor facility, or airport terminal between the hours of sunset and sunrise.

(g) Blasting agents

(g)(1) General Unless otherwise set forth in this paragraph, blasting agents, excluding water gels, shall be transported, stored, and used in the same manner as explosives. Water gels are covered in paragraph (h) of this section.

(g)(2) Fixed location mixing

(g)(2)(i) [Reserved]

(g)(2)(ii) Buildings used for the mixing of blasting agents shall conform to the requirements of this section.

(g)(2)(ii)(A) Buildings shall be of noncombustible construction or sheet metal on wood studs.

(g)(2)(ii)(B) Floors in a mixing plant shall be of concrete or of other nonabsorbent materials.

(g)(2)(ii)(C) All fuel oil storage facilities shall be separated from the mixing plant and located in such a manner that in case of tank rupture, the oil will drain away from the mixing plant building.

(g)(2)(ii)(D) The building shall be well ventilated.

(g)(2)(ii)(E) Heating units which do not depend on combustion processes, when properly designed and located, may be used in the building. All direct sources of heat shall be provided exclusively from units located outside the mixing building.

(g)(2)(ii)(F) All internal-combustion engines used for electric power generation shall be located outside the mixing plant building, or shall be properly ventilated and isolated by a firewall. The exhaust systems on all such engines shall be located so any spark emission cannot be a hazard to any materials in or adjacent to the plant.

(g)(2)(iii) Equipment used for mixing blasting agents shall conform to the requirements of this subdivision.

(g)(2)(iii)(A) The design of the mixer shall minimize the possibility of frictional heating, compaction, and especially confinement. All bearings and drive assemblies shall be mounted outside the mixer and protected against the accumulation of dust. All surfaces shall be accessible for cleaning.

(g)(2)(iii)(B) Mixing and packaging equipment shall be constructed of materials compatible with the fuel-ammonium nitrate composition.

(g)(2)(iii)(C) Suitable means shall be provided to prevent the flow of fuel oil to the mixer in case of fire. In gravity flow systems an automatic spring-loaded shutoff valve with fusible link shall be installed.

(g)(2)(iv) The provisions of this subdivision shall be considered when determining blasting agent compositions.

(g)(2)(iv)(A) The sensitivity of the blasting agent shall be determined by means of a No. 8 test blasting cap at regular intervals and after every change in formulation.

(g)(2)(iv)(B) Oxidizers of small particle size, such as crushed ammonium nitrate prills or fines, may be more sensitive than coarser products and shall, therefore, be handled with greater care.

(g)(2)(iv)(C) No hydrocarbon liquid fuel with flashpoint lower than that of No. 2 diesel fuel oil 125 °F. minimum shall be used.

(g)(2)(iv)(D) Crude oil and crankcase oil shall not be used.

(g)(2)(iv)(E) Metal powders such as aluminum shall be kept dry and shall be stored in containers or bins which are moisture-resistant or weathertight. Solid fuels shall be used in such manner as to minimize dust explosion hazards.

(g)(2)(iv)(F) Peroxides and chlorates shall not be used.

(g)(2)(v) All electrical switches, controls, motors, and lights located in the mixing room shall conform to the requirements in Subpart S of this part for Class II, Division 2 locations; otherwise they shall be located outside the mixing room. The frame of the mixer and all other equipment that may be used shall be electrically bonded and be provided with a continuous path to the ground.

(g)(2)(vi) Safety precautions at mixing plants shall include the requirements of this subdivision.

(g)(2)(vi)(A) Floors shall be constructed so as to eliminate floor drains and piping into which molten materials could flow and be confined in case of fire.

(g)(2)(vi)(B) The floors and equipment of the mixing and packaging room shall be cleaned regularly and thoroughly to prevent accumulation of oxidizers or fuels and other sensitizers.

(g)(2)(vi)(C) The entire mixing and packaging plant shall be cleaned regularly and thoroughly to prevent excessive accumulation of dust.

(g)(2)(vi)(D) Smoking, matches, open flames, spark-producing devices, and firearms (except firearms carried by guards) shall not be permitted inside of or within 50 feet of any building or facility used for the mixing of blasting agents.

(g)(2)(vi)(E) The land surrounding the mixing plant shall be kept clear of brush, dried grass, leaves, and other materials for a distance of at least 25 feet.

(g)(2)(vi)(F) Empty ammonium nitrate bags shall be disposed of daily in a safe manner.

(g)(2)(vi)(G) No welding shall be permitted or open flames used in or around the mixing or storage area of the plant unless the equipment or area has been completely washed down and all oxidizer material removed.

(g)(2)(vi)(H) Before welding or repairs to hollow shafts, all oxidizer material shall be removed from the outside and inside of the shaft and the shaft vented with a minimum one-half inch diameter opening.

(g)(2)(vi)(I) Explosives shall not be permitted inside of or within 50 feet of any building or facility used for the mixing of blasting agents.

(g)(3) **Bulk delivery and mixing vehicles**

(g)(3)(i) The provisions of this paragraph shall apply to off-highway private operations as well as to all public highway movements.

(g)(3)(ii) A bulk vehicle body for delivering and mixing blasting agents shall conform with the requirements of this paragraph (ii).

(g)(3)(ii)(A) The body shall be constructed of noncombustible materials.

(g)(3)(ii)(B) Vehicles used to transport bulk premixed blasting agents on public highways shall have closed bodies.

(g)(3)(ii)(C) All moving parts of the mixing system shall be designed as to prevent a heat buildup. Shafts or axles which contact the product shall have outboard bearings with 1-inch minimum clearance between the bearings and the outside of the product container. Particular attention shall be given to the clearances on all moving parts.

(g)(3)(ii)(D) A bulk delivery vehicle shall be strong enough to carry the load without difficulty and be in good mechanical condition.

(g)(3)(iii) Operation of bulk delivery vehicles shall conform to the requirements of this subdivision. These include the placarding requirements as specified by Department of Transportation.

(g)(3)(iii)(A) The operator shall be trained in the safe operation of the vehicle together with its mixing, conveying, and related equipment. The employer shall assure that the operator is familiar with the commodities being delivered and the general procedure for handling emergency situations.

(g)(3)(iii)(B) The hauling of either blasting caps or other explosives but not both, shall be permitted on bulk trucks provided that a special wood or nonferrous-lined container is installed for the explosives. Such blasting caps or other explosives shall be in DOT-specified shipping containers: see 49 CFR chapter I.

(g)(3)(iii)(C) No person shall smoke, carry matches or any flame-producing device, or carry any firearms while in or about bulk vehicles effecting the mixing transfer or down-the-hole loading of blasting agents at or near the blasting site.

(g)(3)(iii)(D) Caution shall be exercised in the movement of the vehicle in the blasting area to avoid driving the vehicle over or dragging hoses over firing lines, cap wires, or explosive materials. The employer shall assure that the driver, in moving the vehicle, has assistance of a second person to guide his movements.

(g)(3)(iii)(E) No intransit mixing of materials shall be performed.

(g)(3)(iv) Pneumatic loading from bulk delivery vehicles into blastholes primed with electric blasting caps or other static-sensitive systems shall conform to the requirements of this subdivision.

(g)(3)(iv)(A) A positive grounding device shall be used to prevent the accumulation of static electricity.

(g)(3)(iv)(B) A discharge hose shall be used that has a resistance range that will prevent conducting stray currents, but that is conductive enough to bleed off static buildup.

(g)(3)(iv)(C) A qualified person shall evaluate all systems to determine if they will adequately dissipate static under potential field conditions.

(g)(3)(v) Repairs to bulk delivery vehicles shall conform to the requirements of this section.

(g)(3)(v)(A) No welding or open flames shall be used on or around any part of the delivery equipment unless it has been completely washed down and all oxidizer material removed.

(g)(3)(v)(B) Before welding or making repairs to hollow shafts, the shaft shall be thoroughly cleaned inside and out and vented with a minimum one-half-inch diameter opening.

(g)(4) **Bulk storage bins**

(g)(4)(i) The bin, including supports, shall be constructed of compatible materials, waterproof, and adequately supported and braced to withstand the combination of all loads including impact forces arising from product movement within the bin and accidental vehicle contact with the support legs.

(g)(4)(ii) The bin discharge gate shall be designed to provide a closure tight enough to prevent leakage of the stored product. Provision shall also be made so that the gate can be locked.

(g)(4)(iii) Bin loading manways or access hatches shall be hinged or otherwise attached to the bin and be designed to permit locking.

(g)(4)(iv) Any electrically driven conveyors for loading or unloading bins shall conform to the requirements of Subpart S of this part. They shall be designed to minimize damage from corrosion.

(g)(4)(v) Bins containing blasting agent shall be located, with respect to inhabited buildings, passenger railroads, and public highways, in accordance with Table-21 and separation from other blasting agent storage and explosives storage shall be in conformity with Table H–22.

(g)(4)(vi) Bins containing ammonium nitrate shall be separated from blasting agent storage and explosives storage in conformity with Table H–22.

Table H–22
Table of Recommended Separation Distances of Ammonium Nitrate and Blasting Agents From Explosives or Blasting Agents[1-6]

Donor weight		Minimum separation distance of receptor when barricaded[2] (ft.)		Minimum thickness of artificial barricades[5] (in.)
Pounds over	Pounds not over	Ammonium nitrate[3]	Blasting agent[4]	
	100	3	11	12
100	300	4	14	12
300	600	5	18	12
600	1,000	6	22	12
1,000	1,600	7	25	12
1,600	2,000	8	29	12
2,000	3,000	9	32	15
3,000	4,000	10	36	15
4,000	6,000	11	40	15
6,000	8,000	12	43	20
8,000	10,000	13	47	20
10,000	12,000	14	50	20
12,000	16,000	15	54	25
16,000	20,000	16	58	25
20,000	25,000	18	65	25
25,000	30,000	19	68	30
30,000	35,000	20	72	30
35,000	40,000	21	76	30
40,000	45,000	22	79	35
45,000	50,000	23	83	35
50,000	55,000	24	86	35
55,000	60,000	25	90	35
60,000	70,000	26	94	40
70,000	80,000	28	101	40
80,000	90,000	30	108	40
90,000	100,000	32	115	40
100,000	120,000	34	122	50
120,000	140,000	37	133	50
140,000	160,000	40	144	50
160,000	180,000	44	158	50
180,000	200,000	48	173	50

Note: Table data continues on next page.

Donor weight		Minimum separation distance of receptor when barricaded[2](ft.)		Minimum thickness of artificial barricades[5](in.)
Pounds over	Pounds not over	Ammonium nitrate[3]	Blasting agent[4]	
200,000	220,000	52	187	60
220,000	250,000	56	202	60
250,000	275,000	60	216	60
275,000	300,000	64	230	60

[1] These distances apply to the separation of stores only. Table H–21 shall be used in determining separation distances from inhabited buildings, passenger railways, and public highways.

[2] When the ammonium nitrate and/or blasting agent is not barricaded, the distances shown in the table shall be multiplied by six. These distances allow for the possibility of high velocity metal fragments from mixers, hoppers, truck bodies, sheet metal structures, metal container, and the like which may enclose the "donor". Where storage is in bullet-resistant magazines recommended for explosives or where the storage is protected by a bullet-resistant wall, distances, and barricade thicknesses in excess of those prescribed in Table H–21 are not required.

[3] The distances in the table apply to ammonium nitrate that passes the insensitivity test prescribed in the definition of ammonium nitrate fertilizer promulgated by the National Plant Food Institute*; and ammonium nitrate failing to pass said test shall be stored at separation distances determined by competent persons. (*Definition and Test Procedures for Ammonium Nitrate Fertilizer, National Plant Food Institute, November 1964.)

[4] These distances apply to nitro-carbo-nitrates and blasting agents which pass the insensitivity test prescribed in the U.S. Department of Transportation (DOT) regulations.

[5] Earth, or sand dikes, or enclosures filled with the prescribed minimum thickness of earth or sand are acceptable artificial barricades. Natural barricades, such as hills or timber of sufficient density that the surrounding exposures which require protection cannot be seen from the "donor" when the trees are bare of leaves, are also acceptable.

[6] When the ammonium nitrate must be counted in determining the distances to be maintained from inhabited buildings, passenger railways and public highways, it may be counted at one-half its actual weight because its blast effect is lower.

Note 7: Guide to use of table of recommended separation distances of ammonium nitrate and blasting agents from explosives or blasting agents.

(a) Sketch location of all potential donor and acceptor materials together with the maximum mass of material to be allowed in that vicinity. (Potential donors are high explosives, blasting agents, and combination of masses of detonating materials. Potential acceptors are high explosives, blasting agents, and ammonium nitrate.)

(b) Consider separately each donor mass in combination with each acceptor mass. If the masses are closer than table allowance (distances measured between nearest edges), the combination of masses becomes a new potential donor of weight equal to the total mass. When individual masses are considered as donors, distances to potential acceptors shall be measured between edges. When combined masses within propagating distance of each other are considered as a donor, the appropriate distance to the edge of potential acceptors shall be computed as a weighted distance from the combined masses.

Calculation of weighted distance from combined masses:

Let $M_2, M_3 \ldots M_n$ be donor masses to be combined.

M_1 is a potential acceptor mass.

D_{12} is distance from M_1 to M_2 (edge to edge).

D_{13} is distance from M_1 to M_3 (edge to edge), etc.

To find weighted distance [$D_1(_{2,3 \cdot \cdot \cdot n})$] from combined masses to M_1, add the products of the individual masses and distances and divide the total by the sum of the masses thus:

$D_1(_{2,3 \cdot \cdot \cdot n}) = M_2 \times D_{12} + M_3 \times D_{12} \ldots + M_n \times D_{12}\ M_2 + M_3 \ldots + M_n$

Propagation is possible if either an individual donor mass is less than the tabulated distance from an acceptor or a combined mass is less than the weighted distance from an acceptor.

(c) In determining the distances separating highways, railroads, and inhabited buildings from potential explosions (as prescribed in Table H–21), the sum of all masses which may propagate (i.e., lie at distances less than prescribed in the Table) from either individual or combined donor masses are included. However, when the ammonium nitrate must be included, only 50 percent of its weight shall be used because of its reduced blast effects. In applying Table H–21 to distances from highways, railroads, and inhabited buildings, distances are measured from the nearest edge of potentially explodable material as prescribed in Table H–21, Note 5.

(d) When all or part of a potential acceptor comprises Explosives Class A as defined in DOT regulations, storage in bullet-resistant magazines is required. Safe distances to stores in bullet-resistant magazines may be obtained from the intermagazine distances prescribed in Table H–21.

(e) Barricades must not have line-of-sight openings between potential donors and acceptors which permit blast or missiles to move directly between masses.

(f) Good housekeeping practices shall be maintained around any bin containing ammonium nitrate or blasting agent. This includes keeping weeds and other combustible materials cleared within 25 feet of such bin. Accumulation of spilled product on the ground shall be prevented.

(g)(5) Storage of blasting agents and supplies

(g)(5)(i) Blasting agents and oxidizers used for mixing of blasting agents shall be stored in the manner set forth in this subdivision.

(g)(5)(i)(A) Blasting agents or ammonium nitrate, when stored in conjunction with explosives, shall be stored in the manner set forth in paragraph (c) of this section for explosives. The mass of blasting agents and one-half the mass of ammonium nitrate shall be included when computing the total quantity of explosives for determining distance requirements.

(g)(5)(i)(B) Blasting agents, when stored entirely separate from explosives, may be stored in the manner set forth in paragraph (c) of this section or in one-story warehouses (without basements) which shall be:

(g)(5)(i)(B)(1) Noncombustible or fire resistive;

(g)(5)(i)(B)(2) Constructed so as to eliminate open floor drains and piping into which molten materials could flow and be confined in case of fire;

(g)(5)(i)(B)(3) Weather resistant;

(g)(5)(i)(B)(4) Well ventilated; and

(g)(5)(i)(B)(5) Equipped with a strong door kept securely locked except when open for business.

(g)(5)(i)(C) Semitrailer or full-trailer vans used for highway or onsite transportation of the blasting agents are satisfactory for temporarily storing these materials, provided they are located in accordance with Table H–22 with respect to one another. Trailers shall be provided with substantial means for locking, and the trailer doors shall be kept locked, except during the time of placement and removal of stocks of blasting agents.

(g)(5)(ii) Warehouses used for the storage of blasting agents separate from explosives shall be located as set forth in this subdivision.

(g)(5)(ii)(A) Warehouses used for the storage of blasting agents shall be located in Table H–22 with respect to one another.

(g)(5)(ii)(B) If both blasting agents and ammonium nitrate are handled or stored within the distance limitations prescribed through paragraph (g)(2) of this section, one-half the mass of the ammonium nitrate shall be added to the mass of the blasting agent when computing the total quantity of explosives for determining the proper distance for compliance with Table H–21.

(g)(5)(iii) Smoking, matches, open flames, spark producing devices, and firearms are prohibited inside of or within 50 feet of any warehouse used for the storage of blasting agents. Combustible materials shall not be stored within 50 feet of warehouses used for the storage of blasting agents.

(g)(5)(iv) The interior of warehouses used for the storage of blasting agents shall be kept clean and free from debris and empty containers. Spilled materials shall be cleaned up promptly and safely removed. Combustible materials, flammable liquids, corrosive acids, chlorates, or nitrates shall not be stored in any warehouse used for blasting agents unless separated therefrom by a fire resistive separation of not less than 1 hour resistance. The provisions of this subdivision shall not prohibit the storage of blasting agents together with nonexplosive blasting supplies.

(g)(5)(v) Piles of ammonium nitrate and warehouses containing ammonium nitrate shall be adequately separated from readily combustible fuels.

(g)(5)(vi) Caked oxidizers, either in bags or in bulk, shall not be loosened by blasting.

(g)(5)(vii) Every warehouse used for the storage of blasting agents shall be under the supervision of a competent person.

(g)(6) Transportation of packaged blasting agents

(g)(6)(i) When blasting agents are transported in the same vehicle with explosives, all of the requirements of paragraph (d) of this section shall be complied with.

(g)(6)(ii) Vehicles transporting blasting agents shall only be driven by and be in charge of a driver in possession of a valid motor vehicle operator's license. Such a person shall also be familiar with the State's vehicle and traffic laws.

(g)(6)(iii) No matches, firearms, acids, or other corrosive liquids shall be carried in the bed or body of any vehicle containing blasting agents.

(g)(6)(iv) No person shall be permitted to ride upon, drive, load, or unload a vehicle containing blasting agents while smoking or under the influence of intoxicants, narcotics, or other dangerous drugs.

(g)(6)(v) [Reserved]

(g)(6)(vi) Vehicles transporting blasting agents shall be in safe operating condition at all times.

(g)(7) Use of blasting agents. Persons using blasting agents shall comply with all of the applicable provisions of paragraph (e) of this section.

(h) OI Water gel (Slurry) explosives and blasting agents

(h)(1) General provisions Unless otherwise set forth in this paragraph, water gels shall be transported, stored and used in the same manner as explosives or blasting agents in accordance with the classification of the product.

(h)(2) Types and classifications

(h)(2)(i) Water gels containing a substance in itself classified as an explosive shall be classified as an explosive and manufactured, transported, stored, and used as specified for "explosives" in this section, except as noted in subdivision (iv) of this subparagraph.

(h)(2)(ii) Water gels containing no substance in itself classified as an explosive and which are cap-sensitive as defined in paragraph (a) of this section under Blasting Agent shall be classified as an explosive and manufactured, transported, stored and used as specified for "explosives" in this section.

(h)(2)(iii) Water gels containing no substance in itself classified as an explosive and which are not cap-sensitive as defined in paragraph (a) of this section under Blasting Agent shall be classified as blasting agents and manufactured, transported, stored, and used as specified for "blasting agents" in this section.

(h)(2)(iv) When tests on specific formulations of water gels result in Department of Transportation classification as a Class B explosive, bullet-resistant magazines are not required, see paragraph (c)(2)(ii) of this section.

(h)(3) **Fixed location mixing**

(h)(3)(i) [Reserved]

(h)(3)(ii) Buildings used for the mixing of water gels shall conform to the requirements of this subdivision.

(h)(3)(ii)(A) Buildings shall be of noncombustible construction or sheet metal on wood studs.

(h)(3)(ii)(B) Floors in a mixing plant shall be of concrete or of other nonabsorbent materials.

(h)(3)(ii)(C) Where fuel oil is used all fuel oil storage facilities shall be separated from the mixing plant and located in such a manner that in case of tank rupture, the oil will drain away from the mixing plant building.

(h)(3)(ii)(D) The building shall be well ventilated.

(h)(3)(ii)(E) Heating units that do not depend on combustion processes, when properly designed and located, may be used in the building. All direct sources of heat shall be provided exclusively from units located outside of the mixing building.

(h)(3)(ii)(F) All internal-combustion engines used for electric power generation shall be located outside the mixing plant building, or shall be properly ventilated and isolated by a firewall. The exhaust systems on all such engines shall be located so any spark emission cannot be a hazard to any materials in or adjacent to the plant.

(h)(3)(iii) Ingredients of water gels shall conform to the requirements of this subdivision.

(h)(3)(iii)(A) Ingredients in themselves classified as Class A or Class B explosives shall be stored in conformity with paragraph (c) of this section.

(h)(3)(iii)(B) Nitrate-water solutions may be stored in tank cars, tank trucks, or fixed tanks without quantity or distance limitations. Spills or leaks which may contaminate combustible materials shall be cleaned up immediately.

(h)(3)(iii)(C) Metal powders such as aluminum shall be kept dry and shall be stored in containers or bins which are moisture-resistant or weathertight. Solid fuels shall be used in such manner as to minimize dust explosion hazards.

(h)(3)(iii)(D) Ingredients shall not be stored with incompatible materials.

(h)(3)(iii)(E) Peroxides and chlorates shall not be used.

(h)(3)(iv) Mixing equipment shall comply with the requirements of this subdivision.

(h)(3)(iv)(A) The design of the processing equipment, including mixing and conveying equipment, shall be compatible with the relative sensitivity of the materials being handled. Equipment shall be designed to minimize the possibility of frictional heating, compaction, overloading, and confinement.

(h)(3)(iv)(B) Both equipment and handling procedures shall be designed to prevent the introduction of foreign objects or materials.

(h)(3)(iv)(C) Mixers, pumps, valves, and related equipment shall be designed to permit regular and periodic flushing, cleaning, dismantling, and inspection.

(h)(3)(iv)(D) All electrical equipment including wiring, switches, controls, motors, and lights, shall conform to the requirements of Subpart S of this part.

(h)(3)(iv)(E) All electric motors and generators shall be provided with suitable overload protection devices. Electrical generators, motors, proportioning devices, and all other electrical enclosures shall be electrically bonded. The grounding conductor to all such electrical equipment shall be effectively bonded to the service-entrance ground connection and to all equipment ground connections in a manner so as to provide a continuous path to ground.

(h)(3)(v) Mixing facilities shall comply with the fire prevention requirements of this subdivision.

(h)(3)(v)(A) The mixing, loading, and ingredient transfer areas where residues or spilled materials may accumulate shall be cleaned periodically. A cleaning and collection system for dangerous residues shall be provided.

(h)(3)(v)(B) A daily visual inspection shall be made of mixing, conveying, and electrical equipment to establish that such equipment is in good operating condition. A program of systematic maintenance shall be conducted on regular schedule.

(h)(3)(v)(C) Heaters which are not dependent on the combustion process within the heating unit may be used within the confines of processing buildings, or compartments, if provided with temperature and safety controls and located away from combustible materials and the finished product.

(h)(4) **Bulk delivery and mixing vehicles**

(h)(4)(i) The design of vehicles shall comply with the requirements of this subdivision.

(h)(4)(i)(A) Vehicles used over public highways for the bulk transportation of water gels or of ingredients classified as dangerous commodities, shall meet the requirements of the Department of Transportation and shall meet the requirements of paragraphs (d) and (g)(6) of this section.

(h)(4)(i)(B) When electric power is supplied by a self-contained motor generator located on the vehicle the generator shall be at a point separate from where the water gel is discharged.

(h)(4)(i)(C) The design of processing equipment and general requirements shall conform to subparagraphs (3)(iii) and (iv) of this paragraph.

(h)(4)(i)(D) A positive action parking brake, which will set the wheel brakes on at least one axle shall be provided on vehicles when equipped with air brakes and shall be used during bulk delivery operations. Wheel chocks shall supplement parking brakes whenever conditions may require.

(h)(4)(ii) Operation of bulk delivery and mixing vehicles shall comply with the requirements of this subdivision.

(h)(4)(ii)(A) The placarding requirements contained in DOT regulations apply to vehicles carrying water gel explosives or blasting agents.

(h)(4)(ii)(B) The operator shall be trained in the safe operation of the vehicle together with its mixing, conveying, and related equipment. He shall be familiar with the commodities being delivered and the general procedure for handling emergency situations.

(h)(4)(ii)(C) The hauling of either blasting caps or other explosives, but not both, shall be permitted on bulk trucks provided that a special wood or nonferrous-lined container is installed for the explosives. Such blasting caps or other explosives shall be in DOT-specified shipping containers; see 49 CFR chapter I.

(h)(4)(ii)(D) No person shall be allowed to smoke, carry matches or any flame-producing device, or carry any firearms while in or about bulk vehicles effecting the mixing, transfer, or down-the-hole loading of water gels at or near the blasting site.

(h)(4)(ii)(E) Caution shall be exercised in the movement of the vehicle in the blasting area to avoid driving the vehicle over or dragging hoses over firing lines, cap wires, or explosive materials. The employer shall furnish the driver the assistance of a second person to guide the driver's movements.

(h)(4)(ii)(F) No intransit mixing of materials shall be performed.

(h)(4)(ii)(G) The location chosen for water gel or ingredient transfer from a support vehicle into the borehole loading vehicle shall be away from the blasthole site when the boreholes are loaded or in the process of being loaded.

(i) **Storage of ammonium nitrate**

(i)(1) **Scope and definitions**

(i)(1)(i)(A) Except as provided in paragraph (i)(1)(i)(D) of this paragraph applies to the storage of ammonium nitrate in the form of crystals, flakes, grains, or prills including fertilizer grade, dynamite grade, nitrous oxide grade, technical grade, and other mixtures containing 60 percent or more ammonium nitrate by weight but does not apply to blasting agents.

(i)(1)(i)(B) This paragraph does not apply to the transportation of ammonium nitrate.

(i)(1)(i)(C) This paragraph does not apply to storage under the jurisdiction of and in compliance with the regulations of the U.S. Coast Guard (see 46 CFR parts 146–149).

(i)(1)(i)(D) The storage of ammonium nitrate and ammonium nitrate mixtures that are more sensitive than allowed by the "Definition of Test Procedures for Ammonium Nitrate Fertilizer" is prohibited.

(i)(1)(ii)(A) [Reserved]

(i)(1)(ii)(B) The standards for ammonium nitrate (nitrous oxide grade) are those found in the "Specifications, Properties, and Recommendations for Packaging, Transportation, Storage, and Use of Ammonium Nitrate", available from the Compressed Gas Association, Inc., which is incorporated by reference as specified in §1910.6.

(i)(2) General provisions

(i)(2)(i) This paragraph applies to all persons storing, having, or keeping ammonium nitrate, and to the owner or lessee of any building, premises, or structure in which ammonium nitrate is stored in quantities of 1,000 pounds or more.

(i)(2)(ii) Approval of large quantity storage shall be subject to due consideration of the fire and explosion hazards, including exposure to toxic vapors from burning or decomposing ammonium nitrate.

(i)(2)(iii)(A) Storage buildings shall not have basements unless the basements are open on at least one side. Storage buildings shall not be over one story in height.

(i)(2)(iii)(B) Storage buildings shall have adequate ventilation or be of a construction that will be self-ventilating in the event of fire.

(i)(2)(iii)(C) The wall on the exposed side of a storage building within 50 feet of a combustible building, forest, piles of combustible materials and similar exposure hazards shall be of fire-resistive construction. In lieu of the fire-resistive wall, other suitable means of exposure protection such as a free standing wall may be used. The roof coverings shall be Class C or better, as defined in the Manual on Roof Coverings, NFPA 203M–1970, which is incorporated by reference as specified in §1910.6.

(i)(2)(iii)(D) All flooring in storage and handling areas, shall be of noncombustible material or protected against impregnation by ammonium nitrate and shall be without open drains, traps, tunnels, pits, or pockets into which any molten ammonium nitrate could flow and be confined in the event of fire.

(i)(2)(iii)(E) The continued use of an existing storage building or structure not in strict conformity with this paragraph may be approved in cases where such continued use will not constitute a hazard to life.

(i)(2)(iii)(F) Buildings and structures shall be dry and free from water seepage through the roof, walls, and floors.

(i)(3) Storage of ammonium nitrate in bags, drums, or other containers

(i)(3)(i)(A) Bags and containers used for ammonium nitrate must comply with specifications and standards required for use in interstate commerce (see 49 CFR chapter I).

(i)(3)(i)(B) Containers used on the premises in the actual manufacturing or processing need not comply with provisions of paragraph (i)(3)(i)(A) of this paragraph.

(i)(3)(ii)(A) Containers of ammonium nitrate shall not be accepted for storage when the temperature of the ammonium nitrate exceeds 130 °F.

(i)(3)(ii)(B) Bags of ammonium nitrate shall not be stored within 30 inches of the storage building walls and partitions.

(i)(3)(ii)(C) The height of piles shall not exceed 20 feet. The width of piles shall not exceed 20 feet and the length 50 feet except that where the building is of noncombustible construction or is protected by automatic sprinklers the length of piles shall not be limited. In no case shall the ammonium nitrate be stacked closer than 36 inches below the roof or supporting and spreader beams overhead.

(i)(3)(ii)(D) Aisles shall be provided to separate piles by a clear space of not less than 3 feet in width. At least one service or main aisle in the storage area shall be not less than 4 feet in width.

(i)(4) Storage of bulk ammonium nitrate

(i)(4)(i)(A) Warehouses shall have adequate ventilation or be capable of adequate ventilation in case of fire.

(i)(4)(i)(B) Unless constructed of noncombustible material or unless adequate facilities for fighting a roof fire are available, bulk storage structures shall not exceed a height of 40 feet.

(i)(4)(ii)(A) Bins shall be clean and free of materials which may contaminate ammonium nitrate.

(i)(4)(ii)(B) Due to the corrosive and reactive properties of ammonium nitrate, and to avoid contamination, galvanized iron, copper, lead, and zinc shall not be used in a bin construction unless suitably protected. Aluminum bins and wooden bins protected against impregnation by ammonium nitrate are permissible. The partitions dividing the ammonium nitrate storage from other products which would contaminate the ammonium nitrate shall be of tight construction.

(i)(4)(ii)(C) The ammonium nitrate storage bins or piles shall be clearly identified by signs reading "Ammonium Nitrate" with letters at least 2 inches high.

(i)(4)(iii)(A) Piles or bins shall be so sized and arranged that all material in the pile is moved out periodically in order to minimize possible caking of the stored ammonium nitrate.

(i)(4)(iii)(B) Height or depth of piles shall be limited by the pressure-setting tendency of the product. However, in no case shall the ammonium nitrate be piled higher at any point than 36 inches below the roof or supporting and spreader beams overhead.

(i)(4)(iii)(C) Ammonium nitrate shall not be accepted for storage when the temperature of the product exceeds 130 °F.

(i)(4)(iii)(D) Dynamite, other explosives, and blasting agents shall not be used to break up or loosen caked ammonium nitrate.

(i)(5) Contaminants

(i)(5)(i)(A) Ammonium nitrate shall be in a separate building or shall be separated by approved type firewalls of not less than 1 hour fire-resistance rating from storage of organic chemicals, acids, or other corrosive materials, materials that may require blasting during processing or handling, compressed flammable gases, flammable and combustible materials or other contaminating substances, including but not limited to animal fats, baled cotton, baled rags, baled scrap paper, bleaching powder, burlap or cotton bags, caustic soda, coal, coke, charcoal, cork, camphor, excelsior, fibers of any kind, fish oils, fish meal, foam rubber, hay, lubricating oil, linseed oil, or other oxidizable or drying oils, naphthalene, oakum, oiled clothing, oiled paper, oiled textiles, paint, straw, sawdust, wood shavings, or vegetable oils. Walls referred to in this subdivision need extend only to the underside of the roof.

(i)(5)(i)(B) In lieu of separation walls, ammonium nitrate may be separated from the materials referred to in paragraph (a) of this section by a space of at least 30 feet.

(i)(5)(i)(C) Flammable liquids such as gasoline, kerosene, solvents, and light fuel oils shall not be stored on the premises except when such storage conforms to §1910.106, and when walls and sills or curbs are provided in accordance with paragraphs (i)(5)(i)(A) or (B) of this section.

(i)(5)(i)(D) LP-Gas shall not be stored on the premises except when such storage conforms to §1910.110.

(i)(5)(ii)(A) Sulfur and finely divided metals shall not be stored in the same building with ammonium nitrate except when such storage conforms to paragraphs (a) through (h) of this section.

(i)(5)(ii)(B) Explosives and blasting agents shall not be stored in the same building with ammonium nitrate except on the premises of makers, distributors, and user-compounders of explosives or blasting agents.

(i)(5)(ii)(C) Where explosives or blasting agents are stored in separate buildings, other than on the premises of makers, distributors, and user-compounders of explosives or blasting agents, they shall be separated from the ammonium nitrate by the distances and/or barricades specified in Table H–22 of this Subpart, but by not less than 50 feet.

(i)(5)(ii)(D) Storage and/or operations on the premises of makers, distributors, and user-compounders of explosives or blasting agents shall be in conformity with paragraphs (a) through (h) of this section.

(i)(6) General precautions

(i)(6)(i) Electrical installations shall conform to the requirements of Subpart S of this part, for ordinary locations. They shall be designed to minimize damage from corrosion.

(i)(6)(ii) In areas where lightning storms are prevalent, lightning protection shall be provided. (See the Lightning Protection Code, NFPA 78–1968, which is incorporated by reference as specified in §1910.6.)

(i)(6)(iii) Provisions shall be made to prevent unauthorized personnel from entering the ammonium nitrate storage area.

(i)(7) Fire protection

(i)(7)(i) Not more than 2,500 tons (2270 tonnes) of bagged ammonium nitrate shall be stored in a building or structure not equipped with an automatic sprinkler system. Sprinkler systems shall be of the approved type and installed in accordance with §1910.159.

(i)(7)(ii)(A) Suitable fire control devices such as small hose or portable fire extinguishers shall be provided throughout the warehouse and in the loading and unloading areas. Suitable fire control devices shall comply with the requirements of §1910.157 and §1910.158.

(i)(7)(ii)(B) Water supplies and fire hydrants shall be available in accordance with recognized good practices.

(j) Small arms ammunition, small arms primers, and small arms propellants

(j)(1) Scope This paragraph does not apply to in-process storage and intraplant transportation during manufacture of small arms ammunition, small arms primers, and smokeless propellants.

(j)(2) Small arms ammunition

(j)(2)(i) No quantity limitations are imposed on the storage of small arms ammunition in warehouses, retail stores, and other general occupancy facilities, except those imposed by limitations of storage facilities.

(j)(2)(ii) Small arms ammunition shall be separated from flammable liquids, flammable solids as classified in 49 CFR part 172, and from oxidizing materials, by a fire-resistive wall of 1-hour rating or by a distance of 25 feet.

(j)(2)(iii) Small arms ammunition shall not be stored together with Class A or Class B explosives unless the storage facility is adequate for this latter storage.

(j)(3) **Smokeless propellants**

(j)(3)(i) All smokeless propellants shall be stored in shipping containers specified in 49 CFR 173.93 for smokeless propellants.

(j)(3)(ii) [Reserved]

(j)(3)(iii) Commercial stocks of smokeless propellants over 20 pounds and not more than 100 pounds shall be stored in portable wooden boxes having walls of at least 1 inch nominal thickness.

(j)(3)(iv) Commercial stocks in quantities not to exceed 750 pounds shall be stored in nonportable storage cabinets having wooden walls of at least 1 inch nominal thickness. Not more than 400 pounds shall be permitted in any one cabinet.

(j)(3)(v) Quantities in excess of 750 pounds shall be stored in magazines in accordance with paragraph (c) of this section.

(j)(4) **Small arms ammunition primers**

(j)(4)(i) Small arms ammunition primers shall not be stored except in the original shipping container in accordance with the requirements of 49 CFR 173.107 for small arms ammunition primers.

(j)(4)(ii) [Reserved]

(j)(4)(iii) Small arms ammunition primers shall be separated from flammable liquids, flammable solids as classified in 49 CFR part 172, and oxidizing materials by a fire-resistive wall of 1-hour rating or by a distance of 25 feet.

(j)(4)(iv) Not more than 750,000 small arms ammunition primers shall be stored in any one building, except as provided in paragraph (j)(4)(v) of this paragraph. Not more than 100,000 shall be stored in any one pile. Piles shall be at least 15 feet apart.

(j)(4)(v) Quantities of small arms ammunition primers in excess of 750,000 shall be stored in magazines in accordance with paragraph (c) of this section.

(k) **Scope**

(k)(1) This section applies to the manufacture, keeping, having, storage, sale, transportation, and use of explosives, blasting agents, and pyrotechnics. The section does not apply to the sale and use (public display) of pyrotechnics, commonly known as fireworks, nor the use of explosives in the form prescribed by the official U.S. Pharmacopeia.

(k)(2) [OI] The manufacture of explosives as defined in paragraph (a)(3) of this section shall also meet the requirements contained in §1910.119.

(k)(3) [OI] The manufacture of pyrotechnics as defined in paragraph (a)(10) of this section shall also meet the requirements contained in §1910.119.

[39 FR 23502, June 27, 1974, as amended at 43 FR 49747, Oct. 24, 1978; 45 FR 60704, Sept. 12, 1980; 53 FR 12122, Apr. 12, 1988; 57 FR 6403, Feb. 24, 1992; 58 FR 35309, June 30, 1993; 61 FR 9237, Mar. 7, 1996; 63 FR 33466, June 18, 1998]

§1910.110 [OI] Storage and handling of liquefied petroleum gases

(a) **Definitions applicable to this section** As used in this section:

(a)(1) **API-ASME container**—A container constructed in accordance with the requirements of paragraph (b)(3)(iii) of this section.

(a)(2) **ASME container**—A container constructed in accordance with the requirements of paragraph (b)(3)(i) of this section.

(a)(3) **Container assembly**—An assembly consisting essentially of the container and fittings for all container openings, including shutoff valves, excess flow valves, liquid-level gaging devices, safety relief devices, and protective housing.

(a)(4) **Containers**—All vessels, such as tanks, cylinders, or drums, used for transportation or storing liquefied petroleum gases.

(a)(5) **DOT**—Department of Transportation.

(a)(6) **DOT container**—A container constructed in accordance with the applicable requirements of 49 CFR chapter 1.

(a)(7) **"Liquefied petroleum gases"**—"LPG" and "LP-Gas"—Any material which is composed predominantly of any of the following hydrocarbons, or mixtures of them; propane, propylene, butanes (normal butane or iso-butane), and butylenes.

(a)(8) **Movable fuel storage tenders or farm carts**—Containers not in excess of 1,200 gallons water capacity, equipped with wheels to be towed from one location of usage to another. They are basically nonhighway vehicles, but may occasionally be moved over public roads or highways. They are used as a fuel supply for farm tractors, construction machinery and similar equipment.

(a)(9) **P.S.I.G.**—pounds per square inch gauge.

(a)(10) **P.S.I.A.**—pounds per square inch absolute.

(a)(11) **Systems**—an assembly of equipment consisting essentially of the container or containers, major devices such as vaporizers, safety relief valves, excess flow valves, regulators, and piping connecting such parts.

(a)(12) **Vaporizer-burner**—an integral vaporizer-burner unit, dependent upon the heat generated by the burner as the source of heat to vaporize the liquid used for dehydrators or dryers.

(a)(13) **Ventilation, adequate**—when specified for the prevention of fire during normal operation, ventilation shall be considered adequate when the concentration of the gas in a gas-air mixture does not exceed 25 percent of the lower flammable limit.

(a)(14) **Approved**—unless otherwise indicated, listing or approval by a nationally recognized testing laboratory. Refer to §1910.7 for definition of nationally recognized testing laboratory.

(a)(15) **Listed**—see "approved" in §1910.110(a)(14).

(a)(16) **DOT Specifications**—regulations of the Department of Transportation published in 49 CFR chapter I.

(a)(17)–(18) [Reserved]

(a)(19) **DOT cylinders**—cylinders meeting the requirements of 49 CFR chapter I.

(b) **Basic rules**

(b)(1) **Odorizing gases**

(b)(1)(i) All liquefied petroleum gases shall be effectively odorized by an approved agent of such character as to indicate positively, by distinct odor, the presence of gas down to concentration in air of not over one-fifth the lower limit of flammability. Odorization, however, is not required if harmful in the use of further processing of the liquefied petroleum gas, or if odorization will serve no useful purpose as a warning agent in such use or further processing.

(b)(1)(ii) The odorization requirement of paragraph (b)(1)(i) of this section shall be considered to be met by the use of 1.0 pounds of ethyl mercaptan, 1.0 pounds of thiophane or 1.4 pounds of amyl mercaptan per 10,000 gallons of LP-Gas. However, this listing of odorants and quantities shall not exclude the use of other odorants that meet the odorization requirements of paragraph (b)(1)(i) of this section.

(b)(2) **Approval of equipment and systems**

(b)(2)(i) Each system utilizing DOT containers in accordance with 49 CFR part 178 shall have its container valves, connectors, manifold valve assemblies, and regulators approved.

(b)(2)(ii) Each system for domestic or commercial use utilizing containers of 2,000 gallons or less water capacity, other than those constructed in accordance with 49 CFR part 178, shall consist of a container assembly and one or more regulators, and may include other parts. The system as a unit or the container assembly as a unit, and the regulator or regulators, shall be individually listed.

(b)(2)(iii) In systems utilizing containers of over 2,000 gallons water capacity, each regulator, container valve, excess flow valve, gaging device, and relief valve installed on or at the container, shall have its correctness as to design, construction, and performance determined by listing by a nationally recognized testing laboratory. Refer to §1910.7 for definition of nationally recognized testing laboratory.

(b)(3) **Requirements for construction and original test of containers**

(b)(3)(i) Containers used with systems embodied in paragraphs (d), (e), (g), and (h) of this section, except as provided in paragraphs (e)(3)(iii) and (g)(2)(i) of this section, shall be designed, constructed, and tested in accordance with the Rules for Construction of Unfired Pressure Vessels, section VIII, Division 1, American Society of Mechanical Engineers (ASME) Boiler and Pressure Vessel Code, 1968 edition, which is incorporated by reference as specified in §1910.6.

(b)(3)(ii) Containers constructed according to the 1949 and earlier editions of the ASME Code do not have to comply with paragraphs U–2 through U–10 and U–19 thereof. Containers constructed according to paragraph U–70 in the 1949 and earlier editions are not authorized.

(b)(3)(iii) Containers designed, constructed, and tested prior to July 1, 1961, according to the Code for Unfired Pressure Vessels for Petroleum Liquids and Gases, 1951 edition with 1954 Addenda, of the American Petroleum Institute and the American Society of Mechanical Engineers, which is incorporated by reference as specified in §1910.6, shall be considered in conformance. Containers constructed according to API-ASME Code do not have to comply with section I or with Appendix to section I. Paragraphs W–601 to W–606 inclusive in the 1943 and earlier editions do not apply.

(b)(3)(iv) The provisions of paragraph (b)(3)(i) of this section shall not be construed as prohibiting the continued use or reinstallation of containers constructed and maintained in accordance with the standard for the Storage and Handling of Liquefied Petroleum Gases NFPA No. 58 in effect at the time of fabrication.

(b)(3)(v) Containers used with systems embodied in paragraph (b), (d)(3)(iii), and (f) of this section, shall be constructed, tested, and stamped in accordance with DOT specifications effective at the date of their manufacture.

(b)(4) **Welding of containers**

(b)(4)(i) Welding to the shell, head, or any other part of the container subject to internal pressure, shall be done in compliance with the code under which the tank was fabricated. Other welding is permitted only on saddle plates, lugs, or brackets attached to the container by the tank manufacturer.

(b)(4)(ii) Where repair or modification involving welding of DOT containers is required, the container shall be returned to a qualified manufacturer making containers of the same type, and the repair or modification made in compliance with DOT regulations.

(b)(5) **Markings on containers**

(b)(5)(i) Each container covered in paragraph (b)(3)(i) of this section, except as provided in paragraph (b)(3)(iv) of this section shall be marked as specified in the following:

(b)(5)(i)(A) With a marking identifying compliance with, and other markings required by, the rules of the reference under which the container is constructed; or with the stamp and other markings required by the National Board of Boiler and Pressure Vessel Inspectors;

(b)(5)(i)(B) With notation as to whether the container is designed for underground or aboveground installation or both. If intended for both and different style hoods are provided, the marking shall indicate the proper hood for each type of installation;

(b)(5)(i)(C) With the name and address of the supplier of the container, or with the trade name of the container;

(b)(5)(i)(D) With the water capacity of the container in pounds or gallons, U.S. Standard;

(b)(5)(i)(E) With the pressure in p.s.i.g., for which the container is designed;

(b)(5)(i)(F) With the wording "This container shall not contain a product having a vapor pressure in excess of ___ p.s.i.g. at 100 °F.," see subparagraph (14)(viii) of this paragraph;

(b)(5)(i)(G) With the tare weight in pounds or other identified unit of weight for containers with a water capacity of 300 pounds or less;

(b)(5)(i)(H) With marking indicating the maximum level to which the container may be filled with liquid at temperatures between 20 °F. and 130 °F., except on containers provided with fixed maximum level indicators or which are filled by weighing. Markings shall be increments of not more than 20 °F. This marking may be located on the liquid level gaging device;

(b)(5)(i)(I) With the outside surface area in square feet.

(b)(5)(ii) Markings specified shall be on a metal nameplate attached to the container and located in such a manner as to remain visible after the container is installed.

(b)(5)(iii) When LP-Gas and one or more other gases are stored or used in the same area, the containers shall be marked to identify their content. Marking shall conform to the marking requirements set forth in §1910.253(b)(1)(ii).

(b)(6) [OI] **Location of containers and regulating equipment**

(b)(6)(i) Containers, and first stage regulating equipment if used, shall be located outside of buildings, except under one or more of the following:

(b)(6)(i)(A) In buildings used exclusively for container charging, vaporization pressure reduction, gas mixing, gas manufacturing, or distribution;

(b)(6)(i)(B) When portable use is necessary and in accordance with paragraph (c)(5) of this section;

(b)(6)(i)(C) LP-Gas fueled stationary or portable engines in accordance with paragraph (e) (11) or (12) of this section;

(b)(6)(i)(D) LP-Gas fueled industrial trucks used in accordance with paragraph (e)(13) of this section;

(b)(6)(i)(E) LP-Gas fueled vehicles garaged in accordance with paragraph (e)(14) of this section;

(b)(6)(i)(F) Containers awaiting use or resale when stored in accordance with paragraph (f) of this section.

(b)(6)(ii) [OI] Each individual container shall be located with respect to the nearest important building or group of buildings in accordance with Table H–23.

Table H–23

Water capacity per container	Minimum distances		
	Containers		Between aboveground containers
	Underground	Aboveground	
Less than 125 gals[1]	10 feet	None	None.
125 to 250 gals	10 feet	10 feet	None.
251 to 500 gals	10 feet	10 feet	3 feet.
501 to 2,000 gals	25 feet[2]	25 feet[2]	3 feet.
2,001 to 30,000 gals	50 feet	50 feet	5 feet.
30,001 to 70,000 gals	50 feet	75 feet[3]	
70,001 to 90,000 gals	50 feet	100 feet[3]	

[1] If the aggregate water capacity of a multi-container installation at a consumer site is 501 gallons or greater, the minimum distance shall comply with the appropriate portion of this table, applying the aggregate capacity rather than the capacity per container. If more than one installation is made, each installation shall be separated from another installation by at least 25 feet. Do not apply the MINIMUM DISTANCES BETWEEN ABOVE-GROUND CONTAINERS to such installations.

[2] The above distance requirements may be reduced to not less than 10 feet for a single container of 1,200 gallons water capacity or less, providing such a container is at least 25 feet from any other LP-Gas container of more than 125 gallons water capacity.

[3] ¼ of sum of diameters of adjacent containers.

(b)(6)(iii) Containers installed for use shall not be stacked one above the other.

(b)(6)(iv) [Reserved]

(b)(6)(v) In the case of buildings devoted exclusively to gas manufacturing and distributing operations, the distances required by Table H–23 may be reduced provided that in no case shall containers of water capacity exceeding 500 gallons be located closer than 10 feet to such gas manufacturing and distributing buildings.

(b)(6)(vi) Readily ignitible material such as weeds and long dry grass shall be removed within 10 feet of any container.

(b)(6)(vii) The minimum separation between liquefied petroleum gas containers and flammable liquid tanks shall be 20 feet, and the minimum separation between a container and the centerline of the dike shall be 10 feet. The foregoing provision shall not apply when LP-Gas containers of 125 gallons or less capacity are installed adjacent to Class III flammable liquid tanks of 275 gallons or less capacity.

(b)(6)(viii) Suitable means shall be taken to prevent the accumulation of flammable liquids under adjacent liquefied petroleum gas containers, such as by diking, diversion curbs, or grading.

(b)(6)(ix) When dikes are used with flammable liquid tanks, no liquefied petroleum gas containers shall be located within the diked area.

(b)(7) **Container valves and container accessories**

(b)(7)(i) Valves, fittings, and accessories connected directly to the container including primary shutoff valves, shall have a rated working pressure of at least 250 p.s.i.g. and shall be of material and design suitable for LP-Gas service. Cast iron shall not be used for container valves, fittings, and accessories. This does not prohibit the use of container valves made of malleable or nodular iron.

(b)(7)(ii) Connections to containers, except safety relief connections, liquid level gaging devices, and plugged openings, shall have shutoff valves located as close to the container as practicable.

(b)(7)(iii) Excess flow valves, where required shall close automatically at the rated flows of vapor or liquid as specified by the manufacturer. The connections or line including valves, fittings, etc., being protected by an excess flow valve shall have a greater capacity than the rated flow of the excess flow valve.

(b)(7)(iv) Liquid level gaging devices which are so constructed that outward flow of container contents shall not exceed that passed by a No. 54 drill size opening, need not be equipped with excess flow valves.

(b)(7)(v) Openings from container or through fittings attached directly on container to which pressure gage connection is made, need not be equipped with shutoff or excess flow valves if such openings are restricted to not larger than No. 54 drill size opening.

(b)(7)(vi) Except as provided in paragraph (c)(5)(i)(B) of this section, excess flow and back pressure check valves where required by this section shall be located inside of the container or at a point outside where the line enters the container; in the latter case, installation shall be made in such manner that any undue strain beyond the excess flow or back pressure check valve will not cause breakage between the container and such valve.

(b)(7)(vii) Excess flow valves shall be designed with a bypass, not to exceed a No. 60 drill size opening to allow equalization of pressures.

(b)(7)(viii) Containers of more than 30 gallons water capacity and less than 2,000 gallons water capacity, filled on a volumetric basis, and manufactured after December 1, 1963, shall be equipped for filling into the vapor space.

(b)(8) Piping—including pipe, tubing, and fittings

(b)(8)(i) Pipe, except as provided in paragraphs (e)(6)(i) and (g)(10)(iii), of this section shall be wrought iron or steel (black or galvanized), brass, copper, or aluminum alloy. Aluminum alloy pipe shall be at least Schedule 40 in accordance with the specifications for Aluminum Alloy Pipe, American National Standards Institute (ANSI) H38.7–1969 (ASTM, B241–69), which is incorporated by reference as specified in §1910.6, except that the use of alloy 5456 is prohibited and shall be suitably marked at each end of each length indicating compliance with American National Standard Institute Specifications. Aluminum Alloy pipe shall be protected against external corrosion when it is in contact with dissimilar metals other than galvanized steel, or its location is subject to repeated wetting by such liquids as water (except rain water), detergents, sewage, or leaking from other piping, or it passes through flooring, plaster, masonry, or insulation. Galvanized sheet steel or pipe, galvanized inside and out, may be considered suitable protection. The maximum nominal pipe size for aluminum pipe shall be three-fourths inch and shall not be used for pressures exceeding 20 p.s.i.g. Aluminum alloy pipe shall not be installed within 6 inches of the ground.

(b)(8)(i)(A) Vapor piping with operating pressures not exceeding 125 p.s.i.g. shall be suitable for a working pressure of at least 125 p.s.i.g. Pipe shall be at least Schedule 40 (ASTM A–53–69, Grade B Electric Resistance Welded and Electric Flash Welded Pipe, which is incorporated by reference as specified in §1910.6, or equal).

(b)(8)(i)(B) Vapor piping with operating pressures over 125 p.s.i.g. and all liquid piping shall be suitable for a working pressure of at least 250 p.s.i.g. Pipe shall be at least Schedule 80 if joints are threaded or threaded and back welded. At least Schedule 40 (ASTM A–53–69 Grade B Electric Resistance Welded and Electric Flash Welded Pipe or equal) shall be used if joints are welded, or welded and flanged.

(b)(8)(ii) Tubing shall be seamless and of copper, brass, steel, or aluminum alloy. Copper tubing shall be of type K or L or equivalent as covered in the Specification for Seamless Copper Water Tube, ANSI H23.1–1970 (ASTM B88–69), which is incorporated by reference as specified in §1910.6. Aluminum alloy tubing shall be of Type A or B or equivalent as covered in Specification ASTM B210–68 (which is incorporated by reference as specified in §1910.6) and shall be suitably marked every 18 inches indicating compliance with ASTM Specifications. The minimum nominal wall thickness of copper tubing and aluminum alloy tubing shall be as specified in Table H–24 and Table H–25.

Aluminum alloy tubing shall be protected against external corrosion when it is in contact with dissimilar metals other than galvanized steel, or its location is subject to repeated wetting by liquids such as water (except rainwater), detergents, sewage, or leakage from other piping, or it passes through flooring, plaster, masonry, or insulation. Galvanized sheet steel or pipe, galvanized inside and out, may be considered suitable protection. The maximum outside diameter for aluminum alloy tubing shall be three-fourths inch and shall not be used for pressures exceeding 20 p.s.i.g. Aluminum alloy tubing shall not be installed within 6 inches of the ground.

Table H–24
Wall Thickness of Copper Tubing[1]

Standard size (inches)	Nominal outside diameter (inches)	Nominal wall thickness (inches)	
		Type K	Type L
¼	0.375	0.035	0.030
⅜	0.500	0.049	0.035
½	0.625	0.049	0.040
⅝	0.750	0.049	0.042
¾	0.875	0.065	0.045
1	1.125	0.065	0.050
1¼	1.375	0.065	0.055
1½	1.625	0.072	0.060
2	2.125	0.083	0.070

[1] Based on data in Specification for Seamless Copper Water Tube, ANSI H23.1–1970 (ASTM B–88–69).

Note: The standard size by which tube is designated is 1/8 inch smaller than its nominal outside diameter.

Table H–25
Wall Thickness of Aluminum Alloy Tubing[1]

Outside diameter (inches)	Nominal wall thickness (inches)	
	Type A	Type B
⅜	0.035	0.049
½	0.035	0.049
⅝	0.042	0.049
¾	0.049	0.058

[1] Based on data in Standard Specification for Aluminum-Alloy Drawn Seamless Coiled Tubes for Special Purpose Applications, ASTM B210–68.

(b)(8)(iii) In systems where the gas in liquid form without pressure reduction enters the building, only heavy walled seamless brass or copper tubing with an internal diameter not greater than three thirty-seconds inch, and a wall thickness of not less than three sixty-fourths inch shall be used. This requirement shall not apply to research and experimental laboratories, buildings, or separate fire divisions of buildings used exclusively for housing internal combustion engines, and to commercial gas plants or bulk stations where containers are charged, nor to industrial vaporizer buildings, nor to buildings, structures, or equipment under construction or undergoing major renovation.

(b)(8)(iv) Pipe joints may be screwed, flanged, welded, soldered, or brazed with a material having a melting point exceeding 1,000 °F. Joints on seamless copper, brass, steel, or aluminum alloy gas tubing shall be made by means of approved gas tubing fittings, or soldered or brazed with a material having a melting point exceeding 1,000 °F.

(b)(8)(v) For operating pressures of 125 p.s.i.g. or less, fittings shall be designed for a pressure of at least 125 p.s.i.g. For operating pressures above 125 p.s.i.g., fittings shall be designed for a minimum of 250 p.s.i.g.

(b)(8)(vi) The use of threaded cast iron pipe fittings such as ells, tees, crosses, couplings, and unions is prohibited. Aluminum alloy fittings shall be used with aluminum alloy pipe and tubing. Insulated fittings shall be used where aluminum alloy pipe or tubing connects with a dissimilar metal.

(b)(8)(vii) Strainers, regulators, meters, compressors, pumps, etc., are not to be considered as pipe fittings. This does not prohibit the use of malleable, nodular, or higher strength gray iron for such equipment.

(b)(8)(viii) All materials such as valve seats, packing, gaskets, diaphragms, etc., shall be of such quality as to be resistant to the action of liquefied petroleum gas under the service conditions to which they are subjected.

(b)(8)(ix) All piping, tubing, or hose shall be tested after assembly and proved free from leaks at not less than normal operating pressures. After installation, piping and tubing of all domestic and commercial systems shall be tested and proved free of leaks using a manometer or equivalent device that will indicate a drop in pressure. Test shall not be made with a flame.

(b)(8)(x) Provision shall be made to compensate for expansion, contraction, jarring, and vibration, and for settling. This may be accomplished by flexible connections.

(b)(8)(xi) Piping outside buildings may be buried, above ground, or both, but shall be well supported and protected against physical damage. Where soil conditions warrant, all piping shall be protected against corrosion. Where condensation may occur, the piping shall be pitched back to the container, or suitable means shall be provided for revaporization of the condensate.

(b)(9) Hose specifications

(b)(9)(i) Hose shall be fabricated of materials that are resistant to the action of LP-Gas in the liquid and vapor phases. If wire braid is used for reinforcing the hose, it shall be of corrosion-resistant material such as stainless steel.

(b)(9)(ii) Hose subject to container pressure shall be marked "LP-Gas" or "LPG" at not greater than 10-foot intervals.

(b)(9)(iii) Hose subject to container pressure shall be designed for a bursting pressure of not less than 1,250 p.s.i.g.

(b)(9)(iv) Hose subject to container pressure shall have its correctness as to design construction and performance determined by being listed (see §1910.110(a)(15)).

(b)(9)(v) Hose connections subject to container pressure shall be capable of withstanding, without leakage, a test pressure of not less than 500 p.s.i.g.

(b)(9)(vi) Hose and hose connections on the low-pressure side of the regulator or reducing valve shall be designed for a bursting pressure of not less than 125 p.s.i.g. or five times the set pressure of the relief devices protecting that portion of the system, whichever is higher.

(b)(9)(vii) Hose may be used on the low-pressure side of regulators to connect to other than domestic and commercial gas appliances under the following conditions:

(b)(9)(vii)(A) The appliances connected with hose shall be portable and need a flexible connection;

(b)(9)(vii)(B) For use inside buildings the hose shall be of minimum practical length, but shall not exceed 6 feet except as provided in paragraph (c)(5)(i)(g) of this section and shall not extend from one room to another, nor pass through any walls, partitions, ceilings, or floors. Such hose shall not be concealed from view or used in a concealed location. For use outside of buildings, the hose may exceed this length but shall be kept as short as practical;

(b)(9)(vii)(C) The hose shall be approved and shall not be used where it is likely to be subjected to temperatures above 125 °F. The hose shall be securely connected to the appliance and the use of rubber slip ends shall not be permitted;

(b)(9)(vii)(D) The shutoff valve for an appliance connected by hose shall be in the metal pipe or tubing and not at the appliance end of the hose. When shutoff valves are installed close to each other, precautions shall be taken to prevent operation of the wrong valve;

(b)(9)(vii)(E) Hose used for connecting to wall outlets shall be protected from physical damage.

(b)(10) Safety devices

(b)(10)(i) Every container except those constructed in accordance with DOT specifications and every vaporizer (except motor fuel vaporizers and except vaporizers described in paragraph (B)(11)(ii)(C) of this section and paragraph (d)(4)(v)(a) of this section) whether heated by artificial means or not, shall be provided with one or more safety relief valves of spring-loaded or equivalent type. These valves shall be arranged to afford free vent to the outer air with discharge not less than 5 feet horizontally away from any opening into the building which is below such discharge. The rate of discharge shall be in accordance with the requirements of paragraph (b)(10)(ii) or (b)(10)(iii) of this section in the case of vaporizers.

(b)(10)(ii) Minimum required rate of discharge in cubic feet per minute of air at 120 percent of the maximum permitted start to discharge pressure for safety relief valves to be used on containers other than those constructed in accordance with DOT specification shall be as follows:

Surface area (sq. ft.)	Flow rate CFM air
20 or less	626
25	751
30	872
35	990
40	1,100
45	1,220
50	1,330
55	1,430
60	1,540
65	1,640
70	1,750
75	1,850
80	1,950
85	2,050
90	2,150
95	2,240
100	2,340
105	2,440
110	2,530
115	2,630
120	2,720
125	2,810
130	2,900
135	2,990
140	3,080
145	3,170
150	3,260
155	3,350
160	3,440
165	3,530
170	3,620
175	3,700
180	3,790
185	3,880
190	3,960
195	4,050
200	4,130
210	4,300
220	4,470
230	4,630
240	4,800
250	4,960
260	5,130
270	5,290
280	5,450
290	5,610
300	5,760
310	5,920
320	6,080
330	6,230
340	6,390
350	6,540
360	6,690
370	6,840
380	7,000
390	7,150
400	7,300
450	8,040
500	8,760
550	9,470
600	10,170
650	10,860
700	11,550
750	12,220
800	12,880
850	13,540
900	14,190
950	14,830
1,000	15,470
1,050	16,100
1,100	16,720
1,150	17,350
1,200	17,960
1,250	18,570
1,300	19,180
1,350	19,780
1,400	20,380
1,450	20,980
1,500	21,570
1,550	22,160
1,600	22,740

Surface area (sq. ft.)	Flow rate CFM air
1,650	23,320
1,700	23,900
1,750	24,470
1,800	25,050
1,850	25,620
1,900	26,180
1,950	26,750
2,000	27,310

Surface area = total outside surface area of container in square feet.
When the surface area is not stamped on the nameplate or when the marking is not legible, the area can be calculated by using one of the following formulas:

(1) Cylindrical container with hemispherical heads:
Area = Overall length × outside diameter × 3.1416.

(2) Cylindrical container with other than hemispherical heads:
Area = (Overall length + 0.3 outside diameter) × outside diameter × 3.1416.
Note: This formula is not exact, but will give results within the limits of practical accuracy for the sole purpose of sizing relief valves.

(3) Spherical container:
Area = Outside diameter squared × 3.1416.
Flow Rate-CFM Air = Required flow capacity in cubic feet per minute of air at standard conditions, 60 F. and atmospheric pressure (14.7 p.s.i.a.).
The rate of discharge may be interpolated for intermediate values of surface area. For containers with total outside surface area greater than 2,000 square feet, the required flow rate can be calculated using the formula, Flow Rate-CFM Air=53.632 A0.82.
A = total outside surface area of the container in square feet.

Valves not marked "Air" have flow rate marking in cubic feet per minute of liquefied petroleum gas. These can be converted to ratings in cubic feet per minute of air by multiplying the liquefied petroleum gas ratings by factors listed below. Air flow ratings can be converted to ratings in cubic feet per minute of liquefied petroleum gas by dividing the air ratings by the factors listed below.

Air Conversion Factors

Container type	100	125	150	175	200
Air conversion factor	1.162	1.142	1.113	1.078	1.010

(b)(10)(iii) Minimum Required Rate of Discharge for Safety Relief Valves for Liquefied Petroleum Gas Vaporizers (Steam Heated, Water Heated, and Direct Fired).

The minimum required rate of discharge for safety relief valves shall be determined as follows:

(b)(10)(iii)(A) Obtain the total surface area by adding the surface area of vaporizer shell in square feet directly in contact with LP-Gas and the heat exchanged surface area in square feet directly in contact with LP-Gas.

(b)(10)(iii)(B) Obtain the minimum required rate of discharge in cubic feet of air per minute, at 60 °F. and 14.7 p.s.i.a. from paragraph (b)(10)(ii) of this section, for this total surface area.

(b)(10)(iv) Container and vaporizer safety relief valves shall be set to start-to-discharge, with relation to the design pressure of the container, in accordance with Table H–26.

(b)(10)(v) Safety relief devices used with systems employing containers other than those constructed according to DOT specifications shall be so constructed as to discharge at not less than the rates shown in paragraph (b)(10)(ii) of this section, before the pressure is in excess of 120 percent of the maximum (not including the 10 percent referred to in paragraph (b)(10)(iv) of this section) permitted start to discharge pressure setting of the device.

Table H–26

Containers	Minimum (percent)	Maximum (percent)
ASME Code; Par. U–68, U–69—1949 and earlier editions	110	[1]25
ASME Code; Par. U–200, U–201—1949 edition	88	[1]100
ASME Code—1950, 1952, 1956, 1959, 1962, 1965 and 1968 (Division I) editions	88	[1]100
API—ASME Code—all editions	88	[1]100
DOT—As prescribed in 49 CFR Chapter I		

[1] Manufacturers of safety relief valves are allowed a plus tolerance not exceeding 10 percent of the set pressure marked on the valve.

(b)(10)(vi) In certain locations sufficiently sustained high temperatures prevail which require the use of a lower vapor pressure product to be stored or the use of a higher designed pressure vessel in order to prevent the safety valves opening as the result of these temperatures. As an alternative the tanks may be protected by cooling devices such as by spraying, by shading, or other effective means.

(b)(10)(vii) Safety relief valves shall be arranged so that the possibility of tampering will be minimized. If pressure setting or adjustment is external, the relief valves shall be provided with approved means for sealing adjustment.

(b)(10)(viii) Shutoff valves shall not be installed between the safety relief devices and the container, or the equipment or piping to which the safety relief device is connected except that a shutoff valve may be used where the arrangement of this valve is such that full required capacity flow through the safety relief device is always afforded.

(b)(10)(ix) Safety relief valves shall have direct communication with the vapor space of the container at all times.

(b)(10)(x) Each container safety relief valve used with systems covered by paragraphs (d), (e), (g), and (h) of this section, except as provided in paragraph (e)(3)(iii) of this section shall be plainly and permanently marked with the following: "Container Type" of the pressure vessel on which the valve is designed to be installed; the pressure in p.s.i.g. at which the valve is set to discharge; the actual rate of discharge of the valve in cubic feet per minute of air at 60 °F. and 14.7 p.s.i.a.; and the manufacturer's name and catalog number, for example: T200–250–4050 AIR—indicating that the valve is suitable for use on a Type 200 container, that it is set to start to discharge at 250 p.s.i.g.; and that its rate of discharge is 4,050 cubic feet per minute of air as determined in subdivision (ii) of this subparagraph.

(b)(10)(xi) Safety relief valve assemblies, including their connections, shall be of sufficient size so as to provide the rate of flow required for the container on which they are installed.

(b)(10)(xii) A hydrostatic relief valve shall be installed between each pair of shut-off valves on liquefied petroleum gas liquid piping so as to relieve into a safe atmosphere. The start-to-discharge pressure setting of such relief valves shall not be in excess of 500 p.s.i.g. The minimum setting on relief valves installed in piping connected to other than DOT containers shall not be lower than 140 percent of the container relief valve setting and in piping connected to DOT containers not lower than 400 p.s.i.g. The start-to-discharge pressure setting of such a relief valve, if installed on the discharge side of a pump, shall be greater than the maximum pressure permitted by the recirculation device in the system.

(b)(10)(xiii) The discharge from any safety relief device shall not terminate in or beneath any building, except relief devices covered by paragraphs (b)(6)(i)(A) through (E) of this section, or paragraphs (c)(4)(i) or (5) of this section.

(b)(10)(xiv) Container safety relief devices and regulator relief vents shall be located not less than five (5) feet in any direction from air openings into sealed combustion system appliances or mechanical ventilation air intakes.

(b)(11) Vaporizer and housing

(b)(11)(i) Indirect fired vaporizers utilizing steam, water, or other heating medium shall be constructed and installed as follows:

(b)(11)(i)(A) Vaporizers shall be constructed in accordance with the requirements of paragraph (b)(3)(i)–(iii) of this section and shall be permanently marked as follows:

(b)(11)(i)(A)(1) With the code marking signifying the specifications to which the vaporizer is constructed;

(b)(11)(i)(A)(2) With the allowable working pressure and temperature for which the vaporizer is designed;

(b)(11)(i)(A)(3) With the sum of the outside surface area and the inside heat exchange surface area expressed in square feet;

(b)(11)(i)(A)(4) With the name or symbol of the manufacturer.

(b)(11)(i)(B) Vaporizers having an inside diameter of 6 inches or less exempted by the ASME Unfired Pressure Vessel Code, Section VIII of the ASME Boiler and Pressure Vessel Code—1968 shall have a design pressure not less than 250 p.s.i.g. and need not be permanently marked.

(b)(11)(i)(C) Heating or cooling coils shall not be installed inside a storage container.

(b)(11)(i)(D) Vaporizers may be installed in buildings, rooms, sheds, or lean-tos used exclusively for gas manufacturing or distribution, or in other structures of light, noncombustible construction or equivalent, well ventilated near the floor line and roof.

When vaporizing and/or mixing equipment is located in a structure or building not used exclusively for gas manufacturing or distribution, either attached to or within such a building, such structure or room shall be separated from the remainder of the building by a wall designed to withstand a static pressure of at least 100 pounds per square foot. This wall shall have no openings or pipe or conduit passing through it. Such structure or room shall be provided with adequate ventilation and shall have a roof or at least one exterior wall of lightweight construction.

(b)(11)(i)(E) Vaporizers shall have, at or near the discharge, a safety relief valve providing an effective rate of discharge in accordance with paragraph (b)(10)(iii) of this section, except as provided in paragraph (d)(4)(v)(A), of this section.

(b)(11)(i)(F) The heating medium lines into and leaving the vaporizer shall be provided with suitable means for preventing the flow of gas into the heat systems in the event of tube rupture in the vaporizer. Vaporizers shall be provided with suitable automatic means to prevent liquid passing through the vaporizers to the gas discharge piping.

(b)(11)(i)(G) The device that supplies the necessary heat for producing steam, hot water, or other heating medium may be installed in a building, compartment, room, or lean-to which shall be ventilated near the floorline and roof to the outside. The device location shall be separated from all compartments or rooms containing liquefied petroleum gas vaporizers, pumps, and central gas mixing devices by a wall designed to withstand a static pressure of at least 100 pounds per square foot. This wall shall have no openings or pipes or conduit passing through it. This requirement does not apply to the domestic water heaters which may supply heat for a vaporizer in a domestic system.

(b)(11)(i)(H) Gas-fired heating systems supplying heat exclusively for vaporization purposes shall be equipped with automatic safety devices to shut off the flow of gas to main burners, if the pilot light should fail.

(b)(11)(i)(I) Vaporizers may be an integral part of a fuel storage container directly connected to the liquid section or gas section or both.

(b)(11)(i)(J) Vaporizers shall not be equipped with fusible plugs.

(b)(11)(i)(K) Vaporizer houses shall not have unprotected drains to sewers or sump pits.

(b)(11)(ii) Atmospheric vaporizers employing heat from the ground or surrounding air shall be installed as follows:

(b)(11)(ii)(A) Buried underground; or

(b)(11)(ii)(B) Located inside the building close to a point at which pipe enters the building provided the capacity of the unit does not exceed 1 quart;

(b)(11)(ii)(C) Vaporizers of less than 1 quart capacity heated by the ground or surrounding air, need not be equipped with safety relief valves provided that adequate tests demonstrate that the assembly is safe without safety relief valves.

(b)(11)(iii) Direct gas-fired vaporizers shall be constructed, marked, and installed as follows:

(b)(11)(iii)(A)(1) In accordance with the requirements of the American Society of Mechanical Engineers Boiler and Pressure Vessel Code—1968 that are applicable to the maximum working conditions for which the vaporizer is designed;

(b)(11)(iii)(A)(2) With the name of the manufacturer; rated BTU input to the burner; the area of the heat exchange surface in square feet; the outside surface of the vaporizer in square feet; and the maximum vaporizing capacity in gallons per hour.

(b)(11)(iii)(B)(1) Vaporizers may be connected to the liquid section or the gas section of the storage container, or both; but in any case there shall be at the container a manually operated valve in each connection to permit completely shutting off when desired, of all flow of gas or liquid from container to vaporizer;

(b)(11)(iii)(B)(2) Vaporizers with capacity not exceeding 35 gallons per hour shall be located at least 5 feet from container shutoff valves. Vaporizers having capacity of more than 35 gallons but not exceeding 100 gallons per hour shall be located at least 10 feet from the container shutoff valves. Vaporizers having a capacity greater than 100 gallons per hour shall be located at least 15 feet from container shutoff valves.

(b)(11)(iii)(C) Vaporizers may be installed in buildings, rooms, housings, sheds, or lean-tos used exclusively for vaporizing or mixing of liquefied petroleum gas. Vaporizing housing structures shall be of noncombustible construction, well ventilated near the floorline and the highest point of the roof. When vaporizer and/or mixing equipment is located in a structure or room attached to or within a building, such structure or room shall be separated from the remainder of the building by a wall designed to withstand a static pressure of at least 100 pounds per square foot. This wall shall have no openings or pipes or conduit passing through it. Such structure or room shall be provided with adequate ventilation, and shall have a roof or at least one exterior wall of lightweight construction.

(b)(11)(iii)(D) Vaporizers shall have at or near the discharge, a safety relief valve providing an effective rate of discharge in accordance with paragraph (b)(10)(iii) of this section. The relief valve shall be so located as not to be subjected to temperatures in excess of 140 °F.

(b)(11)(iii)(E) Vaporizers shall be provided with suitable automatic means to prevent liquid passing from the vaporizer to the gas discharge piping of the vaporizer.

(b)(11)(iii)(F) Vaporizers shall be provided with means for manually turning off the gas to the main burner and pilot.

(b)(11)(iii)(G) Vaporizers shall be equipped with automatic safety devices to shut off the flow of gas to main burners if the pilot light should fail. When the flow through the pilot exceeds 2,000 BTU per hour, the pilot also shall be equipped with an automatic safety device to shut off the flow of gas to the pilot should the pilot flame be extinguished.

(b)(11)(iii)(H) Pressure regulating and pressure reducing equipment if located within 10 feet of a direct fire vaporizer shall be separated from the open flame by a substantially airtight noncombustible partition or partitions.

(b)(11)(iii)(I) Except as provided in (C) of this subdivision, the following minimum distances shall be maintained between direct fired vaporizers and the nearest important building or group of buildings:

Ten feet for vaporizers having a capacity of 15 gallons per hour or less vaporizing capacity.

Twenty-five feet for vaporizers having a vaporizing capacity of 16 to 100 gallons per hour.

Fifty feet for vaporizers having a vaporizing capacity exceeding 100 gallons per hour.

(b)(11)(iii)(J) Direct fired vaporizers shall not raise the product pressure above the design pressure of the vaporizer equipment nor shall they raise the product pressure within the storage container above the pressure shown in the second column of Table H–31.

(b)(11)(iii)(K) Vaporizers shall not be provided with fusible plugs.

(b)(11)(iii)(L) Vaporizers shall not have unprotected drains to sewers or sump pits.

(b)(11)(iv) Direct gas-fired tank heaters shall be constructed and installed as follows:

(b)(11)(iv)(A) Direct gas-fired tank heaters, and tanks to which they are applied, shall only be installed above ground.

(b)(11)(iv)(B) Tank heaters shall be permanently marked with the name of the manufacturer, the rated BTU input to the burner, and the maximum vaporizing capacity in gallons per hour.

(b)(11)(iv)(C) Tank heaters may be an integral part of a fuel storage container directly connected to the container liquid section, or vapor section, or both.

(b)(11)(iv)(D) Tank heaters shall be provided with a means for manually turning off the gas to the main burner and pilot.

(b)(11)(iv)(E) Tank heaters shall be equipped with an automatic safety device to shut off the flow of gas to main burners, if the pilot light should fail. When flow through pilot exceeds 2,000 BTU per hour, the pilot also shall be equipped with an automatic safety device to shut off the flow of gas to the pilot should the pilot flame be extinguished.

(b)(11)(iv)(F) Pressure regulating and pressure reducing equipment if located within 10 feet of a direct fired tank heater shall be separated from the open flame by a substantially airtight noncombustible partition.

(b)(11)(iv)(G) The following minimum distances shall be maintained between a storage tank heated by a direct fired tank heater and the nearest important building or group of buildings:

Ten feet for storage containers of less than 500 gallons water capacity.

Twenty-five feet for storage containers of 500 to 1,200 gallons water capacity.

Fifty feet for storage containers of over 1,200 gallons water capacity.

(b)(11)(iv)(H) No direct fired tank heater shall raise the product pressure within the storage container over 75 percent of the pressure set out in the second column of Table H–31.

(b)(11)(v) The vaporizer section of vaporizer-burners used for dehydrators or dryers shall be located outside of buildings; they shall be constructed and installed as follows:

(b)(11)(v)(A) Vaporizer-burners shall have a minimum design pressure of 250 p.s.i.g. with a factor of safety of five;

(b)(11)(v)(B) Manually operated positive shut-off valves shall be located at the containers to shut off all flow to the vaporizer-burners;

(b)(11)(v)(C) Minimum distances between storage containers and vaporizer-burners shall be as follows:

Water capacity per container (gallons)	Minimum distances (feet)
Less than 501	10
501 to 2,000	25
Over 2,000	50

(b)(11)(v)(D) The vaporizer section of vaporizer-burners shall be protected by a hydrostatic relief valve. The relief valve shall be located so as not to be subjected to temperatures in excess of 140 °F. The start-to-discharge pressure setting shall be such as to protect the components involved, but not less than 250 p.s.i.g. The discharge shall be directed upward and away from component parts of the equipment and away from operating personnel;

(b)(11)(v)(E) Vaporizer-burners shall be provided with means for manually turning off the gas to the main burner and pilot;

(b)(11)(v)(F) Vaporizer-burners shall be equipped with automatic safety devices to shut off the flow of gas to the main burner and pilot in the event the pilot is extinguished;

(b)(11)(v)(G) Pressure regulating and control equipment shall be located or protected so that the temperatures surrounding this equipment shall not exceed 140 °F. except that equipment components may be used at higher temperatures if designed to withstand such temperatures;

(b)(11)(v)(H) Pressure regulating and control equipment when located downstream of the vaporizer shall be designed to withstand the maximum discharge temperature of the vapor;

(b)(11)(v)(I) The vaporizer section of vaporizer-burners shall not be provided with fusible plugs;

(b)(11)(v)(J) Vaporizer coils or jackets shall be made of ferrous metal or high temperature alloys;

(b)(11)(v)(K) Equipment utilizing vaporizer-burners shall be equipped with automatic shutoff devices upstream and downstream of the vaporizer section connected so as to operate in the event of excessive temperature, flame failure, and, if applicable, insufficient airflow.

(b)(12) Filling densities

(b)(12)(i) The "filling density" is defined as the percent ratio of the weight of the gas in a container to the weight of water the container will hold at 60 °F. All containers shall be filled according to the filling densities shown in Table H–27.

Table H–27
Maximum Permitted Filling Density

Specific gravity at 60 °F. (15.6 °C.)	Above ground containers: 0 to 1,200 U.S. gals. (1,000 imp. gal., 4,550 liters) total water cap.	Above ground containers: Over 1,200 U.S. gals. (1,000 imp. gal., 4,550 liters) total water cap.	Under ground containers, all capacities
	Percent	Percent	Percent
0 .496–0.503	41	44	45
.504– .510	42	45	46
.511– .519	43	46	47
.520– .527	44	47	48
.528– .536	45	48	49
.537– .544	46	49	50
.545– .552	47	50	51
.553– .560	48	51	52
.561– .568	49	52	53
.569– .576	50	53	54
.577– .584	51	54	55
.585– .592	52	55	56
.593– .600	53	56	57

(b)(12)(ii) Except as provided in paragraph (b)(12)(iii) of this section, any container including mobile cargo tanks and portable tank containers regardless of size or construction, shipped under DOT jurisdiction or constructed in accordance with 49 CFR chapter I Specifications shall be charged according to 49 CFR chapter I requirements.

(b)(12)(iii) Portable containers not subject to DOT jurisdiction (such as, but not limited to, motor fuel containers on industrial and lift trucks, and farm tractors covered in paragraph (e) of this section, or containers recharged at the installation) may be filled either by weight, or by volume using a fixed length dip tube gaging device.

(b)(13) LP-Gas in buildings

(b)(13)(i) Vapor shall be piped into buildings at pressures in excess of 20 p.s.i.g. only if the buildings or separate areas thereof, (a) are constructed in accordance with this section; (b) are used excusively to house equipment for vaporization, pressure reduction, gas mixing, gas manufacturing, or distribution, or to house internal combustion engines, industrial processes, research and experimental laboratories, or equipment and processes using such gas and having similar hazard; (c) buildings, structures, or equipment under construction or undergoing major renovation.

(b)(13)(ii) Liquid may be permitted in buildings as follows:

(b)(13)(ii)(A) Buildings, or separate areas of buildings, used exclusively to house equipment for vaporization, pressure reduction, gas mixing, gas manufacturing, or distribution, or to house internal combustion engines, industrial processes, research and experimental laboratories, or equipment and processes using such gas and having similar hazard; and when such buildings, or separate areas thereof are constructed in accordance with this section;

(b)(13)(ii)(B) Buildings, structures, or equipment under construction or undergoing major renovation provided the temporary piping meets the following conditions:

(b)(13)(ii)(B)(1) Liquid piping inside the building shall conform to the requirements of paragraph (b)(8) of this section, and shall not exceed three-fourths iron pipe size. Copper tubing with an outside diameter of three-fourths inch or less may be used provided it conforms to Type K of Specifications for Seamless Water Tube, ANSI H23.1–1970 (ASTM B88–69) (see Table H–24). All such piping shall be protected against construction hazards. Liquid piping inside buildings shall be kept to a minimum. Such piping shall be securely fastened to walls or other surfaces so as to provide adequate protection from breakage and so located as to subject the liquid line to lowest ambient temperatures;

(b)(13)(ii)(B)(2) A shutoff valve shall be installed in each intermediate branch line where it takes off the main line and shall be readily accessible. A shutoff valve shall also be placed at the appliance end of the intermediate branch line. Such shutoff valve shall be upstream of any flexible connector used with the appliance;

(b)(13)(ii)(B)(3) Suitable excess flow valves shall be installed in the container outlet line supplying liquid LP-Gas to the building. A suitable excess flow valve shall be installed immediately downstream of each shutoff valve. Suitable excess flow valves shall be installed where piping size is reduced and shall be sized for the reduced size piping;

(b)(13)(ii)(B)(4) Hydrostatic relief valves shall be installed in accordance with paragraph (b)(10)(xii) of this section;

(b)(13)(ii)(B)(5) The use of hose to carry liquid between the container and the building or at any point in the liquid line, except at the appliance connector, shall be prohibited;

(b)(13)(ii)(B)(6) Where flexible connectors are necessary for appliance installation, such connectors shall be as short as practicable and shall comply with paragraph (b)(8)(ii) or (9) of this section;

(b)(13)(ii)(B)(7) Release of fuel when any section of piping or appliances is disconnected shall be minimized by either of the following methods:

(b)(13)(ii)(B)(7)(i) Using an approved automatic quick-closing coupling (a type closing in both directions when coupled in the fuel line); or

(b)(13)(ii)(B)(7)(ii) Closing the valve nearest to the appliance and allowing the appliance to operate until the fuel in the line is consumed;

(b)(13)(ii)(B)(7)(iii) Portable containers shall not be taken into buildings except as provided in paragraph (b)(6)(i) of this section.

(b)(14) Transfer of liquids The employer shall assure that:

(b)(14)(i) [OI] At least one attendant shall remain close to the transfer connection from the time the connections are first made until they are finally disconnected, during the transfer of the product;

(b)(14)(ii) Containers shall be filled or used only upon authorization of the owner;

(b)(14)(iii) Containers manufactured in accordance with specifications of 49 CFR part 178 and authorized by 49 CFR chapter 1 as a "single trip" or "nonrefillable container" shall not be refilled or reused in LP-Gas service;

(b)(14)(iv) Gas or liquid shall not be vented to the atmosphere to assist in transferring contents of one container to another, except as provided in paragraph (e)(5)(iv) of this section and except that this shall not preclude the use of listed pump utilizing LP-Gas in the vapor phase as a source of energy and venting such gas to the atmosphere at a rate not to exceed that from a No. 31 drill size opening and provided that such venting and liquid transfer shall be located not less than 50 feet from the nearest important building;

(b)(14)(v) Filling of fuel containers for industrial trucks or motor vehicles from industrial bulk storage containers shall be performed not less than 10 feet from the nearest important masonry-walled building or not less than 25 feet from the nearest important building or other construction and, in any event, not less than 25 feet from any building opening;

(b)(14)(vi) Filling of portable containers, containers mounted on skids, fuel containers on farm tractors, or similar applications, from storage containers used in domestic or commercial service, shall be performed not less than 50 feet from the nearest important building;

(b)(14)(vii) The filling connection and the vent from the liquid level gages in containers, filled at point of installation, shall not be less than 10 feet in any direction from air openings into sealed combustion system appliances or mechanical ventilation air intakes;

(b)(14)(viii) Fuel supply containers shall be gaged and charged only in the open air or in buildings especially provided for that purpose;

(b)(14)(ix) The maximum vapor pressure of the product at 100 °F. which may be transferred into a container shall be in accordance with paragraphs (d)(2) and (e)(3) of this section. (For DOT containers use DOT requirements.)

(b)(14)(x) Marketers and users shall exercise precaution to assure that only those gases for which the system is designed, examined, and listed, are employed in its operation, particularly with regard to pressures;

(b)(14)(xi) Pumps or compressors shall be designed for use with LP-Gas. When compressors are used they shall normally take suction from the vapor space of the container being filled and discharge to the vapor space of the container being emptied;

(b)(14)(xii) Pumping systems, when equipped with a positive displacement pump, shall include a recirculating device which shall limit the differential pressure on the pump under normal operating conditions to the maximum differential pressure rating of the pump. The discharge of the pumping system shall be protected so that pressure does not exceed 350 p.s.i.g. If a recirculation system discharges into the supply tank and contains a manual shutoff valve, an adequate secondary safety recirculation system shall be incorporated which shall have no means of rendering it inoperative. Manual shutoff valves in recirculation systems shall be kept open except during an emergency or when repairs are being made to the system;

(b)(14)(xiii) When necessary, unloading piping or hoses shall be provided with suitable bleeder valves for relieving pressure before disconnection;

(b)(14)(xiv) Agricultural air moving equipment, including crop dryers, shall be shut down when supply containers are being filled unless the air intakes and sources of ignition on the equipment are located 50 feet or more from the container;

(b)(14)(xv) Agricultural equipment employing open flames or equipment with integral containers, such as flame cultivators, weed burners, and, in addition, tractors, shall be shut down during refueling.

(b)(15) **Tank car or transport truck loading or unloading points and operations**

(b)(15)(i) The track of tank car siding shall be relatively level.

(b)(15)(ii) A "Tank Car Connected" sign, as covered by DOT rules, shall be installed at the active end or ends of the siding while the tank car is connected.

(b)(15)(iii) While cars are on sidetrack for loading or unloading, the wheels at both ends shall be blocked on the rails.

(b)(15)(iv) The employer shall insure that an employee is in attendance at all times while the tank car, cars, or trucks are being loaded or unloaded.

(b)(15)(v) A backflow check valve, excess-flow valve, or a shutoff valve with means of remote closing, to protect against uncontrolled discharge of LP-Gas from storage tank piping shall be installed close to the point where the liquid piping and hose or swing joint pipe is connected.

(b)(15)(vi) Where practical, the distance of the unloading or loading point shall conform to the distances in subparagraph (6)(ii) of this paragraph.

(b)(16) **Instructions** Personnel performing installation, removal, operation, and maintenance work shall be properly trained in such function.

(b)(17) **Electrical equipment and other sources of ignition**

(b)(17)(i) Electrical equipment and wiring shall be of a type specified by and shall be installed in accordance with Subpart S of this part, for ordinary locations except that fixed electrical equipment in classified areas shall comply with subparagraph (18) of this paragraph.

(b)(17)(ii) Open flames or other sources of ignition shall not be permitted in vaporizer rooms (except those housing direct-fired vaporizers), pumphouses, container charging rooms or other similar locations. Direct-fired vaporizers shall not be permitted in pumphouses or container charging rooms.

(b)(17)(iii) Liquefied petroleum gas storage containers do not require lightning protection.

(b)(17)(iv) Since liquefied petroleum gas is contained in a closed system of piping and equipment, the system need not be electrically conductive or electrically bonded for protection against static electricity.

(b)(17)(v) Open flames (except as provided for in paragraph (b)(11) of this section), cutting or welding, portable electric tools, and extension lights capable of igniting LP-Gas, shall not be permitted within classified areas specified in Table H–28 unless the LP-Gas facilities have been freed of all liquid and vapor, or special precautions observed under carefully controlled conditions.

Table H–28

Part	Location	Extent of classified area[1]	Equipment shall be suitable for Class 1, Group D[2]
A	Storage containers other than DOT cylinders	Within 15 feet in all directions from connections, except connections otherwise covered in Table H–28	Division 2
B	Tank vehicle and tank car loading and unloading[3]	Within 5 feet in all directions from connections regularly made or disconnected for product transfer Beyond 5 feet but within 15 feet in all directions from a point where connections are regularly made or disconnected and within the cylindrical volume between the horizontal equator of the sphere and grade (See Figure H–1)	Division 1 Division 2
C	Gage vent openings other than those on DOT cylinders	Within 5 feet in all directions from point of discharge Beyond 5 feet but within 15 feet in all directions from point of discharge	Division 1 Division 2
D	Relief valve discharge other than those on DOT cylinders	Within direct path of discharge Within 5 feet in all directions from point of discharge Beyond 5 feet but within 15 feet in all directions from point of discharge except within the direct path of discharge	Division 1 Division 1 Division 2
E	Pumps, compressors, gas-air mixers and vaporizers other than direct fired		
	Indoors without ventilation	Entire room and any adjacent room not separated by a gastight partition Within 15 feet of the exterior side of any exterior wall or roof that is not vaportight or within 15 feet of any exterior opening	Division 1 Division 2
	Indoors with adequate ventilation[4] Outdoors in open air at or abovegrade	Entire room and any adjacent room not separated by a gastight partition Within 15 feet in all directions from this equipment and within the cylindrical volume between the horizontal equator of the sphere and grade. See Figure H–1	Division 2 Division 2
F	Service Station Dispensing Units	Entire space within dispenser enclosure, and 18 inches horizontally from enclosure exterior up to an elevation 4 ft. above dispenser base. Entire pit or open space beneath dispenser Up to 18 inches abovegrade within 20 ft. horizontally from any edge of enclosure **Note:** For pits within this area, see part F of this table.	Division 1 Division 2

Part	Location	Extent of classified area[1]	Equipment shall be suitable for Class 1, Group D[2]
G	Pits or trenches containing or located beneath LP-Gas valves, pumps, compressors, regulators, and similar equipment		
	Without mechanical ventilation	Entire pit or trench Entire room and any adjacent room not separated by a gastight partition Within 15 feet in all directions from pit or trench when located outdoors	Division 1 Division 1 Division 2
	With adequate mechanical ventilation	Entire pit or trench Entire room and any adjacent room not separated by a gastight partition Within 15 feet in all directions from pit or trench when located outdoors	Division 2 Division 2 Division 2
H	Special buildings or rooms for storage of portable containers	Entire room	Division 2
I	Pipelines and connections containing operational bleeds, drips, vents or drains	Within 5 ft. in all directions from point of discharge Beyond 5 ft. from point of discharge, same as part E of this table	Division 1
J	Container filling:		
	Indoors without ventilation	Entire room	Division 1
	Indoors with adequate ventilation[4]	Within 5 feet in all directions from connections regularly made or disconnected for product transfer Beyond 5 feet and entire room	Division 1 Division 1
	Outdoors in open air	Within 5 feet in all directions from connections regularly made or disconnected for product transfer Beyond 5 feet but within 15 feet in all direction from a point where connections are regularly made or disconnected and within the cylindrical volume between the horizontal equator of the sphere and grade. (See Figure H–1)	Division 1 Division 1

[1] The classified area shall not extend beyond an unpierced wall, roof, or solid vaportight partition.
[2] See Subpart S of this part.
[3] When classifying extent of hazardous area, consideration shall be given to possible variations in the spotting of tank cars and tank vehicles at the unloading points and the effect these variations of actual spotting point may have on the point of connection.
[4] Ventilation, either natural or mechanical, is considered adequate when the concentration of the gas in a gas-air mixture does not exceed 25 percent of the lower flammable limit under normal operating conditions.

Figure H-1

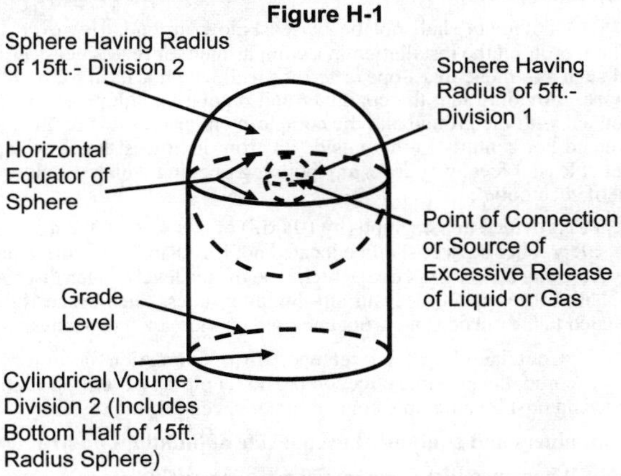

(b)(18) Fixed electrical equipment in classified areas Fixed electrical equipment and wiring installed within classified areas specified in Table H–28 shall comply with Table H–28 and shall be installed in accordance with Subpart S of this part. This provision does not apply to fixed electrical equipment at residential or commercial installations of LP-Gas systems or to systems covered by paragraph (e) or (g) of this section.

(b)(19) Liquid-level gaging device

(b)(19)(i) Each container manufactured after December 31, 1965, and filled on a volumetric basis shall be equipped with a fixed liquid-level gage to indicate the maximum permitted filling level as provided in paragraph (b)(19)(v) of this section. Each container manufactured after December 31, 1969, shall have permanently attached to the container adjacent to the fixed level gage a marking showing the percentage full that will be shown by that gage. When a variable liquid-level gage is also provided, the fixed liquid-level gage will also serve as a means for checking the variable gage. These gages shall be used in charging containers as required in paragraph (b)(12) of this section.

(b)(19)(ii) All variable gaging devices shall be arranged so that the maximum liquid level for butane, for a 50–50 mixture of butane and propane, and for propane, to which the container may be charged is readily determinable. The markings indicating the various liquid levels from empty to full shall be on the system nameplate or gaging device or part may be on the system nameplate and part on the gaging device. Dials of magnetic or rotary gages shall show whether they are for cylindrical or spherical containers and whether for aboveground or underground service. The dials of gages intended for use only on aboveground containers of over 1,200 gallons water capacity shall be so marked.

(b)(19)(iii) Gaging devices that require bleeding of the product to the atmosphere, such as the rotary tube, fixed tube, and slip tube, shall be designed so that the bleed valve maximum opening is not larger than a No. 54 drill size, unless provided with excess flow valve.

(b)(19)(iv) Gaging devices shall have a design working pressure of at least 250 p.s.i.g.

(b)(19)(v) Length of tube or position of fixed liquid-level gage shall be designed to indicate the maximum level to which the container may be filled for the product contained. This level shall be based on the volume of the product at 40 °F. at its maximum permitted filling density for aboveground containers and at 50 °F. for underground containers. The employer shall calculate the filling point for which the fixed liquid level gage shall be designed according to the method in this subdivision.

(b)(19)(v)(A) It is impossible to set out in a table the length of a fixed dip tube for various capacity tanks because of the varying tank diameters and lengths and because the tank may be installed either in a vertical or horizontal position. Knowing the maximum permitted filling volume in gallons, however, the length of the fixed tube can be determined by the use of a strapping table obtained from the container manufacturer. The length of the fixed tube should be such that when its lower end touches the surface of the liquid in the container, the contents of the container will be the maximum permitted volume as determined by the following formula:

$$\frac{\text{(Water capacity (gals.) of container* × filling density**)}}{\text{(Specific gravity of LP-Gas* × volume correction factor × 100)}} = \text{Maximum volume of LP-Gas}$$

*Measured at 60 °F.

**From subparagraph (12) of this paragraph "Filling Densities."

For aboveground containers the liquid temperature is assumed to be 40 °F. and for underground containers the liquid temperature is assumed to be 50 °F. To correct the liquid volumes at these temperatures to 60 °F. the following factors shall be used.

(b)(19)(v)(B) Formula for determining maximum volume of liquefied petroleum gas for which a fixed length of dip tube shall be set:

Table H–29
Volume Correction Factors

Specific gravity	Aboveground	Underground
0.500	1.033	1.017
.510	1.031	1.016
.520	1.029	1.015
.530	1.028	1.014
.540	1.026	1.013
.550	1.025	1.013
.560	1.024	1.012
.570	1.023	1.011
.580	1.021	1.011
.590	1.020	1.010

(b)(19)(v)(C) The maximum volume of LP-Gas which can be placed in a container when determining the length of the dip tube expressed as a percentage of total water content of the container is calculated by the following formula.

(b)(19)(v)(D) The maximum weight of LP-Gas which may be placed in a container for determining the length of a fixed dip tube is determined by multiplying the maximum volume of liquefied petroleum gas obtained by the formula in paragraph (b)(19)(v)(B) of this section by the pounds of liquefied petroleum gas in a gallon at 40 °F. for abovegound and at 50 °F. for underground containers. For example, typical pounds per gallon are specified below:

Example: Assume a 100-gallon total water capacity tank for aboveground storage of propane having a specific gravity of 0.510 of 60 °F.

[(100 (gals.) × 42 (filling density from subparagraph (12) of this paragraph)) ÷ (0.510 × 1.031 (correction factor from Table H–29) × 100)] = (4200÷52.6)

(4200 ÷ 52.6) = 79.8 gallons propane, the maximum amount permitted to be placed in a 100-gallon total water capacity aboveground container equipped with a fixed dip tube.

[(Maximum volume of LP-Gas (from formula in subdivision (b) of this subdivision) × 100) ÷ Total water content of container in gallons] = Maximum percent of LP-Gas

	Aboveground, pounds per gallon	Underground, pounds per gallon
Propane	4.37	4.31
N Butane	4.97	4.92

(b)(19)(vi) Fixed liquid-level gages used on containers other than DOT containers shall be stamped on the exterior of the gage with the letters "DT" followed by the vertical distance (expressed in inches and carried out to one decimal place) from the top of container to the end of the dip tube or to the centerline of the gage when it is located at the maximum permitted filling level. For portable containers that may be filled in the horizontal and/or vertical position the letters "DT" shall be followed by "V" with the vertical distance from the top of the container to the end of the dip tube for vertical filling and with "H" followed by the proper distance for horizontal filling. For DOT containers the stamping shall be placed both on the exterior of the gage and on the container. On above-ground or cargo containers where the gages are positioned at specific levels, the marking may be specified in percent of total tank contents and the marking shall be stamped on the container.

(b)(19)(vii) Gage glasses of the columnar type shall be restricted to charging plants where the fuel is withdrawn in the liquid phase only. They shall be equipped with valves having metallic handwheels, with excess flow valves, and with extra-heavy glass adequately protected with a metal housing applied by the gage manufacturer. They shall be shielded against the direct rays of the sun. Gage glasses of the columnar type are prohibited on tank trucks, and on motor fuel tanks, and on containers used in domestic, commercial, and industrial installations.

(b)(19)(viii) Gaging devices of the float, or equivalent type which do not require flow for their operation and having connections extending to a point outside the container do not have to be equipped with excess flow valves provided the piping and fittings are adequately designed to withstand the container pressure and are properly protected against physical damage and breakage.

(b)(20) **Requirements for appliances**

(b)(20)(i) Except as provided in paragraph (b)(20)(ii) of this section, new commercial and industrial gas consuming appliances shall be approved.

(b)(20)(ii) Any appliance that was originally manufactured for operation with a gaseous fuel other than LP-Gas and is in good condition may be used with LP-Gas only after it is properly converted, adapted, and tested for performance with LP-Gas before the appliance is placed in use.

(b)(20)(iii) Unattended heaters used inside buildings for the purpose of animal or poultry production or care shall be equipped with an approved automatic device designed to shut off the flow of gas to the main burners, and pilot if used, in the event of flame extinguishment.

(b)(20)(iv) All commercial, industrial, and agricultural appliances or equipment shall be installed in accordance with the requirements of this section and in accordance with the following NFPA consensus standards, which are incorporated by reference as specified in §1910.6:

(b)(20)(iv)(A) Domestic and commercial appliances—NFPA 54–1969, Standard for the Installation of Gas Appliances and Gas Piping.

(b)(20)(iv)(B) Industrial appliances—NFPA 54A–1969, Standard for the Installation of Gas Piping and Gas Equipment on Industrial Premises and Certain Other Premises.

(b)(20)(iv)(C) Standard for the Installation and Use of Stationary Combustion Engines and Gas Turbines—NFPA 37–1970.

(b)(20)(iv)(D) Standard for the Installation of Equipment for the Removal of Smoke and Grease-Laden Vapors from Commercial Cooking Equipment, NFPA 96–1970.

(c) **Cylinder systems**

(c)(1) **Application** This paragraph applies specifically to systems utilizing containers constructed in accordance with DOT Specifications. All requirements of paragraph (b) of this section apply to this paragraph unless otherwise noted in paragraph (b) of this section.

(c)(2) **Marking of containers** Containers shall be marked in accordance with DOT regulations. Additional markings not in conflict with DOT regulations may be used.

(c)(3) **Description of a system** A system shall include the container base or bracket, containers, container valves, connectors, manifold valve assembly, regulators, and relief valves.

(c)(4) **Containers and regulating equipment installed outside of buildings or structures**

(c)(4)(i) Containers shall not be buried below ground. However, this shall not prohibit the installation in a compartment or recess below grade level such as a niche in a slope or terrace wall which is used for no other purpose, providing that the container and regulating equipment are not in contact with the ground and the compartment or recess is drained and ventilated horizontally to the outside air from its lowest level, with the outlet at least 3 feet away from any building opening which is below the level of such outlet.

Except as provided in paragraph (b)(10)(xiii) of this section, the discharge from safety relief devices shall be located not less than 3 feet horizontally away from any building opening which is below the level of such discharge and shall not terminate beneath any building unless such space is well ventilated to the outside and is not enclosed on more than two sides.

(c)(4)(ii) Containers shall be set upon firm foundation or otherwise firmly secured; the possible effect on the outlet piping of settling shall be guarded against by a flexible connection or special fitting.

(c)(5) **Containers and equipment used inside of buildings or structures**

(c)(5)(i) When operational requirements make portable use of containers necessary and their location outside of buildings or structure is impracticable, containers and equipment are permitted to be used inside of buildings or structures in accordance with (A) through (L) of this subdivision, and, in addition, such other provisions of this subparagraph as are applicable to the particular use or occupancy.

(c)(5)(i)(A) Containers in use shall mean connected for use.

(c)(5)(i)(B) Systems utilizing containers having a water capacity greater than 2½ pounds (nominal 1 pound LP-Gas capacity) shall be equipped with excess flow valves. Such excess flow valves shall be either integral with the container valves or in the connections to the container valve outlets. In either case, an excess flow valve shall be installed in such a manner that any undue strain beyond the excess flow valve will not cause breakage between the container and the excess flow valve. The installation of excess flow valves shall take into account the type of valve protection provided.

(c)(5)(i)(C) Regulators, if used, shall be either directly connected to the container valves or to manifolds connected to the container values. The regulator shall be suitable for use with LP-Gas. Manifolds and fittings connecting containers to pressure regulator inlets shall be designed for at least 250 p.s.i.g. service pressure.

(c)(5)(i)(D) Valves on containers having a water capacity greater than 50 pounds (nominal 20 pounds LP-Gas capacity) shall be protected while in use.

(c)(5)(i)(E) Containers shall be marked in accordance with paragraph (b)(5)(iii) of this section and paragraph (c)(2) of this section.

(c)(5)(i)(F) Pipe or tubing shall conform to paragraph (b)(8) of this section except that aluminum pipe or tubing shall not be used.

(c)(5)(i)(G)(1) Hose shall be designed for a working pressure of at least 250 p.s.i.g. Hose and hose connections shall have their correctness as to design, construction and performance determined by listing by a nationally recognized testing laboratory. The hose length may exceed the length specified in paragraph (b)(9)(vii)(B) of this section, but shall be as short as practicable. Refer to §1910.7 for definition of nationally recognized testing laboratory.

(c)(5)(i)(G)(2) Hose shall be long enough to permit compliance with spacing provisions of this subparagraph without kinking or straining or causing hose to be so close to a burner as to be damaged by heat.

(c)(5)(i)(H) Portable heaters, including salamanders, shall be equipped with an approved automatic device to shut off the flow of gas to the main burner, and pilot if used, in the event of flame extinguishment. Such heaters having inputs above 50,000 BTU manufactured on or after May 17, 1967, and such heaters having inputs above 100,000 BTU manufactured before May 17, 1967, shall be equipped with either.

(c)(5)(i)(H)(1) A pilot which must be lighted and proved before the main burner can be turned on; or

(c)(5)(i)(H)(2) An electric ignition system.

The provisions of this paragraph (h) do not apply to tar kettle burners, torches, melting pots, nor do they apply to portable heaters under 7,500 BTUH input when used with containers having a maximum water capacity of 2½ pounds. Container valves, connectors, regulators, manifolds, piping, and tubing shall not be used as structural supports for heaters.

(c)(5)(i)(I) Containers, regulating equipment, manifolds, pipe, tubing, and hose shall be located so as to minimize exposure to abnormally high temperatures (such as may result from exposure to convection or radiation from heating equipment or installation in confined spaces), physical damage, or tampering by unauthorized persons.

(c)(5)(i)(J) Heat producing equipment shall be located and used so as to minimize the possibility of ignition of combustibles.

(c)(5)(i)(K) Containers having a water capacity greater than 2½ pounds (nominal 1 pound LP-Gas capacity) connected for use, shall stand on a firm and substantially level surface and, when necessary, shall be secured in an upright position.

(c)(5)(i)(L) Containers, including the valve protective devices, shall be installed so as to minimize the probability of impingement of discharge of safety relief devices upon containers.

(c)(5)(ii) Containers having a maximum water capacity of 2½ pounds (nominal 1 pound LP-Gas capacity) are permitted to be used inside of buildings as part of approved self-contained hand torch assemblies or similar appliances.

(c)(5)(iii) Containers having a maximum water capacity of 12 pounds (nominal 5 pounds LP-Gas capacity) are permitted to be used temporarily inside of buildings for public exhibition or demonstration purposes, including use for classroom demonstrations.

(c)(5)(iv) [Reserved]

(c)(5)(v) Containers are permitted to be used in buildings or structures under construction or undergoing major renovation when such buildings or structures are not occupied by the public, as follows:

(c)(5)(v)(A) The maximum water capacity of individual containers shall be 245 pounds (nominal 100 pounds LP-Gas capacity);

(c)(5)(v)(B) For temporary heating such as curing concrete, drying plaster and similar applications, heaters (other than integral heater-container units) shall be located at least 6 feet from any LP-Gas container. This shall not prohibit the use of heaters specifically designed for attachment to the container or to a supporting standard, provided they are designed and installed so as to prevent direct or radiant heat application from the heater onto the container. Blower and radiant type heaters shall not be directed toward any LP-Gas container within 20 feet;

(c)(5)(v)(C) If two or more heater-container units, of either the integral or nonintegral type, are located in an unpartitioned area on the same floor, the container or containers of each unit shall be separated from the container or containers of any other unit by at least 20 feet;

(c)(5)(v)(D) When heaters are connected to containers for use in an unpartitioned area on the same floor, the total water capacity of containers manifolded together for connection to a heater or heaters shall not be greater than 735 pounds (nominal 300 pounds LP-Gas capacity). Such manifolds shall be separated by at least 20 feet;

(c)(5)(v)(E) On floors on which heaters are not connected for use, containers are permitted to be manifolded together for connection to a heater or heaters on another floor, Provided:

(c)(5)(v)(E)(1) The total water capacity of containers connected to any one manifold is not greater than 2,450 pounds (nominal 1,000 pounds LP-Gas capacity) and;

(c)(5)(v)(E)(2) Where more than one manifold having a total water capacity greater than 735 pounds (nominal 300 pounds LP-Gas capacity) are located in the same unpartitioned area, they shall be separated by at least 50 feet.

(c)(5)(v)(F) Storage of containers awaiting use shall be in accordance with paragraph (f) of this section.

(c)(5)(vi) Containers are permitted to be used in industrial occupancies for processing, research, or experimental purposes as follows:

(c)(5)(vi)(A) The maximum water capacity of individual containers shall be 245 pounds (nominal 100 pounds LP-Gas capacity);

(c)(5)(vi)(B) Containers connected to a manifold shall have a total water capacity not greater than 735 pounds (nominal 300 pounds LP-Gas capacity) and not more than one such manifold may be located in the same room unless separated at least 20 feet from a similar unit;

(c)(5)(vi)(C) The amount of LP-Gas in containers for research and experimental use shall be limited to the smallest practical quantity.

(c)(5)(vii)(A) Containers are permitted to be used in industrial occupancies with essentially noncombustible contents where portable equipment for space heating is essential and where a permanent heating installation is not practical, as follows:

(c)(5)(vii)(B) Containers and heaters shall comply with and be used in accordance with paragraph (c)(5)(v) of this section.

(c)(5)(viii) Containers are permitted to be used in buildings for temporary emergency heating purposes, if necessary to prevent damage to the buildings or contents, when the permanent heating system is temporarily out of service, as follows:

(c)(5)(viii)(A) Containers and heaters shall comply with and be used in accordance with paragraph (c)(5)(v) of this section.

(c)(5)(viii)(B) The temporary heating equipment shall not be left unattended.

(c)(5)(ix) Containers are permitted to be used temporarily in buildings for training purposes related in installation and use of LP-Gas systems, as follows:

(c)(5)(ix)(A) The maximum water capacity of individual containers shall be 245 pounds (nominal 100 pounds LP-Gas capacity), but the maximum quantity of LP-Gas that may be placed in each container shall be 20 pounds.

(c)(5)(ix)(B) If more than one such container is located in the same room, the containers shall be separated by at least 20 feet.

(c)(6) Container valves and accessories

(c)(6)(i) Valves in the assembly of multiple container systems shall be arranged so that replacement of containers can be made without shutting off the flow of gas in the system.

Note: *This provision is not to be construed as requiring an automatic changeover device.*

(c)(6)(ii) Regulators and low-pressure relief devices shall be rigidly attached to the cylinder valves, cylinders, supporting standards, the building walls or otherwise rigidly secured and shall be so installed or protected that the elements (sleet, snow, or ice) will not affect their operation.

(c)(6)(iii) Valves and connections to the containers shall be protected while in transit, in storage, and while being moved into final utilization, as follows:

(c)(6)(iii)(A) By setting into the recess of the container to prevent the possibility of their being struck if the container is dropped upon a flat surface, or

(c)(6)(iii)(B) By ventilated cap or collar, fastened to the container capable of withstanding a blow from any direction equivalent to that of a 30-pound weight dropped 4 feet. Construction must be such that a blow will not be transmitted to the valve or other connection.

(c)(6)(iv) When containers are not connected to the system, the outlet valves shall be kept tightly closed or plugged, even though containers are considered empty.

(c)(6)(v) Containers having a water capacity in excess of 50 pounds (approximately 21 pounds LP-Gas capacity), recharged at the installation, shall be provided with excess flow or backflow check valves to prevent the discharge of container contents in case of failure of the filling or equalizing connection.

(c)(7) Safety devices

(c)(7)(i) Containers shall be provided with safety devices as required by DOT regulations.

(c)(7)(ii) A final stage regulator of an LP-Gas system (excluding any appliance regulator) shall be equipped on the low-pressure side with a relief valve which is set to start to discharge within the limits specified in Table H–30.

Table H–30

Regulator delivery pressure	Relief valve start-to-discharge pressure setting (percent of regulator delivery pressure)	
	Minimum	Maximum
1 p.s.i.g. or less	200	300
Above 1 p.s.i.g. but not over 3 p.s.i.g	140	200
Above 3 p.s.i.g	125	200

(c)(7)(iii) When a regulator or pressure relief valve is used inside a building for other than purposes specified in paragraphs (b)(6)(i)(A)–(G) of this section, the relief valve and the space above the regulator and relief valve diaphragms shall be vented to the outside air with the discharge outlet located not less than 3 feet horizontally away from any building opening which is below such discharge. These provisions do not apply to individual appliance regulators when protection is otherwise provided nor to paragraph (c)(5) of this section and paragraph (b)(10)(xiii) of this section. In buildings devoted exclusively to gas distribution purposes, the space above the diaphragm need not be vented to the outside.

(c)(8) **Reinstallation of containers** Containers shall not be reinstalled unless they are requalified in accordance with DOT regulations.

(c)(9) **Permissible product** A product shall not be placed in a container marked with a service pressure less than four-fifths of the maximum vapor pressure of product at 130 °F.

(d) **Systems utilizing containers other than DOT containers**

(d)(1) **Application** This paragraph applies specifically to systems utilizing storage containers other than those constructed in accordance with DOT specifications. Paragraph (b) of this section applies to this paragraph unless otherwise noted in paragraph (b) of this section.

(d)(2) **Design pressure and classification of storage containers** Storage containers shall be designed and classified in accordance with Table H–31.

Table H–31

Container type	For gases with vapor press. Not to exceed lb. per sq. in. gage at 100 °F. (37.8 °C.)	Minimum design pressure of container, lb. per sq. in. gage	
		1949 and earlier editions of ASME Code (Par. U–68, U–69)	1949 edition of ASME Code (Par. U–200, U–201); 1950, 1952, 1956, 1959, 1962, 1965, and 1968 (Division 1) editions of ASME Code; All editions of API-ASME Code[3]
[1]80	[1]80	[1]80	[1]100
100	100	100	125
125	125	125	156
150	150	150	187
175	175	175	219
[2]200	215	200	250

[1] New storage containers of the 80 type have not been authorized since Dec. 31, 1947.

[2] Container type may be increased by increments of 25. The minimum design pressure of containers shall be 100% of the container type designation when constructed under 1949 or earlier editions of the ASME Code (Par. U–68 and U–69). The minimum design pressure of containers shall be 125% of the container type designation when constructed under: (1) the 1949 ASME Code (Par. U–200 and U–201), (2) 1950, 1952, 1956, 1959, 1962, 1965, and 1968 (Division 1) editions of the ASME Code, and (3) all editions of the API-ASME Code.

[3] Construction of containers under the API-ASME Code is not authorized after July 1, 1961.

(d)(3) **Container valves and accessories, filler pipes, and discharge pipes**

(d)(3)(i) The filling pipe inlet terminal shall not be located inside a building. For containers with a water capacity of 125 gallons or more, such terminals shall be located not less than 10 feet from any building (see paragraph (b)(6)(ii) of this section), and preferably not less than 5 feet from any driveway, and shall be located in a protective housing built for the purpose.

(d)(3)(ii) The filling connection shall be fitted with one of the following:

(d)(3)(ii)(A) Combination back-pressure check valve and excess flow valve;

(d)(3)(ii)(B) One double or two single back-pressure check valves;

(d)(3)(ii)(C) A positive shutoff valve, in conjunction with either:

(d)(3)(ii)(C)(1) An internal back-pressure valve; or

(d)(3)(ii)(C)(2) An internal excess flow valve.

(d)(3)(iii) All openings in a container shall be equipped with approved automatic excess flow valves except in the following: Filling connections as provided in paragraph (d)(3)(ii) of this section; safety relief connections, liquid-level gaging devices as provided in paragraphs (b)(7)(iv), (19)(iii), and (19)(viii) of this section; pressure gage connections as provided in paragraph (b)(7)(v) of this section, as provided in paragraphs (d)(iv), (vi), and (vii) of this section.

(d)(3)(iv) An excess flow valve is not required in the withdrawal service line providing the following are complied with:

(d)(3)(iv)(A) Such systems' total water capacity does not exceed 2,000 U.S. gallons.

(d)(3)(iv)(B) The discharge from the service outlet is controlled by a suitable manually operated shutoff valve which is:

(d)(3)(iv)(B)(1) Threaded directly into the service outlet of the container; or

(d)(3)(iv)(B)(2) Is an integral part of a substantial fitting threaded into or on the service outlet of the container; or

(d)(3)(iv)(B)(3) Threaded directly into a substantial fitting threaded into or on the service outlet of the container.

(d)(3)(iv)(C) The shutoff valve is equipped with an attached handwheel or the equivalent.

(d)(3)(iv)(D) The controlling orifice between the contents of the container and the outlet of the shutoff valve does not exceed five-sixteenths inch in diameter for vapor withdrawal systems and one-eighth inch in diameter for liquid withdrawal systems.

(d)(3)(iv)(E) An approved pressure-reducing regulator is directly attached to the outlet of the shutoff valve and is rigidly supported, or that an approved pressure-reducing regulator is attached to the outlet of the shutoff valve by means of a suitable flexible connection, provided the regulator is adequately supported and properly protected on or at the tank.

(d)(3)(v) All inlet and outlet connections except safety relief valves, liquid level gaging devices and pressure gages on containers of 2,000 gallons water capacity, or more, and on any container used to supply fuel directly to an internal combustion engine, shall be labeled to designate whether they communicate with vapor or liquid space. Labels may be on valves.

(d)(3)(vi) In lieu of an excess flow valve openings may be fitted with a quick-closing internal valve which, except during operating periods shall remain closed. The internal mechanism for such valves may be provided with a secondary control which shall be equipped with a fusible plug (not over 220 °F. melting point) which will cause the internal valve to close automatically in case of fire.

(d)(3)(vii) Not more than two plugged openings shall be permitted on a container of 2,000 gallons or less water capacity.

(d)(3)(viii) Containers of 125 gallons water capacity or more manufactured after July 1, 1961, shall be provided with an approved device for liquid evacuation, the size of which shall be three-fourths inch National Pipe Thread minimum. A plugged opening will not satisfy this requirement.

(d)(4) **Safety devices**

(d)(4)(i) All safety devices shall comply with the following:

(d)(4)(i)(A) All container safety relief devices shall be located on the containers and shall have direct communication with the vapor of space of the container;

(d)(4)(i)(B) In industrial and gas manufacturing plants, discharge pipe from safety relief valves on pipe lines within a building shall discharge vertically upward and shall be piped to a point outside a building;

(d)(4)(i)(C) Safety relief device discharge terminals shall be so located as to provide protection against physical damage and such discharge pipes shall be fitted with loose raincaps. Return bends and restrictive pipefittings shall not be permitted;

(d)(4)(i)(D) If desired, discharge lines from two or more safety relief devices located on the same unit, or similar lines from two or more different units, may be run into a common discharge header, provided that the cross-sectional area of such header be at least equal to the sum of the cross-sectional area of the individual discharge lines, and that the setting of safety relief valves are the same;

(d)(4)(i)(E) Each storage container of over 2,000 gallons water capacity shall be provided with a suitable pressure gage;

(d)(4)(i)(F) A final stage regulator of an LP-Gas system (excluding any appliance regulator) shall be equipped on the low-pressure side with a relief valve which is set to start to discharge within the limits specified in Table H–30;

(d)(4)(i)(G) When a regulator or pressure relief valve is installed inside a building, the relief valve and the space above the regulator and relief valve diaphragms shall be vented to the outside air with the discharge outlet located not less than 3 feet horizontally away from any opening into the building which is below such discharge. (These provisions do not apply to individual appliance regulators when protection is otherwise provided. In buildings devoted exclusively to gas distribution purposes, the space above the diaphragm need not be vented to the outside.)

(d)(4)(ii) Safety devices for aboveground containers shall be provided as follows:

(d)(4)(ii)(A) Containers of 1,200 gallons water capacity or less which may contain liquid fuel when installed above ground shall have the rate of discharge required by paragraph (b)(10)(ii) of this section provided by a spring-loaded relief valve or valves. In addition to the required spring-loaded relief valve(s), suitable fuse plug(s) may be used provided the total discharge area of the fuse plug(s) for each container does not exceed 0.25 square inch;

(d)(4)(ii)(B) The fusible metal of the fuse plugs shall have a yield temperature of 208 °F. minimum and 220 °F. maximum. Relief valves and fuse plugs shall have direct communication with the vapor space of the container;

(d)(4)(ii)(C) On a container having a water capacity greater than 125 gallons, but not over 2,000 gallons, the discharge from the safety relief valves shall be vented away from the container vertically upwards and unobstructed to the open air in such a manner as to prevent any impingement of escaping gas upon the container; loose-fitting rain caps shall be used. Suitable provision shall be made for draining condensate which may accumulate in the relief valve or its discharge pipe;

(d)(4)(ii)(D) On containers of 125 gallons water capacity or less, the discharge from safety relief devices shall be located not less than 5 feet horizontally away from any opening into the building below the level of such discharge;

(d)(4)(ii)(E) On a container having a water capacity greater than 2,000 gallons, the discharge from the safety relief valves shall be vented away from the container vertically upwards to a point at least 7 feet above the container, and unobstructed to the open air in such a manner as to prevent any impingement of escaping gas upon the container; loose-fitting rain caps shall be used. Suitable provision shall be made so that any liquid or condensate that may accumulate inside of the safety relief valve or its discharge pipe will not render the valve inoperative. If a drain is used, a means shall be provided to protect the container, adjacent containers, piping, or equipment against impingement of flame resulting from ignition of product escaping from the drain.

(d)(4)(iii) On all containers which are installed underground and which contain no liquid fuel until buried and covered, the rate of discharge of the spring-loaded relief valve installed thereon may be reduced to a minimum of 30 percent of the rate of discharge specified in paragraph (b)(10)(ii) of this section. Containers so protected shall not be uncovered after installation until the liquid fuel has been removed therefrom. Containers which may contain liquid fuel before being installed under ground and before being completely covered with earth are to be considered aboveground containers when determining the rate of discharge requirement of the relief valves.

(d)(4)(iv) On underground containers of more than 2,000 gallons water capacity, the discharge from safety relief devices shall be piped vertically and directly upward to a point at least 7 feet above the ground.

Where there is a probability of the manhole or housing becoming flooded, the discharge from regulator vent lines shall be above the highest probable water level. All manholes or housings shall be provided with ventilated louvers or their equivalent, the area of such openings equaling or exceeding the combined discharge areas of the safety relief valves and other vent lines which discharge their content into the manhole housing.

(d)(4)(v) Safety devices for vaporizers shall be provided as follows:

(d)(4)(v)(A) Vaporizers of less than 1 quart total capacity, heated by the ground or the surrounding air, need not be equipped with safety relief valves provided that adequate tests certified by any of the authorities referred to in paragraph (b)(2) of this section, demonstrate that the assembly is safe without safety relief valves.

(d)(4)(v)(B) No vaporizer shall be equipped with fusible plugs.

(d)(4)(v)(C) In industrial and gas manufacturing plants, safety relief valves on vaporizers within a building shall be piped to a point outside the building and be discharged upward.

(d)(5) **Reinstallation of containers** Containers may be reinstalled if they do not show any evidence of harmful external corrosion or other damage. Where containers are reinstalled underground, the corrosion resistant coating shall be put in good condition (see paragraph (c)(7)(vi) of this section). Where containers are reinstalled above ground, the safety devices and gaging devices shall comply with paragraph (c)(4) of this section and paragraph (b)(19) of this section respectively for aboveground containers.

(d)(6) **Capacity of containers** A storage container shall not exceed 90,000 gallons water capacity.

(d)(7) **Installation of storage containers**

(d)(7)(i) Containers installed above ground, except as provided in paragraph (c)(7)(vii) of this section, shall be provided with substantial masonry or noncombustible structural supports on firm masonry foundation.

(d)(7)(ii) Aboveground containers shall be supported as follows:

(d)(7)(ii)(A) Horizontal containers shall be mounted on saddles in such a manner as to permit expansion and contraction. Structural metal supports may be employed when they are protected against fire in an approved manner. Suitable means of preventing corrosion shall be provided on that portion of the container in contact with the foundations or saddles.

(d)(7)(ii)(B) Containers of 2,000 gallons water capacity or less may be installed with nonfireproofed ferrous metal supports if mounted on concrete pads or footings, and if the distance from the outside bottom of the container shell to the concrete pad, footing, or the ground does not exceed 24 inches.

(d)(7)(iii) Any container may be installed with nonfireproofed ferrous metal supports if mounted on concrete pads or footings, and if the distance from the outside bottom of the container to the ground does not exceed 5 feet, provided the container is in an isolated location.

(d)(7)(iv) Containers may be partially buried providing the following requirements are met:

(d)(7)(iv)(A) The portion of the container below the surface and for a vertical distance not less than 3 inches above the surface of the ground is protected to resist corrosion, and the container is protected against settling and corrosion as required for fully buried containers;

(d)(7)(iv)(B) Spacing requirements shall be as specified for underground tanks in paragraph (b)(6)(ii) of this section;

(d)(7)(iv)(C) Relief valve capacity shall be as required for aboveground containers;

(d)(7)(iv)(D) Container is located so as not to be subject to vehicular damage, or is adequately protected against such damage;

(d)(7)(iv)(E) Filling densities shall be as required for above-ground containers.

(d)(7)(v) Containers buried underground shall be placed so that the top of the container is not less than 6 inches below grade. Where an underground container might be subject to abrasive action or physical damage due to vehicular traffic or other causes, then it shall be:

(d)(7)(v)(A) Placed not less than 2 feet below grade; or

(d)(7)(v)(B) Otherwise protected against such physical damage.

It will not be necessary to cover the portion of the container to which manhole and other connections are affixed; however, where necessary, protection shall be provided against vehicular damage. When necessary to prevent floating, containers shall be securely anchored or weighted.

(d)(7)(vi)(A) Containers shall be given a protective coating before being placed under ground. This coating shall be equivalent to hot-dip galvanizing or to two coatings of red lead followed by a heavy coating of coal tar or asphalt. In lowering the container into place, care shall be exercised to prevent damage to the coating. Any damage to the coating shall be repaired before backfilling.

(d)(7)(vi)(B) Containers shall be set on a firm foundation (firm earth may be used) and surrounded with earth or sand firmly tamped in place.

(d)(7)(vii) Containers with foundations attached (portable or semiportable containers with suitable steel "runners" or "skids" and popularly known in the industry as "skid tanks") shall be designed, installed, and used in accordance with these rules subject to the following provisions:

(d)(7)(vii)(A) If they are to be used at a given general location for a temporary period not to exceed 6 months they need not have fire-resisting foundations or saddles but shall have adequate ferrous metal supports;

(d)(7)(vii)(B) They shall not be located with the outside bottom of the container shell more than 5 feet above the surface of the ground unless fire-resisting supports are provided;

(d)(7)(vii)(C) The bottom of the skids shall not be less than 2 inches or more than 12 inches below the outside bottom of the container shell;

(d)(7)(vii)(D) Flanges, nozzles, valves, fittings, and the like, having communication with the interior of the container, shall be protected against physical damage;

(d)(7)(vii)(E) When not permanently located on fire-resisting foundations, piping connections shall be sufficiently flexible to minimize the possibility of breakage or leakage of connections if the container settles, moves, or is otherwise displaced;

(d)(7)(vii)(F) Skids, or lugs for attachment of skids, shall be secured to the container in accordance with the code or rules under which the container is designed and built (with a minimum factor of safety of four) to withstand loading in any direction equal to four times the weight of the container and attachments when filled to the maximum permissible loaded weight.

(d)(7)(viii) Field welding where necessary shall be made only on saddle plates or brackets which were applied by the manufacturer of the tank.

(d)(7)(ix) For aboveground containers, secure anchorage or adequate pier height shall be provided against possible container flotation wherever sufficiently high floodwater might occur.

(d)(7)(x) When permanently installed containers are interconnected, provision shall be made to compensate for expansion, contraction, vibration, and settling of containers, and interconnecting piping. Where flexible connections are used, they shall be of an approved type and shall be designed for a bursting pressure of not less than five times the vapor pressure of the product at 100 °F. The use of nonmetallic hose is prohibited for permanently interconnecting such containers.

(d)(7)(xi) Container assemblies listed for interchangeable installation above ground or under ground shall conform to the requirements for aboveground installations with respect to safety relief capacity and filling density. For installation above ground all other requirements for aboveground installations shall apply. For installation under ground all other requirements for underground installations shall apply.

(d)(8) **Protection of container accessories**

(d)(8)(i) Valves, regulating, gaging, and other container accessory equipment shall be protected against tampering and physical damage. Such accessories shall also be so protected during the transit of containers intended for installation underground.

(d)(8)(ii) On underground or combination aboveground-underground containers, the service valve handwheel, the terminal for connecting the hose, and the opening through which there can be a flow from safety relief valves shall be at least 4 inches above the container and this opening shall be located in the dome or housing. Underground systems shall be so installed that all the above openings, including the regulator vent, are located above the normal maximum water table.

(d)(8)(iii) All connections to underground containers shall be located within a substantial dome, housing, or manhole and with access thereto protected by a substantial cover.

(d)(9) **Drips for condensed gas** Where vaporized gas on the low-pressure side of the system may condense to a liquid at normal operating temperatures and pressures, suitable means shall be provided for revaporization of the condensate.

(d)(10) **Damage from vehicles** When damage to LP-Gas systems from vehicular traffic is a possibility, precautions against such damage shall be taken.

(d)(11) **Drains** No drains or blowoff lines shall be directed into or in proximity to sewer systems used for other purposes.

(d)(12) **General provisions applicable to systems in industrial plants (of 2,000 gallons water capacity and more) and to bulk filling plants**

(d)(12)(i) When standard watch service is provided, it shall be extended to the LP-Gas installation and personnel properly trained.

(d)(12)(ii) If loading and unloading are normally done during other than daylight hours, adequate lights shall be provided to illuminate storage containers, control valves, and other equipment.

(d)(12)(iii) Suitable roadways or means of access for extinguishing equipment such as wheeled extinguishers or fire department apparatus shall be provided.

(d)(12)(iv) To minimize trespassing or tampering, the area which includes container appurtenances, pumping equipment, loading and unloading facilities, and cylinder-filling facilities shall be enclosed with at least a 6-foot-high industrial type fence unless otherwise adequately protected. There shall be at least two means of emergency access.

(d)(13) **Container-charging plants**

(d)(13)(i) [OI] The container-charging room shall be located not less than:

(d)(13)(i)(A) Ten feet from bulk storage containers.

(d)(13)(i)(B) [Reserved]

(d)(13)(ii) Tank truck filling station outlets shall be located not less than:

(d)(13)(ii)(A) [Reserved]

(d)(13)(ii)(B) Ten feet from pumps and compressors if housed in one or more separate buildings.

(d)(13)(iii) [OI] The pumps or compressors may be located in the container-charging room or building, in a separate building, or outside of buildings. When housed in a separate building, such building (a small noncombustible weather cover is not to be construed as a building) shall be located not less than:

(d)(13)(iii)(A) Ten feet from bulk storage tanks.

(d)(13)(iii)(B) [Reserved]

(d)(13)(iii)(C) Twenty-five feet from sources of ignition.

(d)(13)(iv) When a part of the container-charging building is to be used for a boiler room or where open flames or similar sources of ignition exist or are employed, the space to be so occupied shall be separated from container charging room by a partition wall or walls of fire-resistant construction continuous from floor to roof or ceiling. Such separation walls shall be without openings and shall be joined to the floor, other walls, and ceiling or roof in a manner to effect a permanent gas-tight joint.

(d)(13)(v) Electrical equipment and installations shall conform with paragraphs (b)(17) and (18) of this section.

(d)(14) **Fire protection**

(d)(14)(i) Each bulk plant shall be provided with at least one approved portable fire extinguisher having a minimum rating of 12–B, C.

(d)(14)(ii) In industrial installations involving containers of 150,000 gallons aggregate water capacity or more, provision shall be made for an adequate supply of water at the container site for fire protection in the container area, unless other adequate means for fire control are provided. Water hydrants shall be readily accessible and so spaced as to provide water protection for all containers. Sufficient lengths of firehose shall be provided at each hydrant location on a hose cart, or other means provided to facilitate easy movement of the hose in the container area. It is desirable to equip the outlet of each hose line with a combination fog nozzle. A shelter shall be provided to protect the hose and its conveyor from the weather.

(d)(15) [Reserved]

(d)(16) **Lighting** Electrical equipment and installations shall conform to paragraphs (b)(17) and (18) of this section.

(d)(17) **Vaporizers for internal combustion engines** The provisions of paragraph (e)(8) of this section shall apply.

(d)(18) **Gas regulating and mixing equipment for internal combustion engines** The provisions of paragraph (e)(9) of this section shall apply.

(e) **Liquefied petroleum gas as a motor fuel**

(e)(1) **Application**

(e)(1)(i) This paragraph applies to internal combustion engines, fuel containers, and pertinent equipment for the use of liquefied petroleum gases as a motor fuel on easily movable, readily portable units including self-propelled vehicles.

(e)(1)(ii) Fuel containers and pertinent equipment for internal combustion engines using liquefied petroleum gas where installation is of the stationary type are covered by paragraph (d) of this section. This paragraph does not apply to containers for transportation of liquefied petroleum gases nor to marine fuel use. All requirements of paragraph (b) of this section apply to this paragraph, unless otherwise noted in paragraph (b) of this section.

(e)(2) **General**

(e)(2)(i) Fuel may be used from the cargo tank of a truck while in transit, but not from cargo tanks on trailers or semitrailers. The use of fuel from the cargo tanks to operate stationary engines is permitted providing wheels are securely blocked.

(e)(2)(ii) Passenger-carrying vehicles shall not be fueled while passengers are on board.

(e)(2)(iii) Industrial trucks (including lift trucks) equipped with permanently mounted fuel containers shall be charged outdoors. Charging equipment shall comply with the provisions of paragraph (h) of this section.

(e)(2)(iv) LP-Gas fueled industrial trucks shall comply with the Standard for Type Designations, Areas of Use, Maintenance and Operation of Powered Industrial Trucks, NFPA 505–1969, which is incorporated by reference as specified in §1910.6.

(e)(2)(v) Engines on vehicles shall be shut down while fueling if the fueling operation involves venting to the atmosphere.

(e)(3) **Design pressure and classification of fuel containers**

(e)(3)(i) Except as covered in paragraphs (e)(3)(ii) and (iii) of this section, containers shall be in accordance with Table H–32.

(e)(3)(ii) Fuel containers for use in industrial trucks (including lift trucks) shall be either DOT containers authorized for LP-Gas service having a minimum service pressure of 240 p.s.i.g. or minimum Container Type 250. Under 1950 and later ASME codes, this means a 312.5–p.s.i.g. design pressure container.

Table H–32

Container type	For gases with vapor press. Not to exceed lb. per sq. in. gage at 100 °F. (37.8 °C.)	Minimum design pressure of container, lb. per sq. in. gage	
		1949 and earlier editions of ASME Code (Par. U–68, U–69)	1949 edition of ASME Code (Par. U–200, U–201); 1950, 1952, 1956, 1959, 1962, 1965, and 1968 (Division 1) editions of ASME Code; All editions of API-ASME Code[2]
[1]200	215Z	200	250

[1] Container type may be increased by increments of 25. The minimum design pressure of containers shall be 100% of the container type designation when constructed under 1949 or earlier editions of the ASME Code (Par. U–68 and U–69). The minimum design pressure of containers shall be 125% of the container type designation when constructed under: (1) the 1949 ASME Code (Par. U–200 and U–201), (2) 1950, 1952, 1956, 1959, 1962, 1965, and 1968 (Division 1) editions of the ASME Code, and (3) all editions of the API-ASME Code.

[2] Construction of containers under the API-ASME Code is not authorized after July 1, 1961.

[OI] indicates an OSHA Letter of Interpretation exists for this specific reference. Please see www.oshainterpretation.us for details.

(e)(3)(iii) Containers manufactured and maintained under DOT specifications and regulations may be used as fuel containers. When so used they shall conform to all requirements of this paragraph.

(e)(3)(iv) All container inlets and outlets except safety relief valves and gaging devices shall be labeled to designate whether they communicate with vapor or liquid space. Labels may be on valves.

(e)(4) **Installation of fuel containers**

(e)(4)(i) [OI] Containers shall be located in a place and in a manner to minimize the possibility of damage to the container. Containers located in the rear of trucks and buses, when protected by substantial bumpers, will be considered in conformance with this requirement. Fuel containers on passenger-carrying vehicles shall be installed as far from the engine as is practicable, and the passenger space and any space containing radio equipment shall be sealed from the container space to prevent direct seepage of gas to these spaces. The container compartment shall be vented to the outside. In case the fuel container is mounted near the engine or the exhaust system, the container shall be shielded against direct heat radiation.

(e)(4)(ii) Containers shall be installed with as much clearance as practicable but never less than the minimum road clearance of the vehicle under maximum spring deflection. This minimum clearance shall be to the bottom of the container or to the lowest fitting on the container or housing, whichever is lower.

(e)(4)(iii) Permanent and removable fuel containers shall be securely mounted to prevent jarring loose, slipping, or rotating, and the fastenings shall be designed and constructed to withstand static loading in any direction equal to twice the weight of the tank and attachments when filled with fuel using a safety factor of not less than four based on the ultimate strength of the material to be used. Field welding, when necessary, shall be made only on saddle plates, lugs or brackets, originally attached to the container by the tank manufacturer.

(e)(4)(iv) Fuel containers on buses shall be permanently installed.

(e)(4)(v) Containers from which vapor only is to be withdrawn shall be installed and equipped with suitable connections to minimize the accidental withdrawal of liquid.

(e)(5) **Valves and accessories**

(e)(5)(i) Container valves and accessories shall have a rated working pressure of at least 250 p.s.i.g., and shall be of a type suitable for liquefied petroleum gas service.

(e)(5)(ii) The filling connection shall be fitted with an approved double back-pressure check valve, or a positive shutoff in conjunction with an internal back-pressure check valve. On a removable container the filler valve may be a hand operated shutoff valve with an internal excess flow valve. Main shutoff valves on the container on liquid and vapor lines must be readily accessible.

(e)(5)(iii) With the exceptions of paragraph (e)(5)(iv)(C) of this section, filling connections equipped with approved automatic back-pressure check valves, and safety relief valves, all connections to containers having openings for the flow of gas in excess of a No. 54 drill size shall be equipped with approved automatic excess flow valves to prevent discharge of content in case connections are broken.

(e)(5)(iv) **Liquid-level gaging devices:**

(e)(5)(iv)(A) Variable liquid-level gages which require the venting of fuel to the atmosphere shall not be used on fuel containers of industrial trucks (including lift trucks);

(e)(5)(iv)(B) On portable containers that may be filled in the vertical and/or horizontal position, the fixed liquid-level gage must indicate maximum permitted filling level for both vertical and horizontal filling with the container oriented to place the safety relief valve in communication with the vapor space;

(e)(5)(iv)(C) In the case of containers used solely in farm tractor service, and charged at a point at least 50 feet from any important building, the fixed liquid-level gaging device may be so constructed that the outward flow of container content exceeds that passed by a No. 54 drill size opening, but in no case shall the flow exceed that passed by a No. 31 drill-size opening. An excess flow valve is not required. Fittings equipped with such restricted drill size opening and container on which they are used shall be marked to indicate the size of the opening;

(e)(5)(iv)(D) All valves and connections on containers shall be adequately protected to prevent damage due to accidental contact with stationary objects or from loose objects thrown up from the road, and all valves shall be safeguarded against damage due to collision, overturning or other accident. For farm tractors where parts of the vehicle provide such protection to valves and fittings, the foregoing requirements shall be considered fulfilled. However, on removable type containers the protection for the fittings shall be permanently attached to the container;

(e)(5)(iv)(E) When removable fuel containers are used, means shall be provided in the fuel system to minimize the escape of fuel when the containers are exchanged. This may be accomplished by either of the following methods:

(e)(5)(iv)(E)(*1*) Using an approved automatic quick-closing coupling (a type closing in both directions when uncoupled) in the fuel line; or

(e)(5)(iv)(E)(*2*) Closing the valve at the fuel container and allowing the engine to run until the fuel in the line is consumed.

(e)(6) **Piping—including pipe, tubing, and fittings**

(e)(6)(i) Pipe from fuel container to first-stage regulator shall be not less than schedule 80 wrought iron or steel (black or galvanized), brass or copper; or seamless copper, brass, or steel tubing. Steel tubing shall have a minimum wall thickness of 0.049 inch. Steel pipe or tubing shall be adequately protected against exterior corrosion. Copper tubing shall be types K or L or equivalent having a minimum wall thickness of 0.032 inch. Approved flexible connections may be used between container and regulator or between regulator and gas-air mixer within the limits of approval. The use of aluminum pipe or tubing is prohibited. In the case of removable containers an approved flexible connection shall be used between the container and the fuel line.

(e)(6)(ii) All piping shall be installed, braced, and supported so as to reduce to a minimum the possibility of vibration strains or wear.

(e)(7) **Safety devices**

(e)(7)(i) Spring-loaded internal type safety relief valves shall be used on all motor fuel containers.

(e)(7)(ii) The discharge outlet from safety relief valves shall be located on the outside of enclosed spaces and as far as practicable from possible sources of ignition, and vented upward within 45 degrees of the vertical in such a manner as to prevent impingement of escaping gas upon containers, or parts of vehicles, or on vehicles in adjacent lines of traffic. A rain cap or other protector shall be used to keep water and dirt from collecting in the valve.

(e)(7)(iii) When a discharge line from the container safety relief valve is used, the line shall be metallic, other than aluminum, and shall be sized, located, and maintained so as not to restrict the required flow of gas from the safety relief valve. Such discharge line shall be able to withstand the pressure resulting from the discharge of vapor when the safety relief valve is in the full open position. When flexibility is necessary, flexible metal hose or tubing shall be used.

(e)(7)(iv) Portable containers equipped for volumetric filling may be filled in either the vertical or horizontal position only when oriented to place the safety relief valve in communication with the vapor space.

(e)(7)(v) Paragraph (b)(10)(xii) of this section for hydrostatic relief valves shall apply.

(e)(8) **Vaporizers**

(e)(8)(i) Vaporizers and any part thereof and other devices that may be subjected to container pressure shall have a design pressure of at least 250 p.s.i.g.

(e)(8)(ii) Each vaporizer shall have a valve or suitable plug which will permit substantially complete draining of the vaporizer. It shall be located at or near the lowest portion of the section occupied by the water or other heating medium.

(e)(8)(iii) Vaporizers shall be securely fastened so as to minimize the possibility of becoming loosened.

(e)(8)(iv) Each vaporizer shall be permanently marked at a visible point as follows:

(e)(8)(iv)(A) With the design pressure of the fuel-containing portion in p.s.i.g.

(e)(8)(iv)(B) With the water capacity of the fuel-containing portion of the vaporizer in pounds.

(e)(8)(v) Devices to supply heat directly to a fuel container shall be equipped with an automatic device to cut off the supply of heat before the pressure inside the fuel container reaches 80 percent of the start to discharge pressure setting of the safety relief device on the fuel container.

(e)(8)(vi) Engine exhaust gases may be used as a direct source of heat supply for the vaporization of fuel if the materials of construction of those parts of the vaporizer in contact with exhaust gases are resistant to the corrosive action of exhaust gases and the vaporizer system is designed to prevent excessive pressures.

(e)(8)(vii) Vaporizers shall not be equipped with fusible plugs.

(e)(9) **Gas regulating and mixing equipment**

(e)(9)(i) Approved automatic pressure reducing equipment shall be installed in a secure manner between the fuel supply container and gas-air mixer for the purpose of reducing the pressure of the fuel delivered to the gas-air mixer.

(e)(9)(ii) An approved automatic shutoff valve shall be provided in the fuel system at some point ahead of the inlet of the gas-air mixer, designed to prevent flow of fuel to the mixer when the ignition is off and the engine is not running. In the case of industrial trucks and engines operating in buildings other than those used exclusively to house engines, the automatic shutoff valve shall be designed to operate if the engine should stop. Atmospheric type regulators (zero governors) shall be considered adequate as an automatic shutoff valve only in cases of outdoor operation such as farm tractors, construction equipment, irrigation pump engines, and other outdoor stationary engine installations.

(e)(9)(iii) The source of the air for combustion shall be completely isolated from the passenger compartment, ventilating system, or air-conditioning system.

(e)(10) [Reserved]

(e)(11) **Stationary engines in buildings** Stationary engines and gas turbines installed in buildings, including portable engines used instead of or to supplement stationary engines, shall comply with the Standard for the Institution and Use of Stationary Combustion Engines and Gas Turbines, NFPA 37–1970, and the appropriate provisions of paragraphs (b), (c), and (d) of this section.

(e)(12) **Portable engines in buildings**

(e)(12)(i) Portable engines may be used in buildings only for emergency use, except as provided by subparagraph (11) of this paragraph.

(e)(12)(ii) Exhaust gases shall be discharged to outside the building or to an area where they will not constitute a hazard.

(e)(12)(iii) Provision shall be made to supply sufficient air for combustion and cooling.

(e)(12)(iv) An approved automatic shutoff valve shall be provided in the fuel system ahead of the engine, designed to prevent flow of fuel to the engine when the ignition is off or if the engine should stop.

(e)(12)(v) The capacity of LP-Gas containers used with such engines shall comply with the applicable occupancy provision of paragraph (c)(5) of this section.

(e)(13) **Industrial trucks inside buildings**

(e)(13)(i) LP-Gas-fueled industrial trucks are permitted to be used in buildings and structures.

(e)(13)(ii) No more than two LP-Gas containers shall be used on an industrial truck for motor fuel purposes.

(e)(13)(iii)–(iv) [Reserved]

(e)(13)(v) Industrial trucks shall not be parked and left unattended in areas of possible excessive heat or sources of ignition.

(e)(14) **Garaging LP-Gas-fueled vehicles**

(e)(14)(i) LP-Gas-fueled vehicles may be stored or serviced inside garages provided there are no leaks in the fuel system and the fuel tanks are not filled beyond the maximum filling capacity specified in paragraph (b)(12)(i) of this section.

(e)(14)(ii) LP-Gas-fueled vehicles being repaired in garages shall have the container shutoff valve closed except when fuel is required for engine operation.

(e)(14)(iii) Such vehicles shall not be parked near sources of heat, open flames, or similar sources of ignition or near open pits unless such pits are adequately ventilated.

(f) **Storage of containers awaiting use or resale**

(f)(1) Application. This paragraph shall apply to the storage of portable containers not in excess of 1,000 pounds water capacity, filled or partially filled, at user location but not connected for use, or in storage for resale by dealers or resellers. This paragraph shall not apply to containers stored at charging plants or at plants devoted primarily to the storage and distribution of LP-Gas or other petroleum products.

(f)(2) **General**

(f)(2)(i) Containers in storage shall be located so as to minimize exposure to excessive temperature rise, physical damage, or tampering by unauthorized persons.

(f)(2)(ii) Containers when stored inside shall not be located near exits, stairways, or in areas normally used or intended for the safe exit of people.

(f)(2)(iii) Container valves shall be protected while in storage as follows:

(f)(2)(iii)(A) By setting into recess of container to prevent the possibility of their being struck if the container is dropped upon a flat surface, or

(f)(2)(iii)(B) By ventilated cap or collar, fastened to container capable of withstanding blow from any direction equivalent to that of a 30-pound weight dropped 4 feet. Construction must be such that a blow will not be transmitted to a valve or other connection.

(f)(2)(iv) The outlet valves of containers in storage shall be closed.

(f)(2)(v) Empty containers which have been in LP-Gas service when stored inside, shall be considered as full containers for the purpose of determining the maximum quantity of LP-Gas permitted by this paragraph.

(f)(3) [Reserved]

(f)(4) **Storage within buildings not frequented by the public (such as industrial buildings)**

(f)(4)(i) The quantity of LP-Gas stored shall not exceed 300 pounds (approximately 2,550 cubic feet in vapor form) except as provided in subparagraph (5) of this paragraph.

(f)(4)(ii) Containers carried as a part of service equipment on highway mobile vehicles are not to be considered in the total storage capacity in subdivision (i) of this subparagraph provided such vehicles are stored in private garages, and are limited to one container per vehicle with an LP-Gas capacity of not more than 100 pounds. All container valves shall be closed.

(f)(5) **Storage within special buildings or rooms**

(f)(5)(i) The quantity of LP-Gas stored in special buildings or rooms shall not exceed 10,000 pounds.

(f)(5)(ii) The walls, floors, and ceilings of container storage rooms that are within or adjacent to other parts of the building shall be constructed of material having at least a 2-hour fire resistance rating.

(f)(5)(iii) A portion of the exterior walls or roof having an area not less than 10 percent of that of the combined area of the enclosing walls and roof shall be of explosion relieving construction.

(f)(5)(iv) Each opening from such storage rooms to other parts of the building shall be protected by a 1 ½ hour (B) fire door listed by a nationally recognized testing laboratory. Refer to §1910.7 for definition of nationally recognized testing laboratory.

(f)(5)(v) Such rooms shall have no open flames for heating or lighting.

(f)(5)(vi) Such rooms shall be adequately ventilated both top and bottom to the outside only. The openings from such vents shall be at least 5 feet away from any other opening into any building.

(f)(5)(vii) The floors of such rooms shall not be below ground level. Any space below the floor shall be of solid fill or properly ventilated to the open air.

(f)(5)(viii) Such storage rooms shall not be located adjoining the line of property occupied by schools, churches, hospitals, athletic fields or other points of public gathering.

(f)(5)(ix) Fixed electrical equipment shall be installed in accordance with paragraph (b)(18) of this section.

(f)(6) **Storage outside of buildings**

(f)(6)(i) Storage outside of buildings, for containers awaiting use or resale, shall be located in accordance with Table H–33 with respect to:

(f)(6)(i)(A) The nearest important building or group of buildings;

(f)(6)(i)(B) [Reserved]

(f)(6)(i)(C) Busy thoroughfares;

Table H–33

Quantity of LP-Gas Stored	Distance
500 pounds or less	0
501 to 2,500 pounds	[1]0
2,501 to 6,000 pounds	10 feet
6,001 to 10,000 pounds	20 feet
Over 10,000 pounds	25 feet

[1] Container or containers shall be at least 10 feet from any building on adjoining property, any sidewalk, or any of the exposures described in §1910.110(f)(6)(i) (c) or (D) of this paragraph.

(f)(6)(ii) Containers shall be in a suitable enclosure or otherwise protected against tampering.

(f)(7) **Fire protection** Storage locations other than supply depots separated and located apart from dealer, reseller, or user establishments shall be provided with at least one approved portable fire extinguisher having a minimum rating of 8–B, C.

(g) [Reserved]

(h) **Liquefied petroleum gas service stations**

(h)(1) **Application** This paragraph applies to storage containers, and dispensing devices, and pertinent equipment in service stations where LP-Gas is stored and is dispensed into fuel tanks of motor vehicles. See paragraph (e) of this section for requirements covering use of LP-Gas as a motor fuel. All requirements of paragraph (b) of this section apply to this paragraph unless otherwise noted.

(h)(2) **Design pressure and classification of storage containers** Storage containers shall be designed and classified in accordance with Table H–34.

Table H–34

Container type	For gases with vapor press. Not to exceed lb. per sq. in. gage at 100 °F. (37.8 °C.)	Minimum design pressure of container, lb. per sq. in. gage	
		1949 and earlier editions of ASME Code (Par. U–68, U–69)	1949 edition of ASME Code (Par. U–200, U–201); 1950, 1952, 1956, 1959, 1962, 1965, and 1968 (Division 1) editions of ASME Code; All editions of API-ASME Code[2]
[1]200	215	200	250

[1] Container type may be increased by increments of 25. The minimum design pressure of containers shall be 100 percent of the container type designation when constructed under 1949 or earlier editions of the ASME Code (Par. U–68 and U–69). The minimum design pressure of containers shall be 125 percent of the container type designation when constructed under: (1) The 1949 ASME Code (Paragraphs U–200 and U–201), (2) 1950, 1952, 1956, 1959, 1962, 1965, and 1968 (Division 1) editions of the ASME Code, and (3) all editions of the API-ASME Code.

[2] Construction of containers under the API-ASME Code is not authorized after July 1, 1961.

(h)(3) Container valves and accessories

(h)(3)(i) A filling connection on the container shall be fitted with one of the following:

(h)(3)(i)(A) A combination back-pressure check and excess flow valve.

(h)(3)(i)(B) One double or two single back-pressure valves.

(h)(3)(i)(C) A positive shutoff valve, in conjunction with either,

(h)(3)(i)(C)(1) An internal back-pressure valve, or

(h)(3)(i)(C)(2) On internal excess flow valve.

In lieu of an excess flow valve, filling connections may be fitted with a quick-closing internal valve, which shall remain closed except during operating periods. The mechanism for such valves may be provided with a secondary control which will cause it to close automatically in case of fire. When a fusible plug is used its melting point shall not exceed 220 °F.

(h)(3)(ii) A filling pipe inlet terminal not on the container shall be fitted with a positive shutoff valve in conjunction with either;

(h)(3)(ii)(A) A black pressure check valve, or

(h)(3)(ii)(B) An excess flow check valve.

(h)(3)(iii) All openings in the container except those listed below shall be equipped with approved excess flow check valves:

(h)(3)(iii)(A) Filling connections as provided in subdivision (i) of this subparagraph.

(h)(3)(iii)(B) Safety relief connections as provided in paragraph (b)(7)(ii) of this section.

(h)(3)(iii)(C) Liquid-level gaging devices as provided in paragraphs (b)(7)(iv) and (19)(iv) of this section.

(h)(3)(iii)(D) Pressure gage connections as provided in paragraph (b)(7)(v) of this section.

(h)(3)(iv) All container inlets and outlets except those listed below shall be labeled to designate whether they connect with vapor or liquid (labels may be on valves):

(h)(3)(iv)(A) Safety relief valves.

(h)(3)(iv)(B) Liquid-level gaging devices.

(h)(3)(iv)(C) Pressure gages.

(h)(3)(v) Each storage container shall be provided with a suitable pressure gage.

(h)(4) Safety-relief valves

(h)(4)(i) All safety-relief devices shall be installed as follows:

(h)(4)(i)(A) On the container and directly connected with the vapor space.

(h)(4)(i)(B) Safety-relief valves and discharge piping shall be protected against physical damage. The outlet shall be provided with loose-fitting rain caps. There shall be no return bends or restrictions in the discharge piping.

(h)(4)(i)(C) The discharge from two or more safety relief valves having the same pressure settings may be run into a common discharge header. The cross-sectional area of such header shall be at least equal to the sum of the cross-sectional areas of the individual discharges.

(h)(4)(i)(D) Discharge from any safety relief device shall not terminate in any building nor beneath any building.

(h)(4)(ii) Aboveground containers shall be provided with safety relief valves as follows:

(h)(4)(ii)(A) The rate of discharge, which may be provided by one or more valves, shall be not less than that specified in paragraph (b)(10)(ii) of this section.

(h)(4)(ii)(B) The discharge from safety relief valves shall be vented to the open air unobstructed and vertically upwards in such a manner as to prevent any impingement of escaping gas upon the container; loose-fitting rain caps shall be used. On a container having a water capacity greater than 2,000 gallons, the discharge from the safety relief valves shall be vented away from the container vertically upwards to a point at least 7 feet above the container. Suitable provisions shall be made so that any liquid or condensate that may accumulate inside of the relief valve or its discharge pipe will not render the valve inoperative. If a drain is used, a means shall be provided to protect the container, adjacent containers, piping, or equipment against impingement of flame resulting from ignition of the product escaping from the drain.

(h)(4)(iii) Underground containers shall be provided with safety relief valves as follows:

(h)(4)(iii)(A) The discharge from safety-relief valves shall be piped vertically upward to a point at least 10 feet above the ground. The discharge lines or pipes shall be adequately supported and protected against physical damage.

(h)(4)(iii)(B) [Reserved]

(h)(4)(iii)(C) If no liquid is put into a container until after it is buried and covered, the rate of discharge of the relief valves may be reduced to not less than 30 percent of the rate shown in paragraph (b)(10)(ii) of this section. If liquid fuel is present during installation of containers, the rate of discharge shall be the same as for aboveground containers. Such containers shall not be uncovered until emptied of liquid fuel.

(h)(5) Capacity of liquid containers Individual liquid storage containers shall not exceed 30,000 gallons water capacity.

(h)(6) Installation of storage containers

(h)(6)(i)(A) Each storage container used exclusively in service station operation shall comply with the following table which specifies minimum distances to a building and groups of buildings.

Water capacity per container (gallons)	Minimum distances	
	Aboveground and underground (feet)	Between aboveground containers (feet)
Up to 2,000	25	3
Over 2,000	50	5

Note: The above distances may be reduced to not less than 10 feet for service station buildings of other than wood frame construction.

(h)(6)(i)(B) Readily ignitible material including weeds and long dry grass, shall be removed within 10 feet of containers.

(h)(6)(i)(C) The minimum separation between LP-Gas containers and flammable liquid tanks shall be 20 feet and the minimum separation between a container and the centerline of the dike shall be 10 feet.

(h)(6)(i)(D) LP-Gas containers located near flammable liquid containers shall be protected against the flow or accumulation of flammable liquids by diking, diversion curbs, or grading.

(h)(6)(i)(E) LP-Gas containers shall not be located within diked areas for flammable liquid containers.

(h)(6)(i)(F) Field welding is permitted only on saddle plates or brackets which were applied by the container manufacturer.

(h)(6)(i)(G) When permanently installed containers are interconnected, provision shall be made to compensate for expansion, contraction, vibration, and settling of containers and interconnecting piping. Where flexible connections are used, they shall be of an approved type and shall be designed for a bursting pressure of not less than five times the vapor pressure of the product at 100 °F. The use of nonmetallic hose is prohibited for interconnecting such containers.

(h)(6)(i)(H) Where high water table or flood conditions may be encountered protection against container flotation shall be provided.

(h)(6)(ii) Aboveground containers shall be installed in accordance with this subdivision.

(h)(6)(ii)(A) Containers may be installed horizontally or vertically.

(h)(6)(ii)(B) Containers shall be protected by crash rails or guards to prevent physical damage unless they are so protected by virtue of their location. Vehicles shall not be serviced within 10 feet of containers.

(h)(6)(ii)(C) Container foundations shall be of substantial masonry or other noncombustible material. Containers shall be mounted on saddles which shall permit expansion and contraction, and shall provide against the excessive concentration of stresses. Corrosion protection shall be provided for tank-mounting areas. Structural metal container supports shall be protected against fire. This protection is not required on prefabricated storage and pump assemblies, mounted on a common base, with container bottom not more than 24 inches above ground and whose water capacity is 2,000 gallons or less if the piping connected to the storage and pump assembly is sufficiently flexible to minimize the possibility of breakage or leakage in the event of failure of the container supports.

(h)(6)(iii) Underground containers shall be installed in accordance with this subdivision.

(h)(6)(iii)(A) Containers shall be given a protective coating before being placed under ground. This coating shall be equivalent to hot-dip galvanizing or to two coatings of red lead followed by a heavy coating of coal tar or asphalt. In lowering the container into place, care shall be exercised to minimize abrasion or other damage to the coating. Damage to the coating shall be repaired before back-filling.

(h)(6)(iii)(B) Containers shall be set on a firm foundation (firm earth may be used) and surrounded with earth or sand firmly tamped in place. Backfill should be free of rocks or other abrasive materials.

(h)(6)(iii)(C) A minimum of 2 feet of earth cover shall be provided. Where ground conditions make compliance with this requirement impractical, equivalent protection against physical damage shall be provided. The portion of the container to which manhole and other connections are attached need not be covered. If the location is subjected to vehicular traffic, containers shall be protected by a concrete slab or other cover adequate to prevent the weight of a loaded vehicle imposing concentrated direct loads on the container shell.

(h)(7) **Protection of container fittings** Valves, regulators, gages, and other container fittings shall be protected against tampering and physical damage.

(h)(8) **Transport truck unloading point**

(h)(8)(i) During unloading, the transport truck shall not be parked on public thoroughfares and shall be at least 5 feet from storage containers, and shall be positioned so that shutoff valves are readily accessible.

(h)(8)(ii) The filling pipe inlet terminal shall not be located within a building nor within 10 feet of any building or driveway. It shall be protected against physical damage.

(h)(9) **Piping, valves, and fittings**

(h)(9)(i) Piping may be underground, above ground, or a combination of both. It shall be well supported and protected against physical damage and corrosion.

(h)(9)(ii) Piping laid beneath driveways shall be installed to prevent physical damage by vehicles.

(h)(9)(iii) Piping shall be wrought iron or steel (black or galvanized), brass or copper pipe; or seamless copper, brass, or steel tubing and shall be suitable for a minimum pressure of 250 p.s.i.g. Pipe joints may be screwed, flanged, brazed, or welded. The use of aluminum alloy piping or tubing is prohibited.

(h)(9)(iv) All shutoff valves (liquid or gas) shall be suitable for liquefied petroleum gas service and designed for not less than the maximum pressure to which they may be subjected. Valves which may be subjected to container pressure shall have a rated working pressure of at least 250 p.s.i.g.

(h)(9)(v) All materials used for valve seats, packing, gaskets, diaphragms, etc., shall be resistant to the action of LP-Gas.

(h)(9)(vi) Fittings shall be steel, malleable iron, or brass having a minimum working pressure of 250 p.s.i.g. Cast iron pipe fittings, such as ells, tees, and unions shall not be used.

(h)(9)(vii) All piping shall be tested after assembly and proved free from leaks at not less than normal operating pressures.

(h)(9)(viii) Provision shall be made for expansion, contraction, jarring, and vibration, and for settling. This may be accomplished by flexible connections.

(h)(10) **Pumps and accessories** All pumps and accessory equipment shall be suitable for LP-Gas service, and designed for not less than the maximum pressure to which they may be subjected. Accessories shall have a minimum rated working pressure of 250 p.s.i.g. Positive displacement pumps shall be equipped with suitable pressure actuated bypass valves permitting flow from pump discharge to storage container or pump suction.

(h)(11) **Dispensing devices**

(h)(11)(i) Meters, vapor separators, valves, and fittings in the dispenser shall be suitable for LP-Gas service and shall be designed for a minimum working pressure of 250 p.s.i.g.

(h)(11)(ii) Provisions shall be made for venting LP-Gas contained in a dispensing device to a safe location.

(h)(11)(iii) Pumps used to transfer LP-Gas shall be equipped to allow control of the flow and to prevent leakage or accidental discharge. Means shall be provided outside the dispensing device to readily shut off the power in the event of fire or accident.

(h)(11)(iv) A manual shutoff valve and an excess flow check valve shall be installed downstream of the pump and ahead of the dispenser inlet.

(h)(11)(v)(A) Dispensing hose shall be resistant to the action of LP-Gas in the liquid phase and designed for a minimum bursting pressure of 1,250 p.s.i.g.

(h)(11)(v)(B) An excess flow check valve or automatic shutoff valve shall be installed at the terminus of the liquid line at the point of attachment of the dispensing hose.

(h)(11)(vi)(A) LP-Gas dispensing devices shall be located not less than 10 feet from aboveground storage containers greater than 2,000 gallons water capacity. The dispensing devices shall not be less than 20 feet from any building (not including canopies), basement, cellar, pit, or line of adjoining property which may be built upon and not less than 10 feet from sidewalks, streets, or thoroughfares. No drains or blowoff lines shall be directed into or in proximity to the sewer systems used for other purposes.

(h)(11)(vi)(B) LP-Gas dispensing devices shall be installed on a concrete foundation or as part of a complete storage and dispensing assembly mounted on a common base, and shall be adequately protected from physical damage.

(h)(11)(vi)(C) LP-Gas dispensing devices shall not be installed within a building except that they may be located under a weather shelter or canopy provided this area is not enclosed on more than two sides. If the enclosing sides are adjacent to each other, the area shall be properly ventilated.

(h)(11)(vii) The dispensing of LP-Gas into the fuel container of a vehicle shall be performed by a competent attendant who shall remain at the LP-Gas dispenser during the entire transfer operation.

(h)(12) **Additional rules** There shall be no smoking on the driveway of service stations in the dispensing areas or transport truck unloading areas. Conspicuous signs prohibiting smoking shall be posted within sight of the customer being served. Letters on such signs shall be not less than 4 inches high. The motors of all vehicles being fueled shall be shut off during the fueling operations.

(h)(13) **Electrical** Electrical equipment and installations shall conform to paragraphs (b)(17) and (18) of this section.

(h)(14) **Fire protection** Each service station shall be provided with at least one approved portable fire extinguisher having at least an 8–B, C, rating.

(i) **Scope**

(i)(1) **Application**

(i)(1)(i) Paragraph (b) of this section applies to installations made in accordance with the requirements of paragraphs (c), (d), (e), (g), and (h) of this section, except as noted in each of those paragraphs.

(i)(1)(ii) Paragraphs (c) through (h) of this section apply as provided in each of those paragraphs.

(i)(2) **Inapplicability** This section does not apply to:

(i)(2)(i) Marine and pipeline terminals, natural gas processing plants, refineries, or tank farms other than those at industrial sites.

(i)(2)(ii) LP-Gas refrigerated storage systems;

(i)(2)(iii) LP-Gas when used with oxygen. The requirements of §1910.253 shall apply to such use;

(i)(2)(iv) LP-Gas when used in utility gas plants. The National Fire Protection Association Standard for the Storage and Handling of Liquefied Petroleum Gases at Utility Gas Plants, NFPA No. 59–1968, shall apply to such use;

(i)(2)(v) Low-pressure (not in excess of one-half pound per square inch or 14 inches water column) LP-Gas piping systems, and the installation and operation of residential and commercial appliances including their inlet connections, supplied through such systems. For such systems, the National Fire Protection Association Standard for the Installation of Gas Appliances and Gas Piping, NFPA 54–1969 shall apply.

(i)(3) **Retroactivity** Unless otherwise stated, it is not intended that the provisions of this section be retroactive.

(i)(3)(i) Existing plants, appliances, equipment, buildings, structures, and installations for the storage, handling or use of LP-Gas, which were in compliance with the current provisions of the National Fire Protection Association Standard for the Storage and Handling of Liquefied Petroleum Gases NFPA No. 58, at the time of manufacture or installation may be continued in use, if such continued use does not constitute a recognized hazard that is causing or is likely to cause death or serious physical harm to employees.

(i)(3)(ii) Stocks of equipment and appliances on hand in such locations as manufacturers' storage, distribution warehouses, and dealers' storage and showrooms, which were in compliance with the current provisions of the National Fire Protection Association Standard for the Storage and Handling of Liquefied Petroleum Gases, NFPA No. 58, at the time of manufacture, may be placed in service, if such use does not constitute a recognized hazard that is causing or is likely to cause death or serious physical harm to employees.

[39 FR 23502, June 27, 1974, as amended at 43 FR 49747, Oct. 24, 1978; 49 FR 5322, Feb. 10, 1984; 53 FR 12122, Apr. 12, 1988; 55 FR 25094, June 20, 1990; 55 FR 32015, Aug. 6, 1990; 58 FR 35309, June 30, 1993; 61 FR 9237, 9238, Mar. 7, 1996; 63 FR 33466, June 18, 1998; 72 FR 71069, Dec. 14, 2007]

§1910.111 Storage and handling of anhydrous ammonia

(a) **General**

(a)(1) **Scope**

(a)(1)(i) This standard is intended to apply to the design, construction, location, installation, and operation of anhydrous ammonia systems including refrigerated ammonia storage systems.

(a)(1)(ii) This standard does not apply to:

(a)(1)(ii)(A) Ammonia manufacturing plants.

(a)(1)(ii)(B) Refrigeration plants where ammonia is used solely as a refrigerant.

(a)(2) **Definitions** As used in this section.

(a)(2)(i) **Appurtenances** All devices such as pumps, compressors, safety relief devices, liquid-level gaging devices, valves and pressure gages.

(a)(2)(ii) **Cylinder** A container of 1,000 pounds of water capacity or less constructed in accordance with Department of Transportation specifications.

(a)(2)(iii) **Code** The Boiler and Pressure Vessel Code, Section VIII, Unfired Pressure Vessels of the American Society of Mechanical Engineers (ASME)—1968.

(a)(2)(iv) **Container** Includes all vessels, tanks, cylinders, or spheres used for transportation, storage, or application of anhydrous ammonia.

(a)(2)(v) **DOT** U.S. Department of Transportation.

(a)(2)(vi) **Design pressure** is identical to the term Maximum Allowable Working Pressure used in the Code.

(a)(2)(vii) **Farm vehicle (implement of husbandry)** A vehicle for use on a farm on which is mounted a container of not over 1,200 gallons water capacity.

(a)(2)(viii) **Filling density** the percent ratio of the weight of the gas in a container to the weight of water at 60 °F. that the container will hold.

(a)(2)(ix) **Gas** Anhydrous ammonia in either the gaseous or liquefied state.

(a)(2)(x) **Gas masks** Gas masks must be approved by the National Institute for Occupational Safety and Health (NIOSH) under 42 CFR part 84 for use with anhydrous ammonia.

(a)(2)(xi) **Capacity** Total volume of the container in standard U.S. gallons.

(a)(2)(xii) **DOT specifications** Regulations of the Department of Transportation published in 49 CFR Chapter I.

(b) **Basic rules** This paragraph applies to all paragraphs of this section unless otherwise noted.

(b)(1) **Approval of equipment and systems** Each appurtenance shall be approved in accordance with paragraph (b)(1)(i), (ii), (iii), or (iv) of this section.

(b)(1)(i) It was installed before February 8, 1973, and was approved, tested, and installed in accordance with either the provisions of the American National Standard for the Storage and Handling of Anhydrous Ammonia, K61.1, or the Fertilizer Institute Standards for the Storage and Handling of Agricultural Anhydrous Ammonia, M–1, (both of which are incorporated by reference as specified in §1910.6) in effect at the time of installation; or

(b)(1)(ii) It is accepted, or certified, or listed, or labeled, or otherwise determined to be safe by a nationally recognized testing laboratory; or

(b)(1)(iii) It is a type which no nationally recognized testing laboratory does, or will undertake to, accept, certify, list, label, or determine to be safe; and such equipment is inspected or tested by any Federal, State, municipal, or other local authority responsible for enforcing occupational safety provisions of a Federal, State, municipal or other local law, code, or regulation pertaining to the storage, handling, transport, and use of anhydrous ammonia, and found to be in compliance with either the provisions of the American National Standard for the Storage and Handling of Anhydrous Ammonia, K61.1, or the Fertilizer Institute Standards for the Storage and Handling of Agricultural Anhydrous Ammonia, M–1, in effect at the time of installation; or

(b)(1)(iv) It is a custom-designed and custom-built unit, which no nationally recognized testing laboratory, or Federal, State, municipal or local authority responsible for the enforcement of a Federal, State, municipal, or local law, code or regulation pertaining to the storage, transportation and use of anhydrous ammonia is willing to undertake to accept, certify, list, label or determine to be safe, and the employer has on file a document attesting to its safe condition following the conduct of appropriate tests. The document shall be signed by a registered professional engineer or other person having special training or experience sufficient to permit him to form an opinion as to safety of the unit involved. The document shall set forth the test bases, test data and results, and also the qualifications of the certifying person.

(b)(1)(v) For the purposes of this paragraph (b)(1), the word listed means that equipment is of a kind mentioned in a list which is published by a nationally recognized laboratory which makes periodic inspection of the production of such equipment, and states such equipment meets nationally recognized standards or has been tested and found safe for use in a specified manner. Labeled means there is attached to it a label, symbol, or other identifying mark of a nationally recognized testing laboratory which, makes periodic inspections of the production of such equipment, and whose labeling indicates compliance with nationally recognized standards or tests to determine safe use in a specified manner. Certified means it has been tested and found by a nationally recognized testing laboratory to meet nationally recognized standards or to be safe for use in a specified manner, or is of a kind whose production is periodically inspected by a nationally recognized testing laboratory, and it bears a label, tag, or other record of certification.

(b)(1)(vi) For the purposes of this paragraph (b)(1), refer to §1910.7 for definition of nationally recognized testing laboratory.

(b)(2) **Requirements for construction, original test and regualification of nonrefrigerated containers**

(b)(2)(i) Containers used with systems covered in paragraphs (c), (f), (g), and (h) of this section shall be constructed and tested in accordance with the Code except that construction under Table UW12 at a basic joint efficiency of under 80 percent is not authorized.

(b)(2)(ii) Containers built according to the Code do not have to comply with Paragraphs UG125 to UG128 inclusive, and Paragraphs UG132 and UG133 of the Code.

(b)(2)(iii) Containers exceeding 36 inches in diameter or 250 gallons water capacity shall be constructed to comply with one or more of the following:

(b)(2)(iii)(A) Containers shall be stress relieved after fabrication in accordance with the Code, or

(b)(2)(iii)(B) Cold-form heads when used, shall be stress relieved, or

(b)(2)(iii)(C) Hot-formed heads shall be used.

(b)(2)(iv) Welding to the shell, head, or any other part of the container subject to internal pressure shall be done in compliance with the Code. Other welding is permitted only on saddle plates, lugs, or brackets attached to the container by the container manufacturer.

(b)(2)(v) Containers used with systems covered in paragraph (e) of this section shall be constructed and tested in accordance with the DOT specifications.

(b)(2)(vi) The provisions of subdivision (i) of this subparagraph shall not be construed as prohibiting the continued use or reinstallation of containers constructed and maintained in accordance with the 1949, 1950, 1952, 1956, 1959, and 1962 editions of the Code or any revisions thereof in effect at the time of fabrication.

(b)(3) **Marking nonrefrigerated containers**

(b)(3)(i) System nameplates, when required, shall be permanently attached to the system so as to be readily accessible for inspection and shall include markings as prescribed in subdivision (ii) of this subparagraph.

(b)(3)(ii) Each container or system covered in paragraphs (c), (f), (g), and (h) of this section shall be marked as specified in the following:

(b)(3)(ii)(A) With a notation "Anhydrous Ammonia.";

(b)(3)(ii)(B) With a marking identifying compliance with the rules of the Code under which the container is constructed;

Under ground: Container and system nameplate;

Above ground: Container.

(b)(3)(ii)(C) With a notation whether the system is designed for underground or aboveground installation or both;

(b)(3)(ii)(D) With the name and address of the supplier of the system or the trade name of the system and with the date of fabrication;

Under ground and above ground: System nameplate.

(b)(3)(ii)(E) With the water capacity of the container in pounds at 60 °F. or gallons, U.S. Standard;

Under ground: Container and system nameplate;

Above ground: Container.

(b)(3)(ii)(F) With the design pressure in pounds per square inch;

Under ground: Container and system nameplate;

Above ground: Container.

(b)(3)(ii)(G) With the wall thickness of the shell and heads;

Under ground: Container and system nameplate;

Above ground: Container.

(b)(3)(ii)(H) With marking indicating the maximum level to which the container may be filled with liquid anhydrous ammonia at temperatures between 20 °F. and 130 °F. except on containers provided with fixed level indicators, such as fixed length dip tubes, or containers that are filled with weight. Markings shall be in increments of not more than 20 °F.

Above ground and under ground: System nameplate or on liquid-level gaging device.

(b)(3)(ii)(I) With the total outside surface area of the container in square feet.

Under ground: System nameplate.

Above ground: No requirement.

(b)(3)(ii)(J) Marking specified on the container shall be on the container itself or on a nameplate permanently attached to it.

(b)(4) **Marking refrigerated containers** Each refrigerated container shall be marked with nameplate on the outer covering in an accessible place as specified in the following:

(b)(4)(i) With the notation, "Anhydrous Ammonia;"

(b)(4)(ii) With the name and address of the builder and the date of fabrication;

(b)(4)(iii) With the water capacity of the container in gallons, U.S. Standard;

(b)(4)(iv) With the design pressure;

(b)(4)(v) With the minimum temperature in degrees Fahrenheit for which the container was designed;

(b)(4)(vi) The maximum allowable water level to which the container may be filled for test purposes;

(b)(4)(vii) With the density of the product in pounds per cubic foot for which the container was designed;

(b)(4)(viii) With the maximum level to which the container may be filled with liquid anhydrous ammonia.

(b)(5) **Location of containers**

(b)(5)(i) Consideration shall be given to the physiological effects of ammonia as well as to adjacent fire hazards in selecting the location for a storage container. Containers shall be located outside of buildings or in buildings or sections thereof especially provided for this purpose.

(b)(5)(ii) Permanent storage containers shall be located at least 50 feet from a dug well or other sources of potable water supply, unless the container is a part of a water-treatment installation.

(b)(5)(iii)–(iv) [Reserved]

(b)(5)(v) Storage areas shall be kept free of readily ignitible materials such as waste, weeds, and long dry grass.

(b)(6) **Container appurtenances**

(b)(6)(i) All appurtenances shall be designed for not less than the maximum working pressure of that portion of the system on which they are installed. All appurtenances shall be fabricated from materials proved suitable for anhydrous ammonia service.

(b)(6)(ii) All connections to containers except safety relief devices, gaging devices, or those fitted with No. 54 drill-size orifice shall have shutoff valves located as close to the container as practicable.

(b)(6)(iii) Excess flow valves where required by these standards shall close automatically at the rated flows of vapor or liquid as specified by the manufacturer. The connections and line including valves and fittings being protected by an excess flow valve shall have a greater capacity than the rated flow of the excess flow valve so that the valve will close in case of failure of the line or fittings.

(b)(6)(iv) Liquid-level gaging devices that require bleeding of the product to the atmosphere and which are so constructed that outward flow will not exceed that passed by a No. 54 drill-size opening need not be equipped with excess flow valves.

(b)(6)(v) Openings from the container or through fittings attached directly on the container to which pressure gage connections are made need not be equipped with excess flow valves if such openings are not larger than No. 54 drill size.

(b)(6)(vi) Excess flow and back pressure check valves where required by the standards in this section shall be located inside of the container or at a point outside as close as practicable to where the line enters the container. In the latter case installation shall be made in such manner that any undue strain beyond the excess flow or back pressure check valve will not cause breakage between the container and the valve.

(b)(6)(vii) Excess flow valves shall be designed with a bypass, not to exceed a No. 60 drill-size opening to allow equalization of pressures.

(b)(6)(viii) All excess flow valves shall be plainly and permanently marked with the name or trademark of the manufacturer, the catalog number, and the rated capacity.

(b)(7) **Piping, tubing, and fittings**

(b)(7)(i) All piping, tubing, and fittings shall be made of material suitable for anhydrous ammonia service.

(b)(7)(ii) All piping, tubing, and fittings shall be designed for a pressure not less than the maximum pressure to which they may be subjected in service.

(b)(7)(iii) All refrigerated piping shall conform to the Refrigeration Piping Code, American National Standards Institute, B31.5–1966 with addenda B31.1a–1968, which is incorporated by reference as specified in §1910.6, as it applies to ammonia.

(b)(7)(iv) [OI] Piping used on non-refrigerated systems shall be at least American Society for Testing and Materials (ASTM) A–53–69 Grade B Electric Resistance Welded and Electric Flash Welded Pipe, which is incorporated by reference as specified in §1910.6, or equal. Such pipe shall be at least schedule 40 when joints are welded, or welded and flanged. Such pipe shall be at least schedule 80 when joints are threaded. Threaded connections shall not be back-welded. Brass, copper, or galvanized steel pipe shall not be used.

(b)(7)(v) Tubing made of brass, copper, or other material subject to attack by ammonia shall not be used.

(b)(7)(vi) Cast iron fittings shall not be used but this shall not prohibit the use of fittings made specifically for ammonia service of malleable, nodular, or high strength gray iron meeting American Society for Testing and Materials (ASTM) A47–68, ASTM 395–68, or ASTM A126–66 Class B or C all of which are incorporated by reference as specified in §1910.6.

(b)(7)(vii) Joint compounds shall be resistant to ammonia.

(b)(8) **Hose specifications**

(b)(8)(i) Hose used in ammonia service shall conform to the joint Agricultural Ammonia Institute—Rubber Manufacturers Association Specifications for Anhydrous Ammonia Hose.

(b)(8)(ii) Hose subject to container pressure shall be designed for a minimum working pressure of 350 p.s.i.g. and a minimum burst pressure of 1,750 p.s.i.g. Hose assemblies, when made up, shall be capable of withstanding a test pressure of 500 p.s.i.g.

(b)(8)(iii) Hose and hose connections located on the low-pressure side of flow control of pressure-reducing valves shall be designed for a bursting pressure of not less than 5 times the pressure setting of the safety relief devices protecting that portion of the system but not less than 125 p.s.i.g. All connections shall be so designed and constructed that there will be no leakage when connected.

(b)(8)(iv) Where hose is to be used for transferring liquid from one container to another, "wet" hose is recommended. Such hose shall be equipped with approved shutoff valves at the discharge end. Provision shall be made to prevent excessive pressure in the hose.

(b)(8)(v) On all hose one-half inch outside diameter and larger, used for the transfer of anhydrous ammonia liquid or vapor, there shall be etched, cast, or impressed at 5-foot intervals the following information.

"Anhydrous Ammonia" xxx p.s.i.g. (maximum working pressure), manufacturer's name or trademark, year of manufacture.

In lieu of this requirement the same information may be contained on a nameplate permanently attached to the hose.

Table H–36

[Minimum required rate of discharge in cubic feet per minute of air at 120 percent of the maximum permitted start to discharge pressure of safety relief valves]

Surface area (sq. ft.)	Flow rate CFM air
20	258
25	310
30	360
35	408
40	455
45	501
50	547
55	591
60	635
65	678
70	720
75	762

Surface area (sq. ft.)	Flow rate CFM air
80	804
85	845
90	885
95	925
100	965
105	1,010
110	1,050
115	1,090
120	1,120
125	1,160
130	1,200
135	1,240
140	1,280
145	1,310
150	1,350
155	1,390
160	1,420
165	1,460
170	1,500
175	1,530
180	1,570
185	1,600
190	1,640
195	1,670
200	1,710
210	1,780
220	1,850
230	1,920
240	1,980
250	2,050
260	2,120
270	2,180
280	2,250
290	2,320
300	2,380
310	2,450
320	2,510
330	2,570
340	2,640
350	2,700
360	2,760
370	2,830
380	2,890
390	2,950
400	3,010
450	3,320
500	3,620
550	3,910
600	4,200
650	4,480
700	4,760
750	5,040

Surface area (sq. ft.)	Flow rate CFM air
800	5,300
850	5,590
900	5,850
950	6,120
1,000	6,380
1,050	6,640
1,100	6,900
1,150	7,160
1,200	7,410
1,250	7,660
1,300	7,910
1,350	8,160
1,400	8,410
1,450	8,650
1,500	8,900
1,550	9,140
1,600	9,380
1,650	9,620
1,700	9,860
1,750	10,090
1,800	10,330
1,850	10,560
1,900	10,800
1,950	11,030
2,000	11,260
2,050	11,490
2,100	11,720
2,150	11,950
2,200	12,180
2,250	12,400
2,300	12,630
2,350	12,850
2,400	13,080
2,450	13,300
2,500	13,520

Surface Area = total outside surface area of container in square feet. When the surface area is not stamped on the nameplate or when the marking is not legible the area can be calculated by using one of the following formulas:

(1) Cylindrical container with hemispherical heads:
Area=overall length in feet times outside diameter in feet times 3.1416;

(2) Cylindrical container with other than hemispherical heads:
Area=(overall length in feet plus 0.3 outside diameter in feet) times outside diameter in feet times 3.1416;

(3) Spherical container:
Area=outside diameter in feet squared times 3.1416.
Flow Rate—CFM Air=cubic feet per minute of air required at standard conditions, 60 °F. and atmospheric pressure (14.7 p.s.i.a.).
The rate of discharge may be interpolated for intermediate values of surface area. For containers with total outside surface area greater than 2,500 square feet, the required flow rate can be calculated using the formula: Flow Rate CFM Air=22.11 A, where A=outside surface area of the container in square feet.

(b)(9) Safety relief devices

(b)(9)(i) Every container used in systems covered by paragraphs (c), (f), (g), and (h) of this section shall be provided with one or more safety relief valves of the spring-loaded or equivalent type. The discharge from safety-relief valves shall be vented away from the container upward and unobstructed to the atmosphere. All relief-valve discharge openings shall have suitable rain caps that will allow free discharge of the vapor and prevent entrance of water. Provision shall be made for draining condensate which may accumulate. The rate of the discharge shall be in accordance with the provisions of Table H–36.

(b)(9)(ii) Container safety-relief valves shall be set to start-to-discharge as follows, with relation to the design pressure of the container:

Containers	Minimum (percent)	Maximum (percent)
ASME-U-68, U-69	110	125
ASME-U-200, U-201	95	100
ASME 1959, 1956, 1952, or 1962	95	100
API-ASME	95	100
U.S. Coast Guard	95	100

As required by DOT Regulations.

(b)(9)(iii) Safety relief devices used in systems covered by paragraphs (c), (f), (g), and (h) of this section shall be constructed to discharge at not less than the rates required in paragraph (b)(9)(i) of this section before the pressure is in excess of 120 percent (not including the 10 percent tolerance referred to in paragraph (b)(9)(ii) of this section) of the maximum permitted start-to-discharge pressure setting of the device.

(b)(9)(iv) Safety-relief valves shall be so arranged that the possibility of tampering will be minimized. If the pressure setting adjustment is external, the relief valves shall be provided with means for sealing the adjustment.

(b)(9)(v) Shutoff valves shall not be installed between the safety-relief valves and the container; except, that a shutoff valve may be used where the arrangement of this valve is such as always to afford full required capacity flow through the relief valves.

(b)(9)(vi) Safety-relief valves shall have direct communication with the vapor space of the container.

(b)(9)(vii) Each container safety-relief valve used with systems covered by paragraphs (c), (f), (g), and (h) of this section shall be plainly and permanently marked with the symbol "NH_3" or "AA"; with the pressure in pounds-per-square-inch gage at which the valve is set to start-to-discharge; with the actual rate of discharge of the valve at its full open position in cubic feet per minute of air at 60 °F. and atmospheric pressure; and with the manufacturer's name and catalog number. Example: "NH_3 250–4050 Air" indicates that the valve is suitable for use on an anhydrous ammonia container, is set to start-to-discharge at a pressure of 250 p.s.i.g., and that its rate of discharge at full open position (subdivisions (ii) and (iii) of this subparagraph) is 4,050 cubic feet per minute of air.

(b)(9)(viii) The flow capacity of the relief valve shall not be restricted by any connection to it on either the upstream or downstream side.

(b)(9)(ix) A hydrostatic relief valve shall be installed between each pair of valves in the liquid ammonia piping or hose where liquid may be trapped so as to relieve into the atmosphere at a safe location.

(b)(10) General

(b)(10)(i) [Reserved]

(b)(10)(ii) Stationary storage installations must have at least two suitable gas masks in readily-accessible locations. Full-face masks with ammonia canisters that have been approved by NIOSH under 42 CFR part 84 are suitable for emergency action involving most anhydrous ammonia leaks, particularly leaks that occur outdoors. For respiratory protection in concentrated ammonia atmospheres, a self-contained breathing apparatus is required.

(b)(10)(iii) Stationary storage installations shall have an easily accessible shower or a 50-gallon drum of water.

(b)(10)(iv) Each vehicle transporting ammonia in bulk except farm applicator vehicles shall carry a container of at least 5 gallons of water and shall be equipped with a full face mask.

(b)(11) Charging of containers

(b)(11)(i) The filling densities for containers that are not refrigerated shall not exceed the following:

Type of container	Percent by weight	Percent by volume
Aboveground-Uninsulated	56	82
Aboveground-Uninsulated		87.5
Aboveground-Insulated	57	83.5
Underground-Uninsulated	58	85
DOT—In accord with DOT regulations.		

(b)(11)(ii) Aboveground uninsulated containers may be charged 87.5 percent by volume provided the temperature of the anhydrous ammonia being charged is determined to be not lower than 30 °F. or provided the charging of the container is stopped at the first indication of frost or ice formation on its outside surface and is not resumed until such frost or ice has disappeared.

(b)(12) Transfer of liquids

(b)(12)(i) Anhydrous ammonia shall always be at a temperature suitable for the material of construction and the design of the receiving container.

(b)(12)(ii) [OI] The employer shall require the continuous presence of an attendant in the vicinity of the operation during such time as ammonia is being transferred.

(b)(12)(iii) Containers shall be charged or used only upon authorization of the owner.

(b)(12)(iv) Containers shall be gaged and charged only in the open atmosphere or in buildings or areas thereof provided for that purpose.

(b)(12)(v) Pumps used for transferring ammonia shall be those manufactured for that purpose.

(b)(12)(v)(A) Pumps shall be designed for at least 250 p.s.i.g. working pressure.

(b)(12)(v)(B) Positive displacement pumps shall have, installed off the discharged port, a constant differential relief valve discharging into the suction port of the pump through a line of sufficient size to carry the full capacity of the pump at relief valve setting, which setting and installation shall be according to the pump manufacturer's recommendations.

(b)(12)(v)(C) On the discharge side of the pump, before the relief valve line, there shall be installed a pressure gage graduated from 0 to 400 p.s.i.

(b)(12)(v)(D) Plant piping shall contain shutoff valves located as close as practical to pump connections.

(b)(12)(vi) Compressors used for transferring or refrigerating ammonia shall be recommended for ammonia service by the manufacturer.

(b)(12)(vi)(A) Compressors shall be designed for at least 250 p.s.i.g. working pressure.

(b)(12)(vi)(B) Plant piping shall contain shutoff valves located as close as practical to compressor connections.

(b)(12)(vi)(C) A relief valve large enough to discharge the full capacity of the compressor shall be connected to the discharge before any shutoff valve.

(b)(12)(vi)(D) Compressors shall have pressure gages at suction and discharge graduated to at least one and one-half times the maximum pressure that can be developed.

(b)(12)(vi)(E) Adequate means, such as drainable liquid trap, shall be provided on the compressor suction to minimize the entry of liquid into the compressor.

(b)(12)(vii) Loading and unloading systems shall be protected by suitable devices to prevent emptying of the storage container or the container being loaded or unloaded in the event of severance of the hose. Backflow check valves or properly sized excess flow valves shall be installed where necessary to provide such protection. In the event that such valves are not practical, remotely operated shutoff valves may be installed.

(b)(13) Tank car unloading points and operations

(b)(13)(i) Provisions for unloading tank cars shall conform to the applicable recommendations contained in the DOT regulations.

(b)(13)(ii) The employer shall insure that unloading operations are performed by reliable persons properly instructed and given the authority to monitor careful compliance with all applicable procedures.

(b)(13)(iii) Caution signs shall be so placed on the track or car as to give necessary warning to persons approaching the car from open end or ends of siding and shall be left up until after the car is unloaded and disconnected from discharge connections. Signs shall be of metal or other suitable material, at least 12 by 15 inches in size and bear the words "STOP—Tank Car Connected" or "STOP—Men at Work" the word, "STOP," being in letters at least 4 inches high and the other words in letters at least 2 inches high.

(b)(13)(iv) The track of a tank car siding shall be substantially level.

(b)(13)(v) Brakes shall be set and wheels blocked on all cars being unloaded.

(b)(14) Liquid-level gaging device

(b)(14)(i) Each container except those filled by weight shall be equipped with an approved liquid-level gaging device. A thermometer well shall be provided in all containers not utilizing a fixed liquid-level gaging device.

(b)(14)(ii) All gaging devices shall be arranged so that the maximum liquid level to which the container is filled is readily determined.

(b)(14)(iii) Gaging devices that require bleeding of the product to the atmosphere such as the rotary tube, fixed tube, and slip tube devices shall be designed so that the maximum opening of the bleed valve is not larger than No. 54 drill size unless provided with an excess flow valve. (This requirement does not apply to farm vehicles used for the application of ammonia as covered in paragraph (h) of this section.)

(b)(14)(iv) Gaging devices shall have a design pressure equal to or greater than the design pressure of the container on which they are installed.

(b)(14)(v) Fixed tube liquid-level gages shall be designed and installed to indicate that level at which the container is filled to 85 percent of its water capacity in gallons.

(b)(14)(vi) Gage glasses of the columnar type shall be restricted to stationary storage installations. They shall be equipped with shutoff valves having metallic handwheels, with excess-flow valves, and with extra heavy glass adequately protected with a metal housing applied by the gage manufacturer. They shall be shielded against the direct rays of the sun.

(b)(15) [Reserved]

(b)(16) **Electrical equipment and wiring**

(b)(16)(i) Electrical equipment and wiring for use in ammonia installations shall be general purpose or weather resistant as appropriate.

(b)(16)(ii) Electrical systems shall be installed and maintained in accordance with Subpart S of this part.

(c) **Systems utilizing stationary, nonrefrigerated storage containers** This paragraph applies to stationary, nonrefrigerated storage installations utilizing containers other than those covered in paragraph (e) of this section. Paragraph (b) of this section applies to this paragraph unless otherwise noted.

(c)(1) Design pressure and construction of containers. The minimum design pressure for nonrefrigerated containers shall be 250 p.s.i.g.

(c)(2) Container valves and accessories, filling and discharge connections.

(c)(2)(i) Each filling connection shall be provided with combination back-pressure check valve and excess-flow valve; one double or two single back-pressure check valves; or a positive shutoff valve in conjunction with either an internal back-pressure check valve or an internal excess flow valve.

(c)(2)(ii) All liquid and vapor connections to containers except filling pipes, safety relief connections, and liquid-level gaging and pressure gage connections provided with orifices not larger than No. 54 drill size as required in paragraphs (b)(6)(iv) and (v) of this section shall be equipped with excess-flow valves.

(c)(2)(iii) Each storage container shall be provided with a pressure gage graduated from 0 to 400 p.s.i. Gages shall be designated for use in ammonia service.

(c)(2)(iv) All containers shall be equipped with vapor return valves.

(c)(3) **Safety-relief devices**

(c)(3)(i) Every container shall be provided with one or more safety-relief valves of the spring-loaded or equivalent type in accordance with paragraph (b)(9) of this section.

(c)(3)(ii) The rate of discharge of spring-loaded safety relief valves installed on underground containers may be reduced to a minimum of 30 percent of the rate of discharge specified in Table H–36. Containers so protected shall not be uncovered after installation until the liquid ammonia has been removed. Containers which may contain liquid ammonia before being installed underground and before being completely covered with earth are to be considered aboveground containers when determining the rate of discharge requirements of the safety-relief valves.

(c)(3)(iii) On underground installations where there is a probability of the manhole or housing becoming flooded, the discharge from vent lines shall be located above the high water level. All manholes or housings shall be provided with ventilated louvers or their equivalent, the area of such openings equalling or exceeding combined discharge areas of safety-relief valves and vent lines which discharge their content into the manhole housing.

(c)(3)(iv) Vent pipes, when used, shall not be restricted or of smaller diameter than the relief-valve outlet connection.

(c)(3)(v) If desired, vent pipes from two or more safety-relief devices located on the same unit, or similar lines from two or more different units may be run into a common discharge header, provided the capacity of such header is at least equal to the sum of the capacities of the individual discharge lines.

(c)(4) **Reinstallation of containers**

(c)(4)(i) Containers once installed under ground shall not later be reinstalled above ground or under ground, unless they successfully withstand hydrostatic pressure retests at the pressure specified for the original hydrostatic test as required by the code under which constructed and show no evidence of serious corrosion.

(c)(4)(ii) Where containers are reinstalled above ground, safety devices or gaging devices shall comply with paragraph (b)(9) of this section and this paragraph respectively for aboveground containers.

(c)(5) **Installation of storage containers**

(c)(5)(i) Containers installed above ground, except as provided in paragraph (c)(5)(v) of this section shall be provided with substantial concrete or masonry supports, or structural steel supports on firm concrete or masonry foundations. All foundations shall extend below the frost line.

(c)(5)(ii) Horizontal aboveground containers shall be so mounted on foundations as to permit expansion and contraction. Every container shall be supported to prevent the concentration of excessive loads on the supporting portion of the shell. That portion of the container in contact with foundations or saddles shall be protected against corrosion.

(c)(5)(iii) Containers installed under ground shall be so placed that the top of the container is below the frost line and in no case less than 2 feet below the surface of the ground. Should ground conditions make compliance with these requirements impracticable, installation shall be made otherwise to prevent physical damage. It will not be necessary to cover the portion of the container to which manhole and other connections are affixed. When necessary to prevent floating, containers shall be securely anchored or weighted.

(c)(5)(iv) Underground containers shall be set on a firm foundation (firm earth may be used) and surrounded with earth or sand well tamped in place. The container, prior to being placed under ground, shall be given a corrosion resisting protective coating. The container thus coated shall be so lowered into place as to prevent abrasion or other damage to the coating.

(c)(5)(v) Containers with foundations attached (portable or semiportable tank containers with suitable steel "runners" or "skids" and commonly known in the industry as "skid tanks") shall be designed and constructed in accordance with paragraph (c)(1) of this section.

(c)(5)(vi) Secure anchorage or adequate pier height shall be provided against container flotation wherever sufficiently high flood water might occur.

(c)(5)(vii) The distance between underground containers of over 2,000 gallons capacity shall be at least 5 feet.

(c)(6) **Protection of appurtenances**

(c)(6)(i) Valves, regulating, gaging, and other appurtenances shall be protected against tampering and physical damage. Such appurtenances shall also be protected during transit of containers.

(c)(6)(ii) All connections to underground containers shall be located within a dome, housing, or manhole and with access thereto by means of a substantial cover.

(c)(7) **Damage from vehicles** Precaution shall be taken against damage to ammonia systems from vehicles.

(d) **Refrigerated storage systems** This paragraph applies to systems utilizing containers with the storage of anhydrous ammonia under refrigerated conditions. All applicable rules of paragraph (b) of this section apply to this paragraph unless otherwise noted.

(d)(1) **Design of containers**

(d)(1)(i) The design temperature shall be the minimum temperature to which the container will be refrigerated.

(d)(1)(ii) Containers with a design pressure exceeding 15 p.s.i.g. shall be constructed in accordance with paragraph (b)(2) of this section, and the materials shall be selected from those listed in API Standard 620, Recommended Rules for Design and Construction of Large, Welded, Low-Pressure Storage Tanks, Fourth Edition, 1970, Tables 2.02, R2.2, R2.2(A), R2.2.1, or R2.3 which are incorporated by reference as specified in §1910.6.

(d)(1)(iii) Containers with a design pressure of 15 p.s.i.g. and less shall be constructed in accordance with the applicable requirements of API Standard 620 including its Appendix R.

(d)(1)(iv) When austenitic steels or nonferrous materials are used, the Code shall be used as a guide in the selection of materials for use at the design temperature.

(d)(1)(v) The filling density for refrigerated storage containers shall be such that the container will not be liquid full at a liquid temperature corresponding to the vapor pressure at the start-to-discharge pressure setting of the safety-relief valve.

(d)(2) **Installation of refrigerated storage containers**

(d)(2)(i) Containers shall be supported on suitable noncombustible foundations designed to accommodate the type of container being used.

(d)(2)(ii) Adequate protection against flotation or other water damage shall be provided wherever high flood water might occur.

(d)(2)(iii) Containers for product storage at less than 32 °F. shall be supported in such a way, or heat shall be supplied, to prevent the effects of freezing and consequent frost heaving.

(d)(3) **Shutoff valves** When operating conditions make it advisable, a check valve shall be installed on the fill connection and a remotely operated shutoff valve on other connections located below the maximum liquid level.

(d)(4) **Safety relief devices**

(d)(4)(i) Safety relief valves shall be set to start-to-discharge at a pressure not in excess of the design pressure of the container and shall have a total relieving capacity sufficient to prevent a maximum pressure in the container of more than 120 percent of the design pressure. Relief valves for refrigerated storage containers shall be self-contained spring-loaded, weight-loaded, or self-contained pilot-operated type.

(d)(4)(ii) The total relieving capacity shall be the larger of:

(d)(4)(ii)(A) Possible refrigeration system upset such as (1) cooling water failure, (2) power failure, (3) instrument air or instrument failure, (4) mechanical failure of any equipment, (5) excessive pumping rates.

(d)(4)(ii)(B) Fire exposure determined in accordance with Compressed Gas Association (CGA) S–1, part 3, Safety Relief Device Standards for Compressed Gas Storage Containers, 1959, which is incorporated by reference as specified in §1910.6, except that "A" shall be the total exposed surface area in square feet up to 25 foot above grade or to the equator of the storage container if it is a sphere, whichever is greater. If the relieving capacity required for fire exposure is greater than that required by (A) of this subdivision, the additional capacity may be provided by weak roof to shell seams in containers operating at essentially atmospheric pressure and having an inherently weak roof-to-shell seam. The weak roof-to-shell seam is not to be considered as providing any of the capacity required in (A) of this subdivision.

(d)(4)(iii) If vent lines are installed to conduct the vapors from the relief valve, the back pressure under full relieving conditions shall not exceed 50 percent of the start-to-discharge pressure for pressure balanced valves or 10 percent of the start-to-discharge pressure for conventional valves. The vent lines shall be installed to prevent accumulation of liquid in the lines.

(d)(4)(iv) The valve or valve installation shall provide weather protection.

(d)(4)(v) Atmospheric storage shall be provided with vacuum breakers. Ammonia gas, nitrogen, methane, or other inert gases can be used to provide a pad.

(d)(5) **Protection of container appurtenances** Appurtenances shall be protected against tampering and physical damage.

(d)(6) **Reinstallation of refrigerated storage containers** Containers of such size as to require field fabrication shall, when moved and reinstalled, be reconstructed and reinspected in complete accordance with the requirements under which they were constructed. The containers shall be subjected to a pressure retest and if rerating is necessary, rerating shall be in accordance with applicable requirements.

(d)(7) **Damage from vehicles** Precaution shall be taken against damage from vehicles.

(d)(8) **Refrigeration load and equipment**

(d)(8)(i) The total refrigeration load shall be computed as the sum of the following:

(d)(8)(i)(A) Load imposed by heat flow into the container caused by the temperature differential between design ambient temperature and storage temperature.

(d)(8)(i)(B) Load imposed by heat flow into the container caused by maximum sun radiation.

(d)(8)(i)(C) Maximum load imposed by filling the container with ammonia warmer than the design storage temperature.

(d)(8)(ii) More than one storage container may be handled by the same refrigeration system.

(d)(9) **Compressors**

(d)(9)(i) A minimum of two compressors shall be provided either of which shall be of sufficient size to handle the loads listed in paragraphs (d)(8)(i)(A) and (B) of this section. Where more than two compressors are provided minimum standby equipment equal to the largest normally operating equipment shall be installed. Filling compressors may be used as standby equipment for holding compressors.

(d)(9)(ii) Compressors shall be sized to operate with a suction pressure at least 10 percent below the minimum setting of the safety valve(s) on the storage container and shall withstand a suction pressure at least equal to 120 percent of the design pressure of the container.

(d)(10) **Compressor drives**

(d)(10)(i) Each compressor shall have its individual driving unit.

(d)(10)(ii) An emergency source of power of sufficient capacity to handle the loads listed in paragraphs (d)(8)(i)(A) and (b) of this section shall be provided unless facilities are available to safely dispose of vented vapors while the refrigeration system is not operating.

(d)(11) **Automatic control equipment**

(d)(11)(i) The refrigeration system shall be arranged with suitable controls to govern the compressor operation in accordance with the load as evidenced by the pressure in the container(s).

(d)(11)(ii) An emergency alarm system shall be installed to function in the event the pressure in the container(s) rises to the maximum allowable operating pressure.

(d)(11)(iii) An emergency alarm and shutoff shall be located in the condenser system to respond to excess discharge pressure caused by failure of the cooling medium.

(d)(11)(iv) All automatic controls shall be installed in a manner to preclude operation of alternate compressors unless the controls will function with the alternate compressors.

(d)(12) **Separators for compressors**

(d)(12)(i) An entrainment separator of suitable size and design pressure shall be installed in the compressor suction line of lubricated compression. The separator shall be equipped with a drain and gaging device.

(d)(12)(ii) [Reserved]

(d)(13) **Condensers** The condenser system may be cooled by air or water or both. The condenser shall be designed for at least 250 p.s.i.g. Provision shall be made for purging noncondensibles either manually or automatically.

(d)(14) **Receiver and liquid drain** A receiver shall be provided with a liquid-level control to discharge the liquid ammonia to storage. The receiver shall be designed for at least 250 p.s.i.g. and be equipped with the necessary connections, safety valves, and gaging device.

(d)(15) **Insulation** Refrigerated containers and pipelines which are insulated shall be covered with a material of suitable quality and thickness for the temperatures encountered. Insulation shall be suitably supported and protected against the weather. Weatherproofing shall be of a type which will not support flame propagation.

(e) [OI] **Systems utilizing portable DOT containers**

(e)(1) **Conformance** Cylinders shall comply with DOT specifications and shall be maintained, filled, packaged, marked, labeled, and shipped to comply with 49 CFR chapter I and the marking requirements set forth in §1910.253(b)(1)(ii).

(e)(2) **Storage** Cylinders shall be stored in an area free from ignitable debris and in such manner as to prevent external corrosion. Storage may be indoors or outdoors.

(e)(3) **Heat protection** Cylinders filled in accordance with DOT regulations will become liquid full at 145 °F. Cylinders shall be protected from heat sources such as radiant flame and steampipes. Heat shall not be applied directly to cylinders to raise the pressure.

(e)(4) **Protection** Cylinders shall be stored in such manner as to protect them from moving vehicles or external damage.

(e)(5) **Valve cap** Any cylinder which is designed to have a valve protection cap shall have the cap securely in place when the cylinder is not in service.

(f) **Tank motor vehicles for the transportation of ammonia**

(f)(1) This paragraph applies to containers and pertinent equipment mounted on tank motor vehicles including semitrailers and full trailers used for the transportation of ammonia. This paragraph does not apply to farm vehicles. For requirements covering farm vehicles, refer to paragraphs (g) and (h) of this section.

Paragraph (b) of this section applies to this paragraph unless otherwise noted. Containers and pertinent equipment for tank motor vehicles for the transportation of anhydrous ammonia, in addition to complying with the requirements of this section, shall also comply with the requirements of DOT.

(f)(2) **Design pressure and construction of containers**

(f)(2)(i) The minimum design pressure for containers shall be that specified in the regulations of the DOT.

(f)(2)(ii) The shell or head thickness of any container shall not be less than three-sixteenth inch.

(f)(2)(iii) All container openings, except safety relief valves, liquid-level gaging devices, and pressure gages, shall be labeled to designate whether they communicate with liquid or vapor space.

(f)(3) **Container appurtenances**

(f)(3)(i) All appurtenances shall be protected against physical damage.

(f)(3)(ii) All connections to containers, except filling connections, safety relief devices, and liquid-level and pressure gage connections, shall be provided with suitable automatic excess flow valves, or in lieu thereof, may be fitted with quick-closing internal valves, which shall remain closed except during delivery operations. The control mechanism for such valves may be provided with a secondary control remote from the delivery connections and such control mechanism shall be provided with a fusible section (melting point 208 °F. to 220 °F.) which will permit the internal valve to close automatically in case of fire.

(f)(3)(iii) Filling connections shall be provided with automatic back-pressure check valves, excess-flow valves, or quick-closing internal valves, to prevent back-flow in case the filling connection is broken. Where the filling and discharge connect to a common opening in the container shell and that opening is fitted with a quick-closing internal valve as specified in paragraph (f)(3)(ii) of this section, the automatic valve shall not be required.

(f)(3)(iv) All containers shall be equipped for spray loading (filling in the vapor space) or with an approved vapor return valve of adequate capacity.

(f)(4) Piping and fittings

(f)(4)(i) All piping, tubing, and fittings shall be securely mounted and protected against damage. Means shall be provided to protect hoses while the vehicle is in motion.

(f)(4)(ii) Fittings shall comply with paragraph (b)(6) of this section. Pipe shall be Schedule 80.

(f)(5) Safety relief devices

(f)(5)(i) The discharge from safety relief valves shall be vented away from the container upward and unobstructed to the open air in such a manner as to prevent any impingement of escaping gas upon the container; loose-fitting rain caps shall be used. Size of discharge lines from safety valves shall not be smaller than the nominal size of the safety-relief valve outlet connection. Suitable provision shall be made for draining condensate which may accumulate in the discharge pipe.

(f)(5)(ii) Any portion of liquid ammonia piping which at any time may be closed at both ends shall be provided with a hydrostatic relief valve.

(f)(6) Transfer of liquids

(f)(6)(i) The content of tank motor vehicle containers shall be determined by weight, by a suitable liquid-level gaging device, or other approved methods. If the content of a container is to be determined by liquid-level measurement, the container shall have a thermometer well so that the internal liquid temperature can be easily determined. This volume when converted to weight shall not exceed the filling density specified by the DOT.

(f)(6)(ii) Any pump, except a constant speed centrifugal pump, shall be equipped with a suitable pressure actuated bypass valve permitting flow from discharge to suction when the discharge pressure rises above a predetermined point. Pump discharge shall also be equipped with a spring-loaded safety relief valve set at a pressure not more than 135 percent of the setting of the bypass valve or more than 400 p.s.i.g., whichever is larger.

(f)(6)(iii) Compressors shall be equipped with manually operated shutoff valves on both suction and discharge connections. Pressure gages of bourdon-tube type shall be installed on the suction and discharge of the compressor before the shutoff valves. The compressor shall not be operated if either pressure gage is removed or is inoperative. A spring-loaded, safety-relief valve capable of discharging to atmosphere the full flow of gas from the compressor at a pressure not exceeding 300 p.s.i.g. shall be connected between the compressor discharge and the discharge shutoff valve.

(f)(6)(iv) Valve functions shall be clearly and legibly identified by metal tags or nameplates permanently affixed to each valve.

(f)(7)–(8) [Reserved]

(f)(9) Chock blocks At least two chock blocks shall be provided. These blocks shall be placed to prevent rolling of the vehicle whenever it is parked during loading and unloading operations.

(f)(10) Portable tank containers (skid tanks) Where portable tank containers are used for farm storage they shall comply with paragraph (c)(1) of this section. When portable tank containers are used in lieu of cargo tanks and are permanently mounted on tank motor vehicles for the transportation of ammonia, they shall comply with the requirements of this paragraph.

(g) Systems mounted on farm vehicles other than for the application of ammonia

(g)(1) Application This paragraph applies to containers of 1,200 gallons capacity or less and pertinent equipment mounted on farm vehicles (implements of husbandry) and used other than for the application of ammonia to the soil. Paragraph (b) of this section applies to this paragraph unless otherwise noted.

(g)(2) Design pressure and classification of containers

(g)(2)(i) The minimum design pressure for containers shall be 250 p.s.i.g.

(g)(2)(ii) The shell or head thickness of any container shall be not less than three-sixteenths of an inch.

(g)(3) Mounting containers

(g)(3)(i) A suitable "stop" or "stops" shall be mounted on the vehicle or on the container in such a way that the container shall not be dislodged from its mounting due to the vehicle coming to a sudden stop. Back slippage shall also be prevented by proper methods.

(g)(3)(ii) A suitable "hold down" device shall be provided which will anchor the container to the vehicle at one or more places on each side of the container.

(g)(3)(iii) When containers are mounted on four-wheel trailers, care shall be taken to insure that the weight is distributed evenly over both axles.

(g)(3)(iv) When the cradle and the tank are not welded together suitable material shall be used between them to eliminate metal-to-metal friction.

(g)(4) Container appurtenances

(g)(4)(i) All containers shall be equipped with a fixed liquid-level gage.

(g)(4)(ii) All containers with a capacity exceeding 250 gallons shall be equipped with a pressure gage having a dial graduated from 0–400 p.s.i.

(g)(4)(iii) The filling connection shall be fitted with combination back-pressure check valve and excess-flow valve; one double or two single back-pressure check valves; or a positive shutoff valve in conjunction with either an internal back-pressure check valve or an internal excess flow valve.

(g)(4)(iv) All containers with a capacity exceeding 250 gallons shall be equipped for spray loading or with an approved vapor return valve.

(g)(4)(v) All vapor and liquid connections except safety-relief valves and those specifically exempted by paragraph (b)(6)(v) of this section shall be equipped with approved excess-flow valves or may be fitted with quick-closing internal valves which, except during operating periods, shall remain closed.

(g)(4)(vi) Fittings shall be adequately protected from damage by a metal box or cylinder with open top securely fastened to the container or by rigid guards, well braced, welded to the container on both sides of the fittings or by a metal dome. If a metal dome is used, the relief valve shall be properly vented through the dome.

(g)(4)(vii) If a liquid withdrawal line is installed in the bottom of a container, the connections thereto, including hose, shall not be lower than the lowest horizontal edge of the vehicle axle.

(g)(4)(viii) Provision shall be made to secure both ends of the hose while in transit.

(g)(5) Marking the container There shall appear on each side and on the rear end of the container in letters at least 4 inches high, the words, **"Caution—Ammonia"** or the container shall be marked in accordance with DOT regulations.

(g)(6) Farm vehicles

(g)(6)(i) Farm vehicles shall conform with State regulations.

(g)(6)(ii) All trailers shall be securely attached to the vehicle drawing them by means of drawbars supplemented by suitable safety chains.

(g)(6)(iii) A trailer shall be constructed so that it will follow substantially in the path of the towing vehicle and will not whip or swerve dangerously from side to side.

(g)(6)(iv) All vehicles shall carry a can containing 5 gallons or more of water.

(h) Systems mounted on farm vehicles for the application of ammonia

(h)(1) This paragraph applies to systems utilizing containers of 250 gallons capacity or less which are mounted on farm vehicles (implement of husbandry) and used for the application of ammonia to the soil. Paragraph (b) of this section applies to this paragraph unless otherwise noted. Where larger containers are used, they shall comply with paragraph (g) of this section.

(h)(2) Design pressure and classification of containers

(h)(2)(i) The minimum design pressure for containers shall be 250 p.s.i.g.

(h)(2)(ii) The shell or head thickness of any container shall not be less than three-sixteenths inch.

(h)(3) Mounting of containers All containers and flow-control devices shall be securely mounted.

(h)(4) Container valves and accessories

(h)(4)(i) Each container shall have a fixed liquid-level gage.

(h)(4)(ii) The filling connection shall be fitted with a combination back-pressure check valve and an excess-flow valve; one double or two single back-pressure check valves: or a positive shutoff valve in conjunction with an internal back-pressure check valve or an internal excess-flow valve.

(h)(4)(iii) The applicator tank may be filled by venting to open air provided the bleeder valve orifice does not exceed seven-sixteenths inch in diameter.

(h)(4)(iv) Regulation equipment may be connected directly to the tank coupling or flange, in which case a flexible connection shall be used between such regulating equipment and the remainder of the liquid withdrawal system. Regulating equipment not so installed shall be flexibly connected to the container shutoff valve.

(h)(4)(v) No excess flow valve is required in the liquid withdrawal line provided the controlling orifice between the contents of the container and the outlet of the shutoff valve does not exceed seven-sixteenths inch in diameter.

[39 FR 23502, June 27, 1974, as amended at 43 FR 49748, Oct. 24, 1978; 49 FR 5322, Feb. 10, 1984; 53 FR 12122, Apr. 12, 1988; 61 FR 9238, Mar. 7, 1996; 63 FR 1269, Jan. 8, 1998; 63 FR 33466, June 18, 1998; 72 FR 71069, Dec. 14, 2007]

§1910.112-§1910.113 [Reserved]

§1910.119 Process safety management of highly hazardous chemicals

Purpose This section contains requirements for preventing or minimizing the consequences of catastrophic releases of toxic, reactive, flammable, or explosive chemicals. These releases may result in toxic, fire or explosion hazards.

(a) Application

(a)(1) This section applies to the following:

(a)(1)(i) A process which involves a chemical at or above the specified threshold quantities listed in Appendix A to this section;

(a)(1)(ii) A process which involves a Category 1 flammable gas (as defined in §1910.1200(c)) or a flammable liquid with a flashpoint below 100 °F (37.8 °C) on site in one location, in a quantity of 10,000 pounds (4535.9 kg) or more except for:

(a)(1)(ii)(A) Hydrocarbon fuels used solely for workplace consumption as a fuel (e.g., propane used for comfort heating, gasoline for vehicle refueling), if such fuels are not a part of a process containing another highly hazardous chemical covered by this standard;

(a)(1)(ii)(B) Flammable liquids stored in atmospheric tanks or transferred which are kept below their normal boiling point without benefit of chilling or refrigeration.

(a)(2) This section does not apply to:

(a)(2)(i) Retail facilities;

(a)(2)(ii) Oil or gas well drilling or servicing operations; or,

(a)(2)(iii) Normally unoccupied remote facilities.

(b) Definitions

Atmospheric tank means a storage tank which has been designed to operate at pressures from atmospheric through 0.5 p.s.i.g. (pounds per square inch gauge, 3.45 Kpa).

Boiling point means the boiling point of a liquid at a pressure of 14.7 pounds per square inch absolute (p.s.i.a.) (760 mm.). For the purposes of this section, where an accurate boiling point is unavailable for the material in question, or for mixtures which do not have a constant boiling point, the 10 percent point of a distillation performed in accordance with the Standard Method of Test for Distillation of Petroleum Products, ASTM D–86–62, which is incorporated by reference as specified in §1910.6, may be used as the boiling point of the liquid.

Catastrophic release means a major uncontrolled emission, fire, or explosion, involving one or more highly hazardous chemicals, that presents serious danger to employees in the workplace.

Facility means the buildings, containers or equipment which contain a process.

Highly hazardous chemical means a substance possessing toxic, reactive, flammable, or explosive properties and specified by paragraph (a)(1) of this section.

Hot work means work involving electric or gas welding, cutting, brazing, or similar flame or spark-producing operations.

Normally unoccupied remote facility means a facility which is operated, maintained or serviced by employees who visit the facility only periodically to check its operation and to perform necessary operating or maintenance tasks. No employees are permanently stationed at the facility. Facilities meeting this definition are not contiguous with, and must be geographically remote from all other buildings, processes or persons.

Process means any activity involving a highly hazardous chemical including any use, storage, manufacturing, handling, or the on-site movement of such chemicals, or combination of these activities. For purposes of this definition, any group of vessels which are interconnected and separate vessels which are located such that a highly hazardous chemical could be involved in a potential release shall be considered a single process.

Replacement in kind means a replacement which satisfies the design specification.

Trade secret means any confidential formula, pattern, process, device, information or compilation of information that is used in an employer's business, and that gives the employer an opportunity to obtain an advantage over competitors who do not know or use it. See Appendix E to §1910.1200—Definition of a Trade Secret (which sets out the criteria to be used in evaluating trade secrets).

(c) Employee participation

(c)(1) Employers shall develop a written plan of action regarding the implementation of the employee participation required by this paragraph.

(c)(2) Employers shall consult with employees and their representatives on the conduct and development of process hazards analyses and on the development of the other elements of process safety management in this standard.

(c)(3) Employers shall provide to employees and their representatives access to process hazard analyses and to all other information required to be developed under this standard.

(d) Process safety information In accordance with the schedule set forth in paragraph (e)(1) of this section, the employer shall complete a compilation of written process safety information before conducting any process hazard analysis required by the standard. The compilation of written process safety information is to enable the employer and the employees involved in operating the process to identify and understand the hazards posed by those processes involving highly hazardous chemicals. This process safety information shall include information pertaining to the hazards of the highly hazardous chemicals used or produced by the process, information pertaining to the technology of the process, and information pertaining to the equipment in the process.

(d)(1) Information pertaining to the hazards of the highly hazardous chemicals in the process This information shall consist of at least the following:

(d)(1)(i) Toxicity information;

(d)(1)(ii) Permissible exposure limits;

(d)(1)(iii) Physical data;

(d)(1)(iv) Reactivity data;

(d)(1)(v) Corrosivity data;

(d)(1)(vi) Thermal and chemical stability data; and

(d)(1)(vii) Hazardous effects of inadvertent mixing of different materials that could foreseeably occur.

Note: *Safety Data Sheets meeting the requirements of 29 CFR §1910.1200(g) may be used to comply with this requirement to the extent they contain the information required by this subparagraph.*

(d)(2) Information pertaining to the technology of the process

(d)(2)(i) Information concerning the technology of the process shall include at least the following:

(d)(2)(i)(A) A block flow diagram or simplified process flow diagram (see Appendix B to this section);

(d)(2)(i)(B) Process chemistry;

(d)(2)(i)(C) Maximum intended inventory;

(d)(2)(i)(D) Safe upper and lower limits for such items as temperatures, pressures, flows or compositions; and,

(d)(2)(i)(E) An evaluation of the consequences of deviations, including those affecting the safety and health of employees.

(d)(2)(ii) Where the original technical information no longer exists, such information may be developed in conjunction with the process hazard analysis in sufficient detail to support the analysis.

(d)(3) Information pertaining to the equipment in the process

(d)(3)(i) Information pertaining to the equipment in the process shall include:

(d)(3)(i)(A) Materials of construction;

(d)(3)(i)(B) Piping and instrument diagrams (P&ID's);

(d)(3)(i)(C) Electrical classification;

(d)(3)(i)(D) Relief system design and design basis;

(d)(3)(i)(E) Ventilation system design;

(d)(3)(i)(F) Design codes and standards employed;

(d)(3)(i)(G) Material and energy balances for processes built after May 26, 1992; and

(d)(3)(i)(H) Safety systems (e.g. interlocks, detection or suppression systems).

(d)(3)(ii) The employer shall document that equipment complies with recognized and generally accepted good engineering practices.

(d)(3)(iii) For existing equipment designed and constructed in accordance with codes, standards, or practices that are no longer in general use, the employer shall determine and document that the equipment is designed, maintained, inspected, tested, and operating in a safe manner.

(e) Process hazard analysis

(e)(1) The employer shall perform an initial process hazard analysis (hazard evaluation) on processes covered by this standard. The process hazard analysis shall be appropriate to the complexity of the process and shall identify, evaluate, and control the hazards involved in the process. Employers shall determine and document the priority order for conducting process hazard analyses based on a rationale which includes such considerations as extent of the process hazards, number of potentially affected employees, age of the process, and operating history of the process. The process hazard analysis shall be conducted as soon as possible, but not later than the following schedule:

(e)(1)(i) No less than 25 percent of the initial process hazards analyses shall be completed by May 26, 1994;

(e)(1)(ii) No less than 50 percent of the initial process hazards analyses shall be completed by May 26, 1995;

(e)(1)(iii) No less than 75 percent of the initial process hazards analyses shall be completed by May 26, 1996;

(e)(1)(iv) All initial process hazards analyses shall be completed by May 26, 1997;

(e)(1)(v) Process hazards analyses completed after May 26, 1987 which meet the requirements of this paragraph are acceptable as initial process hazards analyses. These process hazard analyses shall be updated and revalidated, based on their completion date, in accordance with paragraph (e)(6) of this section.

(e)(2) The employer shall use one or more of the following methodologies that are appropriate to determine and evaluate the hazards of the process being analyzed:

(e)(2)(i) What-If;
(e)(2)(ii) Checklist;
(e)(2)(iii) What-If/Checklist;
(e)(2)(iv) Hazard and Operability Study (HAZOP);
(e)(2)(v) Failure Mode and Effects Analysis (FMEA);
(e)(2)(vi) Fault Tree Analysis; or
(e)(2)(vii) An appropriate equivalent methodology.

(e)(3) O_I The process hazard analysis shall address:

(e)(3)(i) The hazards of the process;

(e)(3)(ii) The identification of any previous incident which had a likely potential for catastrophic consequences in the workplace;

(e)(3)(iii) Engineering and administrative controls applicable to the hazards and their interrelationships such as appropriate application of detection methodologies to provide early warning of releases. (Acceptable detection methods might include process monitoring and control instrumentation with alarms, and detection hardware such as hydrocarbon sensors.);

(e)(3)(iv) Consequences of failure of engineering and administrative controls;

(e)(3)(v) Facility siting;

(e)(3)(vi) Human factors; and

(e)(3)(vii) A qualitative evaluation of a range of the possible safety and health effects of failure of controls on employees in the workplace.

(e)(4) O_I The process hazard analysis shall be performed by a team with expertise in engineering and process operations, and the team shall include at least one employee who has experience and knowledge specific to the process being evaluated. Also, one member of the team must be knowledgeable in the specific process hazard analysis methodology being used.

(e)(5) The employer shall establish a system to promptly address the team's findings and recommendations; assure that the recommendations are resolved in a timely manner and that the resolution is documented; document what actions are to be taken; complete actions as soon as possible; develop a written schedule of when these actions are to be completed; communicate the actions to operating, maintenance and other employees whose work assignments are in the process and who may be affected by the recommendations or actions.

(e)(6) O_I At least every five (5) years after the completion of the initial process hazard analysis, the process hazard analysis shall be updated and revalidated by a team meeting the requirements in paragraph (e)(4) of this section, to assure that the process hazard analysis is consistent with the current process.

(e)(7) Employers shall retain process hazards analyses and updates or revalidations for each process covered by this section, as well as the documented resolution of recommendations described in paragraph (e)(5) of this section for the life of the process.

(f) Operating procedures

(f)(1) The employer shall develop and implement written operating procedures that provide clear instructions for safely conducting activities involved in each covered process consistent with the process safety information and shall address at least the following elements.

(f)(1)(i) Steps for each operating phase

(f)(1)(i)(A) Initial startup;

(f)(1)(i)(B) Normal operations;

(f)(1)(i)(C) Temporary operations;

(f)(1)(i)(D) Emergency shutdown including the conditions under which emergency shutdown is required, and the assignment of shutdown responsibility to qualified operators to ensure that emergency shutdown is executed in a safe and timely manner;

(f)(1)(i)(E) Emergency Operations;

(f)(1)(i)(F) Normal shutdown; and,

(f)(1)(i)(G) Startup following a turnaround, or after an emergency shutdown.

(f)(1)(ii) Operating limits

(f)(1)(ii)(A) Consequences of deviation; and

(f)(1)(ii)(B) Steps required to correct or avoid deviation.

(f)(1)(iii) Safety and health considerations

(f)(1)(iii)(A) Properties of, and hazards presented by, the chemicals used in the process;

(f)(1)(iii)(B) O_I Precautions necessary to prevent exposure, including engineering controls, administrative controls, and personal protective equipment;

(f)(1)(iii)(C) Control measures to be taken if physical contact or airborne exposure occurs;

(f)(1)(iii)(D) Quality control for raw materials and control of hazardous chemical inventory levels; and,

(f)(1)(iii)(E) Any special or unique hazards.

(f)(1)(iv) O_I Safety systems and their functions .

(f)(2) Operating procedures shall be readily accessible to employees who work in or maintain a process.

(f)(3) The operating procedures shall be reviewed as often as necessary to assure that they reflect current operating practice, including changes that result from changes in process chemicals, technology, and equipment, and changes to facilities. The employer shall certify annually that these operating procedures are current and accurate.

(f)(4) O_I The employer shall develop and implement safe work practices to provide for the control of hazards during operations such as lockout/tagout; confined space entry; opening process equipment or piping; and control over entrance into a facility by maintenance, contractor, laboratory, or other support personnel. These safe work practices shall apply to employees and contractor employees.

(g) Training

(g)(1) Initial training

(g)(1)(i) Each employee presently involved in operating a process, and each employee before being involved in operating a newly assigned process, shall be trained in an overview of the process and in the operating procedures as specified in paragraph (f) of this section. The training shall include emphasis on the specific safety and health hazards, emergency operations including shutdown, and safe work practices applicable to the employee's job tasks.

(g)(1)(ii) In lieu of initial training for those employees already involved in operating a process on May 26, 1992, an employer may certify in writing that the employee has the required knowledge, skills, and abilities to safely carry out the duties and responsibilities as specified in the operating procedures.

(g)(2) **Refresher training** Refresher training shall be provided at least every three years, and more often if necessary, to each employee involved in operating a process to assure that the employee understands and adheres to the current operating procedures of the process. The employer, in consultation with the employees involved in operating the process, shall determine the appropriate frequency of refresher training.

(g)(3) **Training documentation** The employer shall ascertain that each employee involved in operating a process has received and understood the training required by this paragraph. The employer shall prepare a record which contains the identity of the employee, the date of training, and the means used to verify that the employee understood the training.

(h) Contractors

(h)(1) **Application** This paragraph applies to contractors performing maintenance or repair, turnaround, major renovation, or specialty work on or adjacent to a covered process. It does not apply to contractors providing incidental services which do not influence process safety, such as janitorial work, food and drink services, laundry, delivery or other supply services.

(h)(2) O_I Employer responsibilities

(h)(2)(i) The employer, when selecting a contractor, shall obtain and evaluate information regarding the contract employer's safety performance and programs.

(h)(2)(ii) The employer shall inform contract employers of the known potential fire, explosion, or toxic release hazards related to the contractor's work and the process.

(h)(2)(iii) The employer shall explain to contract employers the applicable provisions of the emergency action plan required by paragraph (n) of this section.

(h)(2)(iv) O_I The employer shall develop and implement safe work practices consistent with paragraph (f)(4) of this section, to control the entrance, presence and exit of contract employers and contract employees in covered process areas.

(h)(2)(v) The employer shall periodically evaluate the performance of contract employers in fulfilling their obligations as specified in paragraph (h)(3) of this section.

(h)(2)(vi) The employer shall maintain a contract employee injury and illness log related to the contractor's work in process areas.

(h)(3) OI **Contract employer responsibilities**

(h)(3)(i) The contract employer shall assure that each contract employee is trained in the work practices necessary to safely perform his/her job.

(h)(3)(ii) The contract employer shall assure that each contract employee is instructed in the known potential fire, explosion, or toxic release hazards related to his/her job and the process, and the applicable provisions of the emergency action plan.

(h)(3)(iii) The contract employer shall document that each contract employee has received and understood the training required by this paragraph. The contract employer shall prepare a record which contains the identity of the contract employee, the date of training, and the means used to verify that the employee understood the training.

(h)(3)(iv) The contract employer shall assure that each contract employee follows the safety rules of the facility including the safe work practices required by paragraph (f)(4) of this section.

(h)(3)(v) The contract employer shall advise the employer of any unique hazards presented by the contract employer's work, or of any hazards found by the contract employer's work.

(i) **Pre-startup safety review**

(i)(1) The employer shall perform a pre-startup safety review for new facilities and for modified facilities when the modification is significant enough to require a change in the process safety information.

(i)(2) The pre-startup safety review shall confirm that prior to the introduction of highly hazardous chemicals to a process:

(i)(2)(i) Construction and equipment is in accordance with design specifications;

(i)(2)(ii) Safety, operating, maintenance, and emergency procedures are in place and are adequate;

(i)(2)(iii) For new facilities, a process hazard analysis has been performed and recommendations have been resolved or implemented before startup; and modified facilities meet the requirements contained in management of change, paragraph (l);

(i)(2)(iv) Training of each employee involved in operating a process has been completed.

(j) OI **Mechanical integrity**

(j)(1) OI **Application** Paragraphs (j)(2) through (j)(6) of this section apply to the following process equipment:

(j)(1)(i) Pressure vessels and storage tanks;

(j)(1)(ii) Piping systems (including piping components such as valves);

(j)(1)(iii) Relief and vent systems and devices;

(j)(1)(iv) Emergency shutdown systems;

(j)(1)(v) Controls (including monitoring devices and sensors, alarms, and interlocks); and

(j)(1)(vi) Pumps.

(j)(2) OI 8 The employer shall establish and implement written procedures to maintain the on-going integrity of process equipment.

(j)(3) **Training for process maintenance activities** The employer shall train each employee involved in maintaining the on-going integrity of process equipment in an overview of that process and its hazards and in the procedures applicable to the employee's job tasks to assure that the employee can perform the job tasks in a safe manner.

(j)(4) **Inspection and testing**

(j)(4)(i) Inspections and tests shall be performed on process equipment.

(j)(4)(ii) Inspection and testing procedures shall follow recognized and generally accepted good engineering practices.

(j)(4)(iii) The frequency of inspections and tests of process equipment shall be consistent with applicable manufacturers' recommendations and good engineering practices, and more frequently if determined to be necessary by prior operating experience.

(j)(4)(iv) The employer shall document each inspection and test that has been performed on process equipment. The documentation shall identify the date of the inspection or test, the name of the person who performed the inspection or test, the serial number or other identifier of the equipment on which the inspection or test was performed, a description of the inspection or test performed, and the results of the inspection or test.

(j)(5) **Equipment deficiencies** The employer shall correct deficiencies in equipment that are outside acceptable limits (defined by the process safety information in paragraph (d) of this section) before further use or in a safe and timely manner when necessary means are taken to assure safe operation.

(j)(6) **Quality assurance**

(j)(6)(i) OI In the construction of new plants and equipment, the employer shall assure that equipment as it is fabricated is suitable for the process application for which they will be used.

(j)(6)(ii) OI Appropriate checks and inspections shall be performed to assure that equipment is installed properly and consistent with design specifications and the manufacturer's instructions.

(j)(6)(iii) The employer shall assure that maintenance materials, spare parts and equipment are suitable for the process application for which they will be used.

(k) **Hot work permit**

(k)(1) The employer shall issue a hot work permit for hot work operations conducted on or near a covered process.

(k)(2) OI The permit shall document that the fire prevention and protection requirements in 29 CFR §1910.252(a) have been implemented prior to beginning the hot work operations; it shall indicate the date(s) authorized for hot work; and identify the object on which hot work is to be performed. The permit shall be kept on file until completion of the hot work operations.

(l) OI **Management of change**

(l)(1) The employer shall establish and implement written procedures to manage changes (except for "replacements in kind") to process chemicals, technology, equipment, and procedures; and, changes to facilities that affect a covered process.

(l)(2) The procedures shall assure that the following considerations are addressed prior to any change:

(l)(2)(i) OI The technical basis for the proposed change;

(l)(2)(ii) Impact of change on safety and health;

(l)(2)(iii) Modifications to operating procedures;

(l)(2)(iv) Necessary time period for the change; and

(l)(2)(v) Authorization requirements for the proposed change.

(l)(3) Employees involved in operating a process and maintenance and contract employees whose job tasks will be affected by a change in the process shall be informed of, and trained in, the change prior to start-up of the process or affected part of the process.

(l)(4) OI If a change covered by this paragraph results in a change in the process safety information required by paragraph (d) of this section, such information shall be updated accordingly.

(l)(5) OI If a change covered by this paragraph results in a change in the operating procedures or practices required by paragraph (f) of this section, such procedures or practices shall be updated accordingly.

(m) **Incident investigation**

(m)(1) The employer shall investigate each incident which resulted in, or could reasonably have resulted in a catastrophic release of highly hazardous chemical in the workplace.

(m)(2) An incident investigation shall be initiated as promptly as possible, but not later than 48 hours following the incident.

(m)(3) OI An incident investigation team shall be established and consist of at least one person knowledgeable in the process involved, including a contract employee if the incident involved work of the contractor, and other persons with appropriate knowledge and experience to thoroughly investigate and analyze the incident.

(m)(4) A report shall be prepared at the conclusion of the investigation which includes at a minimum:

(m)(4)(i) Date of incident;

(m)(4)(ii) Date investigation began;

(m)(4)(iii) A description of the incident;

(m)(4)(iv) The factors that contributed to the incident; and

(m)(4)(v) Any recommendations resulting from the investigation.

(m)(5) The employer shall establish a system to promptly address and resolve the incident report findings and recommendations. Resolutions and corrective actions shall be documented.

(m)(6) The report shall be reviewed with all affected personnel whose job tasks are relevant to the incident findings including contract employees where applicable.

(m)(7) Incident investigation reports shall be retained for five years.

(n) OI **Emergency planning and response** The employer shall establish and implement an emergency action plan for the entire plant in accordance with the provisions of 29 CFR §1910.38. In addition, the emergency action plan shall include procedures for handling small releases. Employers covered under this standard may also be subject to the hazardous waste and emergency response provisions contained in 29 CFR §1910.120 (a), (p) and (q).

(o) OI **Compliance Audits**

(o)(1) OI Employers shall certify that they have evaluated compliance with the provisions of this section at least every three years to verify that the procedures and practices developed under the standard are adequate and are being followed.

(o)(2) The compliance audit shall be conducted by at least one person knowledgeable in the process.

(o)(3) A report of the findings of the audit shall be developed.

(o)(4) The employer shall promptly determine and document an appropriate response to each of the findings of the compliance audit, and document that deficiencies have been corrected.

(o)(5) Employers shall retain the two (2) most recent compliance audit reports.

(p) **Trade secrets**

(p)(1) Employers shall make all information necessary to comply with the section available to those persons responsible for compiling the process safety information (required by paragraph (d) of this section), those assisting in the development of the process hazard analysis (required by paragraph (e) of this section), those responsible for developing the operating procedures (required by paragraph (f) of this section), and those involved in incident investigations (required by paragraph (m) of this section), emergency planning and response (paragraph (n) of this section) and compliance audits (paragraph (o) of this section) without regard to possible trade secret status of such information.

(p)(2) Nothing in this paragraph shall preclude the employer from requiring the persons to whom the information is made available under paragraph (p)(1) of this section to enter into confidentiality agreements not to disclose the information as set forth in 29 CFR §1910.1200.

(p)(3) Subject to the rules and procedures set forth in 29 CFR §1910.1200(i)(1) through §1910.1200(i)(12), employees and their designated representatives shall have access to trade secret information contained within the process hazard analysis and other documents required to be developed by this standard.

§1910.119 Appendix A OI
List of Highly Hazardous Chemicals, Toxics and Reactives
(Mandatory)

This Appendix contains a listing of toxic and reactive highly hazardous chemicals which present a potential for a catastrophic event at or above the threshold quantity.

CHEMICAL name	CAS*	TQ**
Acetaldehyde	75–07–0	2500
Acrolein (2-Propenal)	107–02–8	150
Acrylyl Chloride	814–68–6	250
Allyl Chloride	107–05–1	1000
Allylamine	107–11–9	1000
Alkylaluminums	Varies	5000
Ammonia, Anhydrous	7664–41–7	10000
Ammonia solutions (>44% ammonia by weight)	7664–41–7	15000
Ammonium Perchlorate	7790–98–9	7500
Ammonium Permanganate	7787–36–2	7500
Arsine (also called Arsenic Hydride)	7784–42–1	100
Bis(Chloromethyl) Ether	542–88–1	100
Boron Trichloride	10294–34–5	2500
Boron Trifluoride	7637–07–2	250
Bromine	7726–95–6	1500
Bromine Chloride	13863–41–7	1500
Bromine Pentafluoride	7789–30–2	2500
Bromine Trifluoride	7787–71–5	15000
3–Bromopropyne (also called Propargyl Bromide)	106–96–7	100
Butyl Hydroperoxide (Tertiary)	75–91–2	5000
Butyl Perbenzoate (Tertiary)	614–45–9	7500
Carbonyl Chloride (see Phosgene)	75–44–5	100
Carbonyl Fluoride	353–50–4	2500
Cellulose Nitrate (concentration >12.6% nitrogen)	9004–70–0	2500
Chlorine	7782–50–5	1500
Chlorine Dioxide	10049–04–4	1000
Chlorine Pentrafluoride	13637–63–3	1000
Chlorine Trifluoride	7790–91–2	1000
Chlorodiethylaluminum (also called Diethylaluminum Chloride)	96–10–6	5000
1-Chloro-2,4-Dinitrobenzene	97–00–7	5000
Chloromethyl Methyl Ether	107–30–2	500
Chloropicrin	76–06–2	500
Chloropicrin and Methyl Bromide mixture	None	1500
Chloropicrin and Methyl Chloride mixture	None	1500
Cumene Hydroperoxide	80–15–9	5000
Cyanogen	460–19–5	2500
Cyanogen Chloride	506–77–4	500
Cyanuric Fluoride	675–14–9	100
Diacetyl Peroxide (Concentration >70%)	110–22–5	5000
Diazomethane	334–88–3	500
Dibenzoyl Peroxide	94–36–0	7500
Diborane	19287–45–7	100
Dibutyl Peroxide (Tertiary)	110–05–4	5000
Dichloro Acetylene	7572–29–4	250
Dichlorosilane	4109–96–0	2500
Diethylzinc	557–20–0	10000
Diisopropyl Peroxydicarbonate	105–64–6	7500
Dilauroyl Peroxide	105–74–8	7500
Dimethyldichlorosilane	75–78–5	1000
Dimethylhydrazine, 1,1-	57–14–7	1000
Dimethylamine, Anhydrous	124–40–3	2500
2,4-Dinitroaniline	97–02–9	5000
Ethyl Methyl Ketone Peroxide (also Methyl Ethyl Ketone Peroxide; concentration >60%)	1338–23–4	5000
Ethyl Nitrite	109–95–5	5000
Ethylamine	75–04–7	7500
Ethylene Fluorohydrin	371–62–0	100
Ethylene Oxide	75–21–8	5000
Ethyleneimine	151–56–4	1000
Fluorine	7782–41–4	1000
Formaldehyde (Formalin)	50–00–0	1000
Furan	110–00–9	500
Hexafluoroacetone	684–16–2	5000
Hydrochloric Acid, Anhydrous	7647–01–0	5000
Hydrofluoric Acid, Anhydrous	7664–39–3	1000
Hydrogen Bromide	10035–10–6	5000
Hydrogen Chloride	7647–01–0	5000
Hydrogen Cyanide, Anhydrous	74–90–8	1000
Hydrogen Fluoride	7664–39–3	1000
Hydrogen Peroxide (52% by weight or greater)	7722–84–1	7500
Hydrogen Selenide	7783–07–5	150
Hydrogen Sulfide	7783–06–4	1500
Hydroxylamine	7803–49–8	2500
Iron, Pentacarbonyl	13463–40–6	250

Note: Table data continues on next page.

CHEMICAL name	CAS*	TQ**
Isopropylamine	75–31–0	5000
Ketene	463–51–4	1000
Methacrylaldehyde	78–85–3	1000
Methacryloyl Chloride	920–46–7	150
Methacryloyloxyethyl Isocyanate	30674–80–7	100
Methyl Acrylonitrile	126–98–7	250
Methylamine, Anhydrous	74–89–5	1000
Methyl Bromide	74–83–9	2500
Methyl Chloride	74–87–3	15000
Methyl Chloroformate	79–22–1	500
Methyl Ethyl Ketone Peroxide (concentration >60%)	1338–23–4	5000
Methyl Fluoroacetate	453–18–9	100
Methyl Fluorosulfate	421–20–5	100
Methyl Hydrazine	60–34–4	100
Methyl Iodide	74–88–4	7500
Methyl Isocyanate	624–83–9	250
Methyl Mercaptan	74–93–1	5000
Methyl Vinyl Ketone	79–84–4	100
Methyltrichlorosilane	75–79–6	500
Nickel Carbonly (Nickel Tetracarbonyl)	13463–39–3	150
Nitric Acid (94.5% by weight or greater)	7697–37–2	500
Nitric Oxide	10102–43–9	250
Nitroaniline (para Nitroaniline)	100–01–6	5000
Nitromethane	75–52–5	2500
Nitrogen Dioxide	10102–44–0	250
Nitrogen Oxides (NO; NO_2; N_2O_4; N_2O_3)	10102–44–0	250
Nitrogen Tetroxide (also called Nitrogen Peroxide)	10544–72–6	250
Nitrogen Trifluoride	7783–54–2	5000
Nitrogen Trioxide	7783–54–2	250
Oleum (65% to 80% by weight; also called Fuming Sulfuric Acid)	8014–94–7	1000
Osmium Tetroxide	20816–12–0	100
Oxygen Difluoride (Fluorine Monoxide)	7783–41–7	100
Ozone	10028–15–6	100
Pentaborane	19624–22–7	100
Peracetic Acid (concentration >60% Acetic Acid; also called Peroxyacetic Acid)	79–21–0	1000
Perchloric Acid (concentration >60% by weight)	7601–90–3	5000
Perchloromethyl Mercaptan	594–42–3	150
Perchloryl Fluoride	7616–94–6	5000
Peroxyacetic Acid (concentration >60% Acetic Acid; also called Peracetic Acid)	79–21–0	1000
Phosgene (also called Carbonyl Chloride)	75–44–5	100
Phosphine (Hydrogen Phosphide)	7803–51–2	100
Phosphorus Oxychloride (also called Phosphoryl Chloride)	10025–87–3	1000
Phosphorus Trichloride	7719–12–2	1000
Phosphoryl Chloride (also called Phosphorus Oxychloride)	10025–87–3	1000
Propargyl Bromide	106–96–7	100
Propyl Nitrate	627–3–4	2500
Sarin	107–44–8	100
Selenium Hexafluoride	7783–79–1	1000
Stibine (Antimony Hydride)	7803–52–3	500
Sulfur Dioxide (liquid)	7446–09–5	1000
Sulfur Pentafluoride	5714–22–7	250
Sulfur Tetrafluoride	7783–60–0	250
Sulfur Trioxide (also called Sulfuric Anhydride)	7446–11–9	1000
Sulfuric Anhydride (also called Sulfur Trioxide)	7446–11–9	1000
Tellurium Hexafluoride	7783–80–4	250
Tetrafluoroethylene	116–14–3	5000
Tetrafluorohydrazine	10036–47–2	5000
Tetramethyl Lead	75–74–1	1000
Thionyl Chloride	7719–09–7	250
Trichloro (chloromethyl) Silane	1558–25–4	100
Trichloro (dichlorophenyl) Silane	27137–85–5	2500
Trichlorosilane	10025–78–2	5000
Trifluorochloroethylene	79–38–9	10000
Trimethyoxysilane	2487–90–3	1500

*Chemical Abstract Service Number.
**Threshold Quantity in Pounds (Amount necessary to be covered by this standard).

§1910.119 Appendix B
Block Flow Diagram and Simplified Process Flow Diagram
(Nonmandatory)

Example of a Block Flow Diagram

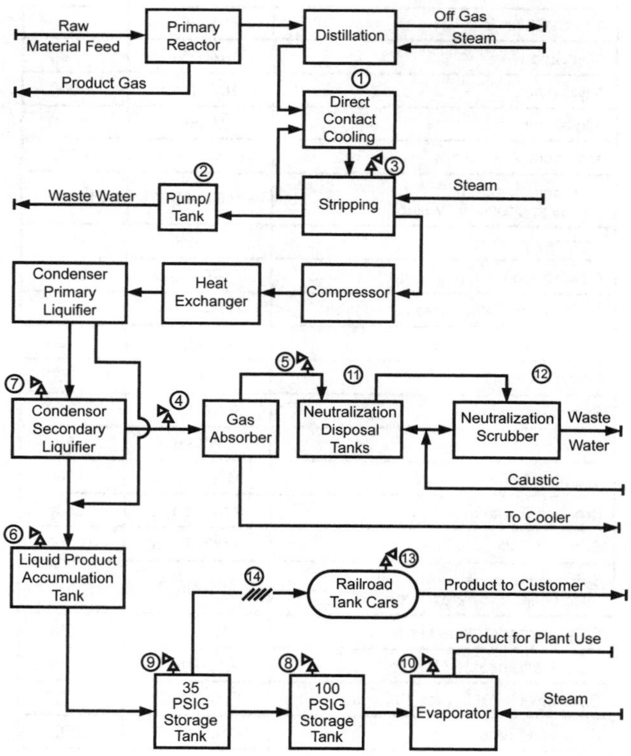

Example of a Process Flow Diagram

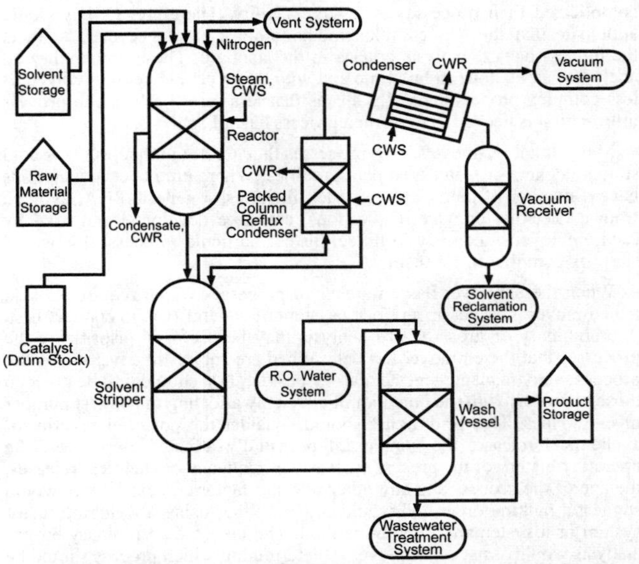

§1910.119 Appendix C Compliance Guidelines and Recommendations for Process Safety Management
(Nonmandatory)

This Appendix serves as a nonmandatory guideline to assist employers and employees in complying with the requirements of this section, as well as provides other helpful recommendations and information. Examples presented in this Appendix are not the only means of achieving the performance goals in the standard. This Appendix neither adds nor detracts from the requirements of the standard.

1. Introduction to Process Safety Management The major objective of process safety management of highly hazardous chemicals is to prevent unwanted releases of hazardous chemicals especially into locations which could expose employees and others to serious hazards. An effective process safety management program requires a systematic approach to evaluating the whole process. Using this approach the process design, process technology, operational and maintenance activities and procedures, nonroutine activities and procedures, emergency preparedness plans and procedures, training programs, and other elements which impact the process are all considered in the evaluation. The various lines of defense that have been incorporated into the design and operation of the process to prevent or mitigate the release of hazardous chemicals need to be evaluated and strengthened to assure their effectiveness at each level. Process safety management is the proactive identification, evaluation and mitigation or prevention of chemical releases that could occur as a result of failures in process, procedures or equipment.

The process safety management standard targets highly hazardous chemicals that have the potential to cause a catastrophic incident. This standard as a whole is to aid employers in their efforts to prevent or mitigate episodic chemical releases that could lead to a catastrophe in the workplace and possibly to the surrounding community. To control these types of hazards, employers need to develop the necessary expertise, experiences, judgement and proactive initiative within their workforce to properly implement and maintain an effective process safety management program as envisioned in the OSHA standard. This OSHA standard is required by the Clean Air Act Amendments as is the Environmental Protection Agency's Risk Management Plan. Employers, who merge the two sets of requirements into their process safety management program, will better assure full compliance with each as well as enhancing their relationship with the local community.

While OSHA believes process safety management will have a positive effect on the safety of employees in workplaces and also offers other potential benefits to employers (increased productivity), smaller businesses which may have limited resources available to them at this time, might consider alternative avenues of decreasing the risks associated with highly hazardous chemicals at their workplaces. One method which might be considered is the reduction in the inventory of the highly hazardous chemical. This reduction in inventory will result in a reduction of the risk or potential for a catastrophic incident. Also, employers including small employers may be able to establish more efficient inventory control by reducing the quantities of highly hazardous chemicals on site below the established threshold quantities. This reduction can be accomplished by ordering smaller shipments and maintaining the minimum inventory necessary for efficient and safe operation. When reduced inventory is not feasible, then the employer might consider dispersing inventory to several locations on site. Dispersing storage into locations where a release in one location will not cause a release in another location is a practical method to also reduce the risk or potential for catastrophic incidents.

2. Employee Involvement in Process Safety Management Section 304 of the Clean Air Act Amendments states that employers are to consult with their employees and their representatives regarding the employers efforts in the development and implementation of the process safety management program elements and hazard assessments. Section 304 also requires employers to train and educate their employees and to inform affected employees of the findings from incident investigations required by the process safety management program. Many employers, under their safety and health programs, have already established means and methods to keep employees and their representatives informed about relevant safety and health issues and employers may be able to adapt these practices and procedures to meet their obligations under this standard. Employers who have not implemented an occupational safety and health program may wish to form a safety and health committee of employees and management representatives to help the employer meet the obligations specified by this standard. These committees can become a significant ally in helping the employer to implement and maintain an effective process safety management program for all employees.

3. Process Safety Information Complete and accurate written information concerning process chemicals, process technology, and process equipment is essential to an effective process safety management program and to a process hazards analysis. The compiled information will be a necessary resource to a variety of users including the team that will perform the process hazards analysis as required under paragraph (e); those developing the training programs and the operating procedures; contractors whose employees will be working with the process; those conducting the pre-startup reviews; local emergency preparedness planners; and insurance and enforcement officials.

The information to be compiled about the chemicals, including process intermediates, needs to be comprehensive enough for an accurate assessment of the fire and explosion characteristics, reactivity hazards, the safety and health hazards to workers, and the corrosion and erosion effects on the process equipment and monitoring tools. Current safety data sheet (SDS) information can be used to help meet this requirement which must be supplemented with process chemistry information including runaway reaction and over pressure hazards if applicable.

Process technology information will be a part of the process safety information package and it is expected that it will include diagrams of the type shown in Appendix B of this section as well as employer established criteria for maximum inventory levels for process chemicals; limits beyond which would be considered upset conditions; and a qualitative estimate of the consequences or results of deviation that could occur if operating beyond the established process limits. Employers are encouraged to use diagrams which will help users understand the process.

A block flow diagram is used to show the major process equipment and interconnecting process flow lines and show flow rates, stream composition, temperatures, and pressures when necessary for clarity. The block flow diagram is a simplified diagram.

Process flow diagrams are more complex and will show all main flow streams including valves to enhance the understanding of the process, as well as pressures and temperatures on all feed and product lines within all major vessels, in and out of headers and heat exchangers, and points of pressure and temperature control. Also, materials of construction information, pump capacities and pressure heads, compressor horsepower and vessel design pressures and temperatures are shown when necessary for clarity. In addition, major components of control loops are usually shown along with key utilities on process flow diagrams.

Piping and instrument diagrams (P&IDs) may be the more appropriate type of diagrams to show some of the above details and to display the information for the piping designer and engineering staff. The P&IDs are to be used to describe the relationships between equipment and instrumentation as well as other relevant information that will enhance clarity. Computer software programs which do P&IDs or other diagrams useful to the information package, may be used to help meet this requirement.

The information pertaining to process equipment design must be documented. In other words, what were the codes and standards relied on to establish good engineering practice. These codes and standards are published by such organizations as the American Society of Mechanical Engineers, American Petroleum Institute, American National Standards Institute, National Fire Protection Association, American Society for Testing and Materials, National Board of Boiler and Pressure Vessel Inspectors, National Association of Corrosion Engineers, American Society of Exchange Manufacturers Association, and model building code groups.

In addition, various engineering societies issue technical reports which impact process design. For example, the American Institute of Chemical Engineers has published technical reports on topics such as two phase flow for venting devices. This type of technically recognized report would constitute good engineering practice.

For existing equipment designed and constructed many years ago in accordance with the codes and standards available at that time and no longer in general use today, the employer must document which codes and standards were used and that the design and construction along with the testing, inspection and operation are still suitable for the intended use. Where the process technology requires a design which departs from the applicable codes and standards, the employer must document that the design and construction is suitable for the intended purpose.

4. Process Hazard Analysis A process hazard analysis (PHA), sometimes called a process hazard evaluation, is one of the most important elements of the process safety management program. A PHA is an organized and systematic effort to identify and analyze the significance of potential hazards associated with the processing or handling of highly hazardous chemicals. A PHA provides information which will assist employers and employees in making decisions for improving safety and reducing the consequences of unwanted or unplanned releases of hazardous chemicals. A PHA is directed toward analyzing potential causes and consequences of fires, explosions, releases of toxic or flammable chemicals and major spills of hazardous chemicals. The PHA focuses on equipment, instrumentation, utilities, human actions (routine and nonroutine), and external factors that might impact the process. These considerations assist in determining the hazards and potential failure points or failure modes in a process.

The selection of a PHA methodology or technique will be influenced by many factors including the amount of existing knowledge about the process. Is it a process that has been operated for a long period of time with little or no innovation and extensive experience has been generated with its use? Or, is it a new process or one which has been changed frequently by the inclusion of innovative features? Also, the size and complexity of the process will influence the decision as to the appropriate PHA methodology to use. All PHA methodologies are subject to certain limitations. For example, the checklist methodology works well when the process is very stable and no changes are made, but it is not as effective when the process has undergone extensive change. The checklist may miss the most recent changes and consequently the changes would not be evaluated. Another limitation to be considered concerns the assumptions made by the team or analyst. The PHA is dependent on good judgement and the assumptions made during the study need to be documented and understood by the team and reviewer and kept for a future PHA.

The team conducting the PHA need to understand the methodology that is going to be used. A PHA team can vary in size from two people to a number of people with varied operational and technical backgrounds. Some team members may only be a part of the team for a limited time. The team leader needs to be fully knowledgeable in the proper implementation of the PHA methodology that is to be used and should be impartial in the evaluation. The other full or part time team members need to provide the team with expertise in areas such as process technology, process design, operating procedures and practices, including how the work is actually performed, alarms, emergency procedures, instrumentation, maintenance procedures, both routine and nonroutine tasks, including how the tasks are authorized, procurement of parts and supplies, safety and health, and any other relevant subject as the need dictates. At least one team member must be familiar with the process.

The ideal team will have an intimate knowledge of the standards, codes, specifications and regulations applicable to the process being studied. The selected team members need to be compatible and the team leader needs to be able to manage the team, and the PHA study. The team needs to be able to work together while benefiting from the expertise of others on the team or outside the team, to resolve issues, and to forge a consensus on the findings of the study and recommendations.

The application of a PHA to a process may involve the use of different methodologies for various parts of the process. For example, a process involving a series of unit operation of varying sizes, complexities, and ages may use different methodologies and team members for each operation. Then the conclusions can be integrated into one final study and evaluation. A more specific example is the use of a checklist PHA for a standard boiler or heat exchanger and the use of a Hazard and Operability PHA for the overall process. Also, for batch type processes like custom batch operations, a generic PHA of a representative batch may be used where there are only small changes of monomer or other ingredient ratios and the chemistry is documented for the full range and ratio of batch ingredients. Another process that might consider using a generic type of PHA is a gas plant. Often these plants are simply moved from site to site and therefore, a generic PHA may be used for these movable plants. Also, when an employer has several similar size gas plants and no sour gas is being processed at the site, then a generic PHA is feasible as long as the variations of the individual sites are accounted for in the PHA. Finally, when an employer has a large continuous process which has several control rooms for different portions of the process such as for a distillation tower and a blending operation, the employer may wish to do each segment separately and then integrate the final results.

Additionally, small businesses which are covered by this rule, will often have processes that have less storage volume, less capacity, and less complicated than processes at a large facility. Therefore, OSHA would anticipate that the less complex methodologies would be used to meet the process hazard analysis criteria in the standard. These process hazard analyses can be done in less time and with a few people being involved. A less complex process generally means that less data, P&IDs, and process information is needed to perform a process hazard analysis.

Many small businesses have processes that are not unique, such as cold storage lockers or water treatment facilities. Where employer associations have a number of members with such facilities, a generic PHA, evolved from a checklist or what-if questions, could be developed and used by each employer effectively to reflect his/her particular process; this would simplify compliance for them.

When the employer has a number of processes which require a PHA, the employer must set up a priority system of which PHAs to conduct first. A preliminary or gross hazard analysis may be useful in prioritizing the processes that the employer has determined are subject to coverage by the process safety management standard. Consideration should first be given to those processes with the potential of adversely affecting the largest number of employees. This prioritizing should consider the potential severity of a chemical release, the number of potentially affected employees, the operating history of the process such as the frequency of chemical releases, the age of the process and any other relevant factors. These factors would suggest a ranking order and would suggest either using a weighing factor system or a systematic ranking method. The use of a preliminary hazard analysis would assist an employer in determining which process should be of the highest priority and thereby the employer would obtain the greatest improvement in safety at the facility.

Detailed guidance on the content and application of process hazard analysis methodologies is available from the American Institute of Chemical Engineers' Center for Chemical Process Safety (see Appendix D).

5. Operating Procedures and Practices Operating procedures describe tasks to be performed, data to be recorded, operating conditions to be maintained, samples to be collected, and safety and health precautions to be taken. The procedures need to be technically accurate, understandable to employees, and revised periodically to ensure that they reflect current operations. The process safety information package is to be used as a resource to better assure that the operating procedures and practices are consistent with the known hazards of the chemicals in the process and that the operating parameters are accurate. Operating procedures should be reviewed by engineering staff and operating personnel to ensure that they are accurate and provide practical instructions on how to actually carry out job duties safely.

Operating procedures will include specific instructions or details on what steps are to be taken or followed in carrying out the stated procedures. These operating instructions for each procedure should include the applicable safety precautions and should contain appropriate information on safety implications. For example, the operating procedures addressing operating parameters will contain operating instructions about pressure limits, temperature ranges, flow rates, what to do when an upset condition occurs, what alarms and instruments are pertinent if an upset condition occurs, and other subjects. Another example of using operating instructions to properly implement operating procedures is in starting up or shutting down the process. In these cases, different parameters will be required from those of normal operation. These operating instructions need to clearly indicate the distinctions between startup and normal operations such as the appropriate allowances for heating up a unit to reach the normal operating parameters. Also the operating instructions need to describe the proper method for increasing the temperature of the unit until the normal operating temperature parameters are achieved.

Computerized process control systems add complexity to operating instructions. These operating instructions need to describe the logic of the software as well as the relationship between the equipment and the control system; otherwise, it may not be apparent to the operator.

Operating procedures and instructions are important for training operating personnel. The operating procedures are often viewed as the standard operating practices (SOPs) for operations. Control room personnel and operating staff, in general, need to have a full understanding of operating procedures. If workers are not fluent in English then procedures and instructions need to be prepared in a second language understood by the workers. In addition, operating procedures need to be changed when there is a change in the process as a result of the management of change procedures. The consequences of operating procedure changes need to be fully evaluated and the information conveyed to the personnel. For example, mechanical changes to the process made by the maintenance department (like changing a valve from steel to brass or other subtle changes) need to be evaluated to determine if operating procedures and practices also need to be changed. All management of change actions must be coordinated and integrated with current operating procedures and operating personnel must be oriented to the changes in procedures before the change is made. When the process is shut down in order to make a change, then the operating procedures must be updated before startup of the process.

Training in how to handle upset conditions must be accomplished as well as what operating personnel are to do in emergencies such as when a pump seal fails or a pipeline ruptures. Communication between operating personnel and workers performing work within the process area, such as nonroutine tasks, also must be maintained. The hazards of the tasks are to be conveyed to operating personnel in accordance with established procedures and to those performing the actual tasks. When the work is completed, operating personnel should be informed to provide closure on the job.

6. Employee Training All employees, including maintenance and contractor employees, involved with highly hazardous chemicals need to fully understand the safety and health hazards of the chemicals and processes they work with for the protection of themselves, their fellow employees and the citizens of nearby communities. Training conducted in compliance with §1910.1200, the Hazard Communication standard, will help employees to be more knowledgeable about the chemicals they work with as well as familiarize them with reading and understanding SDS. However, additional training in subjects such as operating procedures and safety work practices, emergency evacuation and response, safety procedures, routine and nonroutine work authorization activities, and other areas pertinent to process safety and health will need to be covered by an employer's training program.

In establishing their training programs, employers must clearly define the employees to be trained and what subjects are to be covered in their training. Employers in setting up their training program will need to clearly establish the goals and objectives they wish to achieve with the training that they provide to their employees. The learning goals or objectives should be written in clear measurable terms before the training begins. These goals and objectives need to be tailored to each of the specific training modules or segments. Employers should describe the important actions and conditions under which the employee will demonstrate competence or knowledge as well as what is acceptable performance.

Hands-on-training where employees are able to use their senses beyond listening, will enhance learning. For example, operating personnel, who will work in a control room or at control panels, would benefit by being trained at a simulated control panel or panels. Upset conditions of various types could be displayed on the simulator, and then the employee could go through the proper operating procedures to bring the simulator panel back to the normal operating parameters. A training environment could be created to help the trainee feel the full reality of the situation but, of course, under controlled conditions. This realistic type of training can be very effective in teaching employees correct procedures while allowing them to also see the consequences of what might happen if they do not follow established operating procedures. Other training techniques using videos or on-the-job training can also be very effective for teaching other job tasks, duties, or other important information. An effective training program will allow the employee to fully participate in the training process and to practice their skill or knowledge.

Employers need to periodically evaluate their training programs to see if the necessary skills, knowledge, and routines are being properly understood and implemented by their trained employees. The means or methods for evaluating the training should be developed along with the training program goals and objectives. Training program evaluation will help employers to determine the amount of training their employees understood, and whether the desired results were obtained. If, after the evaluation, it appears that the trained employees are not at the level of knowledge and skill that was expected, the employer will need to revise the training program, provide retraining, or provide more frequent refresher training sessions until the deficiency is resolved. Those who conducted the training and those who received the training should also be consulted as to how best to improve the training process. If there is a language barrier, the language known to the trainees should be used to reinforce the training messages and information.

Careful consideration must be given to assure that employees including maintenance and contract employees receive current and updated training. For example, if changes are made to a process, impacted employees must be trained in the changes and understand the effects of the changes on their job tasks (e.g., any new operating procedures pertinent to their tasks). Additionally, as already discussed the evaluation of the employee's absorption of training will certainly influence the need for training.

7. Contractors Employers who use contractors to perform work in and around processes that involve highly hazardous chemicals, will need to establish a screening process so that they hire and use contractors who accomplish the desired job tasks without compromising the safety and health of employees at a facility. For contractors, whose safety performance on the job is not known to the hiring employer, the employer will need to obtain information on injury and illness rates and experience and should obtain contractor references. Additionally, the employer must assure that the contractor has the appropriate job skills, knowledge and certifications (such as for pressure vessel welders). Contractor work methods and experiences should be evaluated. For example, does the contractor conducting demolition work swing loads over operating processes or does the contractor avoid such hazards?

Maintaining a site injury and illness log for contractors is another method employers must use to track and maintain current knowledge of work activities involving contract employees working on or adjacent to covered processes. Injury and illness logs of both the employer's employees and contract employees allow an employer to have full knowledge of process injury and illness experience. This log will also contain information which will be of use to those auditing process safety management compliance and those involved in incident investigations.

Contract employees must perform their work safely. Considering that contractors often perform very specialized and potentially hazardous tasks such as confined space entry activities and nonroutine repair activities it is quite important that their activities be controlled while they are working on or near a covered process. A permit system or work authorization system for these activities would also be helpful to all affected employers. The use of a work authorization system keeps an employer informed of contract employee activities, and as a benefit the employer will have better coordination and more management control over the work being performed in the process area. A well run and well maintained process where employee safety is fully recognized will benefit all of those who work in the facility whether they be contract employees or employees of the owner.

8. Pre-Startup Safety For new processes, the employer will find a PHA helpful in improving the design and construction of the process from a reliability and quality point of view. The safe operation of the new process will be enhanced by making use of the PHA recommendations before final installations are completed. P&IDs are to be completed along with having the operating procedures in place and the operating staff trained to run the process before startup. The initial startup procedures and normal operating procedures need to be fully evaluated as part of the pre-startup review to assure a safe transfer into the normal operating mode for meeting the process parameters.

For existing processes that have been shutdown for turnaround, or modification, etc., the employer must assure that any changes other than "replacement in kind" made to the process during shutdown go through the management of change procedures. P&IDs will need to be updated as necessary, as well as operating procedures and instructions. If the changes made to the process during shutdown are significant and impact the training program, then operating personnel as well as employees engaged in routine and nonroutine work in the process area may need some refresher or additional training in light of the changes. Any incident investigation recommendations, compliance audits or PHA recommendations need to be reviewed as well to see what impacts they may have on the process before beginning the startup.

9. Mechanical Integrity Employers will need to review their maintenance programs and schedules to see if there are areas where "breakdown" maintenance is used rather than an on-going mechanical integrity program. Equipment used to process, store, or handle highly hazardous chemicals needs to be designed, constructed, installed and maintained to minimize the risk of releases of such chemicals. This requires that a mechanical integrity program be in place to assure the continued integrity of process equipment. Elements of a mechanical integrity program include the identification and categorization of equipment and instrumentation, inspections and tests, testing and inspection frequencies, development of maintenance procedures, training of maintenance personnel, the establishment of criteria for acceptable test results, documentation of test and inspection results, and documentation of manufacturer recommendations as to meantime to failure for equipment and instrumentation.

The first line of defense an employer has available is to operate and maintain the process as designed, and to keep the chemicals contained. This line of defense is backed up by the next line of defense which is the controlled release of chemicals through venting to scrubbers or flares, or to surge or overflow tanks which are designed to receive such chemicals, etc. These lines of defense are the primary lines of defense or means to prevent unwanted releases. The secondary lines of defense would include fixed fire protection systems like sprinklers, water spray, or deluge systems, monitor guns, etc., dikes, designed drainage systems, and other systems which would control or mitigate hazardous chemicals once an unwanted release occurs. These primary and secondary lines of defense are what the mechanical integrity program needs to protect and strengthen these primary and secondary lines of defenses where appropriate.

The first step of an effective mechanical integrity program is to compile and categorize a list of process equipment and instrumentation for inclusion in the program. This list would include pressure vessels, storage tanks, process piping, relief and vent systems, fire protection system components, emergency shutdown systems and alarms and interlocks and pumps. For the categorization of instrumentation and the listed equipment the employer would prioritize which pieces of equipment require closer scrutiny than others. Meantime to failure of various instrumentation and equipment parts would be known from the manufacturers data or the employer's experience with the parts, which would then influence the inspection and testing frequency and associated procedures. Also, applicable codes and standards such as the National Board Inspection Code, or those from the American Society for Testing and Material, American Petroleum Institute, National Fire Protection Association, American National Standards Institute, American Society of Mechanical Engineers, and other groups, provide information to help establish an effective testing and inspection frequency, as well as appropriate methodologies.

The applicable codes and standards provide criteria for external inspections for such items as foundation and supports, anchor bolts, concrete or steel supports, guy wires, nozzles and sprinklers, pipe hangers, grounding connections, protective coatings and insulation, and external metal surfaces of piping and vessels, etc. These codes and standards also provide information on methodologies for internal inspection, and a frequency formula based on the corrosion rate of the materials of construction. Also, erosion both internal and external needs to be considered along with corrosion effects for piping and valves. Where the corrosion rate is not known, a maximum inspection frequency is recommended, and methods of developing the corrosion rate are available in the codes. Internal inspections need to cover items such as vessel shell, bottom and head; metallic linings; nonmetallic linings; thickness measurements for vessels and piping; inspection for erosion, corrosion, cracking and bulges; internal equipment like trays, baffles, sensors and screens for erosion, corrosion or cracking and other deficiencies. Some of these inspections may be performed by state of local government inspectors under state and local statutes. However, each employer needs to develop procedures to ensure that tests and inspections are conducted properly and that consistency is maintained even where different employees may be involved. Appropriate training is to be provided to maintenance personnel to ensure that they understand the preventive maintenance program procedures, safe practices, and the proper use amd application of special equipment or unique tools that may be required. This training is part of the overall training program called for in the standard.

A quality assurance system is needed to help ensure that the proper materials of construction are used, that fabrication and inspection procedures are proper, and that installation procedures recognize field installation concerns. The quality assurance program is an essential part of the mechanical integrity program and will help to maintain the primary and secondary lines of defense that have been designed into the process to prevent unwanted chemical releases or those which control or mitigate a release. "As built" drawings, together with certifications of coded vessels and other equipment, and materials of construction need to be verified and retained in the quality assurance documentation. Equipment installation jobs need to be properly inspected in the field for use of proper materials and procedures and to assure that qualified craftsmen are used to do the job. The use of appropriate gaskets, packing, bolts, valves, lubricants and welding rods need to be verified in the field. Also procedures for installation of safety devices need to be verified, such as the torque on the bolts on ruptured disc installations, uniform torque on flange bolts, proper installation of pump seals, etc. If the quality of parts is a problem, it may be appropriate to conduct audits of the equipment supplier's facilities to better assure proper purchases of required equipment which is suitable for its intended service. Any changes in equipment that may become necessary will need to go through the management of change procedures.

10. Nonroutine Work Authorizations Nonroutine work which is conducted in process areas needs to be controlled by the employer in a consistent manner. The hazards identified involving the work that is to be accomplished must be communicated to those doing the work, but also to those operating personnel whose work could affect the safety of the process. A work authorization notice or permit must have a procedure that describes the steps the maintenance supervisor, contractor representative or other person needs to follow to obtain the necessary clearance to get the job started. The work authorization procedures need to reference and coordinate, as applicable, lockout/tagout procedures, line breaking procedures, confined space entry procedures and hot work authorizations. This procedure also needs to provide clear steps to follow once the job is completed in order to provide closure for those that need to know the job is now completed and equipment can be returned to normal.

11. Managing Change To properly manage changes to process chemicals, technology, equipment and facilities, one must define what is meant by change. In this process safety management standard, change includes all modifications to equipment, procedures, raw materials and processing conditions other than "replacement in kind". These changes need to be properly managed by identifying and reviewing them prior to implementation of the change. For example, the operating procedures contain the operating parameters (pressure limits, temperature ranges, flow rates, etc.) and the importance of operating within these limits. While the operator must have the flexibility to maintain safe operation within the established parameters, any operation outside of these parameters requires review and approval by a written management of change procedure.

Management of change covers such as changes in process technology and changes to equipment and instrumentation. Changes in process technology can result from changes in production rates, raw materials, experimentation, equipment unavailability, new equipment, new product development, change in catalyst and changes in operating conditions to improve yield or quality. Equipment changes include among others change in materials of construction, equipment specifications, piping pre-arrangements, experimental equipment, computer program revisions and changes in alarms and interlocks. Employers need to establish means and methods to detect both technical changes and mechanical changes.

Temporary changes have caused a number of catastrophes over the years, and employers need to establish ways to detect temporary changes as well as those that are permanent. It is important that a time limit for temporary changes be established and monitored since, without control, these changes may tend to become permanent. Temporary changes are subject to the management of change provisions. In addition, the management of change procedures are used to insure that the equipment and procedures are returned to their original or designed conditions at the end of the temporary change. Proper documentation and review of these changes is invaluable in assuring that the safety and health considerations are being incorporated into the operating procedures and the process.

Employers may wish to develop a form or clearance sheet to facilitate the processing of changes through the management of change procedures. A typical change form may include a description and the purpose of the change, the technical basis for the change, safety and health considerations, documentation of changes for the operating procedures, maintenance procedures, inspection and testing, P&IDs, electrical classification, training and communications, pre-startup inspection, duration if a temporary change, approvals and authorization. Where the impact of the change is minor and well understood, a check list reviewed by an authorized person with proper communication to others who are affected may be sufficient. However, for a more complex or significant design change, a hazard evaluation procedure with approvals by operations, maintenance, and safety departments may be appropriate. Changes in documents such as P&IDs, raw materials, operating procedures, mechanical integrity programs, electrical classifications, etc., need to be noted so that these revisions can be made permanent when the drawings and procedure manuals are updated. Copies of process changes need to be kept in an accessible location to ensure that design changes are available to operating personnel as well as to PHA team members when a PHA is being done or one is being updated.

12. Investigation of Incidents Incident investigation is the process of identifying the underlying causes of incidents and implementing steps to prevent similar events from occurring. The intent of an incident investigation is for employers to learn from past experiences and thus avoid repeating past mistakes. The incidents for which OSHA expects employers to become aware and to investigate are the types of events which result in or could reasonably have resulted in a catastrophic release. Some of the events are sometimes referred to as "near misses," meaning that a serious consequence did not occur, but could have.

Employers need to develop in-house capability to investigate incidents that occur in their facilities. A team needs to be assembled by the employer and trained in the techniques of investigation including how to conduct interviews of witnesses, needed documentation and report writing. A multi-disciplinary team is better able to gather the facts of the event and to analyze them and develop plausible scenarios as to what happened, and why. Team members should be selected on the basis of their training, knowledge and ability to contribute to a team effort to fully investigate the incident. Employees in the process area where the incident occurred should be consulted, interviewed or made a member of the team. Their knowledge of the events form a significant set of facts about the incident which occurred. The report, its findings and recommendations are to be shared with those who can benefit from the information. The cooperation of employees is essential to an effective incident investigation. The focus of the investigation should be to obtain facts, and not to place blame. The team and the investigation process should clearly deal with all involved individuals in a fair, open and consistent manner.

13. Emergency Preparedness Each employer must address what actions employees are to take when there is an unwanted release of highly hazardous chemicals. Emergency preparedness or the employer's tertiary (third) lines of defense are those that will be relied on along with the secondary lines of defense when the primary lines of defense which are used to prevent an unwanted release fail to stop the release. Employers will need to decide if they want employees to handle and stop small or minor incidental releases. Whether they wish to mobilize the available resources at the plant and have them brought to bear on a more significant release. Or whether employers want their employees to evacuate the danger area and promptly escape to a preplanned safe zone area, and allow the local community emergency response organizations to handle the release. Or whether the employer wants to use some combination of these actions. Employers will need to select how many different emergency preparedness or tertiary lines of defense they plan to have and then develop the necessary plans and procedures, and appropriately train employees in their emergency duties and responsibilities and then implement these lines of defense.

Employers at a minimum must have an emergency action plan which will facilitate the prompt evacuation of employees due to an unwanted release of a highly hazardous chemical. This means that the employer will have a plan that will be activated by an alarm system to alert employees when to evacuate and, that employees who are physically impaired, will have the necessary support and assistance to get them to the safe zone as well. The intent of these requirements is to alert and move employees to a safe zone quickly. Delaying alarms or confusing alarms are to be avoided. The use of process control centers or similar process buildings in the process area as safe areas is discouraged. Recent catastrophes have shown that a large life loss has occurred in these structures because of where they have been sited and because they are not necessarily designed to withstand over-pressures from shockwaves resulting from explosions in the process area.

Unwanted incidental releases of highly hazardous chemicals in the process area must be addressed by the employer as to what actions employees are to take. If the employer wants employees to evacuate the area, then the emergency action plan will be activated. For outdoor processes where wind direction is important for selecting the safe route to a refuge area, the employer should place a wind direction indicator such as a wind sock or pennant at the highest point that can be seen throughout the process area. Employees can move in the direction of cross wind to upwind to gain safe access to the refuge area by knowing the wind direction.

If the employer wants specific employees in the release area to control or stop the minor emergency or incidental release, these actions must be planned for in advance and procedures developed and implemented. Preplanning for handling incidental releases for minor emergencies in the process area needs to be done, appropriate equipment for the hazards must be provided, and training conducted for those employees who will perform the emergency work before they respond to handle an actual release. The employer's training program, including the Hazard Communication standard training is to address the training needs for employees who are expected to handle incidental or minor releases.

Preplanning for releases that are more serious than incidental releases is another important line of defense to be used by the employer. When a serious release of a highly hazardous chemical occurs, the employer through preplanning will have determined in advance what actions employees are to take. The evacuation of the immediate release area and other areas as necessary would be accomplished under the emergency action plan. If the employer wishes to use plant personnel such as a fire brigade, spill control team, a hazardous materials team, or use employees to render aid to those in the immediate release area and control or mitigate the incident, these actions are covered by §1910.120, the Hazardous Waste Operations and Emergency Response (HAZWOPER) standard. If outside assistance is necessary, such as through mutual aid agreements between employers or local government emergency response organizations, these emergency responders are also covered by HAZWOPER. The safety and health protections required for emergency responders are the responsibility of their employers and of the on-scene incident commander.

Responders may be working under very hazardous conditions and therefore the objective is to have them competently led by an on-scene incident commander and the commander's staff, properly equipped to do their assigned work safely, and fully trained to carry out their duties safely before they respond to an emergency. Drills, training exercises, or simulations with the local community emergency response planners and responder organizations is one means to obtain better preparedness. This close cooperation and coordination between plant and local community emergency preparedness managers will also aid the employer in complying with the Environmental Protection Agency's Risk Management Plan criteria.

One effective way for medium to large facilities to enhance coordination and communication during emergencies for on plant operations and with local community organizations is for employers to establish and equip an emergency control center. The emergency control center would be sited in a safe zone area so that it could be occupied throughout the duration of an emergency. The center would serve as the major communication link between the on-scene incident commander and plant or corporate management as well as with the local community officials. The communication equipment in the emergency control center should include a network to receive and transmit information by telephone, radio or other means. It is important to have a backup communication network in case of power failure or one communication means fails. The center should also be equipped with the plant layout and community maps, utility drawings including fire water, emergency lighting, appropriate reference materials such as a government agency notification list, company personnel phone list, SARA Title III reports and safety data sheets, emergency plans and procedures manual, a listing with the location of emergency response equipment, mutual aid information, and access to meteorological or weather condition data and any dispersion modeling data.

14. Compliance Audits Employers need to select a trained individual or assemble a trained team of people to audit the process safety management system and program. A small process or plant may need only one knowledgeable person to conduct an audit. The audit is to include an evaluation of the design and effectiveness of the process safety management system and a field inspection of the safety and health conditions and practices to verify that the employer's systems are effectively implemented. The audit should be conducted or lead by a person knowledgeable in audit techniques and who is impartial towards the facility or area being audited. The essential elements of an audit program include planning, staffing, conduting the audit, evaluation and corrective action, follow-up and documentation.

Planning in advance is essential to the success of the auditing process. Each employer needs to establish the format, staffing, scheduling and verification methods prior to conducting the audit. The format should be designed to provide the lead auditor with a procedure or checklist which details the requirements of each section of the standard. The names of the audit team members should be listed as part of the format as well. The checklist, if properly designed, could serve as the verification sheet which provides the auditor with the necessary information to expedite the review and assure that no requirements of the standard are omitted. This verification sheet format could also identify those elements that will require evaluation or a response to correct deficiencies. This sheet could also be used for developing the follow-up and documentation requirements.

The selection of effective audit team members is critical to the success of the program. Team members should be chosen for their experience, knowledge, and training and should be familiar with the processes and with auditing techniques, practices and procedures. The size of the team will vary depending on the size and complexity of the process under consideration. For a large, complex, highly instrumented plant, it may be desirable to have team members with expertise in process engineering and design, process chemistry, instrumentation and computer controls, electrical hazards and classifications, safety and health disciplines, maintenance, emergency preparedness, warehousing or shipping, and process safety auditing. The team may use part-time members to provide for the depth of expertise required as well as for what is actually done or followed, compared to what is written.

An effective audit includes a review of the relevant documentation and process safety information, inspection of the physical facilities, and interviews with all levels of plant personnel. Utilizing the audit procedure and checklist developed in the preplanning stage, the audit team can systematically analyze compliance with the provisions of the standard and any other corporate policies that are relevant. For example, the audit team will review all aspects of the training program as part of the overall audit. The team will review the written training program for adequacy of content, frequency of training, effectiveness of training in terms of its goals and objectives as well as to how it fits into meeting the standard's requirements, documentation, etc. Through interviews, the team can determine the employee's knowledge and awareness of the safety procedures, duties, rules, emergency response assignments, etc. During the inspection, the team can observe actual practices such as safety and health policies, procedures, and work authorization practices. This approach enables the team to identify deficiencies and determine where corrective actions or improvements are necessary.

An audit is a technique used to gather sufficient facts and information, including statistical information, to verify compliance with standards. Auditors should select as part of their preplanning a sample size sufficient to give a degree of confidence that the audit reflects the level of compliance with the standard. The audit team, through this systematic analysis, should document areas which require corrective action as well as those areas where the process safety management system is effective and working in an effective manner. This provides a record of the audit procedures and findings, and serves as a baseline of operation data for future audits. It will assist future auditors in determining changes or trends from previous audits.

Corrective action is one of the most important parts of the audit. It includes not only addressing the identified deficiencies, but also planning, followup, and documentation. The corrective action process normally begins with a management review of the audit findings. The purpose of this review is to determine what actions are appropriate, and to establish priorities, timetables, resource allocations and requirements and responsibilities. In some cases, corrective action may involve a simple change in procedure or minor maintenance effort to remedy the concern. Management of change procedures need to be used, as appropriate, even for what may seem to be a minor change. Many of the deficiencies can be acted on promptly, while some may require engineering studies or indepth review of actual procedures and practices. There may be instances where no action is necessary and this is a valid response to an audit finding. All actions taken, including an explanation where no action is taken on a finding, needs to be documented as to what was done and why.

It is important to assure that each deficiency identified is addressed, the corrective action to be taken noted, and the audit person or team responsible be properly documented by the employer. To control the corrective action process, the employer should consider the use of a tracking system. This tracking system might include periodic status reports shared with affected levels of management, specific reports such as completion of an engineering study, and a final implementation report to provide closure for audit findings that have been through management of change, if appropriate, and then shared with affected employees and management. This type of tracking system provides the employer with the status of the corrective action. It also provides the documentation required to verify that appropriate corrective actions were taken on deficiencies identified in the audit.

§1910.119 Appendix D
Sources of further information
(Nonmandatory)

1. Center for Chemical Process Safety, American Institute of Chemical Engineers, 345 East 47th Street, New York, NY 10017, (212) 705–7319.
2. "Guidelines for Hazard Evaluation Procedures," American Institute of Chemical Engineers; 345 East 47th Street, New York, NY 10017.
3. "Guidelines for Technical Management of Chemical Process Safety," Center for Chemical Process Safety of the American Institute of Chemical Engineers; 345 East 47th Street, New York, NY 10017.
4. "Evaluating Process Safety in the Chemical Industry," Chemical Manufacturers Association; 2501 M Street NW, Washington, DC 20037.

5. "Safe Warehousing of Chemicals," Chemical Manufacturers Association; 2501 M Street NW, Washington, DC 20037.
6. "Management of Process Hazards," American Petroleum Institute (API Recommended Practice 750); 1220 L Street, N.W., Washington, D.C. 20005.
7. "Improving Owner and Contractor Safety Performance," American Petroleum Institute (API Recommended Practice 2220); API, 1220 L Street N.W., Washington, D.C. 20005.
8. Chemical Manufacturers Association (CMA's Manager Guide), First Edition, September 1991; CMA, 2501 M Street, N.W., Washington, D.C. 20037.
9. "Improving Construction Safety Performance," Report A–3, The Business Roundtable; The Business Roundtable, 200 Park Avenue, New York, NY 10166. (Report includes criteria to evaluate contractor safety performance and criteria to enhance contractor safety performance).
10. "Recommended Guidelines for Contractor Safety and Health," Texas Chemical Council; Texas Chemical Council, 1402 Nueces Street, Austin, TX 78701–1534.
11. "Loss Prevention in the Process Industries," Volumes I and II; Frank P. Lees, Butterworth; London 1983.
12. "Safety and Health Program Management Guidelines," 1989; U.S. Department of Labor, Occupational Safety and Health Administration.
13. "Safety and Health Guide for the Chemical Industry," 1986, (OSHA 3091); U.S. Department of Labor, Occupational Safety and Health Administration; 200 Constitution Avenue, N.W., Washington, D.C. 20210.
14. "Review of Emergency Systems," June 1988; U.S. Environmental Protection Agency (EPA), Office of Solid Waste and Emergency Response, Washington, DC 20460.
15. "Technical Guidance for Hazards Analysis, Emergency Planning for Extremely Hazardous Substances," December 1987; U.S. Environmental Protection Agency (EPA), Federal Emergency Management Administration (FEMA) and U.S. Department of Transportation (DOT), Washington, DC 20460.
16. "Accident Investigation * * * A New Approach," 1983, National Safety Council; 444 North Michigan Avenue, Chicago, IL 60611–3991.
17. "Fire & Explosion Index Hazard Classification Guide," 6th Edition, May 1987, Dow Chemical Company; Midland, Michigan 48674.
18. "Chemical Exposure Index," May 1988, Dow Chemical Company; Midland, Michigan 48674.

[57 FR 6403, Feb. 24, 1992; 57 FR 7847, Mar. 4, 1992, as amended at 61 FR 9238, Mar. 7, 1996; 67 FR 67964, Nov. 7, 2002]

§1910.120 Hazardous waste operations and emergency response

(a) Scope, application, and definitions

(a)(1) Scope This section covers the following operations, unless the employer can demonstrate that the operation does not involve employee exposure or the reasonable possibility for employee exposure to safety or health hazards:

(a)(1)(i) Clean-up operations required by a governmental body, whether Federal, state, local or other involving hazardous substances that are conducted at uncontrolled hazardous waste sites (including, but not limited to, the EPA's National Priority Site List (NPL), state priority site lists, sites recommended for the EPA NPL, and initial investigations of government identified sites which are conducted before the presence or absence of hazardous substances has been ascertained);

(a)(1)(ii) Corrective actions involving clean-up operations at sites covered by the Resource Conservation and Recovery Act of 1976 (RCRA) as amended (42 U.S.C. 6901 et seq.);

(a)(1)(iii) Voluntary clean-up operations at sites recognized by Federal, state, local or other governmental bodies as uncontrolled hazardous waste sites;

(a)(1)(iv) Operations involving hazardous wastes that are conducted at treatment, storage, and disposal (TSD) facilities regulated by 40 CFR parts 264 and 265 pursuant to RCRA; or by agencies under agreement with U.S.E.P.A. to implement RCRA regulations; and

(a)(1)(v) Emergency response operations for releases of, or substantial threats of releases of, hazardous substances without regard to the location of the hazard.

(a)(2) Application

(a)(2)(i) All requirements of Part 1910 and Part 1926 of title 29 of the Code of Federal Regulations apply pursuant to their terms to hazardous waste and emergency response operations whether covered by this section or not. If there is a conflict or overlap, the provision more protective of employee safety and health shall apply without regard to 29 CFR §1910.5(c)(1).

(a)(2)(ii) Hazardous substance clean-up operations within the scope of paragraphs (a)(1)(i) through (a)(1)(iii) of this section must comply with all paragraphs of this section except paragraphs (p) and (q).

(a)(2)(iii) Operations within the scope of paragraph (a)(1)(iv) of this section must comply only with the requirements of paragraph (p) of this section.

Notes and Exceptions:

(A) All provisions of paragraph (p) of this section cover any treatment, storage or disposal (TSD) operation regulated by 40 CFR parts 264 and 265 or by state law authorized under RCRA, and required to have a permit or interim status from EPA pursuant to 40 CFR 270.1 or from a state agency pursuant to RCRA.

(B) Employers who are not required to have a permit or interim status because they are conditionally exempt small quantity generators under 40 CFR 261.5 or are generators who qualify under 40 CFR 262.34 for exemptions from regulation under 40 CFR parts 264, 265 and 270 ("excepted employers") are not covered by paragraphs (p)(1) through (p)(7) of this section. Excepted employers who are required by the EPA or state agency to have their employees engage in emergency response or who direct their employees to engage in emergency response are covered by paragraph (p)(8) of this section, and cannot be exempted by (p)(8)(i) of this section. Excepted employers who are not required to have employees engage in emergency response, who direct their employees to evacuate in the case of such emergencies and who meet the requirements of paragraph (p)(8)(i) of this section are exempt from the balance of paragraph (p)(8) of this section.

(C) If an area is used primarily for treatment, storage or disposal, any emergency response operations in that area shall comply with paragraph (p)(8) of this section. In other areas not used primarily for treatment, storage, or disposal, any emergency response operations shall comply with paragraph (q) of this section. Compliance with the requirements of paragraph (q) of this section shall be deemed to be in compliance with the requirements of paragraph (p)(8) of this section.

(a)(2)(iv) Emergency response operations for releases of, or substantial threats of releases of, hazardous substances which are not covered by paragraphs (a)(1)(i) through (a)(1)(iv) of this section must only comply with the requirements of paragraph (q) of this section.

(a)(3) Definitions

Buddy system means a system of organizing employees into work groups in such a manner that each employee of the work group is designated to be observed by at least one other employee in the work group. The purpose of the buddy system is to provide rapid assistance to employees in the event of an emergency.

Clean-up operation means an operation where hazardous substances are removed, contained, incinerated, neutralized, stabilized, cleared-up, or in any other manner processed or handled with the ultimate goal of making the site safer for people or the environment.

Decontamination means the removal of hazardous substances from employees and their equipment to the extent necessary to preclude the occurrence of foreseeable adverse health affects.

Emergency response or responding to emergencies means a response effort by employees from outside the immediate release area or by other designated responders (i.e., mutual-aid groups, local fire departments, etc.) to an occurrence which results, or is likely to result, in an uncontrolled release of a hazardous substance. Responses to incidental releases of hazardous substances where the substance can be absorbed, neutralized, or otherwise controlled at the time of release by employees in the immediate release area, or by maintenance personnel are not considered to be emergency responses within the scope of this standard. Responses to releases of hazardous substances where there is no potential safety or health hazard (i.e., fire, explosion, or chemical exposure) are not considered to be emergency responses.

Facility means

(A) any building, structure, installation, equipment, pipe or pipeline (including any pipe into a sewer or publicly owned treatment works), well, pit, pond, lagoon, impoundment, ditch, storage container, motor vehicle, rolling stock, or aircraft, or

(B) any site or area where a hazardous substance has been deposited, stored, disposed of, or placed, or otherwise come to be located; but does not include any consumer product in consumer use or any water-borne vessel.

Hazardous materials response (HAZMAT) team means an organized group of employees, designated by the employer, who are expected to perform work to handle and control actual or potential leaks or spills of hazardous substances requiring possible close approach to the substance. The team members perform responses to releases or potential releases of hazardous substances for the purpose of control or stabilization of the incident. A HAZMAT team is not a fire brigade nor is a typical fire brigade a HAZMAT team. A HAZMAT team, however, may be a separate component of a fire brigade or fire department.

Hazardous substance means any substance designated or listed under paragraphs (A) through (D) of this definition, exposure to which results or may result in adverse affects on the health or safety of employees:

(A) Any substance defined under section 101(14) of CERCLA;

(B) Any biological agent and other disease-causing agent which after release into the environment and upon exposure, ingestion, inhalation, or assimilation into any person, either directly from the environment or indirectly by ingestion through food chains, will or may reasonably be anticipated to cause death, disease, behavioral abnormalities, cancer, genetic mutation, physiological malfunctions (including malfunctions in reproduction) or physical deformations in such persons or their offspring;

(C) Any substance listed by the U.S. Department of Transportation as hazardous materials under 49 CFR 172.101 and Appendices; and

(D) Hazardous waste as herein defined.

Hazardous waste means

(A) A waste or combination of wastes as defined in 40 CFR 261.3, or

(B) Those substances defined as hazardous wastes in 49 CFR 171.8.

Hazardous waste operation means any operation conducted within the scope of this standard.

Hazardous waste site or Site means any facility or location within the scope of this standard at which hazardous waste operations take place.

Health hazard means a chemical or a pathogen where acute or chronic health effects may occur in exposed employees. It also includes stress due to temperature extremes. The term health hazard includes chemicals that are classified in accordance with the Hazard Communication Standard, 29 CFR §1910.1200, as posing one of the following hazardous effects: Acute toxicity (any route of exposure); skin corrosion or irritation; serious eye damage or eye irritation; respiratory or skin sensitization; germ cell mutagenicity; carcinogenicity; reproductive toxicity; specific target organ toxicity (single or repeated exposure); aspiration toxicity or simple asphyxiant. (See Appendix A to §1910.1200—Health Hazard Criteria (Mandatory) for the criteria for determining whether a chemical is classified as a health hazard.)

IDLH or Immediately dangerous to life or health means an atmospheric concentration of any toxic, corrosive or asphyxiant substance that poses an immediate threat to life or would cause irreversible or delayed adverse health effects or would interfere with an individual's ability to escape from a dangerous atmosphere.

Oxygen deficiency means that concentration of oxygen by volume below which atmosphere supplying respiratory protection must be provided. It exists in atmospheres where the percentage of oxygen by volume is less than 19.5 percent oxygen.

Permissible exposure limit means the exposure, inhalation or dermal permissible exposure limit specified in 29 CFR Part 1910, Subparts G and Z.

Published exposure level means the exposure limits published in "NIOSH Recommendations for Occupational Health Standards" dated 1986, which is incorporated by reference as specified in §1910.6 or if none is specified, the exposure limits published in the standards specified by the American Conference of Governmental Industrial Hygienists in their publication "Threshold Limit Values and Biological Exposure Indices for 1987–88" dated 1987, which is incorporated by reference as specified in §1910.6.

Post emergency response means that portion of an emergency response performed after the immediate threat of a release has been stabilized or eliminated and clean-up of the site has begun. If post emergency response is performed by an employer's own employees who were part of the initial emergency response, it is considered to be part of the initial response and not post emergency response. However, if a group of an employer's own employees, separate from the group providing initial response, performs the clean-up operation, then the separate group of employees would be considered to be performing post-emergency response and subject to paragraph (q)(11) of this section.

Qualified person means a person with specific training, knowledge and experience in the area for which the person has the responsibility and the authority to control.

Site safety and health supervisor (or official) means the individual located on a hazardous waste site who is responsible to the employer and has the authority and knowledge necessary to implement the site safety and health plan and verify compliance with applicable safety and health requirements.

Small quantity generator means a generator of hazardous wastes who in any calendar month generates no more than 1,000 kilograms (2,205 pounds) of hazardous waste in that month.

Uncontrolled hazardous waste site, means an area identified as an uncontrolled hazardous waste site by a governmental body, whether Federal, state, local or other where an accumulation of hazardous substances creates a threat to the health and safety of individuals or the environment or both. Some sites are found on public lands such as those created by former municipal, county or state landfills where illegal or poorly managed waste disposal has taken place. Other sites are found on private property, often belonging to generators or former generators of hazardous substance wastes. Examples of such sites include, but are not limited to, surface impoundments, landfills, dumps, and tank or drum farms. Normal operations at TSD sites are not covered by this definition.

(b) [OI] Safety and health program

Note to (b): Safety and health programs developed and implemented to meet other Federal, state, or local regulations are considered acceptable in meeting this requirement if they cover or are modified to cover the topics required in this paragraph. An additional or separate safety and health program is not required by this paragraph.

(b)(1) General

(b)(1)(i) Employers shall develop and implement a written safety and health program for their employees involved in hazardous waste operations. The program shall be designed to identify, evaluate, and control safety and health hazards, and provide for emergency response for hazardous waste operations.

(b)(1)(ii) The written safety and health program shall incorporate the following:

(b)(1)(ii)(A) An organizational structure;

(b)(1)(ii)(B) A comprehensive workplan;

(b)(1)(ii)(C) A site-specific safety and health plan which need not repeat the employer's standard operating procedures required in paragraph (b)(1)(ii)(F) of this section;

(b)(1)(ii)(D) The safety and health training program;

(b)(1)(ii)(E) The medical surveillance program;

(b)(1)(ii)(F) The employer's standard operating procedures for safety and health; and

(b)(1)(ii)(G) Any necessary interface between general program and site specific activities.

(b)(1)(iii) Site excavation. Site excavations created during initial site preparation or during hazardous waste operations shall be shored or sloped as appropriate to prevent accidental collapse in accordance with subpart P of 29 CFR Part 1926.

(b)(1)(iv) [OI] Contractors and sub-contractors. An employer who retains contractor or sub-contractor services for work in hazardous waste operations shall inform those contractors, sub-contractors, or their representatives of the site emergency response procedures and any potential fire, explosion, health, safety or other hazards of the hazardous waste operation that have been identified by the employer, including those identified in the employer's information program.

(b)(1)(v) [OI] Program availability. The written safety and health program shall be made available to any contractor or subcontractor or their representative who will be involved with the hazardous waste operation; to employees; to employee designated representatives; to OSHA personnel, and to personnel of other Federal, state, or local agencies with regulatory authority over the site.

(b)(2) Organizational structure part of the site program

(b)(2)(i) The organizational structure part of the program shall establish the specific chain of command and specify the overall responsibilities of supervisors and employees. It shall include, at a minimum, the following elements:

(b)(2)(i)(A) A general supervisor who has the responsibility and authority to direct all hazardous waste operations

(b)(2)(i)(B) A site safety and health supervisor who has the responsibility and authority to develop and implement the site safety and health plan and verify compliance

(b)(2)(i)(C) All other personnel needed for hazardous waste site operations and emergency response and their general functions and responsibilities

(b)(2)(i)(D) The lines of authority, responsibility, and communication.

(b)(2)(ii) The organizational structure shall be reviewed and updated as necessary to reflect the current status of waste site operations.

(b)(3) Comprehensive workplan part of the site program The comprehensive workplan part of the program shall address the tasks and objectives of the site operations and the logistics and resources required to reach those tasks and objectives.

(b)(3)(i) The comprehensive workplan shall address anticipated clean-up activities as well as normal operating procedures which need not repeat the employer's procedures available elsewhere.

(b)(3)(ii) The comprehensive workplan shall define work tasks and objectives and identify the methods for accomplishing those tasks and objectives.

(b)(3)(iii) The comprehensive workplan shall establish personnel requirements for implementing the plan.

(b)(3)(iv) The comprehensive workplan shall provide for the implementation of the training required in paragraph (e) of this section.

(b)(3)(v) The comprehensive workplan shall provide for the implementation of the required informational programs required in paragraph (i) of this section.

(b)(3)(vi) The comprehensive workplan shall provide for the implementation of the medical surveillance program described in paragraph (f) of this section.

(b)(4) O/I Site-specific safety and health plan part of the program

(b)(4)(i) General The site safety and health plan, which must be kept on site, shall address the safety and health hazards of each phase of site operation and include the requirements and procedures for employee protection.

(b)(4)(ii) O/I Elements The site safety and health plan, as a minimum, shall address the following:

(b)(4)(ii)(A) A safety and health risk or hazard analysis for each site task and operation found in the workplan;

(b)(4)(ii)(B) Employee training assignments to assure compliance with paragraph (e) of this section;

(b)(4)(ii)(C) Personal protective equipment to be used by employees for each of the site tasks and operations being conducted as required by the personal protective equipment program in paragraph (g)(5) of this section;

(b)(4)(ii)(D) Medical surveillance requirements in accordance with the program in paragraph (f) of this section;

(b)(4)(ii)(E) Frequency and types of air monitoring, personnel monitoring, and environmental sampling techniques and instrumentation to be used, including methods of maintenance and calibration of monitoring and sampling equipment to be used;

(b)(4)(ii)(F) Site control measures in accordance with the site control program required in paragraph (d) of this section;

(b)(4)(ii)(G) Decontamination procedures in accordance with paragraph (k) of this section;

(b)(4)(ii)(H) An emergency response plan meeting the requirements of paragraph (l) of this section for safe and effective responses to emergencies, including the necessary PPE and other equipment;

(b)(4)(ii)(I) Confined space entry procedures;

(b)(4)(ii)(J) A spill containment program meeting the requirements of paragraph (j) of this section.

(b)(4)(iii) Pre-entry briefing The site specific safety and health plan shall provide for pre-entry briefings to be held prior to initiating any site activity, and at such other times as necessary to ensure that employees are apprised of the site safety and health plan and that this plan is being followed. The information and data obtained from site characterization and analysis work required in paragraph (c) of this section shall be used to prepare and update the site safety and health plan.

(b)(4)(iv) Effectiveness of site safety and health plan. Inspections shall be conducted by the site safety and health supervisor or, in the absence of that individual, another individual who is knowledgeable in occupational safety and health, acting on behalf of the employer as necessary to determine the effectiveness of the site safety and health plan. Any deficiencies in the effectiveness of the site safety and health plan shall be corrected by the employer.

(c) O/I Site characterization and analysis

(c)(1) General Hazardous waste sites shall be evaluated in accordance with this paragraph to identify specific site hazards and to determine the appropriate safety and health control procedures needed to protect employees from the identified hazards.

(c)(2) Preliminary evaluation A preliminary evaluation of a site's characteristics shall be performed prior to site entry by a qualified person in order to aid in the selection of appropriate employee protection methods prior to site entry. Immediately after initial site entry, a more detailed evaluation of the site's specific characteristics shall be performed by a qualified person in order to further identify existing site hazards and to further aid in the selection of the appropriate engineering controls and personal protective equipment for the tasks to be performed.

(c)(3) Hazard identification All suspected conditions that may pose inhalation or skin absorption hazards that are immediately dangerous to life or health (IDLH), or other conditions that may cause death or serious harm, shall be identified during the preliminary survey and evaluated during the detailed survey. Examples of such hazards include, but are not limited to, confined space entry, potentially explosive or flammable situations, visible vapor clouds, or areas where biological indicators such as dead animals or vegetation are located.

(c)(4) Required information The following information to the extent available shall be obtained by the employer prior to allowing employees to enter a site:

(c)(4)(i) Location and approximate size of the site;

(c)(4)(ii) Description of the response activity and/or the job task to be performed;

(c)(4)(iii) Duration of the planned employee activity;

(c)(4)(iv) Site topography and accessibility by air and roads;

(c)(4)(v) Safety and health hazards expected at the site;

(c)(4)(vi) Pathways for hazardous substance dispersion;

(c)(4)(vii) Present status and capabilities of emergency response teams that would provide assistance to hazardous waste clean-up site employees at the time of an emergency;

(c)(4)(viii) Hazardous substances and health hazards involved or expected at the site, and their chemical and physical properties.

(c)(5) Personal protective equipment Personal protective equipment (PPE) shall be provided and used during initial site entry in accordance with the following requirements:

(c)(5)(i) Based upon the results of the preliminary site evaluation, an ensemble of PPE shall be selected and used during initial site entry which will provide protection to a level of exposure below permissible exposure limits and published exposure levels for known or suspected hazardous substances and health hazards, and which will provide protection against other known and suspected hazards identified during the preliminary site evaluation. If there is no permissible exposure limit or published exposure level, the employer may use other published studies and information as a guide to appropriate personal protective equipment;

(c)(5)(ii) If positive-pressure self-contained breathing apparatus is not used as part of the entry ensemble, and if respiratory protection is warranted by the potential hazards identified during the preliminary site evaluation, an escape self-contained breathing apparatus of at least five minute's duration shall be carried by employees during initial site entry;

(c)(5)(iii) If the preliminary site evaluation does not produce sufficient information to identify the hazards or suspected hazards of the site, an ensemble providing protection equivalent to Level B PPE shall be provided as minimum protection, and direct reading instruments shall be used as appropriate for identifying IDLH conditions. (See Appendix B for a description of Level B hazards and the recommendations for Level B protective equipment.);

(c)(5)(iv) Once the hazards of the site have been identified, the appropriate PPE shall be selected and used in accordance with paragraph (g) of this section.

(c)(6) Monitoring The following monitoring shall be conducted during initial site entry when the site evaluation produces information that shows the potential for ionizing radiation or IDLH conditions, or when the site information is not sufficient reasonably to eliminate these possible conditions:

(c)(6)(i) Monitoring with direct reading instruments for hazardous levels of ionizing radiation;

(c)(6)(ii) Monitoring the air with appropriate direct reading test equipment (i.e., combustible gas meters, detector tubes) for IDLH and other conditions that may cause death or serious harm (combustible or explosive atmospheres, oxygen deficiency, toxic substances);

(c)(6)(iii) Visually observing for signs of actual or potential IDLH or other dangerous conditions;

(c)(6)(iv) An ongoing air monitoring program in accordance with paragraph (h) of this section shall be implemented after site characterization has determined the site is safe for the start-up of operations.

(c)(7) O/I Risk identification Once the presence and concentrations of specific hazardous substances and health hazards have been established, the risks associated with these substances shall be identified. Employees who will be working on the site shall be informed of any risks that have been identified. In situations covered by the Hazard Communication Standard, 29 CFR §1910.1200, training required by that standard need not be duplicated.

Note to paragraph (c)(7). Risks to consider include, but are not limited to:

(c)(7)(A) Exposures exceeding the permissible exposure limits and published exposure levels;

(c)(7)(B) IDLH concentrations;

(c)(7)(C) Potential skin absorption and irritation sources;

(c)(7)(D) Potential eye irritation sources;

(c)(7)(E) Explosion sensitivity and flammability ranges;

(c)(7)(F) Oxygen deficiency.

(c)(8) Employee notification Any information concerning the chemical, physical, and toxicologic properties of each substance known or expected to be present on site that is available to the employer and relevant to the duties an employee is expected to perform shall be made available to the affected employees prior to the commencement of their work activities. The employer may utilize information developed for the hazard communication standard for this purpose.

(d) O/I Site control

(d)(1) General Appropriate site control procedures shall be implemented to control employee exposure to hazardous substances before clean-up work begins.

(d)(2) Site control program A site control program for protecting employees which is part of the employer's site safety and health program required in paragraph (b) of this section shall be developed during the planning stages of a hazardous waste clean-up operation and modified as necessary as new information becomes available.

(d)(3) **Elements of the site control program** The site control program shall, as a minimum, include: A site map; site work zones; the use of a "buddy system"; site communications including alerting means for emergencies; the standard operating procedures or safe work practices; and, identification of the nearest medical assistance. Where these requirements are covered elsewhere they need not be repeated.

(e) **Training**

(e)(1) **General**

(e)(1)(i) All employees working on site (such as but not limited to equipment operators, general laborers and others) exposed to hazardous substances, health hazards, or safety hazards and their supervisors and management responsible for the site shall receive training meeting the requirements of this paragraph before they are permitted to engage in hazardous waste operations that could expose them to hazardous substances, safety, or health hazards, and they shall receive review training as specified in this paragraph.

(e)(1)(ii) Employees shall not be permitted to participate in or supervise field activities until they have been trained to a level required by their job function and responsibility.

(e)(2) **Elements to be covered** The training shall thoroughly cover the following:

(e)(2)(i) Names of personnel and alternates responsible for site safety and health;

(e)(2)(ii) Safety, health and other hazards present on the site;

(e)(2)(iii) Use of personal protective equipment;

(e)(2)(iv) Work practices by which the employee can minimize risks from hazards;

(e)(2)(v) Safe use of engineering controls and equipment on the site;

(e)(2)(vi) Medical surveillance requirements, including recognition of symptoms and signs which might indicate overexposure to hazards; and

(e)(2)(vii) The contents of paragraphs (G) through (J) of the site safety and health plan set forth in paragraph (b)(4)(ii) of this section.

(e)(3) **Initial training**

(e)(3)(i) General site workers (such as equipment operators, general laborers and supervisory personnel) engaged in hazardous substance removal or other activities which expose or potentially expose workers to hazardous substances and health hazards shall receive a minimum of 40 hours of instruction off the site, and a minimum of three days actual field experience under the direct supervision of a trained, experienced supervisor.

(e)(3)(ii) Workers on site only occasionally for a specific limited task (such as, but not limited to, ground water monitoring, land surveying, or geo-physical surveying) and who are unlikely to be exposed over permissible exposure limits and published exposure limits shall receive a minimum of 24 hours of instruction off the site, and the minimum of one day actual field experience under the direct supervision of a trained, experienced supervisor.

(e)(3)(iii) Workers regularly on site who work in areas which have been monitored and fully characterized indicating that exposures are under permissible exposure limits and published exposure limits where respirators are not necessary, and the characterization indicates that there are no health hazards or the possibility of an emergency developing, shall receive a minimum of 24 hours of instruction off the site and the minimum of one day actual field experience under the direct supervision of a trained, experienced supervisor.

(e)(3)(iv) Workers with 24 hours of training who are covered by paragraphs (e)(3)(ii) and (e)(3)(iii) of this section, and who become general site workers or who are required to wear respirators, shall have the additional 16 hours and two days of training necessary to total the training specified in paragraph (e)(3)(i).

(e)(4) **Management and supervisor training** On-site management and supervisors directly responsible for, or who supervise employees engaged in, hazardous waste operations shall receive 40 hours initial training, and three days of supervised field experience (the training may be reduced to 24 hours and one day if the only area of their responsibility is employees covered by paragraphs (e)(3)(ii) and (e)(3)(iii) and at least eight additional hours of specialized training at the time of job assignment on such topics as, but not limited to, the employer's safety and health program and the associated employee training program, personal protective equipment program, spill containment program, and health hazard monitoring procedure and techniques.

(e)(5) **Qualifications for trainers** Trainers shall be qualified to instruct employees about the subject matter that is being presented in training. Such trainers shall have satisfactorily completed a training program for teaching the subjects they are expected to teach, or they shall have the academic credentials and instructional experience necessary for teaching the subjects. Instructors shall demonstrate competent instructional skills and knowledge of the applicable subject matter.

(e)(6) **Training certification** Employees and supervisors that have received and successfully completed the training and field experience specified in paragraphs (e)(1) through (e)(4) of this section shall be certified by their instructor or the head instructor and trained supervisor as having successfully completed the necessary training. A written certificate shall be given to each person so certified. Any person who has not been so certified or who does not meet the requirements of paragraph (e)(9) of this section shall be prohibited from engaging in hazardous waste operations.

(e)(7) **Emergency response** Employees who are engaged in responding to hazardous emergency situations at hazardous waste clean-up sites that may expose them to hazardous substances shall be trained in how to respond to such expected emergencies.

(e)(8) **Refresher training** Employees specified in paragraph (e)(1) of this section, and managers and supervisors specified in paragraph (e)(4) of this section, shall receive eight hours of refresher training annually on the items specified in paragraph (e)(2) and/or (e)(4) of this section, any critique of incidents that have occurred in the past year that can serve as training examples of related work, and other relevant topics.

(e)(9) **Equivalent training** Employers who can show by documentation or certification that an employee's work experience and/or training has resulted in training equivalent to that training required in paragraphs (e)(1) through (e)(4) of this section shall not be required to provide the initial training requirements of those paragraphs to such employees and shall provide a copy of the certification or documentation to the employee upon request. However, certified employees or employees with equivalent training new to a site shall receive appropriate, site specific training before site entry and have appropriate supervised field experience at the new site. Equivalent training includes any academic training or the training that existing employees might have already received from actual hazardous waste site work experience.

(f) **Medical surveillance**

(f)(1) **General** Employers engaged in operations specified in paragraphs (a)(1)(i) through (a)(1)(iv) of this section and not covered by (a)(2)(iii) exceptions and employers of employees specified in paragraph (q)(9) shall institute a medical surveillance program in accordance with this paragraph.

(f)(2) **Employees covered** The medical surveillance program shall be instituted by the employer for the following employees:

(f)(2)(i) All employees who are or may be exposed to hazardous substances or health hazards at or above the permissible exposure limits or, if there is no permissible exposure limit, above the published exposure levels for these substances, without regard to the use of respirators, for 30 days or more a year;

(f)(2)(ii) All employees who wear a respirator for 30 days or more a year or as required by §1910.134;

(f)(2)(iii) All employees who are injured, become ill or develop signs or symptoms due to possible overexposure involving hazardous substances or health hazards from an emergency response or hazardous waste operation; and

(f)(2)(iv) Members of HAZMAT teams.

(f)(3) **Frequency of medical examinations and consultations** Medical examinations and consultations shall be made available by the employer to each employee covered under paragraph (f)(2) of this section on the following schedules:

(f)(3)(i) For employees covered under paragraphs (f)(2)(i), (f)(2)(ii), and (f)(2)(iv):

(f)(3)(i)(A) Prior to assignment;

(f)(3)(i)(B) At least once every twelve months for each employee covered unless the attending physician believes a longer interval (not greater than biennially) is appropriate;

(f)(3)(i)(C) At termination of employment or reassignment to an area where the employee would not be covered if the employee has not had an examination within the last six months;

(f)(3)(i)(D) As soon as possible upon notification by an employee that the employee has developed signs or symptoms indicating possible overexposure to hazardous substances or health hazards, or that the employee has been injured or exposed above the permissible exposure limits or published exposure levels in an emergency situation;

(f)(3)(i)(E) At more frequent times, if the examining physician determines that an increased frequency of examination is medically necessary.

(f)(3)(ii) For employees covered under paragraph (f)(2)(iii) and for all employees including those of employers covered by paragraph (a)(1)(v) who may have been injured, received a health impairment, developed signs or symptoms which may have resulted from exposure to hazardous substances resulting from an emergency incident, or exposed during an emergency incident to hazardous substances at concentrations above the permissible exposure limits or the published exposure levels without the necessary personal protective equipment being used:

(f)(3)(ii)(A) As soon as possible following the emergency incident or development of signs or symptoms;

(f)(3)(ii)(B) At additional times, if the examining physician determines that follow-up examinations or consultations are medically necessary.

(f)(4) Content of medical examinations and consultations

(f)(4)(i) [OI] Medical examinations required by paragraph (f)(3) of this section shall include a medical and work history (or updated history if one is in the employee's file) with special emphasis on symptoms related to the handling of hazardous substances and health hazards, and to fitness for duty including the ability to wear any required PPE under conditions (i.e., temperature extremes) that may be expected at the work site.

(f)(4)(ii) The content of medical examinations or consultations made available to employees pursuant to paragraph (f) shall be determined by the attending physician. The guidelines in the Occupational Safety and Health Guidance Manual for Hazardous Waste Site Activities (See Appendix D, Reference #10) should be consulted.

(f)(5) [OI] **Examination by a physician and costs** All medical examinations and procedures shall be performed by or under the supervision of a licensed physician, preferably one knowledgeable in occupational medicine, and shall be provided without cost to the employee, without loss of pay, and at a reasonable time and place.

(f)(6) **Information provided to the physician** The employer shall provide one copy of this Standard and its Appendices to the attending physician, and in addition the following for each employee:

(f)(6)(i) A description of the employee's duties as they relate to the employee's exposures;

(f)(6)(ii) The employee's exposure levels or anticipated exposure levels;

(f)(6)(iii) A description of any personal protective equipment used or to be used;

(f)(6)(iv) Information from previous medical examinations of the employee which is not readily available to the examining physician;

(f)(6)(v) Information required by §1910.134.

(f)(7) [OI] **Physician's written opinion**

(f)(7)(i) The employer shall obtain and furnish the employee with a copy of a written opinion from the attending physician containing the following:

(f)(7)(i)(A) The physician's opinion as to whether the employee has any detected medical conditions which would place the employee at increased risk of material impairment of the employee's health from work in hazardous waste operations or emergency response, or from respirator use;

(f)(7)(i)(B) The physician's recommended limitations upon the employee's assigned work;

(f)(7)(i)(C) The results of the medical examination and tests if requested by the employee;

(f)(7)(i)(D) A statement that the employee has been informed by the physician of the results of the medical examination and any medical conditions which require further examination or treatment.

(f)(7)(ii) The written opinion obtained by the employer shall not reveal specific findings or diagnoses unrelated to occupational exposures.

(f)(8) Recordkeeping

(f)(8)(i) An accurate record of the medical surveillance required by paragraph (f) of this section shall be retained. This record shall be retained for the period specified and meet the criteria of 29 CFR §1910.1020.

(f)(8)(ii) The record required in paragraph (f)(8)(i) of this section shall include at least the following information:

(f)(8)(ii)(A) The name and social security number of the employee;

(f)(8)(ii)(B) Physician's written opinions, recommended limitations, and results of examinations and tests;

(f)(8)(ii)(C) Any employee medical complaints related to exposure to hazardous substances;

(f)(8)(ii)(D) A copy of the information provided to the examining physician by the employer, with the exception of the standard and its appendices.

(g) **Engineering controls, work practices, and personal protective equipment for employee protection** Engineering controls, work practices, personal protective equipment, or a combination of these shall be implemented in accordance with this paragraph to protect employees from exposure to hazardous substances and safety and health hazards.

(g)(1) Engineering controls, work practices and PPE for substances regulated in Subparts G and Z

(g)(1)(i) Engineering controls and work practices shall be instituted to reduce and maintain employee exposure to or below the permissible exposure limits for substances regulated by 29 CFR Part 1910, to the extent required by Subpart Z, except to the extent that such controls and practices are not feasible.

Note to paragraph (g)(1)(i): Engineering controls which may be feasible include the use of pressurized cabs or control booths on equipment, and/or the use of remotely operated material handling equipment. Work practices which may be feasible are removing all non-essential employees from potential exposure during opening of drums, wetting down dusty operations and locating employees upwind of possible hazards.

(g)(1)(ii) Whenever engineering controls and work practices are not feasible or not required, any reasonable combination of engineering controls, work practices and PPE shall be used to reduce and maintain employee exposures to or below the permissible exposure limits or dose limits for substances regulated by 29 CFR Part 1910, Subpart Z.

(g)(1)(iii) The employer shall not implement a schedule of employee rotation as a means of compliance with permissible exposure limits or dose limits except when there is no other feasible way of complying with the airborne or dermal dose limits for ionizing radiation.

(g)(1)(iv) The provisions of 29 CFR, Subpart G, shall be followed.

(g)(2) **Engineering controls, work practices, and PPE for substances not regulated in Subparts G and Z** An appropriate combination of engineering controls, work practices and personal protective equipment shall be used to reduce and maintain employee exposure to or below published exposure levels for hazardous substances and health hazards not regulated by 29 CFR Part 1910, Subparts G and Z. The employer may use the published literature and SDS as a guide in making the employer's determination as to what level of protection the employer believes is appropriate for hazardous substances and health hazards for which there is no permissible exposure limit or published exposure limit.

(g)(3) Personal protective equipment selection

(g)(3)(i) Personal protective equipment (PPE) shall be selected and used which will protect employees from the hazards and potential hazards they are likely to encounter as identified during the site characterization and analysis.

(g)(3)(ii) Personal protective equipment selection shall be based on an evaluation of the performance characteristics of the PPE relative to the requirements and limitations of the site, the task-specific conditions and duration, and the hazards and potential hazards identified at the site.

(g)(3)(iii) Positive pressure self-contained breathing apparatus, or positive pressure air-line respirators equipped with an escape air supply, shall be used when chemical exposure levels present will create a substantial possibility of immediate death, immediate serious illness or injury, or impair the ability to escape.

(g)(3)(iv) Totally-encapsulating chemical protective suits (protection equivalent to Level A protection as recommended in Appendix B) shall be used in conditions where skin absorption of a hazardous substance may result in a substantial possibility of immediate death, immediate serious illness or injury, or impair the ability to escape.

(g)(3)(v) The level of protection provided by PPE selection shall be increased when additional information on site conditions indicates that increased protection is necessary to reduce employee exposures below permissible exposure limits and published exposure levels for hazardous substances and health hazards. (See Appendix B for guidance on selecting PPE ensembles.)

Note to paragraph (g)(3): The level of employee protection provided may be decreased when additional information or site conditions show that decreased protection will not result in hazardous exposures to employees.

(g)(3)(vi) Personal protective equipment shall be selected and used to meet the requirements of 29 CFR Part 1910, Subpart I, and additional requirements specified in this section.

(g)(4) Totally-encapsulating chemical protective suits

(g)(4)(i) Totally-encapsulating suits shall protect employees from the particular hazards which are identified during site characterization and analysis.

(g)(4)(ii) Totally-encapsulating suits shall be capable of maintaining positive air pressure. (See Appendix A for a test method which may be used to evaluate this requirement.)

(g)(4)(iii) Totally-encapsulating suits shall be capable of preventing inward test gas leakage of more than 0.5 percent. (See Appendix A for a test method which may be used to evaluate this requirement.)

(g)(5) **Personal protective equipment (PPE) program** A written personal protective equipment program, which is part of the employer's safety and health program required in paragraph (b) of this section or required in paragraph (p)(1) of this section and which is also a part of the site-specific safety and health plan shall be established. The PPE program shall address the elements listed below. When elements, such as donning and doffing procedures, are provided by the manufacturer of a piece of equipment and are attached to the plan, they need not be rewritten into the plan as long as they adequately address the procedure or element.

(g)(5)(i) PPE selection based upon site hazards;
(g)(5)(ii) PPE use and limitations of the equipment;
(g)(5)(iii) Work mission duration;
(g)(5)(iv) PPE maintenance and storage;
(g)(5)(v) PPE decontamination and disposal;
(g)(5)(vi) PPE training and proper fitting;
(g)(5)(vii) PPE donning and doffing procedures;
(g)(5)(viii) PPE inspection procedures prior to, during, and after use;
(g)(5)(ix) Evaluation of the effectiveness of the PPE program; and
(g)(5)(x) Limitations during temperature extremes, heat stress, and other appropriate medical considerations.

(h) Monitoring

(h)(1) General

(h)(1)(i) Monitoring shall be performed in accordance with this paragraph where there may be a question of employee exposure to hazardous concentrations of hazardous substances in order to assure proper selection of engineering controls, work practices and personal protective equipment so that employees are not exposed to levels which exceed permissible exposure limits, or published exposure levels if there are no permissible exposure limits, for hazardous substances.

(h)(1)(ii) Air monitoring shall be used to identify and quantify airborne levels of hazardous substances and safety and health hazards in order to determine the appropriate level of employee protection needed on site.

(h)(2) **Initial entry** Upon initial entry, representative air monitoring shall be conducted to identify any IDLH condition, exposure over permissible exposure limits or published exposure levels, exposure over a radioactive material's dose limits or other dangerous condition such as the presence of flammable atmospheres or oxygen-deficient environments.

(h)(3) **Periodic monitoring** Periodic monitoring shall be conducted when the possibility of an IDLH condition or flammable atmosphere has developed or when there is indication that exposures may have risen over permissible exposure limits or published exposure levels since prior monitoring. Situations where it shall be considered whether the possibility that exposures have risen are as follows:

(h)(3)(i) When work begins on a different portion of the site;
(h)(3)(ii) When contaminants other than those previously identified are being handled;
(h)(3)(iii) When a different type of operation is initiated (e.g., drum opening as opposed to exploratory well drilling);
(h)(3)(iv) When employees are handling leaking drums or containers or working in areas with obvious liquid contamination (e.g., a spill or lagoon).

(h)(4) **Monitoring of high-risk employees** After the actual clean-up phase of any hazardous waste operation commences; for example, when soil, surface water or containers are moved or disturbed; the employer shall monitor those employees likely to have the highest exposures to hazardous substances and health hazards likely to be present above permissible exposure limits or published exposure levels by using personal sampling frequently enough to characterize employee exposures. If the employees likely to have the highest exposure are over permissible exposure limits or published exposure limits, then monitoring shall continue to determine all employees likely to be above those limits. The employer may utilize a representative sampling approach by documenting that the employees and chemicals chosen for monitoring are based on the criteria stated above.

Note to paragraph (h): *It is not required to monitor employees engaged in site characterization operations covered by paragraph (c) of this section.*

(i) **Informational programs** Employers shall develop and implement a program, which is part of the employer's safety and health program required in paragraph (b) of this section, to inform employees, contractors, and subcontractors (or their representative) actually engaged in hazardous waste operations of the nature, level and degree of exposure likely as a result of participation in such hazardous waste operations. Employees, contractors and subcontractors working outside of the operations part of a site are not covered by this standard.

(j) Handling drums and containers

(j)(1) General

(j)(1)(i) Hazardous substances and contaminated soils, liquids, and other residues shall be handled, transported, labeled, and disposed of in accordance with this paragraph.

(j)(1)(ii) Drums and containers used during the clean-up shall meet the appropriate DOT, OSHA, and EPA regulations for the wastes that they contain.

(j)(1)(iii) When practical, drums and containers shall be inspected and their integrity shall be assured prior to being moved. Drums or containers that cannot be inspected before being moved because of storage conditions (i.e., buried beneath the earth, stacked behind other drums, stacked several tiers high in a pile, etc.) shall be moved to an accessible location and inspected prior to further handling.

(j)(1)(iv) Unlabelled drums and containers shall be considered to contain hazardous substances and handled accordingly until the contents are positively identified and labeled.

(j)(1)(v) Site operations shall be organized to minimize the amount of drum or container movement.

(j)(1)(vi) Prior to movement of drums or containers, all employees exposed to the transfer operation shall be warned of the potential hazards associated with the contents of the drums or containers.

(j)(1)(vii) U.S. Department of Transportation specified salvage drums or containers and suitable quantities of proper absorbent shall be kept available and used in areas where spills, leaks, or ruptures may occur.

(j)(1)(viii) Where major spills may occur, a spill containment program, which is part of the employer's safety and health program required in paragraph (b) of this section, shall be implemented to contain and isolate the entire volume of the hazardous substance being transferred.

(j)(1)(ix) Drums and containers that cannot be moved without rupture, leakage, or spillage shall be emptied into a sound container using a device classified for the material being transferred.

(j)(1)(x) A ground-penetrating system or other type of detection system or device shall be used to estimate the location and depth of buried drums or containers.

(j)(1)(xi) Soil or covering material shall be removed with caution to prevent drum or container rupture.

(j)(1)(xii) Fire extinguishing equipment meeting the requirements of 29 CFR Part 1910, Subpart L, shall be on hand and ready for use to control incipient fires.

(j)(2) **Opening drums and containers** The following procedures shall be followed in areas where drums or containers are being opened:

(j)(2)(i) Where an airline respirator system is used, connections to the source of air supply shall be protected from contamination and the entire system shall be protected from physical damage.
(j)(2)(ii) Employees not actually involved in opening drums or containers shall be kept a safe distance from the drums or containers being opened.
(j)(2)(iii) If employees must work near or adjacent to drums or containers being opened, a suitable shield that does not interfere with the work operation shall be placed between the employee and the drums or containers being opened to protect the employee in case of accidental explosion.
(j)(2)(iv) Controls for drum or container opening equipment, monitoring equipment, and fire suppression equipment shall be located behind the explosion-resistant barrier.
(j)(2)(v) When there is a reasonable possibility of flammable atmospheres being present, material handling equipment and hand tools shall be of the type to prevent sources of ignition.
(j)(2)(vi) Drums and containers shall be opened in such a manner that excess interior pressure will be safely relieved. If pressure can not be relieved from a remote location, appropriate shielding shall be placed between the employee and the drums or containers to reduce the risk of employee injury.
(j)(2)(vii) Employees shall not stand upon or work from drums or containers.

(j)(3) **Material handling equipment** Material handiing equipment used to transfer drums and containers shall be selected, positioned and operated to minimize sources of ignition related to the equipment from igniting vapors released from ruptured drums or containers.

(j)(4) **Radioactive wastes** Drums and containers containing radioactive wastes shall not be handled until such time as their hazard to employees is properly assessed.

(j)(5) **Shock sensitive wastes** As a minimum, the following special precautions shall be taken when drums and containers containing or suspected of containing shock-sensitive wastes are handled:

(j)(5)(i) All non-essential employees shall be evacuated from the area of transfer;
(j)(5)(ii) Material handling equipment shall be provided with explosive containment devices or protective shields to protect equipment operators from exploding containers;
(j)(5)(iii) An employee alarm system capable of being perceived above surrounding light and noise conditions shall be used to signal the commencement and completion of explosive waste handling activities;
(j)(5)(iv) Continuous communications (i.e., portable radios, hand signals, telephones, as appropriate) shall be maintained between the employee-in-charge of the immediate handling area and both the site safety and health supervisor and the command post until such time as the handling operation is completed. Communication equipment or methods that could cause shock sensitive materials to explode shall not be used;

(j)(5)(v) Drums and containers under pressure, as evidenced by bulging or swelling, shall not be moved until such time as the cause for excess pressure is determined and appropriate containment procedures have been implemented to protect employees from explosive relief of the drum;

(j)(5)(vi) Drums and containers containing packaged laboratory wastes shall be considered to contain shock-sensitive or explosive materials until they have been characterized.

Caution: Shipping of shock sensitive wastes may be prohibited under U.S. Department of Transportation regulations. Employers and their shippers should refer to 49 CFR 173.21 and 173.50.

(j)(6) **Laboratory waste packs** In addition to the requirements of paragraph (j)(5) of this section, the following precautions shall be taken, as a minimum, in handling laboratory waste packs (lab packs):

(j)(6)(i) Lab packs shall be opened only when necessary and then only by an individual knowledgeable in the inspection, classification, and segregation of the containers within the pack according to the hazards of the wastes;

(j)(6)(ii) If crystalline material is noted on any container, the contents shall be handled as a shock-sensitive waste until the contents are identified.

(j)(7) **Sampling of drum and container contents** Sampling of containers and drums shall be done in accordance with a sampling procedure which is part of the site safety and health plan developed for and available to employees and others at the specific worksite.

(j)(8) **Shipping and transport**

(j)(8)(i) Drums and containers shall be identified and classified prior to packaging for shipment.

(j)(8)(ii) Drum or container staging areas shall be kept to the minimum number necessary to identify and classify materials safely and prepare them for transport.

(j)(8)(iii) Staging areas shall be provided with adequate access and egress routes.

(j)(8)(iv) Bulking of hazardous wastes shall be permitted only after a thorough characterization of the materials has been completed.

(j)(9) **Tank and vault procedures**

(j)(9)(i) Tanks and vaults containing hazardous substances shall be handled in a manner similar to that for drums and containers, taking into consideration the size of the tank or vault.

(j)(9)(ii) Appropriate tank or vault entry procedures as described in the employer's safety and health plan shall be followed whenever employees must enter a tank or vault.

(k) [OI] **Decontamination**

(k)(1) **General** Procedures for all phases of decontamination shall be developed and implemented in accordance with this paragraph.

(k)(2) **Decontamination procedures**

(k)(2)(i) A decontamination procedure shall be developed, communicated to employees and implemented before any employees or equipment may enter areas on site where potential for exposure to hazardous substances exists.

(k)(2)(ii) Standard operating procedures shall be developed to minimize employee contact with hazardous substances or with equipment that has contacted hazardous substances.

(k)(2)(iii) All employees leaving a contaminated area shall be appropriately decontaminated; all contaminated clothing and equipment leaving a contaminated area shall be appropriately disposed of or decontaminated.

(k)(2)(iv) Decontamination procedures shall be monitored by the site safety and health supervisor to determine their effectiveness. When such procedures are found to be ineffective, appropriate steps shall be taken to correct any deficiencies.

(k)(3) **Location** Decontamination shall be performed in geographical areas that will minimize the exposure of uncontaminated employees or equipment to contaminated employees or equipment.

(k)(4) **Equipment and solvents** All equipment and solvents used for decontamination shall be decontaminated or disposed of properly.

(k)(5) **Personal protective clothing and equipment**

(k)(5)(i) Protective clothing and equipment shall be decontaminated, cleaned, laundered, maintained or replaced as needed to maintain their effectiveness.

(k)(5)(ii) Employees whose non-impermeable clothing becomes wetted with hazardous substances shall immediately remove that clothing and proceed to shower. The clothing shall be disposed of or decontaminated before it is removed from the work zone.

(k)(6) **Unauthorized employees** Unauthorized employees shall not remove protective clothing or equipment from change rooms.

(k)(7) **Commercial laundries or cleaning establishments** Commercial laundries or cleaning establishments that decontaminate protective clothing or equipment shall be informed of the potentially harmful effects of exposures to hazardous substances.

(k)(8) **Showers and change rooms** Where the decontamination procedure indicates a need for regular showers and change rooms outside of a contaminated area, they shall be provided and meet the requirements of 29 CFR §1910.141. If temperature conditions prevent the effective use of water, then other effective means for cleansing shall be provided and used.

(l) [OI] **Emergency response by employees at uncontrolled hazardous waste site**

(l)(1) **Emergency response plan**

(l)(1)(i) An emergency response plan shall be developed and implemented by all employers within the scope of paragraphs (a)(1) (i)–(ii) of this section to handle anticipated emergencies prior to the commencement of hazardous waste operations. The plan shall be in writing and available for inspection and copying by employees, their representatives, OSHA personnel and other governmental agencies with relevant responsibilities.

(l)(1)(ii) Employers who will evacuate their employees from the danger area when an emergency occurs, and who do not permit any of their employees to assist in handling the emergency, are exempt from the requirements of this paragraph if they provide an emergency action plan complying with 29 CFR §1910.38.

(l)(2) **Elements of an emergency response plan** The employer shall develop an emergency response plan for emergencies which shall address, as a minimum, the following:

(l)(2)(i) Pre-emergency planning;

(l)(2)(ii) Personnel roles, lines of authority, and communication;

(l)(2)(iii) Emergency recognition and prevention;

(l)(2)(iv) Safe distances and places of refuge;

(l)(2)(v) Site security and control;

(l)(2)(vi) Evacuation routes and procedures;

(l)(2)(vii) Decontamination procedures which are not covered by the site safety and health plan;

(l)(2)(viii) [OI] Emergency medical treatment and first aid;

(l)(2)(ix) Emergency alerting and response procedures;

(l)(2)(x) Critique of response and follow-up;

(l)(2)(xi) PPE and emergency equipment.

(l)(3) **Procedures for handling emergency incidents**

(l)(3)(i) In addition to the elements for the emergency response plan required in paragraph (l)(2) of this section, the following elements shall be included for emergency response plans:

(l)(3)(i)(A) Site topography, layout, and prevailing weather conditions;

(l)(3)(i)(B) Procedures for reporting incidents to local, state, and federal governmental agencies.

(l)(3)(ii) The emergency response plan shall be a separate section of the Site Safety and Health Plan.

(l)(3)(iii) The emergency response plan shall be compatible and integrated with the disaster, fire and/or emergency response plans of local, state, and federal agencies.

(l)(3)(iv) The emergency response plan shall be rehearsed regularly as part of the overall training program for site operations.

(l)(3)(v) The site emergency response plan shall be reviewed periodically and, as necessary, be amended to keep it current with new or changing site conditions or information.

(l)(3)(vi) An employee alarm system shall be installed in accordance with 29 CFR §1910.165 to notify employees of an emergency situation; to stop work activities if necessary; to lower background noise in order to speed communication; and to begin emergency procedures.

(l)(3)(vii) Based upon the information available at time of the emergency, the employer shall evaluate the incident and the site response capabilities and proceed with the appropriate steps to implement the site emergency response plan.

(m) [OI] **Illumination** Areas accessible to employees shall be lighted to not less than the minimum illumination intensities listed in the following Table H–120.1 while any work is in progress:

Table H–120.1
Minimum Illumination Intensities in Foot-Candles

Foot-candles	Area or operations
5	General site areas.
3	Excavation and waste areas, accessways, active storage areas, loading platforms, refueling, and field maintenance areas.
5	Indoors: Warehouses, corridors, hallways, and exitways.

Foot-candles	Area or operations
5	Tunnels, shafts, and general underground work areas. (Exception: Minimum of 10 foot-candles is required at tunnel and shaft heading during drilling mucking, and scaling. Mine Safety and Health Administration approved cap lights shall be acceptable for use in the tunnel heading.)
10	General shops (e.g., mechanical and electrical equipment rooms, active storerooms, barracks or living quarters, locker or dressing rooms, dining areas, and indoor toilets and workrooms.)
30	First aid stations, infirmaries, and offices.

(n) **Sanitation at temporary workplaces**

(n)(1) Potable water

(n)(1)(i) An adequate supply of potable water shall be provided on the site.

(n)(1)(ii) Portable containers used to dispense drinking water shall be capable of being tightly closed, and equipped with a tap. Water shall not be dipped from containers.

(n)(1)(iii) Any container used to distribute drinking water shall be clearly marked as to the nature of its contents and not used for any other purpose.

(n)(1)(iv) Where single service cups (to be used but once) are supplied, both a sanitary container for the unused cups and a receptacle for disposing of the used cups shall be provided.

(n)(2) Nonpotable water

(n)(2)(i) Outlets for nonpotable water, such as water for firefighting purposes, shall be identified to indicate clearly that the water is unsafe and is not to be used for drinking, washing, or cooking purposes.

(n)(2)(ii) There shall be no cross-connection, open or potential, between a system furnishing potable water and a system furnishing nonpotable water.

(n)(3) **Toilet facilities**

(n)(3)(i) Toilets shall be provided for employees according to the following Table H–120.2.

Table H–120.2
Toilet Facilities

Number of employees	Minimum number of facilities
20 or fewer	One.
More than 20, fewer than 200	One toilet seat and one urinal per 40 employees.
More than 200	One toilet seat and one urinal per 50 employees.

(n)(3)(ii) Under temporary field conditions, provisions shall be made to assure that at least one toilet facility is available.

(n)(3)(iii) Hazardous waste sites not provided with a sanitary sewer shall be provided with the following toilet facilities unless prohibited by local codes:

(n)(3)(iii)(A) Chemical toilets;

(n)(3)(iii)(B) Recirculating toilets;

(n)(3)(iii)(C) Combustion toilets; or

(n)(3)(iii)(D) Flush toilets.

(n)(3)(iv) The requirements of this paragraph for sanitation facilities shall not apply to mobile crews having transportation readily available to nearby toilet facilities.

(n)(3)(v) Doors entering toilet facilities shall be provided with entrance locks controlled from inside the facility.

(n)(4) Food handling All food service facilities and operations for employees shall meet the applicable laws, ordinances, and regulations of the jurisdictions in which they are located.

(n)(5) Temporary sleeping quarters When temporary sleeping quarters are provided, they shall be heated, ventilated, and lighted.

(n)(6) Washing facilities The employer shall provide adequate washing facilities for employees engaged in operations where hazardous substances may be harmful to employees. Such facilities shall be in near proximity to the worksite; in areas where exposures are below permissible exposure limits and published exposure levels and which are under the controls of the employer; and shall be so equipped as to enable employees to remove hazardous substances from themselves.

(n)(7) Showers and change rooms When hazardous waste clean-up or removal operations commence on a site and the duration of the work will require six months or greater time to complete, the employer shall provide showers and change rooms for all employees exposed to hazardous substances and health hazards involved in hazardous waste clean-up or removal operations.

(n)(7)(i) Showers shall be provided and shall meet the requirements of 29 CFR §1910.141(d)(3).

(n)(7)(ii) Change rooms shall be provided and shall meet the requirements of 29 CFR §1910.141(e). Change rooms shall consist of two separate change areas separated by the shower area required in paragraph (n)(7)(i) of this section. One change area, with an exit leading off the worksite, shall provide employees with a clean area where they can remove, store, and put on street clothing. The second area, with an exit to the worksite, shall provide employees with an area where they can put on, remove and store work clothing and personal protective equipment.

(n)(7)(iii) Showers and change rooms shall be located in areas where exposures are below the permissible exposure limits and published exposure levels. If this cannot be accomplished, then a ventilation system shall be provided that will supply air that is below the permissible exposure limits and published exposure levels.

(n)(7)(iv) Employers shall assure that employees shower at the end of their work shift and when leaving the hazardous waste site.

(o) **New technology programs**

(o)(1) The employer shall develop and implement procedures for the introduction of effective new technologies and equipment developed for the improved protection of employees working with hazardous waste clean-up operations, and the same shall be implemented as part of the site safety and health program to assure that employee protection is being maintained.

(o)(2) New technologies, equipment or control measures available to the industry, such as the use of foams, absorbents, adsorbents, neutralizers, or other means to suppress the level of air contaminates while excavating the site or for spill control, shall be evaluated by employers or their representatives. Such an evaluation shall be done to determine the effectiveness of the new methods, materials, or equipment before implementing their use on a large scale for enhancing employee protection. Information and data from manufacturers or suppliers may be used as part of the employer's evaluation effort. Such evaluations shall be made available to OSHA upon request.

(p) **Certain Operations Conducted Under the Resource Conservation and Recovery Act of 1976 (RCRA)** Employers conducting operations at treatment, storage and disposal (TSD) facilities specified in paragraph (a)(1)(iv) of this section shall provide and implement the programs specified in this paragraph. See the "Notes and Exceptions" to paragraph (a)(2)(iii) of this section for employers not covered..

(p)(1) **Safety and health program** The employer shall develop and implement a written safety and health program for employees involved in hazardous waste operations that shall be available for inspection by employees, their representatives and OSHA personnel. The program shall be designed to identify, evaluate and control safety and health hazards in their facilities for the purpose of employee protection, to provide for emergency response meeting the requirements of paragraph (p)(8) of this section and to address as appropriate site analysis, engineering controls, maximum exposure limits, hazardous waste handling procedures and uses of new technologies.

(p)(2) **Hazard communication program** The employer shall implement a hazard communication program meeting the requirements of 29 CFR §1910.1200 as part of the employer's safety and program.

Note to §1910.120: The exemption for hazardous waste provided in §1910.1200 is applicable to this section.

(p)(3) Medical surveillance program The employer shall develop and implement a medical surveillance program meeting the requirements of paragraph (f) of this section.

(p)(4) Decontamination program The employer shall develop and implement a decontamination procedure meeting the requirements of paragraph (k) of this section.

(p)(5) New technology program The employer shall develop and implement procedures meeting the requirements of paragraph (o) of this section for introducing new and innovative equipment into the workplace.

(p)(6) Material handling program Where employees will be handling drums or containers, the employer shall develop and implement procedures meeting the requirements of paragraphs (j)(1)(ii) through (viii) and (xi) of this section, as well as (j)(3) and (j)(8) of this section prior to starting such work.

(p)(7) **Training program**

(p)(7)(i) **New employees** The employer shall develop and implement a training program, which is part of the employer's safety and health program, for employees exposed to health hazards or hazardous substances at TSD operations to enable the employees to perform their assigned duties and functions in a safe and healthful manner so as not endanger themselves or other employees. The initial training shall be for 24 hours and refresher training shall be for eight hours annually. Employees who have received the initial training required by this paragraph shall be given a written certificate attesting that they have successfully completed the necessary training.

(p)(7)(ii) Current employees Employers who can show by an employee's previous work experience and/or training that the employee has had training equivalent to the initial training required by this paragraph, shall be considered as meeting the initial training requirements of this paragraph as to that employee. Equivalent training includes the training that existing employees might have already received from actual site work experience. Current employees shall receive eight hours of refresher training annually.

(p)(7)(iii) Trainers Trainers who teach initial training shall have satisfactorily completed a training course for teaching the subjects they are expected to teach or they shall have the academic credentials and instruction experience necessary to demonstrate a good command of the subject matter of the courses and competent instructional skills.

(p)(8) Emergency response program

(p)(8)(i) Emergency response plan An emergency response plan shall be developed and implemented by all employers. Such plans need not duplicate any of the subjects fully addressed in the employer's contingency planning required by permits, such as those issued by the U.S. Environmental Protection Agency, provided that the contingency plan is made part of the emergency response plan. The emergency response plan shall be a written portion of the employer's safety and health program required in paragraph (p)(1) of this section. Employers who will evacuate their employees from the worksite location when an emergency occurs and who do not permit any of their employees to assist in handling the emergency are exempt from the requirements of paragraph (p)(8) if they provide an emergency action plan complying with 29 CFR §1910.38.

(p)(8)(ii) Elements of an emergency response plan The employer shall develop an emergency response plan for emergencies which shall address, as a minimum, the following areas to the extent that they are not addressed in any specific program required in this paragraph:

(p)(8)(ii)(A) Pre-emergency planning and coordination with outside parties;

(p)(8)(ii)(B) Personnel roles, lines of authority, and communication;

(p)(8)(ii)(C) Emergency recognition and prevention;

(p)(8)(ii)(D) Safe distances and places of refuge;

(p)(8)(ii)(E) Site security and control;

(p)(8)(ii)(F) Evacuation routes and procedures;

(p)(8)(ii)(G) Decontamination procedures;

(p)(8)(ii)(H) Emergency medical treatment and first aid;

(p)(8)(ii)(I) Emergency alerting and response procedures;

(p)(8)(ii)(J) Critique of response and follow-up;

(p)(8)(ii)(K) PPE and emergency equipment.

(p)(8)(iii) Training

(p)(8)(iii)(A) Training for emergency response employees shall be completed before they are called upon to perform in real emergencies. Such training shall include the elements of the emergency response plan, standard operating procedures the employer has established for the job, the personal protective equipment to be worn and procedures for handling emergency incidents.

Exception #1: An employer need not train all employees to the degree specified if the employer divides the work force in a manner such that a sufficient number of employees who have responsibility to control emergencies have the training specified, and all other employees, who may first respond to an emergency incident, have sufficient awareness training to recognize that an emergency response situation exists and that they are instructed in that case to summon the fully trained employees and not attempt control activities for which they are not trained.

Exception #2: An employer need not train all employees to the degree specified if arrangements have been made in advance for an outside fully-trained emergency response team to respond in a reasonable period and all employees, who may come to the incident first, have sufficient awareness training to recognize that an emergency response situation exists and they have been instructed to call the designated outside fully-trained emergency response team for assistance.

(p)(8)(iii)(B) Employee members of TSD facility emergency response organizations shall be trained to a level of competence in the recognition of health and safety hazards to protect themselves and other employees. This would include training in the methods used to minimize the risk from safety and health hazards; in the safe use of control equipment; in the selection and use of appropriate personal protective equipment; in the safe operating procedures to be used at the incident scene; in the techniques of coordination with other employees to minimize risks; in the appropriate response to over exposure from health hazards or injury to themselves and other employees; and in the recognition of subsequent symptoms which may result from over exposures.

(p)(8)(iii)(C) The employer shall certify that each covered employee has attended and successfully completed the training required in paragraph (p)(8)(iii) of this section, or shall certify the employee's competency at least yearly. The method used to demonstrate competency for certification of training shall be recorded and maintained by the employer.

(p)(8)(iv) Procedures for handling emergency incidents

(p)(8)(iv)(A) In addition to the elements for the emergency response plan required in paragraph (p)(8)(ii) of this section, the following elements shall be included for emergency response plans to the extent that they do not repeat any information already contained in the emergency response plan:

(p)(8)(iv)(A)(1) Site topography, layout, and prevailing weather conditions;

(p)(8)(iv)(A)(2) Procedures for reporting incidents to local, state, and federal governmental agencies.

(p)(8)(iv)(B) The emergency response plan shall be compatible and integrated with the disaster, fire and/or emergency response plans of local, state, and federal agencies;

(p)(8)(iv)(C) The emergency response plan shall be rehearsed regularly as part of the overall training program for site operations;

(p)(8)(iv)(D) The site emergency response plan shall be reviewed periodically and, as necessary, be amended to keep it current with new or changing site conditions or information;

(p)(8)(iv)(E) An employee alarm system shall be installed in accordance with 29 CFR §1910.165 to notify employees of an emergency situation; to stop work activities if necessary; to lower background noise in order to speed communication; and to begin emergency procedures;

(p)(8)(iv)(F) Based upon the information available at time of the emergency, the employer shall evaluate the incident and the site response capabilities and proceed with the appropriate steps to implement the site emergency response plan.

(q) Emergency response to hazardous substance releases This paragraph covers employers whose employees are engaged in emergency response no matter where it occurs except that it does not cover employees engaged in operations specified in paragraphs (a)(1)(i) through (a)(1)(iv) of this section. Those emergency response organizations who have developed and implemented programs equivalent to this paragraph for handling releases of hazardous substances pursuant to section 303 of the Superfund Amendments and Reauthorization Act of 1986 (Emergency Planning and Community Right-to-Know Act of 1986, 42 U.S.C. 11003) shall be deemed to have met the requirements of this paragraph.

(q)(1) Emergency response plan An emergency response plan shall be developed and implemented to handle anticipated emergencies prior to the commencement of emergency response operations. The plan shall be in writing and available for inspection and copying by employees, their representatives and OSHA personnel. Employers who will evacuate their employees from the danger area when an emergency occurs, and who do not permit any of their employees to assist in handling the emergency, are exempt from the requirements of this paragraph if they provide an emergency action plan in accordance with 29 CFR §1910.38.

(q)(2) Elements of an emergency response plan The employer shall develop an emergency response plan for emergencies which shall address, as a minimum, the following to the extent that they are not addressed elsewhere:

(q)(2)(i) Pre-emergency planning and coordination with outside parties;

(q)(2)(ii) Personnel roles, lines of authority, training, and communication;

(q)(2)(iii) Emergency recognition and prevention;

(q)(2)(iv) Safe distances and places of refuge;

(q)(2)(v) Site security and control;

(q)(2)(vi) Evacuation routes and procedures;

(q)(2)(vii) Decontamination;

(q)(2)(viii) Emergency medical treatment and first aid;

(q)(2)(ix) Emergency alerting and response procedures;

(q)(2)(x) Critique of response and follow-up;

(q)(2)(xi) PPE and emergency equipment;

(q)(2)(xii) Emergency response organizations may use the local emergency response plan or the state emergency response plan or both, as part of their emergency response plan to avoid duplication. Those items of the emergency response plan that are being properly addressed by the SARA Title III plans may be substituted into their emergency plan or otherwise kept together for the employer and employee's use.

(q)(3) Procedures for handling emergency response

(q)(3)(i) The senior emergency response official responding to an emergency shall become the individual in charge of a site-specific

Incident Command System (ICS). All emergency responders and their communications shall be coordinated and controlled through the individual in charge of the ICS assisted by the senior official present for each employer.

Note to paragraph (q)(3)(i). The "senior official" at an emergency response is the most senior official on the site who has the responsibility for controlling the operations at the site. Initially it is the senior officer on the first-due piece of responding emergency apparatus to arrive on the incident scene. As more senior officers arrive (i.e., battalion chief, fire chief, state law enforcement official, site coordinator, etc.) the position is passed up the line of authority which has been previously established.

(q)(3)(ii) The individual in charge of the ICS shall identify, to the extent possible, all hazardous substances or conditions present and shall address as appropriate site analysis, use of engineering controls, maximum exposure limits, hazardous substance handling procedures, and use of any new technologies.

(q)(3)(iii) Based on the hazardous substances and/or conditions present, the individual in charge of the ICS shall implement appropriate emergency operations, and assure that the personal protective equipment worn is appropriate for the hazards to be encountered. However, personal protective equipment shall meet, at a minimum, the criteria contained in 29 CFR §1910.156(e) when worn while performing fire fighting operations beyond the incipient stage for any incident.

(q)(3)(iv) OI Employees engaged in emergency response and exposed to hazardous substances presenting an inhalation hazard or potential inhalation hazard shall wear positive pressure self-contained breathing apparatus while engaged in emergency response, until such time that the individual in charge of the ICS determines through the use of air monitoring that a decreased level of respiratory protection will not result in hazardous exposures to employees.

(q)(3)(v) The individual in charge of the ICS shall limit the number of emergency response personnel at the emergency site, in those areas of potential or actual exposure to incident or site hazards, to those who are actively performing emergency operations. However, operations in hazardous areas shall be performed using the buddy system in groups of two or more.

(q)(3)(vi) OI Back-up personnel shall stand by with equipment ready to provide assistance or rescue. Advance first aid support personnel, as a minimum, shall also stand by with medical equipment and transportation capability.

(q)(3)(vii) OI The individual in charge of the ICS shall designate a safety official, who is knowledgable in the operations being implemented at the emergency response site, with specific responsibility to identify and evaluate hazards and to provide direction with respect to the safety of operations for the emergency at hand.

(q)(3)(viii) When activities are judged by the safety official to be an IDLH condition and/or to involve an imminent danger condition, the safety official shall have the authority to alter, suspend, or terminate those activities. The safety official shall immediately inform the individual in charge of the ICS of any actions needed to be taken to correct these hazards at the emergency scene.

(q)(3)(ix) After emergency operations have terminated, the individual in charge of the ICS shall implement appropriate decontamination procedures.

(q)(3)(x) OI When deemed necessary for meeting the tasks at hand, approved self-contained compressed air breathing apparatus may be used with approved cylinders from other approved self-contained compressed air breathing apparatus provided that such cylinders are of the same capacity and pressure rating. All compressed air cylinders used with self-contained breathing apparatus shall meet U.S. Department of Transportation and National Institute for Occupational Safety and Health criteria.

(q)(4) OI **Skilled support personnel** Personnel, not necessarily an employer's own employees, who are skilled in the operation of certain equipment, such as mechanized earth moving or digging equipment or crane and hoisting equipment, and who are needed temporarily to perform immediate emergency support work that cannot reasonably be performed in a timely fashion by an employer's own employees, and who will be or may be exposed to the hazards at an emergency response scene, are not required to meet the training required in this paragraph for the employer's regular employees. However, these personnel shall be given an initial briefing at the site prior to their participation in any emergency response. The initial briefing shall include instruction in the wearing of appropriate personal protective equipment, what chemical hazards are involved, and what duties are to be performed. All other appropriate safety and health precautions provided to the employer's own employees shall be used to assure the safety and health of these personnel.

(q)(5) OI **Specialist employees** Employees who, in the course of their regular job duties, work with and are trained in the hazards of specific hazardous substances, and who will be called upon to provide technical advice or assistance at a hazardous substance release incident to the individual in charge, shall receive training or demonstrate competency in the area of their specialization annually.

(q)(6) OI **Training** Training shall be based on the duties and function to be performed by each responder of an emergency response organization. The skill and knowledge levels required for all new responders, those hired after the effective date of this standard, shall be conveyed to them through training before they are permitted to take part in actual emergency operations on an incident. Employees who participate, or are expected to participate, in emergency response, shall be given training in accordance with the following paragraphs:

(q)(6)(i) OI First responder awareness level. First responders at the awareness level are individuals who are likely to witness or discover a hazardous substance release and who have been trained to initiate an emergency response sequence by notifying the proper authorities of the release. They would take no further action beyond notifying the authorities of the release. First responders at the awareness level shall have sufficient training or have had sufficient experience to objectively demonstrate competency in the following areas:

(q)(6)(i)(A) An understanding of what hazardous substances are, and the risks associated with them in an incident;

(q)(6)(i)(B) An understanding of the potential outcomes associated with an emergency created when hazardous substances are present;

(q)(6)(i)(C) The ability to recognize the presence of hazardous substances in an emergency;

(q)(6)(i)(D) The ability to identify the hazardous substances, if possible;

(q)(6)(i)(E) An understanding of the role of the first responder awareness individual in the employer's emergency response plan including site security and control and the U.S. Department of Transportation's Emergency Response Guidebook;

(q)(6)(i)(F) The ability to realize the need for additional resources, and to make appropriate notifications to the communication center.

(q)(6)(ii) OI First responder operations level. First responders at the operations level are individuals who respond to releases or potential releases of hazardous substances as part of the initial response to the site for the purpose of protecting nearby persons, property, or the environment from the effects of the release. They are trained to respond in a defensive fashion without actually trying to stop the release. Their function is to contain the release from a safe distance, keep it from spreading, and prevent exposures. First responders at the operational level shall have received at least eight hours of training or have had sufficient experience to objectively demonstrate competency in the following areas in addition to those listed for the awareness level and the employer shall so certify:

(q)(6)(ii)(A) Knowledge of the basic hazard and risk assessment techniques;

(q)(6)(ii)(B) Know how to select and use proper personal protective equipment provided to the first responder operational level;

(q)(6)(ii)(C) An understanding of basic hazardous materials terms;

(q)(6)(ii)(D) Know how to perform basic control, containment and/or confinement operations within the capabilities of the resources and personal protective equipment available with their unit;

(q)(6)(ii)(E) Know how to implement basic decontamination procedures;

(q)(6)(ii)(F) An understanding of the relevant standard operating procedures and termination procedures.

(q)(6)(iii) OI Hazardous materials technician. Hazardous materials technicians are individuals who respond to releases or potential releases for the purpose of stopping the release. They assume a more aggressive role than a first responder at the operations level in that they will approach the point of release in order to plug, patch or otherwise stop the release of a hazardous substance. Hazardous materials technicians shall have received at least 24 hours of training equal to the first responder operations level and in addition have competency in the following areas and the employer shall so certify:

(q)(6)(iii)(A) Know how to implement the employer's emergency response plan;

(q)(6)(iii)(B) Know the classification, identification and verification of known and unknown materials by using field survey instruments and equipment;

(q)(6)(iii)(C) Be able to function within an assigned role in the Incident Command System;

(q)(6)(iii)(D) OI Know how to select and use proper specialized chemical personal protective equipment provided to the hazardous materials technician;

(q)(6)(iii)(E) Understand hazard and risk assessment techniques;

(q)(6)(iii)(F) Be able to perform advance control, containment, and/or confinement operations within the capabilities of the resources and personal protective equipment available with the unit;

(q)(6)(iii)(G) Understand and implement decontamination procedures.

(q)(6)(iii)(H) Understand termination procedures;

(q)(6)(iii)(I) Understand basic chemical and toxicological terminology and behavior.

(q)(6)(iv) Hazardous materials specialist. Hazardous materials specialists are individuals who respond with and provide support to hazardous materials technicians. Their duties parallel those of the hazardous materials technician, however, those duties require a more directed or specific knowledge of the various substances they may be called upon to contain. The hazardous materials specialist would also act as the site liaison with Federal, state, local and other government authorities in regards to site activities. Hazardous materials specialists shall have received at least 24 hours of training equal to the technician level and in addition have competency in the following areas and the employer shall so certify:

(q)(6)(iv)(A) Know how to implement the local emergency response plan;

(q)(6)(iv)(B) Understand classification, identification and verification of known and unknown materials by using advanced survey instruments and equipment;

(q)(6)(iv)(C) Know of the state emergency response plan;

(q)(6)(iv)(D) Be able to select and use proper specialized chemical personal protective equipment provided to the hazardous materials specialist;

(q)(6)(iv)(E) Understand in-depth hazard and risk techniques;

(q)(6)(iv)(F) Be able to perform specialized control, containment, and/or confinement operations within the capabilities of the resources and personal protective equipment available;

(q)(6)(iv)(G) Be able to determine and implement decontamination procedures;

(q)(6)(iv)(H) Have the ability to develop a site safety and control plan;

(q)(6)(iv)(I) Understand chemical, radiological and toxicological terminology and behavior.

(q)(6)(v) [OI] On scene incident commander. Incident commanders, who will assume control of the incident scene beyond the first responder awareness level, shall receive at least 24 hours of training equal to the first responder operations level and in addition have competency in the following areas and the employer shall so certify:

(q)(6)(v)(A) Know and be able to implement the employer's incident command system;

(q)(6)(v)(B) Know how to implement the employer's emergency response plan;

(q)(6)(v)(C) Know and understand the hazards and risks associated with employees working in chemical protective clothing;

(q)(6)(v)(D) Know how to implement the local emergency response plan;

(q)(6)(v)(E) Know of the state emergency response plan and of the Federal Regional Response Team;

(q)(6)(v)(F) Know and understand the importance of decontamination procedures.

(q)(7) [OI] **Trainers** Trainers who teach any of the above training subjects shall have satisfactorily completed a training course for teaching the subjects they are expected to teach, such as the courses offered by the U.S. National Fire Academy, or they shall have the training and/or academic credentials and instructional experience necessary to demonstrate competent instructional skills and a good command of the subject matter of the courses they are to teach.

(q)(8) [OI] **Refresher training**

(q)(8)(i) Those employees who are trained in accordance with paragraph (q)(6) of this section shall receive annual refresher training of sufficient content and duration to maintain their competencies, or shall demonstrate competency in those areas at least yearly.

(q)(8)(ii) A statement shall be made of the training or competency, and if a statement of competency is made, the employer shall keep a record of the methodology used to demonstrate competency.

(q)(9) [OI] **Medical surveillance and consultation**

(q)(9)(i) [OI] Members of an organized and designated HAZMAT team and hazardous materials specialists shall receive a baseline physical examination and be provided with medical surveillance as required in paragraph (f) of this section.

(q)(9)(ii) Any emergency response employees who exhibits signs or symptoms which may have resulted from exposure to hazardous substances during the course of an emergency incident, either immediately or subsequently, shall be provided with medical consultation as required in paragraph (f)(3)(ii) of this section.

(q)(10) **Chemical protective clothing** Chemical protective clothing and equipment to be used by organized and designated HAZMAT team members, or to be used by hazardous materials specialists, shall meet the requirements of paragraphs (g)(3) through (5) of this section.

(q)(11) [OI] **Post-emergency response operations** Upon completion of the emergency response, if it is determined that it is necessary to remove hazardous substances, health hazards, and materials contaminated with them (such as contaminated soil or other elements of the natural environment) from the site of the incident, the employer conducting the clean-up shall comply with one of the following:

(q)(11)(i) [OI] Meet all of the requirements of paragraphs (b) through (o) of this section; or

(q)(11)(ii) [OI] Where the clean-up is done on plant property using plant or workplace employees, such employees shall have completed the training requirements of the following: 29 CFR §1910.38, §1910.134, §1910.1200, and other appropriate safety and health training made necessary by the tasks they are expected to perform such as personal protective equipment and decontamination procedures. All equipment to be used in the performance of the clean-up work shall be in serviceable condition and shall have been inspected prior to use.

§1910.120 Appendices Hazardous waste operations and emergency response

Note: The following appendices serve as non-mandatory guidelines to assist employees and employers in complying with the appropriate requirements of this section. However §1910.120(g) makes mandatory in certain circumstances the use of Level A and Level B PPE protection.

§1910.120 Appendix A Personal protective equipment test methods

This Appendix sets forth the non-mandatory examples of tests which may be used to evaluate compliance with §1910.120(g)(4)(ii) and (iii). Other tests and other challenge agents may be used to evaluate compliance.

A. Totally-encapsulating chemical protective suit pressure test

1.0 Scope

1.1 This practice measures the ability of a gas tight totally-encapsulating chemical protective suit material, seams, and closures to maintain a fixed positive pressure. The results of this practice allow the gas tight integrity of a totally-encapsulating chemical protective suit to be evaluated.

1.2 Resistance of the suit materials to permeation, penetration, and degradation by specific hazardous substances is not determined by this test method.

2.0 Definition of terms

2.1 **Totally-encapsulated chemical protective suit (TECP suit)** means a full body garment which is constructed of protective clothing materials; covers the wearer's torso, head, arms, legs and respirator; may cover the wearer's hands and feet with tightly attached gloves and boots; completely encloses the wearer and respirator by itself or in combination with the wearer's gloves and boots.

2.2 **Protective clothing material** means any material or combination of materials used in an item of clothing for the purpose of isolating parts of the body from direct contact with a potentially hazardous liquid or gaseous chemicals.

2.3 **Gas tight** means, for the purpose of this test method, the limited flow of a gas under pressure from the inside of a TECP suit to atmosphere at a prescribed pressure and time interval.

3.0 Summary of test method

3.1 The TECP suit is visually inspected and modified for the test. The test apparatus is attached to the suit to permit inflation to the pre-test suit expansion pressure for removal of suit wrinkles and creases. The pressure is lowered to the test pressure and monitored for three minutes. If the pressure drop is excessive, the TECP suit fails the test and is removed from service. The test is repeated after leak location and repair.

4.0 Required Supplies

4.1 Source of compressed air.

4.2 Test apparatus for suit testing, including a pressure measurement device with a sensitivity of at least ¼ inch water gauge.

4.3 Vent valve closure plugs or sealing tape.

4.4 Soapy water solution and soft brush.

4.5 Stop watch or appropriate timing device.

5.0 Safety Precautions

5.1 Care shall be taken to provide the correct pressure safety devices required for the source of compressed air used.

6.0 Test Procedure

6.1 Prior to each test, the tester shall perform a visual inspection of the suit. Check the suit for seam integrity by visually examining the seams and gently pulling on the seams. Ensure that all air supply lines, fittings, visor, zippers, and valves are secure and show no signs of deterioration.

6.1.1 Seal off the vent valves along with any other normal inlet or exhaust points (such as umbilical air line fittings or face piece opening) with tape or other appropriate means (caps, plugs, fixture, etc.). Care should be exercised in the sealing process not to damage any of the suit components.

6.1.2 Close all closure assemblies.

6.1.3 Prepare the suit for inflation by providing an improvised connection point on the suit for connecting an airline. Attach the pressure test apparatus to the suit to permit suit inflation from a compressed air source equipped with a pressure indicating regulator. The leak tightness of the pressure test apparatus should be tested before and after each test by closing off the end of the tubing attached to the suit and assuring a pressure of three inches water gauge for three minutes can be maintained. If a component is removed for the test, that component shall be replaced and a second test conducted with another component removed to permit a complete test of the ensemble.

6.1.4 The pre-test expansion pressure (A) and the suit test pressure (B) shall be supplied by the suit manufacturer, but in no case shall they be less than: (A)=three inches water gauge; and (B)=two inches water gauge. The ending suit pressure (C) shall be no less than 80 percent of the test pressure (B); i.e., the pressure drop shall not exceed 20 percent of the test pressure (B).

6.1.5 Inflate the suit until the pressure inside is equal to pressure (A), the pre-test expansion suit pressure. Allow at least one minute to fill out the wrinkles in the suit. Release sufficient air to reduce the suit pressure to pressure (B), the suit test pressure. Begin timing. At the end of three minutes, record the suit pressure as pressure (C), the ending suit pressure. The difference between the suit test pressure and the ending suit test pressure (B-C) shall be defined as the suit pressure drop.

6.1.6 If the suit pressure drop is more than 20 percent of the suit test pressure (B) during the three-minute test period, the suit fails the test and shall be removed from service.

7.0 Retest Procedure

7.1 If the suit fails the test check for leaks by inflating the suit to pressure (A) and brushing or wiping the entire suit (including seams, closures, lens gaskets, glove-to-sleeve joints, etc.) with a mild soap and water solution. Observe the suit for the formation of soap bubbles, which is an indication of a leak. Repair all identified leaks.

7.2 Retest the TECP suit as outlined in Test procedure 6.0.

8.0 Report

8.1 Each TECP suit tested by this practice shall have the following information recorded:

8.1.1 Unique identification number, identifying brand name, date of purchase, material of construction, and unique fit features, e.g., special breathing apparatus.

8.1.2 The actual values for test pressures (A), (B), and (C) shall be recorded along with the specific observation times. If the ending pressure (C) is less than 80 percent of the test pressure (B), the suit shall be identified as failing the test. When possible, the specific leak location shall be identified in the test records. Retest pressure data shall be recorded as an additional test.

8.1.3 The source of the test apparatus used shall be identified and the sensitivity of the pressure gauge shall be recorded.

8.1.4 Records shall be kept for each pressure test even if repairs are being made at the test location.

Caution: Visually inspect all parts of the suit to be sure they are positioned correctly and secured tightly before putting the suit back into service. Special care should be taken to examine each exhaust valve to make sure it is not blocked.

Care should also be exercised to assure that the inside and outside of the suit is completely dry before it is put into storage.

B. Totally-encapsulating chemical protective suit qualitative leak test

1.0 Scope

1.1 This practice semi-qualitatively tests gas tight totally-encapsulating chemical protective suit integrity by detecting inward leakage of ammonia vapor. Since no modifications are made to the suit to carry out this test, the results from this practice provide a realistic test for the integrity of the entire suit.

1.2 Resistance of the suit materials to permeation, penetration, and degradation is not determined by this test method. ASTM test methods are available to test suit materials for these characteristics and the tests are usually conducted by the manufacturers of the suits.

2.0 Definition of terms

2.1 **Totally-encapsulated chemical protective suit (TECP suit)** means a full body garment which is constructed of protective clothing materials; covers the wearer's torso, head, arms, legs and respirator; may cover the wearer's hands and feet with tightly attached gloves and boots; completely encloses the wearer and respirator by itself or in combination with the wearer's gloves, and boots.

2.2 **Protective clothing** material means any material or combination of materials used in an item of clothing for the purpose of isolating parts of the body from direct contact with a potentially hazardous liquid or gaseous chemicals.

2.3 **Gas tight** means, for the purpose of this test method, the limited flow of a gas under pressure from the inside of a TECP suit to atmosphere at a prescribed pressure and time interval.

2.4 **Intrusion Coefficient** means a number expressing the level of protection provided by a gas tight totally-encapsulating chemical protective suit. The intrusion coefficient is calculated by dividing the test room challenge agent concentration by the concentration of challenge agent found inside the suit. The accuracy of the intrusion coefficient is dependent on the challenge agent monitoring methods. The larger the intrusion coefficient the greater the protection provided by the TECP suit.

3.0 Summary of recommended practice

3.1 The volume of concentrated aqueous ammonia solution (ammonia hydroxide NH4OH) required to generate the test atmosphere is determined using the directions outlined in 6.1. The suit is donned by a person wearing the appropriate respiratory equipment (either a positive pressure self-contained breathing apparatus or a positive pressure supplied air respirator) and worn inside the enclosed test room. The concentrated aqueous ammonia solution is taken by the suited individual into the test room and poured into an open plastic pan. A two-minute evaporation period is observed before the test room concentration is measured, using a high range ammonia length of stain detector tube. When the ammonia vapor reaches a concentration of between 1000 and 1200 ppm, the suited individual starts a standardized exercise protocol to stress and flex the suit. After this protocol is completed, the test room concentration is measured again. The suited individual exits the test room and his stand-by person measures the ammonia concentration inside the suit using a low range ammonia length of stain detector tube or other more sensitive ammonia detector. A stand-by person is required to observe the test individual during the test procedure; aid the person in donning and doffing the TECP suit; and monitor the suit interior. The intrusion coefficient of the suit can be calculated by dividing the average test area concentration by the interior suit concentration. A colorimetric ammonia indicator strip of bromophenol blue or equivalent is placed on the inside of the suit face piece lens so that the suited individual is able to detect a color change and know if the suit has a significant leak. If a color change is observed the individual shall leave the test room immediately.

4.0 Required supplies

4.1 A supply of concentrated aqueous ammonium hydroxide (58% by weight).

4.2 A supply of bromophenol/blue indicating paper or equivalent, sensitive to 5–10 ppm ammonia or greater over a two-minute period of exposure. [pH 3.0 (yellow) to pH 4.6 (blue)]

4.3 A supply of high range (0.5–10 volume percent) and low range (5–700 ppm) detector tubes for ammonia and the corresponding sampling pump. More sensitive ammonia detectors can be substituted for the low range detector tubes to improve the sensitivity of this practice.

4.4 A shallow plastic pan (PVC) at least 12":14":1"; and a half pint plastic container (PVC) with tightly closing lid.

4.5 A graduated cylinder or other volumetric measuring device of at least 50 milliliters in volume with an accuracy of at least ±1 milliliters.

5.0 Safety precautions

5.1 Concentrated aqueous ammonium hydroxide, NH_4 OH, is a corrosive volatile liquid requiring eye, skin, and respiratory protection. The person conducting the test shall review the SDS for aqueous ammonia.

5.2 Since the established permissible exposure limit for ammonia is 35 ppm as a 15 minute STEL, only persons wearing a positive pressure self-contained breathing apparatus or a positive pressure supplied air respirator shall be in the chamber. Normally only the person wearing the totally-encapsulating suit will be inside the chamber. A stand-by person shall have a positive pressure self-contained breathing apparatus, or a positive pressure supplied air respirator available to enter the test area should the suited individual need assistance.

5.3 A method to monitor the suited individual must be used during this test. Visual contact is the simplest but other methods using communication devices are acceptable.

5.4 The test room shall be large enough to allow the exercise protocol to be carried out and then to be ventilated to allow for easy exhaust of the ammonia test atmosphere after the test(s) are completed.

5.5 Individuals shall be medically screened for the use of respiratory protection and checked for allergies to ammonia before participating in this test procedure.

6.0 Test procedure

6.1.1 Measure the test area to the nearest foot and calculate its volume in cubic feet. Multiply the test area volume by 0.2 milliliters of concentrated aqueous ammonia solution per cubic foot of test area volume to determine the approximate volume of concentrated aqueous ammonia required to generate 1000 ppm in the test area.

6.1.2 Measure this volume from the supply of concentrated aqueous ammonia and place it into a closed plastic container.

6.1.3 Place the container, several high range ammonia detector tubes, and the pump in the clean test pan and locate it near the test area entry door so that the suited individual has easy access to these supplies.

6.2.1 In a non-contaminated atmosphere, open a pre-sealed ammonia indicator strip and fasten one end of the strip to the inside of the suit face shield lens where it can be seen by the wearer. Moisten the indicator strip with distilled water. Care shall be taken not to contaminate the detector part of the indicator paper by touching it. A small piece of masking tape or equivalent should be used to attach the indicator strip to the interior of the suit face shield.

6.2.2 If problems are encountered with this method of attachment, the indicator strip can be attached to the outside of the respirator face piece lens being used during the test.

6.3 Don the respiratory protective device normally used with the suit, and then don the TECP suit to be tested. Check to be sure all openings which are intended to be sealed (zippers, gloves, etc.) are completely sealed. DO NOT, however, plug off any venting valves.

6.4 Step into the enclosed test room such as a closet, bathroom, or test booth, equipped with an exhaust fan. No air should be exhausted from the chamber during the test because this will dilute the ammonia challenge concentrations.

6.5 Open the container with the pre-measured volume of concentrated aqueous ammonia within the enclosed test room, and pour the liquid into the empty plastic test pan. Wait two minutes to allow for adequate volatilization of the concentrated aqueous ammonia. A small mixing fan can be used near the evaporation pan to increase the evaporation rate of the ammonia solution.

6.6 After two minutes a determination of the ammonia concentration within the chamber should be made using the high range colorimetric detector tube. A concentration of 1000 ppm ammonia or greater shall be generated before the exercises are started.

6.7 To test the integrity of the suit the following four minute exercise protocol should be followed:

6.7.1 Raising the arms above the head with at least 15 raising motions completed in one minute;

6.7.2 Walking in place for one minute with at least 15 raising motions of each leg in a one-minute period;

6.7.3 Touching the toes with a least 10 complete motions of the arms from above the head to touching of the toes in a one-minute period;

6.7.4 Knee bends with at least 10 complete standing and squatting motions in a one-minute period.

6.8 If at any time during the test the colorimetric indicating paper should change colors, the test should be stopped and section 6.10 and 6.12 initiated (See 4.2).

6.9 After completion of the test exercise, the test area concentration should be measured again using the high range colorimetric detector tube.

6.10 Exit the test area.

6.11 The opening created by the suit zipper or other appropriate suit penetration should be used to determine the ammonia concentration in the suit with the low range length of stain detector tube or other ammonia monitor. The internal TECP suit air should be sampled far enough from the enclosed test area to prevent a false ammonia reading.

6.12 After completion of the measurement of the suit interior ammonia concentration the test is concluded and the suit is doffed and the respirator removed.

6.13 The ventilating fan for the test room should be turned on and allowed to run for enough time to remove the ammonia gas. The fan shall be vented to the outside of the building.

6.14 Any detectable ammonia in the suit interior (five ppm ammonia (NH_3) or more for the length of stain detector tube) indicates that the suit has failed the test. When other ammonia detectors are used a lower level of detection is possible, and it should be specified as the pass/fail criteria.

6.15 By following this test method, an intrusion coefficient of approximately 200 or more can be measured with the suit in a completely operational condition. If the intrusion coefficient is 200 or more, then the suit is suitable for emergency response and field use.

7.0 Retest procedures

7.1 If the suit fails this test, check for leaks by following the pressure test in test A above.

7.2 Retest the TECP suit as outlined in the test procedure 6.0.

8.0 Report

8.1 Each gas tight totally-encapsulating chemical protective suit tested by this practice shall have the following information recorded.

8.1.1 Unique identification number, identifying brand name, date of purchase, material of construction, and unique suit features; e.g., special breathing apparatus.

8.1.2 General description of test room used for test.

8.1.3 Brand name and purchase date of ammonia detector strips and color change data.

8.1.4 Brand name, sampling range, and expiration date of the length of stain ammonia detector tubes. The brand name and model of the sampling pump should also be recorded. If another type of ammonia detector is used, it should be identified along with its minimum detection limit for ammonia.

8.1.5 Actual test results shall list the two test area concentrations, their average, the interior suit concentration, and the calculated intrusion coefficient. Retest data shall be recorded as an additional test.

8.2 The evaluation of the data shall be specified as "suit passed" or "suit failed," and the date of the test. Any detectable ammonia (five ppm or greater for the length of stain detector tube) in the suit interior indicates the suit has failed this test. When other ammonia detectors are used, a lower level of detection is possible and it should be specified as the pass fail criteria.

Caution: Visually inspect all parts of the suit to be sure they are positioned correctly and secured tightly before putting the suit back into service. Special care should be taken to examine each exhaust valve to make sure it is not blocked.

Care should also be exercised to assure that the inside and outside of the suit is completely dry before it is put into storage.

§1910.120 Appendix B
General description and discussion of the levels of protection and protective gear

This Appendix sets forth information about personal protective equipment (PPE) protection levels which may be used to assist employers in complying with the PPE requirements of this section.

As required by the standard, PPE must be selected which will protect employees from the specific hazards which they are likely to encounter during their work on-site.

Selection of the appropriate PPE is a complex process which should take into consideration a variety of factors. Key factors involved in this process are identification of the hazards, or suspected hazards; their routes of potential hazard to employees (inhalation, skin absorption, ingestion, and eye or skin contact); and the performance of the PPE materials (and seams) in providing a barrier to these hazards. The amount of protection provided by PPE is material-hazard specific. That is, protective equipment materials will protect well against some hazardous substances and poorly, or not at all, against others. In many instances, protective equipment materials cannot be found which will provide continuous protection from the particular hazardous substance. In these cases the breakthrough time of the protective material should exceed the work durations.

Other factors in this selection process to be considered are matching the PPE to the employee's work requirements and task-specific conditions. The durability of PPE materials, such as tear strength and seam strength, should be considered in relation to the employee's tasks. The effects of PPE in relation to heat stress and task duration are a factor in selecting and using PPE. In some cases layers of PPE may be necessary to provide sufficient protection, or to protect expensive PPE inner garments, suits or equipment.

The more that is known about the hazards at the site, the easier the job of PPE selection becomes. As more information about the hazards and conditions at the site becomes available, the site supervisor can make decisions to up-grade or down-grade the level of PPE protection to match the tasks at hand.

The following are guidelines which an employer can use to begin the selection of the appropriate PPE. As noted above, the site information may suggest the use of combinations of PPE selected from the different protection levels (i.e., A, B, C, or D) as being more suitable to the hazards of the work. It should be cautioned that the listing below does not fully address the performance of the specific PPE material in relation to the specific hazards at the job site, and that PPE selection, evaluation and re-selection is an ongoing process until sufficient information about the hazards and PPE performance is obtained.

Part A Personal protective equipment is divided into four categories based on the degree of protection afforded. (See part B of this Appendix for further explanation of Levels A, B, C, and D hazards.)

I. Level A —To be selected when the greatest level of skin, respiratory, and eye protection is required.

The following constitute Level A equipment; it may be used as appropriate;

1. Positive pressure, full face-piece self-contained breathing apparatus (SCBA), or positive pressure supplied air respirator with escape SCBA, approved by the National Institute for Occupational Safety and Health (NIOSH)
2. Totally-encapsulating chemical-protective suit
3. Coveralls[1]
4. Long underwear[1]
5. Gloves, outer, chemical-resistant
6. Gloves, inner, chemical-resistant
7. Boots, chemical-resistant, steel toe and shank
8. Hard hat (under suit)[1]
9. Disposable protective suit, gloves and boots (depending on suit construction, may be worn over totally-encapsulating suit)

II. Level B —The highest level of respiratory protection is necessary but a lesser level of skin protection is needed.

The following constitute Level B equipment; it may be used as appropriate.

1. Positive pressure, full-facepiece self-contained breathing apparatus (SCBA), or positive pressure supplied air respirator with escape SCBA (NIOSH approved).
2. Hooded chemical-esistant clothing (overalls and long-sleeved jacket; coveralls; one or two-piece chemical-splash suit; disposable chemical-resistant overalls)
3. Coveralls[1]
4. Gloves, outer, chemical-resistant
5. Gloves, inner, chemical-resistant
6. Boots, outer, chemical-resistant steel toe and shank
7. Boot-covers, outer, chemical-resistant (disposable)[1]
8. Hard hat[1]
9. [Reserved]
10. Face shield[1]

III. Level C —The concentration(s) and type(s) of airborne substance(s) is known and the criteria for using air purifying respirators are met.

The following constitute Level C equipment; it may be used as appropriate.

1. Full-face or half-mask, air purifying respirators (NIOSH approved)
2. Hooded chemical-resistant clothing (overalls; two-piece chemical-splash suit; disposable chemical-resistant overalls)
3. Coveralls[1]
4. Gloves, outer, chemical-resistant
5. Gloves, inner, chemical-resistant
6. Boots (outer), chemical-resistant steel toe and shank[1]
7. Boot-covers, outer, chemical-resistant (disposable)[1]
8. Hard hat[1]
9. Escape mask[1]
10. Face shield[1]

IV. Level D —A work uniform affording minimal protection, used for nuisance contamination only.

The following constitute Level D equipment; it may be used as appropriate:

1. Coveralls
2. Gloves[1]
3. Boots/shoes, chemical-resistant steel toe and shank
4. Boots, outer, chemical-resistant (disposable)[1]
5. Safety glasses or chemical splash goggles*
6. Hard hat[1]
7. Escape mask[1]
8. Face shield[1]

Part B. The types of hazards for which levels A, B, C, and D protection are appropriate are described below:

I. Level A —Level A protection should be used when:

1. The hazardous substance has been identified and requires the highest level of protection for skin, eyes, and the respiratory system based on either the measured (or potential for) high concentration of atmospheric vapors, gases, or particulates; or the site operations and work functions involve a high potential for splash, immersion, or exposure to unexpected vapors, gases, or particulates of materials that are harmful to skin or capable of being absorbed through the skin;
2. Substances with a high degree of hazard to the skin are known or suspected to be present, and skin contact is possible; or
3. Operations are being conducted in confined, poorly ventilated areas, and the absence of conditions requiring Level A have not yet been determined.

II. Level B —Level B protection should be used when:

1. The type and atmospheric concentration of substances have been identified and require a high level of respiratory protection, but less skin protection;
2. The atmosphere contains less than 19.5 percent oxygen; or
3. The presence of incompletely identified vapors or gases is indicated by a direct-reading organic vapor detection instrument, but vapors and gases are not suspected of containing high levels of chemicals harmful to skin or capable of being absorbed through the skin.

   Note: This involves atmospheres with IDLH concentrations of specific substances that present severe inhalation hazards and that do not represent a severe skin hazard; or that do not meet the criteria for use of air-purifying respirators.

III. Level C —Level C protection should be used when:

1. The atmospheric contaminants, liquid splashes, or other direct contact will not adversely affect or be absorbed through any exposed skin;
2. The types of air contaminants have been identified, concentrations measured, and an air-purifying respirator is available that can remove the contaminants; and
3. All criteria for the use of air-purifying respirators are met.

IV. Level D —Level D protection should be used when:

1. The atmosphere contains no known hazard; and
2. Work functions preclude splashes, immersion, or the potential for unexpected inhalation of or contact with hazardous levels of any chemicals.

   Note: As stated before, combinations of personal protective equipment other than those described for Levels A, B, C, and D protection may be more appropriate and may be used to provide the proper level of protection.

As an aid in selecting suitable chemical protective clothing, it should be noted that the National Fire Protection Association (NFPA) has developed standards on chemical protective clothing. The standards that have been adopted by include:

NFPA 1991—Standard on Vapor-Protective Suits for Hazardous Chemical Emergencies (EPA Level A Protective Clothing).

NFPA 1992—Standard on Liquid Splash-Protective Suits for Hazardous Chemical Emergencies (EPA Level B Protective Clothing).

NFPA 1993—Standard on Liquid Splash-Protective Suits for Non-emergency, Non-flammable Hazardous Chemical Situations (EPA Level B Protective Clothing).

These standards apply documentation and performance requirements to the manufacture of chemical protective suits. Chemical protective suits meeting these requirements are labelled as compliant with the appropriate standard. It is recommended that chemical protective suits that meet these standards be used.

§1910.120 Appendix C Compliance guidelines

1. Occupational Safety and Health Program Each hazardous waste site clean-up effort will require an occupational safety and health program headed by the site coordinator or the employer's representative. The purpose of the program will be the protection of employees at the site and will be an extension of the employer's overall safety and health program. The program will need to be developed before work begins on the site and implemented as work proceeds as stated in paragraph (b). The program is to facilitate coordination and communication of safety and health issues among personnel responsible for the various activities which will take place at the site. It will provide the overall means for planning and implementing the needed safety and health training and job orientation of employees who will be working

[1] Optional, as applicable.

at the site. The program will provide the means for identifying and controlling worksite hazards and the means for monitoring program effectiveness. The program will need to cover the responsibilities and authority of the site coordinator or the employer's manager on the site for the safety and health of employees at the site, and the relationships with contractors or support services as to what each employer's safety and health responsibilities are for their employees on the site. Each contractor on the site needs to have its own safety and health program so structured that it will smoothly interface with the program of the site coordinator or principal contractor.

Also those employers involved with treating, storing or disposal of hazardous waste as covered in paragraph (p) must have implemented a safety and health program for their employees. This program is to include the hazard communication program required in paragraph (p)(1) and the training required in paragraphs (p)(7) and (p)(8) as parts of the employers comprehensive overall safety and health program. This program is to be in writing.

Each site or workplace safety and health program will need to include the following: (1) Policy statements of the line of authority and accountability for implementing the program, the objectives of the program and the role of the site safety and health supervisor or manager and staff; (2) means or methods for the development of procedures for identifying and controlling workplace hazards at the site; (3) means or methods for the development and communication to employees of the various plans, work rules, standard operating procedures and practices that pertain to individual employees and supervisors; (4) means for the training of supervisors and employees to develop the needed skills and knowledge to perform their work in a safe and healthful manner; (5) means to anticipate and prepare for emergency situations; and (6) means for obtaining information feedback to aid in evaluating the program and for improving the effectiveness of the program. The management and employees should be trying continually to improve the effectiveness of the program thereby enhancing the protection being afforded those working on the site.

Accidents on the site or workplace should be investigated to provide information on how such occurrences can be avoided in the future. When injuries or illnesses occur on the site or workplace, they will need to be investigated to determine what needs to be done to prevent this incident from occurring again. Such information will need to be used as feedback on the effectiveness of the program and the information turned into positive steps to prevent any reoccurrence. Receipt of employee suggestions or complaints relating to safety and health issues involved with site or workplace activities is also a feedback mechanism that can be used effectively to improve the program and may serve in part as an evaluative tool(s).

For the development and implementation of the program to be the most effective, professional safety and health personnel should be used. Certified Safety Professionals, Board Certified Industrial Hygienists or Registered Professional Safety Engineers are good examples of professional stature for safety and health managers who will administer the employer's program.

2. Training The training programs for employees subject to the requirements of paragraph (e) of this standard should address: the safety and health hazards employees should expect to find on hazardous waste clean-up sites; what control measures or techniques are effective for those hazards; what monitoring procedures are effective in characterizing exposure levels; what makes an effective employer's safety and health program; what a site safety and health plan should include; hands on training with personal protective equipment and clothing they may be expected to use; the contents of the OSHA standard relevant to the employee's duties and function; and, employee's responsibilities under OSHA and other regulations. Supervisors will need training in their responsibilities under the safety and health program and its subject areas such as the spill containment program, the personal protective equipment program, the medical surveillance program, the emergency response plan and other areas.

The training programs for employees subject to the requirements of paragraph (p) of this standard should address: the employers safety and health program elements impacting employees; the hazard communication program; the medical surveillance program; the hazards and the controls for such hazards that employees need to know for their job duties and functions. All require annual refresher training.

The training programs for employees covered by the requirements of paragraph (q) of this standard should address those competencies required for the various levels of response such as: the hazards associated with hazardous substances; hazard identification and awareness; notification of appropriate persons; the need for and use of personal protective equipment including respirators; the decontamination procedures to be used; preplanning activities for hazardous substance incidents including the emergency response plan; company standard operating procedures for hazardous substance emergency responses; the use of the incident command system and other subjects. Hands-on training should be stressed whenever possible. Critiques done after an incident which include an evaluation of what worked and what did not and how could the incident be better handled the next time may be counted as training time.

For hazardous materials specialists (usually members of hazardous materials teams), the training should address the care, use and/or testing of chemical protective clothing including totally encapsulating suits, the medical surveillance program, the standard operating procedures for the hazardous materials team including the use of plugging and patching equipment and other subject areas.

Officers and leaders who may be expected to be in charge at an incident should be fully knowledgeable of their company's incident command system. They should know where and how to obtain additional assistance and be familiar with the local district's emergency response plan and the state emergency response plan.

Specialist employees such as technical experts, medical experts or environmental experts that work with hazardous materials in their regular jobs, who may be sent to the incident scene by the shipper, manufacturer or governmental agency to advise and assist the person in charge of the incident should have training on an annual basis. Their training should include the care and use of personal protective equipment including respirators; knowledge of the incident command system and how they are to relate to it; and those areas needed to keep them current in their respective field as it relates to safety and health involving specific hazardous substances.

Those skilled support personnel, such as employees who work for public works departments or equipment operators who operate bulldozers, sand trucks, backhoes, etc., who may be called to the incident scene to provide emergency support assistance, should have at least a safety and health briefing before entering the area of potential or actual exposure. These skilled support personnel, who have not been a part of the emergency response plan and do not meet the training requirements, should be made aware of the hazards they face and should be provided all necessary protective clothing and equipment required for their tasks.

There are two National Fire Protection Association standards, NFPA 472—"Standard for Professional Competence of Responders to Hazardous Material Incidents" and NFPA 471—"Recommended Practice for Responding to Hazardous Material Incidents", which are excellent resource documents to aid fire departments and other emergency response organizations in developing their training program materials. NFPA 472 provides guidance on the skills and knowledge needed for first responder awareness level, first responder operations level, hazmat technicians, and hazmat specialist. It also offers guidance for the officer corp who will be in charge of hazardous substance incidents.

3. Decontamination Decontamination procedures should be tailored to the specific hazards of the site, and may vary in complexity and number of steps, depending on the level of hazard and the employee's exposure to the hazard. Decontamination procedures and PPE decontamination methods will vary depending upon the specific substance, since one procedure or method may not work for all substances. Evaluation of decontamination methods and procedures should be performed, as necessary, to assure that employees are not exposed to hazards by re-using PPE. References in Appendix D may be used for guidance in establishing an effective decontamination program. In addition, the U.S. Coast Guard's Manual, "Policy Guidance for Response to Hazardous Chemical Releases," U.S. Department of Transportation, Washington, DC (COMDTINST M16465.30) is a good reference for establishing an effective decontamination program.

4. Emergency response plans States, along with designated districts within the states, will be developing or have developed local emergency response plans. These state and district plans should be utilized in the emergency response plans called for in the standard. Each employer should assure that its emergency response plan is compatible with the local plan. The major reference being used to aid in developing the state and local district plans is the Hazardous Materials Emergency Planning Guide, NRT–1. The current Emergency Response Guidebook from the U.S. Department of Transportation, CMA's CHEMTREC and the Fire Service Emergency Management Handbook may also be used as resources.

Employers involved with treatment, storage, and disposal facilities for hazardous waste, which have the required contingency plan called for by their permit, would not need to duplicate the same planning elements. Those items of the emergency response plan that are properly addressed in the contingency plan may be substituted into the emergency response plan required in §1910.120 or otherwise kept together for employer and employee use.

5. Personal protective equipment programs The purpose of personal protective clothing and equipment (PPE) is to shield or isolate individuals from the chemical, physical, and biologic hazards that may be encountered at a hazardous substance site.

As discussed in Appendix B, no single combination of protective equipment and clothing is capable of protecting against all hazards. Thus PPE should be used in conjunction with other protective methods and its effectiveness evaluated periodically.

The use of PPE can itself create significant worker hazards, such as heat stress, physical and psychological stress, and impaired vision, mobility, and communication. For any given situation, equipment and clothing should be selected that provide an adequate level of protection. However, over-protection, as well as under-protection, can be hazardous and should be avoided where possible.

Two basic objectives of any PPE program should be to protect the wearer from safety and health hazards, and to prevent injury to the wearer from incorrect use and/or malfunction of the PPE. To accomplish these goals, a comprehensive PPE program should include hazard identification, medical monitoring, environmental surveillance, selection, use, maintenance, and decontamination of PPE and its associated training.

The written PPE program should include policy statements, procedures, and guidelines. Copies should be made available to all employees, and a reference copy should be made available at the worksite. Technical data on equipment, maintenance manuals, relevant regulations, and other essential information should also be collected and maintained.

6. Incident command system (ICS) §1910.120(q)(3)(ii) requires the implementation of an ICS. The ICS is an organized approach to effectively control and manage operations at an emergency incident. The individual in charge of the ICS is the senior official responding to the incident. The ICS is not much different than the "command post" approach used for many years by the fire service. During large complex fires involving several companies and many pieces of apparatus, a command post would be established. This enabled one individual to be in charge of managing the incident, rather than having several officers from different companies making separate, and sometimes conflicting, decisions. The individual in charge of the command post would delegate responsibility for performing various tasks to subordinate officers. Additionally, all communications were routed through the command post to reduce the number of radio transmissions and eliminate confusion. However, strategy, tactics, and all decisions were made by one individual.

The ICS is a very similar system, except it is implemented for emergency response to all incidents, both large and small, that involve hazardous substances.

For a small incident, the individual in charge of the ICS may perform many tasks of the ICS. There may not be any, or little, delegation of tasks to subordinates. For example, in response to a small incident, the individual in charge of the ICS, in addition to normal command activities, may become the safety officer and may designate only one employee (with proper equipment) as a back-up to provide assistance if needed. OSHA does recommend, however, that at least two employees be designated as back-up personnel since the assistance needed may include rescue.

To illustrate the operation of the ICS, the following scenario might develop during a small incident, such as an overturned tank truck with a small leak of flammable liquid.

The first responding senior officer would implement and take command of the ICS. That person would size-up the incident and determine if additional personnel and apparatus were necessary; would determine what actions to take to control the leak; and, determine the proper level of personal protective equipment. If additional assistance is not needed, the individual in charge of the ICS would implement actions to stop and control the leak using the fewest number of personnel that can effectively accomplish the tasks. The individual in charge of the ICS then would designate himself as the safety officer and two other employees as a back-up in case rescue may become necessary. In this scenario, decontamination procedures would not be necessary.

A large complex incident may require many employees and difficult, time-consuming efforts to control. In these situations, the individual in charge of the ICS will want to delegate different tasks to subordinates in order to maintain a span of control that will keep the number of subordinates, that are reporting, to a manageable level.

Delegation of task at large incidents may be by location, where the incident scene is divided into sectors, and subordinate officers coordinate activities within the sector that they have been assigned.

Delegation of tasks can also be by function. Some of the functions that the individual in charge of the ICS may want to delegate at a large incident are: medical services; evacuation; water supply; resources (equipment, apparatus); media relations; safety; and, site control (integrate activities with police for crowd and traffic control). Also for a large incident, the individual in charge of the ICS will designate several employees as back-up personnel; and a number of safety officers to monitor conditions and recommend safety precautions.

Therefore, no matter what size or complexity an incident may be, by implementing an ICS there will be one individual in charge who makes the decisions and gives directions; and, all actions, and communications are coordinated through one central point of command. Such a system should reduce confusion, improve safety, organize and coordinate actions, and should facilitate effective management of the incident.

7. Site Safety and Control Plans The safety and security of response personnel and others in the area of an emergency response incident site should be of primary concern to the incident commander. The use of a site safety and control plan could greatly assist those in charge of assuring the safety and health of employees on the site.

A comprehensive site safety and control plan should include the following: summary analysis of hazards on the site and a risk analysis of those hazards; site map or sketch; site work zones (clean zone, transition or decontamination zone, work or hot zone); use of the buddy system; site communications; command post or command center; standard operating procedures and safe work practices; medical assistance and triage area; hazard monitoring plan (air contaminate monitoring, etc.); decontamination procedures and area; and other relevant areas. This plan should be a part of the employer's emergency response plan or an extension of it to the specific site.

8. Medical surveillance programs Workers handling hazardous substances may be exposed to toxic chemicals, safety hazards, biologic hazards, and radiation. Therefore, a medical surveillance program is essential to assess and monitor workers' health and fitness for employment in hazardous waste operations and during the course of work; to provide emergency and other treatment as needed; and to keep accurate records for future reference.

The Occupational Safety and Health Guidance Manual for Hazardous Waste Site Activities developed by the National Institute for Occupational Safety and Health (NIOSH), the Occupational Safety and Health Administration (OSHA), the U.S. Coast Guard (USCG), and the Environmental Protection Agency (EPA); October 1985 provides an excellent example of the types of medical testing that should be done as part of a medical surveillance program.

9. New Technology and Spill Containment Programs Where hazardous substances may be released by spilling from a container that will expose employees to the hazards of the materials, the employer will need to implement a program to contain and control the spilled material. Diking and ditching, as well as use of absorbents like diatomaceous earth, are traditional techniques which have proven to be effective over the years. However, in recent years new products have come into the marketplace, the use of which complement and increase the effectiveness of these traditional methods. These new products also provide emergency responders and others with additional tools or agents to use to reduce the hazards of spilled materials.

These agents can be rapidly applied over a large area and can be uniformly applied or otherwise can be used to build a small dam, thus improving the workers' ability to control spilled material. These application techniques enhance the intimate contact between the agent and the spilled material allowing for the quickest effect by the agent or quickest control of the spilled material. Agents are available to solidify liquid spilled materials, to suppress vapor generation from spilled materials, and to do both. Some special agents, which when applied as recommended by the manufacturer, will react in a controlled manner with the spilled material to neutralize acids or caustics, or greatly reduce the level of hazard of the spilled material.

There are several modern methods and devices for use by emergency response personnel or others involved with spill control efforts to safely apply spill control agents to control spilled material hazards. These include portable pressurized applicators similar to hand-held portable fire extinguishing devices, and nozzle and hose systems similar to portable fire fighting foam systems which allow the operator to apply the agent without having to come into contact with the spilled material. The operator is able to apply the agent to the spilled material from a remote position.

The solidification of liquids provides for rapid containment and isolation of hazardous substance spills. By directing the agent at run-off points or at the edges of the spill, the reactant solid will automatically create a barrier to slow or stop the spread of the material. Clean-up of hazardous substances is greatly improved when solidifying agents, acid or caustic neutralizers, or activated carbon adsorbents are used. Properly applied, these agents can totally solidify liquid hazardous substances or neutralize or absorb them, which results in materials which are less hazardous and easier to handle, transport, and dispose of. The concept of spill treatment, to create less hazardous substances, will improve the safety and level of protection of employees working at spill clean-up operations or emergency response operations to spills of hazardous substances.

The use of vapor suppression agents for volatile hazardous substances, such as flammable liquids and those substances which present an inhalation hazard, is important for protecting workers. The rapid and uniform distribution of the agent over the surface of the spilled material can provide quick vapor knockdown. There are temporary and long-term foam-type agents which are effective on vapors and dusts, and activated carbon adsorption agents which are effective for vapor control and soaking-up of the liquid. The proper use of hose lines or hand-held portable pressurized applicators provides good mobility and permits the worker to deliver the agent from a safe distance without having to step into the untreated spilled material. Some of these systems can be recharged in the field to provide coverage of larger spill areas than the design limits of a single charged applicator unit. Some of the more effective agents can solidify the liquid flammable hazardous substances and at the same time elevate the flashpoint above 140 °F so the resulting substance may be handled as a nonhazardous waste material if it meets the U.S. Environmental Protection Agency's 40 CFR part 261 requirements (see particularly §261.21).

All workers performing hazardous substance spill control work are expected to wear the proper protective clothing and equipment for the materials present and to follow the employer's established standard operating procedures for spill control. All involved workers need to be trained in the established operating procedures; in the use and care of spill control equipment; and in the associated hazards and control of such hazards of spill containment work.

These new tools and agents are the things that employers will want to evaluate as part of their new technology program. The treatment of spills of hazardous substances or wastes at an emergency incident as part of the immediate spill containment and control efforts is sometimes acceptable to EPA and a permit exception is described in 40 CFR 264.1(g)(8) and 265.1(c)(11).

§1910.120 Appendix D References

The following references may be consulted for further information on the subject of this standard:

1. OSHA Instruction DFO CPL 2.70—January 29, 1986, Special Emphasis Program: Hazardous Waste Sites.
2. OSHA Instruction DFO CPL 2–2.37A—January 29, 1986, Technical Assistance and Guidelines for Superfund and Other Hazardous Waste Site Activities.
3. OSHA Instruction DTS CPL 2.74—January 29, 1986, Hazardous Waste Activity Form, OSHA 175.
4. Hazardous Waste Inspections Reference Manual, U.S. Department of Labor, Occupational Safety and Health Administration, 1986.
5. Memorandum of Understanding Among the National Institute for Occupational Safety and Health, the Occupational Safety and Health Administration, the United States Coast Guard, and the United States Environmental Protection Agency, Guidance for Worker Protection During Hazardous Waste Site Investigations and Clean-up and Hazardous Substance Emergencies. December 18, 1980.
6. National Priorities List, 1st Edition, October 1984; U.S. Environmental Protection Agency, Revised periodically.
7. The Decontamination of Response Personnel, Field Standard Operating Procedures (F.S.O.P.) 7; U.S. Environmental Protection Agency, Office of Emergency and Remedial Response, Hazardous Response Support Division, December 1984.
8. Preparation of a Site Safety Plan, Field Standard Operating Procedures (F.S.O.P.) 9; U.S. Environmental Protection Agency, Office of Emergency and Remedial Response, Hazardous Response Support Division, April 1985.
9. Standard Operating Safety Guidelines; U.S. Environmental Protection Agency, Office of Emergency and Remedial Response, Hazardous Response Support Division, Environmental Response Team; November 1984.
10. Occupational Safety and Health Guidance Manual for Hazardous Waste Site Activities, National Institute for Occupational Safety and Health (NIOSH), Occupational Safety and Health Administration (OSHA), U.S. Coast Guard (USCG), and Environmental Protection Agency (EPA); October 1985.
11. Protecting Health and Safety at Hazardous Waste Sites: An Overview, U.S. Environmental Protection Agency, EPA/625/9–85/006; September 1985.
12. Hazardous Waste Sites and Hazardous Substance Emergencies, NIOSH Worker Bulletin, U.S. Department of Health and Human Services, Public Health Service, Centers for Disease Control, National Institute for Occupational Safety and Health; December 1982.
13. Personal Protective Equipment for Hazardous Materials Incidents: A Selection Guide; U.S. Department of Health and Human Services, Public Health Service, Centers for Disease Control, National Institute for Occupational Safety and Health; October 1984.
14. Fire Service Emergency Management Handbook, International Association of Fire Chiefs Foundation, 101 East Holly Avenue, Unit 10B, Sterling, VA 22170, January 1985.
15. Emergency Response Guidebook, U.S Department of Transportation, Washington, DC, 1987.
16. Report to the Congress on Hazardous Materials Training, Planning and Preparedness, Federal Emergency Management Agency, Washington, DC, July 1986.
17. Workbook for Fire Command, Alan V. Brunacini and J. David Beageron, National Fire Protection Association, Batterymarch Park, Quincy, MA 02269, 1985.
18. Fire Command, Alan V. Brunacini, National Fire Protection Association, Batterymarch Park,, Quincy, MA 02269, 1985.
19. Incident Command System, Fire Protection Publications, Oklahoma State University, Stillwater, OK 74078, 1983.
20. Site Emergency Response Planning, Chemical Manufacturers Association, Washington, DC 20037, 1986.
21. Hazardous Materials Emergency Planning Guide, NRT–1, Environmental Protection Agency, Washington, DC, March 1987.
22. Community Teamwork: Working Together to Promote Hazardous Materials Transportation Safety. U.S. Department of Transportation, Washington, DC, May 1983.
23. Disaster Planning Guide for Business and Industry, Federal Emergency Management Agency, Publication No. FEMA 141, August 1987.

(The Office of Management and Budget has approved the information collection requirements in this section under control number 1218–0139)

§1910.120 Appendix E Training curriculum guidelines

The following non-mandatory general criteria may be used for assistance in developing site-specific training curriculum used to meet the training requirements of 29 CFR §1910.120(e); 29 CFR §1910.120(p)(7), (p)(8)(iii); and 29 CFR §1910.120(q)(6), (q)(7), and (q)(8). These are generic guidelines and they are not presented as a complete training curriculum for any specific employer. Site-specific training programs must be developed on the basis of a needs assessment of the hazardous waste site, RCRA/TSDF, or emergency response operation in accordance with 29 CFR §1910.120.

It is noted that the legal requirements are set forth in the regulatory text of §1910.120. The guidance set forth here presents a highly effective program that in the areas covered would meet or exceed the regulatory requirements. In addition, other approaches could meet the regulatory requirements.

Suggested General Criteria

Definitions:

"**Competent**" means possessing the skills, knowledge, experience, and judgment to perform assigned tasks or activities satisfactorily as determined by the employer.

"**Demonstration**" means the showing by actual use of equipment or procedures.

"**Hands-on training**" means training in a simulated work environment that permits each student to have experience performing tasks, making decisions, or using equipment appropriate to the job assignment for which the training is being conducted.

"**Initial training**" means training required prior to beginning work.

"**Lecture**" means an interactive discourse with a class lead by an instructor.

"**Proficient**" means meeting a stated level of achievement.

"**Site-specific**" means individual training directed to the operations of a specific job site.

"**Training hours**" means the number of hours devoted to lecture, learning activities, small group work sessions, demonstration, evaluations, or hands-on experience.

Suggested core criteria:

1. **Training facility** The training facility should have available sufficient resources, equipment, and site locations to perform didactic and hands-on training when appropriate. Training facilities should have sufficient organization, support staff, and services to conduct training in each of the courses offered.
2. **Training Director** Each training program should be under the direction of a training director who is responsible for the program. The Training Director should have a minimum of two years of employee education experience.
3. **Instructors** Instructors should be deem competent on the basis of previous documented experience in their area of instruction, successful completion of a "train-the-trainer" program specific to the topics they will teach, and an evaluation of instructional competence by the Training Director.

   Instructors should be required to maintain professional competency by participating in continuing education or professional development programs or by completing successfully an annual refresher course and having an annual review by the Training Director.

   The annual review by the Training Director should include observation of an instructor's delivery, a review of those observations with the trainer, and an analysis of any instructor or class evaluations completed by the students during the previous year.
4. **Course materials** The Training Director should approve all course materials to be used by the training provider. Course materials should be reviewed and updated at least annually. Materials and equipment should be in good working order and maintained properly.

   All written and audio-visual materials in training curricula should be peer reviewed by technically competent outside reviewers or by a standing advisory committee.

   Reviews should possess expertise in the following disciplines were applicable: occupational health, industrial hygiene and safety, chemical/environmental engineering, employee education, or emergency response. One or more of the peer reviewers should be an employee experienced in the work activities to which the training is directed.
5. **Students** The program for accepting students should include:
   a. Assurance that the student is or will be involved in work where chemical exposures are likely and that the student possesses the skills necessary to perform the work.
   b. A policy on the necessary medical clearance.

6. **Ratios** Student-instructor ratios should not exceed 30 students per instructor. Hands-on activity requiring the use of personal protective equipment should have the following student-instructor ratios. For Level C or Level D personal protective equipment the ratio should be 10 students per instructor. For Level A or Level B personal protective equipment the ratio should be 5 students per instructor.
7. **Proficiency assessment** Proficiency should be evaluated and documented by the use of a written assessment and a skill demonstration selected and developed by the Training Director and training staff. The assessment and demonstration should evaluate the knowledge and individual skills developed in the course of training. The level of minimum achievement necessary for proficiency shall be specified in writing by the Training Director.

   If a written test is used, there should be a minimum of 50 questions. If a written test is used in combination with a skills demonstration, a minimum of 25 questions should be used. If a skills demonstration is used, the tasks chosen and the means to rate successful completion should be fully documented by the Training Director.

   The content of the written test or of the skill demonstration shall be relevant to the objectives of the course. The written test and skill demonstration should be updated as necessary to reflect changes in the curriculum and any update should be approved by the Training Director.

   The proficiency assessment methods, regardless of the approach or combination of approaches used, should be justified, documented and approved by the Training Director.

   The proficiency of those taking the additional courses for supervisors should be evaluated and documented by using proficiency assessment methods acceptable to the Training Director. These proficiency assessment methods must reflect the additional responsibilities borne by supervisory personnel in hazardous waste operations or emergency response.
8. **Course certificate** Written documentation should be provided to each student who satisfactorily completes the training course. The documentation should include:
   a. Student's name;
   b. Course title;
   c. Course date;
   d. Statement that the student has successfully completed the course;
   e. Name and address of the training provider;
   f. An individual identification number for the certificate; and
   g. List of the levels of personal protective equipment used by the student to complete the course

   This documentation may include a certificate and an appropriate wallet-sized laminated card with a photograph of the student and the above information. When such course certificate cards are used, the individual identification number for the training certificate should be shown on the card.
9. **Recordkeeping** Training providers should maintain records listing the dates courses were presented, the names of the individual course attenders, the names of those students successfully completing each course, and the number of training certificates issued to each successful student. These records should be maintained for a minimum of five years after the date an individual participated in a training program offered by the training provider. These records should be available and provided upon the student's request or as mandated by law.
10. **Program quality control** The Training Director should conduct or direct an annual written audit of the training program. Program modifications to address deficiencies, if any, should be documented, approved, and implemented by the training provider. The audit and the program modification documents should be maintained at the training facility.

Suggested Program Quality Control Criteria

Factors listed here are suggested criteria for determining the quality and appropriateness of employee health and safety training for hazardous waste operations and emergency response.

A. Training Plan

Adequacy and appropriateness of the training program's curriculum development, instructor training, distribution of course materials, and direct student training should be considered, including

1. The duration of training, course content, and course schedules/ agendas;
2. The different training requirements of the various target populations, as specified in the appropriate generic training curriculum;
3. The process for the development of curriculum, which includes appropriate technical input, outside review, evaluation, program pretesting.
4. The adequate and appropriate inclusion of hands-on, demonstration, and instruction methods; and
5. Adequate monitoring of student safety, progress, and performance during the training.

B. Program management, Training Director, staff, and consultants.

Adequacy and appropriateness of staff performance and delivering an effective training program should be considered, including:

1. Demonstration of the training director's leadership in assuring quality of health and safety training;
2. Demonstration of the competency of the staff to meet the demands of delivering high quality hazardous waste employee health and safety training;
3. Organization charts establishing clear lines of authority;
4. Clearly defined staff duties including the relationship of the training staff to the overall program;
5. Evidence that the training organizational structure suits the needs of the training program;
6. Appropriateness and adequacy of the training methods used by the instructors;
7. Sufficiency of the time committed by the training director and staff to the training program;
8. Adequacy of the ratio of training staff to students;
9. Availability and commitment of the training program of adequate human and equipment resources in the areas of:
   a. Health effects;
   b. Safety;
   c. Personal protective equipment (PPE);
   d. Operational procedures; and
   e. Employee protection practices/procedures.
10. Appropriateness of management controls;
11. Adequacy of the organization and appropriate resources assigned to assure appropriate training;
12. In the case of multiple-site training programs, adequacy of satellite centers management.

C. Training facilities and resources.

Adequacy and appropriateness of the facilities and resources for supporting the training program should be considered, including:

1. Space and equipment to conduct the training;
2. Facilities for representative hands-on training;
3. In the case of multiple-site programs, equipment and facilities at the satellite centers;
4. Adequacy and appropriateness of the quality control and evaluations program to account for instructor performance;
5. Adequacy and appropriateness of the quality control and evaluation program to ensure appropriate course evaluation, feedback, updating, and corrective action;
6. Adequacy and appropriateness of disciplines and expertise being used within the quality control and evaluation program;
7. Adequacy and appropriateness of the role of student evaluations to provide feedback for training program improvement.

D. Quality control and evaluation.

Adequacy and appropriateness of quality control and evaluation plans for training programs should be considered, including:

1. A balanced advisory committee and/or competent outside reviewers to give overall policy guidance;
2. Clear and adequate definition of the composition and active programmatic role of the advisory committee or outside reviewers;
3. Adequacy of the minutes or reports of the advisory committee or outside reviewers' meetings or written communication;
4. Adequacy and appropriateness of the quality control and evaluations program to account for instructor performance;
5. Adequacy and appropriateness of the quality control and evaluation program to ensure appropriate course evaluation, feedback, updating, and corrective action;
6. Adequacy and appropriateness of disciplines and expertise being used within the quality control and evaluation program;
7. Adequacy and appropriateness of the role of student evaluations to provide feedback for training program improvement.

E. Students.

Adequacy and appropriateness of the program for accepting students should be considered, including:

1. Assurance that the student already possess the necessary skills for their job, including necessary documentation;
2. Appropriateness of methods the program uses to ensure that recruits are capable of satisfactorily completing training;
3. Review and compliance with any medical clearance policy.

F. Institutional Environment and Administrative Support.

The adequacy and appropriateness of the institutional environment and administrative support system for the training program should be considered, including:

1. Adequacy of the institutional commitment to the employee training program;

2. Adequacy and appropriateness of the administrative structure and administrative support.

G. Summary of Evaluation Questions.

Key questions for evaluating the quality and appropriateness of an overall training program should include the following:

1. Are the program objectives clearly stated?
2. Is the program accomplishing its objectives?
3. Are appropriate facilities and staff available?
4. Is there an appropriate mix of classroom, demonstration, and hands-on training?
5. Is the program providing quality employee health and safety training that fully meets the intent of regulatory requirements?
6. What are the program's main strengths?
7. What are the program's main weaknesses?
8. What is recommended to improve the program?
9. Are instructors instructing according to their training outlines?
10. Is the evaluation tool current and appropriate for the program content?
11. Is the course material current and relevant to the target group?

Suggested Training Curriculum Guidelines

The following training curriculum guidelines are for those operations specifically identified in 29 CFR §1910.120 as requiring training. Issues such as qualifications of instructors, training certification, and similar criteria appropriate to all categories of operations addressed in §1910.120 have been covered in the preceding section and are not re-addressed in each of the generic guidelines. Basic core requirements for training programs that are addressed include:

1. **General Hazardous Waste Operations;**
2. **RCRA operations—Treatment, storage, and disposal facilities;**
3. **Emergency Response.**

A. General Hazardous Waste Operations and Site-specific Training

1. **Off-site training** Training course content for hazardous waste operations, required by 29 CFR §1910.120(e), should include the following topics or procedures:

a. Regulatory knowledge:

(1) A review of 29 CFR §1910.120 and the core elements of an occupational safety and health program;
(2) The content of a medical surveillance program as outlined in 29 CFR §1910.120(f);
(3) The content of an effective site safety and health plan consistent with the requirements of 29 CFR §1910.120(b)(4)(ii);
(4) Emergency response plan and procedures as outlined in 29 CFR §1910.38 and 29 CFR §1910.120(l);
(5) Adequate illumination;
(6) Sanitation recommendation and equipment;
(7) Review and explanation of OSHA's hazard-communication standard (29 CFR §1910.1200) and lock-out-tag-out standard (29 CFR §1910.147);
(8) Review of other applicable standards including but not limited to those in the construction standards (29 CFR §1926);
(9) Rights and responsibilities of employers and employees under applicable OSHA and EPA laws;

b. Technical knowledge

(1) Type of potential exposures to chemical, biological, and radiological hazards; types of human responses to these hazards and recognition of those responses; principles of toxicology and information about acute and chronic hazards; health and safety considerations of new technology;
(2) Fundamentals of chemical hazards including but not limited to vapor pressure, boiling points, flash points, ph, other physical and chemical properties;
(3) Fire and explosion hazards of chemicals;
(4) General safety hazards such as but not limited to electrical hazards, powered equipment hazards, motor vehicle hazards, walking-working surface hazards, excavation hazards, and hazards associated with working in hot and cold temperature extremes;
(5) Review and knowledge of confined space entry procedures in 29 CFR §1910.146;
(6) Work practices to minimize employee risk from site hazards;
(7) Safe use of engineering controls, equipment, and any new relevant safety technology or safety procedures;
(8) Review and demonstration of competency with air sampling and monitoring equipment that may be used in a site monitoring program;
(9) Container sampling procedures and safeguarding; general drum and container handling procedures including special requirement for laboratory waste packs, shock-sensitive wastes, and radioactive wastes;
(10) The elements of a spill control program;
(11) Proper use and limitations of material handling equipment;
(12) Procedures for safe and healthful preparation of containers for shipping and transport;
(13) Methods of communication including those used while wearing respiratory protection.

c. Technical skills

(1) Selection, use maintenance, and limitations of personal protective equipment including the components and procedures for carrying out a respirator program to comply with 29 CFR §1910.134;
(2) Instruction in decontamination programs including personnel, equipment, and hardware; hands-on training including level A, B, and C ensembles and appropriate decontamination lines; field activities including the donning and doffing of protective equipment to a level commensurate with the employee's anticipated job function and responsibility and to the degree required by potential hazards;
(3) Sources for additional hazard information; exercises using relevant manuals and hazard coding systems.

d. Additional suggested items

(1) A laminated, dated card or certificate with photo, denoting limitations and level of protection for which the employee is trained should be issued to those students successfully completing a course;
(2) Attendance should be required at all training modules, with successful completion of exercises and a final written or oral examination with at least 50 questions;
(3) A minimum of one-third of the program should be devoted to hands-on exercises;
(4) A curriculum should be established for the 8-hour refresher training required by 29 CFR §1910.120(e)(8), with delivery of such courses directed toward those areas of previous training that need improvement or reemphasis;
(5) A curriculum should be established for the required 8-hour training for supervisors. Demonstrated competency in the skills and knowledge provided in a 40-hour course should be a prerequisite for supervisor training.

2. **Refresher training**

The 8-hour annual refresher training required in 29 CFR §1910.120(e)(8) should be conducted by qualified training providers. Refresher training should include at a minimum the following topics and procedures:

(a) Review of and retraining on relevant topics covered in the 40-hour program, as appropriate, using reports by the students on their work experiences;
(b) Update on developments with respect to material covered in the 40-hour course;
(c) Review of changes to pertinent provisions of EPA or OSHA standards or laws;
(d) Introduction of additional subject areas as appropriate;
(e) Hands-on review of new or altered PPE or decontamination equipment or procedures. Review of new developments in personal protective equipment;
(f) Review of newly developed air and contaminant monitoring equipment.

3. **On-site training**

a. The employer should provide employees engaged in hazardous waste site activities with information and training prior to initial assignment into their work area, as follows:

(1) The requirements of the hazard communication program including the location and availability of the written program, required lists of hazardous chemicals, and safety data sheets;
(2) Activities and locations in their work area where hazardous substance may be present;
(3) Methods and observations that may be used to detect the present or release of a hazardous chemical in the work area (such as monitoring conducted by the employer, continuous monitoring devices, visual appearances, or other evidence (sight, sound or smell) of hazardous chemicals being released, and applicable alarms from monitoring devices that record chemical releases;
(4) The physical and health hazards of substances known or potentially present in the work area;
(5) The measures employees can take to help protect themselves from work-site hazards, including specific procedures the employer has implemented;
(6) An explanation of the labeling system and safety data sheets and how employees can obtain and use appropriate hazard information;
(7) The elements of the confined space program including special PPE, permits, monitoring requirements, communication procedures, emergency response, and applicable lock-out procedures.

b. The employer should provide hazardous waste employees information and training and should provide a review and access to the site safety and plan as follows:

(1) Names of personnel and alternate responsible for site safety and health;
(2) Safety and health hazards present on the site;
(3) Selection, use, maintenance, and limitations of personal protective equipment specific to the site;
(4) Work practices by which the employee can minimize risks from hazards;
(5) Safe use of engineering controls and equipment available on site;
(6) Safe decontamination procedures established to minimize employee contact with hazardous substances, including:
(A) Employee decontamination;
(B) Clothing decontamination; and
(C) Equipment decontamination.
(7) Elements of the site emergency response plan, including:
(A) Pre-emergency planning;
(B) Personnel roles and lines of authority and communication;
(C) Emergency recognition and prevention;
(D) Safe distances and places of refuge;
(E) Site security and control;
(F) Evacuation routes and procedures;
(G) Decontamination procedures not covered by the site safety and health plan;
(H) Emergency medical treatment and first aid; and
(I) Emergency equipment and procedures for handling emergency incidents.

c. The employer should provide hazardous waste employees information and training on personal protective equipment used at the site, such as the following:
(1) PPE to be used based upon known or anticipated site hazards;
(2) PPE limitations of materials and construction; limitations during temperature extremes, heat stress, and other appropriate medical considerations; use and limitations of respirator equipment as well as documentation procedures as outlined in 29 CFR §1910.134;
(3) PPE inspection procedures prior to, during, and after use;
(4) PPE donning and doffing procedures;
(5) PPE decontamination and disposal procedures;
(6) PPE maintenance and storage;
(7) Task duration as related to PPE limitations.

d. The employer should instruct the employee about the site medical surveillance program relative to the particular site, including:
(1) Specific medical surveillance programs that have been adapted for the site;
(2) Specific signs and symptoms related to exposure to hazardous materials on the site;
(3) The frequency and extent of periodic medical examinations that will be used on the site;
(4) Maintenance and availability of records;
(5) Personnel to be contacted and procedures to be followed when signs and symptoms of exposures are recognized;

e. The employees will review and discuss the site safety plan as part of the training program. The location of the site safety plan and all written programs should be discussed with employees including a discussion of the mechanisms for access, review, and references described.

B. RCRA Operations Training for Treatment, Storage and Disposal Facilities.

1. As a minimum, the training course required in 29 CFR §1910.120 (p) should include the following topics:
(a) Review of the applicable paragraphs of 29 CFR §1910.120 and the elements of the employer's occupational safety and health plan;
(b) Review of relevant hazards such as, but not limited to, chemical, biological, and radiological exposures; fire and explosion hazards; thermal extremes; and physical hazards
(c) General safety hazards including those associated with electrical hazards, powered equipment hazards, lock-out-tag-out procedures, motor vehicle hazards and walking-working surface hazards;
(d) Confined-space hazards and procedures;
(e) Work practices to minimize employee risk from workplace hazards;
(f) Emergency response plan and procedures including first aid meeting the requirements of paragraph (p)(8);
(g) A review of procedures to minimize exposure to hazardous waste and various type of waste streams, including the materials handling program and spill containment program;
(h) A review of hazard communication programs meeting the requirements of 29 CFR §1910.1200;
(i) A review of medical surveillance programs meeting the requirements of 29 CFR §1910.120(p)(3) including the recognition of signs and symptoms of overexposure to hazardous substance including known synergistic interactions;
(j) A review of decontamination programs and procedures meeting the requirements of 29 CFR §1910.120(p)(4);
(k) A review of an employer's requirements to implement a training program and its elements;
(l) A review of the criteria and programs for proper selection and use of personal protective equipment, including respirators;
(m) A review of the applicable appendices to 29 CFR §1910.120;
(n) Principles of toxicology and biological monitoring as they pertain to occupational health;
(o) Rights and responsibilities of employees and employers under applicable OSHA and EPA laws;
(p) Hands-on exercises and demonstrations of competency with equipment to illustrate the basic equipment principles that may be used during the performance of work duties, including the donning and doffing of PPE;
(q) Sources of reference, efficient use of relevant manuals, and knowledge of hazard coding systems to include information contained in hazardous waste manifests;
(r) At least 8 hours of hands-on training; and
(s) Training in the job skills required for an employee's job function and responsibility before they are permitted to participate in or supervise field activities.

2. The individual employer should provide hazardous waste employees with information and training prior to an employee's initial assignment into a work area. The training and information should cover the following topics:
(a) The Emergency response plan and procedures including first aid;
(b) A review of the employer's hazardous waste handling procedures including the materials handling program and elements of the spill containment program, location of spill response kits or equipment, and the names of those trained to respond to releases;
(c) The hazardous communication program meeting the requirements of 29 CFR §1910.1200;
(d) A review of the employer's medical surveillance program including the recognition of signs and symptoms of exposure to relevant hazardous substance including known synergistic interactions;
(e) A review of the employer's decontamination program and procedures;
(f) A review of the employer's training program and the parties responsible for that program;
(g) A review of the employer's personal protective equipment program including the proper selection and use of PPE based upon specific site hazards;
(h) All relevant site-specific procedures addressing potential safety and health hazards. This may include, as appropriate, biological and radiological exposures, fire and explosion hazards, thermal hazards, and physical hazards such as electrical hazards, powered equipment hazards, lock-out-tag-out hazards, motor vehicle hazards, and walking-working surface hazards.
(i) Safe use engineering controls and equipment on site; and
(j) Names of personnel and alternates responsible for safety and health.

C. Emergency response training.

Federal OSHA standards in 29 CFR §1910.120(q) are directed toward private sector emergency responders. Therefore, the guidelines provided in this portion of the Appendix are directed toward that employee population. However, they also impact indirectly through State OSHA or USEPA regulations some public sector emergency responders. Therefore, the guidelines provided in this portion of the Appendix may be applied to both employee populations.

States with OSHA state plans must cover their employees with regulations at least as effective as the Federal OSHA standards. Public employees in states without approved state OSHA programs covering hazardous waste operations and emergency response are covered by the U.S. EPA under 40 CFR 311, a regulation virtually identical to §1910.120.

Since this is a non-mandatory Appendix and therefore not an enforceable standard, OSHA recommends that those employers, employees or volunteers in public sector emergency response organizations outside Federal OSHA jurisdiction consider the following criteria in developing their own training programs. A unified approach to training at the community level between emergency response organizations covered by Federal OSHA and those not covered directly by Federal OSHA can help ensure an effective community response to the release or potential release of hazardous substances in the community.

a. General considerations.

Emergency response organizations are required to consider the topics listed in §1910.120(q)(6). Emergency response organizations may use some or all of the following topics to supplement those mandatory topics when developing their response training programs. Many of the topics would require an interaction between the response provider and the individuals responsible for the site where the response would be expected.

(1) Hazard recognition, including:
  (A) Nature of hazardous substances present,
  (B) Practical applications of hazard recognition, including presentations on biology, chemistry, and physics.
(2) Principles of toxicology, biological monitoring, and risk assessment;
(3) Safe work practices and general site safety;
(4) Engineering controls and hazardous waste operations;
(5) Site safety plans and standard operating procedures;
(6) Decontamination procedures and practices;
(7) Emergency procedures, first aid, and self-rescue;
(8) Safe use of field equipment;
(9) Storage, handling, use and transportation of hazardous substances;
(10) Use, care, and limitations of personal protective equipment;
(11) Safe sampling techniques;
(12) Rights and responsibilities of employees under OSHA and other related laws concerning right-to-know, safety and health, compensations and liability;
(13) Medical monitoring requirements;
(14) Community relations.

b. Suggested criteria for specific courses.

(1) First responder awareness level
  (A) Review of and demonstration of competency in performing the applicable skills of 29 CFR §1910.120(q);
  (B) Hands-on experience with the U.S. Department of Transportation's Emergency Response Guidebook (ERG) and familiarization with OSHA standard 29 CFR §1910.1201;
  (C) Review of the principles and practices for analyzing an incident to determine both the hazardous substances present and the basic hazard and response information for each hazardous substance present;
  (D) Review of procedures for implementing actions consistent with the local emergency response plan, the organization's standard operating procedures, and the current edition of DOT's ERG including emergency notification procedures and follow-up communications;
  (E) Review of the expected hazards including fire and explosions hazards, confined space hazards, electrical hazards, powered equipment hazards, motor vehicle hazards, and walking-working surface hazards;
  (F) Awareness and knowledge of the competencies for the First Responder at the Awareness Level covered in the National Fire Protection Association's Standard No. 472, Professional Competence of Responders to Hazardous Materials Incidents.

(2) First responder operations level
  (A) Review of and demonstration of competency in performing the applicable skills of 29 CFR §1910.120(q);
  (B) Hands-on experience with the U.S. Department of Transportation's Emergency Response Guidebook (ERG), manufacturer safety data sheets, CHEMTREC/CANUTEC, shipper or manufacturer contacts, and other relevant sources of information addressing hazardous substance releases. Familiarization with OSHA standard 29 CFR §1910.1201;
  (C) Review of the principles and practices for analyzing an incident to determine the hazardous substances present, the likely behavior of the hazardous substance and its container, the types of hazardous substance transportation containers and vehicles, the types and selection of the appropriate defensive strategy for containing the release;
  (D) Review of procedures for implementing continuing response actions consistent with the local emergency response plan, the organization's standard operating procedures, and the current edition of DOT's ERG including extended emergency notification procedures and follow-up communications;
  (E) Review of the principles and practice for proper selection and use of personal protective equipment;
  (F) Review of the principles and practice of personnel and equipment decontamination;
  (G) Review of the expected hazards including fire and explosions hazards, confined space hazards, electrical hazards, powered equipment hazards, motor vehicle hazards, and walking-working surface hazards;
  (H) Awareness and knowledge of the competencies for the First Responder at the Operations Level covered in the National Fire Protection Association's Standard No. 472, Professional Competence of Responders to Hazardous Materials Incidents.

(3) Hazardous materials technician
  (A) Review of and demonstration of competency in performing the applicable skills of 29 CFR §1910.120(q);
  (B) Hands-on experience with written and electronic information relative to response decision making including but not limited to the U.S. Department of Transportation's Emergency Response Guidebook (ERG), manufacturer safety data sheets, CHEMTREC/CANUTEC, shipper or manufacturer contacts, computer data bases and response models, and other relevant sources of information addressing hazardous substance releases. Familiarization with OSHA standard 29 CFR §1910.1201;
  (C) Review of the principles and practices for analyzing an incident to determine the hazardous substances present, their physical and chemical properties, the likely behavior of the hazardous substance and its container, the types of hazardous substance transportation containers and vehicles involved in the release, the appropriate strategy for approaching release sites and containing the release;
  (D) Review of procedures for implementing continuing response actions consistent with the local emergency response plan, the organization's standard operating procedures, and the current edition of DOT's ERG including extended emergency notification procedures and follow-up communications;
  (E) Review of the principles and practice for proper selection and use of personal protective equipment;
  (F) Review of the principles and practices of establishing exposure zones, proper decontamination and medical surveillance stations and procedures;
  (G) Review of the expected hazards including fire and explosions hazards, confined space hazards, electrical hazards, powered equipment hazards, motor vehicle hazards, and walking-working surface hazards;
  (H) Awareness and knowledge of the competencies for the Hazardous Materials Technician covered in the National Fire Protection Association's Standard No. 472, Professional Competence of Responders to Hazardous Materials Incidents.

(4) Hazardous materials specialist
  (A) Review of and demonstration of competency in performing the applicable skills of 29 CFR §1910.120(q);
  (B) Hands-on experience with retrieval and use of written and electronic information relative to response decision making including but not limited to the U.S. Department of Transportation's Emergency Response Guidebook (ERG), manufacturer safety data sheets, CHEMTREC/CANUTEC, shipper or manufacturer contacts, computer data bases and response models, and other relevant sources of information addressing hazardous substance releases Familiarization with OSHA standard 29 CFR §1910.1201;
  (C) Review of the principles and practices for analyzing an incident to determine the hazardous substances present, their physical and chemical properties, and the likely behavior of the hazardous substance and its container, vessel, or vehicle;
  (D) Review of the principles and practices for identification of the types of hazardous substance transportation containers, vessels and vehicles involved in the release; selecting and using the various types of equipment available for plugging or patching transportation containers, vessels or vehicles; organizing and directing the use of multiple teams of hazardous material technicians and selecting the appropriate strategy for approaching release sites and containing or stopping the release;
  (E) Review of procedures for implementing continuing response actions consistent with the local emergency response plan, the organization's standard operating procedures, including knowledge of the available public and private response resources, establishment of an incident command post, direction of hazardous material technician teams, and extended emergency notification procedures and follow-up communications;
  (F) Review of the principles and practice for proper selection and use of personal protective equipment;
  (G) Review of the principles and practices of establishing exposure zones and proper decontamination, monitoring and medical surveillance stations and procedures;
  (H) Review of the expected hazards including fire and explosions hazards, confined space hazards, electrical hazards, powered equipment hazards, motor vehicle hazards, and walking-working surface hazards;
  (I) Awareness and knowledge of the competencies for the Off-site Specialist Employee covered in the National Fire Protection Association's Standard No. 472, Professional Competence of Responders to Hazardous Materials Incidents.

(5) Incident commander

The incident commander is the individual who, at any one time, is responsible for and in control of the response effort. This individual is the person responsible for the direction and coordination of the response effort. An incident commander's position should be occupied by the most senior, appropriately trained individual present at the response site. Yet, as necessary and appropriate by the level of response provided, the position may be occupied by many individuals during a particular response as the need for greater authority, responsibility, or training increases. It is possible for the first responder at the awareness level to assume the duties of incident commander until a more senior and appropriately trained individual arrives at the response site.

Therefore, any emergency responder expected to perform as an incident commander should be trained to fulfill the obligations of the position at the level of response they will be providing including the following:

(A) Ability to analyze a hazardous substance incident to determine the magnitude of the response problem;

(B) Ability to plan and implement an appropriate response plan within the capabilities of available personnel and equipment;

(C) Ability to implement a response to favorably change the outcome of the incident in a manner consistent with the local emergency response plan and the organization's standard operating procedures;

(D) Ability to evaluate the progress of the emergency response to ensure that the response objectives are being met safely, effectively, and efficiently; and

(E) Ability to adjust the response plan to the conditions of the response and to notify higher levels of response when required by the changes to the response plan.

[54 FR 9317, Mar. 6, 1989, as amended at 55 FR 14073, Apr. 13, 1990; 56 FR 15832, Apr. 18, 1991; 59 FR 43270, Aug. 22, 1994; 61 FR 9238, Mar. 7, 1996; 67 FR 67964, Nov. 7, 2002; 71 FR 16672, Apr. 3, 2006]

§1910.121 [Reserved]

Dipping and Coating Operations

Source: 64 FR 13909, Mar. 23, 1999, unless otherwise noted.

§1910.122 Table of Contents

This section lists the paragraph headings contained in §1910.123 through §1910.126.

§1910.123 [OI] Dipping and coating operations: coverage and definitons

(a) [OI] **Does this rule apply to me?**

(a)(1) This rule (§1910.123 through §1910.126) applies when you use a dip tank containing a liquid other than water. It applies when you use the liquid in the tank or its vapor to:

(a)(1)(i) Clean an object;

(a)(1)(ii) Coat an object;

(a)(1)(iii) Alter the surface of an object; or

(a)(1)(iv) Change the character of an object.

(a)(2) This rule also applies to the draining or drying of an object you have dipped or coated.

(b) [OI] **What operations are covered?** Examples of covered operations are paint dipping, electroplating, pickling, quenching, tanning, degreasing, stripping, cleaning, roll coating, flow coating, and curtain coating.

(c) **What operations are not covered?** You are not covered by this rule if your dip-tank operation only uses a molten material (a molten metal, alloy, or salt, for example).

(d) [OI] **How are terms used in §1910.123 through §1910.126 defined?**

Adjacent area means any area within 20 feet (6.1 m) of a vapor area that is not separated from the vapor area by tight partitions.

Approved means that the equipment so designated is listed or approved by a nationally recognized testing laboratory, as defined by §1910.7.

Autoignition temperature means the minimum temperature required to cause self-sustained combustion, independent of any other source of heat.

Combustible liquid means a liquid having a flash point of 100 °F (37.8 °C) or above.

Dip tank means a container holding a liquid other than water and that is used for dipping or coating. An object may be immersed (or partially immersed) in a dip tank or it may be suspended in a vapor coming from the tank.

Flammable liquid means any liquid having a flashpoint at or below 199.4 °F (93 °C).

Flashpoint means the minimum temperature at which a liquid gives off a vapor in sufficient concentration to ignite if tested in accordance with the test methods in Appendix B to §1910.1200—Physical Hazard Criteria.

Lower flammable limit (LFL) means the lowest concentration of a material that will propagate a flame. The LFL is usually expressed as a percent by volume of the material in air (or other oxidant).

Vapor area means any space containing a dip tank, including its drain boards, associated drying or conveying equipment, and any surrounding area where the vapor concentration exceeds 25% of the LFL of the liquid in the tank.

You means the employer, as defined by the Occupational Safety and Health Act of 1970 (29 U.S.C. 651 et seq.).

§1910.124 [OI] General requirements for dipping and coating operations

(a) **What construction requirements apply to dip tanks?** Any container that you use as a dip tank must be strong enough to withstand any expected load.

(b) **What ventilation requirements apply to vapor areas?**

(b)(1) [OI] The ventilation that you provide to a vapor area must keep the airborne concentration of any substance below 25% of its LFL.

(b)(2) When a liquid in a dip tank creates an exposure hazard covered by a standard listed in Subpart Z of this part, you must control worker exposure as required by that standard.

(b)(3) You may use a tank cover or material that floats on the surface of the liquid in a dip tank to replace or supplement ventilation. The method or combination of methods you choose must maintain the airborne concentration of the hazardous material and the worker's exposure within the limits specified in paragraphs (b)(1) and (b)(2) of this section.

(b)(4) When you use mechanical ventilation, it must conform to the following standards that are incorporated by reference as specified in §1910.6:

(b)(4)(i) ANSI Z9.2–1979, Fundamentals Governing the Design and Operation of Local Exhaust Systems;

(b)(4)(ii) NFPA 34–1995, Standard for Dip Tanks Containing Flammable or Combustible Liquids;

(b)(4)(iii) ACGIH's "Industrial Ventilation: A Manual of Recommended Practice" (22nd ed., 1995); or

(b)(4)(iv) ANSI Z9.1–1971, Practices for Ventilation and Operation of Open-Surface Tanks, and NFPA 34–1966, Standard for Dip Tanks Containing Flammable or Combustible Liquids.

(b)(5) When you use mechanical ventilation, it must draw the flow of air into a hood or exhaust duct.

(b)(6) When you use mechanical ventilation, each dip tank must have an independent exhaust system unless the combination of substances being removed will not cause a:

(b)(6)(i) Fire;

(b)(6)(ii) Explosion; or

(b)(6)(iii) Chemical reaction.

(c) **What requirements must I follow to recirculate exhaust air into the workplace?**

(c)(1) You may not recirculate exhaust air when any substance in that air poses a health hazard to employees or exceeds 25% of its LFL.

(c)(2) You must ensure that any exhaust air re-circulated from a dipping or coating operation using flammable liquids or liquids with flashpoints greater than 199.4 °F (93 °C) is:

(c)(2)(i) Free of any solid particulate that poses a health or safety hazard for employees; and

(c)(2)(ii) Monitored by approved equipment.

(c)(3) You must have a system that sounds an alarm and automatically shuts down the operation when the vapor concentration for any substance in the exhaust airstream exceeds 25% of its LFL.

(d) **What must I do when I use an exhaust hood?** You must:

(d)(1) Provide each room having exhaust hoods with a volume of outside air that is at least 90 percent of the volume of the exhaust air; and

(d)(2) Ensure that the outside air supply does not damage exhaust hoods.

(e) **What requirements must I follow when an employee enters a dip tank?** When an employee enters a dip tank, you must meet the entry requirements of §1910.146, OSHA's standard for Permit-Required Confined Spaces, as applicable.

(f) **What first-aid procedures must my employees know?** Your employees must know the first-aid procedures that are appropriate to the dipping or coating hazards to which they are exposed.

(g) **What hygiene facilities must I provide?** When your employees work with liquids that may burn, irritate, or otherwise harm their skin, you must provide:

(g)(1) Locker space or other storage space to prevent contamination of the employee's street clothes;

(g)(2) An emergency shower and eye-wash station close to the dipping or coating operation. In place of this equipment, you may use a water hose that is at least 4 feet (1.22 m) long and at least 3/4 of an inch (18 mm) thick with a quick-opening valve and carrying a pressure of 25 pounds per square inch (1.62 k/cm^2) or less; and

(g)(3) At least one basin with a hot-water faucet for every 10 employees who work with such liquids. (See paragraph (d) of §1910.141.)

(h) **What treatment and first aid must I provide?** When your employees work with liquids that may burn, irritate, or otherwise harm their skin, you must provide:

(h)(1) A physician's approval before an employee with a sore, burn, or other skin lesion that requires medical treatment works in a vapor area;

(h)(2) Treatment by a properly designated person of any small skin abrasion, cut, rash, or open sore;

(h)(3) Appropriate first-aid supplies that are located near the dipping or coating operation; and

(h)(4) For employees who work with chromic acid, periodic examinations of their exposed body parts, especially their nostrils.

(i) **What must I do before an employee cleans a dip tank?** Before permitting an employee to clean the interior of a dip tank, you must:

(i)(1) Drain the contents of the tank and open the cleanout doors; and

(i)(2) Ventilate and clear any pockets where hazardous vapors may have accumulated.

(j) **What must I do to inspect and maintain my dipping or coating operation?** You must:

(j)(1) Inspect the hoods and ductwork of the ventilation system for corrosion or damage:

(j)(1)(i) At least quarterly during operation; and

(j)(1)(ii) Prior to operation after a prolonged shutdown.

(j)(2) Ensure that the airflow is adequate:

(j)(2)(i) At least quarterly during operation; and

(j)(2)(ii) Prior to operation after a prolonged shutdown.

(j)(3) Periodically inspect all dipping and coating equipment, including covers, drains, overflow piping, and electrical and fire-extinguishing systems, and promptly correct any deficiencies;

(j)(4) Provide mechanical ventilation or respirators (selected and used as specified in §1910.134, OSHA's Respiratory Protection standard) to protect employees in the vapor area from exposure to toxic substances released during welding, burning, or open-flame work; and

(j)(5) Have dip tanks thoroughly cleaned of solvents and vapors before permitting welding, burning, or open-flame work on them.

§1910.125
Additional requirements for dipping and coating operations that use flammable liquids or liquids with flashpoints greater than 199.4 °F (93 °C)

If you use flammable liquids, you must comply with the requirements of this section as well as the requirements of §1910.123, §1910.124, and §1910.126, as applicable.

You must comply with this section if:	And:
•The flashpoint of the liquid is 199.4 °F (93 °C) or above	•The liquid is heated as part of the operation; or
	•A heated object is placed in the liquid.

(a) **What type of construction material must be used in making my dip tank?** Your dip tank must be made of noncombustible material.

(b) **When must I provide overflow piping?**

(b)(1) You must provide properly trapped overflow piping that discharges to a safe location for any dip tank having:

(b)(1)(i) A capacity greater than 150 gallons (568 L); or

(b)(1)(ii) A liquid surface area greater than 10 feet^2 (0.95 m2).

(b)(2) You must also ensure that:

(b)(2)(i) Any overflow piping is at least 3 inches (7.6 cm) in diameter and has sufficient capacity to prevent the dip tank from overflowing;

(b)(2)(ii) Piping connections on drains and overflow pipes allow ready access to the interior of the pipe for inspection and cleaning; and

(b)(2)(iii) The bottom of the overflow connection is at least 6 inches (15.2 cm) below the top of the dip tank.

(c) **When must I provide a bottom drain?**

(c)(1) You must provide a bottom drain for dip tanks that contain more than 500 gallons (1893 L) of liquid, unless:

(c)(1)(i) The dip tank is equipped with an automatic closing cover meeting the requirements of paragraph (f)(3) of this section; or

(c)(1)(ii) The viscosity of the liquid at normal atmospheric temperature does not allow the liquid to flow or be pumped easily.

(c)(2) You must ensure that the bottom drain required by this section:

(c)(2)(i) Will empty the dip tank during a fire;

(c)(2)(ii) Is properly trapped;

(c)(2)(iii) Has pipes that permit the dip tank's contents to be removed within five minutes after a fire begins; and

(c)(2)(iv) Discharges to a safe location.

(c)(3) Any bottom drain you provide must be capable of manual and automatic operation, and manual operation must be from a safe and accessible location.

(c)(4) You must ensure that automatic pumps are used when gravity flow from the bottom drain is impractical.

(d) **When must my conveyor system shut down automatically?** If your conveyor system is used with a dip tank, the system must shut down automatically:

(d)(1) If there is a fire; or

(d)(2) If the ventilation rate drops below what is required by paragraph (b) of §1910.124.

(e) **What ignition and fuel sources must be controlled?**

(e)(1) In each vapor area and any adjacent area, you must ensure that:

(e)(1)(i) All electrical wiring and equipment conform to the applicable hazardous (classified)-area requirements of Subpart S of this part (except as specifically permitted in paragraph (g) of §1910.126); and

(e)(1)(ii) There are no flames, spark-producing devices, or other surfaces that are hot enough to ignite vapors.

(e)(2) You must ensure that any portable container used to add liquid to the tank is electrically bonded to the dip tank and positively grounded to prevent static electrical sparks or arcs.

(e)(3) You must ensure that a heating system that is used in a drying operation and could cause ignition:

(e)(3)(i) Is installed in accordance with NFPA 86A–1969, Standard for Ovens and Furnaces (which is incorporated by reference in §1910.6 of this part);

(e)(3)(ii) Has adequate mechanical ventilation that operates before and during the drying operation; and

(e)(3)(iii) Shuts down automatically if any ventilating fan fails to maintain adequate ventilation.

(e)(4) You also must ensure that:

(e)(4)(i) All vapor areas are free of combustible debris and as free as practicable of combustible stock;

(e)(4)(ii) Rags and other material contaminated with liquids from dipping or coating operations are placed in approved waste cans immediately after use; and

(e)(4)(iii) Waste can contents are properly disposed of at the end of each shift.

(e)(5) You must prohibit smoking in a vapor area and must post a readily visible **"No Smoking"** sign near each dip tank.

(f) What fire protection must I provide?

(f)(1) You must provide the fire protection required by this paragraph (f) for:

(f)(1)(i) Any dip tank having a capacity of at least 150 gallons (568 L) or a liquid surface area of at least 4 feet^2 (0.38 m^1); and

(f)(1)(ii) Any hardening or tempering tank having a capacity of at least 500 gallons (1893 L) or a liquid surface area of at least 25 feet^2 (2.37 m^2).

(f)(2) For every vapor area, you must provide:

(f)(2)(i) Manual fire extinguishers that are suitable for flammable and combustible liquid fires and that conform to the requirements of §1910.157; and

(f)(2)(ii) An automatic fire-extinguishing system that conforms to the requirements of Subpart L of this part.

(f)(3) You may substitute a cover that is closed by an approved automatic device for the automatic fire-extinguishing system if the cover:

(f)(3)(i) Can also be activated manually;

(f)(3)(ii) Is noncombustible or tin-clad, with the enclosing metal applied with locked joints; and

(f)(3)(iii) Is kept closed when the dip tank is not in use.

(g) To what temperature may I heat a liquid in a dip tank? You must maintain the temperature of the liquid in a dip tank:

(g)(1) Below the liquid's boiling point; and

(g)(2) At least 100 °F (37.8 °C) below the liquid's autoignition temperature.

§1910.126 [OI]
Additional requirements for special dipping and coating operations

In addition to the requirements in §1910.123 through §1910.125, you must comply with any requirement in this section that applies to your operation.

(a) What additional requirements apply to hardening or tempering tanks?

(a)(1) You must ensure that hardening or tempering tanks:

(a)(1)(i) Are located as far as practicable from furnaces;

(a)(1)(ii) Are on noncombustible flooring; and

(a)(1)(iii) Have noncombustible hoods and vents (or equivalent devices) for venting to the outside. For this purpose, vent ducts must be treated as flues and kept away from combustible materials, particularly roofs.

(a)(2) You must equip each tank with an alarm that will sound if the temperature of the liquid comes within 50 °F (10 °C) of its flashpoint (the alarm set point).

(a)(3) When practicable, you must also provide each tank with a limit switch to shut down the conveyor supplying work to the tank.

(a)(4) If the temperature of the liquid can exceed the alarm set point, you must equip the tank with a circulating cooling system.

(a)(5) If the tank has a bottom drain, the bottom drain may be combined with the oil-circulating system.

(a)(6) You must not use air under pressure when you fill the dip tank or agitate the liquid in the dip tank.

(b) What additional requirements apply to flow coating?

(b)(1) You must use a direct low-pressure pumping system or a 10-gallon (38 L) or smaller gravity tank to supply the paint for flow coating. In case of fire, an approved heat-actuated device must shut down the pumping system.

(b)(2) You must ensure that the piping is substantial and rigidly supported.

(c) What additional requirements apply to roll coating, roll spreading, or roll impregnating? When these operations use a flammable liquid that has a flashpoint below 140 °F (60 °C), you must prevent sparking of static electricity by:

(c)(1) Bonding and grounding all metallic parts (including rotating parts) and installing static collectors; or

(c)(2) Maintaining a conductive atmosphere (for example, one with a high relative humidity) in the vapor area.

(d) What additional requirements apply to vapor degreasing tanks?

(d)(1) You must ensure that the condenser or vapor-level thermostat keeps the vapor level at least 36 inches (91 cm) or one-half the tank width, whichever is less, below the top of the vapor degreasing tank.

(d)(2) When you use gas as a fuel to heat the tank liquid, you must prevent solvent vapors from entering the air-fuel mixture. To do this, you must make the combustion chamber airtight (except for the flue opening).

(d)(3) The flue must be made of corrosion-resistant material, and it must extend to the outside. You must install a draft diverter if mechanical exhaust is used on the flue.

(d)(4) You must not allow the temperature of the heating element to cause a solvent or mixture to decompose or to generate an excessive amount of vapor.

(e) [OI] **What additional requirements apply to cyanide tanks?** You must ensure that cyanide tanks have a dike or other safeguard to prevent cyanide from mixing with an acid if a dip tank fails.

(f) What additional requirements apply to spray cleaning tanks and spray degreasing tanks? If you spray a liquid in the air over an open-surface cleaning or degreasing tank, you must control the spraying to the extent feasible by:

(f)(1) Enclosing the spraying operation; and

(f)(2) Using mechanical ventilation to provide enough inward air velocity to prevent the spray from leaving the vapor area.

(g) What additional requirements apply to electrostatic paint detearing?

(g)(1) You must use only approved electrostatic equipment in paint-detearing operations. Electrodes in such equipment must be substantial, rigidly supported, permanently located, and effectively insulated from ground by nonporous, noncombustible, clean, dry insulators.

(g)(2) You must use conveyors to support any goods being paint deteared.

(g)(3) You must ensure that goods being electrostatically deteared are not manually handled.

(g)(4) Between goods being electrostatically deteared and the electrodes or conductors of the electrostatic equipment, you must maintain a minimum distance of twice the sparking distance. This minimum distance must be displayed conspicuously on a sign located near the equipment.

(g)(5) You must ensure that the electrostatic equipment has automatic controls that immediately disconnect the power supply to the high-voltage transformer and signal the operator if:

(g)(5)(i) Ventilation or the conveyors fail to operate;

(g)(5)(ii) A ground (or imminent ground) occurs anywhere in the high-voltage system; or

(g)(5)(iii) Goods being electrostatically deteared come within twice the sparking distance of the electrodes or conductors of the equipment.

(g)(6) You must use fences, rails, or guards made of conducting material and adequately grounded, to separate paint-detearing operations from storage areas and from personnel.

(g)(7) To protect paint-detearing operations from fire, you must have in place:

(g)(7)(i) Automatic sprinklers; or

(g)(7)(ii) An automatic fire-extinguishing system conforming to the requirements of Subpart L of this part.

(g)(8) To collect paint deposits, you must:

(g)(8)(i) Provide drip plates and screens; and

(g)(8)(ii) Clean these plates and screens in a safe location.

H

Hazardous Materials

Additional requirements for special dipping and coating operations

This page intentionally left blank.

29 CFR PART 1910 Subpart I
Personal Protective Equipment

Section Contents

Subpart I—Personal Protective Equipment

Authority: 29 U.S.C. 653, 655, 657; Secretary of Labor's Order No. 12-71 (36 FR 8754), 8-76 (41 FR 25059), 9-83 (48 FR 35736), 1-90 (55 FR 9033), 6-96 (62 FR 111), 3-2000 (65 FR 50017), 5-2002 (67 FR 65008), 5-2007 (72 FR 31159), 4-2010 (75 FR 55355), or 1-2012 (77 FR 3912), as applicable; and 29 CFR part 1911.

§1910.132
General requirements

(a) **Application** Protective equipment, including personal protective equipment for eyes, face, head, and extremities, protective clothing, respiratory devices, and protective shields and barriers, shall be provided, used, and maintained in a sanitary and reliable condition wherever it is necessary by reason of hazards of processes or environment, chemical hazards, radiological hazards, or mechanical irritants encountered in a manner capable of causing injury or impairment in the function of any part of the body through absorption, inhalation or physical contact.

(b) **Employee-owned equipment** Where employees provide their own protective equipment, the employer shall be responsible to assure its adequacy, including proper maintenance, and sanitation of such equipment.

(c) **Design** All personal protective equipment shall be of safe design and construction for the work to be performed.

(d) **Hazard assessment and equipment selection**

(d)(1) The employer shall assess the workplace to determine if hazards are present, or are likely to be present, which necessitate the use of personal protective equipment (PPE). If such hazards are present, or likely to be present, the employer shall:

(d)(1)(i) Select, and have each affected employee use, the types of PPE that will protect the affected employee from the hazards identified in the hazard assessment;

(d)(1)(ii) Communicate selection decisions to each affected employee; and,

(d)(1)(iii) Select PPE that properly fits each affected employee.

Note: Non-mandatory Appendix B contains an example of procedures that would comply with the requirement for a hazard assessment.

(d)(2) The employer shall verify that the required workplace hazard assessment has been performed through a written certification that identifies the workplace evaluated; the person certifying that the evaluation has been performed; the date(s) of the hazard assessment; and, which identifies the document as a certification of hazard assessment.

(e) **Defective and damaged equipment** Defective or damaged personal protective equipment shall not be used.

(f) **Training**

(f)(1) The employer shall provide training to each employee who is required by this Section to use PPE. Each such employee shall be trained to know at least the following:

(f)(1)(i) When PPE is necessary;

(f)(1)(ii) What PPE is necessary;

(f)(1)(iii) How to properly don, doff, adjust, and wear PPE;

(f)(1)(iv) The limitations of the PPE; and

(f)(1)(v) The proper care, maintenance, useful life and disposal of the PPE.

(f)(2) Each affected employee shall demonstrate an understanding of the training specified in paragraph (f)(1) of this Section, and the ability to use PPE properly, before being allowed to perform work requiring the use of PPE.

(f)(3) When the employer has reason to believe that any affected employee who has already been trained does not have the understanding and skill required by paragraph (f)(2) of this Section, the employer shall retrain each such employee. Circumstances where retraining is required include, but are not limited to, situations where:

(f)(3)(i) Changes in the workplace render previous training obsolete; or

(f)(3)(ii) Changes in the types of PPE to be used render previous training obsolete; or

(f)(3)(iii) Inadequacies in an affected employee's knowledge or use of assigned PPE indicate that the employee has not retained the requisite understanding or skill.

(g) Paragraphs (d) and (f) of this section apply only to §1910.133, §1910.135, §1910.136, §1910.138, and §1910.140. Paragraphs (d) and (f) of this section do not apply to §1910.134 and §1910.137.

(h) **Payment for protective equipment**

(h)(1) Except as provided by paragraphs (h)(2) through (h)(6) of this Section, the protective equipment, including personal protective equipment (PPE), used to comply with this Part, shall be provided by the employer at no cost to employees.

(h)(2) The employer is not required to pay for non-specialty safety-toe protective footwear (including steel-toe shoes or steel-toe boots) and non-specialty prescription safety eyewear, provided that the employer permits such items to be worn off the job-site.

(h)(3) When the employer provides metatarsal guards and allows the employee, at his or her request, to use shoes or boots with built-in metatarsal protection, the employer is not required to reimburse the employee for the shoes or boots.

(h)(4) The employer is not required to pay for:

(h)(4)(i) The logging boots required by 29 CFR §1910.266(d)(1)(v);

(h)(4)(ii) Everyday clothing, such as long-sleeve shirts, long pants, street shoes, and normal work boots; or

(h)(4)(iii) Ordinary clothing, skin creams, or other items, used solely for protection from weather, such as winter coats, jackets, gloves, parkas, rubber boots, hats, raincoats, ordinary sunglasses, and sunscreen.

(h)(5) The employer must pay for replacement PPE, except when the employee has lost or intentionally damaged the PPE.

(h)(6) Where an employee provides adequate protective equipment he or she owns pursuant to paragraph (b) of this Section, the employer may allow the employee to use it and is not required to reimburse the employee for that equipment. The employer shall not require an employee to provide or pay for his or her own PPE, unless the PPE is excepted by paragraphs (h)(2) through (h)(5) of this Section.

(h)(7) This paragraph (h) shall become effective on February 13, 2008. Employers must implement the PPE payment requirements no later than May 15, 2008.

Note to §1910.132(h): When the provisions of another OSHA Standard specify whether or not the employer must pay for specific equipment, the payment provisions of that Standard shall prevail.

[39 FR 23502, June 27, 1974, as amended at 59 FR 16334, Apr. 6, 1994; 59 FR 33910, July 1, 1994; 72 FR 64428, Nov. 15, 2007; 76 FR 33606, June 8, 2011]

§1910.133
Eye and face protection

(a) **General requirements**

(a)(1) The employer shall ensure that each affected employee uses appropriate eye or face protection when exposed to eye or face hazards from flying particles, molten metal, liquid chemicals, acids or caustic liquids, chemical gases or vapors, or potentially injurious light radiation.

(a)(2) The employer shall ensure that each affected employee uses eye protection that provides side protection when there is a hazard from flying objects. Detachable side protectors (e.g. clip-on or slide-on side shields) meeting the pertinent requirements of this Section are acceptable.

(a)(3) The employer shall ensure that each affected employee who wears prescription lenses while engaged in operations that involve eye hazards wears eye protection that incorporates the prescription in its design, or wears eye protection that can be worn over the prescription lenses without disturbing the proper position of the prescription lenses or the protective lenses.

(a)(4) Eye and face PPE shall be distinctly marked to facilitate identification of the manufacturer.

(a)(5) The employer shall ensure that each affected employee uses equipment with filter lenses that have a shade number appropriate for the work being performed for protection from injurious light radiation. The following is a listing of appropriate shade numbers for various operations.

Filter Lenses for Protection Against Radiant Energy			
Operations	**Electrode Size 1/32 in.**	**Arc Current**	**Minimum* Protective Shade**
Shielded metal arc welding	Less than 3	Less than 60	7
	3-5	60-160	8
	5-8	160-250	10
	More than 8	250-550	11
Gas metal arc welding and flux cored arc welding		Less than 60	7
		60-160	10
		160-250	10
		250-500	10
Gas Tungsten arc welding		Less than 50	8
		50-150	8
		150-500	10
Air carbon	(Light)	Less than 500	10
Arc cutting	(Heavy)	500-1000	11
Plasma arc welding		Less than 20	6
		20-100	8
		100-400	10
		400-800	11
Plasma arc cutting	(Light)**	Less than 300	8
	(Medium)**	300-400	9
	(Heavy)**	400-800	10
Torch brazing			3
Torch soldering			2
Carbon arc welding			14

Filter Lenses for Protection Against Radiant Energy			
Operations	**Plate thickness—inches**	**Plate thickness—mm**	**Minimum* Protective Shade**
Gas Welding:			
Light	Under 1/8	Under 3.2	4
Medium	1/8 to 1/2	3.2 to 12.7	5
Heavy	Over 1/2	Over 12.7	6
Oxygen cutting:			
Light	Under 1	Under 25	3
Medium	1 to 6	25 to 150	4
Heavy	Over 6	Over 150	5

* As a rule of thumb, start with a shade that is too dark to see the weld zone. Then go to a lighter shade which gives sufficient view of the weld zone without going below the minimum. In oxyfuel gas welding or cutting where the torch produces a high yellow light, it is desirable to use a filter lens that absorbs the yellow or sodium line in the visible light of the (spectrum) operation.

** These values apply where the actual arc is clearly seen. Experience has shown that lighter filters may be used when the arc is hidden by the workpiece.

(b) Criteria for protective eye and face protection

(b)(1) Protective eye and face protection devices must comply with any of the following consensus standards: :

(b)(1)(i) ANSI/ISEA Z87.1–2010, Occupational and Educational Personal Eye and Face Protection Devices, incorporated by reference in §1910.6; ;

(b)(1)(ii) ANSI Z87.1–2003, Occupational and Educational Personal Eye and Face Protection Devices, incorporated by reference in §1910.6; or

(b)(1)(iii) ANSI Z87.1–1989 (R–1998), Practice for Occupational and Educational Eye and Face Protection, incorporated by reference in §1910.6.

(b)(2) Protective eye and face protection devices that the employer demonstrates are at least as effective as protective eye and face protection devices that are constructed in accordance with one of the above consensus standards will be deemed to be in compliance with the requirements of this Section.

[59 FR 16360, Apr. 6, 1994; 59 FR 33911, July 1, 1994, as amended at 61 FR 9238, Mar. 7, 1996; 61 FR 19548, May 2, 1996; 74 FR 46356, Sept. 9, 2009]

§1910.134 Respiratory protection

This Section applies to General Industry (Part 1910), Shipyards (Part 1915), Marine Terminals (Part 1917), Longshoring (Part 1918), and Construction (Part 1926).

(a) Permissible practice

(a)(1) In the control of those occupational diseases caused by breathing air contaminated with harmful dusts, fogs, fumes, mists, gases, smokes, sprays, or vapors, the primary objective shall be to prevent atmospheric contamination. This shall be accomplished as far as feasible by accepted engineering control measures (for example, enclosure or confinement of the operation, general and local ventilation, and substitution of less toxic materials). When effective engineering controls are not feasible, or while they are being instituted, appropriate respirators shall be used pursuant to this Section.

(a)(2) A respirator shall be provided to each employee when such equipment is necessary to protect the health of such employee. The employer shall provide the respirators which are applicable and suitable for the purpose intended. The employer shall be responsible for the establishment and maintenance of a respiratory protection program, which shall include the requirements outlined in paragraph (c) of this Section. The program shall cover each employee required by this Section to use a respirator.

(b) Definitions The following definitions are important terms used in the respiratory protection Standard in this Section.

Air-purifying respirator means a respirator with an air-purifying filter, cartridge, or canister that removes specific air contaminants by passing ambient air through the air-purifying element.

Assigned protection factor (APF) means the workplace level of respiratory protection that a respirator or class of respirators is expected to provide to employees when the employer implements a continuing, effective respiratory protection program as specified by this Section.

Atmosphere-supplying respirator means a respirator that supplies the respirator user with breathing air from a source independent of the ambient atmosphere, and includes supplied-air respirators (SARs) and self-contained breathing apparatus (SCBA) units.

Canister or cartridge means a container with a filter, sorbent, or catalyst, or combination of these items, which removes specific contaminants from the air passed through the container.

Demand respirator means an atmosphere-supplying respirator that admits breathing air to the facepiece only when a negative pressure is created inside the facepiece by inhalation.

Emergency situation means any occurrence such as, but not limited to, equipment failure, rupture of containers, or failure of control equipment that may or does result in an uncontrolled significant release of an airborne contaminant.

Employee exposure means exposure to a concentration of an airborne contaminant that would occur if the employee were not using respiratory protection.

End-of-service-life indicator (ESLI) means a system that warns the respirator user of the approach of the end of adequate respiratory protection, for example, that the sorbent is approaching saturation or is no longer effective.

Escape-only respirator means a respirator intended to be used only for emergency exit.

Filter or air purifying element means a component used in respirators to remove solid or liquid aerosols from the inspired air.

Filtering facepiece (dust mask) means a negative pressure particulate respirator with a filter as an integral part of the facepiece or with the entire facepiece composed of the filtering medium.

Fit factor means a quantitative estimate of the fit of a particular respirator to a specific individual, and typically estimates the ratio of the concentration of a substance in ambient air to its concentration inside the respirator when worn.

Fit test means the use of a protocol to qualitatively or quantitatively evaluate the fit of a respirator on an individual. (See also Qualitative fit test QLFT and Quantitative fit test QNFT.)

Helmet means a rigid respiratory inlet covering that also provides head protection against impact and penetration.

High efficiency particulate air (HEPA) filter means a filter that is at least 99.97% efficient in removing monodisperse particles of 0.3 micrometers in diameter. The equivalent NIOSH 42 CFR 84 particulate filters are the N100, R100, and P100 filters.

Hood means a respiratory inlet covering that completely covers the head and neck and may also cover portions of the shoulders and torso.

Immediately dangerous to life or health (IDLH) means an atmosphere that poses an immediate threat to life, would cause irreversible adverse health effects, or would impair an individual's ability to escape from a dangerous atmosphere.

Interior structural firefighting means the physical activity of fire suppression, rescue or both, inside of buildings or enclosed structures which are involved in a fire situation beyond the incipient stage. (See 29 CFR §1910.155)

Loose-fitting facepiece means a respiratory inlet covering that is designed to form a partial seal with the face.

Maximum use concentration (MUC) means the maximum atmospheric concentration of a hazardous substance from which an employee can be expected to be protected when wearing a respirator, and is determined by the assigned protection factor of the respirator or class of respirators and the exposure limit of the hazardous substance. The MUC can be determined mathematically by multiplying the assigned protection factor specified for a respirator by the required OSHA permissible exposure limit, short-term exposure limit, or ceiling limit. When no OSHA exposure limit is available for a hazardous substance, an employer must determine an MUC on the basis of relevant available information and informed professional judgment.

Negative pressure respirator (tight fitting) means a respirator in which the air pressure inside the facepiece is negative during inhalation with respect to the ambient air pressure outside the respirator.

Oxygen deficient atmosphere means an atmosphere with an oxygen content below 19.5% by volume.

Physician or other licensed health care professional (PLHCP) means an individual whose legally permitted scope of practice (i.e., license, registration, or certification) allows him or her to independently provide, or be delegated the responsibility to provide, some or all of the health care services required by paragraph (e) of this Section.

Positive pressure respirator means a respirator in which the pressure inside the respiratory inlet covering exceeds the ambient air pressure outside the respirator.

Powered air-purifying respirator (PAPR) means an air-purifying respirator that uses a blower to force the ambient air through air-purifying elements to the inlet covering.

Pressure demand respirator means a positive pressure atmosphere-supplying respirator that admits breathing air to the facepiece when the positive pressure is reduced inside the facepiece by inhalation.

Qualitative fit test (QLFT) means a pass/fail fit test to assess the adequacy of respirator fit that relies on the individual's response to the test agent.

Quantitative fit test (QNFT) means an assessment of the adequacy of respirator fit by numerically measuring the amount of leakage into the respirator.

Respiratory inlet covering means that portion of a respirator that forms the protective barrier between the user's respiratory tract and an air-purifying device or breathing air source, or both. It may be a facepiece, helmet, hood, suit, or a mouthpiece respirator with nose clamp.

Self-contained breathing apparatus (SCBA) means an atmosphere-supplying respirator for which the breathing air source is designed to be carried by the user.

Service life means the period of time that a respirator, filter or sorbent, or other respiratory equipment provides adequate protection to the wearer.

Supplied-air respirator (SAR) or airline respirator means an atmosphere-supplying respirator for which the source of breathing air is not designed to be carried by the user.

This Section means this respiratory protection Standard.

Tight-fitting facepiece means a respiratory inlet covering that forms a complete seal with the face.

User seal check means an action conducted by the respirator user to determine if the respirator is properly seated to the face.

(c) **Respiratory protection program** This paragraph requires the employer to develop and implement a written respiratory protection program with required worksite-specific procedures and elements for required respirator use. The program must be administered by a suitably trained program administrator. In addition, certain program elements may be required for voluntary use to prevent potential hazards associated with the use of the respirator. The Small Entity Compliance Guide contains criteria for the selection of a program administrator and a sample program that meets the requirements of this paragraph. Copies of the Small Entity Compliance Guide will be available on or about April 8, 1998 from the Occupational Safety and Health Administration's Office of Publications, Room N 3101, 200 Constitution Avenue, NW, Washington, DC, 20210 (202–219–4667).

(c)(1) In any workplace where respirators are necessary to protect the health of the employee or whenever respirators are required by the employer, the employer shall establish and implement a written respiratory protection program with worksite-specific procedures. The program shall be updated as necessary to reflect those changes in workplace conditions that affect respirator use. The employer shall include in the program the following provisions of this Section, as applicable:

(c)(1)(i) Procedures for selecting respirators for use in the workplace;

(c)(1)(ii) Medical evaluations of employees required to use respirators;

(c)(1)(iii) Fit testing procedures for tight-fitting respirators;

(c)(1)(iv) Procedures for proper use of respirators in routine and reasonably foreseeable emergency situations;

(c)(1)(v) Procedures and schedules for cleaning, disinfecting, storing, inspecting, repairing, discarding, and otherwise maintaining respirators;

(c)(1)(vi) Procedures to ensure adequate air quality, quantity, and flow of breathing air for atmosphere-supplying respirators;

(c)(1)(vii) Training of employees in the respiratory hazards to which they are potentially exposed during routine and emergency situations;

(c)(1)(viii) Training of employees in the proper use of respirators, including putting on and removing them, any limitations on their use, and their maintenance; and

(c)(1)(ix) Procedures for regularly evaluating the effectiveness of the program.

(c)(2) Where respirator use is not required:

(c)(2)(i) An employer may provide respirators at the request of employees or permit employees to use their own respirators, if the employer determines that such respirator use will not in itself create a hazard. If the employer determines that any voluntary respirator use is permissible, the employer shall provide the respirator users with the information contained in Appendix D to this Section ("Information for Employees Using Respirators When Not Required Under the Standard"); and

(c)(2)(ii) In addition, the employer must establish and implement those elements of a written respiratory protection program necessary to ensure that any employee using a respirator voluntarily is medically able to use that respirator, and that the respirator is cleaned, stored, and maintained so that its use does not present a health hazard to the user. Exception: Employers are not required to include in a written respiratory protection program those employees whose only use of respirators involves the voluntary use of filtering facepieces (dust masks).

(c)(3) The employer shall designate a program administrator who is qualified by appropriate training or experience that is commensurate with the complexity of the program to administer or oversee the respiratory protection program and conduct the required evaluations of program effectiveness.

(c)(4) The employer shall provide respirators, training, and medical evaluations at no cost to the employee.

(d) **Selection of respirators** This paragraph requires the employer to evaluate respiratory hazard(s) in the workplace, identify relevant workplace and user factors, and base respirator selection on these factors. The paragraph also specifies appropriately protective respirators for use in IDLH atmospheres, and limits the selection and use of air-purifying respirators.

(d)(1) **General requirements**

(d)(1)(i) The employer shall select and provide an appropriate respirator based on the respiratory hazard(s) to which the worker is exposed and workplace and user factors that affect respirator performance and reliability.

(d)(1)(ii) The employer shall select a NIOSH-certified respirator. The respirator shall be used in compliance with the conditions of its certification.

(d)(1)(iii) The employer shall identify and evaluate the respiratory hazard(s) in the workplace; this evaluation shall include a reasonable estimate of employee exposures to respiratory hazard(s) and an identification of the contaminant's chemical state and physical form. Where the employer cannot identify or reasonably estimate the employee exposure, the employer shall consider the atmosphere to be IDLH.

(d)(1)(iv) The employer shall select respirators from a sufficient number of respirator models and sizes so that the respirator is acceptable to, and correctly fits, the user.

(d)(2) **Respirators for IDLH atmospheres**

(d)(2(i) The employer shall provide the following respirators for employee use in IDLH atmospheres:

(d)(2)(i)(A) A full facepiece pressure demand SCBA certified by NIOSH for a minimum service life of thirty minutes; or

(d)(2)(i)(B) A combination full facepiece pressure demand supplied-air respirator (SAR) with auxiliary self-contained air supply.

(d)(2)(ii) Respirators provided only for escape from IDLH atmospheres shall be NIOSH-certified for escape from the atmosphere in which they will be used.

(d)(2)(iii) All oxygen-deficient atmospheres shall be considered IDLH. Exception: If the employer demonstrates that, under all foreseeable conditions, the oxygen concentration can be maintained within the ranges specified in Table II of this Section (i.e., for the altitudes set out in the table), then any atmosphere-supplying respirator may be used.

(d)(3) Respirators for atmospheres that are not IDLH

(d)(3)(i) The employer shall provide a respirator that is adequate to protect the health of the employee and ensure compliance with all other OSHA statutory and regulatory requirements, under routine and reasonably foreseeable emergency situations.

(d)(3)(i)(A) [OI] **Assigned Protection Factors (APFs)** Employers must use the assigned protection factors listed in Table 1 to select a respirator that meets or exceeds the required level of employee protection. When using a combination respirator (e.g., airline respirators with an air-purifying filter), employers must ensure that the assigned protection factor is appropriate to the mode of operation in which the respirator is being used.

Table 1
Assigned Protection Factors[5]

Type of respirator[1,2]	Quarter mask	Half mask	Full facepiece	Helmet/hood	Loose-fitting facepiece
1. Air-Purifying Respirator	5	[3]10	50		
2. Powered Air-Purifying Respirator (PAPR)		50	1,000	[4]25/1,000	25
3. Supplied-Air Respirator (SAR) or Airline Respirator					
• Demand mode		10	50		
• Continuous flow mode		50	1,000	[4]25/1,000	25
• Pressure-demand or other positive-pressure mode		50	1,000		
4. Self-Contained Breathing Apparatus (SCBA)					
• Demand mode		10	50	50	
• Pressure-demand or other positive-pressure mode (e.g., open/closed circuit)			10,000	10,000	

[1] Employers may select respirators assigned for use in higher workplace concentrations of a hazardous substance for use at lower concentrations of that substance, or when required respirator use is independent of concentration.

[2] The assigned protection factors in Table 1 are only effective when the employer implements a continuing, effective respirator program as required by this Section (29 CFR §1910.134), including training, fit testing, maintenance, and use requirements

[3] This APF category includes filtering facepieces, and half masks with elastomeric facepieces.

[4] The employer must have evidence provided by the respirator manufacturer that testing of these respirators demonstrates performance at a level of protection of 1,000 or greater to receive an APF of 1,000. This level of performance can best be demonstrated by performing a WPF or SWPF study or equivalent testing. Absent such testing, all other PAPRs and SARs with helmets/hoods are to be treated as loose-fitting facepiece respirators, and receive an APF of 25.

[5] These APFs do not apply to respirators used solely for escape. For escape respirators used in association with specific substances covered by 29 CFR §1910 Subpart Z, employers must refer to the appropriate substance-specific Standards in that Subpart. Escape respirators for other IDLH atmospheres are specified by 29 CFR §1910.134 (d)(2)(ii).

(d)(3)(i)(B) **Maximum Use Concentration (MUC)**

(d)(3)(i)(B)(1) The employer must select a respirator for employee use that maintains the employee's exposure to the hazardous substance, when measured outside the respirator, at or below the MUC.

(d)(3)(i)(B)(2) Employers must not apply MUCs to conditions that are immediately dangerous to life or health (IDLH); instead, they must use respirators listed for IDLH conditions in paragraph (d)(2) of this Standard.

(d)(3)(i)(B)(3) When the calculated MUC exceeds the IDLH level for a hazardous substance, or the performance limits of the cartridge or canister, then employers must set the maximum MUC at that lower limit.

(d)(3)(ii) The respirator selected shall be appropriate for the chemical state and physical form of the contaminant.

(d)(3)(iii) [OI] For protection against gases and vapors, the employer shall provide:

(d)(3)(iii)(A) An atmosphere-supplying respirator; or

(d)(3)(iii)(B) An air-purifying respirator, provided that:

(d)(3)(iii)(B)(1) [OI] The respirator is equipped with an end-of-service-life indicator (ESLI) certified by NIOSH for the contaminant; or

(d)(3)(iii)(B)(2) If there is no ESLI appropriate for conditions in the employer's workplace, the employer implements a change schedule for canisters and cartridges that is based on objective information or data that will ensure that canisters and cartridges are changed before the end of their service life. The employer shall describe in the respirator program the information and data relied upon and the basis for the canister and cartridge change schedule and the basis for reliance on the data.

(d)(3)(iv) For protection against particulates, the employer shall provide:

(d)(3)(iv)(A) An atmosphere-supplying respirator; or

(d)(3)(iv)(B) [OI] An air-purifying respirator equipped with a filter certified by NIOSH under 30 CFR Part 11 as a high efficiency particulate air (HEPA) filter, or an air-purifying respirator equipped with a filter certified for particulates by NIOSH under 42 CFR Part 84; or

(d)(3)(iv)(C) For contaminants consisting primarily of particles with mass median aerodynamic diameters (MMAD) of at least 2 micrometers, an air-purifying respirator equipped with any filter certified for particulates by NIOSH.

Table I
Assigned Protection Factors
[Reserved]

Table II

Altitude (ft.)	Oxygen deficient Atmospheres(%O_2) for which the employer may rely on atmosphere-supplying respirators
Less than 3,001	16.0–19.5
3,001–4,000	16.4–19.5
4,001–5,000	17.1–19.5
5,001–6,000	17.8–19.5
6,001–7,000	18.5–19.5
7,001–8,000[1]	19.3–19.5

[1] Above 8,000 feet the exception does not apply. Oxygen-enriched breathing air must be supplied above 14,000 feet.

(e) [OI] **Medical evaluation** Using a respirator may place a physiological burden on employees that varies with the type of respirator worn, the job and workplace conditions in which the respirator is used, and the medical status of the employee. Accordingly, this paragraph specifies the minimum requirements for medical evaluation that employers must implement to determine the employee's ability to use a respirator.

(e)(1) [OI] **General** The employer shall provide a medical evaluation to determine the employee's ability to use a respirator, before the employee is fit tested or required to use the respirator in the workplace. The employer may discontinue an employee's medical evaluations when the employee is no longer required to use a respirator.

(e)(2) [OI] **Medical evaluation procedures**

(e)(2)(i) [OI] The employer shall identify a physician or other licensed health care professional (PLHCP) to perform medical evaluations using a medical questionnaire or an initial medical examination that obtains the same information as the medical questionnaire.

(e)(2)(ii) The medical evaluation shall obtain the information requested by the questionnaire in Sections 1 and 2, Part A of Appendix C of this Section.

(e)(3) **Follow-up medical examination**

(e)(3)(i) The employer shall ensure that a follow-up medical examination is provided for an employee who gives a positive response to any question among questions 1 through 8 in Section 2, Part A of Appendix C or whose initial medical examination demonstrates the need for a follow-up medical examination.

(e)(3)(ii) The follow-up medical examination shall include any medical tests, consultations, or diagnostic procedures that the PLHCP deems necessary to make a final determination.

(e)(4) **Administration of the medical questionnaire and examinations**

(e)(4)(i) The medical questionnaire and examinations shall be administered confidentially during the employee's normal working hours or at a time and place convenient to the employee. The medical questionnaire shall be administered in a manner that ensures that the employee understands its content.

(e)(4)(ii) The employer shall provide the employee with an opportunity to discuss the questionnaire and examination results with the PLHCP.

(e)(5) **Supplemental information for the PLHCP**

(e)(5)(i) The following information must be provided to the PLHCP before the PLHCP makes a recommendation concerning an employee's ability to use a respirator:

(e)(5)(i)(A) The type and weight of the respirator to be used by the employee;

(e)(5)(i)(B) The duration and frequency of respirator use (including use for rescue and escape);

(e)(5)(i)(C) The expected physical work effort;

(e)(5)(i)(D) Additional protective clothing and equipment to be worn; and

(e)(5)(i)(E) Temperature and humidity extremes that may be encountered.

(e)(5)(ii) Any supplemental information provided previously to the PLHCP regarding an employee need not be provided for a subsequent medical evaluation if the information and the PLHCP remain the same.

(e)(5)(iii) The employer shall provide the PLHCP with a copy of the written respiratory protection program and a copy of this Section.

Note to paragraph (e)(5)(iii): When the employer replaces a PLHCP, the employer must ensure that the new PLHCP obtains this information, either by providing the documents directly to the PLHCP or having the documents transferred from the former PLHCP to the new PLHCP. However, OSHA does not expect employers to have employees medically reevaluated solely because a new PLHCP has been selected.

(e)(6) **Medical determination** In determining the employee's ability to use a respirator, the employer shall:

(e)(6)(i) Obtain a written recommendation regarding the employee's ability to use the respirator from the PLHCP. The recommendation shall provide only the following information:

(e)(6)(i)(A) Any limitations on respirator use related to the medical condition of the employee, or relating to the workplace conditions in which the respirator will be used, including whether or not the employee is medically able to use the respirator;

(e)(6)(i)(B) The need, if any, for follow-up medical evaluations; and

(e)(6)(i)(C) A statement that the PLHCP has provided the employee with a copy of the PLHCP's written recommendation.

(e)(6)(ii) If the respirator is a negative pressure respirator and the PLHCP finds a medical condition that may place the employee's health at increased risk if the respirator is used, the employer shall provide a PAPR if the PLHCP's medical evaluation finds that the employee can use such a respirator; if a subsequent medical evaluation finds that the employee is medically able to use a negative pressure respirator, then the employer is no longer required to provide a PAPR.

(e)(7) **Additional medical evaluations** At a minimum, the employer shall provide additional medical evaluations that comply with the requirements of this Section if:

(e)(7)(i) An employee reports medical signs or symptoms that are related to ability to use a respirator;

(e)(7)(ii) A PLHCP, supervisor, or the respirator program administrator informs the employer that an employee needs to be reevaluated;

(e)(7)(iii) Information from the respiratory protection program, including observations made during fit testing and program evaluation, indicates a need for employee reevaluation; or

(e)(7)(iv) A change occurs in workplace conditions (e.g., physical work effort, protective clothing, temperature) that may result in a substantial increase in the physiological burden placed on an employee.

(f) **Fit testing** This paragraph requires that, before an employee may be required to use any respirator with a negative or positive pressure tight-fitting facepiece, the employee must be fit tested with the same make, model, style, and size of respirator that will be used. This paragraph specifies the kinds of fit tests allowed, the procedures for conducting them, and how the results of the fit tests must be used.

(f)(1) The employer shall ensure that employees using a tight-fitting facepiece respirator pass an appropriate qualitative fit test (QLFT) or quantitative fit test (QNFT) as stated in this paragraph.

(f)(2) The employer shall ensure that an employee using a tight-fitting facepiece respirator is fit tested prior to initial use of the respirator, whenever a different respirator facepiece (size, style, model or make) is used, and at least annually thereafter.

(f)(3) The employer shall conduct an additional fit test whenever the employee reports, or the employer, PLHCP, supervisor, or program administrator makes visual observations of, changes in the employee's physical condition that could affect respirator fit. Such conditions include, but are not limited to, facial scarring, dental changes, cosmetic surgery, or an obvious change in body weight.

(f)(4) If after passing a QLFT or QNFT, the employee subsequently notifies the employer, program administrator, supervisor, or PLHCP that the fit of the respirator is unacceptable, the employee shall be given a reasonable opportunity to select a different respirator facepiece and to be retested.

(f)(5) The fit test shall be administered using an OSHA-accepted QLFT or QNFT protocol. The OSHA-accepted QLFT and QNFT protocols and procedures are contained in Appendix A of this Section.

(f)(6) QLFT may only be used to fit test negative pressure air-purifying respirators that must achieve a fit factor of 100 or less.

(f)(7) If the fit factor, as determined through an OSHA-accepted QNFT protocol, is equal to or greater than 100 for tight-fitting half facepieces, or equal to or greater than 500 for tight-fitting full facepieces, the QNFT has been passed with that respirator.

(f)(8) Fit testing of tight-fitting atmosphere-supplying respirators and tight-fitting powered air-purifying respirators shall be accomplished by performing quantitative or qualitative fit testing in the negative pressure mode, regardless of the mode of operation (negative or positive pressure) that is used for respiratory protection.

(f)(8)(i) Qualitative fit testing of these respirators shall be accomplished by temporarily converting the respirator user's actual facepiece into a negative pressure respirator with appropriate filters, or by using an identical negative pressure air-purifying respirator facepiece with the same sealing surfaces as a surrogate for the atmosphere-supplying or powered air-purifying respirator facepiece.

(f)(8)(ii) Quantitative fit testing of these respirators shall be accomplished by modifying the facepiece to allow sampling inside the facepiece in the breathing zone of the user, midway between the nose and mouth. This requirement shall be accomplished by installing a permanent sampling probe onto a surrogate facepiece, or by using a sampling adapter designed to temporarily provide a means of sampling air from inside the facepiece.

(f)(8)(iii) Any modifications to the respirator facepiece for fit testing shall be completely removed, and the facepiece restored to NIOSH-approved configuration, before that facepiece can be used in the workplace.

(g) **Use of respirators** This paragraph requires employers to establish and implement procedures for the proper use of respirators. These requirements include prohibiting conditions that may result in facepiece seal leakage, preventing employees from removing respirators in hazardous environments, taking actions to ensure continued effective respirator operation throughout the work shift, and establishing procedures for the use of respirators in IDLH atmospheres or in interior structural firefighting situations.

(g)(1) **Facepiece seal protection**

(g)(1)(i) The employer shall not permit respirators with tight-fitting facepieces to be worn by employees who have:

(g)(1)(i)(A) Facial hair that comes between the sealing surface of the facepiece and the face or that interferes with valve function; or

(g)(1)(i)(B) Any condition that interferes with the face-to-facepiece seal or valve function.

(g)(1)(ii) If an employee wears corrective glasses or goggles or other personal protective equipment, the employer shall ensure that such equipment is worn in a manner that does not interfere with the seal of the facepiece to the face of the user.

(g)(1)(iii) For all tight-fitting respirators, the employer shall ensure that employees perform a user seal check each time they put on the respirator using the procedures in Appendix B–1 or procedures recommended by the respirator manufacturer that the employer demonstrates are as effective as those in Appendix B–1 of this Section.

(g)(2) **Continuing respirator effectiveness**

(g)(2)(i) Appropriate surveillance shall be maintained of work area conditions and degree of employee exposure or stress. When there is a change in work area conditions or degree of employee exposure or stress that may affect respirator effectiveness, the employer shall reevaluate the continued effectiveness of the respirator.

(g)(2)(ii) The employer shall ensure that employees leave the respirator use area:

(g)(2)(ii)(A) To wash their faces and respirator facepieces as necessary to prevent eye or skin irritation associated with respirator use; or

(g)(2)(ii)(B) If they detect vapor or gas breakthrough, changes in breathing resistance, or leakage of the facepiece; or

(g)(2)(ii)(C) To replace the respirator or the filter, cartridge, or canister elements.

(g)(2)(iii) If the employee detects vapor or gas breakthrough, changes in breathing resistance, or leakage of the facepiece, the employer must replace or repair the respirator before allowing the employee to return to the work area.

(g)(3) **Procedures for IDLH atmospheres** For all IDLH atmospheres, the employer shall ensure that:

(g)(3)(i) One employee or, when needed, more than one employee is located outside the IDLH atmosphere;

(g)(3)(ii) Visual, voice, or signal line communication is maintained between the employee(s) in the IDLH atmosphere and the employee(s) located outside the IDLH atmosphere;

(g)(3)(iii) The employee(s) located outside the IDLH atmosphere are trained and equipped to provide effective emergency rescue;

(g)(3)(iv) The employer or designee is notified before the employee(s) located outside the IDLH atmosphere enter the IDLH atmosphere to provide emergency rescue;

(g)(3)(v) The employer or designee authorized to do so by the employer, once notified, provides necessary assistance appropriate to the situation;

(g)(3)(vi) Employee(s) located outside the IDLH atmospheres are equipped with:

(g)(3)(vi)(A) Pressure demand or other positive pressure SCBAs, or a pressure demand or other positive pressure supplied-air respirator with auxiliary SCBA; and either

(g)(3)(vi)(B) Appropriate retrieval equipment for removing the employee(s) who enter(s) these hazardous atmospheres where retrieval equipment would contribute to the rescue of the employee(s) and would not increase the overall risk resulting from entry; or

(g)(3)(vi)(C) Equivalent means for rescue where retrieval equipment is not required under paragraph (g)(3)(vi)(B).

(g)(4) **Procedures for interior structural firefighting** In addition to the requirements set forth under paragraph (g)(3), in interior structural fires, the employer shall ensure that:

(g)(4)(i) At least two employees enter the IDLH atmosphere and remain in visual or voice contact with one another at all times;

(g)(4)(ii) At least two employees are located outside the IDLH atmosphere; and

(g)(4)(iii) All employees engaged in interior structural firefighting use SCBAs.

Note to (g): One of the two individuals located outside the IDLH atmosphere may be assigned to an additional role, such as incident commander in charge of the emergency or safety officer, so long as this individual is able to perform assistance or rescue activities without jeopardizing the safety or health of any firefighter working at the incident.

Noteto (g): Nothing in this section is meant to preclude firefighters from performing emergency rescue activities before an entire team has assembled.

(h) **Maintenance and care of respirators** This paragraph requires the employer to provide for the cleaning and disinfecting, storage, inspection, and repair of respirators used by employees.

(h)(1) **Cleaning and disinfecting** The employer shall provide each respirator user with a respirator that is clean, sanitary, and in good working order. The employer shall ensure that respirators are cleaned and disinfected using the procedures in Appendix B–2 of this section, or procedures recommended by the respirator manufacturer, provided that such procedures are of equivalent effectiveness. The respirators shall be cleaned and disinfected at the following intervals:

(h)(1)(i) Respirators issued for the exclusive use of an employee shall be cleaned and disinfected as often as necessary to be maintained in a sanitary condition;

(h)(1)(ii) Respirators issued to more than one employee shall be cleaned and disinfected before being worn by different individuals;

(h)(1)(iii) Respirators maintained for emergency use shall be cleaned and disinfected after each use; and

(h)(1)(iv) Respirators used in fit testing and training shall be cleaned and disinfected after each use.

(h)(2) **Storage** The employer shall ensure that respirators are stored as follows:

(h)(2)(i) All respirators shall be stored to protect them from damage, contamination, dust, sunlight, extreme temperatures, excessive moisture, and damaging chemicals, and they shall be packed or stored to prevent deformation of the facepiece and exhalation valve.

(h)(2)(ii) In addition to the requirements of paragraph (h)(2)(i) of this section, emergency respirators shall be:

(h)(2)(ii)(A) Kept accessible to the work area;

(h)(2)(ii)(B) Stored in compartments or in covers that are clearly marked as containing emergency respirators; and

(h)(2)(ii)(C) Stored in accordance with any applicable manufacturer instructions.

(h)(3) **Inspection**

(h)(3)(i) The employer shall ensure that respirators are inspected as follows:

(h)(3)(i)(A) All respirators used in routine situations shall be inspected before each use and during cleaning;

(h)(3)(i)(B) All respirators maintained for use in emergency situations shall be inspected at least monthly and in accordance with the manufacturer's recommendations, and shall be checked for proper function before and after each use; and

(h)(3)(i)(C) Emergency escape-only respirators shall be inspected before being carried into the workplace for use.

(h)(3)(ii) The employer shall ensure that respirator inspections include the following:

(h)(3)(ii)(A) A check of respirator function, tightness of connections, and the condition of the various parts including, but not limited to, the facepiece, head straps, valves, connecting tube, and cartridges, canisters or filters; and

(h)(3)(ii)(B) A check of elastomeric parts for pliability and signs of deterioration.

(h)(3)(iii) In addition to the requirements of paragraphs (h)(3)(i) and (ii) of this section, self-contained breathing apparatus shall be inspected monthly. Air and oxygen cylinders shall be maintained in a fully charged state and shall be recharged when the pressure falls to 90% of the manufacturer's recommended pressure level. The employer shall determine that the regulator and warning devices function properly.

(h)(3)(iv) For respirators maintained for emergency use, the employer shall:

(h)(3)(iv)(A) Certify the respirator by documenting the date the inspection was performed, the name (or signature) of the person who made the inspection, the findings, required remedial action, and a serial number or other means of identifying the inspected respirator; and

(h)(3)(iv)(B) Provide this information on a tag or label that is attached to the storage compartment for the respirator, is kept with the respirator, or is included in inspection reports stored as paper or electronic files. This information shall be maintained until replaced following a subsequent certification.

(h)(4) **Repairs** The employer shall ensure that respirators that fail an inspection or are otherwise found to be defective are removed from service, and are discarded or repaired or adjusted in accordance with the following procedures:

(h)(4)(i) Repairs or adjustments to respirators are to be made only by persons appropriately trained to perform such operations and shall use only the respirator manufacturer's NIOSH-approved parts designed for the respirator;

(h)(4)(ii) Repairs shall be made according to the manufacturer's recommendations and specifications for the type and extent of repairs to be performed; and

(h)(4)(iii) Reducing and admission valves, regulators, and alarms shall be adjusted or repaired only by the manufacturer or a technician trained by the manufacturer.

(i) **Breathing air quality and use** This paragraph requires the employer to provide employees using atmosphere-supplying respirators (supplied-air and SCBA) with breathing gases of high purity.

(i)(1) The employer shall ensure that compressed air, compressed oxygen, liquid air, and liquid oxygen used for respiration accords with the following specifications:

(i)(1)(i) Compressed and liquid oxygen shall meet the United States Pharmacopoeia requirements for medical or breathing oxygen; and

(i)(1)(ii) Compressed breathing air shall meet at least the requirements for Grade D breathing air described in ANSI/Compressed Gas Association Commodity Specification for Air, G–7.1–1989, to include:

(i)(1)(ii)(A) Oxygen content (v/v) of 19.5–23.5%;

(i)(1)(ii)(B) Hydrocarbon (condensed) content of 5 milligrams per cubic meter of air or less;

(i)(1)(ii)(C) Carbon monoxide (CO) content of 10 ppm or less;

(i)(1)(ii)(D) Carbon dioxide content of 1,000 ppm or less; and

(i)(1)(ii)(E) Lack of noticeable odor.

(i)(2) The employer shall ensure that compressed oxygen is not used in atmosphere-supplying respirators that have previously used compressed air.

(i)(3) The employer shall ensure that oxygen concentrations greater than 23.5% are used only in equipment designed for oxygen service or distribution.

(i)(4) The employer shall ensure that cylinders used to supply breathing air to respirators meet the following requirements:

(i)(4)(i) Cylinders are tested and maintained as prescribed in the Shipping Container Specification Regulations of the Department of Transportation (49 CFR Part 180);

(i)(4)(ii) Cylinders of purchased breathing air have a certificate of analysis from the supplier that the breathing air meets the requirements for Grade D breathing air; and (i)(4)(iii) The moisture content in the cylinder does not exceed a dew point of −50 °F (−45.6 °C) at 1 atmosphere pressure.

(i)(5) The employer shall ensure that compressors used to supply breathing air to respirators are constructed and situated so as to:

(i)(5)(i) Prevent entry of contaminated air into the air-supply system;

(i)(5)(ii) Minimize moisture content so that the dew point at 1 atmosphere pressure is 10 degrees F (5.56 °C) below the ambient temperature;

(i)(5)(iii) Have suitable in-line air-purifying sorbent beds and filters to further ensure breathing air quality. Sorbent beds and filters shall be maintained and replaced or refurbished periodically following the manufacturer's instructions.

(i)(5)(iv) Have a tag containing the most recent change date and the signature of the person authorized by the employer to perform the change. The tag shall be maintained at the compressor.

(i)(6) For compressors that are not oil-lubricated, the employer shall ensure that carbon monoxide levels in the breathing air do not exceed 10 ppm.

(i)(7) OI For oil-lubricated compressors, the employer shall use a high-temperature or carbon monoxide alarm, or both, to monitor carbon monoxide levels. If only high-temperature alarms are used, the air supply shall be monitored at intervals sufficient to prevent carbon monoxide in the breathing air from exceeding 10 ppm.

(i)(8) OI The employer shall ensure that breathing air couplings are incompatible with outlets for nonrespirable worksite air or other gas systems. No asphyxiating substance shall be introduced into breathing air lines.

(i)(9) The employer shall use only the respirator manufacturer's NIOSH-approved breathing-gas containers, marked and maintained in accordance with the Quality Assurance provisions of the NIOSH approval for the SCBA as issued in accordance with the NIOSH respirator-certification Standard at 42 CFR Part 84.

(j) Identification of filters, cartridges, and canisters The employer shall ensure that all filters, cartridges and canisters used in the workplace are labeled and color coded with the NIOSH approval label and that the label is not removed and remains legible.

(k) OI **Training and information** This paragraph requires the employer to provide effective training to employees who are required to use respirators. The training must be comprehensive, understandable, and recur annually, and more often if necessary. This paragraph also requires the employer to provide the basic information on respirators in Appendix D of this section to employees who wear respirators when not required by this section or by the employer to do so.

(k)(1) The employer shall ensure that each employee can demonstrate knowledge of at least the following:

(k)(1)(i) Why the respirator is necessary and how improper fit, usage, or maintenance can compromise the protective effect of the respirator;

(k)(1)(ii) What the limitations and capabilities of the respirator are;

(k)(1)(iii) How to use the respirator effectively in emergency situations, including situations in which the respirator malfunctions;

(k)(1)(iv) How to inspect, put on and remove, use, and check the seals of the respirator;

(k)(1)(v) What the procedures are for maintenance and storage of the respirator;

(k)(1)(vi) How to recognize medical signs and symptoms that may limit or prevent the effective use of respirators; and

(k)(1)(vii) The general requirements of this section.

(k)(2) The training shall be conducted in a manner that is understandable to the employee.

(k)(3) The employer shall provide the training prior to requiring the employee to use a respirator in the workplace.

(k)(4) An employer who is able to demonstrate that a new employee has received training within the last 12 months that addresses the elements specified in paragraph (k)(1)(i) through (vii) is not required to repeat such training provided that, as required by paragraph (k)(1), the employee can demonstrate knowledge of those element(s). Previous training not repeated initially by the employer must be provided no later than 12 months from the date of the previous training.

(k)(5) Retraining shall be administered annually, and when the following situations occur:

(k)(5)(i) Changes in the workplace or the type of respirator render previous training obsolete;

(k)(5)(ii) OI Inadequacies in the employee's knowledge or use of the respirator indicate that the employee has not retained the requisite understanding or skill; or

(k)(5)(iii) Any other situation arises in which retraining appears necessary to ensure safe respirator use.

(k)(6) The basic advisory information on respirators, as presented in Appendix D of this Section, shall be provided by the employer in any written or oral format, to employees who wear respirators when such use is not required by this section or by the employer.

(l) Program evaluation This section requires the employer to conduct evaluations of the workplace to ensure that the written respiratory protection program is being properly implemented, and to consult employees to ensure that they are using the respirators properly.

(l)(1) The employer shall conduct evaluations of the workplace as necessary to ensure that the provisions of the current written program are being effectively implemented and that it continues to be effective.

(l)(2) The employer shall regularly consult employees required to use respirators to assess the employees' views on program effectiveness and to identify any problems. Any problems that are identified during this assessment shall be corrected. Factors to be assessed include, but are not limited to:

(l)(2)(i) Respirator fit (including the ability to use the respirator without interfering with effective workplace performance);

(l)(2)(ii) Appropriate respirator selection for the hazards to which the employee is exposed;

(l)(2)(iii) Proper respirator use under the workplace conditions the employee encounters; and

(l)(2)(iv) Proper respirator maintenance.

(m) OI **Recordkeeping** This section requires the employer to establish and retain written information regarding medical evaluations, fit testing, and the respirator program. This information will facilitate employee involvement in the respirator program, assist the employer in auditing the adequacy of the program, and provide a record for compliance determinations by OSHA.

(m)(1) **Medical evaluation** Records of medical evaluations required by this section must be retained and made available in accordance with 29 CFR §1910.1020.

(m)(2) OI **Fit testing**

(m)(2)(i) The employer shall establish a record of the qualitative and quantitative fit tests administered to an employee including:

(m)(2)(i)(A) The name or identification of the employee tested;

(m)(2)(i)(B) Type of fit test performed;

(m)(2)(i)(C) Specific make, model, style, and size of respirator tested;

(m)(2)(i)(D) Date of test; and

(m)(2)(i)(E) The pass/fail results for QLFTs or the fit factor and strip chart recording or other recording of the test results for QNFTs.

(m)(2)(ii) Fit test records shall be retained for respirator users until the next fit test is administered.

(m)(3) A written copy of the current respirator program shall be retained by the employer.

(m)(4) OI Written materials required to be retained under this paragraph shall be made available upon request to affected employees and to the Assistant Secretary or designee for examination and copying.

(n) Effective date Paragraphs (d)(3)(i)(A) and (d)(3)(i)(B) of this section become effective November 22, 2006.

(o) Appendices Compliance with Appendix A, Appendix B–1, Appendix B–2, Appendix C, and Appendix D to this section are mandatory.

§1910.134 Appendix A OI
Fit testing procedures
(Mandatory)

Part I. OSHA-Accepted Fit Test Protocols

A. Fit Testing Procedures—General Requirements

The employer shall conduct fit testing using the following procedures. The requirements in this Appendix apply to all OSHA-accepted fit test methods, both QLFT and QNFT.

1. The test subject shall be allowed to pick the most acceptable respirator from a sufficient number of respirator models and sizes so that the respirator is acceptable to, and correctly fits, the user.
2. Prior to the selection process, the test subject shall be shown how to put on a respirator, how it should be positioned on the face, how to set strap tension and how to determine an acceptable fit. A mirror shall be available to assist the subject in evaluating the fit and positioning of the respirator. This instruction may not constitute the subject's formal training on respirator use, because it is only a review.
3. The test subject shall be informed that he/she is being asked to select the respirator that provides the most acceptable fit. Each respirator represents a different size and shape, and if fitted and used properly, will provide adequate protection.

4. The test subject shall be instructed to hold each chosen facepiece up to the face and eliminate those that obviously do not give an acceptable fit.
5. The more acceptable facepieces are noted in case the one selected proves unacceptable; the most comfortable mask is donned and worn at least five minutes to assess comfort. Assistance in assessing comfort can be given by discussing the points in the following item A.6. If the test subject is not familiar with using a particular respirator, the test subject shall be directed to don the mask several times and to adjust the straps each time to become adept at setting proper tension on the straps.
6. Assessment of comfort shall include a review of the following points with the test subject and allowing the test subject adequate time to determine the comfort of the respirator:
   (a) Position of the mask on the nose;
   (b) Room for eye protection;
   (c) Room to talk;
   (d) Position of mask on face and cheeks.
7. The following criteria shall be used to help determine the adequacy of the respirator fit:
   (a) Chin properly placed;
   (b) Adequate strap tension, not overly tightened;
   (c) Fit across nose bridge;
   (d) Respirator of proper size to span distance from nose to chin;
   (e) Tendency of respirator to slip;
   (f) Self-observation in mirror to evaluate fit and respirator position.
8. The test subject shall conduct a user seal check, either the negative and positive pressure seal checks described in Appendix B–1 of this section or those recommended by the respirator manufacturer which provide equivalent protection to the procedures in Appendix B–1. Before conducting the negative and positive pressure checks, the subject shall be told to seat the mask on the face by moving the head from side-to-side and up and down slowly while taking in a few slow deep breaths. Another facepiece shall be selected and retested if the test subject fails the user seal check tests.
9. The test shall not be conducted if there is any hair growth between the skin and the facepiece sealing surface, such as stubble beard growth, beard, mustache or sideburns which cross the respirator sealing surface. Any type of apparel which interferes with a satisfactory fit shall be altered or removed.
10. If a test subject exhibits difficulty in breathing during the tests, she or he shall be referred to a physician or other licensed health care professional, as appropriate, to determine whether the test subject can wear a respirator while performing her or his duties.
11. If the employee finds the fit of the respirator unacceptable, the test subject shall be given the opportunity to select a different respirator and to be retested.
12. Exercise regimen. Prior to the commencement of the fit test, the test subject shall be given a description of the fit test and the test subject's responsibilities during the test procedure. The description of the process shall include a description of the test exercises that the subject will be performing. The respirator to be tested shall be worn for at least 5 minutes before the start of the fit test.
13. The fit test shall be performed while the test subject is wearing any applicable safety equipment that may be worn during actual respirator use which could interfere with respirator fit.
14. Test Exercises
    (a) Employers must perform the following test exercises for all fit testing methods prescribed in this Appendix, except for the CNP quantitative fit testing protocol and the CNP REDON quantitative fit testing protocol. For these two protocols, employers must ensure that the test subjects (i.e. , employees) perform the exercise procedure specified in Part I.C.4(b) of this Appendix for the CNP quantitative fit testing protocol, or the exercise procedure described in Part I.C.5(b) of this Appendix for the CNP REDON quantitative fit-testing protocol. For the remaining fit testing methods, employers must ensure that employees perform the test exercises in the appropriate test environment in the following manner:
    (1) Normal breathing. In a normal standing position, without talking, the subject shall breathe normally;
    (2) Deep breathing. In a normal standing position, the subject shall breathe slowly and deeply, taking caution so as not to hyperventilate;
    (3) Turning head side to side. Standing in place, the subject shall slowly turn his/her head from side to side between the extreme positions on each side. The head shall be held at each extreme momentarily so the subject can inhale at each side;
    (4) Moving head up and down. Standing in place, the subject shall slowly move his/her head up and down. The subject shall be instructed to inhale in the up position (i.e., when looking toward the ceiling);
    (5) Talking. The subject shall talk out loud slowly and loud enough so as to be heard clearly by the test conductor. The subject can read from a prepared text such as the Rainbow Passage, count backward from 100, or recite a memorized poem or song.

    Rainbow Passage

    When the sunlight strikes raindrops in the air, they act like a prism and form a rainbow. The rainbow is a division of white light into many beautiful colors. These take the shape of a long round arch, with its path high above, and its two ends apparently beyond the horizon. There is, according to legend, a boiling pot of gold at one end. People look, but no one ever finds it. When a man looks for something beyond reach, his friends say he is looking for the pot of gold at the end of the rainbow.
    (6) Grimace. The test subject shall grimace by smiling or frowning. (This applies only to QNFT testing; it is not performed for QLFT)
    (7) Bending over. The test subject shall bend at the waist as if he/she were to touch his/her toes. Jogging in place shall be substituted for this exercise in those test environments such as shroud type QNFT or QLFT units that do not permit bending over at the waist.
    (8) Normal breathing. Same as exercise (1).

    (b) Each test exercise shall be performed for one minute except for the grimace exercise which shall be performed for 15 seconds. The test subject shall be questioned by the test conductor regarding the comfort of the respirator upon completion of the protocol. If it has become unacceptable, another model of respirator shall be tried. The respirator shall not be adjusted once the fit test exercises begin. Any adjustment voids the test, and the fit test must be repeated.

B. Qualitative Fit Test (QLFT) Protocols

1. General
   (a) The employer shall ensure that persons administering QLFT are able to prepare test solutions, calibrate equipment and perform tests properly, recognize invalid tests, and ensure that test equipment is in proper working order.
   (b) The employer shall ensure that QLFT equipment is kept clean and well maintained so as to operate within the parameters for which it was designed.
2. Isoamyl Acetate Protocol

   Note: This protocol is not appropriate to use for the fit testing of particulate respirators. If used to fit test particulate respirators, the respirator must be equipped with an organic vapor filter.

   (a) Odor Threshold Screening

   Odor threshold screening, performed without wearing a respirator, is intended to determine if the individual tested can detect the odor of isoamyl acetate at low levels.
   (1) Three 1 liter glass jars with metal lids are required.
   (2) Odor-free water (e.g., distilled or spring water) at approximately 25 °C (77 °F) shall be used for the solutions.
   (3) The isoamyl acetate (IAA) (also known at isopentyl acetate) stock solution is prepared by adding 1 ml of pure IAA to 800 ml of odor-free water in a 1 liter jar, closing the lid and shaking for 30 seconds. A new solution shall be prepared at least weekly.
   (4) The screening test shall be conducted in a room separate from the room used for actual fit testing. The two rooms shall be well-ventilated to prevent the odor of IAA from becoming evident in the general room air where testing takes place.
   (5) The odor test solution is prepared in a second jar by placing 0.4 ml of the stock solution into 500 ml of odor-free water using a clean dropper or pipette. The solution shall be shaken for 30 seconds and allowed to stand for two to three minutes so that the IAA concentration above the liquid may reach equilibrium. This solution shall be used for only one day.
   (6) A test blank shall be prepared in a third jar by adding 500 cc of odor-free water.
   (7) The odor test and test blank jar lids shall be labeled (e.g., 1 and 2) for jar identification. Labels shall be placed on the lids so that they can be peeled off periodically and switched to maintain the integrity of the test.
   (8) The following instruction shall be typed on a card and placed on the table in front of the two test jars (i.e., 1 and 2): "The purpose of this test is to determine if you can smell banana oil at a low concentration. The two bottles in front of you contain water. One of these bottles also contains a small amount of banana oil. Be sure the covers are on tight, then shake each bottle for two seconds. Unscrew the lid of each bottle, one at a time, and sniff at the mouth of the bottle. Indicate to the test conductor which bottle contains banana oil."

(9) The mixtures used in the IAA odor detection test shall be prepared in an area separate from where the test is performed, in order to prevent olfactory fatigue in the subject.

(10) If the test subject is unable to correctly identify the jar containing the odor test solution, the IAA qualitative fit test shall not be performed.

(11) If the test subject correctly identifies the jar containing the odor test solution, the test subject may proceed to respirator selection and fit testing.

(b) Isoamyl Acetate Fit Test

(1) The fit test chamber shall be a clear 55-gallon drum liner suspended inverted over a 2-foot diameter frame so that the top of the chamber is about 6 inches above the test subject's head. If no drum liner is available, a similar chamber shall be constructed using plastic sheeting. The inside top center of the chamber shall have a small hook attached.

(2) Each respirator used for the fitting and fit testing shall be equipped with organic vapor cartridges or offer protection against organic vapors.

(3) After selecting, donning, and properly adjusting a respirator, the test subject shall wear it to the fit testing room. This room shall be separate from the room used for odor threshold screening and respirator selection, and shall be well-ventilated, as by an exhaust fan or lab hood, to prevent general room contamination.

(4) A copy of the test exercises and any prepared text from which the subject is to read shall be taped to the inside of the test chamber.

(5) Upon entering the test chamber, the test subject shall be given a 6-inch by 5-inch piece of paper towel, or other porous, absorbent, single-ply material, folded in half and wetted with 0.75 ml of pure IAA. The test subject shall hang the wet towel on the hook at the top of the chamber. An IAA test swab or ampule may be substituted for the IAA wetted paper towel provided it has been demonstrated that the alternative IAA source will generate an IAA test atmosphere with a concentration equivalent to that generated by the paper towel method.

(6) Allow two minutes for the IAA test concentration to stabilize before starting the fit test exercises. This would be an appropriate time to talk with the test subject; to explain the fit test, the importance of his/her cooperation, and the purpose for the test exercises; or to demonstrate some of the exercises.

(7) If at any time during the test, the subject detects the banana-like odor of IAA, the test is failed. The subject shall quickly exit from the test chamber and leave the test area to avoid olfactory fatigue.

(8) If the test is failed, the subject shall return to the selection room and remove the respirator. The test subject shall repeat the odor sensitivity test, select and put on another respirator, return to the test area and again begin the fit test procedure described in (b)(1) through (7) above. The process continues until a respirator that fits well has been found. Should the odor sensitivity test be failed, the subject shall wait at least 5 minutes before retesting. Odor sensitivity will usually have returned by this time.

(9) If the subject passes the test, the efficiency of the test procedure shall be demonstrated by having the subject break the respirator face seal and take a breath before exiting the chamber.

(10) When the test subject leaves the chamber, the subject shall remove the saturated towel and return it to the person conducting the test, so that there is no significant IAA concentration buildup in the chamber during subsequent tests. The used towels shall be kept in a self-sealing plastic bag to keep the test area from being contaminated.

3. Saccharin Solution Aerosol Protocol

The entire screening and testing procedure shall be explained to the test subject prior to the conduct of the screening test.

(a) Taste threshold screening. The saccharin taste threshold screening, performed without wearing a respirator, is intended to determine whether the individual being tested can detect the taste of saccharin.

(1) During threshold screening as well as during fit testing, subjects shall wear an enclosure about the head and shoulders that is approximately 12 inches in diameter by 14 inches tall with at least the front portion clear and that allows free movements of the head when a respirator is worn. An enclosure substantially similar to the 3M hood assembly, parts #FT 14 and #FT 15 combined, is adequate.

(2) The test enclosure shall have a 3/4-inch (1.9 cm) hole in front of the test subject's nose and mouth area to accommodate the nebulizer nozzle.

(3) The test subject shall don the test enclosure. Throughout the threshold screening test, the test subject shall breathe through his/her slightly open mouth with tongue extended. The subject is instructed to report when he/she detects a sweet taste.

(4) Using a DeVilbiss Model 40 Inhalation Medication Nebulizer or equivalent, the test conductor shall spray the threshold check solution into the enclosure. The nozzle is directed away from the nose and mouth of the person. This nebulizer shall be clearly marked to distinguish it from the fit test solution nebulizer.

(5) The threshold check solution is prepared by dissolving 0.83 gram of sodium saccharin USP in 100 ml of warm water. It can be prepared by putting 1 ml of the fit test solution (see (b)(5) below) in 100 ml of distilled water.

(6) To produce the aerosol, the nebulizer bulb is firmly squeezed so that it collapses completely, then released and allowed to fully expand.

(7) Ten squeezes are repeated rapidly and then the test subject is asked whether the saccharin can be tasted. If the test subject reports tasting the sweet taste during the ten squeezes, the screening test is completed. The taste threshold is noted as ten regardless of the number of squeezes actually completed.

(8) If the first response is negative, ten more squeezes are repeated rapidly and the test subject is again asked whether the saccharin is tasted. If the test subject reports tasting the sweet taste during the second ten squeezes, the screening test is completed. The taste threshold is noted as twenty regardless of the number of squeezes actually completed.

(9) If the second response is negative, ten more squeezes are repeated rapidly and the test subject is again asked whether the saccharin is tasted. If the test subject reports tasting the sweet taste during the third set of ten squeezes, the screening test is completed. The taste threshold is noted as thirty regardless of the number of squeezes actually completed.

(10) The test conductor will take note of the number of squeezes required to solicit a taste response.

(11) If the saccharin is not tasted after 30 squeezes (step 10), the test subject is unable to taste saccharin and may not perform the saccharin fit test.

Note to paragraph 3(a): If the test subject eats or drinks something sweet before the screening test, he/she may be unable to taste the weak saccharin solution.

(12) If a taste response is elicited, the test subject shall be asked to take note of the taste for reference in the fit test.

(13) Correct use of the nebulizer means that approximately 1 ml of liquid is used at a time in the nebulizer body.

(14) The nebulizer shall be thoroughly rinsed in water, shaken dry, and refilled at least each morning and afternoon or at least every four hours.

(b) Saccharin solution aerosol fit test procedure.

(1) The test subject may not eat, drink (except plain water), smoke, or chew gum for 15 minutes before the test.

(2) The fit test uses the same enclosure described in 3. (a) above.

(3) The test subject shall don the enclosure while wearing the respirator selected in section I. A. of this Appendix. The respirator shall be properly adjusted and equipped with a particulate filter(s).

(4) A second DeVilbiss Model 40 Inhalation Medication Nebulizer or equivalent is used to spray the fit test solution into the enclosure. This nebulizer shall be clearly marked to distinguish it from the screening test solution nebulizer.

(5) The fit test solution is prepared by adding 83 grams of sodium saccharin to 100 ml of warm water.

(6) As before, the test subject shall breathe through the slightly open mouth with tongue extended, and report if he/she tastes the sweet taste of saccharin.

(7) The nebulizer is inserted into the hole in the front of the enclosure and an initial concentration of saccharin fit test solution is sprayed into the enclosure using the same number of squeezes (either 10, 20 or 30 squeezes) based on the number of squeezes required to elicit a taste response as noted during the screening test. A minimum of 10 squeezes is required.

(8) After generating the aerosol, the test subject shall be instructed to perform the exercises in section I. A. 14. of this Appendix.

(9) Every 30 seconds the aerosol concentration shall be replenished using one half the original number of squeezes used initially (e.g., 5, 10 or 15).

(10) The test subject shall indicate to the test conductor if at any time during the fit test the taste of saccharin is detected. If the test subject does not report tasting the saccharin, the test is passed.

(11) If the taste of saccharin is detected, the fit is deemed unsatisfactory and the test is failed. A different respirator shall be tried and the entire test procedure is repeated (taste threshold screening and fit testing).

(12) Since the nebulizer has a tendency to clog during use, the test operator must make periodic checks of the nebulizer to ensure that it is not clogged. If clogging is found at the end of the test session, the test is invalid.

4. Bitrex™ (Denatonium Benzoate) Solution Aerosol Qualitative Fit Test Protocol

The Bitrex™ (Denatonium benzoate) solution aerosol QLFT protocol uses the published saccharin test protocol because that protocol is widely accepted. Bitrex is routinely used as a taste aversion agent in household liquids which children should not be drinking and is endorsed by the American Medical Association, the National Safety Council, and the American Association of Poison Control Centers. The entire screening and testing procedure shall be explained to the test subject prior to the conduct of the screening test.

(a) Taste Threshold Screening

The Bitrex taste threshold screening, performed without wearing a respirator, is intended to determine whether the individual being tested can detect the taste of Bitrex.

(1) During threshold screening as well as during fit testing, subjects shall wear an enclosure about the head and shoulders that is approximately 12 inches (30.5 cm) in diameter by 14 inches (35.6 cm) tall. The front portion of the enclosure shall be clear from the respirator and allow free movement of the head when a respirator is worn. An enclosure substantially similar to the 3M hood assembly, parts # FT 14 and # FT 15 combined, is adequate.

(2) The test enclosure shall have a ¾ inch (1.9 cm) hole in front of the test subject's nose and mouth area to accommodate the nebulizer nozzle.

(3) The test subject shall don the test enclosure. Throughout the threshold screening test, the test subject shall breathe through his or her slightly open mouth with tongue extended. The subject is instructed to report when he/she detects a bitter taste.

(4) Using a DeVilbiss Model 40 Inhalation Medication Nebulizer or equivalent, the test conductor shall spray the Threshold Check Solution into the enclosure. This Nebulizer shall be clearly marked to distinguish it from the fit test solution nebulizer.

(5) The Threshold Check Solution is prepared by adding 13.5 milligrams of Bitrex to 100 ml of 5% salt (NaCl) solution in distilled water.

(6) To produce the aerosol, the nebulizer bulb is firmly squeezed so that the bulb collapses completely, and is then released and allowed to fully expand.

(7) An initial ten squeezes are repeated rapidly and then the test subject is asked whether the Bitrex can be tasted. If the test subject reports tasting the bitter taste during the ten squeezes, the screening test is completed. The taste threshold is noted as ten regardless of the number of squeezes actually completed.

(8) If the first response is negative, ten more squeezes are repeated rapidly and the test subject is again asked whether the Bitrex is tasted. If the test subject reports tasting the bitter taste during the second ten squeezes, the screening test is completed. The taste threshold is noted as twenty regardless of the number of squeezes actually completed.

(9) If the second response is negative, ten more squeezes are repeated rapidly and the test subject is again asked whether the Bitrex is tasted. If the test subject reports tasting the bitter taste during the third set of ten squeezes, the screening test is completed. The taste threshold is noted as thirty regardless of the number of squeezes actually completed.

(10) The test conductor will take note of the number of squeezes required to solicit a taste response.

(11) If the Bitrex is not tasted after 30 squeezes (step 10), the test subject is unable to taste Bitrex and may not perform the Bitrex fit test.

(12) If a taste response is elicited, the test subject shall be asked to take note of the taste for reference in the fit test.

(13) Correct use of the nebulizer means that approximately 1 ml of liquid is used at a time in the nebulizer body.

(14) The nebulizer shall be thoroughly rinsed in water, shaken to dry, and refilled at least each morning and afternoon or at least every four hours.

(b) Bitrex Solution Aerosol Fit Test Procedure

(1) The test subject may not eat, drink (except plain water), smoke, or chew gum for 15 minutes before the test.

(2) The fit test uses the same enclosure as that described in 4. (a) above.

(3) The test subject shall don the enclosure while wearing the respirator selected according to section I. A. of this Appendix. The respirator shall be properly adjusted and equipped with any type particulate filter(s).

(4) A second DeVilbiss Model 40 Inhalation Medication Nebulizer or equivalent is used to spray the fit test solution into the enclosure. This nebulizer shall be clearly marked to distinguish it from the screening test solution nebulizer.

(5) The fit test solution is prepared by adding 337.5 mg of Bitrex to 200 ml of a 5% salt (NaCl) solution in warm water.

(6) As before, the test subject shall breathe through his or her slightly open mouth with tongue extended, and be instructed to report if he/she tastes the bitter taste of Bitrex.

(7) The nebulizer is inserted into the hole in the front of the enclosure and an initial concentration of the fit test solution is sprayed into the enclosure using the same number of squeezes (either 10, 20 or 30 squeezes) based on the number of squeezes required to elicit a taste response as noted during the screening test.

(8) After generating the aerosol, the test subject shall be instructed to perform the exercises in section I. A. 14. of this Appendix.

(9) Every 30 seconds the aerosol concentration shall be replenished using one half the number of squeezes used initially (e.g., 5, 10 or 15).

(10) The test subject shall indicate to the test conductor if at any time during the fit test the taste of Bitrex is detected. If the test subject does not report tasting the Bitrex, the test is passed.

(11) If the taste of Bitrex is detected, the fit is deemed unsatisfactory and the test is failed. A different respirator shall be tried and the entire test procedure is repeated (taste threshold screening and fit testing).

5. Irritant Smoke (Stannic Chloride) Protocol

This qualitative fit test uses a person's response to the irritating chemicals released in the "smoke" produced by a stannic chloride ventilation smoke tube to detect leakage into the respirator.

(a) General Requirements and Precautions

(1) The respirator to be tested shall be equipped with high efficiency particulate air (HEPA) or P100 series filter(s).

(2) Only stannic chloride smoke tubes shall be used for this protocol.

(3) No form of test enclosure or hood for the test subject shall be used.

(4) The smoke can be irritating to the eyes, lungs, and nasal passages. The test conductor shall take precautions to minimize the test subject's exposure to irritant smoke. Sensitivity varies, and certain individuals may respond to a greater degree to irritant smoke. Care shall be taken when performing the sensitivity screening checks that determine whether the test subject can detect irritant smoke to use only the minimum amount of smoke necessary to elicit a response from the test subject.

(5) The fit test shall be performed in an area with adequate ventilation to prevent exposure of the person conducting the fit test or the build-up of irritant smoke in the general atmosphere.

(b) Sensitivity Screening Check

The person to be tested must demonstrate his or her ability to detect a weak concentration of the irritant smoke.

(1) The test operator shall break both ends of a ventilation smoke tube containing stannic chloride, and attach one end of the smoke tube to a low flow air pump set to deliver 200 milliliters per minute, or an aspirator squeeze bulb. The test operator shall cover the other end of the smoke tube with a short piece of tubing to prevent potential injury from the jagged end of the smoke tube.

(2) The test operator shall advise the test subject that the smoke can be irritating to the eyes, lungs, and nasal passages and instruct the subject to keep his/her eyes closed while the test is performed.

(3) The test subject shall be allowed to smell a weak concentration of the irritant smoke before the respirator is donned to become familiar with its irritating properties and to determine if he/

she can detect the irritating properties of the smoke. The test operator shall carefully direct a small amount of the irritant smoke in the test subject's direction to determine that he/she can detect it.

(c) Irritant Smoke Fit Test Procedure

(1) The person being fit tested shall don the respirator without assistance, and perform the required user seal check(s).

(2) The test subject shall be instructed to keep his/her eyes closed.

(3) The test operator shall direct the stream of irritant smoke from the smoke tube toward the faceseal area of the test subject, using the low flow pump or the squeeze bulb. The test operator shall begin at least 12 inches from the facepiece and move the smoke stream around the whole perimeter of the mask. The operator shall gradually make two more passes around the perimeter of the mask, moving to within six inches of the respirator.

(4) If the person being tested has not had an involuntary response and/or detected the irritant smoke, proceed with the test exercises.

(5) The exercises identified in section I.A. 14. of this Appendix shall be performed by the test subject while the respirator seal is being continually challenged by the smoke, directed around the perimeter of the respirator at a distance of six inches.

(6) If the person being fit tested reports detecting the irritant smoke at any time, the test is failed. The person being retested must repeat the entire sensitivity check and fit test procedure.

(7) Each test subject passing the irritant smoke test without evidence of a response (involuntary cough, irritation) shall be given a second sensitivity screening check, with the smoke from the same smoke tube used during the fit test, once the respirator has been removed, to determine whether he/she still reacts to the smoke. Failure to evoke a response shall void the fit test.

(8) If a response is produced during this second sensitivity check, then the fit test is passed.

C. Quantitative Fit Test (QNFT) Protocols

The following quantitative fit testing procedures have been demonstrated to be acceptable: Quantitative fit testing using a non-hazardous test aerosol (such as corn oil, polyethylene glycol 400 [PEG 400], di-2-ethyl hexyl sebacate [DEHS], or sodium chloride) generated in a test chamber, and employing instrumentation to quantify the fit of the respirator; Quantitative fit testing using ambient aerosol as the test agent and appropriate instrumentation (condensation nuclei counter) to quantify the respirator fit; Quantitative fit testing using controlled negative pressure and appropriate instrumentation to measure the volumetric leak rate of a facepiece to quantify the respirator fit.

1. General

(a) The employer shall ensure that persons administering QNFT are able to calibrate equipment and perform tests properly, recognize invalid tests, calculate fit factors properly and ensure that test equipment is in proper working order.

(b) The employer shall ensure that QNFT equipment is kept clean, and is maintained and calibrated according to the manufacturer's instructions so as to operate at the parameters for which it was designed.

2. Generated Aerosol Quantitative Fit Testing Protocol

(a) Apparatus

(1) Instrumentation Aerosol generation, dilution, and measurement systems using particulates (corn oil, polyethylene glycol 400 [PEG 400], di-2-ethyl hexyl sebacate [DEHS] or sodium chloride) as test aerosols shall be used for quantitative fit testing.

(2) Test chamber The test chamber shall be large enough to permit all test subjects to perform freely all required exercises without disturbing the test agent concentration or the measurement apparatus. The test chamber shall be equipped and constructed so that the test agent is effectively isolated from the ambient air, yet uniform in concentration throughout the chamber.

(3) When testing air-purifying respirators, the normal filter or cartridge element shall be replaced with a high efficiency particulate air (HEPA) or P100 series filter supplied by the same manufacturer.

(4) The sampling instrument shall be selected so that a computer record or strip chart record may be made of the test showing the rise and fall of the test agent concentration with each inspiration and expiration at fit factors of at least 2,000. Integrators or computers that integrate the amount of test agent penetration leakage into the respirator for each exercise may be used provided a record of the readings is made.

(5) The combination of substitute air-purifying elements, test agent and test agent concentration shall be such that the test subject is not exposed in excess of an established exposure limit for the test agent at any time during the testing process, based upon the length of the exposure and the exposure limit duration.

(6) The sampling port on the test specimen respirator shall be placed and constructed so that no leakage occurs around the port (e.g., where the respirator is probed), a free air flow is allowed into the sampling line at all times, and there is no interference with the fit or performance of the respirator. The in-mask sampling device (probe) shall be designed and used so that the air sample is drawn from the breathing zone of the test subject, midway between the nose and mouth and with the probe extending into the facepiece cavity at least 1/4 inch.

(7) The test setup shall permit the person administering the test to observe the test subject inside the chamber during the test.

(8) The equipment generating the test atmosphere shall maintain the concentration of test agent constant to within a 10 percent variation for the duration of the test.

(9) The time lag (interval between an event and the recording of the event on the strip chart or computer or integrator) shall be kept to a minimum. There shall be a clear association between the occurrence of an event and its being recorded.

(10) The sampling line tubing for the test chamber atmosphere and for the respirator sampling port shall be of equal diameter and of the same material. The length of the two lines shall be equal.

(11) The exhaust flow from the test chamber shall pass through an appropriate filter (i.e., high efficiency particulate filter) before release.

(12) When sodium chloride aerosol is used, the relative humidity inside the test chamber shall not exceed 50 percent.

(13) The limitations of instrument detection shall be taken into account when determining the fit factor.

(14) Test respirators shall be maintained in proper working order and be inspected regularly for deficiencies such as cracks or missing valves and gaskets.

(b) Procedural Requirements

(1) When performing the initial user seal check using a positive or negative pressure check, the sampling line shall be crimped closed in order to avoid air pressure leakage during either of these pressure checks.

(2) The use of an abbreviated screening QLFT test is optional. Such a test may be utilized in order to quickly identify poor fitting respirators that passed the positive and/or negative pressure test and reduce the amount of QNFT time. The use of the CNC QNFT instrument in the count mode is another optional method to obtain a quick estimate of fit and eliminate poor fitting respirators before going on to perform a full QNFT.

(3) A reasonably stable test agent concentration shall be measured in the test chamber prior to testing. For canopy or shower curtain types of test units, the determination of the test agent's stability may be established after the test subject has entered the test environment.

(4) Immediately after the subject enters the test chamber, the test agent concentration inside the respirator shall be measured to ensure that the peak penetration does not exceed 5 percent for a half mask or 1 percent for a full facepiece respirator.

(5) A stable test agent concentration shall be obtained prior to the actual start of testing.

(6) Respirator restraining straps shall not be over-tightened for testing. The straps shall be adjusted by the wearer without assistance from other persons to give a reasonably comfortable fit typical of normal use. The respirator shall not be adjusted once the fit test exercises begin.

(7) The test shall be terminated whenever any single peak penetration exceeds 5 percent for half masks and 1 percent for full facepiece respirators. The test subject shall be refitted and retested.

(8) Calculation of fit factors

(i) The fit factor shall be determined for the quantitative fit test by taking the ratio of the average chamber concentration to the concentration measured inside the respirator for each test exercise except the grimace exercise.

(ii) The average test chamber concentration shall be calculated as the arithmetic average of the concentration measured before and after each test (i.e., 7 exercises) or the arithmetic average of the concentration measured before and after each exercise or the true average measured continuously during the respirator sample.

(iii) The concentration of the challenge agent inside the respirator shall be determined by one of the following methods:

(A) Average peak penetration method means the method of determining test agent penetration into the respirator utilizing a strip chart recorder, integrator, or computer. The agent penetration is determined by an average of the peak heights on the graph or by computer integration, for each exercise except the grimace exercise. Integrators or computers that calculate the actual test agent penetration into the respirator for each exercise will also be considered to meet the requirements of the average peak penetration method;

(B) Maximum peak penetration method means the method of determining test agent penetration in the respirator as determined by strip chart recordings of the test. The highest peak penetration for a given exercise is taken to be representative of average penetration into the respirator for that exercise;

(C) Integration by calculation of the area under the individual peak for each exercise except the grimace exercise. This includes computerized integration;

(D) The calculation of the overall fit factor using individual exercise fit factors involves first converting the exercise fit factors to penetration values, determining the average, and then converting that result back to a fit factor. This procedure is described in the following equation:

$$\text{Overall Fit Factor} = \frac{\text{Number of exercises}}{1/ff_1+1/ff_2+1/ff_3+1/ff_4+1/ff_5+1/ff_7+1/ff_8}$$

Where ff1, ff2, ff3, etc. are the fit factors for exercises 1, 2, 3, etc.

(9) The test subject shall not be permitted to wear a half mask or quarter facepiece respirator unless a minimum fit factor of 100 is obtained, or a full facepiece respirator unless a minimum fit factor of 500 is obtained.

(10) Filters used for quantitative fit testing shall be replaced whenever increased breathing resistance is encountered, or when the test agent has altered the integrity of the filter media.

3. Ambient aerosol condensation nuclei counter (CNC) quantitative fit testing protocol

The ambient aerosol condensation nuclei counter (CNC) quantitative fit testing (Portacount™) protocol quantitatively fit tests respirators with the use of a probe. The probed respirator is only used for quantitative fit tests. A probed respirator has a special sampling device, installed on the respirator, that allows the probe to sample the air from inside the mask. A probed respirator is required for each make, style, model, and size that the employer uses and can be obtained from the respirator manufacturer or distributor. The CNC instrument manufacturer, TSI Inc., also provides probe attachments (TSI sampling adapters) that permit fit testing in an employee's own respirator. A minimum fit factor pass level of at least 100 is necessary for a half-mask respirator and a minimum fit factor pass level of at least 500 is required for a full facepiece negative pressure respirator. The entire screening and testing procedure shall be explained to the test subject prior to the conduct of the screening test.

(a) Portacount Fit Test Requirements

(1) Check the respirator to make sure the sampling probe and line are properly attached to the facepiece and that the respirator is fitted with a particulate filter capable of preventing significant penetration by the ambient particles used for the fit test (e.g., NIOSH 42 CFR 84 series 100, series 99, or series 95 particulate filter) per manufacturer's instruction.

(2) Instruct the person to be tested to don the respirator for five minutes before the fit test starts. This purges the ambient particles trapped inside the respirator and permits the wearer to make certain the respirator is comfortable. This individual shall already have been trained on how to wear the respirator properly.

(3) Check the following conditions for the adequacy of the respirator fit: Chin properly placed; Adequate strap tension, not overly tightened; Fit across nose bridge; Respirator of proper size to span distance from nose to chin; Tendency of the respirator to slip; Self-observation in a mirror to evaluate fit and respirator position.

(4) Have the person wearing the respirator do a user seal check. If leakage is detected, determine the cause. If leakage is from a poorly fitting facepiece, try another size of the same model respirator, or another model of respirator.

(5) Follow the manufacturer's instructions for operating the Portacount and proceed with the test.

(6) The test subject shall be instructed to perform the exercises in section I. A. 14. of this Appendix.

(7) After the test exercises, the test subject shall be questioned by the test conductor regarding the comfort of the respirator upon completion of the protocol. If it has become unacceptable, another model of respirator shall be tried.

(b) Portacount Test Instrument

(1) The Portacount will automatically stop and calculate the overall fit factor for the entire set of exercises. The overall fit factor is what counts. The Pass or Fail message will indicate whether or not the test was successful. If the test was a Pass, the fit test is over.

(2) Since the pass or fail criterion of the Portacount is user programmable, the test operator shall ensure that the pass or fail criterion meet the requirements for minimum respirator performance in this Appendix.

(3) A record of the test needs to be kept on file, assuming the fit test was successful. The record must contain the test subject's name; overall fit factor; make, model, style, and size of respirator used; and date tested.

4. Controlled negative pressure (CNP) quantitative fit testing protocol

The CNP protocol provides an alternative to aerosol fit test methods. The CNP fit test method technology is based on exhausting air from a temporarily sealed respirator facepiece to generate and then maintain a constant negative pressure inside the facepiece. The rate of air exhaust is controlled so that a constant negative pressure is maintained in the respirator during the fit test. The level of pressure is selected to replicate the mean inspiratory pressure that causes leakage into the respirator under normal use conditions. With pressure held constant, air flow out of the respirator is equal to air flow into the respirator. Therefore, measurement of the exhaust stream that is required to hold the pressure in the temporarily sealed respirator constant yields a direct measure of leakage air flow into the respirator. The CNP fit test method measures leak rates through the facepiece as a method for determining the facepiece fit for negative pressure respirators. The CNP instrument manufacturer Occupational Health Dynamics of Birmingham, Alabama also provides attachments (sampling manifolds) that replace the filter cartridges to permit fit testing in an employee's own respirator. To perform the test, the test subject closes his or her mouth and holds his/her breath, after which an air pump removes air from the respirator facepiece at a pre-selected constant pressure. The facepiece fit is expressed as the leak rate through the facepiece, expressed as milliliters per minute. The quality and validity of the CNP fit tests are determined by the degree to which the in-mask pressure tracks the test pressure during the system measurement time of approximately five seconds. Instantaneous feedback in the form of a real-time pressure trace of the in-mask pressure is provided and used to determine test validity and quality. A minimum fit factor pass level of 100 is necessary for a half-mask respirator and a minimum fit factor of at least 500 is required for a full facepiece respirator. The entire screening and testing procedure shall be explained to the test subject prior to the conduct of the screening test.

(a) CNP Fit Test Requirements.

(1) The instrument shall have a non-adjustable test pressure of 15.0 mm water pressure.

(2) The CNP system defaults selected for test pressure shall be set at −15 mm of water (-0.58 inches of water) and the modeled inspiratory flow rate shall be 53.8 liters per minute for performing fit tests.

Note: CNP systems have built-in capability to conduct fit testing that is specific to unique work rate, mask, and gender situations that might apply in a specific workplace. Use of system default values, which were selected to represent respirator wear with medium cartridge resistance at a low-moderate work rate, will allow inter-test comparison of the respirator fit.

(3) The individual who conducts the CNP fit testing shall be thoroughly trained to perform the test.

(4) The respirator filter or cartridge needs to be replaced with the CNP test manifold. The inhalation valve downstream from the manifold either needs to be temporarily removed or propped open.

(5) The employer must train the test subject to hold his or her breath for at least 10 seconds.

(6) The test subject must don the test respirator without any assistance from the test administrator who is conducting the CNP fit test. The respirator must not be adjusted once the fit-test exercises begin. Any adjustment voids the test, and the test subject must repeat the fit test.

(7) The QNFT protocol shall be followed according to section I. C. 1. of this Appendix with an exception for the CNP test exercises.

(b) CNP Test Exercises

(1) Normal breathing In a normal standing position, without talking, the subject shall breathe normally for 1 minute. After the normal breathing exercise, the subject needs to hold head straight ahead and hold his or her breath for 10 seconds during the test measurement.

(2) Deep breathing In a normal standing position, the subject shall breathe slowly and deeply for 1 minute, being careful not to hyperventilate. After the deep breathing exercise, the subject shall hold his or her head straight ahead and hold his or her breath for 10 seconds during test measurement.

(3) Turning head side to side Standing in place, the subject shall slowly turn his or her head from side to side between the extreme positions on each side for 1 minute. The head shall be held at each extreme momentarily so the subject can inhale at each side. After the turning head side to side exercise, the subject needs to hold head full left and hold his or her breath for 10 seconds during test measurement. Next, the subject needs to hold head full right and hold his or her breath for 10 seconds during test measurement.

(4) Moving head up and down Standing in place, the subject shall slowly move his or her head up and down for 1 minute. The subject shall be instructed to inhale in the up position (i.e., when looking toward the ceiling). After the moving head up and down exercise, the subject shall hold his or her head full up and hold his or her breath for 10 seconds during test measurement. Next, the subject shall hold his or her head full down and hold his or her breath for 10 seconds during test measurement.

(5) Talking The subject shall talk out loud slowly and loud enough so as to be heard clearly by the test conductor. The subject can read from a prepared text such as the Rainbow Passage, count backward from 100, or recite a memorized poem or song for 1 minute. After the talking exercise, the subject shall hold his or her head straight ahead and hold his or her breath for 10 seconds during the test measurement.

(6) Grimace The test subject shall grimace by smiling or frowning for 15 seconds.

(7) Bending Over The test subject shall bend at the waist as if he or she were to touch his or her toes for 1 minute. Jogging in place shall be substituted for this exercise in those test environments such as shroud-type QNFT units that prohibit bending at the waist. After the bending over exercise, the subject shall hold his or her head straight ahead and hold his or her breath for 10 seconds during the test measurement.

(8) Normal Breathing The test subject shall remove and re-don the respirator within a one-minute period. Then, in a normal standing position, without talking, the subject shall breathe normally for 1 minute. After the normal breathing exercise, the subject shall hold his or her head straight ahead and hold his or her breath for 10 seconds during the test measurement. After the test exercises, the test subject shall be questioned by the test conductor regarding the comfort of the respirator upon completion of the protocol. If it has become unacceptable, another model of a respirator shall be tried.

(c) CNP Test Instrument

(1) The test instrument must have an effective audio-warning device, or a visual-warning device in the form of a screen tracing, that indicates when the test subject fails to hold his or her breath during the test. The test must be terminated and restarted from the beginning when the test subject fails to hold his or her breath during the test. The test subject then may be refitted and retested.

(2) A record of the test shall be kept on file, assuming the fit test was successful. The record must contain the test subject's name; overall fit factor; make, model, style and size of respirator used; and date tested.

5. Controlled negative pressure (CNP) REDON quantitative fit testing protocol

(a) When administering this protocol to test subjects, employers must comply with the requirements specified in paragraphs (a) and (c) of Part I.C.4 of this Appendix ("Controlled negative pressure (CNP) quantitative fit testing protocol"), as well as use the test exercises described below in paragraph (b) of this protocol instead of the test exercises specified in paragraph (b) of Part I.C.4 of this Appendix.

(b) Employers must ensure that each test subject being fit tested using this protocol follows the exercise and measurement procedures, including the order of administration, described below in Table A–1 of this Appendix.

Table A–1
CNP REDON Quantitative Fit Testing Protocol

Exercises[1]	Exercise procedure	Measurement procedure
Facing Forward	Stand and breathe normally, without talking, for 30 seconds	Face forward, while holding breath for 10 seconds
Bending Over	Bend at the waist, as if going to touch his or her toes, for 30 seconds	Face parallel to the floor, while holding breath for 10 seconds
Head Shaking	For about three seconds, shake head back and forth vigorously several times while shouting	Face forward, while holding breath for 10 seconds
REDON 1	Remove the respirator mask, loosen all facepiece straps, and then redon the respirator mask	Face forward, while holding breath for 10 seconds
REDON 2	Remove the respirator mask, loosen all facepiece straps, and then redon the respirator mask again	Face forward, while holding breath for 10 seconds

[1] Exercises are listed in the order in which they are to be administered.

(c) After completing the test exercises, the test administrator must question each test subject regarding the comfort of the respirator. When a test subject states that the respirator is unacceptable, the employer must ensure that the test administrator repeats the protocol using another respirator model.

(d) Employers must determine the overall fit factor for each test subject by calculating the harmonic mean of the fit testing exercises as follows:

$$\text{Overall Fit Factor} = \frac{N}{[1/FF_1 + 1/FF_2 + \ldots 1/FF_n]}$$

Where:
N = The number of exercises;
FF1= The fit factor for the first exercise;
FF2= The fit factor for the second exercise; and
FFN= The fit factor for the nth exercise.

Part II. New Fit Test Protocols

A. Any person may submit to OSHA an application for approval of a new fit test protocol. If the application meets the following criteria, OSHA will initiate a rulemaking proceeding under section 6(b)(7) of the OSH Act to determine whether to list the new protocol as an approved protocol in this Appendix A.

B. The application must include a detailed description of the proposed new fit test protocol. This application must be supported by either:

1. A test report prepared by an independent government research laboratory (e.g., Lawrence Livermore National Laboratory, Los Alamos National Laboratory, the National Institute for Standards and Technology) stating that the laboratory has tested the protocol and had found it to be accurate and reliable; or
2. An article that has been published in a peer-reviewed industrial hygiene journal describing the protocol and explaining how test data support the protocol's accuracy and reliability.

C. If OSHA determines that additional information is required before the Agency commences a rulemaking proceeding under this section, OSHA will so notify the applicant and afford the applicant the opportunity to submit the supplemental information. Initiation of a rulemaking proceeding will be deferred until OSHA has received and evaluated the supplemental information.

§1910.134 Appendix B-1
User seal check procedures
(Mandatory)

The individual who uses a tight-fitting respirator is to perform a user seal check to ensure that an adequate seal is achieved each time the respirator is put on. Either the positive and negative pressure checks listed in this

Appendix, or the respirator manufacturer's recommended user seal check method shall be used. User seal checks are not substitutes for qualitative or quantitative fit tests.

I. Facepiece Positive and/or Negative Pressure Checks

A. Positive pressure check. Close off the exhalation valve and exhale gently into the facepiece. The face fit is considered satisfactory if a slight positive pressure can be built up inside the facepiece without any evidence of outward leakage of air at the seal. For most respirators this method of leak testing requires the wearer to first remove the exhalation valve cover before closing off the exhalation valve and then carefully replacing it after the test.

B. Negative pressure check. Close off the inlet opening of the canister or cartridge(s) by covering with the palm of the hand(s) or by replacing the filter seal(s), inhale gently so that the facepiece collapses slightly, and hold the breath for ten seconds. The design of the inlet opening of some cartridges cannot be effectively covered with the palm of the hand. The test can be performed by covering the inlet opening of the cartridge with a thin latex or nitrile glove. If the facepiece remains in its slightly collapsed condition and no inward leakage of air is detected, the tightness of the respirator is considered satisfactory.

II. Manufacturer's Recommended User Seal Check Procedures

The respirator manufacturer's recommended procedures for performing a user seal check may be used instead of the positive and/or negative pressure check procedures provided that the employer demonstrates that the manufacturer's procedures are equally effective.

§1910.134 Appendix B-2 Respirator cleaning procedures (Mandatory)

These procedures are provided for employer use when cleaning respirators. They are general in nature, and the employer as an alternative may use the cleaning recommendations provided by the manufacturer of the respirators used by their employees, provided such procedures are as effective as those listed here in Appendix B–2. Equivalent effectiveness simply means that the procedures used must accomplish the objectives set forth in Appendix B–2, i.e., must ensure that the respirator is properly cleaned and disinfected in a manner that prevents damage to the respirator and does not cause harm to the user.

I. Procedures for Cleaning Respirators

A. Remove filters, cartridges, or canisters. Disassemble facepieces by removing speaking diaphragms, demand and pressure-demand valve assemblies, hoses, or any components recommended by the manufacturer. Discard or repair any defective parts.

B. Wash components in warm (43 °C [110 °F] maximum) water with a mild detergent or with a cleaner recommended by the manufacturer. A stiff bristle (not wire) brush may be used to facilitate the removal of dirt.

C. Rinse components thoroughly in clean, warm (43 °C [110 °F] maximum), preferably running water. Drain.

D. When the cleaner used does not contain a disinfecting agent, respirator components should be immersed for two minutes in one of the following:

1. Hypochlorite solution (50 ppm of chlorine) made by adding approximately one milliliter of laundry bleach to one liter of water at 43 °C (110 °F); or,
2. Aqueous solution of iodine (50 ppm iodine) made by adding approximately 0.8 milliliters of tincture of iodine (6–8 grams ammonium and/or potassium iodide/100 cc of 45% alcohol) to one liter of water at 43 °C (110 °F); or,
3. Other commercially available cleansers of equivalent disinfectant quality when used as directed, if their use is recommended or approved by the respirator manufacturer.

E. Rinse components thoroughly in clean, warm (43 °C [110 °F] maximum), preferably running water. Drain. The importance of thorough rinsing cannot be overemphasized. Detergents or disinfectants that dry on facepieces may result in dermatitis. In addition, some disinfectants may cause deterioration of rubber or corrosion of metal parts if not completely removed.

F. Components should be hand-dried with a clean lint-free cloth or air-dried.

G. Reassemble facepiece, replacing filters, cartridges, and canisters where necessary.

H. Test the respirator to ensure that all components work properly.

§1910.134 Appendix C OSHA respirator medical evaluation questionnaire (Mandatory)

To the employer:

Answers to questions in Section 1, and to question 9 in Section 2 of Part A, do not require a medical examination.

To the employee:

Your employer must allow you to answer this questionnaire during normal working hours, or at a time and place that is convenient to you. To maintain your confidentiality, your employer or supervisor must not look at or review your answers, and your employer must tell you how to deliver or send this questionnaire to the health care professional who will review it.

Part A. Section 1. (Mandatory)

The following information must be provided by every employee who has been selected to use any type of respirator (please print).

1. Today's date:_____________
2. Your name:____
3. Your age (to nearest year):_______ 4. Sex (circle one): Male / Female
5. Your height: ____ft. ____in. 6. Your weight: _____ lbs.
7. Your job title:____
8. A phone number where you can be reached by the health care professional who reviews this questionnaire (include the Area Code): ______________________
9. The best time to phone you at this number: ______________________
10. Has your employer told you how to contact the health care professional who will review this questionnaire (circle one): Yes / No
11. Check the type of respirator you will use (you can check more than one category):
   a. ___ N, R, or P disposable respirator (filter-mask, non-cartridge type only).
   b. ___ Other type (for example, half- or full-facepiece type, powered-air purifying, supplied-air, self-contained breathing apparatus).
12. Have you worn a respirator (circle one): Yes / No
   If "yes," what type(s): ______________________________

Part A. Section 2. (Mandatory) Questions 1 through 9 below must be answered by every employee who has been selected to use any type of respirator (please circle "yes" or "no").

1. Do you currently smoke tobacco, or have you smoked tobacco in the last month: Yes / No
2. Have you ever had any of the following conditions?
   a. Seizures: Yes / No
   b. Diabetes (sugar disease): Yes / No
   c. Allergic reactions that interfere with your breathing: Yes / No
   d. Claustrophobia (fear of closed-in places): Yes / No
   e. Trouble smelling odors: Yes / No
3. Have you ever had any of the following pulmonary or lung problems?
   a. Asbestosis: Yes / No b. Asthma: Yes / No
   c. Chronic bronchitis: Yes / No
   d. Emphysema: Yes / No e. Pneumonia: Yes / No
   f. Tuberculosis: Yes / No g. Silicosis: Yes / No
   h. Pneumothorax (collapsed lung): Yes / No
   i. Lung cancer: Yes / No
   j. Broken ribs: Yes / No
   k. Any chest injuries or surgeries: Yes / No
   l. Any other lung problem that you've been told about: Yes / No
4. Do you currently have any of the following symptoms of pulmonary or lung illness?
   a. Shortness of breath: Yes / No
   b. Shortness of breath when walking fast on level ground or walking up a slight hill or incline: Yes / No
   c. Shortness of breath when walking with other people at an ordinary pace on level ground: Yes / No
   d. Have to stop for breath when walking at your own pace on level ground: Yes / No
   e. Shortness of breath when washing or dressing yourself: Yes / No
   f. Shortness of breath that interferes with your job: Yes / No
   g. Coughing that produces phlegm (thick sputum): Yes / No
   h. Coughing that wakes you early in the morning: Yes / No
   i. Coughing that occurs mostly when you are lying down: Yes / No
   j. Coughing up blood in the last month: Yes / No
   k. Wheezing: Yes / No
   l. Wheezing that interferes with your job: Yes / No
   m. Chest pain when you breathe deeply: Yes / No
   n. Any other symptoms that you think may be related to lung problems: Yes / No
5. Have you ever had any of the following cardiovascular or heart problems?
   a. Heart attack: Yes / No b. Stroke: Yes / No
   c. Angina: Yes / No d. Heart failure: Yes / No
   e. Swelling in your legs or feet (not caused by walking): Yes / No
   f. Heart arrhythmia (heart beating irregularly): Yes / No
   g. High blood pressure: Yes / No
   h. Any other heart problem that you've been told about: Yes / No

6. Have you ever had any of the following cardiovascular or heart symptoms?
   a. Frequent pain or tightness in your chest: Yes / No
   b. Pain or tightness in your chest during physical activity: Yes / No
   c. Pain or tightness in your chest that interferes with your job: Yes / No
   d. In the past two years, have you noticed your heart skipping or missing a beat: Yes / No
   e. Heartburn or indigestion that is not related to eating: Yes / No
   f. Any other symptoms that you think may be related to heart or circulation problems: Yes / No

7. Do you currently take medication for any of the following problems?
   a. Breathing or lung problems: Yes / No
   b. Heart trouble: Yes / No
   c. Blood pressure: Yes / No
   d. Seizures: Yes / No

8. If you've used a respirator, have you ever had any of the following problems? (If you've never used a respirator, check the following space and go to question 9:) ___ Never used a respirator.
   a. Eye irritation: Yes / No
   b. Skin allergies or rashes: Yes / No
   c. Anxiety: Yes / No
   d. General weakness or fatigue: Yes / No
   e. Any other problem that interferes with your use of a respirator: Yes / No

9. Would you like to talk to the health care professional who will review this questionnaire about your answers to this questionnaire: Yes / No

Questions 10 to 15 below must be answered by every employee who has been selected to use either a full-facepiece respirator or a self-contained breathing apparatus (SCBA). For employees who have been selected to use other types of respirators, answering these questions is voluntary.

10. Have you ever lost vision in either eye (temporarily or permanently): Yes / No

11. Do you currently have any of the following vision problems?
   a. Wear contact lenses: Yes / No
   b. Wear glasses: Yes / No   c. Color blind: Yes / No
   d. Any other eye or vision problem: Yes / No

12. Have you ever had an injury to your ears, including a broken ear drum: Yes / No

13. Do you currently have any of the following hearing problems?
   a. Difficulty hearing: Yes / No
   b. Wear a hearing aid: Yes / No
   c. Any other hearing or ear problem: Yes / No

14. Have you ever had a back injury: Yes / No

15. Do you currently have any of the following musculoskeletal problems?
   a. Weakness in any of your arms, hands, legs, or feet: Yes / No
   b. Back pain: Yes / No
   c. Difficulty fully moving your arms and legs: Yes / No
   d. Pain or stiffness when you lean forward or backward at the waist: Yes / No
   e. Difficulty fully moving your head up or down: Yes / No
   f. Difficulty fully moving your head side to side: Yes / No
   g. Difficulty bending at your knees: Yes / No
   h. Difficulty squatting to the ground: Yes / No
   i. Climbing a flight of stairs or a ladder carrying more than 25 lbs: Yes / No
   j. Any other muscle or skeletal problem that interferes with using a respirator: Yes / No

Part B.

Any of the following questions, and other questions not listed, may be added to the questionnaire at the discretion of the health care professional who will review the questionnaire.

1. In your present job, are you working at high altitudes (over 5,000 feet) or in a place that has lower than normal amounts of oxygen: Yes / No

   If "yes," do you have feelings of dizziness, shortness of breath, pounding in your chest, or other symptoms when you're working under these conditions: Yes / No

2. At work or at home, have you ever been exposed to hazardous solvents, hazardous airborne chemicals (e.g., gases, fumes, or dust), or have you come into skin contact with hazardous chemicals: Yes/No

   If "yes," name the chemicals if you know them:____________________

3. Have you ever worked with any of the materials, or under any of the conditions, listed below:
   a. Asbestos: Yes / No
   b. Silica (e.g., in sandblasting): Yes / No
   c. Tungsten/cobalt (e.g., grinding or welding this material): Yes / No
   d. Beryllium: Yes / No   e. Aluminum: Yes / No
   f. Coal (for example, mining): Yes / No
   g. Iron: Yes / No   h. Tin: Yes / No
   i. Dusty environments: Yes / No
   j. Any other hazardous exposures: Yes / No
   If "yes," describe these exposures:____________________

4. List any second jobs or side businesses you have:____________________

5. List your previous occupations:____________________

6. List your current and previous hobbies:____________________

7. Have you been in the military services? Yes / No

   If "yes," were you exposed to biological or chemical agents (either in training or combat): Yes / No

8. Have you ever worked on a HAZMAT team? Yes / No

9. Other than medications for breathing and lung problems, heart trouble, blood pressure, and seizures mentioned earlier in this questionnaire, are you taking any other medications for any reason (including over-the-counter medications): Yes / No

   If "yes," name the medications if you know them:____________________

10. Will you be using any of the following items with your respirator(s)?
   a. HEPA Filters: Yes / No
   b. Canisters (for example, gas masks): Yes / No
   c. Cartridges: Yes / No

11. How often are you expected to use the respirator(s) (circle "yes" or "no" for all answers that apply to you)?:
   a. Escape only (no rescue): Yes / No
   b. Emergency rescue only: Yes / No
   c. Less than 5 hours per week: Yes / No
   d. Less than 2 hours per day: Yes / No
   e. 2 to 4 hours per day: Yes / No
   f. Over 4 hours per day: Yes / No

12. During the period you are using the respirator(s), is your work effort:

   a. Light (less than 200 kcal per hour): Yes / No

   If "yes," how long does this period last during the average shift: ______hrs. ______mins.

   Examples of a light work effort are sitting while writing, typing, drafting, or performing light assembly work; or standing while operating a drill press (1–3 lbs.) or controlling machines.

   b. Moderate (200 to 350 kcal per hour): Yes / No

   If "yes," how long does this period last during the average shift: ______hrs. ______mins.

   Examples of moderate work effort are sitting while nailing or filing; driving a truck or bus in urban traffic; standing while drilling, nailing, performing assembly work, or transferring a moderate load (about 35 lbs.) at trunk level; walking on a level surface about 2 mph or down a 5-degree grade about 3 mph; or pushing a wheelbarrow with a heavy load (about 100 lbs.) on a level surface.

   c. Heavy (above 350 kcal per hour): Yes / No

   If "yes," how long does this period last during the average shift: ______hrs. ______mins.

   Examples of heavy work are lifting a heavy load (about 50 lbs.) from the floor to your waist or shoulder; working on a loading dock; shoveling; standing while bricklaying or chipping castings; walking up an 8-degree grade about 2 mph; climbing stairs with a heavy load (about 50 lbs.).

13. Will you be wearing protective clothing and/or equipment (other than the respirator) when you're using your respirator: Yes / No

   If "yes," describe this protective clothing and/or equipment: ____________________

14. Will you be working under hot conditions (temperature exceeding 77 °F): Yes / No

15. Will you be working under humid conditions: Yes / No

16. Describe the work you'll be doing while you're using your respirator(s): ____________________

17. Describe any special or hazardous conditions you might encounter when you're using your respirator(s) (for example, confined spaces, life-threatening gases): ____________________

18. Provide the following information, if you know it, for each toxic substance that you'll be exposed to when you're using your respirator(s):

   Name of the first toxic substance:____________________
   Estimated maximum exposure level per shift:____________________
   Duration of exposure per shift____________________
   Name of the second toxic substance:____________________

Estimated maximum exposure level per shift:____________________
Duration of exposure per shift:____________________
Name of the third toxic substance:____________________
Estimated maximum exposure level per shift:____________________
Duration of exposure per shift:____________________

The name of any other toxic substances that you'll be exposed to while using your respirator: ____________________

19. Describe any special responsibilities you'll have while using your respirator(s) that may affect the safety and well-being of others (for example, rescue, security): ____________________

§1910.134 Appendix D Information for employees using respirators when not required under the Standard

(Mandatory)

Respirators are an effective method of protection against designated hazards when properly selected and worn. Respirator use is encouraged, even when exposures are below the exposure limit, to provide an additional level of comfort and protection for workers. However, if a respirator is used improperly or not kept clean, the respirator itself can become a hazard to the worker. Sometimes, workers may wear respirators to avoid exposures to hazards, even if the amount of hazardous substance does not exceed the limits set by OSHA Standards. If your employer provides respirators for your voluntary use, or if you provide your own respirator, you need to take certain precautions to be sure that the respirator itself does not present a hazard.

You should do the following:

1. Read and heed all instructions provided by the manufacturer on use, maintenance, cleaning and care, and warnings regarding the respirators limitations.
2. Choose respirators certified for use to protect against the contaminant of concern. NIOSH, the National Institute for Occupational Safety and Health of the U.S. Department of Health and Human Services, certifies respirators. A label or statement of certification should appear on the respirator or respirator packaging. It will tell you what the respirator is designed for and how much it will protect you.
3. Do not wear your respirator into atmospheres containing contaminants for which your respirator is not designed to protect against. For example, a respirator designed to filter dust particles will not protect you against gases, vapors, or very small solid particles of fumes or smoke.
4. Keep track of your respirator so that you do not mistakenly use someone else's respirator.

[63 FR 1270, Jan. 8, 1998; 63 FR 20098, 20099, Apr. 23, 1998, as amended at 69 FR 46993, Aug. 4, 2004; 71 FR 16672, Apr. 3, 2006; 71 FR 50187, Aug. 24, 2006; 73 FR 75584, Dec. 12, 2008; 76 FR 33607, June 8, 2011]

§1910.135 Head protection

(a) **General requirements**

(a)(1) The employer shall ensure that each affected employee wears a protective helmet when working in areas where there is a potential for injury to the head from falling objects.

(a)(2) The employer shall ensure that a protective helmet designed to reduce electrical shock hazard is worn by each such affected employee when near exposed electrical conductors which could contact the head.

(b) **Criteria for head protection**

(b)(1) Head protection must comply with any of the following consensus standards:

(b)(1)(i) ANSI Z89.1–2009, "American National Standard for Industrial Head Protection," which is incorporated by reference in §1910.6;

(b)()(1)(ii) ANSI Z89.1–2003, "American National Standard for Industrial Head Protection," which is incorporated by reference in §1910.6; or

(b)(1)(iii) ANSI Z89.1–1997, "American National Standard for Personnel Protection—Protective Headwear for Industrial Workers—Requirements," which is incorporated by reference in §1910.6

(b)(2) Head protection devices that the employer demonstrates are at least as effective as head protection devices that are constructed in accordance with one of the above consensus standards will be deemed to be in compliance with the requirements of this section.

[59 FR 16362, Apr. 6, 1994, as amended at 61 FR 9238, Mar. 7, 1996; 61 FR 19548, May 2, 1996; 74 FR 46356, Sept. 9, 2009]

§1910.136 Foot protection

(a) **General requirements** The employer shall ensure that each affected employee uses protective footwear when working in areas where there is a danger of foot injuries due to falling or rolling objects, or objects piercing the sole, or when the use of protective footwear will protect the affected employee from an electrical hazard, such as a static-discharge or electric-shock hazard, that remains after the employer takes other necessary protective measures.

(b) **Criteria for protective footwear**

(b)(1) Protective footwear must comply with any of the following consensus standards:

(b)(1)(i) ASTM F–2412–2005, "Standard Test Methods for Foot Protection," and ASTM F–2413–2005, "Standard Specification for Performance Requirements for Protective Footwear," which are incorporated by reference in §1910.6;

(b)(1)(ii) ANSI Z41–1999, "American National Standard for Personal Protection—Protective Footwear," which is incorporated by reference in §1910.6; or

(b)(1)(iii) ANSI Z41–1991, "American National Standard for Personal Protection—Protective Footwear," which is incorporated by reference in §1910.6.

(b)(2) Protective footwear that the employer demonstrates is at least as effective as protective footwear that is constructed in accordance with one of the above consensus standards will be deemed to be in compliance with the requirements of this section.

[59 FR 16362, Apr. 6, 1994; 59 FR 33911, July 1, 1994, as amended at 61 FR 9238, Mar. 7, 1996; 61 FR 19548, May 2, 1996; 61 FR 21228, May 9, 1996; 74 FR 46356, Sept. 9, 2009]

§1910.137 Electrical protective equipment

(a) **Design requirements for specific types of electrical protective equipment** Rubber insulating blankets, rubber insulating matting, rubber insulating covers, rubber insulating line hose, rubber insulating gloves, and rubber insulating sleeves shall meet the following requirements:

(a)(1) **Manufacture and marking of rubber insulating equipment**

(a)(1)(ii) Blankets, gloves and sleeves shall be produced by a seamless process.

(a)(1)(ii) Each item shall be clearly marked as follows:

(a)(1)(ii)(A) Class 00 equipment shall be marked Class 00.

(a)(1)(ii)(B) Class 0 equipment shall be marked Class 0.

(a)(1)(ii)(C) Class 1 equipment shall be marked Class 1.

(a)(1)(ii)(D) Class 2 equipment shall be marked Class 2.

(a)(1)(ii)(E) Class 3 equipment shall be marked Class 3.

(a)(1)(ii)(F) Class 4 equipment shall be marked Class 4.

(a)(1)(ii)(G) Non-ozone-resistant equipment shall be marked Type I.

(a)(1)(ii)(H) Ozone-resistant equipment shall be marked Type II.

(a)(1)(ii)(H) Other relevant markings, such as the manufacturer's identification and the size of the equipment, may also be provided.

(a)(1)(iii) Markings shall be nonconducting and shall be applied in such a manner as not to impair the insulating qualities of the equipment.

(a)(1)(iv) Markings on gloves shall be confined to the cuff portion of the glove.

(a)(2) **Electrical requirements**

(a)(2)(i) Equipment shall be capable of withstanding the a-c proof-test voltage specified in Table I–1 or the d-c proof test voltage specified in Table I–2.

(a)(2)(i)(A) The proof test shall reliably indicate that the equipment can withstand the voltage involved.

(a)(2)(i)(B) The test voltage shall be applied continuously for 3 minutes for equipment other than matting and shall be applied continuously for 1 minute for matting.

(a)(2)(i)(C) Gloves shall also be capable of separately withstanding the ac proof-test voltage specified in Table I-1 after a 16-hour water soak. (See the note following paragraph (a)(3)(ii)(B) of this section.)

(a)(2)(ii) When the ac proof test is used on gloves, the 60-hertz proof-test current may not exceed the values specified in Table I-1 at any time during the test period.

(a)(2)(ii)(A) If the ac proof test is made at a frequency other than 60 hertz, the permissible proof-test current shall be computed from the direct ratio of the frequencies.

(a)(2)(ii)(B) For the test, gloves (right side out) shall be filled with tap water and immersed in water to a depth that is in accordance with Table

I-3. Water shall be added to or removed from the glove, as necessary, so that the water level is the same inside and outside the glove.

(a)(2)(ii)(C) After the 16-hour water soak specified in paragraph (a)(2)(i)(C) of this section, the 60-hertz proof-test current may not exceed the values given in Table I-1 by more than 2 milliamperes.

(a)(2)(iii) Equipment that has been subjected to a minimum breakdown voltage test may not be used for electrical protection. (See the note following paragraph (a)(3)(ii)(B) of this section.)

(a)(2)(iv) Material used for Type II insulating equipment shall be capable of withstanding an ozone test, with no visible effects. The ozone test shall reliably indicate that the material will resist ozone exposure in actual use. Any visible signs of ozone deterioration of the material, such as checking, cracking, breaks, or pitting, is evidence of failure to meet the requirements for ozone-resistant material. (See the note following paragraph (a)(3)(ii)(B) of this section.)

(a)(3) Workmanship and finish

(a)(3)(i) Equipment shall be free of physical irregularities that can adversely affect the insulating properties of the equipment and that can be detected by the tests or inspections required under this Section.

(a)(3)(ii) Surface irregularities that may be present on all rubber goods (because of imperfections on forms or molds or because of inherent difficulties in the manufacturing process) and that may appear as indentations, protuberances, or imbedded foreign material are acceptable under the following conditions:

(a)(3)(ii)(A) The indentation or protuberance blends into a smooth slope when the material is stretched.

(a)(3)(ii)(B) Foreign material remains in place when the insulating material is folded and stretches with the insulating material surrounding it.

Note to paragraph (a): Rubber insulating equipment meeting the following national consensus standards is deemed to be in compliance with the performance requirements of paragraph (a) of this Section:

American Society for Testing and Materials (ASTM) D120-09, Standard Specification for Rubber Insulating Gloves.

ASTM D178-01 (2010), Standard Specification for Rubber Insulating Matting.

ASTM D1048-12, Standard Specification for Rubber Insulating Blankets.

ASTM D1049-98 (2010), Standard Specification for Rubber Insulating Covers.

ASTM D1050-05 (2011), Standard Specification for Rubber Insulating Line Hose.

ASTM D1051-08, Standard Specification for Rubber Insulating Sleeves.

The preceding standards also contain specifications for conducting the various tests required in paragraph (a) of this section. For example, the ac and dc proof tests, the breakdown test, the water-soak procedure, and the ozone test mentioned in this paragraph are described in detail in these ASTM standards.

ASTM F1236-96 (2012), Standard Guide for Visual Inspection of Electrical Protective Rubber Products, presents methods and techniques for the visual inspection of electrical protective equipment made of rubber. This guide also contains descriptions and photographs of irregularities that can be found in this equipment.

ASTM F819-10, Standard Terminology Relating to Electrical Protective Equipment for Workers, includes definitions of terms relating to the electrical protective equipment covered under this Section.

(b) Design requirements for other types of electrical protective equipment The following requirements apply to the design and manufacture of electrical protective equipment that is not covered by paragraph (a) of this Section:

(b)(1) **Voltage withstand** Insulating equipment used for the protection of employees shall be capable of withstanding, without failure, the voltages that may be imposed upon it.

Note: These voltages include transient overvoltages, such as switching surges, as well as nominal line voltage. See Appendix B to §1910.269 for a discussion of transient overvoltages on electric power transmission and distribution systems. See IEEE Std 516-2009, IEEE Guide for Maintenance Methods on Energized Power Lines, for methods of determining the magnitude of transient overvoltages on an electrical system and for a discussion comparing the ability of insulation equipment to withstand a transient overvoltage based on its ability to withstand ac voltage testing.

(b)(2) Equipment current

(b)(2)(i) Protective equipment used for the primary insulation of employees from energized circuit parts shall be capable of passing a current test when subjected to the highest nominal voltage on which the equipment is to be used.

(b)(2)(ii) When insulating equipment is tested in accordance with paragraph (b)(2)(i) of this section, the equipment current may not exceed 1 microampere per kilovolt of phase-to-phase applied voltage.

Note: This paragraph applies to equipment that provides primary insulation of employees from energized parts. It does not apply to equipment used for secondary insulation or equipment used for brush contact only.

Note: For ac excitation, this current consists of three components: Capacitive current because of the dielectric properties of the insulating material itself; conduction current through the volume of the insulating equipment; and leakage current along the surface of the tool or equipment. The conduction current is normally negligible. For clean, dry insulating equipment, the leakage current is small, and the capacitive current predominate.

Note: Plastic guard equipment is deemed to conform to the performance requirements of paragraph (b) of this section if it meets, and is used in accordance with, ASTM F712-06 (2011), Standard Test Methods and Specifications for Electrically Insulating Plastic Guard Equipment for Protection of Workers.

(c) In-service care and use of electrical protective equipment

(c)(1) **General** Electrical protective equipment shall be maintained in a safe, reliable condition.

(c)(2) **Specific requirements** The following specific requirements apply to rubber insulating blankets, rubber insulating covers, rubber insulating line hose, rubber insulating gloves, and rubber insulating sleeves:

(c)(2)(i) Maximum use voltages shall conform to those listed in Table I–4.

(c)(2)(ii) Insulating equipment shall be inspected for damage before each day's use and immediately following any incident that can reasonably be suspected of causing damage. Insulating gloves shall be given an air test, along with the inspection.

Note: ASTM F1236-96 (2012), Standard Guide for Visual Inspection of Electrical Protective Rubber Products, presents methods and techniques for the visual inspection of electrical protective equipment made of rubber. This guide also contains descriptions and photographs of irregularities that can be found in this equipment.

(c)(2)(iii) Insulating equipment with any of the following defects may not be used:

(c)(2)(iii)(A) A hole, tear, puncture, or cut;

(c)(2)(iii)(B) Ozone cutting or ozone checking (that is, a series of interlacing cracks produced by ozone on rubber under mechanical stress);

(c)(2)(iii)(C) An embedded foreign object;

(c)(2)(iii)(D) Any of the following texture changes: swelling, softening, hardening, or becoming sticky or inelastic.

(c)(2)(iii)(E) Any other defect that damages the insulating properties.

(c)(2)(iv) Insulating equipment found to have other defects that might affect its insulating properties shall be removed from service and returned for testing under paragraphs (c)(2)(viii) and (c)(2)(ix) of this Section.

(c)(2)(v) Insulating equipment shall be cleaned as needed to remove foreign substances.

(c)(2)(vi) Insulating equipment shall be stored in such a location and in such a manner as to protect it from light, temperature extremes, excessive humidity, ozone, and other injurious substances and conditions.

(c)(2)(vii) Protector gloves shall be worn over insulating gloves, except as follows:

(c)(2)(vii)(A) Protector gloves need not be used with Class 0 gloves, under limited-use conditions, when small equipment and parts manipulation necessitate unusually high finger dexterity.

Note: Persons inspecting rubber insulating gloves used under these conditions need to take extra care in visually examining them. Employees using rubber insulating gloves under these conditions need to take extra care to avoid handling sharp objects.

(c)(2)(vii)(B) If the voltage does not exceed 250 volts, ac, or 375 volts, dc, protector gloves need not be used with Class 00 gloves, under limited-use conditions, when small equipment and parts manipulation necessitate unusually high finger dexterity.

Note: Persons inspecting rubber insulating gloves used under these conditions need to take extra care in visually examining them. Employees using rubber insulating gloves under these conditions need to take extra care to avoid handling sharp objects.

(c)(2)(vii)(C) Any other class of glove may be used without protector gloves, under limited-use conditions, when small equipment and parts manipulation necessitate unusually high finger dexterity but only if the employer can demonstrate that the possibility of physical damage to the gloves is small and if the class of glove is one class higher than that required for the voltage involved.

(c)(2)(vii)(D) Insulating gloves that have been used without protector gloves may not be reused until they have been tested under the provisions of paragraphs (c)(2)(viii) and (c)(2)(ix) of this Section.

(c)(2)(viii) Electrical protective equipment shall be subjected to periodic electrical tests. Test voltages and the maximum intervals between tests shall be in accordance with Table I-4 and Table I-5.

(c)(2)(ix) The test method used under paragraphs (c)(2)(viii) and (c)(2)(xi) of this section shall reliably indicate whether the insulating equipment can withstand the voltages involved.

Note: Standard electrical test methods considered as meeting this paragraph are given in the following national consensus standards:

ASTM D120-09, Standard Specification for Rubber Insulating Gloves.

ASTM D178-01 (2010), Standard Specification for Rubber Insulating Matting.

ASTM D1048-12, Standard Specification for Rubber Insulating Blankets.

ASTM D1049-98 (2010), Standard Specification for Rubber Insulating Covers.

ASTM D1050-05 (2011), Standard Specification for Rubber Insulating Line Hose.

ASTM D1051-08, Standard Specification for Rubber Insulating Sleeves.

ASTM F478-09, Standard Specification for In-Service Care of Insulating Line Hose and Covers.

ASTM F479-06 (2011), Standard Specification for In-Service Care of Insulating Blankets.

ASTM F496-08, Standard Specification for In-Service Care of Insulating Gloves and Sleeves.

(c)(2)(x) Insulating equipment failing to pass inspections or electrical tests may not be used by employees, except as follows:

(c)(2)(x)(A) Rubber insulating line hose may be used in shorter lengths with the defective portion cut off.

(c)(2)(x)(B) Rubber insulating blankets may be salvaged by severing the defective area from the undamaged portion of the blanket. The resulting undamaged area may not be smaller than 560 millimeters by 560 millimeters (22 inches by 22 inches) for Class 1, 2, 3, and 4 blankets.

(c)(2)(x)(C) Rubber insulating blankets may be repaired using a compatible patch that results in physical and electrical properties equal to those of the blanket.

(c)(2)(x)(D) Rubber insulating gloves and sleeves with minor physical defects, such as small cuts, tears, or punctures, may be repaired by the application of a compatible patch. Also, rubber insulating gloves and sleeves with minor surface blemishes may be repaired with a compatible liquid compound. The repaired area shall have electrical and physical properties equal to those of the surrounding material. Repairs to gloves are permitted only in the area between the wrist and the reinforced edge of the opening.

(c)(2)(xi) Repaired insulating equipment shall be retested before it may be used by employees.

(c)(2)(xii) The employer shall certify that equipment has been tested in accordance with the requirements of paragraphs (c)(2)(iv), (c)(2)(vii)(D), (c)(2)(viii), (c)(2)(ix), and (c)(2)(xi) of this section. The certification shall identify the equipment that passed the test and the date it was tested and shall be made available upon request to the Assistant Secretary for Occupational Safety and Health and to employees or their authorized representatives.

Note: Marking equipment with, and entering onto logs, the results of the tests and the dates of testing are two acceptable means of meeting the certification requirement.

Table I-1
A-C Proof-Test Requirements

Class of equipment	Proof-test voltage rms V	Maximum proof-test current, mA (gloves only)			
		280-mm (11-in) glove	360-mm (14-in) glove	410-mm (16-in) glove	460-mm (18-in) glove
00	2,500	8	12	....	....
0	5,000	8	12	14	16
1	10,000	....	14	16	18
2	20,000	....	16	18	20
3	30,000	....	18	20	22
4	40,000	....	....	22	24

Table I-2
D-C Proof-Test Requirements

Class of equipment	Proof-test voltage
00	10,000
0	20,000
1	40,000
2	50,000
3	60,000
4	70,000

Note: The d-c voltages listed in this table are not appropriate for proof testing rubber insulating line hose or covers. For this equipment, d-c proof tests shall use a voltage high enough to indicate that the equipment can be safely used at the voltages listed in Table I–4. See ASTM D1050–05 (2011) and ASTMD 1049–98 (2010) for further information on proof tests for rubber insulating line hose and covers, respectively.

Table I–3
Glove Tests—Water Level[1,2]

Class of glove	AC proof-test		DC proof-test	
	mm.	in.	mm.	in.
00	38	1.5	38	1.5
0	38	1.5	38	1.5
1	38	1.5	51	2.0
2	64	2.5	76	3.0
3	89	3.5	102	4.0
4	127	5.0	153	6.0

[1] The water level is given as the clearance from the reinforced edge of the glove to the water line, with a tolerance of ±13 mm. (±0.5 in.).

[2] If atmospheric conditions make the specified clearances impractical, the clearances may be increased by a maximum of 25 mm. (1 in.).

Table I–4
Rubber Insulating Equipment, Voltage Requirements

Class of equipment	Maximum use voltage[1] a-c—rms	Retest voltage[2] a-c—rms	Retest voltage[2] d-c—avg
00	500	2,500	10,000
0	1,000	5,000	20,000
1	7,500	10,000	40,000
2	17,000	20,000	50,000
3	26,500	30,000	60,000
4	36,000	40,000	70,000

[1] The maximum use voltage is the ac voltage (rms) classification of the protective equipment that designates the maximum nominal design voltage of the energized system that may be safely worked. The nominal design voltage is equal to the phase-to-phase voltage on multiphase circuits. However, the phase-to-ground potential is considered to be the nominal design voltage if:

(1) There is no multiphase exposure in a system area and the voltage exposure is limited to the phase-to-ground potential, or

(2) The electric equipment and devices are insulated or isolated or both so that the multiphase exposure on a grounded wye circuit is removed.

[2] The proof-test voltage shall be applied continuously for at least 1 minute, but no more than 3 minutes.

Table I–5
Rubber Insulating Equipment, Test Intervals

Type of equipment	When to test
Rubber insulating line hose	Upon indication that insulating value is suspect and after repair.
Rubber insulating covers	Upon indication that insulating value is suspect and after repair.
Rubber insulating blankets	Before first issue and every 12 months thereafter;[1] upon indication that insulating value is suspect; and after repair.
Rubber insulating gloves	Before first issue and every 6 months thereafter;[1] upon indication that insulating value is suspect; after repair; and after use without protectors.
Rubber insulating sleeves	Before first issue and every 12 months thereafter;[1] upon indication that insulating value is suspect; and after repair.

[1] If the insulating equipment has been electrically tested but not issued for service, the insulating equipment may not be placed into service unless it has been electrically tested within the previous 12 months.

[59 FR 4435, Jan. 31, 1994; 59 FR 33662, June 30, 1994]

§1910.138 Hand protection

(a) **General requirements** Employers shall select and require employees to use appropriate hand protection when employees' hands are exposed to hazards such as those from skin absorption of harmful substances; severe cuts or lacerations; severe abrasions; punctures; chemical burns; thermal burns; and harmful temperature extremes.

(b) **Selection** Employers shall base the selection of the appropriate hand protection on an evaluation of the performance characteristics of the hand protection relative to the task(s) to be performed, conditions present, duration of use, and the hazards and potential hazards identified.

[59 FR 16362, Apr. 6, 1994; 59 FR 33911, July 1, 1994]

§1910.139 [Reserved]

§1910.140 Personal fall protection systems

(a) **Scope and application** This section establishes performance, care, and use criteria for all personal fall protection systems. The employer must ensure that each personal fall protection system used to comply with this Part must meet the requirements of this section.

(b) **Definitions** The following definitions apply to this section:

Anchorage means a secure point of attachment for equipment such as lifelines, lanyards, or deceleration devices.

Belt terminal means an end attachment of a window cleaner's positioning system used for securing the belt or harness to a window cleaner's belt anchor.

Body belt means a strap with means both for securing about the waist and for attaching to other components such as a lanyard used with positioning systems, travel restraint systems, or ladder safety systems.

Body harness means straps that secure about the employee in a manner to distribute the fall arrest forces over at least the thighs, pelvis, waist, chest, and shoulders, with a means for attaching the harness to other components of a personal fall protection system.

Carabiner means a connector generally comprised of a trapezoidal or oval shaped body with a closed gate or similar arrangement that may be opened to attach another object and, when released, automatically closes to retain the object.

Competent person means a person who is capable of identifying existing and predictable hazards in any personal fall protection system or any component of it, as well as in their application and uses with related equipment, and who has authorization to take prompt, corrective action to eliminate the identified hazards.

Connector means a device used to couple (connect) parts of the fall protection system together.

D-ring means a connector used:

(i) In a harness as an integral attachment element or fall arrest attachment;

(ii) In a lanyard, energy absorber, lifeline, or anchorage connector as an integral connector; or

(iii) In a positioning or travel restraint system as an attachment element.

Deceleration device means any mechanism that serves to dissipate energy during a fall.

Deceleration distance means the vertical distance a falling employee travels from the point at which the deceleration device begins to operate, excluding lifeline elongation and free fall distance, until stopping. It is measured as the distance between the location of an employee's body harness attachment point at the moment of activation (at the onset of fall arrest forces) of the deceleration device during a fall, and the location of that attachment point after the employee comes to a full stop.

Equivalent means alternative designs, equipment, materials, or methods that the employer can demonstrate will provide an equal or greater degree of safety for employees compared to the designs, equipment, materials, or methods specified in the Standard.

Free fall means the act of falling before the personal fall arrest system begins to apply force to arrest the fall.

Free fall distance means the vertical displacement of the fall arrest attachment point on the employee's body belt or body harness between onset of the fall and just before the system begins to apply force to arrest the fall. This distance excludes deceleration distance, lifeline and lanyard elongation, but includes any deceleration device slide distance or self-retracting lifeline/lanyard extension before the devices operate and fall arrest forces occur.

Lanyard means a flexible line of rope, wire rope, or strap that generally has a connector at each end for connecting the body belt or body harness to a deceleration device, lifeline, or anchorage.

Lifeline means a component of a personal fall protection system consisting of a flexible line for connection to an anchorage at one end so as to hang vertically (vertical lifeline), or for connection to anchorages at both ends so as to stretch horizontally (horizontal lifeline), and serves as a means for connecting other components of the system to the anchorage.

Personal fall arrest system means a system used to arrest an employee in a fall from a walking-working surface. It consists of a body harness, anchorage, and connector. The means of connection may include a lanyard, deceleration device, lifeline, or a suitable combination of these.

Personal fall protection system means a system (including all components) an employer uses to provide protection from falling or to safely arrest an employee's fall if one occurs.

Examples of personal fall protection systems include personal fall arrest systems, positioning systems, and travel restraint systems.

Positioning system (work-positioning system) means a system of equipment and connectors that, when used with a body harness or body belt, allows an employee to be supported on an elevated vertical surface, such as a wall or window sill, and work with both hands free. Positioning systems also are called "positioning system devices" and "work-positioning equipment."

Qualified describes a person who, by possession of a recognized degree, certificate, or professional standing, or who by extensive knowledge, training, and experience has successfully demonstrated the ability to solve or resolve problems relating to the subject matter, the work, or the project.

Rope grab means a deceleration device that travels on a lifeline and automatically, by friction, engages the lifeline and locks so as to arrest the fall of an employee. A rope grab usually employs the principle of inertial locking, cam/lever locking, or both.

Safety factor means the ratio of the design load and the ultimate strength of the material.

Self-retracting lifeline/lanyard means a deceleration device containing a drum-wound line that can be slowly extracted from, or retracted onto, the drum under slight tension during normal movement by the employee. At the onset of a fall, the device automatically locks the drum and arrests the fall.

Snaphook means a connector comprised of a hook-shaped body with a normally closed gate, or similar arrangement that may be manually opened to permit the hook to receive an object. When released, the snaphook automatically closes to retain the object. Opening a snaphook requires two separate actions. Snaphooks are generally one of two types:

(i) Automatic-locking type (permitted) with a self-closing and self-locking gate that remains closed and locked until intentionally unlocked and opened for connection or disconnection; and

(ii) Non-locking type (prohibited) with a self-closing gate that remains closed, but not locked, until intentionally opened for connection or disconnection.

Travel restraint (tether) line means a rope or wire rope used to transfer forces from a body support to an anchorage or anchorage connector in a travel restraint system.

Travel restraint system means a combination of an anchorage, anchorage connector, lanyard (or other means of connection), and body support that an employer uses to eliminate the possibility of an employee going over the edge of a walking-working surface.

Window cleaner's belt means a positioning belt that consists of a waist belt, an integral terminal runner or strap, and belt terminals.

Window cleaner's belt anchor (window anchor) means specifically designed fall-preventing attachment points permanently affixed to a window frame or to a building part immediately adjacent to the window frame, for direct attachment of the terminal portion of a window cleaner's belt.

Window cleaner's positioning system means a system which consists of a window cleaner's belt secured to window anchors.

Work-positioning system (see Positioning system in this paragraph (b)).

(c) **General requirements** The employer must ensure that personal fall protection systems meet the following requirements. Additional requirements for personal fall arrest systems and positioning systems are contained in paragraphs (d) and (e) of this section, respectively.

(c)(1) Connectors must be drop forged, pressed or formed steel, or made of equivalent materials.

(c)(2) Connectors must have a corrosion-resistant finish, and all surfaces and edges must be smooth to prevent damage to interfacing parts of the system.

(c)(3) When vertical lifelines are used, each employee must be attached to a separate lifeline.

(c)(4) Lanyards and vertical lifelines must have a minimum breaking strength of 5,000 pounds (22.2 kN).

(c)(5) Self-retracting lifelines and lanyards that automatically limit free fall distance to 2 feet (0.61 m) or less must have components capable of sustaining a minimum tensile load of 3,000 pounds (13.3 kN) applied to the device with the lifeline or lanyard in the fully extended position.

(c)(6) A competent person or qualified person must inspect each knot in a lanyard or vertical lifeline to ensure that it meets the requirements of paragraphs (c)(4) and (5) of this section before any employee uses the lanyard or lifeline.

(c)(7) D-rings, snaphooks, and carabiners must be capable of sustaining a minimum tensile load of 5,000 pounds (22.2 kN).

(c)(8) D-rings, snaphooks, and carabiners must be proof tested to a minimum tensile load of 3,600 pounds (16 kN) without cracking, breaking, or incurring permanent deformation. The gate strength of snaphooks and carabiners, must be proof tested to 3,600 lbs. (16 kN) in all directions.

(c)(9) Snaphooks and carabiners must be the automatic locking type that require at least two separate, consecutive movements to open.

(c)(10) Snaphooks and carabiners must not be connected to any of the following unless they are designed for such connections:

(c)(10)(i) Directly to webbing, rope, or wire rope;

(c)(10)(ii) To each other;

(c)(10)(iii) To a D-ring to which another snaphook, carabiner, or connector is attached;

(c)(10)(iv) To a horizontal life line; or

(c)(10)(v) To any object that is incompatibly shaped or dimensioned in relation to the snaphook or carabiner such that unintentional disengagement could occur when the connected object depresses the snaphook or carabiner gate, allowing the components to separate.

(c)(11) The employer must ensure that each horizontal lifeline:

(c)(11)(i) Is designed, installed, and used under the supervision of a qualified person; and

(c)(11)(ii) Is part of a complete personal fall arrest system that maintains a safety factor of at least two.

(c)(12) Anchorages used to attach to personal fall protection equipment must be independent of any anchorage used to suspend employees or platforms on which employees work. Anchorages used to attach to personal fall protection equipment on mobile work platforms on powered industrial trucks must be attached to an overhead member of the platform, at a point located above and near the center of the platform.

(c)(13) Anchorages, except window cleaners' belt anchors covered by paragraph (e) of this section, must be:

(c)(13)(i) Capable of supporting at least 5,000 pounds (22.2 kN) for each employee attached; or

(c)(13)(ii) Designed, installed, and used, under the supervision of qualified person, as part of a complete personal fall protection system that maintains a safety factor of at least two.

(c)(14) Travel restraint lines must be capable of sustaining a tensile load of at least 5,000 pounds (22.2 kN).

(c)(15) Lifelines must not be made of natural fiber rope. Polypropylene rope must contain an ultraviolet (UV) light inhibitor.

(c)(16) Personal fall protection systems and their components must be used exclusively for employee fall protection and not for any other purpose, such as hoisting equipment or materials.

(c)(17) A personal fall protection system or its components subjected to impact loading must be removed from service immediately and not used again until a competent person inspects the system or components and determines that it is not damaged and safe for use for employee personal fall protection.

(c)(18) Personal fall protection systems must be inspected before initial use during each workshift for mildew, wear, damage, and other deterioration, and defective components must be removed from service.

(c)(19) Ropes, belts, lanyards, and harnesses used for personal fall protection must be compatible with all connectors used.

(c)(20) Ropes, belts, lanyards, lifelines, and harnesses used for personal fall protection must be protected from being cut, abraded, melted, or otherwise damaged.

(c)(21) The employer must provide for prompt rescue of each employee in the event of a fall.

(c)(22) Personal fall protection systems must be worn with the attachment point of the body harness located in the center of the employee's back near shoulder level. The attachment point may be located in the pre-sternal position if the free fall distance is limited to 2 feet (0.6 m) or less.

(d) **Personal fall arrest systems**

(d)(1) System performance criteria. In addition to the general requirements in paragraph (c) of this section, the employer must ensure that personal fall arrest systems:

(d)(1)(i) Limit the maximum arresting force on the employee to 1,800 pounds (8 kN);

(d)(1)(ii) Bring the employee to a complete stop and limit the maximum deceleration distance the employee travels to 3.5 feet (1.1 m);

(d)(1)(iii) Have sufficient strength to withstand twice the potential impact energy of the employee free falling a distance of 6 feet (1.8 m), or the free fall distance permitted by the system; and

(d)(1)(iv) Sustain the employee within the system/strap configuration without making contact with the employee's neck and chin area.

(d)(1)(v) If the personal fall arrest system meets the criteria and protocols in Appendix D of this Subpart, and is being used by an employee having a combined body and tool weight of less than 310 pounds (140 kg), the system is considered to be in compliance with the provisions of paragraphs (d)(1)(i) through (iii) of this section. If the system is used by an employee having a combined body and tool weight of 310 pounds (140kg) or more and the employer has appropriately modified the criteria and protocols in Appendix D, then the system will be deemed to be in compliance with the requirements of paragraphs (d)(1)(i) through (iii).

(d)(2) System use criteria. The employer must ensure that:

(d)(2)(i) On any horizontal lifeline that may become a vertical lifeline, the device used to connect to the horizontal lifeline is capable of locking in both directions on the lifeline.

(d)(2)(ii) Personal fall arrest systems are rigged in such a manner that the employee cannot free fall more than 6 feet (1.8 m) or contact a lower level. A free fall may be more than 6 feet (1.8 m) provided the employer can demonstrate the manufacturer designed the system to allow a free fall of more than 6 feet and tested the system to ensure a maximum arresting force of 1,800 pounds (8 kN) is not exceeded.

(d)(3) Body belts. Body belts are prohibited as part of a personal fall arrest system.

(e) **Positioning systems**

(e)(1) **System performance requirements** The employer must ensure that each positioning system meets the following requirements:

(e)(1)(i) **General** All positioning systems, except window cleaners' positioning systems, are capable of withstanding, without failure, a drop test consisting of a 4-foot (1.2-m) drop of a 250-pound (113-kg) weight;

(e)(1)(ii) **Window cleaners' positioning systems** All window cleaners' positioning systems must:

(e)(1)(ii)(A) Be capable of withstanding without failure a drop test consisting of a 6-foot (1.8-m) drop of a 250-pound (113-kg) weight; and

(e)(1)(ii)(B) Limit the initial arresting force on the falling employee to not more than 2,000 pounds (8.9 kN), with a duration not exceeding 2 milliseconds and any subsequent arresting forces to not more than 1,000 pounds (4.5 kN).

(e)(1)(iii) Positioning systems, including window cleaners' positioning systems, that meet the test methods and procedures in Appendix D of this Subpart are considered to be in compliance with paragraphs (e)(1)(i) and (ii).

(e)(1)(iv) Lineman's body belt and pole strap systems. Lineman's body belt and pole strap systems must meet the following tests:

(e)(1)(iv)(A) A dielectric test of 819.7 volts, AC, per centimeter (25,000 volts per foot) for 3 minutes without visible deterioration;

(e)(1)(iv)(B) A leakage test of 98.4 volts, AC, per centimeter (3,000 volts per foot) with a leakage current of no more than 1 mA; and

(e)(1)(iv)(C) A flammability test in accordance with Table I-7 of this section.

Table I-7
Flammability Test

Test Method	Criteria for Passing Test
1. Vertically suspend a 19.7-inch (500-mm length of strapping suporting a 220.5-lb (100-kg) weight; 2. Use a butane or propane burner with a 3-inch (76-mm) flame; 3. Direct the flame to an edge of the strapping at a distance of 1 inch (25mm); 4. Remove the flame after 5 seconds; and 5. Wait for any flames on the positioning strap to stop burning	Any flames on the positioning strap must self-extinguish. The positioning strap must continue to support the 220.5-lb (100-kg) mass.

(e)(2) **System use criteria for window cleaners' positioning systems** The employer must ensure that window cleaners' positioning systems meet and are used in accordance with the following:

(e)(2)(i) Window cleaners' belts are designed and constructed so that:

(e)(2)(i)(A) Belt terminals will not pass through their fastenings on the belt or harness if a terminal comes loose from the window anchor; and

(e)(2)(i)(B) The length of the runner from terminal tip to terminal tip is 8 feet (2.44 m) or less;

(e)(2)(ii) Window anchors to which belts are fastened are installed in the side frames or mullions of the window at a point not less than 42 inches (106.7 cm) and not more than 51 inches (129.5 cm) above the window sill;

(e)(2)(iii) Each window anchor is capable of supporting a minimum load of 6,000 pounds (26.5 kN);

(e)(2)(iv) Use of installed window anchors for any purpose other than attaching the window cleaner's belt is prohibited;

(e)(2)(v) A window anchor that has damaged or deteriorated fastenings or supports is removed, or the window anchor head is detached so the anchor cannot be used;

(e)(2)(vi) Rope that has wear or deterioration that affects its strength is not used;

(e)(2)(vii) Both terminals of the window cleaner's belt are attached to separate window anchors during any cleaning operation;

(e)(2)(viii) No employee works on a window sill or ledge on which there is snow, ice, or any other slippery condition, or one that is weakened or rotted;

(e)(2)(ix) No employee works on a window sill or ledge unless:

(e)(2)(ix)(A) The window sill or ledge is a minimum of 4 inches (10 cm) wide and slopes no more than 15 degrees below horizontal; or

(e)(2)(ix)(B) The 4-inch minimum width of the window sill or ledge is increased 0.4 inches (1 cm) for every degree the sill or ledge slopes beyond 15 degrees, up to a maximum of 30 degrees;

(e)(2)(x) The employee attaches at least one belt terminal to a window anchor before climbing through the window opening, and keeps at least one terminal attached until completely back inside the window opening;

(e)(2)(xi) Except as provided in paragraph (e)(2)(xii) of this section, the employee travels from one window to another by returning inside the window opening and repeating the belt terminal attachment procedure at each window in accordance with paragraph (e)(2)(x) of this section;

(e)(2)(xii) An employee using a window cleaner's positioning system may travel from one window to another while outside of the building, provided:

(e)(2)(xii)(A) At least one belt terminal is attached to a window anchor at all times;

(e)(2)(xii)(B) The distance between window anchors does not exceed 4 feet (1.2 m) horizontally. The distance between windows may be increased up to 6 feet (1.8 m) horizontally if the window sill or ledge is at least 1 foot (0.31 m) wide and the slope is less than 5 degrees;

(e)(2)(xii)(C) The sill or ledge between windows is continuous; and

(e)(2)(xii)(D) The width of the window sill or ledge in front of the mullions is at least 6 inches (15.2 cm) wide.

Subpart I of Part 1910 Appendix A References for further information
(Nonmandatory)

The documents in Appendix A provide information which may be helpful in understanding and implementing the Standards in Subpart I.

1. Bureau of Labor Statistics (BLS). "Accidents Involving Eye Injuries." Report 597, Washington, D.C.: BLS, 1980.
2. Bureau of Labor Statistics (BLS). "Accidents Involving Face Injuries." Report 604, Washington, D.C.: BLS, 1980.
3. Bureau of Labor Statistics (BLS). "Accidents Involving Head Injuries." Report 605, Washington, D.C.: BLS, 1980.
4. Bureau of Labor Statistics (BLS). "Accidents Involving Foot Injuries." Report 626, Washington, D.C.: BLS, 1981.
5. National Safety Council. "Accident Facts", Annual edition, Chicago, IL: 1981.
6. Bureau of Labor Statistics (BLS). "Occupational Injuries and Illnesses in the United States by Industry," Annual edition, Washington, D.C.: BLS.
7. National Society to Prevent Blindness. "A Guide for Controlling Eye Injuries in Industry," Chicago, Il: 1982.

[59 FR 16362, Apr. 6, 1994]

Subpart I to Part 1910 Appendix B Compliance guidelines for hazard assessment and personal protective equipment selection
(Nonmandatory)

This Appendix is intended to provide compliance assistance for employers and employees in implementing requirements for a hazard assessment and the selection of personal protective equipment.

1. **Controlling hazards** PPE devices alone should not be relied on to provide protection against hazards, but should be used in conjunction with guards, engineering controls, and sound manufacturing practices.

2. **Assessment and selection** It is necessary to consider certain general guidelines for assessing the foot, head, eye and face, and hand hazard situations that exist in an occupational or educational operation or process, and to match the protective devices to the particular hazard. It should be the responsibility of the safety officer to exercise common sense and appropriate expertise to accomplish these tasks.

3. **Assessment guidelines** In order to assess the need for PPE the following steps should be taken:

a. **Survey** Conduct a walk-through survey of the areas in question. The purpose of the survey is to identify sources of hazards to workers and co-workers. Consideration should be given to the basic hazard categories:

(a) Impact;
(b) Penetration;
(c) Compression (roll-over);
(d) Chemical;
(e) Heat;
(f) Harmful dust;
(g) Light (optical) radiation

b. **Sources** During the walk-through survey the safety officer should observe: (a) sources of motion; i.e., machinery or processes where any movement of tools, machine elements or particles could exist, or movement of personnel that could result in collision with stationary objects; (b) sources of high temperatures that could result in burns, eye injury or ignition of protective equipment, etc.; (c) types of chemical exposures; (d) sources of harmful dust; (e) sources of light radiation, i.e., welding, brazing, cutting, furnaces, heat treating, high intensity lights, etc.; (f) sources of falling objects or potential for dropping objects; (g) sources of sharp objects which might pierce the feet or cut the hands; (h) sources of rolling or pinching objects which could crush the feet; (i) layout of workplace and location of co-workers; and (j) any electrical hazards. In addition, injury/accident data should be reviewed to help identify problem areas.

c. **Organize data** Following the walk-through survey, it is necessary to organize the data and information for use in the assessment of hazards. The objective is to prepare for an analysis of the hazards in the environment to enable proper selection of protective equipment.

d. **Analyze data** Having gathered and organized data on a workplace, an estimate of the potential for injuries should be made. Each of the basic hazards (paragraph 3.a.) should be reviewed and a determination made as to the type, level of risk, and seriousness of potential injury from each of the hazards found in the area. The possibility of exposure to several hazards simultaneously should be considered.

4. **Selection guidelines** After completion of the procedures in paragraph 3, the general procedure for selection of protective equipment is to: (a) Become familiar with the potential hazards and the type of protective equipment that is available, and what it can do; i.e., splash protection, impact protection, etc.; (b) compare the hazards associated with the environment; i.e., impact velocities, masses, projectile shape, radiation intensities, with the capabilities of the available protective equipment; (c) select the protective equipment which ensures a level of protection greater than the minimum required to protect employees from the hazards; and (d) fit the user with the protective device and give instructions on care and use of the PPE. It is very important that end users be made aware of all warning labels for and limitations of their PPE.

5. **Fitting the device** Careful consideration must be given to comfort and fit. PPE that fits poorly will not afford the necessary protection. Continued wearing of the device is more likely if it fits the wearer comfortably. Protective devices are generally available in a variety of sizes. Care should be taken to ensure that the right size is selected.

6. **Devices with adjustable features** Adjustments should be made on an individual basis for a comfortable fit that will maintain the protective device in the proper position. Particular care should be taken in fitting devices for eye protection against dust and chemical splash to ensure that the devices are sealed to the face. In addition, proper fitting of helmets is important to ensure that it will not fall off during work operations. In some cases a chin strap may be necessary to keep the helmet on an employee's head. (Chin straps should break at a reasonably low force, however, so as to prevent a strangulation hazard). Where manufacturer's instructions are available, they should be followed carefully.

7. **Reassessment of hazards** It is the responsibility of the safety officer to reassess the workplace hazard situation as necessary, by identifying and evaluating new equipment and processes, reviewing accident records, and reevaluating the suitability of previously selected PPE.

8. **Selection chart guidelines for eye and face protection** Some occupations (not a complete list) for which eye protection should be routinely considered are: carpenters, electricians, machinists, mechanics and repairers, millwrights, plumbers and pipe fitters, sheet metal workers and tinsmiths, assemblers, sanders, grinding machine operators, lathe and milling machine operators, sawyers, welders, laborers, chemical process operators and handlers, and timber cutting and logging workers. The following chart provides general guidance for the proper selection of eye and face protection to protect against hazards associated with the listed hazard "source" operations.

Eye and Face Protection Selection Chart

Source	Assessment of Hazard	Protection
IMPACT—Chipping, grinding machining, masonry work, woodworking, sawing, drilling, chiseling, powered fastening, riveting, and sanding	Flying fragments, objects, large chips, particles sand, dirt, etc	Spectacles with side protection, goggles, face shields. See notes (1), (3), (5), (6), (10). For severe exposure, use faceshield.
HEAT—Furnace operations, pouring, casting, hot dipping, and welding	Hot sparks	Faceshields, goggles, spectacles with side protection. For severe exposure use faceshield. See notes (1), (2), (3).
	Splash from molten metals	Faceshields worn over goggles. See notes (1), (2), (3).
	High temperature exposure	Screen face shields, reflective face shields. See notes (1), (2), (3).
CHEMICALS—Acid and chemicals handling, degreasing plating	Splash	Goggles, eyecup and cover types. For severe exposure, use face shield. See notes (3), (11).
	Irritating mists	Special-purpose goggles.
DUST—Woodworking, buffing, general dusty conditions	Nuisance dust	Goggles, eyecup and cover types. See note (8).
LIGHT and/or RADIATION—		
Welding: Electric arc	Optical radiation	Welding helmets or welding shields. Typical shades: 10-14. See notes (9), (12)
Welding: Gas	Optical radiation	Welding goggles or welding face shield. Typical shades: gas welding 4-8, cutting 3-6, brazing 3-4. See note (9)
Cutting, Torch brazing, Torch soldering	Optical radiation	Spectacles or welding face-shield. Typical shades, 1.5-3. See notes (3), (9)
Glare	Poor vision	Spectacles with shaded or special-purpose lenses, as suitable. See notes (9), (10).

Notes to Eye and Face Protection Selection Chart:

(1) Care should be taken to recognize the possibility of multiple and simultaneous exposure to a variety of hazards. Adequate protection against the highest level of each of the hazards should be provided. Protective devices do not provide unlimited protection.
(2) Operations involving heat may also involve light radiation. As required by the Standard, protection from both hazards must be provided.
(3) Faceshields should only be worn over primary eye protection (spectacles or goggles).
(4) As required by the Standard, filter lenses must meet the requirements for shade designations in §1910.133(a)(5). Tinted and shaded lenses are not filter lenses unless they are marked or identified as such.
(5) As required by the Standard, persons whose vision requires the use of prescription (Rx) lenses must wear either protective devices fitted with prescription (Rx) lenses or protective devices designed to be worn over regular prescription (Rx) eyewear.
(6) Wearers of contact lenses must also wear appropriate eye and face protection devices in a hazardous environment. It should be recognized that dusty and/or chemical environments may represent an additional hazard to contact lens wearers.
(7) Caution should be exercised in the use of metal frame protective devices in electrical hazard areas.
(8) Atmospheric conditions and the restricted ventilation of the protector can cause lenses to fog. Frequent cleansing may be necessary.
(9) Welding helmets or faceshields should be used only over primary eye protection (spectacles or goggles).
(10) Non-sideshield spectacles are available for frontal protection only, but are not acceptable eye protection for the sources and operations listed for "impact."
(11) Ventilation should be adequate, but well protected from splash entry. Eye and face protection should be designed and used so that it provides both adequate ventilation and protects the wearer from splash entry.
(12) Protection from light radiation is directly related to filter lens density. See note (4) . Select the darkest shade that allows task performance.

9. **Selection guidelines for head protection** All head protection (helmets) is designed to provide protection from impact and penetration hazards caused by falling objects. Head protection is also available which provides protection from electric shock and burn. When selecting head protection, knowledge of potential electrical hazards is important. Class A helmets, in addition to impact and penetration resistance, provide electrical protection from low-voltage conductors (they are proof tested to 2,200 volts). Class B helmets, in addition to impact and penetration resistance, provide electrical protection from high-voltage conductors (they are proof tested to 20,000 volts). Class C helmets provide impact and penetration resistance (they are usually made of aluminum which conducts electricity), and should not be used around electrical hazards.

Where falling object hazards are present, helmets must be worn. Some examples include: working below other workers who are using tools and materials which could fall; working around or under conveyor belts which are carrying parts or materials; working below machinery or processes which might cause material or objects to fall; and working on exposed energized conductors.

Some examples of occupations for which head protection should be routinely considered are: carpenters, electricians, linemen, mechanics and repairers, plumbers and pipe fitters, assemblers, packers, wrappers, sawyers, welders, laborers, freight handlers, timber cutting and logging, stock handlers, and warehouse laborers.

Beginning with the ANSI Z89.1–1997 Standard, ANSI updated the classification system for protective helmets. Prior revisions used type classifications to distinguish between caps and full brimmed hats. Beginning in 1997, Type I designated helmets designed to reduce the force of impact resulting from a blow only to the top of the head, while Type II designated helmets designed to reduce the force of impact resulting from a blow to the top or sides of the head. Accordingly, if a hazard assessment indicates that lateral impact to the head is foreseeable, employers must select Type II helmets for their employees. To improve comprehension and usefulness, the 1997 revision also redesignated the electrical-protective classifications for helmets as follows: "Class G—General"; helmets designed to reduce the danger of contact with low-voltage conductors; "Class E—Electrical"; helmets designed to reduce the danger of contact with conductors at higher voltage levels; and "Class C—Conductive"; helmets that provide no protection against contact with electrical hazards.

10. **Selection guidelines for foot protection** Safety shoes and boots which meet the ANSI Z41-1991 Standard provide both impact and compression protection. Where necessary, safety shoes can be obtained which provide puncture protection. In some work situations, metatarsal protection should be provided, and in other special situations electrical conductive or insulating safety shoes would be appropriate.

Safety shoes or boots with impact protection would be required for carrying or handling materials such as packages, objects, parts or heavy tools, which could be dropped; and, for other activities where objects might fall onto the feet. Safety shoes or boots with compression protection would be required for work activities involving skid trucks (manual material handling carts) around bulk rolls (such as paper rolls) and around heavy pipes, all of which could potentially roll over an employee's feet. Safety shoes or boots with puncture protection would be required where sharp objects such as nails, wire, tacks, screws, large staples, scrap metal etc., could be stepped on by employees causing a foot injury. Electrically conductive shoes would be required as a supplementary form of protection for work activities in which there is a danger of fire or explosion from the discharge of static electricity. Electrical-hazard or dielectric footwear would be required as a supplementary form of protection when an employee standing on the ground is exposed to hazardous step or touch potential (the difference in electrical potential between the feet or between the hands and feet) or when primary forms of electrical protective equipment, such as rubber insulating gloves and blankets, do not provide complete protection for an employee standing on the ground.

Safety shoes or boots with puncture protection would be required where sharp objects such as nails, wire, tacks, screws, large staples, scrap metal etc., could be stepped on by employees causing a foot injury. Electrically conductive shoes would be required as a supplementary form of protection for work activities in which there is a danger of fire or explosion from the discharge of static electricity. Electrical-hazard or dielectric footwear would be required as a supplementary form of protection when an employee standing on the ground is exposed to hazardous step or touch potential (the difference in electrical potential between the feet or between the hands and feet) or when primary forms of electrical protective equipment, such as rubber insulating gloves and blankets, do not provide complete protection for an employee standing on the ground.

Some occupations (not a complete list) for which foot protection should be routinely considered are: Shipping and receiving clerks, stock clerks, carpenters, electricians, machinists, mechanics and repairers, plumbers and pipe fitters, structural metal workers, assemblers, drywall installers and lathers, packers, wrappers, craters, punch and stamping press operators, sawyers, welders, laborers, freight handlers, gardeners and grounds-keepers, timber cutting and logging workers, stock handlers and warehouse laborers.

11. **Selection guidelines for hand protection** Gloves are often relied upon to prevent cuts, abrasions, burns, and skin contact with chemicals that are capable of causing local or systemic effects following dermal exposure. OSHA is unaware of any gloves that provide protection against all potential hand hazards, and commonly available glove materials provide only limited protection against many chemicals. Therefore, it is important to select the most appropriate glove for a particular application and to determine how long it can be worn, and whether it can be reused.

It is also important to know the performance characteristics of gloves relative to the specific hazard anticipated; e.g., chemical hazards, cut hazards, flame hazards, etc. These performance characteristics should be assessed by using standard test procedures. Before purchasing gloves, the employer should request documentation from the manufacturer that the gloves meet the appropriate test standard(s) for the hazard(s) anticipated.

Other factors to be considered for glove selection in general include:

(A) As long as the performance characteristics are acceptable, in certain circumstances, it may be more cost effective to regularly change cheaper gloves than to reuse more expensive types; and,

(B) The work activities of the employee should be studied to determine the degree of dexterity required, the duration, frequency, and degree of exposure of the hazard, and the physical stresses that will be applied.

With respect to selection of gloves for protection against chemical hazards:

(A) The toxic properties of the chemical(s) must be determined; in particular, the ability of the chemical to cause local effects on the skin and /or to pass through the skin and cause systemic effects;

(B) Generally, any "chemical resistant" glove can be used for dry powders;

(C) For mixtures and formulated products (unless specific test data are available), a glove should be selected on the basis of the chemical component with the shortest breakthrough time, since it is possible for solvents to carry active ingredients through polymeric materials; and,

(D) Employees must be able to remove the gloves in such a manner as to prevent skin contamination.

12. **Cleaning and maintenance** It is important that all PPE be kept clean and properly maintained. Cleaning is particularly important for eye and face protection where dirty or fogged lenses could impair vision.

For the purposes of compliance with §1910.132 (a) and (b), PPE should be inspected, cleaned, and maintained at regular intervals so that the PPE provides the requisite protection.

It is also important to ensure that contaminated PPE which cannot be decontaminated is disposed of in a manner that protects employees from exposure to hazards.

[59 FR 16362, Apr. 6, 1994, as amended at 74 FR 46357, Sept. 9, 2009]

Subpart I of Part 1910 Appendix C Personal Fall Protection Systems Non-Mandatory Guidelines

The following information generally applies to all personal fall protection systems and is intended to assist employers and employees comply with the requirements of §1910.140 for personal fall protection systems.

(a) **Planning considerations** It is important for employers to plan prior to using personal fall protection systems. Probably the most overlooked component of planning is locating suitable anchorage points. Such planning should ideally be done before the structure or building is constructed so that anchorage points can be used later for window cleaning or other building maintenance.

(b) **Selection and use considerations**

(1) The kind of personal fall protection system selected should be appropriate for the employee's specific work situation. Free fall distances should always be kept to a minimum. Many systems are designed for particular work applications, such as climbing ladders and poles; maintaining and servicing equipment; and window cleaning. Consideration should be given to the environment in which the work will be performed. For example, the presence of acids, dirt, moisture, oil, grease, or other substances, and their potential effects on the system selected, should be evaluated. The employer should fully evaluate the work conditions and environment (including seasonal weather changes) before selecting the appropriate personal fall protection system. Hot or cold environments may also affect fall protection systems. Wire rope should not be used where electrical hazards are anticipated. As required by §1910.140(c)(21), the employer must provide a means for promptly rescuing an employee should a fall occur.

(2) Where lanyards, connectors, and lifelines are subject to damage by work operations, such as welding, chemical cleaning, and sandblasting, the component should be protected, or other securing systems should be used. A program for cleaning and maintaining the system may be necessary.

(c) **Testing considerations** Before purchasing a personal fall protection system, an employer should insist that the supplier provide information about its test performance (using recognized test methods) so the employer will know that the system meets the criteria in §1910.140. Otherwise, the employer should test the equipment to ensure that it is in compliance. Appendix D to this Subpart contains test methods which are recommended for evaluating the performance of any system. There are some circumstances in which an employer can evaluate a system based on data and calculations derived from the testing of similar systems. Enough information must be available for the employer to demonstrate that its system and the tested system(s) are similar in both function and design.

(d) **Component compatibility considerations** Ideally, a personal fall protection system is designed, tested, and supplied as a complete system. However, it is common practice for lanyards, connectors, lifelines, deceleration devices, body belts, and body harnesses to be interchanged since some components wear out before others. Employers and employees should realize that not all components are interchangeable. For instance, a lanyard should not be connected between a body harness and a deceleration device of the self-retracting type (unless specifically allowed by the manufacturer) since this can result in additional free fall for which the system was not designed. In addition, positioning components, such as pole straps, ladder hooks and rebar hooks, should not be used in personal fall arrest systems unless they meet the appropriate strength and performance requirements of Part 1910 (e.g., §1910.140, §1910.268 and §1910.269). Any substitution or change to a personal fall protection system should be fully evaluated or tested by a competent person to determine that it meets applicable OSHA Standards before the modified system is put in use. Also, OSHA suggests that rope be used according to manufacturers' recommendations, especially if polypropylene rope is used.

(e) **Employee training considerations** As required by §1910.30 and §1910.132, before an employee uses a fall protection system, the employer must ensure that he or she is trained in the proper use of the system. This may include the following: The limits of the system; proper anchoring and tie-off techniques; estimating free fall distance, including determining elongation and deceleration distance; methods of use; and inspection and storage. Careless or improper use of fall protection equipment can result in serious injury or death. Employers and employees should become familiar with the material in this Standard and Appendix, as well as manufacturers' recommendations, before a system is used. It is important for employees to be aware that certain tie-offs (such as using knots and tying around sharp edges) can reduce the overall strength of a system. Employees also need to know the maximum permitted free fall distance. Training should stress the importance of inspections prior to use, the limitations of the equipment to be used, and unique conditions at the worksite that may be important.

(f) **Instruction considerations** Employers should obtain comprehensive instructions from the supplier or a qualified person as to the system's proper use and application, including, where applicable:

(1) The force measured during the sample force test;

(2) The maximum elongation measured for lanyards during the force test;

(3) The deceleration distance measured for deceleration devices during the force test;

(4) Caution statements on critical use limitations;

(5) Limits of the system;

(6) Proper hook-up, anchoring and tie-off techniques, including the proper D-ring or other attachment point to use on the body harness;

(7) Proper climbing techniques;

(8) Methods of inspection, use, cleaning, and storage; and

(9) Specific lifelines that may be used.

(g) **Inspection considerations** Personal fall protection systems must be inspected before initial use in each workshift. Any component with damage, such as a cut, tear, abrasion, mold, or evidence of undue stretching, an alteration or addition that might affect its effectiveness, damage due to deterioration, fire, acid, or other corrosive damage, distorted hooks or faulty hook springs, tongues that are unfitted to the shoulder of buckles, loose or damaged mountings, non-functioning parts, or wear, or internal deterioration must be removed from service immediately, and should be tagged or marked as unusable, or destroyed. Any personal fall protection system, including components, subjected to impact loading must be removed from service immediately and not used until a competent person inspects the system and determines that it is not damaged and is safe to use for personal fall protection.

(h) **Rescue considerations** As required by §1910.140(c)(21), when personal fall arrest systems are used, special consideration must be given to rescuing an employee promptly should a fall occur. The availability of rescue personnel, ladders, or other rescue equipment needs to be evaluated since there may be instances in which employees cannot self-rescue (e.g., employee unconscious or seriously injured). In some situations, equipment allowing employees to rescue themselves after the fall has been arrested may be desirable, such as devices that have descent capability.

(i) **Tie-off considerations** Employers and employees should at all times be aware that the strength of a personal fall arrest system is based on its being attached to an anchoring system that can support the system. Therefore, if a means of attachment is used that will reduce the strength of the system (such as an eye-bolt/snaphook anchorage), that component should be replaced by a stronger one that will also maintain the appropriate maximum deceleration characteristics. The following is a listing of some situations in which employers and employees should be especially cautious:

(1) Tie-off using a knot in the lanyard or lifeline (at any location). The strength of the line can be reduced by 50 percent or more if a knot is used. Therefore, a stronger lanyard or lifeline should be used to compensate for the knot, or the lanyard length should be reduced (or the tie-off location raised) to minimize free fall distance, or the lanyard or lifeline should be replaced by one which has an appropriately incorporated connector to eliminate the need for a knot.

(2) Tie-off around rough or sharp (e.g., "H" or "I" beams) surfaces. Sharp or rough surfaces can damage rope lines and this reduces strength of the system drastically. Such tie-offs should be avoided whenever possible. An alternate means should be used such as a snaphook/D-ring connection, a tie-off apparatus (steel cable tie-off), an effective padding of the surfaces, or an abrasion-resistant strap around the supporting member. If these alternative means of tie-off are not available, the employer should try to minimize the potential free fall distance.

(3) Knots. Sliding hitch knots should not be used except in emergency situations. The one-and-one sliding hitch knot should never be used because it is unreliable in stopping a fall. The two-and-two, or three-and-three knots (preferable) may be used in emergency situations; however, care should be taken to limit free fall distances because of reduced lifeline/lanyard strength. OSHA requires that a competent or qualified person inspect each knot in a lanyard or vertical lifeline to ensure it meets the strength requirements in §1910.140.

(j) **Horizontal lifelines** Horizontal lifelines, depending on their geometry and angle of sag, may be subjected to greater loads than the impact load imposed by an attached component. When the angle of horizontal lifeline sag is less than 30 degrees, the impact force imparted to the lifeline by an attached lanyard is greatly amplified. For example, with a sag angle of 15 degrees the force amplification is about 2:1, and at 5 degrees sag it is about 6:1. Depending on the angle of sag, and the line's elasticity, the strength of the horizontal lifeline, and the anchorages to which it is attached should be increased a number of times over that of the lanyard. Extreme care should be taken in considering a horizontal lifeline for multiple tie-offs. If there are multiple tie-offs to a horizontal lifeline, and one employee falls, the movement of the falling employee and the horizontal lifeline during arrest of the fall may cause other employees to fall. Horizontal lifeline and anchorage strength should be increased for each additional employee to be tied-off. For these and other reasons, the systems using horizontal lifelines must be designed only by qualified persons. OSHA recommends testing installed lifelines and anchors prior to use. OSHA requires that horizontal lifelines are designed, installed and used under the supervision of a qualified person.

(k) **Eye-bolts** It must be recognized that the strength of an eye-bolt is rated along the axis of the bolt, and that its strength is greatly reduced if the force is applied at right angles to this axis (in the direction of its shear strength). Care should also be exercised in selecting the proper diameter of the eye to avoid creating a roll-out hazard (accidental disengagement of the snaphook from the eye-bolt).

(l) Vertical lifeline considerations. As required by §1910.140(c)(3), each employee must have a separate lifeline when the lifeline is vertical. If multiple tie-offs to a single lifeline are used, and one employee falls, the movement of the lifeline during the arrest of the fall may pull other employees' lanyards, causing them to fall as well.

(m) **Snaphook and carabiner considerations** As required by §1910.140(c)(10), the following connections must be avoided unless the locking snaphook or carabiner has been designed for them because they are conditions that can result in rollout:

(1) Direct connection to webbing, rope, or a horizontal lifeline;

(2) Two (or more) snaphooks or carabiners connected to one D-ring;

(3) Two snaphooks or carabiners connected to each other;

(4) Snaphooks or carabiners connected directly to webbing, rope, or wire rope; and

(5) Improper dimensions of the D-ring, rebar, or other connection point in relation to the snaphook or carabiner dimensions which would allow the gate to be depressed by a turning motion.

(n) **Free fall considerations** Employers and employees should always be aware that a system's maximum arresting force is evaluated under normal use conditions established by the manufacturer. OSHA requires that personal fall arrest systems be rigged so an employee cannot free fall in excess of 6 feet (1.8 m). Even a few additional feet of free fall can significantly increase the arresting force on the employee, possibly to the point of causing injury and possibly exceeding the strength of the system. Because of this, the free fall distance should be kept to a minimum, and, as required by §1910.140(d)(2), must never be greater than 6 feet (1.8 m). To assure this, the tie-off attachment point to the lifeline or anchor should be located at or above the connection point of the fall arrest equipment to the harness. (Otherwise, additional free fall distance is added to the length of the connecting means (i.e., lanyard)). Tying off to the walking-working surface will often result in a free fall greater than 6 feet (1.8 m). For instance, if a 6-foot (1.8-m) lanyard is used, the total free fall distance will be the distance from the walking-working level to the harness connection plus the 6 feet (1.8 m) of lanyard.

(o) **Elongation and deceleration distance considerations** During fall arrest, a lanyard will stretch or elongate, whereas activation of a deceleration device will result in a certain stopping distance. These distances should be available with the lanyard or device's instructions and must be added to the free fall distance to arrive at the total fall distance before an employee is fully stopped. The additional stopping distance may be significant if the lanyard or deceleration device is attached near or at the end of a long lifeline, which may itself add considerable distance due to its own elongation. As required by §1910.140(d)(2), sufficient distance to allow for all of these factors must also be maintained between the employee and obstructions below, to prevent an injury due to impact before the system fully arrests the fall. In addition, a minimum of 12 feet (3.7 m) of lifeline should be allowed below the securing point of a rope-grab-type deceleration device, and the end terminated to prevent the device from sliding off the lifeline. Alternatively, the lifeline should extend to the ground or the next working level below. These measures are suggested to prevent the employee from inadvertently moving past the end of the lifeline and having the rope grab become disengaged from the lifeline.

(p) **Obstruction considerations** In selecting a location for tie-off, employers and employees should consider obstructions in the potential fall path of the employee. Tie-offs that minimize the possibilities of exaggerated swinging should be considered

Subpart I of Part 1910 Appendix D Test Methods and Procedures for Personal Fall Protection Systems Non-Mandatory Guidelines

This Appendix contains test methods for personal fall protection systems which may be used to determine if they meet the system performance criteria specified in paragraphs (d) and (e) of §1910.140.

Test methods for personal fall arrest systems (paragraph (d) of §1910.140).

(a) **General** The following sets forth test procedures for personal fall arrest systems as defined in paragraph (d) of §1910.140.

(b) **General test conditions**

(1) Lifelines, lanyards and deceleration devices should be attached to an anchorage and connected to the body harness in the same manner as they would be when used to protect employees.

(2) The fixed anchorage should be rigid, and should not have a deflection greater than 0.04 inches (1 mm) when a force of 2,250 pounds (10 kN) is applied.

(3) The frequency response of the load measuring instrumentation should be 120 Hz.

(4) The test weight used in the strength and force tests should be a rigid, metal cylindrical or torso-shaped object with a girth of 38 inches plus or minus 4 inches (96 cm plus or minus 10 cm).

(5) The lanyard or lifeline used to create the free fall distance should be supplied with the system, or in its absence, the least elastic lanyard or lifeline available should be used with the system.

(6) The test weight for each test should be hoisted to the required level and should be quickly released without having any appreciable motion imparted to it.

(7) The system's performance should be evaluated, taking into account the range of environmental conditions for which it is designed to be used.

(8) Following the test, the system need not be capable of further operation.

(c) **Strength test**

(1) During the testing of all systems, a test weight of 300 pounds plus or minus 3 pounds (136.4 kg plus or minus 1.4 kg) should be used. (See paragraph (b)(4) of this Appendix.)

(2) The test consists of dropping the test weight once. A new unused system should be used for each test.

(3) For lanyard systems, the lanyard length should be 6 feet plus or minus 2 inches (1.83 m plus or minus 5 cm) as measured from the fixed anchorage to the attachment on the body harness.

(4) For rope-grab-type deceleration systems, the length of the lifeline above the centerline of the grabbing mechanism to the lifeline's anchorage point should not exceed 2 feet (0.61 m).

(5) For lanyard systems, for systems with deceleration devices which do not automatically limit free fall distance to 2 feet (0.61 m) or less, and for systems with deceleration devices which have a connection distance in excess of 1 foot (0.3 m) (measured between the centerline of the lifeline and the attachment point to the body harness), the test weight should be rigged to free fall a distance of 7.5 feet (2.3 m) from a point that is 1.5 feet (46 cm) above the anchorage point, to its hanging location (6 feet (1.83 m) below the anchorage). The test weight should fall without interference, obstruction, or hitting the floor or ground during the test. In some cases a non-elastic wire lanyard of sufficient length may need to be added to the system (for test purposes) to create the necessary free fall distance.

(6) For deceleration device systems with integral lifelines or lanyards that automatically limit free fall distance to 2 feet (0.61 m) or less, the test weight should be rigged to free fall a distance of 4 feet (1.22 m).

(7) Any weight that detaches from the harness should constitute failure for the strength test.

(d) **Force test**

(1) **General** The test consists of dropping the respective test weight specified in paragraph (d)(2)(i) or (d)(3)(i) of this Appendix once. A new, unused system should be used for each test.

(2) **For lanyard systems**

(i) A test weight of 220 pounds plus or minus three pounds (100 kg plus or minus 1.6 kg) should be used. (See paragraph (b)(4) of this Appendix.)

(ii) Lanyard length should be 6 feet plus or minus 2 inches (1.83 m plus or minus 5 cm) as measured from the fixed anchorage to the attachment on the body harness.

(iii) The test weight should fall free from the anchorage level to its hanging location (a total of 6 feet (1.83 m) free fall distance) without interference, obstruction, or hitting the floor or ground during the test.

(3) **For all other systems**

(i) A test weight of 220 pounds plus or minus 2 pounds (100 kg plus or minus 1.0 kg) should be used. (See paragraph (b)(4) of this Appendix.)

(ii) The free fall distance to be used in the test should be the maximum fall distance physically permitted by the system during normal use conditions, up to a maximum free fall distance for the test weight of 6 feet (1.83 m), except as follows:

(A) For deceleration systems having a connection link or lanyard, the test weight should free fall a distance equal to the connection distance (measured between the centerline of the lifeline and the attachment point to the body harness).

(B) For deceleration device systems with integral lifelines or lanyards that automatically limit free fall distance to 2 feet (0.61 m) or less, the test weight should free fall a distance equal to that permitted by the system in normal use. (For example, to test a system with a self-retracting lifeline or lanyard, the test weight should be supported and the system allowed to retract the lifeline or lanyard as it would in normal use. The test weight would then be released and the force and deceleration distance measured).

(4) **Failure** A system fails the force test when the recorded maximum arresting force exceeds 2,520 pounds (11.2 kN) when using a body harness.

(5) **Distances** The maximum elongation and deceleration distance should be recorded during the force test.

(e) **Deceleration device tests**

(1) **General** The device should be evaluated or tested under the environmental conditions (such as rain, ice, grease, dirt, and type of lifeline) for which the device is designed.

(2) **Rope-grab-type deceleration devices**

(i) Devices should be moved on a lifeline 1,000 times over the same length of line a distance of not less than 1 foot (30.5 cm), and the mechanism should lock each time.

(ii) Unless the device is permanently marked to indicate the type of lifelines that must be used, several types (different diameters and different materials), of lifelines should be used to test the device.

(3) **Other self-activating-type deceleration devices** The locking mechanisms of other self-activating-type deceleration devices designed for more than one arrest should lock each of 1,000 times as they would in normal service.

Test methods for positioning systems (paragraph (e) of §1910.140).

(a) **General** The following sets forth test procedures for positioning systems as defined in paragraph (e) of §1910.140. The requirements in this Appendix for personal fall arrest systems set forth procedures that may be used, along with the procedures listed below, to determine compliance with the requirements for positioning systems.

(b) **Test conditions**

(1) The fixed anchorage should be rigid and should not have a deflection greater than 0.04 inches (1 mm) when a force of 2,250 pounds (10 kN) is applied.

(2) For window cleaners' belts, the complete belt should withstand a drop test consisting of a 250 pound (113 kg) weight falling free for a distance of 6 feet (1.83 m). The weight should be a rigid object with a girth of 38 inches plus or minus 4 inches (96 cm plus or minus 10 cm). The weight should be placed in the waistband with the belt buckle drawn firmly against the weight, as when the belt is worn by a window cleaner. One belt terminal should be attached to a rigid anchor and the other terminal should hang free. The terminals should be adjusted to their maximum span. The weight fastened in the freely suspended belt should then be lifted exactly 6 feet (1.83 m) above its "at rest" position and released so as to permit a free fall of 6 feet (1.83 m) vertically below the point of attachment of the terminal anchor. The belt system should be equipped with devices and instrumentation capable of measuring the duration and magnitude of the arrest forces. Failure of the test should consist of any breakage or slippage sufficient to permit the weight to fall free of the system. In addition, the initial and subsequent arresting forces should be measured and should not exceed 2,000 pounds (8.5 kN) for more than 2 milliseconds for the initial impact, or exceed 1,000 pounds (4.5 kN) for the remainder of the arrest time.

(3) All other positioning systems (except for restraint line systems) should withstand a drop test consisting of a 250 pound (113 kg) weight free falling a distance of 4 feet (1.2 m). The weight must be a rigid object with a girth of 38 inches plus or minus 4 inches (96 cm plus or minus 10 cm). The body belt or harness should be affixed to the test weight as it would be to an employee. The system should be connected to the rigid anchor in the manner that the system would be connected in normal use. The weight should be lifted exactly 4 feet (1.2 m) above its "at rest" position and released so as to permit a vertical free fall of 4 feet (1.2 m). Failure of the system should be indicated by any breakage or slippage sufficient to permit the weight to fall free to the ground.

This page intentionally left blank.

Section Contents

Subpart J—General Environmental Controls

Authority: 29 U.S.C. 653, 655, 657; Secretary of Labor's Order No. 12–71 (36 FR 8754), 8–76 (41 FR 25059), 9–83 (48 FR 35736), 1–90 (55 FR 9033), 6–96 (62 FR 111), 3–2000 (65 FR 50017), 5–2007 (72 FR 31159), 4–2010 (75 FR 55355), or 1–2012 (77 FR 3912), as applicable..

Section 1910.141, 1910.142, 1910.145, 1910.146, and 1910.147 also issued under 29 CFR 1911.

§1910.141 Sanitation

(a) **General**

(a)(1) **Scope** This section applies to permanent places of employment.

(a)(2) **Definitions applicable to this section**

Nonwater carriage toilet facility means a toilet facility not connected to a sewer.

Number of employees means, unless otherwise specified, the maximum number of employees present at any one time on a regular shift.

Personal service room, means a room used for activities not directly connected with the production or service function performed by the establishment. Such activities include, but are not limited to, first-aid, medical services, dressing, showering, toilet use, washing, and eating.

Potable water means water that meets the standards for drinking purposes of the State or local authority having jurisdiction, or water that meets the quality standards prescribed by the U.S. Environmental Protection Agency's National Primary Drinking Water Regulations (40 CFR 141).

Toilet facility means a fixture maintained within a toilet room for the purpose of defecation or urination, or both.

Toilet room means a room maintained within or on the premises of any place of employment, containing toilet facilities for use by employees.

Toxic material means a material in concentration or amount which exceeds the applicable limit established by a standard, such as §1910.1000 and §1910.1001 or, in the absence of an applicable standard, which is of such toxicity so as to constitute a recognized hazard that is causing or is likely to cause death or serious physical harm.

Urinal means a toilet facility maintained within a toilet room for the sole purpose of urination.

Water closet means a toilet facility maintained within a toilet room for the purpose of both defecation and urination and which is flushed with water.

Wet process means any process or operation in a workroom which normally results in surfaces upon which employees may walk or stand becoming wet.

(a)(3) **Housekeeping**

(a)(3)(i) All places of employment shall be kept clean to the extent that the nature of the work allows.

(a)(3)(ii) The floor of every workroom shall be maintained, so far as practicable, in a dry condition. Where wet processes are used, drainage shall be maintained and false floors, platforms, mats, or other dry standing places shall be provided, where practicable, or appropriate waterproof footgear shall be provided.

(a)(3)(iii) To facilitate cleaning, every floor, working place, and passageway shall be kept free from protruding nails, splinters, loose boards, and unnecessary holes and openings.

(a)(4) **Waste disposal**

(a)(4)(i) Any receptacle used for putrescible solid or liquid waste or refuse shall be so constructed that it does not leak and may be thoroughly cleaned and maintained in a sanitary condition. Such a receptacle shall be equipped with a solid tight-fitting cover, unless it can be maintained in a sanitary condition without a cover. This requirement does not prohibit the use of receptacles which are designed to permit the maintenance of a sanitary condition without regard to the aforementioned requirements.

(a)(4)(ii) All sweepings, solid or liquid wastes, refuse, and garbage shall be removed in such a manner as to avoid creating a menace to health and as often as necessary or appropriate to maintain the place of employment in a sanitary condition.

(a)(5) **Vermin control** Every enclosed workplace shall be so constructed, equipped, and maintained, so far as reasonably practicable, as to prevent the entrance or harborage of rodents, insects, and other vermin. A continuing and effective extermination program shall be instituted where their presence is detected.

(b) **Water supply**

(b)(1) **Potable water**

(b)(1)(i) Potable water shall be provided in all places of employment, for drinking, washing of the person, cooking, washing of foods, washing of cooking or eating utensils, washing of food preparation or processing premises, and personal service rooms.

(b)(1)(ii) [Reserved]

(b)(1)(iii) Portable drinking water dispensers shall be designed, constructed, and serviced so that sanitary conditions are maintained, shall be capable of being closed, and shall be equipped with a tap.

(b)(1)(iv) [Reserved]

(b)(1)(v) Open containers such as barrels, pails, or tanks for drinking water from which the water must be dipped or poured, whether or not they are fitted with a cover, are prohibited.

(b)(1)(vi) A common drinking cup and other common utensils are prohibited.

(b)(2) **Nonpotable water**

(b)(2)(i) Outlets for nonpotable water, such as water for industrial or firefighting purposes, shall be posted or otherwise marked in a manner that will indicate clearly that the water is unsafe and is not to be used for drinking, washing of the person, cooking, washing of food, washing of cooking or eating utensils, washing of food preparation or processing premises, or personal service rooms, or for washing clothes.

(b)(2)(ii) Construction of nonpotable water systems or systems carrying any other nonpotable substance shall be such as to prevent backflow or backsiphonage into a potable water system.

(b)(2)(iii) Nonpotable water shall not be used for washing any portion of the person, cooking or eating utensils, or clothing. Nonpotable water may be used for cleaning work premises, other than food processing and preparation premises and personal service rooms: Provided, That this nonpotable water does not contain concentrations of chemicals, fecal coliform, or other substances which could create insanitary conditions or be harmful to employees.

(c) **Toilet facilities**

(c)(1) **General**

(c)(1)(i) Except as otherwise indicated in this paragraph (c)(1)(i), toilet facilities, in toilet rooms separate for each sex, shall be provided in all places of employment in accordance with table J–1 of this section. The number of facilities to be provided for each sex shall be based on the number of employees of that sex for whom the facilities are furnished. Where toilet rooms will be occupied by no more than one person at a time, can be locked from the inside, and contain at least one water closet, separate toilet rooms for each sex need not be provided. Where such single-occupancy rooms have more than one toilet facility, only one such facility in each toilet room shall be counted for the purpose of Table J–1.

Table J–1

Number of employees	Minimum number of water closets[1]
1 to 15	1
16 to 35	2
36 to 55	3
56 to 80	4
81 to 110	5
111 to 150	6
Over 150	(2)

[1] Where toilet facilities will not be used by women, urinals may be provided instead of water closets, except that the number of water closets in such cases shall not be reduced to less than 2/3 of the minimum specified.

[2] 1 additional fixture for each additional 40 employees.

(c)(1)(ii) The requirements of paragraph (c)(1)(i) of this section do not apply to mobile crews or to normally unattended work locations so long as employees working at these locations have transportation immediately available to nearby toilet facilities which meet the other requirements of this subparagraph.

(c)(1)(iii) The sewage disposal method shall not endanger the health of employees.

(c)(2) Construction of toilet rooms

(c)(2)(i) Each water closet shall occupy a separate compartment with a door and walls or partitions between fixtures sufficiently high to assure privacy.

(c)(2)(ii) [Reserved]

(d) Washing facilities

(d)(1) General Washing facilities shall be maintained in a sanitary condition.

(d)(2) Lavatories

(d)(2)(i) Lavatories shall be made available in all places of employment. The requirements of this subdivision do not apply to mobile crews or to normally unattended work locations if employees working at these locations have transportation readily available to nearby washing facilities which meet the other requirements of this paragraph.

(d)(2)(ii) Each lavatory shall be provided with hot and cold running water, or tepid running water.

(d)(2)(iii) Hand soap or similar cleansing agents shall be provided.

(d)(2)(iv) Individual hand towels or sections thereof, of cloth or paper, air blowers or clean individual sections of continuous cloth toweling, convenient to the lavatories, shall be provided.

(d)(3) Showers

(d)(3)(i) Whenever showers are required by a particular standard, the showers shall be provided in accordance with paragraphs (d)(3)(ii) through (v) of this section.

(d)(3)(ii) One shower shall be provided for each 10 employees of each sex, or numerical fraction thereof, who are required to shower during the same shift.

(d)(3)(iii) Body soap or other appropriate cleansing agents convenient to the showers shall be provided as specified in paragraph (d)(2)(iii) of this section.

(d)(3)(iv) Showers shall be provided with hot and cold water feeding a common discharge line.

(d)(3)(v) Employees who use showers shall be provided with individual clean towels.

(e) Change rooms Whenever employees are required by a particular standard to wear protective clothing because of the possibility of contamination with toxic materials, change rooms equipped with storage facilities for street clothes and separate storage facilities for the protective clothing shall be provided.

(f) Clothes drying facilities Where working clothes are provided by the employer and become wet or are washed between shifts, provision shall be made to insure that such clothing is dry before reuse.

(g) Consumption of food and beverages on the premises

(g)(1) Application This paragraph shall apply only where employees are permitted to consume food or beverages, or both, on the premises.

(g)(2) Eating and drinking areas No employee shall be allowed to consume food or beverages in a toilet room nor in any area exposed to a toxic material.

(g)(3) Waste disposal containers Receptacles constructed of smooth, corrosion resistant, easily cleanable, or disposable materials, shall be provided and used for the disposal of waste food. The number, size, and location of such receptacles shall encourage their use and not result in overfilling. They shall be emptied not less frequently than once each working day, unless unused, and shall be maintained in a clean and sanitary condition. Receptacles shall be provided with a solid tight-fitting cover unless sanitary conditions can be maintained without use of a cover.

(g)(4) Sanitary storage No food or beverages shall be stored in toilet rooms or in an area exposed to a toxic material.

(h) Food handling All employee food service facilities and operations shall be carried out in accordance with sound hygienic principles. In all places of employment where all or part of the food service is provided, the food dispensed shall be wholesome, free from spoilage, and shall be processed, prepared, handled, and stored in such a manner as to be protected against contamination.

[39 FR 23502, June 27, 1974, as amended at 40 FR 18446, April 28, 1975; 40 FR 23073, May 28, 1975; 43 FR 49748, Oct. 24, 1978; 63 FR 33466, June 18, 1998; 76 FR 33607, June 8, 2011]

§1910.142 Temporary labor camps

(a) Site

(a)(1) All sites used for camps shall be adequately drained. They shall not be subject to periodic flooding, nor located within 200 feet of swamps, pools, sink holes, or other surface collections of water unless such quiescent water surfaces can be subjected to mosquito control measures. The camp shall be located so the drainage from and through the camp will not endanger any domestic or public water supply. All sites shall be graded, ditched, and rendered free from depressions in which water may become a nuisance.

(a)(2) All sites shall be adequate in size to prevent overcrowding of necessary structures. The principal camp area in which food is prepared and served and where sleeping quarters are located shall be at least 500 feet from any area in which livestock is kept.

(a)(3) The grounds and open areas surrounding the shelters shall be maintained in a clean and sanitary condition free from rubbish, debris, waste paper, garbage, or other refuse.

(b) Shelter

(b)(1) Every shelter in the camp shall be constructed in a manner which will provide protection against the elements.

(b)(2) Each room used for sleeping purposes shall contain at least 50 square feet of floor space for each occupant. At least a 7–foot ceiling shall be provided.

(b)(3) Beds, cots, or bunks, and suitable storage facilities such as wall lockers for clothing and personal articles shall be provided in every room used for sleeping purposes. Such beds or similar facilities shall be spaced not closer than 36 inches both laterally and end to end, and shall be elevated at least 12 inches from the floor. If double-deck bunks are used, they shall be spaced not less than 48 inches both laterally and end to end. The minimum clear space between the lower and upper bunk shall be not less than 27 inches. Triple-deck bunks are prohibited.

(b)(4) The floors of each shelter shall be constructed of wood, asphalt, or concrete. Wooden floors shall be of smooth and tight construction. The floors shall be kept in good repair.

(b)(5) All wooden floors shall be elevated not less than 1 foot above the ground level at all points to prevent dampness and to permit free circulation of air beneath.

(b)(6) Nothing in this section shall be construed to prohibit "banking" with earth or other suitable material around the outside walls in areas subject to extreme low temperatures.

(b)(7) All living quarters shall be provided with windows the total of which shall be not less than one-tenth of the floor area. At least one-half of each window shall be so constructed that it can be opened for purposes of ventilation.

(b)(8) All exterior openings shall be effectively screened with 16–mesh material. All screen doors shall be equipped with self-closing devices.

(b)(9) In a room where workers cook, live, and sleep a minimum of 100 square feet per person shall be provided. Sanitary facilities shall be provided for storing and preparing food.

(b)(10) In camps where cooking facilities are used in common, stoves (in ratio of one stove to 10 persons or one stove to two families) shall be provided in an enclosed and screened shelter. Sanitary facilities shall be provided for storing and preparing food.

(b)(11) All heating, cooking, and water heating equipment shall be installed in accordance with State and local ordinances, codes, and regulations governing such installations. If a camp is used during cold weather, adequate heating equipment shall be provided.

(c) **Water supply**

(c)(1) An adequate and convenient water supply, approved by the appropriate health authority, shall be provided in each camp for drinking, cooking, bathing, and laundry purposes.

(c)(2) A water supply shall be deemed adequate if it is capable of delivering 35 gallons per person per day to the campsite at a peak rate of 2 ½ times the average hourly demand.

(c)(3) The distribution lines shall be capable of supplying water at normal operating pressures to all fixtures for simultaneous operation. Water outlets shall be distributed throughout the camp in such a manner that no shelter is more than 100 feet from a yard hydrant if water is not piped to the shelters.

(c)(4) Where water under pressure is available, one or more drinking fountains shall be provided for each 100 occupants or fraction thereof. Common drinking cups are prohibited.

(d) **Toilet facilities**

(d)(1) Toilet facilities adequate for the capacity of the camp shall be provided.

(d)(2) Each toilet room shall be located so as to be accessible without any individual passing through any sleeping room. Toilet rooms shall have a window not less than 6 square feet in area opening directly to the outside area or otherwise be satisfactorily ventilated. All outside openings shall be screened with 16–mesh material. No fixture, water closet, chemical toilet, or urinal shall be located in a room used for other than toilet purposes.

(d)(3) A toilet room shall be located within 200 feet of the door of each sleeping room. No privy shall be closer than 100 feet to any sleeping room, dining room, lunch area, or kitchen.

(d)(4) Where the toilet rooms are shared, such as in multifamily shelters and in barracks type facilities, separate toilet rooms shall be provided for each sex. These rooms shall be distinctly marked "for men" and "for women" by signs printed in English and in the native language of the persons occupying the camp, or marked with easily understood pictures or symbols. If the facilities for each sex are in the same building, they shall be separated by solid walls or partitions extending from the floor to the roof or ceiling.

(d)(5) Where toilet facilities are shared, the number of water closets or privy seats provided for each sex shall be based on the maximum number of persons of that sex which the camp is designed to house at any one time, in the ratio of one such unit to each 15 persons, with a minimum of two units for any shared facility.

(d)(6) Urinals shall be provided on the basis of one unit or 2 linear feet of urinal trough for each 25 men. The floor from the wall and for a distance not less than 15 inches measured from the outward edge of the urinals shall be constructed of materials impervious to moisture. Where water under pressure is available, urinals shall be provided with an adequate water flush. Urinal troughs in privies shall drain freely into the pit or vault and the construction of this drain shall be such as to exclude flies and rodents from the pit.

(d)(7) Every water closet installed on or after August 31, 1971, shall be located in a toilet room.

(d)(8) Each toilet room shall be lighted naturally, or artificially by a safe type of lighting at all hours of the day and night.

(d)(9) An adequate supply of toilet paper shall be provided in each privy, water closet, or chemical toilet compartment.

(d)(10) Privies and toilet rooms shall be kept in a sanitary condition. They shall be cleaned at least daily.

(e) **Sewage disposal facilities** In camps where public sewers are available, all sewer lines and floor drains from buildings shall be connected thereto.

(f) **Laundry, handwashing, and bathing facilities**

(f)(1) Laundry, handwashing, and bathing facilities shall be provided in the following ratio:

- (f)(1)(i) Handwash basin per family shelter or per six persons in shared facilities;
- (f)(1)(ii) Shower head for every 10 persons;
- (f)(1)(iii) Laundry tray or tub for every 30 persons.
- (f)(1)(iv) Slop sink in each building used for laundry, hand washing, and bathing.

(f)(2) Floors shall be of smooth finish but not slippery materials; they shall be impervious to moisture. Floor drains shall be provided in all shower baths, shower rooms, or laundry rooms to remove waste water and facilitate cleaning. All junctions of the curbing and the floor shall be coved. The walls and partitions of shower rooms shall be smooth and impervious to the height of splash.

(f)(3) An adequate supply of hot and cold running water shall be provided for bathing and laundry purposes. Facilities for heating water shall be provided.

(f)(4) Every service building shall be provided with equipment capable of maintaining a temperature of at least 70 °F. during cold weather.

(f)(5) Facilities for drying clothes shall be provided.

(f)(6) All service buildings shall be kept clean.

(g) **Lighting** Where electric service is available, each habitable room in a camp shall be provided with at least one ceiling-type light fixture and at least one separate floor- or wall-type convenience outlet. Laundry and toilet rooms and rooms where people congregate shall contain at least one ceiling- or wall-type fixture. Light levels in toilet and storage rooms shall be at least 20 foot-candles 30 inches from the floor. Other rooms, including kitchens and living quarters, shall be at least 30 foot-candles 30 inches from the floor.

(h) **Refuse disposal**

(h)(1) Fly-tight, rodent-tight, impervious, cleanable or single service containers, approved by the appropriate health authority shall be provided for the storage of garbage. At least one such container shall be provided for each family shelter and shall be located within 100 feet of each shelter on a wooden, metal, or concrete stand.

(h)(2) Garbage containers shall be kept clean.

(h)(3) Garbage containers shall be emptied when full, but not less than twice a week.

(i) **Construction and operation of kitchens, dining hall, and feeding facilities**

(i)(1) In all camps where central dining or multiple family feeding operations are permitted or provided, the food handling facilities shall comply with the requirements of the "Food Service Sanitation Ordinance and Code," Part V of the "Food Service Sanitation Manual," U.S. Public Health Service Publication 934 (1965), which is incorporated by reference as specified in §1910.6.

(i)(2) A properly constructed kitchen and dining hall adequate in size, separate from the sleeping quarters of any of the workers or their families, shall be provided in connection with all food handling facilities. There shall be no direct opening from living or sleeping quarters into a kitchen or dining hall.

(i)(3) No person with any communicable disease shall be employed or permitted to work in the preparation, cooking, serving, or other handling of food, foodstuffs, or materials used therein, in any kitchen or dining room operated in connection with a camp or regularly used by persons living in a camp.

(j) **Insect and rodent control** Effective measures shall be taken to prevent infestation by and harborage of animal or insect vectors or pests.

(k) **First aid**

(k)(1) Adequate first aid facilities approved by a health authority shall be maintained and made available in every labor camp for the emergency treatment of injured persons.

(k)(2) Such facilities shall be in charge of a person trained to administer first aid and shall be readily accessible for use at all times.

(l) **Reporting communicable disease**

(l)(1) It shall be the duty of the camp superintendent to report immediately to the local health officer the name and address of any individual in the camp known to have or suspected of having a communicable disease.

(l)(2) Whenever there shall occur in any camp a case of suspected food poisoning or an unusual prevalence of any illness in which fever, diarrhea, sore throat, vomiting, or jaundice is a prominent symptom, it shall be the duty of the camp superintendent to report immediately the existence of the outbreak to the health authority by telegram, telephone, electronic mail or any other method that is equally fast.

[39 FR 23502, June 27, 1974, as amended at 47 FR 14696, Apr. 6, 1982; 49 FR 18295, Apr. 30, 1984; 61 FR 9238, Mar. 7, 1996; 63 FR 33466, June 18, 1998; 70 FR 1141, Jan. 5, 2005; 70 FR 53929, Sept. 13, 2005]

§1910.143 Nonwater carriage disposal systems [Reserved]

§1910.144 Safety color code for marking physical hazards

(a) **Color identification**

(a)(1) **Red** Red shall be the basic color for the identification of:

(a)(1)(i) **Fire protection equipment and apparatus** [Reserved]

(a)(1)(ii) **Danger** Safety cans or other portable containers of flammable liquids having a flash point at or below 80 °F, table containers of flammable liquids (open cup tester), excluding shipping containers, shall be painted red with some additional clearly visible identification either in the form of a yellow band around the can or the name of the contents conspicuously stenciled or painted on the can in yellow. Red lights shall be provided at barricades and at temporary obstructions. Danger signs shall be painted red.

(a)(1)(iii) Stop Emergency stop bars on hazardous machines such as rubber mills, wire blocks, flat work ironers, etc., shall be red. Stop buttons or electrical switches which letters or other markings appear, used for emergency stopping of machinery shall be red.

(a)(2) [Reserved]

(a)(3) **Yellow** Yellow shall be the basic color for designating caution and for marking physical hazards such as: Striking against, stumbling, falling, tripping, and "caught in between."

(b) [Reserved]

[39 FR 23502, June 27, 1974, as amended at 43 FR 49748, Oct. 24, 1978; 49 FR 5322, Feb. 10, 1984; 61 FR 9239, Mar. 7, 1996; 72 FR 71069, Dec. 14, 2007]

§1910.145
Specification for accident prevention signs and tags

(a) Scope

(a)(1) These specifications apply to the design, application, and use of signs or symbols (as included in paragraphs (c) through (e) of this section) intended to indicate and, insofar as possible, to define specific hazards of a nature such that failure to designate them may lead to accidental injury to workers or the public, or both, or to property damage. These specifications are intended to cover all safety signs except those designed for streets, highways, and railroads. These specifications do not apply to plant bulletin boards or to safety posters.

(a)(2) All new signs and replacements of old signs shall be in accordance with these specifications.

(b) Definitions As used in this section, the word sign refers to a surface on prepared for the warning of, or safety instructions of, industrial workers or members of the public who may be exposed to hazards. Excluded from this definition, however, are news releases, displays commonly known as safety posters, and bulletins used for employee education.

(c) Classification of signs according to use

(c)(1) Danger signs

(c)(1)(i) There shall be no variation in the type of design of signs posted to warn of specific dangers and radiation hazards.

(c)(1)(ii) All employees shall be instructed that danger signs indicate immediate danger and that special precautions are necessary.

(c)(2) Caution signs

(c)(2)(i) Caution signs shall be used only to warn against potential hazards or to caution against unsafe practices.

(c)(2)(ii) All employees shall be instructed that caution signs indicate a possible hazard against which proper precaution should be taken.

(c)(3) **Safety instruction signs** Safety instruction signs shall be used where there is a need for general instructions and suggestions relative to safety measures.

(d) Sign design

(d)(1) Design features All signs shall be furnished with rounded or blunt corners and shall be free from sharp edges, burrs, splinters, or other sharp projections. The ends or heads of bolts or other fastening devices shall be located in such a way that they do not constitute a hazard.

(d)(2) Danger signs The colors red, black, and white shall be those of opaque glossy samples as specified in Table 1, "Fundamental Specification of Safety Colors for CIE Standard Source 'C,' " of ANSI Z53.1–1967 or in Table 1, "Specification of the Safety Colors for CIE Illuminate C and the CIE 1931, 2ß Standard Observer," of ANSI Z535.1– 2006(R2011), incorporated by reference in §1910.6.

(d)(3) [Reserved]

(d)(4) Caution signs The standard color of the background shall be yellow; and the panel, black with yellow letters. Any letters used against the yellow background shall be black. The colors shall be those of opaque glossy samples as specified in Table 1 of ANSI Z53.1– 1967 or Table 1 of ANSI Z535.1– 2006(R2011), incorporated by reference in §1910.6.

(d)(5) [Reserved]

(d)(6) Safety instruction signs The standard color of the background shall be white; and the panel, green with white letters. Any letters used against the white background shall be black. The colors shall be those of opaque glossy samples as specified in Table 1 of ANSI Z53.1–1967 or in Table 1 of ANSI Z535.1–2006(R2011), incorporated by reference in §1910.6.

(d)(7)–(9) [Reserved]

(d)(10) Slow-moving vehicle emblem This emblem (see fig. J–7) consists of a fluorescent yellow-orange triangle with a dark red reflective border. The yellow-orange fluorescent triangle is a highly visible color for daylight exposure. The reflective border defines the shape of the fluorescent color in daylight and creates a hollow red triangle in the path of motor vehicle headlights at night. The emblem is intended as a unique identification for, and it shall be used only on, vehicles which by design move slowly (25 m.p.h. or less) on the public roads. The emblem is not a clearance marker for wide machinery nor is it intended to replace required lighting or marking of slow-moving vehicles. Neither the color film pattern and its dimensions nor the backing shall be altered to permit use of advertising or other markings. The material, location, mounting, etc., of the emblem shall be in accordance with the American Society of Agricultural Engineers Emblem for Identifying Slow-Moving Vehicles, ASAE R276, 1967, or ASAE S276.2 (ANSI B114.1–1971), which are incorporated by reference as specified in §1910.6.

Figure J–7
Slow-Moving Vehicle Emblem
Note: All dimensions are in inches.

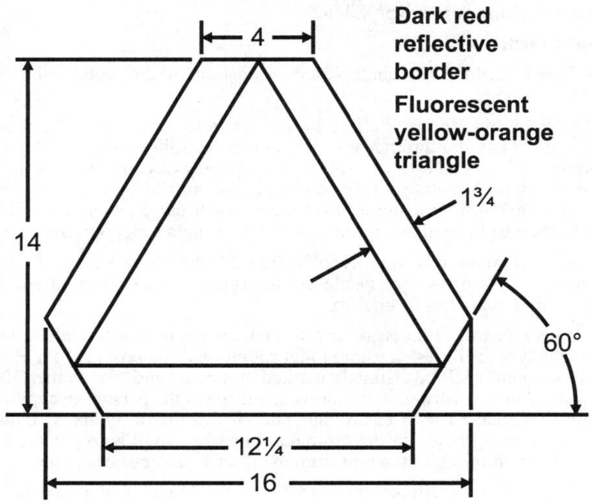

(e) Sign wordings

(e)(1) [Reserved]

(e)(2) Nature of wording The wording of any sign should be easily read and concise. The sign should contain sufficient information to be easily understood. The wording should make a positive, rather than negative suggestion and should be accurate in fact.

(e)(3) [Reserved]

(e)(4) Biological hazard signs The biological hazard warning shall be used to signify the actual or potential presence of a biohazard and to identify equipment, containers, rooms, materials, experimental animals, or combinations thereof, which contain, or are contaminated with, viable hazardous agents. For the purpose of this subparagraph the term "biological hazard," or "biohazard," shall include only those infectious agents presenting a risk or potential risk to the well-being of man.

(f) Accident prevention tags

(f)(1) Scope and application

(f)(1)(i) This paragraph (f) applies to all accident prevention tags used to identify hazardous conditions and provide a message to employees with respect to hazardous conditions as set forth in paragraph (f)(3) of this section, or to meet the specific tagging requirements of other OSHA standards.

(f)(1)(ii) This paragraph (f) does not apply to construction or agriculture.

(f)(2) Definitions

Biological hazard or BIOHAZARD means those infectious agents presenting a risk of death, injury or illness to employees.

Major message means that portion of a tag's inscription that is more specific than the signal word and that indicates the specific hazardous condition or the instruction to be communicated to the employee. Examples include: "High Voltage," "Close Clearance," "Do Not Start," or "Do Not Use" or a corresponding pictograph used with a written text or alone.

Pictograph means a pictorial representation used to identify a hazardous condition or to convey a safety instruction.

Signal word means that portion of a tag's inscription that contains the word or words that are intended to capture the employee's immediate attention.

Tag means a device usually made of card, paper, pasteboard, plastic or other material used to identify a hazardous condition.

(f)(3) Use Tags shall be used as a means to prevent accidental injury or illness to employees who are exposed to hazardous or potentially hazardous conditions, equipment or operations which are out of the ordinary, unexpected or not readily apparent. Tags shall be used until such time as the identified hazard is eliminated or the hazardous operation is completed. Tags need not be used where signs, guarding or other positive means of protection are being used.

(f)(4) **General tag criteria** All required tags shall meet the following criteria:

(f)(4)(i) Tags shall contain a signal word and a major message;

(f)(4)(i)(A) The signal word shall be either "Danger," "Caution," or "Biological Hazard," "BIOHAZARD," or the biological hazard symbol;

(f)(4)(i)(B) The major message shall indicate the specific hazardous condition or the instruction to be communicated to the employee.

(f)(4)(ii) The signal word shall be readable at a minimum distance of five feet (1.52 m) or such greater distance as warranted by the hazard;

(f)(4)(iii) The tag's major message shall be presented in either pictographs, written text or both;

(f)(4)(iv) The signal word and the major message shall be understandable to all employees who may be exposed to the identified hazard;

(f)(4)(v) All employees shall be informed as to the meaning of the various tags used throughout the workplace and what special precautions are necessary;

(f)(4)(vi) Tags shall be affixed as close as safely possible to their respective hazards by a positive means such as string, wire, or adhesive that prevents their loss or unintentional removal.

(f)(5) **Danger tags** Danger tags shall be used in major hazard situations where an immediate hazard presents a threat of death or serious injury to employees. Danger tags shall be used only in these situations.

(f)(6) **Caution tags** Caution tags shall be used in minor hazard situations where a non-immediate or potential hazard or unsafe practice presents a lesser threat of employee injury. Caution tags shall be used only in these situations.

(f)(7) **Warning tags** Warning tags may be used to represent a hazard level between "Caution" and "Danger," instead of the required "Caution" tag, provided that they have a signal word of "Warning," an appropriate major message, and otherwise meet the general tag criteria of paragraph (f)(4) of this section.

(f)(8) **Biological hazard tags**

(f)(8)(i) Biological hazard tags shall be used to identify the actual or potential presence of a biological hazard and to identify equipment, containers, rooms, experimental animals, or combinations thereof, that contain or are contaminated with hazardous biological agents.

(f)(8)(ii) The symbol design for biological hazard tags shall conform to the design shown below:

Biological Hazard Symbol

(f)(9) **Other tags** Other tags may be used in addition to those required by this paragraph (f), or in other situations where this paragraph (f) does not require tags, provided that they do not detract from the impact or visibility of the signal word and major message of any required tag.

§1910.145(f) Appendices
Accident prevention tags

§1910.145(f) Appendix A
Recommended color coding

While the standard does not specifically mandate colors to be used on accident prevention tags, the following color scheme is recommended by OSHA for meeting the requirements of this section:

"DANGER"—Red, or predominantly red, with lettering or symbols in a contrasting color.

"CAUTION"—Yellow, or predominantly yellow, with lettering or symbols in a contrasting color.

"WARNING"—Orange, or predominantly orange, with lettering or symbols in a contrasting color.

"BIOLOGICAL HAZARD"—Fluorescent orange or orange-red, or predominantly so, with lettering or symbols in a contrasting color.

§1910.145(f) Appendix B
References for further information

The following references provide information which can be helpful in understanding the requirements contained in various sections of the standard:

1. Bresnahan, Thomas F., and Bryk, Joseph, "The Hazard Association Values of Accident Prevention Signs", Journal of American Society of Safety Engineers; January 1975.
2. Dreyfuss, H., Symbol Sourcebook, McGraw Hill; New York, NY, 1972.
3. Glass, R.A. and others, Some Criteria for Colors and Signs in Workplaces, National Bureau of Standards, Washington DC, 1983.
4. Graphic Symbols for Public Areas and Occupational Environments, Treasury Board of Canada, Ottawa, Canada, July 1980.
5. Howett, G.L., Size of Letters Required for Visibility as a Function of Viewing Distance and Observer Acuity, National Bureau of Standards, Washington DC, July 1983.
6. Lerner, N.D. and Collins, B.L., The Assessment of Safety Symbol Understandability by Different Testing Methods, National Bureau of Standards, Washington DC, 1980.
7. Lerner, N.D. and Collins, B.L., Workplace Safety Symbols, National Bureau of Standards, Washington DC, 1980.
8. Modley, R. and Meyers, W.R., Handbook of Pictorial Symbols, Dover Publication, New York, NY, 1976.
9. Product Safety Signs and Labels, FMC Corporation, Santa Clara, CA, 1978.
10. Safety Color Coding for Marking Physical Hazards, Z53.1, American National Standards Institute, New York, NY, 1979.
11. Signs and Symbols for the Occupational Environment, Can. 3–Z–321–77, Canadian Standards Association, Ottawa, September 1977.
12. Symbols for Industrial Safety, National Bureau of Standards, Washington DC, April 1982.
13. Symbol Signs, U.S. Department of Transportation, Washington DC, November 1974.

[39 FR 23502, June 27, 1974, as amended at 43 FR 49749, Oct. 24, 1978; 43 FR 51759, Nov. 7, 1978; 49 FR 5322, Feb. 10, 1984; 51 FR 33260, Sept. 19, 1986; 61 FR 9239, Mar. 7, 1996; 76 FR 24698, May 2, 2011; 76 FR 44265, July 25, 2011]

§1910.146 OI
Permit-required confined spaces

(a) OI **Scope and application** This section contains requirements for practices and procedures to protect employees in general industry from the hazards of entry into permit-required confined spaces. This section does not apply to agriculture, to construction, or to shipyard employment (Parts 1928, 1926, and 1915 of this chapter, respectively).

(b) OI **Definitions**

Acceptable entry conditions means the conditions that must exist in a permit space to allow entry and to ensure that employees involved with a permit-required confined space entry can safely enter into and work within the space.

Attendant means an individual stationed outside one or more permit spaces who monitors the authorized entrants and who performs all attendant's duties assigned in the employer's permit space program.

Authorized entrant means an employee who is authorized by the employer to enter a permit space.

Blanking or blinding means the absolute closure of a pipe, line, or duct by the fastening of a solid plate (such as a spectacle blind or a skillet blind) that completely covers the bore and that is capable of withstanding the maximum pressure of the pipe, line, or duct with no leakage beyond the plate.

Confined space means a space that:

(1) Is large enough and so configured that an employee can bodily enter and perform assigned work; and

(2) Has limited or restricted means for entry or exit (for example, tanks, vessels, silos, storage bins, hoppers, vaults, and pits are spaces that may have limited means of entry.); and

(3) Is not designed for continuous employee occupancy.

Double block and bleed means the closure of a line, duct, or pipe by closing and locking or tagging two in-line valves and by opening and locking or tagging a drain or vent valve in the line between the two closed valves.

Emergency means any occurrence (including any failure of hazard control or monitoring equipment) or event internal or external to the permit space that could endanger entrants.

Engulfment means the surrounding and effective capture of a person by a liquid or finely divided (flowable) solid substance that can be aspirated to cause death by filling or plugging the respiratory system or that can exert enough force on the body to cause death by strangulation, constriction, or crushing.

Entry means the action by which a person passes through an opening into a permit-required confined space. Entry includes ensuing work activities in that space and is considered to have occurred as soon as any part of the entrant's body breaks the plane of an opening into the space.

Entry permit (permit) means the written or printed document that is provided by the employer to allow and control entry into a permit space and that contains the information specified in paragraph (f) of this section.

Entry supervisor means the person (such as the employer, foreman, or crew chief) responsible for determining if acceptable entry conditions are present at a permit space where entry is planned, for authorizing entry and overseeing entry operations, and for terminating entry as required by this section.

Note: An entry supervisor also may serve as an attendant or as an authorized entrant, as long as that person is trained and equipped as required by this section for each role he or she fills. Also, the duties of entry supervisor may be passed from one individual to another during the course of an entry operation.

Hazardous atmosphere means an atmosphere that may expose employees to the risk of death, incapacitation, impairment of ability to self-rescue (that is, escape unaided from a permit space), injury, or acute illness from one or more of the following causes:

(1) Flammable gas, vapor, or mist in excess of 10 percent of its lower flammable limit (LFL);

(2) Airborne combustible dust at a concentration that meets or exceeds its LFL;

Note: This concentration may be approximated as a condition in which the dust obscures vision at a distance of 5 feet (1.52 m) or less.

(3) Atmospheric oxygen concentration below 19.5 percent or above 23.5 percent;

(4) Atmospheric concentration of any substance for which a dose or a permissible exposure limit is published in Subpart G, Occupational Health and Environmental Control, or in Subpart Z, Toxic and Hazardous Substances, of this part and which could result in employee exposure in excess of its dose or permissible exposure limit;

Note: An atmospheric concentration of any substance that is not capable of causing death, incapacitation, impairment of ability to self-rescue, injury, or acute illness due to its health effects is not covered by this provision.

(5) Any other atmospheric condition that is immediately dangerous to life or health.

Note: For air contaminants for which OSHA has not determined a dose or permissible exposure limit, other sources of information, such as Safety Data Sheets that comply with the Hazard Communication Standard, §1910.1200 of this part, published information, and internal documents can provide guidance in establishing acceptable atmospheric conditions.

Hot work permit means the employer's written authorization to perform operations (for example, riveting, welding, cutting, burning, and heating) capable of providing a source of ignition.

Immediately dangerous to life or health (IDLH) means any condition that poses an immediate or delayed threat to life or that would cause irreversible adverse health effects or that would interfere with an individual's ability to escape unaided from a permit space.

Note: Some materials—hydrogen fluoride gas and cadmium vapor, for example—may produce immediate transient effects that, even if severe, may pass without medical attention, but are followed by sudden, possibly fatal collapse 12–72 hours after exposure. The victim "feels normal" from recovery from transient effects until collapse. Such materials in hazardous quantities are considered to be "immediately" dangerous to life or health.

Inerting means the displacement of the atmosphere in a permit space by a noncombustible gas (such as nitrogen) to such an extent that the resulting atmosphere is noncombustible.

Note: This procedure produces an IDLH oxygen-deficient atmosphere.

Isolation means the process by which a permit space is removed from service and completely protected against the release of energy and material into the space by such means as: blanking or blinding; misaligning or removing sections of lines, pipes, or ducts; a double block and bleed system; lockout or tagout of all sources of energy; or blocking or disconnecting all mechanical linkages.

Line breaking means the intentional opening of a pipe, line, or duct that is or has been carrying flammable, corrosive, or toxic material, an inert gas, or any fluid at a volume, pressure, or temperature capable of causing injury.

Non-permit confined space means a confined space that does not contain or, with respect to atmospheric hazards, have the potential to contain any hazard capable of causing death or serious physical harm.

Oxygen deficient atmosphere means an atmosphere containing less than 19.5 percent oxygen by volume.

Oxygen enriched atmosphere means an atmosphere containing more than 23.5 percent oxygen by volume.

Permit-required confined space (permit space) means a confined space that has one or more of the following characteristics:

(1) Contains or has a potential to contain a hazardous atmosphere;

(2) Contains a material that has the potential for engulfing an entrant;

(3) Has an internal configuration such that an entrant could be trapped or asphyxiated by inwardly converging walls or by a floor which slopes downward and tapers to a smaller cross- section; or

(4) Contains any other recognized serious safety or health hazard.

Permit-required confined space program (permit space program) means the employer's overall program for controlling, and, where appropriate, for protecting employees from, permit space hazards and for regulating employee entry into permit spaces.

Permit system means the employer's written procedure for preparing and issuing permits for entry and for returning the permit space to service following termination of entry.

Prohibited condition means any condition in a permit space that is not allowed by the permit during the period when entry is authorized.

Rescue service means the personnel designated to rescue employees from permit spaces.

Retrieval system means the equipment (including a retrieval line, chest or full-body harness, wristlets, if appropriate, and a lifting device or anchor) used for non-entry rescue of persons from permit spaces.

Testing means the process by which the hazards that may confront entrants of a permit space are identified and evaluated. Testing includes specifying the tests that are to be performed in the permit space.

Note: Testing enables employers both to devise and implement adequate control measures for the protection of authorized entrants and to determine if acceptable entry conditions are present immediately prior to, and during, entry.

(c) OI **General requirements**

(c)(1) OI The employer shall evaluate the workplace to determine if any spaces are permit- required confined spaces.

Note: Proper application of the decision flow chart in Appendix A to §1910.146 would facilitate compliance with this requirement.

(c)(2) OI If the workplace contains permit spaces, the employer shall inform exposed employees, by posting danger signs or by any other equally effective means, of the existence and location of and the danger posed by the permit spaces.

Note: A sign reading "DANGER—PERMIT-REQUIRED CONFINED SPACE, DO NOT ENTER" or using other similar language would satisfy the requirement for a sign.

(c)(3) OI If the employer decides that its employees will not enter permit spaces, the employer shall take effective measures to prevent its employees from entering the permit spaces and shall comply with paragraphs (c)(1), (c)(2), (c)(6), and (c)(8) of this section.

(c)(4) OI If the employer decides that its employees will enter permit spaces, the employer shall develop and implement a written permit space program that complies with this section. The written program shall be available for inspection by employees and their authorized representatives.

(c)(5) OI An employer may use the alternate procedures specified in paragraph (c)(5)(ii) of this section for entering a permit space under the conditions set forth in paragraph (c)(5)(i) of this section.

(c)(5)(i) OI An employer whose employees enter a permit space need not comply with paragraphs (d) through (f) and (h) through (k) of this section, provided that:

(c)(5)(i)(A) The employer can demonstrate that the only hazard posed by the permit space is an actual or potential hazardous atmosphere;

(c)(5)(i)(B) The employer can demonstrate that continuous forced air ventilation alone is sufficient to maintain that permit space safe for entry;

(c)(5)(i)(C) The employer develops monitoring and inspection data that supports the demonstrations required by paragraphs (c)(5)(i)(A) and (c)(5)(i)(B) of this section;

(c)(5)(i)(D) If an initial entry of the permit space is necessary to obtain the data required by paragraph (c)(5)(i)(C) of this section, the entry is performed in compliance with paragraphs (d) through (k) of this section;

(c)(5)(i)(E) The determinations and supporting data required by paragraphs (c)(5)(i)(A), (c)(5)(i)(B), and (c)(5)(i)(C) of this section are documented by the employer and are made available to each employee who enters the permit space under the terms of paragraph (c)(5) of this section or to that employee's authorized representative; and

(c)(5)(i)(F) Entry into the permit space under the terms of paragraph (c)(5)(i) of this section is performed in accordance with the requirements of paragraph (c)(5)(ii) of this section.

Note: See paragraph (c)(7) of this section for reclassification of a permit space after all hazards within the space have been eliminated.

(c)(5)(ii) The following requirements apply to entry into permit spaces that meet the conditions set forth in paragraph (c)(5)(i) of this section.

(c)(5)(ii)(A) Any conditions making it unsafe to remove an entrance cover shall be eliminated before the cover is removed.

(c)(5)(ii)(B) When entrance covers are removed, the opening shall be promptly guarded by a railing, temporary cover, or other temporary barrier that will prevent an accidental fall through the opening and that will protect each employee working in the space from foreign objects entering the space.

(c)(5)(ii)(C) Before an employee enters the space, the internal atmosphere shall be tested, with a calibrated direct-reading instrument, for oxygen content, for flammable gases and vapors, and for potential toxic air contaminants, in that order. Any employee who enters the space, or that employee's authorized representative, shall be provided an opportunity to observe the pre-entry testing required by this paragraph.

(c)(5)(ii)(D) There may be no hazardous atmosphere within the space whenever any employee is inside the space.

(c)(5)(ii)(E) OI Continuous forced air ventilation shall be used, as follows:

(c)(5)(ii)(E)(1) An employee may not enter the space until the forced air ventilation has eliminated any hazardous atmosphere;

(c)(5)(ii)(E)(2) The forced air ventilation shall be so directed as to ventilate the immediate areas where an employee is or will be present within the space and shall continue until all employees have left the space;

(c)(5)(ii)(E)(3) The air supply for the forced air ventilation shall be from a clean source and may not increase the hazards in the space.

(c)(5)(ii)(F) The atmosphere within the space shall be periodically tested as necessary to ensure that the continuous forced air ventilation is preventing the accumulation of a hazardous atmosphere. Any employee who enters the space, or that employee's authorized representative, shall be provided with an opportunity to observe the periodic testing required by this paragraph.

(c)(5)(ii)(G) If a hazardous atmosphere is detected during entry:

(c)(5)(ii)(G)(1) Each employee shall leave the space immediately;

(c)(5)(ii)(G)(2) The space shall be evaluated to determine how the hazardous atmosphere developed; and

(c)(5)(ii)(G)(3) Measures shall be implemented to protect employees from the hazardous atmosphere before any subsequent entry takes place.

(c)(5)(ii)(H) The employer shall verify that the space is safe for entry and that the pre-entry measures required by paragraph (c)(5)(ii) of this section have been taken, through a written certification that contains the date, the location of the space, and the signature of the person providing the certification. The certification shall be made before entry and shall be made available to each employee entering the space or to that employee's authorized representative .

(c)(6) When there are changes in the use or configuration of a non-permit confined space that might increase the hazards to entrants, the employer shall reevaluate that space and, if necessary, reclassify it as a permit-required confined space.

(c)(7) OI A space classified by the employer as a permit-required confined space may be reclassified as a non-permit confined space under the following procedures:

(c)(7)(i) OI If the permit space poses no actual or potential atmospheric hazards and if all hazards within the space are eliminated without entry into the space, the permit space may be reclassified as a non-permit confined space for as long as the non-atmospheric hazards remain eliminated;

(c)(7)(ii) OI If it is necessary to enter the permit space to eliminate hazards, such entry shall be performed under paragraphs (d) through (k) of this section. If testing and inspection during that entry demonstrate that the hazards within the permit space have been eliminated, the permit space may be reclassified as a non-permit confined space for as long as the hazards remain eliminated;

Note: Control of atmospheric hazards through forced air ventilation does not constitute elimination of the hazards. Paragraph (c)(5) covers permit space entry where the employer can demonstrate that forced air ventilation alone will control all hazards in the space.

(c)(7)(iii) OI The employer shall document the basis for determining that all hazards in a permit space have been eliminated, through a certification that contains the date, the location of the space, and the signature of the person making the determination. The certification shall be made available to each employee entering the space or to that employee's authorized representative;

(c)(7)(iv) OI If hazards arise within a permit space that has been declassified to a non-permit space under paragraph (c)(7) of this section, each employee in the space shall exit the space. The employer shall then reevaluate the space and determine whether it must be reclassified as a permit space, in accordance with other applicable provisions of this section.

(c)(8) OI When an employer (host employer) arranges to have employees of another employer (contractor) perform work that involves permit space entry, the host employer shall:

(c)(8)(i) OI Inform the contractor that the workplace contains permit spaces and that permit space entry is allowed only through compliance with a permit space program meeting the requirements of this section;

(c)(8)(ii) OI Apprise the contractor of the elements, including the hazards identified and the host employer's experience with the space, that make the space in question a permit space;

(c)(8)(iii) OI Apprise the contractor of any precautions or procedures that the host employer has implemented for the protection of employees in or near permit spaces where contractor personnel will be working;

(c)(8)(iv) OI Coordinate entry operations with the contractor, when both host employer personnel and contractor personnel will be working in or near permit spaces, as required by paragraph (d)(11) of this section; and

(c)(8)(v) OI Debrief the contractor at the conclusion of the entry operations regarding the permit space program followed and regarding any hazards confronted or created in permit spaces during entry operations.

(c)(9) OI In addition to complying with the permit space requirements that apply to all employers, each contractor who is retained to perform permit space entry operations shall:

(c)(9)(i) Obtain any available information regarding permit space hazards and entry operations from the host employer;

(c)(9)(ii) Coordinate entry operations with the host employer, when both host employer personnel and contractor personnel will be working in or near permit spaces, as required by paragraph (d)(11) of this section; and

(c)(9)(iii) Inform the host employer of the permit space program that the contractor will follow and of any hazards confronted or created in permit spaces, either through a debriefing or during the entry operation.

(d) OI **Permit-required confined space program (permit space program)** Under the permit space program required by paragraph (c)(4) of this section, the employer shall:

(d)(1) Implement the measures necessary to prevent unauthorized entry;

(d)(2) Identify and evaluate the hazards of permit spaces before employees enter them;

(d)(3) OI Develop and implement the means, procedures, and practices necessary for safe permit space entry operations, including, but not limited to, the following:

(d)(3)(i) Specifying acceptable entry conditions;

(d)(3)(ii) Providing each authorized entrant or that employee's authorized representative with the opportunity to observe any monitoring or testing of permit spaces;

(d)(3)(iii) Isolating the permit space;

(d)(3)(iv) Purging, inerting, flushing, or ventilating the permit space as necessary to eliminate or control atmospheric hazards;

(d)(3)(v) Providing pedestrian, vehicle, or other barriers as necessary to protect entrants from external hazards; and

(d)(3)(vi) Verifying that conditions in the permit space are acceptable for entry throughout the duration of an authorized entry.

(d)(4) Provide the following equipment (specified in paragraphs (d)(4)(i) through (d)(4)(ix) of this section) at no cost to employees, maintain that equipment properly, and ensure that employees use that equipment properly:

(d)(4)(i) Testing and monitoring equipment needed to comply with paragraph (d)(5) of this section;

(d)(4)(ii) Ventilating equipment needed to obtain acceptable entry conditions;

(d)(4)(iii) Communications equipment necessary for compliance with paragraphs (h)(3) and (i)(5) of this section;

(d)(4)(iv) Personal protective equipment insofar as feasible engineering and work practice controls do not adequately protect employees;

(d)(4)(v) Lighting equipment needed to enable employees to see well enough to work safely and to exit the space quickly in an emergency;

(d)(4)(vi) Barriers and shields as required by paragraph (d)(3)(iv) of this section;

(d)(4)(vii) Equipment, such as ladders, needed for safe ingress and egress by authorized entrants;

(d)(4)(viii) Rescue and emergency equipment needed to comply with paragraph (d)(9) of this section, except to the extent that the equipment is provided by rescue services; and

(d)(4)(ix) Any other equipment necessary for safe entry into and rescue from permit spaces.

(d)(5) OI Evaluate permit space conditions as follows when entry operations are conducted:

(d)(5)(i) Test conditions in the permit space to determine if acceptable entry conditions exist before entry is authorized to begin, except that, if isolation of the space is infeasible because the space is large or is part of a continuous system (such as a sewer), pre-entry testing shall be performed to the extent feasible before entry is authorized and, if entry is authorized, entry conditions shall be continuously monitored in the areas where authorized entrants are working;

(d)(5)(ii) OI Test or monitor the permit space as necessary to determine if acceptable entry conditions are being maintained during the course of entry operations; and

(d)(5)(iii) OI When testing for atmospheric hazards, test first for oxygen, then for combustible gases and vapors, and then for toxic gases and vapors.

(d)(5)(iv) Provide each authorized entrant or that employee's authorized representative an opportunity to observe the pre-entry and any subsequent testing or monitoring of permit spaces;

(d)(5)(v) Reevaluate the permit space in the presence of any authorized entrant or that employee's authorized representative who requests that the employer conduct such reevaluation because the entrant or representative has reason to believe that the evaluation of that space may not have been adequate;

(d)(5)(vi) Immediately provide each authorized entrant or that employee's authorized representative with the results of any testing conducted in accord with paragraph (d) of this section.

Note: Atmospheric testing conducted in accordance with Appendix B to §1910.146 would be considered as satisfying the requirements of this paragraph. For permit space operations in sewers, atmospheric testing conducted in accordance with Appendix B, as supplemented by Appendix E to §1910.146, would be considered as satisfying the requirements of this paragraph.

(d)(6) Provide at least one attendant outside the permit space into which entry is authorized for the duration of entry operations;

Note: Attendants may be assigned to monitor more than one permit space provided the duties described in paragraph (i) of this section can be effectively performed for each permit space that is monitored. Likewise, attendants may be stationed at any location outside the permit space to be monitored as long as the duties described in paragraph (i) of this section can be effectively performed for each permit space that is monitored.

(d)(7) If multiple spaces are to be monitored by a single attendant, include in the permit program the means and procedures to enable the attendant to respond to an emergency affecting one or more of the permit spaces being monitored without distraction from the attendant's responsibilities under paragraph (i) of this section;

(d)(8) Designate the persons who are to have active roles (as, for example, authorized entrants, attendants, entry supervisors, or persons who test or monitor the atmosphere in a permit space) in entry operations, identify the duties of each such employee, and provide each such employee with the training required by paragraph (g) of this section;

(d)(9) Develop and implement procedures for summoning rescue and emergency services, for rescuing entrants from permit spaces, for providing necessary emergency services to rescued employees, and for preventing unauthorized personnel from attempting a rescue;

(d)(10) Develop and implement a system for the preparation, issuance, use, and cancellation of entry permits as required by this section;

(d)(11) OI Develop and implement procedures to coordinate entry operations when employees of more than one employer are working simultaneously as authorized entrants in a permit space, so that employees of one employer do not endanger the employees of any other employer;

(d)(12) Develop and implement procedures (such as closing off a permit space and canceling the permit) necessary for concluding the entry after entry operations have been completed;

(d)(13) Review entry operations when the employer has reason to believe that the measures taken under the permit space program may not protect employees and revise the program to correct deficiencies found to exist before subsequent entries are authorized; and

Note: Examples of circumstances requiring the review of the permit space program are: any unauthorized entry of a permit space, the detection of a permit space hazard not covered by the permit, the detection of a condition prohibited by the permit, the occurrence of an injury or near-miss during entry, a change in the use or configuration of a permit space, and employee complaints about the effectiveness of the program.

(d)(14) Review the permit space program, using the canceled permits retained under paragraph (e)(6) of this section within 1 year after each entry and revise the program as necessary, to ensure that employees participating in entry operations are protected from permit space hazards.

Note: Employers may perform a single annual review covering all entries performed during a 12-month period. If no entry is performed during a 12-month period, no review is necessary.

Appendix C to §1910.146 presents examples of permit space programs that are considered to comply with the requirements of paragraph (d) of this section.

(e) **Permit system**

(e)(1) Before entry is authorized, the employer shall document the completion of measures required by paragraph (d)(3) of this section by preparing an entry permit.

Note: Appendix D to §1910.146 presents examples of permits whose elements are considered to comply with the requirements of this section.

(e)(2) Before entry begins, the entry supervisor identified on the permit shall sign the entry permit to authorize entry.

(e)(3) The completed permit shall be made available at the time of entry to all authorized entrants or their authorized representatives, by posting it at the entry portal or by any other equally effective means, so that the entrants can confirm that pre-entry preparations have been completed.

(e)(4) The duration of the permit may not exceed the time required to complete the assigned task or job identified on the permit in accordance with paragraph (f)(2) of this section.

(e)(5) The entry supervisor shall terminate entry and cancel the entry permit when:

(e)(5)(i) The entry operations covered by the entry permit have been completed; or

(e)(5)(ii) A condition that is not allowed under the entry permit arises in or near the permit space.

(e)(6) The employer shall retain each canceled entry permit for at least 1 year to facilitate the review of the permit-required confined space program required by paragraph (d)(14) of this section. Any problems encountered during an entry operation shall be noted on the pertinent permit so that appropriate revisions to the permit space program can be made.

(f) **Entry permit** The entry permit that documents compliance with this section and authorizes entry to a permit space shall identify:

(f)(1) The permit space to be entered;

(f)(2) The purpose of the entry;

(f)(3) The date and the authorized duration of the entry permit;

(f)(4) The authorized entrants within the permit space, by name or by such other means (for example, through the use of rosters or tracking systems) as will enable the attendant to determine quickly and accurately, for the duration of the permit, which authorized entrants are inside the permit space;

Note: This requirement may be met by inserting a reference on the entry permit as to the means used, such as a roster or tracking system, to keep track of the authorized entrants within the permit space.

(f)(5) The personnel, by name, currently serving as attendants;

(f)(6) The individual, by name, currently serving as entry supervisor, with a space for the signature or initials of the entry supervisor who originally authorized entry;

(f)(7) The hazards of the permit space to be entered;

(f)(8) The measures used to isolate the permit space and to eliminate or control permit space hazards before entry;

Note: Those measures can include the lockout or tagging of equipment and procedures for purging, inerting, ventilating, and flushing permit spaces.

(f)(9) The acceptable entry conditions;

(f)(10) The results of initial and periodic tests performed under paragraph (d)(5) of this section, accompanied by the names or initials of the testers and by an indication of when the tests were performed;

(f)(11) The rescue and emergency services that can be summoned and the means (such as the equipment to use and the numbers to call) for summoning those services;

(f)(12) The communication procedures used by authorized entrants and attendants to maintain contact during the entry;

(f)(13) Equipment, such as personal protective equipment, testing equipment, communications equipment, alarm systems, and rescue equipment, to be provided for compliance with this section;

(f)(14) Any other information whose inclusion is necessary, given the circumstances of the particular confined space, in order to ensure employee safety; and

(f)(15) Any additional permits, such as for hot work, that have been issued to authorize work in the permit space.

(g) **Training**

(g)(1) The employer shall provide training so that all employees whose work is regulated by this section acquire the understanding, knowledge, and skills necessary for the safe performance of the duties assigned under this section.

(g)(2) Training shall be provided to each affected employee:

(g)(2)(i) Before the employee is first assigned duties under this section;

(g)(2)(ii) Before there is a change in assigned duties;

(g)(2)(iii) Whenever there is a change in permit space operations that presents a hazard about which an employee has not previously been trained;

(g)(2)(iv) Whenever the employer has reason to believe either that there are deviations from the permit space entry procedures required by paragraph (d)(3) of this section or that there are inadequacies in the employee's knowledge or use of these procedures.

(g)(3) The training shall establish employee proficiency in the duties required by this section and shall introduce new or revised procedures, as necessary, for compliance with this section.

(g)(4) The employer shall certify that the training required by paragraphs (g)(1) through (g)(3) of this section has been accomplished. The certification shall contain each employee's name, the signatures or initials of the trainers, and the dates of training. The certification shall be available for inspection by employees and their authorized representatives.

(h) **Duties of authorized entrants** The employer shall ensure that all authorized entrants:

(h)(1) Know the hazards that may be faced during entry, including information on the mode, signs or symptoms, and consequences of the exposure;

(h)(2) Properly use equipment as required by paragraph (d)(4) of this section;

(h)(3) Communicate with the attendant as necessary to enable the attendant to monitor entrant status and to enable the attendant to alert entrants of the need to evacuate the space as required by paragraph (i)(6) of this section;

(h)(4) Alert the attendant whenever:

(h)(4)(i) The entrant recognizes any warning sign or symptom of exposure to a dangerous situation; or

(h)(4)(ii) The entrant detects a prohibited condition; and

(h)(5) Exit from the permit space as quickly as possible whenever:

(h)(5)(i) An order to evacuate is given by the attendant or the entry supervisor;

(h)(5)(ii) The entrant recognizes any warning sign or symptom of exposure to a dangerous situation;

(h)(5)(iii) The entrant detects a prohibited condition; or

(h)(5)(iv) An evacuation alarm is activated.

(i) [OI] **Duties of attendants** The employer shall ensure that each attendant:

(i)(1) Knows the hazards that may be faced during entry, including information on the mode, signs or symptoms, and consequences of the exposure;

(i)(2) Is aware of possible behavioral effects of hazard exposure in authorized entrants;

(i)(3) Continuously maintains an accurate count of authorized entrants in the permit space and ensures that the means used to identify authorized entrants under paragraph (f)(4) of this section accurately identifies who is in the permit space;

(i)(4) Remains outside the permit space during entry operations until relieved by another attendant;

Note: When the employer's permit entry program allows attendant entry for rescue, attendants may enter a permit space to attempt a rescue if they have been trained and equipped for rescue operations as required by paragraph (k)(1) of this section and if they have been relieved as required by paragraph (i)(4) of this section.

(i)(5) Communicates with authorized entrants as necessary to monitor entrant status and to alert entrants of the need to evacuate the space under paragraph (i)(6) of this section;

(i)(6) Monitors activities inside and outside the space to determine if it is safe for entrants to remain in the space and orders the authorized entrants to evacuate the permit space immediately under any of the following conditions;

(i)(6)(i) If the attendant detects a prohibited condition;

(i)(6)(ii) If the attendant detects the behavioral effects of hazard exposure in an authorized entrant;

(i)(6)(iii) If the attendant detects a situation outside the space that could endanger the authorized entrants; or

(i)(6)(iv) If the attendant cannot effectively and safely perform all the duties required under paragraph (i) of this section;

(i)(7) Summon rescue and other emergency services as soon as the attendant determines that authorized entrants may need assistance to escape from permit space hazards;

(i)(8) Takes the following actions when unauthorized persons approach or enter a permit space while entry is underway:

(i)(8)(i) Warn the unauthorized persons that they must stay away from the permit space;

(i)(8)(ii) Advise the unauthorized persons that they must exit immediately if they have entered the permit space; and

(i)(8)(iii) Inform the authorized entrants and the entry supervisor if unauthorized persons have entered the permit space;

(i)(9) Performs non-entry rescues as specified by the employer's rescue procedure; and

(i)(10) Performs no duties that might interfere with the attendant's primary duty to monitor and protect the authorized entrants.

(j) **Duties of entry supervisors** The employer shall ensure that each entry supervisor:

(j)(1) Knows the hazards that may be faced during entry, including information on the mode, signs or symptoms, and consequences of the exposure;

(j)(2) Verifies, by checking that the appropriate entries have been made on the permit, that all tests specified by the permit have been conducted and that all procedures and equipment specified by the permit are in place before endorsing the permit and allowing entry to begin;

(j)(3) Terminates the entry and cancels the permit as required by paragraph (e)(5) of this section;

(j)(4) Verifies that rescue services are available and that the means for summoning them are operable;

(j)(5) Removes unauthorized individuals who enter or who attempt to enter the permit space during entry operations; and

(j)(6) Determines, whenever responsibility for a permit space entry operation is transferred and at intervals dictated by the hazards and operations performed within the space, that entry operations remain consistent with terms of the entry permit and that acceptable entry conditions are maintained.

(k) [OI] **Rescue and emergency services**

(k)(1) [OI] An employer who designates rescue and emergency services, pursuant to paragraph (d)(9) of this section, shall:

(k)(1)(i) Evaluate a prospective rescuer's ability to respond to a rescue summons in a timely manner, considering the hazard(s) identified;

Note to paragraph (k)(1)(i): What will be considered timely will vary according to the specific hazards involved in each entry. For example, §1910.134, Respiratory Protection, requires that employers provide a standby person or persons capable of immediate action to rescue employee(s) wearing respiratory protection while in work areas defined as IDLH atmospheres.

(k)(1)(ii) Evaluate a prospective rescue service's ability, in terms of proficiency with rescue-related tasks and equipment, to function appropriately while rescuing entrants from the particular permit space or types of permit spaces identified;

(k)(1)(iii) Select a rescue team or service from those evaluated that:

(k)(1)(iii)(A) Has the capability to reach the victim(s) within a time frame that is appropriate for the permit space hazard(s) identified;

(k)(1)(iii)(B) Is equipped for and proficient in performing the needed rescue services;

(k)(1)(iv) Inform each rescue team or service of the hazards they may confront when called on to perform rescue at the site; and

(k)(1)(v) Provide the rescue team or service selected with access to all permit spaces from which rescue may be necessary so that the rescue service can develop appropriate rescue plans and practice rescue operations.

Note to paragraph (k)(1): Non-mandatory Appendix F contains examples of criteria which employers can use in evaluating prospective rescuers as required by paragraph (k)(1) of this section.

(k)(2) An employer whose employees have been designated to provide permit space rescue and emergency services shall take the following measures:

(k)(2)(i) Provide affected employees with the personal protective equipment (PPE) needed to conduct permit space rescues safely and train affected employees so they are proficient in the use of that PPE, at no cost to those employees;

(k)(2)(ii) Train affected employees to perform assigned rescue duties. The employer must ensure that such employees successfully complete the training required to establish proficiency as an authorized entrant, as provided by paragraphs (g) and (h) of this section;

(k)(2)(iii) [OI] Train affected employees in basic first-aid and cardiopulmonary resuscitation (CPR). The employer shall ensure that at least one member of the rescue team or service holding a current certification in first aid and CPR is available; and

(k)(2)(iv) Ensure that affected employees practice making permit space rescues at least once every 12 months, by means of simulated rescue operations in which they remove dummies, manikins, or actual persons from the actual permit spaces or from representative permit spaces. Representative permit spaces shall, with respect to opening size, configuration, and accessibility, simulate the types of permit spaces from which rescue is to be performed.

(k)(3) To facilitate non-entry rescue, retrieval systems or methods shall be used whenever an authorized entrant enters a permit space, unless the retrieval equipment would increase the overall risk of entry or would not contribute to the rescue of the entrant. Retrieval systems shall meet the following requirements.

(k)(3)(i) Each authorized entrant shall use a chest or full body harness, with a retrieval line attached at the center of the entrant's back near shoulder level, above the entrant's head, or at another point which the employer can establish presents a profile small enough for the successful removal of the entrant. Wristlets may be used in lieu of the chest or full body harness if the employer can demonstrate that the use of a chest or full body harness is infeasible or creates a greater hazard and that the use of wristlets is the safest and most effective alternative.

(k)(3)(ii) The other end of the retrieval line shall be attached to a mechanical device or fixed point outside the permit space in such a manner that rescue can begin as soon as the rescuer becomes aware that rescue is necessary. A mechanical device shall be available to retrieve personnel from vertical type permit spaces more than 5 feet (1.52 m) deep.

(k)(4) If an injured entrant is exposed to a substance for which a Safety Data Sheet (SDS) or other similar written information is required to be kept at the worksite, that SDS or written information shall be made available to the medical facility treating the exposed entrant.

(l) **Employee participation**

(l)(1) Employers shall consult with affected employees and their authorized representatives on the development and implementation of all aspects of the permit space program required by paragraph (c) of this section.

(l)(2) Employers shall make available to affected employees and their authorized representatives all information required to be developed by this section.

§1910.146 Appendices Permit–required confined spaces

Note: Appendices A through F serve to provide information and nonmandatory guidelines to assist employers and employees in complying with the appropriate requirements of this section.

§1910.146 Appendix A Permit–required confined spaces decision flow chart

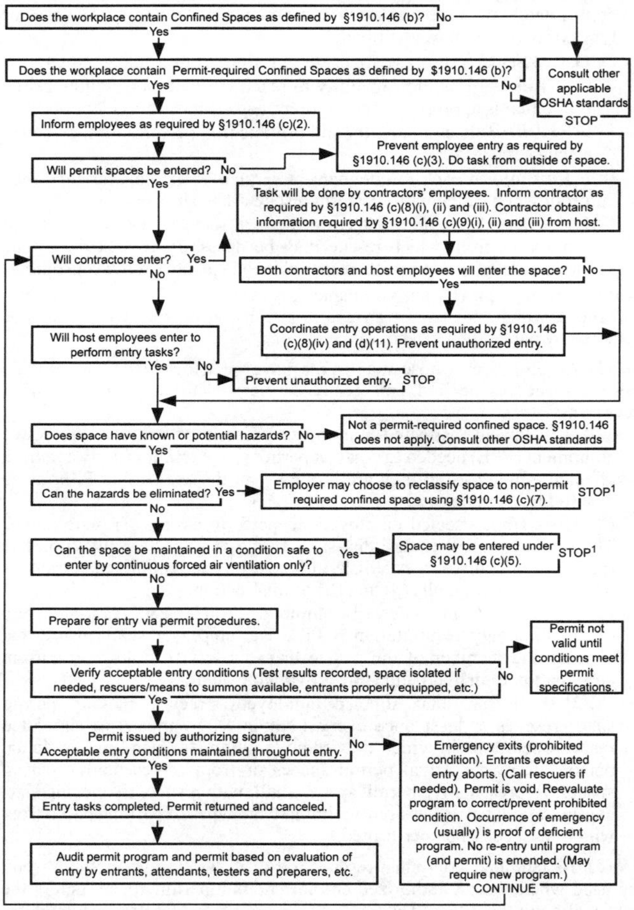

[1]Spaces may have to be evacuated and re-evaluated if hazards arise during entry

§1910.146 Appendix B Procedures for atmospheric testing

Atmospheric testing is required for two distinct purposes: evaluation of the hazards of the permit space and verification that acceptable entry conditions for entry into that space exist.

(1) Evaluation testing The atmosphere of a confined space should be analyzed using equipment of sufficient sensitivity and specificity to identify and evaluate any hazardous atmospheres that may exist or arise, so that appropriate permit entry procedures can be developed and acceptable entry conditions stipulated for that space. Evaluation and interpretation of these data, and development of the entry procedure, should be done by, or reviewed by, a technically qualified professional (e.g., OSHA consultation service, or certified industrial hygienist, registered safety engineer, certified safety professional, certified marine chemist, etc.) based on evaluation of all serious hazards.

(2) Verification testing The atmosphere of a permit space which may contain a hazardous atmosphere should be tested for residues of all contaminants identified by evaluation testing using permit specified equipment to determine that residual concentrations at the time of testing and entry are within the range of acceptable entry conditions. Results of testing (i.e., actual concentration, etc.) should be recorded on the permit in the space provided adjacent to the stipulated acceptable entry condition.

(3) Duration of testing Measurement of values for each atmospheric parameter should be made for at least the minimum response time of the test instrument specified by the manufacturer.

(4) Testing stratified atmospheres When monitoring for entries involving a descent into atmospheres that may be stratified, the atmospheric envelope should be tested a distance of approximately 4 feet (1.22 m) in the direction of travel and to each side. If a sampling probe is used, the entrant's rate of progress should be slowed to accommodate the sampling speed and detector response.

(5) Order of testing A test for oxygen is performed first because most combustible gas meters are oxygen dependent and will not provide reliable readings in an oxygen deficient atmosphere. Combustible gasses are tested for next because the threat of fire or explosion is both more immediate and more life threatening, in most cases, than exposure to toxic gasses and vapors. If tests for toxic gasses and vapors are necessary, they are performed last.

§1910.146 Appendix C Examples of permit–required confined space programs

Example 1

Workplace Sewer entry.

Potential hazards The employees could be exposed to the following:

Engulfment

Presence of toxic gases. Equal to or more than 10 ppm hydrogen sulfide measured as an 8-hour time-weighted average. If the presence of other toxic contaminants is suspected, specific monitoring programs will be developed.

Presence of explosive/flammable gases. Equal to or greater than 10% of the lower flammable limit (LFL).

Oxygen Deficiency. A concentration of oxygen in the atmosphere equal to or less than 19.5% by volume.

A. Entry Without Permit/Attendant

Certification Confined spaces may be entered without the need for a written permit or attendant provided that the space can be maintained in a safe condition for entry by mechanical ventilation alone, as provided in §1910.146(c)(5). All spaces shall be considered permit-required confined spaces until the pre-entry procedures demonstrate otherwise. Any employee required or permitted to pre-check or enter an enclosed/confined space shall have successfully completed, -as a minimum, the training as required by the following sections of these procedures. A written copy of operating and rescue procedures as required by these procedures shall be at the work site for the duration of the job. The Confined Space Pre-Entry Check List must be completed by the LEAD WORKER before entry into a confined space. This list verifies completion of items listed below. This check list shall be kept at the job site for duration of the job. If circumstances dictate an interruption in the work, the permit space must be re-evaluated and a new check list must be completed.

Control of atmospheric and engulfment hazards

Pumps and Lines. All pumps and lines which may reasonably cause contaminants to flow into the space shall be disconnected, blinded and locked out, or effectively isolated by other means to prevent development of dangerous air contamination or engulfment. Not all laterals to sewers or storm drains require blocking. However, where experience or knowledge of industrial use indicates there is a reasonable potential for contamination of air or engulfment into an occupied sewer, then all affected laterals shall be blocked. If blocking and/or isolation requires entry into the space the provisions for entry into a permit-required confined space must be implemented.

Surveillance The surrounding area shall be surveyed to avoid hazards such as drifting vapors from the tanks, piping, or sewers.

Testing The atmosphere within the space will be tested to determine whether dangerous air contamination and/or oxygen deficiency exists. Detector tubes, alarm only gas monitors and explosion meters are examples of monitoring equipment that may be used to test permit space atmospheres. Testing shall be performed by the LEAD WORKER who has successfully completed the Gas Detector training for the monitor he will use. The minimum parameters to be monitored are oxygen deficiency, LFL, and hydrogen sulfide concentration. A written record of the pre-entry test results shall be made and kept at the work site for the duration of the job. The supervisor will certify in writing, based upon the results of the pre-entry testing, that all hazards have been eliminated. Affected employees shall be able to review the testing results. The most hazardous conditions shall govern when work is being performed in two adjoining, connecting spaces.

Entry Procedures If there are no non-atmospheric hazards present and if the pre-entry tests show there is no dangerous air contamination and/or oxygen deficiency within the space and there is no reason to believe that any is likely to develop, entry into and work within may proceed. Continuous testing of the atmosphere in the immediate vicinity of the workers within the space shall be accomplished. The workers will immediately leave the permit space when any of the gas monitor alarm set points are reached as defined. Workers will not return to the area until a SUPERVISOR who has completed the gas detector training has used a direct reading gas detector to evaluate the situation and has determined that it is safe to enter.

Rescue Arrangements for rescue services are not required where there is no attendant. See the rescue portion of section B., below, for instructions regarding rescue planning where an entry permit is required.

B. Entry Permit Required

Permits Confined Space Entry Permit. All spaces shall be considered permit-required confined spaces until the pre-entry procedures demonstrate otherwise. Any employee required or permitted to pre-check or enter a permit-required confined space shall have successfully completed, as a minimum, the training as required by the following sections of these procedures. A written copy of operating and rescue procedures as required by these procedures shall be at the work site for the duration of the job. The Confined Space Entry Permit must be completed before approval can be given to enter a permit-required confined space. This permit verifies completion of items listed below. This permit shall be kept at the job site for the duration of the job. If circumstances cause an interruption in the work or a change in the alarm conditions for which entry was approved, a new Confined Space Entry Permit must be completed.

Control of atmospheric and engulfment hazards

Surveillance The surrounding area shall be surveyed to avoid hazards such as drifting vapors from tanks, piping or sewers.

Testing The confined space atmosphere shall be tested to determine whether dangerous air contamination and/or oxygen deficiency exists. A direct reading gas monitor shall be used. Testing shall be performed by the SUPERVISOR who has successfully completed the gas detector training for the monitor he will use. The minimum parameters to be monitored are oxygen deficiency, LFL and hydrogen sulfide concentration. A written record of the pre- entry test results shall be made and kept at the work site for the duration of the job. Affected employees shall be able to review the testing results. The most hazardous conditions shall govern when work is being performed in two adjoining, connected spaces.

Space Ventilation Mechanical ventilation systems, where applicable, shall be set at 100% outside air. Where possible, open additional manholes to increase air circulation. Use portable blowers to augment natural circulation if needed. After a suitable ventilating period, repeat the testing. Entry may not begin until testing has demonstrated that the hazardous atmosphere has been eliminated.

Entry Procedures The following procedure shall be observed under any of the following conditions:

1. Testing demonstrates the existence of dangerous or deficient conditions and additional ventilation cannot reduce concentrations to safe levels;
2. The atmosphere tests as safe but unsafe conditions can reasonably be expected to develop;
3. It is not feasible to provide for ready exit from spaces equipped with automatic fire suppression systems and it is not practical or safe to deactivate such systems; or
4. An emergency exists and it is not feasible to wait for pre-entry procedures to take effect.

All personnel must be trained A self contained breathing apparatus shall be worn by any person entering the space. At least one worker shall stand by the outside of the space ready to give assistance in case of emergency. The standby worker shall have a self contained breathing apparatus available for immediate use. There shall be at least one additional worker within sight or call of the standby worker. Continuous powered communications shall be maintained between the worker within the confined space and standby personnel.

If at any time there is any questionable action or non- movement by the worker inside, a verbal check will be made. If there is no response, the worker will be moved immediately. Exception: If the worker is disabled due to falling or impact, he/she shall not be removed from the confined space unless there is immediate danger to his/her life. Local fire department rescue personnel shall be notified immediately. The standby worker may only enter the confined space in case of an emergency (wearing the self contained breathing apparatus) and only after being relieved by another worker. Safety belt or harness with attached lifeline shall be used by all workers entering the space with the free end of the line secured outside the entry opening. The standby worker shall attempt to remove a disabled worker via his lifeline before entering the space.

When practical, these spaces shall be entered through side openings—those within 3 1/2 feet (1.07 m) of the bottom. When entry must be through a top opening, the safety belt shall be of the harness type that suspends a person upright and a hoisting device or similar apparatus shall be available for lifting workers out of the space.

In any situation where their use may endanger the worker, use of a hoisting device or safety belt and attached lifeline may be discontinued.

When dangerous air contamination is attributable to flammable and/or explosive substances, lighting and electrical equipment shall be Class 1, Division 1 rated per National Electrical Code and no ignition sources shall be introduced into the area.

Continuous gas monitoring shall be performed during all confined space operations. If alarm conditions change adversely, entry personnel shall exit the confined space and a new confined space permit issued.

Rescue Call the fire department services for rescue. Where immediate hazards to injured personnel are present, workers at the site shall implement emergency procedures to fit the situation.

Example 2

Workplace Meat and poultry rendering plants.

Cookers and dryers are either batch or continuous in their operation. Multiple batch cookers are operated in parallel. When one unit of a multiple set is shut down for repairs, means are available to isolate that unit from the others which remain in operation.

Cookers and dryers are horizontal, cylindrical vessels equipped with a center, rotating shaft and agitator paddles or discs. If the inner shell is jacketed, it is usually heated with steam at pressures up to 150 psig (1034.25 kPa). The rotating shaft assembly of the continuous cooker or dryer is also steam heated.

Potential Hazards The recognized hazards associated with cookers and dryers are the risk that employees could be:

1. Struck or caught by rotating agitator;
2. Engulfed in raw material or hot, recycled fat;
3. Burned by steam from leaks into the cooker/dryer steam jacket or the condenser duct system if steam valves are not properly closed and locked out;
4. Burned by contact with hot metal surfaces, such as the agitator shaft assembly, or inner shell of the cooker/dryer;
5. Heat stress caused by warm atmosphere inside cooker/dryer;
6. Slipping and falling on grease in the cooker/dryer;
7. Electrically shocked by faulty equipment taken into the cooker/dryer;
8. Burned or overcome by fire or products of combustion; or
9. Overcome by fumes generated by welding or cutting done on grease covered surfaces.

Permits The supervisor in this case is always present at the cooker/dryer or other permit entry confined space when entry is made. The supervisor must follow the pre-entry isolation procedures described in the entry permit in preparing for entry, and ensure that the protective clothing, ventilating equipment and any other equipment required by the permit are at the entry site.

Control of hazards Mechanical. Lock out main power switch to agitator motor at main power panel. Affix tag to the lock to inform others that a permit entry confined space entry is in progress.

Engulfment Close all valves in the raw material blow line. Secure each valve in its closed position using chain and lock. Attach a tag to the valve and chain warning that a permit entry confined space entry is in progress. The same procedure shall be used for securing the fat recycle valve.

Burns and heat stress Close steam supply valves to jacket and secure with chains and tags. Insert solid blank at flange in cooker vent line to condenser manifold duct system. Vent cooker/dryer by opening access door at discharge end and top center door to allow natural ventilation throughout the entry. If faster cooling is needed, use a portable ventilation fan to increase ventilation. Cooling water may be circulated through the jacket to reduce both outer and inner surface temperatures of cooker/dryers faster. Check air and inner surface temperatures in cooker/dryer to assure they are within acceptable limits before entering, or use proper protective clothing.

Fire and fume hazards Careful site preparation, such as cleaning the area within 4 inches (10.16 cm) of all welding or torch cutting operations, and proper ventilation are the preferred controls. All welding and cutting operations shall be done in accordance with the requirements of 29 CFR Part 1910, Subpart Q, OSHA's welding standard. Proper ventilation may be achieved by local exhaust ventilation, or the use of portable ventilation fans, or a combination of the two practices.

Electrical shock Electrical equipment used in cooker/dryers shall be in serviceable condition.

Slips and falls Remove residual grease before entering cooker/dryer.

Attendant The supervisor shall be the attendant for employees entering cooker/dryers.

Permit The permit shall specify how isolation shall be done and any other preparations needed before making entry. This is especially important in parallel arrangements of cooker/dryers so that the entire operation need not be shut down to allow safe entry into one unit.

Rescue When necessary, the attendant shall call the fire department as previously arranged.

Example 3

Workplace Workplaces where tank cars, trucks, and trailers, dry bulk tanks and trailers, railroad tank cars, and similar portable tanks are fabricated or serviced.

A. During fabrication These tanks and dry-bulk carriers are entered repeatedly throughout the fabrication process. These products are not configured identically, but the manufacturing processes by which they are made are very similar.

Sources of hazards In addition to the mechanical hazards arising from the risks that an entrant would be injured due to contact with components of the tank or the tools being used, there is also the risk that a worker could be injured by breathing fumes from welding materials or mists or vapors from materials used to coat the tank interior. In addition, many of these vapors and mists are flammable, so the failure to properly ventilate a tank could lead to a fire or explosion.

Control of hazards

Welding Local exhaust ventilation shall be used to remove welding fumes once the tank or carrier is completed to the point that workers may enter and exit only through a manhole. (Follow the requirements of 29 CFR §1910, Subpart Q, OSHA's welding standard, at all times.) Welding gas tanks may never be brought into a tank or carrier that is a permit entry confined space.

Application of interior coatings/linings Atmospheric hazards shall be controlled by forced air ventilation sufficient to keep the atmospheric concentration of flammable materials below 10% of the lower flammable limit (LFL) (or lower explosive limit (LEL), whichever term is used locally). The appropriate respirators are provided and shall be used in addition to providing forced ventilation if the forced ventilation does not maintain acceptable respiratory conditions.

Permits Because of the repetitive nature of the entries in these operations, an "Area Entry Permit" will be issued for a 1 month period to cover those production areas where tanks are fabricated to the point that entry and exit are made using manholes.

Authorization Only the area supervisor may authorize an employee to enter a tank within the permit area. The area supervisor must determine that conditions in the tank trailer, dry bulk trailer or truck, etc. meet permit requirements before authorizing entry.

Attendant The area supervisor shall designate an employee to maintain communication by employer specified means with employees working in tanks to ensure their safety. The attendant may not enter any permit entry confined space to rescue an entrant or for any other reason, unless authorized by the rescue procedure and, and even then, only after calling the rescue team and being relieved by as attendant by another worker.

Communications and observation Communications between attendant and entrant(s) shall be maintained throughout entry. Methods of communication that may be specified by the permit include voice, voice powered radio, tapping or rapping codes on tank walls, signalling tugs on a rope, and the attendant's observation that work activities such as chipping, grinding, welding, spraying, etc., which require deliberate operator control continue normally. These activities often generate so much noise that the necessary hearing protection makes communication by voice difficult.

Rescue procedures Acceptable rescue procedures include entry by a team of employee-rescuers, use of public emergency services, and procedures for breaching the tank. The area permit specifies which procedures are available, but the area supervisor makes the final decision based on circumstances. (Certain injuries may make it necessary to breach the tank to remove a person rather than risk additional injury by removal through an existing manhole. However, the supervisor must ensure that no breaching procedure used for rescue would violate terms of the entry permit. For instance, if the tank must be breached by cutting with a torch, the tank surfaces to be cut must be free of volatile or combustible coatings within 4 inches (10.16 cm) of the cutting line and the atmosphere within the tank must be below the LFL.

Retrieval line and harnesses The retrieval lines and harnesses generally required under this standard are usually impractical for use in tanks because the internal configuration of the tanks and their interior baffles and other structures would prevent rescuers from hauling out injured entrants. However, unless the rescue procedure calls for breaching the tank for rescue, the rescue team shall be trained in the use of retrieval lines and harnesses for removing injured employees through manholes.

B. Repair or service of "used" tanks and bulk trailers

Sources of hazards In addition to facing the potential hazards encountered in fabrication or manufacturing, tanks or trailers which have been in service may contain residues of dangerous materials, whether left over from the transportation of hazardous cargoes or generated by chemical or bacterial action on residues of non-hazardous cargoes.

Control of atmospheric hazards A "used" tank shall be brought into areas where tank entry is authorized only after the tank has been emptied, cleansed (without employee entry) of any residues, and purged of any potential atmospheric hazards.

Welding In addition to tank cleaning for control of atmospheric hazards, coating and surface materials shall be removed 4 inches (10.16 cm) or more from any surface area where welding or other torch work will be done and care taken that the atmosphere within the tank remains well below the LFL. (Follow the requirements of 29 CFR §1910, Subpart Q, OSHA's welding standard, at all times.)

Permits An entry permit valid for up to 1 year shall be issued prior to authorization of entry into used tank trailers, dry bulk trailers or trucks. In addition to the pre-entry cleaning requirement, this permit shall require the employee safeguards specified for new tank fabrication or construction permit areas.

Authorization Only the area supervisor may authorize an employee to enter a tank trailer, dry bulk trailer or truck within the permit area. The area supervisor must determine that the entry permit requirements have been met before authorizing entry.

§1910.146 Appendix D
Sample Permits

Appendix D–1 Confined Space Entry Permit

Date & Time Issued: ______________ Date and Time Expires: ______________

Job site/Space I.D.: ______________ Job Supervisor: ______________

Equipment to be worked on: ______________ Work to be performed: ______________

Stand-by personnel: ______________

1. Atmospheric Checks: Time ______ Oxygen ______ % Explosive ______ % L.F.L Toxic ______ PPM
2. Tester's signature: ______________
3. Source isolation (No Entry):

	N/A	Yes	No
Pumps or lines blinded,	( )	( )	( )
disconnected, or blocked	( )	( )	( )

4. Ventilation Modification:

	N/A	Yes	No
Mechanical	( )	( )	( )
Natural Ventilation only	( )	( )	( )

5. Atmospheric check after isolation and Ventilation:

Oxygen ______ %		> 19.5 %
Explosive ______ %	L.F.L.	< 10 %
Toxic ______	PPM	< 10 PPM H_2S
Time ______		
Testers Signature ______________		

6. Communication procedures: ______________
7. Rescue procedures: ______________
8. Entry, standby, and back up persons:

	Yes	No
Successfully completed required training	( )	( )
Is it current?	( )	( )

9. Equipment:

	N/A	Yes	No
Direct reading gas monitor - tested	( )	( )	( )
Safety harnesses and lifelines for entry and standby persons	( )	( )	( )
Hosting equipment	( )	( )	( )
Powered communications	( )	( )	( )
SCBA's for entry and standby person	( )	( )	( )
Protective Clothing	( )	( )	( )
All electric equipment listed Class I, Division I, Division I, Group D and Non-sparking tools	( )	( )	( )

10. Periodic atmospheric tests:

Oxygen ______ %	Time ______	Oxygen ______ %	Time ______
Oxygen ______ %	Time ______	Oxygen ______ %	Time ______
Explosive ______ %	Time ______	Explosive ______ %	Time ______
Explosive ______ %	Time ______	Explosive ______ %	Time ______
Toxic ______ %	Time ______	Toxic ______ %	Time ______
Toxic ______ %	Time ______	Toxic ______ %	Time ______

We have reviewed the work authorized by this permit and the information contained here-in. Written instructions and safety procedures have been received and are understood. Entry cannot be approved if any squares are marked in the "No" column. This permit is not valid unless all appropriate items are completed.

	(print name)	(signature)
Permit Prepared By: (Supervisor)	______________	______________
Approved By: (Unit Supervisor)	______________	______________
Reviewed By: (Cs Operations Personnel)	______________	______________

This permit to be kept at job site. Return job site copy to Safety Officer following job completion.
Copies: White (Original (Safety Officer) Yellow (Unit Supervisor) Hard (Job site)

Appendix D–2 Entry Permit

PERMIT VALID FOR 8 HOURS ONLY. ALL PERMIT COPIES REMAIN AT SITE UNTIL JOB COMPLETED.

DATE: ______________ SITE LOCATION/DESCRIPTION ______________

PURPOSE OF ENTRY ______________

SUPERVISOR(S) in charge of crews ______________ Type of Crew ______________ Phone # ______________

COMMUNICATION PROCEDURES ______________

RESCUE PROCEDURES (PHONE NUMBERS AT BOTTOM) ______________

* BOLD DENOTES MINIMUM REQUIREMENTS TO BE COMPLETED AND REVIEWED PRIOR TO ENTRY *

REQUIREMENTS COMPLETED	DATE	TIME	REQUIREMENTS COMPLETED	DATE	TIME
Lock Out/De-energize/Try-Out			Full Body Harness w/"D" ring		
Line(s) Broken-Capped-Blank			Emergency Escape Retrieval Eq		
Purge-Flush and Vent			Lifelines		
Ventilation			Fire Extinguishers		
Secure Area (Post and Flag)			Lighting (Explosive Proof)		
Breathing Apparatus			Protective Clothing		
Resuscitator - Inhalator			Respirator(s) (Air Purifying)		
Standby Safety Personnel			Burning and Welding Permit		

Note: Items that do not apply enter N/A in the blank.

** RECORD CONTINUOUS MONITORING RESULTS EVERY 2 HOURS

CONTINUOUS MONITORING**	Permissible									
TEST(S) TO BE TAKEN	Entry Level									
PERCENT OF OXYGEN	19.5% TO 23.5%									
LOWER FLAMMABLE LIMIT	UNDER 10%									
CARBON MONOXIDE	+35 PPM									
Aromatic Hydrocarbon	+ 1 PPM *5 PPM									
Hydrogen Cyanide	(Skin) *4 PPM									
Hydrogen Sulfide	+10 PPM *15 PPM									
Sulfur Dioxide	+2 PPM *5 PPM									
Ammonia	*35 PPM									

*Short-term exposure limit: Employee can work in the area up to 15 minutes.
+8 hr. Time Weighted Ave.: Employee can work in area 8 hrs (longer with appropriate respiratory protection).

REMARKS: ______________

GAS TESTER NAME & CHECK #	INSTRUMENT(S) USED	MODEL &/OR TYPE	SERIAL &/OR UNIT #

SAFETY STANDBY PERSON IS REQUIRED FOR ALL CONFINED SPACE WORK

SAFETY STANDBY PERSON(S)	CHECK #	CONFINED SPACE ENTRANT(S)	CHECK #	CONFINED SPACE ENTRANT(S)	CHECK #

SUPERVISOR AUTHORIZATION - ALL CONDITIONS SATISFIED ______________ DEPARTMENT/PHONE ______________

AMBULANCE 2800 FIRE 2900 Safety 4901 Gas Coordinator 4529/5387

§1910.146 Appendix E
Sewer system entry

Sewer entry differs in three vital respects from other permit entries; first, there rarely exists any way to completely isolate the space (a section of a continuous system) to be entered; second, because isolation is not complete, the atmosphere may suddenly and unpredictably become lethally hazardous (toxic, flammable or explosive) from causes beyond the control of the entrant or employer, and third, experienced sewer workers are especially knowledgeable in entry and work in their permit spaces because of their frequent entries. Unlike other employments where permit space entry is a rare and exceptional event, sewer workers' usual work environment is a permit space.

(1) Adherence to procedure The employer should designate as entrants only employees who are thoroughly trained in the employer's sewer entry procedures and who demonstrate that they follow these entry procedures exactly as prescribed when performing sewer entries.

(2) Atmospheric monitoring Entrants should be trained in the use of, and be equipped with, atmospheric monitoring equipment which sounds an audible alarm, in addition to its visual readout, whenever one of the following conditions are encountered: Oxygen concentration less than 19.5 percent; flammable gas or vapor at 10 percent or more of the lower flammable limit (LFL); or hydrogen sulfide or carbon monoxide at or above 10 ppm or 35 ppm, respectively, measured as an 8-hour time-weighted average. Atmospheric monitoring equipment needs to be calibrated according to the manufacturer's instructions. The oxygen sensor/broad range sensor is best suited for initial use in situations where the actual or potential contaminants have not been identified, because broad range sensors, unlike substance-specific sensors, enable employers to obtain an overall reading of the hydrocarbons (flammables) present in the space. However, such sensors only indicate that a hazardous threshold of a class of chemicals has been exceeded. They do not measure the levels of contamination of specific substances. Therefore, substance-specific devices, which measure the actual levels of specific substances, are best suited for use where actual and potential contaminants have been identified. The measurements obtained with substance-specific devices are of vital importance to the employer when decisions are made concerning the measures necessary to protect entrants (such as ventilation or personal protective equipment) and the setting and attainment of appropriate entry conditions. However, the sewer environment may suddenly and unpredictably change, and the substance-specific devices may not detect the potentially lethal atmospheric hazards which may enter the sewer environment.

Although OSHA considers the information and guidance provided above to be appropriate and useful in most sewer entry situations, the Agency emphasizes that each employer must consider the unique circumstances, including the predictability of the atmosphere, of the sewer permit spaces in the employer's workplace in preparing for entry. Only the employer can decide, based upon his or her knowledge of, and experience with permit spaces in sewer systems, what the best type of testing instrument may be for any specific entry operation.

The selected testing instrument should be carried and used by the entrant in sewer line work to monitor the atmosphere in the entrant's environment, and in advance of the entrant's direction of movement, to warn the entrant of any deterioration in atmospheric conditions. Where several entrants are working together in the same immediate location, one instrument, used by the lead entrant, is acceptable.

(3) Surge flow and flooding Sewer crews should develop and maintain liaison, to the extent possible, with the local weather bureau and fire and emergency services in their area so that sewer work may be delayed or interrupted and entrants withdrawn whenever sewer lines might be suddenly flooded by rain or fire suppression activities, or whenever flammable or other hazardous materials are released into sewers during emergencies by industrial or transportation accidents.

(4) Special Equipment Entry into large bore sewers may require the use of special equipment. Such equipment might include such items as atmosphere monitoring devices with automatic audible alarms, escape self-contained breathing apparatus (ESCBA) with at least 10 minute air supply (or other NIOSH approved self-rescuer), and waterproof flashlights, and may also include boats and rafts, radios and rope stand-offs for pulling around bends and corners as needed.

§1910.146 Appendix F
Rescue team or rescue service evaluation criteria
(Nonmandatory)

(1) This Appendix provides guidance to employers in choosing an appropriate rescue service. It contains criteria that may be used to evaluate the capabilities both of prospective and current rescue teams. Before a rescue team can be trained or chosen, however, a satisfactory permit program, including an analysis of all permit-required confined spaces to identify all potential hazards in those spaces, must be completed. OSHA believes that compliance with all the provisions of §1910.146 will enable employers to conduct permit space operations without recourse to rescue services in nearly all cases. However, experience indicates that circumstances will arise where entrants will need to be rescued from permit spaces. It is therefore important for employers to select rescue services or teams, either on-site or off-site, that are equipped and capable of minimizing harm to both entrants and rescuers if the need arises.

(2) For all rescue teams or services, the employer's evaluation should consist of two components: an initial evaluation, in which employers decide whether a potential rescue service or team is adequately trained and equipped to perform permit space rescues of the kind needed at the facility and whether such rescuers can respond in a timely manner, and a performance evaluation, in which employers measure the performance of the team or service during an actual or practice rescue. For example, based on the initial evaluation, an employer may determine that maintaining an on-site rescue team will be more expensive than obtaining the services of an off-site team, without being significantly more effective, and decide to hire a rescue service. During a performance evaluation, the employer could decide, after observing the rescue service perform a practice rescue, that the service's training or preparedness was not adequate to effect a timely or effective rescue at his or her facility and decide to select another rescue service, or to form an internal rescue team.

A. Initial Evaluation

I. The employer should meet with the prospective rescue service to facilitate the evaluations required by §1910.146(k)(1)(i) and §1910.146(k)(1)(ii). At a minimum, if an off-site rescue service is being considered, the employer must contact the service to plan and coordinate the evaluations required by the standard. Merely posting the service's number or planning to rely on the 911 emergency phone number to obtain these services at the time of a permit space emergency would not comply with paragraph (k)(1) of the standard.

II. The capabilities required of a rescue service vary with the type of permit spaces from which rescue may be necessary and the hazards likely to be encountered in those spaces. Answering the questions below will assist employers in determining whether the rescue service is capable of performing rescues in the permit spaces present at the employer's workplace.

1. What are the needs of the employer with regard to response time (time for the rescue service to receive notification, arrive at the scene, and set up and be ready for entry)? For example, if entry is to be made into an IDLH atmosphere, or into a space that can quickly develop an IDLH atmosphere (if ventilation fails or for other reasons), the rescue team or service would need to be standing by at the permit space. On the other hand, if the danger to entrants is restricted to mechanical hazards that would cause injuries (e.g., broken bones, abrasions) a response time of 10 or 15 minutes might be adequate.
2. How quickly can the rescue team or service get from its location to the permit spaces from which rescue may be necessary? Relevant factors to consider would include: the location of the rescue team or service relative to the employer's workplace, the quality of roads and highways to be traveled, potential bottlenecks or traffic congestion that might be encountered in transit, the reliability of the rescuer's vehicles, and the training and skill of its drivers.
3. What is the availability of the rescue service? Is it unavailable at certain times of the day or in certain situations? What is the likelihood that key personnel of the rescue service might be unavailable at times? If the rescue service becomes unavailable while an entry is underway, does it have the capability of notifying the employer so that the employer can instruct the attendant to abort the entry immediately?
4. Does the rescue service meet all the requirements of paragraph (k)(2) of the standard? If not, has it developed a plan that will enable it to meet those requirements in the future? If so, how soon can the plan be implemented?
5. For off-site services, is the service willing to perform rescues at the employer's workplace? (An employer may not rely on a rescuer who declines, for whatever reason, to provide rescue services.)
6. Is an adequate method for communications between the attendant, employer and prospective rescuer available so that a rescue request can be transmitted to the rescuer without delay? How soon after notification can a prospective rescuer dispatch a rescue team to the entry site?
7. For rescues into spaces that may pose significant atmospheric hazards and from which rescue entry, patient packaging and retrieval cannot be safely accomplished in a relatively short time (15–20 minutes), employers should consider using airline respirators (with escape bottles) for the rescuers and to supply rescue air to the patient. If the employer decides to use SCBA, does the prospective rescue service have an ample supply of replacement cylinders and procedures for rescuers to enter and exit (or be retrieved) well within the SCBA's air supply limits?
8. If the space has a vertical entry over 5 feet in depth, can the prospective rescue service properly perform entry rescues? Does the service have the technical knowledge and equipment to perform rope work or elevated rescue, if needed?

9. Does the rescue service have the necessary skills in medical evaluation, patient packaging and emergency response?
10. Does the rescue service have the necessary equipment to perform rescues, or must the equipment be provided by the employer or another source?

B. Performance Evaluation

Rescue services are required by paragraph (k)(2)(iv) of the standard to practice rescues at least once every 12 months, provided that the team or service has not successfully performed a permit space rescue within that time. As part of each practice session, the service should perform a critique of the practice rescue, or have another qualified party perform the critique, so that deficiencies in procedures, equipment, training, or number of personnel can be identified and corrected. The results of the critique, and the corrections made to respond to the deficiencies identified, should be given to the employer to enable it to determine whether the rescue service can quickly be upgraded to meet the employer's rescue needs or whether another service must be selected. The following questions will assist employers and rescue teams and services evaluate their performance.

1. Have all members of the service been trained as permit space entrants, at a minimum, including training in the potential hazards of all permit spaces, or of representative permit spaces, from which rescue may be needed? Can team members recognize the signs, symptoms, and consequences of exposure to any hazardous atmospheres that may be present in those permit spaces?
2. Is every team member provided with, and properly trained in, the use and need for PPE, such as SCBA or fall arrest equipment, which may be required to perform permit space rescues in the facility? Is every team member properly trained to perform his or her functions and make rescues, and to use any rescue equipment, such as ropes and backboards, that may be needed in a rescue attempt?
3. Are team members trained in the first aid and medical skills needed to treat victims overcome or injured by the types of hazards that may be encountered in the permit spaces at the facility?
4. Do all team members perform their functions safely and efficiently? Do rescue service personnel focus on their own safety before considering the safety of the victim?
5. If necessary, can the rescue service properly test the atmosphere to determine if it is IDLH?
6. Can the rescue personnel identify information pertinent to the rescue from entry permits, hot work permits, and SDSs?
7. Has the rescue service been informed of any hazards to personnel that may arise from outside the space, such as those that may be caused by future work near the space?
8. If necessary, can the rescue service properly package and retrieve victims from a permit space that has a limited size opening (less than 24 inches (60.9 cm) in diameter), limited internal space, or internal obstacles or hazards?
9. If necessary, can the rescue service safely perform an elevated (high angle) rescue?
10. Does the rescue service have a plan for each of the kinds of permit space rescue operations at the facility? Is the plan adequate for all types of rescue operations that may be needed at the facility? Teams may practice in representative spaces, or in spaces that are "worst-case" or most restrictive with respect to internal configuration, elevation, and portal size. The following characteristics of a practice space should be considered when deciding whether a space is truly representative of an actual permit space:
    (1) Internal configuration.
        (a) Open—there are no obstacles, barriers, or obstructions within the space. One example is a water tank.
        (b) Obstructed—the permit space contains some type of obstruction that a rescuer would need to maneuver around. An example would be a baffle or mixing blade. Large equipment, such as a ladder or scaffold, brought into a space for work purposes would be considered an obstruction if the positioning or size of the equipment would make rescue more difficult.
    (2) Elevation.
        (a) Elevated—a permit space where the entrance portal or opening is above grade by 4 feet or more. This type of space usually requires knowledge of high angle rescue procedures because of the difficulty in packaging and transporting a patient to the ground from the portal.
        (b) Non-elevated—a permit space with the entrance portal located less than 4 feet above grade. This type of space will allow the rescue team to transport an injured employee normally.
    (3) Portal size.
        (a) Restricted—A portal of 24 inches or less in the least dimension. Portals of this size are too small to allow a rescuer to simply enter the space while using SCBA. The portal size is also too small to allow normal spinal immobilization of an injured employee.
        (b) Unrestricted—A portal of greater than 24 inches in the least dimension. These portals allow relatively free movement into and out of the permit space.
    (4) Space access.
        (a) Horizontal—The portal is located on the side of the permit space. Use of retrieval lines could be difficult.
        (b) Vertical—The portal is located on the top of the permit space, so that rescuers must climb down, or the bottom of the permit space, so that rescuers must climb up to enter the space. Vertical portals may require knowledge of rope techniques, or special patient packaging to safely retrieve a downed entrant.

[58 FR 4549, Jan. 14, 1993; 58 FR 34845, 34846, June 29, 1993, as amended at 59 FR 26114, May 19, 1994; 63 FR 66038, 66039, Dec. 1, 1998]

§1910.147 [OI] The control of hazardous energy (lockout/tagout)

(a) [OI] **Scope, application, and purpose**

(a)(1) Scope

(a)(1)(i) [OI] This standard covers the servicing and maintenance of machines and equipment in which the unexpected energization or start up of the machines or equipment, or release of stored energy could cause injury to employees. This standard establishes minimum performance requirements for the control of such hazardous energy.

(a)(1)(ii) This standard does not cover the following:

(a)(1)(ii)(A) Construction and agriculture employment;

(a)(1)(ii)(B) Employment covered by parts 1915, 1917, and 1918 of this title;

(a)(1)(ii)(C) Installations under the exclusive control of electric utilities for the purpose of power generation, transmission and distribution, including related equipment for communication or metering;

(a)(1)(ii)(D) Exposure to electrical hazards from work on, near, or with conductors or equipment in electric-utilization installations, which is covered by Subpart S of this part; and

(a)(1)(ii)(E) Oil and gas well drilling and servicing.

(a)(2) Application

(a)(2)(i) This standard applies to the control of energy during servicing and/or maintenance of machines and equipment.

(a)(2)(ii) [OI] Normal production operations are not covered by this standard (See Subpart 0 of this part). Servicing and/or maintenance which takes place during normal production operations is covered by this standard only if;:

(a)(2)(ii)(A) [OI] An employee is required to remove or bypass a guard or other safety device; or

(a)(2)(ii)(B) [OI] An employee is required to place any part of his or her body into an area on a machine or piece of equipment where work is actually performed upon the material being processed (point of operation) or where an associated danger zone exists during a machine operating cycle.

Note: Exception to paragraph (a)(2)(ii): Minor tool changes and adjustments, and other minor servicing activities, which take place during normal production operations, are not covered by this standard if they are routine, repetitive, and integral to the use of the equipment for production, provided that the work is performed using alternative measures which provide effective protection (See Subpart 0 of this part).

(a)(2)(iii) This standard does not apply to the following.

(a)(2)(iii)(A) [OI] Work on cord and plug connected electric equipment for which exposure to the hazards of unexpected energization or start up of the equipment is controlled by the unplugging of the equipment from the energy source and by the plug being under the exclusive control of the employee performing the servicing or maintenance.

(a)(2)(iii)(B) Hot tap operations involving transmission and distribution systems for substances such as gas, steam, water or petroleum products when they are performed on pressurized pipelines, provided that the employer demonstrates that

(1) continuity of service is essential;

(2) shutdown of the system is impractical; and

(3) documented procedures are followed, and special equipment is used which will provide proven effective protection for employees.

(a)(3) **Purpose**

(a)(3)(i) This section requires employers to establish a program and utilize procedures for affixing appropriate lockout devices or tagout devices to energy isolating devices, and to otherwise disable machines or equipment to prevent unexpected energization, start-up or release of stored energy in order to prevent injury to employees.

(a)(3)(ii) When other standards in this part require the use of lockout or tagout, they shall be used and supplemented by the procedural and training requirements of this section.

(b) **Definitions applicable to this section**

Affected employee An employee whose job requires him/her to operate or use a machine or equipment on which servicing or maintenance is being performed under lockout or tagout, or whose job requires him/her to work in an area in which such servicing or maintenance is being performed.

Authorized employee A person who locks out or tags out machines or equipment in order to perform servicing or maintenance on that machine or equipment. An affected employee becomes an authorized employee when that employee's duties include performing servicing or maintenance covered under this section.

Capable of being locked out An energy isolating device is capable of being locked out if it has a hasp or other means of attachment to which, or through which, a lock can be affixed, or it has a locking mechanism built into it. Other energy isolating devices are capable of being locked out, if lockout can be achieved without the need to dismantle, rebuild, or replace the energy isolating device or permanently alter its energy control capability.

Energized Connected to an energy source or containing residual or stored energy.

Energy isolating device A mechanical device that physically prevents the transmission or release of energy, including but not limited to the following: A manually operated electrical circuit breaker; a disconnect switch; a manually operated switch by which the conductors of a circuit can be disconnected from all ungrounded supply conductors, and, in addition, no pole can be operated independently; a line valve; a block; and any similar device used to block or isolate energy. Push buttons, selector switches and other control circuit type devices are not energy isolating devices.

Energy source Any source of electrical, mechanical, hydraulic, pneumatic, chemical, thermal, or other energy.

Hot tap A procedure used in the repair, maintenance and services activities which involves welding on a piece of equipment (pipelines, vessels or tanks) under pressure, in order to install connections or appurtenances. It is commonly used to replace or add sections of pipeline without the interruption of service for air, gas, water, steam, and petrochemical distribution systems.

Lockout The placement of a lockout device on an energy isolating device, in accordance with an established procedure, ensuring that the energy isolating device and the equipment being controlled cannot be operated until the lockout device is removed.

Lockout device A device that utilizes a positive means such as a lock, either key or combination type, to hold an energy isolating device in a safe position and prevent the energizing of a machine or equipment. Included are blank flanges and bolted slip blinds.

Normal production operations The utilization of a machine or equipment to perform its intended production function.

Servicing and/or maintenance Workplace activities such as constructing, installing, setting up, adjusting, inspecting, modifying, and maintaining and/or servicing machines or equipment. These activities include lubrication, cleaning or unjamming of machines or equipment and making adjustments or tool changes, where the employee may be exposed to the unexpected energization or startup of the equipment or release of hazardous energy.

Setting up Any work performed to prepare a machine or equipment to perform its normal production operation.

Tagout The placement of a tagout device on an energy isolating device, in accordance with an established procedure, to indicate that the energy isolating device and the equipment being controlled may not be operated until the tagout device is removed.

Tagout device A prominent warning device, such as a tag and a means of attachment, which can be securely fastened to an energy isolating device in accordance with an established procedure, to indicate that the energy isolating device and the equipment being controlled may not be operated until the tagout device is removed.

(c) **General**

(c)(1) **Energy control program** The employer shall establish a program consisting of energy control procedures, employee training and periodic inspections to ensure that before any employee performs any servicing or maintenance on a machine or equipment where the unexpected energizing, start up or release of stored energy could occur and cause injury, the machine or equipment shall be isolated from the energy source, and rendered inoperative.

(c)(2) **Lockout/tagout**

(c)(2)(i) If an energy isolating device is not capable of being locked out, the employer's energy control program under paragraph (c)(1) of this section shall utilize a tagout system.

(c)(2)(ii) If an energy isolating device is capable of being locked out, the employer's energy control program under paragraph (c)(1) of this section shall utilize lockout, unless the employer can demonstrate that the utilization of a tagout system will provide full employee protection as set forth in paragraph (c)(3) of this section.

(c)(2)(iii) After January 2, 1990, whenever replacement or major repair, renovation or modification of a machine or equipment is performed, and whenever new machines or equipment are installed, energy isolating devices for such machine or equipment shall be designed to accept a lockout device.

(c)(3) **Full employee protection**

(c)(3)(i) When a tagout device is used on an energy isolating device which is capable of being locked out, the tagout device shall be attached at the same location that the lockout device would have been attached, and the employer shall demonstrate that the tagout program will provide a level of safety equivalent to that obtained by using a lockout program.

(c)(3)(ii) In demonstrating that a level of safety is achieved in the tagout program which is equivalent to the level of safety obtained by using a lockout program, the employer shall demonstrate full compliance with all tagout-related provisions of this standard together with such additional elements as are necessary to provide the equivalent safety available from the use of a lockout device. Additional means to be considered as part of the demonstration of full employee protection shall include the implementation of additional safety measures such as the removal of an isolating circuit element, blocking of a controlling switch, opening of an extra disconnecting device, or the removal of a valve handle to reduce the likelihood of inadvertent energization.

(c)(4) **Energy control procedure**

(c)(4)(i) Procedures shall be developed, documented and utilized for the control of potentially hazardous energy when employees are engaged in the activities covered by this section.

Note: Exception: The employer need not document the required procedure for a particular machine or equipment, when all of the following elements exist:

(1) The machine or equipment has no potential for stored or residual energy or reaccumulation of stored energy after shut down which could endanger employees;
(2) The machine or equipment has a single energy source which can be readily identified and isolated;
(3) The isolation and locking out of that energy source will completely deenergize and deactivate the machine or equipment;
(4) The machine or equipment is isolated from that energy source and locked out during servicing or maintenance;
(5) A single lockout device will achieve a locked-out condition;
(6) the lockout device is under the exclusive control of the authorized employee performing the servicing or maintenance;
(7) The servicing or maintenance does not create hazards for other employees; and
(8) The employer, in utilizing this exception, has had no accidents involving the unexpected activation or reenergization of the machine or equipment during servicing or maintenance.

(c)(4)(ii) The procedures shall clearly and specifically outline the scope, purpose, authorization, rules, and techniques to be utilized for the control of hazardous energy, and the means to enforce compliance including, but not limited to, the following:

(c)(4)(ii)(A) A specific statement of the intended use of the procedure;

(c)(4)(ii)(B) Specific procedural steps for shutting down, isolating, blocking and securing machines or equipment to control hazardous energy;

(c)(4)(ii)(C) Specific procedural steps for the placement, removal and transfer of lockout devices or tagout devices and the responsibility for them; and

(c)(4)(ii)(D) Specific requirements for testing a machine or equipment to determine and verify the effectiveness of lockout devices, tagout devices, and other energy control measures.

(c)(5) **Protective materials and hardware**

(c)(5)(i) Locks, tags, chains, wedges, key blocks, adapter pins, self-locking fasteners, or other hardware shall be provided by the employer for isolating, securing or blocking of machines or equipment from energy sources.

(c)(5)(ii) Lockout devices and tagout devices shall be singularly identified; shall be the only devices(s) used for controlling energy; shall not be used for other purposes; and shall meet the following requirements:

(c)(5)(ii)(A) **Durable**

(c)(5)(ii)(A)(1) Lockout and tagout devices shall be capable of withstanding the environment to which they are exposed for the maximum period of time that exposure is expected.

(c)(5)(ii)(A)(2) Tagout devices shall be constructed and printed so that exposure to weather conditions or wet and damp locations will not cause the tag to deteriorate or the message on the tag to become illegible.

(c)(5)(ii)(A)(3) Tags shall not deteriorate when used in corrosive environments such as areas where acid and alkali chemicals are handled and stored.

(c)(5)(ii)(B) **Standardized** Lockout and tagout devices shall be standardized within the facility in at least one of the following criteria: Color; shape; or size; and additionally, in the case of tagout devices, print and format shall be standardized.

(c)(5)(ii)(C) **Substantial**

(c)(5)(ii)(C)(1) **Lockout devices** Lockout devices shall be substantial enough to prevent removal without the use of excessive force or unusual techniques, such as with the use of bolt cutters or other metal cutting tools.

(c)(5)(ii)(C)(2) **Tagout devices** Tagout devices, including and their means of attachment, shall be substantial enough to prevent inadvertent or accidental removal. Tagout device attachment means shall be of a non-reusable type, attachable by hand, self-locking, and non-releasable with a minimum unlocking strength of no less than 50 pounds and having the general design and basic characteristics of being at least equivalent to a one-piece, all-environment-tolerant nylon cable tie.

(c)(5)(ii)(D) **Identifiable** Lockout devices and tagout devices shall indicate the identity of the employee applying the device(s).

(c)(5)(iii) Tagout devices shall warn against hazardous conditions if the machine or equipment is energized and shall include a legend such as the following: **Do Not Start, Do Not Open, Do Not Close, Do Not Energize, Do Not Operate.**

(c)(6) **Periodic inspection**

(c)(6)(i) The employer shall conduct a periodic inspection of the energy control procedure at least annually to ensure that the procedure and the requirements of this standard are being followed.

(c)(6)(i)(A) The periodic inspection shall be perfomed by an authorized employee other than the ones(s) utilizing the energy control procedure being inspected.

(c)(6)(i)(B) The periodic inspection shall be conducted to correct any deviations or inadequacies identified.

(c)(6)(i)(C) Where lockout is used for energy control, the periodic inspection shall include a review, between the inspector and each authorized employee, of that employee's responsibilities under the energy control procedure being inspected.

(c)(6)(i)(D) Where tagout is used for energy control, the periodic inspection shall include a review, between the inspector and each authorized and affected employee, of that employee's responsibilities under the energy control procedure being inspected, and the elements set forth in paragraph (c)(7)(ii) of this section.

(c)(6)(ii) The employer shall certify that the periodic inspections have been performed. The certification shall identify the machine or equipment on which the energy control procedure was being utilized, the date of the inspection, the employees included in the inspection, and the person performing the inspection.

(c)(7) **Training and communication**

(c)(7)(i) The employer shall provide training to ensure that the purpose and function of the energy control program are understood by employees and that the knowledge and skills required for the safe application, usage, and removal of the energy controls are acquired by employees. The training shall include the following:

(c)(7)(i)(A) Each authorized employee shall receive training in the recognition of applicable hazardous energy sources, the type and magnitude of the energy available in the workplace, and the methods and means necessary for energy isolation and control.

(c)(7)(i)(B) Each affected employee shall be instructed in the purpose and use of the energy control procedure.

(c)(7)(i)(C) All other employees whose work operations are or may be in an area where energy control procedures may be utilized, shall be instructed about the procedure, and about the prohibition relating to attempts to restart or reenergize machines or equipment which are locked out or tagged out.

(c)(7)(ii) When tagout systems are used, employees shall also be trained in the following limitations of tags:

(c)(7)(ii)(A) Tags are essentially warning devices affixed to energy isolating devices, and do not provide the physical restraint on those devices that is provided by a lock.

(c)(7)(ii)(B) When a tag is attached to an energy isolating means, it is not to be removed without authorization of the authorized person responsible for it, and it is never to be bypassed, ignored, or otherwise defeated.

(c)(7)(ii)(C) Tags must be legible and understandable by all authorized employees, affected employees, and all other employees whose work operations are or may be in the area, in order to be effective.

(c)(7)(ii)(D) Tags and their means of attachment must be made of materials which will withstand the environmental conditions encountered in the workplace.

(c)(7)(ii)(E) Tags may evoke a false sense of security, and their meaning needs to be understood as part of the overall energy control program.

(c)(7)(ii)(F) Tags must be securely attached to energy isolating devices so that they cannot be inadvertently or accidentally detached during use.

(c)(7)(iii) **Employee retraining**

(c)(7)(iii)(A) Retraining shall be provided for all authorized and affected employees whenever there is a change in their job assignments, a change in machines, equipment or processes that present a new hazard, or when there is a change in the energy control procedures.

(c)(7)(iii)(B) Additional retraining shall also be conducted whenever a periodic inspection under paragraph (c)(6) of this section reveals, or whenever the employer has reason to believe, that there are deviations from or inadequacies in the employee's knowledge or use of the energy control procedures.

(c)(7)(iii)(C) The retraining shall reestablish employee proficiency and introduce new or revised control methods and procedures, as necessary.

(c)(7)(iv) The employer shall certify that employee training has been accomplished and is being kept up to date. The certification shall contain each employee's name and dates of training.

(c)(8) **Energy isolation** Lockout or tagout shall be performed only by the authorized employees who are performing the servicing or maintenance.

(c)(9) **Notification of employees** Affected employees shall be notified by the employer or authorized employee of the application and removal of lockout devices or tagout devices. Notification shall be given before the controls are applied, and after they are removed from the machine or equipment.

(d) **Application of control** The established procedures for the application of energy control (the lockout or tagout procedures) shall cover the following elements and actions and shall be done in the following sequence:

(d)(1) **Preparation for shutdown** Before an authorized or affected employee turns off a machine or equipment, the authorized employee shall have knowledge of the type and magnitude of the energy, the hazards of the energy to be controlled, and the method or means to control the energy.

(d)(2) **Machine or equipment shutdown** The machine or equipment shall be turned off or shut down using the procedures established for the machine or equipment. An orderly shutdown must be utilized to avoid any additional or increased hazard(s) to employees as a result of the equipment stoppage.

(d)(3) **Machine or equipment isolation** All energy isolating devices that are needed to control the energy to the machine or equipment shall be physically located and operated in such a manner as to isolate the machine or equipment from the energy source(s).

(d)(4) **Lockout or tagout device application**

(d)(4)(i) Lockout or tagout devices shall be affixed to each energy isolating device by authorized employees.

(d)(4)(ii) Lockout devices, where used, shall be affixed in a manner to that will hold the energy isolating devices in a "safe" or "off" position.

(d)(4)(iii) Tagout devices, where used, shall be affixed in such a manner as will clearly indicate that the operation or movement of energy isolating devices from the "safe" or "off" position is prohibited.

(d)(4)(iii)(A) Where tagout devices are used with energy isolating devices designed with the capability of being locked, the tag attachment shall be fastened at the same point at which the lock would have been attached.

(d)(4)(iii)(B) Where a tag cannot be affixed directly to the energy isolating device, the tag shall be located as close as safely possible to the device, in a position that will be immediately obvious to anyone attempting to operate the device.

(d)(5) **Stored energy**

(d)(5)(i) Following the application of lockout or tagout devices to energy isolating devices, all potentially hazardous stored or residual energy shall be relieved, disconnected, restrained, and otherwise rendered safe.

(d)(5)(ii) [OI] If there is a possibility of reaccumulation of stored energy to a hazardous level, verification of isolation shall be continued until the servicing or maintenance is completed, or until the possibility of such accumulation no longer exists.

(d)(6) **Verification of isolation** Prior to starting work on machines or equipment that have been locked out or tagged out, the authorized employee shall verify that isolation and deenergization of the machine or equipment have been accomplished.

(e) **Release from lockout or tagout** Before lockout or tagout devices are removed and energy is restored to the machine or equipment, procedures shall be followed and actions taken by the authorized employee(s) to ensure the following:

(e)(1) **The machine or equipment** The work area shall be inspected to ensure that nonessential items have been removed and to ensure that machine or equipment components are operationally intact.

(e)(2) **Employees**

(e)(2)(i) The work area shall be checked to ensure that all employees have been safely positioned or removed.

(e)(2)(ii) After lockout or tagout devices have been removed and before a machine or equipment is started, affected employees shall be notified that the lockout or tagout device(s) have been removed.

(e)(3) [OI] **Lockout or tagout devices removal** Each lockout or tagout device shall be removed from each energy isolating device by the employee who applied the device. Exception to paragraph (e)(3): When the authorized employee who applied the lockout or tagout device is not available to remove it, that device may be removed under the direction of the employer, provided that specific procedures and training for such removal have been developed, documented and incorporated into the employer's energy control program. The employer shall demonstrate that the specific procedure provides equivalent safety to the removal of the device by the authorized employee who applied it. The specific procedure shall include at least the following elements:

(e)(3)(i) Verification by the employer that the authorized employee who applied the device is not at the facility;

(e)(3)(ii) Making all reasonable efforts to contact the authorized employee to inform him/her that his/her lockout or tagout device has been removed; and

(e)(3)(iii) Ensuring that the authorized employee has this knowledge before he/she resumes work at that facility.

(f) **Additional requirements**

(f)(1) [OI] Testing or positioning of machines, equipment or components thereof. In situations in which lockout or tagout devices must be temporarily removed from the energy isolating device and the machine or equipment energized to test or position the machine, equipment or component thereof, the following sequence of actions shall be followed:

(f)(1)(i) Clear the machine or equipment of tools and materials in accordance with paragraph (e)(1) of this section;

(f)(1)(ii) Remove employees from the machine or equipment area in accordance with paragraph (e)(2) of this section;

(f)(1)(iii) Remove the lockout or tagout devices as specified in paragraph (e)(3) of this section;

(f)(1)(iv) Energize and proceed with testing or positioning;

(f)(1)(v) Deenergize all systems and reapply energy control measures in accordance with paragraph (d) of this section to continue the servicing and/or maintenance.

(f)(2) **Outside personnel (contractors, etc.)**

(f)(2)(i) [OI] Whenever outside servicing personnel are to be engaged in activities covered by the scope and application of this standard, the on-site employer and the outside employer shall inform each other of their respective lockout or tagout procedures.

(f)(2)(ii) The on-site employer shall ensure that his/her employees understand and comply with the restrictions and prohibitions of the outside employer's energy control program.

(f)(3) [OI] **Group lockout or tagout**

(f)(3)(i) When servicing and/or maintenance is performed by a crew, craft, department or other group, they shall utilize a procedure which affords the employees a level of protection equivalent to that provided by the implementation of a personal lockout or tagout device.

(f)(3)(ii) [OI] Group lockout or tagout devices shall be used in accordance with the procedures required by paragraph (c)(4) of this section including, but not necessarily limited to, the following specific requirements:

(f)(3)(ii)(A) Primary responsibility is vested in an authorized employee for a set number of employees working under the protection of a group lockout or tagout device (such as an operations lock);

(f)(3)(ii)(B) Provision for the authorized employee to ascertain the exposure status of individual group members with regard to the lockout or tagout of the machine or equipment and

(f)(3)(ii)(C) When more than one crew, craft, department, etc. is involved, assignment of overall job-associated lockout or tagout control responsibility to an authorized employee designated to coordinate affected work forces and ensure continuity of protection; and

(f)(3)(ii)(D) Each authorized employee shall affix a personal lockout or tagout device to the group lockout device, group lockbox, or comparable mechanism when he or she begins work, and shall remove those devices when he or she stops working on the machine or equipment being serviced or maintained.

(f)(4) **Shift or personnel changes** Specific procedures shall be utilized during shift or personnel changes to ensure the continuity of lockout or tagout protection, including provision for the orderly transfer of lockout or tagout device protection between off-going and oncoming employees, to minimize exposure to hazards from the unexpected energization or start-up of the machine or equipment, or the release of stored energy.

Note: The following Appendix to §1910.147 services as a non-mandatory guideline to assist employers and employees in complying with the requirements of this section, as well as to provide other helpful information. Nothing in the Appendix adds to or detracts from any of the requirements of this section.

§1910.147 Appendix A
Typical minimal lockout procedure

General

The following simple lockout procedure is provided to assist employers in developing their procedures so they meet the requirements of this standard. When the energy isolating devices are not lockable, tagout may be used, provided the employer complies with the provisions of the standard which require additional training and more rigorous periodic inspections. When tagout is used and the energy isolating devices are lockable, the employer must provide full employee protection (see paragraph (c)(3)) and additional training and more rigorous periodic inspections are required. For more complex systems, more comprehensive procedures may need to be developed, documented and utilized.

Lockout Procedure

Lockout procedure for:

____

(Name of Company for single procedure or identification of equipment if multiple procedures are used)

Purpose

This procedure establishes the minimum requirements for the lockout of energy isolating devices whenever maintenance or servicing is done on machines or equipment. It shall be used to ensure that the machine or equipment is stopped, isolated from all potentially hazardous energy sources and locked out before employees perform any servicing or maintenance where the unexpected energization or start-up of the machine or equipment or release of stored energy could cause injury.

Compliance With This Program

All employees are required to comply with the restrictions and limitations imposed upon them during the use of lockout. The authorized employees are required to perform the lockout in accordance with this procedure. All employees, upon observing a machine or piece of equipment which is locked out to perform servicing or maintenance shall not attempt to start, energize or use that machine or equipment.

____

Type of compliance enforcement to be taken for violation of the above.

Sequence of Lockout

(1) Notify all affected employees that servicing or maintenance is required on a machine or equipment and that the machine or equipment must be shut down and locked out to perform the servicing or maintenance.

____

Name(s)/Job Title(s) of affected employees and how to notify.

(2) The authorized employee shall refer to the company procedure to identify the type and magnitude of the energy that the machine or equipment utilizes, shall understand the hazards of the energy, and shall know the methods to control the energy.

____

Type(s) and magnitude(s) of energy, its hazards and the methods to control the energy.

(3) If the machine or equipment is operating, shut it down by the normal stopping procedure (depress stop button, open switch, close valve, etc.).

Type(s) and location(s) of machine or equipment operating controls.

(4) De-activate the energy isolating device(s) so that the machine or equipment is isolated from the energy source(s).

Type(s) and location(s) of energy isolating devices.

(5) Lock out the energy isolating device(s) with assigned individual lock(s).

(6) Stored or residual energy (such as that in capacitors, springs, elevated machine members, rotating flywheels, hydraulic systems, and air, gas, steam, or water pressure, etc.) must be dissipated or restrained by methods such as grounding, repositioning, blocking, bleeding down, etc.

Type(s) of stored energy—methods to dissipate or restrain.

(7) Ensure that the equipment is disconnected from the energy source(s) by first checking that no personnel are exposed, then verify the isolation of the equipment by operating the push button or other normal operating control(s) or by testing to make certain the equipment will not operate.

Caution: Return operating control(s) to neutral or "off" position after verifying the isolation of the equipment.

Method of verifying the isolation of the equipment.

(8) The machine or equipment is now locked out.

Restoring Equipment to Service. When the servicing or maintenance is completed and the machine or equipment is ready to return to normal operating condition, the following steps shall be taken.

(1) Check the machine or equipment and the immediate area around the machine or equipment to ensure that nonessential items have been removed and that the machine or equipment components are operationally intact.

(2) Check the work area to ensure that all employees have been safely positioned or removed from the area.

(3) Verify that the controls are in neutral.

(4) Remove the lockout devices and reenergize the machine or equipment.

Note: The removal of some forms of blocking may require reenergization of the machine before safe removal.

(5) Notify affected employees that the servicing or maintenance is completed and the machine or equipment is ready for use.

[54 FR 36687, Sept. 1, 1989, as amended at 54 FR 42498, Oct. 17, 1989; 55 FR 38685, 38686, Sept. 20, 1990; 76 FR 24698, May 2, 2011; 76 FR 44265, July 25, 2011]

This page intentionally left blank.

29 CFR PART 1910 Subpart K
Medical and First Aid

Section Contents

Subpart K—Medical and First Aid

Authority: Sections 4, 6, and 8 of the Occupational Safety and Health Act of 1970, 29 U.S.C. 653, 655, and 657; Secretary of Labor's Order No. 12–71 (36 FR 8754), 8–76 (41 FR 25059), 9–83 (48 FR 35736), 1–90 (55 FR 9033), 6–96 (62 FR 111), or 3–2000 (65 FR 50017), as applicable, and 29 CFR part 1911.

§1910.151 OI
Medical services and first aid

(a) OI The employer shall ensure the ready availability of medical personnel for advice and consultation on matters of plant health.

(b) OI In the absence of an infirmary, clinic, or hospital in near proximity to the workplace which is used for the treatment of all injured employees, a person or persons shall be adequately trained to render first aid. Adequate first aid supplies shall be readily available.

(c) OI Where the eyes or body of any person may be exposed to injurious corrosive materials, suitable facilities for quick drenching or flushing of the eyes and body shall be provided within the work area for immediate emergency use.

§1910.151 Appendix A
First aid kits
(Nonmandatory)

First aid supplies are required to be readily available under paragraph §1910.151(b). An example of the minimal contents of a generic first aid kit is described in American National Standard (ANSI) Z308.1–1998 "Minimum Requirements for Workplace First-aid Kits." The contents of the kit listed in the ANSI standard should be adequate for small worksites. When larger operations or multiple operations are being conducted at the same location, employers should determine the need for additional first aid kits at the worksite, additional types of first aid equipment and supplies and additional quantities and types of supplies and equipment in the first aid kits.

§1910.152
[Reserved]

This page intentionally left blank.

29 CFR PART 1910 Subpart L
Fire Protection

Section Contents

Authority: Sections 4, 6, and 8 of the Occupational Safety and Health Act of 1970 (29 U.S.C. 653, 655, and 657); Secretary of Labor's Order No. 12–71 (36 FR 8754), 8–76 (41 FR 25059), 9–83 (48 FR 35736), 1–90 (55 FR 9033), 6–96 (62 FR 111), 3–2000 (65 FR 50017), 5–2002 (67 FR 65008), or 5–2007 (72 FR 31160), as applicable, and 29 CFR Part §1911.

§1910.155
Scope, application and definitions applicable to this Subpart

(a) **Scope** This Subpart contains requirements for fire brigades, and all portable and fixed fire suppression equipment, fire detection systems, and fire or employee alarm systems installed to meet the fire protection requirements of 29 CFR Part §1910.

(b) **Application** This Subpart applies to all employments except for maritime, construction, and agriculture.

(c) **Definitions applicable to this Subpart**

(c)(1) **After-flame** means the time a test specimen continues to flame after the flame source has been removed.

(c)(2) **Aqueous film forming foam (AFFF)** means a fluorinated surfactant with a foam stabilizer which is diluted with water to act as a temporary barrier to exclude air from mixing with the fuel vapor by developing an aqueous film on the fuel surface of some hydrocarbons which is capable of suppressing the generation of fuel vapors.

(c)(3) **Approved** means acceptable to the Assistant Secretary under the following criteria:

(c)(3)(i) If it is accepted, or certified, or listed, or labeled or otherwise determined to be safe by a nationally recognized testing laboratory; or

(c)(3)(ii) With respect to an installation or equipment of a kind which no nationally recognized testing laboratory accepts, certifies, lists, labels, or determines to be safe, if it is inspected or tested by another Federal agency and found in compliance with the provisions of the applicable National Fire Protection Association Fire Code; or

(c)(3)(iii) With respect to custom-made equipment or related installations which are designed, fabricated for, and intended for use by its manufacturer on the basis of test data which the employer keeps and makes available for inspection to the Assistant Secretary.

(c)(3)(iv) For the purposes of paragraph (c)(3) of this section:

(c)(3)(iv)(A) Equipment is listed if it is of a kind mentioned in a list which is published by a nationally recognized testing laboratory which makes periodic inspections of the production of such equipment and which states that such equipment meets nationally recognized standards or has been tested and found safe for use in a specified manner;

(c)(3)(iv)(B) Equipment is labeled if there is attached to it a label, symbol, or other identifying mark of a nationally recognized testing laboratory which makes periodic inspections of the production of such equipment, and whose labeling indicates compliance with nationally recognized standards or tests to determine safe use in a specified manner;

(c)(3)(iv)(C) Equipment is accepted if it has been inspected and found by a nationally recognized testing laboratory to conform to specified plans or to procedures of applicable codes; and

(c)(3)(iv)(D) Equipment is certified if it has been tested and found by a nationally recognized testing laboratory to meet nationally recognized standards or to be safe for use in a specified manner or is of a kind whose production is periodically inspected by a nationally recognized testing laboratory, and if it bears a label, tag, or other record of certification.

(c)(3)(iv)(E) Refer to §1910.7 for definition of nationally recognized testing laboratory.

(c)(4) **Assistant Secretary** means the Assistant Secretary of Labor for Occupational Safety and Health or designee.

(c)(5) **Automatic fire detection device** means a device designed to automatically detect the presence of fire by heat, flame, light, smoke or other products of combustion.

(c)(6) **Buddy-breathing device** means an accessory to self-contained breathing apparatus which permits a second person to share the same air supply as that of the wearer of the apparatus.

(c)(7) **Carbon dioxide** means a colorless, odorless, electrically nonconductive inert gas (chemical formula CO2) that is a medium for extinguishing fires by reducing the concentration of oxygen or fuel vapor in the air to the point where combustion is impossible.

(c)(8) **Class A fire** means a fire involving ordinary combustible materials such as paper, wood, cloth, and some rubber and plastic materials.

(c)(9) **Class B fire** means a fire involving flammable or combustible liquids, flammable gases, greases and similar materials, and some rubber and plastic materials.

(c)(10) **Class C fire** means a fire involving energized electrical equipment where safety to the employee requires the use of electrically nonconductive extinguishing media.

(c)(11) **Class D fire** means a fire involving combustible metals such as magnesium, titanium, zirconium, sodium, lithium and potassium.

(c)(12) **Dry chemical** means an extinguishing agent composed of very small particles of chemicals such as, but not limited to, sodium bicarbonate, potassium bicarbonate, urea-based potassium bicarbonate, potassium chloride, or monoammonium phosphate supplemented by special treatment to provide resistance to packing and moisture absorption (caking) as well as to provide proper flow capabilities. Dry chemical does not include dry powders.

(c)(13) **Dry powder** means a compound used to extinguish or control Class D fires.

(c)(14) **Education** means the process of imparting knowledge or skill through systematic instruction. It does not require formal classroom instruction.

(c)(15) **Enclosed structure** means a structure with a roof or ceiling and at least two walls which may present fire hazards to employees, such as accumulations of smoke, toxic gases and heat, similar to those found in buildings.

(c)(16) **Extinguisher classification** means the letter classification given an extinguisher to designate the class or classes of fire on which an extinguisher will be effective.

(c)(17) **Extinguisher rating** means the numerical rating given to an extinguisher which indicates the extinguishing potential of the unit based on standardized tests developed by Underwriters' Laboratories, Inc.

(c)(18) **Fire brigade (private fire department, industrial fire department)** means an organized group of employees who are knowledgeable, trained, and skilled in at least basic fire fighting operations.

(c)(19) **Fixed extinguishing system** means a permanently installed system that either extinguishes or controls a fire at the location of the system.

(c)(20) **Flame resistance** is the property of materials, or combinations of component materials, to retard ignition and restrict the spread of flame.

(c)(21) **Foam** means a stable aggregation of small bubbles which flow freely over a burning liquid surface and form a coherent blanket which seals combustible vapors and thereby extinguishes the fire.

(c)(22) **Gaseous agent** is a fire extinguishing agent which is in the gaseous state at normal room temperature and pressure. It has low viscosity, can expand or contract with changes in pressure and temperature, and has the ability to diffuse readily and to distribute itself uniformly throughout an enclosure.

(c)(23) **Halon 1211** means a colorless, faintly sweet smelling, electrically nonconductive liquefied gas (chemical formula CBrC1F2) which is a medium for extinguishing fires by inhibiting the chemical chain reaction of fuel and oxygen. It is also known as bromochlorodifluoromethane.

(c)(24) **Halon 1301** means a colorless, odorless, electrically nonconductive gas (chemical formula CBrF3) which is a medium for extinguishing fires by inhibiting the chemical chain reaction of fuel and oxygen. It is also known as bromotrifluoromethane.

(c)(25) **Helmet** is a head protective device consisting of a rigid shell, energy absorption system, and chin strap intended to be worn to provide protection for the head or portions thereof, against impact, flying or falling objects, electric shock, penetration, heat and flame.

(c)(26) **Incipient stage fire** means a fire which is in the initial or beginning stage and which can be controlled or extinguished by portable fire extinguishers, Class II standpipe or small hose systems without the need for protective clothing or breathing apparatus.

(c)(27) **Inspection** means a visual check of fire protection systems and equipment to ensure that they are in place, charged, and ready for use in the event of a fire.

(c)(28) **Interior structural fire fighting** means the physical activity of fire suppression, rescue or both, inside of buildings or enclosed structures which are involved in a fire situation beyond the incipient stage.

(c)(29) **Lining** means a material permanently attached to the inside of the outer shell of a garment for the purpose of thermal protection and padding.

(c)(30) **Local application system** means a fixed fire suppression system which has a supply of extinguishing agent, with nozzles arranged to automatically discharge extinguishing agent directly on the burning material to extinguish or control a fire.

(c)(31) **Maintenance** means the performance of services on fire protection equipment and systems to assure that they will perform as expected in the event of a fire. Maintenance differs from inspection in that maintenance requires the checking of internal fittings, devices and agent supplies.

(c)(32) **Multipurpose dry chemical** means a dry chemical which is approved for use on Class A, Class B and Class C fires.

(c)(33) **Outer shell** is the exterior layer of material on the fire coat and protective trousers which forms the outermost barrier between the fire fighter and the environment. It is attached to the vapor barrier and liner and is usually constructed with a storm flap, suitable closures, and pockets.

(c)(34) **Positive-pressure breathing apparatus** means self-contained breathing apparatus in which the pressure in the breathing zone is positive in relation to the immediate environment during inhalation and exhalation.

(c)(35) **Pre-discharge employee alarm** means an alarm which will sound at a set time prior to actual discharge of an extinguishing system so that employees may evacuate the discharge area prior to system discharge.

(c)(36) **Quick disconnect valve** means a device which starts the flow of air by inserting of the hose (which leads from the facepiece) into the regulator of self-contained breathing apparatus, and stops the flow of air by disconnection of the hose from the regulator.

(c)(37) **Sprinkler alarm** means an approved device installed so that any waterflow from a sprinkler system equal to or greater than that from single automatic sprinkler will result in an audible alarm signal on the premises.

(c)(38) **Sprinkler system** means a system of piping designed in accordance with fire protection engineering standards and installed to control or extinguish fires. The system includes an adequate and reliable water supply, and a network of specially sized piping and sprinklers which are interconnected. The system also includes a control valve and a device for actuating an alarm when the system is in operation.

(c)(39) **Standpipe systems**

(c)(39)(i) Class I standpipe system means a 2½-inch; (6.3 cm) hose connection for use by fire departments and those trained in handling heavy fire streams.

(c)(39)(ii) Class II standpipe system means a 1½-inch; (3.8 cm) hose system which provides a means for the control or extinguishment of incipient stage fires.

(c)(39)(iii) Class III standpipe system means a combined system of hose which is for the use of employees trained in the use of hose operations and which is capable of furnishing effective water discharge during the more advanced stages of fire (beyond the incipient stage) in the interior of workplaces. Hose outlets are available for both 1½"; (3.8 cm) and 2 ½"; (6.3 cm) hose.

(c)(39)(iv) Small hose system means a system of hose ranging in diameter from ⅝"; (1.6 cm up to 1½"; (3.8 cm) which is for the use of employees and which provides a means for the control and extinguishment of incipient stage fires.

(c)(40) **Total flooding system** means a fixed suppression system which is arranged to automatically discharge a predetermined concentration of agent into an enclosed space for the purpose of fire extinguishment or control.

(c)(41) **Training** means the process of making proficient through instruction and hands-on practice in the operation of equipment, including respiratory protection equipment, that is expected to be used and in the performance of assigned duties.

(c)(42) **Vapor barrier** means that material used to prevent or substantially inhibit the transfer of water, corrosive liquids and steam or other hot vapors from the outside of a garment to the wearer's body.

[45 FR 60704, Sept. 12, 1980, as amended at 53 FR 12122, Apr. 12, 1988]

§1910.156 Fire brigades

(a) **Scope and application**

(a)(1) **Scope** This section contains requirements for the organization, training, and personal protective equipment of fire brigades whenever they are established by an employer.

(a)(2) **Application** The requirements of this section apply to fire brigades, industrial fire departments and private or contractual type fire departments. Personal protective equipment requirements apply only to members of fire brigades performing interior structural fire fighting. The requirements of this section do not apply to airport crash rescue or forest fire fighting operations.

(b) **Organization**

(b)(1) **Organizational statement** The employer shall prepare and maintain a statement or written policy which establishes the existence of a fire brigade; the basic organizational structure; the type, amount, and frequency of training to be provided to fire brigade members; the expected number of members in the fire brigade; and the functions that the fire brigade is to perform at the workplace. The organizational statement shall be available for inspection by the Assistant Secretary and by employees or their designated representatives.

(b)(2) **Personnel** The employer shall assure that employees who are expected to do interior structural fire fighting are physically capable of performing duties which may be assigned to them during emergencies. The employer shall not permit employees with known heart disease, epilepsy, or emphysema, to participate in fire brigade emergency activities unless a physician's certificate of the employees' fitness to participate in such activities is provided. For employees assigned to fire brigades before September 15, 1980, this paragraph is effective on September 15, 1990. For employees assigned to fire brigades on or after September 15, 1980, this paragraph is effective December 15, 1980.

(c) **Training and education**

(c)(1) The employer shall provide training and education for all fire brigade members commensurate with those duties and functions that fire brigade members are expected to perform. Such training and education shall be provided to fire brigade members before they perform fire brigade emergency activities. Fire brigade leaders and training instructors shall be provided with training and education which is more comprehensive than that provided to the general membership of the fire brigade.

(c)(2) The employer shall assure that training and education is conducted frequently enough to assure that each member of the fire brigade is able to perform the member's assigned duties and functions satisfactorily and in a safe manner so as not to endanger fire brigade members or other employees. All fire brigade members shall be provided with training at least annually. In addition, fire brigade members who are expected to perform interior structural fire fighting shall be provided with an education session or training at least quarterly.

(c)(3) The quality of the training and education program for fire brigade members shall be similar to those conducted by such fire training schools as the Maryland Fire and Rescue Institute; Iowa Fire Service Extension; West Virginia Fire Service Extension; Georgia Fire Academy, New York State Department, Fire Prevention and Control; Louisiana State University Firemen Training Program, or Washington State's Fire Service Training Commission for Vocational Education. (For example: for the oil refinery industry, with its unique hazards, the training and education program for those fire brigade members shall be similar to those conducted by Texas A & M University, Lamar University, Reno Fire School, or the Delaware State Fire School.)

(c)(4) The employer shall inform fire brigade members about special hazards such as storage and use of flammable liquids and gases, toxic chemicals, radioactive sources, and water reactive substances, to which they may be exposed during fire and other emergencies. The fire brigade members shall also be advised of any changes that occur in relation to the special hazards. The employer shall develop and make available for inspection by fire brigade members, written procedures that describe the actions to be taken in situations involving the special hazards and shall include these in the training and education program.

(d) **Fire fighting equipment** The employer shall maintain and inspect, at least annually, fire fighting equipment to assure the safe operational condition of the equipment. Portable fire extinguishers and respirators shall be inspected at least monthly. Fire fighting equipment that is in damaged or unserviceable condition shall be removed from service and replaced.

(e) OI **Protective clothing** The following requirements apply to those employees who perform interior structural fire fighting. The requirements do not apply to employees who use fire extinguishers or standpipe systems to control or extinguish fires only in the incipient stage.

(e)(1) **General**

(e)(1)(i) The employer shall provide at no cost to the employee and assure the use of protective clothing which complies with the requirements of this paragraph. The employer shall assure that protective clothing ordered or purchased after July 1, 1981, meets the requirements contained in this paragraph. As the new equipment is provided, the employer shall assure that all fire brigade members wear the equipment when performing interior structural fire fighting. After July 1, 1985, the employer shall assure that all fire brigade members wear protective clothing meeting the requirements of this paragraph when performing interior structural fire fighting.

(e)(1)(ii) The employer shall assure that protective clothing protects the head, body, and extremities, and consists of at least the following components: foot and leg protection; hand protection; body protection; eye, face and head protection.

(e)(2) **Foot and leg protection**

(e)(2)(i) Foot and leg protection shall meet the requirements of paragraphs (e)(2)(ii) and (e)(2)(iii) of this section, and may be achieved by either of the following methods:

(e)(2)(i)(A) Fully extended boots which provide protection for the legs; or

(e)(2)(i)(B) Protective shoes or boots worn in combination with protective trousers that meet the requirements of paragraph (e)(3) of this section.

(e)(2)(ii) Protective footwear shall meet the requirements of §1910.136 for Class 75 footwear. In addition, protective footwear shall be water-resistant for at least 5 inches (12.7 cm) above the bottom of the heel and shall be equipped with slip-resistant outer soles.

(e)(2)(iii) Protective footwear shall be tested in accordance with paragraph (1) of Appendix E, and shall provide protection against penetration of the midsole by a size 8D common nail when at least 300 pounds (1330 N) of static force is applied to the nail.

(e)(3) **Body protection**

(e)(3)(i) Body protection shall be coordinated with foot and leg protection to ensure full body protection for the wearer. This shall be achieved by one of the following methods:

(e)(3)(i)(A) Wearing of a fire-resistive coat meeting the requirements of paragraph (e)(3)(ii) of this section in combination with fully extended boots meeting the requirements of paragraphs (e)(2)(ii) and (e)(2)(iii) of this section; or

(e)(3)(i)(B) Wearing of a fire-resistive coat in combination with protective trousers both of which meet the requirements of paragraph (e)(3)(ii) of this section.

(e)(3)(ii) The performance, construction, and testing of fire-resistive coats and protective trousers shall be at least equivalent to the requirements of the National Fire Protection Association (NFPA) standard NFPA No. 1971–1975, "Protective Clothing for Structural Fire Fighting," which is incorporated by reference as specified in §1910.6, (See Appendix D to Subpart L) with the following permissible variations from those requirements:

(e)(3)(ii)(A) Tearing strength of the outer shell shall be a minimum of 8 pounds (35.6 N) in any direction when tested in accordance with paragraph (2) of Appendix E; and

(e)(3)(ii)(B) The outer shell may discolor but shall not separate or melt when placed in a forced air laboratory oven at a temperature of 500 °F (260 °C) for a period of five minutes. After cooling to ambient temperature and using the test method specified in paragraph (3) of Appendix E, char length shall not exceed 4.0 inches (10.2 cm) and after-flame shall not exceed 2.0 seconds.

(e)(4) **Hand protection**

(e)(4)(i) Hand protection shall consist of protective gloves or glove system which will provide protection against cut, puncture, and heat penetration. Gloves or glove system shall be tested in accordance with the test methods contained in the National Institute for Occupational Safety and Health (NIOSH) 1976 publication, "The Development of Criteria for Fire Fighter's Gloves; Vol. II, Part II: Test Methods," which is incorporated by reference as specified in §1910.6, (See Appendix D to Subpart L) and shall meet the following criteria for cut, puncture, and heat penetration:

(e)(4)(i)(A) Materials used for gloves shall resist surface cut by a blade with an edge having a 60° included angle and a .001 inch (.0025 cm.) radius, under an applied force of 16 lbf (72N), and at a slicing velocity of greater or equal to 60 in/min (2.5 cm./sec);

(e)(4)(i)(B) Materials used for the palm and palm side of the fingers shall resist puncture by a penetrometer (simulating a 4d lath nail), under an applied force of 13.2 lbf (60N), and at a velocity greater or equal to 20 in/min (.85 cm./sec); and

(e)(4)(i)(C) The temperature inside the palm and gripping surface of the fingers of gloves shall not exceed 135 °F (57 °C) when gloves or glove system are exposed to 932 °F (500 °C) for five seconds at 4 psi (28 kPa) pressure.

(e)(4)(ii) Exterior materials of gloves shall be flame resistant and shall be tested in accordance with paragraph (3) of Appendix E. Maximum allowable afterflame shall be 2.0 seconds, and the maximum char length shall be 4.0 inches (10.2 cm).

(e)(4)(iii) When design of the fire-resistive coat does not otherwise provide protection for the wrists, protective gloves shall have wristlets of at least 4.0 inches (10.2 cm) in length to protect the wrist area when the arms are extended upward and outward from the body.

(e)(5) **Head, eye and face protection**

(e)(5)(i) Head protection shall consist of a protective head device with ear flaps and chin strap which meet the performance, construction, and testing requirements of the National Fire Safety and Research Office of the National Fire Prevention and Control Administration, U.S. Department of Commerce (now known as the U.S. Fire Administration), which are contained in "Model Performance Criteria for Structural Firefighters' Helmets" (August 1977) which is incorporated by reference as specified in §1910.6, (See Appendix D to Subpart L).

(e)(5)(ii) Protective eye and face devices which comply with §1910.133 shall be used by fire brigade members when performing operations where the hazards of flying or falling materials which may cause eye and face injuries are present. Protective eye and face devices provided as accessories to protective head devices (face shields) are permitted when such devices meet the requirements of §1910.133.

(e)(5)(iii) Full facepieces, helmets, or hoods of breathing apparatus which meet the requirements of §1910.134 and paragraph (f) of this section, shall be acceptable as meeting the eye and face protection requirements of paragraph (e)(5)(ii) of this section.

(f) OI **Respiratory protection devices**

(f)(1) **General requirements**

(f)(1)(i) The employer must ensure that respirators are provided to, and used by, each fire brigade member, and that the respirators meet the requirements of 29 CFR §1910.134 for each employee required by this section to use a respirator.

(f)(1)(ii) Approved self-contained breathing apparatus with full-facepiece, or with approved helmet or hood configuration, shall be provided to and worn by fire brigade members while working inside buildings or confined spaces where toxic products of combustion or an oxygen deficiency may be present.

Such apparatus shall also be worn during emergency situations involving toxic substances.

(f)(1)(iii) Approved self-contained breathing apparatus may be equipped with either a "buddy-breathing" device or a quick disconnect valve, even if these devices are not certified by NIOSH. If these accessories are used, they shall not cause damage to the apparatus, or restrict the air flow of the apparatus, or obstruct the normal operation of the apparatus.

(f)(1)(iv) OI Approved self-contained compressed air breathing apparatus may be used with approved cylinders from other approved self-contained compressed air breathing apparatus provided that such cylinders are of the same capacity and pressure rating. All compressed air cylinders used with self-contained breathing apparatus shall meet DOT and NIOSH criteria.

(f)(1)(v) Self-contained breathing apparatuses must have a minimum service-life rating of 30 minutes in accordance with the methods and requirements specified by NIOSH under 42 CFR Part 84, except for escape self-contained breathing apparatus (ESCBAs) used only for emergency escape purposes.

(f)(1)(vi) Self-contained breathing apparatus shall be provided with an indicator which automatically sounds an audible alarm when the remaining service life of the apparatus is reduced to within a range of 20 to 25 percent of its rated service time.

(f)(2) **Positive-pressure breathing apparatus**

(f)(2)(i) The employer shall assure that self-contained breathing apparatus ordered or purchased after July 1, 1981, for use by fire brigade members performing interior structural fire fighting operations, are of the pressure-demand or other positive-pressure type. Effective July 1,

1983, only pressure-demand or other positive-pressure self-contained breathing apparatus shall be worn by fire brigade members performing interior structural fire fighting.

(f)(2)(ii) This paragraph does not prohibit the use of a self-contained breathing apparatus where the apparatus can be switched from a demand to a positive-pressure mode. However, such apparatus shall be in the positive-pressure mode when fire brigade members are performing interior structural fire fighting operations.

[45 FR 60706, Sept. 12, 1980; 46 FR 24557, May 1, 1981; 49 FR 18295, Apr. 30, 1984; 61 FR 9239, Mar. 7, 1996; 63 FR 1284, Jan. 8, 1998; 63 FR 33467, June 18, 1998; 73 FR 75584, Dec. 12, 2008]

PORTABLE FIRE SUPPRESSION EQUIPMENT

§1910.157 Portable fire extinguishers

(a) **Scope and application** The requirements of this section apply to the placement, use, maintenance, and testing of portable fire extinguishers provided for the use of employees. Paragraph (d) of this section does not apply to extinguishers provided for employee use on the outside of workplace buildings or structures. Where extinguishers are provided but are not intended for employee use and the employer has an emergency action plan and a fire prevention plan that meet the requirements of 29 CFR §1910.38 and 29 CFR §1910.39 respectively, then only the requirements of paragraphs (e) and (f) of this section apply.

(b) **Exemptions**

(b)(1) Where the employer has established and implemented a written fire safety policy which requires the immediate and total evacuation of employees from the workplace upon the sounding of a fire alarm signal and which includes an emergency action plan and a fire prevention plan which meet the requirements of 29 CFR §1910.38 and 29 CFR §1910.39 respectively, and when extinguishers are not available in the workplace, the employer is exempt from all requirements of this section unless a specific standard in Part §1910 requires that a portable fire extinguisher be provided.

(b)(2) Where the employer has an emergency action plan meeting the requirements of §1910.38 which designates certain employees to be the only employees authorized to use the available portable fire extinguishers, and which requires all other employees in the fire area to immediately evacuate the affected work area upon the sounding of the fire alarm, the employer is exempt from the distribution requirements in paragraph (d) of this section.

(c) **General requirements**

(c)(1) The employer shall provide portable fire extinguishers and shall mount, locate and identify them so that they are readily accessible to employees without subjecting the employees to possible injury.

(c)(2) Only approved portable fire extinguishers shall be used to meet the requirements of this section.

(c)(3) The employer shall not provide or make available in the workplace portable fire extinguishers using carbon tetrachloride or chlorobromomethane extinguishing agents.

(c)(4) The employer shall assure that portable fire extinguishers are maintained in a fully charged and operable condition and kept in their designated places at all times except during use.

(c)(5) The employer shall remove from service all soldered or riveted shell self-generating soda acid or self-generating foam or gas cartridge water type portable fire extinguishers which are operated by inverting the extinguisher to rupture the cartridge or to initiate an uncontrollable pressure generating chemical reaction to expel the agent.

(d) **Selection and distribution**

(d)(1) Portable fire extinguishers shall be provided for employee use and selected and distributed based on the classes of anticipated workplace fires and on the size and degree of hazard which would affect their use.

(d)(2) The employer shall distribute portable fire extinguishers for use by employees on Class A fires so that the travel distance for employees to any extinguisher is 75 feet (22.9 m) or less.

(d)(3) The employer may use uniformly spaced standpipe systems or hose stations connected to a sprinkler system installed for emergency use by employees instead of Class A portable fire extinguishers, provided that such systems meet the respective requirements of §1910.158 or §1910.159, that they provide total coverage of the area to be protected, and that employees are trained at least annually in their use.

(d)(4) The employer shall distribute portable fire extinguishers for use by employees on Class B fires so that the travel distance from the Class B hazard area to any extinguisher is 50 feet (15.2 m) or less.

(d)(5) The employer shall distribute portable fire extinguishers used for Class C hazards on the basis of the appropriate pattern for the existing Class A or Class B hazards.

(d)(6) The employer shall distribute portable fire extinguishers or other containers of Class D extinguishing agent for use by employees so that the travel distance from the combustible metal working area to any extinguishing agent is 75 feet (22.9 m) or less. Portable fire extinguishers for Class D hazards are required in those combustible metal working areas where combustible metal powders, flakes, shavings, or similarly sized products are generated at least once every two weeks.

(e) **Inspection, maintenance and testing**

(e)(1) The employer shall be responsible for the inspection, maintenance and testing of all portable fire extinguishers in the workplace.

(e)(2) Portable extinguishers or hose used in lieu thereof under paragraph (d)(3) of this section shall be visually inspected monthly.

(e)(3) The employer shall assure that portable fire extinguishers are subjected to an annual maintenance check. Stored pressure extinguishers do not require an internal examination. The employer shall record the annual maintenance date and retain this record for one year after the last entry or the life of the shell, whichever is less. The record shall be available to the Assistant Secretary upon request.

(e)(4) The employer shall assure that stored pressure dry chemical extinguishers that require a 12-year hydrostatic test are emptied and subjected to applicable maintenance procedures every 6 years. Dry chemical extinguishers having non-refillable disposable containers are exempt from this requirement. When recharging or hydrostatic testing is performed, the 6-year requirement begins from that date.

(e)(5) The employer shall assure that alternate equivalent protection is provided when portable fire extinguishers are removed from service for maintenance and recharging.

(f) **Hydrostatic testing**

(f)(1) The employer shall assure that hydrostatic testing is performed by trained persons with suitable testing equipment and facilities.

(f)(2) The employer shall assure that portable extinguishers are hydrostatically tested at the intervals listed in Table L–1 of this section, except under any of the following conditions:

(f)(2)(i) When the unit has been repaired by soldering, welding, brazing, or use of patching compounds;

(f)(2)(ii) When the cylinder or shell threads are damaged;

(f)(2)(iii) When there is corrosion that has caused pitting, including corrosion under removable name plate assemblies;

(f)(2)(iv) When the extinguisher has been burned in a fire; or

(f)(2)(v) When a calcium chloride extinguishing agent has been used in a stainless steel shell.

(f)(3) In addition to an external visual examination, the employer shall assure that an internal examination of cylinders and shells to be tested is made prior to the hydrostatic tests.

Table L–1

Type of extinguishers	Test interval (years)
Soda acid (soldered brass shells) (until 1/1/82)	([1])
Soda acid (stainless steel shell)	5
Cartridge operated water and/or antifreeze	5
Stored pressure water and/or antifreeze	5
Wetting agent	5
Foam (soldered brass shells) (until 1/1/82)	([1])
Foam (stainless steel shell)	5
Aqueous Film Forming foam (AFFF)	5
Loaded stream	5
Dry chemical with stainless steel	5
Carbon dioxide	5
Dry chemical, stored pressure, with mild steel, brazed brass or aluminum shells	12
Dry chemical, cartridge or cylinder operated, with mild steel shells	12
Halon 1211	12

Type of extinguishers	Test interval (years)
Halon 1301	12
Dry powder, cartridge or cylinder operated with mild steel shells	12

[1] Extinguishers having shells constructed of copper or brass joined by soft solder or rivets shall not be hydrostatically tested and shall be removed from service by January 1, 1982. (Not permitted)

(f)(4) The employer shall assure that portable fire extinguishers are hydrostatically tested whenever they show new evidence of corrosion or mechanical injury, except under the conditions listed in paragraphs (f)(2)(i)–(v) of this section.

(f)(5) The employer shall assure that hydrostatic tests are performed on extinguisher hose assemblies which are equipped with a shut-off nozzle at the discharge end of the hose. The test interval shall be the same as specified for the extinguisher on which the hose is installed.

(f)(6) The employer shall assure that carbon dioxide hose assemblies with a shut-off nozzle are hydrostatically tested at 1,250 psi (8,620 kPa).

(f)(7) The employer shall assure that dry chemical and dry powder hose assemblies with a shut-off nozzle are hydrostatically tested at 300 psi (2,070 kPa).

(f)(8) Hose assemblies passing a hydrostatic test do not require any type of recording or stamping.

(f)(9) The employer shall assure that hose assemblies for carbon dioxide extinguishers that require a hydrostatic test are tested within a protective cage device.

(f)(10) The employer shall assure that carbon dioxide extinguishers and nitrogen or carbon dioxide cylinders used with wheeled extinguishers are tested every 5 years at 5/3 of the service pressure as stamped into the cylinder. Nitrogen cylinders which comply with 49 CFR 173.34(e)(15) may be hydrostatically tested every 10 years.

(f)(11) The employer shall assure that all stored pressure and Halon 1211 types of extinguishers are hydrostatically tested at the factory test pressure not to exceed two times the service pressure.

(f)(12) The employer shall assure that acceptable self-generating type soda acid and foam extinguishers are tested at 350 psi (2,410 kPa).

(f)(13) Air or gas pressure may not be used for hydrostatic testing.

(f)(14) Extinguisher shells, cylinders, or cartridges which fail a hydrostatic pressure test, or which are not fit for testing shall be removed from service and from the workplace.

(f)(15)(i) The equipment for testing compressed gas type cylinders shall be of the water jacket type. The equipment shall be provided with an expansion indicator which operates with an accuracy within one percent of the total expansion or .1cc (.1mL) of liquid.

(f)(15)(ii) The equipment for testing non-compressed gas type cylinders shall consist of the following:

(f)(15)(ii)(A) A hydrostatic test pump, hand or power operated, capable of producing not less than 150 percent of the test pressure, which shall include appropriate check valves and fittings;

(f)(15)(ii)(B) A flexible connection for attachment to fittings to test through the extinguisher nozzle, test bonnet, or hose outlet, as is applicable; and

(f)(15)(ii)(C) A protective cage or barrier for personal protection of the tester, designed to provide visual observation of the extinguisher under test.

(f)(16) The employer shall maintain and provide upon request to the Assistant Secretary evidence that the required hydrostatic testing of fire extinguishers has been performed at the time intervals shown in Table L–1. Such evidence shall be in the form of a certification record which includes the date of the test, the signature of the person who performed the test and the serial number, or other identifier, of the fire extinguisher that was tested. Such records shall be kept until the extinguisher is hydrostatically retested at the time interval specified in Table L–1 or until the extinguisher is taken out of service, whichever comes first.

(g) Training and education

(g)(1) Where the employer has provided portable fire extinguishers for employee use in the workplace, the employer shall also provide an educational program to familiarize employees with the general principles of fire extinguisher use and the hazards involved with incipient stage fire fighting.

(g)(2) The employer shall provide the education required in paragraph (g)(1) of this section upon initial employment and at least annually thereafter.

(g)(3) The employer shall provide employees who have been designated to use fire fighting equipment as part of an emergency action plan with training in the use of the appropriate equipment.

(g)(4) The employer shall provide the training required in paragraph (g)(3) of this section upon initial assignment to the designated group of employees and at least annually thereafter.

[45 FR 60708, Sept. 12, 1980; 46 FR 24557, May 1, 1981, as amended at 51 FR 34560, Sept. 29, 1986; 61 FR 9239, Mar. 7, 1996; 67 FR 67964, Nov. 7, 2002]

§1910.158 Standpipe and hose systems

(a) Scope and application

(a)(1) Scope This section applies to all small hose, Class II, and Class III standpipe systems installed to meet the requirements of a particular OSHA standard.

(a)(2) Exception This section does not apply to Class I standpipe systems.

(b) Protection of standpipes The employer shall assure that standpipes are located or otherwise protected against mechanical damage. Damaged standpipes shall be repaired promptly.

(c) Equipment

(c)(1) Reels and cabinets Where reels or cabinets are provided to contain fire hose, the employer shall assure that they are designed to facilitate prompt use of the hose valves, the hose, and other equipment at the time of a fire or other emergency. The employer shall assure that the reels and cabinets are conspicuously identified and used only for fire equipment.

(c)(2) Hose outlets and connections

(c)(2)(i) The employer shall assure that hose outlets and connections are located high enough above the floor to avoid being obstructed and to be accessible to employees.

(c)(2)(ii) The employer shall standardize screw threads or provide appropriate adapters throughout the system and assure that the hose connections are compatible with those used on the supporting fire equipment.

(c)(3) Hose

(c)(3)(i) The employer shall assure that every 1½"; (3.8 cm) or smaller hose outlet used to meet this standard is equipped with hose connected and ready for use. In extremely cold climates where such installation may result in damaged equipment, the hose may be stored in another location provided it is readily available and can be connected when needed.

(c)(3)(ii) Standpipe systems installed after January 1, 1981, for use by employees, shall be equipped with lined hose. Unlined hose may remain in use on existing systems. However, after the effective date of this standard, unlined hose which becomes unserviceable shall be replaced with lined hose.

(c)(3)(iii) The employer shall provide hose of such length that friction loss resulting from water flowing through the hose will not decrease the pressure at the nozzle below 30 psi (210 kPa). The dynamic pressure at the nozzle shall be within the range of 30 psi (210 kPa) to 125 psi (860 kPa).

(c)(4) Nozzles The employer shall assure that standpipe hose is equipped with shut-off type nozzles.

(d) Water supply The minimum water supply for standpipe and hose systems, which are provided for the use of employees, shall be sufficient to provide 100 gallons per minute (6.3 l/s) for a period of at least thirty minutes.

(e) Tests and maintenance

(e)(1) Acceptance tests

(e)(1)(i) The employer shall assure that the piping of Class II and Class III systems installed after January 1, 1981, including yard piping, is hydrostatically tested for a period of at least 2 hours at not less than 200 psi (1380 kPa), or at least 50 psi (340 kPa) in excess of normal pressure when such pressure is greater than 150 psi (1030 kPa).

(e)(1)(ii) The employer shall assure that hose on all standpipe systems installed after January 1, 1981, is hydrostatically tested with couplings in place, at a pressure of not less than 200 psi (1380 kPa), before it is placed in service. This pressure shall be maintained for at least 15 seconds and not more than one minute during which time the hose shall not leak nor shall any jacket thread break during the test.

(e)(2) Maintenance

(e)(2)(i) The employer shall assure that water supply tanks are kept filled to the proper level except during repairs. When pressure tanks are used, the employer shall assure that proper pressure is maintained at all times except during repairs.

(e)(2)(ii) The employer shall assure that valves in the main piping connections to the automatic sources of water supply are kept fully open at all times except during repair.

(e)(2)(iii) The employer shall assure that hose systems are inspected at least annually and after each use to assure that all of the equipment and hose are in place, available for use, and in serviceable condition.

(e)(2)(iv) When the system or any portion thereof is found not to be serviceable, the employer shall remove it from service immediately and replace it with equivalent protection such as extinguishers and fire watches.

(e)(2)(v) The employer shall assure that hemp or linen hose on existing systems is unracked, physically inspected for deterioration, and reracked using a different fold pattern at least annually. The employer shall assure that defective hose is replaced in accordance with paragraph (c)(3)(ii) of this section.

(e)(2)(vi) The employer shall designate trained persons to conduct all inspections required under this section.

[45 FR 60710, Sept. 12, 1980, as amended at 61 FR 9239, Mar. 7, 1996]

FIXED FIRE SUPPRESSION EQUIPMENT

§1910.159 Automatic sprinkler systems

(a) **Scope and application**

(a)(1) The requirements of this section apply to all automatic sprinkler systems installed to meet a particular OSHA standard.

(a)(2) For automatic sprinkler systems used to meet OSHA requirements and installed prior to the effective date of this standard, compliance with the National Fire Protection Association (NFPA) or the National Board of Fire Underwriters (NBFU) standard in effect at the time of the system's installation will be acceptable as compliance with this section.

(b) **Exemptions** Automatic sprinkler systems installed in workplaces, but not required by OSHA, are exempt from the requirements of this section.

(c) **General requirements**

(c)(1) **Design**

(c)(1)(i) All automatic sprinkler designs used to comply with this standard shall provide the necessary discharge patterns, densities, and water flow characteristics for complete coverage in a particular workplace or zoned subdivision of the workplace.

(c)(1)(ii) The employer shall assure that only approved equipment and devices are used in the design and installation of automatic sprinkler systems used to comply with this standard.

(c)(2) **Maintenance** The employer shall properly maintain an automatic sprinkler system installed to comply with this section. The employer shall assure that a main drain flow test is performed on each system annually. The inspector's test valve shall be opened at least every two years to assure that the sprinkler system operates properly.

(c)(3) **Acceptance tests** The employer shall conduct proper acceptance tests on sprinkler systems installed for employee protection after January 1, 1981, and record the dates of such tests. Proper acceptance tests include the following:

(c)(3)(i) Flushing of underground connections;
(c)(3)(ii) Hydrostatic tests of piping in system;
(c)(3)(iii) Air tests in dry-pipe systems;
(c)(3)(iv) Dry-pipe valve operation; and
(c)(3)(v) Test of drainage facilities.

(c)(4) **Water supplies** The employer shall assure that every automatic sprinkler system is provided with at least one automatic water supply capable of providing design water flow for at least 30 minutes. An auxiliary water supply or equivalent protection shall be provided when the automatic water supply is out of service, except for systems of 20 or fewer sprinklers.

(c)(5) **Hose connections for fire fighting use** The employer may attach hose connections for fire fighting use to wet pipe sprinkler systems provided that the water supply satisfies the combined design demand for sprinklers and standpipes.

(c)(6) **Protection of piping** The employer shall assure that automatic sprinkler system piping is protected against freezing and exterior surface corrosion.

(c)(7) **Drainage** The employer shall assure that all dry sprinkler pipes and fittings are installed so that the system may be totally drained.

(c)(8) **Sprinklers**

(c)(8)(i) The employer shall assure that only approved sprinklers are used on systems.

(c)(8)(ii) The employer may not use older style sprinklers to replace standard sprinklers without a complete engineering review of the altered part of the system.

(c)(8)(iii) The employer shall assure that sprinklers are protected from mechanical damage.

(c)(9) **Sprinkler alarms** On all sprinkler systems having more than twenty (20) sprinklers, the employer shall assure that a local waterflow alarm is provided which sounds an audible signal on the premises upon water flow through the system equal to the flow from a single sprinkler.

(c)(10) **Sprinkler spacing** The employer shall assure that sprinklers are spaced to provide a maximum protection area per sprinkler, a minimum of interference to the discharge pattern by building or structural members or building contents and suitable sensitivity to possible fire hazards. The minimum vertical clearance between sprinklers and material below shall be 18 inches (45.7 cm).

(c)(11) **Hydraulically designed systems** The employer shall assure that hydraulically designed automatic sprinkler systems or portions thereof are identified and that the location, number of sprinklers in the hydraulically designed section, and the basis of the design is indicated. Central records may be used in lieu of signs at sprinkler valves provided the records are available for inspection and copying by the Assistant Secretary.

[45 FR 60710, Sept. 12, 1980; 46 FR 24557, May 1, 1981]

§1910.160 Fixed extinguishing systems, general

(a) **Scope and application**

(a)(1) This section applies to all fixed extinguishing systems installed to meet a particular OSHA standard except for automatic sprinkler systems which are covered by §1910.159.

(a)(2) This section also applies to fixed systems not installed to meet a particular OSHA standard, but which, by means of their operation, may expose employees to possible injury, death, or adverse health consequences caused by the extinguishing agent. Such systems are only subject to the requirements of paragraphs (b)(4) through (b)(7) and (c) of this section.

(a)(3) Systems otherwise covered in paragraph (a)(2) of this section which are installed in areas with no employee exposure are exempted from the requirements of this section.

(b) **General requirements**

(b)(1) Fixed extinguishing system components and agents shall be designed and approved for use on the specific fire hazards they are expected to control or extinguish.

(b)(2) If for any reason a fixed extinguishing system becomes inoperable, the employer shall notify employees and take the necessary temporary precautions to assure their safety until the system is restored to operating order. Any defects or impairments shall be properly corrected by trained personnel.

(b)(3) The employer shall provide a distinctive alarm or signaling system which complies with §1910.165 and is capable of being perceived above ambient noise or light levels, on all extinguishing systems in those portions of the workplace covered by the extinguishing system to indicate when the extinguishing system is discharging. Discharge alarms are not required on systems where discharge is immediately recognizable.

(b)(4) The employer shall provide effective safeguards to warn employees against entry into discharge areas where the atmosphere remains hazardous to employee safety or health.

(b)(5) The employer shall post hazard warning or caution signs at the entrance to, and inside of, areas protected by fixed extinguishing systems which use agents in concentrations known to be hazardous to employee safety and health.

(b)(6) The employer shall assure that fixed systems are inspected annually by a person knowledgeable in the design and function of the system to assure that the system is maintained in good operating condition.

(b)(7) The employer shall assure that the weight and pressure of refillable containers is checked at least semi-annually. If the container shows a loss in net content or weight of more than 5 percent, or a loss in pressure of more than 10 percent, it shall be subjected to maintenance.

(b)(8) The employer shall assure that factory charged nonrefillable containers which have no means of pressure indication are weighed at least semi-annually. If a container shows a loss in net weight or more than 5 percent it shall be replaced.

(b)(9) The employer shall assure that inspection and maintenance dates are recorded on the container, on a tag attached to the container, or in a central location. A record of the last semi-annual check shall be maintained until the container is checked again or for the life of the container, whichever is less.

(b)(10) The employer shall train employees designated to inspect, maintain, operate, or repair fixed extinguishing systems and annually review their training to keep them up-to-date in the functions they are to perform.

(b)(11) The employer shall not use chlorobromomethane or carbon tetrachloride as an extinguishing agent where employees may be exposed.

(b)(12) The employer shall assure that systems installed in the presence of corrosive atmospheres are constructed of non-corrosive material or otherwise protected against corrosion.

(b)(13) Automatic detection equipment shall be approved, installed and maintained in accordance with §1910.164.

(b)(14) The employer shall assure that all systems designed for and installed in areas with climatic extremes shall operate effectively at the expected extreme temperatures.

(b)(15) The employer shall assure that at least one manual station is provided for discharge activation of each fixed extinguishing system.

(b)(16) The employer shall assure that manual operating devices are identified as to the hazard against which they will provide protection.

(b)(17) The employer shall provide and assure the use of the personal protective equipment needed for immediate rescue of employees trapped in hazardous atmospheres created by an agent discharge.

(c) Total flooding systems with potential health and safety hazards to employees

(c)(1) The employer shall provide an emergency action plan in accordance with §1910.38 for each area within a workplace that is protected by a total flooding system which provides agent concentrations exceeding the maximum safe levels set forth in paragraphs (b)(5) and (b)(6) of §1910.162.

(c)(2) Systems installed in areas where employees cannot enter during or after the system's operation are exempt from the requirements of paragraph (c) of this section.

(c)(3) On all total flooding systems the employer shall provide a pre-discharge employee alarm which complies with §1910.165, and is capable of being perceived above ambient light or noise levels before the system discharges, which will give employees time to safely exit from the discharge area prior to system discharge.

(c)(4) The employer shall provide automatic actuation of total flooding systems by means of an approved fire detection device installed and interconnected with a pre-discharge employee alarm system to give employees time to safely exit from the discharge area prior to system discharge.

[45 FR 60711, Sept. 12, 1980]

§1910.161 Fixed extinguishing systems, dry chemical

(a) Scope and application This section applies to all fixed extinguishing systems, using dry chemical as the extinguishing agent, installed to meet a particular OSHA standard. These systems shall also comply with §1910.160.

(b) Specific requirements

(b)(1) The employer shall assure that dry chemical agents are compatible with any foams or wetting agents with which they are used.

(b)(2) The employer may not mix together dry chemical extinguishing agents of different compositions. The employer shall assure that dry chemical systems are refilled with the chemical stated on the approval nameplate or an equivalent compatible material.

(b)(3) When dry chemical discharge may obscure vision, the employer shall provide a pre-discharge employee alarm which complies with §1910.165 and which will give employees time to safely exit from the discharge area prior to system discharge.

(b)(4) The employer shall sample the dry chemical supply of all but stored pressure systems at least annually to assure that the dry chemical supply is free of moisture which may cause the supply to cake or form lumps.

(b)(5) The employer shall assure that the rate of application of dry chemicals is such that the designed concentration of the system will be reached within 30 seconds of initial discharge.

[45 FR 60712, Sept. 12, 1980]

§1910.162 Fixed extinguishing systems, gaseous agent

(a) Scope and application

(a)(1) **Scope** This section applies to all fixed extinguishing systems, using a gas as the extinguishing agent, installed to meet a particular OSHA standard. These systems shall also comply with §1910.160. In some cases, the gas may be in a liquid state during storage.

(a)(2) **Application** The requirements of paragraphs (b)(2) and (b)(4) through (b)(6) shall apply only to total flooding systems.

(b) Specific requirements

(b)(1) Agents used for initial supply and replenishment shall be of the type approved for the system's application. Carbon dioxide obtained by dry ice conversion to liquid is not acceptable unless it is processed to remove excess water and oil.

(b)(2) Except during overhaul, the employer shall assure that the designed concentration of gaseous agents is maintained until the fire has been extinguished or is under control.

(b)(3) The employer shall assure that employees are not exposed to toxic levels of gaseous agent or its decomposition products.

(b)(4) The employer shall assure that the designed extinguishing concentration is reached within 30 seconds of initial discharge except for Halon systems which must achieve design concentration within 10 seconds.

(b)(5) The employer shall provide a distinctive pre-discharge employee alarm capable of being perceived above ambient light or noise levels when agent design concentrations exceed the maximum safe level for employee exposure. A pre-discharge employee alarm for alerting employees before system discharge shall be provided on Halon 1211 and carbon dioxide systems with a design concentration of 4 percent or greater and for Halon 1301 systems with a design concentration of 10 percent or greater. The pre-discharge employee alarm shall provide employees time to safely exit the discharge area prior to system discharge.

(b)(6)(i) Where egress from an area cannot be accomplished within one minute, the employer shall not use Halon 1301 in concentrations greater than 7 percent.

(b)(6)(ii) Where egress takes greater than 30 seconds but less than one minute, the employer shall not use Halon 1301 in a concentration greater than 10 percent.

(b)(6)(iii) Halon 1301 concentrations greater than 10 percent are only permitted in areas not normally occupied by employees provided that any employee in the area can escape within 30 seconds. The employer shall assure that no unprotected employees enter the area during agent discharge.

[45 FR 60712, Sept. 12, 1980; 46 FR 24557, May 1, 1981]

§1910.163 Fixed extinguishing systems, water spray and foam

(a) Scope and application This section applies to all fixed extinguishing systems, using water or foam solution as the extinguishing agent, installed to meet a particular OSHA standard. These systems shall also comply with §1910.160. This section does not apply to automatic sprinkler systems which are covered under §1910.159.

(b) Specific requirements

(b)(1) The employer shall assure that foam and water spray systems are designed to be effective in at least controlling fire in the protected area or on protected equipment.

(b)(2) The employer shall assure that drainage of water spray systems is directed away from areas where employees are working and that no emergency egress is permitted through the drainage path.

[45 FR 60712, Sept. 12, 1980]

OTHER FIRE PROTECTION SYSTEMS

§1910.164 Fire detection systems

(a) Scope and application This section applies to all automatic fire detection systems installed to meet the requirements of a particular OSHA standard.

(b) Installation and restoration

(b)(1) The employer shall assure that all devices and equipment constructed and installed to comply with this standard are approved for the purpose for which they are intended.

(b)(2) The employer shall restore all fire detection systems and components to normal operating condition as promptly as possible after each test or alarm. Spare detection devices and components which are normally destroyed in the process of detecting fires shall be available on the premises or from a local supplier in sufficient quantities and locations for prompt restoration of the system.

(c) Maintenance and testing

(c)(1) The employer shall maintain all systems in an operable condition except during repairs or maintenance.

(c)(2) The employer shall assure that fire detectors and fire detection systems are tested and adjusted as often as needed to maintain proper reliability and operating condition except that factory calibrated detectors need not be adjusted after installation.

(c)(3) The employer shall assure that pneumatic and hydraulic operated detection systems installed after January 1, 1981, are equipped with supervised systems.

(c)(4) The employer shall assure that the servicing, maintenance and testing of fire detection systems, including cleaning and necessary sensitivity adjustments are performed by a trained person knowledgeable in the operations and functions of the system.

(c)(5) The employer shall also assure that fire detectors that need to be cleaned of dirt, dust, or other particulates in order to be fully operational are cleaned at regular periodic intervals.

(d) **Protection of fire detectors**

(d)(1) The employer shall assure that fire detection equipment installed outdoors or in the presence of corrosive atmospheres be protected from corrosion. The employer shall provide a canopy, hood, or other suitable protection for detection equipment requiring protection from the weather.

(d)(2) The employer shall locate or otherwise protect detection equipment so that it is protected from mechanical or physical impact which might render it inoperable.

(d)(3) The employer shall assure that detectors are supported independently of their attachment to wires or tubing.

(e) **Response time**

(e)(1) The employer shall assure that fire detection systems installed for the purpose of actuating fire extinguishment or suppression systems shall be designed to operate in time to control or extinguish a fire.

(e)(2) The employer shall assure that fire detection systems installed for the purpose of employee alarm and evacuation be designed and installed to provide a warning for emergency action and safe escape of employees.

(e)(3) The employer shall not delay alarms or devices initiated by fire detector actuation for more than 30 seconds unless such delay is necessary for the immediate safety of employees. When such delay is necessary, it shall be addressed in an emergency action plan meeting the requirements of §1910.38.

(f) **Number, location and spacing of detecting devices** The employer shall assure that the number, spacing and location of fire detectors is based upon design data obtained from field experience, or tests, engineering surveys, the manufacturer's recommendations, or a recognized testing laboratory listing.

[45 FR 60713, Sept. 12, 1980]

§1910.165 Employee alarm systems

(a) **Scope and application**

(a)(1) This section applies to all emergency employee alarms installed to meet a particular OSHA standard. This section does not apply to those discharge or supervisory alarms required on various fixed extinguishing systems or to supervisory alarms on fire suppression, alarm or detection systems unless they are intended to be employee alarm systems.

(a)(2) The requirements in this section that pertain to maintenance, testing and inspection shall apply to all local fire alarm signaling systems used for alerting employees regardless of the other functions of the system.

(a)(3) All pre-discharge employee alarms installed to meet a particular OSHA standard shall meet the requirements of paragraphs (b)(1) through (4), (c), and (d)(1) of this section.

(b) **General requirements**

(b)(1) The employee alarm system shall provide warning for necessary emergency action as called for in the emergency action plan, or for reaction time for safe escape of employees from the workplace or the immediate work area, or both.

(b)(2) The employee alarm shall be capable of being perceived above ambient noise or light levels by all employees in the affected portions of the workplace. Tactile devices may be used to alert those employees who would not otherwise be able to recognize the audible or visual alarm.

(b)(3) The employee alarm shall be distinctive and recognizable as a signal to evacuate the work area or to perform actions designated under the emergency action plan.

(b)(4) The employer shall explain to each employee the preferred means of reporting emergencies, such as manual pull box alarms, public address systems, radio or telephones. The employer shall post emergency telephone numbers near telephones, or employee notice boards, and other conspicuous locations when telephones serve as a means of reporting emergencies. Where a communication system also serves as the employee alarm system, all emergency messages shall have priority over all non-emergency messages.

(b)(5) The employer shall establish procedures for sounding emergency alarms in the workplace. For those employers with 10 or fewer employees in a particular workplace, direct voice communication is an acceptable procedure for sounding the alarm provided all employees can hear the alarm. Such workplaces need not have a back-up system.

(c) **Installation and restoration**

(c)(1) The employer shall assure that all devices, components, combinations of devices or systems constructed and installed to comply with this standard are approved. Steam whistles, air horns, strobe lights or similar lighting devices, or tactile devices meeting the requirements of this section are considered to meet this requirement for approval.

(c)(2) The employer shall assure that all employee alarm systems are restored to normal operating condition as promptly as possible after each test or alarm. Spare alarm devices and components subject to wear or destruction shall be available in sufficient quantities and locations for prompt restoration of the system.

(d) **Maintenance and testing**

(d)(1) The employer shall assure that all employee alarm systems are maintained in operating condition except when undergoing repairs or maintenance.

(d)(2) The employer shall assure that a test of the reliability and adequacy of non-supervised employee alarm systems is made every two months. A different actuation device shall be used in each test of a multi-actuation device system so that no individual device is used for two consecutive tests.

(d)(3) The employer shall maintain or replace power supplies as often as is necessary to assure a fully operational condition. Back-up means of alarm, such as employee runners or telephones, shall be provided when systems are out of service.

(d)(4) The employer shall assure that employee alarm circuitry installed after January 1, 1981, which is capable of being supervised is supervised and that it will provide positive notification to assigned personnel whenever a deficiency exists in the system. The employer shall assure that all supervised employee alarm systems are tested at least annually for reliability and adequacy.

(d)(5) The employer shall assure that the servicing, maintenance and testing of employee alarms are done by persons trained in the designed operation and functions necessary for reliable and safe operation of the system.

(e) **Manual operation** The employer shall assure that manually operated actuation devices for use in conjunction with employee alarms are unobstructed, conspicuous and readily accessible.

[45 FR 60713, Sept. 12, 1980]

Subpart L of §1910 Appendices

Note: The following Appendices to Subpart L, except Appendix E, serve as nonmandatory guidelines to assist employers in complying with the appropriate requirements of Subpart L.

Subpart L of §1910 Appendix A Fire protection

§1910.156 Fire brigades

1. Scope This section does not require an employer to organize a fire brigade. However, if an employer does decide to organize a fire brigade, the requirements of this section apply.

2. Pre-fire planning It is suggested that pre-fire planning be conducted by the local fire department and/or the workplace fire brigade in order for them to be familiar with the workplace and process hazards. Involvement with the local fire department or fire prevention bureau is encouraged to facilitate coordination and cooperation between members of the fire brigade and those who might be called upon for assistance during a fire emergency.

3. Organizational statement In addition to the information required in the organizational statement, §1910.156(b)(1), it is suggested that the organizational statement also contain the following information: a description of the duties that the fire brigade members are expected to perform; the line authority of each fire brigade officer; the number of the fire brigade officers and number of training instructors; and a list and description of the types of awards or recognition that brigade members may be eligible to receive.

4. Physical capability The physical capability requirement applies only to those fire brigade members who perform interior structural fire fighting. Employees who cannot meet the physical capability requirement may still be members of the fire brigade as long as such employees do not perform interior structural fire fighting. It is suggested that fire brigade members who are unable to perform interior structural fire fighting be assigned less stressful and physically demanding fire brigade duties, e.g., certain types of training, recordkeeping, fire prevention inspection and maintenance, and fire pump operations.

Physically capable can be defined as being able to perform those duties specified in the training requirements of §1910.156(c). Physically capable can also be determined by physical performance tests or by a physical examination when the examining physician is aware of the duties that the fire brigade member is expected to perform.

It is also recommended that fire brigade members participate in a physical fitness program. There are many benefits which can be attributed to being physically fit. It is believed that physical fitness may help to reduce the number of sprain and strain injuries as well as contributing to the improvement of the cardiovascular system.

5. Training and education The paragraph on training and education does not contain specific training and education requirements because the type, amount, and frequency of training and education will be as varied as are the purposes for which fire brigades are organized. However, the paragraph does require that training and education be commensurate with those functions that the fire brigade is expected to perform; i.e., those functions specified in the organizational statement. Such a performance requirement provides the necessary flexibility to design a training program which meets the needs of individual fire brigades.

At a minimum, hands-on training is required to be conducted annually for all fire brigade members. However, for those fire brigade members who are expected to perform interior structural fire fighting, some type of training or education session must be provided at least quarterly.

In addition to the required hands-on training, it is strongly recommended that fire brigade members receive other types of training and education such as: classroom instruction, review of emergency action procedures, pre-fire planning, review of special hazards in the workplace, and practice in the use of self-contained breathing apparatus.

It is not necessary for the employer to duplicate the same training or education that a fire brigade member receives as a member of a community volunteer fire department, rescue squad, or similar organization. However, such training or education must have been provided to the fire brigade member within the past year and it must be documented that the fire brigade member has received the training or education. For example: there is no need for a fire brigade member to receive another training class in the use of positive-pressure self-contained breathing apparatus if the fire brigade member has recently completed such training as a member of a community fire department. Instead, the fire brigade member should receive training or education covering other important equipment or duties of the fire brigade as they relate to the workplace hazards, facilities and processes.

It is generally recognized that the effectiveness of fire brigade training and education depends upon the expertise of those providing the training and education as well as the motivation of the fire brigade members. Fire brigade training instructors must receive a higher level of training and education than the fire brigade members they will be teaching. This includes being more knowledgeable about the functions to be performed by the fire brigade and the hazards involved. The instructors should be qualified to train fire brigade members and demonstrate skills in communication, methods of teaching, and motivation. It is important for instructors and fire brigade members alike to be motivated toward the goals of the fire brigade and be aware of the importance of the service that they are providing for the protection of other employees and the workplace.

It is suggested that publications from the International Fire Service Training Association, the National Fire Protection Association (NFPA–1041), the International Society of Fire Service Instructors and other fire training sources be consulted for recommended qualifications of fire brigade training instructors.

In order to be effective, fire brigades must have competent leadership and supervision. It is important for those who supervise the fire brigade during emergency situations, e.g., fire brigade chiefs, leaders, etc., to receive the necessary training and education for supervising fire brigade activities during these hazardous and stressful situations. These fire brigade members with leadership responsibilities should demonstrate skills in strategy and tactics, fire suppression and prevention techniques, leadership principles, pre-fire planning, and safety practices. It is again suggested that fire service training sources be consulted for determining the kinds of training and education which are necessary for those with fire brigade leadership responsibilities.

It is further suggested that fire brigade leaders and fire brigade instructors receive more formalized training and education on a continuing basis by attending classes provided by such training sources as universities and university fire extension services.

The following recommendations should not be considered to be all of the necessary elements of a complete comprehensive training program, but the information may be helpful as a guide in developing a fire brigade training program.

All fire brigade members should be familiar with exit facilities and their location, emergency escape routes for handicapped workers, and the workplace "emergency action plan."

In addition, fire brigade members who are expected to control and extinguish fires in the incipient stage should, at a minimum, be trained in the use of fire extinguishers, standpipes, and other fire equipment they are assigned to use. They should also be aware of first aid medical procedures and procedures for dealing with special hazards to which they may be exposed. Training and education should include both classroom instruction and actual operation of the equipment under simulated emergency conditions. Hands-on type training must be conducted at least annually but some functions should be reviewed more often.

In addition to the above training, fire brigade members who are expected to perform emergency rescue and interior structural fire fighting should, at a minimum, be familiar with the proper techniques in rescue and fire suppression procedures. Training and education should include fire protection courses, classroom training, simulated fire situations including "wet drills" and, when feasible, extinguishment of actual mock fires. Frequency of training or education must be at least quarterly, but some drills or classroom training should be conducted as often as monthly or even weekly to maintain the proficiency of fire brigade members.

There are many excellent sources of training and education that the employer may want to use in developing a training program for the workplace fire brigade. These sources include publications, seminars, and courses offered by universities.

There are also excellent fire school courses by such facilities as Texas A and M University, Delaware State Fire School, Lamar University, and Reno Fire School, that deal with those unique hazards which may be encountered by fire brigades in the oil and chemical industry. These schools, and others, also offer excellent training courses which would be beneficial to fire brigades in other types of industries. These courses should be a continuing part of the training program, and employers are strongly encouraged to take advantage of these excellent resources.

It is also important that fire brigade members be informed about special hazards to which they may be exposed during fire and other emergencies. Such hazards as storage and use areas of flammable liquids and gases, toxic chemicals, water-reactive substances, etc., can pose difficult problems. There must be written procedures developed that describe the actions to be taken in situations involving special hazards. Fire brigade members must be trained in handling these special hazards as well as keeping abreast of any changes that occur in relation to these special hazards.

6. Fire fighting equipment It is important that fire fighting equipment that is in damaged or unserviceable condition be removed from service and replaced. This will prevent fire brigade members from using unsafe equipment by mistake.

Fire fighting equipment, except portable fire extinguishers and respirators, must be inspected at least annually. Portable fire extinguishers and respirators are required to be inspected at least monthly.

7. Protective clothing

(A) General Paragraph (e) of §1910.156 does not require all fire brigade members to wear protective clothing. It is not the intention of these standards to require employers to provide a full ensemble of protective clothing for every fire brigade member without consideration given to the types of hazardous environments to which the fire brigade member might be exposed. It is the intention of these standards to require adequate protection for those fire brigade members who might be exposed to fires in an advanced stage, smoke, toxic gases, and high temperatures. Therefore, the protective clothing requirements only apply to those fire brigade members who perform interior structural fire fighting operations.

Additionally, the protective clothing requirements do not apply to the protective clothing worn during outside fire fighting operations (brush and forest fires, crash crew operations) or other special fire fighting activities. It is important that the protective clothing to be worn during these types of fire fighting operations reflect the hazards which are expected to be encountered by fire brigade members.

(B) Foot and leg protection §1910.156 permits an option to achieve foot and leg protection.

The section recognizes the interdependence of protective clothing to cover one or more parts of the body. Therefore, an option is given so that fire brigade members may meet the foot and leg requirements by either wearing long fire-resistive coats in combination with fully extended boots, or by wearing shorter fire-resistive costs in combination with protective trousers and protective shoes or shorter boots.

(C) Body protection Paragraph (e)(3) of §1910.156 provides an option for fire brigade members to achieve body protection. Fire brigade members may wear a fire-resistive coat in combination with fully extended boots, or they may wear a fire-resistive coat in combination with protective trousers.

Fire-resistive coats and protective trousers meeting all of the requirements contained in NFPA 1971–1975 "Protective Clothing for Structural Fire Fighters," are acceptable as meeting the requirements of this standard.

The lining is required to be permanently attached to the outer shell. However, it is permissible to attach the lining to the outer shell material by stitching in one area such as at the neck. Fastener tape or snap fasteners may be used to secure the rest of the lining to the outer shell to facilitate cleaning. Reference to permanent lining does not refer to a winter liner which is a detachable extra lining used to give added protection to the wearer against the effects of cold weather and wind.

(D) Hand protection The requirements of the paragraph on hand protection may be met by protective gloves or a glove system. A glove system consists of a combination of different gloves. The usual components of a glove system consist of a pair of gloves, which provide thermal insulation to the hands, worn in combination with a second pair of gloves which provide protection against flame, cut, and puncture.

It is suggested that protective gloves provide dexterity and a sense of feel for objects. Criteria and test methods for dexterity are contained in the NIOSH publications, "The Development of Criteria for Firefighters' Gloves; Vol. I: Glove Requirements" and "Vol. II: Glove Criteria and Test Methods." These NIOSH publications also contain a permissible modified version of Federal Test Method 191, Method 5903, (paragraph (3) of Appendix E) for flame resistance when gloves, rather than glove material, are tested for flame resistance.

(E) Head, eye, and face protection Head protective devices which meet the requirements contained in NFPA No. 1972 are acceptable as meeting the requirements of this standard for head protection.

Head protective devices are required to be provided with ear flaps so that the ear flaps will be available if needed. It is recommended that ear protection always be used while fighting interior structural fires.

Many head protective devices are equipped with face shields to protect the eyes and face. These face shields are permissible as meeting the eye and face protection requirements of this paragraph as long as such face shields meet the requirements of §1910.133 of the General Industry Standards.

Additionally, full facepieces, helmets or hoods of approved breathing apparatus which meet the requirements of §1910.134 and paragraph (f) of §1910.156 are also acceptable as meeting the eye and face protection requirements.

It is recommended that a flame resistant protective head covering such as a hood or snood, which will not adversely affect the seal of a respirator facepiece, be worn during interior structural fire fighting operations to protect the sides of the face and hair.

8. Respiratory protective devices Respiratory protection is required to be worn by fire brigade members while working inside buildings or confined spaces where toxic products of combustion or an oxygen deficiency is likely to be present; respirators are also to be worn during emergency situations involving toxic substances. When fire brigade members respond to emergency situations, they may be exposed to unknown contaminants in unknown concentrations. Therefore, it is imperative that fire brigade members wear proper respiratory protective devices during these situations. Additionally, there are many instances where toxic products of combustion are still present during mop-up and overhaul operations. Therefore, fire brigade members should continue to wear respirators during these types of operations.

Self-contained breathing apparatus are not required to be equipped with either a buddy-breathing device or a quick-disconnect valve. However, these accessories may be very useful and are acceptable as long as such accessories do not cause damage to the apparatus, restrict the air flow of the apparatus, or obstruct the normal operation of the apparatus.

Buddy-breathing devices are useful for emergency situations where a victim or another fire brigade member can share the same air supply with the wearer of the apparatus for emergency escape purposes.

The employer is encouraged to provide fire brigade members with an alternative means of respiratory protection to be used only for emergency escape purposes if the self-contained breathing apparatus becomes inoperative. Such alternative means of respiratory protection may be either a buddy-breathing device or an escape self-contained breathing apparatus (ESCBA). The ESCBA is a short-duration respiratory protective device which is approved for only emergency escape purposes. It is suggested that if ESCBA units are used, that they be of at least 5 minutes service life.

Quick-disconnect valves are devices which start the flow of air by insertion of the hose (which leads to the facepiece) into the regulator of self-contained breathing apparatus, and stop the flow of air by disconnecting the hose from the regulator. These devices are particularly useful for those positive-pressure self-contained breathing apparatus which do not have the capability of being switched from the demand to the positive-pressure mode.

The use of a self-contained breathing apparatus where the apparatus can be switched from a demand to a positive-pressure mode is acceptable as long as the apparatus is in the positive-pressure mode when performing interior structural fire fighting operations. Also acceptable are approved respiratory protective devices which have been converted to the positive-pressure type when such modification is accomplished by trained and experienced persons using kits or parts approved by NIOSH and provided by the manufacturer and by following the manufacturer's instructions.

There are situations which require the use of respirators which have a duration of 2 hours or more. Presently, there are no approved positive-pressure apparatus with a rated service life of more than 2 hours. Consequently, negative-pressure self-contained breathing apparatus with a rated service life of more than 2 hours and which have a minimum protection factor of 5,000 as determined by an acceptable quantitative fit test performed on each individual, will be acceptable for use during situations which require long duration apparatus. Long duration apparatus may be needed in such instances as working in tunnels, subway systems, etc. Such negative-pressure breathing apparatus will continue to be acceptable for a maximum of 18 months after a positive-pressure apparatus with the same or longer rated service life of more than 2 hours is certified by NIOSH/MSHA. After this 18 month phase-in period, all self-contained breathing apparatus used for these long duration situations will have to be of the positive-pressure type.

Protection factor (sometimes called fit factor) is defined as the ratio of the contaminant concentrations outside of the respirator to the contaminant concentrations inside the facepiece of the respirator.

$$PF = \frac{\text{Concentration outside respirator}}{\text{Concentration inside facepiece}}$$

Protection factors are determined by quantitative fit tests. An acceptable quantitative fit test should include the following elements:

1. A fire brigade member who is physically and medically capable of wearing respirators, and who is trained in the use of respirators, dons a self-contained breathing apparatus equipped with a device that will monitor the concentration of a contaminant inside the facepiece.

2. The fire brigade member then performs a qualitative fit test to assure the best face to facepiece seal as possible. A qualitative fit test can consist of a negative-pressure test, positive-pressure test, isoamyl acetate vapor (banana oil) test, or an irritant smoke test. For more details on respirator fitting see the NIOSH booklet entitled "A Guide to Industrial Respiratory Protection" June, 1976, and HEW publication No. (NIOSH) 76–189.

3. The wearer should then perform physical activity which reflects the level of work activity which would be expected during fire fighting activities. The physical activity should include simulated fire-ground work activity or physical exercise such as running-in-place, a step test, etc.

4. Without readjusting the apparatus, the wearer is placed in a test atmosphere containing a non-toxic contaminant with a known, constant, concentration.

The protection factor is then determined by dividing the known concentration of the contaminant in the test atmosphere by the concentration of the contaminant inside the facepiece when the following exercises are performed:

(a) Normal breathing with head motionless for one minute;
(b) Deep breathing with head motionless for 30 seconds;
(c) Turning head slowly from side to side while breathing normally, pausing for at least two breaths before changing direction. Continue for at least one minute;
(d) Moving head slowly up and down while breathing normally, pausing for at least two breaths before changing direction. Continue for at least two minutes;
(e) Reading from a prepared text, slowly and clearly, and loudly enough to be heard and understood. Continue for one minute; and
(f) Normal breathing with head motionless for at least one minute. The protection factor which is determined must be at least 5,000. The quantitative fit test should be conducted at least three times. It is acceptable to conduct all three tests on the same day. However, there should be at least one hour between tests to reflect the protection afforded by the apparatus during different times of the day.

The above elements are not meant to be a comprehensive, technical description of a quantitative fit test protocol. However, quantitative fit test procedures which include these elements are acceptable for determining protection factors. Procedures for a quantitative fit test are required to be available for inspection by the Assistant Secretary or authorized representative.

Organizations such as Los Alamos Scientific Laboratory, Lawrence Livermore Laboratory, NIOSH, and American National Standards Institute (ANSI) are excellent sources for additional information concerning qualitative and quantitative fit testing.

§1910.157 Portable fire extinguishers

1. Scope and application The scope and application of this section is written to apply to three basic types of workplaces. First, there are those workplaces where the employer has chosen to evacuate all employees from the workplace at the time of a fire emergency. Second, there are those workplaces where the employer has chosen to permit certain employees to fight fires and to evacuate all other non-essential employees at the time of a fire emergency. Third, there are those workplaces where the employer has chosen to permit all employees in the workplace to use portable fire extinguishers to fight fires.

The section also addresses two kinds of work areas. The entire workplace can be divided into outside (exterior) work areas and inside (interior) work areas. This division of the workplace into two areas is done in recognition of the different types of hazards employees may be exposed to during fire fighting operations. Fires in interior workplaces, pose a greater hazard to employees; they can produce greater exposure to quantities of smoke, toxic gases, and heat because of the capability of a building or structure to contain or entrap these products of combustion until the building can be ventilated. Exterior work areas, normally open to the environment, are somewhat less hazardous, because the products of combustion are generally carried away by the thermal column of the fire. Employees also have a greater selection of evacuation routes if it is necessary to abandon fire fighting efforts.

In recognition of the degree of hazard present in the two types of work areas, the standards for exterior work areas are somewhat less restrictive in regards to extinguisher distribution. Paragraph (a) explains this by specifying which paragraphs in the section apply.

2. Portable fire extinguisher exemptions In recognition of the three options given to employers in regard to the amount of employee evacuation to be carried out, the standards permit certain exemptions based on the number of employees expected to use fire extinguishers.

Where the employer has chosen to totally evacuate the workplace at the time of a fire emergency and when fire extinguishers are not provided, the requirements of this section do not apply to that workplace.

Where the employer has chosen to partially evacuate the workplace or the effected area at the time of a fire emergency and has permitted certain designated employees to remain behind to operate critical plant operations or to fight fires with extinguishers, then the employer is exempt from the distribution requirements of this section. Employees who will be remaining behind to perform incipient fire fighting or members of a fire brigade must be trained in their duties. The training must result in the employees becoming familiar with the locations of fire extinguishers. Therefore, the employer must locate the extinguishers in convenient locations where the employees know they can be found. For example, they could be mounted in the fire truck or cart that the fire brigade uses when it responds to a fire emergency. They can also be distributed as set forth in the National Fire Protection Association's Standard No. 10, "Portable Fire Extinguishers."

Where the employer has decided to permit all employees in the workforce to use fire extinguishers, then the entire OSHA section applies.

3. Portable fire extinguisher mounting Previous standards for mounting fire extinguishers have been criticized for requiring specific mounting locations. In recognition of this criticism, the standard has been rewritten to permit as much flexibility in extinguisher mounting as is acceptable to assure that fire extinguishers are available when needed and that employees are not subjected to injury hazards when they try to obtain an extinguisher.

It is the intent of OSHA to permit the mounting of extinguishers in any location that is accessible to employees without the use of portable devices such as a ladder. This limitation is necessary because portable devices can be moved or taken from the place where they are needed and, therefore, might not be available at the time of an emergency.

Employers are given as much flexibility as possible to assure that employees can obtain extinguishers as fast as possible. For example, an acceptable method of mounting extinguishers in areas where fork lift trucks or tow-motors are used is to mount the units on retractable boards which, by means of counterweighting, can be raised above the level where they could be struck by vehicular traffic. When needed, they can be lowered quickly for use. This method of mounting can also reduce vandalism and unauthorized use of extinguishers. The extinguishers may also be mounted as outlined in the National Fire Protection Association's Standard No. 10, "Portable Fire Extinguishers."

4. Selection and distribution The employer is responsible for the proper selection and distribution of fire extinguishers and the determination of the necessary degree of protection. The selection and distribution of fire extinguishers must reflect the type and class of fire hazards associated with a particular workplace.

Extinguishers for protecting Class A hazards may be selected from the following types: water, foam, loaded stream, or multipurpose dry chemical. Extinguishers for protecting Class B hazards may be selected from the following types: Halon 1301, Halon 1211, carbon dioxide, dry chemicals, foam, or loaded stream. Extinguishers for Class C hazards may be selected from the following types: Halon 1301, Halon 1211, carbon dioxide, or dry chemical.

Combustible metal (Class D hazards) fires pose a different type of fire problem in the workplace. Extinguishers using water, gas, or certain dry chemicals cannot extinguish or control this type of fire. Therefore, certain metals have specific dry powder extinguishing agents which can extinguish or control this type of fire. Those agents which have been specifically approved for use on certain metal fires provide the best protection; however, there are also some "universal" type agents which can be used effectively on a variety of combustible metal fires if necessary. The "universal" type agents include: Foundry flux, Lith-X powder, TMB liquid, pyromet powder, TEC powder, dry talc, dry graphite powder, dry sand, dry sodium chloride, dry soda ash, lithium chloride, zirconium silicate, and dry dolomite.

Water is not generally accepted as an effective extinguishing agent for metal fires. When applied to hot burning metal, water will break down into its basic atoms of oxygen and hydrogen. This chemical breakdown contributes to the combustion of the metal. However, water is also a good universal coolant and can be used on some combustible metals, but only under proper conditions and application, to reduce the temperature of the burning metal below the ignition point. For example, automatic deluge systems in magnesium plants can discharge such large quantities of water on burning magnesium that the fire will be extinguished. The National Fire Protection Association has specific standards for this type of automatic sprinkler system. Further information on the control of metal fires with water can be found in the National Fire Protection Association's Fire Protection Handbook.

An excellent source of selection and distribution criteria is found in the National Fire Protection Association's Standard No. 10. Other sources of information include the National Safety Council and the employer's fire insurance carrier.

5. Substitution of standpipe systems for portable fire extinguishers The employer is permitted to substitute acceptable standpipe systems for portable fire extinguishers under certain circumstances. It is necessary to assure that any substitution will provide the same coverage that portable units provide. This means that fire hoses, because of their limited portability, must be spaced throughout the protected area so that they can reach around obstructions such as columns, machinery, etc. and so that they can reach into closets and other enclosed areas.

6. Inspection, maintenance and testing The ultimate responsibility for the inspection, maintenance and testing of portable fire extinguishers lies with the employer. The actual inspection, maintenance, and testing may, however, be conducted by outside contractors with whom the employer has arranged to do the work. When contracting for such work, the employer should assure that the contractor is capable of performing the work that is needed to comply with this standard.

If the employer should elect to perform the inspection, maintenance, and testing requirements of this section in-house, then the employer must make sure that those persons doing the work have been trained to do the work and to recognize problem areas which could cause an extinguisher to be inoperable. The National Fire Protection Association provides excellent guidelines in its standard for portable fire extinguishers. The employer may also check with the manufacturer of the unit that has been purchased and obtain guidelines on inspection, maintenance, and testing. Hydrostatic testing is a process that should be left to contractors or individuals using suitable facilities and having the training necessary to perform the work.

Anytime the employer has removed an extinguisher from service to be checked or repaired, alternate equivalent protection must be provided. Alternate equivalent protection could include replacing the extinguisher with one or more units having equivalent or equal ratings, posting a fire watch, restricting the unprotected area from employee exposure, or providing a hose system ready to operate.

7. Hydrostatic testing As stated before, the employer may contract for hydrostatic testing. However, if the employer wishes to provide the testing service, certain equipment and facilities must be available. Employees should be made aware of the hazards associated with hydrostatic testing and the importance of using proper guards and water pressures. Severe injury can result if extinguisher shells fail violently under hydrostatic pressure.

Employers are encouraged to use contractors who can perform adequate and reliable service. Firms which have been certified by the Materials Transportation Board (MTB) of the U.S. Department of Transportation (DOT) or State licensed extinguisher servicing firms or recognized by the National Association of Fire Equipment Distributors in Chicago, Illinois, are generally acceptable for performing this service.

8. Training and education This part of the standard is of the utmost importance to employers and employees if the risk of injury or death due to extinguisher use is to be reduced. If an employer is going to permit an employee to fight a workplace fire of any size, the employer must make sure that the employee knows everything necessary to assure the employee's safety.

Training and education can be obtained through many channels. Often, local fire departments in larger cities have fire prevention bureaus or similar organizations which can provide basic fire prevention training programs. Fire insurance companies will have data and information available. The National Fire Protection Association and the National Safety Council will provide, at a small cost, publications that can be used in a fire prevention program.

Actual fire fighting training can be obtained from various sources in the country. The Texas A & M University, the University of Maryland's Fire and Rescue Institute, West Virginia University's Fire Service Extension, Iowa State University's Fire Service Extension and other State training schools and land grant colleges have fire fighting programs directed to industrial applications. Some manufacturers of extinguishers, such as the Ansul Company and Safety First, conduct fire schools for customers in the proper use of extinguishers. Several large corporations have taken time to develop their own on-site training programs which expose employees to the actual "feeling" of fire fighting. Simulated fires for training of employees in the proper use of extinguishers are also an acceptable part of a training program.

In meeting the requirements of this section, the employer may also provide educational materials, without classroom instruction, through the use of employee notice campaigns using instruction sheets or flyers or similar types of informal programs. The employer must make sure that employees are trained and educated to recognize not only what type of fire is being fought and how to fight it, but also when it is time to get away from it and leave fire suppression to more experienced fire fighters.

§1910.158 Standpipe and hose systems

1. Scope and application This section has been written to provide adequate coverage of those standpipe and hose systems that an employer may install in the workplace to meet the requirements of a particular OSHA standard. For example, OSHA permits the substitution of hose systems for portable fire extinguishers in §1910.157. If an employer chooses to provide hose systems instead of portable Class A fire extinguishers, then those hose systems used for substitution would have to meet the applicable requirements of §1910.157. All other standpipe and hose systems not used as a substitute would be exempt from these requirements.

The section specifically exempts Class I large hose systems. By large hose systems, OSHA means those 2½"; (6.3 cm) hose lines that are usually associated with fire departments of the size that provide their own water supply through fire apparatus. When the fire gets to the size that outside protection of that degree is necessary, OSHA believes that in most industries employees will have been evacuated from the fire area and the "professional" fire fighters will take control.

2. Protection of standpipes Employers must make sure that standpipes are protected so that they can be relied upon during a fire emergency. This means protecting the pipes from mechanical and physical damage. There are various means for protecting the equipment such as, but not limited to, enclosing the supply piping in the construction of the building, locating the standpipe in an area which is inaccessible to vehicles, or locating the standpipe in a stairwell.

3. Hose covers and cabinets The employer should keep fire protection hose equipment in cabinets or inside protective covers which will protect it from the weather elements, dirt or other damaging sources. The use of protective covers must be easily removed or opened to assure that hose and nozzle are accessible. When the employer places hose in a cabinet, the employer must make sure that the hose and nozzle are accessible to employees without subjecting them to injury. In order to make sure that the equipment is readily accessible, the employer must also make sure that the cabinets used to store equipment are kept free of obstructions and other equipment which may interfere with the fast distribution of the fire hose stored in the cabinet.

4. Hose outlets and connections. The employer must assure that employees who use standpipe and hose systems can reach the hose rack and hose valve without the use of portable equipment such as ladders. Hose reels are encouraged for use because one employee can retrieve the hose, charge it, and place it into service without much difficulty.

5. Hose When the employer elects to provide small hose in lieu of portable fire extinguishers, those hose stations being used for the substitution must have hose attached and ready for service. However, if more than the necessary amount of small hose outlets are provided, hose does not have to be attached to those outlets that would provide redundant coverage. Further, where the installation of hose on outlets may expose the hose to extremely cold climates, the employer may store the hose in houses or similar protective areas and connect it to the outlet when needed.

There is approved lined hose available that can be used to replace unlined hose which is stored on racks in cabinets. The lined hose is constructed so that it can be folded and placed in cabinets in the same manner as unlined hose.

Hose is considered to be unserviceable when it deteriorates to the extent that it can no longer carry water at the required pressure and flow rates. Dry rotted linen or hemp hose, cross threaded couplings, and punctured hose are examples of unserviceable hose.

6. Nozzles Variable stream nozzles can provide useful variations in water flow and spray patterns during fire fighting operations and they are recommended for employee use. It is recommended that 100 psi (700kPa) nozzle pressure be used to provide good flow patterns for variable stream nozzles. The most desirable attribute for nozzles is the ability of the nozzle person to shut off the water flow at the nozzle when it is necessary. This can be accomplished in many ways. For example, a shut-off nozzle with a lever or rotation of the nozzle to stop flow would be effective, but in other cases a simple globe valve placed between a straight stream nozzle and the hose could serve the same purpose. For straight stream nozzles 50 psi nozzle pressure is recommended. The intent of this standard is to protect the employee from "run-away" hoses if it becomes necessary to drop a pressurized hose line and retreat from the fire front and other related hazards.

7. Design and installation Standpipe and hose systems designed and installed in accordance with NFPA Standard No. 14, "Standpipe and Hose Systems," are considered to be in compliance with this standard.

§1910.159 Automatic sprinkler systems

1. Scope and application This section contains the minimum requirements for design, installation and maintenance of sprinkler systems that are needed for employee safety. The Occupational Safety and Health Administration is aware of the fact that the National Board of Fire Underwriters is no longer an active organization, however, sprinkler systems still exist that were designed and installed in accordance with that organization's standards. Therefore, OSHA will recognize sprinkler systems designed to, and maintained in accordance with, NBFU and earlier NFPA standards.

2. Exemptions In an effort to assure that employers will continue to use automatic sprinkler systems as the primary fire protection system in workplaces, OSHA is exempting from coverage those systems not required by a particular OSHA standard and which have been installed in workplaces solely for the purpose of protecting property. Many of these types of systems are installed in areas or buildings with little or no employee exposure. An example is those warehouses where employees may enter occasionally to take inventory or move stock. Some employers may choose to shut down those systems which are not specifically required by OSHA rather than upgrade them to comply with the standards. OSHA does not intend to regulate such systems. OSHA only intends to regulate those systems which are installed to comply with a particular OSHA standard.

3. Design There are two basic types of sprinkler system design. Pipe schedule designed systems are based on pipe schedule tables developed to protect hazards with standard sized pipe, number of sprinklers, and pipe lengths. Hydraulic designed systems are based on an engineered design of pipe size which will produce a given water density or flow rate at any particular point in the system. Either design can be used to comply with this standard.

The National Fire Protection Association's Standard No. 13, "Automatic Sprinkler Systems," contains the tables needed to design and install either type of system. Minimum water supplies, densities, and pipe sizes are given for all types of occupancies.

The employer may check with a reputable fire protection engineering consultant or sprinkler design company when evaluating existing systems or designing a new installation.

With the advent of new construction materials for the manufacute of sprinkler pipe, materials, other than steel have been approved for use as sprinkler pipe. Selection of pipe material should be made on the basis of the type of installation and the acceptability of the material to local fire and building officials where such systems may serve more than one purpose.

Before new sprinkler systems are placed into service, an acceptance test is to be conducted. The employer should invite the installer, designer, insurance representative, and a local fire official to witness the test. Problems found during the test are to be corrected before the system is placed into service.

4. Maintenance It is important that any sprinkler system maintenance be done only when there is minimal employee exposure to the fire hazard. For example, if repairs or changes to the system are to be made, they should be made during those hours when employees are not working or are not occupying that portion of the workplace protected by the portion of the system which has been shut down.

The procedures for performing a flow test via a main drain test or by the use of an inspector's test valve can be obtained from the employer's fire insurance company or from the National Fire Protection Association's Standard No. 13A, "Sprinkler System, Maintenance."

5. Water supplies The water supply to a sprinkler system is one of the most important factors an employer should consider when evaluating a system. Obviously, if there is no water supply, the system is useless. Water supplies can be lost for various reasons such as improperly closed valves, excessive demand, broken water mains, and broken fire pumps. The employer must be able to determine if or when this type of condition exists either by performing a main drain test or visual inspection. Another problem may be an inadequate water supply. For example, a light hazard occupancy may, through rehabilitation or change in tenants, become an ordinary or high hazard occupancy. In such cases, the existing water supply may not be able to provide the pressure or duration necessary for proper protection. Employers must assure that proper design and tests have been made to assure an adequate water supply. These tests can be arranged through the employer's fire insurance carrier or through a local sprinkler maintenance company or through the local fire prevention organization.

Anytime the employer must shut down the primary water supply for a sprinkler system, the standard requires that equivalent protection be provided. Equivalent protection may include a fire watch with extinguishers or hose lines in place and manned, or a secondary water supply such as a tank truck and pump, or a tank or fire pond with fire pumps, to protect the areas where the primary water supply is limited or shut down. The employer may also require evacuation of the workplace and have an emergency action plan which specifies such action.

6. Protection of piping Piping which is exposed to corrosive atmospheres, either chemical or natural, can become defective to the extent that it is useless. Employers must assure that piping is protected from corrosion by its material of construction, e.g., stainless steel, or by a protective coating, e.g., paint.

7. Sprinklers When an employer finds it necessary to replace sprinkler system components or otherwise change a sprinkler's design, employer should make a complete fire protection engineering survey of that part of the system being changed. This review should assure that the changes to the system will not alter the effectiveness of the system as it is presently designed. Water supplies, densities and flow characteristics should be maintained.

8. Protection of sprinklers All components of the system must be protected from mechanical impact damage. This can be achieved with the use of mechanical guards or screens or by locating components in areas where physical contact is impossible or limited.

9. Sprinkler alarms The most recognized sprinkler alarm is the water motor gong or bell that sounds when water begins to flow through the system. This is not however, the only type of acceptable water flow alarm. Any alarm that gives an indication that water is flowing through the system is acceptable. For example, a siren, a whistle, a flashing light, or similar alerting device which can transmit a signal to the necessary persons would be acceptable. The purpose of the alarm is to alert persons that the system is operating, and that some type of planned action is necessary.

10. Sprinkler spacing For a sprinkler system to be effective there must be an adequate discharge of water spray from the sprinkler head. Any obstructions which hinder the designed density or spray pattern of the water may create unprotected areas which can cause fire to spread. There are some sprinklers that, because of the system's design, are deflected to specific areas. This type of obstruction is acceptable if the system's design takes it into consideration in providing adequate coverage.

§1910.160 Fixed extinguishing systems, general

1. Scope and application This section contains the general requirements that are applicable to all fixed extinguishing systems installed to meet OSHA standards. It also applies to those fixed extinguishing systems, generally total flooding, which are not required by OSHA, but which, because of the agent's discharge, may expose employees to hazardous concentrations of extinguishing agents or combustion by-products. Employees who work around fixed extinguishing systems must be warned of the possible hazards associated with the system and its agent. For example, fixed dry chemical extinguishing systems may generate a large enough cloud of dry chemical particles that employees may become visually disoriented. Certain gaseous agents can expose employees to hazardous by-products of combustion when the agent comes into contact with hot metal or other hot surface. Some gaseous agents may be present in hazardous concentrations when the system has totally discharged because an extra rich concentration is necessary to extinguish deep-seated fires. Certain local application systems may be designed to discharge onto the flaming surface of a liquid, and it is possible that the liquid can splatter when hit with the discharging agent. All of these hazards must be determined before the system is placed into operation, and must be discussed with employees.

Based on the known toxicological effects of agents such as carbon tetrachloride and chlorobromomethane, OSHA is not permitting the use of these agents in areas where employees can be exposed to the agent or its side effects. However, chlorobromomethane has been accepted and may be used as an explosion suppression agent in unoccupied spaces. OSHA is permitting the use of this agent only in areas where employees will not be exposed.

2. Distinctive alarm signals A distinctive alarm signal is required to indicate that a fixed system is discharging. Such a signal is necessary on those systems where it is not immediately apparent that the system is discharging. For example, certain gaseous agents make a loud noise when they discharge. In this case no alarm signal is necessary. However, where systems are located in remote locations or away from the general work area and where it is possible that a system could discharge without anyone knowing that it is doing so, then a distinctive alarm is necessary to warn employees of the hazards that may exist. The alarm can be a bell, gong, whistle, horn, flashing light, or any combination of signals as long as it is identifiable as a discharge alarm.

3. Maintenance The employer is responsible for the maintenance of all fixed systems, but this responsibility does not preclude the use of outside contractors to do such work. New systems should be subjected to an acceptance test before placed in service. The employer should invite the installer, designer, insurance representative and others to witness the test. Problems found during the test need to be corrected before the system is considered operational.

4. Manual discharge stations There are instances, such as for mechanical reasons and others, where the standards call for a manual back-up activation device. While the location of this device is not specified in the standard, the employer should assume that the device should be located where employees can easily reach it. It could, for example, be located along the main means of egress from the protected area so that employees could activate the system as they evacuate the work area.

5. Personal protective equipment The employer is required to provide the necessary personal protective equipment to rescue employees who may be trapped in a totally flooded environment which may be hazardous to their health. This equipment would normally include a positive-pressure self-contained breathing apparatus and any necessary first aid equipment. In cases where the employer can assure the prompt arrival of the local fire department or plant emergency personnel which can provide the equipment, this can be considered as complying with the standards.

§1910.161 Fixed extinguishing systems, dry chemical

1. Scope and application The requirements of this section apply only to dry chemical systems. These requirements are to be used in conjunction with the requirements of §1910.160.

2. Maintenance The employer is responsible for assuring that dry chemical systems will operate effectively. To do this, periodic maintenance is necessary. One test that must be conducted during the maintenance check is one which will determine if the agent has remained free of moisture. If an agent absorbs any moisture, it may tend to cake and thereby clog the system. An easy test for acceptable moisture content is to take a lump of dry chemical from the container and drop it from a height of four inches. If the lump crumbles into fine particles, the agent is acceptable.

§1910.162 Fixed extinguishing systems, gaseous agent

1. Scope and application This section applies only to those systems which use gaseous agents. The requirements of §1910.160 also apply to the gaseous agent systems covered in this section.

2. Design concentrations Total flooding gaseous systems are based on the volume of gas which must be discharged in order to produce a certain designed concentration of gas in an enclosed area. The concentration needed to extinguish a fire depends on several factors including the type of fire hazard and the amount of gas expected to leak away from the area during discharge. At times it is necessary to "super-saturate" a work area to provide for expected leakage from the enclosed area. In such cases, employers must assure that the flooded area has been ventilated before employees are permitted to reenter the work area without protective clothing and respirators.

3. Toxic decomposition Certain halogenated hydrocarbons will break down or decompose when they are combined with high temperatures found in the fire environment. The products of the decomposition can include toxic elements or compounds. For example, when Halon 1211 is placed into contact with hot metal it will break down and form bromide or fluoride fumes. The employer must find out which toxic products may result from decomposition of a particular agent from the manufacturer, and take the necessary precautions to prevent employee exposure to the hazard.

§1910.163 Fixed extinguishing systems, water spray and foam

1. Scope and application This section applies to those systems that use water spray or foam. The requirements of §1910.160 also apply to this type of system.

2. Characteristics of foams When selecting the type of foam for a specific hazard, the employer should consider the following limitations of some foams.

a. Some foams are not acceptable for use on fires involving flammable gases and liquefied gases with boiling points below ambient workplace temperatures. Other foams are not effective when used on fires involving polar solvent liquids.

b. Any agent using water as part of the mixture should not be used on fire involving combustible metals unless it is applied under proper conditions to reduce the temperature of burning metal below the ignition temperature. The employer should use only those foams that have been tested and accepted for this application by a recognized independent testing laboratory.

c. Certain types of foams may be incompatible and break down when they are mixed together.

d. For fires involving water miscible solvents, employers should use only those foams tested and approved for such use. Regular protein foams may not be effective on such solvents.

Whenever employers provide a foam or water spray system, drainage facilities must be provided to carry contaminated water or foam overflow away from the employee work areas and egress routes. This drainage system should drain to a central impounding area where it can be collected and disposed of properly. Other government agencies may have regulations concerning environmental considerations.

§1910.164 Fire detection systems

1. Installation and restoration Fire detection systems must be designed by knowledgeable engineers or other professionals, with expertise in fire detection systems and when the systems are installed, there should be an acceptance test performed on the system to insure it operates properly. The manufacturer's recommendations for system design should be consulted. While entire systems may not be approved, each component used in the system is required to be approved. Custom fire detection systems should be designed by knowledgeable fire protection or electrical engineers who are familiar with the workplace hazards and conditions. Some systems may only have one or two individual detectors for a small workplace, but good design and installation is still important. An acceptance test should be performed on all systems, including these smaller systems.

OSHA has a requirement that spare components used to replace those which may be destroyed during an alarm situation be available in sufficient quantities and locations for prompt restoration of the system. This does not mean that the parts or components have to be stored at the workplace. If the employer can assure that the supply of parts is available in the local community or the general metropolitan area of the workplace, then the requirements for storage and availability have been met. The intent is to make sure that the alarm system is fully operational when employees are occupying the workplace, and that when the system operates it can be returned to full service the next day or sooner.

2. Supervision Fire detection systems should be supervised. The object of supervision is detection of any failure of the circuitry, and the employer should use any method that will assure that the system's circuits are operational. Electrically operated sensors for air pressure, fluid pressure, or electrical circuits, can provide effective monitoring and are the typical types of supervision.

3. Protection of fire detectors Fire detectors must be protected from corrosion either by protective coatings, by being manufactured from non-corrosive materials or by location. Detectors must also be protected from mechanical impact damage, either by suitable cages or metal guards where such hazards are present, or by locating them above or out of contact with materials or equipment which may cause damage.

4. Number, location, and spacing of detectors This information can be obtained from the approval listing for detectors or NFPA standards. It can also be obtained from fire protection engineers or consultants or manufacturers of equipment who have access to approval listings and design methods.

§1910.165 Employee alarm systems

1. Scope and application This section is intended to apply to employee alarm systems used for all types of employee emergencies except those which occur so quickly and at such a rapid rate (e.g., explosions) that any action by the employee is extremely limited following detection.

In small workplaces with 10 or less employees the alarm system can be by direct voice communication (shouting) where any one individual can quickly alert all other employees. Radio may be used to transmit alarms from remote workplaces where telephone service is not available, provided that radio messages will be monitored by emergency services, such as fire, police or others, to insure alarms are transmitted and received.

2. Alarm signal alternatives In recognition of physically impaired individuals, OSHA is accepting various methods of giving alarm signals. For example, visual, tactile or audible alarm signals are acceptable methods for giving alarms to employees. Flashing lights or vibrating devices can be used in areas where the employer has hired employees with hearing or vision impairments. Vibrating devices, air fans, or other tactile devices can be used where visually and hearing impaired employees work. Employers are cautioned that certain frequencies of flashing lights have been claimed to initiate epileptic seizures in some employees and that this fact should be considered when selecting an alarm device. Two way radio communications would be most appropriate for transmitting emergency alarms in such workplaces which may be remote or where telephones may not be available.

3. Reporting alarms Employee alarms may require different means of reporting, depending on the workplace involved. For example, in small workplaces, a simple shout throughout the workplace may be sufficient to warn employees of a fire or other emergency. In larger workplaces, more sophisticated equipment is necessary so that entire plants or high-rise buildings are not evacuated for one small emergency. In remote areas, such as pumping plants, radio communication with a central base station may be necessary. The goal of this standard is to assure that all employees who need to know that an emergency exists can be notified of the emergency. The method of transmitting the alarm should reflect the situation found at the workplace.

Personal radio transmitters, worn by an individual, can be used where the individual may be working such as in a remote location. Such personal radio transmitters shall send a distinct signal and should clearly indicate who is having an emergency, the location, and the nature of the emergency. All radio transmitters need a feedback system to assure that the emergency alarm is sent to the people who can provide assistance.

For multi-story buildings or single story buildings with interior walls for subdivisions, the more traditional alarm systems are recommended for these types of workplaces. Supervised telephone or manual fire alarm or pull box stations with paging systems to transmit messages throughout the building is the recommended alarm system. The alarm box stations should be available within a travel distance of 200 feet. Water flow detection on a sprinkler system, fire detection systems (guard's supervisory station) or tour signal (watchman's service), or other related systems may be part of the overall system. The paging system may be used for nonemergency operations provided the emergency messages and uses will have precedence over all other uses of the system.

4. Supervision The requirements for supervising the employee alarm system circuitry and power supply may be accomplished in a variety of ways. Typically, electrically operated sensors for air pressure, fluid pressure, steam pressure, or electrical continuity of circuitry may be used to continuously monitor the system to assure it is operational and to identify trouble in the system and give a warning signal.

[45 FR 60715, Sept. 12, 1980; 46 FR 24557, May 1, 1981]

Subpart L of §1910 Appendix B National consensus standards

The following table contains a cross-reference listing of those current national consensus standards which contains information and guidelines that would be considered acceptable in complying with requirements in the specific sections of Subpart L.

Subpart L section	National consensus standard
1910.156	ANSI/NFPA No. 1972; Structural Fire Fighter's Helmets.
	ANSI Z88.5 American National Standard, Practice for Respirator Protection for the Fire Service.
	ANSI/NFPA No. 1971, Protective Clothing for Structural Fire Fighters.
	NFPA No. 1041, Fire Service Instructor Professional Qualifications.
1910.157	ANSI/NFPA No. 10, Portable Fire Extinguishers.
1910.158	ANSI/NFPA No. 18, Wetting Agents.
	ANSI/NFPA No. 20, Centrifugal Fire Pumps.
	NFPA No. 21, Steam Fire Pumps.
	ANSI/NFPA No. 22, Water Tanks.
	NFPA No. 24, Outside Protection.
	NFPA No. 26, Supervision of Valves.
	NFPA No. 13E, Fire Department Operations in Properties Protected by Sprinkler, Standpipe Systems.
	ANSI/NFPA No. 194, Fire Hose Connections.
	NFPA No. 197, Initial Fire Attack, Training for.
	NFPA No. 1231, Water Supplies for Suburban and Rural Fire Fighting.
1910.159	ANSI-NFPA No. 13, Sprinkler Systems.
	NFPA No. 13A, Sprinkler Systems, Maintenance.
	ANSI/NFPA No. 18, Wetting Agents.
	ANSI/NFPA No. 20, Centrifugal Fire Pumps.
	ANSI/NFPA No. 22, Water Tanks.
	NFPA No. 24, Outside Protection.
	NFPA No. 26, Supervision of Valves.
	ANSI/NFPA No. 72B, Auxiliary Signaling Systems.
	NFPA No. 1231, Water Supplies for Suburban and Rural Fire Fighting.
1910.160	ANSI/NFPA No. 11, Foam Systems.
	ANSI/NFPA 11A, High Expansion Foam Extinguishing Systems.
	ANSI/NFPA No. 11B, Synthetic Foam and Combined Agent Systems.
	ANSI/NFPA No. 12, Carbon Dioxide Systems.
	ANSI/NFPA No. 12A, Halon 1301 Systems.
	ANSI/NFPA No. 12B, Halon 1211 Systems.
	ANSI/NFPA No. 15, Water Spray Systems.
	ANSI/NFPA 16 Foam-Water Spray Systems.
	ANSI/NFPA No. 17, Dry Chemical Systems.
	ANSI/NFPA 69, Explosion Suppression Systems.
1910.161	ANSI/NFPA No. 11B, Synthetic Foam and Combined Agent Systems.
	ANSI/NFPA No. 17, Dry Chemical Systems.
1910.162	ANSI/NFPA No. 12, Carbon Dioxide Systems.
	ANSI/NFPA No. 12A, Halon 1211 Systems.
	ANSI/NFPA No. 12B, Halon 1301 Systems.
	ANSI/NFPA No. 69, Explosion Suppression Systems.

Subpart L section	National consensus standard
1910.163	ANSI/NFPA No. 11, Foam Extinguishing Systems.
	ANSI/NFPA No. 11A, High Expansion Foam Extinguishing Systems.
	ANSI/NFPA No. 11B, Synthetic Foam and Combined Agent Systems.
	ANSI/NFPA No. 15, Water Spray Fixed Systems.
	ANSI/NFPA No. 16, Foam-Water Spray Systems.
	ANSI/NFPA No. 18, Wetting Agents.
	NFPA No. 26, Supervision of Valves.
1910.164	ANSI/NFPA No. 71, Central Station Signaling Systems.
	ANSI/NFPA No. 72A, Local Protective Signaling Systems.
	ANSI/NFPA No. 72B, Auxiliary Signaling Systems.
	ANSI/NFPA No. 72D, Proprietary Protective Signaling Systems.
	ANSI/NFPA No. 72E, Automatic Fire Detectors.
	ANSI/NFPA No. 101, Life Safety Code.
1910.165	ANSI/NFPA No. 71, Central Station Signaling Systems.
	ANSI/NFPA No. 72A, Local Protective Signaling Systems.
	ANSI/NFPA No. 72B, Auxiliary Protective Signaling Systems.
	ANSI/NFPA No. 72C, Remote Station Protective Signaling Systems.
	ANSI/NFPA No. 72D, Proprietary Protective Signaling Systems.
	ANSI/NFPA No. 101, Life Safety Code.
Metric Conversion	ANSI/ASTM No. E380, American National Standard for Metric Practice.

NFPA standards are available from the National Fire Protection Association, Batterymarch Park, Quincy, MA 02269.
ANSI Standards are available from the American National Standards Institute, 1430 Broadway, New York, NY 10018.

[45 FR 60715, Sept. 12, 1980, as amended at 58 FR 35309, June 30, 1993]

Subpart L of §1910 Appendix C Fire protection references for further information

I. Appendix general references. The following references provide information which can be helpful in understanding the requirements contained in all of the sections of Subpart L:

A. Fire Protection Handbook, National Fire Protection Association, Batterymarch Park, Quincy, MA 02269.

B. Accident Prevention Manual for Industrial Operations, National Safety Council; 425 North Michigan Avenue, Chicago, IL 60611.

C. Various associations also publish information which may be useful in understanding these standards. Examples of these associations are: Fire Equipment Manufacturers Association (FEMA) of Arlington, VA 22204 and the National Association of Fire Equipment Distributors (NAFED) of Chicago, IL 60601.

II. Appendix references applicable to individual sections. The following references are grouped according to individual sections contained in Subpart L. These references provide information which may be helpful in understanding and implementing the standards of each section of Subpart L.

A. §1910.156. Fire brigades:

1. Private Fire Brigades, NFPA 27; National Fire Protection Association, Batterymarch Park, Quincy, MA 02269.
2. Initial Fire Attack, Training Standard On, NFPA 197; National Fire Protection Association, Batterymarch Park, Quincy, MA 02269.
3. Fire Fighter Professional Qualifications, NFPA 1001; National Fire Protection Association, Batterymarch Park, Quincy, MA 02269.
4. Organization for Fire Services, NFPA 1201; National Fire Protection Association, Batterymarch Park, Quincy, MA 02269.
5. Organization of a Fire Department, NFPA 1202; National Fire Protection Association, Batterymarch Park, Quincy, MA 02269 .
6. Protective Clothing for Structural Fire Fighting, ANSI/NFPA 1971; .
7. American National Standard for Men's Safety-Toe Footwear, ANSI Z41.1; American National Standards Institute, New York, NY 10018.
8. American National Standard for Occupational and Educational Eye and Face Protection, ANSI Z87.1; American National Standards Institute, New York, NY 10018.
9. American National Standard, Safety Requirements for Industrial Head Protection, ANSI Z89.1; American National Standards Institute, New York, NY 10018.
10 Specifications for Protective Headgear for Vehicular Users, ANSI Z90.1; American National Standards Institute, New York, NY 10018.
11. Testing Physical Fitness; Davis and Santa Maria. Fire Command. April 1975.
12. Development of a Job-Related Physical Performance Examination for Fire Fighters; Dotson and Others. A summary report for the National Fire Prevention and Control Administration. Washington, DC. March 1977.
13. Proposed Sample Standards for Fire Fighters' Protective Clothing and Equipment; International Association of Fire Fighters, Washington, DC.
14. A Study of Facepiece Leakage of Self-Contained Breathing Apparatus by DOP Man Tests; Los Alamos Scientific Laboratory, Los Alamos, NM.
15. The Development of Criteria for Fire Fighters' Gloves; Vol. II: Glove Criteria and Test Methods; National Institute for Occupational Safety and Health, Cincinnati, OH. 1976.
16. Model Performance Criteria for Structural Fire Fighters' Helmets; National Fire Prevention and Control Administration, Washington, DC. 1977.
17. Firefighters; Job Safety and Health Magazine, Occupational Safety and Health Administration, Washington, DC. June 1978.
18. Eating Smoke—The Dispensable Diet; Utech, H.P. The Fire Independent, 1975.
19. Project Monoxide—A Medical Study of an Occupational Hazard of Fire Fighters; International Association of Fire Fighters, Washington, DC.
20. Occupational Exposures to Carbon Monoxide in Baltimore Firefighters; Radford and Levine. Johns Hopkins University, Baltimore, MD. Journal of Occupational Medicine, September, 1976.
21. Fire Brigades; National Safety Council, Chicago, IL. 1966.
22. American National Standard, Practice for Respiratory Protection for the Fire Service; ANSI Z88.5; American National Standards Institute, New York, NY 10018.
23. Respirator Studies for the Nuclear Regulatory Commission; October 1, 1977—September 30, 1978. Evaluation and Performance of Open Circuit Breathing Apparatus. NU REG/CR–1235. Los Alamos Scientific Laboratory; Los Alamos, NM. 87545, January, 1980.

B. §1910.157. Portable fire extinguishers:

1. Standard for Portable Fire Extinguishers, ANSI/NFPA 10; National Fire Protection Association, Batterymarch Park, Quincy, MA 02269
2. Methods for Hydrostatic Testing of Compressed Gas Cylinders, C–1; Compressed Gas Association, 1235 Jefferson Davis Highway, Arlington, VA 22202.
3. Recommendations for the Disposition of Unserviceable Compressed Gas Cylinders, C–2; Compressed Gas Association, 1235 Jefferson Davis Highway, Arlington, VA 22202.
4. Standard for Visual Inspection of Compressed Gas Cylinders, C–6; Compressed Gas Association, 1235 Jefferson Davis Highway, Arlington, VA 22202.
5. Portable Fire Extinguisher Selection Guide, National Association of Fire Equipment Distributors; 111 East Wacker Drive, Chicago, IL 60601.

C. §1910.158. Standpipe and hose systems:

1. Standard for the Installation of Sprinkler Systems, ANSI/NFPA 13; National Fire Protection Association, Batterymarch Park, Quincy, MA 02269.
2. Standard of the Installation of Standpipe and Hose Systems, ANSI/NFPA 14; National Fire Protection Association, Batterymarch Park, Quincy, MA 02269.
3. Standard for the Installation of Centrifugal Fire Pumps, ANSI/NFPA 20; National Fire Protection Association, Batterymarch Park, Quincy, MA 02269.
4. Standard for Water Tanks for Private Fire Protection, ANSI/NFPA 22; National Fire Protection Association, Batterymarch Park, Quincy, MA 02269.
5. Standard for Screw Threads and Gaskets for Fire Hose Connections, ANSI/NFPA 194; National Fire Protection Association, Batterymarch Park, Quincy, MA 02269 .

6. Standard for Fire Hose, NFPA 196; National Fire Protection Association, Batterymarch Park, Quincy, MA 02269.
7. Standard for the Care of Fire Hose, NFPA 198; National Fire Protection Association, Batterymarch Park, Quincy, MA 02269.

D. §1910.159. Automatic sprinkler systems:

1. Standard of the Installation of Sprinkler Systems, ANSI-NFPA 13; National Fire Protection Association, Batterymarch Park, Quincy, MA 02269.
2. Standard for the Care and Maintenance of Sprinkler Systems, ANSI/NFPA 13A; National Fire Protection Association, Batterymarch Park, Quincy, MA 02269.
3. Standard for the Installation of Standpipe and Hose Systems, ANSI/NFPA 14; National Fire Protection Association, Batterymarch Park, Quincy, MA 02269.
4. Standard for the Installation of Centrifugal Fire Pumps, ANSI/NFPA 20; National Fire Protection Association, Batterymarch Park, Quincy, MA 02269 .
5. Standard for Water Tanks for Private Fire Protection, ANSI-NFPA 22; National Fire Protection Association, Batterymarch Park, Quincy, MA 02269.
6. Standard for Indoor General Storage, ANSI/NFPA 231; National Fire Protection Association, Batterymarch Park, Quincy, MA 02269.
7. Standard for Rack Storage of Materials, ANSI/NFPA 231C; National Fire Protection Association, Batterymarch Park, Quincy, MA 02269.

E. §1910.160. Fixed extinguishing systems—general information:

1. Standard for Foam Extinguishing Systems, ANSI-NFPA 11; National Fire Protection Association, Batterymarch Park, Quincy, MA 02269.
2. Standard for Hi-Expansion Foam Systems, ANSI/NFPA 11A; National Fire Protection Association, Batterymarch Park, Quincy, MA 02269.
3. Standard on Synthetic Foam and Combined Agent Systems, ANSI/NFPA 11B; National Fire Protection Association, Batterymarch Park, Quincy, MA 02269.
4. Standard on Carbon Dioxide Extinguishing Systems, ANSI/NFPA 12; National Fire Protection Association, Batterymarch Park, Quincy, MA 02269.
5. Standard on Halon 1301, ANSI/NFPA 12A; National Fire Protection Association, Batterymarch Park, Quincy, MA 02269.
6. Standard on Halon 1211, ANSI/NFPA 12B; National Fire Protection Association, Batterymarch Park, Quincy, MA 02269 .
7. Standard for Water Spray Systems, ANSI/NFPA 15; National Fire Protection Association, Batterymarch Park, Quincy, MA 02269.
8. Standard for Foam-Water Sprinkler Systems and Foam-Water Spray Systems, ANSI/NFPA 16; National Fire Protection Association, National Fire Protection Association, Batterymarch Park, Quincy, MA 02269.
9. Standard for Dry Chemical Extinguishing Systems, ANSI/NFPA 17; National Fire Protection Association, Batterymarch Park, Quincy, MA 02269.

F. §1910.161. Fixed extinguishing systems—dry chemical:

1. Standard for Dry Chemical Extinguishing Systems, ANSI/NFPA 17; National Fire Protection Association, Batterymarch Park, Quincy, MA 02269.
2. National Electrical Code, ANSI/NFPA 70; National Fire Protection Association, Batterymarch Park, Quincy, MA 02269.
3. Standard for the Installation of Equipment for the Removal of Smoke and Grease-Laden Vapor from Commercial Cooking Equipment, NFPA 96; National Fire Protection Association, Batterymarch Park, Quincy, MA 02269.

G. §1910.162. Fixed extinguishing systems—gaseous agents:

1. Standard on Carbon Dioxide Extinguishing Systems, ANSI/NFPA 12; National Fire Protection Association, Batterymarch Park, Quincy, MA 02269.
2. Standard on Halon 1301, ANSI/NFPA 12B; National Fire Protection Association, Batterymarch Park, Quincy, MA 02269.
3. Standard on Halon 1211, ANSI/NFPA 12B; National Fire Protection Association, Batterymarch Park, Quincy, MA 02269.
4. Standard on Explosion Prevention Systems, ANSI/NFPA 69; National Fire Protection Association, Batterymarch Park, Quincy, MA 02269.
5. National Electrical Code, ANSI/NFPA 70; National Fire Protection Association, Batterymarch Park, Quincy, MA 02269.
6. Standard on Automatic Fire Detectors, ANSI/NFPA 72E; National Fire Protection Association, Batterymarch Park, Quincy, MA 02269.

7. Determination of Halon 1301/1211 Threshold Extinguishing Concentrations Using the Cup Burner Method; Riley and Olson, Ansul Report AL–530–A.

H. §1910.163. Fixed extinguishing systems—water spray and foam agents:

1. Standard for Foam Extinguisher Systems, ANSI/NFPA 11; National Fire Protection Association, Batterymarch Park, Quincy, MA 02269.
2. Standard for High Expansion Foam Systems, ANSI/NFPA 11A; National Fire Protection Association, Batterymarch Park, Quincy, MA 02269
3. Standard for Water Spray Fixed Systems for Fire Protection, ANSI/NFPA 15; National Fire Protection Association, Batterymarch Park, Quincy, MA 02269.
4. Standard for the Installation of Foam-Water Sprinkler Systems and Foam-Water Spray Systems, ANSI/NFPA 16; National Fire Protection Association, Batterymarch Park, Quincy, MA 02269.

I. §1910.164. Fire Detection systems:

1. National Electrical Code, ANSI/NFPA 70; National Fire Protection Association, Batterymarch Park, Quincy, MA 02269.
2. Standard for Central Station Signaling Systems, ANSI/NFPA 71; National Fire Protection Association, Batterymarch Park, Quincy, MA 02269.
3. Standard on Automatic Fire Detectors, ANSI/NFPA 72E; National Fire Protection Association, Batterymarch Park, Quincy, MA 02269.

J. §1910.165. Employee alarm systems:

1. National Electrical Code, ANSI/NFPA 70; National Fire Protection Association, Batterymarch Park, Quincy, MA 02269.
2. Standard for Central Station Signaling systems, ANSI/NFPA 71; National Fire Protection Association, Batterymarch Park, Quincy, MA 02269.
3. Standard for Local Protective Signaling Systems, ANSI/NFPA 72A; National Fire Protection Association, Batterymarch Park, Quincy, MA 02269.
4. Standard for Auxiliary Protective Signaling Systems, ANSI/NFPA 72B; National Fire Protection Association, Batterymarch Park, Quincy, MA 02269.
5. Standard for Remote Station Protective Signaling Systems, ANSI/NFPA 72C; National Fire Protection Association, Batterymarch Park, Quincy, MA 02269 .
6. Standard for Proprietary Protective Signaling Systems, ANSI/NFPA 72D; National Fire Protection Association, Batterymarch Park, Quincy, MA 02269.
7. Vocal Emergency Alarms in Hospitals and Nursing Facilities: Practice and Potential. National Bureau of Standards. Washington, D.C., July 1977.
8. Fire Alarm and Communication Systems. National Bureau of Standards. Washington, D.C., April 1978.

[45 FR 60715, Sept. 12, 1980, as amended at 58 FR 35309, June 30, 1993]

Subpart L of §1910 Appendix D Availability of publications incorporated by reference in §1910.156 Fire brigades

The final standard for fire brigades, §1910.156, contains provisions which incorporate certain publications by reference. The publications provide criteria and test methods for protective clothing worn by those fire brigade members who are expected to perform interior structural fire fighting. The standard references the publications as the chief sources of information for determining if the protective clothing affords the required level of protection.

It is appropriate to note that the final standard does not require employers to purchase a copy of the referenced publications. Instead, employers can specify (in purchase orders to the manufacturers) that the protective clothing meet the criteria and test methods contained in the referenced publications and can rely on the manufacturers' assurances of compliance. Employers, however, may desire to obtain a copy of the referenced publications for their own information.

The paragraph designation of the standard where the referenced publications appear, the title of the publications, and the availability of the publications are as follows:

Paragraph designation	Referenced publication	Available from
1910.156(e)(3)(ii)	"Protective Clothing for Structural Fire Fighting," NFPA No. 1971 (1975)	National Fire Protection Association, Batterymarch Park, Quincy, MA 02269.

Paragraph designation	Referenced publication	Available from
1910.156(e)(4)(i)	"Development of Criteria for Fire Fighter's Gloves; Vol. II, Part II: Test Methods" (1976)	U.S. Government Printing Office, Washington, D.C. 20402. Stock No. for Vol. II is: 071–033–0201–1.
1910.156(e)(5)(i)	"Model Performance Criteria for Structural Firefighter's Helmets" (1977)	U.S. Fire Administration, National Fire Safety and Research Office, Washington, D.C. 20230.

The referenced publications (or a microfiche of the publications) are available for review at many universities and public libraries throughout the country. These publications may also be examined at the OSHA Technical Data Center, Room N2439–Rear, United States Department of Labor, 200 Constitution Ave., N.W., Washington, D.C. 20210 (202–219–7500), or at any OSHA Regional Office (see telephone directories under United States Government-Labor Department).

[45 FR 60715, Sept. 12, 1980, as amended at 58 FR 33509, June 30, 1993; 61 FR 9239, Mar. 7, 1996]

Subpart L of §1910 Appendix E Test methods for protective clothing

This Appendix contains test methods which must be used to determine if protective clothing affords the required level of protection as specified in §1910.156, fire brigades.

(1) Puncture resistance test method for foot protection

A. Apparatus The puncture resistance test shall be performed on a testing machine having a movable platform adjusted to travel at ¼"/min (0.1 cm/sec). Two blocks of hardwood, metal, or plastic shall be prepared as follows: the blocks shall be of such size and thickness as to insure a suitable rigid test ensemble and allow for at least one-inch of the pointed end of an 8D nail to be exposed for the penetration. One block shall have a hole drilled to hold an 8D common nail firmly at an angle of 98°. The second block shall have a maximum ½" (1.3 cm) diameter hole drilled through it so that the hole will allow free passage of the nail after it penetrates the insole during the test.

B. Procedure The test ensemble consisting of the sample unit, the two prepared blocks, a piece of leather outsole 10 to 11 irons thick, and a new 8D nail, shall be placed as follows: the 8D nail in the hole, the sample of outsole stock superimposed above the nail, the area of the sole plate to be tested placed on the outsole, and the second block with hole so placed as to allow for free passage of the nail after it passes through the outsole stock and sole plate in that order. The machine shall be started and the pressure, in pounds required for the nail to completely penetrate the outsole and sole plate, recorded to the nearest five pounds. Two determinations shall be made on each sole plate and the results averaged. A new nail shall be used for each determination.

C. Source These test requirements are contained in "Military Specification For Fireman's Boots," MIL-B-2885D (1973 and amendment dated 1975) and are reproduced for your convenience.

(2) Test method for determining the strength of cloth by tearing: Trapezoid Method

A. Test specimen The specimen shall be a rectangle of cloth 3-inches by 6-inches (7.6 cm by 15.2 cm). The long dimension shall be parallel to the warp for warp tests and parallel to the filling for filling tests. No two specimens for warp tests shall contain the same warp yarns, nor shall any two specimens for filling tests contain the same filling yarns. The specimen shall be taken no nearer the selvage than 1/10 the width of the cloth. An isosceles trapezoid having an altitude of 3-inches (7.6 cm) and bases of 1 inch (2.5cm) and 4 inches (10.2 cm) in length, respectively, shall be marked on each specimen, preferably with the aid of a template. A cut approximately ⅜" (1 cm) in length shall then be made in the center of a perpendicular to the 1-inch (2.5 cm) edge.

B. Apparatus

(i) Six-ounce (.17 kg) weight tension clamps shall be used so designed that the six ounces (.17 kg) of weight are distributed evenly across the complete width of the sample.

(ii) The machine shall consist of three main parts: Straining mechanism, clamps for holding specimen, and load and elongation recording mechanisms.

(iii) A machine wherein the specimen is held between two clamps and strained by a uniform movement of the pulling clamp shall be used.

(iv) The machine shall be adjusted so that the pulling clamp shall have a uniform speed of 12 ± 10.5 inches per minute (0.5 ± .02 cm/sec).

(v) The machine shall have two clamps with two jaws on each clamp. The design of the two clamps shall be such that one gripping surface or jaw may be an integral part of the rigid frame of the clamp or be fastened to allow a slight vertical movement, while the other gripping surface or jaw shall be completely moveable. The dimension of the immovable jaw of each clamp parallel to the application of the load shall measure one-inch, and the dimension of the jaw perpendicular to this direction shall measure three inches or more. The face of the movable jaw of each clamp shall measure one-inch by three inches.

Each jaw face shall have a flat smooth, gripping surface. All edges which might cause a cutting action shall be rounded to a radius of not over 1/64-inch (.04 cm). In cases where a cloth tends to slip when being tested, the jaws may be faced with rubber or other material to prevent slippage. The distance between the jaws (gage length) shall be one-inch at the start of the test.

(vi) Calibrated dial; scale or chart shall be used to indicate applied load and elongation. The machine shall be adjusted or set, so that the maximum load required to break the specimen will remain indicated on the calibrated dial or scale after the test specimen has ruptured.

(vii) The machine shall be of such capacity that the maximum load required to break the specimen shall be not greater than 85 percent or less than 15 percent of the rated capacity.

(viii) The error of the machine shall not exceed 2 percent up to and including a 50-pound load (22.6 kg) and 1 percent over a 50-pound load (22.6 kg) at any reading within its loading range.

(ix) All machine attachments for determining maximum loads shall be disengaged during this test.

C. Procedure

(i) The specimen shall be clamped in the machine along the nonparallel sides of the trapezoid so that these sides lie along the lower edge of the upper clamp and the upper edge of the lower clamp with the cut halfway between the clamps. The short trapezoid base shall be held taut and the long trapezoid base shall lie in the folds.

(ii) The machine shall be started and the force necessary to tear the cloth shall be observed by means of an autographic recording device. The speed of the pulling clamp shall be 12" ± 0.5 inch per minute (0.5 ± .02 cm/sec).

(iii) If a specimen slips between the jaws, breaks in or at the edges of the jaws, or if for any reason attributable to faulty technique, an individual measurement falls markedly below the average test results for the sample unit, such result shall be discarded and another specimen shall be tested.

(iv) The tearing strength of the specimen shall be the average of the five highest peak loads of resistance registered for 3" (7.6 cm) of separation of the tear.

D. Report

(i) Five specimens in each of the warp and filling directions shall be tested from each sample unit.

(ii) The tearing strength of the sample unit shall be the average of the results obtained from the specimens tested in each of the warp and filling directions and shall be reported separately to the nearest 0.1-pound (.05 kg).

E. Source These test requirements are contained in "Federal Test Method Standard 191, Method 5136" and are reproduced for your convenience.

(3) Test method for determining flame resistance of cloth; vertical

A. Test specimen The specimen shall be a rectangle of cloth 2¾" (7.0 cm) by 12" (30.5 cm) with the long dimension parallel to either the warp or filling direction of the cloth. No two warp specimens shall contain the same warp yarns, and no two filling specimens shall contain the same filling yarn.

B. Number of determinations Five specimens from each of the warp and filling directions shall be tested from each sample unit.

C. Apparatus

(i) Cabinet. A cabinet and accessories shall be fabricated in accordance with the requirements specified in Figures L–1, L–2, and L–3. Galvanized sheet metal or other suitable metal shall be used. The entire inside back wall of the cabinet shall be painted black to facilitate the viewing of the test specimen and pilot flame.

(ii) Burner. The burner shall be equipped with a variable orifice to adjust the flame height, a barrel having a ⅜" (1 cm) inside diameter and a pilot light.

(a) The burner may be constructed by combining a ⅜" (1 cm) inside diameter barrel 3 ± ¼" (7.6 ± .6 cm) long from a fixed orifice burner with a base from a variable orifice burner.

(b) The pilot light tube shall have a diameter of approximately 1⁄16" (.2 cm) and shall be spaced ⅛" (.3 cm) away from the burner edge with a pilot flame⅛" (.3 cm) long.

(c) The necessary gas connections and the applicable plumbing shall be as specified in Figure L–4 except that a solenoid valve may be used in lieu of the stopcock valve to which the burner is attached. The stopcock valve or solenoid valve, whichever is used, shall be capable of being fully opened or fully closed in 0.1-second.

(d) On the side of the barrel of the burner, opposite the pilot light there shall be a metal rod of approximately ⅛" (.3 cm) diameter spaced ½" (1.3 cm) from the barrel and extending above the burner. The rod shall have two 5⁄16" (.8 cm) prongs marking the distances of ¾" (1.9 cm) and 1½" (3.8 cm) above the top of the burner.

(e) The burner shall be fixed in a position so that the center of the barrel of the burner is directly below the center of the specimen.

(iii) There shall be a control valve system with a delivery rate designed to furnish gas to the burner under a pressure of 2½ ± ¼ (psi) (17.5 ± 1.8 kPa) per square inch at the burner inlet (see (g)(3)(vi)(A)). The manufacturer's recommended delivery rate for the valve system shall be included in the required pressure.

(iv) A synthetic gas mixture shall be of the following composition within the following limits (analyzed at standard conditions): 55 ± 3 percent hydrogen, 24 ± 1 percent methane, 3 ± 1 percent ethane, and 18 ±1 percent carbon monoxide which will give a specific gravity of 0.365 ± 0.018 (air = 1) and a B.T.U. content of 540 ± 20 per cubic foot (20.1 ± 3.7 kJ/L)(dry basis) at 69.8 °F (21 °C).

(v) There shall be metal hooks and weights to produce a series of total loads to determine length of char. The metal hooks shall consist of No. 19 gage steel wire or equivalent and shall be made from 3" (7.6 cm) lengths of wire and bent ½" (1.3 cm) from one end to a 45 degree hook. One end of the hook shall be fastened around the neck of the weight to be used.

(vi) There shall be a stop watch or other device to measure the burning time to 0.2-second.

(vii) There shall be a scale, graduated in 0.1" (.3 cm) to measure the length of char.

D. Procedure

(i) The material undergoing test shall be evaluated for the characteristics of after-flame time and char length on each specimen.

(ii) All specimens to be tested shall be at moisture equilibrium under standard atmospheric conditions in accordance with paragraph (3) C of this Appendix. Each specimen to be tested shall be exposed to the test flame within 20 seconds after removal from the standard atmosphere. In case of dispute, all testing will be conducted under Standard Atmospheric Conditions in accordance with paragraph (3)C of this Appendix.

(iii) The specimen in its holder shall be suspended vertically in the cabinet in such a manner that the entire length of the specimen is exposed and the lower end is ¾" (1.9 cm) above the top of the gas burner. The apparatus shall be set up in a draft free area.

(iv) Prior to inserting the specimen, the pilot flame shall be adjusted to approximately ⅛-inch (.3 cm) in height measured from its lowest point to the tip.

The burner flame shall be adjusted by means of the needle valve in the base of the burner to give a flame height of 1½" (3.8 cm) with the stopcock fully open and the air supply to the burner shut off and taped. The 1½-inch (3.8 cm) flame height is obtained by adjusting the valve so that the uppermost portion (tip) of the flame is level with the tip of the metal prong (see Figure L–2) specified for adjustment of flame height. It is an important aspect of the evaluation that the flame height be adjusted with the tip of the flame level with the tip of the metal prong. After inserting the specimen, the stopcock shall be fully opened, and the burner flame applied vertically at the middle of the lower edge of the specimen for 12 seconds and the burner turned off. The cabinet door shall remain shut during testing.

(v) The after-flame shall be the time the specimen continues to flame after the burner flame is shut off.

(vi) After each specimen is removed, the test cabinet shall be cleared of fumes and smoke prior to testing the next specimen.

(vii) After both flaming and glowing have ceased, the char length shall be measured. The char length shall be the distance from the end of the specimen, which was exposed to the flame, to the end of a tear (made lengthwise) of the specimen through the center of the charred area as follows: The specimen shall be folded lengthwise and creased by hand along a line through the highest peak of the charred area. The hook shall be inserted in the specimen (or a hole, ¼-inch (.6 cm) diameter or less, punched out for the hook) at one side of the charred area ¼" (.6 cm) from the adjacent outside edge and ¼" (.6 cm) in from the lower end. A weight of sufficient size such that the weight and hook together shall equal the total tearing load required in Table L–2 of this section shall be attached to the hook.

(viii) A tearing force shall be applied gently to the specimen by grasping the corner of the cloth at the opposite edge of the char from the load and raising the specimen and weight clear of the supporting surface. The end of the tear shall be marked off on the edge and the char length measurement made along the undamaged edge.

Loads for determining char length applicable to the weight of the test cloth shall be as shown in Table L–2.

Table L–2[1]

Specified weight per square yard of cloth before any fire retardant treatment or coating—ounces	Total tearing weight for determining the charred length—pound
2.0 to 6.0	0.25
Over 6.0 to 15.0	0.50
Over 15.0 to 23.0	0.75
Over 23.0	1.0

[1] TochangeintoS.I.(SystemInternational)units,1ounce=28.35grams, 1 pound = 453 grams, 1 yard =.91 meter

(ix) The after-flame time of the specimen shall be recorded to the nearest 0.2-second and the char length to the nearest 0.1" (.3 cm).

E. Report

(i) The after-flame time and char length of the sample unit shall be the average of the results obtained from the individual specimens tested. All values obtained from the individual specimens shall be recorded.

(ii) The after-flame time shall be reported to the nearest 0.2-second and the char length to the nearest 0.1" (.3 cm).

F. Source These test requirements are contained in "Federal Test Method Standard 191, Method 5903 (1971)" and are reproduced for your convenience.

Figure L–1 Vertical Flame Resistance Textile Apparatus

All given dimensions are in inches.
System International (S.I.) Unit: 1-inch = 2.54 cm.

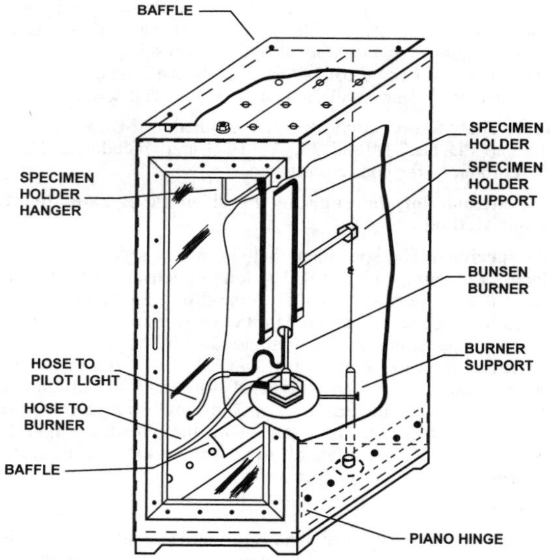

Figure L–2 Vertical Flame Resistance Textile Apparatus Door and Top View w/Baffle

All given dimensions are in inches. System International (S.I.) Unit: 1-inch = 2.54 cm.

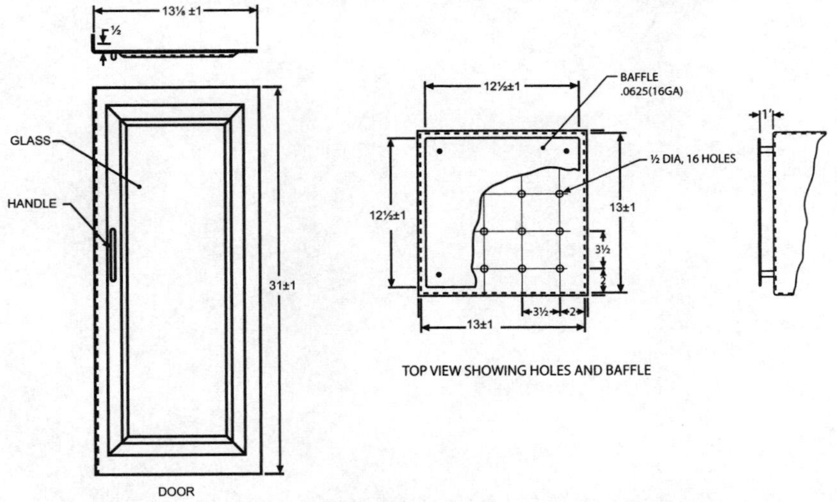

Figure L–3 Vertical Flame Resistance Textile Apparatus, View and Details

All given dimensions are in inches. System International (S.I.) Unit: 1-inch = 2.54 cm.

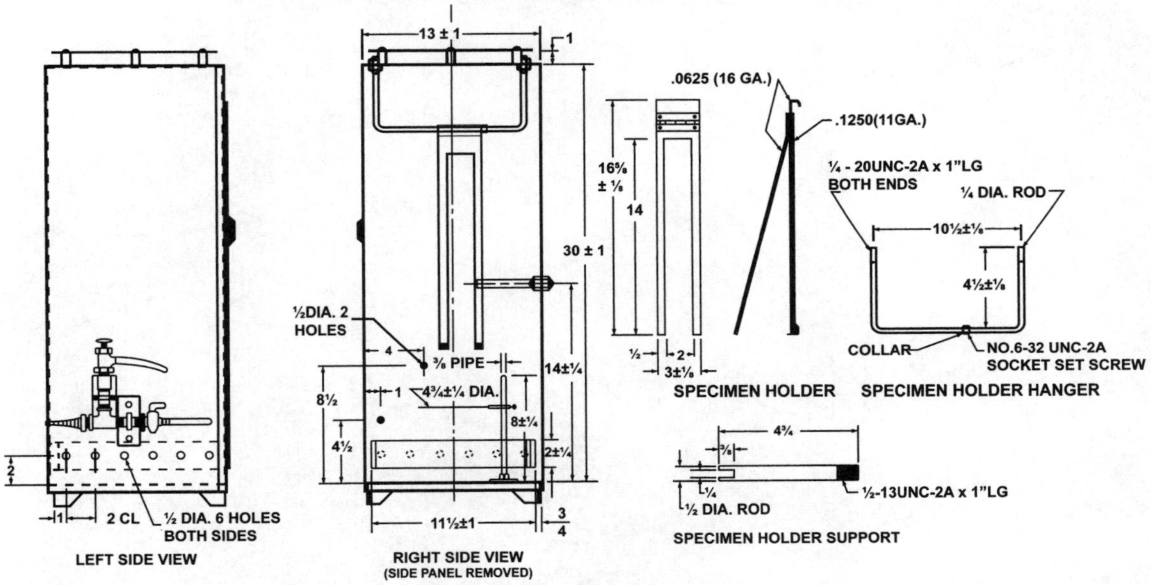

Figure L–4 Vertical Flame Resistance Textile Apparatus

All given dimensions are in inches. System International (S.I.) Unit: 1-inch = 2.54 cm.

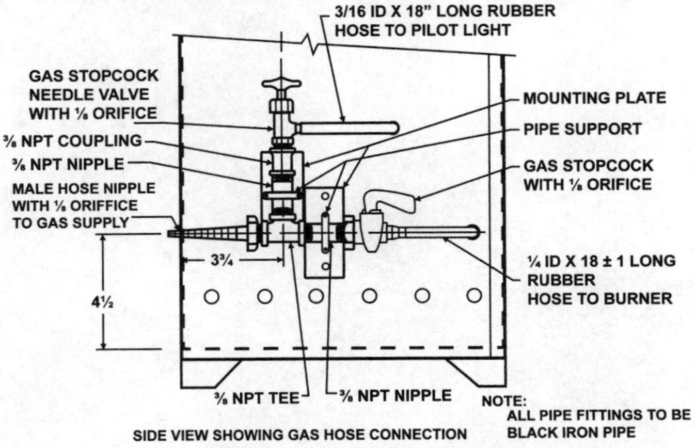

Vertical flame resistance textile apparatus. All given dimensions are in inches. System International (S.I.) Unit: 1 inch = 2.54 cm.

[45 FR 60715, Sept. 12, 1980; 46 FR 24557, May 1, 1981]

This page intentionally left blank.

29 CFR PART 1910 Subpart M
Compressed Gas and Compressed Air Equipment

Section Contents

Subpart M—Compressed Gas and Compressed Air Equipment

Authority: Sections 4, 6, and 8 of the Occupational Safety and Health Act of 1970 (29 U.S.C. 653, 655, 657); Secretary of Labor's Order No. 12–71 (36 FR 8754), 8–76 (41 FR 25059), 9–83 (48 FR 35736), or 1–90 (55 FR 9033), as applicable.

§1910.166–§1910.168 [Reserved]

§1910.169 Air receivers

(a) **General requirements**

(a)(1) **Application** This section applies to compressed air receivers, and other equipment used in providing and utilizing compressed air for performing operations such as cleaning, drilling, hoisting, and chipping. On the other hand, however, this section does not deal with the special problems created by using compressed air to convey materials nor the problems created when men work in compressed air as in tunnels and caissons. This section is not intended to apply to compressed air machinery and equipment used on transportation vehicles such as steam railroad cars, electric railway cars, and automotive equipment.

(a)(2) **New and existing equipment**

(a)(2)(i) All new air receivers installed after the effective date of these regulations shall be constructed in accordance with the 1968 edition of the A.S.M.E. Boiler and Pressure Vessel Code Section VIII, which is incorporated by reference as specified in §1910.6.

(a)(2)(ii) All safety valves used shall be constructed, installed, and maintained in accordance with the A.S.M.E. Boiler and Pressure Vessel Code, Section VIII Edition 1968.

(b) **Installation and equipment requirements**

(b)(1) **Installation** Air receivers shall be so installed that all drains, handholes, and manholes therein are easily accessible. Under no circumstances shall an air receiver be buried underground or located in an inaccessible place.

(b)(2) **Drains and traps** A drain pipe and valve shall be installed at the lowest point of every air receiver to provide for the removal of accumulated oil and water. Adequate automatic traps may be installed in addition to drain valves. The drain valve on the air receiver shall be opened and the receiver completely drained frequently and at such intervals as to prevent the accumulation of excessive amounts of liquid in the receiver.

(b)(3) **Gages and valves**

(b)(3)(i) Every air receiver shall be equipped with an indicating pressure gage (so located as to be readily visible) and with one or more spring-loaded safety valves. The total relieving capacity of such safety valves shall be such as to prevent pressure in the receiver from exceeding the maximum allowable working pressure of the receiver by more than 10 percent.

(b)(3)(ii) No valve of any type shall be placed between the air receiver and its safety valve or valves.

(b)(3)(iii) Safety appliances, such as safety valves, indicating devices and controlling devices, shall be constructed, located, and installed so that they cannot be readily rendered inoperative by any means, including the elements.

(b)(3)(iv) All safety valves shall be tested frequently and at regular intervals to determine whether they are in good operating condition.

[39 FR 23502, June 27, 1974, as amended at 49 FR 5322, Feb. 10, 1984; 61 FR 9239, Mar. 7, 1996]

This page intentionally left blank.

29 CFR PART 1910 Subpart N
Materials Handling and Storage

Section Contents

Subpart N—Materials Handling and Storage

Authority: 29 U.S.C. 653, 655, 657; Secretary of Labor's Order No. 12-71 (36 FR 8754), 8-76 (41 FR 25059), 9-83 (48 FR 35736), 1-90 (55 FR 9033), 6-96 (62 FR 111), 3-2000 (65 FR 50017), 5-2002 (67 FR 65008), 5-2007 (72 FR 31159), 4-2010 (75 FR 55355), or 1-2012 (77 FR 3912), as applicable; and 29 CFR part 1911.

§1910.176 [OI]
Handling materials—general

(a) **Use of mechanical equipment** Where mechanical handling equipment is used, sufficient safe clearances shall be allowed for aisles, at loading docks, through doorways and wherever turns or passage must be made. Aisles and passageways shall be kept clear and in good repair, with no obstruction across or in aisles that could create a hazard. Permanent aisles and passageways shall be appropriately marked.

(b) **Secure storage** Storage of material shall not create a hazard. Bags, containers, bundles, etc., stored in tiers shall be stacked, blocked, interlocked and limited in height so that they are stable and secure against sliding or collapse.

(c) **Housekeeping** Storage areas shall be kept free from accumulation of materials that constitute hazards from tripping, fire, explosion, or pest harborage. Vegetation control will be exercised when necessary.

(d) [Reserved]

(e) **Clearance limits** Clearance signs to warn of clearance limits shall be provided.

(f) **Rolling railroad cars** Derail and/or bumper blocks shall be provided on spur railroad tracks where a rolling car could contact other cars being worked, enter a building, work or traffic area.

(g) **Guarding** Covers and/or guardrails shall be provided to protect personnel from the hazards of open pits, tanks, vats, ditches, etc.

[39 FR 23052, June 27, 1974, as amended at 43 FR 49749, Oct. 24, 1978]

§1910.177 [OI]
Servicing multi–piece and single piece rim wheels

(a) **Scope**

(a)(1) This Section applies to the servicing of multi-piece and single piece rim wheels used on large vehicles such as trucks, tractors, trailers, buses and off-road machines. It does not apply to the servicing of rim wheels used on automobiles, or on pickup trucks and vans utilizing automobile tires or truck tires designated "LT".

(a)(2) [OI] This Section does not apply to employers and places of employment regulated under the Longshoring Standards, 29 CFR Part 1918; Construction Safety Standards, 29 CFR Part 1926; or Agriculture Standards, 29 CFR Part 1928.

(a)(3) All provisions of this Section apply to the servicing of both single piece rim wheels and multi-piece rim wheels unless designated otherwise.

(b) **Definitions**

Barrier means a fence, wall or other structure or object placed between a single piece rim wheel and an employee during tire inflation, to contain the rim wheel components in the event of the sudden release of the contained air of the single piece rim wheel.

Charts means the U.S. Department of Labor, Occupational Safety and Health Administration publications entitled "Demounting and Mounting Procedures for Truck/Bus Tires" and "Multi-piece Rim Matching Chart," the National Highway Traffic Safety Administration (NHTSA) publications entitled "Demounting and Mounting Procedures Truck/Bus Tires" and "Multi-piece Rim Matching Chart," or any other poster which contains at least the same instructions, safety precautions and other information contained in the charts that is applicable to the types of wheels being serviced.

Installing a rim wheel means the transfer and attachment of an assembled rim wheel onto a vehicle axle hub. Removing means the opposite of installing.

Mounting a tire means the assembly or putting together of the wheel and tire components to form a rim wheel, including inflation. Demounting means the opposite of mounting.

Multi-piece rim wheel means the assemblage of a multi-piece wheel with the tire tube and other components.

Multi-piece wheel means a vehicle wheel consisting of two or more parts, one of which is a side or locking ring designed to hold the tire on the wheel by interlocking components when the tire is inflated.

Restraining device means an apparatus such as a cage, rack, assemblage of bars and other components that will constrain all rim wheel components during an explosive separation of a multi-piece rim wheel, or during the sudden release of the contained air of a single piece rim wheel.

Rim manual means a publication containing instructions from the manufacturer or other qualified organization for correct mounting, demounting, maintenance, and safety precautions peculiar to the type of wheel being serviced.

Rim wheel means an assemblage of tire, tube and liner (where appropriate), and wheel components.

Service or servicing means the mounting and demounting of rim wheels, and related activities such as inflating, deflating, installing, removing, and handling.

Service area means that part of an employer's premises used for the servicing of rim wheels, or any other place where an employee services rim wheels.

Single piece rim wheel means the assemblage of single piece rim wheel with the tire and other components.

Single piece wheel means a vehicle wheel consisting of one part, designed to hold the tire on the wheel when the tire is inflated.

Trajectory means any potential path or route that a rim wheel component may travel during an explosive separation, or the sudden release of the pressurized air, or an area at which an airblast from a single piece rim wheel may be released. The trajectory may deviate from paths which are perpendicular to the assembled position of the rim wheel at the time of separation or explosion. (See Appendix A for examples of trajectories.)

Wheel means that portion of a rim wheel which provides the method of attachment of the assembly to the axle of a vehicle and also provides the means to contain the inflated portion of the assembly (i.e., the tire and/or tube).

(c) **Employee training**

(c)(1) The employer shall provide a program to train all employees who service rim wheels in the hazards involved in servicing those rim wheels and the safety procedures to be followed.

(c)(1)(i) The employer shall assure that no employee services any rim wheel unless the employee has been trained and instructed in correct procedures of servicing the type of wheel being serviced, and in the safe operating procedures described in paragraphs (f) and (g) of this Section.

(c)(1)(ii) Information to be used in the training program shall include, at a minimum, the applicable data contained in the charts (rim manuals) and the contents of this standard.

(c)(1)(iii) Where an employer knows or has reason to believe that any of his employees is unable to read and understand the charts or rim manual, the employer shall assure that the employee is instructed concerning the contents of the charts and rim manual in a manner which the employee is able to understand.

(c)(2) The employer shall assure that each employee demonstrates and maintains the ability to service rim wheels safely, including performance of the following tasks:

(c)(2)(i) Demounting of tires (including deflation);

(c)(2)(ii) Inspection and identification of the rim wheel components;

(c)(2)(iii) Mounting of tires (including inflation with a restraining device or other safeguard required by this Section);

(c)(2)(iv) Use of the restraining device or barrier, and other equipment required by this Section;

(c)(2)(v) Handling of rim wheels;

(c)(2)(vi) Inflation of the tire when a single piece rim wheel is mounted on a vehicle;

(c)(2)(vii) An understanding of the necessity of standing outside the trajectory both during inflation of the tire and during inspection of the rim wheel following inflation; and

(c)(2)(viii) Installation and removal of rim wheels.

(c)(3) The employer shall evaluate each employee's ability to perform these tasks and to service rim wheels safely, and shall provide additional training as necessary to assure that each employee maintains his or her proficiency.

(d) **Tire servicing equipment**

(d)(1) The employer shall furnish a restraining device for inflating tires on multi-piece wheels.

(d)(2) The employer shall provide a restraining device or barrier for inflating tires on single piece wheels unless the rim wheel will be bolted onto a vehicle during inflation.

(d)(3) Restraining devices and barriers shall comply with the following requirements:

(d)(3)(i) Each restraining device or barrier shall have the capacity to withstand the maximum force that would be transferred to it during a rim wheel separation occurring at 150 percent of the maximum tire specification pressure for the type of rim wheel being serviced.

(d)(3)(ii) Restraining devices and barriers shall be capable of preventing the rim wheel components from being thrown outside or beyond the device or barrier for any rim wheel positioned within or behind the device;

(d)(3)(iii) Restraining devices and barriers shall be visually inspected prior to each day's use and after any separation of the rim wheel components or sudden release of contained air. Any restraining device or barrier exhibiting damage such as the following defects shall be immediately removed from service:

(d)(3)(iii)(A) Cracks at welds;

(d)(3)(iii)(B) Cracked or broken components;

(d)(3)(iii)(C) Bent or sprung components caused by mishandling, abuse, tire explosion or rim wheel separation;

(d)(3)(iii)(D) Pitting of components due to corrosion; or

(d)(3)(iii)(E) Other structural damage which would decrease its effectiveness.

(d)(3)(iv) Restraining devices or barriers removed from service shall not be returned to service until they are repaired and reinspected. Restraining devices or barriers requiring structural repair such as component replacement or rewelding shall not be returned to service until they are certified by either the manufacturer or a Registered Professional Engineer as meeting the strength requirements of paragraph (d)(3)(i) of this Section.

(d)(4) The employer shall furnish and assure that an air line assembly consisting of the following components be used for inflating tires:

(d)(4)(i) A clip-on chuck;

(d)(4)(ii) An in-line valve with a pressure gauge or a presettable regulator; and

(d)(4)(iii) A sufficient length of hose between the clip-on chuck and the in-line valve (if one is used) to allow the employee to stand outside the trajectory.

(d)(5) Current charts or rim manuals containing instructions for the type of wheels being serviced shall be available in the service area.

(d)(6) The employer shall furnish and assure that only tools recommended in the rim manual for the type of wheel being serviced are used to service rim wheels.

(e) **Wheel component acceptability**

(e)(1) Multi-piece wheel components shall not be interchanged except as provided in the charts or in the applicable rim manual.

(e)(2) Multi-piece wheel components and single piece wheels shall be inspected prior to assembly. Any wheel or wheel component which is bent out of shape, pitted from corrosion, broken, or cracked shall not be used and shall be marked or tagged unserviceable and removed from the service area. Damaged or leaky valves shall be replaced.

(e)(3) Rim flanges, rim gutters, rings, bead seating surfaces and the bead areas of tires shall be free of any dirt, surface rust, scale or loose or flaked rubber build-up prior to mounting and inflation.

(e)(4) The size (bead diameter and tire/wheel widths) and type of both the tire and the wheel shall be checked for compatibility prior to assembly of the rim wheel.

(f) **Safe operating procedure—multi-piece rim wheels** The employer shall establish a safe operating procedure for servicing multi-piece rim wheels and shall assure that employees are instructed in and follow that procedure. The procedure shall include at least the following elements:

(f)(1) Tires shall be completely deflated before demounting by removal of the valve core.

(f)(2) Tires shall be completely deflated by removing the valve core before a rim wheel is removed from the axle in either of the following situations:

(f)(2)(i) When the tire has been driven underinflated at 80% or less of its recommended pressure; or

(f)(2)(ii) When there is obvious or suspected damage to the tire or wheel components.

(f)(3) Rubber lubricant shall be applied to bead and rim mating surfaces during assembly of the wheel and inflation of the tire, unless the tire or wheel manufacturer recommends against it.

(f)(4) If a tire on a vehicle is underinflated but has more than 80% of the recommended pressure, the tire may be inflated while the rim wheel is on the vehicle provided remote control inflation equipment is used, and no employees remain in the trajectory during inflation.

(f)(5) Tires shall be inflated outside a restraining device only to a pressure sufficient to force the tire bead onto the rim ledge and create an airtight seal with the tire and bead.

(f)(6) Whenever a rim wheel is in a restraining device the employee shall not rest or lean any part of his body or equipment on or against the restraining device.

(f)(7) After tire inflation, the tire and wheel components shall be inspected while still within the restraining device to make sure that they are properly seated and locked. If further adjustment to the tire or wheel components is necessary, the tire shall be deflated by removal of the valve core before the adjustment is made.

(f)(8) No attempt shall be made to correct the seating of side and lock rings by hammering, striking or forcing the components while the tire is pressurized.

(f)(9) Cracked, broken, bent or otherwise damaged rim components shall not be reworked, welded, brazed, or otherwise heated.

(f)(10) Whenever multi-piece rim wheels are being handled, employees shall stay out of the trajectory unless the employer can demonstrate that performance of the servicing makes the employee's presence in the trajectory necessary.

(f)(11) No heat shall be applied to a multi-piece wheel or wheel component.

(g) Safe operating procedure—single piece rim wheels. The employer shall establish a safe operating procedure for servicing single piece rim wheels and shall assure that employees are instructed in and follow that procedure. The procedure shall include at least the following elements:

(g)(1) Tires shall be completely deflated by removal of the valve core before demounting.

(g)(2) Mounting and demounting of the tire shall be done only from the narrow ledge side of the wheel. Care shall be taken to avoid damaging the tire beads while mounting tires on wheels. Tires shall be mounted only on compatible wheels of matching bead diameter and width.

(g)(3) Nonflammable rubber lubricant shall be applied to bead and wheel mating surfaces before assembly of the rim wheel, unless the tire or wheel manufacturer recommends against the use of any rubber lubricant.

(g)(4) If a tire changing machine is used, the tire shall be inflated only to the minimum pressure necessary to force the tire bead onto the rim ledge while on the tire changing machine.

(g)(5) If a bead expander is used, it shall be removed before the valve core is installed and as soon as the rim wheel becomes airtight (the tire bead slips onto the bead seat).

(g)(6) Tires may be inflated only when contained within a restraining device, positioned behind a barrier or bolted on the vehicle with the lug nuts fully tightened.

(g)(7) Tires shall not be inflated when any flat, solid surface is in the trajectory and within one foot of the sidewall.

(g)(8) Employees shall stay out of the trajectory when inflating a tire.

(g)(9) Tires shall not be inflated to more than the inflation pressure stamped in the sidewall unless a higher pressure is recommended by the manufacturer.

(g)(10) Tires shall not be inflated above the maximum pressure recommended by the manufacturer to seat the tire bead firmly against the rim flange.

(g)(11) No heat shall be applied to a single piece wheel.

(g)(12) Cracked, broken, bent, or otherwise damaged wheels shall not be reworked, welded, brazed, or otherwise heated.

§1910.177 Appendix A Trajectory

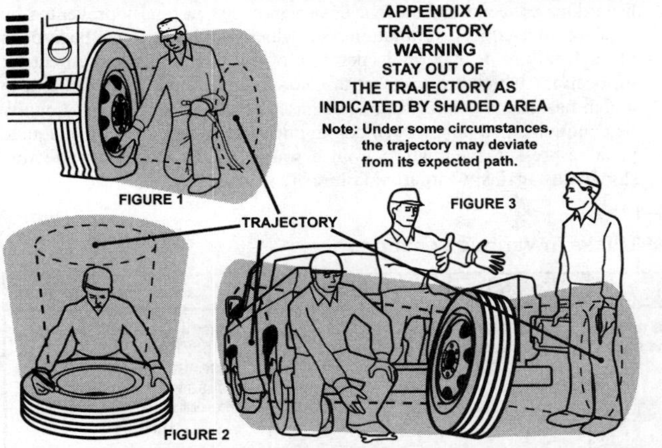

§1910.177 Appendix B Ordering information for the OSHA charts

OSHA has printed two charts entitled “Demounting and Mounting Procedures for Truck/Bus Tires” and “Multi-piece Rim Matching Chart,” as part of a continuing campaign to reduce accidents among employees who service large vehicle rim wheels.

Reprints of the charts are available through the Occupational Safety and Health Administration (OSHA) Area and Regional Offices. The address and telephone number of the nearest OSHA office can be obtained by looking in the local telephone directory under U.S. Government, U.S. Department of Labor, Occupational Safety and Health Administration. Single copies are available without charge.

Individuals, establishments and other organizations desiring single or multiple copies of these charts may order them from the OSHA Publications Office, U.S. Department of Labor, Room N–3101, Washington, DC 20210, Telephone (202) 219–4667.

[49 FR 4350, Feb. 3, 1984, as amended at 52 FR 36026, Sept. 25, 1987; 53 FR 34737, Sept. 8, 1988; 61 FR 9239, Mar. 7, 1996; 76 FR 24698, May 2, 2011]

§1910.178 Powered industrial trucks

(a) General requirements

(a)(1) This Section contains safety requirements relating to fire protection, design, maintenance, and use of fork trucks, tractors, platform lift trucks, motorized hand trucks, and other specialized industrial trucks powered by electric motors or internal combustion engines. This Section does not apply to compressed air or nonflammable compressed gas-operated industrial trucks, nor to farm vehicles, nor to vehicles intended primarily for earth moving or over-the-road hauling.

(a)(2) All new powered industrial trucks acquired and used by an employer shall meet the design and construction requirements for powered industrial trucks established in the “American National Standard for Powered Industrial Trucks, Part II, ANSI B56.1–1969”, which is incorporated by reference as specified in §1910.6, except for vehicles intended primarily for earth moving or over-the-road hauling.

(a)(3) Approved trucks shall bear a label or some other identifying mark indicating approval by the testing laboratory. See paragraph (a)(7) of this Section and paragraph 405 of “American National Standard for Powered Industrial Trucks, Part II, ANSI B56.1–1969”, which is incorporated by reference in paragraph (a)(2) of this Section and which provides that if the powered industrial truck is accepted by a nationally recognized testing laboratory it should be so marked.

(a)(4) Modifications and additions which affect capacity and safe operation shall not be performed by the customer or user without manufacturers prior written approval. Capacity, operation, and maintenance instruction plates, tags, or decals shall be changed accordingly.

(a)(5) If the truck is equipped with front-end attachments other than factory installed attachments, the user shall request that the truck be marked to identify the attachments and show the approximate weight of the truck and attachment combination at maximum elevation with load laterally centered.

(a)(6) The user shall see that all nameplates and markings are in place and are maintained in a legible condition.

(a)(7) As used in this Section, the term, **approved truck or approved industrial truck** means a truck that is listed or approved for fire safety purposes for the intended use by a nationally recognized testing laboratory, using nationally recognized testing standards. Refer to §1910.155(c)(3)(iv)(A) for definition of listed, and to §1910.7 for definition of nationally recognized testing laboratory.

(b) Designations For the purpose of this standard there are eleven different designations of industrial trucks or tractors as follows: D, DS, DY, E, ES, EE, EX, G, GS, LP, and LPS.

(b)(1) The D designated units are units similar to the G units except that they are diesel engine powered instead of gasoline engine powered.

(b)(2) The DS designated units are diesel powered units that are provided with additional safeguards to the exhaust, fuel and electrical systems. They may be used in some locations where a D unit may not be considered suitable.

(b)(3) The DY designated units are diesel powered units that have all the safeguards of the DS units and in addition do not have any electrical equipment including the ignition and are equipped with temperature limitation features.

(b)(4) The E designated units are electrically powered units that have minimum acceptable safeguards against inherent fire hazards.

(b)(5) The ES designated units are electrically powered units that, in addition to all of the requirements for the E units, are provided with additional safeguards to the electrical system to prevent emission of hazardous sparks and to limit surface temperatures. They may be used in some locations where the use of an E unit may not be considered suitable.

(b)(6) The EE designated units are electrically powered units that have, in addition to all of the requirements for the E and ES units, the electric motors and all other electrical equipment completely enclosed. In certain locations the EE unit may be used where the use of an E and ES unit may not be considered suitable.

(b)(7) The EX designated units are electrically powered units that differ from the E, ES, or EE units in that the electrical fittings and equipment are so designed, constructed and assembled that the units may be used in certain atmospheres containing flammable vapors or dusts.

(b)(8) The G designated units are gasoline powered units having minimum acceptable safeguards against inherent fire hazards.

(b)(9) The GS designated units are gasoline powered units that are provided with additional safeguards to the exhaust, fuel, and electrical systems. They may be used in some locations where the use of a G unit may not be considered suitable.

(b)(10) The LP designated unit is similar to the G unit except that liquefied petroleum gas is used for fuel instead of gasoline.

(b)(11) The LPS designated units are liquefied petroleum gas powered units that are provided with additional safeguards to the exhaust, fuel, and electrical systems. They may be used in some locations where the use of an LP unit may not be considered suitable.

(b)(12) The atmosphere or location shall have been classified as to whether it is hazardous or nonhazardous prior to the consideration of industrial trucks being used therein and the type of industrial truck required shall be as provided in paragraph (d) of this Section for such location.

(c) Designated locations

(c)(1) The industrial trucks specified under subparagraph (2) of this paragraph are the minimum types required but industrial trucks having greater safeguards may be used if desired.

(c)(2) For specific areas of use, see Table N–1 which tabulates the information contained in this Section. References are to the corresponding classification as used in Subpart S of this Part.

(c)(2)(i) Power-operated industrial trucks shall not be used in atmospheres containing hazardous concentration of acetylene, butadiene, ethylene oxide, hydrogen (or gases or vapors equivalent in hazard to hydrogen, such as manufactured gas), propylene oxide, acetaldehyde, cyclopropane, diethyl ether, ethylene, isoprene, or unsymmetrical dimethyl hydrazine (UDMH).

(c)(2)(ii)(A) Power-operated industrial trucks shall not be used in atmospheres containing hazardous concentrations of metal dust, including aluminum, magnesium, and their commercial alloys, other metals of similarly hazardous characteristics, or in atmospheres containing carbon black, coal or coke dust except approved power-operated industrial trucks designated as EX may be used in such atmospheres.

(c)(2)(ii)(B) In atmospheres where dust of magnesium, aluminum or aluminum bronze may be present, fuses, switches, motor controllers, and circuit breakers of trucks shall have enclosures specifically approved for such locations.

(c)(2)(iii) O I Only approved power-operated industrial trucks designated as EX may be used in atmospheres containing acetone, acrylonitrile, alcohol, ammonia, benzine, benzol, butane, ethylene dichloride, gasoline, hexane, lacquer solvent vapors, naphtha, natural gas, propane, propylene, styrene, vinyl acetate, vinyl chloride, or xylenes in quantities sufficient to produce explosive or ignitable mixtures and where such concentrations of these gases or vapors exist continuously, intermittently or periodically under normal operating conditions or may exist frequently because of repair, maintenance operations, leakage, breakdown or faulty operation of equipment.

(c)(2)(iv) O I Power-operated industrial trucks designated as DY, EE, or EX may be used in locations where volatile flammable liquids or flammable gases are handled, processed or used, but in which the hazardous liquids, vapors or gases will normally be confined within closed containers or closed systems from which they can escape only in case of accidental rupture or breakdown of such containers or systems, or in the case of abnormal operation of equipment; also in locations in which hazardous concentrations of gases or vapors are normally prevented by positive mechanical ventilation but which might become hazardous through failure or abnormal operation of the ventilating equipment; or in locations which are adjacent to Class I, Division 1 locations, and to which hazardous concentrations of gases or vapors might occasionally be communicated unless such communication is prevented by adequate positive-pressure ventilation from a source of clear air, and effective safeguards against ventilation failure are provided.

Table N–1

Summary Table on Use of Industrial Trucks in Various Locations

Classes	Unclassified	Class I locations	Class II locations	Class III locations
Description of classes	Locations not possessing atmospheres as described in other columns	Locations in which flammable gases or vapors are, or may be, present in the air in quantities sufficient to produce explosive or ignitible mixtures	Locations which are hazardous because of the presence of combustible dust	Locations where easily ignitible fibers or flyings are present but not likely to be in suspension in quantities sufficient to produce ignitible mixtures

Groups in classes	None	A	B	C	D	E	F	G	None
Examples of locations or atmospheres in classes and groups	Piers and wharves inside and outside general storage, general industrial or commercial properties.	Acetylene	Hydrogen	Ethyl ether	Gasoline Naphtha Alcohols Acetone Lacquer solvent Benzene	Metal dust	Carbon black coal dust, coke dust	Grain dust, flour dust, starch dust, organic dust	Baled waste, cocoa fiber, cotton, excelsior, hemp, istle, jute, kapok, oakum, sisal, Spanish moss, synthetic fibers, tow.

		1	2	1	2	1	2
Divisions (nature of hazardous conditions)	None	Above condition exists continuously, intermittently, or periodically under normal operating conditions.	Above condition may occur accidentally as due to a puncture of a storage drum.	Explosive mixture may be present under normal operating conditions, or where failure of equipment may cause the condition to exist simultaneously with arcing or sparking of electrical equipment, or where dusts of an electrically conducting nature may be present.	Explosive mixture not normally present, but where deposits of dust may cause heat rise in electrical equipment, or where such deposits may be ignited by arcs or sparks from electrical equipment.	Locations in which easily ignitible fibers or materials producing combustible flyings are handled, manufactured, or used.	Locations in which easily ignitible fibers are stored or handled (except in the process of manufacture).

Authorized uses of trucks by types in groups of classes and divisions

Groups in classes	None	A	B	C	D	A	B	C	D	E	F	G	E	F	G	None	None
Type of truck authorized:																	
Diesel:																	
Type D	D**																
Type DS									DS						DS		DS
Type DY									DY						DY	DY	DY
Electric:																	
Type E	E**																E
Type ES									ES						ES		ES
Type EE									EE						EE	EE	EE
Type EX					EX				EX		EX	EX			EX	EX	EX
Gasoline:																	
Type G	G**																
Type GS									GS						GS		GS
LP-Gas																	

Authorized uses of trucks by types in groups of classes and divisions																	
Groups in classes	None	A	B	C	D	A	B	C	D	E	F	G	E	F	G	None	None
Type LP	LP**																
Type LPS									LPS						LPS		LPS
Paragraph Ref. in No. 505.	210.211		201 (a)		203 (a)		209 (a)		204 (a), (b)		202 (a)	205 (a)		209 (a)	206 (a), (b)	207 (a)	208 (a)

**Trucks conforming to these types may also be used—see subdivision (c)(2)(x) and (c)(2)(xii) of this Section.

(c)(2)(v) In locations used for the storage of hazardous liquids in sealed containers or liquefied or compressed gases in containers, approved power-operated industrial trucks designated as DS, ES, GS, or LPS may be used. This classification includes locations where volatile flammable liquids or flammable gases or vapors are used, but which, would become hazardous only in case of an accident or of some unusual operating condition. The quantity of hazardous material that might escape in case of accident, the adequacy of ventilating equipment, the total area involved, and the record of the industry or business with respect to explosions or fires are all factors that should receive consideration in determining whether or not the DS or DY, ES, EE, GS, LPS designated truck possesses sufficient safeguards for the location. Piping without valves, checks, meters and similar devices would not ordinarily be deemed to introduce a hazardous condition even though used for hazardous liquids or gases. Locations used for the storage of hazardous liquids or of liquefied or compressed gases in sealed containers would not normally be considered hazardous unless subject to other hazardous conditions also.

(c)(2)(vi)(A) Only approved power operated industrial trucks designated as EX shall be used in atmospheres in which combustible dust is or may be in suspension continuously, intermittently, or periodically under normal operating conditions, in quantities sufficient to produce explosive or ignitable mixtures, or where mechanical failure or abnormal operation of machinery or equipment might cause such mixtures to be produced.

(c)(2)(vi)(B) The EX classification usually includes the working areas of grain handling and storage plants, room containing grinders or pulverizers, cleaners, graders, scalpers, open conveyors or spouts, open bins or hoppers, mixers, or blenders, automatic or hopper scales, packing machinery, elevator heads and boots, stock distributors, dust and stock collectors (except all-metal collectors vented to the outside), and all similar dust producing machinery and equipment in grain processing plants, starch plants, sugar pulverizing plants, malting plants, hay grinding plants, and other occupancies of similar nature; coal pulverizing plants (except where the pulverizing equipment is essentially dust tight); all working areas where metal dusts and powders are produced, processed, handled, packed, or stored (except in tight containers); and other similar locations where combustible dust may, under normal operating conditions, be present in the air in quantities sufficient to produce explosive or ignitable mixtures.

(c)(2)(vii) Only approved power-operated industrial trucks designated as DY, EE, or EX shall be used in atmospheres in which combustible dust will not normally be in suspension in the air or will not be likely to be thrown into suspension by the normal operation of equipment or apparatus in quantities sufficient to produce explosive or ignitable mixtures but where deposits or accumulations of such dust may be ignited by arcs or sparks originating in the truck.

(c)(2)(viii) Only approved power-operated industrial trucks designated as DY, EE, or EX shall be used in locations which are hazardous because of the presence of easily ignitable fibers or flyings but in which such fibers or flyings are not likely to be in suspension in the air in quantities sufficient to produce ignitable mixtures.

(c)(2)(ix) Only approved power-operated industrial trucks designated as DS, DY, ES, EE, EX, GS, or LPS shall be used in locations where easily ignitable fibers are stored or handled, including outside storage, but are not being processed or manufactured. Industrial trucks designated as E, which have been previously used in these locations may be continued in use.

(c)(2)(x) On piers and wharves handling general cargo, any approved power-operated industrial truck designated as Type D, E, G, or LP may be used, or trucks which conform to the requirements for these types may be used.

(c)(2)(xi) If storage warehouses and outside storage locations are hazardous only the approved power-operated industrial truck specified for such locations in this paragraph (c)(2) shall be used. If not classified as hazardous, any approved power-operated industrial truck designated as Type D, E, G, or LP may be used, or trucks which conform to the requirements for these types may be used.

(c)(2)(xii) If general industrial or commercial properties are hazardous, only approved power-operated industrial trucks specified for such locations in this paragraph (c)(2) shall be used. If not classified as hazardous, any approved power-operated industrial truck designated as Type D, E, G, or LP may be used, or trucks which conform to the requirements of these types may be used.

(d) **Converted industrial trucks** Power-operated industrial trucks that have been originally approved for the use of gasoline for fuel, when converted to the use of liquefied petroleum gas fuel in accordance with paragraph (q) of this Section, may be used in those locations where G, GS or LP, and LPS designated trucks have been specified in the preceding paragraphs.

(e) **Safety guards**

(e)(1) High Lift Rider trucks shall be fitted with an overhead guard manufactured in accordance with paragraph (a)(2) of this Section, unless operating conditions do not permit.

(e)(2) If the type of load presents a hazard, the user shall equip fork trucks with a vertical load backrest extension manufactured in accordance with paragraph (a)(2) of this Section.

(f) **Fuel handling and storage**

(f)(1) The storage and handling of liquid fuels such as gasoline and diesel fuel shall be in accordance with NFPA Flammable and Combustible Liquids Code (NFPA No. 30–1969), which is incorporated by reference as specified in §1910.6.

(f)(2) The storage and handling of liquefied petroleum gas fuel shall be in accordance with NFPA Storage and Handling of Liquefied Petroleum Gases (NFPA No. 58–1969), which is incorporated by reference as specified in §1910.6.

(g) **Changing and charging storage batteries**

(g)(1) Battery charging installations shall be located in areas designated for that purpose.

(g)(2) Facilities shall be provided for flushing and neutralizing spilled electrolyte, for fire protection, for protecting charging apparatus from damage by trucks, and for adequate ventilation for dispersal of fumes from gassing batteries.

(g)(3) [Reserved]

(g)(4) A conveyor, overhead hoist, or equivalent material handling equipment shall be provided for handling batteries.

(g)(5) Reinstalled batteries shall be properly positioned and secured in the truck.

(g)(6) A carboy tilter or siphon shall be provided for handling electrolyte.

(g)(7) When charging batteries, acid shall be poured into water; water shall not be poured into acid.

(g)(8) Trucks shall be properly positioned and brake applied before attempting to change or charge batteries.

(g)(9) Care shall be taken to assure that vent caps are functioning. The battery (or compartment) cover(s) shall be open to dissipate heat.

(g)(10) Smoking shall be prohibited in the charging area.

(g)(11) Precautions shall be taken to prevent open flames, sparks, or electric arcs in battery charging areas.

(g)(12) Tools and other metallic objects shall be kept away from the top of uncovered batteries.

(h) **Lighting for operating areas**

(h)(1) [Reserved]

(h)(2) Where general lighting is less than 2 lumens per square foot, auxiliary directional lighting shall be provided on the truck.

(i) **Control of noxious gases and fumes**

(i)(1) Concentration levels of carbon monoxide gas created by powered industrial truck operations shall not exceed the levels specified in §1910.1000.

(j) **Dockboards (bridge plates)** See Subpart D of this Part

(k) **Trucks and railroad cars**

(k)(1) The brakes of highway trucks shall be set and wheel chocks placed under the rear wheels to prevent the trucks from rolling while they are boarded with powered industrial trucks.

(k)(2) Wheel stops or other recognized positive protection shall be provided to prevent railroad cars from moving during loading or unloading operations.

(k)(3) Fixed jacks may be necessary to support a semitrailer and prevent upending during the loading or unloading when the trailer is not coupled to a tractor.

(k)(4) Positive protection shall be provided to prevent railroad cars from being moved while dockboards or bridge plates are in position.

(l) **Operator training**

(l)(1) **Safe operation**

(l)(1)(i) The employer shall ensure that each powered industrial truck operator is competent to operate a powered industrial truck safely, as demonstrated by the successful completion of the training and evaluation specified in this paragraph (l).

(l)(1)(ii) Prior to permitting an employee to operate a powered industrial truck (except for training purposes), the employer shall ensure that each operator has successfully completed the training required by this paragraph (l), except as permitted by paragraph (l)(5).

(l)(2) **Training program implementation**

(l)(2)(i) Trainees may operate a powered industrial truck only:

(l)(2)(i)(A) Under the direct supervision of persons who have the knowledge, training, and experience to train operators and evaluate their competence; and

(l)(2)(i)(B) Where such operation does not endanger the trainee or other employees.

(l)(2)(ii) Training shall consist of a combination of formal instruction (e.g., lecture, discussion, interactive computer learning, video tape, written material), practical training (demonstrations performed by the trainer and practical exercises performed by the trainee), and evaluation of the operator's performance in the workplace.

(l)(2)(iii) All operator training and evaluation shall be conducted by persons who have the knowledge, training, and experience to train powered industrial truck operators and evaluate their competence.

(l)(3) **Training program content** Powered industrial truck operators shall receive initial training in the following topics, except in topics which the employer can demonstrate are not applicable to safe operation of the truck in the employer's workplace.

(l)(3)(i) **Truck-related topics:**

(l)(3)(i)(A) Operating instructions, warnings, and precautions for the types of truck the operator will be authorized to operate;

(l)(3)(i)(B) Differences between the truck and the automobile;

(l)(3)(i)(C) Truck controls and instrumentation: where they are located, what they do, and how they work;

(l)(3)(i)(D) Engine or motor operation;

(l)(3)(i)(E) Steering and maneuvering;

(l)(3)(i)(F) Visibility (including restrictions due to loading);

(l)(3)(i)(G) Fork and attachment adaptation, operation, and use limitations;

(l)(3)(i)(H) Vehicle capacity;

(l)(3)(i)(I) Vehicle stability;

(l)(3)(i)(J) Any vehicle inspection and maintenance that the operator will be required to perform;

(l)(3)(i)(K) Refueling and/or charging and recharging of batteries;

(l)(3)(i)(L) Operating limitations;

(l)(3)(i)(M) Any other operating instructions, warnings, or precautions listed in the operator's manual for the types of vehicle that the employee is being trained to operate.

(l)(3)(ii) **Workplace-related topics:**

(l)(3)(ii)(A) Surface conditions where the vehicle will be operated;

(l)(3)(ii)(B) Composition of loads to be carried and load stability;

(l)(3)(ii)(C) Load manipulation, stacking, and unstacking;

(l)(3)(ii)(D) Pedestrian traffic in areas where the vehicle will be operated;

(l)(3)(ii)(E) Narrow aisles and other restricted places where the vehicle will be operated;

(l)(3)(ii)(F) Hazardous (classified) locations where the vehicle will be operated;

(l)(3)(ii)(G) Ramps and other sloped surfaces that could affect the vehicle's stability;

(l)(3)(ii)(H) Closed environments and other areas where insufficient ventilation or poor vehicle maintenance could cause a buildup of carbon monoxide or diesel exhaust;

(l)(3)(ii)(I) Other unique or potentially hazardous environmental conditions in the workplace that could affect safe operation.

(l)(3)(iii) The requirements of this Section

(l)(4) **Refresher training and evaluation**

(l)(4)(i) Refresher training, including an evaluation of the effectiveness of that training, shall be conducted as required by paragraph (l)(4)(ii) to ensure that the operator has the knowledge and skills needed to operate the powered industrial truck safely.

(l)(4)(ii) Refresher training in relevant topics shall be provided to the operator when:

(l)(4)(ii)(A) The operator has been observed to operate the vehicle in an unsafe manner;

(l)(4)(ii)(B) The operator has been involved in an accident or near-miss incident;

(l)(4)(ii)(C) The operator has received an evaluation that reveals that the operator is not operating the truck safely;

(l)(4)(ii)(D) The operator is assigned to drive a different type of truck; or

(l)(4)(ii)(E) A condition in the workplace changes in a manner that could affect safe operation of the truck.

(l)(4)(iii) An evaluation of each powered industrial truck operator's performance shall be conducted at least once every three years.

(l)(5) **Avoidance of duplicative training** If an operator has previously received training in a topic specified in paragraph (l)(3) of this Section, and such training is appropriate to the truck and working conditions encountered, additional training in that topic is not required if the operator has been evaluated and found competent to operate the truck safely.

(l)(6) **Certification** The employer shall certify that each operator has been trained and evaluated as required by this paragraph (l). The certification shall include the name of the operator, the date of the training, the date of the evaluation, and the identity of the person(s) performing the training or evaluation.

(l)(7) **Dates** The employer shall ensure that operators of powered industrial trucks are trained, as appropriate, by the dates shown in the following table.

If the employee was hired:	The initial training and evaluation of that employee must be completed:
Before December 1, 1999	By December 1, 1999.
After December 1, 1999	Before the employee is assigned to operate a powered industrial truck.

(l)(8) Appendix A to this Section provides non-mandatory guidance to assist employers in implementing this paragraph. (l). This Appendix does not add to, alter, or reduce the requirements of this Section.

(m) **Truck operations**

(m)(1) Trucks shall not be driven up to anyone standing in front of a bench or other fixed object.

(m)(2) No person shall be allowed to stand or pass under the elevated portion of any truck, whether loaded or empty.

(m)(3) Unauthorized personnel shall not be permitted to ride on powered industrial trucks. A safe place to ride shall be provided where riding of trucks is authorized.

(m)(4) The employer shall prohibit arms or legs from being placed between the uprights of the mast or outside the running lines of the truck.

(m)(5)

(m)(5)(i) When a powered industrial truck is left unattended, load engaging means shall be fully lowered, controls shall be neutralized, power shall be shut off, and brakes set. Wheels shall be blocked if the truck is parked on an incline.

(m)(5)(ii) A powered industrial truck is unattended when the operator is 25 ft. or more away from the vehicle which remains in his view, or whenever the operator leaves the vehicle and it is not in his view.

(m)(5)(iii) When the operator of an industrial truck is dismounted and within 25 ft. of the truck still in his view, the load engaging means shall be fully lowered, controls neutralized, and the brakes set to prevent movement.

(m)(6) A safe distance shall be maintained from the edge of ramps or platforms while on any elevated dock, or platform or freight car. Trucks shall not be used for opening or closing freight doors.

(m)(7) Brakes shall be set and wheel blocks shall be in place to prevent movement of trucks, trailers, or railroad cars while loading or unloading.

Fixed jacks may be necessary to support a semitrailer during loading or unloading when the trailer is not coupled to a tractor. The flooring of trucks, trailers, and railroad cars shall be checked for breaks and weakness before they are driven onto.

(m)(8) There shall be sufficient headroom under overhead installations, lights, pipes, sprinkler system, etc.

(m)(9) An overhead guard shall be used as protection against falling objects. It should be noted that an overhead guard is intended to offer protection from the impact of small packages, boxes, bagged material, etc., representative of the job application, but not to withstand the impact of a falling capacity load.

(m)(10) A load backrest extension shall be used whenever necessary to minimize the possibility of the load or part of it from falling rearward.

(m)(11) Only approved industrial trucks shall be used in hazardous locations.

(m)(12)–(13) [Reserved]

(m)(14) Fire aisles, access to stairways, and fire equipment shall be kept clear.

(n) **Traveling**

(n)(1) All traffic regulations shall be observed, including authorized plant speed limits. A safe distance shall be maintained approximately three truck lengths from the truck ahead, and the truck shall be kept under control at all times.

(n)(2) The right of way shall be yielded to ambulances, fire trucks, or other vehicles in emergency situations.

(n)(3) Other trucks traveling in the same direction at intersections, blind spots, or other dangerous locations shall not be passed.

(n)(4) The driver shall be required to slow down and sound the horn at cross aisles and other locations where vision is obstructed. If the load being carried obstructs forward view, the driver shall be required to travel with the load trailing.

(n)(5) Railroad tracks shall be crossed diagonally wherever possible. Parking closer than 8 feet from the center of railroad tracks is prohibited.

(n)(6) The driver shall be required to look in the direction of, and keep a clear view of the path of travel.

(n)(7) Grades shall be ascended or descended slowly.

(n)(7)(i) When ascending or descending grades in excess of 10 percent, loaded trucks shall be driven with the load upgrade.

(n)(7)(ii) [Reserved]

(n)(7)(iii) On all grades the load and load engaging means shall be tilted back if applicable, and raised only as far as necessary to clear the road surface.

(n)(8) OI Under all travel conditions the truck shall be operated at a speed that will permit it to be brought to a stop in a safe manner.

(n)(9) Stunt driving and horseplay shall not be permitted.

(n)(10) The driver shall be required to slow down for wet and slippery floors.

(n)(11) Dockboard or bridgeplates, shall be properly secured before they are driven over. Dockboard or bridgeplates shall be driven over carefully and slowly and their rated capacity never exceeded.

(n)(12) Elevators shall be approached slowly, and then entered squarely after the elevator car is properly leveled. Once on the elevator, the controls shall be neutralized, power shut off, and the brakes set.

(n)(13) Motorized hand trucks must enter elevator or other confined areas with load end forward.

(n)(14) Running over loose objects on the roadway surface shall be avoided.

(n)(15) OI While negotiating turns, speed shall be reduced to a safe level by means of turning the hand steering wheel in a smooth, sweeping motion. Except when maneuvering at a very low speed, the hand steering wheel shall be turned at a moderate, even rate.

(o) **Loading**

(o)(1) OI Only stable or safely arranged loads shall be handled. Caution shall be exercised when handling off-center loads which cannot be centered.

(o)(2) Only loads within the rated capacity of the truck shall be handled.

(o)(3) The long or high (including multiple-tiered) loads which may affect capacity shall be adjusted.

(o)(4) Trucks equipped with attachments shall be operated as partially loaded trucks when not handling a load.

(o)(5) A load engaging means shall be placed under the load as far as possible; the mast shall be carefully tilted backward to stabilize the load.

(o)(6) Extreme care shall be used when tilting the load forward or backward, particularly when high tiering. Tilting forward with load engaging means elevated shall be prohibited except to pick up a load. An elevated load shall not be tilted forward except when the load is in a deposit position over a rack or stack. When stacking or tiering, only enough backward tilt to stabilize the load shall be used.

(p) OI **Operation of the truck**

(p)(1) OI If at any time a powered industrial truck is found to be in need of repair, defective, or in any way unsafe, the truck shall be taken out of service until it has been restored to safe operating condition.

(p)(2) Fuel tanks shall not be filled while the engine is running. Spillage shall be avoided.

(p)(3) Spillage of oil or fuel shall be carefully washed away or completely evaporated and the fuel tank cap replaced before restarting engine.

(p)(4) No truck shall be operated with a leak in the fuel system until the leak has been corrected.

(p)(5) Open flames shall not be used for checking electrolyte level in storage batteries or gasoline level in fuel tanks.

(q) OI **Maintenance of industrial trucks**

(q)(1) OI Any power-operated industrial truck not in safe operating condition shall be removed from service. All repairs shall be made by authorized personnel.

(q)(2) No repairs shall be made in Class I, II, and III locations.

(q)(3) Those repairs to the fuel and ignition systems of industrial trucks which (q)involve fire hazards shall be conducted only in locations designated for such repairs.

(q)(4) Trucks in need of repairs to the electrical system shall have the battery disconnected prior to such repairs.

(q)(5) OI All parts of any such industrial truck requiring replacement shall be replaced only by parts equivalent as to safety with those used in the original design.

(q)(6) OI Industrial trucks shall not be altered so that the relative positions of the various parts are different from what they were when originally received from the manufacturer, nor shall they be altered either by the addition of extra parts not provided by the manufacturer or by the elimination of any parts, except as provided in paragraph (q)(12) of this Section. Additional counterweighting of fork trucks shall not be done unless approved by the truck manufacturer.

(q)(7) OI Industrial trucks shall be examined before being placed in service, and shall not be placed in service if the examination shows any condition adversely affecting the safety of the vehicle. Such examination shall be made at least daily.

Where industrial trucks are used on a round-the-clock basis, they shall be examined after each shift. Defects when found shall be immediately reported and corrected.

(q)(8) Water mufflers shall be filled daily or as frequently as is necessary to prevent depletion of the supply of water below 75 percent of the filled capacity. Vehicles with mufflers having screens or other parts that may become clogged shall not be operated while such screens or parts are clogged. Any vehicle that emits hazardous sparks or flames from the exhaust system shall immediately be removed from service, and not returned to service until the cause for the emission of such sparks and flames has been eliminated.

(q)(9) When the temperature of any part of any truck is found to be in excess of its normal operating temperature, thus creating a hazardous condition, the vehicle shall be removed from service and not returned to service until the cause for such overheating has been eliminated.

(q)(10) Industrial trucks shall be kept in a clean condition, free of lint, excess oil, and grease. Noncombustible agents should be used for cleaning trucks. Low flash point (below 100 °F.) solvents shall not be used. High flash point (at or above 100 °F.) solvents may be used. Precautions regarding toxicity, ventilation, and fire hazard shall be consonant with the agent or solvent used.

(q)(11) [Reserved]

(q)(12) Industrial trucks originally approved for the use of gasoline for fuel may be converted to liquefied petroleum gas fuel provided the complete conversion results in a truck which embodies the features specified for LP or LPS designated trucks. Such conversion equipment shall be approved. The description of the component parts of this conversion system and the recommended method of installation on specific trucks are contained in the "Listed by Report."

N Materials Handling and Storage — Powered industrial trucks

§1910.178 Appendix A
Stability of powered industrial trucks
(Nonmandatory Appendix to paragraph (L) of this section)

A–1. Definitions

The following definitions help to explain the principle of stability:

Center of gravity is the point on an object at which all of the object's weight is concentrated. For symmetrical loads, the center of gravity is at the middle of the load.

Counterweight is the weight that is built into the truck's basic structure and is used to offset the load's weight and to maximize the vehicle's resistance to tipping over.

Fulcrum is the truck's axis of rotation when it tips over.

Grade is the slope of a surface, which is usually measured as the number of feet of rise or fall over a hundred foot horizontal distance (the slope is expressed as a percent).

Lateral stability is a truck's resistance to overturning sideways.

Line of action is an imaginary vertical line through an object's center of gravity.

Load center is the horizontal distance from the load's edge (or the fork's or other attachment's vertical face) to the line of action through the load's center of gravity.

Longitudinal stability is the truck's resistance to overturning forward or rearward.

Moment is the product of the object's weight times the distance from a fixed point (usually the fulcrum). In the case of a powered industrial truck, the distance is measured from the point at which the truck will tip over to the object's line of action. The distance is always measured perpendicular to the line of action.

Track is the distance between the wheels on the same axle of the truck.

Wheelbase is the distance between the centerline of the vehicle's front and rear wheels.

A–2. General

A–2.1. Determining the stability of a powered industrial truck is simple once a few basic principles are understood. There are many factors that contribute to a vehicle's stability: the vehicle's wheelbase, track, and height; the load's weight distribution; and the vehicle's counterweight location (if the vehicle is so equipped).

A–2.2. The "stability triangle," used in most stability discussions, demonstrates stability simply.

A–3. Basic Principles

A–3.1. Whether an object is stable depends on the object's moment at one end of a system being greater than, equal to, or smaller than the object's moment at the system's other end. This principle can be seen in the way a see-saw or teeter-totter works: that is, if the product of the load and distance from the fulcrum (moment) is equal to the moment at the device's other end, the device is balanced and it will not move. However, if there is a greater moment at one end of the device, the device will try to move downward at the end with the greater moment.

A–3.2. The longitudinal stability of a counterbalanced powered industrial truck depends on the vehicle's moment and the load's moment. In other words, if the mathematic product of the load moment (the distance from the front wheels, the approximate point at which the vehicle would tip forward) to the load's center of gravity times the load's weight is less than the vehicle's moment, the system is balanced and will not tip forward. However, if the load's moment is greater than the vehicle's moment, the greater load-moment will force the truck to tip forward.

A–4. The Stability Triangle

A–4.1. Almost all counterbalanced powered industrial trucks have a three-point suspension system, that is, the vehicle is supported at three points. This is true even if the vehicle has four wheels. The truck's steer axle is attached to the truck by a pivot pin in the axle's center. When the points are connected with imaginary lines, this three-point support forms a triangle called the stability triangle. Figure 1 depicts the stability triangle.

Figure 1

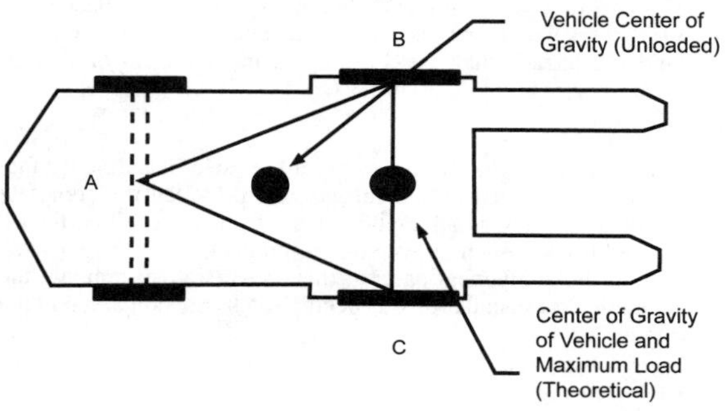

Notes:

1. When the vehicle is loaded, the combined center of gravity (CG) shifts toward line B–C. Theoretically the maximum load will result in the CG at the line B–C. In actual practice, the combined CG should never be at line B–C.
2. The addition of additional counterweight will cause the truck CG to shift toward point A and result in a truck that is less stable laterally.

A–4.2. When the vehicle's line of action, or load center, falls within the stability triangle, the vehicle is stable and will not tip over. However, when the vehicle's line of action or the vehicle/load combination falls outside the stability triangle, the vehicle is unstable and may tip over. (See Figure 2.)

Figure 2

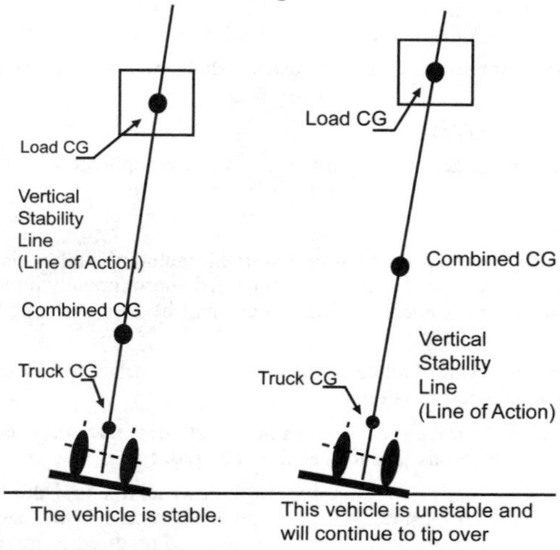

A–5. Longitudinal Stability

A–5.1. The axis of rotation when a truck tips forward is the front wheels' points of contact with the pavement. When a powered industrial truck tips forward, the truck will rotate about this line. When a truck is stable, the vehicle-moment must exceed the load-moment. As long as the vehicle-moment is equal to or exceeds the load-moment, the vehicle will not tip over. On the other hand, if the load moment slightly exceeds the vehicle-moment, the truck will begin to tip forward, thereby causing the rear to lose contact with the floor or ground and resulting in loss of steering control. If the load-moment greatly exceeds the vehicle moment, the truck will tip forward.

A–5.2. To determine the maximum safe load-moment, the truck manufacturer normally rates the truck at a maximum load at a given distance from the front face of the forks. The specified distance from the front face of the forks to the line of action of the load is commonly called the load center. Because larger trucks normally handle loads that are physically larger, these vehicles have greater load centers. Trucks with a capacity of 30,000 pounds or less are normally rated at a given load weight at a 24-inch load center. Trucks with a capacity greater than 30,000 pounds are normally rated at a given load weight at a 36- or 48-inch load center. To safely operate the vehicle, the operator should always check the data plate to determine the maximum allowable weight at the rated load center.

A–5.3. Although the true load-moment distance is measured from the front wheels, this distance is greater than the distance from the front face of the forks. Calculating the maximum allowable load-moment using the load-center distance always provides a lower load-moment than the truck was designed to handle. When handling unusual loads, such as those that are larger than 48 inches long (the center of gravity is greater than 24 inches) or that have an offset center of gravity, etc., a maximum allowable load-moment should be calculated and used to determine whether a load can be safely handled. For example, if an operator is operating a 3000 pound capacity truck (with a 24-inch load center), the maximum allowable load-moment is 72,000 inch-pounds (3,000 times 24). If a load is 60 inches long (30-inch load center), then the maximum that this load can weigh is 2,400 pounds (72,000 divided by 30).

A–6. Lateral Stability

A–6.1. The vehicle's lateral stability is determined by the line of action's position (a vertical line that passes through the combined vehicle's and load's center of gravity) relative to the stability triangle. When the vehicle is not loaded, the truck's center of gravity location is the only factor to be considered in determining the truck's stability. As long as the line of action of the combined vehicle's and load's center of gravity falls within the stability triangle, the truck is stable and will not tip over. However, if the line of action falls outside the stability triangle, the truck is not stable and may tip over. Refer to Figure 2.

A–6.2. Factors that affect the vehicle's lateral stability include the load's placement on the truck, the height of the load above the surface on which the vehicle is operating, and the vehicle's degree of lean.

A–7. Dynamic Stability

A–7.1. Up to this point, the stability of a powered industrial truck has been discussed without considering the dynamic forces that result when the vehicle and load are put into motion. The weight's transfer and the resultant shift in the center of gravity due to the dynamic forces created when the machine is moving, braking, cornering, lifting, tilting, and lowering loads, etc., are important stability considerations.

A–7.2. When determining whether a load can be safely handled, the operator should exercise extra caution when handling loads that cause the vehicle to approach its maximum design characteristics. For example, if an operator must handle a maximum load, the load should be carried at the lowest position possible, the truck should be accelerated slowly and evenly, and the forks should be tilted forward cautiously. However, no precise rules can be formulated to cover all of these eventualities.

[39 FR 23502, June 27, 1974, as amended at 40 FR 23073, May 28, 1975; 43 FR 49749, Oct. 24, 1978; 49 FR 5322, Feb. 10, 1984; 53 FR 12122, Apr. 12, 1988; 55 FR 32015, Aug 6, 1990; 61 FR 9239, Mar. 7, 1996; 63 FR 66270, Dec. 1, 1998; 68 FR 32638, June 2, 2003; 71 FR 16672, Apr. 3, 2006]

§1910.179 [OI] Overhead and gantry cranes

(a) **Definitions applicable to this Section**

(a)(1) A **crane** is a machine for lifting and lowering a load and moving it horizontally, with the hoisting mechanism an integral part of the machine. Cranes whether fixed or mobile are driven manually or by power.

(a)(2) [OI] An **automatic crane** is a crane which when activated operates through a preset cycle or cycles.

(a)(3) A **cab-operated crane** is a crane controlled by an operator in a cab located on the bridge or trolley.

(a)(4) **Cantilever gantry crane** means a gantry or semigantry crane in which the bridge girders or trusses extend transversely beyond the crane runway on one or both sides.

(a)(5) **Floor-operated crane** means a crane which is pendant or nonconductive rope controlled by an operator on the floor or an independent platform.

(a)(6) **Gantry crane** means a crane similar to an overhead crane except that the bridge for carrying the trolley or trolleys is rigidly supported on two or more legs running on fixed rails or other runway.

(a)(7) **Hot metal handling crane** means an overhead crane used for transporting or pouring molten material.

(a)(8) **Overhead crane** means a crane with a movable bridge carrying a movable or fixed hoisting mechanism and traveling on an overhead fixed runway structure.

(a)(9) **Power-operated crane** means a crane whose mechanism is driven by electric, air, hydraulic, or internal combustion means.

(a)(10) A **pulpit-operated crane** is a crane operated from a fixed operator station not attached to the crane.

(a)(11) A **remote-operated crane** is a crane controlled by an operator not in a pulpit or in the cab attached to the crane, by any method other than pendant or rope control.

(a)(12) A **semigantry crane** is a gantry crane with one end of the bridge rigidly supported on one or more legs that run on a fixed rail or runway, the other end of the bridge being supported by a truck running on an elevated rail or runway.

(a)(13) **Storage bridge crane** means a gantry type crane of long span usually used for bulk storage of material; the bridge girders or trusses are rigidly or nonrigidly supported on one or more legs. It may have one or more fixed or hinged cantilever ends.

(a)(14) **Wall crane** means a crane having a jib with or without trolley and supported from a side wall or line of columns of a building. It is a traveling type and operates on a runway attached to the side wall or columns.

(a)(15) **Appointed** means assigned specific responsibilities by the employer or the employer's representative.

(a)(16) **ANSI** means the American National Standards Institute.

(a)(17) An **auxiliary hoist** is a supplemental hoisting unit of lighter capacity and usually higher speed than provided for the main hoist.

(a)(18) A **brake** is a device used for retarding or stopping motion by friction or power means.

(a)(19) A **drag brake** is a brake which provides retarding force without external control.

(a)(20) A **holding brake** is a brake that automatically prevents motion when power is off.

(a)(21) **Bridge** means that part of a crane consisting of girders, trucks, end ties, footwalks, and drive mechanism which carries the trolley or trolleys.

(a)(22) **Bridge travel** means the crane movement in a direction parallel to the crane runway.

(a)(23) A **bumper (buffer)** is an energy absorbing device for reducing impact when a moving crane or trolley reaches the end of its permitted travel; or when two moving cranes or trolleys come in contact.

(a)(24) The **cab** is the operator's compartment on a crane.

(a)(25) **Clearance** means the distance from any part of the crane to a point of the nearest obstruction.

(a)(26) **Collectors current** are contacting devices for collecting current from runway or bridge conductors.

(a)(27) **Conductors, bridge** are the electrical conductors located along the bridge structure of a crane to provide power to the trolley.

(a)(28) **Conductors, runway (main)** are the electrical conductors located along a crane runway to provide power to the crane.

(a)(29) The **control braking** means is a method of controlling crane motor speed when in an overhauling condition.

(a)(30) **Countertorque** means a method of control by which the power to the motor is reversed to develop torque in the opposite direction.

(a)(31) **Dynamic** means a method of controlling crane motor speeds when in the overhauling condition to provide a retarding force.

(a)(32) **Regenerative** means a form of dynamic braking in which the electrical energy generated is fed back into the power system.

(a)(33) **Mechanical** means a method of control by friction.

(a)(34) **Controller, spring return** means a controller which when released will return automatically to a neutral position.

(a)(35) [OI] **Designated** means selected or assigned by the employer or the employer's representative as being qualified to perform specific duties.

(a)(36) A **drift point** means a point on a travel motion controller which releases the brake while the motor is not energized. This allows for coasting before the brake is set.

(a)(37) The **drum** is the cylindrical member around which the ropes are wound for raising or lowering the load.

(a)(38) An **equalizer** is a device which compensates for unequal length or stretch of a rope.

(a)(39) **Exposed** means capable of being contacted inadvertently. Applied to hazardous objects not adequately guarded or isolated.

(a)(40) **Fail-safe** means a provision designed to automatically stop or safely control any motion in which a malfunction occurs.

(a)(41) **Footwalk** means the walkway with handrail, attached to the bridge or trolley for access purposes.

(a)(42) A **hoist** is an apparatus which may be a part of a crane, exerting a force for lifting or lowering.

(a)(43) **Hoist chain** means the load bearing chain in a hoist.

Note: Chain properties do not conform to those shown in ANSI B30.9–1971, Safety Code for Slings.

(a)(44) **Hoist motion** means that motion of a crane which raises and lowers a load.

(a)(45) **Load** means the total superimposed weight on the load block or hook.

(a)(46) The **load block** is the assembly of hook or shackle, swivel, bearing, sheaves, pins, and frame suspended by the hoisting rope.

(a)(47) **Magnet** means an electromagnetic device carried on a crane hook to pick up loads magnetically.

(a)(48) **Main hoist** means the hoist mechanism provided for lifting the maximum rated load.

(a)(49) A **man trolley** is a trolley having an operator's cab attached thereto.

(a)(50) **Rated load** means the maximum load for which a crane or individual hoist is designed and built by the manufacturer and shown on the equipment nameplate(s).

(a)(51) **Rope** refers to wire rope, unless otherwise specified.

(a)(52) **Running sheave** means a sheave which rotates as the load block is raised or lowered.

(a)(53) **Runway** means an assembly of rails, beams, girders, brackets, and framework on which the crane or trolley travels.

(a)(54) **Side pull** means that portion of the hoist pull acting horizontally when the hoist lines are not operated vertically.

(a)(55) **Span** means the horizontal distance center to center of runway rails.

(a)(56) **Standby crane** means a crane which is not in regular service but which is used occasionally or intermittently as required.

(a)(57) A **stop** is a device to limit travel of a trolley or crane bridge. This device normally is attached to a fixed structure and normally does not have energy absorbing ability.

(a)(58) A **switch** is a device for making, breaking, or for changing the connections in an electric circuit.

(a)(59) An **emergency stop** switch is a manually or automatically operated electric switch to cut off electric power independently of the regular operating controls.

(a)(60) A **limit switch** is a switch which is operated by some part or motion of a power-driven machine or equipment to alter the electric circuit associated with the machine or equipment.

(a)(61) A **main switch** is a switch controlling the entire power supply to the crane.

(a)(62) A **master switch** is a switch which dominates the operation of contactors, relays, or other remotely operated devices.

(a)(63) The **trolley** is the unit which travels on the bridge rails and carries the hoisting mechanism.

(a)(64) **Trolley travel** means the trolley movement at right angles to the crane runway.

(a)(65) **Truck** means the unit consisting of a frame, wheels, bearings, and axles which supports the bridge girders or trolleys.

(b) General requirements

(b)(1) **Application** This Section applies to overhead and gantry cranes, including semigantry, cantilever gantry, wall cranes, storage bridge cranes, and others having the same fundamental characteristics. These cranes are grouped because they all have trolleys and similar travel characteristics.

(b)(2) **New and existing equipment** All new overhead and gantry cranes constructed and installed on or after August 31, 1971, shall meet the design specifications of the American National Standard Safety Code for Overhead and Gantry Cranes, ANSI B30.2.0–1967, which is incorporated by reference as specified in §1910.6.

(b)(3) **Modifications** Cranes may be modified and rerated provided such modifications and the supporting structure are checked thoroughly for the new rated load by a qualified engineer or the equipment manufacturer. The crane shall be tested in accordance with paragraph (k)(2) of this Section. New rated load shall be displayed in accordance with subparagraph (5) of this paragraph.

(b)(4) **Wind indicators and rail clamps** Outdoor storage bridges shall be provided with automatic rail clamps. A wind-indicating device shall be provided which will give a visible or audible alarm to the bridge operator at a predetermined wind velocity. If the clamps act on the rail heads, any beads or weld flash on the rail heads shall be ground off.

(b)(5) **Rated load marking** The rated load of the crane shall be plainly marked on each side of the crane, and if the crane has more than one hoisting unit, each hoist shall have its rated load marked on it or its load block and this marking shall be clearly legible from the ground or floor.

(b)(6) Clearance from obstruction

(b)(6)(i) Minimum clearance of 3 inches overhead and 2 inches laterally shall be provided and maintained between crane and obstructions in conformity with Crane Manufacturers Association of America, Inc., Specification No. 61, which is incorporated by reference as specified in §1910.6 (formerly the Electric Overhead Crane Institute, Inc).

(b)(6)(ii) Where passageways or walkways are provided obstructions shall not be placed so that safety of personnel will be jeopardized by movements of the crane.

(b)(7) **Clearance between parallel cranes** If the runways of two cranes are parallel, and there are no intervening walls or structure, there shall be adequate clearance provided and maintained between the two bridges.

(b)(8) **Designated personnel** — Only designated personnel shall be permitted to operate a crane covered by this Section.

(c) Cabs

(c)(1) Cab location

(c)(1)(i) The general arrangement of the cab and the location of control and protective equipment shall be such that all operating handles are within convenient reach of the operator when facing the area to be served by the load hook, or while facing the direction of travel of the cab. The arrangement shall allow the operator a full view of the load hook in all positions.

(c)(1)(ii) The cab shall be located to afford a minimum of 3 inches clearance from all fixed structures within its area of possible movement.

(c)(2) **Access to crane** Access to the car and/or bridge walkway shall be by a conveniently placed fixed ladder, stairs, or platform requiring no step over any gap exceeding 12 inches (30 cm). Fixed ladders must comply with Subpart D of this Part.

(c)(3) **Fire extinguisher** Carbon tetrachloride extinguishers shall not be used.

(c)(4) **Lighting** Light in the cab shall be sufficient to enable the operator to see clearly enough to perform his work.

(d) Footwalks and ladders

(d)(1) Location of footwalks

(d)(1)(i) If sufficient headroom is available on cab-operated cranes, a footwalk shall be provided on the drive side along the entire length of the bridge of all cranes having the trolley running on the top of the girders.

(d)(1)(ii) Where footwalks are located in no case shall less than 48 inches of headroom be provided.

(d)(2) Construction of footwalks

(d)(2)(i) Footwalks shall be of rigid construction and designed to sustain a distributed load of at least 50 pounds per square foot.

(d)(2)(ii) Footwalks shall have a walking surface of antislip type.

Note: Wood will meet this requirement.

(d)(2)(iii) [Reserved]

(d)(2)(iv) The inner edge shall extend at least to the line of the outside edge of the lower cover plate or flange of the girder.

(d)(3) **Toeboards and handrails for footwalks** Toeboards and handrails must comply with Subpart D of this Part.

(d)(4) Ladders and stairways

(d)(4)(i) Gantry cranes shall be provided with ladders or stairways extending from the ground to the footwalk or cab platform.

(d)(4)(ii) Stairways shall be equipped with rigid and substantial metal handrails. Walking surfaces shall be of an antislip type.

(d)(4)(iii) Ladders shall be permanently and securely fastened in place and constructed in compliance with Subpart D of this Part.

(e) Stops, bumpers, rail sweeps, and guards

(e)(1) Trolley stops

(e)(1)(i) Stops shall be provided at the limits of travel of the trolley.

(e)(1)(ii) Stops shall be fastened to resist forces applied when contacted.

(e)(1)(iii) A stop engaging the tread of the wheel shall be of a height at least equal to the radius of the wheel.

(e)(2) Bridge bumpers

(e)(2)(i) A crane shall be provided with bumpers or other automatic means providing equivalent effect, unless the crane travels at a slow rate of speed and has a faster deceleration rate due to the use of sleeve bearings, or is not operated near the ends of bridge and trolley travel, or is restricted to a limited distance by the nature of the crane operation and there is no hazard of striking any object in this limited distance, or is used in similar operating conditions. The bumpers shall be capable of stopping the crane (not including the lifted load) at an average rate of deceleration not to exceed 3 ft/s/s when traveling in either direction at 20 percent of the rated load speed.

(e)(2)(i)(A) The bumpers shall have sufficient energy absorbing capacity to stop the crane when traveling at a speed of at least 40 percent of rated load speed.

(e)(2)(i)(B) The bumper shall be so mounted that there is no direct shear on bolts.

(e)(2)(ii) Bumpers shall be so designed and installed as to minimize parts falling from the crane in case of breakage.

(e)(3) Trolley bumpers

(e)(3)(i) A trolley shall be provided with bumpers or other automatic means of equivalent effect, unless the trolley travels at a slow rate of speed, or is not operated near the ends of bridge and trolley travel, or is restricted to a limited distance of the runway and there is no hazard of striking any object in this limited distance, or is used in similar operating conditions. The bumpers shall be capable of stopping the trolley (not including the lifted load) at an average rate of deceleration not to exceed 4.7 ft/s/s when traveling in either direction at one-third of the rated load speed.

(e)(3)(ii) When more than one trolley is operated on the same bridge, each shall be equipped with bumpers or equivalent on their adjacent ends.

(e)(3)(iii) Bumpers or equivalent shall be designed and installed to minimize parts falling from the trolley in case of age.

(e)(4) **Rail sweeps** Bridge trucks shall be equipped with sweeps which extend below the top of the rail and project in front of the truck wheels.

(e)(5) Guards for hoisting ropes

(e)(5)(i) If hoisting ropes run near enough to other parts to make fouling or chafing possible, guards shall be installed to prevent this condition.

(e)(5)(ii) A guard shall be provided to prevent contact between bridge conductors and hoisting ropes if they could come into contact.

(e)(6) **Guards for moving parts**

(e)(6)(i) Exposed moving parts such as gears, set screws, projecting keys, chains, chain sprockets, and reciprocating components which might constitute a hazard under normal operating conditions shall be guarded.

(e)(6)(ii) Guards shall be securely fastened.

(e)(6)(iii) Each guard shall be capable of supporting without permanent distortion the weight of a 200–pound person unless the guard is located where it is impossible for a person to step on it.

(f) **Brakes**

(f)(1) **Brakes for hoists**

(f)(1)(i) OI Each independent hoisting unit of a crane shall be equipped with at least one self-setting brake, hereafter referred to as a holding brake, applied directly to the motor shaft or some part of the gear train.

(f)(1)(ii) OI Each independent hoisting unit of a crane, except worm-geared hoists, the angle of whose worm is such as to prevent the load from accelerating in the lowering direction shall, in addition to a holding brake, be equipped with control braking means to prevent overspeeding.

(f)(2) **Holding brakes**

(f)(2)(i) Holding brakes for hoist motors shall have not less than the following percentage of the full load hoisting torque at the point where the brake is applied.

(f)(2)(i)(A) 125 percent when used with a control braking means other than mechanical.

(f)(2)(i)(B) 100 percent when used in conjunction with a mechanical control braking means.

(f)(2)(i)(C) 100 percent each if two holding brakes are provided.

(f)(2)(ii) Holding brakes on hoists shall have ample thermal capacity for the frequency of operation required by the service.

(f)(2)(iii) Holding brakes on hoists shall be applied automatically when power is removed.

(f)(2)(iv) Where necessary holding brakes shall be provided with adjustment means to compensate for wear.

(f)(2)(v) The wearing surface of all holding-brake drums or discs shall be smooth.

(f)(2)(vi) Each independent hoisting unit of a crane handling hot metal and having power control braking means shall be equipped with at least two holding brakes.

(f)(3) **Control braking means**

(f)(3)(i) A power control braking means such as regenerative, dynamic or countertorque braking, or a mechanically controlled braking means shall be capable of maintaining safe lowering speeds of rated loads.

(f)(3)(ii) The control braking means shall have ample thermal capacity for the frequency of operation required by service.

(f)(4) **Brakes for trolleys and bridges**

(f)(4)(i) Foot-operated brakes shall not require an applied force of more than 70 pounds to develop manufacturer's rated brake torque.

(f)(4)(ii) Brakes may be applied by mechanical, electrical, pneumatic, hydraulic, or gravity means.

(f)(4)(iii) Where necessary brakes shall be provided with adjustment means to compensate for wear.

(f)(4)(iv) The wearing surface of all brakedrums or discs shall be smooth.

(f)(4)(v) All foot-brake pedals shall be constructed so that the operator's foot will not easily slip off the pedal.

(f)(4)(vi) Foot-operated brakes shall be equipped with automatic means for positive release when pressure is released from the pedal.

(f)(4)(vii) Brakes for stopping the motion of the trolley or bridge shall be of sufficient size to stop the trolley or bridge within a distance in feet equal to 10 percent of full load speed in feet per minute when traveling at full speed with full load.

(f)(4)(viii) If holding brakes are provided on the bridge or trolleys, they shall not prohibit the use of a drift point in the control circuit.

(f)(4)(ix) Brakes on trolleys and bridges shall have ample thermal capacity for the frequency of operation required by the service to prevent impairment of functions from overheating.

(f)(5) **Application of trolley brakes**

(f)(5)(i) On cab-operated cranes with cab on trolley, a trolley brake shall be required as specified under paragraph (f)(4) of this Section.

(f)(5)(ii) A drag brake may be applied to hold the trolley in a desired position on the bridge and to eliminate creep with the power off.

(f)(6) **Application of bridge brakes**

(f)(6)(i) On cab-operated cranes with cab on bridge, a bridge brake is required as specified under paragraph (f)(4) of this Section.

(f)(6)(ii) On cab-operated cranes with cab on trolley, a bridge brake of the holding type shall be required.

(f)(6)(iii) On all floor, remote and pulpit-operated crane bridge drives, a brake of noncoasting mechanical drive shall be provided.

(g) **Electric equipment**

(g)(1) **General**

(g)(1)(i) Wiring and equipment shall comply with Subpart S of this Part.

(g)(1)(ii) The control circuit voltage shall not exceed 600 volts for a.c. or d.c. current.

(g)(1)(iii) The voltage at pendant push-buttons shall not exceed 150 volts for a.c. and 300 volts for d.c.

(g)(1)(iv) Where multiple conductor cable is used with a suspended pushbutton station, the station must be supported in some satisfactory manner that will protect the electrical conductors against strain.

(g)(1)(v) Pendant control boxes shall be constructed to prevent electrical shock and shall be clearly marked for identification of functions.

(g)(2) **Equipment**

(g)(2)(i) Electrical equipment shall be so located or enclosed that live parts will not be exposed to accidental contact under normal operating conditions.

(g)(2)(ii) Electric equipment shall be protected from dirt, grease, oil, and moisture.

(g)(2)(iii) Guards for live parts shall be substantial and so located that they cannot be accidently deformed so as to make contact with the live parts.

(g)(3) **Controllers**

(g)(3)(i) Cranes not equipped with spring-return controllers or momentary contact pushbuttons shall be provided with a device which will disconnect all motors from the line on failure of power and will not permit any motor to be restarted until the controller handle is brought to the "off" position, or a reset switch or button is operated.

(g)(3)(ii) Lever operated controllers shall be provided with a notch or latch which in the "off" position prevents the handle from being inadvertently moved to the "on" position. An "off" detent or spring return arrangement is acceptable.

(g)(3)(iii) The controller operating handle shall be located within convenient reach of the operator.

(g)(3)(iv) As far as practicable, the movement of each controller handle shall be in the same general directions as the resultant movements of the load.

(g)(3)(v) The control for the bridge and trolley travel shall be so located that the operator can readily face the direction of travel.

(g)(3)(vi) For floor-operated cranes, the controller or controllers if rope operated, shall automatically return to the "off" position when released by the operator.

(g)(3)(vii) Pushbuttons in pendant stations shall return to the "off" position when pressure is released by the crane operator.

(g)(3)(viii) Automatic cranes shall be so designed that all motions shall fail-safe if any malfunction of operation occurs.

(g)(3)(ix) Remote-operated cranes shall function so that if the control signal for any crane motion becomes ineffective the crane motion shall stop.

(g)(4) **Resistors**

(g)(4)(i) Enclosures for resistors shall have openings to provide adequate ventilation, and shall be installed to prevent the accumulation of combustible matter too near to hot parts.

(g)(4)(ii) Resistor units shall be supported so as to be as free as possible from vibration.

(g)(4)(iii) Provision shall be made to prevent broken parts or molten metal falling upon the operator or from the crane.

(g)(5) **Switches**

(g)(5)(i) The power supply to the runway conductors shall be controlled by a switch or circuit breaker located on a fixed structure, accessible from the floor, and arranged to be locked in the open position.

(g)(5)(ii) On cab-operated cranes a switch or circuit breaker of the enclosed type, with provision for locking in the open position, shall be provided in the leads from the runway conductors. A means of opening this switch or circuit breaker shall be located within easy reach of the operator.

(g)(5)(iii) On floor-operated cranes, a switch or circuit breaker of the enclosed type, with provision for locking in the open position, shall be provided in the leads from the runway conductors. This disconnect shall be mounted on the bridge or footwalk near the runway collectors. One of the following types of floor-operated disconnects shall be provided:

(g)(5)(iii)(A) Nonconductive rope attached to the main disconnect switch.

(g)(5)(iii)(B) An undervoltage trip for the main circuit breaker operated by an emergency stop button in the pendant pushbutton in the pendant pushbutton station.

(g)(5)(iii)(C) A main line contactor operated by a switch or pushbutton in the pendant pushbutton station.

(g)(5)(iv) The hoisting motion of all electric traveling cranes shall be provided with an overtravel limit switch in the hoisting direction.

(g)(5)(v) All cranes using a lifting magnet shall have a magnet circuit switch of the enclosed type with provision for locking in the open position. Means for discharging the inductive load of the magnet shall be provided.

(g)(6) **Runway conductors** Conductors of the open type mounted on the crane runway beams or overhead shall be so located or so guarded that persons entering or leaving the cab or crane footwalk normally could not come into contact with them.

(g)(7) **Extension lamps** If a service receptacle is provided in the cab or on the bridge of cab-operated cranes, it shall be a grounded three-prong type permanent receptacle, not exceeding 300 volts.

(h) **Hoisting equipment**

(h)(1) **Sheaves**

(h)(1)(i) Sheave grooves shall be smooth and free from surface defects which could cause rope damage.

(h)(1)(ii) Sheaves carrying ropes which can be momentarily unloaded shall be provided with close-fitting guards or other suitable devices to guide the rope back into the groove when the load is applied again.

(h)(1)(iii) The sheaves in the bottom block shall be equipped with close-fitting guards that will prevent ropes from becoming fouled when the block is lying on the ground with ropes loose.

(h)(1)(iv) Pockets and flanges of sheaves used with hoist chains shall be of such dimensions that the chain does not catch or bind during operation.

(h)(1)(v) All running sheaves shall be equipped with means for lubrication. Permanently lubricated, sealed and/or shielded bearings meet this requirement.

(h)(2) **Ropes**

(h)(2)(i) [OI] In using hoisting ropes, the crane manufacturer's recommendation shall be followed. The rated load divided by the number of parts of rope shall not exceed 20 percent of the nominal breaking strength of the rope.

(h)(2)(ii) Socketing shall be done in the manner specified by the manufacturer of the assembly.

(h)(2)(iii) Rope shall be secured to the drum as follows:

(h)(2)(iii)(A) [OI] No less than two wraps of rope shall remain on the drum when the hook is in its extreme low position.

(h)(2)(iii)(B) Rope end shall be anchored by a clamp securely attached to the drum, or by a socket arrangement approved by the crane or rope manufacturer.

(h)(2)(iv) Eye splices. [Reserved]

(h)(2)(v) Rope clips attached with U-bolts shall have the U-bolts on the dead or short end of the rope. Spacing and number of all types of clips shall be in accordance with the clip manufacturer's recommendation. Clips shall be drop-forged steel in all sizes manufactured commercially. When a newly installed rope has been in operation for an hour, all nuts on the clip bolts shall be retightened.

(h)(2)(vi) Swaged or compressed fittings shall be applied as recommended by the rope or crane manufacturer.

(h)(2)(vii) Wherever exposed to temperatures, at which fiber cores would be damaged, rope having an independent wirerope or wire-strand core, or other temperature-damage resistant core shall be used.

(h)(2)(viii) Replacement rope shall be the same size, grade, and construction as the original rope furnished by the crane manufacturer, unless otherwise recommended by a wire rope manufacturer due to actual working condition requirements.

(h)(3) **Equalizers** If a load is supported by more than one part of rope, the tension in the parts shall be equalized.

(h)(4) **Hooks** Hooks shall meet the manufacturer's recommendations and shall not be overloaded.

(i) [OI] **Warning device** Except for floor-operated cranes a gong or other effective warning signal shall be provided for each crane equipped with a power traveling mechanism.

(j) **Inspection**

(j)(1) [OI] **Inspection classification**

(j)(1)(i) **Initial inspection** Prior to initial use all new and altered cranes shall be inspected to insure compliance with the provisions of this Section.

(j)(1)(ii) Inspection procedure for cranes in regular service is divided into two general classifications based upon the intervals at which inspection should be performed. The intervals in turn are dependent upon the nature of the critical components of the crane and the degree of their exposure to wear, deterioration, or malfunction. The two general classifications are herein designated as "frequent" and "periodic" with respective intervals between inspections as defined below:

(j)(1)(ii)(A) Frequent inspection—Daily to monthly intervals;

(j)(1)(ii)(B) Periodic inspection—1 to 12– month intervals.

(j)(2) **Frequent inspection** The following items shall be inspected for defects at intervals as defined in paragraph (j)(1)(ii) of this Section or as specifically indicated, including observation during operation for any defects which might appear between regular inspections. All deficiencies such as listed shall be carefully examined and determination made as to whether they constitute a safety hazard:

(j)(2)(i) All functional operating mechanisms for maladjustment interfering with proper operation. Daily;

(j)(2)(ii) Deterioration or leakage in lines, tanks, valves, drain pumps, and other parts of air or hydraulic systems. Daily;

(j)(2)(iii) Hooks with deformation or cracks. Visual inspection daily; monthly inspection with a certification record which includes the date of inspection, the signature of the person who performed the inspection and the serial number, or other identifier, of the hook inspected. For hooks with cracks or having more than 15 percent in excess of normal throat opening or more than 10° twist from the plane of the unbent hook refer to paragraph (l)(3)(iii)(A) of this Section;

(j)(2)(iv) Hoist chains, including end connections, for excessive wear, twist, distorted links interfering with proper function, or stretch beyond manufacturer's recommendations. Visual inspection daily; monthly inspection with a certification record which includes the date of inspection, the signature of the person who performed the inspection and an identifier of the chain which was inspected

(j)(2)(v) [Reserved]

(j)(2)(vi) All functional operating mechanisms for excessive wear of components.

(j)(2)(vii) Rope reeving for noncompliance with manufacturer's recommendations.

(j)(3) [OI] **Periodic inspection** Complete inspections of the crane shall be performed at intervals as generally defined in paragraph (j)(1)(ii)(b) of this Section, depending upon its activity, severity of service, and environment, or as specifically indicated below. These inspections shall include the requirements of paragraph (j)(2) of this Section and in addition, the following items. Any deficiencies such as listed shall be carefully examined and determination made as to whether they constitute a safety hazard:

(j)(3)(i) Deformed, cracked, or corroded members;

(j)(3)(ii) Loose bolts or rivets;

(j)(3)(iii) Cracked or worn sheaves and drums;

(j)(3)(iv) Worn, cracked or distorted parts such as pins, bearings, shafts, gears, rollers, locking and clamping devices;

(j)(3)(v) Excessive wear on brake system parts, linings, pawls, and ratchets;

(j)(3)(vi) Load, wind, and other indicators over their full range, for any significant inaccuracies;

(j)(3)(vii) Gasoline, diesel, electric, or other powerplants for improper performance or noncompliance with applicable safety requirements;

(j)(3)(viii) Excessive wear of chain drive sprockets and excessive chain stretch;

(j)(3)(ix) [Reserved];

(j)(3)(x) Electrical apparatus, for signs of pitting or any deterioration of controller contactors, limit switches and pushbutton stations.

(j)(4) **Cranes not in regular use**

(j)(4)(i) A crane which has been idle for a period of 1 month or more, but less than 6 months, shall be given an inspection conforming with requirements of paragraph (j)(2) of this Section and paragraph (m)(2) of this Section before placing in service.

(j)(4)(ii) A crane which has been idle for a period of over 6 months shall be given a complete inspection conforming with requirements of paragraphs (j)(2) and (3) of this Section and paragraph (m)(2) of this Section before placing in service.

(j)(4)(iii) Standby cranes shall be inspected at least semi-annually in accordance with requirements of paragraph (j)(2) of this Section and paragraph (m)(2) of this Section.

(k) **Testing**

(k)(1) **Operational tests**

(k)(1)(i) Prior to initial use all new and altered cranes shall be tested to insure compliance with this Section including the following functions:

(k)(1)(i)(A) Hoisting and lowering;

(k)(1)(i)(B) Trolley travel;

(k)(1)(i)(C) Bridge travel;

(k)(1)(i)(D) Limit switches, locking and safety devices.

(k)(1)(ii) The trip setting of hoist limit switches shall be determined by tests with an empty hook traveling in increasing speeds up to the maximum speed. The actuating mechanism of the limit switch shall be located so that it will trip the switch, under all conditions, in sufficient time to prevent contact of the hook or hook block with any part of the trolley.

(k)(2) **Rated load test** Test loads shall not be more than 125 percent of the rated load unless otherwise recommended by the manufacturer. The test reports shall be placed on file where readily available to appointed personnel.

(l) **Maintenance**

(l)(1) **Preventive maintenance** A preventive maintenance program based on the crane manufacturer's recommendations shall be established.

(l)(2) **Maintenance procedure**

(l)(2)(i) Before adjustments and repairs are started on a crane the following precautions shall be taken;

(l)(2)(i)(A) The crane to be repaired shall be run to a location where it will cause the least interference with other cranes and operations in the area;

(l)(2)(i)(B) All controllers shall be at the off position;

(l)(2)(i)(C) The main or emergency switch shall be open and locked in the open position;

(l)(2)(i)(D) Warning or "out of order" signs shall be placed on the crane, also on the floor beneath or on the hook where visible from the floor;

(l)(2)(i)(E) Where other cranes are in operation on the same runway, rail stops or other suitable means shall be provided to prevent interference with the idle crane.

(l)(2)(ii) After adjustments and repairs have been made the crane shall not be operated until all guards have been reinstalled, safety devices reactivated and maintenance equipment removed.

(l)(3) **Adjustments and repairs**

(l)(3)(i) Any unsafe conditions disclosed by the inspection requirements of paragraph (j) of this Section shall be corrected before operation of the crane is resumed. Adjustments and repairs shall be done only by designated personnel.

(l)(3)(ii) Adjustments shall be maintained to assure correct functioning of components. The following are examples:

(l)(3)(ii)(A) All functional operating mechanisms;

(l)(3)(ii)(B) Limit switches;

(l)(3)(ii)(C) Control systems;

(l)(3)(ii)(D) Brakes;

(l)(3)(ii)(E) Power plants.

(l)(3)(iii) Repairs or replacements shall be provided promptly as needed for safe operation. The following are examples:

(l)(3)(iii)(A) Crane hooks showing defects described in paragraph (j)(2)(iii) of this Section shall be discarded. Repairs by welding or reshaping are not generally recommended. If such repairs are attempted they shall only be done under competent supervision and the hook shall be tested to the load requirements of paragraph (k)(2) of this Section before further use;

(l)(3)(iii)(B) Load attachment chains and rope slings showing defects described in paragraph (j)(2)(iv) and (v) of this Section respectively;

(l)(3)(iii)(C) All critical parts which are cracked, broken, bent, or excessively worn;

(l)(3)(iii)(D) Pendant control stations shall be kept clean and function labels kept legible.

(m) **Rope inspection**

(m)(1) **Running ropes** A thorough inspection of all ropes shall be made at least once a month and a certification record which includes the date of inspection, the signature of the person who performed the inspection and an identifier for the ropes which were inspected shall be kept on file where readily available to appointed personnel. Any deterioration, resulting in appreciable loss of original strength, shall be carefully observed and determination made as to whether further use of the rope would constitute a safety hazard. Some of the conditions that could result in an appreciable loss of strength are the following:

(m)(1)(i) Reduction of rope diameter below nominal diameter due to loss of core support, internal or external corrosion, or wear of outside wires;

(m)(1)(ii) A number of broken outside wires and the degree of distribution or concentration of such broken wires;

(m)(1)(iii) Worn outside wires;

(m)(1)(iv) Corroded or broken wires at end connections;

(m)(1)(v) Corroded, cracked, bent, worn, or improperly applied end connections;

(m)(1)(vi) Severe kinking, crushing, cutting, or unstranding.

(m)(2) **Other ropes** All rope which has been idle for a period of a month or more due to shutdown or storage of a crane on which it is installed shall be given a thorough inspection before it is used. This inspection shall be for all types of deterioration and shall be performed by an appointed person whose approval shall be required for further use of the rope. A certification record shall be available for inspection which includes the date of inspection, the signature of the person who performed the inspection and an identifier for the rope which was inspected.

(n) **Handling the load**

(n)(1) **Size of load** The crane shall not be loaded beyond its rated load except for test purposes as provided in paragraph (k) of this Section.

(n)(2) **Attaching the load**

(n)(2)(i) The hoist chain or hoist rope shall be free from kinks or twists and shall not be wrapped around the load.

(n)(2)(ii) The load shall be attached to the load block hook by means of slings or other approved devices.

(n)(2)(iii) Care shall be taken to make certain that the sling clears all obstacles.

(n)(3) **Moving the load**

(n)(3)(i) The load shall be well secured and properly balanced in the sling or lifting device before it is lifted more than a few inches.

(n)(3)(ii) Before starting to hoist the following conditions shall be noted:

(n)(3)(ii)(A) Hoist rope shall not be kinked.

(n)(3)(ii)(B) Multiple part lines shall not be twisted around each other.

(n)(3)(ii)(C) The hook shall be brought over the load in such a manner as to prevent swinging.

(n)(3)(iii) During hoisting care shall be taken that:

(n)(3)(iii)(A) There is no sudden acceleration or deceleration of the moving load.

(n)(3)(iii)(B) The load does not contact any obstructions.

(n)(3)(iv) Cranes shall not be used for side pulls except when specifically authorized by a responsible person who has determined that the stability of the crane is not thereby endangered and that various parts of the crane will not be overstressed.

(n)(3)(v) While any employee is on the load or hook, there shall be no hoisting, lowering, or traveling.

(n)(3)(vi) The employer shall require that the operator avoid carrying loads over people.

(n)(3)(vii) The operator shall test the brakes each time a load approaching the rated load is handled. The brakes shall be tested by raising the load a few inches and applying the brakes.

(n)(3)(viii) The load shall not be lowered below the point where less than two full wraps of rope remain on the hoisting drum.

(n)(3)(ix) When two or more cranes are used to lift a load one qualified responsible person shall be in charge of the operation. He shall analyze the operation and instruct all personnel involved in the proper positioning, rigging of the load, and the movements to be made.

(n)(3)(x) The employer shall insure that the operator does not leave his position at the controls while the load is suspended.

(n)(3)(xi) When starting the bridge and when the load or hook approaches near or over personnel, the warning signal shall be sounded.

(n)(4) **Hoist limit switch**

(n)(4)(i) At the beginning of each operator's shift, the upper limit switch of each hoist shall be tried out under no load. Extreme care shall be exercised; the block shall be "inched" into the limit or run in at slow speed. If the switch does not operate properly, the appointed person shall be immediately notified.

(n)(4)(ii) The hoist limit switch which controls the upper limit of travel of the load block shall never be used as an operating control.

(o) **Other requirements, general**

(o)(1) **Ladders**

(o)(1)(i) The employer shall insure that hands are free from encumbrances while personnel are using ladders.

(o)(1)(ii) Articles which are too large to be carried in pockets or belts shall be lifted and lowered by hand line.

(o)(2) **Cabs**

(o)(2)(i) Necessary clothing and personal belongings shall be stored in such a manner as not to interfere with access or operation.

(o)(2)(ii) Tools, oil cans, waste, extra fuses, and other necessary articles shall be stored in the tool box, and shall not be permitted to lie loose in or about the cab.

(o)(3) **Fire extinguishers** The employer shall insure that operators are familiar with the operation and care of fire extinguishers provided.

[39 FR 23502, June 27, 1974, as amended at 40 FR 27400, June 27, 1975; 49 FR 5322, Feb. 10, 1984; 51 FR 34560, Sept. 29, 1986; 55 FR 32015, Aug. 6, 1990; 61 FR 9239, Mar. 7, 1996]

§1910.180 [OI]
Crawler locomotive and truck cranes

(a) **Definitions applicable to this Section**

(a)(1) A **crawler crane** consists of a rotating superstructure with power plant, operating machinery, and boom, mounted on a base, equipped with crawler treads for travel. Its function is to hoist and swing loads at various radii.

(a)(2) A **locomotive crane** consists of a rotating superstructure with power-plant, operating machinery and boom, mounted on a base or car equipped for travel on railroad track. It may be self-propelled or propelled by an outside source. Its function is to hoist and swing loads at various radii.

(a)(3) A **truck crane** consists of a rotating superstructure with powerplant, operating machinery and boom, mounted on an automotive truck equipped with a powerplant for travel. Its function is to hoist and swing loads at various radii.

(a)(4) A **wheel mounted crane (wagon crane)** consists of a rotating superstructure with powerplant, operating machinery and boom, mounted on a base or platform equipped with axles and rubber-tired wheels for travel. The base is usually propelled by the engine in the superstructure, but it may be equipped with a separate engine controlled from the superstructure. Its function is to hoist and swing loads at various radii.

(a)(5) An **accessory** is a secondary part or assembly of parts which contributes to the overall function and usefulness of a machine.

(a)(6) **Appointed** means assigned specific responsibilities by the employer or the employer's representative.

(a)(7) **ANSI** means the American National Standards Institute.

(a)(8) An **angle indicator (boom)** is an accessory which measures the angle of the boom to the horizontal.

(a)(9) The **axis of rotation** is the vertical axis around which the crane superstructure rotates.

(a)(10) **Axle** means the shaft or spindle with which or about which a wheel rotates. On truck- and wheel-mounted cranes it refers to an automotive type of axle assembly including housings, gearing, differential, bearings, and mounting appurtenances.

(a)(11) **Axle (bogie)** means two or more automotive-type axles mounted in tandem in a frame so as to divide the load between the axles and permit vertical oscillation of the wheels.

(a)(12) The **base (mounting)** is the traveling base or carrier on which the rotating superstructure is mounted such as a car, truck, crawlers, or wheel platform.

(a)(13) The **boom (crane)** is a member hinged to the front of the rotating superstructure with the outer end supported by ropes leading to a gantry or A-frame and used for supporting the hoisting tackle.

(a)(14) The **boom angle** is the angle between the longitudinal centerline of the boom and the horizontal. The boom longitudinal centerline is a straight line between the boom foot pin (heel pin) centerline and boom point sheave pin centerline.

(a)(15) The **boom hoist** is a hoist drum and rope reeving system used to raise and lower the boom. The rope system may be all live reeving or a combination of live reeving and pendants.

(a)(16) The **boom stop** is a device used to limit the angle of the boom at the highest position.

(a)(17) A **brake** is a device used for retarding or stopping motion by friction or power means.

(a)(18) A **cab** is a housing which covers the rotating superstructure machinery and/or operator's station. On truck-crane trucks a separate cab covers the driver's station.

(a)(19) The **clutch** is a friction, electromagnetic, hydraulic, pneumatic, or positive mechanical device for engagement or disengagement of power.

(a)(20) The **counterweight** is a weight used to supplement the weight of the machine in providing stability for lifting working loads.

(a)(21) **Designated** means selected or assigned by the employer or the employer's representative as being qualified to perform specific duties.

(a)(22) The **drum** is the cylindrical members around which ropes are wound for raising and lowering the load or boom.

(a)(23) **Dynamic (loading)** means loads introduced into the machine or its components by forces in motion.

(a)(24) The **gantry (A-frame)** is a structural frame, extending above the superstructure, to which the boom support ropes are reeved.

(a)(25) A **jib** is an extension attached to the boom point to provide added boom length for lifting specified loads. The jib may be in line with the boom or offset to various angles.

(a)(26) **Load (working)** means the external load, in pounds, applied to the crane, including the weight of load-attaching equipment such as load blocks, shackles, and slings.

(a)(27) **Load block (upper)** means the assembly of hook or shackle, swivel, sheaves, pins, and frame suspended from the boom point.

(a)(28) **Load block (lower)** means the assembly of hook or shackle, swivel, sheaves, pins, and frame suspended by the hoisting ropes.

(a)(29) A **load hoist** is a hoist drum and rope reeving system used for hoisting and lowering loads.

(a)(30) **Load ratings** are crane ratings in pounds established by the manufacturer in accordance with paragraph (c) of this Section.

(a)(31) **Outriggers** are extendable or fixed metal arms, attached to the mounting base, which rest on supports at the outer ends.

(a)(32) **Rail clamp** means a tong-like metal device, mounted on a locomotive crane car, which can be connected to the track.

(a)(33) **Reeving** means a rope system in which the rope travels around drums and sheaves.

(a)(34) **Rope** refers to a wire rope unless otherwise specified.

(a)(35) **Side loading** means a load applied at an angle to the vertical plane of the boom.

(a)(36) A **standby crane** is a crane which is not in regular service but which is used occasionally or intermittently as required.

(a)(37) A **standing (guy) rope** is a supporting rope which maintains a constant distance between the points of attachment to the two components connected by the rope.

(a)(38) **Structural competence** means the ability of the machine and its components to withstand the stresses imposed by applied loads.

(a)(39) **Superstructure** means the rotating upper frame structure of the machine and the operating machinery mounted thereon.

(a)(40) **Swing** means the rotation of the superstructure for movement of loads in a horizontal direction about the axis of rotation.

(a)(41) **Swing mechanism** means the machinery involved in providing rotation of the superstructure.

(a)(42) **Tackle** is an assembly of ropes and sheaves arranged for hoisting and pulling.

(a)(43) **Transit** means the moving or transporting of a crane from one jobsite to another.

(a)(44) **Travel** means the function of the machine moving from one location to another, on a jobsite.

(a)(45) The **travel mechanism** is the machinery involved in providing travel.

(a)(46) **Wheelbase** means the distance between centers of front and rear axles. For a multiple axle assembly the axle center for wheelbase measurement is taken as the midpoint of the assembly.

(a)(47) The **whipline (auxiliary hoist)** is a separate hoist rope system of lighter load capacity and higher speed than provided by the main hoist.

(a)(48) A **winch head** is a power driven spool for handling of loads by means of friction between fiber or wire rope and spool.

(b) **General requirements**

(b)(1) [OI] **Application** This Section applies to crawler cranes, locomotive cranes, wheel mounted cranes of both truck and self-propelled wheel type, and any variations thereof which retain the same fundamental characteristics. This Section includes only cranes of the above types, which are basically powered by internal combustion engines or electric motors and which utilize drums and ropes. Cranes designed for railway and automobile wreck clearances are excepted. The requirements of this Section are applicable only to machines when used as lifting cranes.

(b)(2) **New and existing equipment** All new crawler, locomotive, and truck cranes constructed and utilized on or after August 31, 1971, shall meet the design specifications of the American National Standard Safety Code for Crawler, Locomotive, and Truck Cranes, ANSI B30.5–1968, which is incorporated by reference as specified in §1910.6. Crawler, locomotive, and truck cranes constructed prior to August 31, 1971, should be modified to conform to those design specifications by February 15, 1972, unless it can be shown that the crane cannot feasibly or economically be altered and that the crane substantially complies with the requirements of this Section.

(b)(3) **Designated personnel** Only designated personnel shall be permitted to operate a crane covered by this Section.

(c) **Load ratings**

(c)(1) Load ratings — where stability governs lifting performance.

(c)(1)(i) The margin of stability for determination of load ratings, with booms of stipulated lengths at stipulated working radii for the various types of crane mountings, is established by taking a percentage of the loads which will produce a condition of tipping or balance with the boom in the least stable direction, relative to the mounting. The load ratings shall not exceed the following percentages for cranes, with the indicated types of mounting under conditions stipulated in paragraphs (c)(1)(ii) and (iii) of this Section.

Type of crane mounting	Maximum load ratings (percent of tipping loads)
Locomotive, without outriggers:	
Booms 60 feet or less	[1]85
Booms over 60 feet	[1]85
Locomotive, using outriggers fully extended	80
Crawler, without outriggers	75
Crawler, using outriggers fully extended	85
Truck and wheel mounted without outriggers or using outriggers fully extended	85

[1] Unless this results in less than 30,000 pound-feet net stabilizing moment about the rail, which shall be minimum with such booms.

(c)(1)(ii) The following stipulations shall govern the application of the values in paragraph (c)(1)(i) of this Section for locomotive cranes:

(c)(1)(ii)(A) Tipping with or without the use of outriggers occurs when half of the wheels farthest from the load leave the rail.

(c)(1)(ii)(B) The crane shall be standing on track which is level within 1 percent grade.

(c)(1)(ii)(C) Radius of the load is the horizontal distance from a projection of the axis of rotation to the rail support surface, before loading, to the center of vertical hoist line or tackle with load applied.

(c)(1)(ii)(D) Tipping loads from which ratings are determined shall be applied under static conditions only, i.e., without dynamic effect of hoisting, lowering, or swinging.

(c)(1)(ii)(E) The weight of all auxiliary handling devices such as hoist blocks, hooks, and slings shall be considered a part of the load rating.

(c)(1)(iii) Stipulations governing the application of the values in paragraph (c)(1)(i) of this Section for crawler, truck, and wheel-mounted cranes shall be in accordance with Crane Load-Stability Test Code, Society of Automotive Engineers (SAE) J765, which is incorporated by reference as specified in §1910.6.

(c)(1)(iv) The effectiveness of these preceding stability factors will be influenced by such additional factors as freely suspended loads, track, wind, or ground conditions, condition and inflation of rubber tires, boom lengths, proper operating speeds for existing conditions, and, in general, careful and competent operation. All of these shall be taken into account by the user.

(c)(2) **Load rating chart** A substantial and durable rating chart with clearly legible letters and figures shall be provided with each crane and securely fixed to the crane cab in a location easily visible to the operator while seated at his control station.

(d) [OI] **Inspection classification**

(d)(1) Initial inspection. Prior to initial use all new and altered cranes shall be inspected to insure compliance with provisions of this Section.

(d)(2) Regular inspection. Inspection procedure for cranes in regular service is divided into two general classifications based upon the intervals at which inspection should be performed. The intervals in turn are dependent upon the nature of the critical components of the crane and the degree of their exposure to wear, deterioration, or malfunction. The two general classifications are herein designated as "frequent" and "periodic", with respective intervals between inspections as defined below:

(d)(2)(i) Frequent inspection: Daily to monthly intervals.

(d)(2)(ii) Periodic inspection: 1- to 12-month intervals, or as specifically recommended by the manufacturer.

(d)(3) **Frequent inspection** Items such as the following shall be inspected for defects at intervals as defined in paragraph (d)(2)(i) of this Section or as specifically indicated including observation during operation for any defects which might appear between regular inspections. Any deficiencies such as listed shall be carefully examined and determination made as to whether they constitute a safety hazard:

(d)(3)(i) All control mechanisms for maladjustment interfering with proper operation: Daily;

(d)(3)(ii) All control mechanisms for excessive wear of components and contamination by lubricants or other foreign matter;

(d)(3)(iii) All safety devices for malfunction;

(d)(3)(iv) Deterioration or leakage in air or hydraulic systems: Daily;

(d)(3)(v) Crane hooks with deformations or cracks. For hooks with cracks or having more than 15 percent in excess of normal throat opening or more than 10° twist from the plane of the unbent hook;

(d)(3)(vi) Rope reeving for noncompliance with manufacturer's recommendations;

(d)(3)(vii) Electrical apparatus for malfunctioning, signs of excessive deterioration, dirt, and moisture accumulation.

(d)(4) **Periodic inspection** Complete inspections of the crane shall be performed at intervals as generally defined in paragraph (d)(2)(ii) of this Section depending upon its activity, severity of service, and environment, or as specifically indicated below. These inspections shall include the requirements of paragraph (d)(3) of this Section and in addition, items such as the following. Any deficiencies such as listed shall be carefully examined and determination made as to whether they constitute a safety hazard:

(d)(4)(i) Deformed, cracked, or corroded members in the crane structure and boom;

(d)(4)(ii) Loose bolts or rivets;

(d)(4)(iii) Cracked or worn sheaves and drums;

(d)(4)(iv) Worn, cracked, or distorted parts such as pins, bearings, shafts, gears, rollers and locking devices;

(d)(4)(v) Excessive wear on brake and clutch system parts, linings, pawls, and ratchets;

(d)(4)(vi) Load, boom angle, and other indicators over their full range, for any significant inaccuracies;

(d)(4)(vii) Gasoline, diesel, electric, or other power plants for improper performance or noncompliance with safety requirements;

(d)(4)(viii) Excessive wear of chain-drive sprockets and excessive chain stretch;

(d)(4)(ix) Travel steering, braking, and locking devices, for malfunction;

(d)(4)(x) Excessively worn or damaged tires.

(d)(5) **Cranes not in regular use**

(d)(5)(i) A crane which has been idle for a period of one month or more, but less than 6 months, shall be given an inspection conforming with requirements of paragraph (d)(3) of this Section and paragraph (g)(2)(ii) of this Section before placing in service.

(d)(5)(ii) A crane which has been idle for a period of six months shall be given a complete inspection conforming with requirements of paragraphs (d)(3) and (4) of this Section and paragraph (g)(2)(ii) of this Section before placing in service.

(d)(5)(iii) Standby cranes shall be inspected at least semiannually in accordance with requirements of paragraph (d)(3) of this Section and paragraph (g)(2)(ii) of this Section. Such cranes which are exposed to adverse environment should be inspected more frequently.

(d)(6) **Inspection records** Certification records which include the date of inspection, the signature of the person who performed the inspection and the serial number, or other identifier, of the crane which was inspected shall be made monthly on critical items in use such as brakes, crane hooks, and ropes. This certification record shall be kept readily available.

(e) **Testing**

(e)(1) **Operational tests**

(e)(1)(i) In addition to prototype tests and quality-control measures, each new production crane shall be tested by the manufacturer to the extent necessary to insure compliance with the operational requirements of this paragraph including functions such as the following:

(e)(1)(i)(A) Load hoisting and lowering mechanisms;

(e)(1)(i)(B) Boom hoisting and lower mechanisms;

(e)(1)(i)(C) Swinging mechanism;

(e)(1)(i)(D) Travel mechanism;

(e)(1)(i)(E) Safety devices.

(e)(1)(ii) Where the complete production crane is not supplied by one manufacturer such tests shall be conducted at final assembly.

(e)(1)(iii) Certified production-crane test results shall be made available.

(e)(2) **Rated load test**

(e)(2)(i) Written reports shall be available showing test procedures and confirming the adequacy of repairs or alterations.

(e)(2)(ii) Test loads shall not exceed 110 percent of the rated load at any selected working radius.

(e)(2)(iii) Where rerating is necessary:

(e)(2)(iii)(A) Crawler, truck, and wheel-mounted cranes shall be tested in accordance with SAE Recommended Practice, Crane Load Stability Test Code J765 (April 1961).

(e)(2)(iii)(B) Locomotive cranes shall be tested in accordance with paragraph (c)(1)(i) and (ii) of this Section.

(e)(2)(iii)(C) Rerating test report shall be readily available.

(e)(2)(iv) No cranes shall be rerated in excess of the original load ratings unless such rating changes are approved by the crane manufacturer or final assembler.

(f) **Maintenance procedure—General** After adjustments and repairs have been made the crane shall not be operated until all guards have been reinstalled, safety devices reactivated, and maintenance equipment removed.

(g) **Rope inspection**

(g)(1) **Running ropes** A thorough inspection of all ropes in use shall be made at least once a month and a certification record which includes the date of inspection, the signature of the person who performed the inspection and an identifier for the ropes shall be prepared and kept on file where readily available. All inspections shall be performed by an appointed or authorized person. Any deterioration, resulting in appreciable loss of original strength shall be carefully observed and detemination made as to whether further use of the rope would constitute a safety hazard. Some of the conditions that could result in an appreciable loss of strength are the following:

(g)(1)(i) Reduction of rope diameter below nominal diameter due to loss of core support, internal or external corrosion, or wear of outside wires;

(g)(1)(ii) A number of broken outside wires and the degree of distribution of concentration of such broken wires;

(g)(1)(iii) Worn outside wires;

(g)(1)(iv) Corroded or broken wires at end connections;

(g)(1)(v) Corroded, cracked, bent, worn, or improperly applied end connections;

(g)(1)(vi) Severe kinking, crushing, cutting, or unstranding.

(g)(2) **Other ropes**

(g)(2)(i) Heavy wear and/or broken wires may occur in sections in contact with equalizer sheaves or other sheaves where rope travel is limited, or with saddles. Particular care shall be taken to inspect ropes at these locations.

(g)(2)(ii) All rope which has been idle for a period of a month or more due to shutdown or storage of a crane on which it is installed shall be given a thorough inspection before it is used. This inspection shall be for all types of deterioration and shall be performed by an appointed or authorized person whose approval shall be required for further use of the rope. A certification record which includes the date of inspection, the signature of the person who performed the inspection, and an identifier for the rope which was inspected shall be prepared and kept readily available.

(g)(2)(iii) Particular care shall be taken in the inspection of nonrotating rope.

(h) **Handling the load**

(h)(1) **Size of load**

(h)(1)(i) No crane shall be loaded beyond the rated load, except for test purposes as provided in paragraph (e) of this Section.

(h)(1)(ii) When loads which are limited by structural competence rather than by stability are to be handled, it shall be ascertained that the weight of the load has been determined within plus or minus 10 percent before it is lifted.

(h)(2) **Attaching the load**

(h)(2)(i) The hoist rope shall not be wrapped around the load.

(h)(2)(ii) The load shall be attached to the hook by means of slings or other approved devices.

(h)(3) **Moving the load**

(h)(3)(i) The employer shall assure that:

(h)(3)(i)(A) The crane is level and where necessary blocked properly.

(h)(3)(i)(B) The load is well secured and properly balanced in the sling or lifting device before it is lifted more than a few inches.

(h)(3)(ii) Before starting to hoist, the following conditions shall be noted:

(h)(3)(ii)(A) Hoist rope shall not be kinked.

(h)(3)(ii)(B) Multiple part lines shall not be twisted around each other.

(h)(3)(ii)(C) The hook shall be brought over the load in such a manner as to prevent swinging.

(h)(3)(iii) During hoisting care shall be taken that:

(h)(3)(iii)(A) There is no sudden acceleration or deceleration of the moving load.

(h)(3)(iii)(B) The load does not contact any obstructions.

(h)(3)(iv) Side loading of booms shall be limited to freely suspended loads. Cranes shall not be used for dragging loads sideways.

(h)(3)(v) OI No hoisting, lowering, swinging, or traveling shall be done while anyone is on the load or hook.

(h)(3)(vi) The operator should avoid carrying loads over people.

(h)(3)(vii) On truck-mounted cranes, no loads shall be lifted over the front area except as approved by the crane manufacturer.

(h)(3)(viii) The operator shall test the brakes each time a load approaching the rated load is handled by raising it a few inches and applying the brakes.

(h)(3)(ix) Outriggers shall be used when the load to be handled at that particular radius exceeds the rated load without outriggers as given by the manufacturer for that crane. Where floats are used they shall be securely attached to the outriggers. Wood blocks used to support outriggers shall:

(h)(3)(ix)(A) Be strong enough to prevent crushing.

(h)(3)(ix)(B) Be free from defects.

(h)(3)(ix)(C) Be of sufficient width and length to prevent shifting or toppling under load.

(h)(3)(x) Neither the load nor the boom shall be lowered below the point where less than two full wraps of rope remain on their respective drums.

(h)(3)(xi) Before lifting loads with locomotive cranes without using outriggers, means shall be applied to prevent the load from being carried by the truck springs.

(h)(3)(xii) When two or more cranes are used to lift one load, one designated person shall be responsible for the operation. He shall be required to analyze the operation and instruct all personnel involved in the proper positioning, rigging of the load, and the movements to be made.

(h)(3)(xiii) In transit the following additional precautions shall be exercised:

(h)(3)(xiii)(A) The boom shall be carried in line with the direction of motion.

(h)(3)(xiii)(B) The superstructure shall be secured against rotation, except when negotiating turns when there is an operator in the cab or the boom is supported on a dolly.

(h)(3)(xiii)(C) The empty hook shall be lashed or otherwise restrained so that it cannot swing freely.

(h)(3)(xiv) Before traveling a crane with load, a designated person shall be responsible for determining and controlling safety. Decisions such as position of load, boom location, ground support, travel route, and speed of movement shall be in accord with his determinations.

(h)(3)(xv) A crane with or without load shall not be traveled with the boom so high that it may bounce back over the cab.

(h)(3)(xvi) When rotating the crane, sudden starts and stops shall be avoided. Rotational speed shall be such that the load does not swing out beyond the radii at which it can be controlled. A tag or restraint line shall be used when rotation of the load is hazardous.

(h)(3)(xvii) When a crane is to be operated at a fixed radius, the boom-hoist pawl or other positive locking device shall be engaged.

(h)(3)(xviii) Ropes shall not be handled on a winch head without the knowledge of the operator.

(h)(3)(xix) While a winch head is being used, the operator shall be within convenient reach of the power unit control lever.

(h)(4) **Holding the load**

(h)(4)(i) The operator shall not be permitted to leave his position at the controls while the load is suspended.

(h)(4)(ii) No person should be permitted to stand or pass under a load on the hook.

(h)(4)(iii) If the load must remain suspended for any considerable length of time, the operator shall hold the drum from rotating in the lowering direction by activating the positive controllable means of the operator's station.

(i) **Other requirements**

(i)(1) **Rail clamps** Rail clamps shall not be used as a means of restraining tipping of a locomotive crane.

(i)(2) **Ballast or counterweight** Cranes shall not be operated without the full amount of any ballast or counterweight in place as specified by the maker, but truck cranes that have dropped the ballast or counterweight may be operated temporarily with special care and only for light loads without full ballast or counterweight in place. The ballast or counterweight in place specified by the manufacturer shall not be exceeded.

(i)(3) **Cabs**

(i)(3)(i) Necessary clothing and personal belongings shall be stored in such a manner as to not interfere with access or operation.

(i)(3)(ii) Tools, oil cans, waste, extra fuses, and other necessary articles shall be stored in the tool box, and shall not be permitted to lie loose in or about the cab.

(i)(4) **Refueling**

(i)(4)(i) Refueling with small portable containers shall be done with an approved safety type can equipped with an automatic closing cap and flame arrester. Refer to §1910.155(c)(3) for definition of approved.

(i)(4)(ii) Machines shall not be refueled with the engine running.

(i)(5) **Fire extinguishers**

(i)(5)(i) A carbon dioxide, dry chemical, or equivalent fire extinguisher shall be kept in the cab or vicinity of the crane.

(i)(5)(ii) Operating and maintenance personnel shall be made familiar with the use and care of the fire extinguishers provided.

(i)(6) **Swinging locomotive cranes** A locomotive crane shall not be swung into a position where railway cars on an adjacent track might strike it, until it has been ascertained that cars are not being moved on the adjacent track and proper flag protection has been established.

(j) **Operations near overhead lines** For operations near overhead electric lines, see §1910.333(c)(3).

[39 FR 23502, June 27, 1974, as amended at 49 FR 5323, Feb. 10, 1984; 51 FR 34561, Sept. 29, 1986; 53 FR 12122, Apr. 12, 1988; 55 FR 32015, Aug 6, 1990; 61 FR 9239, Mar. 7, 1996]

§1910.181 Derricks

(a) **Definitions applicable to this Section**

(a)(1) A **derrick** is an apparatus consisting of a mast or equivalent member held at the head by guys or braces, with or without a boom, for use with a hoisting mechanism and operating ropes.

(a)(2) **A-frame derrick** means a derrick in which the boom is hinged from a cross member between the bottom ends of two upright members spread apart at the lower ends and joined at the top; the boom point secured to the junction of the side members, and the side members are braced or guyed from this junction point.

A–FRAME DERRICK

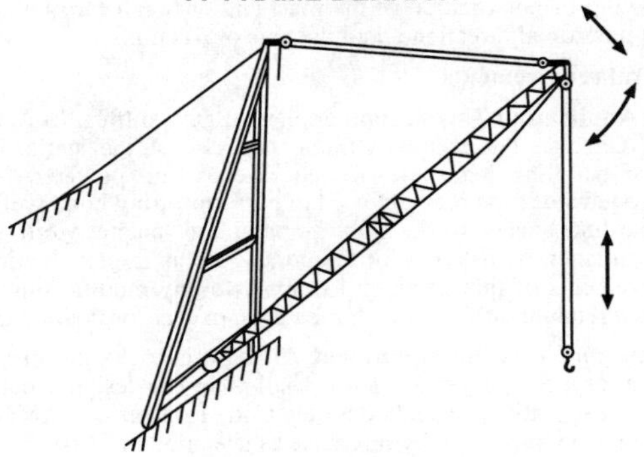

(a)(3) A **basket derrick** is a derrick without a boom, similar to a gin pole, with its base supported by ropes attached to corner posts or other parts of the structure. The base is at a lower elevation than its supports. The location of the base of a basket derrick can be changed by varying the length of the rope supports. The top of the pole is secured with multiple reeved guys to position the top of the pole to the desired location by varying the length of the upper guy lines. The load is raised and lowered by ropes through a sheave or block secured to the top of the pole.

BASKET DERRICK

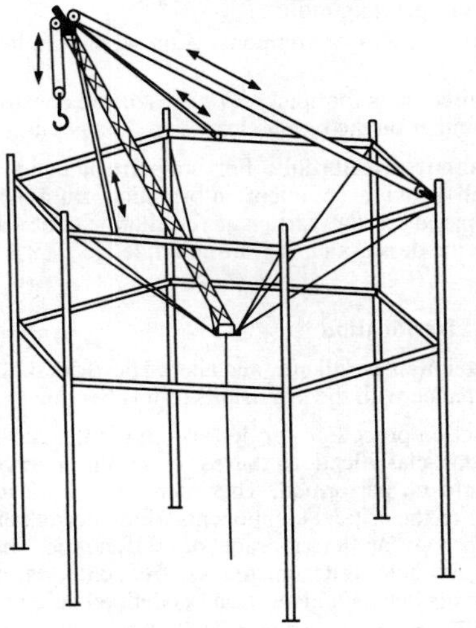

(a)(4) **Breast derrick** means a derrick without boom. The mast consists of two side members spread farther apart at the base than at the top and tied together at top and bottom by rigid members. The mast is prevented from tipping forward by guys connected to its top. The load is raised and lowered by ropes through a sheave or block secured to the top crosspiece.

BREAST DERRICK

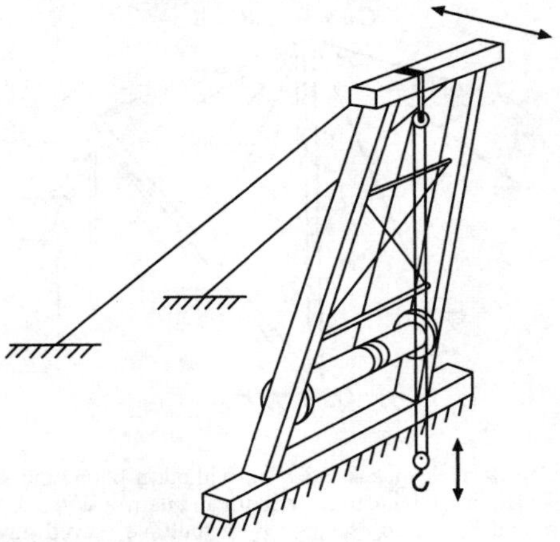

(a)(5) **Chicago boom derrick** means a boom which is attached to a structure, an outside upright member of the structure serving as the mast, and the boom being stepped in a fixed socket clamped to the upright. The derrick is complete with load, boom, and boom point swing line falls.

CHICAGO BOOM DERRICK

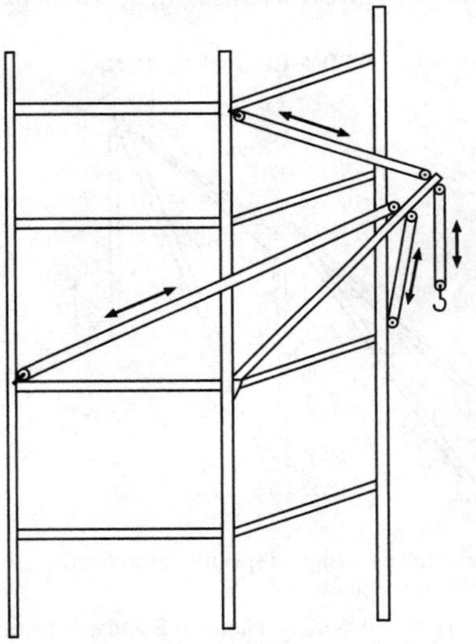

(a)(6) A **gin pole derrick** is a derrick without a boom. Its guys are so arranged from its top as to permit leaning the mast in any direction. The load is raised and lowered by ropes reeved through sheaves or blocks at the top of the mast.

GIN POLE DERRICK

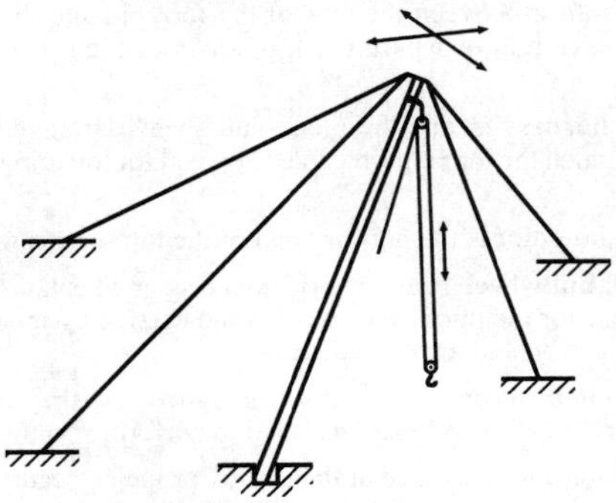

N

Materials Handling and Storage

Derricks

(a)(7) **Guy derrick** means a fixed derrick consisting of a mast capable of being rotated, supported in a vertical position by guys, and a boom whose bottom end is hinged or pivoted to move in a vertical plane with a reeved rope between the head of the mast and the boom point for raising and lowering the boom, and a reeved rope from the boom point for raising and lowering the load.

GUY DERRICK

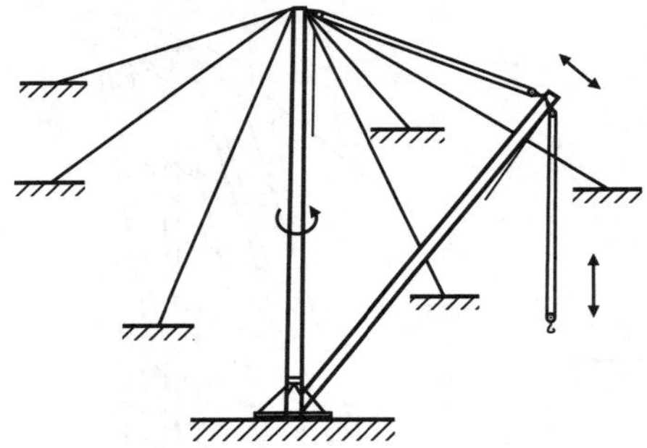

(a)(8) **Shearleg derrick** means a derrick without a boom and similar to a breast derrick. The mast, wide at the bottom and narrow at the top, is hinged at the bottom and has its top secured by a multiple reeved guy to permit handling loads at various radii by means of load tackle suspended from the mast top.

(a)(9) A **stiffleg derrick** is a derrick similar to a guy derrick except that the mast is supported or held in place by two or more stiff members, called stiffiegs, which are capable of resisting either tensile or compressive forces. Sills are generally provided to connect the lower ends of the stiffiegs to the foot of the mast.

STIFF LEG DERRICK

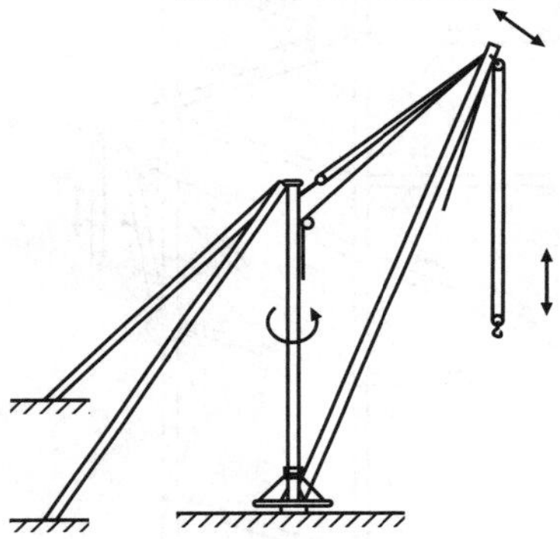

(a)(10) **Appointed** means assigned specific responsibilities by the employer or the employer's representative.

(a)(11) **ANSI** means the American National Standards Institute.

(a)(12) A **boom** is a timber or metal section or strut, pivoted or hinged at the heel (lower end) at a location fixed in height on a frame or mast or vertical member, and with its point (upper end) supported by chains, ropes, or rods to the upper end of the frame, mast, or vertical member. A rope for raising and lowering the load is reeved through sheaves or a block at the boom point. The length of the boom shall be taken as the straight line distance between the axis of the foot pin and the axis of the boom point sheave pin, or where used, the axis of the upper load block attachment pin.

(a)(13) **Boom harness** means the block and sheave arrangement on the boom point to which the topping lift cable is reeved for lowering and raising the boom.

(a)(14) The **boom point** is the outward end of the top section of the boom.

(a)(15) **Derrick bullwheel** means a horizontal ring or wheel, fastened to the foot of a derrick, for the purpose of turning the derrick by means of ropes leading from this wheel to a powered drum.

(a)(16) **Designated** means selected or assigned by the employer or employer's representative as being qualified to perform specific duties.

(a)(17) **Eye** means a loop formed at the end of a rope by securing the dead end to the live end at the base of the loop.

(a)(18) A **fiddle block** is a block consisting of two sheaves in the same plane held in place by the same cheek plates.

(a)(19) The **foot bearing or foot block (sill block)** is the lower support on which the mast rotates.

(a)(20) A **gudgeon pin** is a pin connecting the mast cap to the mast allowing rotation of the mast.

(a)(21) A **guy** is a rope used to steady or secure the mast or other member in the desired position.

(a)(22) **Load, working** means the external load, in pounds, applied to the derrick, including the weight of load attaching equipment such as load blocks, shackles, and slings.

(a)(23) **Load block, lower** means the assembly of sheaves, pins, and frame suspended by the hoisting rope.

(a)(24) **Load block, upper** means the assembly of sheaves, pins, and frame suspended from the boom.

(a)(25) **Mast** means the upright member of the derrick.

(a)(26) **Mast cap (spider)** means the fitting at the top of the mast to which the guys are connected.

(a)(27) **Reeving** means a rope system in which the rope travels around drums and sheaves.

(a)(28) **Rope** refers to wire rope unless otherwise specified.

(a)(29) [OI] **Safety hook** means a hook with a latch to prevent slings or load from accidentally slipping off the hook.

(a)(30) **Side loading** is a load applied at an angle to the vertical plane of the boom.

(a)(31) The **sill** is a member connecting the foot block and stiffleg or a member connecting the lower ends of a double member mast.

(a)(32) A **standby derrick** is a derrick not in regular service which is used occasionally or intermittently as required.

(a)(33) **Stiffleg** means a rigid member supporting the mast at the head.

(a)(34) **Swing** means rotation of the mast and/or boom for movements of loads in a horizontal direction about the axis of rotation.

(b) **General requirements**

(b)(1) [OI] **Application** This Section applies to guy, stiffleg, basket, breast, gin pole, Chicago boom and A-frame derricks of the stationary type, capable of handling loads at variable reaches and powered by hoists through systems of rope reeving, used to perform lifting hook work, single or multiple line bucket work, grab, grapple, and magnet work. Derricks may be permanently installed for temporary use as in construction work. The requirements of this Section also apply to any modification of these types which retain their fundamental features, except for floating derricks.

(b)(2) **New and existing equipment** All new derricks constructed and installed on or after August 31, 1971, shall meet the design specifications of the American National Standard Safety Code for Derricks, ANSI B30.6–1969, which is incorporated by reference as specified in §1910.6.

(b)(3) **Designated personnel** Only designated personnel shall be permitted to operate a derrick covered by this Section.

(c) **Load ratings**

(c)(1) **Rated load marking** For permanently installed derricks with fixed lengths of boom, guy, and mast, a substantial, durable, and clearly legible rating chart shall be provided with each derrick and securely affixed where it is visible to personnel responsible for the safe operation of the equipment. The chart shall include the following data:

(c)(1)(i) Manufacturer's approved load ratings at corresponding ranges of boom angle or operating radii;

(c)(1)(ii) Specific lengths of components on which the load ratings are based;

(c)(1)(iii) Required parts for hoist reeving. Size and construction of rope may be shown either on the rating chart or in the operating manual.

(c)(2) **Nonpermanent installations** For nonpermanent installations, the manufacturer shall provide sufficient information from which capacity charts can be prepared for the particular installation. The capacity charts shall be located at the derricks or the jobsite office.

(d) **Inspection**

(d)(1) **Inspection classification**

(d)(1)(i) Prior to initial use all new and altered derricks shall be inspected to insure compliance with the provisions of this Section.

(d)(1)(ii) Inspection procedure for derricks in regular service is divided into two general classifications based upon the intervals at which inspection should be performed. The intervals in turn are dependent upon the nature of the critical components of the derrick and the degree of their exposure to wear, deterioration, or malfunction. The two general classifications are herein designated as frequent and periodic with respective intervals between inspections as defined below:

(d)(1)(ii)(A) Frequent inspection—Daily to monthly intervals;

(d)(1)(ii)(B) Periodic inspection—1- to 12-month intervals, or as specified by the manufacturer.

(d)(2) Frequent inspection Items such as the following shall be inspected for defects at intervals as defined in paragraph (d)(1)(ii)(A) of this Section or as specifically indicated, including observation during operation for any defects which might appear between regular inspections. Deficiencies shall be carefully examined for any safety hazard:

(d)(2)(i) All control mechanisms: Inspect daily for adjustment, wear, and lubrication;

(d)(2)(ii) All chords and lacing: Inspect daily, visually;

(d)(2)(iii) Tension in guys: Daily;

(d)(2)(iv) Plumb of the mast;

(d)(2)(v) Deterioration or leakage in air or hydraulic systems: Daily;

(d)(2)(vi) Derrick hooks for deformations or cracks; for hooks with cracks or having more than 15 percent in excess of normal throat opening or more than 10° twist from the plane of the unbent hook, refer to paragraph (e)(3)(iii) of this Section;

(d)(2)(vii) Rope reeving; visual inspection for noncompliance with derrick manufacturer's recommendations;

(d)(2)(viii) Hoist brakes, clutches, and operating levers: check daily for proper functioning before beginning operations;

(d)(2)(ix) Electrical apparatus for malfunctioning, signs of excessive deterioration, dirt, and moisture accumulation.

(d)(3) Periodic inspection

(d)(3)(i) Complete inspections of the derrick shall be performed at intervals as generally defined in paragraph (d)(1)(ii)(B) of this Section depending upon its activity, severity of service, and environment, or as specifically indicated below. These inspections shall include the requirements of paragraph (d)(2) of this Section and in addition, items such as the following. Deficiencies shall be carefully examined and a determination made as to whether they constitute a safety hazard:

(d)(3)(i)(A) Structural members for deformations, cracks, and corrosion;

(d)(3)(i)(B) Bolts or rivets for tightness;

(d)(3)(i)(C) Parts such as pins, bearings, shafts, gears, sheaves, drums, rollers, locking and clamping devices, for wear, cracks, and distortion;

(d)(3)(i)(D) Gudgeon pin for cracks, wear, and distortion each time the derrick is to be erected;

(d)(3)(i)(E) Powerplants for proper performance and compliance with applicable safety requirements;

(d)(3)(i)(F) Hooks.

(d)(3)(ii) Foundation or supports shall be inspected for continued ability to sustain the imposed loads.

(d)(4) Derricks not in regular use

(d)(4)(i) A derrick which has been idle for a period of 1 month or more, but less than 6 months, shall be given an inspection conforming with requirements of paragraph (d)(2) of this Section and paragraph (g)(3) of this Section before placing in service.

(d)(4)(ii) A derrick which has been idle for a period of over 6 months shall be given a complete inspection conforming with requirements of paragraphs (d)(2) and (3) of this Section and paragraph (g)(3) of this Section before placing in service.

(d)(4)(iii) Standby derricks shall be inspected at least semiannually in accordance with requirements of paragraph (d)(2) of this Section and paragraph (g)(3) of this Section.

(e) Testing

(e)(1) Operational tests Prior to initial use all new and altered derricks shall be tested to insure compliance with this Section including the following functions:

(e)(1)(i) Load hoisting and lowering;

(e)(1)(ii) Boom up and down;

(e)(1)(iii) Swing;

(e)(1)(iv) Operation of clutches and brakes of hoist.

(e)(2) Anchorages All anchorages shall be approved by the appointed person. Rock and hairpin anchorages may require special testing.

(f) Maintenance

(f)(1) Preventive maintenance A preventive maintenance program based on the derrick manufacturer's recommendations shall be established.

(f)(2) Maintenance procedure

(f)(2)(i) Before adjustments and repairs are started on a derrick the following precautions shall be taken:

(f)(2)(i)(A) The derrick to be repaired shall be arranged so it will cause the least interference with other equipment and operations in the area.

(f)(2)(i)(B) All hoist drum dogs shall be engaged.

(f)(2)(i)(C) The main or emergency switch shall be locked in the open position, if an electric hoist is used.

(f)(2)(i)(D) Warning or out of order signs shall be placed on the derrick and hoist.

(f)(2)(i)(E) The repairs of booms of derricks shall either be made when the booms are lowered and adequately supported or safely tied off.

(f)(2)(i)(F) A good communication system shall be set up between the hoist operator and the appointed individual in charge of derrick operations before any work on the equipment is started.

(f)(2)(ii) After adjustments and repairs have been made the derrick shall not be operated until all guards have been reinstalled, safety devices reactivated, and maintenance equipment removed.

(f)(3) Adjustments and repairs

(f)(3)(i) Any unsafe conditions disclosed by inspection shall be corrected before operation of the derrick is resumed.

(f)(3)(ii) Adjustments shall be maintained to assure correct functioning of components.

(f)(3)(iii) Repairs or replacements shall be provided promptly as needed for safe operation. The following are examples of conditions requiring prompt repair or replacement:

(f)(3)(iii)(A) Hooks showing defects described in paragraph (d)(2)(vi) of this Section shall be discarded.

(f)(3)(iii)(B) All critical parts which are cracked, broken, bent, or excessively worn.

(f)(3)(iii)(C) [Reserved]

(f)(3)(iii)(D) All replacement and repaired parts shall have at least the original safety factor.

(g) Rope inspection

(g)(1) Running ropes A thorough inspection of all ropes in use shall be made at least once a month and a certification record which includes the date of inspection, the signature of the person who performed the inspection, and an identifier for the ropes which were inspected shall be prepared and kept on file where readily available. Any deterioration, resulting in appreciable loss of original strength shall be carefully observed and determination made as to whether further use of the rope would constitute a safety hazard. Some of the conditions that could result in an appreciable loss of strength are the following:

(g)(1)(i) Reduction of rope diameter below nominal diameter due to loss of core support, internal or external corrosion, or wear of outside wires;

(g)(1)(ii) A number of broken outside wires and the degree of distribution or concentration of such broken wires;

(g)(1)(iii) Worn outside wires;

(g)(1)(iv) Corroded or broken wires at end connections;

(g)(1)(v) Corroded, cracked, bent, worn, or improperly applied end connections;

(g)(1)(vi) Severe kinking, crushing, cutting, or unstranding.

(g)(2) Limited travel ropes Heavy wear and/or broken wires may occur in sections in contact with equalizer sheaves or other sheaves where rope travel is limited, or with saddles. Particular care shall be taken to inspect ropes at these locations.

(g)(3) Idle ropes All rope which has been idle for a period of a month or more due to shutdown or storage of a derrick on which it is installed shall be given a thorough inspection before it is used. This inspection shall be for all types of deterioration. A certification record shall be prepared and kept readily available which includes the date of inspection, the signature of the person who performed the inspection, and an identifier for the ropes which were inspected.

(g)(4) Nonrotating ropes Particular care shall be taken in the inspection of nonrotating rope.

(h) Operations of derricks Derrick operations shall be directed only by the individual specifically designated for that purpose.

(i) Handling the load

(i)(1) Size of load

(i)(1)(i) No derrick shall be loaded beyond the rated load.

(i)(1)(ii) When loads approach the maximum rating of the derrick, it shall be ascertained that the weight of the load has been determined within plus or minus 10 percent before it is lifted.

(i)(2) Attaching the load

(i)(2)(i) The hoist rope shall not be wrapped around the load.

(i)(2)(ii) The load shall be attached to the hook by means of slings or other suitable devices.

(i)(3) **Moving the load**

(i)(3)(i) The load shall be well secured and properly balanced in the sling or lifting device before it is lifted more than a few inches.

(i)(3)(ii) Before starting to hoist, the following conditions shall be noted:

(i)(3)(ii)(A) Hoist rope shall not be kinked.

(i)(3)(ii)(B) Multiple part lines shall not be twisted around each other.

(i)(3)(ii)(C) The hook shall be brought over the load in such a manner as to prevent swinging.

(i)(3)(iii) During hoisting, care shall be taken that:

(i)(3)(iii)(A) There is no sudden acceleration or deceleration of the moving load.

(i)(3)(iii)(B) Load does not contact any obstructions.

(i)(3)(iv) A derrick shall not be used for side loading except when specifically authorized by a responsible person who has determined that the various structural components will not be overstressed.

(i)(3)(v) No hoisting, lowering, or swinging shall be done while anyone is on the load or hook.

(i)(3)(vi) The operator should avoid carrying loads over people.

(i)(3)(vii) The operator shall test the brakes each time a load approaching the rated load is handled by raising it a few inches and applying the brakes.

(i)(3)(viii) Neither the load nor boom shall be lowered below the point where less than two full wraps of rope remain on their respective drums.

(i)(3)(ix) When rotating a derrick, sudden starts and stops shall be avoided. Rotational speed shall be such that the load does not swing out beyond the radius at which it can be controlled.

(i)(3)(x) Boom and hoisting rope systems shall not be twisted.

(i)(4) **Holding the load**

(i)(4)(i) The operator shall not be allowed to leave his position at the controls while the load is suspended.

(i)(4)(ii) People should not be permitted to stand or pass under a load on the hook.

(i)(4)(iii) If the load must remain suspended for any considerable length of time, a dog, or pawl and ratchet, or other equivalent means, rather than the brake alone, shall be used to hold the load.

(i)(5) **Use of winch heads**

(i)(5)(i) Ropes shall not be handled on a winch head without the knowledge of the operator.

(i)(5)(ii) While a winch head is being used, the operator shall be within convenient reach of the power unit control lever.

(i)(6) **Securing boom** Dogs, pawls, or other positive holding mechanism on the hoist shall be engaged. When not in use, the derrick boom shall:

(i)(6)(i) Be laid down;

(i)(6)(ii) Be secured to a stationary member, as nearly under the head as possible, by attachment of a sling to the load block; or

(i)(6)(iii) Be hoisted to a vertical position and secured to the mast.

(j) **Other requirements**

(j)(1) **Guards**

(j)(1)(i) Exposed moving parts, such as gears, ropes, setscrews, projecting keys, chains, chain sprockets, and reciprocating components, which constitute a hazard under normal operating conditions shall be guarded.

(j)(1)(ii) Guards shall be securely fastened.

(j)(1)(iii) Each guard shall be capable of supporting without permanent distortion, the weight of a 200–pound person unless the guard is located where it is impossible for a person to step on it.

(j)(2) **Hooks**

(j)(2)(i) Hooks shall meet the manufacturer's recommendations and shall not be overloaded.

(j)(2)(ii) Safety latch type hooks shall be used wherever possible.

(j)(3) **Fire extinguishers**

(j)(3)(i) A carbon dioxide, dry chemical, or equivalent fire extinguisher shall be kept in the immediate vicinity of the derrick.

(j)(3)(ii) Operating and maintenance personnel shall be familiar with the use and care of the fire extinguishers provided.

(j)(4) **Refueling**

(j)(4)(i) Refueling with portable containers shall be done with approved safety type containers equipped with automatic closing cap and flame arrester. Refer to §1910.155(c)(3) for definition of Approved.

(j)(4)(ii) Machines shall not be refueled with the engine running.

(j)(5) **Operations near overhead lines** For operations near overhead electric lines, see §1910.333(c)(3).

(j)(6) **Cab or operating enclosure**

(j)(6)(i) Necessary clothing and personal belongings shall be stored in such a manner as to not interfere with access or operation.

(j)(6)(ii) Tools, oilcans, waste, extra fuses, and other necessary articles shall be stored in the toolbox, and shall not be permitted to lie loose in or about the cab or operating enclosure.

[37 FR 22102, Oct. 18, 1972, as amended at 38 FR 14373, June 1, 1973; 43 FR 49750, Oct. 24, 1978; 49 FR 5323, Feb. 10, 1984; 51 FR 34561, Sept. 29, 1986; 53 FR 12122, Apr. 12, 1988; 55 FR 32015, Aug. 6, 1990; 61 FR 9240, Mar. 7, 1996]

§1910.183 Helicopters

(a) [Reserved]

(b) **Briefing** Prior to each day's operation a briefing shall be conducted. This briefing shall set forth the plan of operation for the pilot and ground personnel.

(c) **Slings and tag lines** Loads shall be properly slung. Tag lines shall be of a length that will not permit their being drawn up into the rotors. Pressed sleeve, swedged eyes, or equivalent means shall be used for all freely suspended loads to prevent hand splices from spinning open or cable clamps from loosening.

(d) **Cargo hooks** All electrically operated cargo hooks shall have the electrical activating device so designed and installed as to prevent inadvertent operation. In addition, these cargo hooks shall be equipped with an emergency mechanical control for releasing the load. The employer shall ensure that the hooks are tested prior to each day's operation by a competent person to determine that the release functions properly, both electrically and mechanically.

(e) **Personal protective equipment**

(e)(1) Personal protective equipment shall be provided and the employer shall ensure its use by employees receiving the load. Personal protective equipment shall consist of complete eye protection and hardhats secured by chinstraps.

(e)(2) Loose-fitting clothing likely to flap in rotor downwash, and thus be snagged on the hoist line, may not be worn.

(f) **Loose gear and objects** The employer shall take all necessary precautions to protect employees from flying objects in the rotor downwash. All loose gear within 100 feet of the place of lifting the load or depositing the load, or within all other areas susceptible to rotor downwash, shall be secured or removed.

(g) **Housekeeping** Good housekeeping shall be maintained in all helicopter loading and unloading areas.

(h) **Load safety** The size and weight of loads, and the manner in which loads are connected to the helicopter shall be checked. A lift may not be made if the helicopter operator believes the lift cannot be made safely.

(i) **Hooking and unhooking loads** When employees perform work under hovering craft, a safe means of access shall be provided for employees to reach the hoist line hook and engage or disengage cargo slings. Employees may not be permitted to perform work under hovering craft except when necessary to hook or unhook loads.

(j) **Static charge** Static charge on the suspended load shall be dissipated with a grounding device before ground personnel touch the suspended load, unless protective rubber gloves are being worn by all ground personnel who may be required to touch the suspended load.

(k) **Weight limitation** The weight of an external load shall not exceed the helicopter manufacturer's rating.

(l) **Ground lines** Hoist wires or other gear, except for pulling lines or conductors that are allowed to "pay out" from a container or roll off a reel, shall not be attached to any fixed ground structure, or allowed to foul on any fixed structure.

(m) **Visibility** Ground personnel shall be instructed and the employer shall ensure that when visibility is reduced by dust or other conditions, they shall exercise special caution to keep clear of main and stabilizing rotors. Precautions shall also be taken by the employer to eliminate, as far as practical, the dust or other conditions reducing the visibility.

(n) **Signal systems** The employer shall instruct the aircrew and ground personnel on the signal systems to be used and shall review the system with the employees in advance of hoisting the load. This applies to both radio and hand signal systems. Hand signals, where used, shall be as shown in Figure N–1.

(o) **Approach distance** No employee shall be permitted to approach within 50 feet of the helicopter when the rotor blades are turning, unless his work duties require his presence in that area.

(p) **Approaching helicopter** The employer shall instruct employees, and shall ensure, that whenever approaching or leaving a helicopter which has its blades rotating, all employees shall remain in full view of the pilot and keep in a crouched position. No employee shall be permitted to work in the area from the cockpit or cabin rearward while blades are rotating, unless authorized by the helicopter operator to work there.

(q) **Personnel** Sufficient ground personnel shall be provided to ensure that helicopter loading and unloading operations can be performed safely.

(r) **Communications** There shall be constant reliable communication between the pilot and a designated employee of the ground crew who acts as a signalman during the period of loading and unloading. The signalman shall be clearly distinguishable from other ground personnel.

(s) **Fires** Open fires shall not be permitted in areas where they could be spread by the rotor downwash.

Figure N–1
Helicopter Hand Signals

[40 FR 13440, Mar. 26, 1975, as amended at 63 FR 33467, June 18, 1998]

§1910.184 Slings

(a) **Scope** This Section applies to slings used in conjunction with other material handling equipment for the movement of material by hoisting, in employments covered by this Part. The types of slings covered are those made from alloy steel chain, wire rope, metal mesh, natural or synthetic fiber rope (conventional three strand construction), and synthetic web (nylon, polyester, and polypropylene).

(b) **Definitions**

Angle of loading is the inclination of a leg or branch of a sling measured from the horizontal or vertical plane as shown in Fig. N–184–5; provided that an angle of loading of five degrees or less from the vertical may be considered a vertical angle of loading.

Basket hitch is a sling configuration whereby the sling is passed under the load and has both ends, end attachments, eyes or handles on the hook or a single master link.

Braided wire rope is a wire rope formed by plaiting component wire ropes.

Bridle wire rope sling is a sling composed of multiple wire rope legs with the top ends gathered in a fitting that goes over the lifting hook.

Cable laid endless sling-mechanical joint is a wire rope sling made endless by joining the ends of a single length of cable laid rope with one or more metallic fittings.

Cable laid grommet-hand tucked is an endless wire rope sling made from one length of rope wrapped six times around a core formed by hand tucking the ends of the rope inside the six wraps.

Cable laid rope is a wire rope composed of six wire ropes wrapped around a fiber or wire rope core.

Cable laid rope sling-mechanical joint is a wire rope sling made from a cable laid rope with eyes fabricated by pressing or swaging one or more metal sleeves over the rope junction.

Choker hitch is a sling configuration with one end of the sling passing under the load and through an end attachment, handle or eye on the other end of the sling.

Coating is an elastomer or other suitable material applied to a sling or to a sling component to impart desirable properties.

Cross rod is a wire used to join spirals of metal mesh to form a complete fabric. (See Fig. N–184–2.)

Designated means selected or assigned by the employer or the employer's representative as being qualified to perform specific duties.

Equivalent entity is a person or organization (including an employer) which, by possession of equipment, technical knowledge and skills, can perform with equal competence the same repairs and tests as the person or organization with which it is equated.

Fabric (metal mesh) is the flexible portion of a metal mesh sling consisting of a series of transverse coils and cross rods.

Female handle (choker) is a handle with a handle eye and a slot of such dimension as to permit passage of a male handle thereby allowing the use of a metal mesh sling in a choker hitch. (See Fig. N–184–1.)

Handle is a terminal fitting to which metal mesh fabric is attached. (See Fig. N–184–1.)

Handle eye is an opening in a handle of a metal mesh sling shaped to accept a hook, shackle or other lifting device. (See Fig. N–184–1.)

Hitch is a sling configuration whereby the sling is fastened to an object or load, either directly to it or around it.

Link is a single ring of a chain.

Male handle (triangle) is a handle with a handle eye.

Master coupling link is an alloy steel welded coupling link used as an intermediate link to join alloy steel chain to master links. (See Fig. N–184–3.)

Master link or gathering ring is a forged or welded steel link used to support all members (legs) of an alloy steel chain sling or wire rope sling. (See Fig. N–184–3.)

Mechanical coupling link is a nonwelded, mechanically closed steel link used to attach master links, hooks, etc., to alloy steel chain.

Figure N–184-1
Metal Mesh Sling (Typical)

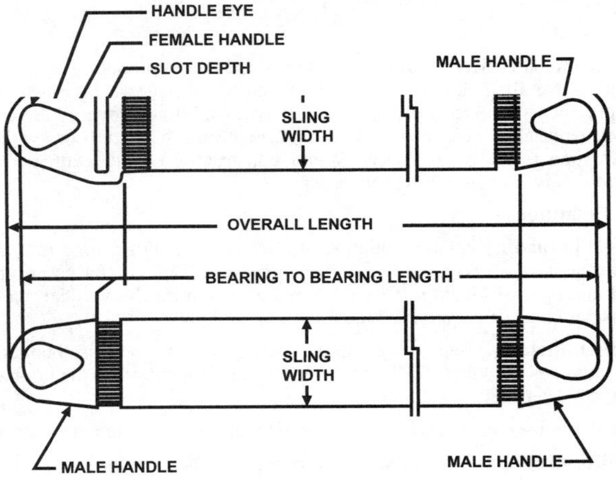

Figure N–184–2
Metal Mesh Construction

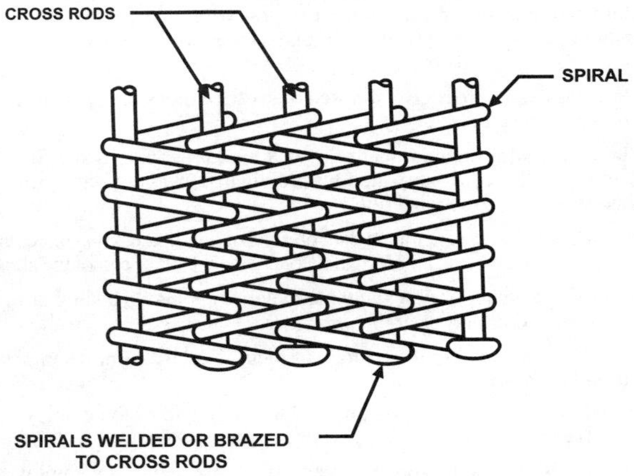

Figure N–184–3
Major Components of a Quadruple Sling

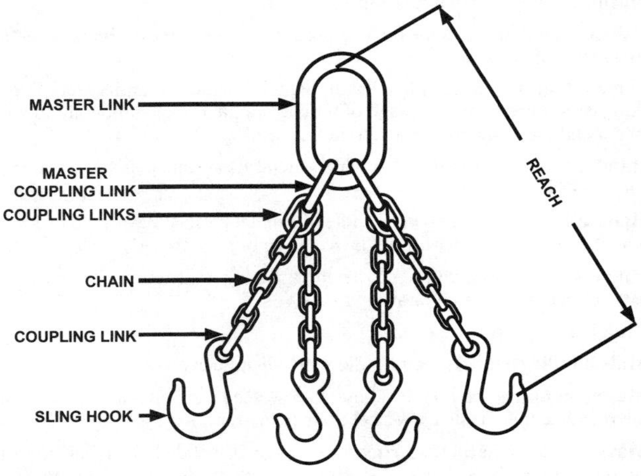

Proof load is the load applied in performance of a proof test.

Proof test is a nondestructive tension test performed by the sling manufacturer or an equivalent entity to verify construction and workmanship of a sling.

Rated capacity or working load limit is the maximum working load permitted by the provisions of this Section.

Reach is the effective length of an alloy steel chain sling measured from the top bearing surface of the upper terminal component to the bottom bearing surface of the lower terminal component.

Selvage edge is the finished edge of synthetic webbing designed to prevent unraveling.

Sling is an assembly which connects the load to the material handling equipment.

Sling manufacturer is a person or organization that assembles sling components into their final form for sale to users.

Spiral is a single transverse coil that is the basic element from which metal mesh is fabricated. (See Fig. N–184–2.)

Strand laid endless sling-mechanical joint is a wire rope sling made endless from one length of rope with the ends joined by one or more metallic fittings.

Strand laid grommet-hand tucked is an endless wire rope sling made from one length of strand wrapped six times around a core formed by hand tucking the ends of the strand inside the six wraps.

Strand laid rope is a wire rope made with strands (usually six or eight) wrapped around a fiber core, wire strand core, or independent wire rope core (IWRC).

Vertical hitch is a method of supporting a load by a single, vertical part or leg of the sling. (See Fig. N–184–4.)

(c) Safe operating practices Whenever any sling is used, the following practices shall be observed:

(c)(1) Slings that are damaged or defective shall not be used;

(c)(2) Slings shall not be shortened with knots or bolts or other makeshift devices;

(c)(3) Sling legs shall not be kinked;

(c)(4) Slings shall not be loaded in excess of their rated capacities;

(c)(5) Slings used in a basket hitch shall have the loads balanced to prevent slippage;

(c)(6) Slings shall be securely attached to their loads;

(c)(7) Slings shall be padded or protected from the sharp edges of their loads;

(c)(8) Suspended loads shall be kept clear of all obstructions;

(c)(9) All employees shall be kept clear of loads about to be lifted and of suspended loads;

(c)(10) Hands or fingers shall not be placed between the sling and its load while the sling is being tightened around the load;

(c)(11) Shock loading is prohibited;

(c)(12) A sling shall not be pulled from under a load when the load is resting on the sling;

(c)(13) Employers must not load a sling in excess of its recommended safe working load as prescribed by the sling manufacturer on the identification markings permanently affixed to the sling;

(c)(14) Employers must not use slings without affixed and legible identification markings.

(d) Inspections Each day before being used, the sling and all fastenings and attachments shall be inspected for damage or defects by a competent person designated by the employer. Additional inspections shall be performed during sling use, where service conditions warrant. Damaged or defective slings shall be immediately removed from service.

(e) Alloy steel chain slings

(e)(1) Sling identification Alloy steel chain slings shall have permanently affixed durable identification stating size, grade, rated capacity, and reach.

(e)(2) Attachments

(e)(2)(i) Hooks, rings, oblong links, pear shaped links, welded or mechanical coupling links or other attachments shall have a rated capacity at least equal to that of the alloy steel chain with which they are used or the sling shall not be used in excess of the rated capacity of the weakest component.

(e)(2)(ii) Makeshift links or fasteners formed from bolts or rods, or other such attachments, shall not be used.

(e)(3) Inspections

(e)(3)(i) In addition to the inspection required by paragraph (d) of this Section, a thorough periodic inspection of alloy steel chain slings in use shall be made on a regular basis, to be determined on the basis of (A) frequency of sling use; (B) severity of service conditions; (C) nature of lifts being made; and (D) experience gained on the service life of slings used in similar circumstances. Such inspections shall in no event be at intervals greater than once every 12 months.

(e)(3)(ii) The employer shall make and maintain a record of the most recent month in which each alloy steel chain sling was thoroughly inspected, and shall make such record available for examination.

(e)(3)(iii) The thorough inspection of alloy steel chain slings shall be performed by a competent person designated by the employer, and shall include a thorough inspection for wear, defective welds, deformation and increase in length. Where such defects or deterioration are present, the sling shall be immediately removed from service.

(e)(4) **Proof testing** The employer shall ensure that before use, each new, repaired, or reconditioned alloy steel chain sling, including all welded components in the sling assembly, shall be proof tested by the sling manufacturer or equivalent entity, in accordance with paragraph 5.2 of the American Society of Testing and Materials Specification A391–65, which is incorporated by reference as specified in §1910.6 (ANSI G61.1– 1968). The employer shall retain a certificate of the proof test and shall make it available for examination.

(e)(5) [Reserved]

(e)(6) **Safe operating temperatures** Employers must permanently remove an alloy steel-chain slings from service if it is heated above 1000 degrees F. When exposed to service temperatures in excess of 600 degrees F, employers must reduce the maximum working-load limits permitted by the chain manufacturer in accordance with the chain or sling manufacturer's recommendations.

(e)(7) **Repairing and reconditioning alloy steel chain slings**

(e)(7)(i) Worn or damaged alloy steel chain slings or attachments shall not be used until repaired. When welding or heat testing is performed, slings shall not be used unless repaired, reconditioned and proof tested by the sling manufacturer or an equivalent entity.

(e)(7)(ii) Mechanical coupling links or low carbon steel repair links shall not be used to repair broken lengths of chain.

(e)(8) **Effect of wear** If the chain size at any point of the link is less than that stated in Table N–184–1, the employer must remove the chain from service.

(e)(9) **Deformed attachments**

(e)(9)(i) Alloy steel chain slings with cracked or deformed master links, coupling links or other components shall be removed from service.

Table N–184–1
Minimum Allowable Chain Size At Any Point of Link

Chain size, inches	Minimum allowable chain size, inches
1/4	13/64
3/8	19/64
1/2	25/64
5/8	31/64
3/8	19/32
7/8	4 5/64
1	13/16
1 1/8	29/32
1 1/4	1
1 3/8	1 3/32
1 1/2	1 3/16
1 3/4	1 13/32

(e)(9)(ii) Slings shall be removed from service if hooks are cracked, have been opened more than 15 percent of the normal throat opening measured at the narrowest point or twisted more than 10 degrees from the plane of the unbent hook.

(f) **Wire-rope slings**

(f)(1) **Sling use** Employers must use only wire-rope slings that have permanently affixed and legible identification markings as prescribed by the manufacturer, and that indicate the recommended safe working load for the type(s) of hitch(es) used, the angle upon which it is based, and the number of legs if more than one.

(f)(2) **Minimum sling lengths**

(f)(2)(i) Cable laid and 6×19 and 6×37 slings shall have a minimum clear length of wire rope 10 times the component rope diameter between splices, sleeves or end fittings.

(f)(2)(ii) Braided slings shall have a minimum clear length of wire rope 40 times the component rope diameter between the loops or end fittings.

(f)(2)(iii) Cable laid grommets, strand laid grommets and endless slings shall have a minimum circumferential length of 96 times their body diameter.

(f)(3) **Safe operating temperatures** Fiber core wire rope slings of all grades shall be permanently removed from service if they are exposed to temperatures in excess of 200 °F. When nonfiber core wire rope slings of any grade are used at temperatures above 400 °F or below minus 60 °F, recommendations of the sling manufacturer regarding use at that temperature shall be followed.

(f)(4) **End attachments**

(f)(4)(i) Welding of end attachments, except covers to thimbles, shall be performed prior to the assembly of the sling.

(f)(4)(ii) All welded end attachments shall not be used unless proof tested by the manufacturer or equivalent entity at twice their rated capacity prior to initial use. The employer shall retain a certificate of the proof test, and make it available for examination.

(f)(5) **Removal from service** Wire rope slings shall be immediately removed from service if any of the following conditions are present:

(f)(5)(i) Ten randomly distributed broken wires in one rope lay, or five broken wires in one strand in one rope lay;

(f)(5)(ii) Wear or scraping of one-third the original diameter of outside individual wires;

(f)(5)(iii) Kinking, crushing, bird caging or any other damage resulting in distortion of the wire rope structure;

(f)(5)(iv) Evidence of heat damage;

(f)(5)(v) End attachments that are cracked, deformed or worn;

(f)(5)(vi) Hooks that have been opened more than 15 percent of the normal throat opening measured at the narrowest point or twisted more than 10 degrees from the plane of the unbent hook;

(f)(5)(vii) Corrosion of the rope or end attachments.

(g) **Metal mesh slings**

(g)(1) **Sling marking** Each metal mesh sling shall have permanently affixed to it a durable marking that states the rated capacity for vertical basket hitch and choker hitch loadings.

(g)(2) **Handles** Handles shall have a rated capacity at least equal to the metal fabric and exhibit no deformation after proof testing.

(g)(3) **Attachments of handles to fabric** The fabric and handles shall be joined so that:

(g)(3)(i) The rated capacity of the sling is not reduced

(g)(3)(ii) The load is evenly distributed across the width of the fabric.

(g)(3)(iii) Sharp edges will not damage the fabric.

(g)(4) **Sling coatings** Coatings which diminish the rated capacity of a sling shall not be applied.

(g)(5) **Sling testing** All new and repaired metal mesh slings, including handles, shall not be used unless proof tested by the manufacturer or equivalent entity at a minimum of 1½ times their rated capacity. Elastomer impregnated slings shall be proof tested before coating.

(g)(6) [Reserved]

(g)(7) **Safe operating temperatures** Metal mesh slings which are not impregnated with elastomers may be used in a temperature range from minus 20 °F to plus 550 °F without decreasing the working load limit. Metal mesh slings impregnated with polyvinyl chloride or neoprene may be used only in a temperature range from zero degrees to plus 200 °F. For operations outside these temperature ranges or for metal mesh slings impregnated with other materials, the sling manufacturer's recommendations shall be followed.

(g)(8) **Repairs**

(g)(8)(i) Metal mesh slings which are repaired shall not be used unless repaired by a metal mesh sling manufacturer or an equivalent entity.

(g)(8)(ii) Once repaired, each sling shall be permanently marked or tagged, or a written record maintained, to indicate the date and nature of the repairs and the person or organization that performed the repairs. Records of repairs shall be made available for examination.

(g)(9) **Removal from service** Metal mesh slings shall be immediately removed from service if any of the following conditions are present:

(g)(9)(i) A broken weld or broken brazed joint along the sling edge;

(g)(9)(ii) Reduction in wire diameter of 25 per cent due to abrasion or 15 percent due to corrosion;

(g)(9)(iii) Lack of flexibility due to distortion of the fabric;

(g)(9)(iv) Distortion of the female handle so that the depth of the slot is increased more than 10 percent;

(g)(9)(v) Distortion of either handle so that the width of the eye is decreased more than 10 percent;

(g)(9)(vi) A 15 percent reduction of the original cross sectional area of metal at any point around the handle eye;

(g)(9)(vii) Distortion of either handle out of its plane.

(h) **Natural and synthetic fiber-rope slings**

(h)(1) **Sling use** Employers must use natural and synthetic fiber-rope slings that have permanently affixed and legible identification markings stating the rated capacity for the type(s) of hitch(es) used and the angle upon which it is based, type of fiber material, and the number of legs if more than one.

(h)(2) **Safe operating temperatures** Natural and synthetic fiber rope slings, except for wet frozen slings, may be used in a temperature range from minus 20 °F to plus 180 °F without decreasing the working load limit. For operations outside this temperature range and for wet frozen slings, the sling manufacturer's recommendations shall be followed.

(h)(3) **Splicing** Spliced fiber rope slings shall not be used unless they have been spliced in accordance with the following minimum requirements and in accordance with any additional recommendations of the manufacturer:

(h)(3)(i) In manila rope, eye splices shall consist of at least three full tucks, and short splices shall consist of at least six full tucks, three on each side of the splice center line.

(h)(3)(ii) In synthetic fiber rope, eye splices shall consist of at least four full tucks, and short splices shall consist of at least eight full tucks, four on each side of the center line.

(h)(3)(iii) Strand end tails shall not be trimmed flush with the surface of the rope immediately adjacent to the full tucks. This applies to all types of fiber rope and both eye and short splices. For fiber rope under one inch in diameter, the tail shall project at least six rope diameters beyond the last full tuck. For fiber rope one inch in diameter and larger, the tail shall project at least six inches beyond the last full tuck. Where a projecting tail interferes with the use of the sling, the tail shall be tapered and spliced into the body of the rope using at least two additional tucks (which will require a tail length of approximately six rope diameters beyond the last full tuck).

(h)(3)(iv) Fiber rope slings shall have a minimum clear length of rope between eye splices equal to 10 times the rope diameter.

(h)(3)(v) Knots shall not be used in lieu of splices.

(h)(3)(vi) Clamps not designed specifically for fiber ropes shall not be used for splicing.

(h)(3)(vii) For all eye splices, the eye shall be of such size to provide an included angle of not greater than 60 degrees at the splice when the eye is placed over the load or support.

(h)(4) **End attachments** Fiber rope slings shall not be used if end attachments in contact with the rope have sharp edges or projections.

(h)(5) **Removal from service** Natural and synthetic fiber rope slings shall be immediately removed from service if any of the following conditions are present:

(h)(5)(i) Abnormal wear;

(h)(5)(ii) Powdered fiber between strands;

(h)(5)(iii) Broken or cut fibers;

(h)(5)(iv) Variations in the size or roundness of strands;

(h)(5)(v) Discoloration or rotting; and

(h)(5)(vi) Distortion of hardware in the sling.

(h)(6) **Repairs** Only fiber rope slings made from new rope shall be used. Use of repaired or reconditioned fiber rope slings is prohibited.

(i) **Synthetic web slings**

(i)(1) **Sling identification** Each sling shall be marked or coded to show the rated capacities for each type of hitch and type of synthetic web material.

(i)(2) **Webbing** Synthetic webbing shall be of uniform thickness and width and selvage edges shall not be split from the webbing's width.

(i)(3) **Fittings** Fittings shall be:

(i)(3)(i) Of a minimum breaking strength equal to that of the sling; and

(i)(3)(ii) Free of all sharp edges that could in any way damage the webbing.

(i)(4) **Attachment of end fittings to webbing and formation of eyes** Stitching shall be the only method used to attach end fittings to webbing and to form eyes. The thread shall be in an even pattern and contain a sufficient number of stitches to develop the full breaking strength of the sling.

(i)(5) [Reserved]

(i)(6) **Environmental conditions** When synthetic web slings are used, the following precautions shall be taken:

(i)(6)(i) Nylon web slings shall not be used where fumes, vapors, sprays, mists or liquids of acids or phenolics are present.

(i)(6)(ii) Polyester and polypropylene web slings shall not be used where fumes, vapors, sprays, mists or liquids of caustics are present.

(i)(6)(iii) Web slings with aluminum fittings shall not be used where fumes, vapors, sprays, mists or liquids of caustics are present.

Figure N–184–6
Basic Synthetic Web Sling Constructions

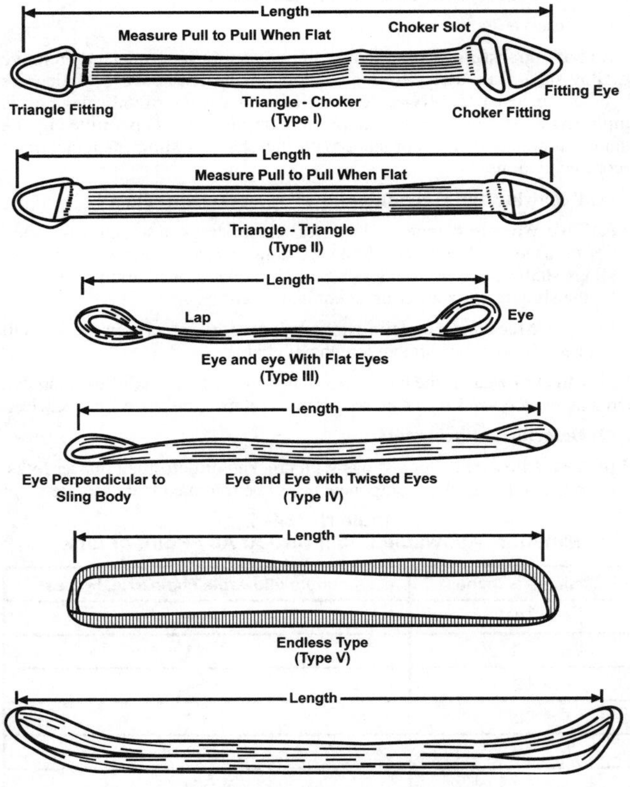

(i)(7) **Safe operating temperatures** Synthetic web slings of polyester and nylon shall not be used at temperatures in excess of 180 °F. Polypropylene web slings shall not be used at temperatures in excess of 200 °F.

(i)(8) [OI] **Repairs**

(i)(8)(i) Synthetic web slings which are repaired shall not be used unless repaired by a sling manufacturer or an equivalent entity.

(i)(8)(ii) Each repaired sling shall be proof tested by the manufacturer or equivalent entity to twice the rated capacity prior to its return to service. The employer shall retain a certificate of the proof test and make it available for examination.

(i)(8)(iii) Slings, including webbing and fittings, which have been repaired in a temporary manner shall not be used.

(i)(9) [OI] Removal from service. Synthetic web slings shall be immediately removed from service if any of the following conditions are present:

(i)(9)(i) Acid or caustic burns;

(i)(9)(ii) Melting or charring of any part of the sling surface;

(i)(9)(iii) Snags, punctures, tears or cuts;

(i)(9)(iv) Broken or worn stitches; or

(i)(9)(v) Distortion of fittings.

[40 FR 27369, June 27, 1975, as amended at 40 FR 31598, July 28, 1975; 41 FR 13353, Mar. 30, 1976; 58 FR 35309, June 30, 1993; 61 FR 9240, Mar. 7, 1996; 76 FR 33607, June 8, 2011]

[OI] indicates an OSHA Letter of Interpretation exists for this specific reference. Please see www.oshainterpretation.us for details.

29 CFR PART 1910 Subpart O
Machinery and Machine Guarding

Section Contents

Subpart O—Machinery and Machine Guarding

Authority: 29 U.S.C. 653, 655, 657; Secretary of Labor's Order No. 12-71 (36 FR 8754), 8-76 (41 FR 25059), 9-83 (48 FR 35736), 1-90 (55 FR 9033), 5-2002 (67 FR 65008), or 1-2012 (77 FR 3912), as applicable; 20 CFR Part §1911. Sections §1910.217 and §1910.219 also issued under 5 U.S.C. 553.

§1910.211 Definitions

(a) As used in §1910.213 and §1910.214 unless the context clearly requires otherwise, the following woodworking machinery terms shall have the meaning prescribed in this paragraph.

(a)(1) **Point of operations** means that point at which cutting, shaping, boring, or forming is accomplished upon the stock.

(a)(2) **Push stick** means a narrow strip of wood or other soft material with a notch cut into one end and which is used to push short pieces of material through saws.

(a)(3) **Block** means a short block of wood, provided with a handle similar to that of a plane and a shoulder at the rear end, which is used for pushing short stock over revolving cutters.

(b) As used in §1910.215 unless the context clearly requires otherwise, the following abrasive wheel machinery terms shall have the meanings prescribed in this paragraph.

(b)(1) **Type 1 straight wheels** means wheels having diameter, thickness, and hole size dimensions, and they should be used only on the periphery. Type 1 wheels shall be mounted between flanges.

Limitation: Hole dimension (H) should not be greater than two-thirds of wheel diameter dimension (D) for precision, cylindrical, centerless, or surface grinding applications. Maximum hole size for all other applications should not exceed one-half wheel diameter.

Figure No. 0–1
Type 1 Straight Wheels

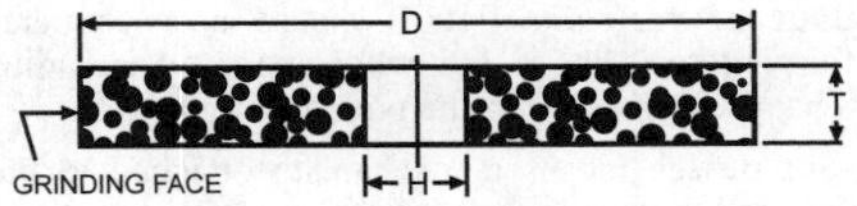

Peripheral grinding wheel having a diameter, thickness and hole.

(b)(2) **Type 2 cylinder wheels** means wheels having diameter, wheel thickness, and rim thickness dimensions. Grinding is performed on the rim face only, dimension W. Cylinder wheels may be plain, plate mounted, inserted nut, or of the projecting stud type.

Limitation: Rim height, T dimension, is generally equal to or greater than rim thickness, W dimension.

Figure No. 0–2
Type 2 Cylinder Wheels

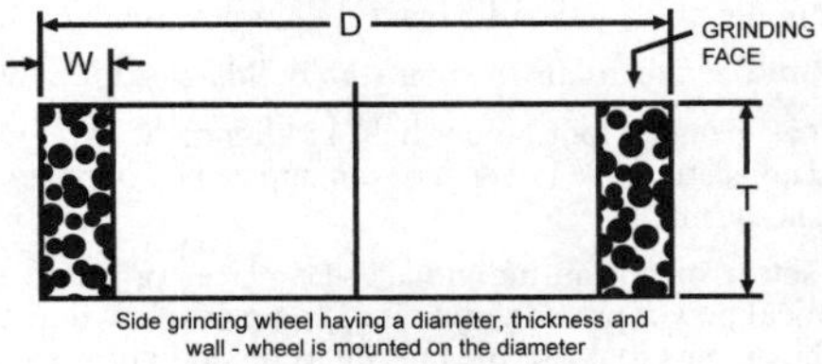

Side grinding wheel having a diameter, thickness and wall - wheel is mounted on the diameter

(b)(3) **Type 6 straight cup wheels** means wheels having diameter, thickness, hole size, rim thickness, and back thickness dimensions. Grinding is always performed on rim face, W dimension.

Limitation: Minimum back thickness, E dimension, should not be less than one-fourth T dimension. In addition, when unthreaded hole wheels are specified, the inside flat, K dimension, must be large enough to accommodate a suitable flange.

Figure No. O–3
Type 6 Straight Cup Wheels

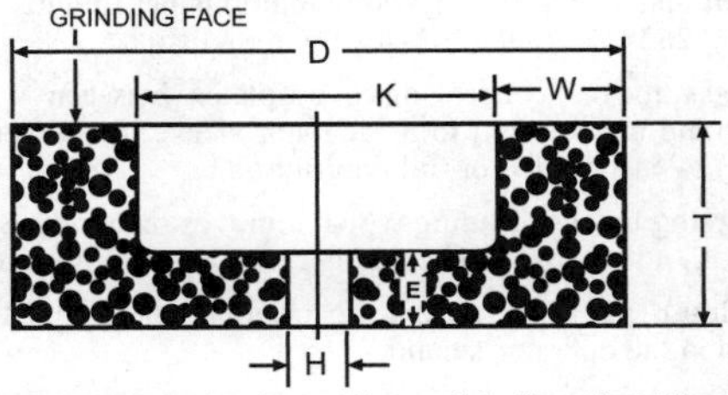

Side grinding wheel having a diameter, thickness and hole with one side straight or flat and the opposite side recessed. This type, however, differs from Type 5 in that the grinding is performed on the wall of the abrasive created by the difference between the diameter of the recess and the outside diameter of the wheel. Therefore, the wall dimension "W" takes precedence over the diameter of the recess as an essential intermediate dimension to describe this shape type.

(b)(4) **Type 11 flaring cup wheels** mean wheels having double diameter dimensions D and J, and in addition have thickness, hole size, rim and back thickness dimensions. Grinding is always performed on rim face, W dimension. Type 11 wheels are subject to all limitations of use and mounting listed for type 6 straight sided cup wheels definition.

Limitation: Minimum back thickness, E dimension, should not be less than one-fourth T dimension. In addition when unthreaded hole wheels are specified the inside flat, K dimension, shall be large enough to accommodate a suitable flange.

Figure No. O–4
Type 11 Flaring Cup Wheels

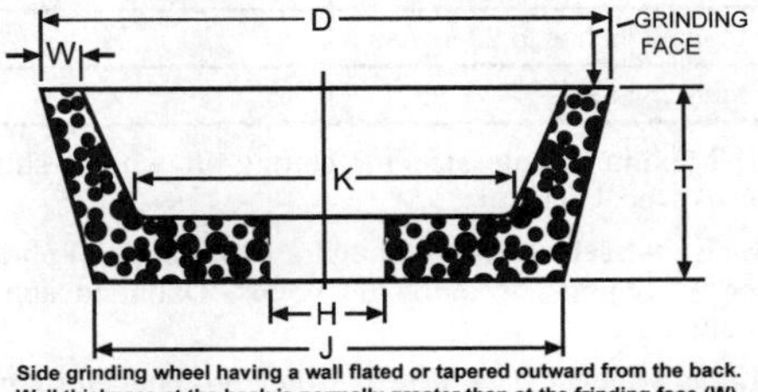

Side grinding wheel having a wall flated or tapered outward from the back. Wall thickness at the back is normally greater than at the frinding face (W).

(b)(5) **Modified types 6 and 11 wheels (terrazzo)** mean some type 6 and 11 cup wheels used in the terrazzo trade having tapered K dimensions to match a special tapered flange furnished by the machine builder.

Limitation: These wheels shall be mounted only with a special tapered flange.

Figure No. O–5
Tapered "K" Dimension Tapered "K" Dimension

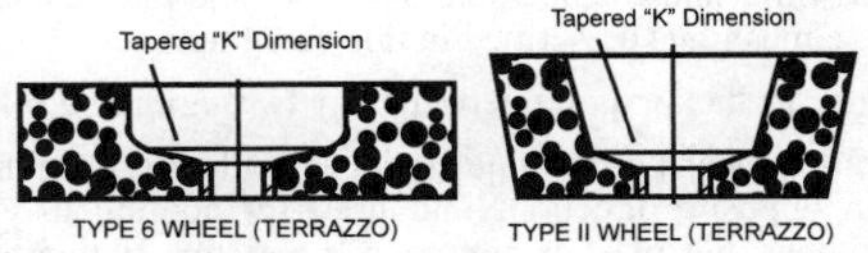

Typical examples of modified types 6 and 11 wheels (terrazzo) showing tapered K dimensions.

(b)(6) **Types 27 and 28 depressed center wheels** mean wheels having diameter, thickness, and hole size dimensions. Both types are reinforced, organic bonded wheels having offset hubs which permit side and peripheral grinding operations without interference with the mounting. Type 27 wheels are manufactured with flat grinding rims permitting notching and cutting operations. Type 28 wheels have saucer shaped grinding rims.

(b)(6)(i) Limitations: Special supporting, back adapter and inside flange nuts are required for the proper mounting of these types of wheels subject to limitations of §1910.215(c)(4)(i) and (ii).

(b)(6)(ii) Mounts which are affixed to the wheel by the manufacturer may not require an inside nut and shall not be reused.

(b)(7) **Type 27A depressed center, cutting-off wheels** mean wheels having diameter, thickness, and hole size dimensions. They are reinforced, organic bonded, offset hub type wheels, usually 16 inches diameter and larger, specially designed for use on cutting-off machines where mounting nut or outer flange interference cannot be tolerated.

Limitations:See §1910.215(c)(1).

(b)(8) **Surface feet per minute (s.f.p.m.)** means the distance in feet any one abrasive grain on the peripheral surface of a grinding wheel travels in 1 minute.

Surface Feet Per Minute = 3.1416 × diameter in inches × r.p.m. ÷ 12 or .262 × diameter in inches × r.p.m.

Examples:

(a) 24-inch diameter wheel, 1,000 revolutions per minute. Surface Feet per minute .262×24×1,000=6,288 s.f.p.m.

(b) 12-inch diameter wheel, 1,000 revolutions per minute. Surface Feet per minute .262×12×1,000=3,144 s.f.p.m.

(b)(9) **Flanges** means collars, discs or plates between which wheels are mounted and are referred to as adaptor, sleeve, or back up type. See paragraph (c) of §1910.215 for full description.

(b)(10) **Snagging** means grinding which removes relatively large amounts of material without regard to close tolerances or surface finish requirements.

(b)(11) **Off-hand grinding** means the grinding of any material or part which is held in the operator's hand.

(b)(12) **Safety guard** means an enclosure designed to restrain the pieces of the grinding wheel and furnish all possible protection in the event that the wheel is broken in operation. See paragraph (b) of §1910.215.

(b)(13) **Cutting off wheels** means wheels having diameter thickness and hole size dimensions and are subject to all limitations of mounting and use listed for type 1 wheels, the definition in subparagraph (1) of this paragraph and paragraph (d) of §1910.215. They may be steel centered, diamond abrasive or organic bonded abrasive of the plain or reinforced type.

(b)(13)(i) Limitation: Cutting off wheels are recommended only for use on specially designed and fully guarded machines and are subject to the following maximum thickness and hole size limitations.

Wheel diameter	Max. thickness (inch)
6 inch and smaller	3/16
Larger than 6 inches to 12 inches	1/4
Larger than 12 inches to 23 inches	3/8
Larger than 23 inches	1/2

(b)(13)(ii) Maximum hole size for cutting-off wheels should not be larger than 1/4-wheel diameter.

(b)(14) **Abrasive wheel** means a cutting tool consisting of abrasive grains held together by organic or inorganic bonds. Diamond and reinforced wheels are included.

(b)(15) **Organic wheels** means wheels which are bonded by means of an organic material such as resin, rubber, shellac, or other similar bonding agent.

(b)(16) **Inorganic wheels** means wheels which are bonded by means of inorganic material such as clay, glass, porcelain, sodium silicate, magnesium oxychloride, or metal. Wheels bonded with clay, glass, porcelain or related ceramic materials are characterized as vitrified bonded wheels.

(c) As used in §1910.216, unless the context clearly requires otherwise, the following mills and calenders in the rubber and plastic industries terms shall have the meanings prescribed in this paragraph.

(c)(1) **Bite** means the nip point between any two inrunning rolls.

(c)(2) **Calender** means a machine equipped with two or more metal rolls revolving in opposite directions and used for continuously sheeting or plying up rubber and plastics compounds and for frictioning or coating materials with rubber and plastics compounds.

(c)(3) **Mill** means a machine consisting of two adjacent metal rolls, set horizontally, which revolve in opposite directions (i.e., toward each other as viewed from above) used for the mechanical working of rubber and plastics compounds.

(d) As used in §1910.217, unless the context clearly requires otherwise, the following power press terms shall have the meaning prescribed in this paragraph.

(d)(1) **Antirepeat** means the part of the clutch/brake control system designed to limit the press to a single stroke if the tripping means is held operated. Antirepeat requires release of all tripping mechanisms before another stroke can be initiated. Antirepeat is also called single stroke reset or reset circuit.

(d)(2) **Brake** means the mechanism used on a mechanical power press to stop and/or hold the crankshaft, either directly or through a gear train, when the clutch is disengaged.

(d)(3) **Bolster plate** means the plate attached to the top of the bed of the press having drilled holes or T-slots for attaching the lower die or die shoe.

(d)(4) **Clutch** means the coupling mechanism used on a mechanical power press to couple the flywheel to the crankshaft, either directly or through a gear train.

(d)(5) **Full revolution clutch** means a type of clutch that, when tripped, cannot be disengaged until the crankshaft has completed a full revolution and the press slide a full stroke.

(d)(6) **Part revolution clutch** means a type of clutch that can be disengaged at any point before the crankshaft has completed a full revolution and the press slide a full stroke.

(d)(7) **Direct drive** means the type of driving arrangement wherein no clutch is used; coupling and decoupling of the driving torque is accomplished by energization and deenergization of a motor. Even though not employing a clutch, direct drives match the operational characteristics of "part revolution clutches" because the driving power may be disengaged during the stroke of the press.

(d)(8) **Concurrent** means acting in conjunction, and is used to describe a situation wherein two or more controls exist in an operated condition at the same time.

(d)(9) **Continuous** means uninterrupted multiple strokes of the slide without intervening stops (or other clutch control action) at the end of individual strokes.

(d)(10) **Counterbalance** means the mechanism that is used to balance or support the weight of the connecting rods, slide, and slide attachments.

(d)(11) **Device** means a press control or attachment that:

(d)(11)(i) Restrains the operator from inadvertently reaching into the point of operation, or

(d)(11)(ii) Prevents normal press operation if the operator's hands are inadvertently within the point of operation, or

(d)(11)(iii) Automatically withdraws the operator's hands if the operator's hands are inadvertently within the point of operation as the dies close, or

(d)(11)(iv) Prevents the initiation of a stroke, or stops of stroke in progress, when there is an intrusion through the sensing field by any part of the operator's body or by any other object.

(d)(12) **Presence sensing device** means a device designed, constructed and arranged to create a sensing field or area that signals the clutch/brake control to deactivate the clutch and activate the brake of the press when any part of the operator's body or a hand tool is within such field or area.

(d)(13) **Gate or movable barrier device** means a movable barrier arranged to enclose the point of operation before the press stroke can be started.

(d)(14) **Holdout or restraint device** means a mechanism, including attachments for operator's hands, that when anchored and adjusted prevent the operator's hands from entering the point of operation.

(d)(15) **Pull-out device** means a mechanism attached to the operator's hands and connected to the upper die or slide of the press, that is designed, when properly adjusted, to withdraw the operator's hands as the dies close, if the operator's hands are inadvertently within the point of operation.

(d)(16) **Sweep device** means a single or double arm (rod) attached to the upper die or slide of the press and designed to move the operator's hands to a safe position as the dies close, if the operator's hands are inadvertently within the point of operation.

(d)(17) **Two hand control device** means a two hand trip that further requires concurrent pressure from both hands of the operator during a substantial part of the die-closing portion of the stroke of the press.

(d)(18) **Die** means the tooling used in a press for cutting or forming material. An upper and a lower die make a complete set.

(d)(19) **Die builder** means any person who builds dies for power presses.

(d)(20) **Die set** means a tool holder held in alignment by guide posts and bushings and consisting of a lower shoe, an upper shoe or punch holder, and guide posts and bushings.

(d)(21) **Die setter** means an individual who places or removes dies in or from mechanical power presses, and who, as a part of his duties, makes the necessary adjustments to cause the tooling to function properly and safely.

(d)(22) **Die setting** means the process of placing or removing dies in or from a mechanical power press, and the process of adjusting the dies, other tooling and safeguarding means to cause them to function properly and safely.

(d)(23) **Die shoe** means a plate or block upon which a die holder is mounted. A die shoe functions primarily as a base for the complete die assembly, and, when used, is bolted or clamped to the bolster plate or the face of slide.

(d)(24) **Ejector** means a mechanism for removing work or material from between the dies.

(d)(25) **Face of slide** means the bottom surface of the slide to which the punch or upper die is generally attached.

(d)(26) **Feeding** means the process of placing or removing material within or from the point of operation.

(d)(27) **Automatic feeding** means feeding wherein the material or part being processed is placed within or removed from the point of operation by a method or means not requiring action by an operator on each stroke of the press.

(d)(28) **Semiautomatic feeding** means feeding wherein the material or part being processed is placed within or removed from the point of operation by an auxiliary means controlled by operator on each stroke of the press.

(d)(29) **Manual feeding** means feeding wherein the material or part being processed is handled by the operator on each stroke of the press.

(d)(30) **Foot control** means the foot operated control mechanism designed to be used with a clutch or clutch/brake control system.

(d)(31) **Foot pedal** means the foot operated lever designed to operate the mechanical linkage that trips a full revolution clutch.

(d)(32) **Guard** means a barrier that prevents entry of the operator's hands or fingers into the point of operation.

(d)(33) **Die enclosure guard** means an enclosure attached to the die shoe or stripper, or both, in a fixed position.

(d)(34) **Fixed barrier guard** means a die space barrier attached to the press frame.

(d)(35) **Interlocked press barrier guard** means a barrier attached to the press frame and interlocked so that the press stroke cannot be started normally unless the guard itself, or its hinged or movable sections, enclose the point of operation.

(d)(36) **Adjustable barrier guard** means a barrier requiring adjustment for each job or die setup.

(d)(37) **Guide post** means the pin attached to the upper or lower die shoe operating within the bushing on the opposing die shoe, to maintain the alignment of the upper and lower dies.

(d)(38) **Hand feeding tool** means any hand held tool designed for placing or removing material or parts to be processed within or from the point of operation.

(d)(39) **Inch** means an intermittent motion imparted to the slide (on machines using part revolution clutches) by momentary operation of the Inch operating means. Operation of the Inch operating means engages the driving clutch so that a small portion of one stroke or indefinite stroking can occur, depending upon the length of time the Inch operating means is held operated. Inch is a function used by the die setter for setup of dies and tooling, but is not intended for use during production operations by the operator.

(d)(40) **Jog** means an intermittent motion imparted to the slide by momentary operation of the drive motor, after the clutch is engaged with the flywheel at rest.

(d)(41) **Knockout** means a mechanism for releasing material from either die.

(d)(42) **Liftout** means the mechanism also known as knockout.

(d)(43) **Operator's station** means the complete complement of controls used by or available to an operator on a given operation for stroking the press.

(d)(44) **Pinch point** means any point other than the point of operation at which it is possible for a part of the body to be caught between the moving parts of a press or auxiliary equipment, or between moving and stationary parts of a press or auxiliary equipment or between the material and moving part or parts of the press or auxiliary equipment.

(d)(45) **Point of operation** means the area of the press where material is actually positioned and work is being performed during any process such as shearing, punching, forming, or assembling.

(d)(46) **Press** means a mechanically powered machine that shears, punches, forms or assembles metal or other material by means of cutting, shaping, or combination dies attached to slides. A press consists of a stationary bed or anvil, and a slide (or slides) having a controlled reciprocating motion toward and away from the bed surface, the slide being guided in a definite path by the frame of the press.

(d)(47) **Repeat** means an unintended or unexpected successive stroke of the press resulting from a malfunction.

(d)(48) **Safety block** means a prop that, when inserted between the upper and lower dies or between the bolster plate and the face of the slide, prevents the slide from falling of its own deadweight.

(d)(49) **Single stroke** means one complete stroke of the slide, usually initiated from a full open (or up) position, followed by closing (or down), and then a return to the full open position.

(d)(50) **Single stroke mechanism** means an arrangement used on a full revolution clutch to limit the travel of the slide to one complete stroke at each engagement of the clutch.

(d)(51) **Slide** means the main reciprocating press member. A slide is also called a ram, plunger, or platen.

(d)(52) **Stop control** means an operator control designed to immediately deactivate the clutch control and activate the brake to stop slide motion.

(d)(53) **Stripper** means a mechanism or die part for removing the parts or material from the punch.

(d)(54) **Stroking selector** means the part of the clutch/brake control that determines the type of stroking when the operating means is actuated. The stroking selector generally includes positions for "Off" (Clutch Control), "Inch," "Single Stroke," and "Continuous" (when Continuous is furnished).

(d)(55) **Trip or (tripping)** means activation of the clutch to "run" the press.

(d)(56) **Turnover bar** means a bar used in die setting to manually turn the crankshaft of the press.

(d)(57) **Two-hand trip** means a clutch actuating means requiring the concurrent use of both hands of the operator to trip the press.

(d)(58) **Unitized tooling** means a type of die in which the upper and lower members are incorporated into a selfcontained unit so arranged as to hold the die members in alignment.

(d)(59) **Control system** means sensors, manual input and mode selection elements, interlocking and decision-making circuitry, and output elements to the press operating mechanism.

(d)(60) **Brake monitor** means a sensor designed, constructed, and arranged to monitor the effectiveness of the press braking system.

(d)(61) **Presence sensing device initiation** means an operating mode of indirect manual initiation of a single stroke by a presence sensing device when it senses that work motions of the operator, related to feeding and/or removing parts, are completed and all parts of the operator's body or hand tools are safely clear of the point of operation.

(d)(62) **Safety system** means the integrated total system, including the pertinent elements of the press, the controls, the safeguarding and any required supplemental safeguarding, and their interfaces with the operator, and the environment, designed, constructed and arranged to operate together as a unit, such that a single failure or single operating error will not cause injury to personnel due to point of operation hazards.

(d)(63) **Authorized person** means one to whom the authority and responsibility to perform a specific assignment has been given by the employer.

(d)(64) **Certification or certify** means, in the case of design certification/validation, that the manufacturer has reviewed and tested the design and manufacture, and in the case of installation certification/validation and annual recertification/revalidation, that the employer has reviewed and tested the installation, and concludes in both cases that the requirements of §1910.217 (a) through (h) and Appendix A have been met. The certifications are made to the validation organization.

(d)(65) **Validation or validate** means for PSDI safety systems that an OSHA recognized third-party validation organization:

(d)(65)(i) For design certification/validation has reviewed the manufacturer's certification that the PSDI safety system meets the requirements of §1910.217 (a) through (h) and Appendix A and the underlying tests and analyses performed by the manufacturer, has performed additional tests and analyses which may be required by §1910.217 (a) through (h) and Appendix A, and concludes that the requirements of §1910.217 (a) through (h) and Appendix A have been met; and

(d)(65)(ii) For installation certification/validation and annual recertification/revalidation has reviewed the employer's certification that the PSDI safety system meets the requirements of §1910.217 (a) through (h) and Appendix A and the underlying tests performed by the employer, has performed additional tests and analyses which may be required by §1910.217 (a) through (h) and Appendix A, and concludes that the requirements of §1910.217 (a) through (h) and Appendix A have been met.

(d)(66) **Certification/validation and certify/validate** means the combined process of certification and validation.

(e) As used in §1910.218, unless the context clearly requires otherwise, the following forging and hot metal terms shall have the meaning prescribed in this paragraph.

(e)(1) **Forging** means the product of work on metal formed to a desired shape by impact or pressure in hammers, forging machines (upsetters), presses, rolls, and related forming equipment. Forging hammers, counterblow equipment and high-energy-rate forging machines impart impact to the workpiece, while most other types of forging equipment impart squeeze pressure in shaping the stock. Some metals can be forged at room temperature, but the majority of metals are made more plastic for forging by heating.

(e)(2) **Open framehammers (or blacksmith hammers)** mean hammers used primarily for the shaping of forgings by means of impact with flat dies. Open frame hammers generally are so constructed that the anvil assembly is separate from the operating mechanism and machine supports; it rests on its own independent foundation. Certain exceptions are forging hammers made with frame mounted on the anvil; e.g., the smaller, single-frame hammers are usually made with the anvil and frame in one piece.

(e)(3) **Steam hammers** mean a type of drop hammer where the ram is raised for each stroke by a double-action steam cylinder and the energy delivered to the workpiece is supplied by the velocity and weight of the ram and attached upper die driven downward by steam pressure. Energy delivered during each stroke may be varied.

(e)(4) **Gravity hammers** mean a class of forging hammer wherein energy for forging is obtained by the mass and velocity of a freely falling ram and the attached upper die. Examples: board hammers and air-lift hammers.

(e)(5) **Forging presses** mean a class of forging equipment wherein the shaping of metal between dies is performed by mechanical or hydraulic pressure, and usually is accomplished with a single workstroke of the press for each die station.

(e)(6) **Trimming presses** mean a class of auxiliary forging equipment which removes flash or excess metal from a forging. This trimming operation can also be done cold, as can coining, a product sizing operation.

(e)(7) **High-energy-rate forging machines** mean a class of forging equipment wherein high ram velocities resulting from the sudden release of a compressed gas against a free piston impart impact to the workpiece.

(e)(8) **Forging rolls** mean a class of auxiliary forging equipment wherein stock is shaped between power driven rolls bearing contoured dies. Usually used for preforming, roll forging is often employed to reduce thickness and increase length of stock.

(e)(9) **Ring rolls** mean a class for forging equipment used for shaping weldless rings from pierced discs or thick-walled, ring-shaped blanks between rolls which control wall thickness, ring diameter, height and contour.

(e)(10) **Bolt-headers** mean the same as an upsetter or forging machine except that the diameter of stock fed into the machine is much smaller, i.e., commonly three-fourths inch or less.

(e)(11) **Rivet making machines** mean the same as upsetters and boltheaders when producing rivets with stock diameter of 1-inch or more. Rivet making with less than 1-inch diameter is usually a cold forging operation, and therefore not included in this Subpart.

(e)(12) **Upsetters (or forging machines, or headers)** type of forging equipment, related to the mechanical press, in which the main forming energy is applied horizontally to the workpiece which is gripped and held by prior action of the dies.

(f) As used in §1910.219, unless the context clearly requires otherwise, the following mechanical power-transmission guarding terms shall have the meaning prescribed in this paragraph.

(f)(1) **Belts** include all power transmission belts, such as flat belts, round belts, V-belts, etc., unless otherwise specified.

(f)(2) **Belt shifter** means a device for mechanically shifting belts from tight to loose pulleys or vice versa, or for shifting belts on cones of speed pulleys.

(f)(3) **Belt pole (sometimes called a belt shipper or shipper pole)** means a device used in shifting belts on and off fixed pulleys on line or countershaft where there are no loose pulleys.

(f)(4) **Exposed to contact** means that the location of an object is such that a person is likely to come into contact with it and be injured.

(f)(5) **Flywheels** include flywheels, balance wheels, and flywheel pulleys mounted and revolving on crankshaft of engine or other shafting.

(f)(6) **Maintenance runway** means any permanent runway or platform used for oiling, maintenance, running adjustment, or repair work, but not for passageway.

(f)(7) **Nip-point belt and pulley guard** means a device which encloses the pulley and is provided with rounded or rolled edge slots through which the belt passes.

(f)(8) **Point of operation** means that point at which cutting, shaping, or forming is accomplished upon the stock and shall include such other points as may offer a hazard to the operator in inserting or manipulating the stock in the operation of the machine.

(f)(9) **Prime movers** include steam, gas, oil, and air engines, motors, steam and hydraulic turbines, and other equipment used as a source of power.

(f)(10) **Sheaves** mean grooved pulleys, and shall be so classified unless used as flywheels.

[39 FR 23502, June 27, 1974, as amended at 39 FR 41846, Dec. 3, 1974; 53 FR 8353, Mar. 14, 1988]

§1910.212 General requirements for all machines

(a) **Machine guarding**

(a)(1) **Types of guarding** One or more methods of machine guarding shall be provided to protect the operator and other employees in the machine area from hazards such as those created by point of operation, ingoing nip points, rotating parts, flying chips and sparks. Examples of guarding methods are—barrier guards, two-hand tripping devices, electronic safety devices, etc.

(a)(2) **General requirements for machine guards** Guards shall be affixed to the machine where possible and secured elsewhere if for any reason attachment to the machine is not possible. The guard shall be such that it does not offer an accident hazard in itself.

(a)(3) **Point of operation guarding**

(a)(3)(i) Point of operation is the area on a machine where work is actually performed upon the material being processed.

(a)(3)(ii) The point of operation of machines whose operation exposes an employee to injury, shall be guarded. The guarding device shall be in conformity with any appropriate standards therefor, or, in the absence of applicable specific standards, shall be so designed and constructed as to prevent the operator from having any part of his body in the danger zone during the operating cycle.

(a)(3)(iii) Special handtools for placing and removing material shall be such as to permit easy handling of material without the operator placing a hand in the danger zone. Such tools shall not be in lieu of other guarding required by this section, but can only be used to supplement protection provided.

(a)(3)(iv) The following are some of the machines which usually require point of operation guarding:

(a)(3)(iv)(A) Guillotine cutters;
(a)(3)(iv)(B) Shears;
(a)(3)(iv)(C) Alligator shears;
(a)(3)(iv)(D) Power presses;
(a)(3)(iv)(E) Milling machines;
(a)(3)(iv)(F) Power saws;
(a)(3)(iv)(G) Jointers;
(a)(3)(iv)(H) Portable power tools;
(a)(3)(iv)(I) Forming rolls and calenders.

(a)(4) **Barrels, containers, and drums** Revolving drums, barrels, and containers shall be guarded by an enclosure which is interlocked with the drive mechanism, so that the barrel, drum, or container cannot revolve unless the guard enclosure is in place.

(a)(5) **Exposure of blades** When the periphery of the blades of a fan is less than seven (7) feet above the floor or working level, the blades shall be guarded. The guard shall have openings no larger than one-half (½) inch.

(b) **Anchoring fixed machinery** Machines designed for a fixed location shall be securely anchored to prevent walking or moving.

§1910.213 Woodworking machinery requirements

(a) **Machine construction general**

(a)(1) Each machine shall be so constructed as to be free from sensible vibration when the largest size tool is mounted and run idle at full speed.

(a)(2) Arbors and mandrels shall be constructed so as to have firm and secure bearing and be free from play.

(a)(3) [Reserved]

(a)(4) Any automatic cutoff saw that strokes continuously without the operator being able to control each stroke shall not be used.

(a)(5) Saw frames or tables shall be constructed with lugs cast on the frame or with an equivalent means to limit the size of the saw blade that can be mounted, so as to avoid overspeed caused by mounting a saw larger than intended.

(a)(6) Circular saw fences shall be so constructed that they can be firmly secured to the table or table assembly without changing their alignment with the saw. For saws with tilting tables or tilting arbors the fence shall be so constructed that it will remain in a line parallel with the saw, regardless of the angle of the saw with the table.

(a)(7) Circular saw gages shall be so constructed as to slide in grooves or tracks that are accurately machined, to insure exact alignment with the saw for all positions of the guide.

(a)(8) Hinged saw tables shall be so constructed that the table can be firmly secured in any position and in true alignment with the saw.

(a)(9) All belts, pulleys, gears, shafts, and moving parts shall be guarded in accordance with the specific requirements of §1910.219.

(a)(10) It is recommended that each power-driven woodworking machine be provided with a disconnect switch that can be locked in the off position.

(a)(11) The frames and all exposed, noncurrent-carrying metal parts of portable electric woodworking machinery operated at more than 90 volts to ground shall be grounded and other portable motors driving electric tools which are held in the hand while being operated shall be grounded if they operate at more than 90 volts to ground. The ground shall be provided through use of a separate ground wire and polarized plug and receptacle.

(a)(12) For all circular saws where conditions are such that there is a possibility of contact with the portion of the saw either beneath or behind the table, that portion of the saw shall be covered with an exhaust hood, or, if no exhaust system is required, with a guard that shall be so arranged as to prevent accidental contact with the saw.

(a)(13) Revolving double arbor saws shall be fully guarded in accordance with all the requirements for circular crosscut saws or with all the requirements for circular ripsaws, according to the kind of saws mounted on the arbors.

(a)(14) No saw, cutter head, or tool collar shall be placed or mounted on a machine arbor unless the tool has been accurately machined to size and shape to fit the arbor.

(a)(15) Combs (featherboards) or suitable jigs shall be provided at the workplace for use when a standard guard cannot be used, as in dadoing, grooving, jointing, moulding, and rabbeting.

(b) **Machine controls and equipment**

(b)(1) A mechanical or electrical power control shall be provided on each machine to make it possible for the operator to cut off the power from each machine without leaving his position at the point of operation.

(b)(2) On machines driven by belts and shafting, a locking-type belt shifter or an equivalent positive device shall be used.

(b)(3) OI On applications where injury to the operator might result if motors were to restart after power failures, provision shall be made to prevent machines from automatically restarting upon restoration of power.

(b)(4) Power controls and operating controls should be located within easy reach of the operator while he is at his regular work location, making it unnecessary for him to reach over the cutter to make adjustments. This does not apply to constant pressure controls used only for setup purposes.

(b)(5) On each machine operated by electric motors, positive means shall be provided for rendering such controls or devices inoperative while repairs or adjustments are being made to the machines they control.

(b)(6) Each operating treadle shall be protected against unexpected or accidental tripping.

(b)(7) Feeder attachments shall have the feed rolls or other moving parts so covered or guarded as to protect the operator from hazardous points.

(c) OI **Hand-fed ripsaws**

(c)(1) Each circular hand-fed ripsaw shall be guarded by a hood which shall completely enclose that portion of the saw above the table and that portion of the saw above the material being cut. The hood and mounting shall be arranged so that the hood will automatically adjust itself to the thickness of and remain in contact with the material being cut but it shall not offer any considerable resistance to insertion of material to saw or to passage of the material being sawed. The hood shall be made of adequate strength to resist blows and strains incidental to reasonable operation, adjusting, and handling, and shall be so designed as to protect the operator from flying splinters and broken saw teeth. It shall be made of material that is soft enough so that it will be unlikely to cause tooth breakage. The hood shall be so mounted as to insure that its operation will be positive, reliable, and in true alignment with the saw; and the mounting shall be adequate in strength to resist any reasonable side thrust or other force tending to throw it out of line.

(c)(2) Each hand-fed circular ripsaw shall be furnished with a spreader to prevent material from squeezing the saw or being thrown back on the operator. The spreader shall be made of hard tempered steel, or its equivalent, and shall be thinner than the saw kerf. It shall be of sufficient width to provide adequate stiffness or rigidity to resist any reasonable side thrust or blow tending to bend or throw it out of position. The spreader shall be attached so that it will remain in true alignment with the saw even when either the saw or table is tilted. The provision of a spreader in connection with grooving, dadoing, or rabbeting is not required. On the completion of such operations, the spreader shall be immediately replaced.

(c)(3) OI Each hand-fed circular ripsaw shall be provided with nonkickback fingers or dogs so located as to oppose the thrust or tendency of the saw to pick up the material or to throw it back toward the operator. They shall be designed to provide adequate holding power for all the thicknesses of materials being cut.

(d) **Hand-fed crosscut table saws**

(d)(1) Each circular crosscut table saw shall be guarded by a hood which shall meet all the requirements of paragraph (c)(1) of this section for hoods for circular ripsaws.

(d)(2) [Reserved]

(e) **Circular resaws**

(e)(1) Each circular resaw shall be guarded by a hood or shield of metal above the saw. This hood or shield shall be so designed as to guard against danger from flying splinters or broken saw teeth.

(e)(2) Each circular resaw (other than self-feed saws with a roller or wheel at back of the saw) shall be provided with a spreader fastened securely behind the saw. The spreader shall be slightly thinner than the saw kerf and slightly thicker than the saw disk.

(f) **Self-feed circular saws**

(f)(1) Feed rolls and saws shall be protected by a hood or guard to prevent the hands of the operator from coming in contact with the in-running rolls at any point. The guard shall be constructed of heavy material, preferably metal, and the bottom of the guard shall come down to within three-eighths inch of the plane formed by the bottom or working surfaces of the feed rolls. This distance (three-eighths inch) may be increased to three-fourths inch, provided the lead edge of the hood is extended to be not less than 5½ inches in front of the nip point between the front roll and the work.

(f)(2) OI Each self-feed circular ripsaw shall be provided with sectional non-kickback fingers for the full width of the feed rolls. They shall be located in front of the saw and so arranged as to be in continual contact with the wood being fed.

(g) **Swing cutoff saws** The requirements of this paragraph are also applicable to sliding cutoff saws mounted above the table.

(g)(1) Each swing cutoff saw shall be provided with a hood that will completely enclose the upper half of the saw, the arbor end, and the point of operation at all positions of the saw. The hood shall be constructed in such a manner and of such material that it will protect the operator from flying splinters and broken saw teeth. Its hood shall be so designed that it will automatically cover the lower portion of the blade, so that when the saw is returned to the back of the table the hood will rise on top of the fence, and when the saw is moved forward the hood will drop on top of and remain in contact with the table or material being cut.

(g)(2) Each swing cutoff saw shall be provided with an effective device to return the saw automatically to the back of the table when released at any point of its travel. Such a device shall not depend for its proper functioning upon any rope, cord, or spring. If there is a counterweight, the bolts supporting the bar and counterweight shall be provided with cotter pins; and the counterweight shall be prevented from dropping by either a bolt passing through both the bar and counterweight, or a bolt put through the extreme end of the bar, or, where the counterweight does not encircle the bar, a safety chain attached to it.

(g)(3) Limit chains or other equally effective devices shall be provided to prevent the saw from swinging beyond the front or back edges of the table, or beyond a forward position where the gullets of the lowest saw teeth will rise above the table top.

(g)(4) Inverted swing cutoff saws shall be provided with a hood that will cover the part of the saw that protrudes above the top of the table or above the material being cut. It shall automatically adjust itself to the thickness of and remain in contact with the material being cut.

(h) OI **Radial saws**

(h)(1) OI The upper hood shall completely enclose the upper portion of the blade down to a point that will include the end of the saw arbor. The upper hood shall be constructed in such a manner and of such material that it will protect the operator from flying splinters, broken saw teeth, etc., and will deflect sawdust away from the operator. The sides of the lower exposed portion of the blade shall be guarded to the full diameter of the blade by a device that will automatically adjust itself to the thickness of the stock and remain in contact with stock being cut to give maximum protection possible for the operation being performed.

(h)(2) Each radial saw used for ripping shall be provided with nonkickback fingers or dogs located on both sides of the saw so as to oppose the thrust or tendency of the saw to pick up the material or to throw it back toward the operator. They shall be designed to provide adequate holding power for all the thicknesses of material being cut.

(h)(3) An adjustable stop shall be provided to prevent the forward travel of the blade beyond the position necessary to complete the cut in repetitive operations.

(h)(4) Installation shall be in such a manner that the front end of the unit will be slightly higher than the rear, so as to cause the cutting head to return gently to the starting position when released by the operator.

(h)(5) Ripping and ploughing shall be against the direction in which the saw turns. The direction of the saw rotation shall be conspicuously marked on the hood. In addition, a permanent label not less than 1½ inches by ¾ inch shall be affixed to the rear of the guard at approximately the level of the arbor, reading as follows: "Danger: Do Not Rip or Plough From This End".

(i) **Bandsaws and band resaws**

(i)(1) All portions of the saw blade shall be enclosed or guarded, except for the working portion of the blade between the bottom of the guide rolls and the table. Bandsaw wheels shall be fully encased. The outside periphery of the enclosure shall be solid. The front and back of the band wheels shall be either enclosed by solid material or by wire mesh or perforated metal. Such mesh or perforated metal shall be not less than 0.037 inch (U.S. Gage No. 20), and the openings shall be not greater than three-eighths inch. Solid material used for this purpose shall be of an equivalent strength and firmness. The guard for the portion of the blade between the sliding guide and the upper-saw-wheel guard shall protect the saw blade at the front and outer side. This portion of the guard shall be self-adjusting to raise and lower with the guide. The upper-wheel guard shall be made to conform to the travel of the saw on the wheel.

(i)(2) Each bandsaw machine shall be provided with a tension control device to indicate a proper tension for the standard saws used on the machine, in order to assist in the elimination of saw breakage due to improper tension.

(i)(3) Feed rolls of band resaws shall be protected with a suitable guard to prevent the hands of the operator from coming in contact with the in-running rolls at any point. The guard shall be constructed of heavy material, preferably metal, and the edge of the guard shall come to within three-eighths inch of the plane formed by the inside face of the feed roll in contact with the stock being cut.

(j) **Jointers**

(j)(1) Each hand-fed planer and jointer with horizontal head shall be equipped with a cylindrical cutting head, the knife projection of which shall not exceed one-eighth inch beyond the cylindrical body of the head.

(j)(2) The opening in the table shall be kept as small as possible. The clearance between the edge of the rear table and the cutter head shall be not more than one-eighth inch. The table throat opening shall be not more than 2½ inches when tables are set or aligned with each other for zero cut.

(j)(3) Each hand-fed jointer with a horizontal cutting head shall have an automatic guard which will cover all the section of the head on the working side of the fence or gage. The guard shall effectively keep the operator's hand from coming in contact with the revolving knives. The guard shall automatically adjust itself to cover the unused portion of the head and shall remain in contact with the material at all times.

(j)(4) Each hand-fed jointer with horizontal cutting head shall have a guard which will cover the section of the head back of the gage or fence.

(j)(5) Each wood jointer with vertical head shall have either an exhaust hood or other guard so arranged as to enclose completely the revolving head, except for a slot of such width as may be necessary and convenient for the application of the material to be jointed.

(k) **Tenoning machines**

(k)(1) Feed chains and sprockets of all double end tenoning machines shall be completely enclosed, except for that portion of chain used for conveying the stock.

(k)(2) At the rear ends of frames over which feed conveyors run, sprockets and chains shall be guarded at the sides by plates projecting beyond the periphery of sprockets and the ends of lugs.

(k)(3) Each tenoning machine shall have all cutting heads, and saws if used, covered by metal guards. These guards shall cover at least the unused part of the periphery of the cutting head. If such a guard is constructed of sheet metal, the material used shall be not less than one-sixteenth inch in thickness, and if cast iron is used, it shall be not less than three-sixteenths inch in thickness.

(k)(4) Where an exhaust system is used, the guard shall form part or all of the exhaust hood and shall be constructed of metal of a thickness not less than that specified in subparagraph (3) of this paragraph.

(l) **Boring and mortising machines**

(l)(1) Safety-bit chucks with no projecting set screws shall be used.

(l)(2) Boring bits should be provided with a guard that will enclose all portions of the bit and chuck above the material being worked.

(l)(3) The top of the cutting chain and driving mechanism shall be enclosed.

(l)(4) If there is a counterweight, one of the following or equivalent means shall be used to prevent its dropping:

(l)(4)(i) It shall be bolted to the bar by means of a bolt passing through both bar and counterweight;

(l)(4)(ii) A bolt shall be put through the extreme end of the bar;

(l)(4)(iii) Where the counterweight does not encircle the bar, a safety chain shall be attached to it;

(l)(4)(iv) Other types of counterweights shall be suspended by chain or wire rope and shall travel in a pipe or other suitable enclosure wherever they might fall and cause injury.

(l)(5) Universal joints on spindles of boring machines shall be completely enclosed in such a way as to prevent accidental contact by the operator.

(l)(6) Each operating treadle shall be covered by an inverted U-shaped metal guard, fastened to the floor, and of adequate size to prevent accidental tripping.

(m) **Wood shapers and similar equipment**

(m)(1) The cutting heads of each wood shaper, hand-fed panel raiser, or other similar machine not automatically fed, shall be enclosed with a cage or adjustable guard so designed as to keep the operator's hand away from the cutting edge. The diameter of circular shaper guards shall be not less than the greatest diameter of the cutter. In no case shall a warning device of leather or other material attached to the spindle be acceptable.

(m)(2) [Reserved]

(m)(3) All double-spindle shapers shall be provided with a spindle starting and stopping device for each spindle.

(n) **Planing, molding, sticking, and matching machines**

(n)(1) Each planing, molding, sticking, and matching machine shall have all cutting heads, and saws if used, covered by a metal guard. If such guard is constructed of sheet metal, the material used shall be not less than 1/16 inch in thickness, and if cast iron is used, it shall be not less than three-sixteenths inch in thickness.

(n)(2) Where an exhaust system is used, the guards shall form part or all of the exhaust hood and shall be constructed of metal of a thickness not less than that specified in paragraph (h)(1) of this section.

(n)(3) Feed rolls shall be guarded by a hood or suitable guard to prevent the hands of the operator from coming in contact with the in-running rolls at any point. The guard shall be fastened to the frame carrying the rolls so as to remain in adjustment for any thickness of stock.

(n)(4) Surfacers or planers used in thicknessing multiple pieces of material simultaneously shall be provided with sectional infeed rolls having sufficient yield in the construction of the sections to provide feeding contact pressure on the stock, over the permissible range of variation in stock thickness specified or for which the machine is designed. In lieu of such yielding sectional rolls, suitable section kickback finger devices shall be provided at the infeed end.

(o) **Profile and swing-head lathes and wood heel turning machine**

(o)(1) Each profile and swing-head lathe shall have all cutting heads covered by a metal guard. If such a guard is constructed of sheet metal, the material used shall be not less than one-sixteenth inch in thickness; and if cast iron is used, it shall not be less than three-sixteenths inch in thickness.

(o)(2) Cutting heads on wood-turning lathes, whether rotating or not, shall be covered as completely as possible by hoods or shields.

(o)(3) Shoe last and spoke lathes, doweling machines, wood heel turning machines, and other automatic wood-turning lathes of the rotating knife type shall be equipped with hoods enclosing the cutter blades completely except at the contact points while the stock is being cut.

(o)(4) Lathes used for turning long pieces of wood stock held only between the two centers shall be equipped with long curved guards extending over the tops of the lathes in order to prevent the work pieces from being thrown out of the machines if they should become loose.

(o)(5) Where an exhaust system is used, the guard shall form part or all of the exhaust hood and shall be constructed of metal of a thickness not less than that specified in subparagraph (1) of this paragraph.

(p) **Sanding machines**

(p)(1) Feed rolls of self-feed sanding machines shall be protected with a semicylindrical guard to prevent the hands of the operator from coming in contact with the in-running rolls at any point. The guard shall be constructed of heavy material, preferably metal, and firmly secured to the frame carrying the rolls so as to remain in adjustment for any thickness of stock. The bottom of the guard should come down to within three-eighths inch of a plane formed by the bottom or contact face of the feed roll where it touches the stock.

(p)(2) Each drum sanding machine shall have an exhaust hood, or other guard if no exhaust system is required, so arranged as to enclose the revolving drum, except for that portion of the drum above the table, if a table is used, which may be necessary and convenient for the application of the material to be finished.

(p)(3) Each disk sanding machine shall have the exhaust hood, or other guard if no exhaust system is required, so arranged as to enclose the revolving disk, except for that portion of the disk above the table, if a table is used, which may be necessary for the application of the material to be finished.

(p)(4) Belt sanding machines shall be provided with guards at each nip point where the sanding belt runs on to a pulley. These guards shall effectively prevent the hands or fingers of the operator from coming in contact with the nip points. The unused run of the sanding belt shall be guarded against accidental contact.

(q) **Veneer cutters and wringers**

(q)(1) Veneer slicer knives shall be guarded to prevent accidental contact with knife edge, at both front and rear.

(q)(2) Veneer clippers shall have automatic feed or shall be provided with a guard which will make it impossible to place a finger or fingers under the knife while feeding or removing the stock.

(q)(3) Sprockets on chain or slat-belt conveyors shall be enclosed.

(q)(4) Where practicable, hand and footpower guillotine veneer cutters shall be provided with rods or plates or other satisfactory means, so arranged on the feeding side that the hands cannot reach the cutting edge of the knife while feeding or holding the stock in place.

(q)(5) Power-driven guillotine veneer cutters, except continuous feed trimmers, shall be equipped with:

(q)(5)(i) Starting devices which require the simultaneous action of both hands to start the cutting motion and of at least one hand on a control during the complete stroke of the knife; or

(q)(5)(ii) An automatic guard which will remove the hands of the operator from the danger zone at every descent of the blade, used in conjunction with one-hand starting devices which require two distinct movements of the device to start the cutting motion, and so designed as to return positively to the nonstarting position after each complete cycle of the knife.

(q)(6) Where two or more workers are employed at the same time on the same power-driven guillotine veneer cutter equipped with two-hand control, the device shall be so arranged that each worker shall be required to use both hands simultaneously on the controls to start the cutting motion, and at least one hand on a control to complete the cut.

(q)(7) Power-driven guillotine veneer cutters, other than continuous trimmers, shall be provided, in addition to the brake or other stopping mechanism, with an emergency device which will prevent the machine from operating in the event of failure of the brake when the starting mechanism is in the nonstarting position.

(r) **Miscellaneous woodworking machines**

(r)(1) The feed rolls of roll type glue spreaders shall be guarded by a semicylindrical guard. The bottom of the guard shall come to within three-eighths inch of a plane formed by bottom or contact face of the feed roll where it touches the stock.

(r)(2) Drag saws shall be so located as to give at least a 4-foot clearance for passage when the saw is at the extreme end of the stroke; or if such clearance is not obtainable, the saw and its driving mechanism shall be provided with a standard enclosure.

(r)(3) For combination or universal woodworking machines each point of operation of any tool shall be guarded as required for such a tool in a separate machine.

(r)(4) [OI] The mention of specific machines in paragraphs (a) thru (q) and this paragraph (r) of this section, inclusive, is not intended to exclude other woodworking machines from the requirement that suitable guards and exhaust hoods be provided to reduce to a minimum the hazard due to the point of operation of such machines.

(s) **Inspection and maintenance of woodworking machinery**

(s)(1) Dull, badly set, improperly filed, or improperly tensioned saws shall be immediately removed from service, before they begin to cause the material to stick, jam, or kick back when it is fed to the saw at normal speed. Saws to which gum has adhered on the sides shall be immediately cleaned.

(s)(2) All knives and cutting heads of woodworking machines shall be kept sharp, properly adjusted, and firmly secured. Where two or more knives are used in one head, they shall be properly balanced.

(s)(3) Bearings shall be kept free from lost motion and shall be well lubricated.

(s)(4) Arbors of all circular saws shall be free from play.

(s)(5) Sharpening or tensioning of saw blades or cutters shall be done only by persons of demonstrated skill in this kind of work.

(s)(6) Emphasis is placed upon the importance of maintaining cleanliness around woodworking machinery, particularly as regards the effective functioning of guards and the prevention of fire hazards in switch enclosures, bearings, and motors.

(s)(7) All cracked saws shall be removed from service.

(s)(8) The practice of inserting wedges between the saw disk and the collar to form what is commonly known as a "wobble saw" shall not be permitted.

(s)(9) Push sticks or push blocks shall be provided at the work place in the several sizes and types suitable for the work to be done.

(s)(10)–(11) [Reserved]

(s)(12) The knife blade of jointers shall be so installed and adjusted that it does not protrude more than one-eighth inch beyond the cylindrical body of the head. Push sticks or push blocks shall be provided at the work place in the several sizes and types suitable for the work to be done.

(s)(13) Whenever veneer slicers or rotary veneer-cutting machines have been shutdown for the purpose of inserting logs or to make adjustments, operators shall make sure that machine is clear and other workmen are not in a hazardous position before starting the machine.

(s)(14) Operators shall not ride the carriage of a veneer slicer.

[39 FR 23502, June 27, 1974, as amended at 43 FR 49750, Oct. 24, 1978; 49 FR 5323, Feb. 10, 1984]

§1910.214 [OI] Cooperage machinery [Reserved]

§1910.215 [OI] Abrasive wheel machinery

(a) [OI] **General requirements**

(a)(1) [OI] **Machine guarding** Abrasive wheels shall be used only on machines provided with safety guards as defined in the following paragraphs of this section, except:

(a)(1)(i) Wheels used for internal work while within the work being ground;

(a)(1)(ii) Mounted wheels, used in portable operations, 2 inches and smaller in diameter; and

(a)(1)(iii) Types 16, 17, 18, 18R, and 19 cones, plugs, and threaded hole pot balls where the work offers protection.

(a)(2) [OI] **Guard design** The safety guard shall cover the spindle end, nut, and flange projections. The safety guard shall be mounted so as to maintain proper alignment with the wheel, and the strength of the fastenings shall exceed the strength of the guard, except:

(a)(2)(i) [OI] Safety guards on all operations where the work provides a suitable measure of protection to the operator, may be so constructed that the spindle end, nut, and outer flange are exposed; and where the nature of the work is such as to entirely cover the side of the wheel, the side covers of the guard may be omitted; and

(a)(2)(ii) The spindle end, nut, and outer flange may be exposed on machines designed as portable saws.

(a)(3) **Flanges** Grinding machines shall be equipped with flanges in accordance with paragraph (c) of this section.

(a)(4) **Work rests** On offhand grinding machines, work rests shall be used to support the work. They shall be of rigid construction and designed to be adjustable to compensate for wheel wear. Work rests shall be kept adjusted closely to the wheel with a maximum opening of one-eighth inch to prevent the work from being jammed between the wheel and the rest, which may cause wheel breakage. The work rest shall be securely clamped after each adjustment. The adjustment shall not be made with the wheel in motion.

(a)(5) **Excluded machinery** Natural sandstone wheels and metal, wooden, cloth, or paper discs, having a layer of abrasive on the surface are not covered by this section.

(b) **Guarding of abrasive wheel machinery**

(b)(1) **Cup wheels** Cup wheels (Types 6 and 11) shall be protected by

(b)(1)(i) Safety guards as specified in paragraphs (b)(1) through (10) of this section;

(b)(1)(ii) Band type guards as specified in paragraph (b)(11) of this section; and

(b)(1)(iii) Special "Revolving Cup Guards" which mount behind the wheel and turn with it. They shall be made of steel or other material with adequate strength and shall enclose the wheel sides upward from the back for one-third of the wheel thickness. The mounting features shall conform with all requirements of this section. It is necessary to maintain clearance between the wheel side and the guard. This clearance shall not exceed one-sixteenth inch.

(b)(2) **Guard exposure angles** The maximum exposure angles specified in paragraphs (b)(3) through (8) of this section shall not be exceeded. Visors or other accessory equipment shall not be included as a part of the guard when measuring the guard opening, unless such equipment has strength equal to that of the guard.

(b)(3) **Bench and floor stands** The angular exposure of the grinding wheel periphery and sides for safety guards used on machines known as bench and floor stands should not exceed 90° or one-fourth of the periphery. This exposure shall begin at a point not more than 65° above the horizontal plane of the wheel spindle. (See Figures O–6 and O–7 and paragraph (b)(9) of this section.)

Figure No. O–6

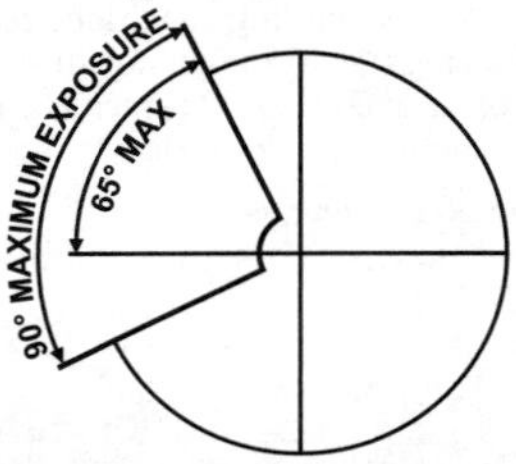

Figure No. O–7

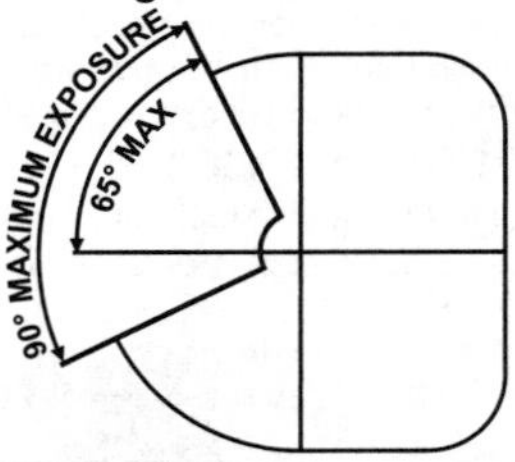

Wherever the nature of the work requires contact with the wheel below the horizontal plane of the spindle, the exposure shall not exceed 125°. (See Figures O–8 and O–9.)

Figure No. O–8

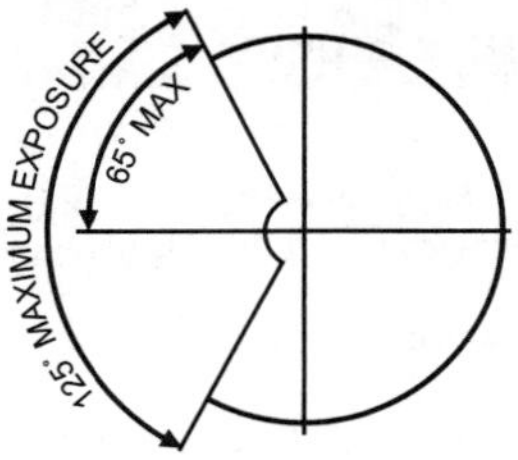

Figure No. O–9

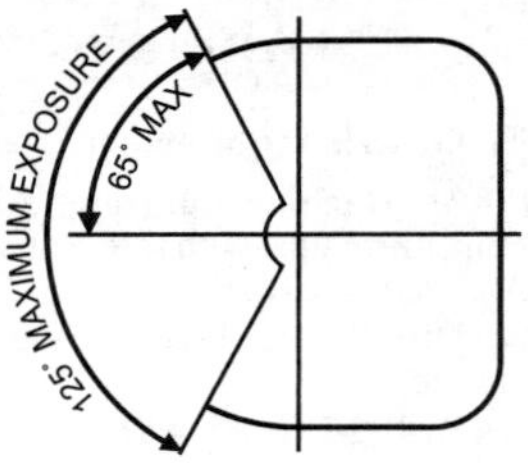

(b)(4) **Cylindrical grinders** The maximum angular exposure of the grinding wheel periphery and sides for safety guards used on cylindrical grinding machines shall not exceed 180°. This exposure shall begin at a point not more than 65° above the horizontal plane of the wheel spindle. (See Figures O–10 and O–11 and subparagraph (9) of this paragraph.)

Figure No. O–10

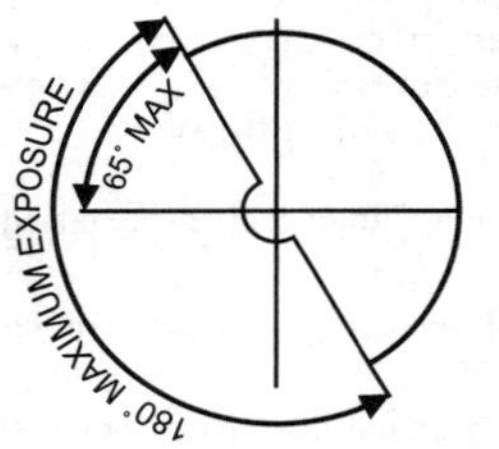

Figure No. O–11

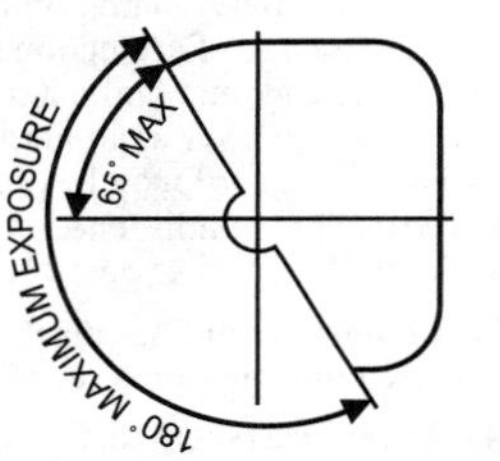

(b)(5) **Surface grinders and cutting-off machines** The maximum angular exposure of the grinding wheel periphery and sides for safety guards used on cutting-off machines and on surface grinding machines which employ the wheel periphery shall not exceed 150°. This exposure shall begin at a point not less than 15° below the horizontal plane of the wheel spindle. (See Figures O–12 and O–13.)

Figure No. O–12

Figure No. O–13

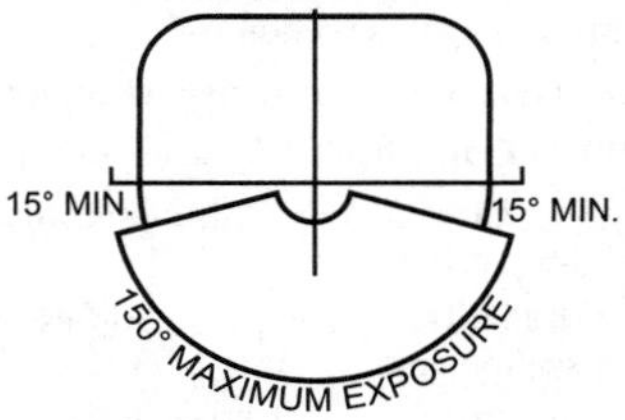

(b)(6) **Swing frame grinders** The maximum angular exposure of the grinding wheel periphery and sides for safety guards used on machines known as swing frame grinding machines shall not exceed 180°, and the top half of the wheel shall be enclosed at all times. (See Figures O–14 and O–15.)

Figure No. O–14

Figure No. O–15

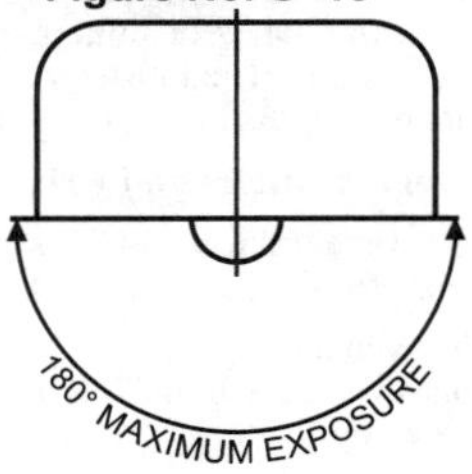

(b)(7) **Automatic snagging machines** The maximum angular exposure of the grinding wheel periphery and sides for safety guards used on grinders known as automatic snagging machines shall not exceed 180° and the top half of the wheel shall be enclosed at all times. (See Figures O–14 and O–15.)

(b)(8) **Top grinding** Where the work is applied to the wheel above the horizontal centerline, the exposure of the grinding wheel periphery shall be as small as possible and shall not exceed 60°. (See Figures O–16 and O–17.)

Figure No. O–16

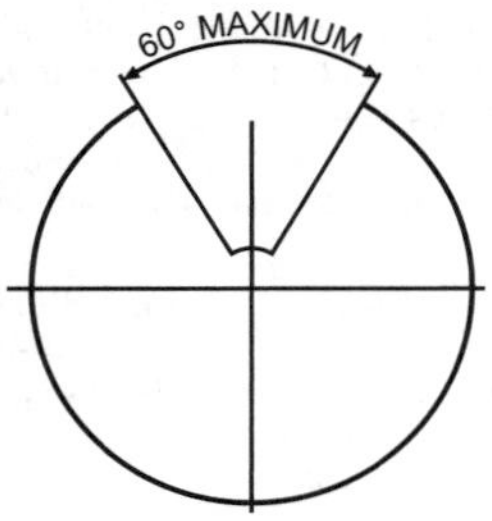

Figure No. O–17

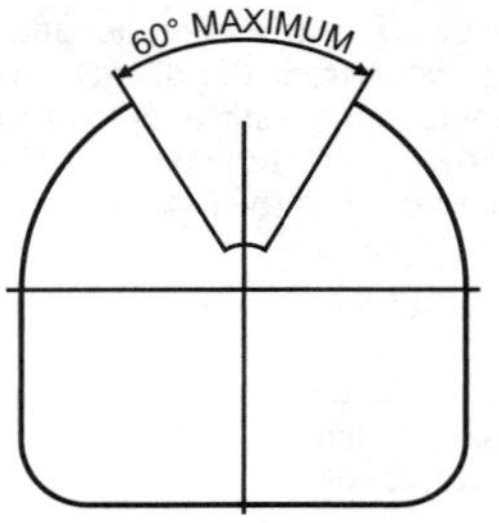

(b)(9) **Exposure adjustment** Safety guards of the types described in subparagraphs (3) and (4) of this paragraph, where the operator stands in front of the opening, shall be constructed so that the peripheral protecting member can be adjusted to the constantly decreasing diameter of the wheel. The maximum angular exposure above the horizontal plane of the wheel spindle as specified in paragraphs (b)(3) and (4) of this section shall never be exceeded, and the distance between the wheel periphery and the adjustable tongue or the end of the peripheral member at the top shall never exceed one-fourth inch. (See Figures O–18, O–19, O–20, O–21, O–22, and O–23.)

(b)(10) **Material requirements and minimum dimensions**

(b)(10)(i) See Figures O–36 and O–37 and Table O–9 for minimum basic thickness of peripheral and side members for various types of safety guards and classes of service.

(b)(10)(ii) If operating speed does not exceed 8,000 surface feet per minute cast iron safety guards, malleable iron guards or other guards as described in paragraph (b)(10)(iii) of this section shall be used.

(b)(10)(iii) Cast steel, or structural steel, safety guards as specified in Figures O–36 and O–37 and Table O–9 shall be used where operating speeds of wheels are faster than 8,000 surface feet per minute up to a maximum of 16,000 surface feet per minute.

(b)(10)(iv) For cutting-off wheels 16 inches diameter and smaller and where speed does not exceed 16,000 surface feet per minute, cast iron or malleable iron safety guards as specified in Figures O–36 and O–37, and in Table O–9 shall be used.

Figure No. O–18 **Figure No. O–19**

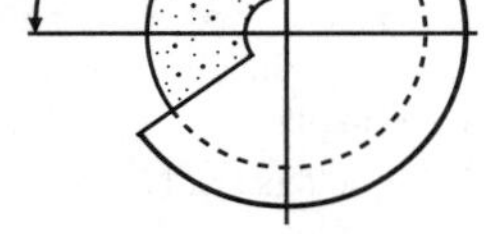

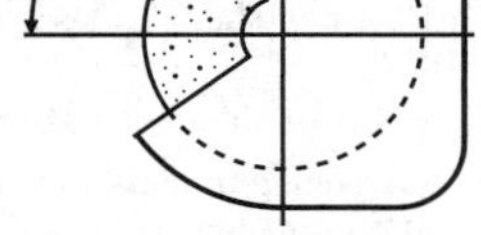

CORRECT
Showing adjustable tongue giving required angular protection for all sizes of wheel used.

Figure No. O–20 Figure No. O–21

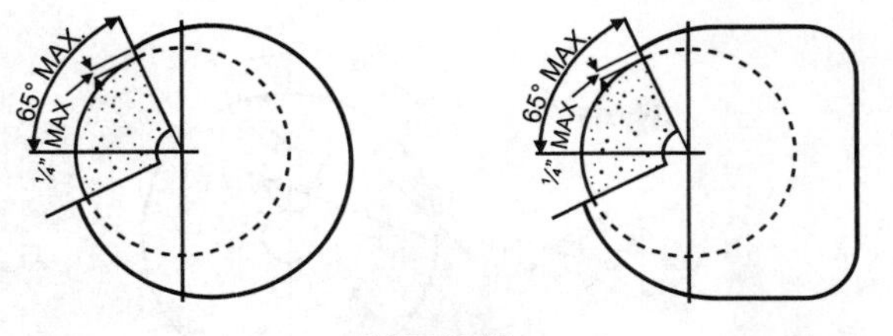

CORRECT
Showing movable guard with opening small enough to give required protection for smaller size wheel used.

Figure No. O–22 Figure No. O–23

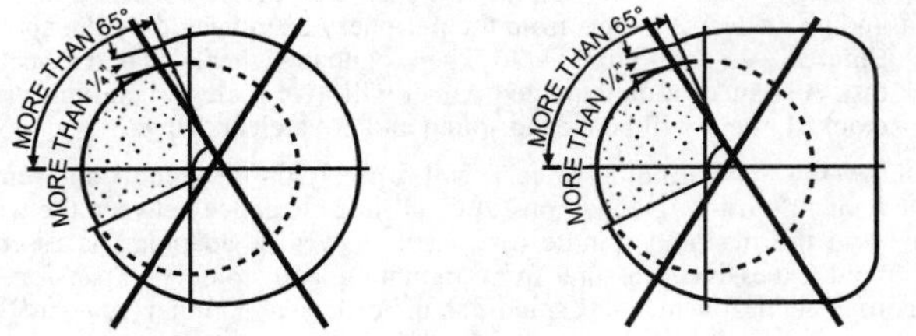

INCORRECT
Showing movable guard with size of opening correct for full size wheel but too large for smaller wheels.

(b)(10)(v) For cutting-off wheels larger than 16 inches diameter and where speed does not exceed 14,200 surface feet per minute, safety guards as specified in Figures O–27 and O–28, and in Table O–1 shall be used.

(b)(10)(vi) For thread grinding wheels not exceeding 1 inch in thickness cast iron or malleable iron safety guards as specified in Figures O–36 and O–37, and in Table O–9 shall be used.

(b)(11) Band type guards—general specifications Band type guards shall conform to the following general specifications:

(b)(11)(i) The bands shall be of steel plate or other material of equal or greater strength. They shall be continuous, the ends being either riveted, bolted, or welded together in such a manner as to leave the inside free from projections.

(b)(11)(ii) The inside diameter of the band shall not be more than 1 inch larger than the outside diameter of the wheel, and shall be mounted as nearly concentric with the wheel as practicable.

(b)(11)(iii) The band shall be of sufficient width and its position kept so adjusted that at no time will the wheel protrude beyond the edge of the band a distance greater than that indicated in Figure O–29 and in Table O–2 or the wall thickness (W), whichever is smaller.

(b)(12) Guard design specifications Abrasive wheel machinery guards shall meet the design specifications of the American National Standard Safety Code for the Use, Care, and Protection of Abrasive Wheels, ANSI B7.1–1970, which is incorporated by reference as specified in §1910.6. This requirement shall not apply to natural sandstone wheels or metal, wooden, cloth, or paper discs, having a layer of abrasive on the surface.

(c) Flanges

(c)(1) General requirements All abrasive wheels shall be mounted between flanges which shall not be less than one-third the diameter of the wheel.

(c)(1)(i) Exceptions

(c)(1)(i)(A) Mounted wheels;

(c)(1)(i)(B) Portable wheels with threaded inserts or projecting studs;

(c)(1)(i)(C) Abrasive discs (inserted nut, inserted washer and projecting stud type);

(c)(1)(i)(D) Plate mounted wheels;

(c)(1)(i)(E) Cylinders, cup, or segmental wheels that are mounted in chucks;

(c)(1)(i)(F) Types 27 and 28 wheels;

(c)(1)(i)(G) Certain internal wheels;

(c)(1)(i)(H) Modified types 6 and 11 wheels (terrazzo);

(c)(1)(i)(I) Cutting-off wheels, Types 1 and 27A (see paragraphs (c)(1)(ii) and (iii) of this section)

(c)(1)(ii) Type 1 cutting-off wheels are to be mounted between properly relieved flanges which have matching bearing surfaces. Such flanges shall be at least one-fourth the wheel diameter.

(c)(1)(iii) Type 27A cutting-off wheels are designed to be mounted by means of flat, not relieved, flanges having matching bearing surfaces and which may be less than one-third but shall not be less than one-fourth the wheel diameter. (See Figure O–24 for one such type of mounting.)

(c)(1)(iv) There are three general types of flanges:

(c)(1)(iv)(A) Straight relieved flanges (see Figure O–32);

(c)(1)(iv)(B) Straight unrelieved flanges (see Figure O–30);

(c)(1)(iv)(C) Adaptor flanges (see Figures O–33 and O–34);

(c)(1)(v) Regardless of flange type used, the wheel shall always be guarded. Blotters shall be used in accordance with paragraph (c)(6) of this section.

Figure No. O–24

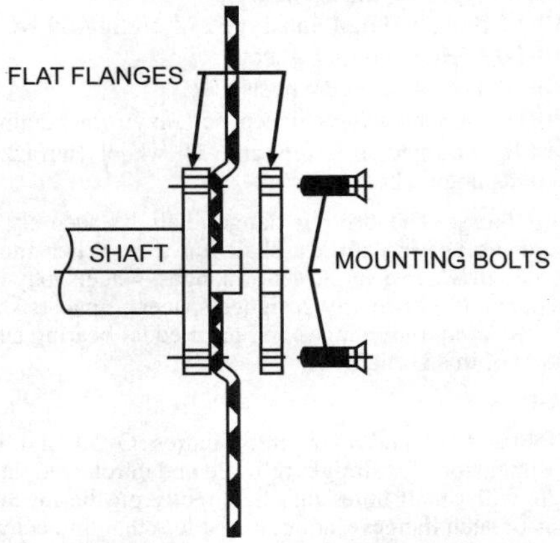

The Type 27 A Wheel is mounted between flat non–relieved flanges of equal bearing surfaces.

(c)(2) [Reserved]

(c)(3) Finish and balance Flanges shall be dimensionally accurate and in good balance. There shall be no rough surfaces or sharp edges.

(c)(4) Uniformity of diameter

(c)(4)(i) Both flanges, of any type, between which a wheel is mounted, shall be of the same diameter and have equal bearing surface. Exceptions are set forth in the remaining subdivisions of this subparagraph.

(c)(4)(ii) Type 27 and Type 28 wheels, because of their shape and usage, require specially designed adaptors. The back flange shall extend beyond the central hub or raised portion and contact the wheel to counteract the side pressure on the wheel in use. The adaptor nut which is less than the minimum one-third diameter of wheel fits in the depressed side of wheel to prevent interference in side grinding and serves to drive the wheel by its clamping force against the depressed portion of the back flange. The variance in flange diameters, the adaptor nut being less than one-third wheel diameter, and the use of side pressure in wheel operation limits the use to reinforced organic bonded wheels. Mounts which are affixed to the wheel by the manufacturer shall not be reused. Type 27 and Type 28 wheels shall be used only with a safety guard located between wheel and operator during use. (See Figure O–24–A.)

Figure No. O–24–A

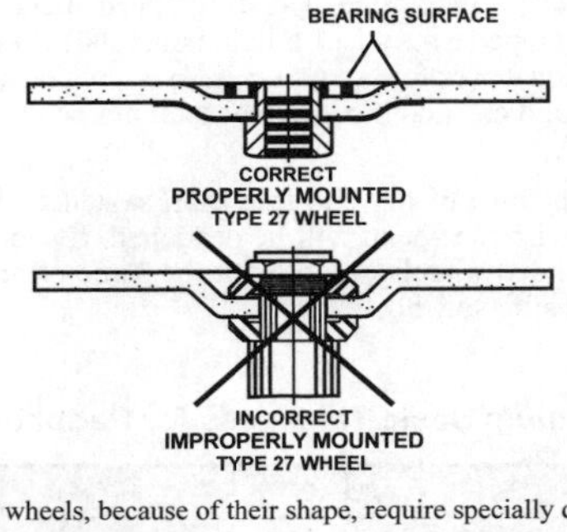

Types 27 and 28 wheels, because of their shape, require specially designed adaptors.

(c)(4)(iii) Modified Types 6 and 11 wheels (terrazzo) with tapered K dimension.

(c)(5) Recess and undercut

(c)(5)(i) Straight relieved flanges made according to Table O–6 and Figure O–32 shall be recessed at least one-sixteenth inch on the side next to the wheel for a distance as specified in Table O–6.

(c)(5)(ii) Straight flanges of the adaptor or sleeve type (Table O–7 and Figures O–33 and O–34) shall be undercut so that there will be no bearing on the sides of the wheel within one-eighth inch of the arbor hole.

(c)(6) **Blotters**

(c)(6)(i) Blotters (compressible washers) shall always be used between flanges and abrasive wheel surfaces to insure uniform distribution of flange pressure. (See paragraph (d)(5) of this section.)

(c)(6)(ii) Exception:

(c)(6)(ii)(A) Mounted wheels;

(c)(6)(ii)(B) Abrasive discs (inserted nut, inserted washer, and projecting stud type);

(c)(6)(ii)(C) Plate mounted wheels;

(c)(6)(ii)(D) Cylinders, cups, or segmental wheels that are mounted in chucks;

(c)(6)(ii)(E) Types 27 and 28 wheels;

(c)(6)(ii)(F) Certain Type 1 and Type 27A cutting-off wheels;

(c)(6)(ii)(G) Certain internal wheels;

(c)(6)(ii)(H) Type 4 tapered wheels;

(c)(6)(ii)(I) Diamond wheels, except certain vitrified diamond wheels;

(c)(6)(ii)(J) Modified Types 6 and 11 wheel (terrazzo)—blotters applied flat side of wheel only.

(c)(7) **Driving flange** The driving flange shall be securely fastened to the spindle and the bearing surface shall run true. When more than one wheel is mounted between a single set of flanges, wheels may be cemented together or separated by specially designed spacers. Spacers shall be equal in diameter to the mounting flanges and have equal bearing surfaces. (See paragraph (d)(6) of this section.)

(c)(8) **Dimensions**

(c)(8)(i) Tables O–4 and O–6 and Figures O–30 and O–32 show minimum dimensions for straight relieved and unrelieved flanges for use with wheels with small holes that fit directly on the machine spindle. Dimensions of such flanges shall never be less than indicated.

(c)(8)(ii) Table O–5, and Table O–7 and Figures O–31, O–33, O–34 show minimum dimensions for straight adaptor flanges for use with wheels having holes larger than the spindle. Dimensions of such adaptor flanges shall never be less than indicated.

(c)(8)(iii) Table O–8 and Figure O–35 show minimum dimensions for straight flanges that are an integral part of wheel sleeves which are frequently used on precision grinding machines. Dimensions of such flanges shall never be less than indicated.

(c)(9) **Repairs and maintenance** All flanges shall be maintained in good condition. When the bearing surfaces become worn, warped, sprung, or damaged they should be trued or refaced. When refacing or truing, care shall be exercised to make sure that proper relief and rigidity is maintained as specified in paragraphs (c)(2) and (5) of this section and they shall be replaced when they do not conform to these subparagraphs and Table O–4, Figure O–30, Table O–5, Figure O–31, Table O–6, Figure O–32, and Table O–8, Figure O–35. Failure to observe these rules might cause excessive flange pressure around the hole of the wheel. This is especially true of wheel-sleeve or adaptor flanges.

(d) **Mounting**

(d)(1) **Inspection** Immediately before mounting, all wheels shall be closely inspected and sounded by the user (ring test) to make sure they have not been damaged in transit, storage, or otherwise. The spindle speed of the machine shall be checked before mounting of the wheel to be certain that it does not exceed the maximum operating speed marked on the wheel. Wheels should be tapped gently with a light nonmetallic implement, such as the handle of a screwdriver for light wheels, or a wooden mallet for heavier wheels. If they sound cracked (dead), they shall not be used. This is known as the "Ring Test".

(d)(1)(i) Wheels must be dry and free from sawdust when applying the ring test, otherwise the sound will be deadened. It should also be noted that organic bonded wheels do not emit the same clear metallic ring as do vitrified and silicate wheels.

Figure No. O–25

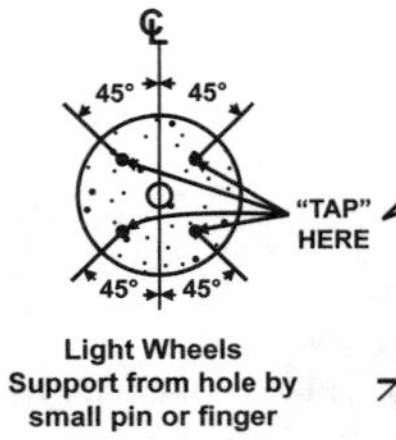

Figure No. O–26

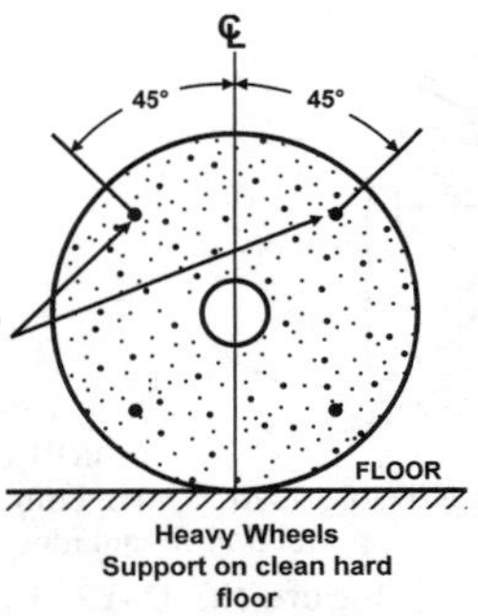

(d)(1)(ii) "Tap" wheels about 45° each side of the vertical centerline and about 1 or 2 inches from the periphery as indicated by the spots in Figure O–25 and Figure O–26. Then rotate the wheel 45° and repeat the test. A sound and undamaged wheel will give a clear metallic tone. If cracked, there will be a dead sound and not a clear "ring."

(d)(2)**Arbor size** Grinding wheels shall fit freely on the spindle and remain free under all grinding conditions. A controlled clearance between the wheel hole and the machine spindle (or wheel sleeves or adaptors) is essential to avoid excessive pressure from mounting and spindle expansion. To accomplish this, the machine spindle shall be made to nominal (standard) size plus zero minus .002 inch, and the wheel hole shall be made suitably oversize to assure safety clearance under the conditions of operating heat and pressure.

(d)(3) [OI] **Surface condition** All contact surfaces of wheels, blotters and flanges shall be flat and free of foreign matter.

(d)(4) **Bushing** When a bushing is used in the wheel hole it shall not exceed the width of the wheel and shall not contact the flanges.

(d)(5) **Blotters** When blotters or flange facings of compressible material are required, they shall cover entire contact area of wheel flanges. Blotters need not be used with the following types of wheels:

(d)(5)(i) Mounted wheels;

(d)(5)(ii) Abrasive discs (inserted nut, inserted washer, and projecting-stud type);

(d)(5)(iii) Plate mounted wheels;

(d)(5)(iv) Cylinders, cups, or segmental wheels that are mounted in chucks;

(d)(5)(v) Types 27 and 28 wheels;

(d)(5)(vi) Certain Type 1 and Type 27A cutting-off wheels;

(d)(5)(vii) Certain internal wheels;

(d)(5)(viii) Type 4 tapered wheels;

(d)(5)(ix) Diamond wheels, except certain vitrified diamond wheels.

(d)(6) **Multiple wheel mounting** When more than one wheel is mounted between a single set of flanges, wheels may be cemented together or separated by specially designed spacers. Spacers shall be equal in diameter to the mounting flanges and have equal bearing surfaces. When mounting wheels which have not been cemented together, or ones which do not utilize separating spacers, care must be exercised to use wheels specially manufactured for that purpose.

Figure No. O–27

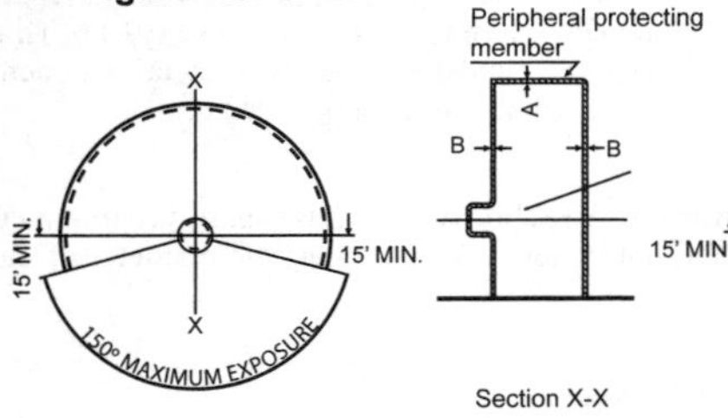

Figure No. O–28

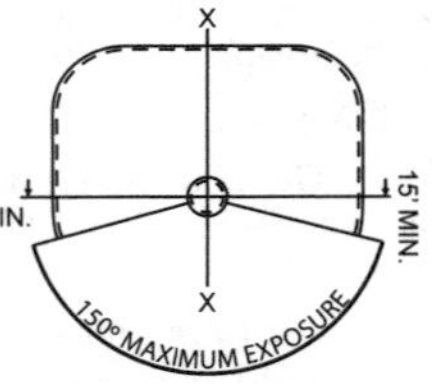

Table O–1
Minimum Basic Thickness for Peripheral and Side Members for Safety Guards Used With Cutting-Off Wheels

Material used in construction of guard	Maximum thickness of cutting off wheel	Speed not to exceed	Cutting off wheel diameters									
			6 to 11 inches		Over 11 to 20 inches		Over 20 to 30 inches		Over 30 to 48 inches		Over 48 to 72 inches	
			A	B	A	B	A	B	A	B	A	B
Structural steel (min. tensile strength 60,000 p.s.i.)	1/2 inch or less	14,200 SFPM	1/16	1/16	3/32	3/32	1/8	1/8	3/16	3/16	1/4	1/4
	1/2 inch or less	16,000 SFPM	3/32	1/8	1/8	1/8	3/16	1/8	1/4	3/16	5/16	1/4

Figure No. O–29

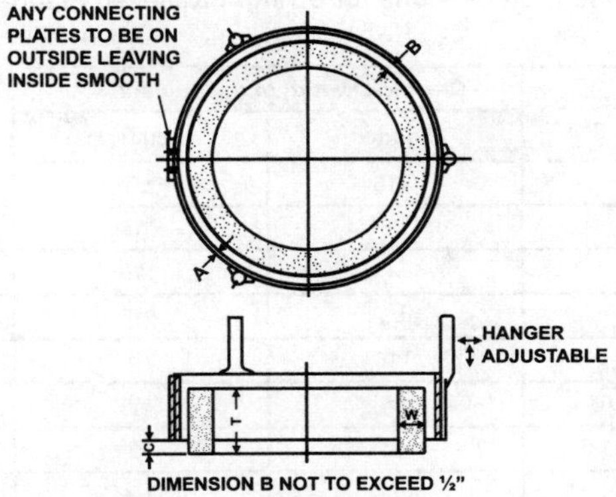

Table O–3
Guide for Construction of Band Type Guards [Maximum Wheel Speed 7,000 SFPM]

Minimum material specifications	Diameter of wheel	Minimum thickness of band A	Minimum diameter of rivets	Maximum distance between centers of rivets
		Inches		
Hot rolled steel SAE 1008	Under 8	1/16	3/16	3/4
	8 to 24	1/8	1/4	1
	Over 24 to 30	1/4	3/8	1 1/4

Figure No. O–30

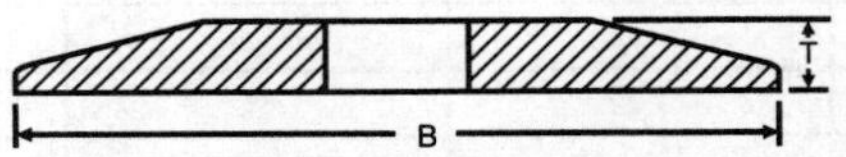

Driving flange secured to spindle for use only on portable wheels with threaded inserts or projecting studs.

Figure No. O–31

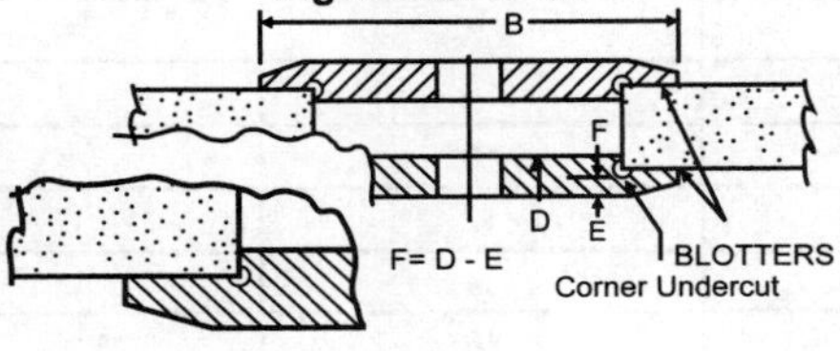

Table O–5
Minimum Dimensions for Straight Adaptor Flange—for Organic Bonded Wheels Over 1 1/4 Inches Thick[1]
[In inches]

Wheel diameter	Wheel hole diameter	B—Minimum flange diameter	D—Minimun thickness of flange at bore	E—Minimum thickness of flange at edge of undercut	F[1]—(D-E) minimum thickness
12 to 14	4	6	7/8	3/8	1/2
	5	7	7/8	3/8	1/2
	6	8	7/8	3/8	1/2
Larger than 14 to 18	4	6	7/8	3/8	1/2
	5	7	7/8	3/8	1/2
	6	8	7/8	3/8	1/2
	7	9	7/8	3/8	1/2
	8	10	7/8	3/8	1/2
Larger than 18 to 24	6	8	1	1/2	1/2
	7	9	1	1/2	1/2
	8	10	1	1/2	1/2
	10	12	1	1/2	1/2
	12	14	1	1/2	1/2
Larger than 24 to 30	12	15	1	1/2	1/2
Larger than 30 to 36	12	15	1 3/8	7/8	1/2

[1] For wheels under 1¼ inches thick F dimension shall not exceed 40 percent of wheel thickness.

Figure No. O–32

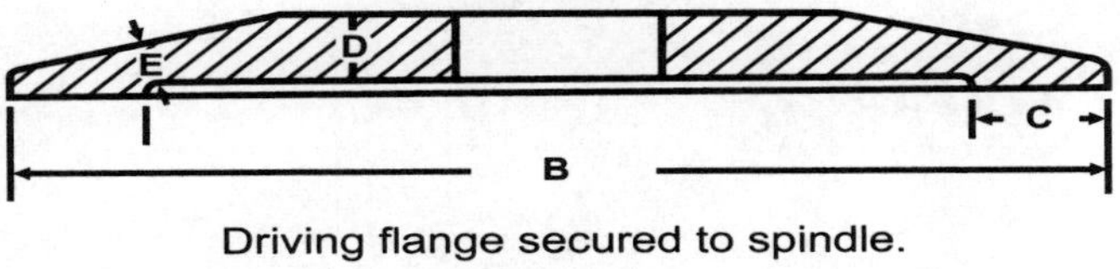

Driving flange secured to spindle.

O

Machinery and Machine Guarding

Abrasive wheel machinery

Table O–6
Minimum Dimensions for Straight Relieved Flanges[1]
[In inches]

A—Diameter of wheel	B—Minimum outside diameter of flanges	C—Radial width of bearing surface		D—Minimum thickness of flange at bore	E—Minimum thickness of flange at edge of recess
		Minimum	Maximum		
1	3/8	1/16	1/8	1/16	1/16
2	3/4	1/8	3/16	1/8	3/32
3	1	1/8	3/16	3/16	3/32
4	1 3/8	1/8	3/16	3/16	1/8
5	1 3/4	3/16	1/4	1/4	1/8
6	2	1/4	1/2	3/8	3/16
7	2 1/2	1/4	1/2	3/8	3/16
8	3	1/4	1/2	3/8	3/16
10	3 1/2	5/16	5/8	3/8	1/4
12	4	5/16	5/8	1/2	5/16
14	4 1/2	3/8	3/4	1/2	5/16
16	5 1/2	1/2	1	1/2	5/16
18	6	1/2	1	5/8	3/8
20	7	5/8	1 1/4	5/8	3/8
22	7 1/2	5/8	1 1/4	5/8	7/16
24	8	3/4	1 1/4	5/8	7/16
26	8 1/2	3/4	1 1/4	5/8	1/2
28	10	7/8	1 1/2	3/4	1/2
30	10	7/8	1 1/2	3/4	5/8
36	12	1	2	7/8	3/4
42	14	1	2	7/8	3/4
48	16	1 1/4	2	1 1/8	1
60	20	1 1/4	2	1 1/4	1 1/8
72	24	1 1/2	2 1/2	1 3/8	1 1/4

[1] Flanges for wheels under 2 inches diameter may be unrelieved and shall be maintained flat and true.

Figure No. O–33

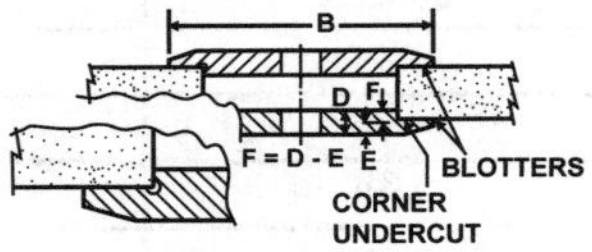

Central Nut Mounting
Driving flange secured to spindle.

Figure No. O–34

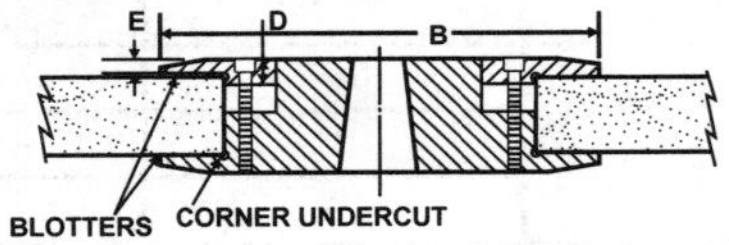

Multiple Screw Mounting
Driving flange secured to spindle.

Table O–7
Minimum Dimensions for Straight Flanges—for Mechanical Grinders 12,500 S.F.P.M. to 16,500 S.F.P.M.[1]

Wheel diameter	Wheel hole diameter	B—Minimum flange diameter	D—Minimum thickness of flange at bore	E—Minimum thickness of flange at edge of undercut	F[2]—(D-E) minimum thickness
20	6	8	1	½	½
20	8	10	1½	¾	¾
24	12	15	2	1	1
30	12	15	2	1	1
36	12	15	2	1	

[1] Flanges shall be of steel, quality SAE 1040 or equivalent, annealed plate, heat treated to R. 25–30.

[2] For wheels under 1 1/4 inch thick F dimension shall not exceed 40 percent of wheel thickness.

Figure No. O–35

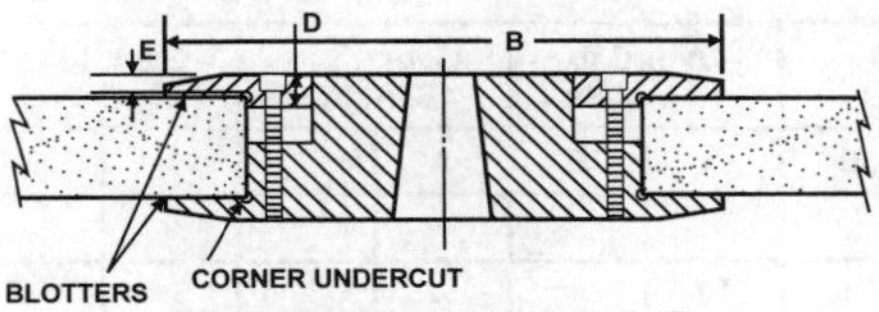

Driving flange secured to spindle

Table O–8
Minimum Dimensions for Straight Flanges Used as Wheel Sleeves for Precision Grinding Only
[In inches]

Wheel diameter	Wheel hole diameter	B—Minimum outside diameter of flange	D—Minimum thickness of flange at bore	E—Minimum thickness of flange at edge of undercut
12 to 14	5	7	1/2	7/16
Larger than 14 to 20	5	7	5/8	7/16
	6	8	5/8	7/16
	8	10	5/8	7/16
	10	11 1/2	5/8	7/16
	12	13 1/2	5/8	7/16
Larger than 20 to 30	8	10	3/4	1/2
	10	11 1/2	3/4	1/2
	12	13 1/2	3/4	1/2
	16	17 1/2	3/4	1/2
Larger than 30 to 42	12	13 1/2	3/4	1/2
	16	17 1/2	3/4	1/2
	18	19 1/2	3/4	1/2
	20	21 1/2	3/4	1/2
Larger than 42 to 60	16	20	1	3/4
	20	24	1	3/4
	24	29	1 1/8	7/8

Note: These flanges may be clamped together by means of a central nut, or by a series of bolts or some other equivalent means of fastening. For hole sizes smaller than shown in this table, use table 12.

Figure No. O–36

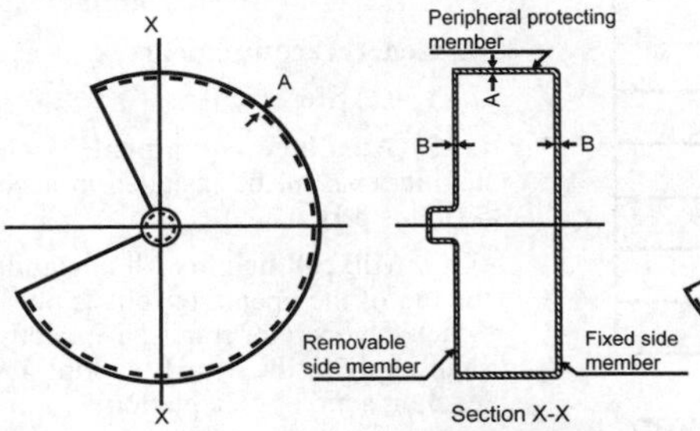

Figure No. O–37

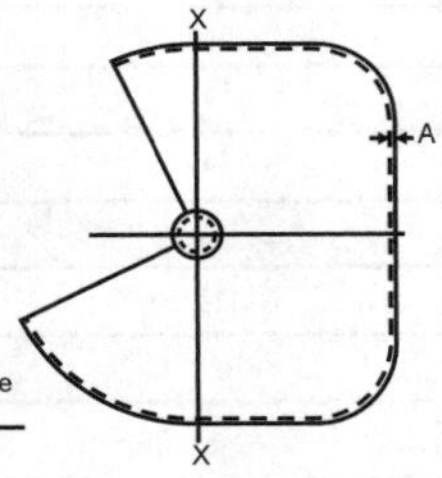

Table O–9
Minimum Basic Thicknesses of Peripheral and Side Members for Safety Guards
[In inches]

Material used in construction of guard	Maximum thickness of grinding wheel	Grinding wheel diameters													
		3 to 6 inches		Over 6 to 12 inches		Over 12 to 16 inches		Over 16 to 20 inches		Over 20 to 24 inches		Over 24 to 30 inches		Over 30 to 48 inches	
		A	B	A	B	A	B	A	B	A	B	A	B	A	B
Material satisfactory[1] for speeds up to 8,000 SFPM.	2	1/4	1/4	3/8	5/16	1/2	3/8	5/8	1/2	7/8	5/8	1	3/4	1 1/4	1
	4	5/16	5/16	3/8	5/16	1/2	3/8	3/4	5/8	1	5/8	1 1/8	3/4	1 3/8	1
	6	3/8	5/16	1/2	7/16	5/8	1/2	1	5/8	1 1/8	3/4	1 1/4	7/8	1 1/2	1 1/8
	8			5/8	9/16	7/8	3/4	1	3/4	1 1/8	3/4	1 1/4	7/8	1 1/2	1 1/8
	10			3/4	11/16	7/8	3/4	1	3/4	1 1/8	3/4	1 1/4	7/8	1 1/2	1 1/8
Cast iron (min. tensile strength 20,000 p.s.i.) Class 20.	16					1 1/8	1	1 1/4	1	1 5/16	1	1 7/16	1 1/16	1 3/4	1 3/8
	20							1 3/8	1 1/8	1 3/8	1 1/8	1 1/2	1 3/8	2	1 5/8

Note: Table date continues on next page.

Material used in construction of guard	Maximum thickness of grinding wheel	Grinding wheel diameters													
		3 to 6 inches		Over 6 to 12 inches		Over 12 to 16 inches		Over 16 to 20 inches		Over 20 to 24 inches		Over 24 to 30 inches		Over 30 to 48 inches	
		A	B	A	B	A	B	A	B	A	B	A	B	A	B
Material satisfactory[1] for speeds up to 9,000 SFPM	2	1/4	1/4	3/8	5/16	1/2	3/8	5/8	1/2	3/4	5/8	7/8	3/4	1	7/8
	4	5/16	5/16	3/8	5/16	1/2	3/8	5/8	1/2	3/4	5/8	7/8	3/4	1 1/8	7/8
	6	3/8	5/16	1/2	7/16	5/8	1/2	3/4	5/8	7/8	5/8	1	3/4	1 1/4	7/8
	8			1/2	7/16	5/8	1/2	3/4	5/8	7/8	5/8	1	3/4	1 1/4	7/8
	10			1/2	7/16	5/8	1/2	3/4	5/8	7/8	5/8	1	3/4	1 1/4	7/8
Malleable iron (min. tensile strength 50,000 p.s.i.) Grade 32510	16					13/16	11/16	13/16	11/16	1	3/4	1 1/8	7/8	1 3/8	1
	20							7/8	3/4	1	3/4	1 1/8	7/8	1 1/2	1 1/8
Materials satisfactory[1] for speeds up to 16,000 SFPM	2	1/4	1/4	5/16	5/16	3/8	3/8	1/2	7/16	5/8	1/2	3/4	5/8	7/8	3/4
	4	1/4	1/4	1/2	1/2	1/2	1/2	9/16	1/2	5/8	1/2	3/4	5/8	1	3/4
	6	3/8	1/4	3/4	5/8	3/4	5/8	3/4	5/8	13/16	11/16	13/16	11/16	1 1/8	3/4
	8			7/8	3/4	7/8	3/4	7/8	3/4	7/8	3/4	15/16	13/16	1 3/8	1
	10			1	7/8	1	7/8	1	7/8	1 1/8	15/16	1 1/8	1	1 7/16	1 1/16
Steel castings (min. tensile strength 60,000 p.s.i.) Grade V60-30	16					1 1/4	1 1/8	1 1/4	1 1/8	1 1/4	1 1/8	1 1/4	1 1/8	1 13/16	1 7/16
	20							1 3/8	1 1/4	1 3/8	1 1/4	1 7/16	1 5/16	2 1/16	1 11/16
Structural steel (min. tensile strength 60,000 p.s.i.)	2	1/8	1/16	5/16	1/4	5/16	1/4	5/16	1/4	5/16	1/4	3/8	5/16	1/2	3/8
	4	1/8	1/16	3/8	5/16	3/8	5/16	3/8	5/16	3/8	5/16	3/8	5/16	1/2	3/8
	6	3/16	1/16	1/2	3/8	7/16	3/8	7/16	3/8	7/16	3/8	7/16	3/8	3/4	1/2
	8			1/2	3/8	9/16	7/16	9/16	7/16	9					
	10	9/16	7/6	5/8	1/2	5/8	1/2	5/8	1/2	5/8	1/2	7/8	5/8		
	16					5/8	9/16	3/4	5/8	3/4	5/8	13/16	11/16	1 1/16	13/16
	20							1 3/16	1 1/16	13/16	11/16	7/8	3/4	1 3/16	15/16

[1] The recommendations listed in the above table are guides for the conditions stated. Other material, designs or dimensions affording equal or superior protection are also acceptable.

Table O–2
Exposure Versus Wheel Thickness
[In inches]

Overall thickness of wheel (T)	Maximum exposure of wheel (C)
1/2	1/4
1	1/2
2	3/4
3	1
4	1 1/2
5 and over	2

Table O–4
Minimum Dimensions for Straight Unrelieved Flanges for Wheels with Threaded Inserts or Projecting Studs

A—Diameter of wheel	B[1]—Minimum outside diameter of flange	T—Minimum thickness of flange
1	5/8	1/8
2	1	1/8
3	1	3/16
4	1 3/8	3/16
5	1 3/4	1/4
6	2	3/8

[1] Note: Must be large enough to extend beyond the bushing. Where prong anchor or cupback bushing are used, this footnote does not apply.

[39 FR 23502, June 27, 1974, as amended at 43 FR 49750, Oct. 24, 1978; 49 FR 5323, Feb. 10, 1984; 61 FR 9240, Mar. 7, 1996]

§1910.216
Mills and calenders in the rubber and plastics industries

(a) **General requirements**

(a)(1)–(2) [Reserved]

(a)(3) **Auxiliary equipment** Mechanical and electrical equipment and auxiliaries shall be installed in accordance with this section and Subpart S of this part.

(a)(4) **Mill roll heights** All new mill installations shall be installed so that the top of the operating rolls is not less than 50 inches above the level on which the operator stands, irrespective of the size of the mill. This distance shall apply to the actual working level, whether it be at the general floor level, in a pit, or on a platform.

(b) **Mill safety controls**

(b)(1) **Safety trip control** A safety trip control shall be provided in front and in back of each mill. It shall be accessible and shall operate readily on contact. The safety trip control shall be one of the following types or a combination thereof:

(b)(1)(i) **Pressure-sensitive body bars** Installed at front and back of each mill having a 46-inch roll height or over. These bars shall operate readily by pressure of the mill operator's body.

(b)(1)(ii) **Safety triprod** Installed in the front and in the back of each mill and located within 2 inches of a vertical plane tangent to the front and rear rolls. The top rods shall be not more than 72 inches above the level on which the operator stands. The triprods shall be accessible and shall operate readily whether the rods are pushed or pulled.

(b)(1)(iii) **Safety tripwire cable or wire center cord** Installed in the front and in the back of each mill and located within 2 inches of a vertical plane tangent to the front and rear rolls. The cables shall not be more than 72 inches above the level on which the operator stands. The tripwire cable or wire center cord shall operate readily whether cable or cord is pushed or pulled.

(b)(2) [Reserved]

(b)(3) **Auxiliary equipment** All auxiliary equipment such as mill divider, support bars, spray pipes, feed conveyors, strip knives, etc., shall be located in such a manner as to avoid interference with access to and operation of safety devices.

(c) **Calender safety controls**

(c)(1) **Safety trip, face** A safety triprod, cable, or wire center cord shall be provided across each pair of in-running rolls extending the length of the face of the rolls. It shall be readily accessible and operate whether pushed or pulled. The safety tripping devices shall be located within reach of the operator and the bite.

(c)(2) **Safety trip, side** On both sides of the calender and near each end of the face of the roll, there shall be a cable or wire center cord connected to the safety trip. They shall operate readily when pushed or pulled.

(d) **Protection by location**

(d)(1) **Mills** Where a mill is so installed that persons cannot normally reach through, over, under, or around to come in contact with the roll bite or be caught between a roll and an adjacent object, then, provided such elements are made a fixed part of a mill, safety control devices listed in paragraph (b) of this section shall not apply.

(d)(2) **Calenders** Where a calender is so installed that persons cannot normally reach through, over, under, or around to come in contact with the roll bite or be caught between a roll and an adjacent object, then, provided such elements are made a fixed part of a calender, safety control devices listed in paragraph (c) of this section shall not apply.

(e) **Trip and emergency switches** All trip and emergency switches shall not be of the automatically resetting type, but shall require manual resetting.

(f) **Stopping limits**

(f)(1) **Determination of distance of travel** All measurements on mills and calenders shall be taken with the rolls running empty at maximum operating speed. Stopping distances shall be expressed in inches of surface travel of the roll from the instant the emergency stopping device is actuated.

(f)(2) **Stopping limits for mills** All mills irrespective of the size of the rolls or their arrangement (individually or group-driven) shall be stopped within a distance, as measured in inches of surface travel, not greater than 1 ½ percent of the peripheral no-load surface speeds of the respective rolls as determined in feet per minute.

(f)(3) **Stopping limits for calenders**

(f)(3)(i) All calenders, irrespective of size of the rolls or their configuration, shall be stopped within a distance, as measured in inches of surface travel, not greater than 1¾ percent of the peripheral no-load surface speeds of the respective calender rolls as determined in feet per minute.

(f)(3)(ii) Where speeds above 250 feet per minute as measured on the surface of the drive roll are used, stopping distances of more than 1¾ percent are permissible. Such stopping distances shall be subject to engineering determination.

[39 FR 23502, June 27, 1974, as amended at 49 FR 5323, Feb. 10, 1984; 61 FR 9240, Mar. 7, 1996]

§1910.217 Mechanical power presses

(a) **General requirements**

(a)(1)–(3) [Reserved]

(a)(4) **Reconstruction and modification** It shall be the responsibility of any person reconstructing, or modifying a mechanical power press to do so in accordance with paragraph (b) of this section.

(a)(5) **Excluded machines** Press brakes, hydraulic and pneumatic power presses, bulldozers, hot bending and hot metal presses, forging presses and hammers, riveting machines and similar types of fastener applicators are excluded from the requirements of this section.

(b) **Mechanical power press guarding and construction, general**

(b)(1) **Hazards to personnel associated with broken or falling machine components** Machine components shall be designed, secured, or covered to minimize hazards caused by breakage, or loosening and falling or release of mechanical energy (i.e. broken springs).

(b)(2) **Brakes** Friction brakes provided for stopping or holding a slide movement shall be inherently self-engaging by requiring power or force from an external source to cause disengagement. Brake capacity shall be sufficient to stop the motion of the slide quickly and capable of holding the slide and its attachments at any point in its travel.

(b)(3) **Machines using full revolution positive clutches**

(b)(3)(i) Machines using full revolution clutches shall incorporate a single-stroke mechanism.

(b)(3)(ii) If the single-stroke mechanism is dependent upon spring action, the spring(s) shall be of the compression type, operating on a rod or guided within a hole or tube, and designed to prevent interleaving of the spring coils in event of breakage.

(b)(4) **Foot pedals (treadle)**

(b)(4)(i) The pedal mechanism shall be protected to prevent unintended operation from falling or moving objects or by accidental stepping onto the pedal.

(b)(4)(ii) A pad with a nonslip contact area shall be firmly attached to the pedal.

(b)(4)(iii) The pedal return spring(s) shall be of the compression type, operating on a rod or guided within a hole or tube, or designed to prevent interleaving of spring coils in event of breakage.

(b)(4)(iv) If pedal counterweights are provided, the path of the travel of the weight shall be enclosed.

(b)(5) **Hand operated levers**

(b)(5)(i) Hand-lever-operated power presses shall be equipped with a spring latch on the operating lever to prevent premature or accidental tripping.

(b)(5)(ii) The operating levers on hand-tripped presses having more than one operating station shall be interlocked to prevent the tripping of the press except by the "concurrent" use of all levers.

(b)(6) **Two-hand trip**

(b)(6)(i) A two-hand trip shall have the individual operator's hand controls protected against unintentional operation and have the individual operator's hand controls arranged by design and construction and/or separation to require the use of both hands to trip the press and use a control arrangement requiring concurrent operation of the individual operator's hand controls.

(b)(6)(ii) Two-hand trip systems on full revolution clutch machines shall incorporate an antirepeat feature.

(b)(6)(iii) If two-hand trip systems are used on multiple operator presses, each operator shall have a separate set of controls.

(b)(7) **Machines using part revolution clutches**

(b)(7)(i) The clutch shall release and the brake shall be applied when the external clutch engaging means is removed, deactivated, or deenergized.

(b)(7)(ii) A red color stop control shall be provided with the clutch/brake control system. Momentary operation of the stop control shall immediately deactivate the clutch and apply the brake. The stop control shall override any other control, and reactuation of the clutch shall require use of the operating (tripping) means which has been selected.

(b)(7)(iii) A means of selecting Off, "Inch," Single Stroke, and Continuous (when the continuous function is furnished) shall be supplied with the clutch/brake control to select type of operation of the press. Fixing of selection shall be by means capable of supervision by the employer.

(b)(7)(iv) The "Inch" operating means shall be designed to prevent exposure of the workers hands within the point of operation by:

(b)(7)(iv)(A) Requiring the concurrent use of both hands to actuate the clutch, or

(b)(7)(iv)(B) Being a single control protected against accidental actuation and so located that the worker cannot reach into the point of operation while operating the single control.

(b)(7)(v) Two-hand controls for single stroke shall conform to the following requirements:

(b)(7)(v)(A) Each hand control shall be protected against unintended operation and arranged by design, construction, and/or separation so that the concurrent use of both hands is required to trip the press.

(b)(7)(v)(B) The control system shall be designed to permit an adjustment which will require concurrent pressure from both hands during the die closing portion of the stroke.

(b)(7)(v)(C) The control system shall incorporate an antirepeat feature.

(b)(7)(v)(D) The control systems shall be designed to require release of all operators' hand controls before an interrupted stroke can be resumed. This requirement pertains only to those single-stroke, two-hand controls manufactured and installed on or after August 31, 1971.

(b)(7)(vi) [Reserved]

(b)(7)(vii) Controls for more than one operating station shall be designed to be activated and deactivated in complete sets of two operator's hand controls per operating station by means capable of being supervised by the employer. The clutch/brake control system shall be designed and constructed to prevent actuation of the clutch if all operating stations are bypassed.

(b)(7)(viii) Those clutch/brake control systems which contain both single and continuous functions shall be designed so that completion of continuous circuits may be supervised by the employer. The initiation of continuous run shall require a prior action or decision by the operator in addition to the selection of Continuous on the stroking selector, before actuation of the operating means will result in continuous stroking.

(b)(7)(ix) If foot control is provided, the selection method between hand and foot control shall be separate from the stroking selector and shall be designed so that the selection may be supervised by the employer.

(b)(7)(x) Foot operated tripping controls, if used, shall be protected so as to prevent operation from falling or moving objects, or from unintended operation by accidental stepping onto the foot control.

(b)(7)(xi) The control of air-clutch machines shall be designed to prevent a significant increase in the normal stopping time due to a failure within the operating value mechanism, and to inhibit further operation if such failure does occur. This requirement shall apply only to those clutch/brake air-valve controls manufactured and installed on or after August 31, 1971, but shall not apply to machines intended only for continuous, automatic feeding applications.

(b)(7)(xii) The clutch/brake control shall incorporate an automatic means to prevent initiation or continued activation of the Single Stroke or Continuous functions unless the press drive motor is energized and in the forward direction.

(b)(7)(xiii) The clutch/brake control shall automatically deactivate in event of failure of the power or pressure supply for the clutch engaging means. Reactivation of the clutch shall require restoration of normal supply and the use of the tripping mechanism(s).

(b)(7)(xiv) The clutch/brake control shall automatically deactivate in event of failure of the counterbalance(s) air supply. Reactivation of the clutch shall require restoration of normal air supply and use of the tripping mechanism(s).

(b)(7)(xv) Selection of bar operation shall be by means capable of being supervised by the employer. A separate pushbutton shall be employed to activate the clutch, and the clutch shall be activated only if the driver motor is deenergized.

(b)(8) Electrical

(b)(8)(i) A main power disconnect switch capable of being locked only in the Off position shall be provided with every power press control system.

(b)(8)(ii) The motor start button shall be protected against accidental operation.

(b)(8)(iii) All mechanical power press controls shall incorporate a type of drive motor starter that will disconnect the drive motor from the power source in event of control voltage or power source failure, and require operation of the motor start button to restart the motor when voltage conditions are restored to normal.

(b)(8)(iv) All a.c. control circuits and solenoid value coils shall be powered by not more than a nominal 120-volt a.c. supply obtained from a transformer with an isolated secondary. Higher voltages that may be necessary for operation of machine or control mechanisms shall be isolated from any control mechanism handled by the operator, but motor starters with integral Start-Stop buttons may utilize line voltage control. All d.c. control circuits shall be powered by not more than a nominal 240-volt d.c. supply isolated from any higher voltages.

(b)(8)(v) All clutch/brake control electrical circuits shall be protected against the possibility of an accidental ground in the control circuit causing false operation of the press.

(b)(8)(vi) Electrical clutch/brake control circuits shall incorporate features to minimize the possibility of an unintended stroke in the event of the failure of a control component to function properly, including relays, limit switches, and static output circuits.

(b)(9) Slide counterbalance systems

(b)(9)(i) Spring counterbalance systems when used shall incorporate means to retain system parts in event of breakage.

(b)(9)(ii) Spring counterbalances when used shall have the capability to hold the slide and its attachments at midstroke, without brake applied.

(b)(9)(iii) Air counterbalance cylinders shall incorporate means to retain the piston and rod in case of breakage or loosening.

(b)(9)(iv) Air counterbalance cylinders shall have adequate capability to hold the slide and its attachments at any point in stroke, without brake applied.

(b)(9)(v) Air counterbalance cylinders shall incorporate means to prevent failure of capability (sudden loss of pressure) in event of air supply failure.

(b)(10) **Air controlling equipment** Air controlling equipment shall be protected against foreign material and water entering the pneumatic system of the press. A means of air lubrication shall be provided when needed.

(b)(11) **Hydraulic equipment** The maximum anticipated working pressures in any hydraulic system on a mechanical power press shall not exceed the safe working pressure rating of any component used in that system.

(b)(12) **Pressure vessels** All pressure vessels used in conjunction with power presses shall conform to the American Society of Mechanical Engineers Code for Pressure Vessels, 1968 Edition, which is incorporated by reference as specified in §1910.6.

(b)(13) OI **Control reliability** When required by paragraph (c)(5) of this section, the control system shall be constructed so that a failure within the system does not prevent the normal stopping action from being applied to the press when required, but does prevent initiation of a successive stroke until the failure is corrected. The failure shall be detectable by a simple test, or indicated by the control system. This requirement does not apply to those elements of the control system which have no effect on the protection against point of operation injuries.

(b)(14) **Brake system monitoring** When required by paragraph (c)(5) of this section, the brake monitor shall meet the following requirements:

(b)(14)(i) Be so constructed as to automatically prevent the activation of a successive stroke if the stopping time or braking distance deteriorates to a point where the safety distance being utilized does not meet the requirements set forth in paragraph (c)(3)(iii)(E) or (c)(3)(vii)(C) of this section. The brake monitor used with the Type B gate or movable barrier device shall be installed in a manner to detect slide top-stop overrun beyond the normal limit reasonably established by the employer.

(b)(14)(ii) Be installed on a press such that it indicates when the performance of the braking system has deteriorated to the extent described in paragraph (b)(14)(i) of this section; and

(b)(14)(iii) Be constructed and installed in a manner to monitor brake system performance on each stroke.

(c) OI Safeguarding the point of operation

(c)(1) OI General requirements

(c)(1)(i) OI It shall be the responsibility of the employer to provide and insure the usage of "point of operation guards" or properly applied and adjusted point of operation devices on every operation performed on a mechanical power press. See Table O–10.

(c)(1)(ii) The requirement of paragraph (c)(1)(i) of this section shall not apply when the point of operation opening is one-fourth inch or less. See Table O–10.

(c)(2) Point of operation guards

(c)(2)(i) Every point of operation guard shall meet the following design, construction, application, and adjustment requirements:

(c)(2)(i)(A) It shall prevent entry of hands or fingers into the point of operation by reaching through, over, under or around the guard;

(c)(2)(i)(B) It shall conform to the maximum permissible openings of Table O–10;

(c)(2)(i)(C) It shall, in itself, create no pinch point between the guard and moving machine parts;

(c)(2)(i)(D) It shall utilize fasteners not readily removable by operator, so as to minimize the possibility of misuse or removal of essential parts;

(c)(2)(i)(E) It shall facilitate its inspection; and

(c)(2)(i)(F) It shall offer maximum visibility of the point of operation consistent with the other requirements.

(c)(2)(ii) A die enclosure guard shall be attached to the die shoe or stripper in a fixed position.

(c)(2)(iii) A fixed barrier guard shall be attached securely to the frame of the press or to the bolster plate.

(c)(2)(iv) An interlocked press barrier guard shall be attached to the press frame or bolster and shall be interlocked with the press clutch control so that the clutch cannot be activated unless the guard itself, or the hinged or movable sections of the guard are in position to conform to the requirements of Table O–10.

(c)(2)(v) The hinged or movable sections of an interlocked press barrier guard shall not be used for manual feeding. The guard shall prevent opening of the interlocked section and reaching into the point of operation prior to die closure or prior to the cessation of slide motion. See paragraph (c)(3)(ii) of this section regarding manual feeding through interlocked press barrier devices.

(c)(2)(vi) The adjustable barrier guard shall be securely attached to the press bed, bolster plate, or die shoe, and shall be adjusted and operated in conformity with Table O–10 and the requirements of this subparagraph. Adjustments shall be made only by authorized personnel whose qualifications include a knowledge of the provisions of Table O–10 and this subparagraph.

(c)(2)(vii) A point of operation enclosure which does not meet the requirements of this subparagraph and Table O–10 shall be used only in conjunction with point of operation devices.

(c)(3) OI Point of operation devices

(c)(3)(i) Point of operation devices shall protect the operator by:

(c)(3)(i)(A) Preventing and/or stopping normal stroking of the press if the operator's hands are inadvertently placed in the point of operation; or

OI indicates an OSHA Letter of Interpretation exists for this specific reference. Please see www.oshainterpretation.us for details.

(c)(3)(i)(B) Preventing the operator from inadvertently reaching into the point of operation, or withdrawing his hands if they are inadvertently located in the point of operation, as the dies close; or

(c)(3)(i)(C) Preventing the operator from inadvertently reaching into the point of operation at all times; or

(c)(3)(i)(D) [Reserved]

(c)(3)(i)(E) Requiring application of both of the operator's hands to machine operating controls and locating such controls at such a safety distance from the point of operation that the slide completes the downward travel or stops before the operator can reach into the point of operation with his hands; or

(c)(3)(i)(F) Enclosing the point of operation before a press stroke can be initiated, and maintaining this closed condition until the motion of the slide had ceased; or

(c)(3)(i)(G) Enclosing the point of operation before a press stroke can be initiated, so as to prevent an operator from reaching into the point of operation prior to die closure or prior to cessation of slide motion during the downward stroke.

(c)(3)(ii) A gate or movable barrier device shall protect the operator as follows:

(c)(3)(ii)(A) A Type A gate or movable barrier device shall protect the operator in the manner specified in paragraph (c)(3)(i)(F) of this section, and

(c)(3)(ii)(B) A Type B gate or movable barrier device shall protect the operator in the manner specified in paragraph (c)(3)(i)(G) of this section.

(c)(3)(iii) [OI] A presence sensing point of operation device shall protect the operator as provided in paragraph (c)(3)(i)(A) of this section, and shall be interlocked into the control circuit to prevent or stop slide motion if the operator's hand or other part of his body is within the sensing field of the device during the downstroke of the press slide.

(c)(3)(iii)(A) The device may not be used on machines using full revolution clutches.

(c)(3)(iii)(B) The device may not be used as a tripping means to initiate slide motion, except when used in total conformance with paragraph (h) of this section.

(c)(3)(iii)(C) The device shall be constructed so that a failure within the system does not prevent the normal stopping action from being applied to the press when required, but does prevent the initiation of a successive stroke until the failure is corrected. The failure shall be indicated by the system.

(c)(3)(iii)(D) Muting (bypassing of the protective function) of such device, during the upstroke of the press slide, is permitted for the purpose of parts ejection, circuit checking, and feeding.

(c)(3)(iii)(E) The safety distance (D_s) from the sensing field to the point of operation shall be greater than the distance determined by the following formula:

$$D_s = 63 \text{ inches/second} \times T_s$$

where:

D_s = minimum safety distance (inches); 63 inches/second = hand speed constant; and

T_s = stopping time of the press measured at approximately 90° position of crankshaft rotation (seconds).

(c)(3)(iii)(F) Guards shall be used to protect all areas of entry to the point of operation not protected by the presence sensing device.

(c)(3)(iv) The pull-out device shall protect the operator as specified in paragraph (c)(3)(i)(B) of this section, and shall include attachments for each of the operator's hands.

(c)(3)(iv)(A) Attachments shall be connected to and operated only by the press slide or upper die.

(c)(3)(iv)(B) Attachments shall be adjusted to prevent the operator from reaching into the point of operation or to withdraw the operator's hands from the point of operation before the dies close.

(c)(3)(iv)(C) A separate pull-out device shall be provided for each operator if more than one operator is used on a press.

(c)(3)(iv)(D) Each pull-out device in use shall be visually inspected and checked for proper adjustment at the start of each operator shift, following a new die set-up, and when operators are changed. Necessary maintenance or repair or both shall be performed and completed before the press is operated. Records of inspections and maintenance shall be kept in accordance with paragraph (e) of this section.

(c)(3)(v) The sweep device may not be used for point of operation safeguarding.

(c)(3)(vi) A holdout or a restraint device shall protect the operator as specified in paragraph (c)(3)(i)(C) of this section and shall include attachments for each of the operator's hands. Such attachments shall be securely anchored and adjusted in such a way that the operator is restrained from reaching into the point of operation. A separate set of restraints shall be provided for each operator if more than one operator is required on a press.

(c)(3)(vii) The two hand control device shall protect the operator as specified in paragraph (c)(3)(i)(E) of this section.

(c)(3)(vii)(A) When used in press operations requiring more than one operator, separate two hand controls shall be provided for each operator, and shall be designed to require concurrent application of all operators' controls to activate the slide. The removal of a hand from any control button shall cause the slide to stop.

(c)(3)(vii)(B) Each two hand control shall meet the construction requirements of paragraph (b)(7)(v) of this section.

(c)(3)(vii)(C) The safety distance (D_s) between each two hand control device and the point of operation shall be greater than the distance determined by the following formula:

$$D_s = 63 \text{ inches/second} \times T_s;$$

where:

D_s = minimum safety distance (inches); 63 inches/second = hand speed constant; and

T_s = stopping time of the press measured at approximately 90° position of crankshaft rotation (seconds).

(c)(3)(vii)(D) Two hand controls shall be fixed in position so that only a supervisor or safety engineer is capable of relocating the controls.

(c)(3)(viii) The two hand trip device shall protect the operator as specified in paragraph (c)(3)(i)(E) of this section.

(c)(3)(viii)(A) When used in press operations requiring more than one operator, separate two hand trips shall be provided for each operator, and shall be designed to require concurrent application of all operators' to activate the slide.

(c)(3)(viii)(B) Each two hand trip shall meet the construction requirements of paragraph (b)(6) of this section.

(c)(3)(viii)(C) The safety distance (D_m) between the two hand trip and the point of operation shall be greater than the distance determined by the following formula:

$$D_m = 63 \text{ inches/second} \times T_m;$$

Where:

D_m = minimum safety distance (inches); 63 inches/second=hand speed constant; and

T_m = the maximum time the press takes for the die closure after it has been tripped (seconds). For full revolution clutch presses with only one engaging point T_m is equal to the time necessary for one and one-half revolutions of the crankshaft. For full revolution clutch presses with more than one engaging point, T_m shall be calculated as follows:

$T_m = [½ + (1 \div \text{Number of engaging points per revolution})] \times$ time necessary to complete one revolution of the crankshaft (seconds).

(c)(3)(viii)(D) Two hand trips shall be fixed in position so that only a supervisor or safety engineer is capable of relocating the controls.

(c)(4) **Hand feeding tools** Hand feeding tools are intended for placing and removing materials in and from the press. Hand feeding tools are not a point of operation guard or protection device and shall not be used in lieu of the "guards" or devices required in this section.

(c)(5) **Additional requirements for safe-guarding** Where the operator feeds or removes parts by placing one or both hands in the point of operation, and a two hand control, presence sensing device, Type B gate or movable barrier (on a part revolution clutch) is used for safeguarding:

(c)(5)(i) The employer shall use a control system and a brake monitor which comply with paragraphs (b)(13) and (14) of this section;

(c)(5)(ii) The exception in paragraph (b)(7)(v)(D) of this section for two hand controls manufactured and installed before August 31, 1971 is not applicable under this paragraph (c)(5);

(c)(5)(iii) The control of air clutch machines shall be designed to prevent a significant increase in the normal stopping time due to a failure within the operating valve mechanism, and to inhibit further operation if such failure does occur, where a part revolution clutch is employed. The exception in paragraph (b)(7)(xi) of this section for controls manufactured and installed before August 31, 1971, is not applicable under this paragraph (c)(5).

(d) Design, construction, setting and feeding of dies

(d)(1) **General requirements** The employer shall:

(d)(1)(i) Use dies and operating methods designed to control or eliminate hazards to operating personnel; and

(d)(1)(ii) Furnish and enforce the use of hand tools for freeing and removing stuck work or scrap pieces from the die, so that no employee need reach into the point of operation for such purposes.

(d)(2) [Reserved]

(d)(3) **Scrap handling** The employer shall provide means for handling scrap from roll feed or random length stock operations. Scrap cutters used in conjunction with scrap handling systems shall be safeguarded in accordance with paragraph (c) of this section and with §1910.219.

(d)(4) **Guide post hazard** The hazard created by a guide post (when it is located in the immediate vicinity of the operator) when separated from its bushing by more than one-fourth inch shall be considered as a point of operation hazard and be protected in accordance with paragraph (c) of this section.

(d)(5) **Unitized tooling** If unitized tooling is used, the opening between the top of the punch holder and the face of the slide, or striking pad, shall be safeguarded in accordance with the requirements of paragraph (c) of this section.

(d)(6) **Tonnage, stroke, and weight designation**. All dies shall be:

(d)(6)(i) Stamped with the tonnage and stroke requirements, or have these characteristics recorded if these records are readily available to the die setter;

(d)(6)(ii) Stamped to indicate upper die weight when necessary for air counterbalance pressure adjustment; and

(d)(6)(iii) Stamped to indicate complete die weight when handling equipment may become overloaded.

(d)(7) **Die fastening** Provision shall be made in both the upper and lower shoes for securely mounting the die to the bolster and slide. Where clamp caps or setscrews are used in conjunction with punch stems, additional means of securing the upper shoe to the slide shall be used.

(d)(8) **Die handling** Handling equipment attach points shall be provided on all dies requiring mechanical handling.

(d)(9) **Diesetting**

(d)(9)(i) The employer shall establish a diesetting procedure that will insure compliance with paragraph (c) of this section.

(d)(9)(ii) The employer shall provide spring loaded turnover bars, for presses designed to accept such turnover bars.

(d)(9)(iii) The employer shall provide die stops or other means to prevent losing control of the die while setting or removing dies in presses which are inclined.

(d)(9)(iv) The employer shall provide and enforce the use of safety blocks for use whenever dies are being adjusted or repaired in the press.

(d)(9)(v) The employer shall provide brushes, swabs, lubricating rolls, and automatic or manual pressure guns so that operators and diesetters shall not be required to reach into the point of operation or other hazard areas to lubricate material, punches or dies.

(e) **Inspection, maintenance, and modification of presses**

(e)(1) **Inspection and maintenance records** The employer shall establish and follow an inspection program having a general component and a directed component.

(e)(1)(i) Under the general component of the inspection program, the employer shall:

(e)(1)(i)(A) Conduct periodic and regular inspections of each power press to ensure that all of its parts, auxiliary equipment, and safeguards, including the clutch/brake mechanism, antirepeat feature, and single-stroke mechanism, are in a safe operating condition and adjustment;

(e)(1)(i)(B) Perform and complete necessary maintenance or repair, or both, before operating the press; and

(e)(1)(i)(C) Maintain a certification record of each inspection, and each maintenance and repair task performed, under the general component of the inspection program that includes the date of the inspection, maintenance, or repair work, the signature of the person who performed the inspection, maintenance, or repair work, and the serial number, or other identifier, of the power press inspected, maintained, and repaired.

(e)(1)(ii) Under the directed component of the inspection program, the employer shall:

(e)(1)(ii)(A) Inspect and test each press on a regular basis at least once a week to determine the condition of the clutch/brake mechanism, antirepeat feature, and single-stroke mechanism;

(e)(1)(ii)(B) Perform and complete necessary maintenance or repair, or both, on the clutch/brake mechanism, antirepeat feature, and single-stroke mechanism before operating the press; and

(e)(1)(ii)(C) Maintain a certification record of each maintenance task performed under the directed component of the inspection program that includes the date of the maintenance task, the signature of the person who performed the maintenance task, and the serial number, or other identifier, of the power press maintained.

Note to paragraph (e)(1)(ii): Inspections of the clutch/brake mechanism, antirepeat feature, and single-stroke mechanism conducted under the directed component of the inspection program are exempt from the requirement to maintain certification records specified by paragraph (e)(1)(i)(C) of this section, but inspections of the clutch/brake mechanism, antirepeat feature, and single-stroke mechanism conducted under the general component of the inspection program are not exempt from this requirement.

(e)(1)(iii) Paragraph (e)(1)(ii) of this section does not apply to presses that comply with paragraphs (b)(13) and (14) of this section.

(e)(2) **Modification** It shall be the responsibility of any person modifying a power press to furnish instructions with the modification to establish new or changed guidelines for use and care of the power press so modified.

(e)(3) **Training of maintenance personnel** It shall be the responsibility of the employer to insure the original and continuing competence of personnel caring for, inspecting, and maintaining power presses.

(f) **Operation of power presses**

(f)(1) [Reserved]

(f)(2) **Instruction to operators** The employer shall train and instruct the operator in the safe method of work before starting work on any operation covered by this section. The employer shall insure by adequate supervision that correct operating procedures are being followed.

(f)(3) **Work area** The employer shall provide clearance between machines so that movement of one operator will not interfere with the work of another. Ample room for cleaning machines, handling material, work pieces, and scrap shall also be provided. All surrounding floors shall be kept in good condition and free from obstructions, grease, oil, and water.

(f)(4) **Overloading** The employer shall operate his presses within the tonnage and attachment weight ratings specified by the manufacturer.

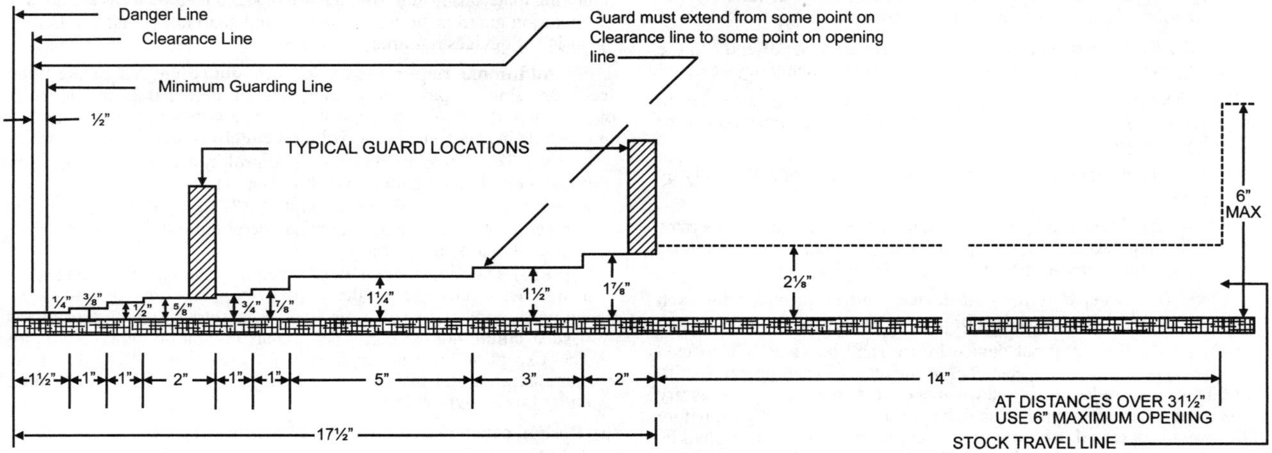

Explanation of above diagram:

This diagram shows the accepted safe openings between the bottom edge of a guard and feed table at various distances from the danger line (point of operation).

The clearance line marks the distance required to prevent contact between guard and moving parts.

The minimum guarding line is the distance between the infeed side of the guard and the danger line which is one-half inch from the danger line.

The various openings are such that for average size hands an operator's fingers won't reach the point of operation.

After installation of point of operation guards and before a job is released for operation a check should be made to verify that the guard will prevent the operator's hands from reaching the point of operation.

Table O–10
[In inches]

Distance of opening from point of operation hazard	Maximum width of opening
½ to 1 ½	¼
1 ½ to 2 ½	⅜
2 ½ to 3 ½	½
3 ½ to 5 ½	⅝
5 ½ to 6 ½	¾
6 ½ to 7 ½	⅞
7 ½ to 12 ½	1 ¼
12 ½ to 15 ½	1 ½
15 ½ to 17 ½	1 ⅞
17 ½ to 31 ½	2 ⅛

This table shows the distances that guards shall be positioned from the danger line in accordance with the required openings.

(g) Reports of injuries to employees operating mechanical power presses

(g)(1) The employer shall report, within 30 days of the occurrence, all point-of-operation injuries to operators or other employees to either the Director of the Directorate of Standards and Guidance at OSHA, U.S. Department of Labor, Washington, DC 20210 or electronically at http://www.osha.gov/pls/oshaweb/mechanical.html; or to the State Agency administering a plan approved by the Assistant Secretary of Labor for Occupational Safety and Health.

(g)(2) The report shall include the following information:

(g)(2)(i) Employer's name, address and location of the workplace (establishment);

(g)(2)(ii) Employee's name, injury sustained, and the task being performed (operation, set-up, maintenance, or other);

(g)(2)(iii) Type of clutch used on the press (full revolution, part revolution, or direct drive);

(g)(2)(iv) Type of safeguard(s) being used (two hand control, two hand trip, pull-outs, sweeps, or other). If the safeguard is not described in this section, give a complete description;

(g)(2)(v) Cause of the accident (repeat of press, safeguard failure, removing stuck part or scrap, no safeguard provided, no safeguard in use, or other);

(g)(2)(vi) Type of feeding (manual with hands in dies or with hands out of dies, semiautomatic, automatic, or other);

(g)(2)(vii) Means used to actuate press stroke (foot trip, foot control, hand trip, hand control, or other);

(g)(2)(viii) Number of operators required for the operation and the number of operators provided with controls and safeguards.

(h) Presence sensing device initiation (PSDI)

(h)(1) General

(h)(1)(i) The requirements of paragraph (h) shall apply to all part revolution mechanical power presses used in the PSDI mode of operation.

(h)(1)(ii) The relevant requirements of paragraphs (a) through (g) of this section also shall apply to all presses used in the PSDI mode of operation, whether or not cross referenced in this paragraph (h). Such cross-referencing of specific requirements from paragraphs (a) through (g) of this section is intended only to enhance convenience and understanding in relating to the new provisions to the existing standard, and is not to be construed as limiting the applicability of other provisions in paragraphs (a) through (g) of this section.

(h)(1)(iii) Full revolution mechanical power presses shall not be used in the PSDI mode of operation.

(h)(1)(iv) Mechanical power presses with a configuration which would allow a person to enter, pass through, and become clear of the sensing field into the hazardous portion of the press shall not be used in the PSDI mode of operation.

(h)(1)(v) The PSDI mode of operation shall be used only for normal production operations. Die-setting and maintenance procedures shall comply with paragraphs (a) through (g) of this section, and shall not be done in the PSDI mode.

(h)(2) Brake and clutch requirements

(h)(2)(i) Presses with flexible steel band brakes or with mechanical linkage actuated brakes or clutches shall not be used in the PSDI mode.

(h)(2)(ii) Brake systems on presses used in the PSDI mode shall have sufficient torque so that each average value of stopping times (Ts) for stops initiated at approximately 45 degrees, 60 degrees, and 90 degrees, respectively, of crankshaft angular position, shall not be more than 125 percent of the average value of the stopping time at the top crankshaft position. Compliance with this requirement shall be determined by using the heaviest upper die to be used on the press, and operating at the fastest press speed if there is speed selection.

(h)(2)(iii) Where brake engagement and clutch release is effected by spring action, such spring(s) shall operate in compression on a rod or within a hole or tube, and shall be of non-interleaving design.

(h)(3) Pneumatic systems

(h)(3)(i) Air valve and air pressure supply/control

(h)(3)(i)(A) The requirements of paragraphs (b)(7)(xiii), (b)(7)(xiv), (b)(10), (b)(12) and (c)(5)(iii) of this section apply to the pneumatic systems of machines used in the PSDI mode.

(h)(3)(i)(B) The air supply for pneumatic clutch/brake control valves shall incorporate a filter, an air regulator, and, when necessary for proper operation, a lubricator.

(h)(3)(i)(C) The air pressure supply for clutch/brake valves on machines used in the PSDI mode shall be regulated to pressures less than or equal to the air pressure used when making the stop time measurements required by paragraph (h)(2)(ii) of this section.

(h)(3)(ii) Air counterbalance systems

(h)(3)(ii)(A) Where presses that have slide counterbalance systems are used in the PSDI mode, the counterbalance system shall also meet the requirements of paragraph (b)(9) of this section.

(h)(3)(ii)(B) Counterbalances shall be adjusted in accordance with the press manufacturer's recommendations to assure correct counterbalancing of the slide attachment (upper die) weight for all operations performed on presses used in the PSDI mode. The adjustments shall be made before performing the stopping time measurements required by paragraphs (h)(2)(ii), (h)(5)(iii), and (h)(9)(v) of this section.

(h)(4) Flywheels and bearings Presses whose designs incorporate flywheels running on journals on the crankshaft or back shaft, or bull gears running on journals mounted on the crankshaft, shall be inspected, lubricated, and maintained as provided in paragraph (h)(10) of this section to reduce the possibility of unintended and uncontrolled press strokes caused by bearing seizure.

(h)(5) Brake monitoring

(h)(5)(i) Presses operated in the PSDI mode shall be equipped with a brake monitor that meets the requirements of paragraphs (b)(13) and (b)(14) of this section. In addition, the brake monitor shall be adjusted during installation certification to prevent successive stroking of the press if increases in stopping time cause an increase in the safety distance above that required by paragraph (h)(9)(v) of this section.

(h)(5)(ii) Once the PSDI safety system has been certified/validated, adjustment of the brake monitor shall not be done without prior approval of the validation organization for both the brake monitor adjustment and the corresponding adjustment of the safety distance. The validation organization shall in its installation validation, state that in what circumstances, if any, the employer has advance approval for adjustment, when prior oral approval is appropriate and when prior approval must be in writing. The adjustment shall be done under the supervision of an authorized person whose qualifications include knowledge of safety distance requirements and experience with the brake system and its adjustment. When brake wear or other factors extend press stopping time beyond the limit permitted by the brake monitor, adjustment, repair, or maintenance shall be performed on the brake or other press system element that extends the stopping time.

(h)(5)(iii) The brake monitor setting shall allow an increase of no more than 10 percent of the longest stopping time for the press, or 10 milliseconds, whichever is longer, measured at the top of the stroke.

(h)(6) Cycle control and control systems

(h)(6)(i) The control system on presses used in the PSDI mode shall meet the applicable requirements of paragraphs (b)(7), (b)(8), (b)(13), and (c)(5) of this section.

(h)(6)(ii) The control system shall incorporate a means of dynamically monitoring for decoupling of the rotary position indicating mechanism drive from the crankshaft. This monitor shall stop slide motion and prevent successive press strokes if decoupling occurs, or if the monitor itself fails.

(h)(6)(iii) The mode selection means of paragraph (b)(7)(iii) of this section shall have at least one position for selection of the PSDI mode. Where more than one interruption of the light sensing field is used in the initiation of a stroke, either the mode selection means must have one position for each function, or a separate selection means shall be provided which becomes operable when the PSDI mode is selected. Selection of PSDI mode and the number of interruptions/withdrawals of the light sensing field required to initiate a press cycle shall be by means capable of supervision by the employer.

(h)(6)(iv) A PSDI set-up/reset means shall be provided which requires an overt action by the operator, in addition to PSDI mode selection, before operation of the press by means of PSDI can be started.

(h)(6)(v) An indicator visible to the operator and readily seen by the employer shall be provided which shall clearly indicate that the system is set-up for cycling in the PSDI mode.

(h)(6)(vi) The control system shall incorporate a timer to deactivate PSDI when the press does not stroke within the period of time set by the timer. The timer shall be manually adjustable, to a maximum time of 30 seconds. For any timer setting greater than 15 seconds, the adjustment shall be made by the use of a special tool available only to authorized persons. Following a deactivation of PSDI by the timer, the system shall make it necessary to reset the set-up/reset means in order to reactivate the PSDI mode.

(h)(6)(vii) Reactivation of PSDI operation following deactivation of the PSDI mode from any other cause, such as activation of the red color stop control required by paragraph (b)(7)(ii) of this section, interruption of the presence sensing field, opening of an interlock, or reselection of the number of sensing field interruptions/withdrawals required to cycle the press, shall require resetting of the set-up/reset means.

(h)(6)(viii) The control system shall incorporate an automatic means to prevent initiation or continued operation in the PSDI mode unless the press drive motor is energized in the forward direction of crankshaft rotation.

(h)(6)(ix) The control design shall preclude any movement of the slide caused by operation of power on, power off, or selector switches, or from checks for proper operations as required by paragraph (h)(6)(xiv) of this section.

(h)(6)(x) All components and subsystems of the control system shall be designed to operate together to provide total control system compliance with the requirements of this section.

(h)(6)(xi) Where there is more than one operator of a press used for PSDI, each operator shall be protected by a separate, independently functioning, presence sensing device. The control system shall require that each sensing field be interrupted the selected number of times prior to initiating a stroke. Further, each operator shall be provided with a set-up/reset means that meets the requirements of paragraph (h)(6) of this section, and which must be actuated to initiate operation of the press in the PSDI mode.

(h)(6)(xii) [Reserved]

(h)(6)(xiii) The control system shall incorporate interlocks for supplemental guards, if used, which will prevent stroke initiation or will stop a stroke in progress if any supplemental guard fails or is deactivated.

(h)(6)(xiv) The control system shall perform checks for proper operation of all cycle control logic element switches and contacts at least once each cycle. Control elements shall be checked for correct status after power "on" and before the initial PSDI stroke.

(h)(6)(xv) The control system shall have provisions for an "inch" operating means meeting the requirements of paragraph (b)(7)(iv) of this section. Die-setting shall not be done in the PSDI mode. Production shall not be done in the "inch" mode.

(h)(6)(xvi) The control system shall permit only a single stroke per initiation command.

(h)(6)(xvii) Controls with internally stored programs (e.g., mechanical, electro-mechanical, or electronic) shall meet the requirements of paragraph (b)(13) of this section, and shall default to a predetermined safe condition in the event of any single failure within the system. Programmable controllers which meet the requirements for controls with internally stored programs stated above shall be permitted only if all logic elements affecting the safety system and point of operation safety are internally stored and protected in such a manner that they cannot be altered or manipulated by the user to an unsafe condition.

(h)(7) Environmental requirements Control components shall be selected, constructed, and connected together in such a way as to withstand expected operational and environmental stresses, at least including those outlined in Appendix A. Such stresses shall not so affect the control system as to cause unsafe operation.

(h)(8) Safety system

(h)(8)(i) Mechanical power presses used in the PSDI mode shall be operated under the control of a safety system which, in addition to meeting the applicable requirements of paragraphs (b)(13) and (c)(5) and other applicable provisions of this section, shall function such that a single failure or single operating error shall not cause injury to personnel from point of operation hazards.

(h)(8)(ii) The safety system shall be designed, constructed, and arranged as an integral total system, including all elements of the press, the controls, the safeguarding and any required supplemental safeguarding, and their interfaces with the operator and that part of the environment which has effect on the protection against point of operation hazards.

(h)(9) Safeguarding the point of operation

(h)(9)(i) The point of operation of presses operated in the PSDI mode shall be safeguarded in accordance with the requirements of paragraph (c) of this section, except that the safety distance requirements of paragraph (h)(9)(v) of this section shall be used for PSDI operation.

(h)(9)(ii)(A) PSDI shall be implemented only by use of light curtain (photo-electric) presence sensing devices which meet the requirements of paragraph (c)(3)(iii)(c) of this section unless the requirements of the following paragraph have been met.

(h)(9)(ii)(B) Alternatives to photo-electric light curtains may be used for PSDI when the employer can demonstrate, through tests and analysis by the employer or the manufacturer, that the alternative is as safe as the photo-electric light curtain, that the alternative meets the conditions of this section, has the same long term reliability as light curtains and can be integrated into the entire safety system as provided for in this section. Prior to use, both the employer and manufacturer must certify that these requirements and all the other applicable requirements of this section are met and these certifications must be validated by an OSHA-recognized third-party validation organization to meet these additional requirements and all the other applicable requirements of paragraphs (a) through (h) and Appendix A of this section. Three months prior to the operation of any alternative system, the employer must notify the OSHA Directorate of Safety Standards Programs of the name of the system to be installed, the manufacturer and the OSHA-recognized third-party validation organization immediately. Upon request, the employer must make available to that office all tests and analyses for OSHA review.

(h)(9)(iii) Individual sensing fields of presence sensing devices used to initiate strokes in the PSDI mode shall cover only one side of the press.

(h)(9)(iv) Light curtains used for PSDI operation shall have minimum object sensitivity not to exceed one and one-fourth inches (31.75 mm). Where light curtain object sensitivity is user-adjustable, either discretely or continuously, design features shall limit the minimum object sensitivity adjustment not to exceed one and one-fourth inches (31.75 mm). Blanking of the sensing field is not permitted.

(h)(9)(v) The safety distance (D_s) from the sensing field of the presence sensing device to the point of operation shall be greater than or equal to the distance determined by the formula:

$$D_s = H_s \times (T_s + T_p + T_r + 2T_m) + D_p$$

Where:

D_s = Minimum safety distance.

H_s = Hand speed constant of 63 inches per second (1.6 m/s);

T_s = Longest press stopping time, in seconds, computed by taking averages of multiple measurements at each of three positions (45 degrees, 60 degrees, and 90 degrees) of crankshaft angular position; the longest of the three averages is the stopping time to use. (T_s is defined as the sum of the kinetic energy dissipation time plus the pneumatic/magnetic/hydraulic reaction time of the clutch/brake operating mechanism(s);)

T_p = Longest presence sensing device response time, in seconds;

T_r = Longest response time, in seconds, of all interposing control elements between the presence sensing device and the clutch/brake operating mechanism(s);

T_m = Increase in the press stopping time at the top of the stroke, in seconds, allowed by the brake monitor for brake wear. The time increase allowed shall be limited to no more than 10 percent of the longest press stopping time measured at the top of the stroke, or 10 milliseconds, whichever is longer;

D_p = Penetration depth factor, required to provide for possible penetration through the presence sensing field by fingers or hand before detection occurs. The penetration depth factor shall be determined from Graph h–1 using the minimum object sensitivity size.

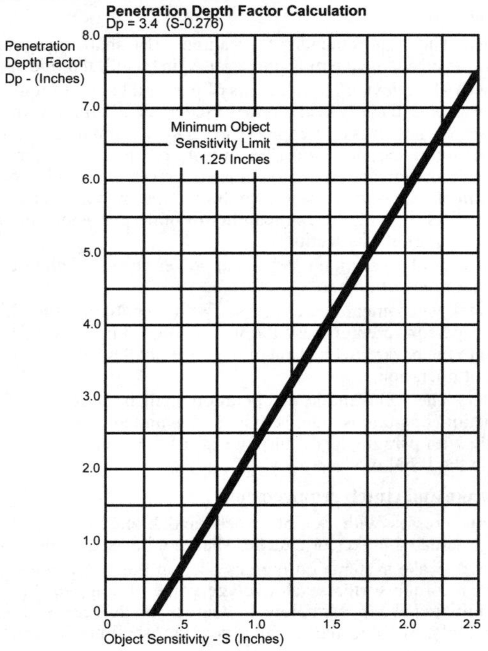

(h)(9)(vi) The presence sensing device location shall either be set at each tool change and set-up to provide at least the minimum safety distance, or fixed in location to provide a safety distance greater than or equal to the minimum safety distance for all tooling set-ups which are to be used on that press.

(h)(9)(vii) Where presence sensing device location is adjustable, adjustment shall require the use of a special tool available only to authorized persons.

(h)(9)(viii) Supplemental safeguarding shall be used to protect all areas of access to the point of operation which are unprotected by the PSDI presence sensing device. Such supplemental safeguarding shall consist of either additional light curtain (photo-electric) presence sensing devices or other types of guards which meet the requirements of paragraphs (c) and (h) of this section.

(h)(9)(viii)(A) Presence sensing devices used as supplemental safeguarding shall not initiate a press stroke, and shall conform to the requirements of paragraph (c)(3)(iii) and other applicable provisions of this section, except that the safety distance shall comply with paragraph (h)(9)(v) of this section.

(h)(9)(viii)(B) Guards used as supplemental safeguarding shall conform to the design, construction and application requirements of paragraph (c)(2) of this section, and shall be interlocked with the press control to prevent press PSDI operation if the guard fails, is removed, or is out of position.

(h)(9)(ix) Barriers shall be fixed to the press frame or bolster to prevent personnel from passing completely through the sensing field, where safety distance or press configuration is such that personnel could pass through the PSDI presence sensing field and assume a position where the point of operation could be accessed without detection by the PSDI presence sensing device. As an alternative, supplemental presence sensing devices used only in the safeguard mode may be provided. If used, these devices shall be located so as to detect all operator locations and positions not detected by the PSDI sensing field, and shall prevent stroking or stop a stroke in process when any supplemental sensing field(s) are interrupted.

(h)(9)(x) Hand tools. Where tools are used for feeding, removal of scrap, lubrication of parts, or removal of parts that stick on the die in PSDI operations:

(h)(9)(x)(A) The minimum diameter of the tool handle extension shall be greater than the minimum object sensitivity of the presence sensing device(s) used to initiate press strokes; or

(h)(9)(x)(B) The length of the hand tool shall be such as to ensure that the operator's hand will be detected for any safety distance required by the press set-ups.

(h)(10) **Inspection and maintenance**

(h)(10)(i) Any press equipped with presence sensing devices for use in PSDI, or for supplemental safeguarding on presses used in the PSDI mode, shall be equipped with a test rod of diameter specified by the presence sensing device manufacturer to represent the minimum object sensitivity of the sensing field. Instructions for use of the test rod shall be noted on a label affixed to the presence sensing device.

(h)(10)(ii) The following checks shall be made at the beginning of each shift and whenever a die change is made.

(h)(10)(ii)(A) A check shall be performed using the test rod according to the presence sensing device manufacturer's instructions to determine that the presence sensing device used for PSDI is operational.

(h)(10)(ii)(B) The safety distance shall be checked for compliance with (h)(9)(v) of this section.

(h)(10)(ii)(C) A check shall be made to determine that all supplemental safeguarding is in place. Where presence sensing devices are used for supplemental safeguarding, a check for proper operation shall be performed using the test rod according to the presence sensing device manufacturer's instructions.

(h)(10)(ii)(D) A check shall be made to assure that the barriers and/or supplemental presence sensing devices required by paragraph (h)(9)(ix) of this section are operating properly.

(h)(10)(ii)(E) A system or visual check shall be made to verify correct counterbalance adjustment for die weight according to the press manufacturer's instructions, when a press is equipped with a slide counterbalance system.

(h)(10)(iii) When presses used in the PSDI mode have flywheel or bullgear running on crankshaft mounted journals and bearings, or a flywheel mounted on back shaft journals and bearings, periodic inspections following the press manufacturer's recommendations shall be made to ascertain that bearings are in good working order, and that automatic lubrication systems for these bearings (if automatic lubrication is provided) are supplying proper lubrication. On presses with provision for manual lubrication of flywheel or bullgear bearings, lubrication shall be provided according to the press manufacturer's recommendations.

(h)(10)(iv) Periodic inspections of clutch and brake mechanisms shall be performed to assure they are in proper operating condition. The press manufacturer's recommendations shall be followed.

(h)(10)(v) When any check of the press, including those performed in accordance with the requirements of paragraphs (h)(10)(ii), (iii) or (iv) of this section, reveals a condition of noncompliance, improper adjustment, or failure, the press shall not be operated until the condition has been corrected by adjustment, replacement, or repair.

(h)(10)(vi) It shall be the responsibility of the employer to ensure the competence of personnel caring for, inspecting, and maintaining power presses equipped for PSDI operation, through initial and periodic training.

(h)(11) Safety system certification/validation.

(h)(11)(i) Prior to the initial use of any mechanical press in the PSDI mode, two sets of certification and validation are required:

(h)(11)(i)(A) The design of the safety system required for the use of a press in the PSDI mode shall be certified and validated prior to installation. The manufacturer's certification shall be validated by an OSHA-recognized third-party validation organization to meet all applicable requirements of paragraphs (a) through (h) and Appendix A of this section;

(h)(11)(i)(B) After a press has been equipped with a safety system whose design has been certified and validated in accordance with paragraph (h)(11)(i) of this section, the safety system installation shall be certified by the employer, and then shall be validated by an OSHA-recognized third-party validation organization to meet all applicable requirements of paragraphs (a) through (h) and Sppendix A of this section.

(h)(11)(ii) At least annually thereafter, the safety system on a mechanical power press used in the PSDI mode shall be recertified by the employer and revalidated by an OSHA-recognized third-party validation organization to meet all applicable requirements of paragraphs (a) through (h) and Appendix A of this section. Any press whose safety system has not been recertified and revalidated within the preceding 12 months shall be removed from service in the PSDI mode until the safety system is recertified and revalidated.

(h)(11)(iii) A label shall be affixed to the press as part of each installation certification/validation and the most recent recertification/revalidation. The label shall indicate the press serial number, the minimum safety distance (Ds) required by paragraph (h)(9)(v) of this section, the fulfillment of design certification/validation, the employer's signed certification, the identification of the OSHA-recognized third-party validation organization, its signed validation, and the date the certification/validation and recertification/revalidation are issued.

(h)(11)(iv) Records of the installation certification and validation and the most recent recertification and revalidation shall be maintained for each safety system equipped press by the employer as long as the press is in use. The records shall include the manufacture and model number of each component and subsystem, the calculations of the safety distance as required by paragraph (h)(9)(v) of this section, and the stopping time measurements required by paragraph (h)(2)(ii) of this section. The most recent records shall be made available to OSHA upon request.

(h)(11)(v) The employer shall notify the OSHA-recognized third-party validation organization within five days whenever a component or a subsystem of the safety system fails or modifications are made which may affect the safety of the system. The failure of a critical component shall necessitate the removal of the safety system from service until it is recertified and revalidated, except recertification by the employer without revalidation is permitted when a non-critical component or subsystem is replaced by one of the same manufacture and design as the original, or determined by the third-party validation organization to be equivalent by similarity analysis, as set forth in Appendix A.

(h)(11)(vi) The employer shall notify the OSHA-recognized third-party validation organization within five days of the occurrence of any point of operation injury while a press is used in the PSDI mode. This is in addition to the report of injury required by paragraph (g) of this section; however, a copy of that report may be used for this purpose.

(h)(12) **Die setting and work set-up.**

(h)(12)(i) Die setting on presses used in the PSDI mode shall be performed in accordance with paragraphs (d) and (h) of this section.

(h)(12)(ii) The PSDI mode shall not be used for die setting or set-up. An alternative manual cycle initiation and control means shall be supplied for use in die setting which meets the requirements of paragraph (b)(7) of this section.

(h)(12)(iii) Following a die change, the safety distance, the proper application of supplemental safeguarding, and the slide counterbalance adjustment (if the press is equipped with a counterbalance) shall be checked and maintained by authorized persons whose qualifications include knowledge of the safety distance, supplemental safeguarding requirements, and the manufacturer's specifications for counterbalance adjustment. Adjustment of the location of the PSDI presence sensing device shall require use of a special tool available only to the authorized persons.

(h)(13) **Operator training**

(h)(13)(i) The operator training required by paragraph (f)(2) of this section shall be provided to the employee before the employee initially operates the press and as needed to maintain competence, but not less than annually thereafter. It shall include instruction relative to the following items for presses used in the PSDI mode.

(h)(13)(i)(A) The manufacturer's recommended test procedures for checking operation of the presence sensing device. This shall include the use of the test rod required by paragraph (h)(10)(i) of this section.

(h)(13)(i)(B) The safety distance required.

(h)(13)(i)(C) The operation, function and performance of the PSDI mode.

(h)(13)(i)(D) The requirements for hand tools that may be used in the PSDI mode.

(h)(13)(i)(E) The severe consequences that can result if he or she attempts to circumvent or by-pass any of the safeguard or operating functions of the PSDI system.

(h)(13)(ii) The employer shall certify that employees have been trained by preparing a certification record which includes the identity of the person trained, the signature of the employer or the person who conducted the training, and the date the training was completed. The certification record shall be prepared at the completion of training and shall be maintained on file for the duration of the employee's employment. The certification record shall be made available upon request to the Assistant Secretary for Occupational Safety and Health.

§1910.217 Appendix A Mandatory requirements for certification/validation of safety systems for presence sensing device initiation of mechanical power presses

Purpose

The purpose of the certification/validation of safety systems for presence sensing device initiation (PSDI) of mechanical power presses is to ensure that the safety systems are designed, installed, and maintained in accordance with all applicable requirements of 29 CFR §1910.217 (a) through (h) and this Appendix A.

General

The certification/validation process shall utilize an independent third-party validation organization recognized by OSHA in accordance with the requirements specified in Appendix C of this section.

While the employer is responsible for assuring that the certification/validation requirements in §1910.217(h)(11) are fulfilled, the design certification of PSDI safety systems may be initiated by manufacturers, employers, and/or their representatives. The term manufacturers refers to the manufacturer of any of the components of the safety system. An employer who assembles a PSDI safety system would be a manufacturer as well as employer for purposes of this Standard and Appendix.

The certification/validation process includes two stages. For design certification, in the first stage, the manufacturer (which can be an employer) certifies that the PSDI safety system meets the requirements of 29 CFR §1910.217 (a) through (h) and this Appendix A, based on appropriate design criteria and tests. In the second stage, the OSHA-recognized third-party validation organization validates that the PSDI safety system meets the requirements of 29 CFR §1910.217 (a) through (h) and this Appendix A and the manufacturer's certification by reviewing the manufacturer's design and test data and performing any additional reviews required by this standard or which it believes appropriate.

For installation certification/validation and annual recertification/revalidation, in the first stage the employer certifies or recertifies that the employer is installing or utilizing a PSDI safety system validated as meeting the design requirements of 29 CFR §1910.217 (a) through (h) and this Appendix A by an OSHA-recognized third-party validation organization and that the installation, operation and maintenance meet the requirements of 29 CFR §1910.217 (a) through (h) and this Appendix A. In the second stage, the OSHA-recognized third-party validation organization validates or revalidates that the PSDI safety system installation meets the requirements of 29 CFR §1910.217 (a) through (h) and this Appendix A and the employer's certification, by reviewing that the PSDI safety system has been certified; the employer's certification, designs and tests, if any; the installation, operation, maintenance and training; and by performing any additional tests and reviews which the validation organization believes is necessary.

Summary

The certification/validation of safety systems for PSDI shall consider the press, controls, safeguards, operator, and environment as an integrated system which shall comply with all of the requirements in 29 CFR §1910.217 (a) through (h) and this Appendix A. The certification/validation process shall verify that the safety system complies with the OSHA safety requirements as follows:

A. Design Certification/Validation

1. The major parts, components and subsystems used shall be defined by part number or serial number, as appropriate, and by manufacturer to establish the configuration of the system.

2. The identified parts, components and subsystems shall be certified by the manufacturer to be able to withstand the functional and operational environments of the PSDI safety system.

3. The total system design shall be certified by the manufacturer as complying with all requirements in 29 CFR §1910.217 (a) through (h) and this Appendix A.

4. The third-party validation organization shall validate the manufacturer's certification under paragraphs 2 and 3.

B. Installation Certification/Validation

1. The employer shall certify that the PSDI safety system has been design certified and validated, that the installation meets the operational and environmental requirements specified by the manufacturer, that the installation drawings are accurate, and that the installation meets the requirements of 29 CFR §1910.217 (a) through (h) and this Appendix A. (The operational and installation requirements of the PSDI safety system may vary for different applications.)

2. The third-party validation organization shall validate the employer's certifications that the PSDI safety system is design certified and validated, that the installation meets the installation and environmental requirements specified by the manufacturer, and that the installation meets the requirements of 29 CFR §1910.217 (a) through (h) and this Appendix A.

C. Recertification/Revalidation

1. The PSDI safety system shall remain under certification/validation for the shorter of one year or until the system hardware is changed, modified or refurbished, or operating conditions are changed (including environmental, application or facility changes), or a failure of a critical component has occurred.

2. Annually, or after a change specified in paragraph 1., the employer shall inspect and recertify the installation as meeting the requirements set forth under B., Installation Certification/Validation.

3. The third-party validation organization, annually or after a change specified in paragraph 1., shall validate the employer's certification that the requirements of paragraph B., Installation Certification/Validation have been met.

(*Note:* Such changes in operational conditions as die changes or press relocations not involving disassembly or revision to the safety system would not require recertification/revalidation.)

Certification/Validation Requirements

A. General Design Certification/Validation Requirements

1. Certification/Validation Program Requirements The manufacturer shall certify and the OSHA-recognized third-party validation organization shall validate that:

(a) The design of components, subsystems, software and assemblies meets OSHA performance requirements and are ready for the intended use; and

(b) The performance of combined subsystems meets OSHA's operational requirements.

2. Certification/Validation Program Level of Risk Evaluation Requirements The manufacturer shall evaluate and certify, and the OSHA-recognized third-party validation organization shall validate, the design and operation of the safety system by determining conformance with the following:

a. The safety system shall have the ability to sustain a single failure or a single operating error and not cause injury to personnel from point of operation hazards. Acceptable design features shall demonstrate, in the following order or precedence, that:

(1) No single failure points may cause injury; or

(2) Redundancy, and comparison and/or diagnostic checking, exist for the critical items that may cause injury, and the electrical, electronic, electromechanical and mechanical parts and components are selected so that they can withstand operational and external environments. The safety factor and/or derated percentage shall be specifically noted and complied with.

b. The manufacturer shall design, evaluate, test and certify, and the third-party validation organization shall evaluate and validate, that the PSDI safety system meets appropriate requirements in the following areas.

(1) Environmental Limits

(a) Temperature

(b) Relative humidity

(c) Vibration

(d) Fluid compatibility with other materials

(2) Design Limits
- (a) Power requirements
- (b) Power transient tolerances
- (c) Compatibility of materials used
- (d) Material stress tolerances and limits
- (e) Stability to long term power fluctuations
- (f) Sensitivity to signal acquisition
- (g) Repeatability of measured parameter without inadvertent initiation of a press stroke
- h) Operational life of components in cycles, hours, or both
- (i) Electromagnetic tolerance to:
  - (1) Specific operational wave lengths; and
  - (2) Externally generated wave lengths

(3) New Design Certification/Validation Design certification/validation for a new safety system, i.e., a new design or new integration of specifically identified components and subsystems, would entail a single certification/validation which would be applicable to all identical safety systems. It would not be necessary to repeat the tests on individual safety systems of the same manufacture or design. Nor would it be necessary to repeat these tests in the case of modifications where determined by the manufacturer and validated by the third-party validation organization to be equivalent by similarity analysis. Minor modifications not affecting the safety of the system may be made by the manufacturer without revalidation.

Substantial modifications would require testing as a new safety system, as deemed necessary by the validation organization.

B. Additional Detailed Design Certification/Validation Requirements

1. General The manufacturer or the manufacturer's representative shall certify to and submit to an OSHA-recognized third-party validation organization the documentation necessary to demonstrate that the PSDI safety system design is in full compliance with the requirements of 29 CFR §1910.217(a)–(h) and this Appendix A, as applicable, by means of analysis, tests, or combination of both, establishing that the following additional certification/validation requirements are fulfilled.

2. Reaction Times For the purpose of demonstrating compliance with the reaction time required by §1910.217(h), the tests shall use the following definitions and requirements:

a. **Reaction time** means the time, in seconds, it takes the signal, required to activate/deactivate the system, to travel through the system, measured from the time of signal initiation to the time the function being measured is completed.

b. **Full stop or No movement of the slide or ram** means when the crankshaft rotation has slowed to two or less revolutions per minute, just before stopping completely.

c. **Function completion** means for, electrical, electromechanical and electronic devices, when the circuit produces a change of state in the output element of the device.

d. When the change of state is motion, the measurement shall be made at the completion of the motion.

e. The generation of the test signal introduced into the system for measuring reaction time shall be such that the initiation time can be established with an error of less than 0.5 percent of the reaction time measured.

f. The instrument used to measure reaction time shall be calibrated to be accurate to within 0.001 second.

3. Compliance with §1910.217(h)(2)(ii) For compliance with these requirements, the average value of the stopping time, T_s, shall be the arithmetic mean of at least 25 stops for each stop angle initiation measured with the brake and/or clutch unused, 50 percent worn, and 90 percent worn. The recommendations of the brake system manufacturer shall be used to simulate or estimate the brake wear. The manufacturer's recommended minimum lining depth shall be identified and documented, and an evaluation made that the minimum depth will not be exceeded before the next (annual) recertification/revalidation. A correlation of the brake and/or clutch degradation based on the above tests and/or estimates shall be made and documented. The results shall document the conditions under which the brake and/or clutch will and will not comply with the requirement. Based upon this determination, a scale shall be developed to indicate the allowable 10 percent of the stopping time at the top of the stroke for slide or ram overtravel due to brake wear. The scale shall be marked to indicate that brake adjustment and/or replacement is required. The explanation and use of the scale shall be documented.

The test specification and procedure shall be submitted to the validation organization for review and validation prior to the test. The validation organization representative shall witness at least one set of tests.

4. Compliance with §1910.217(h)(5)(iii) and (h)(9)(v) Each reaction time required to calculate the Safety Distance, including the brake monitor setting, shall be documented in separate reaction time tests. These tests shall specify the acceptable tolerance band sufficient to assure that tolerance build-up will not render the safety distance unsafe.

a. Integrated test of the press fully equipped to operate in the PSDI mode shall be conducted to establish the total system reaction time.

b. Brakes which are the adjustable type shall be adjusted properly before the test.

5. Compliance with §1910.217(h)(2)(iii)

a. Prior to conducting the brake system test required by paragraph (h)(2)(ii), a visual check shall be made of the springs. The visual check shall include a determination that the spring housing or rod does not show damage sufficient to degrade the structural integrity of the unit, and the spring does not show any tendency to interleave.

b. Any detected broken or unserviceable springs shall be replaced before the test is conducted. The test shall be considered successful if the stopping time remains within that which is determined by paragraph (h)(9)(v) for the safety distance setting. If the increase in press stopping time exceeds the brake monitor setting limit defined in paragraph (h)(5)(iii), the test shall be considered unsuccessful, and the cause of the excessive stopping time shall be investigated. It shall be ascertained that the springs have not been broken and that they are functioning properly.

6. Compliance with §1910.217(h)(7)

a. Tests which are conducted by the manufacturers of electrical components to establish stress, life, temperature and loading limits must be tests which are in compliance with the provisions of the National Electrical Code.

b. Electrical and/or electronic cards or boards assembled with discreet components shall be considered a subsystem and shall require separate testing that the subsystems do not degrade in any of the following conditions:
- (1) Ambient temperature variation from −20 °C to +50 °C.
- (2) Ambient relative humidity of 99 percent.
- (3) Vibration of 45G for one millisecond per stroke when the item is to be mounted on the press frame.
- (4) Electromagnetic interference at the same wavelengths used for the radiation sensing field, at the power line frequency fundamental and harmonics, and also from outogenous radiation due to system switching.
- (5) Electrical power supply variations of ±15 percent.

c. The manufacturer shall specify the test requirements and procedures from existing consensus tests in compliance with the provisions of the National Electrical Code.

d. Tests designed by the manufacturer shall be made available upon request to the validation organization. The validation organization representative shall witness at least one set of each of these tests.

7. Compliance with §1910.217(h)(9)(iv).

a. The manufacturer shall design a test to demonstrate that the prescribed minimum object sensitivity of the presence sensing device is met.

b. The test specifications and procedures shall be made available upon request to the validation organization.

8. Compliance with §1910.217(h)(9)(x)

a. The manufacturer shall design a test(s) to establish the hand tool extension diameters allowed for variations in minimum object sensitivity response.

b. The test(s) shall document the range of object diameter sizes which will produce both single and double break conditions.

c. The test(s) specifications and procedures shall be made available upon request to the validation organization.

9. Integrated Tests Certification/Validation

a. The manufacturer shall design a set of integrated tests to demonstrate compliance with the following requirements:
Sections §1910.217(h)(6)(ii); (iii); (iv); (v); (vi); (vii); (viii); (ix); (xi); (xii); (xiii); (xiv); (xv); and (xvii).

b. The integrated test specifications and procedures shall be made available to the validation organization.

10. Analysis

a. The manufacturer shall submit to the validation organization the technical analysis such as Hazard Analysis, Failure Mode and Effect Analysis, Stress Analysis, Component and Material Selection Analysis, Fluid Compatibility, and/or other analyses which may be necessary to demonstrate, compliance with the following requirements:
Sections §1910.217(h)(8)(i) and (ii); (h)(2) ii) and (iii); (h)(3)(i)(A) and (C), and (ii); (h)(5)(i), (ii) and (iii); (h)(6)(i), (iii), (iv), (vi), (vii), (viii), (ix), (x), (xi), (xiii), (xiv), (xv), (xvi), and (xvii); (h)(7)(i) and (ii); (h)(9)(iv), (v), (viii), (ix) and (x); (h)(10)(i) and (ii).

11. Types of Tests Acceptable for Certification/Validation

a. Test results obtained from development testing may be used to certify/validate the design.

b. The test results shall provide the engineering data necessary to establish confidence that the hardware and software will meet specifications, the manufacturing process has adequate quality control and the data acquired was used to establish processes, procedures, and test levels supporting subsequent hardware design, production, installation and maintenance.

12. Validation for Design Certification/Validation If, after review of all documentation, tests, analyses, manufacturer's certifications, and any additional tests which the third-party validation organization believes are necessary, the third-party validation organization determines that the PSDI safety system is in full compliance with the applicable requirements of 29 CFR §1910.217(a) through (h) and this Appendix A, it shall validate the manufacturer's certification that it so meets the stated requirements.

C. Installation Certification/Validation Requirements

1. The employer shall evaluate and test the PSDI system installation, shall submit to the OSHA-recognized third-party validation organization the necessary supporting documentation, and shall certify that the requirements of §1910.217(a) through (h) and this Appendix A have been met and that the installation is proper.

2. The OSHA-recognized third-party validation organization shall conduct tests, and/or review and evaluate the employer's installation tests, documentation and representations. If it so determines, it shall validate the employer's certification that the PSDI safety system is in full conformance with all requirements of 29 CFR §1910.217(a) through (h) and this Appendix A.

D. Recertification/Revalidation Requirements

1. A PSDI safety system which has received installation certification/validation shall undergo recertification/revalidation the earlier of:

a. Each time the systems hardware is significantly changed, modified, or refurbished;

b. Each time the operational conditions are significantly changed (including environmental, application or facility changes, but excluding such changes as die changes or press relocations not involving revision to the safety system);

c. When a failure of a significant component has occurred or a change has been made which may affect safety; or

d. When one year has elapsed since the installation certification/validation or the last recertification/revalidation.

2. Conduct or recertification/revalidation. The employer shall evaluate and test the PSDI safety system installation, shall submit to the OSHA-recognized third-party validation organization the necessary supporting documentation, and shall recertify that the requirements of §1910.217(a) through (h) and this Appendix are being met. The documentation shall include, but not be limited to, the following items:

a. Demonstration of a thorough inspection of the entire press and PSDI safety system to ascertain that the installation, components and safeguarding have not been changed, modified or tampered with since the installation certification/validation or last recertification/revalidation was made.

b. Demonstrations that such adjustments as may be needed (such as to the brake monitor setting) have been accomplished with proper changes made in the records and on such notices as are located on the press and safety system.

c. Demonstration that review has been made of the reports covering the design certification/validation, the installation certification/validation, and all recertification/revalidations, in order to detect any degradation to an unsafe condition, and that necessary changes have been made to restore the safety system to previous certification/validation levels.

3. The OSHA-recognized third-party validation organization shall conduct tests, and/or review and evaluate the employer's installation, tests, documentation and representations. If it so determines, it shall revalidate the employer's recertification that the PSDI system is in full conformance with all requirements of 29 CFR §1910.217(a) through (h) and this Appendix A.

§1910.217 Appendix B Nonmandatory guidelines for certification/validation of safety systems for presence sensing device initiation of mechanical power presses

Objectives

This Appendix provides employers, manufacturers, and their representatives, with nonmandatory guidelines for use in developing certification documents. Employers and manufacturers are encouraged to recommend other approaches if there is a potential for improving safety and reducing cost. The guidelines apply to certification/validation activity from design evaluation through the completion of the installation test and the annual recertification/revalidation tests.

General Guidelines

A. The certification/validation process should confirm that hazards identified by hazard analysis, (HA), failure mode effect analysis (FMEA), and other system analyses have been eliminated by design or reduced to an acceptable level through the use of appropriate design features, safety devices, warning devices, or special procedures. The certification/validation process should also confirm that residual hazards identified by operational analysis are addressed by warning, labeling safety instructions or other appropriate means.

B. The objective of the certification/validation program is to demonstrate and document that the system satisfies specification and operational requirements for safe operations.

Quality Control

The safety attributes of a certified/validated PSDI safety system are more likely to be maintained if the quality of the system and its parts, components and subsystem is consistently controlled. Each manufacturer supplying parts, components, subsystems, and assemblies needs to maintain the quality of the product, and each employer needs to maintain the system in a non-degraded condition.

Analysis Guidelines

A. Certification/validation of hardware design below the system level should be accomplished by test and/or analysis.

B. Analytical methods may be used in lieu of, in combination with, or in support of tests to satisfy specification requirements.

C. Analyses may be used for certification/validation when existing data are available or when test is not feasible.

D. Similarity analysis may be used in lieu of tests where it can be shown that the article is similar in design, manufacturing process, and quality control to another article that was previously certified/validated in accordance with equivalent or more stringent criteria. If previous design, history and application are considered to be similar, but not equal to or more exacting than earlier experiences, the additional or partial certification/validation tests should concentrate on the areas of changed or increased requirements.

Analysis Reports

The analysis reports should identify: (1) The basis for the analysis; (2) the hardware or software items analyzed; (3) conclusions; (4) safety factors; and (5) limit of the analysis. The assumptions made during the analysis should be clearly stated and a description of the effects of these assumptions on the conclusions and limits should be included.

Certification/validation by similarity analysis reports should identify, in addition to the above, application of the part, component or subsystem for which certification/validation is being sought as well as data from previous usage establishing adequacy of the item. Similarity analysis should not be accepted when the internal and external stresses on the item being certified/validated are not defined.

Usage experience should also include failure data supporting adequacy of the design.

§1910.217 Appendix C Mandatory requirements for OSHA recognition of third–party validation organizations for the PSDI standard

This Appendix prescribes mandatory requirements and procedures for OSHA recognition of third-party validation organizations to validate employer and manufacturer certifications that their equipment and practices meet the requirements of the PSDI standard. The scope of the Appendix includes the three categories of certification/validation required by the PSDI standard: Design Certification/Validation, Installation Certification/Validation, and Annual Recertification/Revalidation.

If further detailing of these provisions will assist the validation organization or OSHA in this activity, this detailing will be done through appropriate OSHA Program Directives.

I. Procedure for OSHA Recognition of Validation Organizations

A. Applications

1. **Eligibility**
   a. Any person or organization considering itself capable of conducting a PSDI-related third-party validation function may apply for OSHA recognition.
   b. However, in determining eligibility for a foreign-based third-party validation organization, OSHA shall take into consideration whether there is reciprocity of treatment by the foreign government after consultation with relevant U.S. government agencies.

2. **Content of application**
   a. The application shall identify the scope of the validation activity for which the applicant wishes to be recognized, based on one of the following alternatives:
      (1) Design Certification/Validation, Installation Certification/Validation, and Annual Recertification/Revalidation;
      (2) Design Certification/Validation only; or
      (3) Installation/Certification/Validation and Annual Recertification/Revalidation.
   b. The application shall provide information demonstrating that it and any validating laboratory utilized meet the qualifications set forth in section II of this Appendix.
   c. The applicant shall provide information demonstrating that it and any validating laboratory utilized meet the program requirements set forth in section III of this Appendix.
   d. The applicant shall identify the test methods it or the validating laboratory will use to test or judge the components and operations of the PSDI safety system required to be tested by the PSDI standard and Appendix A, and shall specify the reasons the test methods are appropriate.
   e. The applicant may include whatever enclosures, attachments, or exhibits the applicant deems appropriate. The application need not be submitted on a Federal form.
   f. The applicant shall certify that the information submitted is accurate.

3. **Filing office location** The application shall be filed with: PSDI Certification/Validation Program, Office of Variance Determination, Occupational Safety and Health Administration, U.S. Department of Labor, Room N3653, 200 Constitution Avenue, NW., Washington, DC 20210.

4. **Amendments and withdrawals**
   a. An application may be revised by an applicant at any time prior to the completion of the final staff recommendation.
   b. An application may be withdrawn by an applicant, without prejudice, at any time prior to the final decision by the Assistant Secretary in paragraph I..B.8.b.(4) of this Appendix.

B. Review and Decision Process

1. **Acceptance and field inspection** All applications submitted will be accepted by OSHA, and their receipt acknowledged in writing. After receipt of an application, OSHA may request additional information if it believes information relevant to the requirements for recognition have been omitted. OSHA may inspect the facilities of the third-party validation organization and any validating laboratory, and while there shall review any additional documentation underlying the application. A report shall be made of each field inspection.

2. **Requirements for recognition** The requirements for OSHA recognition of a third-party validation organization for the PSDI standard are that the program has fulfilled the requirements of section II of this Appendix for qualifications and of section III of this Appendix for program requirements, and the program has identified appropriate test and analysis methods to meet the requirements of the PSDI standard and Appendix A.

3. **Preliminary approval** If, after review of the application, any additional information, and the inspection report, the applicant and any validating laboratory appear to have met the requirements for recognition, a written recommendation shall be submitted by the responsible OSHA personnel to the Assistant Secretary to approve the application with a supporting explanation.

4. **Preliminary disapproval** If, after review of the application, additional information, and inspection report, the applicant does not appear to have met the requirements for recognition, the Director of the PSDI certification/validation program shall notify the applicant in writing, listing the specific requirements of this Appendix which the applicant has not met, and the reasons.

5. **Revision of application** After receipt of a notification of preliminary disapproval, the applicant may submit a revised application for further review by OSHA pursuant to subsection I.B. of this Appendix or may request that the original application be submitted to the Assistant Secretary with a statement of reasons supplied by the applicant as to why the application should be approved.

6. **Preliminary decision by Assistant Secretary**
   a. The Assistant Secretary, or a special designee for this purpose, will make a preliminary decision whether the applicant has met the requirements for recognition based on the completed application file and the written staff recommendation, as well as the statement of reasons by the applicant if there is a recommendation of disapproval.
   b. This preliminary decision will be sent to the applicant and subsequently published in the Federal Register.

7. **Public review and comment period**
   a. The Federal Register notice of preliminary decision will provide a period of not less than 60 calendar days for the written comments on the applicant's fulfillment of the requirements for recognition. The application, supporting documents, staff recommendation, statement of applicant's reasons, and any comments received, will be available for public inspection in the OSHA Docket Office.
   b. If the preliminary decision is in favor of recognition, a member of the public, or if the preliminary decision is against recognition, the applicant may request a public hearing by the close of the comment period, if it supplies detailed reasons and evidence challenging the basis of the Assistant Secretary's preliminary decision and justifying the need for a public hearing to bring out evidence which could not be effectively supplied through written submissions.

8. **Final decision by Assistant Secretary**
   a. Without hearing. If there are no valid requests for a hearing, based on the application, supporting documents, staff recommendation, evidence and public comment, the Assistant Secretary shall issue the final decision (including reasons) of the Department of Labor on whether the applicant has demonstrated by a preponderance of the evidence that it meets the requirements for recognition.
   b. After hearing. If there is a valid request for a hearing pursuant to paragraph I.B.7.b. of this Appendix, the following procedures will be used:
      (1) The Assistant Secretary will issue a notice of hearing before an administrative law judge of the Department of Labor pursuant to the rules specified in 29 CFR part 1905, Subpart C.
      (2) After the hearing, pursuant to Subpart C, the administrative law judge shall issue a decision (including reasons) based on the application, the supporting documentation, the staff recommendation, the public comments and the evidence submitted during the hearing (the record), stating whether it has been demonstrated, based on a preponderance of evidence, that the applicant meets the requirements for recognition. If no exceptions are filed, this is the final decision of the Department of Labor.
      (3) Upon issuance of the decision, any party to the hearing may file exceptions within 20 days pursuant to Subpart C. If exceptions are filed, the administrative law judge shall forward the decision, exceptions and record to the Assistant Secretary for the final decision on the application.
      (4) The Assistant Secretary shall review the record, the decision by the administrative law judge, and the exceptions. Based on this, the Assistant Secretary shall issue the final decision (including reasons) of the Department of Labor stating whether the applicant has demonstrated by a preponderance of evidence that it meets the requirements for recognition.
   c. Publication. A notification of the final decision shall be published in the Federal Register.

C. Terms and Conditions of Recognition, Renewal and Revocation

1. The following terms and conditions shall be part of every recognition:
   a. The recognition of any validation organization will be evidenced by a letter of recognition from OSHA. The letter will provide the specific details of the scope of the OSHA recognition as well as any conditions imposed by OSHA, including any Federal monitoring requirements.
   b. The recognition of each validation organization will be valid for five years, unless terminated before or renewed after the expiration of the period. The dates of the period of recognition will be stated in the recognition letter.

c. The recognized validation organization shall continue to satisfy all the requirements of this Appendix and the letter of recognition during the period of recognition.

2. A recognized validation organization may change a test method of the PSDI safety system certification/validation program by notifying the Assistant Secretary of the change, certifying that the revised method will be at least as effective as the prior method, and providing the supporting data upon which its conclusions are based.

3. A recognized validation organization may renew its recognition by filing a renewal request at the address in paragraph I.A.3. of this Appendix, above, not less than 180 calendar days, nor more than one year, before the expiration date of its current recognition. When a recognized validation organization has filed such a renewal request, its current recognition will not expire until a final decision has been made on the request. The renewal request will be processed in accordance with subsection I.B. of this Appendix, above, except that a reinspection is not required but may be performed by OSHA. A hearing will be granted to an objecting member of the public if evidence of failure to meet the requirements of this Appendix is supplied to OSHA.

4. A recognized validation organization may apply to OSHA for an expansion of its current recognition to cover other categories of PSDI certification/validation in addition to those included in the current recognition. The application for expansion will be acted upon and processed by OSHA in accordance with subsection I.B. of this Appendix, subject to the possible reinspection exception. If the validation organization has been recognized for more than one year, meets the requirements for expansion of recognition, and there is no evidence that the recognized validation organization has not been following the requirements of this Appendix and the letter of recognition, an expansion will normally be granted. A hearing will be granted to an objecting member of the public only if evidence of failure to meet the requirements of this Appendix is supplied to OSHA.

5. A recognized validation organization may voluntarily terminate its recognition, either in its entirety or with respect to any area covered in its recognition, by giving written notice to OSHA at any time. The written notice shall indicate the termination date. A validation organization may not terminate its installation certification and recertification validation functions earlier than either one year from the date of the written notice, or the date on which another recognized validation organization is able to perform the validation of installation certification and recertification.

6. a. OSHA may revoke its recognition of a validation organization if its program either has failed to continue to satisfy the requirements of this Appendix or its letter of recognition, has not been performing the validation functions required by the PSDI Standard and Appendix A, or has misrepresented itself in its applications. Before proposing to revoke recognition, the Agency will notify the recognized validation organization of the basis of the proposed revocation and will allow rebuttal or correction of the alleged deficiencies. If the deficiencies are not corrected, OSHA may revoke recognition, effective in 60 days, unless the validation organization requests a hearing within that time.

b. If a hearing is requested, it shall be held before an administrative law judge of the Department of Labor pursuant to the rules specified in 29 CFR part 1905, Subpart C.

c. The parties shall be OSHA and the recognized validation organization. The decision shall be made pursuant to the procedures specified in paragraphs I.B.8.b.(2) through (4) of this Appendix except that the burden of proof shall be on OSHA to demonstrate by a preponderance of the evidence that the recognition should be revoked because the validation organization either is not meeting the requirements for recognition, has not been performing the validation functions required by the PSDI Standard and Appendix A, or has misrepresented itself in its applications.

D. Provisions of OSHA Recognition

Each recognized third-party validation organization and its validating laboratories shall:

1. Allow OSHA to conduct unscheduled reviews or on-site audits of it or the validating laboratories on matters relevant to PSDI, and cooperate in the conduct of these reviews and audits;
2. Agree to terms and conditions established by OSHA in the grant of recognition on matters such as exchange of data, submission of accident reports, and assistance in studies for improving PSDI or the certification/validation process.

II. Qualifications

The third-party validation organization, the validating laboratory, and the employees of each shall meet the requirements set forth in this section of this Appendix.

A. Experience of Validation Organization

1. The third-party validation organization shall have legal authority to perform certification/validation activities.
2. The validation organization shall demonstrate competence and experience in either power press design, manufacture or use, or testing, quality control or certification/validation of equipment comparable to power presses and associated control systems.
3. The validation organization shall demonstrate a capability for selecting, reviewing, and/or validating appropriate standards and test methods to be used for validating the certification of PSDI safety systems, as well as for reviewing judgements on the safety of PSDI safety systems and their conformance with the requirements of this section.
4. The validating organization may utilize the competence, experience, and capability of its employees to demonstrate this competence, experience and capability.

B. Independence of Validation Organization

1. The validation organization shall demonstrate that:
   a. It is financially capable to conduct the work;
   b. It is free of direct influence or control by manufacturers, suppliers, vendors, representatives of employers and employees, and employer or employee organizations; and
   c. Its employees are secure from discharge resulting from pressures from manufacturers, suppliers, vendors, employers or employee representatives.
2. A validation organization may be considered independent even if it has ties with manufacturers, employers or employee representatives if these ties are with at least two of these three groups; it has a board of directors (or equivalent leadership responsible for the certification/validation activities) which includes representatives of the three groups; and it has a binding commitment of funding for a period of three years or more.

C. Validating Laboratory

The validation organization's laboratory (which organizationally may be a part of the third-party validation organization):

1. Shall have legal authority to perform the validation of certification;
2. Shall be free of operational control and influence of manufacturers, suppliers, vendors, employers, or employee representatives that would impair its integrity of performance; and
3. Shall not engage in the design, manufacture, sale, promotion, or use of the certified equipment.

D. Facilities and Equipment

The validation organization's validating laboratory shall have available all testing facilities and necessary test and inspection equipment relevant to the validation of the certification of PSDI safety systems, installations and operations.

E. Personnel

The validation organization and the validating laboratory shall be adequately staffed by personnel who are qualified by technical training and/or experience to conduct the validation of the certification of PSDI safety systems.

1. The validation organization shall assign overall responsibility for the validation of PSDI certification to an Administrative Director. Minimum requirements for this position are a Bachelor's degree and five years professional experience, at least one of which shall have been in responsible charge of a function in the areas of power press design or manufacture or a broad range of power press use, or in the areas of testing, quality control, or certification/validation of equipment comparable to power presses or their associated control systems.
2. The validating laboratory, if a separate organization from the validation organization, shall assign technical responsibility for the validation of PSDI certification to a Technical Director. Minimum requirements for this position are a Bachelor's degree in a technical field and five years of professional experience, at least one of which shall have been in responsible charge of a function in the area of testing, quality control or certification/validation of equipment comparable to power presses or their associated control systems.
3. If the validation organization and the validating laboratory are the same organization, the administrative and technical responsibilities may be combined in a single position, with minimum requirements as described in E.1. and 2. for the combined position.
4. The validation organization and validating laboratory shall have adequate administrative and technical staffs to conduct the validation of the certification of PSDI safety systems.

F. Certification/Validation Mark or Logo

1. The validation organization or the validating laboratory shall own a registered certification/validation mark or logo.

2. The mark or logo shall be suitable for incorporation into the label required by paragraph (h)(11)(iii) of this section.

III. Program Requirements

A. Test and Certification/Validation Procedures

1. The validation organization and/or validating laboratory shall have established written procedures for test and certification/validation of PSDI safety systems. The procedures shall be based on pertinent OSHA standards and test methods, or other publicly available standards and test methods generally recognized as appropriate in the field, such as national consensus standards or published standards of professional societies or trade associations.
2. The written procedures for test and certification/validation of PSDI systems, and the standards and test methods on which they are based, shall be reproducible and be available to OSHA and to the public upon request.

B. Test Reports

1. A test report shall be prepared for each PSDI safety system that is tested. The test report shall be signed by a technical staff representative and the Technical Director.
2. The test report shall include the following:
   a. Name of manufacturer and catalog or model number of each subsystem or major component;
   b. Identification and description of test methods or procedures used; (This may be through reference to published sources which describe the test methods or procedures used.)
   c. Results of all tests performed;
   d. All safety distance calculations.
3. A copy of the test report shall be maintained on file at the validation organization and/or validating laboratory, and shall be available to OSHA upon request.

C. Certification/Validation Reports

1. A certification/validation report shall be prepared for each PSDI safety system for which the certification is validated. The certification/validation report shall be signed by the Administrative Director and the Technical Director.
2. The certification/validation report shall include the following:
   a. Name of manufacturer and catalog or model number of each subsystem or major component;
   b. Results of all tests which serve as the basis for the certification;
   c. All safety distance calculations;
   d. Statement that the safety system conforms with all requirements of the PSDI Standard and Appendix A.
3. A copy of the certification/validation report shall be maintained on file at the validation organization and/or validating laboratory, and shall be available to the public upon request.
4. A copy of the certification/validation report shall be submitted to OSHA within 30 days of its completion.

D. Publications System

The validation organization shall make available upon request a list of PSDI safety systems which have been certified/validated by the program.

E. Follow-up Activities

1. The validation organization or validating laboratory shall have a follow-up system for inspecting or testing manufacturer's production of design certified/validated PSDI safety system components and subassemblies where deemed appropriate by the validation organization.
2. The validation organization shall notify the appropriate product manufacturer(s) of any reports from employers of point of operation injuries which occur while a press is operated in a PSDI mode.

F. Records

The validation organization or validating laboratory shall maintain a record of each certification/validation of a PSDI safety system, including manufacturer and/or employer certification documentation, test and working data, test report, certification/validation report, any follow-up inspections or testing, and reports of equipment failures, any reports of accidents involving the equipment, and any other pertinent information. These records shall be available for inspection by OSHA and OSHA State Plan offices.

G. Dispute Resolution Procedures

1. The validation organization shall have a reasonable written procedure for acknowledging and processing appeals or complaints from program participants (manufacturers, producers, suppliers, vendors and employers) as well as other interested parties (employees or their representatives, safety personnel, government agencies, etc.), concerning certification or validation.
2. The validation organization may charge any complainant the reasonable charge for repeating tests needed for the resolution of disputes.

§1910.217 Appendix D Nonmandatory supplementary information

This Appendix provides nonmandatory supplementary information and guidelines to assist in the understanding and use of 29 CFR §1910.217(h) to allow presence sensing device initiation (PSDI) of mechanical power presses. Although this Appendix as such is not mandatory, it references sections and requirements which are made mandatory by other parts of the PSDI Standard and Appendices.

1. General

OSHA intends that PSDI continue to be prohibited where present state-of-the-art technology will not allow it to be done safely. Only part revolution type mechanical power presses are approved for PSDI. Similarly, only presses with a configuration such that a person's body cannot completely enter the bed area are approved for PSDI.

2. Brake and Clutch

Flexible steel band brakes do not possess a long-term reliability against structural failure as compared to other types of brakes, and therefore are not acceptable on presses used in the PSDI mode of operation.

Fast and consistent stopping times are important to safety for the PSDI mode of operation. Consistency of braking action is enhanced by high brake torque. The requirement in paragraph (h)(2)(ii) defines a high torque capability which should ensure fast and consistent stopping times.

Brake design parameters important to PSDI are high torque, low moment of inertia, low air volume (if pneumatic) mechanisms, non-interleaving engagement springs, and structural integrity which is enhanced by over-design. The requirement in paragrapah (h)(2)(iii) reduces the possibility of significantly increased stopping time if a spring breaks.

As an added precaution to the requirements in paragraph (h)(2)(iii), brake adjustment locking means should be secured. Where brake springs are externally accessible, lock nuts or other means may be provided to reduce the possibility of backing off of the compression nut which holds the springs in place.

3. Pneumatic Systems

Elevated clutch/brake air pressure results in longer stopping time. The requirement in paragraph (h)(3)(i)(C) is intended to prevent degradation in stopping speed from higher air pressure. Higher pressures may be permitted, however, to increase clutch torque to free "jammed" dies, provided positive measures are provided to prevent the higher pressure at other times.

4. Flywheels and Bearings

Lubrication of bearings is considered the single greatest deterrent to their failure. The manufacturer's recommended procedures for maintenance and inspection should be closely followed.

5. Brake Monitoring

The approval of brake monitor adjustments, as required in paragraph (h)(5)(ii), is not considered a recertification, and does not necessarily involve an on-site inspection by a representative of the validation organization. It is expected that the brake monitor adjustment normally could be evaluated on the basis of the effect on the safety system certification/validation documentation retained by the validation organization.

Use of a brake monitor does not eliminate the need for periodic brake inspection and maintenance to reduce the possibility of catastrophic failures.

6. Cycle Control and Control Systems

The PSDI set-up/reset means required by paragraph (h)(6)(iv) may be initiated by the actuation of a special momentary pushbutton or by the actuation of a special momentary pushbutton and the initiation of a first stroke with two hand controls.

It would normally be preferable to limit the adjustment of the time required in paragraph (h)(6)(vi) to a maximum of 15 seconds. However, where an operator must do many operations outside the press, such as lubricating, trimming, deburring, etc., a longer interval up to 30 seconds is permitted.

When a press is equipped for PSDI operation, it is recommended that the presence sensing device be active as a guarding device in other production modes. This should enhance the reliability of the device and ensure that it remains operable.

An acceptable method for interlocking supplemental guards as required by paragraph (h)(6)(xiii) would be to incorporate the supplemental guard and the PSDI presence sensing device into a hinged arrangement in which the alignment of the presence sensing device serves, in effect, as the interlock. If the supplemental guards are moved, the presence sensing device would become misaligned and the press control would be deactivated. No extra microswitches or interlocking sensors would be required.

Paragraph (h)(6)(xv) of the standard requires that the control system have provisions for an "inch" operating means; that die-setting not be done in the PSDI mode; and that production not be done in the "inch" mode. It should be noted that the sensing device would be by-passed in the "inch" mode. For that reason, the prohibitions against die-setting in the PSDI mode, and against production in the "inch" mode are cited to emphasize that "inch" operation is of reduced safety and is not compatible with PSDI or other production modes.

7. Environmental Requirements

It is the intent of paragraph (h)(7) that control components be provided with inherent design protection against operating stresses and environmental factors affecting safety and reliability.

8. Safety system

The safety system provision continues the concept of paragraph (b)(13) that the probability of two independent failures in the length of time required to make one press cycle is so remote as to be a negligible risk factor in the total array of equipment and human factors. The emphasis is on an integrated total system including all elements affecting point of operation safety.

It should be noted that this does not require redundancy for press components such as structural elements, clutch/brake mechanisms, plates, etc., for which adequate reliability may be achieved by proper design, maintenance, and inspection.

9. Safeguarding the Point of Operation

The intent of paragraph (h)(9)(iii) is to prohibit use of mirrors to "bend" a single light curtain sensing field around corners to cover more than one side of a press. This prohibition is needed to increase the reliability of the presence sensing device in initiating a stroke only when the desired work motion has been completed.

Object sensitivity describes the capability of a presence sensing device to detect an object in the sensing field, expressed as the linear measurement of the smallest interruption which can be detected at any point in the field. Minimum object sensitivity describes the largest acceptable size of the interruption in the sensing field. A minimum object sensitivity of one and one-fourth inches (31.75 mm) means that a one and one-fourth inch (31.75 mm) diameter object will be continuously detected at all locations in the sensing field.

In deriving the safety distance required in paragraph (h)(9)(v), all stopping time measurements should be made with clutch/brake air pressure regulated to the press manufacturer's recommended value for full clutch torque capability. The stopping time measurements should be made with the heaviest upper die that is planned for use in the press. If the press has a slide counterbalance system, it is important that the counterbalance be adjusted correctly for upper die weight according to the manufacturer's instructions. While the brake monitor setting is based on the stopping time it actually measures, i.e., the normal stopping time at the top of the stroke, it is important that the safety distance be computed from the longest stopping time measured at any of the indicated three downstroke stopping positions listed in the explanation of Ts. The use in the formula of twice the stopping time increase, Tm, allowed by the brake monitor for brake wear allows for greater increases in the downstroke stopping time than occur in normal stopping time at the top of the stroke.

10. Inspection and Maintenance [Reserved]

11. Safety System Certification/Validation

Mandatory requirements for certification/validation of the PSDI safety system are provided in Appendix A and Appendix C to this standard. Nonmandatory supplementary information and guidelines relating to certification/validation of the PSDI safety system are provided to Appendix B to this standard.

[39 FR 32502, June 27, 1974, as amended at 39 FR 41846, Dec. 23, 1974; 40 FR 3982, Jan. 27, 1975; 43 FR 49750, Oct. 24, 1978; 45 FR 8594, Feb. 8, 1980; 49 FR 18295, Apr. 30, 1984; 51 FR 34561, Sept. 29, 1986; 53 FR 8353, 8358 Mar. 14, 1988; 54 FR 24333, June 7, 1989; 61 FR 9240, Mar. 7, 1996; 69 FR 31882, June 8, 2004]

§1910.218 [OI]
Forging machines

(a) General requirements

(a)(1) Use of lead The safety requirements of this subparagraph apply to lead casts or other use of lead in the forge shop or die shop.

(a)(1)(i) Thermostatic control of heating elements shall be provided to maintain proper melting temperature and prevent overheating.

(a)(1)(ii) Fixed or permanent lead pot installations shall be exhausted.

(a)(1)(iii) Portable units shall be used only in areas where good, general room ventilation is provided.

(a)(1)(iv) Personal protective equipment (gloves, goggles, aprons, and other items) shall be worn.

(a)(1)(v) A covered container shall be provided to store dross skimmings.

(a)(1)(vi) Equipment shall be kept clean, particularly from accumulations of yellow lead oxide.

(a)(2) Inspection and maintenance It shall be the responsibility of the employer to maintain all forge shop equipment in a condition which will insure continued safe operation. This responsibility includes:

(a)(2)(i) Establishing periodic and regular maintenance safety checks and keeping certification records of these inspections which include the date of inspection, the signature of the person who performed the inspection and the serial number, or other identifier, for the forging machine which was inspected.

(a)(2)(ii) Scheduling and recording the inspection of guards and point of operation protection devices at frequent and regular intervals. Recording of inspections shall be in the form of a certification record which includes the date the inspection was performed, the signature of the person who performed the inspection and the serial number, or other identifier, of the equipment inspected.

(a)(2)(iii) Training personnel for the proper inspection and maintenance of forging machinery and equipment.

(a)(2)(iv) All overhead parts shall be fastened or protected in such a manner that they will not fly off or fall in event of failure.

(a)(3) Hammers and presses

(a)(3)(i) All hammers shall be positioned or installed in such a manner that they remain on or are anchored to foundations sufficient to support them according to applicable engineering standards.

(a)(3)(ii) All presses shall be installed in such a manner that they remain where they are positioned or they are anchored to foundations sufficient to support them according to applicable engineering standards.

Table O–11
Strength and Dimensions for Wood Ram Props

Size of timber, inches[1]	Square inches in cross section	Minimum allowable crushing strength parallel to grain, p.s.i.[2]	Maximum static load within short column range[3]	Safety factor	Maximum recommended weight of forging hammer for timber used	Maximum allowable length of timber, inches
4x4	16	5,000	80,000	10	8,000	44
6x6	36	5,000	180,000	10	18,000	66
8x8	64	5,000	320,000	10	32,000	88
10x10	100	5,000	500,000	10	50,000	100
12x12	144	5,000	720,000	10	72,000	132

[1] Actual dimension.

[2] Adapted from U.S. Department of Agriculture Technical Bulletin 479. Hardwoods recommended are those whose ultimate crushing strengths in compression parallel to grain are 5,000 p.s.i. (pounds per square inch) or greater.

[3] Slenderness ratio formula for short columns is L/d = 11, where L = length of timber in inches and d = least dimension in inches; this ratio should not exceed 11.

(a)(3)(iii) Means shall be provided for disconnecting the power to the machine and for locking out or rendering cycling controls inoperable.

(a)(3)(iv) The ram shall be blocked when dies are being changed or other work is being done on the hammer. Blocks or wedges shall be made of material the strength and construction of which should meet or exceed the specifications and dimensions shown in Table O–11.

(a)(3)(v) Tongs shall be of sufficient length to clear the body of the worker in case of kickback, and shall not have sharp handle ends.

(a)(3)(vi) Oil swabs, or scale removers, or other devices to remove scale shall be provided. These devices shall be long enough to enable a man to reach the full length of the die without placing his hand or arm between the dies.

(a)(3)(vii) Material handling equipment shall be of adequate strength, size, and dimension to handle diesetting operations safely.

(a)(3)(viii) A scale guard of substantial construction shall be provided at the back of every hammer, so arranged as to stop flying scale.

(a)(3)(ix) A scale guard of substantial construction shall be provided at the back of every press, so arranged as to stop flying scale.

(b) **Hammers, general**

(b)(1) **Keys** Die keys and shims shall be made from a grade of material that will not unduly crack or splinter.

(b)(2) **Foot operated devices** All foot operated devices (i.e., treadles, pedals, bars, valves, and switches) shall be substantially and effectively protected from unintended operation.

(c) **Presses** All manually operated valves and switches shall be clearly identified and readily accessible.

(d) **Power-driven hammers**

(d)(1) **Safety cylinder head** Every steam or airhammer shall have a safety cylinder head to act as a cushion if the rod should break or pullout of the ram.

(d)(2) **Shutoff valve** Steam hammers shall be provided with a quick closing emergency valve in the admission pipeline at a convenient location. This valve shall be closed and locked in the off position while the hammer is being adjusted, repaired, or serviced, or when the dies are being changed.

(d)(3) **Cylinder draining** Steam hammers shall be provided with a means of cylinder draining, such as a self-draining arrangement or a quick-acting drain cock.

(d)(4) **Pressure pipes** Steam or air piping shall conform to the specifications of American National Standard ANSI B31.1.0–1967, Power Piping with Addenda issued before April 28, 1971, which is incorporated by reference as specified in §1910.6.

(e) **Gravity hammers**

(e)(1) **Air-lift hammers**

(e)(1)(i) Air-lift hammers shall have a safety cylinder head as required in paragraph (d)(1) of this section.

(e)(1)(ii) Air-lift hammers shall have an air shutoff valve as required in paragraph (d)(2) of this section.

(e)(1)(iii) Air-lift hammers shall be provided with two drain cocks: one on main head cylinder, and one on clamp cylinder.

(e)(1)(iv) Air piping shall conform to the specifications of the ANSI B31.1.0–1967, Power Piping with Addenda issued before April 28, 1971, which is incorporated by reference as specified in §1910.6.

(e)(2) **Board drophammers**

(e)(2)(i) A suitable enclosure shall be provided to prevent damaged or detached boards from falling. The board enclosure shall be securely fastened to the hammer.

(e)(2)(ii) All major assemblies and fittings which can loosen and fall shall be properly secured in place.

(f) **Forging presses**

(f)(1) **Mechanical forging presses** When dies are being changed or maintenance is being performed on the press, the following shall be accomplished:

(f)(1)(i) The power to the press shall be locked out.

(f)(1)(ii) The flywheel shall be at rest.

(f)(1)(iii) The ram shall be blocked with a material the strength of which shall meet or exceed the specifications or dimensions shown in Table O–11.

(f)(2) **Hydraulic forging presses** When dies are being changed or maintenance is being performed on the press, the following shall be accomplished:

(f)(2)(i) The hydraulic pumps and power apparatus shall be locked out.

(f)(2)(ii) The ram shall be blocked with a material the strength of which shall meet or exceed the specifications or dimensions shown in Table O–11.

(g) **Trimming presses**

(g)(1) **Hot trimming presses** The requirements of paragraph (f)(1) of this section shall also apply to hot trimming presses.

(g)(2) **Cold trimming presses** Cold trimming presses shall be safeguarded in accordance with §1910.217(c).

(h) **Upsetters**

(h)(1) **General requirements** All upsetters shall be installed so that they remain on their supporting foundations.

(h)(2) **Lockouts** Upsetters shall be provided with a means for locking out the power at its entry point to the machine and rendering its cycling controls inoperable.

(h)(3) **Manually operated controls** All manually operated valves and switches shall be clearly identified and readily accessible.

(h)(4) **Tongs** Tongs shall be of sufficient length to clear the body of the worker in case of kickback, and shall not have sharp handle ends.

(h)(5) **Changing dies** When dies are being changed, maintenance performed, or any work done on the machine, the power to the upsetter shall be locked out, and the flywheel shall be at rest.

(i) **Other forging equipment**

(i)(1) **Boltheading** The provisions of paragraph (h) of this section shall apply to boltheading.

(i)(2) **Rivet making** The provisions of paragraph (h) of this section shall apply to rivet making.

(j) **Other forge facility equipment**

(j)(1) **Billet shears** A positive-type lockout device for disconnecting the power to the shear shall be provided.

(j)(2) **Saws** Every saw shall be provided with a guard of not less than one-eighth inch sheet metal positioned to stop flying sparks.

(j)(3) **Conveyors** Conveyor power transmission equipment shall be guarded in accordance with ANSI B20.1–1957, Safety Code for Conveyors, Cableways, and Related Equipment, which is incorporated by reference as specified in §1910.6.

(j)(4) **Shot blast** The cleaning chamber shall have doors or guards to protect operators.

(j)(5) **Grinding** Personal protective equipment shall be used in grinding operations, and equipment shall be used and maintained in accordance with ANSI B7.1–1970, Safety Code for the Use, Care, and Protection of Abrasive Wheels, which is incorporated by reference as specified in §1910.6, and with §1910.215.

[39 FR 23502, June 27, 1974, as amended at 49 FR 5323, Feb. 10, 1984; 51 FR 34561, Sept. 29, 1986; 61 FR 9240, Mar. 7, 1996]

§1910.219 Mechanical power–transmission apparatus

(a) **General requirements**

(a)(1) This section covers all types and shapes of power-transmission belts, except the following when operating at two hundred and fifty (250) feet per minute or less:

(a)(1)(i) Flat belts one (1) inch or less in width,

(a)(1)(ii) flat belts two (2) inches or less in width which are free from metal lacings or fasteners,

(a)(1)(iii) round belts one-half (½) inch or less in diameter; and

(a)(1)(iv) single strand V-belts, the width of which is thirteen thirty-seconds (13/32) inch or less.

(a)(2) Vertical and inclined belts (paragraphs (e)(3) and (4) of this section) if not more than two and one-half (2½) inches wide and running at a speed of less than one thousand (1,000) feet per minute, and if free from metal lacings or fastenings may be guarded with a nip-point belt and pulley guard.

(a)(3) For the Textile Industry, because of the presence of excessive deposits of lint, which constitute a serious fire hazard, the sides and face sections only of nip-point belt and pulley guards are required, provided the guard shall extend at least six (6) inches beyond the rim of the pulley on the in-running and off-running sides of the belt and at least two (2) inches away from the rim and face of the pulley in all other directions.

(a)(4) This section covers the principal features with which power transmission safeguards shall comply.

(b) **Prime-mover guards**

(b)(1) **Flywheels** Flywheels located so that any part is seven (7) feet or less above floor or platform shall be guarded in accordance with the requirements of this subparagraph:

(b)(1)(i) With an enclosure of sheet, perforated, or expanded metal, or woven wire;

(b)(1)(ii) With guard rails placed not less than fifteen (15) inches nor more than twenty (20) inches from rim. When flywheel extends into pit or is within 12 inches of floor, a standard toeboard shall also be provided;

(b)(1)(iii) When the upper rim of flywheel protrudes through a working floor, it shall be entirely enclosed or surrounded by a guardrail and toeboard.

(b)(1)(iv) For flywheels with smooth rims five (5) feet or less in diameter, where the preceding methods cannot be applied, the following may be used: A disk attached to the flywheel in such manner as to cover the spokes of the wheel on the exposed side and present a smooth surface and edge, at the same time providing means for periodic inspection. An open space, not exceeding four (4) inches in width, may be left between the outside edge of the disk and the rim of the wheel if desired, to facilitate turning the wheel over. Where a disk is used, the keys or other dangerous projections not covered by disk shall be cut off or covered. This subdivision does not apply to flywheels with solid web centers.

(b)(1)(v) Adjustable guard to be used for starting engine or for running adjustment may be provided at the flywheel of gas or oil engines. A slot opening for jack bar will be permitted.

(b)(1)(vi) Wherever flywheels are above working areas, guards shall be installed having sufficient strength to hold the weight of the flywheel in the event of a shaft or wheel mounting failure.

(b)(2) **Cranks and connecting rods** Cranks and connecting rods, when exposed to contact, shall be guarded in accordance with paragraphs (m) and (n) of this section, or by a guardrail as described in paragraph (o)(5) of this section.

(b)(3) **Tail rods or extension piston rods** Tail rods or extension piston rods shall be guarded in accordance with paragraphs (m) and (o) of this section, or by a guardrail on sides and end, with a clearance of not less than fifteen (15) nor more than twenty (20) inches when rod is fully extended.

(c) **Shafting**

(c)(1) **Installation**

(c)(1)(i) Each continuous line of shafting shall be secured in position against excessive endwise movement.

(c)(1)(ii) Inclined and vertical shafts, particularly inclined idler shafts, shall be securely held in position against endwise thrust.

(c)(2) **Guarding horizontal shafting**

(c)(2)(i) [OI] All exposed parts of horizontal shafting seven (7) feet or less from floor or working platform, excepting runways used exclusively for oiling, or running adjustments, shall be protected by a stationary casing enclosing shafting completely or by a trough enclosing sides and top or sides and bottom of shafting as location requires.

(c)(2)(ii) Shafting under bench machines shall be enclosed by a stationary casing, or by a trough at sides and top or sides and bottom, as location requires. The sides of the trough shall come within at least six (6) inches of the underside of table, or if shafting is located near floor within six (6) inches of floor. In every case the sides of trough shall extend at least two (2) inches beyond the shafting or protuberance.

(c)(3) Guarding vertical and inclined shafting. Vertical and inclined shafting seven (7) feet or less from floor or working platform, excepting maintenance runways, shall be enclosed with a stationary casing in accordance with requirements of paragraphs (m) and (o) of this section.

(c)(4) **Projecting shaft ends**

(c)(4)(i) Projecting shaft ends shall present a smooth edge and end and shall not project more than one-half the diameter of the shaft unless guarded by nonrotating caps or safety sleeves.

(c)(4)(ii) Unused keyways shall be filled up or covered.

(c)(5) [OI] **Power-transmission apparatus located in basements** All mechanical power transmission apparatus located in basements, towers, and rooms used exclusively for power transmission equipment shall be guarded in accordance with this section, except that the requirements for safeguarding belts, pulleys, and shafting need not be complied with when the following requirements are met:

(c)(5)(i) The basement, tower, or room occupied by transmission equipment is locked against unauthorized entrance.

(c)(5)(ii) The vertical clearance in passageways between the floor and power transmission beams, ceiling, or any other objects, is not less than five feet six inches (5 ft. 6 in.).

(c)(5)(iii) The intensity of illumination conforms to the requirements of ANSI A11.1–1965 (R–1970), which is incorporated by reference as specified in §1910.6.

(c)(5)(iv) [Reserved]

(c)(5)(v) The route followed by the oiler is protected in such manner as to prevent accident.

(d) **Pulleys**

(d)(1) [OI] **Guarding** Pulleys, any parts of which are seven (7) feet or less from the floor or working platform, shall be guarded in accordance with the standards specified in paragraphs (m) and (o) of this section. Pulleys serving as balance wheels (e.g., punch presses) on which the point of contact between belt and pulley is more than six feet six inches (6 ft. 6 in.) from the floor or platform may be guarded with a disk covering the spokes.

(d)(2) **Location of pulleys**

(d)(2)(i) Unless the distance to the nearest fixed pulley, clutch, or hanger exceeds the width of the belt used, a guide shall be provided to prevent the belt from leaving the pulley on the side where insufficient clearance exists.

(d)(2)(ii) **[Reserved]**

(d)(3) **Broken pulleys** Pulleys with cracks, or pieces broken out of rims, shall not be used.

(d)(4) **Pulley speeds** Pulleys intended to operate at rim speed in excess of manufacturers normal recommendations shall be specially designed and carefully balanced for the speed at which they are to operate.

(e) **Belt, rope, and chain drives**

(e)(1) **Horizontal belts and ropes**

(e)(1)(i) Where both runs of horizontal belts are seven (7) feet or less from the floor level, the guard shall extend to at least fifteen (15) inches above the belt or to a standard height except that where both runs of a horizontal belt are 42 inches or less from the floor, the belt shall be fully enclosed in accordance with paragraphs (m) and (o) of this section.

(e)(1)(ii) In powerplants or power-development rooms, a guardrail may be used in lieu of the guard required by subdivision (i) of this subparagraph.

(e)(2) **Overhead horizontal belts**

(e)(2)(i) Overhead horizontal belts, with lower parts seven (7) feet or less from the floor or platform, shall be guarded on sides and bottom in accordance with paragraph (o)(3) of this section.

(e)(2)(ii) Horizontal overhead belts more than seven (7) feet above floor or platform shall be guarded for their entire length under the following conditions:

(e)(2)(ii)(A) If located over passageways or work places and traveling 1,800 feet or more per minute.

(e)(2)(ii)(B) If center to center distance between pulleys is ten (10) feet or more.

(e)(2)(ii)(C) If belt is eight (8) inches or more in width.

(e)(2)(iii) Where the upper and lower runs of horizontal belts are so located that passage of persons between them would be possible, the passage shall be either:

(e)(2)(iii)(A) Completely barred by a guardrail or other barrier in accordance with paragraphs (m) and (o) of this section; or

(e)(2)(iii)(B) Where passage is regarded as necessary, there shall be a platform over the lower run guarded on either side by a railing completely filled in with wire mesh or other filler, or by a solid barrier. The upper run shall be so guarded as to prevent contact therewith either by the worker or by objects carried by him. In powerplants only the lower run of the belt need be guarded.

(e)(2)(iv) Overhead chain and link belt drives are governed by the same rules as overhead horizontal belts and shall be guarded in the same manner as belts.

(e)(3) **Vertical and inclined belts**

(e)(3)(i) Vertical and inclined belts shall be enclosed by a guard conforming to standards in paragraphs (m) and (o) of this section.

(e)(3)(ii) All guards for inclined belts shall be arranged in such a manner that a minimum clearance of seven (7) feet is maintained between belt and floor at any point outside of guard.

(e)(4) **Vertical belts** Vertical belts running over a lower pulley more than seven (7) feet above floor or platform shall be guarded at the bottom in the same manner as horizontal overhead belts, if conditions are as stated in paragraphs (e)(2)(ii)(A) and (C) of this Section.

(e)(5) Cone-pulley belts

(e)(5)(i) The cone belt and pulley shall be equipped with a belt shifter so constructed as to adequately guard the nip point of the belt and pulley. If the frame of the belt shifter does not adequately guard the nip point of the belt and pulley, the nip point shall be further protected by means of a vertical guard placed in front of the pulley and extending at least to the top of the largest step of the cone.

(e)(5)(ii) If the belt is of the endless type or laced with rawhide laces, and a belt shifter is not desired, the belt will be considered guarded if the nip point of the belt and pulley is protected by a nip point guard located in front of the cone extending at least to the top of the largest step of the cone, and formed to show the contour of the cone in order to give the nip point of the belt and pulley the maximum protection.

(e)(5)(iii) If the cone is located less than 3 feet from the floor or working platform, the cone pulley and belt shall be guarded to a height of 3 feet regardless of whether the belt is endless or laced with rawhide.

(e)(6) Belt tighteners

(e)(6)(i) Suspended counterbalanced tighteners and all parts thereof shall be of substantial construction and securely fastened; the bearings shall be securely capped. Means must be provided to prevent tightener from falling, in case the belt breaks.

(e)(6)(ii) Where suspended counterweights are used and not guarded by location, they shall be so encased as to prevent accident.

(f) Gears, sprockets, and chains

(f)(1) **Gears** Gears shall be guarded in accordance with one of the following methods:

(f)(1)(i) By a complete enclosure; or

(f)(1)(ii) By a standard guard as described in paragraph (o) of this section, at least seven (7) feet high extending six (6) inches above the mesh point of the gears; or

(f)(1)(iii) By a band guard covering the face of gear and having flanges extended inward beyond the root of the teeth on the exposed side or sides. Where any portion of the train of gears guarded by a band guard is less than six (6) feet from the floor a disk guard or a complete enclosure to the height of six (6) feet shall be required.

(f)(2) **Hand-operated gears** Paragraph (f)(1) of this section does not apply to hand-operated gears used only to adjust machine parts and which do not continue to move after hand power is removed. However, the guarding of these gears is highly recommended.

(f)(3) **Sprockets and chains** All sprocket wheels and chains shall be enclosed unless they are more than seven (7) feet above the floor or platform. Where the drive extends over other machine or working areas, protection against falling shall be provided. This subparagraph does not apply to manually operated sprockets.

(f)(4) **Openings for oiling** When frequent oiling must be done, openings with hinged or sliding self-closing covers shall be provided. All points not readily accessible shall have oil feed tubes if lubricant is to be added while machinery is in motion.

(g) **Guarding friction drives** The driving point of all friction drives when exposed to contact shall be guarded, all arm or spoke friction drives and all web friction drives with holes in the web shall be entirely enclosed, and all projecting belts on friction drives where exposed to contact shall be guarded.

(h) Keys, setscrews, and other projections

(h)(1) All projecting keys, setscrews, and other projections in revolving parts shall be removed or made flush or guarded by metal cover. This subparagraph does not apply to keys or setscrews within gear or sprocket casings or other enclosures, nor to keys, setscrews, or oilcups in hubs of pulleys less than twenty (20) inches in diameter where they are within the plane of the rim of the pulley.

(h)(2) It is recommended, however, that no projecting setscrews or oilcups be used in any revolving pulley or part of machinery.

(i) Collars and couplings

(i)(1) **Collars** All revolving collars, including split collars, shall be cylindrical, and screws or bolts used in collars shall not project beyond the largest periphery of the collar.

(i)(2) [OI] **Couplings** Shaft couplings shall be so constructed as to present no hazard from bolts, nuts, setscrews, or revolving surfaces. Bolts, nuts, and setscrews will, however, be permitted where they are covered with safety sleeves or where they are used parallel with the shafting and are countersunk or else do not extend beyond the flange of the coupling.

(j) **Bearings and facilities for oiling** All drip cups and pans shall be securely fastened.

(k) Guarding of clutches, cutoff couplings, and clutch pulleys

(k)(1) **Guards** Clutches, cutoff couplings, or clutch pulleys having projecting parts, where such clutches are located seven (7) feet or less above the floor or working platform, shall be enclosed by a stationary guard constructed in accordance with this section. A "U" type guard is permissible.

(k)(2) **Engine rooms** In engine rooms a guardrail, preferably with toeboard, may be used instead of the guard required by paragraph (k)(1) of this section, provided such a room is occupied only by engine room attendants.

(l) Belt shifters, clutches, shippers, poles, perches, and fasteners

(l)(1) Belt shifters

(l)(1)(i) Tight and loose pulleys on all new installations made on or after August 31, 1971, shall be equipped with a permanent belt shifter provided with mechanical means to prevent belt from creeping from loose to tight pulley. It is recommended that old installations be changed to conform to this rule.

(l)(1)(ii) Belt shifter and clutch handles shall be rounded and be located as far as possible from danger of accidental contact, but within easy reach of the operator. Where belt shifters are not directly located over a machine or bench, the handles shall be cut off six feet six inches (6 ft. 6 in.) above floor level.

(l)(2) **Belt shippers and shipper poles** The use of belt poles as substitutes for mechanical shifters is not recommended.

(l)(3) **Belt perches** Where loose pulleys or idlers are not practicable, belt perches in form of brackets, rollers, etc., shall be used to keep idle belts away from the shafts.

(l)(4) **Belt fasteners** Belts which of necessity must be shifted by hand and belts within seven (7) feet of the floor or working platform which are not guarded in accordance with this section shall not be fastened with metal in any case, nor with any other fastening which by construction or wear will constitute an accident hazard.

(m) [OI] Standard guards—general requirements

(m)(1) [OI] Materials

(m)(1)(i) Standard conditions shall be secured by the use of the following materials. Expanded metal, perforated or solid sheet metal, wire mesh on a frame of angle iron, or iron pipe securely fastened to floor or to frame of machine.

(m)(1)(ii) All metal should be free from burrs and sharp edges.

(m)(2) Methods of manufacture

(m)(2)(i) Expanded metal, sheet or perforated metal, and wire mesh shall be securely fastened to frame.

(m)(2)(ii) [Reserved]

(n) [Reserved]

(o) Approved materials

(o)(1) **Minimum requirements** The materials and dimensions specified in this paragraph shall apply to all guards, except horizontal overhead belts, rope, cable, or chain guards more than seven (7) feet above floor, or platform.

(o)(1)(i) [Reserved]

(o)(1)(i)(A) All guards shall be rigidly braced every three (3) feet or fractional part of their height to some fixed part of machinery or building structure. Where guard is exposed to contact with moving equipment additional strength may be necessary.

(o)(1)(i)(B) [Reserved]

(o)(1)(ii) [Reserved]

(o)(2) Wood guards

(o)(2)(i) Wood guards may be used in the woodworking and chemical industries, in industries where the presence of fumes or where manufacturing conditions would cause the rapid deterioration of metal guards; also in construction work and in locations outdoors where extreme cold or extreme heat make metal guards and railings undesirable. In all other industries, wood guards shall not be used.

(o)(2)(ii) [Reserved]

(o)(3) Guards for horizontal overhead belts

(o)(3)(i) Guards for horizontal overhead belts shall run the entire length of the belt and follow the line of the pulley to the ceiling or be carried to the nearest wall, thus enclosing the belt effectively. Where belts are so located as to make it impracticable to carry the guard to wall or ceiling, construction of guard shall be such as to enclose completely the top and bottom runs of belt and the face of pulleys.

(o)(3)(ii) [Reserved]

(o)(3)(iii) Suitable reinforcement shall be provided for the ceiling rafters or overhead floor beams, where such is necessary, to sustain safely the weight and stress likely to be imposed by the guard. The interior surface of all guards, by which is meant the surface of the guard with which a belt will come in contact, shall be smooth and free from all projections of any character, except where construction demands it; protruding shallow roundhead rivets may be used. Overhead belt guards shall be at least one-quarter wider than belt which they protect, except that this clearance need not in any case exceed six (6) inches on each side. Overhead rope drive and block and roller-chain-drive guards shall be not less than six (6) inches wider than the drive on each side. In overhead silent chain-drive guards where the chain is held from lateral displacement on the sprockets, the side clearances required on drives of twenty (20) inch centers or under shall be not less than one-fourth inch from the nearest moving chain part, and on drives of over twenty (20) inch centers a minimum of one-half inch from the nearest moving chain part.

(o)(4) **Guards for horizontal overhead rope and chain drives** Overhead-rope and chain-drive guard construction shall conform to the rules for overhead-belt guard.

(o)(5) **Guardrails and toeboards**

(o)(5)(i) Guardrail shall be forty-two (42) inches in height, with midrail between top rail and floor.

(o)(5)(ii) Posts shall be not more than eight (8) feet apart; they are to be permanent and substantial, smooth, and free from protruding nails, bolts, and splinters. If made of pipe, the post shall be one and one-fourth (1¼) inches inside diameter, or larger. If made of metal shapes or bars, their section shall be equal in strength to that of one and one-half (1½) by one and one-half (1½) by three-sixteenths (3/16) inch angle iron. If made of wood, the posts shall be two by four (2 × 4) inches or larger. The upper rail shall be two by four (2 × 4) inches, or two one by four (1 × 4) strips, one at the top and one at the side of posts. The midrail may be one by four (1 × 4) inches or more. Where panels are fitted with expanded metal or wire mesh the middle rails may be omitted. Where guard is exposed to contact with moving equipment, additional strength may be necessary.

(o)(5)(iii) Toeboards shall be four (4) inches or more in height, of wood, metal, or of metal grill not exceeding one (1) inch mesh.

(p) **Care of equipment**

(p)(1) OI **General** All power-transmission equipment shall be inspected at intervals not exceeding 60 days and be kept in good working condition at all times.

(p)(2) OI **Shafting**

(p)(2)(i) Shafting shall be kept in alignment, free from rust and excess oil or grease.

(p)(2)(ii) Where explosives, explosive dusts, flammable vapors or flammable liquids exist, the hazard of static sparks from shafting shall be carefully considered.

(p)(3) OI **Bearings** Bearings shall be kept in alignment and properly adjusted.

(p)(4) OI **Hangers** Hangers shall be inspected to make certain that all supporting bolts and screws are tight and that supports of hanger boxes are adjusted properly.

(p)(5) OI **Pulleys**

(p)(5)(i) Pulleys shall be kept in proper alignment to prevent belts from running off.

(p)(5)(ii) [Reserved]

(p)(6) OI **Care of belts**

(p)(6)(i) [Reserved]

(p)(6)(ii) Inspection shall be made of belts, lacings, and fasteners and such equipment kept in good repair.

(p)(7) OI **Lubrication** The regular oilers shall wear tight-fitting clothing. Machinery shall be oiled when not in motion, wherever possible.

[39 FR 23502, June 27, 1974, as amended at 43 FR 49750, Oct. 24, 1978; 43 FR 51760; Nov. 7, 1978; 49 FR 5323, Feb. 10, 1984; 61 FR 9240, Mar. 7, 1996; 69 FR 31882, June 8, 2004]

29 CFR PART 1910 Subpart P
Hand and Portable Powered Tools and Other Hand–Held Equipment

Section Contents

Subpart P—Hand and Portable Powered Tools and Other Hand–Held Eqipment

Authority: Sections 4, 6, and 8 of the Occupational Safety and Health Act of 1970 (29 U.S.C. 653, 655, 657); Secretary of Labor's Order No. 12–71 (36 FR 8754), 8–76 (41 FR 25059), 9–83 (48 FR 35736), 1–90 (55 FR 9033), or 5–2007 (72 FR 31159), as applicable; 29 CFR Part §1911.

Section §1910.243 also issued under 29 CFR Part §1910.

§1910.241 Definitions

As used in this Subpart:

(a) **Explosive-actuated fastening tool terms**

(a)(1) **Hammer-operated piston tool — low-velocity type** A tool which, by means of a heavy mass hammer supplemented by a load, moves a piston designed to be captive to drive a stud, pin, or fastener into a work surface, always starting the fastener at rest and in contact with the work surface. It shall be so designed that when used with any load that accurately chambers in it and that is commercially available at the time the tool is submitted for approval, it will not cause such stud, pin, or fastener to have a mean velocity in excess of 300 feet per second when measured 6.5 feet from the muzzle end of the barrel.

(a)(2) **High-velocity tool** A tool or machine which, when used with a load, propels or discharges a stud, pin, or fastener, at velocities in excess of 300 feet per second when measured 6.5 feet from the muzzle end of the barrel, for the purpose of impinging it upon, affixing it to, or penetrating another object or material.

(a)(3) **Low-velocity piston tool** A tool that utilizes a piston designed to be captive to drive a stud, pin, or fastener into a work surface. It shall be so designed that when used with any load that accurately chambers in it and that is commercially available at the time the tool is submitted for approval, it will not cause such stud, pin, or fastener to have a mean velocity in excess of 300 feet per second when measured 6.5 feet from the muzzle end of the barrel.

(a)(4) **Stud, pin, or fastener** A fastening device specifically designed and manufactured for use in explosive-actuated fastening tools.

(a)(5) **To chamber** To fit properly without the use of excess force, the case being duly supported.

(a)(6) **Explosive powerload, also known as load** Any substance in any form capable of producing a propellant force.

(a)(7) **Tool** An explosive-actuated fastening tool, unless otherwise indicated, and all accessories pertaining thereto.

(a)(8) **Protective shield or guard** A device or guard attached to the muzzle end of the tool, which is designed to confine flying particles.

(b) **Abrasive wheel terms**

(b)(1) **Mounted wheels** Mounted wheels, usually 2-inch diameter or smaller, and of various shapes, may be either organic or inorganic bonded abrasive wheels. They are secured to plain or threaded steel mandrels.

(b)(2) **Tuck pointing** Removal, by grinding, of cement, mortar, or other nonmetallic jointing material.

(b)(3) **Tuck pointing wheels** Tuck pointing wheels, usually Type 1, reinforced organic bonded wheels have diameter, thickness and hole size dimension. They are subject to the same limitations of use and mounting as Type 1 wheels defined in subparagraph (10) of this paragraph.

Limitation: Wheels used for tuck pointing should be reinforced, organic bonded. (See §1910.243(c)(1)(ii)(C))

(b)(4) **Portable grinding** A grinding operation where the grinding machine is designed to be hand held and may be easily moved from one location to another.

(b)(5) **Organic bonded wheels** Organic wheels are wheels which are bonded by means of an organic material such as resin, rubber, shellac, or other similar bonding agent.

(b)(6) **Safety guard** A safety guard is an enclosure designed to restrain the pieces of the grinding wheel and furnish all possible protection in the event that the wheel is broken in operation.

(b)(7) **Reinforced wheels** The term reinforced as applied to grinding wheels shall define a class of organic wheels which contain strengthening fabric or filament. The term reinforced does not cover wheels using such mechanical additions as steel rings, steel cup backs or wire or tape winding.

(b)(8) **Type 11 flaring cup wheels** Type 11 flaring cup wheels have double diameter dimensions D and J, and in addition have thickness, hole size, rim and back thickness dimensions. Grinding is always performed on rim face, W dimension. Type 11 wheels are subject to all limitations of use and mounting listed for Type 6 straight sided cup wheels definition in subparagraph (9) of this paragraph.

Figure P-1
Type 11 Flaring Cup Wheels

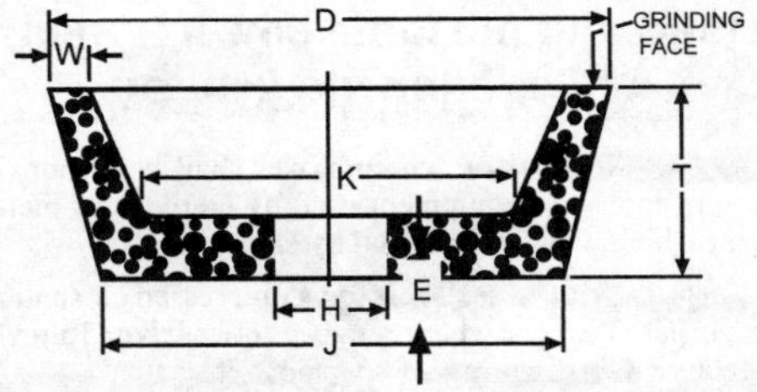

Side grinding wheel having a wall flared or tapered outward from the back. Wall thickness at the back is normally greater than at the grinding face (W).

Limitation: Minimum back thickness, E dimension, should not be less than one-fourth T dimension. In addition when unthreaded hole wheels are specified the inside flat, K dimension, shall be large enough to accommodate a suitable flange.

(b)(9) **Type 6 straight cup wheels**. Type 6 cup wheels have diameter, thickness, hole size, rim thickness, and back thickness dimensions. Grinding is always performed on rim face, W dimension.

Limitation: Minimum back thickness, E dimension, should not be less than one-fourth T dimension. In addition, when unthreaded hole wheels are specified, the inside flat, K dimension, must be large enough to accommodate a suitable flange.

Figure No. P-2
Type 6 Straight Cup Wheels

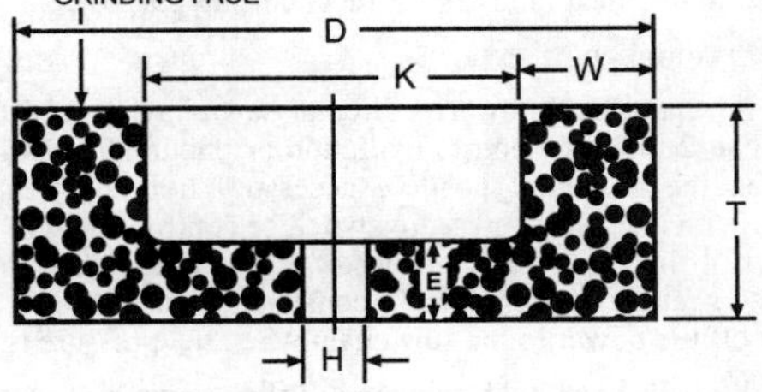

Side grinding wheel having a diameter, thickness and hole with one side straight or flat and the opposite side recessed. This type, however, differs from Type 5 in that the grinding is performed on the wall of the abrasive created by the difference between the diameter of the recess and the outside diameter of the wheel. Therefore, the wall dimension "W" takes precedence over the diameter of the recess as an essential intermediate dimension to describe this shape type.

(b)(10) **Type 1 straight wheels**. Type 1 straight wheels have diameter, thickness, and hole size dimensions and should be used only on the periphery. Type 1 wheels shall be mounted between flanges.

Limitation: Hole dimension (H) should not be greater than two-thirds of wheel diameter dimension (D) for precision, cylindrical, centerless, or surface grinding applications. Maximum hole size for all other applications should not exceed one-half wheel diameter.

Figure No. P-3
Type 1 Straight Wheels

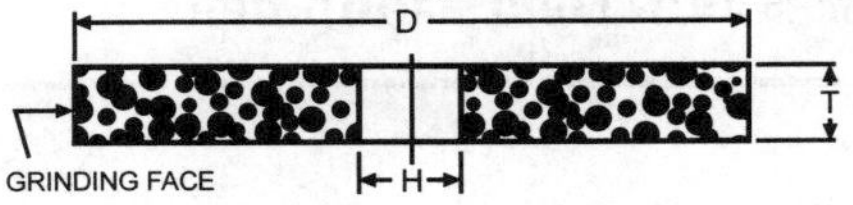

Peripheral grinding wheel having a diameter, thickness and hole.

(c) [Reserved]

(d) Jack terms

(d)(1) Jack A jack is an appliance for lifting and lowering or moving horizontally a load by application of a pushing force.

Note: Jacks may be of the following types: Lever and ratchet, screw and hydraulic.

(d)(2) Rating The rating of a jack is the maximum working load for which it is designed to lift safely that load throughout its specified amount of travel.

Note: To raise the rated load of a jack, the point of application of the load, the applied force, and the length of lever arm should be those designated by the manufacturer for the particular jack considered.

[39 FR 23502, June 27, 1974, as amended at 43 FR 49750, Oct. 24, 1978]

§1910.242 Hand and portable powered tools and equipment, general

(a) General requirements Each employer shall be responsible for the safe condition of tools and equipment used by employees, including tools and equipment which may be furnished by employees.

(b) Compressed air used for cleaning Compressed air shall not be used for cleaning purposes except where reduced to less than 30 p.s.i. and then only with effective chip guarding and personal protective equipment.

§1910.243 Guarding of portable powered tools

(a) Portable powered tool

(a)(1) Portable circular saws

(a)(1)(i) All portable, power-driven circular saws having a blade diameter greater than 2 in. shall be equipped with guards above and below the base plate or shoe. The upper guard shall cover the saw to the depth of the teeth, except for the minimum arc required to permit the base to be tilted for bevel cuts. The lower guard shall cover the saw to the depth of the teeth, except for the minimum arc required to allow proper retraction and contact with the work. When the tool is withdrawn from the work, the lower guard shall automatically and instantly return to covering position.

(a)(1)(ii) Paragraph (a)(1)(i) of this section does not apply to circular saws used in the meat industry for meat cutting purposes.

(a)(2) Switches and controls

(a)(2)(i) All hand-held powered circular saws having a blade diameter greater than 2 inches, electric, hydraulic or pneumatic chain saws, and percussion tools without positive accessory holding means shall be equipped with a constant pressure switch or control that will shut off the power when the pressure is released. All hand-held gasoline powered chain saws shall be equipped with a constant pressure throttle control that will shut off the power to the saw chain when the pressure is released.

(a)(2)(ii) All hand-held powered drills, tappers, fastener drivers, horizontal, vertical, and angle grinders with wheels greater than 2 inches in diameter, disc sanders with discs greater than 2 inches in diameter, belt sanders, reciprocating saws, saber, scroll, and jig saws with blade shanks greater than a nominal one-fourth inch, and other similarly operating powered tools shall be equipped with a constant pressure switch or control, and may have a lock-on control provided that turnoff can be accomplished by a single motion of the same finger or fingers that turn it on.

(a)(2)(iii)(A) All other hand-held powered tools, such as, but not limited to, platen sanders, grinders with wheels 2 inches in diameter or less, disc sanders with discs 2 inches in diameter or less, routers, planers, laminate trimmers, nibblers, shears, saber, scroll, and jig saws with blade shanks a nominal one-fourth of an inch wide or less, may be equipped with either a positive "on-off" control, or other controls as described by paragraph (a)(2)(i) and (ii) of this section.

(a)(2)(iii)(B) Saber, scroll, and jig saws with nonstandard blade holders may use blades with shanks which are nonuniform in width, provided the narrowest portion of the blade shank is an integral part in mounting the blade.

(a)(2)(iii)(C) Blade shank width shall be measured at the narrowest portion of the blade shank when saber, scroll, and jig saws have nonstandard blade holders.

(a)(2)(iii)(D) Nominal in this subparagraph means ± 0.05 inch.

(a)(2)(iv) The operating control on hand-held power tools shall be so located as to minimize the possibility of its accidental operation, if such accidental operation would constitute a hazard to employees.

(a)(2)(v) This subparagraph does not apply to concrete vibrators, concrete breakers, powered tampers, jack hammers, rock drills, garden appliances, household and kitchen appliances, personal care appliances, medical or dental equipment, or to fixed machinery.

(a)(3) Portable belt sanding machines Belt sanding machines shall be provided with guards at each nip point where the sanding belt runs onto a pulley. These guards shall effectively prevent the hands or fingers of the operator from coming in contact with the nip points. The unused run of the sanding belt shall be guarded against accidental contact.

(a)(4) Cracked saws All cracked saws shall be removed from service.

(a)(5) Grounding Portable electric powered tools shall meet the electrical requirements of Subpart S of this part.

(b) Pneumatic powered tools and hose

(b)(1) Tool retainer A tool retainer shall be installed on each piece of utilization equipment which, without such a retainer, may eject the tool.

(b)(2) Airhose Hose and hose connections used for conducting compressed air to utilization equipment shall be designed for the pressure and service to which they are subjected.

(c) Portable abrasive wheels

(c)(1) General requirements Abrasive wheels shall be used only on machine provided with safety guards as defined in paragraph (c)(1) through (4) of this section.

(c)(1)(i) Exceptions The requirements of this paragraph (c)(1) shall not apply to the following classes of wheels and conditions.

(c)(1)(i)(A) Wheels used for internal work while within the work being ground;

(c)(1)(i)(B) Mounted wheels used in portable operations 2 inches and smaller in diameter; (see definition §1910.241(b)(1)); and

(c)(1)(i)(C) Types 16, 17, 18, 18R, and 19 cones, and plugs, and threaded hole pot balls where the work offers protection.

(c)(1)(ii)(A) A safety guard shall cover the spindle end, nut and flange projections. The safety guard shall be mounted so as to maintain proper alignment with the wheel, and the strength of the fastenings shall exceed the strength of the guard.

(c)(1)(ii)(B) Exception Safety guards on all operations where the work provides a suitable measure of protection to the operator may be so constructed that the spindle end, nut and outer flange are exposed. Where the nature of the work is such as to entirely cover the side of the wheel, the side covers of the guard may be omitted.

(c)(1)(ii)(C) Exception The spindle end, nut, and outer flange may be exposed on portable machines designed for, and used with, type 6, 11, 27, and 28 abrasive wheels, cutting off wheels, and tuck pointing wheels.

(c)(2) Cup wheels Cup wheels (Types 6 and 11) shall be protected by:

(c)(2)(i) Safety guards as specified in paragraph (c)(1) of this section; or,

(c)(2)(ii) Special "revolving cup guards" which mount behind the wheel and turn with it. They shall be made of steel or other material with adequate strength and shall enclose the wheel sides upward from the back for one-third of the wheel thickness. The mounting features shall conform with all regulations. (See paragraph (c)(5) of this section.) It is necessary to maintain clearance between the wheel side and the guard. The clearance shall not exceed one-sixteenth inch; or,

(c)(2)(iii) Some other form of guard that will insure as good protection as that which would be provided by the guards specified in paragraph (c)(1)(i) or (ii) of this subparagraph.

(c)(3) Vertical portable grinders Safety guards used on machines known as right angle head or vertical portable grinders shall have a maximum exposure angle of 180°, and the guard shall be so located so as to be between the operator and the wheel during use. Adjustment of guard shall be such that pieces of an accidentally broken wheel will be deflected away from the operator. (See Figure P–4.)

Figure No. P–4

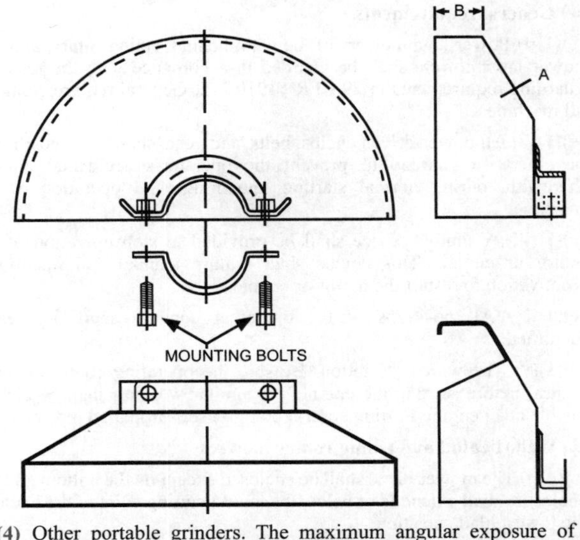

(c)(4) Other portable grinders. The maximum angular exposure of the grinding wheel periphery and sides for safety guards used on other portable grinding machines shall not exceed 180° and the top half of the wheel shall be enclosed at all times. (See Figures P–5 and P–6.)

Figure No. P–5

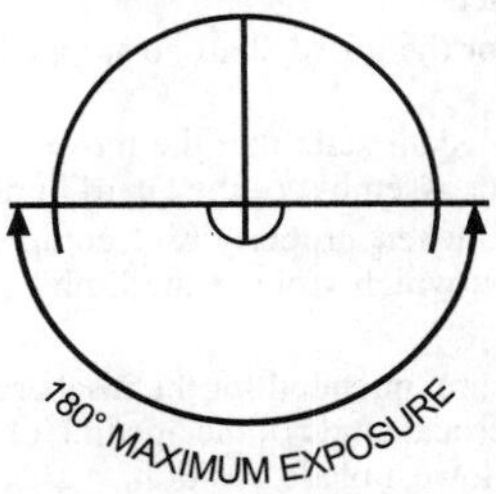

Figure No. P–6

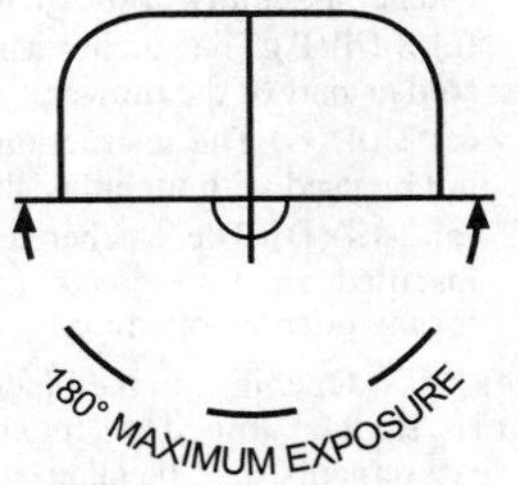

(c)(5) Mounting and inspection of abrasive wheels

(c)(5)(i) Immediately before mounting, all wheels shall be closely inspected and sounded by the user (ring test, see Subpart O, §1910.215(d)(1)) to make sure they have not been damaged in transit, storage, or otherwise. The spindle speed of the machine shall be checked before mounting of the wheel to be certain that it does not exceed the maximum operating speed marked on the wheel.

(c)(5)(ii) Grinding wheels shall fit freely on the spindle and remain free under all grinding conditions. A controlled clearance between the wheel hole and the machine spindle (or wheel sleeves or adaptors) is essential to avoid excessive pressure from mounting and spindle expansion. To accomplish this, the machine spindle shall be made to nominal (standard) size plus zero minus .002 inch, and the wheel hole shall be made suitably oversize to assure safety clearance under the conditions of operating heat and pressure.

(c)(5)(iii) All contact surfaces of wheels, blotters, and flangers shall be flat and free of foreign matter.

(c)(5)(iv) When a bushing is used in the wheel hole it shall not exceed the width of the wheel and shall not contact the flanges.

(c)(5)(v) Requirements for the use of flanges and blotters, see Subpart O, §1910.215(c).

(c)(6) **Excluded machinery** Natural sandstone wheels and metal, wooden, cloth, or paper discs, having a layer of abrasive on the surface are not covered by this paragraph.

(d) OI **Explosive actuated fastening tools**

(d)(1) **General requirements**

(d)(1)(i) Explosive-actuated fastening tools that are actuated by explosives or any similar means, and propel a stud, pin, fastener, or other object for the purpose of affixing it by penetration to any other object shall meet the design requirements specified by paragraph (d)(2) of this section. This requirement does not apply to devices designed for attaching objects to soft construction materials, such as wood, plaster, tar, dry wallboard, and the like, or to stud-welding equipment.

(d)(1)(ii) Operators and assistants using tools shall be safeguarded by means of eye protection. Head and face protection shall be used, as required by working conditions, as set forth in Subpart I.

(d)(2) **Inspection, maintenance, and tool handling**

(d)(2)(i) High-velocity tools. Tools of this type shall have the characteristics outlined in (a) through (h) of this section.

(d)(2)(i)(A) The muzzle end of the tool shall have a protective shield or guard at least 3½" in diameter, mounted perpendicular to and concentric with the barrel, and designed to confine any flying fragments or particles that might otherwise create a hazard at the time of firing.

(d)(2)(i)(B) Where a standard shield or guard cannot be used, or where it does not cover all apparent avenues through which flying particles might escape, a special shield, guard, fixture, or jig designed and built by the manufacturer of the tool being used, which provides this degree of protection, shall be used as a substitute.

(d)(2)(i)(C) The tool shall be so designed that it cannot be fired unless it is equipped with a standard protective shield or guard, or a special shield, guard, fixture, or jig.

(d)(2)(i)(D)(1) The firing mechanism shall be so designed that the tool cannot fire during loading or preparation to fire, or if the tool should be dropped while loaded.

(d)(2)(i)(D)(2) Firing of the tool shall be dependent upon at least two separate and distinct operations of the operator, with the final firing movement being separate from the operation of bringing the tool into the firing position.

(d)(2)(i)(E) The tool shall be so designed as not to be operable other than against a work surface, and unless the operator is holding the tool against the work surface with a force at least 5 pounds greater than the total weight of the tool.

(d)(2)(i)(F) The tool shall be so designed that it will not operate when equipped with the standard guard indexed to the center position if any bearing surface of the guard is tilted more than 8° from contact with the work surface.

(d)(2)(i)(G) The tool shall be so designed that positive means of varying the power are available or can be made available to the operator as part of the tool, or as an auxiliary, in order to make it possible for the operator to select a power level adequate to perform the desired work without excessive force.

(d)(2)(i)(H) The tool shall be so designed that all breeching parts will be reasonably visible to allow a check for any foreign matter that may be present.

(d)(2)(ii) Tools of the low-velocity-piston type shall have the characteristics outlined in paragraphs (d)(2)(ii)(A) through (E) of this section and any additional safety features he may wish to incorporate.

(d)(2)(ii)(A) The muzzle end of the tool shall be designed so that suitable protective shields, guards, jigs, or fixtures, designed and built by the manufacturer of the tool being used, can be mounted perpendicular to the barrel. A standard spall shield shall be supplied with each tool.

(d)(2)(ii)(B)(1) The tool shall be designed so that it shall not in ordinary usage propel or discharge a stud, pin, or fastener while loading or during preparation to fire, or if the tool should be dropped while loaded.

(d)(2)(ii)(B)(2) Firing of the tool shall be dependent upon at least two separate and distinct operations of the operator, with the final firing movement being separate from the operation of bringing the tool into the firing position.

(d)(2)(ii)(C) The tool shall be so designed as not to be operable other than against a work surface, and unless the operator is holding the tool against the work surface with a force at least 5 pounds greater than the total weight of the tool.

(d)(2)(ii)(D) The tool shall be so designed that positive means of varying the power are available or can be made available to the operator as part of the tool, or as an auxiliary, in order to make it possible for the operator to select a power level adequate to perform the desired work without excessive force.

(d)(2)(ii)(E) The tool shall be so designed that all breeching parts will be reasonably visible to allow a check for any foreign matter that may be present.

(d)(2)(iii) Tools of the hammer-operated piston tools—low-velocity type shall have the characteristics outlined in paragraphs (d)(2)(iii)(A) through (E) of this section.

(d)(2)(iii)(A) The muzzle end of the tool shall be so designed that suitable protective shields, guards, jigs, or fixtures, designed and built by the manufacturer of the tool being used, can be mounted perpendicular to the barrel. A standard spall shield shall be supplied with each tool.

(d)(2)(iii)(B) The tool shall be so designed that it shall not in ordinary usage propel or discharge a stud, pin, or fastener while loading, or during preparation to fire, or if the tool should be dropped while loaded.

(d)(2)(iii)(C) Firing of the tool shall be dependent upon at least two separate and distinct operations of the operator, with the final firing movement being separate from the operation of bringing the tool into the firing position.

(d)(2)(iii)(D) The tool shall be so designed that positive means of varying the power are available or can be made available to the operator as part of the tool, or as an auxiliary, in order to make it possible for the operator to select a power level adequate to perform the desired work without excessive force.

(d)(2)(iii)(E) The tool shall be so designed that all breeching parts will be reasonably visible to allow a check for any foreign matter that may be present.

(d)(3) Requirements for loads and fasteners

(d)(3)(i) There shall be a standard means of identifying the power levels of loads used in tools.

(d)(3)(ii) [Reserved]

(d)(3)(iii) No load (cased or caseless) shall be used if it will accurately chamber in any existing approved commercially available low-velocity piston tool or hammer operated piston tool—low-velocity type and will cause a fastener to have a mean velocity in excess of 300 feet per second when measured 6.5 feet from the muzzle end of the barrel. No individual test firing of a series shall exceed 300 feet per second by more than 8 percent.

(d)(3)(iv) Fasteners used in tools shall be only those specifically manufactured for use in such tools.

(d)(4) [OI] Operating requirements

(d)(4)(i) Before using a tool, the operator shall inspect it to determine to his satisfaction that it is clean, that all moving parts operate freely, and that the barrel is free from obstructions.

(d)(4)(ii) When a tool develops a defect during use, the operator shall immediately cease to use it, until it is properly repaired.

(d)(4)(iii) Tools shall not be loaded until just prior to the intended firing time. Neither loaded nor empty tools are to be pointed at any workmen.

(d)(4)(iv) No tools shall be loaded unless being prepared for immediate use, nor shall an unattended tool be left loaded.

(d)(4)(v) In case of a misfire, the operator shall hold the tool in the operating position for at least 30 seconds. He shall then try to operate the tool a second time. He shall wait another 30 seconds, holding the tool in the operating position; then he shall proceed to remove the explosive load in strict accordance with the manufacturer's instructions.

(d)(4)(vi) A tool shall never be left unattended in a place where it would be available to unauthorized persons.

(d)(4)(vii) Fasteners shall not be driven into very hard or brittle materials including, but not limited to, cast iron, glazed tile, surface-hardened steel, glass block, live rock, face brick, or hollow tile.

(d)(4)(viii) Driving into materials easily penetrated shall be avoided unless such materials are backed by a substance that will prevent the pin or fastener from passing completely through and creating a flying-missile hazard on the other side.

(d)(4)(ix)(A) Fasteners shall not be driven directly into materials such as brick or concrete closer than 3 inches from the unsupported edge or corner, or into steel surfaces closer than one-half inch from the unsupported edge or corner, unless a special guard, fixture, or jig is used. (Exception: Low-velocity tools may drive no closer than 2 inches from an edge in concrete or one-fourth inch in steel.)

(d)(4)(ix)(B) When fastening other materials, such as a 2- by 4-inch wood section to a concrete surface, it is permissible to drive a fastener of no greater than 7/32" shank diameter not closer than 2 inches from the unsupported edge or corner of the work surface.

(d)(4)(x) Fasteners shall not be driven through existing holes unless a positive guide is used to secure accurate alignment.

(d)(4)(xi) No fastener shall be driven into a spalled area caused by an unsatisfactory fastening.

(d)(4)(xii) Tools shall not be used in an explosive or flammable atmosphere.

(d)(4)(xiii) All tools shall be used with the correct shield, guard, or attachment recommended by the manufacturer.

(d)(4)(xiv) Any tool found not in proper working order shall be immediately removed from service. The tool shall be inspected at regular intervals and shall be repaired in accordance with the manufacturer's specifications.

(e) Power lawnmowers

(e)(1) General requirements

(e)(1)(i) Power lawnmowers of the walk-behind, riding-rotary, and reel power lawnmowers shall be guarded in accordance with the machine guarding requirements in 29 CFR §1910.212, General requirements for all machines.

(e)(1)(ii) All power-driven chains, belts, and gears shall be so positioned or otherwise guarded to prevent the operator's accidental contact therewith, during normal starting, mounting, and operation of the machine.

(e)(1)(iii) A shutoff device shall be provided to stop operation of the motor or engine. This device shall require manual and intentional reactivation to restart the motor or engine.

(e)(1)(iv) All positions of the operating controls shall be clearly identified.

(e)(1)(v) The words, "Caution. Be sure the operating control(s) is in neutral before starting the engine," or similar wording shall be clearly visible at an engine starting control point on self-propelled mowers.

(e)(2) Walk-behind and riding rotary mowers

(e)(2)(i) The mower blade shall be enclosed except on the bottom and the enclosure shall extend to or below the lowest cutting point of the blade in the lowest blade position.

(e)(2)(ii) Guards which must be removed to install a catcher assembly shall comply with the following:

(e)(2)(ii)(A) Warning instructions shall be affixed to the mower near the opening stating that the mower shall not be used without either the catcher assembly or the guard in place.

(e)(2)(ii)(B) The catcher assembly or the guard shall be shipped and sold as part of the mower.

(e)(2)(ii)(C) The instruction manual shall state that the mower shall not be used without either the catcher assembly or the guard in place.

(e)(2)(ii)(D) The catcher assembly, when properly and completely installed, shall not create a condition which violates the limits given for the guarded opening.

(e)(2)(iii) Openings in the blade enclosure, intended for the discharge of grass, shall be limited to a maximum vertical angle of the opening of 30°. Measurements shall be taken from the lowest blade position.

(e)(2)(iv) The total effective opening area of the grass discharge opening(s) shall not exceed 1,000 square degrees on units having a width of cut less than 27½", or 2,000 square degrees on units having a width of cut 27 ½ inches or over.

(e)(2)(v) The word "Caution." or stronger wording, shall be placed on the mower at or near each discharge opening.

(e)(2)(vi) [Reserved]

(e)(2)(vii) Blade(s) shall stop rotating from the manufacturer's specified maximum speed within 15 seconds after declutching, or shutting off power.

(e)(2)(viii) In a multipiece blade, the means of fastening the cutting members to the body of the blade or disc shall be so designed that they will not become worn to a hazardous condition before the cutting members themselves are worn beyond use.

(e)(2)(ix) The maximum tip speed of any blade shall be 19,000 feet per minute.

(e)(3) Walk-behind rotary mowers

(e)(3)(i) The horizontal angle of the opening(s) in the blade enclosure, intended for the discharge of grass, shall not contact the operator area.

(e)(3)(ii) There shall be one of the following at all openings in the blade enclosure intended for the discharge of grass:

(e)(3)(ii)(A) A minimum unobstructed horizontal distance of 3 inches from the end of the discharge chute to the blade tip circle.

(e)(3)(ii)(B) A rigid bar fastened across the discharge opening, secured to prevent removal without the use of tools. The bottom of the bar shall be no higher than the bottom edge of the blade enclosure.

(e)(3)(iii) The highest point(s) of the front of the blade enclosure, except discharge openings, shall be such that any line extending a maximum of 15° downward from the horizontal toward the blade shaft axis (axes) shall not intersect the horizontal plane within the blade tip circle. The highest point(s) on the blade enclosure front, except discharge-openings, shall not exceed 1¼ inches above the lowest cutting point of the blade in the lowest blade position. Mowers with a swingover handle are to be considered as having no front in the blade enclosure and therefore shall comply with paragraph (e)(2)(i) of this section.

(e)(3)(iv) The mower handle shall be fastened to the mower so as to prevent loss of control by unintentional uncoupling while in operation.

(e)(3)(v) A positive upstop or latch shall be provided for the mower handle in the normal operating position(s). The upstop shall not be subject to unintentional disengagement during normal operation of the mower. The upstop or latch shall not allow the center or the handle grips to come closer than 17 inches horizontally behind the closest path of the mower blade(s) unless manually disengaged.

(e)(3)(vi) A swing-over handle, which complies with the above requirements, will be permitted.

(e)(3)(vii) Wheel drive disengaging controls, except deadman controls, shall move opposite to the direction of the vehicle motion in order to disengage the drive. Deadman controls shall automatically interrupt power to a drive when the operator's actuating force is removed, and may operate in any direction to disengage the drive.

(e)(4) **Riding rotary mowers**

(e)(4)(i) The highest point(s) of all openings in the blade enclosure, front shall be limited by a vertical angle of opening of 15° and a maximum distance of 1¼" above the lowest cutting point of the blade in the lowest blade position.

(e)(4)(ii) Opening(s) shall be placed so that grass or debris will not discharge directly toward any part of an operator seated in a normal operator position.

(e)(4)(iii) There shall be one of the following at all openings in the blade enclosure intended for the discharge of grass:

(e)(4)(iii)(A) A minimum unobstructed horizontal distance of 6 inches from the end of the discharge chute to the blade tip circle.

(e)(4)(iii)(B) A rigid bar fastened across the discharge opening, secured to prevent removal without the use of tools. The bottom of the bar shall be no higher than the bottom edge of the blade enclosure.

(e)(4)(iv) Mowers shall be provided with stops to prevent jackknifing or locking of the steering mechanism.

(e)(4)(v) Vehicle stopping means shall be provided.

(e)(4)(vi) Hand-operated wheel drive disengaging controls shall move opposite to the direction of vehicle motion in order to disengage the drive. Foot-operated wheel drive disengaging controls shall be depressed to disengage the drive. Deadman controls, both hand and foot operated, shall automatically interrupt power to a drive when the operator's actuating force is removed, and may operate in any direction to disengage the drive.

[39 FR 23502, June 27, 1974, as amended at 43 FR 49750, Oct. 24, 1978; 49 FR 5323, Feb. 10, 1984; 50 FR 4649, Feb. 1, 1985; 61 FR 9240, Mar. 7, 1996; 70 FR 53929, Sept. 13, 2005; 72 FR 71070, Dec. 14, 2007]

§1910.244
Other portable tools and equipment

(a) **Jacks**

(a)(1) **Loading and marking**

(a)(1)(i) The operator shall make sure that the jack used has a rating sufficient to lift and sustain the load.

(a)(1)(ii) The rated load shall be legibly and permanently marked in a prominent location on the jack by casting, stamping, or other suitable means.

(a)(2) Operation and maintenance.

(a)(2)(i) In the absence of a firm foundation, the base of the jack shall be blocked. If there is a possibility of slippage of the cap, a block shall be placed in between the cap and the load.

(a)(2)(ii) The operator shall watch the stop indicator, which shall be kept clean, in order to determine the limit of travel. The indicated limit shall not be overrun.

(a)(2)(iii) After the load has been raised, it shall be cribbed, blocked, or otherwise secured at once.

(a)(2)(iv) Hydraulic jacks exposed to freezing temperatures shall be supplied with an adequate antifreeze liquid.

(a)(2)(v) All jacks shall be properly lubricated at regular intervals.

(a)(2)(vi) Each jack shall be thoroughly inspected at times which depend upon the service conditions. Inspections shall be not less frequent than the following:

(a)(2)(vi)(A) For constant or intermittent use at one locality, once every 6 months,

(a)(2)(vi)(B) For jacks sent out of shop for special work, when sent out and when returned,

(a)(2)(vi)(C) For a jack subjected to abnormal load or shock, immediately before and immediately thereafter.

(a)(2)(vii) [OI] Repair or replacement parts shall be examined for possible defects.

(a)(2)(viii) Jacks which are out of order shall be tagged accordingly, and shall not be used until repairs are made.

(b) [OI] **Abrasive blast cleaning nozzles**. The blast cleaning nozzles shall be equipped with an operating valve which must be held open manually. A support shall be provided on which the nozzle may be mounted when it is not in use.

[39 FR 23502, June 27, 1974, as amended at 49 FR 5323, Feb. 10, 1984]

This page intentionally left blank.

29 CFR PART 1910 Subpart Q
Welding, Cutting and Brazing

Section Contents

Subpart Q—Welding, Cutting and Brazing

Authority: Sections 4, 6, and 8 of the Occupational Safety and Health Act of 1970 (29 U.S.C. 653, Sections 4, 6, and 8 of the Occupational Safety and Health Act of 1970 (29 U.S.C. 653, 655, and 657); Secretary of Labor's Orders Nos. 12–71 (36 FR 8754), 8–76 (41 FR 25059), 9–83 (48 FR 35736), 1–90 (55 FR 9033), 6–96 (62 FR 111), 3–2000 (65 FR 50017), or 5–2007 (72 FR 31159), as applicable; and 29 CFR Part §1911.

Source: 55 FR 13696, Apr. 11, 1990, unless otherwise noted.

§1910.251 Definitions

As used in this Subpart:

(a) **Welder and welding operator** mean any operator of electric or gas welding and cutting equipment.

(b) **Approved** means listed or approved by a nationally recognized testing laboratory. Refer to §1910.155(c)(3) for definitions of listed and approved, and §1910.7 for nationally recognized testing laboratory.

[55 FR 13696, Apr. 11, 1990, as amended at 61 FR 9240, Mar. 7, 1996; 72 FR 71070, Dec. 14, 2007]

§1910.252 General requirements

(a) **Fire prevention and protection**

(a)(1) **Basic precautions** For elaboration of these basic precautions and of the special precautions of paragraph (a)(2) of this section as well as a delineation of the fire protection and prevention responsibilities of welders and cutters, their supervisors (including outside contractors) and those in management on whose property cutting and welding is to be performed, see Standard for Fire Prevention in Use of Cutting and Welding Processes, NFPA Standard 51B, 1962, which is incorporated by reference as specified in §1910.6. The basic precautions for fire prevention in welding or cutting work are:

(a)(1)(i) Fire hazards. If the object to be welded or cut cannot readily be moved, all movable fire hazards in the vicinity shall be taken to a safe place.

(a)(1)(ii) Guards. If the object to be welded or cut cannot be moved and if all the fire hazards cannot be removed, then guards shall be used to confine the heat, sparks, and slag, and to protect the immovable fire hazards.

(a)(1)(iii) Restrictions. If the requirements stated in paragraphs (a)(1)(i) and (a)(1)(ii) of this section cannot be followed then welding and cutting shall not be performed.

(a)(2) **Special precautions** When the nature of the work to be performed falls within the scope of paragraph (a)(1)(ii) of this section certain additional precautions may be necessary:

(a)(2)(i) **Combustible material** Wherever there are floor openings or cracks in the flooring that cannot be closed, precautions shall be taken so that no readily combustible materials on the floor below will be exposed to sparks which might drop through the floor. The same precautions shall be observed with regard to cracks or holes in walls, open doorways and open or broken windows.

(a)(2)(ii) **Fire extinquishers** Suitable fire extinguishing equipment shall be maintained in a state of readiness for instant use. Such equipment may consist of pails of water, buckets of sand, hose or portable extinguishers depending upon the nature and quantity of the combustible material exposed.

(a)(2)(iii) **Fire watch**

(a)(2)(iii)(A) Fire watchers shall be required whenever welding or cutting is performed in locations where other than a minor fire might develop, or any of the following conditions exist:

(a)(2)(iii)(A)(1) Appreciable combustible material, in building construction or contents, closer than 35 feet (10.7 m) to the point of operation.

(a)(2)(iii)(A)(2) Appreciable combustibles are more than 35 feet (10.7 m) away but are easily ignited by sparks.

(a)(2)(iii)(A)(3) Wall or floor openings within a 35-foot (10.7 m) radius expose combustible material in adjacent areas including concealed spaces in walls or floors.

(a)(2)(iii)(A)(4) Combustible materials are adjacent to the opposite side of metal partitions, walls, ceilings, or roofs and are likely to be ignited by conduction or radiation.

(a)(2)(iii)(B) Fire watchers shall have fire extinguishing equipment readily available and be trained in its use. They shall be familiar with facilities for sounding an alarm in the event of a fire. They shall watch for fires in all exposed areas, try to extinguish them only when obviously within the capacity of the equipment available, or otherwise sound the alarm. A fire watch shall be maintained for at least a half hour after completion of welding or cutting operations to detect and extinguish possible smoldering fires.

(a)(2)(iv) **Authorization** Before cutting or welding is permitted, the area shall be inspected by the individual responsible for authorizing cutting and welding operations. He shall designate precautions to be followed in granting authorization to proceed preferably in the form of a written permit.

(a)(2)(v) **Floors** Where combustible materials such as paper clippings, wood shavings, or textile fibers are on the floor, the floor shall be swept clean for a radius of 35 feet (10.7 m). Combustible floors shall be kept wet, covered with damp sand, or protected by fire-resistant shields. Where floors have been wet down, personnel operating arc welding or cutting equipment shall be protected from possible shock.

(a)(2)(vi) **Prohibited areas** Cutting or welding shall not be permitted in the following situations:

(a)(2)(vi)(A) In areas not authorized by management.

(a)(2)(vi)(B) In sprinklered buildings while such protection is impaired.

(a)(2)(vi)(C) In the presence of explosive atmospheres (mixtures of flammable gases, vapors, liquids, or dusts with air), or explosive atmospheres that may develop inside uncleaned or improperly prepared tanks or equipment which have previously contained such materials, or that may develop in areas with an accumulation of combustible dusts.

(a)(2)(vi)(D) In areas near the storage of large quantities of exposed, readily ignitible materials such as bulk sulfur, baled paper, or cotton.

(a)(2)(vii) **Relocation of combustibles** Where practicable, all combustibles shall be relocated at least 35 feet (10.7 m) from the work site. Where relocation is impracticable, combustibles shall be protected with flameproofed covers or otherwise shielded with metal or asbestos guards or curtains.

(a)(2)(viii) **Ducts** Ducts and conveyor systems that might carry sparks to distant combustibles shall be suitably protected or shut down.

(a)(2)(ix) **Combustible walls** Where cutting or welding is done near walls, partitions, ceiling or roof of combustible construction, fire-resistant shields or guards shall be provided to prevent ignition.

(a)(2)(x) **Noncombustible walls** If welding is to be done on a metal wall, partition, ceiling or roof, precautions shall be taken to prevent ignition of combustibles on the other side, due to conduction or radiation, preferably by relocating combustibles. Where combustibles are not relocated, a fire watch on the opposite side from the work shall be provided.

(a)(2)(xi) **Combustible cover** Welding shall not be attempted on a metal partition, wall, ceiling or roof having a combustible covering nor on walls or partitions of combustible sandwich-type panel construction.

(a)(2)(xii) **Pipes** Cutting or welding on pipes or other metal in contact with combustible walls, partitions, ceilings or roofs shall not be undertaken if the work is close enough to cause ignition by conduction.

(a)(2)(xiii) **Management** Management shall recognize its responsibility for the safe usage of cutting and welding equipment on its property and:

(a)(2)(xiii)(A) Based on fire potentials of plant facilities, establish areas for cutting and welding, and establish procedures for cutting and welding, in other areas.

(a)(2)(xiii)(B) Designate an individual responsible for authorizing cutting and welding operations in areas not specifically designed for such processes.

(a)(2)(xiii)(C) Insist that cutters or welders and their supervisors are suitably trained in the safe operation of their equipment and the safe use of the process.

(a)(2)(xiii)(D) Advise all contractors about flammable materials or hazardous conditions of which they may not be aware.

(a)(2)(xiv) **Supervisor** The Supervisor:

(a)(2)(xiv)(A) Shall be responsible for the safe handling of the cutting or welding equipment and the safe use of the cutting or welding process.

(a)(2)(xiv)(B) Shall determine the combustible materials and hazardous areas present or likely to be present in the work location.

(a)(2)(xiv)(C) Shall protect combustibles from ignition by the following:

(a)(2)(xiv)(C)(1) Have the work moved to a location free from dangerous combustibles.

(a)(2)(xiv)(C)(2) If the work cannot be moved, have the combustibles moved to a safe distance from the work or have the combustibles properly shielded against ignition.

(a)(2)(xiv)(C)(3) See that cutting and welding are so scheduled that plant operations that might expose combustibles to ignition are not started during cutting or welding.

(a)(2)(xiv)(D) Shall secure authorization for the cutting or welding operations from the designated management representative.

(a)(2)(xiv)(E) Shall determine that the cutter or welder secures his approval that conditions are safe before going ahead.

(a)(2)(xiv)(F) Shall determine that fire protection and extinguishing equipment are properly located at the site.

(a)(2)(xiv)(G) Where fire watches are required, he shall see that they are available at the site.

(a)(2)(xv) **Fire prevention precautions** Cutting or welding shall be permitted only in areas that are or have been made fire safe. When work cannot be moved practically, as in most construction work, the area shall be made safe by removing combustibles or protecting combustibles from ignition sources.

(a)(3) **Welding or cutting containers**

(a)(3)(i) **Used containers** No welding, cutting, or other hot work shall be performed on used drums, barrels, tanks or other containers until they have been cleaned so thoroughly as to make absolutely certain that there are no flammable materials present or any substances such as greases, tars, acids, or other materials which when subjected to heat, might produce flammable or toxic vapors. Any pipe lines or connections to the drum or vessel shall be disconnected or blanked.

(a)(3)(ii) **Venting and purging** All hollow spaces, cavities or containers shall be vented to permit the escape of air or gases before preheating, cutting or welding. Purging with inert gas is recommended.

(a)(4) **Confined spaces**

(a)(4)(i) OI **Accidental contact** When arc welding is to be suspended for any substantial period of time, such as during lunch or overnight, all electrodes shall be removed from the holders and the holders carefully located so that accidental contact cannot occur and the machine be disconnected from the power source.

(a)(4)(ii) **Torch valve** In order to eliminate the possibility of gas escaping through leaks or improperly closed valves, when gas welding or cutting, the torch valves shall be closed and the gas supply to the torch positively shut off at some point outside the confined area whenever the torch is not to be used for a substantial period of time, such as during lunch hour or overnight. Where practicable, the torch and hose shall also be removed from the confined space.

(b) **Protection of personnel**

(b)(1) **General**

(b)(1)(i) **Railing** A welder or helper working on platforms, scaffolds, or runways shall be protected against falling. This may be accomplished by the use of railings, safety belts, life lines, or some other equally effective safeguards.

(b)(1)(ii) **Welding cable** Welders shall place welding cable and other equipment so that it is clear of passageways, ladders, and stairways.

(b)(2) OI **Eye protection**

(b)(2)(i) **Selection**

(b)(2)(i)(A) Helmets or hand shields shall be used during all arc welding or arc cutting operations, excluding submerged arc welding. Helpers or attendants shall be provided with proper eye protection.

(b)(2)(i)(B) Goggles or other suitable eye protection shall be used during all gas welding or oxygen cutting operations. Spectacles without side shields, with suitable filter lenses are permitted for use during gas welding operations on light work, for torch brazing or for inspection.

(b)(2)(i)(C) All operators and attendants of resistance welding or resistance brazing equipment shall use transparent face shields or goggles, depending on the particular job, to protect their faces or eyes, as required.

(b)(2)(i)(D) Eye protection in the form of suitable goggles shall be provided where needed for brazing operations not covered in paragraphs (b)(2)(i)(A) through (b)(2)(i)(C) of this section.

(b)(2)(ii) OI **Specifications for protectors**

(b)(2)(ii)(A) Helmets and hand shields shall be made of a material which is an insulator for heat and electricity. Helmets, shields and goggles shall be not readily flammable and shall be capable of withstanding sterilization.

(b)(2)(ii)(B) Helmets and hand shields shall be arranged to protect the face, neck and ears from direct radiant energy from the arc.

(b)(2)(ii)(C) Helmets shall be provided with filter plates and cover plates designed for easy removal.

(b)(2)(ii)(D) All parts shall be constructed of a material which will not readily corrode or discolor the skin.

(b)(2)(ii)(E) Goggles shall be ventilated to prevent fogging of the lenses as much as practicable.

(b)(2)(ii)(F) All glass for lenses shall be tempered, substantially free from striae, air bubbles, waves and other flaws. Except when a lens is ground to provide proper optical correction for defective vision, the front and rear surfaces of lenses and windows shall be smooth and parallel.

(b)(2)(ii)(G) Lenses shall bear some permanent distinctive marking by which the source and shade may be readily identified.

(b)(2)(ii)(H) The following is a guide for the selection of the proper shade numbers. These recommendations may be varied to suit the individual's needs.

Welding operation	Shade No.
Shielded metal-arc welding— 1/16-, 3/32-, 1/8-, 5/32-inch electrodes	10
Gas-shielded arc welding (nonferrous)— 1/16-, 3/32-, 1/8-, 5/32-inch electrodes	11
Gas-shielded arc welding (ferrous)— 1/16-, 3/32-, 1/8-, 5/32-inch electrodes	12
Shielded metal-arc welding: 3/16-, 7/32-, 1/4-inch electrodes 5/16-, 3/8-inch electrodes	 12 14
Atomic hydrogen welding	10-14
Carbon arc welding	14
Soldering	2
Torch brazing	3 or 4
Light cutting, up to 1 inch	3 or 4
Medium cutting, 1 inch to 6 inches	4 or 5
Heavy cutting, 6 inches and over	5 or 6
Gas welding (light) up to 1/8 inch	4 or 5
Gas welding (medium) 1/8 inch to 1/2 inch	5 or 6
Gas welding (heavy) 1/2 inch and over	6 or 8

Note: In gas welding or oxygen cutting where the torch produces a high yellow light, it is desirable to use a filter or lens that absorbs the yellow or sodium line in the visible light of the operation.

(b)(2)(ii)(I) OI Filter lenses must meet the test for transmission of radiant energy prescribed by any of the consensus standards listed in 29 CFR §1910.133(b)(1).

(b)(2)(iii) **Protection from arc welding rays** Where the work permits, the welder should be enclosed in an individual booth painted with a finish of low reflectivity such as zinc oxide (an important factor for absorbing ultraviolet radiations) and lamp black, or shall be enclosed with noncombustible screens similarly painted. Booths and screens shall permit circulation of air at floor level. Workers or other persons adjacent to the welding areas shall be protected from the rays by noncombustible or flameproof screens or shields or shall be required to wear appropriate goggles.

(b)(3) OI **Protective clothing—General requirements** Employees exposed to the hazards created by welding, cutting, or brazing operations shall be protected by personal protective equipment in accordance with the requirements of §1910.132 of this part. Appropriate protective clothing required for any welding operation will vary with the size, nature and location of the work to be performed.

(b)(4) **Work in confined spaces**

(b)(4)(i) OI **General** As used herein confined space is intended to mean a relatively small or restricted space such as a tank, boiler, pressure vessel, or small compartment of a ship.

(b)(4)(ii) **Ventilation** Ventilation is a prerequisite to work in confined spaces. For ventilation requirements see paragraph (c) of this section.

(b)(4)(iii) **Securing cylinders and machinery** When welding or cutting is being performed in any confined spaces the gas cylinders and welding machines shall be left on the outside. Before operations are started, heavy portable equipment mounted on wheels shall be securely blocked to prevent accidental movement.

(b)(4)(iv) **Lifelines** Where a welder must enter a confined space through a manhole or other small opening, means shall be provided for quickly removing him in case of emergency. When safety belts and lifelines are used for this purpose they shall be so attached to the welder's body that his body cannot be jammed in a small exit opening. An attendant with a pre-planned rescue procedure shall be stationed outside to observe the welder at all times and be capable of putting rescue operations into effect.

(b)(4)(v) **Electrode removal** When arc welding is to be suspended for any substantial period of time, such as during lunch or overnight, all electrodes shall be removed from the holders and the holders carefully located so that accidental contact cannot occur and the machine disconnected from the power source.

(b)(4)(vi) **Gas cylinder shutoff** In order to eliminate the possibility of gas escaping through leaks of improperly closed valves, when gas welding or cutting, the torch valves shall be closed and the fuel-gas and oxygen supply to the torch positively shut off at some point outside the confined area whenever the torch is not to be used for a substantial period of time, such as during lunch hour or overnight. Where practicable the torch and hose shall also be removed from the confined space.

(b)(4)(vii) OI **Warning sign** After welding operations are completed, the welder shall mark the hot metal or provide some other means of warning other workers.

(c) OI Health protection and ventilation

(c)(1) General

(c)(1)(i) **Contamination** The requirements in this paragraph have been established on the basis of the following three factors in arc and gas welding which govern the amount of contamination to which welders may be exposed:

(c)(1)(i)(A) Dimensions of space in which welding is to be done (with special regard to height of ceiling);

(c)(1)(i)(B) Number of welders;

(c)(1)(i)(C) Possible evolution of hazardous fumes, gases, or dust according to the metals involved.

(c)(1)(ii) **Screens** When welding must be performed in a space entirely screened on all sides, the screens shall be so arranged that no serious restriction of ventilation exists. It is desirable to have the screens so mounted that they are about 2 feet (0.61 m) above the floor unless the work is performed at so low a level that the screen must be extended nearer to the floor to protect nearby workers from the glare of welding.

(c)(1)(iii) **Maximum allowable concentration** Local exhaust or general ventilating systems shall be provided and arranged to keep the amount of toxic fumes, gases, or dusts below the maximum allowable concentration as specified in §1910.1000 of this part.

(c)(1)(iv) **Hazard communication** The employer shall include the potentially hazardous materials employed in fluxes, coatings, coverings, and filler metals, all of which are potentially used in welding and cutting, or are released to the atmosphere during welding and cutting, in the program established to comply with the Hazard Communication Standard (HCS) (§1910.1200). The employer shall ensure that each employee has access to labels on containers of such materials and safety data sheets, and is trained in accordance with the provisions of §1910.1200. Potentially hazardous materials shall include but not be limited to the materials itemized in paragraphs (c)(5) through (c)(12) of this section.

(c)(1)(v) Additional considerations for hazard communication in welding, cutting, and brazing.

(c)(1)(v)(A) The suppliers shall determine and shall label in accordance with §1910.1200 any hazards associated with the use of their materials in welding, cutting, and brazing.

(c)(1)(v)(B) In addition to any requirements imposed by §1910.1200, all filler metals and fusible granular materials shall carry the following notice, as a minimum, on tags, boxes, or other containers:

Do not use in areas without adequate ventilation. See ANSI Z49.1–1967 Safety in Welding, Cutting, and Allied Processes published by the American Welding Society.

(c)(1)(v)(C) Where brazing (welding) filler metals contain cadmium in significant amounts, the labels shall indicate the hazards associated with cadmium including cancer, lung and kidney effects, and acute toxicity effects.

(c)(1)(v)(D) Where brazing and gas welding fluxes contain fluorine compounds, the labels shall indicate the hazards associated with fluorine compounds including eye and respiratory tract effects.

(c)(1)(vi) Prior to June 1, 2015, employers may include the following information on labels in lieu of the labeling requirements in paragraph (c)(1)(v) of this section:

(c)(1)(vi)(A) All filler metals and fusible granular materials shall carry the following notice, as a minimum, on tags, boxes, or other containers:

CAUTION

Welding may produce fumes and gases hazardous to health. Avoid breathing these fumes and gases. Use adequate ventilation. See ANSI Z49.1 – 1967 Safety in Welding and Cutting published by the American Welding Society.

(c)(1)(vi)(B) Brazing (welding) filler metals containing cadmium in significant amounts shall carry the following notice on tags, boxes, or other containers:

WARNING
CONTAINS CADMIUM
POISONOUS FUMES MAY BE FORMED ON HEATING

Do not breathe fumes. Use only with adequate ventilation such as fume collectors, exhaust ventilators, or air-supplied respirators. See ANSI Z49.1 – 1967. If chest pain, cough, or fever develops after use call physician immediately.

(c)(1)(vi)(C) Brazing and gas welding fluxes containing fluorine compounds shall have a cautionary wording to indicate that they contain fluorine compounds. One such cautionary wording recommended by the American Welding Society for brazing and gas welding fluxes reads as follows:

CAUTION
CONTAINS FLUORIDES

This flux when heated gives off fumes that may irritate eyes, nose and throat.

1. Avoid fumes—use only in well-ventilated spaces.
2. Avoid contact of flux with eyes or skin.
3. Do not take internally.

(c)(2) Ventilation for general welding and cutting

(c)(2)(i) **General** Mechanical ventilation shall be provided when welding or cutting is done on metals not covered in paragraphs (c)(5) through (c)(12) of this section. (For specific materials, see the ventilation requirements of paragraphs (c)(5) through (c)(12) of this section.)

(c)(2)(i)(A) In a space of less than 10,000 cubic feet (284 m3) per welder.

(c)(2)(i)(B) In a room having a ceiling height of less than 16 feet (5 m).

(c)(2)(i)(C) In confined spaces or where the welding space contains partitions, balconies, or other structural barriers to the extent that they significantly obstruct cross ventilation.

(c)(2)(ii) **Minimum rate** Such ventilation shall be at the minimum rate of 2,000 cubic feet (57 m^3) per minute per welder, except where local exhaust hoods and booths as per paragraph (c)(3) of this section, or airline respirators approved by the Mine Safety and Health Administration and the National Institute for Occupational Safety and Health, pursuant to the provisions of 30 CFR part 11, are provided. Natural ventilation is considered sufficient for welding or cutting operations where the restrictions in paragraph (c)(2)(i) of this section are not present.

(c)(3) **Local exhaust hoods and booths** Mechanical local exhaust ventilation may be by means of either of the following:

(c)(3)(i) **Hoods** Freely movable hoods intended to be placed by the welder as near as practicable to the work being welded and provided with a rate of air-flow sufficient to maintain a velocity in the direction of the hood of 100 linear feet (30 m) per minute in the zone of welding when the hood is at its most remote distance from the point of welding. The rates of ventilation required to accomplish this control velocity using a 3-inch (7.6 cm) wide flanged suction opening are shown in the following table:

Welding zone	Minimum air flow[1] cubic feet/minute	Duct diameter, inches[2]
4 to 6 inches from arc or torch	150	3
6 to 8 inches from arc or torch	275	3½
8 to 10 inches from arc or torch	425	4½
10 to 12 inches from arc or torch	600	5½

[1] When brazing with cadmium bearing materials or when cutting on such materials increased rates of ventilation may be required.
[2] Nearest half-inch duct diameter based on 4,000 feet per minute velocity in pipe.

(c)(3)(ii) **Fixed enclosure** A fixed enclosure with a top and not less than two sides which surround the welding or cutting operations and with a rate of airflow sufficient to maintain a velocity away from the welder of not less than 100 linear feet (30 m) per minute.

OI indicates an OSHA Letter of Interpretation exists for this specific reference. Please see www.oshainterpretation.us for details.

(c)(4) [OI] **Ventilation in confined spaces**

(c)(4)(i) **Air replacement** All welding and cutting operations carried on in confined spaces shall be adequately ventilated to prevent the accumulation of toxic materials or possible oxygen deficiency. This applies not only to the welder but also to helpers and other personnel in the immediate vicinity. All air replacing that withdrawn shall be clean and respirable.

(c)(4)(ii) **Airline respirators** In circumstances for which it is impossible to provide such ventilation, airline respirators or hose masks approved for this purpose by the National Institute for Occupational Safety and Health (NIOSH) under 42 CFR part 84 must be used.

(c)(4)(iii) **Self-contained units** In areas immediately hazardous to life, a full-facepiece, pressure-demand, self-contained breathing apparatus or a combination full-facepiece, pressure-demand supplied-air respirator with an auxiliary, self-contained air supply approved by NIOSH under 42 CFR part 84 must be used.

(c)(4)(iv) **Outside helper** Where welding operations are carried on in confined spaces and where welders and helpers are provided with hose masks, hose masks with blowers or self-contained breathing equipment approved by the Mine Safety and Health Administration and the National Institute for Occupational Safety and Health, a worker shall be stationed on the outside of such confined spaces to insure the safety of those working within.

(c)(4)(v) **Oxygen for ventilation** Oxygen shall never be used for ventilation.

(c)(5) **Fluorine compounds**

(c)(5)(i) **General** In confined spaces, welding or cutting involving fluxes, coverings, or other materials which contain fluorine compounds shall be done in accordance with paragraph (c)(4) of this section. A fluorine compound is one that contains fluorine, as an element in chemical combination, not as a free gas.

(c)(5)(ii) **Maximum allowable concentration** The need for local exhaust ventilation or airline respirators for welding or cutting in other than confined spaces will depend upon the individual circumstances. However, experience has shown such protection to be desirable for fixed-location production welding and for all production welding on stainless steels. Where air samples taken at the welding location indicate that the fluorides liberated are below the maximum allowable concentration, such protection is not necessary.

(c)(6) **Zinc**

(c)(6)(i) **Confined spaces** In confined spaces welding or cutting involving zinc-bearing base or filler metals or metals coated with zinc-bearing materials shall be done in accordance with paragraph (c)(4) of this section.

(c)(6)(ii) **Indoors** Indoors, welding or cutting involving zinc-bearing base or filler metals coated with zinc-bearing materials shall be done in accordance with paragraph (c)(3) of this section.

(c)(7) **Lead**

(c)(7)(i) **Confined spaces** In confined spaces, welding involving lead-base metals (erroneously called lead-burning) shall be done in accordance with paragraph (c)(4) of this section.

(c)(7)(ii) **Indoors** Indoors, welding involving lead-base metals shall be done in accordance with paragraph (c)(3) of this section.

(c)(7)(iii) **Local ventilation** In confined spaces or indoors, welding or cutting operations involving metals containing lead, other than as an impurity, or metals coated with lead-bearing materials, including paint, must be done using local exhaust ventilation or airline respirators. Such operations, when done outdoors, must be done using respirators approved for this purpose by NIOSH under 42 CFR part 84. In all cases, workers in the immediate vicinity of the cutting operation must be protected by local exhaust ventilation or airline respirators.

(c)(8) **Beryllium** Welding or cutting indoors, outdoors, or in confined spaces involving beryllium-containing base or filler metals shall be done using local exhaust ventilation and airline respirators unless atmospheric tests under the most adverse conditions have established that the workers' exposure is within the acceptable concentrations defined by §1910.1000 of this part. In all cases, workers in the immediate vicinity of the welding or cutting operations shall be protected as necessary by local exhaust ventilation or airline respirators.

(c)(9) [OI] **Cadmium**

(c)(9)(i) **General** In confined spaces or indoors, welding or cutting operations involving cadmium-bearing or cadmium-coated base metals must be done using local exhaust ventilation or airline respirators unless atmospheric tests under the most adverse conditions show that employee exposure is within the acceptable concentrations specified by 29 CFR §1910.1000. Such operations, when done outdoors, must be done using respirators, such as fume respirators, approved for this purpose by NIOSH under 42 CFR part 84.

(c)(9)(ii) **Confined space** Welding (brazing) involving cadmium-bearing filler metals shall be done using ventilation as prescribed in paragraph (c)(3) or (c)(4) of this section if the work is to be done in a confined space.

(c)(10) [OI] **Mercury** In confined spaces or indoors, welding or cutting operations involving metals coated with mercury-bearing materials, including paint, must be done using local exhaust ventilation or airline respirators unless atmospheric tests under the most adverse conditions show that employee exposure is within the acceptable concentrations specified by 29 CFR §1910.1000. Such operations, when done outdoors, must be done using respirators approved for this purpose by NIOSH under 42 CFR Part 84.

(c)(11) **Cleaning compounds**

(c)(11)(i) **Manufacturer's instructions** In the use of cleaning materials, because of their possible toxicity or flammability, appropriate precautions such as manufacturers instructions shall be followed.

(c)(11)(ii) **Degreasing** Degreasing and other cleaning operations involving chlorinated hydrocarbons shall be so located that no vapors from these operations will reach or be drawn into the atmosphere surrounding any welding operation. In addition, trichloroethylene and perchlorethylene should be kept out of atmospheres penetrated by the ultraviolet radiation of gas-shielded welding operations.

(c)(12) **Cutting of stainless steels** Oxygen cutting, using either a chemical flux or iron powder or gas-shielded arc cutting of stainless steel, shall be done using mechanical ventilation adequate to remove the fumes generated.

(c)(13) **First-aid equipment** First-aid equipment shall be available at all times. All injuries shall be reported as soon as possible for medical attention. First aid shall be rendered until medical attention can be provided.

(d) **Industrial applications**

(d)(1) **Transmission pipeline**

(d)(1)(i) **General** The requirements of paragraphs (b) and (c) of this section and §1910.254 of this part shall be observed.

(d)(1)(ii) **Field shop operations** Where field shop operations are involved for fabrication of fittings, river crossings, road crossings, and pumping and compressor stations the requirements of paragraphs (a), (b), and (c) of this section and §1910.253 and §1910.254 of this part shall be observed.

(d)(1)(iii) **Electric shock** When arc welding is performed in wet conditions, or under conditions of high humidity, special protection against electric shock shall be supplied.

(d)(1)(iv) **Pressure testing** In pressure testing of pipelines, the workers and the public shall be protected against injury by the blowing out of closures or other pressure restraining devices. Also, protection shall be provided against expulsion of loose dirt that may have become trapped in the pipe.

(d)(1)(v) **Construction standards** The welded construction of transmission pipelines shall be conducted in accordance with the Standard for Welding Pipe Lines and Related Facilities, API Std. 1104—1968, which is incorporated by reference as specified in §1910.6.

(d)(1)(vi) **Flammable substance lines** The connection, by welding, of branches to pipelines carrying flammable substances shall be performed in accordance with Welding or Hot Tapping on Equipment Containing Flammables, API Std. PSD No. 2201—1963, which is incorporated by reference as specified in §1910.6.

(d)(1)(vii) **X-ray inspection** The use of X-rays and radioactive isotopes for the inspection of welded pipeline joints shall be carried out in conformance with the American National Standard Safety Standard for Non-Medical X-ray and Sealed Gamma-Ray Sources, ANSI Z54.1—1963, which is incorporated by reference as specified in §1910.6.

(d)(2) **Mechanical piping systems**

(d)(2)(i) **General** The requirements of paragraphs (a), (b), and (c) of this section and §1910.253 and §1910.254 of this part shall be observed.

(d)(2)(ii) **X-ray inspection** The use of X-rays and radioactive isotopes for the inspection of welded piping joints shall be in conformance with the American National Standard Safety Standard for Non-Medical X-ray and Sealed Gamma-Ray Sources, ANSI Z54.1—1963.

[55 FR 13696, Apr. 11, 1990, as amended at 61 FR 9240, Mar. 7, 1996; 63 FR 1284, Jan. 8, 1998; 74 FR 46357, Sept. 9, 2009]

§1910.253 [OI]
Oxygen–fuel gas welding and cutting

(a) **General requirements**

(a)(1) **Flammable mixture** Mixtures of fuel gases and air or oxygen may be explosive and shall be guarded against. No device or attachment facilitating or permitting mixtures of air or oxygen with flammable gases prior to consumption, except at the burner or in a standard torch, shall be allowed unless approved for the purpose.

(a)(2) **Maximum pressure** Under no condition shall acetylene be generated, piped (except in approved cylinder manifolds) or utilized at a pressure in excess of 15 psig (103 kPa gauge pressure) or 30 psia (206 kPa absolute). The 30 psia (206 kPa absolute) limit is intended to prevent unsafe use of acetylene in pressurized chambers such as caissons, underground excavations or tunnel construction.) This requirement is not intended to apply to storage of acetylene dissolved in a suitable solvent in cylinders manufactured and maintained according to U.S. Department of Transportation requirements, or to acetylene for chemical use. The use of liquid acetylene shall be prohibited.

(a)(3) **Apparatus** Only approved apparatus such as torches, regulators or pressure-reducing valves, acetylene generators, and manifolds shall be used.

(a)(4) [OI] **Personnel** Workmen in charge of the oxygen or fuel-gas supply equipment, including generators, and oxygen or fuel-gas distribution piping systems shall be instructed and judged competent by their employers for this important work before being left in charge. Rules and instructions covering the operation and maintenance of oxygen or fuel-gas supply equipment including generators, and oxygen or fuel-gas distribution piping systems shall be readily available.

(b) **Cylinders and containers**

(b)(1) **Approval and marking**

(b)(1)(i) All portable cylinders used for the storage and shipment of compressed gases shall be constructed and maintained in accordance with the regulations of the U.S. Department of Transportation, 49 CFR parts 171–179.

(b)(1)(ii) Compressed gas cylinders shall be legibly marked, for the purpose of identifying the gas content, with either the chemical or the trade name of the gas. Such marking shall be by means of stenciling, stamping, or labeling, and shall not be readily removable. Whenever practical, the marking shall be located on the shoulder of the cylinder.

(b)(1)(iii) Compressed gas cylinders shall be equipped with connections complying with the American National Standard Compressed Gas Cylinder Valve Outlet and Inlet Connections, ANSI B57.1—1965, which is incorporated by reference as specified in §1910.6.

(b)(1)(iv) [OI] All cylinders with a water weight capacity of over 30 pounds (13.6 kg) shall be equipped with means of connecting a valve protection cap or with a collar or recess to protect the valve.

(b)(2) [OI] **Storage of cylinders—general**

(b)(2)(i) Cylinders shall be kept away from radiators and other sources of heat.

(b)(2)(ii) Inside of buildings, cylinders shall be stored in a well-protected, well-ventilated, dry location, at least 20 feet (6.1 m) from highly combustible materials such as oil or excelsior. Cylinders should be stored in definitely assigned places away from elevators, stairs, or gangways. Assigned storage spaces shall be located where cylinders will not be knocked over or damaged by passing or falling objects, or subject to tampering by unauthorized persons. Cylinders shall not be kept in unventilated enclosures such as lockers and cupboards.

(b)(2)(iii) Empty cylinders shall have their valves closed.

(b)(2)(iv) Valve protection caps, where cylinder is designed to accept a cap, shall always be in place, hand-tight, except when cylinders are in use or connected for use.

(b)(3) [OI] **Fuel-gas cylinder storage** Inside a building, cylinders, except those in actual use or attached ready for use, shall be limited to a total gas capacity of 2,000 cubic feet (56 m^3) or 300 pounds (135.9 kg) of liquefied petroleum gas.

(b)(3)(i) For storage in excess of 2,000 cubic feet (56 m^3) total gas capacity of cylinders or 300 (135.9 kg) pounds of liquefied petroleum gas, a separate room or compartment conforming to the requirements specified in paragraphs (f)(6)(i)(H) and (f)(6)(i)(I) of this section shall be provided, or cylinders shall be kept outside or in a special building. Special buildings, rooms or compartments shall have no open flame for heating or lighting and shall be well ventilated. They may also be used for storage of calcium carbide in quantities not to exceed 600 (271.8 kg) pounds, when contained in metal containers complying with paragraphs (g)(1)(i) and (g)(1)(ii) of this section.

(b)(3)(ii) Acetylene cylinders shall be stored valve end up.

(b)(4) [OI] **Oxygen storage**

(b)(4)(i) Oxygen cylinders shall not be stored near highly combustible material, especially oil and grease; or near reserve stocks of carbide and acetylene or other fuel-gas cylinders, or near any other substance likely to cause or accelerate fire; or in an acetylene generator compartment.

(b)(4)(ii) Oxygen cylinders stored in outside generator houses shall be separated from the generator or carbide storage rooms by a noncombustible partition having a fire-resistance rating of at least 1 hour. This partition shall be without openings and shall be gastight.

(b)(4)(iii) Oxygen cylinders in storage shall be separated from fuel-gas cylinders or combustible materials (especially oil or grease), a minimum distance of 20 feet (6.1 m) or by a noncombustible barrier at least 5 feet (1.5 m) high having a fire-resistance rating of at least one-half hour.

(b)(4)(iv) Where a liquid oxygen system is to be used to supply gaseous oxygen for welding or cutting and the system has a storage capacity of more than 13,000 cubic feet (364 m^3) of oxygen (measured at 14.7 psia (101 kPa) and 70 °F (21.1 °C)), connected in service or ready for service, or more than 25,000 cubic feet (700 m^3) of oxygen (measured at 14.7 psia (101 kPa) and 70 °F (21.1 °C), including unconnected reserves on hand at the site, it shall comply with the provisions of the Standard for Bulk Oxygen Systems at Consumer Sites, NFPA No. 566—1965, which is incorporated by reference as specified in §1910.6.

(b)(5) **Operating procedures**

(b)(5)(i) Cylinders, cylinder valves, couplings, regulators, hose, and apparatus shall be kept free from oily or greasy substances. Oxygen cylinders or apparatus shall not be handled with oily hands or gloves. A jet of oxygen must never be permitted to strike an oily surface, greasy clothes, or enter a fuel oil or other storage tank.

(b)(5)(ii)(A) [OI] When transporting cylinders by a crane or derrick, a cradle, boat, or suitable platform shall be used. Slings or electric magnets shall not be used for this purpose. Valve-protection caps, where cylinder is designed to accept a cap, shall always be in place.

(b)(5)(ii)(B) [OI] Cylinders shall not be dropped or struck or permitted to strike each other violently.

(b)(5)(ii)(C) Valve-protection caps shall not be used for lifting cylinders from one vertical position to another. Bars shall not be used under valves or valve-protection caps to pry cylinders loose when frozen to the ground or otherwise fixed; the use of warm (not boiling) water is recommended. Valve-protection caps are designed to protect cylinder valves from damage.

(b)(5)(ii)(D) [OI] Unless cylinders are secured on a special truck, regulators shall be removed and valve-protection caps, when provided for, shall be put in place before cylinders are moved.

(b)(5)(ii)(E) Cylinders not having fixed hand wheels shall have keys, handles, or nonadjustable wrenches on valve stems while these cylinders are in service. In multiple cylinder installations only one key or handle is required for each manifold.

(b)(5)(ii)(F) Cylinder valves shall be closed before moving cylinders.

(b)(5)(ii)(G) Cylinder valves shall be closed when work is finished.

(b)(5)(ii)(H) Valves of empty cylinders shall be closed.

(b)(5)(ii)(I) [OI] Cylinders shall be kept far enough away from the actual welding or cutting operation so that sparks, hot slag, or flame will not reach them, or fire-resistant shields shall be provided.

(b)(5)(ii)(J) Cylinders shall not be placed where they might become part of an electric circuit. Contacts with third rails, trolley wires, etc., shall be avoided. Cylinders shall be kept away from radiators, piping systems, layout tables, etc., that may be used for grounding electric circuits such as for arc welding machines. Any practice such as the tapping of an electrode against a cylinder to strike an arc shall be prohibited.

(b)(5)(ii)(K) Cylinders shall never be used as rollers or supports, whether full or empty.

(b)(5)(ii)(L) The numbers and markings stamped into cylinders shall not be tampered with.

(b)(5)(ii)(M) No person, other than the gas supplier, shall attempt to mix gases in a cylinder. No one, except the owner of the cylinder or person authorized by him, shall refill a cylinder.

(b)(5)(ii)(N) No one shall tamper with safety devices in cylinders or valves.

(b)(5)(ii)(O) Cylinders shall not be dropped or otherwise roughly handled.

(b)(5)(ii)(P) Unless connected to a manifold, oxygen from a cylinder shall not be used without first attaching an oxygen regulator to the cylinder valve. Before connecting the regulator to the cylinder valve, the valve shall be opened slightly for an instant and then closed. Always stand to one side of the outlet when opening the cylinder valve.

(b)(5)(ii)(Q) A hammer or wrench shall not be used to open cylinder valves. If valves cannot be opened by hand, the supplier shall be notified.

(b)(5)(ii)(R)(1) Cylinder valves shall not be tampered with nor should any attempt be made to repair them. If trouble is experienced, the supplier should be sent a report promptly indicating the character of the trouble and the cylinder's serial number. Supplier's instructions as to its disposition shall be followed.

(b)(5)(ii)(R)(2) Complete removal of the stem from a diaphragm-type cylinder valve shall be avoided.

(b)(5)(iii)(A) Fuel-gas cylinders shall be placed with valve end up whenever they are in use. Liquefied gases shall be stored and shipped with the valve end up.

(b)(5)(iii)(B) Cylinders shall be handled carefully. Rough handling, knocks, or falls are liable to damage the cylinder, valve or safety devices and cause leakage.

(b)(5)(iii)(C) Before connecting a regulator to a cylinder valve, the valve shall be opened slightly and closed immediately. The valve shall be opened while standing to one side of the outlet; never in front of it. Never crack a fuel-gas cylinder valve near other welding work or near sparks, flame, or other possible sources of ignition.

(b)(5)(iii)(D) Before a regulator is removed from a cylinder valve, the cylinder valve shall be closed and the gas released from the regulator.

(b)(5)(iii)(E) Nothing shall be placed on top of an acetylene cylinder when in use which may damage the safety device or interfere with the quick closing of the valve.

(b)(5)(iii)(F) If cylinders are found to have leaky valves or fittings which cannot be stopped by closing of the valve, the cylinders shall be taken outdoors away from sources of ignition and slowly emptied.

(b)(5)(iii)(G) A warning should be placed near cylinders having leaking fuse plugs or other leaking safety devices not to approach them with a lighted cigarette or other source of ignition. Such cylinders should be plainly tagged; the supplier should be promptly notified and his instructions followed as to their return.

(b)(5)(iii)(H) Safety devices shall not be tampered with.

(b)(5)(iii)(I) Fuel-gas shall never be used from cylinders through torches or other devices equipped with shutoff valves without reducing the pressure through a suitable regulator attached to the cylinder valve or manifold.

(b)(5)(iii)(J) The cylinder valve shall always be opened slowly.

(b)(5)(iii)(K) An acetylene cylinder valve shall not be opened more than one and one-half turns of the spindle, and preferably no more than three-fourths of a turn.

(b)(5)(iii)(L) Where a special wrench is required it shall be left in position on the stem of the valve while the cylinder is in use so that the fuel-gas flow can be quickly turned off in case of emergency. In the case of manifolded or coupled cylinders at least one such wrench shall always be available for immediate use.

(c) Manifolding of cylinders

(c)(1) Fuel-gas manifolds

(c)(1)(i) Manifolds shall be approved either separately for each component part or as an assembled unit.

(c)(1)(ii) Except as provided in paragraph (c)(1)(iii) of this section fuel-gas cylinders connected to one manifold inside a building shall be limited to a total capacity not exceeding 300 pounds (135.9 kg) of liquefied petroleum gas or 3,000 cubic feet (84 m^3) of other fuel-gas. More than one such manifold with connected cylinders may be located in the same room provided the manifolds are at least 50 feet (15 m) apart or separated by a noncombustible barrier at least 5 feet (1.5 m) high having a fire-resistance rating of at least one-half hour.

(c)(1)(iii) Fuel-gas cylinders connected to one manifold having an aggregate capacity exceeding 300 pounds (135.9 kg) of liquefied petroleum gas or 3,000 cubic feet (84 m^3) of other fuel-gas shall be located outdoors, or in a separate building or room constructed in accordance with paragraphs (f)(6)(i)(H) and (f)(6)(i)(I) of this section.

(c)(1)(iv) Separate manifold buildings or rooms may also be used for the storage of drums of calcium carbide and cylinders containing fuel gases as provided in paragraph (b)(3) of this section. Such buildings or rooms shall have no open flames for heating or lighting and shall be well-ventilated.

(c)(1)(v) High-pressure fuel-gas manifolds shall be provided with approved pressure regulating devices.

(c)(2) High-pressure oxygen manifolds (for use with cylinders having a Department of Transportation service pressure above 200 psig (1.36 MPa)).

(c)(2)(i) Manifolds shall be approved either separately for each component part or as an assembled unit.

(c)(2)(ii) Oxygen manifolds shall not be located in an acetylene generator room. Oxygen manifolds shall be separated from fuel-gas cylinders or combustible materials (especially oil or grease), a minimum distance of 20 feet (6.1 m) or by a noncombustible barrier at least 5 feet (1.5 m) high having a fire-resistance rating of at least one-half hour.

(c)(2)(iii) Except as provided in paragraph (c)(2)(iv) of this section, oxygen cylinders connected to one manifold shall be limited to a total gas capacity of 6,000 cubic feet (168 m^3). More than one such manifold with connected cylinders may be located in the same room provided the manifolds are at least 50 feet (15 m) apart or separated by a noncombustible barrier at least 5 feet (1.5 m) high having a fire-resistance rating of at least one-half hour.

(c)(2)(iv) An oxygen manifold, to which cylinders having an aggregate capacity of more than 6,000 cubic feet (168 m^3) of oxygen are connected, should be located outdoors or in a separate noncombustible building. Such a manifold, if located inside a building having other occupancy, shall be located in a separate room of noncombustible construction having a fire-resistance rating of at least one-half hour or in an area with no combustible material within 20 feet (6.1 m) of the manifold.

(c)(2)(v) An oxygen manifold or oxygen bulk supply system which has storage capacity of more than 13,000 cubic feet (364 m^3) of oxygen (measured at 14.7 psia (101 kPa) and 70 °F (21.1 °C)), connected in service or ready for service, or more than 25,000 cubic feet (700 m^3) of oxygen (measured at 14.7 psia (101 kPa) and 70 °F (21.1 °C)), including unconnected reserves on hand at the site, shall comply with the provisions of the Standard for Bulk Oxygen Systems at Consumer Sites, NFPA No. 566–1965.

(c)(2)(vi) High-pressure oxygen manifolds shall be provided with approved pressure-regulating devices.

(c)(3) **Low-pressure oxygen manifolds** (for use with cylinders having a Department of Transportation service pressure not exceeding 200 psig (1.36 MPa)).

(c)(3)(i) Manifolds shall be of substantial construction suitable for use with oxygen at a pressure of 250 psig (1.7 MPa). They shall have a minimum bursting pressure of 1,000 psig (6.8 MPa) and shall be protected by a safety relief device which will relieve at a maximum pressure of 500 psig (3.4 MPa). DOT–4L200 cylinders have safety devices which relieve at a maximum pressure of 250 psig (1.7 MPa) (or 235 psig (1.6 MPa) if vacuum insulation is used).

(c)(3)(ii) Hose and hose connections subject to cylinder pressure shall comply with paragraph (e)(5) of this section. Hose shall have a minimum bursting pressure of 1,000 psig (6.8 MPa).

(c)(3)(iii) The assembled manifold including leads shall be tested and proven gas-tight at a pressure of 300 psig (2.04 MPa). The fluid used for testing oxygen manifolds shall be oil-free and not combustible.

(c)(3)(iv) The location of manifolds shall comply with paragraphs (c)(2)(ii), (c)(2)(iii), (c)(2)(iv), and (c)(2)(v) of this section.

(c)(3)(v) The following sign shall be conspicuously posted at each manifold:

Low-Pressure Manifold
Do Not Connect High-Pressure Cylinders
Maximum Pressure—250 psig (1.7 MPa)

(c)(4) Portable outlet headers

(c)(4)(i) Portable outlet headers shall not be used indoors except for temporary service where the conditions preclude a direct supply from outlets located on the service piping system.

(c)(4)(ii) Each outlet on the service piping from which oxygen or fuel-gas is withdrawn to supply a portable outlet header shall be equipped with a readily accessible shutoff valve.

(c)(4)(iii) Hose and hose connections used for connecting the portable outlet header to the service piping shall comply with paragraph (e)(5) of this section.

(c)(4)(iv) Master shutoff valves for both oxygen and fuel-gas shall be provided at the entry end of the portable outlet header.

(c)(4)(v) Portable outlet headers for fuel-gas service shall be provided with an approved hydraulic back-pressure valve installed at the inlet and preceding the service outlets, unless an approved pressure-reducing regulator, an approved back-flow check valve, or an approved hydraulic back-pressure valve is installed at each outlet. Outlets provided on headers for oxygen service may be fitted for use with pressure-reducing regulators or for direct hose connection.

(c)(4)(vi) Each service outlet on portable outlet headers shall be provided with a valve assembly that includes a detachable outlet seal cap, chained or otherwise attached to the body of the valve.

(c)(4)(vii) Materials and fabrication procedures for portable outlet headers shall comply with paragraphs (d)(1), (d)(2), and (d)(5) of this section.

(c)(4)(viii) Portable outlet headers shall be provided with frames which will support the equipment securely in the correct operating position and protect them from damage during handling and operation.

(c)(5) Manifold operation procedures

(c)(5)(i) Cylinder manifolds shall be installed under the supervision of someone familiar with the proper practices with reference to their construction and use.

(c)(5)(ii) All manifolds and parts used in methods of manifolding shall be used only for the gas or gases for which they are approved.

(c)(5)(iii) When acetylene cylinders are coupled, approved flash arresters shall be installed between each cylinder and the coupler block. For outdoor use only, and when the number of cylinders coupled does not exceed three, one flash arrester installed between the coupler block and regulator is acceptable.

(c)(5)(iv) The aggregate capacity of fuel-gas cylinders connected to a portable manifold inside a building shall not exceed 3,000 cubic feet (84 m^3) of gas.

(c)(5)(v) Acetylene and liquefied fuel-gas cylinders shall be manifolded in a vertical position.

(c)(5)(vi) The pressure in the gas cylinders connected to and discharged simultaneously through a common manifold shall be approximately equal.

(d) Service piping systems

(d)(1) Materials and design

(d)(1)(i)(A) Piping and fittings shall comply with section 2, Industrial Gas and Air Piping Systems, of the American National Standard Code for Pressure Piping ANSI B31.1, 1967, which is incorporated by reference as specified in §1910.6, insofar as it does not conflict with paragraphs (d)(1)(i)(A)(1) and (d)(1)(i)(A)(2) of this section:

(d)(1)(i)(A)(1) Pipe shall be at least Schedule 40 and fittings shall be at least standard weight in sizes up to and including 6-inch nominal.

(d)(1)(i)(A)(2) Copper tubing shall be Types K or L in accordance with the Standard Specification for Seamless Copper Water Tube, ASTM B88–66a, which is incorporated by reference as specified in §1910.6.

(d)(1)(i)(B) Piping shall be steel, wrought iron, brass or copper pipe, or seamless copper, brass or stainless steel tubing, except as provided in paragraphs (d)(1)(ii) and (d)(1)(iii) of this section.

(d)(1)(ii)(A) Oxygen piping and fittings at pressures in excess of 700 psi (4.8 MPa), shall be stainless steel or copper alloys.

(d)(1)(ii)(B) Hose connections and hose complying with paragraph (e)(5) of this section may be used to connect the outlet of a manifold pressure regulator to piping providing the working pressure of the piping is 250 psi (1.7 MPa) or less and the length of the hose does not exceed 5 feet (1.5 m). Hose shall have a minimum bursting pressure of 1,000 psig (6.8 MPa).

(d)(1)(ii)(C) When oxygen is supplied to a service piping system from a low-pressure oxygen manifold without an intervening pressure regulating device, the piping system shall have a minimum design pressure of 250 psig (1.7 MPa). A pressure regulating device shall be used at each station outlet when the connected equipment is for use at pressures less than 250 psig (1.7 MPa).

(d)(1)(iii)(A) Piping for acetylene or acetylenic compounds shall be steel or wrought iron.

(d)(1)(iii)(B) Unalloyed copper shall not be used for acetylene or acetylenic compounds except in listed equipment.

(d)(2) Piping joints

(d)(2)(i) Joints in steel or wrought iron piping shall be welded, threaded or flanged. Fittings, such as ells, tees, couplings, and unions, may be rolled, forged or cast steel, malleable iron or nodular iron. Gray or white cast iron fittings are prohibited.

(d)(2)(ii) Joints in brass or copper pipe shall be welded, brazed, threaded, or flanged. If of the socket type, they shall be brazed with silver-brazing alloy or similar high melting point (not less than 800 °F (427 °C)) filler metal.

(d)(2)(iii) Joints in seamless copper, brass, or stainless steel tubing shall be approved gas tubing fittings or the joints shall be brazed. If of the socket type, they shall be brazed with silver-brazing alloy or similar high melting point (not less than 800 °F (427 °C)) filler metal.

(d)(3) Installation

(d)(3)(i) Distribution lines shall be installed and maintained in a safe operating condition.

(d)(3)(ii) All piping shall be run as directly as practicable, protected against physical damage, proper allowance being made for expansion and contraction, jarring and vibration. Pipe laid underground in earth shall be located below the frost line and protected against corrosion. After assembly, piping shall be thoroughly blown out with air, nitrogen, or carbon dioxide to remove foreign materials. For oxygen piping, only oil-free air, oil-free nitrogen, or oil-free carbon dioxide shall be used.

(d)(3)(iii) Only piping which has been welded or brazed shall be installed in tunnels, trenches or ducts. Shutoff valves shall be located outside such conduits. Oxygen piping may be placed in the same tunnel, trench or duct with fuel-gas pipelines, provided there is good natural or forced ventilation.

(d)(3)(iv) Low points in piping carrying moist gas shall be drained into drip pots constructed so as to permit pumping or draining out the condensate at necessary intervals. Drain valves shall be installed for this purpose having outlets normally closed with screw caps or plugs. No open end valves or petcocks shall be used, except that in drips located out of doors, underground, and not readily accessible, valves may be used at such points if they are equipped with means to secure them in the closed position. Pipes leading to the surface of the ground shall be cased or jacketed where necessary to prevent loosening or breaking.

(d)(3)(v) Gas cocks or valves shall be provided for all buildings at points where they will be readily accessible for shutting off the gas supply to these buildings in any emergency. There shall also be provided a shutoff valve in the discharge line from the generator, gas holder, manifold or other source of supply.

(d)(3)(vi) Shutoff valves shall not be installed in safety relief lines in such a manner that the safety relief device can be rendered ineffective.

(d)(3)(vii) Fittings and lengths of pipe shall be examined internally before assembly and, if necessary freed from scale or dirt. Oxygen piping and fittings shall be washed out with a suitable solution which will effectively remove grease and dirt but will not react with oxygen. Hot water solutions of caustic soda or trisodium phosphate are effective cleaning agents for this purpose.

(d)(3)(viii) Piping shall be thoroughly blown out after assembly to remove foreign materials. For oxygen piping, oil-free air, oil-free nitrogen, or oil-free carbon dioxide shall be used. For other piping, air or inert gas may be used.

(d)(3)(ix) When flammable gas lines or other parts of equipment are being purged of air or gas, open lights or other sources of ignition shall not be permitted near uncapped openings.

(d)(3)(x) No welding or cutting shall be performed on an acetylene or oxygen pipeline, including the attachment of hangers or supports, until the line has been purged. Only oil-free air, oil-free nitrogen, or oil-free carbon dioxide shall be used to purge oxygen lines.

(d)(4) Painting and signs

(d)(4)(i) Underground pipe and tubing and outdoor ferrous pipe and tubing shall be covered or painted with a suitable material for protection against corrosion.

(d)(4)(ii) Aboveground piping systems shall be marked in accordance with the American National Standard Scheme for the Identification of Piping Systems, ANSI A13.1−1956, which is incorporated by reference as specified in §1910.6.

(d)(4)(iii) Station outlets shall be marked to indicate the name of the gas.

(d)(5) Testing

(d)(5)(i) Piping systems shall be tested and proved gastight at 1½ times the maximum operating pressure, and shall be thoroughly purged of air before being placed in service. The material used for testing oxygen lines shall be oil free and noncombustible. Flames shall not be used to detect leaks.

(d)(5)(ii) When flammable gas lines or other parts of equipment are being purged of air or gas, sources of ignition shall not be permitted near uncapped openings.

(e) Protective equipment, hose, and regulators

(e)(1) **General** Equipment shall be installed and used only in the service for which it is approved and as recommended by the manufacturer.

(e)(2) **Pressure relief devices** Service piping systems shall be protected by pressure relief devices set to function at not more than the design pressure of the systems and discharging upwards to a safe location.

(e)(3) Piping protective equipment

(e)(3)(i) The fuel-gas and oxygen piping systems, including portable outlet headers shall incorporate the protective equipment shown in Figures Q–1, Q–2, and Q–3. When only a portion of a fuel-gas system is to be used with oxygen, only that portion need comply with this paragraph (e)(3)(i).

Figure Q–1 **Figure Q–2** **Figure Q–3**

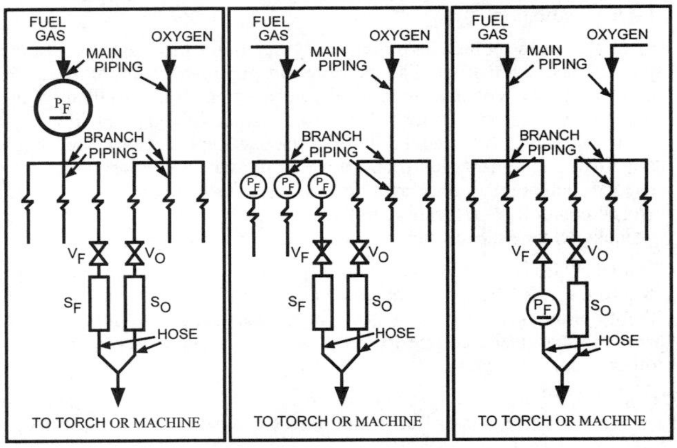

LEGEND
P_F – Protective equipment in fuel gas piping
V_F – Fuel gas station outlet valve
V_O – Oxygen station outlet valve
S_F – Backflow prevention device(s) at fuel gas station outlet
S_O – Backflow prevention device(s) at oxygen station outlet

(e)(3)(ii) Approved protective equipment (designated PF in Figures Q–1, Q–2, and Q–3) shall be installed in fuel-gas piping to prevent:

(e)(3)(ii)(A) Backflow of oxygen into the fuel-gas supply system;

(e)(3)(ii)(B) Passage of a flash back into the fuel-gas supply system; and

(e)(3)(ii)(C) Excessive back pressure of oxygen in the fuel-gas supply system. The three functions of the protective equipment may be combined in one device or may be provided by separate devices.

(e)(3)(ii)(C)(1) The protective equipment shall be located in the main supply line, as in Figure Q–1 or at the head of each branch line, as in Figure Q–2 or at each location where fuel-gas is withdrawn, as in Figure Q–3. Where branch lines are of 2-inch pipe size or larger or of substantial length, protective equipment (designated as P_F) shall be located as shown in either Q–2 and Q–3.

(e)(3)(ii)(C)(2) Backflow protection shall be provided by an approved device that will prevent oxygen from flowing into the fuel-gas system or fuel from flowing into the oxygen system (see S_F, in Figures Q–1 and Q–2).

(e)(3)(ii)(C)(3) Flash-back protection shall be provided by an approved device that will prevent flame from passing into the fuel-gas system.

(e)(3)(ii)(C)(4) Back-pressure protection shall be provided by an approved pressure-relief device set at a pressure not greater than the pressure rating of the backflow or the flashback protection device, whichever is lower. The pressure-relief device shall be located on the downstream side of the backflow and flashback protection devices. The vent from the pressure-relief device shall be at least as large as the relief device inlet and shall be installed without low points that may collect moisture. If low points are unavoidable, drip pots with drains closed with screw plugs or caps shall be installed at the low points. The vent terminus shall not endanger personnel or property through gas discharge; shall be located away from ignition sources; and shall terminate in a hood or bend.

(e)(3)(iii) If pipeline protective equipment incorporates a liquid, the liquid level shall be maintained, and a suitable antifreeze may be used to prevent freezing.

(e)(3)(iv) Fuel gas for use with equipment not requiring oxygen shall be withdrawn upstream of the piping protective devices.

(e)(4) Station outlet protective equipment

(e)(4)(i) A check valve, pressure regulator, hydraulic seal, or combination of these devices shall be provided at each station outlet, including those on portable headers, to prevent backflow, as shown in Figures Q–1, Q–2, and Q–3 and designated as S_F and S_O.

(e)(4)(ii) When approved pipeline protective equipment (designated P_F) is located at the station outlet as in Figure Q–3, no additional check valve, pressure regulator, or hydraulic seal is required.

(e)(4)(iii) A shutoff valve (designated V_F and V_O) shall be installed at each station outlet and shall be located on the upstream side of other station outlet equipment.

(e)(4)(iv) If the station outlet is equipped with a detachable regulator, the outlet shall terminate in a union connection that complies with the Regulator Connection Standards, 1958, Compressed Gas Association, which is incorporated by reference as specified in §1910.6.

(e)(4)(v) If the station outlet is connected directly to a hose, the outlet shall terminate in a union connection complying with the Standard Hose Connection Specifications, 1957, Compressed Gas Association, which is incorporated by reference as specified in §1910.6.

(e)(4)(vi) Station outlets may terminate in pipe threads to which permanent connections are to be made, such as to a machine.

(e)(4)(vii) Station outlets shall be equipped with a detachable outlet seal cap secured in place. This cap shall be used to seal the outlet except when a hose, a regulator, or piping is attached.

(e)(4)(viii) Where station outlets are equipped with approved backflow and flashback protective devices, as many as four torches may be supplied from one station outlet through rigid piping, provided each outlet from such piping is equipped with a shutoff valve and provided the fuel-gas capacity of any one torch does not exceed 15 cubic feet (0.42 m^3) per hour. This paragraph (e)(4)(viii) does not apply to machines.

(e)(5) Hose and hose connections

(e)(5)(i) Hose for oxy-fuel gas service shall comply with the Specification for Rubber Welding Hose, 1958, Compressed Gas Association and Rubber Manufacturers Association, which is incorporated by reference as specified in §1910.6.

(e)(5)(ii) When parallel lengths of oxygen and acetylene hose are taped together for convenience and to prevent tangling, not more than 4 inches (10.2 cm) out of 12 inches (30.5 cm) shall be covered by tape.

(e)(5)(iii) Hose connections shall comply with the Standard Hose Connection Specifications, 1957, Compressed Gas Association.

(e)(5)(iv) Hose connections shall be clamped or otherwise securely fastened in a manner that will withstand, without leakage, twice the pressure to which they are normally subjected in service, but in no case less than a pressure of 300 psi (2.04 MPa). Oil-free air or an oil-free inert gas shall be used for the test.

(e)(5)(v) Hose showing leaks, burns, worn places, or other defects rendering it unfit for service shall be repaired or replaced.

(e)(6) Pressure-reducing regulators

(e)(6)(i) Pressure-reducing regulators shall be used only for the gas and pressures for which they are intended. The regulator inlet connections shall comply with Regulator Connection Standards, 1958, Compressed Gas Association.

(e)(6)(ii) When regulators or parts of regulators, including gages, need repair, the work shall be performed by skilled mechanics who have been properly instructed.

(e)(6)(iii) Gages on oxygen regulators shall be marked "USE NO OIL."

(e)(6)(iv) Union nuts and connections on regulators shall be inspected before use to detect faulty seats which may cause leakage of gas when the regulators are attached to the cylinder valves.

(f) Acetylene generators

(f)(1) Approval and marking

(f)(1)(i) Generators shall be of approved construction and shall be plainly marked with the maximum rate of acetylene in cubic feet per hour for which they are designed; the weight and size of carbide necessary for a single charge; the manufacturer's name and address; and the name or number of the type of generator.

(f)(1)(ii) Carbide shall be of the size marked on the generator nameplate.

(f)(2) Rating and pressure limitations

(f)(2)(i) The total hourly output of a generator shall not exceed the rate for which it is approved and marked. Unless specifically approved for higher ratings, carbide-feed generators shall be rated at 1 cubic foot (0.028 m^3) per hour per pound of carbide required for a single complete charge.

(f)(2)(ii) Relief valves shall be regularly operated to insure proper functioning. Relief valves for generating chambers shall be set to open at a pressure not in excess of 15 psig (103 kPa gauge pressure). Relief valves for hydraulic back pressure valves shall be set to open at a pressure not in excess of 20 psig (137 kPa gauge pressure).

(f)(2)(iii) Nonautomatic generators shall not be used for generating acetylene at pressures exceeding l psig (7 kPa gauge pressure), and all water overflows shall be visible.

(f)(3) **Location** The space around the generator shall be ample for free, unobstructed operation and maintenance and shall permit ready adjustment and charging.

(f)(4) **Stationary acetylene generators (automatic and nonautomatic)**

(f)(4)(i)(A) The foundation shall be so arranged that the generator will be level and so that no excessive strain will be placed on the generator or its connections. Acetylene generators shall be grounded.

(f)(4)(i)(B) Generators shall be placed where water will not freeze. The use of common salt (sodium chloride) or other corrosive chemicals for protection against freezing is not permitted. (For heating systems see paragraph (f)(6)(iii) of this section.)

(f)(4)(i)(C) Except when generators are prepared in accordance with paragraph (f)(7)(v) of this section, sources of ignition shall be prohibited in outside generator houses or inside generator rooms.

(f)(4)(i)(D) Water shall not be supplied through a continuous connection to the generator except when the generator is provided with an adequate open overflow or automatic water shutoff which will effectively prevent overfilling of the generator. Where a noncontinuous connection is used, the supply line shall terminate at a point not less than 2 inches (5 cm) above the regularly provided opening for filling so that the water can be observed as it enters the generator.

(f)(4)(i)(E) Unless otherwise specifically approved, generators shall not be fitted with continuous drain connections leading to sewers, but shall discharge through an open connection into a suitably vented outdoor receptacle or residue pit which may have such connections. An open connection for the sludge drawoff is desirable to enable the generator operator to observe leakage of generating water from the drain valve or sludge cock.

(f)(4)(ii)(A) Each generator shall be provided with a vent pipe.

(f)(4)(ii)(B) The escape or relief pipe shall be rigidly installed without traps and so that any condensation will drain back to the generator.

(f)(4)(ii)(C) The escape or relief pipe shall be carried full size to a suitable point outside the building. It shall terminate in a hood or bend located at least 12 feet (3.7 m) above the ground, preferably above the roof, and as far away as practicable from windows or other openings into buildings and as far away as practicable from sources of ignition such as flues or chimneys and tracks used by locomotives. Generating chamber relief pipes shall not be inter-connected but shall be separately led to the outside air. The hood or bend shall be so constructed that it will not be obstructed by rain, snow, ice, insects, or birds. The outlet shall be at least 3 feet (0.9 m) from combustible construction.

(f)(4)(iii)(A) Gas holders shall be constructed on the gasometer principle, the bell being suitably guided. The gas bell shall move freely without tendency to bind and shall have a clearance of at least 2 inches (5 cm) from the shell.

(f)(4)(iii)(B) The gas holder may be located in the generator room, in a separate room or out of doors. In order to prevent collapse of the gas bell or infiltration of air due to a vacuum caused by the compressor or booster pump or cooling of the gas, a compressor or booster cutoff shall be provided at a point 12 inches (0.3 m) or more above the landing point of the bell. When the gas holder is located indoors, the room shall be ventilated in accordance with paragraph (f)(6)(ii) of this section and heated and lighted in accordance with paragraphs (f)(6)(iii) and (f)(6)(iv) of this section.

(f)(4)(iii)(C) When the gas holder is not located within a heated building, gas holder seals shall be protected against freezing.

(f)(4)(iii)(D) Means shall be provided to stop the generator-feeding mechanism before the gas holder reaches the upper limit of its travel.

(f)(4)(iii)(E) When the gas holder is connected to only one generator, the gas capacity of the holder shall be not less than one-third of the hourly rating of the generator.

(f)(4)(iii)(F) If acetylene is used from the gas holder without increase in pressure at some points but with increase in pressure by a compressor or booster pump at other points, approved piping protective devices shall be installed in each supply line. The low-pressure protective device shall be located between the gas holder and the shop piping, and the medium-pressure protective device shall be located between the compressor or booster pump and the shop piping (see Figure Q–4). Approved protective equipment (designated P_F) is used to prevent: Backflow of oxygen into the fuel-gas supply system; passage of a flashback into the fuel-gas supply system; and excessive back pressure of oxygen in the fuel-gas supply system. The three functions of the protective equipment may be combined in one device or may be provided by separate devices.

Figure Q–4

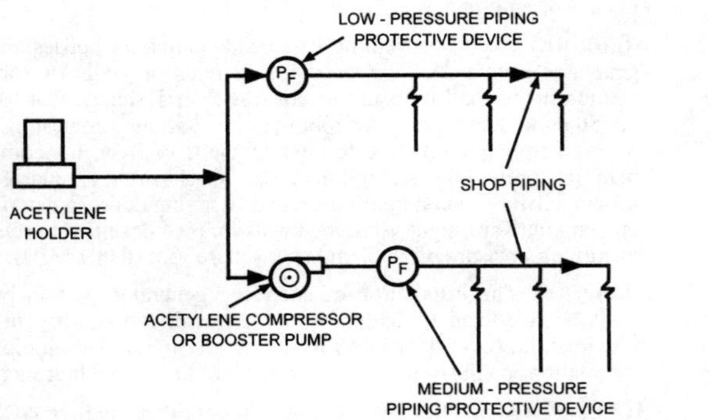

(f)(4)(iv)(A) The compressor or booster system shall be of an approved type.

(f)(4)(iv)(B) Wiring and electric equipment in compressor or booster pump rooms or enclosures shall conform to the provisions of Subpart S of this part for Class I, Division 2 locations.

(f)(4)(iv)(C) Compressors and booster pump equipment shall be located in well-ventilated areas away from open flames, electrical or mechanical sparks, or other ignition sources.

(f)(4)(iv)(D) Compressor or booster pumps shall be provided with pressure relief valves which will relieve pressure exceeding 15 psig (103 kPa gauge pressure) to a safe outdoor location as provided in paragraph (f)(4)(ii) of this section, or by returning the gas to the inlet side or to the gas supply source.

(f)(4)(iv)(E) Compressor or booster pump discharge outlets shall be provided with approved protective equipment. (See paragraph (e) of this section.)

(f)(5) **Portable acetylene generators**

(f)(5)(i)(A) All portable generators shall be of a type approved for portable use.

(f)(5)(i)(B) Portable generators shall not be used within 10 feet (3 m) of combustible material other than the floor.

(f)(5)(i)(C) Portable generators shall not be used in rooms of total volume less than 35 times the total gas-generating capacity per charge of all generators in the room. Generators shall not be used in rooms having a ceiling height of less than 10 feet (3 m). (To obtain the gas-generating capacity in cubic feet per charge, multiply the pounds of carbide per charge by 4.5.)

(f)(5)(i)(D) Portable generators shall be protected against freezing. The use of salt or other corrosive chemical to prevent freezing is prohibited.

(f)(5)(ii)(A) Portable generators shall be cleaned and recharged and the air mixture blown off outside buildings.

(f)(5)(ii)(B) When charged with carbide, portable generators shall not be moved by crane or derrick.

(f)(5)(ii)(C) When not in use, portable generators shall not be stored in rooms in which open flames are used unless the generators contain no carbide and have been thoroughly purged of acetylene. Storage rooms shall be well ventilated.

(f)(5)(ii)(D) When portable acetylene generators are to be transported and operated on vehicles, they shall be securely anchored to the vehicles. If transported by truck, the motor shall be turned off during charging, cleaning, and generating periods.

(f)(5)(ii)(E) Portable generators shall be located at a safe distance from the welding position so that they will not be exposed to sparks, slag, or misdirection of the torch flame or overheating from hot materials or processes.

(f)(6) **Outside generator houses and inside generator rooms for stationary acetylene generators**

(f)(6)(i)(A) No opening in any outside generator house shall be located within 5 feet (1.5 m) of any opening in another building.

(f)(6)(i)(B) Walls, floors, and roofs of outside generator houses shall be of noncombustible construction.

(f)(6)(i)(C) When a part of the generator house is to be used for the storage or manifolding of oxygen cylinders, the space to be so occupied shall be separated from the generator or carbide storage section by partition walls continuous from floor to roof or ceiling, of the type of construction stated in paragraph (f)(6)(i)(H) of this section. Such separation walls shall be without openings and shall be joined to the floor, other walls and ceiling or roof in a manner to effect a permanent gas-tight joint.

(f)(6)(i)(D) Exit doors shall be located so as to be readily accessible in case of emergency.

(f)(6)(i)(E) Explosion venting for outside generator houses and inside generator rooms shall be provided in exterior walls or roofs. The venting areas shall be equal to not less than 1 square foot (0.09 m^2) per 50 cubic feet (1.4 m^3) of room volume and may consist of any one or any combination of the following: Walls of light, noncombustible material preferably single-thickness, single-strength glass; lightly fastened hatch covers; lightly fastened swinging doors in exterior walls opening outward; lightly fastened walls or roof designed to relieve at a maximum pressure of 25 pounds per square foot (0.001 MPa).

(f)(6)(i)(F) The installation of acetylene generators within buildings shall be restricted to buildings not exceeding one story in height; provided, however, that this will not be construed as prohibiting such installations on the roof or top floor of a building exceeding such height.

(f)(6)(i)(G) Generators installed inside buildings shall be enclosed in a separate room.

(f)(6)(i)(H) The walls, partitions, floors, and ceilings of inside generator rooms shall be of noncombustible construction having a fire-resistance rating of at least 1 hour. The walls or partitions shall be continuous from floor to ceiling and shall be securely anchored. At least one wall of the room shall be an exterior wall.

(f)(6)(i)(I) Openings from an inside generator room to other parts of the building shall be protected by a swinging type, self-closing fire door for a Class B opening and having a rating of at least 1 hour. Windows in partitions shall be wired glass and approved metal frames with fixed sash. Installation shall be in accordance with the Standard for the Installation of Fire Doors and Windows, NFPA 80–1970, which is incorporated by reference as specified in §1910.6.

(f)(6)(ii) Inside generator rooms or outside generator houses shall be well ventilated with vents located at floor and ceiling levels.

(f)(6)(iii) Heating shall be by steam, hot water, enclosed electrically heated elements or other indirect means. Heating by flames or fires shall be prohibited in outside generator houses or inside generator rooms, or in any enclosure communicating with them.

(f)(6)(iv)(A) Generator houses or rooms shall have natural light during daylight hours. Where artificial lighting is necessary it shall be restricted to electric lamps installed in a fixed position. Unless specifically approved for use in atmospheres containing acetylene, such lamps shall be provided with enclosures of glass or other noncombustible material so designed and constructed as to prevent gas vapors from reaching the lamp or socket and to resist breakage. Rigid conduit with threaded connections shall be used.

(f)(6)(iv)(B) Lamps installed outside of wired-glass panels set in gas-tight frames in the exterior walls or roof of the generator house or room are acceptable.

(f)(6)(v) Electric switches, telephones, and all other electrical apparatus which may cause a spark, unless specifically approved for use inside acetylene generator rooms, shall be located outside the generator house or in a room or space separated from the generator room by a gas-tight partition, except that where the generator system is designed so that no carbide fill opening or other part of the generator is open to the generator house or room during the operation of the generator, and so that residue is carried in closed piping from the residue discharge valve to a point outside the generator house or room, electrical equipment in the generator house or room shall conform to the provisions of Subpart S of this part for Class I, Division 2 locations.

(f)(7) Maintenance and operation

(f)(7)(i) Unauthorized persons shall not be permitted in outside generator houses or inside generator rooms.

(f)(7)(i)(A) Operating instructions shall be posted in a conspicuous place near the generator or kept in a suitable place available for ready reference.

(f)(7)(i)(B) When recharging generators the order of operations specified in the instructions supplied by the manufacturer shall be followed.

(f)(7)(i)(C) In the case of batch-type generators, when the charge of carbide is exhausted and before additional carbide is added, the generating chamber shall always be flushed out with water, renewing the water supply in accordance with the instruction card furnished by the manufacturer.

(f)(7)(i)(D) The water-carbide residue mixture drained from the generator shall not be discharged into sewer pipes or stored in areas near open flames. Clear water from residue settling pits may be discharged into sewer pipes.

(f)(7)(ii) The carbide added each time the generator is recharged shall be sufficient to refill the space provided for carbide without ramming the charge. Steel or other ferrous tools shall not be used in distributing the charge.

(f)(7)(iii) Generator water chambers shall be kept filled to proper level at all times except while draining during the recharging operation.

(f)(7)(iv) Whenever repairs are to be made or the generator is to be charged or carbide is to be removed, the water chamber shall be filled to the proper level.

(f)(7)(v) Previous to making repairs involving welding, soldering, or other hot work or other operations which produce a source of ignition, the carbide charge and feed mechanism shall be completely removed. All acetylene shall be expelled by completely flooding the generator shell with water and the generator shall be disconnected from the piping system. The generator shall be kept filled with water, if possible, or positioned to hold as much water as possible.

(f)(7)(vi) Hot repairs shall not be made in a room where there are other generators unless all the generators and piping have been purged of acetylene.

(g) Calcium carbide storage

(g)(1) Packaging

(g)(1)(i) Calcium carbide shall be contained in metal packages of sufficient strength to prevent rupture. The packages shall be provided with a screw top or equivalent. These packages shall be constructed water- and air-tight. Solder shall not be used in such a manner that the package would fail if exposed to fire.

(g)(1)(ii) Packages containing calcium carbide shall be conspicuously marked "Calcium Carbide—Dangerous If Not Kept Dry" or with equivalent warning.

(g)(1)(iii) Caution: Metal tools, even the so-called spark resistant type may cause ignition of an acetylene and air mixture when opening carbide containers.

(g)(1)(iv) Sprinkler systems shall not be installed in carbide storage rooms.

(g)(2) Storage indoors

(g)(2)(i) Calcium carbide in quantities not to exceed 600 pounds (272.2 kg) may be stored indoors in dry, waterproof, and well-ventilated locations.

(g)(2)(i)(A) Calcium carbide not exceeding 600 pounds (272.2 kg) may be stored indoors in the same room with fuel-gas cylinders.

(g)(2)(i)(B) Packages of calcium carbide, except for one of each size, shall be kept sealed. The seals shall not be broken when there is carbide in excess of 1 pound (0.5 kg) in any other unsealed package of the same size of carbide in the room.

(g)(2)(ii) Calcium carbide exceeding 600 pounds (272.2 kg) but not exceeding 5,000 pounds (2,268 kg) shall be stored:

(g)(2)(ii)(A) In accordance with paragraph (g)(2)(iii) of this section;

(g)(2)(ii)(B) In an inside generator room or outside generator house; or

(g)(2)(ii)(C) In a separate room in a one-story building which may contain other occupancies, but without cellar or basement beneath the carbide storage section. Such rooms shall be constructed in accordance with paragraphs (f)(6)(i)(H) and (f)(6)(i)(I) of this section and ventilated in accordance with paragraph (f)(6)(ii) of this section. These rooms shall be used for no other purpose.

(g)(2)(iii) Calcium carbide in excess of 5,000 pounds (2,268 kg) shall be stored in one-story buildings without cellar or basement and used for no other purpose, or in outside generator houses. If the storage building is of noncombustible construction, it may adjoin other one-story buildings if separated therefrom by unpierced firewalls; if it is detached less than 10 feet (3 m) from such building or buildings, there shall be no opening in any of the mutually exposing sides of such buildings within 10 feet (3 m). If the storage building is of combustible construction, it shall be at least 20 feet (6.1 m) from any other one- or two-story building, and at least 30 feet (9.1 m) from any other building exceeding two stories.

(g)(3) Storage outdoors

(g)(3)(i) Calcium carbide in unopened metal containers may be stored outdoors.

(g)(3)(ii) Carbide containers to be stored outdoors shall be examined to make sure that they are in good condition. Periodic reexaminations shall be made for rusting or other damage to a container that might affect its water or air tightness.

(g)(3)(iii) The bottom tier of each row shall be placed on wooden planking or equivalent, so that the containers will not come in contact with the ground or ground water.

(g)(3)(iv) Containers of carbide which have been in storage the longest shall be used first.

[55 FR 13696, Apr. 11, 1990, as amended at 55 FR 32015, Aug 6, 1990; 55 FR 46053, Nov. 1, 1990; 61 FR 9241, Mar. 7, 1996; 72 FR 71070, Dec. 14, 2007]

§1910.254 Arc welding and cutting

(a) General

(a)(1) Equipment selection Welding equipment shall be chosen for safe application to the work to be done as specified in paragraph (b) of this section.

(a)(2) Installation Welding equipment shall be installed safely as specified by paragraph (c) of this section.

(a)(3) Instruction Workmen designated to operate arc welding equipment shall have been properly instructed and qualified to operate such equipment as specified in paragraph (d) of this section.

(b) Application of arc welding equipment

(b)(1) General Assurance of consideration of safety in design is obtainable by choosing apparatus complying with the Requirements for Electric Arc-Welding Apparatus, NEMA EW–1–1962, National Electrical Manufacturers Association or the Safety Standard for Transformer-Type Arc-Welding Machines, ANSI C33.2—1956, Underwriters' Laboratories, both of which are incorporated by reference as specified in §1910.6.

(b)(2) Environmental conditions

(b)(2)(i) Standard machines for arc welding service shall be designed and constructed to carry their rated load with rated temperature rises where the temperature of the cooling air does not exceed 40 °C (104 °F) and where the altitude does not exceed 3,300 feet (1,005.8 m), and shall be suitable for operation in atmospheres containing gases, dust, and light rays produced by the welding arc.

(b)(2)(ii) Unusual service conditions may exist, and in such circumstances machines shall be especially designed to safely meet the requirements of the service. Chief among these conditions are:

(b)(2)(ii)(A) Exposure to unusually corrosive fumes;
(b)(2)(ii)(B) Exposure to steam or excessive humidity;
(b)(2)(ii)(C) Exposure to excessive oil vapor;
(b)(2)(ii)(D) Exposure to flammable gases;
(b)(2)(ii)(E) Exposure to abnormal vibration or shock;
(b)(2)(ii)(F) Exposure to excessive dust;
(b)(2)(ii)(G) Exposure to weather;
(b)(2)(ii)(H) Exposure to unusual seacoast or shipboard conditions.

(b)(3) Voltage The following limits shall not be exceeded:

(b)(3)(i) Alternating-current machines

(b)(3)(i)(A) Manual arc welding and cutting—80 volts

(b)(3)(i)(B) Automatic (machine or mechanized) arc welding and cutting—100 volts

(b)(3)(ii) Direct-current machines

(b)(3)(ii)(A) Manual arc welding and cutting—100 volts

(b)(3)(ii)(B) Automatic (machine or mechanized) arc welding and cutting-100 volts

(b)(3)(iii) When special welding and cutting processes require values of open circuit voltages higher than the above, means shall be provided to prevent the operator from making accidental contact with the high voltage by adequate insulation or other means.

(b)(3)(iv) For a.c. welding under wet conditions or warm surroundings where perspiration is a factor, the use of reliable automatic controls for reducing no load voltage is recommended to reduce the shock hazard.

(b)(4) Design

(b)(4)(i) A controller integrally mounted in an electric motor driven welder shall have capacity for carrying rated motor current, shall be capable of making and interrupting stalled rotor current of the motor, and may serve as the running overcurrent device if provided with the number of overcurrent units as specified by Subpart S of this part.

(b)(4)(ii) On all types of arc welding machines, control apparatus shall be enclosed except for the operating wheels, levers, or handles.

(b)(4)(iii) Input power terminals, tap change devices and live metal parts connected to input circuits shall be completely enclosed and accessible only by means of tools.

(b)(4)(iv) Terminals for welding leads should be protected from accidental electrical contact by personnel or by metal objects, i.e., vehicles, crane hooks, etc. Protection may be obtained by use of: Dead-front receptacles for plug connections; recessed openings with nonremovable hinged covers; heavy insulating sleeving or taping or other equivalent electrical and mechanical protection. If a welding lead terminal which is intended to be used exclusively for connection to the work is connected to the grounded enclosure, it must be done by a conductor at least two AWG sizes smaller than the grounding conductor and the terminal shall be marked to indicate that it is grounded.

(b)(4)(v) No connections for portable control devices such as push buttons to be carried by the operator shall be connected to an a.c. circuit of higher than 120 volts. Exposed metal parts of portable control devices operating on circuits above 50 volts shall be grounded by a grounding conductor in the control cable.

(b)(4)(vi) Auto transformers or a.c. reactors shall not be used to draw welding current directly from any a.c. power source having a voltage exceeding 80 volts.

(c) Installation of arc welding equipment

(c)(1) General Installation including power supply shall be in accordance with the requirements of Subpart S of this part.

(c)(2) Grounding

(c)(2)(i) The frame or case of the welding machine (except engine-driven machines) shall be grounded under the conditions and according to the methods prescribed in Subpart S of this part.

(c)(2)(ii) Conduits containing electrical conductors shall not be used for completing a work-lead circuit. Pipelines shall not be used as a permanent part of a work-lead circuit, but may be used during construction, extension or repair providing current is not carried through threaded joints, flanged bolted joints, or caulked joints and that special precautions are used to avoid sparking at connection of the work-lead cable.

(c)(2)(iii) Chains, wire ropes, cranes, hoists, and elevators shall not be used to carry welding current.

(c)(2)(iv) Where a structure, conveyor, or fixture is regularly employed as a welding current return circuit, joints shall be bonded or provided with adequate current collecting devices.

(c)(2)(v) All ground connections shall be checked to determine that they are mechanically strong and electrically adequate for the required current.

(c)(3) Supply connections and conductors

(c)(3)(i) A disconnecting switch or controller shall be provided at or near each welding machine which is not equipped with such a switch or controller mounted as an integral part of the machine. The switch shall be in accordance with Subpart S of this part. Overcurrent protection shall be provided as specified in Subpart S of this part. A disconnect switch with overload protection or equivalent disconnect and protection means, permitted by Subpart S of this part, shall be provided for each outlet intended for connection to a portable welding machine.

(c)(3)(ii) For individual welding machines, the rated current-carrying capacity of the supply conductors shall be not less than the rated primary current of the welding machines.

(c)(3)(iii) For groups of welding machines, the rated current-carrying capacity of conductors may be less than the sum of the rated primary currents of the welding machines supplied. The conductor rating shall be determined in each case according to the machine loading based on the use to be made of each welding machine and the allowance permissible in the event that all the welding machines supplied by the conductors will not be in use at the same time.

(c)(3)(iv) In operations involving several welders on one structure, d.c. welding process requirements may require the use of both polarities; or supply circuit limitations for a.c. welding may require distribution of machines among the phases of the supply circuit. In such cases no load voltages between electrode holders will be 2 times normal in d.c. or 1, 1.41, 1.73, or 2 times normal on a.c. machines. Similar voltage differences will exist if both a.c. and d.c. welding are done on the same structure.

(c)(3)(iv)(A) All d.c. machines shall be connected with the same polarity.

(c)(3)(iv)(B) All a.c. machines shall be connected to the same phase of the supply circuit and with the same instantaneous polarity.

(d) Operation and maintenance

(d)(1) General Workers assigned to operate or maintain arc welding equipment shall be acquainted with the requirements of this section and with §1910.252 (a), (b), and (c) of this part.

(d)(2) Machine hook up Before starting operations all connections to the machine shall be checked to make certain they are properly made. The work lead shall be firmly attached to the work; magnetic work clamps shall be freed from adherent metal particles of spatter on contact surfaces. Coiled welding cable shall be spread out before use to avoid serious overheating and damage to insulation.

(d)(3) Grounding Grounding of the welding machine frame shall be checked. Special attention shall be given to safety ground connections of portable machines.

(d)(4) Leaks There shall be no leaks of cooling water, shielding gas or engine fuel.

(d)(5) Switches It shall be determined that proper switching equipment for shutting down the machine is provided.

(d)(6) **Manufacturers' instructions** Printed rules and instructions covering operation of equipment supplied by the manufacturers shall be strictly followed.

(d)(7) **Electrode holders** Electrode holders when not in use shall be so placed that they cannot make electrical contact with persons, conducting objects, fuel or compressed gas tanks.

(d)(8) **Electric shock** Cables with splices within 10 feet (3 m) of the holder shall not be used. The welder should not coil or loop welding electrode cable around parts of his body.

(d)(9) **Maintenance**

(d)(9)(i) The operator should report any equipment defect or safety hazard to his supervisor and the use of the equipment shall be discontinued until its safety has been assured. Repairs shall be made only by qualified personnel.

(d)(9)(ii) Machines which have become wet shall be thoroughly dried and tested before being used.

(d)(9)(iii) [OI] Cables with damaged insulation or exposed bare conductors shall be replaced. Joining lengths of work and electrode cables shall be done by the use of connecting means specifically intended for the purpose. The connecting means shall have insulation adequate for the service conditions.

[55 FR 13696, Apr. 11, 1990, as amended at 61 FR 9241, Mar. 7, 1996; 70 FR 53929, Sept. 13, 2005]

§1910.255 [OI] Resistance welding

(a) **General**

(a)(1) **Installation** All equipment shall be installed by a qualified electrician in conformance with Subpart S of this part. There shall be a safety-type disconnecting switch or a circuit breaker or circuit interrupter to open each power circuit to the machine, conveniently located at or near the machine, so that the power can be shut off when the machine or its controls are to be serviced.

(a)(2) **Thermal protection** Ignitron tubes used in resistance welding equipment shall be equipped with a thermal protection switch.

(a)(3) **Personnel** Workmen designated to operate resistance welding equipment shall have been properly instructed and judged competent to operate such equipment.

(a)(4) **Guarding** Controls of all automatic or air and hydraulic clamps shall be arranged or guarded to prevent the operator from accidentally activating them.

(b) **Spot and seam welding machines (nonportable)**

(b)(1) **Voltage** All external weld initiating control circuits shall operate on low voltage, not over 120 volts, for the safety of the operators.

(b)(2) **Capacitor welding** Stored energy or capacitor discharge type of resistance welding equipment and control panels involving high voltage (over 550 volts) shall be suitably insulated and protected by complete enclosures, all doors of which shall be provided with suitable interlocks and contacts wired into the control circuit (similar to elevator interlocks). Such interlocks or contacts shall be so designed as to effectively interrupt power and short circuit all capacitors when the door or panel is open. A manually operated switch or suitable positive device shall be installed, in addition to the mechanical interlocks or contacts, as an added safety measure assuring absolute discharge of all capacitors.

(b)(3) **Interlocks** All doors and access panels of all resistance welding machines and control panels shall be kept locked and interlocked to prevent access, by unauthorized persons, to live portions of the equipment.

(b)(4) **Guarding** All press welding machine operations, where there is a possibility of the operator's fingers being under the point of operation, shall be effectively guarded by the use of a device such as an electronic eye safety circuit, two hand controls or protection similar to that prescribed for punch press operation, §1910.217 of this part. All chains, gears, operating bus linkage, and belts shall be protected by adequate guards, in accordance with §1910.219 of this part.

(b)(5) **Shields** The hazard of flying sparks shall be, wherever practical, eliminated by installing a shield guard of safety glass or suitable fire-resistant plastic at the point of operation. Additional shields or curtains shall be installed as necessary to protect passing persons from flying sparks. (See §1910.252(b)(2)(i)(C) of this part.)

(b)(6) **Foot switches** All foot switches shall be guarded to prevent accidental operation of the machine.

(b)(7) **Stop buttons** Two or more safety emergency stop buttons shall be provided on all special multispot welding machines, including 2-post and 4-post weld presses.

(b)(8) **Safety pins** On large machines, four safety pins with plugs and receptacles (one in each corner) shall be provided so that when safety pins are removed and inserted in the ram or platen, the press becomes inoperative.

(b)(9) **Grounding** Where technically practical, the secondary of all welding transformers used in multispot, projection and seam welding machines shall be grounded. This may be done by permanently grounding one side of the welding secondary current circuit. Where not technically practical, a center tapped grounding reactor connected across the secondary or the use of a safety disconnect switch in conjunction with the welding control are acceptable alternates. Safety disconnect shall be arranged to open both sides of the line when welding current is not present.

(c) **Portable welding machines**

(c)(1) **Counterbalance** All portable welding guns shall have suitable counterbalanced devices for supporting the guns, including cables, unless the design of the gun or fixture makes counterbalancing impractical or unnecessary.

(c)(2) **Safety chains** All portable welding guns, transformers and related equipment that is suspended from overhead structures, eye beams, trolleys, etc., shall be equipped with safety chains or cables. Safety chains or cables shall be capable of supporting the total shock load in the event of failure of any component of the supporting system.

(c)(3) **Clevis** Each clevis shall be capable of supporting the total shock load of the suspended equipment in the event of trolley failure.

(c)(4) **Switch guards** All initiating switches, including retraction and dual schedule switches, located on the portable welding gun shall be equipped with suitable guards capable of preventing accidental initiation through contact with fixturing, operator's clothing, etc. Initiating switch voltage shall not exceed 24 volts.

(c)(5) **Moving holder** The movable holder, where it enters the gun frame, shall have sufficient clearance to prevent the shearing of fingers carelessly placed on the operating movable holder.

(c)(6) **Grounding** The secondary and case of all portable welding transformers shall be grounded. Secondary grounding may be by center tapped secondary or by a center tapped grounding reactor connected across the secondary.

(d) **Flash welding equipment**

(d)(1) **Ventilation and flash guard** Flash welding machines shall be equipped with a hood to control flying flash. In cases of high production, where materials may contain a film of oil and where toxic elements and metal fumes are given off, ventilation shall be provided in accordance with §1910.252(c) of this part.

(d)(2) **Fire curtains** For the protection of the operators of nearby equipment, fire-resistant curtains or suitable shields shall be set up around the machine and in such a manner that the operators movements are not hampered.

(e) [OI] **Maintenance** Periodic inspection shall be made by qualified maintenance personnel, and a certification record maintained. The certification record shall include the date of inspection, the signature of the person who performed the inspection and the serial number, or other identifier, for the equipment inspected. The operator shall be instructed to report any equipment defects to his supervisor and the use of the equipment shall be discontinued until safety repairs have been completed.

29 CFR PART 1910 Subpart R
Special Industries

Section Contents

Subpart E—Special Industries

Authority: 29 U.S.C. 653, 655, 657; Secretary of Labor's Order No. 12-71 (36 FR 8754), 8-76 (41 FR 25059), 9-83 (48 FR 35736), 1-90 (55 FR 9033), 6-96 (62 FR 111), 5-2007 (72 FR 31159), 4-2010 (75 FR 55355), or 1-2012 (77 FR 3912), as applicable; and 29 CFR Part 1911.

§1910.261 [OI]
Pulp, paper, and paperboard mills

(a) [OI] General requirements

(a)(1) [OI] Application This Section applies to establishments where pulp, paper, and paperboard are manufactured and converted. This Section does not apply to logging and the transportation of logs to pulp, paper, and paperboard mills.

(a)(2) Standards incorporated by reference Standards covering issues of occupational safety and health which have general application without regard to any specific industry are incorporated by reference in paragraphs (b) through (m) of this Section and in subparagraphs (3) and (4) of this paragraph and made applicable under this Section. Such standards shall be construed according to the rules set forth in §1910.5.

(a)(3) General incorporation of standards Establishments subject to this Section shall comply with the following standards of the American National Standards Institute, which are incorporated by reference as specified in §1910.6:

(a)(3)(i) Practice for Industrial Lighting, A11.1—1965 (R–1970);

(a)(3)(ii) Scheme for the Identification of Piping Systems, A13.1—1956;

(a)(3)(iii) Safety Code for Elevators, Dumbwaiters, and Moving Walks, A17.1—1965, including Supplements A17.1a—1967, A17.1b—1968, A17.1c—1969, and A17.1d—1970;

(a)(3)(iv) Practice for the Inspection of Elevators (Inspector's Manual), A17.2—1960, including Suppelements A17.2a—1965 and A17.2b—1967;

(a)(3)(v) [OI] Safety Code for Conveyors, Cableways, and Related Equipment, B20.1—1957;

(a)(3)(vi) Power Piping, B31.1.0—1967 and addenda B31.10a—1969. Fuel Gas Piping, B31.2—1968;

(a)(3)(vii) Identification of Gas-Mask Canisters, K13.1—1967;

(a)(3)(viii) Prevention of Sulfur Fires and Explosions, Z12.12—1968;

(a)(3)(ix) Installation of Blower and Exhaust Systems for Dust, Stock, and Vapor Removal or Conveying, Z33.1—1961.

(a)(4) Other standards The following standards, which are incorporated by reference as specified in §1910.6, shall be considered standards under this Section:

(a)(4)(i) ASME Boiler and Pressure Vessel Code, Section VIII, Unfired Pressure Vessels, including addenda 1969;

(a)(4)(ii) [OI] Building Exits Code for Life Safety from Fire, NFPA 101—1970;

(a)(4)(iii) Safety in the Handling and Use of Explosives, IME Pamphlet No. 17, July 1960, Institute of Makers of Explosives.

(b) Safe practices

(b)(1) [OI] Lockouts Devices such as padlocks shall be provided for locking out the source of power at the main disconnect switch. Before any maintenance, inspection, cleaning, adjusting, or servicing of equipment (electrical, mechanical, or other) that requires entrance into or close contact with the machinery or equipment, the main power disconnect switch or valve, or both, controlling its source of power or flow of material, shall be locked out or blocked off with padlock, blank flange, or similar device.

(b)(2) Emergency lighting Emergency lighting shall be provided wherever it is necessary for employees to remain at their machines or stations to shut down equipment in case of power failure. Emergency lighting shall be provided at stairways and passageways or aisleways used by employees for emergency exit in case of power failure. Emergency lighting shall be provided in all plant first aid and medical facilities.

(c) Handling and storage of pulpwood and pulp chips

(c)(1) Handling pulpwood with forklift trucks Where large forklift trucks, or lift trucks with clam-jaws, are used in the yard, the operator's enclosed cab shall be provided with an escape hatch, whenever the hydraulic arm blocks escape through the side doors.

(c)(2) Handling pulpwood with cranes or stackers

(c)(2)(i) Where locomotive cranes are used for loading or unloading pulpwood, the pulpwood shall be piled so as to allow a clearance of not less than 24 inches between the pile and the end of the cab of any locomotive crane in use, when the cab is turned in any working position.

(c)(2)(ii) The minimum distance of the pulpwood pile from the centerline of a standard-gage track shall be maintained at not less than 8½ feet.

(c)(2)(iii) Logs shall be piled in an orderly and stable manner, with no projection into walkways or roadways.

(c)(2)(iv) Railroad cars shall not be spotted on tracks adjacent to the locomotive cranes unless a 24-inch clearance is maintained, as required in paragraph (c)(2)(i) of this Section.

(c)(2)(v) The handling and storage of other materials shall conform to paragraphs (c)(2)(i) and (ii) of this Section with respect to clearance.

(c)(2)(vi) No person shall be permitted to walk beneath a suspended load, bucket, or hook.

(c)(3) Handling pulpwood from ships

(c)(3)(i) [Reserved]

(c)(3)(ii) The hatch tender shall be required to signal the hoisting engineer to move the load only after the men working in the hold are in the clear.

(c)(3)(iii) The air in the ship's hold, tanks, or closed vessels shall be tested for oxygen deficiency and for both toxic and explosive gases and vapors.

(c)(4) Handling pulpwood from flatcars and all other railway cars

(c)(4)(i) Railroad flatcars for the conveyance of pulpwood loaded parallel to the length of the car shall be equipped with safety-stake pockets.

(c)(4)(ii) Where pulpwood is loaded crosswise on a flatcar sufficient stakes of sizes not smaller than 4 by 4 inches shall be used to prevent the load from shifting.

(c)(4)(iii) When it is necessary to cut stakes, those on the unloading side should be partially cut through first, and then the binder wires cut on the opposite side. Wire cutters equipped with long extension handles shall be used. No person shall be permitted along the dumping side of the car after the stakes have been cut.

(c)(4)(iv) When steel straps without stakes are used, the steel straps shall be cut from a safe area to prevent employees from being struck by the falling logs.

(c)(4)(v) Flatcars and all other cars shall be chocked during unloading. Where equipment is not provided with hand brakes, rail clamping chocks shall be used.

(c)(4)(vi) A derail shall be used to prevent movement of other rail equipment into cars where persons are working.

(c)(5) Handling pulpwood from trucks

(c)(5)(i) Cutting of stakes and binder wires shall be done in accordance with paragraph (c)(4)(iii) of this Section.

(c)(5)(ii) Where binder chain and steel stakes are used, the binder chains shall be released and the stakes tripped from the opposite side of the load spillage.

(c)(5)(iii) Where binder chains and crane slings are used, the crane slings shall be attached and taut before the binder chains are released. The hooker shall see that the helper is clear before signaling for the movement of the load.

(c)(6) Handling pulp chips from railway cars All cars shall be securely fastened in place and all employees in the clear before dumping is started.

(c)(7) Handling pulp chips from trucks and trailers All trucks and trailers shall be securely fastened in place and all employees in the clear before dumping is started.

(c)(8) Cranes

(c)(8)(i) [Reserved]

(c)(8)(ii) A safety device such as a heavy chain or cable at least equal in strength to the lifting cables shall be fastened to the boom and to the frame of the boom crane (if it is other than locomotive) at the base. Alternatively, a telescoping safety device shall be fastened to the boom and to the cab frame, so as to prevent the boom from snapping back over the cab in the event of lifting cable breakage.

(c)(8)(iii) A crane shall not be operated where any part thereof may come within 10 feet of overhead powerlines (or other overhead obstructions) unless the powerlines have been deenergized. The boom shall be painted bright yellow from and including the head sheave to a point 6 feet down the boom towards the cab.

(c)(8)(iv) Standard signals for the operation of cranes shall be established for all movements of the crane, in accordance with American National Standards B30.2—1943 (reaffirmed 1968) and B30.2.0—1967.

(c)(8)(v) Only one member of the crew shall be authorized to give signals to the crane operator.

(c)(8)(vi) All cranes shall be equipped with a suitable warning device such as a horn or whistle.

(c)(8)(vii) A sheave guard shall be provided beneath the head sheave of the boom.

(c)(9) Traffic warning signs or signals

(c)(9)(i) A flagman shall direct the movement of cranes or locomotives being moved across railroad tracks or roads, and at any points where the vision of the operator is restricted. The flagman must always remain in sight of the operator when the crane or locomotive is in motion. The blue flag policy shall be used to mark stationary cars day and night. This policy shall include marking the track in advance of the spotted cars (flag for daytime, light for darkness).

(c)(9)(ii) After cars are spotted for loading or unloading, warning flags or signs shall be placed in the center of the track at least 50 feet away from the cars and a derail set to protect workmen in the car.

(c)(10) **Illumination** Artificial illumination shall be provided when loading or unloading is performed after dark, in accordance with American National Standard A11.1—1965 (R—1970).

(c)(11) [Reserved]

(c)(12) **Barking devices** When barking drums are employed in the yard, the requirements of paragraph (e)(12) of this Section shall apply.

(c)(13) **Hand tools** Handles of wood hooks shall be locked to the shank to prevent them from rotating.

(c)(14) Removal of pulpwood

(c)(14)(i) The ends of a woodpile shall be properly sloped and cross-tiered into the pile. Upright poles shall not be used at the ends of woodpiles. To knock down wood from the woodpile, mechanical equipment shall be used to permit employees to keep in the clear of loosened wood.

(c)(14)(ii) If dynamite is used to loosen the pile, only authorized personnel shall be permitted to handle and discharge the explosive. An electric detonator is preferable for firing; if a fuse is used, it shall be an approved safety fuse with a burning rate of not less than 120 seconds per yard and a minimum length of 3 feet, in accordance with Safety in the Handling and Use of Explosives, IME Pamphlet No. 17, July 1960.

(c)(15) Belt conveyors

(c)(15)(i) The sides of the conveyor shall be constructed so that the wood will not fall off.

(c)(15)(ii) Where conveyors cross passageways or roadways, a horizontal platform shall be provided under the conveyor, extended out from the sides of the conveyor a distance equal to ¹½ times the length of the wood handled. The platform shall extend the width of the road plus 2 feet (61 cm) on each side, and shall be kept free of wood and rubbish. The edges of the platform shall be provided with toeboards or other protection that meet the requirements of Subpart D of this Part, to prevent wood from falling.

(c)(15)(iii) All conveyors for pulpwood shall have the inrunning nips between chain and sprockets guarded; also, turning drums shall be guarded.

(c)(15)(iv) Every belt conveyor shall have an emergency stop cable extending the length of the conveyor so that it may be stopped from any location along the line, or conveniently located stop buttons within 10 feet of each work station, in accordance with American National Standard B20.1—1957.

(c)(16) **Signs** When conveyors cross walkways or roadways in the yards, the employer must erect signs reading "Danger—Overhead Conveyor" or an equivalent warning, in accordance with ANSI Z35.1–1968 or ANSI Z535.2–2011, incorporated by reference in §1910.6.

(d) Handling and storage of raw materials other than pulpwood or pulp chips

(d)(1) **Personal protective equipment** Whenever possible, all dust, fumes, and gases incident to handling materials shall be controlled at the source, in accordance with American National Standard Z9.2—1960. Where control at the source is not possible, respirators with goggles or protective masks shall be provided, and employees shall wear them when handling alum, clay, soda ash, lime, bleach powder, sulfur, chlorine, and similar materials, and when opening rag bales.

(d)(2) Clearance

(d)(2)(i) When materials are being piled inside a building and upon platforms, an aisle clearance at least 3 feet greater than the widest truck in use shall be provided.

(d)(2)(ii) Baled paper and rags stored inside a building shall not be piled closer than 18 inches to walls, partitions, or sprinkler heads.

(d)(3) Piling and unpil.04ing pulp

(d)(3)(i) Piles of wet lap pulp (unless palletized) shall be stepped back one-half the width of the sheet for each 8 feet of pile height. Sheets of pulp shall be interlapped to make the pile secure. Pulp shall not be piled over pipelines to jeopardize pipes, or so as to cause overloading of floors, or to within 18 inches below sprinkler heads.

(d)(3)(ii) Piles of pulp shall not be undermined when being unpiled.

(d)(3)(iii) Floor capacities shall be clearly marked on all floors.

(d)(4)(i) [Reserved]

(d)(4)(ii) Where rolls are pyramided two or more high, chocks shall be installed between each roll on the floor and at every row. Where pulp and paper rolls are stored on smooth floors in processing areas, rubber chocks with wooden core shall be used.

(d)(4)(iii) When rolls are decked two or more high, the bottom rolls shall be chocked on each side to prevent shifting in either direction.

(e) Preparing pulpwood

(e)(1) **Gang and slasher saws** A guard shall be provided in front of all gang and slasher saws to protect workers from wood thrown by saws. A guard shall be placed over tail sprockets.

(e)(2) **Slasher tables** Saws shall be stopped and power switches shall be locked out and tagged whenever it is necessary for any person to be on the slasher table.

(e)(3) [Reserved]

(e)(4) **Runway to the jack ladder** TThe runway from the pond or unloading dock to the table shall be protected with standard handrails and toeboards. Inclined portions shall have cleats or equivalent nonslip surfacing that complies with Subpart D of this Part. Protective equipment shall be provided for persons working over water.

(e)(5) **Guards below table** Where not protected by the frame of the machine, the underside of the slasher saws shall be enclosed with guards.

(e)(6) **Conveyors** The requirements of paragraph (c)(15)(iv) of this Section shall apply.

(e)(7) [Reserved]

(e)(8) **Barker feed** Each barker shall be equipped with a feed and turnover device which will make it unnecessary for the operator to hold a bolt or log by hand during the barking operation. Eye, ear, and head protection shall be provided for the operator, in accordance with paragraph (b)(2) of this Section.

(e)(9) [Reserved]

(e)(10) **Stops** All control devices shall be locked out and tagged when knives are being changed.

(e)(11) **Speed governor** Water wheels, when directly connected to barker disks or grinders, shall be provided with speed governors, if operated with gate wide open.

(e)(12) Continuous barking drums

(e)(12)(i) When platforms or floors allow access to the sides of the drums, a standard railing shall be constructed around the drums. When two or more drums are arranged side by side, proper walkways with standard handrails shall be provided between each set, in accordance with paragraph (b)(3) of this Section.

(e)(12)(ii) Sprockets and chains, gears, and trunnions shall have standard guards, in accordance with paragraph (b)(1) of this Section.

(e)(12)(iii) Whenever it becomes necessary for a workman to go within a drum, the driving mechanism shall be locked and tagged, at the main disconnect switch, in accordance with paragraph (b)(4) of this Section.

(e)(13) **Intermittent barking drums** In addition to motor switch, clutch, belt shifter, or other power disconnecting device, intermittent barking drums shall be equipped with a device which may be locked to prevent the drum from moving while it is being emptied or filled.

(e)(14) **Hydraulic barkers** Hydraulic barkers shall be enclosed with strong baffles at the inlet and the outlet. The operator shall be protected by at least five-ply laminated glass.

(e)(15) **Splitter block** The block upon or against which the wood is rested shall have a corrugated surface or other means provided that the wood will not slip. Wood to be split, and also the splitting block, shall be free of ice, snow, or chips. The operator shall be provided with eye and foot protection. A clear and unobstructed view shall be maintained between equipment and workers around the block and the workers' help area.

(e)(16) **Power control** Power for the operation of the splitter shall be controlled by a clutch or equivalent device.

(e)(17) **Knot cleaners** The operators of knot cleaners of the woodpecker type shall wear eye protection equipment.

(e)(18) **Chipper spout** The feed system to the chipper spout shall be arranged in such a way that the operator does not stand in a direct line with the chipper spout. All chipper spouts shall be enclosed to a height of at least 42 inches from the floor or operator's platform. When other protection is not sufficient, the operator shall wear a safety belt line. The safety belt line shall be fastened in such a manner as to make it impossible for the operator to fall into the throat of the chipper. Ear protection equipment shall be worn by the operator and others in the immediate area if there is any possibility that the noise level may be harmful (see §1910.95).

(e)(19) **Carriers for knives** Carriers shall be provided and used for transportation of knives.

(f) **Rag and old paper preparation**

(f)(1) **Ripping and trimming tools**

(f)(1)(i) Hand knives and scissors shall have blunt points, shall be fastened to the table with chain or thong, and shall not be carried on the person but placed safely in racks or sheaths when not in use.

(f)(1)(ii) Hand knives and sharpening steels shall be provided with guards at the junction of the handle and the blade.

(f)(2) **Shredders, cutters, and dusters**

(f)(2)(i) Rotating heads or cylinders shall be completely enclosed except for an opening at the feed side sufficient to permit only the entry of stock. The enclosure shall extend over the top of the feed rolls. It shall be constructed either of solid material or with mesh or openings not exceeding one-half inch and substantial enough to contain flying particles and prevent accidental contact with moving parts. The enclosure shall be bolted or locked into place.

(f)(2)(ii) A smooth-pivoted idler roll resting on the stock or feed table shall be provided in front of feed rolls except when arrangements prevent the operator from standing closer than 36 inches to any part of the feed rolls.

(f)(2)(iii) Any manually fed cutter, shredder, or duster shall be provided with an idler roll as per subdivision (ii) of this subparagraph or the operator shall use special hand-feeding tools.

(f)(2)(iv) Hoods of cutters, shredders, and dusters shall have exhaust ventilation, in accordance with American National Standard Z9.2—1960.

(f)(3) **Blowers**

(f)(3)(i) Blowers used for transporting rags shall be provided with feed hoppers having outer edges located not less than 48 inches from the fan.

(f)(3)(ii) The arrangement of the blower discharge outlets and work areas shall be such as to prevent material from falling on workers.

(f)(4) **Conveyors** Conveyors and conveyor drive belts and pulleys shall be fully enclosed or, if open and within 7 feet of the floor, shall be constructed and guarded in accordance with paragraph (c)(15) of this Section and American National Standards B15.1—1953 (Reaffirmed 1958) and B20.1—1957.

(f)(5) **Dust** Measures for the control of dust shall be provided, in accordance with American National Standards Z33.1—1961, Z87.1—1968, and Z88.2—1969.

(f)(6) **Rag cookers**

(f)(6)(i) When cleaning, inspection, or other work requires that persons enter rag cookers, all steam and water valves, or other control devices, shall be locked and tagged in the closed or "off" position. Blank flanging of pipelines is acceptable in place of closed and locked valves.

(f)(6)(ii) When cleaning, inspection, or other work requires that persons must enter the cooker, one person shall be stationed outside in a position to observe and assist in case of emergency, in accordance with paragraph (b)(5) of this Section.

(f)(6)(iii) [Reserved]

(f)(6)(iv) Rag cookers shall be provided with safety valves in accordance with the ASME Boiler and Pressure Vessel Code, Section VIII, Unfired Pressure Vessels—1968, with Addenda.

(g) **Chemical processes of making pulp**

(g)(1) **Sulfur burners**

(g)(1)(i) Sulfur-burner houses shall be safely and adequately ventilated, and every precaution shall be taken to guard against dust explosion hazards and fires, in accordance with American National Standards Z9.2—1960 and Z12.12—1968.

(g)(1)(ii) Nonsparking tools and equipment shall be used in handling dry sulfur.

(g)(1)(iii) Sulfur storage bins shall be kept free of sulfur dust accumulation, in accordance with American National Standard Z9.2—1960.

(g)(1)(iv) Sulfur-melting equipment shall not be located in the burner room.

(g)(2) **Protection for employees (acid plants)**

(g)(2)(i) Supplied air respirators shall be strategically located for emergency and rescue use.

(g)(2)(ii) The worker shall be provided with eye protection, a supplied air respirator and a personal fall protection system that meets the requirements of Subpart I of this Part, during inspection, repairs or maintenance of acid towers. The line shall be extended to an attendant stationed outside the tower opening.

(g)(3) **Acid tower structure** Outside elevators shall be inspected daily during winter months when ice materially affects safety. Elevators, runways, stairs, etc., for the acid tower shall be inspected monthly for defects that may occur because of exposure to acid or corrosive gases.

(g)(4) **Tanks (acid)**

(g)(4)(i) Tanks shall be free of acid and shall be washed out with water, and fresh air shall be blown into them before allowing men to enter. Men entering the tanks shall be provided with supplied air respirators, lifebelts, and attached lifelines.

(g)(4)(ii) A man shall be stationed outside to summon assistance if necessary. All intake valves to a tank shall be blanked off or disconnected.

(g)(5) **Clothing** Where lime slaking takes place, employees shall be provided with rubber boots, rubber gloves, protective aprons, and eye protection. A deluge shower and eye fountain shall be provided to flush the skin and eyes to counteract lime or acid burns.

(g)(6) **Lead burning** When lead burning is being done within tanks, fresh air shall be forced into the tanks so that fresh air will reach the face of the worker first and the direction of the current will never be from the source of the fumes toward the face of the workers. Supplied air respirators (constant-flow type) shall be provided.

(g)(7) **Hoops for acid storage tanks** Hoops of tanks shall be made of rods rather than flat strips and shall be safely maintained by scheduled inspections.

(g)(8) **Chip and sawdust bins** Steam or compressed-air lances, or other facilities, shall be used for breaking down the arches caused by jamming in chip lofts. No worker shall be permitted to enter a bin unless provided with a safety belt, with line attached, and an attendant stationed at the bin to summon assistance.

(g)(9) OI **Exits (digester building)** At least one unobstructed exit at each end of the room shall be provided on each floor of a digester building.

(g)(10) **Gas masks (digester building)** Gas masks must be available, and they must furnish adequate protection against sulfurous acid and chlorine gases and be inspected and repaired in accordance with 29 CFR §1910.134.

(g)(11) **Elevators**

(g)(11)(i) Elevators shall be constructed in accordance with American National Standard A17.1—1965.

(g)(11)(ii) Elevators shall be equipped with gas masks for the maximum number of passengers.

(g)(11)(iii) Elevators shall be equipped with an alarm system to advise of failure.

(g)(12) **Blowoff valves and piping**

(g)(12)(i) The blowoff valve of a digester shall be arranged so as to be operated from another room, remote from safety valves.

(g)(12)(ii) OI Through bolts instead of cap bolts shall be used on all digester pipings.

(g)(12)(iii) Heavy duty pipe, valves, and fittings shall be used between the digester and blow pit. These valves, fittings, and pipes shall be inspected at least semiannually to determine the degree of deterioration.

(g)(12)(iv) OI Digester blow valves shall be pinned or locked in closed position throughout the entire cooking period.

(g)(13) **Blow pits and blow tanks**

(g)(13)(i) Blow-pit openings preferably shall be on the side of the pit instead of on the top. Openings shall be as small as possible when located on top, and shall be protected in accordance with Subpart D of this Part.

(g)(13)(ii) A specially constructed ladder shall be used for access to blow pits, to be constructed so that the door of the blow pit cannot be closed when the ladder is in place; other means shall be provided to prevent the closing of the pit door when anyone is in the pit.

(g)(13)(iii) A signaling device shall be installed in the digester and blow-pit rooms and chip bins to be operated as a warning before and while digesters are being blown.

(g)(13)(iv) Blow-pit hoops shall be maintained in a safe condition.

(g)(14) **Blowing digester**

(g)(14)(i) Blowoff valves shall be opened slowly.

(g)(14)(ii) After the digester has started to be blown, the blowoff valve shall be left open, and the hand plate shall not be removed until the digester cook signals the blow-pit man that the blow is completed. Whenever it becomes necessary to remove the hand plate to clear stock, operators shall wear eye protection equipment and protective clothing to guard against burns from hot stock.

(g)(14)(iii) Means shall be provided whereby the digester cook shall signal the man in the chip bin before starting to load the digester.

(g)(15) **Inspecting and repairing digester**

(g)(15)(i) Valves controlling lines leading into a digester shall be locked out and tagged. The keys to the locks shall be in the possession of a person or persons doing the inspecting or making repairs.

(g)(15)(ii) Fresh air shall be blown into the digester constantly while workmen are inside. Supplied air respirators shall be available in the event the fresh air supply fails or is inadequate.

(g)(15)(iii) No inspector shall enter a digester unless a lifeline is securely fastened to his body by means of a safety belt and at least one other experienced employee is stationed outside the digester to handle the line and to summon assistance. All ladders and lifelines shall be inspected before each use.

(g)(15)(iv) All employees entering digesters for inspection or repair work shall be provided with protective headgear. Eye protection and dust masks shall be provided to workmen while the old brick lining is being removed, in accordance with American National Standards, Z87.1—1968, Z88.2—1969, and Z99.1—1969.

(g)(16) **Pressure tanks-accumulators (acid)**

(g)(16)(i) Safety regulations governing inspection and repairing of pressure tanks-accumulators (acid) shall be the same as those specified in subparagraph (15) of this paragraph.

(g)(16)(ii) The pressure tanks-accumulators shall be inspected twice annually. (See the ASME Boiler and Pressure Vessel Code, Section VIII, Unfired Pressure Vessels—1968, with Addenda.)

(g)(17) **Pressure vessels (safety devices)**

(g)(17)(i) A safety valve shall be installed in a separate line from each pressure vessel; no hand valve shall be installed between this safety valve and the pressure vessel. Safety valves shall be checked between each cook to be sure they have not become plugged or corroded to the point of being inoperative. (See the ASME Boiler and Pressure Vessel Code, Section VIII, Unfired Pressure Vessels—1968, with Addenda.)

(g)(17)(ii) All safety devices shall conform to Paragraph U–2 in the ASME Boiler and Pressure Vessel Code, Section VIII, Unfired Pressure Vessels—1968, with Addenda.

(g)(18) **Miscellaneous** Insofar as the processes of the sulfate and soda operations are similar to those of the sulfite processes, the standard of paragraphs (g)(1) through (17) of this Section shall apply.

(g)(18)(i) Quick operating showers, bubblers, etc., shall be available for emergency use in case of caustic soda burns.

(g)(18)(ii) Rotary tenders, smelter operators, and those cleaning smelt spouts shall be provided with eye protection equipment (fitted with lenses that filter out the harmful rays emanating from the light source) when actively engaged in their duties, in accordance with American National Standard Z87.1—1968.

(g)(18)(iii) Heavy-duty pipe, valves, and fittings shall be used between digester and blow pit. These shall be inspected at least semiannually to determine the degree of deterioration and repaired or replaced when necessary, in accordance with American National Standards B31.1—1955, B31.1a—1963, B31.1.0—1967, and B31.2—1968.

(g)(18)(iv) Smelt-dissolving tanks shall be covered and the cover kept closed, except when samples are being taken.

(g)(18)(v) Smelt tanks shall be provided with vent stacks and explosion doors, in accordance with American National Standard Z9.1—1951.

(g)(19) **Blow lines**

(g)(19)(i)–(ii) [Reserved]

(g)(19)(iii) When blow lines from more than one digester lead into one pipe, the cock or valve of the blow line from the tank being inspected or repaired shall be locked or tagged out, or the line shall be disconnected and blocked off.

(g)(20) **Furnace room** Exhaust ventilation shall be provided where niter cake is fed into a rotary furnace and shall be so designed and maintained as to keep the concentration of hydrogen sulfide gas below the parts per million listed in §1910.1000.

(g)(21) **Inspection and repair of tanks** All piping leading to tanks shall be blanked off or valved and locked or tagged. Any lines to sewers shall be blanked off to protect workers from air contaminants.

(g)(22) **Welding** Welding on blow tanks, accumulator tanks, or any other vessels where turpentine vapor or other combustible vapor could gather shall be done only after the vessel has been completely purged of fumes. Fresh air shall be supplied workers inside of vessels.

(g)(23) **Turpentine systems and storage tanks** Nonsparking tools and ground hose shall be used when pumping out the tank. The tank shall be surrounded by a berm or moat.

(h) **Bleaching**

(h)(1) **Bleaching engines** Bleaching engines, except the Bellmer type, shall be completely covered on the top, with the exception of one small opening large enough to allow filling, but too small to admit an employee. Platforms leading from one engine to another shall have standard guardrails that meet the requirements in Subpart D of this Part.

(h)(2) **Bleach mixing rooms**

(h)(2)(i) The room in which the bleach powder is mixed shall be provided with adequate exhaust ventilation, located at the floor level, in accordance with American National Standard Z9.1—1951.

(h)(2)(ii) Chlorine gas shall be carried away from the work place and breathing area by an exhaust system. The gas shall be rendered neutral or harmless before being discharged into the atmosphere. The requirements of American National Standard Z9.2—1960 shall apply to this subdivision.

(h)(2)(iii) For emergency and rescue operations, the employer must provide employees with self-contained breathing apparatuses or supplied-air respirators, and ensure that employees use these respirators, in accordance with the requirements of 29 CFR §1910.134.

(h)(3) **Liquid chlorine**

(h)(3)(i) Tanks of liquid chlorine shall be stored in an adequately ventilated unoccupied room, where their possible leakage cannot affect workers.

(h)(3)(ii) Gas masks capable of absorbing chlorine shall be supplied, conveniently placed, and regularly inspected, and workers who may be exposed to chlorine gas shall be instructed in their use.

(h)(3)(iii) For emergency and rescue work, independent self-contained oxygen-type masks or supplied air equipment shall be provided.

(h)(3)(iv) At least two exits, remote from each other, shall be provided for all rooms in which chlorine is stored.

(h)(3)(v) Spur tracks upon which tank cars containing chlorine and caustic are spotted and connected to pipelines shall be protected by means of a derail in front of the cars.

(h)(3)(vi) All chlorine, caustic, and acid lines shall be marked for positive identification, in accordance with American National Standard A13.1—1967.

(h)(4) **Bagged or drummed chemicals** Bagged or drummed chemicals require efficient handling to prevent damage and spillage. Certain oxidizing chemicals used in bleaching pulp and also in some sanitizing work require added precautions for safety in storage and handling. In storage, these chemicals must be isolated from combustible materials and other chemicals with which they will react such as acids. They must also be kept dry, clean and uncontaminated.

(i) **Mechanical pulp process**

(i)(1) **Pulp grinders**

(i)(1)(i) Water wheels directly connected to pulp grinders shall be provided with speed governors limiting the peripheral speed of the grinder to that recommended by the manufacturer.

(i)(1)(ii) Doors of pocket grinders shall be arranged so as to keep them from closing accidentally.

(i)(2) **Butting saws** Hood guards shall be provided on butting saws, in accordance with American National Standard O1.1—1954 (reaffirmed 1961).

(i)(3) **Floors and platforms** The requirements of paragraph (b)(3) of this Section shall apply.

(i)(4) **Personal protection** Persons exposed to falling material shall wear eye, head, foot, and shin protection equipment, in accordance with American National Standards Z87.1—1968, Z88.2—1969, Z89.1—1969, and Z41.1—1967.

(j) **Stock preparation**

(j)(1) **Pulp shredders**

(j)(1)(i) Cutting heads shall be completely enclosed except for an opening at the feed side sufficient to permit only entry of stock. The enclosure shall be bolted or locked in place. The enclosure shall be of solid material or with mesh or other openings not exceeding one-half inch.

(j)(1)(ii) Either a slanting feed table with its outer edge not less than 36 inches from the cutting head or an automatic feeding device shall be provided.

(j)(1)(iii) Repairs for cleaning of blockage shall be done only when the shredder is shutdown and control devices locked.

(j)(2) **Pulp conveyors** Pulp conveyors and conveyor drive belts and pulleys shall be fully enclosed, or if open and within 7 feet of the floor, shall be constructed and guarded in accordance with American National Standard B20.1—1957.

(j)(3) [Reserved]

(j)(4) **Beaters**

(j)(4)(i) Beater rolls shall be provided with covers.

(j)(4)(ii) When cleaning, inspecting, or other work requires that persons enter the beaters, all control devices shall be locked or tagged out, in accordance with paragraph (b)(4) of this Section.

(j)(4)(iii) When beaters are fed from the floor above, the chute opening, if less than 42 inches (1.06 m) from the floor, shall be provided with a guardrail system that meets the requirements in Subpart D of this Part, or other equivalent enclosures. Openings for manual feeding shall be sufficient only for entry of stock, and shall be provided with at least two permanently secured crossrails or other fall protection system that meet the requirements in Subpart D.

(j)(4)(iv) [Reserved]

(j)(4)(v) Floors around beaters shall be provided with sufficient drainage to remove wastes.

(j)(5) Pulpers

(j)(5)(i) All pulpers having the top or any other opening of a vessel less than 42 inches (107 cm) from the floor or work platform shall have such openings guarded by guardrail systems that meet the requirements in Subpart D of this Part, or other equivalent enclosures. For manual changing, openings shall be sufficient only to permit the entry of stock, and shall be provided with at least two permanently secured crossrails, or other fall protection systems that meet the requirements in Subpart D.

(j)(5)(ii) When cleaning, inspecting, or other work requires that persons enter the pulpers, they shall be equipped with safety belt and lifeline, and one person shall be stationed outside at a position to observe and assist in case of emergency.

(j)(5)(iii) When cleaning, inspecting, or other work requires that persons enter pulpers, all steam, water, or other control devices shall be locked or tagged out. Blank flanging and tagging of pipe lines is acceptable in place of closed and locked or tagged valves. Blank flanging of steam and water lines shall be acceptable in place of valve locks.

(j)(6) Stock chests

(j)(6)(i) All control devices shall be locked or tagged out when persons enter stock chests, in accordance with paragraph (b)(4) of this Section.

(j)(6)(ii) When cleaning, inspecting, or other work requires that persons enter stock chests, they shall be provided with a low-voltage extension light.

(k) Machine room

(k)(1) Emergency stops Paper machines shall be equipped with devices that will stop the machine quickly in an emergency. The devices shall consist of push buttons for electric motive power (or electrically operated engine stops), pull cords connected directly to the prime mover, control clutches, or other devices, interlocked with adequate braking action. The devices shall be tested periodically by making use of them when stopping the machine and shall be so located that any person working on the machine can quickly disconnect the machine from the source of power in case of emergency.

(k)(2) Drives

(k)(2)(i) All drives shall be provided with lockout devices at the power switch which interrupts the flow of current to the unit.

(k)(2)(ii) All ends of rotating shafts including dryer drum shafts shall be completely guarded.

(k)(2)(iii) All accessible disengaged doctor blades should be covered.

(k)(2)(iv) All exposed shafts shall be guarded. Crossovers shall be provided.

(k)(2)(v) Oil cups and grease fittings shall be placed in a safe area remote from nip and heat hazards.

(k)(3) Protective equipment Face shields, aprons, and rubber gloves shall be provided for workmen handling acids in accordance with paragraphs (b)(2) and (d)(1) of this Section.

(k)(4)–(5) [Reserved]

(k)(6) Steps Steps of uniform rise and tread with nonslip surfaces that meet the requirements in subpart D of this part shall be provided at each press.

(k)(7) Plank walkways A removable plank shall be provided along each press, with standard guardrails installed. The planks shall have nonslip surfaces in accordance with paragraph (b)(3) of this Section.

(k)(8) Dryer lubrication If a gear bearing must be oiled while the machine is in operation, an automatic oiling device to protect the oiler shall be provided, or oil cups and grease fittings shall be placed along the walkways out of reach of hot pipes and dryer gears.

(k)(9) Levers All levers carrying weights shall be constructed so that weights will not slip or fall off.

(k)(10) First dryer Either a permanent guardrail or apron guard or both shall be installed in front of the first dryer in each section in accordance with paragraph (b)(1) of this Section.

(k)(11) [OI] **Steam and hot-water pipes** All exposed steam and hot-water pipes within 7 feet of the floor or working platform or within 15 inches measured horizontally from stairways, ramps, or fixed ladders shall be covered with an insulating material, or guarded in such manner as to prevent contact.

(k)(12) Dryer gears Dryer gears shall be guarded excepting where the oilers' walkway is removed out of reach of the gears' nips and spokes and hot pipes in accordance with American National Standard B15.1—1953 (reaffirmed 1958).

(k)(12)(i) A guardrail shall be provided at broke holes in accordance with §1910.23.

(k)(13) Broke hole

(k)(13)(i) A guardrail that complies with subpart D of this part shall be provided at broke holes.

(k)(13)(ii) Where pulpers are located directly below the broke hole on a paper machine and where the broke hole opening is large enough to permit a worker to fall through, any employee pushing broke down the hole shall wear a safety belt attached to a safety belt line. The safety belt line shall be fastened in such a manner that it is impossible for the person to fall into the pulper.

(k)(13)(iii) An alarm bell or a flashing light shall be actuated before dropping material through the broke hole.

(k)(14) Feeder belt A feeder belt or other effective device shall be provided for starting paper through the calender stack.

(k)(15) Steps Steps or ladders that comply with subpart D of this part and tread with nonslip surfaces shall be provided at each calendar stack. Handrails and hand grips complying with Subpart D shall be provided at each calendar stack.

(k)(16) [Reserved]

(k)(17) Sole plates All exposed sole plates between dryers, calenders, reels, and rewinders shall have a nonskid surface.

(k)(18) Nip points The hazard of the nip points on all calender rolls shall be eliminated or minimized by means of an effective barrier device, or by feeding the paper into the rolls by means of a rope carrier, air jets, or hand feeding devices.

(k)(19) Platforms [Reserved]

(k)(20) Scrapers Alloy steel scrapers with pullthrough blades approximately 3 by 5 inches in size shall be used to remove "scabs" from calender rolls.

(k)(21) Illumination Permanent lighting shall be installed in all areas where employees are required to make machine adjustments and sheet transfers in accordance with the American National Standard A11.1—1965 (R 1970).

(k)(22) Control panels All control panel handles and buttons shall be protected from accidental contact.

(k)(23) [Reserved]

(k)(24) Lifting reels

(k)(24)(i) The reels shall stop rotating before being lifted from bearings.

(k)(24)(ii) All lifting equipment (clamps, cables, and slings) shall be maintained in a safe condition and inspected regularly.

(k)(24)(iii) Reel shafts with square block ends shall be guarded.

(k)(25) Feeder belts Feeder belts, carrier ropes, air carriage, or other equally effective means shall be provided for starting paper into the nip or drum-type reels.

(k)(26) Inrunning nip

(k)(26)(i) Where the nipping points of all drum winders and rewinders is on the operator's side, it shall be guarded by barrier guards interlocked with the drive mechanism.

(k)(26)(ii) [Reserved]

(k)(27) Core collars Set screws for securing core collars to winding and unwinding shafts shall not protrude above the face of the collar. All edges of the collar with which an operator's hand comes in contact shall be beveled to remove all sharp corners.

(k)(28) Slitter knives Slitter knives shall be guarded so as to prevent accidental contact. Carriers shall be provided and used for transportation of slitter knives.

(k)(29) Winder shaft The winder shall have a guide rail to align the shaft for easy entrance into the opened rewind shaft bearing housings.

(k)(30) Core shaft When the core shaft weighs in excess of the safe standard, a mechanical device such as a dolly shall be provided for carrying all or part of the weight when it is being removed from the set of paper and placed in the dressing brackets on the winder.

(k)(31) Winder area A nonskid surface shall be provided in the front vicinity of the winder to prevent accidental slipping.

(k)(32) Radiation Special standards regarding the use of radiation equipment shall be posted and followed as required by §1910.96.

(l) Finishing room

(l)(1) Cleaning rolls Rolls shall be cleaned only on the outrunning side.

(l)(2) **Emergency stops** Electrically or manually operated quick power disconnecting devices, interlocked with braking action, shall be provided on all operating sides of the machine within easy reach of all employees. These devices shall be tested by making use of them when stopping the machine.

(l)(3) **Core collars** The requirements of paragraph (k)(27) of this Section and the American National Standard B15.1—1953 (reaffirmed 1958) shall apply.

(l)(4) **Elevators** These shall be in accordance with American National Standard A17.1—1965.

(l)(5) **Control panels** The requirements of paragraph (k)(22) of this Section shall apply.

(l)(6) **Guillotine-type cutters**

(l)(6)(i) Each guillotine-type cutter shall be equipped with a control which requires the operator and his helper, if any, to use both hands to engage the clutch.

(l)(6)(ii) Each guillotine-type cutter shall be equipped with a nonrepeat device.

(l)(6)(iii) Carriers shall be provided and used for transportation of guillotine-type cutter knives.

(l)(7) **Rotary cutter**

(l)(7)(i) On single-knife machines a guard shall be provided at a point of contact to the knife.

(l)(7)(ii) On duplex cutters the protection required for single-knife machines shall be provided for the first knife, and a hood shall be provided for the second knife.

(l)(7)(iii) Safe access shall be provided to the knives of a rotary cutter by means of catwalks with nonslip surfaces, railings, and toeboards in accordance with paragraph (b)(3) of this Section.

(l)(7)(iv) A guard shall be provided for the spreader or squeeze roll at the nip side on sheet cutters.

(l)(7)(v) Electrically or manually operated quick power disconnecting devices with adequate braking action shall be provided on all operating sides of the machine within easy reach of all operators.

(l)(7)(vi) The outside slitters shall be guarded.

(l)(8) **Platers**

(l)(8)(i) A guard shall be arranged across the face of the rolls to serve as a warning that the operator's hand is approaching the danger zone.

(l)(8)(ii) A quick power disconnecting device shall be installed on each machine within easy reach of the operator.

(l)(9) **Finishing room rewinders**

(l)(9)(i) The nipping points of all drum winders and rewinders located on the operator's side shall be guarded by either automatic or manually operated barrier guards of sufficient height to protect fully anyone working around them. The barrier guard shall be interlocked with the drive mechanism to prevent operating above jog speed without the guard in place.

A zero speed switch should be installed to prevent the guard from being raised while the roll is turning.

(l)(9)(ii) A nonskid surface shall be provided in front of the rewinder to prevent an employee from slipping in accordance with paragraph (b)(3) of this Section.

(l)(9)(iii) Mechanical lifting devices shall be provided for placing and removing rolls from the machine.

(l)(10) **Control panels** The requirements of paragraph (k)(22) of this Section shall apply.

(l)(11) **Roll-type embosser** The nipping point located on the operator's side shall be guarded by either automatic or manually operated barrier guards interlocked with the drive.

(l)(12) **Sorting and counting tables**

(l)(12)(i) Tables shall be smooth and free from splinters, with edges and corners rounded.

(l)(12)(ii) Paddles shall be smooth and free from splinters.

(l)(13) **Roll splitters** The nip point and cutter knife shall be guarded by either automatic or manually operated barrier guards.

(m) **Materials handling**

(m)(1) **Hand trucks** No person shall be permitted to ride on a powered hand truck unless it is so designed by the manufacturer. A limit switch shall be on operating handle—30 degrees each way from a 45-degree angle up and down.

(m)(2) [Reserved]

(m)(3) **Cartons** The carton-stitching machine shall be guarded to prevent the operator from coming in contact with the stitching head.

(m)(4) [Reserved]

(m)(5) **Unloading cars** Flag signals, derails, or other protective devices shall be used to protect men during switching operations. The blue flag policy shall be invoked according to paragraph (c)(9)(i) of this Section.

[39 FR 23502, June 27, 1974, as amended at 40 FR 23073, May 28, 1975; 43 FR 49751, Oct. 24, 1978; 49 FR 5323, Feb. 10, 1984; 55 FR 32015, Aug. 6, 1990; 61 FR 9241, Mar. 7, 1996; 63 FR 1285, Jan. 8, 1998; 63 FR 33467, June 18, 1998; 72 FR 71070, Dec. 14, 2007]

§1910.262 OI
Textiles

(a) **Application requirements**

(a)(1) **Application** The requirements of this Subpart for textile safety apply to the design, installation, processes, operation, and maintenance of textile machinery, equipment, and other plant facilities in all plants engaged in the manufacture and processing of textiles, except those processes used exclusively in the manufacture of synthetic fibers.

(a)(2) **Standards incorporated by reference** Standards covering issues of occupational safety and health which are of general application without regard to any specific industry are incorporated by reference in paragraphs of this Section and made applicable to textiles. All such standards shall be construed according to the rules of construction set out in §1910.5.

(b) **Definitions applicable to this Section**

(b)(1) **Belt shifter** A belt shifter is a device for mechanically shifting a belt from one pulley to another.

(b)(2) **Belt shifter lock** A belt shifter lock is a device for positively locking the belt shifter in position while the machine is stopped and the belt is idling on the loose pulleys.

(b)(3) **Calender** A calender in essence consists of a set of heavy rollers mounted on vertical side frames and arranged to pass cloth between them. Calenders may have two to ten rollers, or bowls, some of which can be heated.

(b)(4) **Embossing calender** An embossing calender is a calender with two or more rolls, one of which is engraved for producing figured effects of various kinds on a fabric.

(b)(5) **Cans (drying)** Drying cans are hollow cylindrical drums mounted in a frame so they can rotate. They are heated with steam and are used to dry fabrics or yarn as it passes around the perimeter of the can.

(b)(6) **Carbonizing** Carbonizing means the removing of vegetable matter such as burns, straws, etc., from wool by treatment with acid, followed by heat. The undesired matter is reduced to a carbon-like form which may be removed by dusting or shaking.

(b)(7) **Card** A card machine consists of cylinders of various sizes—and in certain cases flats—covered with card clothing and set in relation to each other so that fibers in staple form may be separated into individual relationship. The speed of the cylinders and their direction of rotation varies. The finished product is delivered as a sliver. Cards of different types are: The revolving flat card, the roller-and-clearer card, etc.

(b)(8) **Card clothing** Card clothing is the material with which many of the surfaces of a card are covered; e.g., the cylinder, doffer, etc. It consists of a thick foundation material, usually made of textile fabrics, through which are pressed many fine, closely spaced, specially bent wires.

(b)(9) **Comber** A comber is a machine for combing fibers of cotton, wool, etc. The essential parts are a device for feeding forward a fringe of fibers at regular intervals and an arrangement of combs or pins which, at the right time, pass through the fringe. All tangled fibers, short fibers, and neps are removed and the long fibers are laid parallel.

(b)(10) **Combing machinery** Combing machinery is a general classification, including combers, sliver lap machines, ribbon lap machines, and gill boxes, but excluding cards.

(b)(11) **Cutter (rotary staple)** A rotary staple cutter is a machine consisting of one or more rotary blades used for the purpose of cutting textile fibers into staple lengths.

(b)(12) **Exposed to contact** Exposed to contact shall mean that the location of an object, material, nip point, or point of operation is such that a person is liable to come in contact with it in his normal course of employment.

(b)(13) **Garnett machine** A Garnett machine means any of a number of types of machines for opening hard twisted waste of wool, cotton, silk, etc. Essentially, such machines consist of a lickerin; one or more cylinders, each having a complement worker and stripper rolls; and a fancy roll and doffer. The action of such machines is somewhat like that of a wool card, but it is much more severe in that the various rolls are covered with garnett wire instead of card clothing.

(b)(14) **Gill box** A gill box is a machine used in the worsted system of manufacturing yarns. Its function is to arrange the fibers in parallel order. Essentially, it consists of a pair of feed rolls and a series of followers where the followers move at a faster surface speed and perform a combing action.

(b)(15) **Interlock** An interlock is a device that operates to prevent the operation of machine while the cover or door of the machine is open or unlocked, and which will also hold the cover or door closed and locked while the machine is in motion.

(b)(16) **Jig (dye)** A dye jig is a machine for dyeing piece goods. The cloth, at full width, passes from a roller through the dye liquor in an open vat and is then wound on another roller. The operation is repeated until the desired shade is obtained.

(b)(17) **Kier** A kier is a large metal vat, usually a pressure type, in which fabrics may be boiled out, bleached, etc.

(b)(18) **Lapper (ribbon)** A ribbon lapper is a machine used to prepare laps for feeding a cotton comb; its purpose is to provide a uniform lap in which the fibers have been straightened as much as possible.

(b)(19) **Lapper (sliver)** A sliver lapper is a machine in which a number of parallel card slivers are drafted slightly, laid side by side in a compact sheet, and wound into a cylindrical package.

(b)(20) **Loom** A loom is a machine for effecting the interlacing of two series of yarns crossing one another at right angles. The warp yarns are wound on a warp beam and pass through heddles and reed. The filling is shot across in a shuttle and settled in place by reed and lay, and the fabric is wound on a cloth beam.

(b)(21) **Mangle (starch)** A starch mangle is a mangle that is used specifically for starching cotton goods. It commonly consists of two large rolls and a shallow open vat with several immersion rolls. The vat contains the starch solution.

(b)(22) **Mangle (water)** A water mangle is a calender having two or more rolls used for squeezing water from fabrics before drying. Water mangles also may be used in other ways during the finishing of various fabrics.

(b)(23) **Mule** A mule is a type of spinning frame having a head stock and a carriage as its two main sections. The head stock is stationary. The carriage is movable and it carries the spindles which draft and spin the roving into the yarn. The carriage extends over the whole width of the machine and moves slowly toward and away from the head stock during the spinning operation.

(b)(24) **Nip** Nip shall mean the point of contact between two in-running rolls.

(b)(25) **Openers and pickers** Openers and pickers means a general classification which includes breaker pickers, intermediate pickers, finisher pickers, single process pickers, multiple process pickers, willow machines, card and picker waste cleaners, thread extractors, shredding machines, roving waste openers, shoddy pickers, bale breakers, feeders, vertical openers, lattice cleaners, horizontal cleaners, and any similar machinery equipped with either cylinders, screen section, calender section, rolls, or beaters used for the preparation of stock for further processing.

(b)(26) **Paddler** A paddler consists of a trough for a solution and two or more squeeze rolls between which cloth passes after being passed through a mordant or dye bath.

(b)(27) **Point of operation** Point of operation shall mean that part of the machine where the work of cutting, shearing, squeezing, drawing, or manipulating the stock in any other way is done.

(b)(28) **Printing machine (roller type)** A roller printing machine is a machine consisting of a large central cylinder, or pressure bowl, around the lower part of the perimeter of which is placed a series of engraved color rollers (each having a color trough), a furnisher roller, doctor blades, etc. The machine is used for printing fabrics.

(b)(29) **Ranges (bleaching continuous)** Continuous bleaching ranges are of several types and may be made for cloth in rope or open-width form. The goods, after wetting out, pass through a squeeze roll into a saturator containing a solution of caustic soda and then to an enclosed J-box. A V-shaped arrangement is attached to the front part of the J-box for uniform and rapid saturation of the cloth with steam before it is packed down in the J-box. The cloth, in a single strand rope form, passes over a guide roll down the first arm of the "V" and up the second. Steam is injected into the "V" at the upper end of the second arm so that the cloth is rapidly saturated with steam at this point. The J-box capacity is such that cloth will remain hot for a sufficient time to complete the scouring action. It then passes a series of washers with a squeeze roll in between. The cloth then passes through a second set of saturator, J-box, and washer, where it is treated with the peroxide solution. By slight modification of the form of the unit, the same process can be applied to open-width cloth.

(b)(30) **Range (mercerizing)** A mercerizing range consists generally of a 3-bowl mangle, a tenter frame, and a number of boxes for washing and scouring. The whole setup is in a straight line and all parts operate continuously. The combination is used to saturate the cloth with sodium hydroxide, stretch it while saturated, and washing out most of the caustic before releasing tension.

(b)(31) **Sanforizing machine** A sanforizing machine is a machine consisting of a large steam-heated cylinder, an endless, thick, woolen felt blanket which is in close contact with the cylinder for most of its perimeter, and an electrically heated shoe which presses the cloth against the blanket while the latter is in a stretched condition as it curves around feed-in roll.

(b)(32) **Shearing machine** A shearing machine is a machine used in shearing cloth. Cutting action is provided by a number of steel blades spirally mounted on a roller. The roller rotates in close contact with a fixed ledger blade. There may be from one to six such rollers on a machine.

(b)(33) **Singeing machine** A singeing machine is a machine used particularly with cotton; it comprises of a heated roller, plate, or an open gas flame. The material is rapidly passed over the roller or the plate or through the open gas flame to remove, fuzz or hairiness on yarn or cloth by burning.

(b)(34) **Slasher** A slasher is a machine used for applying a size mixture to warp yarns. Essentially, it consists of a stand for holding section beams, a size box, one or more cylindrical dryers or an enclosed hot air dryer, and a beaming end for finding the yarn on the loom beams.

(b)(35) **Solvent (industrial organic)** Industrial organic solvent means any organic volatile liquid or compound, or any combination of these substances which are used to dissolve or suspend a nonvolatile or slightly volatile substance for industrial utilization. It shall also apply to such substances when used as detergents or cleansing agents. It shall not apply to petroleum products when such products are used as fuel.

(b)(36) **Tenter frame** A tenter frame is a machine for drying cloth under tension. It essentially consists of a pair of endless traveling chains fitted with clips of fine pins and carried on tracks. The cloth is firmly held at the selvages by the two chains which diverge as they move forward so that the cloth is brought to the desired width.

(b)(37) **Warper** A warper is any machine for preparing and arranging the yarns intended for the warp of a fabric, specifically, a beam warper.

(c) **General safety requirements**

(c)(1) **Means of stopping machines** Every textile machine shall be provided with individual mechanical or electrical means for stopping such machines. On machines driven by belts and shafting, a locking-type shifter or an equivalent positive device shall be used. On operations where injury to the operator might result if motors were to restart after power failures, provision shall be made to prevent machines from automatically restarting upon restoration of power.

(c)(2) **Handles** Stopping and starting handles shall be designed to the proper length to prevent the worker's hand or fingers from striking against any revolving part, gear guard, or any other part of the machine.

(c)(3)–(4) [Reserved]

(c)(5) **Inspection and maintenance** All guards and other safety devices, including starting and stopping devices, shall be properly maintained.

(c)(6) **Lighting** Lighting shall conform to American National Standard A11.1—1965, which is incorporated by reference as specified in §1910.6.

(c)(7) **Identification of piping systems** Identification of piping systems shall conform to American National Standard A13.1—1956, which is incorporated by reference as specified in §1910.6.

(c)(8) **Identification of physical hazards** Identification of physical hazards shall be in accordance with the requirements of §1910.144.

(c)(9) OI **Steam pipes** All pipes carrying steam or hot water for process or servicing machinery, when exposed to contact and located within seven feet of the floor or working platform shall be covered with a heat-insulating material, or otherwise properly guarded.

(d) **Openers and pickers**

(d)(1) **Beater guards** When any opening or picker machinery is equipped with a beater, such beater shall be provided with metal covers which will prevent contact with the beater. Such covers shall be provided with an interlock which will prevent the cover from being raised while the machine is in motion and prevent the operation of the machine while the cover is open.

(d)(2) **Cleanout holes** Cleanout holes within reaching distance of the fan or picker beater shall have their covers securely fastened and they shall not be opened while the machine is in motion.

(d)(3) **Feed rolls** The feed rolls on all opening and picking machinery shall be covered with a guard designed to prevent the operator from reaching the nip while the machinery is in operation.

(d)(4) **Removal of foreign ferrous material** All textile opener lines shall be equipped with magnetic separators, tramp iron separators, or other means for the removal of foreign ferrous material.

(e) **Cotton cards**

(e)(1) **Enclosures** Cylinder and lickerins shall be completely protected and the doffers should be enclosed.

(e)(2) **Enclosure fastenings** The enclosures or covers shall be kept in place while the machine is in operation, except when stripping or grinding.

(e)(3) **Stripping rolls** On operations calling for flat strippings which are allowed to fall on the doffer cover, where such strippings are removed by hand, the doffer cover shall be kept closed and securely fastened to prevent the opening of the cover while the machine is in operation. When it becomes necessary to clean the cards while they are in motion, a long-handled brush or dust mop shall be used.

(f) Garnett machines

(f)(1) Lickerin Garnett lickerins shall be enclosed.

(f)(2) Fancy rolls Garnett fancy rolls shall be enclosed by covers. These shall be installed in a way that keeps worker rolls reasonably accessible for removal or adjustment.

(f)(3) Underside of machine The underside of the garnett shall be guarded by a screen mesh or other form of enclosure to prevent access.

(g) Spinning mules A substantial fender of metal or hardwood shall be installed in front of the carriage wheels, the fender to extend to within one-fourth inch of the rail.

(h) Slashers

(h)(1) Cylinder dryers

(h)(1)(i) Reducing valves, safety valves, and pressure gages Reducing valves, safety valves, and pressure gages shall conform to the ASME Pressure Vessel Code, Section VIII, Unfired Pressure Vessels, 1968, which is incorporated by reference as specified in §1910.6.

(h)(1)(ii) Vacuum relief valves Vacuum relief valves shall conform to the ASME Code for Pressure Vessels, Section VIII, Unfired Pressure Vessels, 1968.

(h)(1)(iii) Lever control When slashers are operated by control levers, these levers shall be connected to a horizontal bar or treadle located not more than 69 inches above the floor to control the operation from any point.

(h)(1)(iv) Pushbutton control Slashers operated by pushbutton control shall have stop and start buttons located at each end of the machine, and additional buttons located on both sides of the machine, at the size box and the delivery end. If calender rolls are used, additional buttons shall be provided at both sides of the machine at points near the nips, except when slashers are equipped with an enclosed dryer.

(h)(1)(v) Nip guards All nip guards shall comply with the requirements of paragraph (h)(2)(iv) of this Section.

(h)(1)(vi) Cylinder enclosure When enclosures or hoods are used over cylinder drying rolls, such enclosures or hoods shall be provided with an exhaust system which will effectively prevent wet air and steam from escaping into the workroom.

(h)(1)(vii) Expansion chambers Slasher kettles and cookers shall be provided with expansion chambers in the covers, or drains, to prevent surging over. Steam-control valves shall be so located that they can be operated without exposing the worker to moving parts, hot surfaces, or steam.

(h)(2) Enclosed hot air dryer

(h)(2)(i) Lever control When slashers are operated by control levers, these levers shall be connected to a horizontal bar or treadle located not more than 69 inches above the floor to control the operation from any point.

(h)(2)(ii) Push-button control Slashers operated by push-button control shall have one start button at each end of the machine and stop buttons shall be located on both sides of the machines at intervals spaced not more than 6 feet on centers. Inching buttons should be installed.

(h)(2)(iii) Dryer enclosure The dryer enclosure shall be provided with an exhaust system which will effectively prevent wet air and steam from escaping into the workroom.

(h)(2)(iv) Nip guards All nip guards shall comply with Table R–1.

Table R–1
Guard Openings
[Openings in the guard or between the guard and working surface shall not be greater than the following]

Distance of opening from nip point	Maximum width of opening
0 to 1½	¼
1½ to 2½	⅜
2½ to 3½	½
3½ to 5½	⅝
5½ to 6½	¾
6½ to 7½	⅞
7½ to 8½	1¼

The measurements in Table R–1 are all in inches.

(h)(2)(v) Expansion chambers. Slasher kettles and cookers shall be provided with expansion chambers in the covers, or drains, to prevent surging over. Steam control valves shall be so located that they can be operated without exposing the worker to moving parts, hot surfaces, or steam.

(i) Warpers

(i)(1) Swiveled double-bar gates Swiveled double-bar gates shall be installed on all warpers operating in excess of 450 yards per minute. These gates shall be so interlocked that the machine cannot be operated until the gate is in the "closed position," except for the purpose of inching or jogging.

(i)(2) Closed position Closed position shall mean that the top bar of the gate shall be at least 42 inches from the floor or working platform; and the lower bar shall be at least 21 inches from the floor or working platform; and the gate shall be located 15 inches from the vertical tangent to the beam head.

(j) Drawing frames, slubbers, roving parts, cotton combers, ring spinning frames, twisters Gear housing covers on all installations of drawing frames, slubbers, roving frames, cotton combers, ring spinning frames, and twisters shall be equipped with interlocks.

(k) Gill boxes

(k)(1) Pin guard A guard shall be placed ahead of the feed end and shall be so designed that it will prevent the worker's fingers from being caught in the pins of the intersecting fallers.

(k)(2) Nip guards All nip guards shall comply with the requirements of paragraph (h)(2)(iv) of this Section.

(l) Heavy draw boxes, finishers, and speeders used in worsted drawing

(l)(1) Band pulley covers Covers for band pulleys shall be closed when the machine is in motion.

(l)(2) Benches or working platforms Branches or working platforms approximately 10 inches in height and 8 inches in width should be installed along the entire running length of the machine for the worker to stand on while creeling the machine. Such benches or platforms shall be covered with an abrasive or nonslip material.

(m) Sliver and ribbon lappers (cotton) Cover guard. An interlocking cover guard shall be installed over the large calender drums and the lap spool, designed to prevent the operator from coming in contact with the nip.

(n) Looms

(n)(1) Shuttle guard Each loom shall be equipped with a guard designed to minimize the danger of the shuttle flying out of the shed.

(n)(2) Protection for loom fixer Provisions shall be made so that every loom fixer can prevent the loom from being started while he is at work on the loom. This may be accomplished by means of a lock, the key to which is retained in the possession of the loom fixer, or by some other effective means to prevent starting the loom.

(o) Shearing machines All revolving blades on shearing machines shall be guarded so that the opening between the cloth surface and the bottom of the guard will not exceed three-eighths inch.

(p) Continuous bleach range (cotton and rayon)

(p)(1) J-box protection Each valve controlling the flow of steam, injurious gases, or liquids into a J-box shall be equipped with a chain, lock, and key, so that any worker who enters the J-box can lock the valve and retain the key in his possession. Any other method which will prevent steam, injurious gases, or liquids from entering the J-box while the worker is in it will be acceptable.

(p)(2) Open-width bleaching The nip of all in-running rolls on open-width bleaching machine rolls shall be protected with a guard to prevent the worker from being caught at the nip. The guard shall extend across the entire length of the nip.

(q) Kiers

(q)(1) Reducing valves, safety valves, and pressure gages Reducing valves, safety valves, and pressure gages shall conform to the ASME Code for Unfired Pressure Vessels, Section VIII, Unfired/Pressure Vessels, 1968.

(q)(2) Kier valve protection Each valve controlling the flow of steam, injurious gases, or liquids into a kier shall be equipped with a chain, lock, and key, so that any worker who enters the kier can lock the valve and retain the key in his possession. Any other method which will prevent steam, injurious gases, or liquids from entering the kier while the worker is in it will be acceptable.

(r) Gray and white bins On new installations guardrails that comply with Subpart D of this Part shall be provided where workers are required to plait by hand from the top of the bin so as to protect the worker from falling to a lower level.

(s) Mercerizing range (piece goods)

(s)(1) Stopping devices A stopping device shall be provided at each end of the machine.

(s)(2) Frame ends A guard shall be installed at each end of the frame between the in-running chain and the clip opener, to prevent the worker's fingers from being caught.

(s)(3) Mangle and washers The nip at the in-running rolls shall conform to §1910.264.

(t) Tenter frames

(t)(1) Stopping devices A stopping device shall be provided at each end of the machine.

(t)(2) Frame ends A guard shall be installed at each end of the frame at the in-running chain and clip opener.

(t)(3) Oil cups Oil cups shall be safely located to permit easy access.

(u) Dyeing jigs

(u)(1) Stopping devices Each dye jig shall be equipped with individual mechanical or electrical means for stopping the machine.

(u)(2) Roll arms Roll arms on jigs shall be built to allow for extra large batches, and to prevent the center bar from being forced off, causing the batch to fall.

(v) Padders—Nip guards All nip guards shall comply with the requirements of paragraph (h)(2)(iv) of this Section.

(w) Drying cans

(w)(1) Pressure reducing valves and pressure gages Pressure reducing valves and pressure gages shall conform to the ASME Code for Pressure Vessels, Section VIII, 1968, Unfired Pressure Vessels.

(w)(2) Vacuum collapse If cans are not designed to prevent vacuum collapse, each can shall be equipped with one or more vacuum relief valves with openings of sufficient size to prevent the collapse of the can if vacuum occurs.

(x) Flat-work ironer

(x)(1) Feed rolls The feed rolls shall be guarded to conform to §1910.264.

(x)(2) Pressure rolls Pressure rolls shall be covered or guarded to conform to §1910.264.

(y) Extractors

(y)(1) Centrifugal extractor

(y)(1)(i) Cover Each extractor shall be equipped with a metal cover.

(y)(1)(ii) Interlocking device Each extractor shall be equipped with an interlocking device that will prevent the cover from being opened while the basket is in motion, and also prevent the power operation of the basket while the cover is open.

(y)(1)(iii) Brakes Each extractor shall be equipped with a mechanically or electrically operated brake to quickly stop the basket when the power driving the basket is shut off.

(y)(1)(iv) Maximum allowable speed Each centrifugal extractor shall be effectively secured in position on the floor or foundation so as to eliminate unnecessary vibration, and should not be operated at a speed greater than the manufacturer's rating, which shall be stamped where easily visible in letters not less than one-quarter inch in height. The maximum allowable speed shall be given in revolutions per minute (rpm).

(y)(2) Engine drum extractor—Over-speed governor Each engine individually driving an extractor shall be provided with an approved engine stop and speed limit governor.

(y)(3) Squeezer or wringer extractor—Nip guards All nip guards shall comply with the requirements of paragraph (h)(2)(iv) of this Section.

(z) Nip guards All nip guards for water mangle, starch mangle, back-washer (worsted yarn) crabbing machines, decating machines, shall comply with the requirements of paragraph (h)(2)(iv).

(aa) Sanforizing and palmer machine A safety trip rod, cable, or wire center cord shall be provided across the front and back of all palmer cylinders extending the length of the face of the cylinder. It shall operate readily whether pushed or pulled. This safety trip shall be not more than 72 inches above the level on which the operator stands and shall be readily accessible.

(bb) Rope washers

(bb)(1) Splash guard Splash guards shall be installed on all rope washers unless the machine is so designed as to prevent the water or liquid from splashing the operator, the floor, or working surface.

(bb)(2) Safety stop bar A safety trip rod, cable or wire center cord shall be provided across the front and back of all rope washers extending the length of the face of the washer. It shall operate readily whether pushed or pulled. This safety trip shall be not more than 72 inches above the level on which the operator stands and shall be readily accessible.

(cc) Laundry washer tumbler or shaker

(cc)(1) [OI] **Interlocking device** Each drying tumbler, each double cylinder shaker or clothes tumbler, and each washing machine shall be equipped with an interlock device which will prevent the power operation of the inside cylinder when the outer door on the case or shell is open, and which will also prevent the outer door on the case or shell from being opened without shutting off the power.

(cc)(2) Means of holding covers or doors in open position Each enclosed barrel shall also be equipped with adequate means for holding open the doors or covers of the inner and outer cylinders or shells while it is being loaded or unloaded.

(dd) Printing machine (roller type)

(dd)(1) Nip guards All nip guards shall comply with the requirements of paragraph (h)(2)(iv) of this Section.

(dd)(2) Crown wheel and roller gear nip protection The engraved roller gears and the large crown wheel shall be provided with a protective disc which will enclose the nips of the in-running gears. Individual discs for each nip will be acceptable.

(ee) Calenders The nip at the in-running side of the rolls shall be provided with a guard extending across the entire length of the nip and arranged to prevent the fingers of the workers from being pulled in between the rolls or between the guard and the rolls, and constructed so that the cloth can be fed into the rolls safely.

(ff) Rotary staple cutters A guard shall be installed completely enclosing the cutters to prevent the hands of the operator from reaching the cutting zone.

(gg) [Reserved]

(hh) Hand bailing machine An angle-iron-handle stop guard shall be installed at the right angle to the frame of the machine. The stop guard shall be so designed and so located that it will prevent the handle from traveling beyond the vertical position should the handle slip from the operator's hand when the pawl has been released from the teeth of the takeup gear.

(ii) Roll bench Cleats shall be installed on the ends of roll benches.

(jj) Cuttle or swing folder (overhead type) The bottom of the overhead folders shall be located not less than 7 feet from the floor or working surface.

(kk) Color-mixing room Floors in color-mixing rooms shall be constructed to drain easily.

(ll) Open tanks and vats for mixing and storage of hot or corrosive liquids—Shutoff valves Boiling tanks, caustic tanks, and hot liquid containers, so located that the operator cannot see the contents from the floor or working area, shall have emergency shutoff valves controlled from a point not subject to danger of splash. Valves shall conform to the ASME Pressure Vessel Code, Section VIII, Unfired Pressure Vessels, 1968.

(mm) Dye kettles and vats Pipes or drains of sufficient capacity to carry the contents safely away from the working area shall be installed where there are dye kettles and vats which may at any time contain hot or corrosive liquids. These shall not empty directly onto the floor.

(nn) Acid carboys Carboys shall be provided with inclinators, or the acid shall be withdrawn from the carboys by means of pumping without pressure in the carboy, or by means of hand operated siphons.

(oo) Handling caustic soda and caustic potash Means shall be provided for handling and emptying caustic soda and caustic potash containers to prevent workers from coming in contact with the caustic (see paragraph (qq) of this Section).

(pp) First aid Wherever acids or caustics are used, provision shall be made for a copious and flowing supply of fresh, clean water.

[39 FR 23502, June 27, 1974, as amended at 40 FR 23073, May 28, 1975; 49 FR 5324, Feb. 10, 1984; 61 FR 9241, Mar. 7, 1996; 63 FR 33467, June 18, 1998]

§1910.263 [OI] Bakery equipment

(a) General requirements

(a)(1) Application The requirements of this Section shall apply to the design, installation, operation and maintenance of machinery and equipment used within a bakery.

(a)(2) [Reserved]

(b) [Reserved]

(c) General machine guarding

(c)(1) [Reserved]

(c)(2) Gears All gears shall be completely enclosed regardless of location.

(c)(3) Sprockets and V-belt drives Sprockets and V-belt drives located within reach from platforms or passageways or located within 8 feet 6 inches from the floor shall be completely enclosed.

(c)(4) [Reserved]

(c)(5) Lubrication Where machinery must be lubricated while in motion, stationary lubrication fittings inside a machine shall be provided with extension piping to a point of safety so that the employee will not have to reach into any dangerous part of the machine when lubricating.

(c)(6)–(7) [Reserved]

(c)(8) Hot pipes Exposed hot water and steam pipes shall be covered with insulating material wherever necessary to protect employee from contact.

(d) Flour-handling equipment

(d)(1) General requirements for flour handling

(d)(1)(i) Wherever any of the various pieces of apparatus comprising a flour-handling system are run in electrical unity with one another the following safeguards shall apply:

(d)(1)(i)(A) [Reserved]

(d)(1)(i)(B) Wherever a flour-handling system is of such size that the beginning of its operation is far remote from its final delivery end, all electric motors operating each apparatus comprising this system shall be controlled at each of two points, one located at each remote end, either of which will stop all motors.

(d)(1)(i)(C) [Reserved]

(d)(1)(i)(D) Control circuits for magnetic controllers shall be so arranged that the opening of any one of several limit switches, which may be on an individual unit, will serve to de-energize all of the motors of that unit.

(d)(1)(ii) [Reserved]

(d)(2) Bag chutes and bag lifts (bag-arm elevators)

(d)(2)(i) Bag chutes (gravity chutes for handling flour bags) shall be so designed so as to keep to a minimum the speed of flour bags. If the chute inclines more than 30° from the horizontal, there shall be an upturn at the lower end of the chute to slow down the bags.

(d)(2)(ii) Bag-arm elevators with manual takeoff shall be designed to operate at a capacity not exceeding seven bags per minute. The arms on the conveyor chain shall be so spaced as to obtain the full capacity of the elevator with the lowest possible chain speed. There shall be an electric limit switch at the unloading end of the bag-arm elevator so installed as to automatically stop the conveyor chain if any bag fails to clear the conveyor arms.

(d)(2)(iii) [Reserved]

(d)(2)(iv) Man lifts shall be prohibited in bakeries. Bag or barrel lifts shall not be used as man lifts.

(d)(3) Dumpbin and blender

(d)(3)(i)–(iv) [Reserved]

(d)(3)(v) All dumpbin and blender hoods shall be of sufficient capacity to prevent circulation of flour dust outside the hoods.

(d)(3)(vi) All dumpbins shall be of a suitable height from floor to enable the operator to dump flour from bags, without causing undue strain or fatigue. Where the edge of any bin is more than 24 inches above the flour, a bag rest step shall be provided.

(d)(3)(vii) A control device for stopping the dumpbin and blender shall be provided close to the normal location of the operator.

(d)(4)–(5) [Reserved]

(d)(6) Storage bins

(d)(6)(i) [Reserved]

(d)(6)(ii) Storage bins shall be provided with gaskets and locks or latches to keep the cover closed, or other equivalent devices in order to insure the dust tightness of the cover. Covers at openings where an employee may enter the bin shall also be provided with a hasp and a lock, so located that the employee may lock the cover in the open position whenever it is necessary to enter the bin.

(d)(6)(iii) Storage bins where the side is more than 5 feet in depth shall be provided with standard stationary safety ladders, both inside and outside, to reach from floor level to top of bin and from top of bin to inside bottom, keeping the ladder end away from the moving screw conveyor.

(d)(6)(iv)–(v) [Reserved]

(d)(6)(vi) The main entrance cover of large storage bins located at the interior exit ladder shall be provided with an electric interlock for motors operating both feed and unloading screw, so that these motors cannot operate while the cover is open.

(d)(7) Screw conveyors

(d)(7)(i)–(ii) [Reserved]

(d)(7)(iii) The covers of all screw conveyors shall be made removable in convenient sections, held on with stationary clamps located at proper intervals keeping all covers dust-tight. Where drop or hinged bottom sections are provided this provision shall not apply.

(d)(8) Sifters

(d)(8)(i) Enclosures of all types of flour sifters shall be so constructed that they are dust-tight but readily accessible for interior inspection.

(d)(8)(ii) [Reserved]

(d)(9) Flour scales

(d)(9)(i)–(ii) [Reserved]

(d)(9)(iii) Traveling or track-type flour scales shall be equipped with bar handles for moving same. The bar should be at least 1 inch in diameter and well away from trolley track wheels.

(e) Mixers

(e)(1) Horizontal dough mixers

(e)(1)(i) Mixers with external power application shall have all belts, chains, gears, pulleys, sprockets, clutches, and other moving parts completely enclosed.

(e)(1)(ii) [Reserved]

(e)(1)(iii) Each mixer shall be equipped with an individual motor and control, and with a conveniently located manual switch to prevent the mixer from being started in the usual manner while the machine is being serviced and cleaned.

(e)(1)(iv) All electrical control stations shall be so located that the operator must be in full view of the bowl in its open position. No duplication of such controls other than a stop switch shall be permitted.

(e)(1)(v) All mixers with power and manual dumping arrangements shall be equipped with safety devices which shall:

(e)(1)(v)(A) Engage both hands of the operator, when the agitator is in motion under power, and while the bowl is opened more than one-fifth of its total opening.

(e)(1)(v)(B) Prevent the agitator from being started, while the bowl is more than one-fifth open, without engaging both hands of the operator.

(e)(1)(vi)–(vii) [Reserved]

(e)(1)(viii) Every mixer shall be equipped with a full enclosure over the bowl which is closed at all times while the agitator is in motion. Only minor openings in this enclosure, such as ingredient doors, flour inlets, etc., each representing less than 1½ square feet in area, shall be capable of being opened while the mixer is in operation.

(e)(1)(ix) [Reserved]

(e)(1)(x) Overhead covers or doors which are subject to accidental closure shall be counterbalanced to remain in an open position or provided with means to hold them open until positively released by the operator.

(e)(1)(xi)–(xvii) [Reserved]

(e)(1)(xviii) Valves and controls to regulate the coolant in mixer jackets shall be located so as to permit access by the operator without jeopardizing his safety.

(e)(2) Vertical mixers

(e)(2)(i) Vertical mixers shall comply with paragraphs (e)(1)(i), (iii), (ix) and (x), of this Section.

(e)(2)(ii) [Reserved]

(e)(2)(iii) Bowl locking devices shall be of a positive type which require the attention of the operator for unlocking.

(e)(2)(iv) Devices shall be made available for moving bowls weighing more than 80 pounds, with contents, into and out of the mixing position on the machine.

(f) Dividers

(f)(1)–(2) [Reserved]

(f)(3) **Rear of divider** The back of the divider shall have a complete cover to enclose all of the moving parts, or each individual part shall be enclosed or guarded to remove the separate hazards. The rear cover shall be provided with a limit switch in order that the machine cannot operate when this cover is open. The guard on the back shall be hinged so that it cannot be completely removed and if a catch or brace is provided for holding the cover open, it shall be designed so that it will not release due to vibrations or minor bumping whereby the cover may drop on an employee.

(g) Moulders

(g)(1) **Hoppers** Mechanical feed moulders shall be provided with hoppers so designed and connected to the proofer that an employee's hands cannot get into the hopper where they will come in contact with the in-running rolls.

(g)(2) **Hand-fed moulders** Hand-fed moulders shall be provided with a belt-feed device or the hopper shall be extended high enough so that the hands of the operator cannot get into the feed rolls. The top edge of such a hopper shall be well rounded to prevent injury when it is struck or bumped by the employee's hand.

(g)(3) **Stopping devices** There shall be a stopping device within easy reach of the operator who feeds the moulder and another stopping device within the reach of the employee taking the dough away from the moulder.

(h) Manually fed dough brakes

(h)(1) **Top-roll protection** The top roll shall be protected by a heavy gage metal shield extending over the roll to go within 6 inches of the hopper bottom board. The shield may be perforated to permit observation of the dough entering the rolls.

(h)(2) **Emergency stop bar** An emergency stop bar shall be provided, and so located that the body of the operator will press against the bar if the operator slips and falls toward the rolls, or if the operator gets his hand caught in the rolls. The bar shall apply the body pressure to open positively a circuit that will deenergize the drive motor. In addition, a brake which is inherently self-engaging by requiring power or force from an external source to cause disengagement shall be activated at the same time causing the rolls to stop instantly. The emergency stop bar shall be checked for proper operation every 30 days.

(i) Miscellaneous equipment

(i)(1) Proof boxes All door locks shall be operable both from within and outside the box. Guide rails shall be installed to center the rack as it enters, passes through, and leaves the proof box.

(i)(2) Fermentation room Fermentation room doors shall have nonshatterable wire glass or plastic panels for vision through doors.

(i)(3) Troughs Troughs shall be mounted on antifriction bearing casters thus making it possible for the operator to move and direct the motion of the trough with a minimum of effort.

(i)(4) Hand trucks

(i)(4)(i) Casters shall be set back from corners to be out of the way of toes and heels, but not far enough back to cause the truck to be unstable.

(i)(4)(ii) A lock or other device shall be provided to hold the handle in vertical position when the truck is not in use.

(i)(5) Lift trucks A lock or other device shall be provided to hold the handle in vertical position when the truck is not in use.

(i)(6) Racks

(i)(6)(i) [Reserved]

(i)(6)(ii) Racks shall be equipped with handles so located with reference to the frame of the rack that no part of the operator's hands extends beyond the outer edge of the frame when holding onto the handles.

(i)(6)(iii) Antifriction bearing casters shall be used to give the operator better control of the rack.

(i)(7) Conveyors

(i)(7)(i) Wherever a conveyor passes over a main aisleway, regularly occupied work area, or passageway, the underside of the conveyor shall be completely enclosed to prevent broken chains or other material from falling in the passageway.

(i)(7)(ii) Stop bumpers shall be installed on all delivery ends of conveyors, wherever manual removal of the product carried is practiced.

(i)(7)(iii) Where hazard of getting caught exists a sufficient number of stop buttons shall be provided to enable quick stopping of the conveyor.

(i)(8)–(10) [Reserved]

(i)(11) Ingredient premixers, emulsifiers, etc.

(i)(11)(i) All top openings shall be provided with covers attached to the machines. These covers should be so arranged and interlocked that power will be shut off whenever the cover is opened to a point where the operator's fingers might come in contact with the beaters.

(i)(11)(ii) [Reserved]

(i)(12) Chain tackle

(i)(12)(i) All chain tackle shall be marked prominently, permanently, and legibly with maximum load capacity.

(i)(12)(ii) All chain tackle shall be marked permanently and legibly with minimum support specification.

(i)(12)(iii) Safety hooks shall be used.

(i)(13) Trough hoists, etc.

(i)(13)(i) All hoists shall be marked prominently, permanently, and legibly with maximum load capacity.

(i)(13)(ii) All hoists shall be marked permanently and legibly with minimum support specifications.

(i)(13)(iii) Safety catches shall be provided for the chain so that the chain will hold the load in any position.

(i)(13)(iv) Safety hooks shall be used.

(i)(14) Air-conditioning units

(i)(14)(i) [Reserved]

(i)(14)(ii) On large units with doors to chambers large enough to be entered, all door locks shall be operable from both inside and outside.

(i)(15) Pan washing tanks

(i)(15)(i) [Reserved]

(i)(15)(ii) The surface of the floor of the working platform shall be maintained in nonslip condition.

(i)(15)(iii)–(iv) [Reserved]

(i)(15)(v) Power ventilated exhaust hoods shall be provided over the tanks.

(i)(16)–(19) [Reserved]

(i)(20) Bread coolers, rack type

(i)(20)(i) [Reserved]

(i)(20)(ii) All door locks shall be operable from both within and outside the cooler.

(i)(21) [Reserved]

(i)(22) Doughnut machines Separate flues shall be provided, (i) for venting vapors from the frying section, and (ii) for venting products of combustion from the combustion chamber used to heat the fat.

(i)(23) Open fat kettles

(i)(23)(i) The floor around kettles shall be maintained in nonslip condition.

(i)(23)(ii)–(iii) [Reserved]

(i)(23)(iv) The top of the kettle shall be not less than 36 inches above floor or working level.

(i)(24) Steam kettles

(i)(24)(i) Positive locking devices shall be provided to hold kettles in the desired position.

(i)(24)(ii) Kettles with steam jackets shall be provided with safety valves in accordance with the ASME Pressure Vessel Code, Section VIII, Unfired Pressure Vessels, 1968, which is incorporated by reference as specified in §1910.6.

(j) Slicers and wrappers

(j)(1) Slicers

(j)(1)(i)–(ii) [Reserved]

(j)(1)(iii) The cover over the knife head of reciprocating-blade slicers shall be provided with an interlocking arrangement so that the machine cannot operate unless the cover is in place.

(j)(1)(iv) On slicers with endless band knives, each motor shall be equipped with a magnet brake which operates whenever the motor is not energized. Each door, panel, or other point of access to the cutting blades shall be arranged by means of mechanical or electric interlocks so that the motor will be deenergized if all such access doors, panels, or access points are not closed.

(j)(1)(v) When it is necessary to sharpen slicer blades on the machine, a barrier shall be provided leaving only sufficient opening for the sharpening stone to reach the knife blades.

(j)(1)(vi) [Reserved]

(j)(1)(vii) Slicer wrapper conditions:

(j)(1)(vii)(A)–(B) [Reserved]

(j)(1)(vii)(C) Mechanical control levers for starting and stopping both slicing machine conveyors and wrapping machines shall be extended or so located that an operator in one location can control both machines. Such levers should be provided wherever necessary, but these should be so arranged that there is only one station capable of starting the wrapping machine and conveyor assembly, and this starting station should be so arranged or guarded as to prevent accidental starting. The electric control station for starting and stopping the electric motor driving the wrapping machine and conveyor should be located near the clutch starting lever.

(j)(2) Wrappers

(j)(2)(i)–(ii) [Reserved]

(j)(2)(iii) Electrical heaters on wrappers shall be protected by a cover plate properly separated or insulated from the heaters in order that accidental contact with this cover plate will not cause a burn to the operator.

(k) Biscuit and cracker equipment

(k)(1) Meal, peanut, and fig grinders

(k)(1)(i) If the hopper is removable it shall be provided with an electric interlock so that the machine cannot be put in operation when the hopper is removed.

(k)(1)(ii) Where grid guards cannot be used, feed conveyors to hoppers, or baffle-type hoppers, shall be provided. Hoppers in such cases shall be enclosed and provided with hinged covers, and equipped with electric interlock to prevent operation of the machine with the cover open.

(k)(2) Sugar and spice pulverizers

(k)(2)(i) All drive belts used in connection with sugar and spice pulverizers shall be grounded by means of metal combs or other effective means of removing static electricity. All pulverizing of sugar or spice grinding shall be done in accordance with NFPA 62—1967 (Standard for Dust Hazards of Sugar and Cocoa) and NFPA 656—1959 (Standard for Dust Hazards in Spice Grinding Plants), which are incorporated by reference as specified in §1910.6.

(k)(2)(ii) Magnetic separators shall be provided to reduce fire and explosion hazards.

(k)(3) **Cheese, fruit, and food cutters** These machines shall be protected in accordance with the requirements of paragraph (k)(1) of this Section.

(k)(4) [Reserved]

(k)(5) **Reversible dough brakes** Reversible brakes shall be provided with a guard or tripping mechanism on each side of the rolls. These guards shall be so arranged as to stop the machine or reverse the direction of the rolls so that they are outrunning if the guard is moved by contact of the operator.

(k)(6) **Cross-roll brakes** Cross-roll brakes shall be provided with guards that are similar in number and equal in effectiveness to guards on hand-fed brakes.

(k)(7) **Box-and roll-type dough sheeters**

(k)(7)(i) [Reserved]

(k)(7)(ii) Hoppers for sheeters shall have an automatic stop bar or automatic stopping device along the back edge of the hopper. If construction does not permit location at the back edge, the automatic stop bar or automatic stopping device shall be located where it will be most effective to accomplish the desired protection.

(k)(8) [Reserved]

(k)(9) **Rotary, die machines, pretzel rolling, and pretzel-stick extruding machines** Dough hoppers shall have the entire opening protected with substantial grid-type guards to prevent the employee from getting his hands caught in moving parts, or the hopper shall be extended high enough so that the operator's hands cannot get into moving parts.

(k)(10)–(11) [Reserved]

(k)(12) **Pan cooling towers**

(k)(12)(i) Where pan cooling towers extend to two or more floors, a lockout switch shall be provided on each floor in order that mechanics working on the tower may positively lock the mechanism against starting. Only one start switch shall be used in the motor control circuit.

(k)(12)(ii) [Reserved]

(k)(13) **Chocolate melting, refining, and mixing kettles** Each kettle shall be provided with a cover to enclose the top of the kettle. The bottom outlet of each kettle shall be of such size and shape that the operator cannot reach in to touch the revolving paddle or come in contact with the shear point between the paddle and the side of the kettle.

(k)(14)–(16) [Reserved]

(k)(17) **Peanut cooling trucks** Mechanically operated peanut cooling trucks shall have a grid-type cover over the entire top.

(l) **Ovens**

(l)(1) **General location**

(l)(1)(i)–(vi) [Reserved]

(l)(1)(vii) Ovens shall be located so that possible fire or explosion will not expose groups of persons to possible injury. For this reason ovens shall not adjoin lockers, lunch or sales rooms, main passageways, or exits.

(l)(2) [Reserved]

(l)(3) **Safeguards of mechanical parts**

(l)(3)(i) Emergency stop buttons shall be provided on mechanical ovens near the point where operators are stationed.

(l)(3)(ii) All piping at ovens shall be tested to be gastight.

(l)(3)(iii) Main shutoff valves, operable separately from any automatic valve, shall be provided to permit turning off the fuel or steam in case of an emergency.

(l)(3)(iii)(A) Main shutoff valves shall be located so that explosions, fires, etc. will not prevent access to these valves.

(l)(3)(iii)(B) Main shutoff valves shall be locked in the closed position when men must enter the oven or when the oven is not in service.

(l)(4)–(7) [Reserved]

(l)(8) **Electrical heating equipment**

(l)(8)(i)–(ii) [Reserved]

(l)(8)(iii) A main disconnect switch or circuit breaker shall be provided. This switch or circuit breaker shall be so located that it can be reached quickly and safely. The main switch or circuit breaker shall have provisions for locking it in the open position if any work on the electrical equipment or inside the oven must be performed.

(l)(9) **General requirements**

(l)(9)(i) [OI] Protecting devices shall be properly maintained and kept in working order.

(l)(9)(ii) [OI] All safety devices on ovens shall be inspected at intervals of not less than twice a month by an especially appointed, properly instructed bakery employee, and not less than once a year by representatives of the oven manufacturers.

(l)(9)(iii)(A) Protection of gas pilot lights shall be provided when it is impracticable to protect the main flame of the burner and where the pilot flame cannot contact the flame electrode without being in the path of the main flame of the burner. Failure of any gas pilot shall automatically shut off the fuel supply to the burner.

(l)(9)(iii)(B) Ovens with multiple burners shall be equipped with individual atmospheric pilot lights where there is sufficient secondary air in the baking chamber and where gas is available; or else each burner shall be equipped with an electric spark-type ignition device.

(l)(9)(iv) Burners of a capacity exceeding 150,000 B.t.u. per hour equipped with electric ignition shall be protected in addition by quick-acting combustion safeguards.

(l)(9)(iv)(A) [OI] The high-tension current for any electric spark-type ignition device shall originate in a power supply line which is interlocked with the fuel supply for the oven in such a way that in case of current failure both the source of electricity to the high-tension circuits and the fuel supply shall be turned off simultaneously.

(l)(9)(iv)(B) [Reserved]

(l)(9)(iv)(C) Combustion safeguards used in connection with electric ignition systems on ovens shall be so designed as to prevent an explosive mixture from accumulating inside the oven before ignition has taken place.

(l)(9)(v) When fuel is supplied and used at line pressure, safety shutoff valves shall be provided in the fuel line leading to the burner.

(l)(9)(v)(A) When fuel is supplied in excess of line pressure, safety shutoff valves shall be provided in the fuel line leading to the burners, unless the fuel supply lines are equipped with other automatic valves which will prevent the flow of fuel when the compressing equipment is stopped.

(l)(9)(v)(B) The safety shutoff valve shall be positively tight and shall be tested at least twice monthly.

(l)(9)(v)(C)–(D) [Reserved]

(l)(9)(v)(E) A safety shutoff valve shall require manual operation for reopening after it has closed, or the electric circuit shall be so arranged that it will require a manual operation for reopening the safety shutoff valve.

(l)(9)(v)(F) Manual reset-type safety shutoff valves shall be so arranged that they cannot be locked in an open position by external means.

(l)(9)(v)(G) Where blowers are used for supplying the air for combustion the safety shutoff valve shall be interlocked so that it will close in case of air failure.

(l)(9)(v)(H) Where gas or electric ignition is used, the safety shutoff valve shall close in case of ignition failure. On burners equipped with combustion safeguards, the valve shall close in case of burner flame failure.

(l)(9)(vi) One main, manually operated, fuel shutoff valve shall be provided on each oven, and shall be located ahead of all other valves in the system.

(l)(9)(vii) All individual gas or oil burners with a heating capacity over 150,000 B.t.u. per hour shall be protected by a safeguard which is actuated by the flame and which will react to flame failure in a time interval not to exceed 2 seconds. All safeguards, once having shut down a gas or oil burner, shall require manual resetting and starting of the burner or burners.

(l)(9)(viii) Any space in an oven (except direct fired ovens) which could be filled with an explosive mixture shall be protected by explosion vents. Explosion vents shall be made of minimum weight consistent with adequate insulation.

(l)(9)(viii)(A) Explosion doors which have a substantial weight shall be attached by chains or similar means to prevent flying parts from injuring the personnel in case of an explosion.

(l)(9)(viii)(B) Where explosion vents are so located that flying parts or gases might endanger the personnel working on or near the oven, internal or external protecting means shall be provided in the form of heavily constructed shields or deflectors made from noncombustible material.

(l)(9)(viii)(C) Specifically exempted from the provisions of paragraph paragraph (l)(8)(viii) of this Section are heating systems on ovens in which the fuel is admitted only to enclosed spaces which shall have been tested to prove that their construction will resist repeated explosions without deformation are exempt from the requirements of paragraph (l)(8)(viii)(A) and (B) of this Section.

(l)(9)(ix)–(x) [Reserved]

(l)(9)(xi) Where the gas supply pressure is substantially higher than that at which the burners of an oven are designed to operate, a gas pressure regulator shall be employed.

(l)(9)(xi)(A)–(C) [Reserved]

(l)(9)(xi)(D) A relief valve shall be placed on the outlet side of gas pressure regulators where gas is supplied at high pressure. The discharge from this valve shall be piped to the outside of the building.

(l)(10) **Direct-fired ovens**

(l)(10)(i) Direct-fired ovens shall be safeguarded against failure of fuel, air, or ignition.

(l)(10)(ii) To prevent the possible accumulation of explosive gases from being ignited after a shutdown, all direct-fired ovens with a heating capacity over 150,000 B.t.u. per hour shall be ventilated before the ignition system, combustion air blower, and the fuel can be turned on. The preventilation shall insure at least four complete changes of atmosphere in the baking chamber by discharging the oven atmosphere to the outside of the building and entraining fresh air into it. The preventilation shall be repeated whenever the heating equipment is shut down by a safety device.

(l)(11) **Direct recirculating ovens**

(l)(11)(i) Each circulating fan in direct recirculating ovens shall be interconnected with the burner in such a manner that the fuel is shut off by a safety valve when the fan is not running.

(l)(11)(ii) The flame of the burner or burners in direct recirculating ovens shall be protected by a quick-acting flame-sensitive safeguard which will automatically shut off the fuel supply in case of burner failure.

(l)(12)–(14) [Reserved]

(l)(15) **Indirect recirculating ovens**

(l)(15)(i)–(ii) [Reserved]

(l)(15)(iii) Duct systems (in ovens) operating under pressure shall be tested for tightness in the initial starting of the oven and also at intervals not farther apart than 6 months.

[39 FR 23502, June 27, 1974, as amended at 43 FR 49765, Oct. 24, 1978; 43 FR 51760, Nov. 7, 1978; 61 FR 9241, Mar. 7, 1996]

§1910.264 [OI] Laundry machinery and operations

(a) [Reserved]

(b) **General requirements** This Section applies to moving parts of equipment used in laundries and to conditions peculiar to this industry, with special reference to the point of operation of laundry machines. This Section does not apply to dry-cleaning operations.

(c) **Point-of-operation guards**

(c)(1) **Washroom machines**

(c)(1)(i) [Reserved]

(c)(1)(ii) **Washing machine**

(c)(1)(ii)(A) [Reserved]

(c)(1)(ii)(B) Each washing machine shall be provided with means for holding open the doors or covers of inner and outer cylinders or shells while being loaded or unloaded.

(c)(2) **Starching and drying machines**

(c)(2)(i)–(ii) [Reserved]

(c)(2)(iii) Drying tumbler

(c)(2)(iii)(A) [Reserved]

(c)(2)(iii)(B) Each drying tumbler shall be provided with means for holding open the doors or covers of inner and outer cylinders or shells while being loaded or unloaded.

(c)(2)(iv) Shaker (clothes tumbler)

(c)(2)(iv)(A) [Reserved]

(c)(2)(iv)(B)(1) [Reserved]

(c)(2)(iv)(B)(2) Each shaker or clothes tumbler of the double-cylinder type shall be provided with means for holding open the doors or covers of inner and outer cylinders or shells while being loaded or unloaded.

(c)(2)(v) Exception. Provisions of paragraph (c)(2)(iii), (iv)(A)(1), and (iv)(B) of this Section shall not apply to shakeout or conditioning tumblers where the clothes are loaded into the open end of the revolving cylinder and are automatically discharged out of the opposite end.

(c)(3) [Reserved]

(c)(4) **Miscellaneous machines and equipment**

(c)(4)(i)–(ii) [Reserved]

(c)(4)(iii) Steam pipes

(c)(4)(iii)(A) All steam pipes that are within 7 feet of the floor or working platform, and with which the worker may come into contact, shall be insulated or covered with a heat-resistive material or shall be otherwise properly guarded.

(c)(4)(iii)(B) Where pressure-reducing valves are used, one or more relief or safety valves shall be provided on the low-pressure side of the reducing valve, in case the piping or equipment on the low-pressure side does not meet the requirements for full initial pressure. The relief or safety valve shall be located adjacent to, or as close as possible to, the reducing valve. Proper protection shall be provided to prevent injury or damage caused by fluid escaping from relief or safety valves if vented to the atmosphere. The vents shall be of ample size and as short and direct as possible. The combined discharge capacity of the relief valves shall be such that the pressure rating of the lower-pressure piping and equipment will not be exceeded if the reducing valve sticks or fails to open.

(d) **Operating rules**

(d)(1) **General**

(d)(1)(i)–(ii) [Reserved]

(d)(1)(iii) **Markers** Markers and others handling soiled clothes shall be warned against touching the eyes, mouth, or any part of the body on which the skin has been broken by a scratch or abrasion; and they shall be cautioned not to touch or eat food until their hands have been thoroughly washed.

(d)(1)(iv) [Reserved]

(d)(1)(v) **Instruction of employees** Employees shall be properly instructed as to the hazards of their work and be instructed in safe practices, by bulletins, printed rules, and verbal instructions.

(d)(2) **Mechanical**

(d)(2)(i) **Safety guards**

(d)(2)(i)(A) No safeguard, safety appliance, or device attached to, or forming an integral part of any machinery shall be removed or made ineffective except for the purpose of making immediate repairs or adjustments. Any such safeguard, safety appliance, or device removed or made ineffective during the repair or adjustment of such machinery shall be replaced immediately upon the completion of such repairs or adjustments.

(d)(2)(i)(B) [Reserved]

[39 FR 23502, June 27, 1974, as amended at 43 FR 49767, Oct. 24, 1978; 43 FR 51760, Nov. 7, 1978]

§1910.265 [OI] Sawmills

(a) **General requirements—Application** This Section includes safety requirements for sawmill operations including, but not limited to, log and lumber handling, sawing, trimming, and planing; waste disposal; operation of dry kilns; finishing; shipping; storage; yard and yard equipment; and for power tools and affiliated equipment used in connection with such operations, but excluding the manufacture of plywood, cooperage, and veneer.

(b) **Definitions applicable to this Section**

(b)(1) **A-frame** The term A-frame means a structure made of two independent columns fastened together at the top and separated at the bottom for stability.

(b)(2) **Annealing** The term annealing means heating then cooling to soften and render less brittle.

(b)(3) **Binder** The term binder means a chain, cable, rope, or other approved material used for binding loads.

(b)(4) **Boom** The term boom means logs or timbers fastened together end to end and used to contain floating logs. The term includes enclosed logs.

(b)(5) **Brow log** The term brow log means a log placed parallel to a roadway at a landing or dump to protect vehicles while loading or unloading.

(b)(6) **Bunk** The term bunk means a cross support for a load.

(b)(7) **Cant** The term cant means a log slabbed on one or more sides.

(b)(8) **Carriage (log carriage)** The term carriage means a framework mounted on wheels which runs on tracks or in grooves in a direction parallel to the face of the saw, and which contains apparatus to hold a log securely and advance it towards the saw.

(b)(9) **Carrier** The term carrier means an industrial truck so designed and constructed that it straddles the load to be transported with mechanisms to pick up the load and support it during transportation.

(b)(10) **Chipper** The term chipper means a machine which cuts material into chips.

(b)(11) **Chock (bunk block) (cheese block)** The terms chock, bunk block, and cheese block mean a wedge that prevents logs or loads from moving.

(b)(12) **Cold deck** The term cold deck means a pile of logs stored for future removal.

(b)(13) **Crotch lines** The term crotch lines means two short lines attached to a hoisting line by a ring or shackle, the lower ends being attached to loading hooks.

(b)(14) **Dog (carriage dog)** The term dog means a steel tooth, one or more of which are attached to each carriage knee to hold log firmly in place on carriage.

(b)(15) **Drag saw** The term drag saw means a power-driven, reciprocating crosscut saw mounted on suitable frame and used for bucking logs.

(b)(16) **Head block** The term head block means that part of a carriage which holds the log and upon which it rests. It generally consists of base, knee, taper set, and mechanism.

(b)(17) **Head rig** The term head rig means a combination of head saw and log carriage used for the initial breakdown of logs into timbers, cants, and boards.

(b)(18) **Hog** The term hog means a machine for cutting or grinding slabs and other coarse residue from the mill.

(b)(19) **Husk** The term husk means a head saw framework on a circular mill.

(b)(20) **Industrial truck** The term industrial truck means a mobile powerdriven truck or tractor.

(b)(21) **Kiln tender** The term kiln tender means the operator of a kiln.

(b)(22) **Lift truck** The term lift truck means an industrial truck used for lateral transportation and equipped with a power-operated lifting device, usually in the form of forks, for piling or unpiling lumber units or packages.

(b)(23) **Live rolls** The term live rolls means cylinders of wood or metal mounted on horizontal axes and rotated by power, which are used to convey slabs, lumber, and other wood products.

(b)(24) **Loading boom** The term loading boom means any structure projecting from a pivot point to guide a log when lifted.

(b)(25) **Log deck** The term Log deck means a platform in the sawmill on which the logs remain until needed for sawing.

(b)(26) **Lumber hauling truck** The term lumber hauling truck means an industrial truck, other than a lift truck or a carrier, used for the transport of lumber.

(b)(27) **Log haul** The term log haul means a conveyor for transferring logs to mill.

(b)(28) **Package** The term package means a unit of lumber.

(b)(29) **Peavy** The term peavy means a stout wooden handle fitted with a spike and hook and used for rolling logs.

(b)(30) **Pike pole** The term pike pole means a long pole whose end is shod with a sharp pointed spike.

(b)(31) **Pitman rod** The term pitman rod means connecting rod.

(b)(32) **Resaw** The term resaw means band, circular, or sash gang saws used to break down slabs, cants, or flitches into lumber.

(b)(33) **Running line** The term running line means any moving rope as distinguished from a stationary rope such as a guyline.

(b)(34) **Safety factor** The term safety factor means a calculated reduction factor which may be applied to laboratory test values to obtain safe working stresses for wooden beams and other mechanical members; ratio of breaking load to safe load.

(b)(35) **Saw guide** The term saw guide means a device for steadying a circular or bandsaw.

(b)(36) **Setwork** The term setwork means a mechanism on a sawmill carriage which enables an operator to move the log into position for another cut.

(b)(37) **Sorting gaps** The term sorting gaps means the areas on a log pond enclosed by boom sticks into which logs are sorted.

(b)(38) **Spreader wheel** The term spreader wheel means a metal wheel that separates the board from the log in back of circular saws to prevent binding.

(b)(39) **Splitter** The term splitter means a knife-type, nonrotating spreader.

(b)(40) **Sticker** The term sticker means a strip of wood or other material used to separate layers of lumber.

(b)(41) **Stiff boom** The term stiff boom means the anchored, stationary boom sticks which are tied together and on which boom men work.

(b)(42) **Swifter** The term swifter is a means of tying boom sticks together to prevent them from spreading while being towed.

(b)(43) **Telltale** The term telltale means a device used to serve as a warning for overhead objects.

(b)(44) **Top saw** The term top saw means the upper of two circular saws on a head rig, both being on the same husk.

(b)(45) **Tramway** The term tramway means a way for trams, usually consisting of parallel tracks laid on wooden beams.

(b)(46) **Trestle** The term trestle means a braced framework of timbers, piles or steelwork for carrying a road or railroad over a depression.

(c) Building facilities, and isolated equipment

(c)(1) **Safety factor** All buildings, docks, tramways, walkways, log dumps, and other structures shall be designed, constructed and maintained so as to support the imposed load in accordance with a safety factor.

(c)(2) **Work areas** Work areas under mills shall be as evenly surfaced as local conditions permit. They shall be free from unnecessary obstructions and provided with lighting facilities in accordance with American National Standard for Industrial Lighting A11.1—1965, which is incorporated by reference as specified in §1910.6.

(c)(3) **Floors** Flooring in buildings and on ramps and walkways shall be constructed and installed in accordance with established principles of mechanics and sound engineering practices. They shall be of adequate strength to support the estimated or actual dead and live loads acting on them with the resultant stress not exceeding the allowable stress for the material being used.

(c)(3)(i) [Reserved]

(c)(3)(ii) **Areas beneath floor openings** Areas under floor openings shall, where practical, be fenced off. When this is not practical, they shall be plainly marked and telltales shall be installed to hang over these areas.

(c)(3)(iii) **Floor maintenance** The flooring of buildings, docks, and passageways shall be kept in good repair. When a hazardous condition develops that cannot be immediately repaired, the area shall be guarded until adequate repairs are made.

(c)(3)(iv) **Nonslip floors** Floors, footwalks, and passageways in the work area around machines or other places where a person is required to stand or walk shall be provided with effective means to minimize slipping.

(c)(4) Walkways, docks, and platforms

(c)(4)(i) **Width** Walkways, docks, and platforms shall be of sufficient width to provide adequate passage and working areas.

(c)(4)(ii) **Maintenance** Walkways shall be evenly floored and kept in good repair.

(c)(4)(iii) **Docks** Docks and runways used for the operation of lift trucks and other vehicles shall have a substantial guard or shear timber except where loading and unloading are being performed.

(c)(4)(iv) **Elevated walks** All elevated walks, runways, or platforms, if 4 feet or more from the floor level, shall be provided with a standard railing except on loading or unloading sides of platforms. If height exceeds 6 feet, a standard toe board also shall be provided to prevent material from rolling or falling off.

(c)(4)(v) **Elevated platforms** Where elevated platforms are used routinely on a daily basis, they shall be equipped with stairways or fixed ladders that comply with Subpart D of this Part.

(c)(4)(vi) **Hazardous locations** Where required, walkways and stairways with standard handrails shall be provided in elevated and hazardous locations. Where such passageways are over walkways or work areas, standard toe boards shall be provided.

(c)(5) Stairways

(c)(5)(i) **Construction** Stairways shall be constructed in accordance with Subpart D of this Part.

(c)(5)(ii) **Handrails** Stairways shall be provided with a standard handrail on at least one side or on any open side. Where stairs are more than four feet wide there shall be a standard handrail at each side, and where more than eight feet wide, a third standard handrail shall be erected in the center of the stairway.

(c)(5)(iii) **Lighting** All stairways shall be adequately lighted as prescribed in paragraph (c)(9) of this Section.

(c)(6) Emergency exits including doors and fire escapes

(c)(6)(i) **Opening** Doors shall not open directly on or block a flight of stairs, and shall swing in the direction of exit travel.

(c)(6)(ii) **Identification** Exits shall be located and identified in a manner that affords ready exit from all work areas.

(c)(6)(iii) **Swinging doors** All swinging doors shall be provided with windows; with one window for each section of double swinging doors. Such windows shall be of shatterproof or safety glass unless otherwise protected against breakage.

(c)(6)(iv) **Sliding doors** Where sliding doors are used as exits, an inner door shall be cut inside each of the main doors and arranged to open outward.

(c)(6)(v) **Barriers and warning signs** Where a doorway opens upon a railroad track or upon a tramway or dock over which vehicles travel, a barrier or other warning device shall be placed to prevent workmen from stepping into moving traffic.

(c)(7) **Air requirements** Ventilation shall be provided to supply adequate fresh healthful air to rooms, buildings, and work areas.

(c)(8) **Vats and tanks** All open vats and tanks into which workmen could fall shall be guarded.

(c)(9) **Lighting**

(c)(9)(i) **Adequacy** Illumination shall be provided and designed to supply adequate general and local lighting to rooms, buildings, and work areas during the time of use.

(c)(9)(ii) **Effectiveness** Factors upon which the adequacy and effectiveness of illumination will be judged, include the following:

(c)(9)(ii)(A) The quantity of light in foot-candle intensity shall be sufficient for the work being done.

(c)(9)(ii)(B) The quality of the light shall be such that it is free from glare, and has correct direction, diffusion, and distribution.

(c)(9)(ii)(C) Shadows and extreme contrasts shall be avoided or kept to a minimum.

(c)(10) [Reserved]

(c)(11) **Hazard marking** Physical hazard marking shall be as specified in §1910.144 of this Part.

(c)(12) [Reserved]

(c)(13) **Hydraulic systems** Means shall be provided to block, chain, or otherwise secure equipment normally supported by hydraulic pressure so as to provide for safe maintenance.

(c)(14) [Reserved]

(c)(15) **Gas piping and appliances** All gas piping and appliances shall be installed in accordance with the American National Standard Requirements for the Installation of Gas Appliances and Gas Piping Z21.30—1964, which is incorporated by reference as specified in §1910.6.

(c)(16)–(17) [Reserved]

(c)(18) OI **Conveyors**

(c)(18)(i) **Standards** Construction, operation, and maintenance of conveyors shall be in accordance with American National Standard B20.1—1957, which is incorporated by reference as specified in §1910.6.

(c)(18)(ii) **Guarding** Spiked live rolls shall be guarded.

(c)(19) **Stationary tramways and trestles**

(c)(19)(i) **Foundations and walkways** Tramways and trestles shall have substantial mud sills or foundations which shall be frequently inspected and kept in repair. When vehicles are operated on tramways and trestles which are used for foot passage, traffic shall be controlled or a walkway with standard handrails at the outer edge and shear timber on the inner edge shall be provided. This walkway shall be wide enough to allow adequate clearance to vehicles. When walkways cross over other thoroughfares, they shall be solidly fenced at the outer edge to a height of 42 inches over such thoroughfares.

(c)(19)(ii) **Clearance** Stationary tramways and trestles shall have a vertical clearance of 22 feet over railroad rails. When constructed over carrier docks or roads, they shall have a clearance of 6 feet above the driver's foot rest on the carrier, and in no event shall this clearance be less than 12 feet from the roadway. In existing operations where it is impractical to obtain such clearance, telltales, electric signals, signs or other precautionary measures shall be installed.

(c)(20) **Blower, collecting, and exhaust systems**

(c)(20)(i) **Design, construction, and maintenance** Blower collecting, and exhaust systems should be designed, constructed, and maintained in accordance with American National Standards Z33.1—1961 (For the Installation of Blower and Exhaust Systems for Dust, Stock, and Vapor Removal or Conveying) and Z12.2—1962 (R1969) (Code for the Prevention of Dust Explosion in Woodworking and Wood Flour Manufacturing Plants), which are incorporated by reference as specified in §1910.6.

(c)(20)(ii) **Collecting systems** All mills containing one or more machines that create dust, shavings, chips, or slivers during a period of time equal to or greater than one-fourth of the working day, shall be equipped with a collecting system. It may be either continuous or automatic, and shall be of sufficient strength and capacity to enable it to remove such refuse from points of operation and immediate vicinities of machines and work areas.

(c)(20)(iii) **Exhaust or conveyor systems** Each woodworking machine that creates dust, shavings, chips, or slivers shall be equipped with an exhaust or conveyor system located and adjusted to remove the maximum amount of refuse from the point of operation and immediate vicinity.

(c)(20)(iv) [Reserved]

(c)(20)(v) **Dust chambers** Exhaust pipes shall not discharge into an unconfined outside pile if uncontrolled fire or explosion hazards are created. They may empty into settling or dust chambers, designed to prevent the dust or refuse from entering any work area. Such chambers shall be constructed and operated to minimize the danger of fire or dust explosion.

(c)(20)(vi) **Hand removal of refuse** Provision for the daily removal of refuse shall be made in all operations not required to have an exhaust system or having refuse too heavy, bulky, or otherwise unsuitable to be handled by the exhaust system.

(c)(21) **Chippers**

(c)(21)(i) **Whole-log chippers** The feed system to the chipper shall be arranged so the operator does not stand in direct line with the chipper spout (hopper). The chipper spout shall be enclosed to a height of not less than 36 inches from the floor or the operator's platform. A safety belt and lifeline shall be worn by workmen when working at or near the spout unless the spout is guarded. The lifeline shall be short enough to prevent workers from falling into the chipper.

(c)(21)(ii) **Hogs**

(c)(21)(ii)(A) Hog mills shall be so designed and arranged that from no position on the rim of the chute shall the distance to the cutter knives be less than 40 inches.

(c)(21)(ii)(B) Hog feed chutes shall be provided with suitable and approved baffles, which shall minimize material from being thrown from the mill.

(c)(21)(ii)(C) Employees feeding hog mills shall be provided with safety belts and lines unless guarded.

(c)(22) [Reserved]

(c)(23) **Bins, bunkers, hoppers, and fuel houses**

(c)(23)(i) **Guarding** Open bins, bunkers, and hoppers whose upper edges extend less than 3 feet above working level shall be equipped with standard handrails and toe boards, or have their tops covered by a substantial grill or grating with openings small enough to prevent a man from falling through.

(c)(23)(ii) **Use of wheeled equipment to load bins** Where automotive or other wheeled equipment is used to move materials into bins, bunkers, and hoppers, adequate guard rails shall be installed along each side of the runway, and a substantial bumper stop provided when necessary.

(c)(23)(iii) **Exits, lighting, and safety devices** Fuel houses and bins shall have adequate exits and lighting, and all necessary safety devices shall be provided and shall be used by persons entering these structures.

(c)(23)(iv) **Walkways** Where needed, fuel houses and bins shall have a standard railed platform or walkway near the top.

(c)(24) **Ropes, cables, slings, and chains**

(c)(24)(i) **Safe usage** Ropes, cables, slings, and chains shall be used in accordance with safe use practices recommended by the manufacturer or within safe limits recommended by the equipment manufacturer when used in conjunction with it.

(c)(24)(ii) **Hooks** No open hook shall be used in rigging to lift any load where there is hazard from relieving the tension on the hook from the load or hook catching or fouling.

(c)(24)(iii) **Work by qualified persons** Installation, inspection, maintenance, repair, and testing of ropes, cables, slings, and chains shall be done only by persons qualified to do such work.

(c)(24)(iv) **Slings** Proper storage shall be provided for slings while not in use.

(c)(24)(v) **Ropes or cables**

(c)(24)(v)(A) Wire rope or cable shall be inspected when installed and once each week thereafter, when in use. It shall be removed from hoisting or load-carrying service when kinked or when one of the following conditions exists:

(c)(24)(v)(A)(1) When three broken wires are found in one lay of 6 by 6 wire rope.

(c)(24)(v)(A)(2) When six broken wires are found in one lay of 6 by 19 wire rope.

(c)(24)(v)(A)(3) When nine broken wires are found in one lay of 6 by 37 wire rope.

(c)(24)(v)(A)(4) When eight broken wires are found in one lay of 8 by 19 wire rope.

(c)(24)(v)(A)(5) When marked corrosion appears.

(c)(24)(v)(A)(6) Wire rope of a type not described herein shall be removed from service when 4 percent of the total number of wires composing such rope are found to be broken in one lay.

(c)(24)(v)(B) Wire rope removed from service due to defects shall be plainly marked or identified as being unfit for further use on cranes, hoists, and other load-carrying devices.

(c)(24)(v)(C) The ratio between the rope diameter and the drum, block, sheave, or pulley tread diameter shall be such that the rope will adjust itself to the bend without excessive wear, deformation, or injury. In no case shall the safe value of drums, blocks, sheaves, or pulleys be reduced when replacing such items unless compensating changes are made for rope used and for safe loading limits.

(c)(24)(vi) **Drums, sheaves, and pulleys** Drums, sheaves, and pulleys shall be smooth and free from surface defects liable to injure rope. Drums, sheaves, or pulleys having eccentric bores or cracked hubs, spokes, or flanges shall be removed from service.

(c)(24)(vii) **Connections** Connections, fittings, fastenings, and other parts used in connection with ropes and cables shall be of good quality and of proper size and strength, and shall be installed in accordance with the manufacturer's recommendations.

(c)(24)(viii) **Socketing, splicing, and seizing**

(c)(24)(viii)(A) Socketing, splicing, and seizing of cables shall be performed only by qualified persons.

(c)(24)(viii)(B) All eye splices shall be made in an approved manner and wire rope thimbles of proper size shall be fitted in the eye, except that in slings the use of thimbles shall be optional.

(c)(24)(viii)(C) Wire rope clips attached with U-bolts shall have these bolts on the dead or short end of the rope. The U-bolt nuts shall be retightened immediately after initial load carrying use and at frequent intervals thereafter.

(c)(24)(viii)(D) When a wedge socket-type fastening is used, the dead or short end of the cable shall be clipped with a U-bolt or otherwise made secure against loosening.

(c)(24)(viii)(E) **Fittings** Hooks, shackles, rings, pad eyes, and other fittings that show excessive wear or that have been bent, twisted, or otherwise damaged shall be removed from service.

(c)(24)(viii)(F) **Running lines** Running lines of hoisting equipment located within 6 feet 6 inches of the ground or working level shall be boxed off or otherwise guarded, or the operating area shall be restricted.

(c)(24)(viii)(G) **Number of wraps on drum** There shall be not less than two full wraps of hoisting cable on the drum of cranes and hoists at all times of operation.

(c)(24)(viii)(H) **Drum flanges** Drums shall have a flange at each end to prevent the cable from slipping off.

(c)(24)(viii)(I) **Sheave guards** Bottom sheaves shall be protected by close fitting guards to prevent cable from jumping the sheave.

(c)(24)(viii)(J) **Preventing abrasion** The reeving of a rope shall be so arranged as to minimize chafing or abrading while in use.

(c)(24)(ix) **Chains**

(c)(24)(ix)(A) Chains used in load carrying service shall be inspected before initial use and weekly thereafter.

(c)(24)(ix)(B) Chain shall be normalized or annealed periodically as recommended by the manufacturer.

(c)(24)(ix)(C) If at any time any 3-foot length of chain is found to have stretched one-third the length of a link it shall be discarded.

(c)(24)(ix)(D) Bolts or nails shall not be placed between two links to shorten or join chains.

(c)(24)(ix)(E) Broken chains shall not be spliced by inserting a bolt between two links with the head of the bolt and nut sustaining the load, or by passing one link through another and inserting a bolt or nail to hold it.

(c)(24)(x) **Fiber rope**

(c)(24)(x)(A) Frozen fiber rope shall not be used in load carrying service.

(c)(24)(x)(B) Fiber rope that has been subjected to acid or excessive heat shall not be used for load carrying purposes.

(c)(24)(x)(C) Fiber rope shall be protected from abrasion by padding where it is fastened or drawn over square corners or sharp or rough surfaces.

(c)(25) [Reserved]

(c)(26) **Mechanical stackers and unstackers**

(c)(26)(i) [Reserved]

(c)(26)(ii) **Lumber lifting devices** Lumber lifting devices on all stackers shall be designed and arranged so as to minimize the possibility of lumber falling from such devices.

(c)(26)(iii) **Blocking hoisting platform** Means shall be provided to positively block the hoisting platform when employees must go beneath the stacker or unstacker hoist.

(c)(26)(iv) **Identifying controls** Every manually operated control switch shall be properly identified and so located as to be readily accessible to the operator.

(c)(26)(v) **Locking main control switches** Main control switches shall be so designed that they can be locked in the open position.

(c)(26)(vi) **Guarding side openings** The hoistway side openings at the top level of the stacker and unstacker shall be protected by enclosures of standard railings.

(c)(26)(vii) **Guarding hoistway openings** When the hoist platform or top of the load is below the working platform, the hoistway openings shall be guarded.

(c)(26)(viii) **Guarding lower landing area** The lower landing area of stackers and unstackers shall be guarded by enclosures that prevent entrance to the area or pit below the hoist platform. Entrances should be protected by electrically interlocked gates which, when open, will disconnect the power and set the hoist brakes. When the interlock is not installed, other positive means of protecting the entrance shall be provided.

(c)(26)(ix) **Inspection** Every stacker and unstacker shall be inspected at frequent intervals and all defective parts shall be immediately repaired or replaced.

(c)(26)(x) **Cleaning pits** Safe means of entrance and exit shall be provided to permit cleaning of pits.

(c)(26)(xi) **Preventing entry to hazardous area** Where the return of trucks from unstacker to stacker is by mechanical power or gravity, adequate signs, warning devices, or barriers shall be erected to prevent entry into the hazardous area.

(c)(27) **Lumber piling and storage**

(c)(27)(i) **Pile foundations** In stacking units of lumber, pile foundations shall be designed and arranged to support maximum loads without sinking, sagging, or permitting the piles to topple. In unit package piles, substantial bolsters or unit separators shall be placed between each package directly over the stickers.

(c)(27)(ii) **Stacking dissimilar unit packages** Long units of lumber shall not be stacked upon shorter packages except where a stable pile can be made with the use of package separators.

(c)(27)(iii) **Unstable piles** Piles of lumber which have become unstable shall be immediately made safe, or the area into which they might fall shall be fenced or barricaded and employees prohibited from entering it.

(c)(27)(iv) **Stickers** Unit packages of lumber shall be provided with stickers as necessary to insure stability under ordinary operating conditions.

(c)(27)(v) **Sticker alignment** Stickers shall extend the full width of the package, shall be uniformly spaced, and shall be aligned one above the other. Stickers may be lapped with a minimum overlapping of 12 inches. Stickers shall not protrude more than 2 inches beyond the sides of the package.

(c)(27)(vi) **Pile height** The height of unit package piles shall be dependent on the dimensions of the packages and shall be such as to provide stability under normal operating conditions. Adjacent lumber piles may be tied together with separators to increase stability.

(c)(28) **Lumber loading** Loads shall be built and secured to insure stability in transit.

(c)(29) **Burners**

(c)(29)(i) **Guying** If the burner stack is not self-supporting, it shall be guyed or otherwise supported.

(c)(29)(ii) **Runway** The conveyor runway to the burner shall be equipped with a standard handrail. If the runway crosses a roadway or thoroughfare, standard toe boards shall be provided in addition.

(c)(30) **Vehicles**

(c)(30)(i) **Scope** Vehicles shall include all mobile equipment normally used in sawmill, planing mill, storage, shipping, and yard operations.

(c)(30)(ii) **Warning signals and spark arrestors** All vehicles shall be equipped with audible warning signals and where practicable shall have spark arrestors.

(c)(30)(iii) **Lights** All vehicles operated in the dark or in poorly lighted areas shall be equipped with head and tail lights.

(c)(30)(iv) **Overhead guard** All vehicles operated in areas where overhead hazards exist shall be equipped with an approved overhead guard. See American National Standard Safety Code for Powered Industrial Trucks, B56.1—1969, which is incorporated by reference as specified in §1910.6.

(c)(30)(v) **Platform guard** Where the operator is exposed to hazard from backing the vehicle into objects, an approved platform guard shall be provided and so arranged as to not impede exit of driver from vehicle.

(c)(30)(vi) [Reserved]

(c)(30)(vii) **Operation in buildings** Vehicles powered by internal combustion engines shall not operate in buildings unless the buildings are adequately ventilated.

(c)(30)(viii) **Load limits** No vehicle shall be operated with loads exceeding its safe load capacity.

(c)(30)(ix) **Brakes** All vehicles shall be equipped with brakes capable of holding and controlling the vehicle and capacity load upon any incline or grade over which they may be operated.

(c)(30)(x) [Reserved]

(c)(30)(xi) **Carriers**

(c)(30)(xi)(A) Carriers shall be so designed and constructed that the operator's field of vision shall not be unnecessarily restricted.

(c)(30)(xi)(B) Carriers shall be provided with an access ladder or equivalent.

(c)(30)(xii) **Lumber hauling trucks**

(c)(30)(xii)(A) On trucks where movement of load on stopping would endanger the operator, a substantial bulkhead shall be installed behind the operator's seat. This shall extend to the top of the operator's compartment.

(c)(30)(xii)(B) Stakes, stake pockets, racks, tighteners, and binders shall provide adequate means to secure the load against any movement during transit.

(c)(30)(xii)(C) Where rollers are used, at least two shall be equipped with locks which shall be locked when supporting loads during transit.

(c)(31) **Traffic control and flow**

(c)(31)(i) **Hazardous crossings** Railroad tracks and other hazardous crossings shall be plainly posted.

(c)(31)(ii) **Restricted overhead clearance** All areas of restricted side or overhead clearance shall be plainly marked.

(c)(31)(iii) **Pickup and unloading points** Pickup and unloading points and paths for lumber packages on conveyors and transfers and other areas where accurate spotting is required, shall be plainly marked and wheel stops provided where necessary.

(c)(31)(iv) **Aisles, passageways, and roadways** Aisles, passageways, and roadways shall be sufficiently wide to provide safe side clearance. One-way aisles may be used for two-way traffic if suitable turnouts are provided.

(d) **Log handling, sorting, and storage**

(d)(1) **Log unloading methods, equipment, and facilities**

(d)(1)(i) **Unloading methods**

(d)(1)(i)(A) Stakes and chocks which trip shall be constructed in such manner that the tripping mechanism that releases the stake or chocks is activated at the opposite side of the load being tripped.

(d)(1)(i)(B) Binders on logs shall not be released prior to securing with unloading lines or other unloading device.

(d)(1)(i)(C) Binders shall be released only from the side on which the unloader operates, except when released by remote control devices or except when person making release is protected by racks or stanchions or other equivalent means.

(d)(1)(i)(D) Loads on which a binder is fouled by the unloading machine shall have an extra binder or metal band of equal strength placed around the load, or the load shall be otherwise secured so the fouled binder can be safely removed.

(d)(1)(ii) **Unloading equipment and facilities**

(d)(1)(ii)(A) Machines used for hoisting, unloading, or lowering logs shall be equipped with brakes capable of controlling or holding the maximum load in midair.

(d)(1)(ii)(B) The lifting cylinders of all hydraulically operated log handling machines shall be equipped with a positive device for preventing the uncontrolled lowering of the load or forks in case of a failure in the hydraulic system.

(d)(1)(ii)(C) A limit switch shall be installed on powered log handling machines to prevent the lift arms from traveling too far in the event the control switch is not released in time.

(d)(1)(ii)(D) When forklift-type machines are used to load trailers, a means of securing the loading attachment to the fork shall be installed and used.

(d)(1)(ii)(E) A-frames and similar log unloading devices shall have adequate height to provide safe clearance for swinging loads and to provide for adequate crotch lines and spreader bar devices.

(d)(1)(ii)(F) Log handling machines used to stack logs or lift loads above operator's head shall be equipped with adequate overhead protection.

(d)(1)(ii)(G) All mobile log handling machines shall be equipped with headlights and backup lights.

(d)(1)(ii)(H) Unloading devices shall be equipped with a horn or other plainly audible signaling device.

(d)(1)(ii)(I) Movement of unloading equipment shall be coordinated by audible or hand signals when operator's vision is impaired or operating in the vicinity of other employees.

(d)(1)(ii)(J) Wood pike poles shall be made of straight-grained, select material. Metal or conductive pike poles shall not be used around exposed energized electrical conductors. Defective, blunt, or dull pike poles shall not be used.

(d)(2) **Log unloading and storage areas**

(d)(2)(i) **General**

(d)(2)(i)(A) Log dumps, booms, ponds, or storage areas used at night shall be illuminated in accordance with the requirements of American National Standard A11.1–1965 (R–1970) Standard Practice for Industrial Lighting, which is incorporated by reference as specified in §1910.6.

(d)(2)(i)(B) Log unloading areas shall be arranged and maintained to provide a safe working area.

(d)(2)(i)(C) Where skids are used, space adequate to clear a man's body shall be maintained between the top of the skids and the ground.

(d)(2)(i)(D) Signs prohibiting unauthorized foot or vehicle traffic in log unloading and storage areas shall be posted.

(d)(2)(ii) **Water log dumps**

(d)(2)(ii)(A) Ungrounded electrically powered hoists using handheld remote control in grounded locations, such as log dumps or mill log lifts, shall be actuated by circuits operating at less than 50 volts to ground.

(d)(2)(ii)(B) Roadbeds at log dumps shall be of sufficient width and evenness to insure safe operation of equipment.

(d)(2)(ii)(C) An adequate brow log or skid timbers or the equivalent shall be provided where necessary. Railroad-type dumps, when located where logs are dumped directly into water or where entire loads are lifted from vehicle, may be exempted providing such practice does not create a hazardous exposure of personnel or equipment.

(d)(2)(ii)(D) Unloading lines shall be arranged so that it is not necessary for the employees to attach them from the pond or dump side of the load except when entire loads are lifted from the log-transporting vehicle.

(d)(2)(ii)(E) Unloading lines, crotch lines, or equally effective means shall be arranged and used in a manner to minimize the possibility of any log from swinging or rolling back.

(d)(2)(ii)(F) When logs are unloaded with peavys or similar manual methods, means shall be provided and used that will minimize the danger from rolling or swinging logs.

(d)(2)(ii)(G) Guardrails, walkways, and standard handrails shall be installed.

(d)(2)(ii)(H) Approved life rings (see: 46 CFR 160.099 and 46 CFR 160.050) with line attached and maintained to retain buoyancy shall be provided.

(d)(2)(iii) **Log booms and ponds**

(d)(2)(iii)(A) Walkways and floats shall be installed and securely anchored to provide adequate passageway for employees.

(d)(2)(iii)(B) All regular boom sticks and foot logs shall be reasonably straight, with no protruding knots and bark, and shall be capable of supporting, above the water line at either end, the weight of an employee and equipment.

(d)(2)(iii)(C) Permanent cable swifters shall be so arranged that it will not be necessary to roll boom sticks in order to attach or detach them.

(d)(2)(iii)(D) Periodic inspection of cable or dogging lines shall be made to determine when repair or removal from service is necessary.

(d)(2)(iii)(E) The banks of the log pond in the vicinity of the log haul shall be reinforced to prevent caving in.

(d)(2)(iii)(F) Artificial log ponds shall be drained, cleaned, and refilled when unhealthy stagnation or pollution occurs.

(d)(2)(iii)(G) Employees whose duties require them to work from boats, floating logs, boom sticks, or walkways along or on water shall be provided with and shall wear appropriate buoyant devices while performing such duties.

(d)(2)(iii)(H) Stiff booms shall be two float logs wide secured by boom chains or other connecting devices, and of a width adequate for the working needs. Walking surfaces shall be free of loose material and maintained in good repair.

(d)(2)(iii)(I) Boom sticks shall be fastened together with adequate crossties or couplings.

(d)(2)(iii)(J) Floating donkeys or other power-driven machinery used on booms shall be placed on a raft or float with enough buoyancy to keep the deck well above water.

(d)(2)(iii)(K) All sorting gaps shall have a substantial stiff boom on each side.

(d)(2)(iv) Pond boats and rafts The applicable provisions of the Standard for Fire Protection for Motorcraft, NFPA No. 302—1968, which is incorporated by reference as specified in §1910.6, shall be complied with.

(d)(2)(iv)(A) Decks of pond boats shall be covered with nonslip material.

(d)(2)(iv)(B) Powered pond boats or rafts shall be provided with at least one approved fire extinguisher, and one lifering with line attached.

(d)(2)(iv)(C) Boat fuel shall be transported and stored in approved safety containers. Refer to §1910.155(c)(3) for definition of approved.

(d)(2)(iv)(D) Inspection, maintenance, and ventilation of the bilge area shall be provided to prevent accumulation of highly combustible materials.

(d)(2)(iv)(E) Adequate ventilation shall be provided for the cabin area on enclosed cabin-type boats to prevent accumulation of harmful gases or vapors.

(d)(2)(v) Dry deck storage

(d)(2)(v)(A) Dry deck storage areas shall be kept orderly and shall be maintained in a condition which is conducive to safe operation of mobile equipment.

(d)(2)(v)(B) Logs shall be stored in a safe and orderly manner, and roadways and traffic lanes shall be maintained at a width adequate for safe travel of log handling equipment.

(d)(2)(v)(C) Logs shall be arranged to minimize the chance of accidentally rolling from the deck.

(d)(2)(vi) Log hauls and slips

(d)(2)(vi)(A) Walkways along log hauls shall have a standard handrail on the outer edge, and cleats or other means to assure adequate footing and enable employees to walk clear of the log chute.

(d)(2)(vi)(B) Log haul bull chains or cable shall be designed, installed, and maintained to provide adequate safety for the work need.

(d)(2)(vi)(C) Log haul gear and bull chain drive mechanism shall be guarded.

(d)(2)(vi)(D) Substantial troughs for the return strand of log haul chains shall be provided over passageways.

(d)(2)(vi)(E) Log haul controls shall be located and identified to operate from a position where the operator will, at all times, be in the clear of logs, machinery, lines, and rigging. In operations where control is by lever exposed to incoming logs, the lever shall be arranged to operate the log haul only when moved toward the log slip or toward the log pond.

(d)(2)(vi)(F) A positive stop shall be installed on all log hauls to prevent logs from traveling too far ahead in the mill.

(d)(2)(vi)(G) Overhead protection shall be provided for employees working below logs being moved to the log deck.

(d)(2)(vi)(H) Log wells shall be provided with safeguards to minimize the possibility of logs rolling back into well from log deck.

(d)(3) Log decks

(d)(3)(i) Access Safe access to the head rig shall be provided.

(d)(3)(ii) Stops Log decks shall be provided with adequate stops, chains, or other safeguards to prevent logs from rolling down the deck onto the carriage or its runway.

(d)(3)(iii) Barricade A barricade or other positive stop of sufficient strength to stop any log shall be erected between the sawyer's stand and the log deck.

(d)(3)(iv) Loose chains Loose chains from overhead canting devices or other equipment shall not be allowed to hang over the log deck in such manner as to strike employees.

(d)(3)(v) Swing saws Swing saws on log decks shall be equipped with a barricade and stops for protection of employees who may be on the opposite side of the log haul chute.

(d)(3)(vi) Drag saws Where reciprocating log cutoff saws (drag saws) are provided, they shall not project into walkway or aisle.

(d)(3)(vii) Circular cutoff saws Circular log bucking or cutoff saws shall be so located and guarded as to allow safe entrance to and exit from the building.

(d)(3)(viii) Entrance doorway Where the cutoff saw partially blocks the entrance from the log haul runway, the entrance shall be guarded.

(d)(4) Mechanical barkers

(d)(4)(i) Rotary barkers Rotary barking devices shall be so guarded as to protect employees from flying chips, bark, or other extraneous material.

(d)(4)(ii) Elevating ramp If an elevating ramp or gate is used, it shall be provided with a safety chain, hook, or other means of suspension while employees are underneath.

(d)(4)(iii) Area around barkers The hazardous area around ring barkers and their conveyors shall be fenced off or posted as a prohibited area for unauthorized persons.

(d)(4)(iv) Enclosing hydraulic barkers Hydraulic barkers shall be enclosed with strong baffles at the inlet and outlet. The operator shall be protected by adequate safety glass or equivalent.

(d)(4)(v) Holddown rolls Holddown rolls shall be installed at the infeed and outfeed sections of mechanical ring barkers to control the movement of logs.

(e) Log breakdown and related machinery and facilities

(e)(1) Log carriages and carriage runways

(e)(1)(i) Bumpers A substantial stop or bumper with adequate shock-absorptive qualities shall be installed at each end of the carriage runway.

(e)(1)(ii) Footing Rider-type carriages shall be floored to provide secure footing and a firm working platform for the block setter.

(e)(1)(iii) Sheave housing Sheaves on rope-driven carriages shall be guarded at floor line with substantial housings.

(e)(1)(iv) Carriage control A positive means shall be provided to prevent unintended movement of the carriage. This may involve a control locking device, a carriage tie-down, or both.

(e)(1)(v) Barriers and warning signs A barrier shall be provided to prevent employees from entering the space necessary for travel of the carriage, with headblocks fully receded, for the full length and extreme ends of carriage runways. Warning signs shall be posted at possible entry points to this area.

(e)(1)(vi) Overhead clearance For a rider-type carriage adequate overhead clear space above the carriage deck shall be provided for the full carriage runway length.

(e)(1)(vii) Sweeping devices Carriage track sweeping devices shall be used to keep track rails clear of debris.

(e)(1)(viii) Dogs Dogging devices shall be adequate to secure logs, cants, or boards, during sawing operations.

(e)(2) Head saws

(e)(2)(i) Band head saws

(e)(2)(i)(A) Band head saws shall not be operated at speeds in excess of those recommended by the manufacturer.

(e)(2)(i)(B) Band head saws shall be thoroughly inspected for cracks, splits, broken teeth, and other defects. A bandsaw with a crack greater than one-tenth the width of the saw shall not be placed in service until width of saw is reduced to eliminate crack, until cracked section is removed, or crack development is stopped.

(e)(2)(i)(C) Provisions shall be made for alerting and warning employees before starting band head saws, and measures shall be taken to insure that all persons are in the clear.

(e)(2)(ii) Bandsaw wheels

(e)(2)(ii)(A) No bandsaw wheel shall be run at a peripheral speed in excess of that recommended by the manufacturer. The manufacturer's recommended maximum speed shall be stamped in plainly legible figures on some portion of the wheel.

(e)(2)(ii)(B) Band head saw wheels shall be subjected to monthly inspections. Hubs, spokes, rims, bolts, and rivets shall be thoroughly examined in the course of such inspections. A loose or damaged hub, a rim crack, or loose spokes shall make the wheel unfit for service.

(e)(2)(ii)(C) Band wheels shall be completely encased or guarded, except for a portion of the upper wheel immediately around the point where the blade leaves the wheel, to permit operator to observe movement of equipment. Necessary ventilating and observation ports may be permitted. Substantial doors or gates are allowed for repair, lubrication, and saw changes; such doors or gates shall be closed securely during operation. Band head rigs shall be equipped with a saw catcher or guard of substantial construction.

(e)(2)(iii) Single circular head saws

(e)(2)(iii)(A) Circular head saws shall not be operated at speeds in excess of those specified by the manufacturer. Maximum speed shall be etched on the saw.

(e)(2)(iii)(B) Circular head saws shall be equipped with safety guides which can be readily adjusted without use of hand tools.

(e)(2)(iii)(C) The upper saw of a double circular mill shall be provided with a substantial hood or guard. A screen or other suitable device shall be placed so as to protect the sawyer from flying particles.

(e)(2)(iii)(D) All circular sawmills where live rolls are not used behind the head saw shall be equipped with a spreader wheel or splitter.

(e)(2)(iv) Twin circular head saws Twin circular head saw rigs such as scrag saws shall meet the specifications for single circular head saws in paragraph (e)(1)(iii) of this Section where applicable.

(e)(2)(v) **Whole-log sash gang saws (Swedish gangs)**

(e)(2)(v)(A) Cranks, pitman rods, and other moving parts shall be adequately guarded.

(e)(2)(v)(B) Feed rolls shall be enclosed by a cover over the top, front, and open ends except where guarded by location. Drive mechanism to feed rolls shall be enclosed.

(e)(2)(v)(C) Carriage cradles of whole-log sash gang saws (Swedish gangs), shall be of adequate height to prevent logs from kicking out while being loaded.

(e)(3) **Resaws**

(e)(3)(i) **Band resaws** Band resaws shall meet the specifications for band head saws as required by paragraph (e)(2)(i) of this Section.

(e)(3)(ii) **Circular gang resaws**

(e)(3)(ii)(A) Banks of circular gang resaws shall be guarded by a hood.

(e)(3)(ii)(B) Circular gang resaws shall be provided with safety fingers or other antikickback devices.

(e)(3)(ii)(C) Circular gang resaws shall not be operated at speeds exceeding those recommended by the manufacturer.

(e)(3)(ii)(D) [Reserved]

(e)(3)(ii)(E) Feed rolls shall be guarded.

(e)(3)(ii)(F) Each circular gang resaw, except self-feed saws with a live roll or wheel at back of saw, shall be provided with spreaders.

(e)(3)(iii) **Sash gang resaws** Sash gang resaws shall meet the safety specifications of whole-log sash gang saws in accordance with the requirements of paragraph (e)(2)(v) of this Section.

(e)(4) **Trimmer saws**

(e)(4)(i) **Maximum speed** Trimmer saws shall not be run at peripheral speeds in excess of those recommended by the manufacturer.

(e)(4)(ii) **Guards**

(e)(4)(ii)(A) Trimmer saws shall be guarded in front by adequate baffles to protect against flying debris and they shall be securely bolted to a substantial frame. These guards for a series of saws shall be set as close to the top of the trimmer table as is practical.

(e)(4)(ii)(B) The end saws on trimmer shall be guarded.

(e)(4)(ii)(C) The rear of trimmer saws shall have a guard the full width of the saws and as much wider as practical.

(e)(4)(iii) **Safety stops** Automatic trimmer saws shall be provided with safety stops or hangers to prevent saws from dropping on table.

(e)(5) **Edgers**

(e)(5)(i) **Location**

(e)(5)(i)(A) Where vertical arbor edger saws are located ahead of the main saw, they shall be so guarded that an employee cannot contact any part of the edger saw from his normal position.

(e)(5)(i)(B) Edgers shall not be located in the main roll case behind the head saws.

(e)(5)(ii) **Guards**

(e)(5)(ii)(A) The top and the openings in end and side frames of edgers shall be adequately guarded and gears and chains shall be fully housed. Guards may be hinged or otherwise arranged to permit oiling and the removal of saws.

(e)(5)(ii)(B) All edgers shall be equipped with pressure feed rolls.

(e)(5)(ii)(C) Pressure feed rolls on edgers shall be guarded against accidental contact.

(e)(5)(iii) **Antikickback devices**

(e)(5)(iii)(A) Edgers shall be provided with safety fingers or other approved methods of preventing kickbacks or guarding against them. A barricade in line with the edger, if properly fenced off, may be used if safety fingers are not feasible to install.

(e)(5)(iii)(B) A controlling device shall be installed and located so that the operator can stop the feed mechanism without releasing the tension of the pressure rolls.

(e)(5)(iv) **Operating speed of live rolls** Live rolls and tailing devices in back of edger shall operate at a speed not less than the speed of the edger feed rolls.

(e)(6) **Planers**

(e)(6)(i) **Guards**

(e)(6)(i)(A) All cutting heads shall be guarded.

(e)(6)(i)(B) Side head hoods shall be of sufficient height to safeguard the head setscrew.

(e)(6)(i)(C) Pressure feed rolls and "pineapples" shall be guarded.

(e)(6)(i)(D) Levers or controls shall be so arranged or guarded as to reduce the possibility of accidental operation.

(f) **Dry kilns and facilities**

(f)(1) **Kiln foundations** Dry kilns shall be constructed upon solid foundations to prevent tracks from sagging.

(f)(2) **Passageways** A passageway shall be provided to give adequate clearance on at least one side or in the center of end-piled kilns and on two sides of cross-piled kilns.

(f)(3) **Doors**

(f)(3)(i) **Main kiln doors**

(f)(3)(i)(A) Main kiln doors shall be provided with a method of holding them open while kiln is being loaded.

(f)(3)(i)(B) Counterweights on vertical lift doors shall be boxed or otherwise guarded.

(f)(3)(i)(C) Adequate means shall be provided to firmly secure main doors, when they are disengaged from carriers and hangers, to prevent toppling.

(f)(3)(ii) **Escape doors**

(f)(3)(ii)(A) If operating procedures require access to kilns, kilns shall be provided with escape doors that operate easily from the inside, swing in the direction of exit, and are located in or near the main door at the end of the passageway.

(f)(3)(ii)(B) Escape doors shall be of adequate height and width to accommodate an average size man.

(f)(4) **Pits** Pits shall be well ventilated, drained, and lighted, and shall be large enough to safely accommodate the kiln operator together with operating devices such as valves, dampers, damper rods, and traps.

(f)(5) **Steam mains** All high-pressure steam mains located in or adjacent to an operating pit shall be covered with heat-insulating material.

(f)(6) **Ladders** A fixed ladder complying with the requirements of Subpart D of this Part, or other adequate means, shall be provided to permit access to the roof. Where controls and machinery are mounted on the roof, a permanent stairway with standard handrail shall be installed in accordance with the requirements in Subpart D.

(f)(7) **Chocks** A means shall be provided for chocking or blocking cars.

(f)(8) **Kiln tender room** A warm room shall be provided for kiln employees to stay in during cold weather after leaving a hot kiln.

[39 FR 23502, June 27, 1974, as amended at 40 FR 23073, May 28, 1975; 43 FR 49751, Oct. 24, 1978; 43 FR 51760, Nov. 7, 1978; 53 FR 12123, Apr. 12, 1988; 55 FR 32015, Aug. 6, 1990; 61 FR 9241, Mar. 7, 1996; 63 FR 33467, June 18, 1998; 70 FR 53929, Sept. 13, 2005]

§1910.266 Logging operations

(a) **Table of contents** This paragraph contains the list of paragraphs and appendices contained in this Section.

3. Bucking and limbing
4. Chipping
5. Yarding
6. Loading and unloading
7. Transport
8. Storage

i. Training
j. Appendices
Appendix A—Minimum First-aid Supplies
Appendix B—Minimum First-aid Training
Appendix C—Corresponding ISO Agreements

(b) Scope and application

(b)(1) This standard establishes safety practices, means, methods and operations for all types of logging, regardless of the end use of the wood. These types of logging include, but are not limited to, pulpwood and timber harvesting and the logging of sawlogs, veneer bolts, poles, pilings and other forest products. This standard does not cover the construction or use of cable yarding systems.

(b)(2) This standard applies to all logging operations as defined by this Section.

(b)(3) Hazards and working conditions not specifically addressed by this Section are covered by other applicable Sections of Part 1910.

(c) Definitions applicable to this Section

Arch An open-framed trailer or built-up framework used to suspend the leading ends of trees or logs when they are skidded.

Backcut (felling cut) The final cut in a felling operation.

Ballistic nylon A nylon fabric of high tensile properties designed to provide protection from lacerations.

Buck To cut a felled tree into logs.

Butt The bottom of the felled part of a tree.

Cable yarding The movement of felled trees or logs from the area where they are felled to the landing on a system composed of a cable suspended from spars and/or towers. The trees or logs may be either dragged across the ground on the cable or carried while suspended from the cable.

Chock A block, often wedge shaped, which is used to prevent movement; e.g., a log from rolling, a wheel from turning.

Choker A sling used to encircle the end of a log for yarding. One end is passed around the load, then through a loop eye, end fitting or other device at the other end of the sling. The end that passed through the end fitting or other device is then hooked to the lifting or pulling machine.

Danger tree A standing tree that presents a hazard to employees due to conditions such as, but not limited to, deterioration or physical damage to the root system, trunk, stem or limbs, and the direction and lean of the tree.

Debark To remove bark from trees or logs.

Deck A stack of trees or logs.

Designated person An employee who has the requisite knowledge, training and experience to perform specific duties.

Domino felling The partial cutting of multiple trees which are left standing and then pushed over with a pusher tree.

Fell (fall) To cut down trees.

Feller (faller) An employee who fells trees.

Grounded The placement of a component of a machine on the ground or on a device where it is firmly supported.

Guarded Covered, shielded, fenced, enclosed, or otherwise protected by means of suitable enclosures, covers, casings, shields, troughs, railings, screens, mats, or platforms, or by location, to prevent injury.

Health care provider A health care practitioner operating with the scope of his/her license, certificate, registration or legally authorized practice.

Landing Any place where logs are laid after being yarded, and before transport from the work site.

Limbing To cut branches off felled trees.

Lodged tree (hung tree) A tree leaning against another tree or object which prevents it from falling to the ground.

Log A segment sawed or split from a felled tree, such as, but not limited to, a section, bolt, or tree length.

Logging operations Operations associated with felling and moving trees and logs from the stump to the point of delivery, such as, but not limited to, marking danger trees and trees/logs to be cut to length, felling, limbing, bucking, debarking, chipping, yarding, loading, unloading, storing, and transporting machines, equipment and personnel to, from and between logging sites.

Machine A piece of stationary or mobile equipment having a self-contained powerplant, that is operated off-road and used for the movement of material. Machines include, but are not limited to, tractors, skidders, front-end loaders, scrapers, graders, bulldozers, swing yarders, log stackers, log loaders, and mechanical felling devices, such as tree shears and feller-bunchers. Machines do not include airplanes or aircraft (e.g., helicopters).

Rated capacity The maximum load a system, vehicle, machine or piece of equipment was designed by the manufacturer to handle.

Root wad The ball of a tree root and dirt that is pulled from the ground when a tree is uprooted.

Serviceable condition A state or ability of a tool, machine, vehicle or other device to operate as it was intended by the manufacturer to operate.

Skidding The yarding of trees or logs by pulling or towing them across the ground.

Slope (grade) The increase or decrease in altitude over a horizontal distance expressed as a percentage. For example, a change of altitude of 20 feet (6 m) over a horizontal distance of 100 feet (30 m) is expressed as a 20 percent slope.

Snag Any standing dead tree or portion thereof.

Spring pole A tree, segment of a tree, limb, or sapling which is under stress or tension due to the pressure or weight of another object.

Tie down Chain, cable, steel strips or fiber webbing and binders attached to a truck, trailer or other conveyance as a means to secure loads and to prevent them from shifting or moving when they are being transported.

Undercut A notch cut in a tree to guide the direction of the tree fall and to prevent splitting or kickback.

Vehicle A car, bus, truck, trailer or semi-trailer owned, leased or rented by the employer that is used for transportation of employees or movement of material.

Winching The winding of cable or rope onto a spool or drum.

Yarding The movement of logs from the place they are felled to a landing.

(d) General requirements

(d)(1) Personal protective equipment

(d)(1)(i) The employer shall assure that personal protective equipment, including any personal protective equipment provided by an employee, is maintained in a serviceable condition.

(d)(1)(ii) The employer shall assure that personal protective equipment, including any personal protective equipment provided by an employee, is inspected before initial use during each workshift. Defects or damage shall be repaired or the unserviceable personal protective equipment shall be replaced before work is commenced.

(d)(1)(iii) The employer shall provide, at no cost to the employee, and assure that each employee handling wire rope wears, hand protection which provides adequate protection from puncture wounds, cuts and lacerations.

(d)(1)(iv) The employer shall provide, at no cost to the employee, and assure that each employee who operates a chain saw wears leg protection constructed with cut-resistant material, such as ballistic nylon. The leg protection shall cover the full length of the thigh to the top of the boot on each leg to protect against contact with a moving chain saw. Exception: This requirement does not apply when an employee is working as a climber if the employer demonstrates that a greater hazard is posed by wearing leg protection in the particular situation, or when an employee is working from a vehicular mounted elevating and rotating work platform meeting the requirements of 29 CFR §1910.67.

(d)(1)(v) The employer shall assure that each employee wears foot protection, such as heavy-duty logging boots that are waterproof or water repellant, cover and provide support to the ankle. The employer shall assure that each employee who operates a chain saw wears foot protection that is constructed with cut-resistant material which will protect the employee against contact with a running chain saw. Sharp, calk-soled boots or other slip-resistant type boots may be worn where the employer demonstrates that they are necessary for the employee's job, the terrain, the timber type, and the weather conditions, provided that foot protection otherwise required by this paragraph is met.

(d)(1)(vi) The employer shall provide, at no cost to the employee, and assure that each employee who works in an area where there is potential for head injury from falling or flying objects wears head protection meeting the requirements of Subpart I of Part 1910.

(d)(1)(vii) The employer shall provide, at no cost to the employee, and assure that each employee wears the following:

(d)(1)(vii)(A) Eye protection meeting the requirements of Subpart I of Part 1910 where there is potential for eye injury due to falling or flying objects; and

(d)(1)(vii)(B) Face protection meeting the requirements of Subpart I of Part 1910 where there is potential for facial injury such as, but not limited to, operating a chipper. Logger-type mesh screens may be worn by employees performing chain-saw operations and yarding.

Note to paragraph (d)(1)(vii): The employee does not have to wear a separate eye protection device where face protection covering both the eyes and face is worn.

(d)(2) First-aid kits

(d)(2)(i) The employer shall provide first-aid kits at each work site where trees are being cut (e.g., felling, bucking, limbing), at each active landing, and on each employee transport vehicle. The number of first-aid kits and the content of each kit shall reflect the degree of isolation, the number of employees, and the hazards reasonably anticipated at the work site.

(d)(2)(ii) At a minimum, each first-aid kit shall contain the items listed in Appendix A at all times.

(d)(2)(iii) The employer also may have the number and content of first-aid kits reviewed and approved annually by a health care provider.

(d)(2)(iv) The employer shall maintain the contents of each first-aid kit in a serviceable condition.

(d)(3) **Seat belts** For each vehicle or machine (equipped with ROPS/FOPS or overhead guards), including any vehicle or machine provided by an employee, the employer shall assure:

(d)(3)(i) That a seat belt is provided for each vehicle or machine operator;

(d)(3)(ii) That each employee uses the available seat belt while the vehicle or machine is being operated;

(d)(3)(iii) That each employee securely and tightly fastens the seat belt to restrain the employee within the vehicle or machine cab;

(d)(3)(iv) That each machine seat belt meets the requirements of the Society of Automotive Engineers Standard SAE J386, June 1985, "Operator Restraint Systems for Off-Road Work Machines", which is incorporated by reference as specified in §1910.6.

(d)(3)(v) That seat belts are not removed from any vehicle or machine. The employer shall replace each seat belt which has been removed from any vehicle or machine that was equipped with seat belts at the time of manufacture; and

(d)(3)(vi) That each seat belt is maintained in a serviceable condition.

(d)(4) **Fire extinguishers** The employer shall provide and maintain portable fire extinguishers on each machine and vehicle in accordance with the requirements of Subpart L of Part 1910.

(d)(5) **Environmental conditions** All work shall terminate and each employee shall move to a place of safety when environmental conditions, such as but not limited to, electrical storms, strong winds which may affect the fall of a tree, heavy rain or snow, extreme cold, dense fog, fires, mudslides, and darkness, create a hazard for the employee in the performance of the job.

(d)(6) **Work areas**

(d)(6)(i) Employees shall be spaced and the duties of each employee shall be organized so the actions of one employee will not create a hazard for any other employee.

(d)(6)(ii) Work areas shall be assigned so that trees cannot fall into an adjacent occupied work area. The distance between adjacent occupied work areas shall be at least two tree lengths of the trees being felled. The distance between adjacent occupied work areas shall reflect the degree of slope, the density of the growth, the height of the trees, the soil structure and other hazards reasonably anticipated at that work site. A distance of greater than two tree lengths shall be maintained between adjacent occupied work areas on any slope where rolling or sliding of trees or logs is reasonably foreseeable.

(d)(6)(iii) Each employee performing a logging operation at a logging work site shall work in a position or location that is within visual or audible contact with another employee.

(d)(6)(iv) The employer shall account for each employee at the end of each workshift.

(d)(7) **Signaling and signal equipment**

(d)(7)(i) Hand signals or audible contact, such as but not limited to, whistles, horns, or radios, shall be utilized whenever noise, distance, restricted visibility, or other factors prevent clear understanding of normal voice communications between employees.

(d)(7)(ii) Engine noise, such as from a chain saw, is not an acceptable means of signaling. Other locally and regionally recognized signals may be used.

(d)(7)(iii) Only a designated person shall give signals, except in an emergency.

(d)(8) **Overhead electric lines**

(d)(8)(i) Logging operations near overhead electric lines shall be done in accordance with the requirements of 29 CFR §1910.333(c)(3).

(d)(8)(ii) The employer shall notify the power company immediately if a felled tree makes contact with any power line. Each employee shall remain clear of the area until the power company advises that there are no electrical hazards.

(d)(9) **Flammable and combustible liquids**

(d)(9)(i) Flammable and combustible liquids shall be stored, handled, transported, and used in accordance with the requirements of Subpart H of Part 1910.

(d)(9)(ii) Flammable and combustible liquids shall not be transported in the driver compartment or in any passenger-occupied area of a machine or vehicle.

(d)(9)(iii) Each machine, vehicle, and portable powered tool shall be shut off during fueling. Diesel-powered machines and vehicles may be fueled while they are at idle, provided that continued operation is intended and that the employer follows safe fueling and operating procedures.

(d)(9)(iv) Flammable and combustible liquids, including chain-saw and diesel fuel, may be used to start a fire, provided the employer assures that in the particular situation its use does not create a hazard for an employee.

(d)(10) **Explosives and blasting agents**

(d)(10)(i) Explosives and blasting agents shall be stored, handled, transported, and used in accordance with the requirements of Subpart H of Part 1910.

(d)(10)(ii) Only a designated person shall handle or use explosives and blasting agents.

(d)(10)(iii) Explosives and blasting agents shall not be transported in the driver compartment or in any passenger-occupied area of a machine or vehicle.

(e) **Hand and portable powered tools**

(e)(1) **General requirements**

(e)(1)(i) The employer shall assure that each hand and portable powered tool, including any tool provided by an employee, is maintained in serviceable condition.

(e)(1)(ii) The employer shall assure that each tool, including any tool provided by an employee, is inspected before initial use during each workshift. At a minimum, the inspection shall include the following:

(e)(1)(ii)(A) Handles and guards, to assure that they are sound, tight-fitting, properly shaped, free of splinters and sharp edges, and in place;

(e)(1)(ii)(B) Controls, to assure proper function;

(e)(1)(ii)(C) Chain-saw chains, to assure proper adjustment;

(e)(1)(ii)(D) Chain-saw mufflers, to assure that they are operational and in place;

(e)(1)(ii)(E) Chain brakes and nose shielding devices, to assure that they are in place and function properly;

(e)(1)(ii)(F) Heads of shock, impact-driven and driving tools, to assure that there is no mushrooming;

(e)(1)(ii)(G) Cutting edges, to assure that they are sharp and properly shaped; and

(e)(1)(ii)(H) All other safety devices, to assure that they are in place and function properly.

(e)(1)(iii) The employer shall assure that each tool is used only for purposes for which it has been designed.

(e)(1)(iv) When the head of any shock, impact-driven or driving tool begins to chip, it shall be repaired or removed from service.

(e)(1)(v) The cutting edge of each tool shall be sharpened in accordance with manufacturer's specifications whenever it becomes dull during the workshift.

(e)(1)(vi) Each tool shall be stored in the provided location when not being used at a work site.

(e)(1)(vii) Racks, boxes, holsters or other means shall be provided, arranged and used for the transportation of tools so that a hazard is not created for any vehicle operator or passenger.

(e)(2) **Chain saws**

(e)(2)(i) Each chain saw placed into initial service after the effective date of this Section shall be equipped with a chain brake and shall otherwise meet the requirements of the ANSI B175.1–1991 "Safety Requirements for Gasoline-Powered Chain Saws", which is incorporated by reference as specified in §1910.6. Each chain saw placed into service before the effective date of this Section shall be equipped with a protective device that minimizes chain-saw kickback. No chain-saw kickback device shall be removed or otherwise disabled.

(e)(2)(ii) Each gasoline-powered chain saw shall be equipped with a continuous pressure throttle control system which will stop the chain when pressure on the throttle is released.

(e)(2)(iii) The chain saw shall be operated and adjusted in accordance with the manufacturer's instructions.

(e)(2)(iv) The chain saw shall be fueled at least 10 feet (3 m) from any open flame or other source of ignition.

(e)(2)(v) The chain saw shall be started at least 10 feet (3 m) from the fueling area.

(e)(2)(vi) The chain saw shall be started on the ground or where otherwise firmly supported. Drop starting a chain saw is prohibited.

(e)(2)(vii) The chain saw shall be started with the chain brake engaged.

(e)(2)(viii) The chain saw shall be held with the thumbs and fingers of both hands encircling the handles during operation unless the employer demonstrates that a greater hazard is posed by keeping both hands on the chain saw in that particular situation.

(e)(2)(ix) The chain-saw operator shall be certain of footing before starting to cut. The chain saw shall not be used in a position or at a distance that could cause the operator to become off-balance, to have insecure footing, or to relinquish a firm grip on the saw.

(e)(2)(x) Prior to felling any tree, the chain-saw operator shall clear away brush or other potential obstacles which might interfere with cutting the tree or using the retreat path.

(e)(2)(xi) The chain saw shall not be used to cut directly overhead.

(e)(2)(xii) The chain saw shall be carried in a manner that will prevent operator contact with the cutting chain and muffler.

(e)(2)(xiii) The chain saw shall be shut off or the throttle released before the feller starts his retreat.

(e)(2)(xiv) The chain saw shall be shut down or the chain brake shall be engaged whenever a saw is carried further than 50 feet (15.2 m). The chain saw shall be shut down or the chain brake shall be engaged when a saw is carried less than 50 feet if conditions such as, but not limited to, the terrain, underbrush and slippery surfaces, may create a hazard for an employee.

(f) **Machines**

(f)(1) **General requirements**

(f)(1)(i) The employer shall assure that each machine, including any machine provided by an employee, is maintained in serviceable condition.

(f)(1)(ii) The employer shall assure that each machine, including any machine provided by an employee, is inspected before initial use during each workshift. Defects or damage shall be repaired or the unserviceable machine shall be replaced before work is commenced.

(f)(1)(iii) The employer shall assure that operating and maintenance instructions are available on the machine or in the area where the machine is being operated. Each machine operator and maintenance employee shall comply with the operating and maintenance instructions.

(f)(2) **Machine operation**

(f)(2)(i) The machine shall be started and operated only by a designated person.

(f)(2)(ii) Stationary logging machines and their components shall be anchored or otherwise stabilized to prevent movement during operation.

(f)(2)(iii) The rated capacity of any machine shall not be exceeded.

(f)(2)(iv) To maintain stability, the machine must be operated within the limitations imposed by the manufacturer as described in the operating and maintenance instructions for that machine.

(f)(2)(v) Before starting or moving any machine, the operator shall determine that no employee is in the path of the machine.

(f)(2)(vi) The machine shall be operated only from the operator's station or as otherwise recommended by the manufacturer.

(f)(2)(vii) The machine shall be operated at such a distance from employees and other machines such that operation will not create a hazard for an employee.

(f)(2)(viii) No employee other than the operator shall ride on any mobile machine unless seating, seat belts and other protection equivalent to that provided for the operator are provided.

(f)(2)(ix) No employee shall ride on any load.

(f)(2)(x) Before the operator leaves the operator's station of a machine, it shall be secured as follows:

(f)(2)(x)(A) The parking brake or brake locks shall be applied.

(f)(2)(x)(B) The transmission shall be placed in the manufacturer's specified park position.

(f)(2)(x)(C) Each moving element such as, but not limited to blades, buckets, saws and shears, shall be lowered to the ground or otherwise secured.

(f)(2)(xi) If a hydraulic or pneumatic storage device can move the moving elements such as, but not limited to, blades, buckets, saws and shears, after the machine is shut down, the pressure or stored energy from the element shall be discharged as specified by the manufacturer.

(f)(2)(xii) The rated capacity of any vehicle transporting a machine shall not be exceeded.

(f)(2)(xiii) The machine shall be loaded, secured and unloaded so that it will not create a hazard for any employee.

(f)(3) **Protective structures**

(f)(3)(i) Each tractor, skidder, swing yarder, log stacker, log loader and mechanical felling device, such as tree shears or feller-buncher, placed into initial service after February 9, 1995, shall be equipped with falling object protective structure (FOPS) and/or rollover protective structure (ROPS). The employer shall replace FOPS or ROPS which have been removed from any machine. Exception: This requirement does not apply to machines which are capable of 360 degree rotation.

(f)(3)(ii)(A) ROPS shall be tested, installed, and maintained in serviceable condition.

(f)(3)(ii)(B) Each machine manufactured after August 1, 1996, shall have ROPS tested, installed, and maintained in accordance with the Society of Automotive Engineers SAE J1040, April 1988, "Performance Criteria for Rollover Protective Structures (ROPS) for Construction, Earthmoving, Forestry, and Mining Machines", which is incorporated by reference as specified in §1910.6.

(f)(3)(ii)(C) This incorporation by reference was approved by the Director of the Federal Register in accordance with 5 U.S.C. 552(a) and 1 CFR Part 51. Copies may be obtained from the Society of Automotive Engineers, 400 Commonwealth Drive, Warrendale, PA 15096. Copies may be inspected at the Docket Office, Occupational Safety and Health Administration, U.S. Department of Labor, 200 Constitution Avenue NW., room N2625, Washington, DC 20210, or at the National Archives and Records Administration (NARA). For information on the availability of this material at NARA, call 202–741–6030, or go to: http://www.archives.gov/federal_register/code_of_federal_regulations/ibr_locations.html.

(f)(3)(iii) FOPS shall be installed, tested and maintained in accordance with the Society of Automotive Engineers SAE J231, January 1981, "Minimum Performance Criteria for Falling Object Protective Structures (FOPS)", which is incorporated by reference as specified in §1910.6.

(f)(3)(iv) ROPS and FOPS shall meet the requirements of the Society of Automotive Engineers SAE J397, April 1988, "Deflection Limiting Volume-ROPS/FOPS Laboratory Evaluation", which is incorporated by reference as specified in §1910.6.

(f)(3)(v) Each protective structure shall be of a size that does not impede the operator's normal movements.

(f)(3)(vi) The overhead covering of each cab shall be of solid material and shall extend over the entire canopy.

(f)(3)(vii) Each machine manufactured after August 1, 1996, shall have a cab that is fully enclosed with mesh material with openings no greater than 2 inches (5.08 cm) at its least dimension. The cab may be enclosed with other material(s) where the employer demonstrates such material(s) provides equivalent protection and visibility. Exception: Equivalent visibility is not required for the lower portion of the cab where there are control panels or similar obstructions in the cab, or where visibility is not necessary for safe operation of the machine.

(f)(3)(viii) Each machine manufactured on or before August 1, 1996 shall have a cab which meets the requirements specified in paragraph (f)(3)(vii) or a protective canopy for the operator which meets the following requirements:

(f)(3)(viii)(A) The protective canopy shall be constructed to protect the operator from injury due to falling trees, limbs, saplings or branches which might enter the compartment side areas and from snapping winch lines or other objects.

(f)(3)(viii)(B) The lower portion of the cab shall be fully enclosed with solid material, except at entrances, to prevent the operator from being injured from obstacles entering the cab.

(f)(3)(viii)(C) The upper rear portion of the cab shall be fully enclosed with open mesh material with openings of such size as to reject the entrance of an object larger than 2 inches in diameter. It shall provide maximum rearward visibility.

(f)(3)(viii)(D) Open mesh shall be extended forward as far as possible from the rear corners of the cab sides so as to give the maximum protection against obstacles, branches, etc., entering the cab area.

(f)(3)(ix) The enclosure of the upper portion of each cab shall allow maximum visibility.

(f)(3)(x) When transparent material is used to enclose the upper portion of the cab, it shall be made of safety glass or other material that the employer demonstrates provides equivalent protection and visibility.

(f)(3)(xi) Transparent material shall be kept clean to assure operator visibility.

(f)(3)(xii) Transparent material that may create a hazard for the operator, such as but not limited to, cracked, broken or scratched safety glass, shall be replaced.

(f)(3)(xiii) Deflectors shall be installed in front of each cab to deflect whipping saplings and branches. Deflectors shall be located so as not to impede visibility and access to the cab.

(f)(3)(xiv) [OI] The height of each cab entrance shall be at least 52 inches (1.3 meters) from the floor of the cab.

(f)(3)(xv) Each machine operated near cable yarding operations shall be equipped with sheds or roofs of sufficient strength to provide protection from breaking lines.

(f)(4) **Overhead guards** Each forklift shall be equipped with an overhead guard meeting the requirements of the American Society of Mechanical Engineers, ASME B56.6–1992 (with addenda), "Safety Standard for Rough Terrain Forklift Trucks", which is incorporated by reference as specified in §1910.6.

(f)(5) **Machine access**

(f)(5)(i) Machine access systems, meeting the specifications of the Society of Automotive Engineers, SAE J185, June 1988, "Recommended Practice for Access Systems for Off-Road Machines", which is incorporated by reference as specified in §1910.6, shall be provided for each machine where the operator or any other employee must climb onto the machine to enter the cab or to perform maintenance.

(f)(5)(ii) Each machine cab shall have a second means of egress.

(f)(5)(iii) Walking and working surfaces of each machine and machine work station shall have a slip resistant surface to assure safe footing.

(f)(5)(iv) The walking and working surface of each machine shall be kept free of waste, debris and any other material which might result in fire, slipping, or falling.

(f)(6) **Exhaust systems**

(f)(6)(i) The exhaust pipes on each machine shall be located so exhaust gases are directed away from the operator.

(f)(6)(ii) The exhaust pipes on each machine shall be mounted or guarded to protect each employee from accidental contact.

(f)(6)(iii) The exhaust pipes shall be equipped with spark arresters. Engines equipped with turbochargers do not require spark arresters.

(f)(6)(iv) Each machine muffler provided by the manufacturer, or their equivalent, shall be in place at all times the machine is in operation.

(f)(7) **Brakes**

(f)(7)(i) Service brakes shall be sufficient to stop and hold each machine and its rated load capacity on the slopes over which it is being operated.

(f)(7)(ii) Each machine placed into initial service on or after September 8, 1995 shall also be equipped with: back-up or secondary brakes that are capable of stopping the machine regardless of the direction of travel or whether the engine is running; and parking brakes that are capable of continuously holding a stopped machine stationary.

(f)(8) **Guarding**

(f)(8)(i) Each machine shall be equipped with guarding to protect employees from exposed moving elements, such as but not limited to, shafts, pulleys, belts on conveyors, and gears, in accordance with the requirements of Subpart O of Part 1910.

(f)(8)(ii) Each machine used for debarking, limbing and chipping shall be equipped with guarding to protect employees from flying wood chunks, logs, chips, bark, limbs and other material in accordance with the requirements of Subpart O of Part 1910.

(f)(8)(iii) The guarding on each machine shall be in place at all times the machine is in operation.

(g) **Vehicles**

(g)(1) The employer shall assure that each vehicle used to perform any logging operation is maintained in serviceable condition.

(g)(2) The employer shall assure that each vehicle used to perform any logging operation is inspected before initial use during each workshift. Defects or damage shall be repaired or the unserviceable vehicle shall be replaced before work is commenced.

(g)(3) The employer shall assure that operating and maintenance instructions are available in each vehicle. Each vehicle operator and maintenance employee shall comply with the operating and maintenance instructions.

(g)(4) The employer shall assure that each vehicle operator has a valid operator's license for the class of vehicle being operated.

(g)(5) Mounting steps and handholds shall be provided for each vehicle wherever it is necessary to prevent an employee from being injured when entering or leaving the vehicle.

(g)(6) The seats of each vehicle shall be securely fastened.

(g)(7) The requirements of paragraphs (f)(2)(iii), (f)(2)(v), (f)(2)(vii), (f)(2)(x), (f)(2)(xiii), and (f)(7) of this Section shall also apply to each vehicle used to transport any employee off public roads or to perform any logging operation, including any vehicle provided by an employee.

(h) **Tree harvesting**

(h)(1) **General requirements**

(h)(1)(i) Trees shall not be felled in a manner that may create a hazard for an employee, such as but not limited to, striking a rope, cable, power line, or machine.

(h)(1)(ii) The immediate supervisor shall be consulted when unfamiliar or unusually hazardous conditions necessitate the supervisor's approval before cutting is commenced.

(h)(1)(iii) While manual felling is in progress, no yarding machine shall be operated within two tree lengths of trees being manually felled. Exception: This provision does not apply to yarding machines performing tree pulling operations.

(h)(1)(iv) No employee shall approach a feller closer than two tree lengths of trees being felled until the feller has acknowledged that it is safe to do so, unless the employer demonstrates that a team of employees is necessary to manually fell a particular tree.

(h)(1)(v) No employee shall approach a mechanical felling operation closer than two tree lengths of the trees being felled until the machine operator has acknowledged that it is safe to do so.

(h)(1)(vi) Each danger tree shall be felled, removed or avoided. Each danger tree, including lodged trees and snags, shall be felled or removed using mechanical or other techniques that minimize employee exposure before work is commenced in the area of the danger tree. If the danger tree is not felled or removed, it shall be marked and no work shall be conducted within two tree lengths of the danger tree unless the employer demonstrates that a shorter distance will not create a hazard for an employee.

(h)(1)(vii) Each danger tree shall be carefully checked for signs of loose bark, broken branches and limbs or other damage before they are felled or removed. Accessible loose bark and other damage that may create a hazard for an employee shall be removed or held in place before felling or removing the tree.

(h)(1)(viii) Felling on any slope where rolling or sliding of trees or logs is reasonably foreseeable shall be done uphill from, or on the same level as, previously felled trees.

(h)(1)(ix) Domino felling of trees is prohibited.

Note to paragraph (h)(1)(ix): The definition of domino felling does not include the felling of a single danger tree by felling another single tree into it.

(h)(2) **Manual felling**

(h)(2)(i) Before felling is started, the feller shall plan and clear a retreat path. The retreat path shall extend diagonally away from the expected felling line unless the employer demonstrates that such a retreat path poses a greater hazard than an alternate path. Once the backcut has been made the feller shall immediately move a safe distance away from the tree on the retreat path.

(h)(2)(ii) [OI] Before each tree is felled, conditions such as, but not limited to, snow and ice accumulation, the wind, the lean of tree, dead limbs, and the location of other trees, shall be evaluated by the feller and precautions taken so a hazard is not created for an employee.

(h)(2)(iii) Each tree shall be checked for accumulations of snow and ice. Accumulations of snow and ice that may create a hazard for an employee shall be removed before felling is commenced in the area or the area shall be avoided.

(h)(2)(iv) When a spring pole or other tree under stress is cut, no employee other than the feller shall be closer than two trees lengths when the stress is released.

(h)(2)(v) An undercut shall be made in each tree being felled unless the employer demonstrates that felling the particular tree without an undercut will not create a hazard for an employee. The undercut shall be of a size so the tree will not split and will fall in the intended direction.

(h)(2)(vi) A backcut shall be made in each tree being felled. The backcut shall leave sufficient hinge wood to hold the tree to the stump during most of its fall so that the hinge is able to guide the tree's fall in the intended direction.

(h)(2)(vii) [OI] The backcut shall be above the level of the horizontal facecut in order to provide an adequate platform to prevent kickback. Exception: The backcut may be at or below the horizontal facecut in tree pulling operations.

Note to paragraph (h)(2)(vii): This requirement does not apply to open face felling where two angled facecuts rather than a horizontal facecut are used.

(h)(3) **Limbing and bucking**

(h)(3)(i) Limbing and bucking on any slope where rolling or sliding of trees or logs is reasonably foreseeable shall be done on the uphill side of each tree or log.

(h)(3)(ii) Before bucking or limbing wind-thrown trees, precautions shall be taken to prevent the root wad, butt or logs from striking an employee. These precautions include, but are not limited to, chocking or moving the tree to a stable position.

(h)(4) Chipping (in-woods locations)

(h)(4)(i) Chipper access covers or doors shall not be opened until the drum or disc is at a complete stop.

(h)(4)(ii) Infeed and discharge ports shall be guarded to prevent contact with the disc, knives, or blower blades.

(h)(4)(iii) The chipper shall be shut down and locked out in accordance with the requirements of 29 CFR §1910.147 when an employee performs any servicing or maintenance.

(h)(4)(iv) Detached trailer chippers shall be chocked during usage on any slope where rolling or sliding of the chipper is reasonably foreseeable.

(h)(5) Yarding

(h)(5)(i) No log shall be moved until each employee is in the clear.

(h)(5)(ii) Each choker shall be hooked and unhooked from the uphill side or end of the log, unless the employer demonstrates that is it not feasible in the particular situation to hook or unhook the choker from the uphill side. Where the choker is hooked or unhooked from the downhill side or end of the log, the log shall be securely chocked to prevent rolling, sliding or swinging.

(h)(5)(iii) Each choker shall be positioned near the end of the log or tree length.

(h)(5)(iv) Each machine shall be positioned during winching so the machine and winch are operated within their design limits.

(h)(5)(v) No yarding line shall be moved unless the yarding machine operator has clearly received and understood the signal to do so. When in doubt, the yarding machine operator shall repeat the signal and wait for a confirming signal before moving any line.

(h)(5)(vi) No load shall exceed the rated capacity of the pallet, trailer, or other carrier.

(h)(5)(vii) Towed equipment, such as but not limited to, skid pans, pallets, arches, and trailers, shall be attached to each machine or vehicle in such a manner as to allow a full 90 degree turn; to prevent overrunning of the towing machine or vehicle; and to assure that the operator is always in control of the towed equipment.

(h)(5)(viii) The yarding machine or vehicle, including its load, shall be operated with safe clearance from all obstructions that may create a hazard for an employee.

(h)(5)(ix) Each yarded tree shall be placed in a location that does not create a hazard for an employee and an orderly manner so that the trees are stable before bucking or limbing is commenced.

(h)(6) Loading and unloading

(h)(6)(i) The transport vehicle shall be positioned to provide working clearance between the vehicle and the deck.

(h)(6)(ii) Only the loading or unloading machine operator and other personnel the employer demonstrates are essential shall be in the loading or unloading work area during this operation.

(h)(6)(iii) No transport vehicle operator shall remain in the cab during loading and unloading if the logs are carried or moved over the truck cab, unless the employer demonstrates that it is necessary for the operator to do so. Where the transport vehicle operator remains in the cab, the employer shall provide operator protection, such as but not limited to, reinforcement of the cab.

(h)(6)(iv) Each log shall be placed on a transport vehicle in an orderly manner and tightly secured.

(h)(6)(v) The load shall be positioned to prevent slippage or loss during handling and transport.

(h)(6)(vi) Each stake and chock which is used to trip loads shall be so constructed that the tripping mechanism is activated on the side opposite the release of the load.

(h)(6)(vii) Each tie down shall be left in place over the peak log to secure all logs until the unloading lines or other protection the employer demonstrates is equivalent has been put in place. A stake of sufficient strength to withstand the forces of shifting or moving logs, shall be considered equivalent protection provided that the logs are not loaded higher than the stake.

(h)(6)(viii) Each tie down shall be released only from the side on which the unloading machine operates, except as follows:

(h)(6)(viii)(A) When the tie down is released by a remote control device; and

(h)(6)(viii)(B) When the employee making the release is protected by racks, stanchions or other protection the employer demonstrates is capable of withstanding the force of the logs.

(h)(7) Transport The transport vehicle operator shall assure that each tie down is tight before transporting the load. While en route, the operator shall check and tighten the tie downs whenever there is reason to believe that the tie downs have loosened or the load has shifted.

(h)(8) Storage Each deck shall be constructed and located so it is stable and provides each employee with enough room to safely move and work in the area.

(i) Training

(i)(1) The employer shall provide training for each employee, including supervisors, at no cost to the employee.

(i)(2) Frequency Training shall be provided as follows:

(i)(2)(i) As soon as possible but not later than the effective date of this Section for initial training for each current and new employee;

(i)(2)(ii) Prior to initial assignment for each new employee;

(i)(2)(iii) Whenever the employee is assigned new work tasks, tools, equipment, machines or vehicles; and

(i)(2)(iv) Whenever an employee demonstrates unsafe job performance.

(i)(3) Content At a minimum, training shall consist of the following elements:

(i)(3)(i) Safe performance of assigned work tasks;

(i)(3)(ii) [OI] Safe use, operation and maintenance of tools, machines and vehicles the employee uses or operates, including emphasis on understanding and following the manufacturer's operating and maintenance instructions, warnings and precautions;

(i)(3)(iii) Recognition of safety and health hazards associated with the employee's specific work tasks, including the use of measures and work practices to prevent or control those hazards;

(i)(3)(iv) Recognition, prevention and control of other safety and health hazards in the logging industry;

(i)(3)(v) Procedures, practices and requirements of the employer's work site; and

(i)(3)(vi) The requirements of this standard.

(i)(4) Training of an employee due to unsafe job performance, or assignment of new work tasks, tools, equipment, machines, or vehicles; may be limited to those elements in paragraph (i)(3) of this Section which are relevant to the circumstances giving rise to the need for training.

(i)(5) Portability of training

(i)(5)(i) Each current employee who has received training in the particular elements specified in paragraph (i)(3) of this Section shall not be required to be retrained in those elements.

(i)(5)(ii) Each new employee who has received training in the particular elements specified in paragraph (i)(3) of this Section shall not be required to be retrained in those elements prior to initial assignment.

(i)(5)(iii) The employer shall train each current and new employee in those elements for which the employee has not received training.

(i)(5)(iv) The employer is responsible for ensuring that each current and new employee can properly and safely perform the work tasks and operate the tools, equipment, machines, and vehicles used in their job.

(i)(6) Each new employee and each employee who is required to be trained as specified in paragraph (i)(2) of this Section, shall work under the close supervision of a designated person until the employee demonstrates to the employer the ability to safely perform their new duties independently.

(i)(7) [OI] **First-aid training**

(i)(7)(i) The employer shall assure that each employee, including supervisors, receives or has received first-aid and CPR training meeting at least the requirements specified in Appendix B.

(i)(7)(ii) The employer shall assure that each employee's first-aid and CPR training and/or certificate of training remain current.

(i)(8) All training shall be conducted by a designated person.

(i)(9) The employer shall assure that all training required by this Section is presented in a manner that the employee is able to understand. The employer shall assure that all training materials used are appropriate in content and vocabulary to the educational level, literacy, and language skills of the employees being trained.

(i)(10) Certification of training

(i)(10)(i) The employer shall verify compliance with paragraph (i) of this Section by preparing a written certification record. The written certification record shall contain the name or other identity of the employee trained, the date(s) of the training, and the signature of the person who conducted the training or the signature of the employer. If the employer relies on training conducted prior to the employee's hiring or completed prior to the effective date of this Section, the certification record shall indicate the date the employer determined the prior training was adequate.

(i)(10)(ii) The most recent training certification shall be maintained.

(i)(11) **Safety and health meetings** The employer shall hold safety and health meetings as necessary and at least each month for each employee. Safety and health meetings may be conducted individually, in crew meetings, in larger groups, or as part of other staff meetings.

(j) **Appendices** Appendices A and B of this Section are mandatory. The information contained in Appendix C of this Section is informational and is not intended to create any additional obligations not otherwise imposed or to detract from existing regulations.

Note: In the Federal Register of August 9, 1995, OSHA extended the stay of the following paragraphs of §1910.266 until September 8, 1995. The remaining requirements of §1910.266, which became effective on February 9, 1995, are unaffected by the extension of the partial stay:

1. (d)(1)(v)—insofar as it requires foot protection to be chain-saw resistant;
2. (d)(1)(vii)—insofar as it required face protection;
3. (d)(2)(iii);
4. (f)(2)(iv);
5. (f)(2)(xi);
6. (f)(3)(ii);
7. (f)(3)(vii);
8. (f)(3)(viii);
9. (f)(7)(ii)—insofar as it requires parking brakes to be able to stop a moving machine;
10. (g)(1) and (g)(2) insofar as they require inspection and maintenance of employee-owned vehicles;
11. (h)(2)(vii)—insofar as it precludes backcuts at the level of the horizontal cut of the undercut when the Humboldt cutting method is used.

§1910.266 Appendix A First–Aid Kits (Mandatory)

The following list sets forth the minimally acceptable number and type of first-aid supplies for first-aid kits required under paragraph (d)(2) of the logging standard. The contents of the first-aid kit listed should be adequate for small work sites, consisting of approximately two to three employees. When larger operations or multiple operations are being conducted at the same location, additional first-aid kits should be provided at the work site or additional quantities of supplies should be included in the first-aid kits:

1. Gauze pads (at least 4×4 inches);
2. Two large gauze pads (at least 8×10 inches);
3. Box adhesive bandages (band-aids);
4. One package gauze roller bandage at least 2 inches wide;
5. Two triangular bandages;
6. Wound cleaning agent such as sealed moistened towelettes;
7. Scissors;
8. At least one blanket;
9. Tweezers;
10. Adhesive tape;
11. Latex gloves;
12. Resuscitation equipment such as resuscitation bag, airway, or pocket mask;;
13. Two elastic wraps;
14. Splint;
15. Directions for requesting emergency assistance

§1910.266 Appendix B First–Aid and CPR training (Mandatory)

The following is deemed to be the minimal acceptable first-aid and CPR training program for employees engaged in logging activities.

First-aid and CPR training shall be conducted using the conventional methods of training such as lecture, demonstration, practical exercise and examination (both written and practical). The length of training must be sufficient to assure that trainees understand the concepts of first aid and can demonstrate their ability to perform the various procedures contained in the outline below.

At a minimum, first-aid and CPR training shall consist of the following:

1. The definition of first aid
2. Legal issues of applying first aid (Good Samaritan Laws)
3. Basic anatomy
4. Patient assessment and first aid for the following:
   a. Respiratory arrest
   b. Cardiac arrest
   c. Hemorrhage
   d. Lacerations/abrasions
   e. Amputations
   f. Musculoskeletal injuries
   g Shock
   h. Eye injuries
   i. Burns
   j. Loss of consciousness
   k. Extreme temperature exposure (hypothermia/hyperthermia)
   l. Paralysis
   m. Poisoning
   n. Loss of mental functioning (psychosis/hallucinations, etc.). Artificial ventilation
   o. Drug overdose
5. CPR.
6. Application of dressings and slings
7. Treatment of strains, sprains, and fractures
8. Immobilization of injured persons
9. Handling and transporting injured persons
10. Treatment of bites, stings, or contact with poisonous plants or animals

§1910.266 Appendix C Comparable ISO standards (Nonmandatory)

The following International Labor Organization (ISO) standards are comparable to the corresponding Society of Automotive Engineers (Standards that are referenced in this standard).

Utilization of the ISO standards in lieu of the corresponding SAE standards should result in a machine that meets the OSHA standard.

SAE standard	ISO standard	Subject
SAE J1040	ISO 3471–1	Performance Criteria for Rollover Protective Structures (ROPS) for Construction, Earthmoving, Forestry and Mining Machines
SAE J397	ISO 3164	Deflection Limiting Volume—ROPS/FOPS Laboratory Evaluation
SAE J231	ISO 3449	Minimum Performance Criteria for Falling Object Protective Structures (FOPS)
SAE J386	ISO 6683	Operator Restraint Systems for Off-Road Work Machines
SAE J185	ISO 2897	Access Systems for Off-Road Machines

[59 FR 51741, Oct. 12, 1994, as amended at 60 FR 7449, Feb. 8, 1995; 60 FR 40458, Aug. 9, 1996; 60 FR 47035–47037, Sept. 8, 1995; 61 FR 9241, 9242, Mar. 7, 1996; 69 FR 18803, Apr. 9, 2004; 71 FR 16673, Apr. 3, 2006]

§1910.268 Telecommunications

(a) **Application**

(a)(1) This Section sets forth safety and health standards that apply to the work conditions, practices, means, methods, operations, installations and processes performed at telecommunications centers and at telecommunications field installations, which are located outdoors or in building spaces used for such field installations. Center work includes the installation, operation, maintenance, rearrangement, and removal of communications equipment and other associated equipment in telecommunications switching centers. Field work includes the installation, operation, maintenance, rearrangement, and removal of conductors and other equipment used for signal or communication service, and of their supporting or containing structures, overhead or underground, on public or private rights of way, including buildings or other structures.

(a)(2) These standards do not apply:

(a)(2)(i) To construction work, as defined in §1910.12, nor

(a)(2)(ii) To installations under the exclusive control of electric utilities used for the purpose of communications or metering, or for generation, control, transformation, transmission, and distribution of electric energy, which are located in buildings used exclusively by the electric utilities for such purposes, or located outdoors on property owned or leased by the electric utilities or on public highways, streets, roads, etc., or outdoors by established rights on private property.

(a)(3) Operations or conditions not specifically covered by this Section are subject to all the applicable standards contained in this Part 1910. See §1910.5(c). Operations which involve construction work, as defined in §1910.12 are subject to all the applicable standards contained in Part 1926 of this chapter.

(b) General

(b)(1) Buildings containing telecommunications centers

(b)(1)(i) **Illumination** Lighting in telecommunication centers shall be provided in an adequate amount such that continuing work operations, routine observations, and the passage of employees can be carried out in a safe and healthful manner. Certain specific tasks in centers, such as splicing cable and the maintenance and repair of equipment frame lineups, may require a higher level of illumination. In such cases, the employer shall install permanent lighting or portable supplemental lighting to attain a higher level of illumination shall be provided as needed to permit safe performance of the required task.

(b)(1)(ii) **Working surfaces** Guard rails and toe boards may be omitted on distribution frame mezzanine platforms to permit access to equipment. This exemption applies only on the side or sides of the platform facing the frames and only on those portions of the platform adjacent to equipped frames.

(b)(1)(iii) **Working spaces** Maintenance aisles, or wiring aisles, between equipment frame lineups are working spaces and are not an exit route for purposes of 29 CFR §1910.34.

(b)(1)(iv) **Special doors** When blastproof or power actuated doors are installed in specially designed hardsite security buildings and spaces, they shall be designed and installed so that they can be used as a means of egress in emergencies.

(b)(1)(v) **Equipment, machinery and machine guarding** When power plant machinery in telecommunications centers is operated with commutators and couplings uncovered, the adjacent housing shall be clearly marked to alert personnel to the rotating machinery.

(b)(2) Battery handling

(b)(2)(i) Eye protection devices which provide side as well as frontal eye protection for employees shall be provided when measuring storage battery specific gravity or handling electrolyte, and the employer shall ensure that such devices are used by the employees. The employer shall also ensure that acid resistant gloves and aprons shall be worn for protection against spattering. Facilities for quick drenching or flushing of the eyes and body shall be provided unless the storage batteries are of the enclosed type and equipped with explosion proof vents, in which case sealed water rinse or neutralizing packs may be substituted for the quick drenching or flushing facilities. Employees assigned to work with storage batteries shall be instructed in emergency procedures such as dealing with accidental acid spills.

(b)(2)(ii) Electrolyte (acid or base, and distilled water) for battery cells shall be mixed in a well ventilated room. Acid or base shall be poured gradually, while stirring, into the water. Water shall never be poured into concentrated (greater than 75 percent) acid solutions. Electrolyte shall never be placed in metal containers nor stirred with metal objects.

(b)(2)(iii) When taking specific gravity readings, the open end of the hydrometer shall be covered with an acid resistant material while moving it from cell to cell to avoid splashing or throwing the electrolyte.

(b)(3) Employers must provide employees with readily accessible, adequate, and appropriate first aid supplies. A non-mandatory example of appropriate supplies is listed in Appendix A to 29 CFR §1910.151.

(b)(4) **Hazardous materials** Highway mobile vehicles and trailers stored in garages in accordance with §1910.110 may be equipped to carry more than one LP-gas container, but the total capacity of LP-gas containers per work vehicle stored in garages shall not exceed 100 pounds of LP-gas. All container valves shall be closed when not in use.

(b)(5) **Compressed gas** When using or transporting nitrogen cylinders in a horizontal position, special compartments, racks, or adequate blocking shall be provided to prevent cylinder movement. Regulators shall be removed or guarded before a cylinder is transported.

(b)(6) **Support structures** No employee, or any material or equipment, may be supported or permitted to be supported on any portion of a pole structure, platform, ladder, walkway or other elevated structure or aerial device unless the employer ensures that the support structure is first inspected by a competent person and it is determined to be adequately strong, in good working condition and properly secured in place.

(b)(7) Approach distances to exposed energized overhead power lines and parts. The employer shall ensure that no employee approaches or takes any conductive object closer to any electrically energized overhead power lines and parts than prescribed in Table R–2, unless:

(b)(7)(i) The employee is insulated or guarded from the energized parts (insulating gloves rated for the voltage involved shall be considered adequate insulation), or

(b)(7)(ii) The energized parts are insulated or guarded from the employee and any other conductive object at a different potential, or

(b)(7)(iii) The power conductors and equipment are deenergized and grounded.

Table R–2

Approach Distances to Exposed Energized Overhead Power Lines and Parts

Voltage range (phase to phase, RMS)	Approach distance (inches)
300V and less	([1])
Over 300V, not over 750V	12
Over 750V not over 2 kV	18
Over 2 kV, not over 15 kV	24
Over 15 kV, not over 37 kV	36
Over 37 kV, not over 87.5 kV	42
Over 87.5 kV, not over 121 kV	48
Over 121 kV, not over 140 kV	54

[1] Avoid contact.

(b)(8) **Illumination of field work** Whenever natural light is insufficient to adequately illuminate the worksite, artificial illumination shall be provided to enable the employee to perform the work safely.

(c) **Training** Employers shall provide training in the various precautions and safe practices described in this Section and shall insure that employees do not engage in the activities to which this Section applies until such employees have received proper training in the various precautions and safe practices required by this Section. However, where the employer can demonstrate that an employee is already trained in the precautions and safe practices required by this Section prior to his employment, training need not be provided to that employee in accordance with this Section. Where training is required, it shall consist of on-the-job training or classroom-type training or a combination of both. The employer shall certify that employees have been trained by preparing a certification record which includes the identity of the person trained, the signature of the employer or the person who conducted the training, and the date the training was completed. The certification record shall be prepared at the completion of training and shall be maintained on file for the duration of the employee's employment. The certification record shall be made available upon request to the Assistant Secretary for Occupational Safety and Health. Such training shall, where appropriate, include the following subjects:

(c)(1) [OI] Recognition and avoidance of dangers relating to encounters with harmful substances and animal, insect, or plant life;

(c)(2) [OI] Procedures to be followed in emergency situations; and

(c)(3) [OI] First aid training, including instruction in artificial respiration.

(d) Employee protection in public work areas

(d)(1) Before work is begun in the vicinity of vehicular or pedestrian traffic which may endanger employees, warning signs and/or flags or other traffic control devices shall be placed conspicuously to alert and channel approaching traffic. Where further protection is needed, barriers shall be utilized. At night, warning lights shall be prominently displayed, and excavated areas shall be enclosed with protective barricades.

(d)(2) If work exposes energized or moving parts that are normally protected, danger signs shall be displayed and barricades erected, as necessary, to warn other personnel in the area.

(d)(3) The employer shall insure that an employee finding any crossed or fallen wires which create or may create a hazardous situation at the work area: (i) Remains on guard or adopts other adequate means to warn other employees of the danger and (ii) has the proper authority notified at the earliest practical moment.

(e) **Tools and personal protective equipment—Generally** Personal protective equipment, protective devices and special tools needed for the work of employees shall be provided and the employer shall ensure that they are used by employees. Before each day's use the employer shall ensure that these personal protective devices, tools, and equipment are carefully inspected by a competent person to ascertain that they are in good condition.

(f) Rubber insulating equipment

(f)(1) Rubber insulating equipment designed for the voltage levels to be encountered shall be provided and the employer shall ensure that they are used by employees as required by this Section. The requirements of §1910.137, Electrical Protective Equipment, shall be followed except for Table I–6.

(f)(2) The employer is responsible for the periodic retesting of all insulating gloves, blankets, and other rubber insulating equipment. This retesting shall be electrical, visual and mechanical. The following maximum retesting intervals shall apply:

Gloves, blankets, and other insulating equipment	Natural rubber	Synthetic rubber
	Months	
New	12	18
Re-issued	9	15

(f)(3) Gloves and blankets shall be marked to indicate compliance with the retest schedule, and shall be marked with the date the next test is due. Gloves found to be defective in the field or by the tests set forth in paragraph (f)(2) of this Section shall be destroyed by cutting them open from the finger to the gauntlet.

(g) O_I **Personal climbing equipment**

(g)(1) O_I **General** Safety belts and straps shall be provided and the employer shall ensure their use when work is performed at positions more than 4 feet above ground, on poles, and on towers, except as provided in paragraphs (n)(7) and (n)(8) of this Section. No safety belts, safety straps or lanyards acquired after July 1, 1975 may be used unless they meet the tests set forth in paragraph (g)(2) of this Section. The employer shall ensure that all safety belts and straps are inspected by a competent person prior to each day's use to determine that they are in safe working condition.

(g)(2) **Pole climbers**

(g)(2)(i) Pole climbers may not be used if the gaffs are less than 1¼ inches in length as measured on the underside of the gaff. The gaffs of pole climbers shall be covered with safety caps when not being used for their intended use.

(g)(2)(ii) The employer shall ensure that pole climbers are inspected by a competent person for the following conditions: Fractured or cracked gaffs or leg irons, loose or dull gaffs, broken straps or buckles. If any of these conditions exist, the defect shall be corrected before the climbers are used.

(g)(2)(iii) Pole climbers shall be inspected as required in this paragraph (g)(3) before each day's use and a gaff cut-out test performed at least weekly when in use.

(g)(2)(iv) Pole climbers may not be worn when:

(g)(2)(iv)(A) O_I Working in trees (specifically designed tree climbers shall be used for tree climbing),

(g)(2)(iv)(B) Working on ladders,

(g)(2)(iv)(C) Working in an aerial lift,

(g)(2)(iv)(D) Driving a vehicle, nor

(g)(2)(iv)(E) Walking on rocky, hard, frozen, brushy or hilly terrain.

(h) O_I **Ladders** Ladders, step bolts, and manhole steps shall meet the applicable requirements in Subpart D of this Part

(i) **Other tools and personal protective equipment**

(i)(1) **Head protection** Head protection meeting the requirements of ANSI Z89.2–1971, "Safety Requirements for Industrial Protective Helmets for Electrical Workers, Class B" shall be provided whenever there is exposure to possible high voltage electrical contact, and the employer shall ensure that the head protection is used by employees. ANSI Z89.2–1971 is incorporated by reference as specified in §1910.6.

(i)(2) **Eye protection** Eye protection meeting the requirements of §1910.133 (a)(2) thru (a)(6) shall be provided and the employer shall ensure its use by employees where foreign objects may enter the eyes due to work operations such as but not limited to:

(i)(2)(i) Drilling or chipping stone, brick or masonry, breaking concrete or pavement, etc. by hand tools (sledgehammer, etc.) or power tools such as pneumatic drills or hammers;

(i)(2)(ii) Working on or around high speed emery or other grinding wheels unprotected by guards;

(i)(2)(iii) Cutting or chipping terra cotta ducts, tile, etc.;

(i)(2)(iv) Working under motor vehicles requiring hammering;

(i)(2)(v) Cleaning operations using compressed air, steam, or sand blast;

(i)(2)(vi) Acetylene welding or similar operations where sparks are thrown off;

(i)(2)(vii) Using powder actuated stud drivers;

(i)(2)(viii) Tree pruning or cutting underbrush;

(i)(2)(ix) Handling battery cells and solutions, such as taking battery readings with a hydrometer and thermometer;

(i)(2)(x) Removing or rearranging strand or open wire; and

(i)(2)(xi) Performing lead sleeve wiping and while soldering.

(i)(3) **Tent heaters** Flame-type heaters may not be used within ground tents or on platforms within aerial tents unless:

(i)(3)(i) The tent covers are constructed of fire resistant materials, and

(i)(3)(ii) Adequate ventilation is provided to maintain safe oxygen levels and avoid harmful buildup of combustion products and combustible gases.

(i)(4) **Torches** Torches may be used on aerial splicing platforms or in buckets enclosed by tents provided the tent material is constructed of fire resistant material and the torch is turned off when not in actual use. Aerial tents shall be adequately ventilated while the torch is in operation.

(i)(5) **Portable power equipment** Nominal 120V, or less, portable generators used for providing power at work locations do not require grounding if the output circuit is completely isolated from the frame of the unit.

(i)(6) **Vehicle-mounted utility generators** Vehicle-mounted utility generators used for providing nominal 240V AC or less for powering portable tools and equipment need not be grounded to earth if all of the following conditions are met:

(i)(6)(i) One side of the voltage source is solidly strapped to the metallic structure of the vehicle;

(i)(6)(ii) Grounding-type outlets are used, with a "grounding" conductor between the outlet grounding terminal and the side of the voltage source that is strapped to the vehicle;

(i)(6)(iii) All metallic encased tools and equipment that are powered from this system are equipped with three-wire cords and grounding-type attachment plugs, except as designated in paragraph (i)(7) of this Section.

(i)(7) **Portable lights, tools, and appliances** Portable lights, tools, and appliances having noncurrent-carrying external metal housing may be used with power equipment described in paragraph (i)(5) of this Section without an equipment grounding conductor. When operated from commercial power such metal parts of these devices shall be grounded, unless these tools or appliances are protected by a system of double insulation, or its equivalent. Where such a system is employed, the equipment shall be distinctively marked to indicate double insulation.

(i)(8) **Soldering devices** Grounding shall be omitted when using soldering irons, guns or wire-wrap tools on telecommunications circuits.

(i)(9) **Lead work** The wiping of lead joints using melted solder, gas fueled torches, soldering irons or other appropriate heating devices, and the soldering of wires or other electrical connections do not constitute the welding, cutting and brazing described in Subpart Q of this Part. When operated from commercial power the metal housing of electric solder pots shall be grounded. Electric solder pots may be used with the power equipment described in paragraph (i)(5) of this Section without a grounding conductor. The employer shall ensure that wiping gloves or cloths and eye protection are used in lead wiping operations. A drip pan to catch hot lead drippings shall also be provided and used.

(j) **Vehicle-mounted material handling devices and other mechanical equipment**

(j)(1) **General**

(j)(1)(i) The employer shall ensure that visual inspections are made of the equipment by a competent person each day the equipment is to be used to ascertain that it is in good condition.

(j)(1)(ii) The employer shall ensure that tests shall be made at the beginning of each shift by a competent person to insure the vehicle brakes and operating systems are in proper working condition.

(j)(2) **Scrapers, loaders, dozers, graders and tractors**

(j)(2)(i) All rubber-tired, self-propelled scrapers, rubber-tired front end loaders, rubber-tired dozers, agricultural and industrial tractors, crawler tractors, crawler-type loaders, and motor graders, with or without attachments, that are used in telecommunications work shall have rollover protective structures that meet the requirements of Subpart W of Part 1926 of this Title.

(j)(2)(ii) Eye protection shall be provided and the employer shall ensure that it is used by employees when working in areas where flying material is generated.

(j)(3) **Vehicle-mounted elevating and rotating work platforms** These devices shall not be operated with any conductive part of the equipment closer to exposed energized power lines than the clearances set forth in Table R–2 of this Section.

(j)(4) **Derrick trucks and similar equipment**

(j)(4)(i) This equipment shall not be operated with any conductive part of the equipment closer to exposed energized power lines than the clearances set forth in Table R–2 of this Section.

(j)(4)(ii) When derricks are used to handle poles near energized power conductors, these operations shall comply with the requirements contained in paragraphs (b)(7) and (n)(11) of this Section.

(j)(4)(iii) Moving parts of equipment and machinery carried on or mounted on telecommunications line trucks shall be guarded. This may be done with barricades as specified in paragraph (d)(2) of this Section.

(j)(4)(iv) Derricks and the operation of derricks shall comply with the following requirements:

(j)(4)(iv)(A) Manufacturer's specifications, load ratings and instructions for derrick operation shall be strictly observed.

(j)(4)(iv)(B) Rated load capacities and instructions related to derrick operation shall be conspicuously posted on a permanent weather-resistant plate or decal in a location on the derrick that is plainly visible to the derrick operator.

(j)(4)(iv)(C) Prior to derrick operation the parking brake must be set and the stabilizers extended if the vehicle is so equipped. When the vehicle is situated on a grade, at least two wheels must be chocked on the downgrade side.

(j)(4)(iv)(D) Only persons trained in the operation of the derrick shall be permitted to operate the derrick.

(j)(4)(iv)(E) Hand signals to derrick operators shall be those prescribed by ANSI B30.6–1969, "Safety Code for Derricks", which is incorporated by reference as specified in §1910.6.

(j)(4)(iv)(F) The employer shall ensure that the derrick and its associated equipment are inspected by a competent person at intervals set by the manufacturer but in no case less than once per year. Records shall be maintained including the dates of inspections, and necessary repairs made, if corrective action was required.

(j)(4)(iv)(G) Modifications or additions to the derrick and its associated equipment that alter its capacity or affect its safe operation shall be made only with written certification from the manufacturer, or other equivalent entity, such as a nationally recognized testing laboratory, that the modification results in the equipment being safe for its intended use. Such changes shall require the changing and posting of revised capacity and instruction decals or plates. These new ratings or limitations shall be as provided by the manufacturer or other equivalent entity.

(j)(4)(iv)(H) Wire rope used with derricks shall be of improved plow steel or equivalent. Wire rope safety factors shall be in accordance with American National Standards Institute B30.6–1969.

(j)(4)(iv)(I) Wire rope shall be taken out of service, or the defective portion removed, when any of the following conditions exist:

(j)(4)(iv)(I)(1) The rope strength has been significantly reduced due to corrosion, pitting, or excessive heat, or

(j)(4)(iv)(I)(2) The thickness of the outer wires of the rope has been reduced to two-thirds or less of the original thickness, or

(j)(4)(iv)(I)(3) There are more than six broken wires in any one rope lay, or

(j)(4)(iv)(I)(4) There is excessive permanent distortion caused by kinking, crushing, or severe twisting of the rope.

(k) **Materials handling and storage**

(k)(1) **Poles** When working with poles in piles or stacks, work shall be performed from the ends of the poles as much as possible, and precautions shall be taken for the safety of employees at the other end of the pole. During pole hauling operations, all loads shall be secured to prevent displacement. Lights, reflectors and/or flags shall be displayed on the end and sides of the load as necessary. The requirements for installation, removal, or other handling of poles in pole lines are prescribed in paragraph (n) of this Section which pertains to overhead lines. In the case of hoisting machinery equipped with a positive stop loadholding device, it shall be permissible for the operator to leave his position at the controls (while a load is suspended) for the sole purpose of assisting in positioning the load prior to landing it. Prior to unloading steel, poles, crossarms, and similar material, the load shall be thoroughly examined to ascertain that the load has not shifted, that binders or stakes have not broken, and that the load is not otherwise hazardous to employees.

(k)(2) **Cable reels** Cable reels in storage shall be checked or otherwise restrained when there is a possibility that they might accidentally roll from position.

(l) **Cable fault locating and testing**

(l)(1) Employees involved in using high voltages to locate trouble or test cables shall be instructed in the precautions necessary for their own safety and the safety of other employees.

(l)(2) Before the voltage is applied, cable conductors shall be isolated to the extent practicable. Employees shall be warned, by such techniques as briefing and tagging at all affected locations, to stay clear while the voltage is applied.

(m) **Grounding for employee protection—pole lines**

(m)(1) **Power conductors** Electric power conductors and equipment shall be considered as energized unless the employee can visually determine that they are bonded to one of the grounds listed in paragraph (m)(4) of this Section.

(m)(2) **Nonworking open wire** Nonworking open wire communications lines shall be bonded to one of the grounds listed in paragraph (m)(4) of this Section.

(m)(3) **Vertical power conduit, power ground wires and street light fixtures**

(m)(3)(i) Metal power conduit on joint use poles, exposed vertical power ground wires, and street light fixtures which are below communications attachments or less than 20 inches above these attachments, shall be considered energized and shall be tested for voltage unless the employee can visually determine that they are bonded to the communications suspension strand or cable sheath.

(m)(3)(ii) If no hazardous voltage is shown by the voltage test, a temporary bond shall be placed between such street light fixture, exposed vertical power grounding conductor, or metallic power conduit and the communications cable strand. Temporary bonds used for this purpose shall have sufficient conductivity to carry at least 500 amperes for a period of one second without fusing.

(m)(4) **Suitable protective grounding** Acceptable grounds for protective grounding are as follows:

(m)(4)(i) A vertical ground wire which has been tested, found safe, and is connected to a power system multigrounded neutral or the grounded neutral of a power secondary system where there are at least three services connected;

(m)(4)(ii) Communications cable sheath or shield and its supporting strand where the sheath or shield is:

(m)(4)(ii)(A) Bonded to an underground or buried cable which is connected to a central office ground, or

(m)(4)(ii)(B) Bonded to an underground metallic piping system, or

(m)(4)(ii)(C) Bonded to a power system multigrounded neutral or grounded neutral of a power secondary system which has at least three services connected;

(m)(4)(iii) Guys which are bonded to the grounds specified in paragraphs (m)(4)(i) and (ii) of this Section and which have continuity uninterrupted by an insulator; and

(m)(4)(iv) If all of the preceding grounds are not available, arrays of driven ground rods where the resultant resistance to ground will be low enough to eliminate danger to personnel or permit prompt operation of protective devices.

(m)(5) **Attaching and removing temporary bonds** When attaching grounds (bonds), the first attachment shall be made to the protective ground. When removing bonds, the connection to the line or equipment shall be removed first. Insulating gloves shall be worn during these operations.

(m)(6) **Temporary grounding of suspension strand**

(m)(6)(i) The suspension strand shall be grounded to the existing grounds listed in paragraph (m)(4) of this Section when being placed on jointly used poles or during thunderstorm activity.

(m)(6)(ii) Where power crossings are encountered on nonjoint lines, the strand shall be bonded to an existing ground listed in paragraph (m)(4) of this Section as close as possible to the crossing. This bonding is not required where crossings are made on a common crossing pole unless there is an upward change in grade at the pole.

(m)(6)(iii) Where roller-type bonds are used, they shall be restrained so as to avoid stressing the electrical connections.

(m)(6)(iv) Bonds between the suspension strand and the existing ground shall be at least No. 6AWG copper.

(m)(6)(v) Temporary bonds shall be left in place until the strand has been tensioned, dead-ended, and permanently grounded.

(m)(6)(vi) The requirements of paragraphs (m)(6)(i) through (m)(6)(v) of this Section do not apply to the installation of insulated strand.

(m)(7) **Antenna work-radio transmitting stations 3–30 MHZ**

(m)(7)(i) Prior to grounding a radio transmitting station antenna, the employer shall insure that the rigger in charge:

(m)(7)(i)(A) Prepares a danger tag signed with his signature;

(m)(7)(i)(B) Requests the transmitting technician to shutdown the transmitter and to ground the antenna with its grounding switch;

(m)(7)(i)(C) Is notified by the transmitting technician that the transmitter has been shutdown; and

(m)(7)(i)(D) Tags the antenna ground switch personally in the presence of the transmitting technician after the antenna has been grounded by the transmitting technician.

(m)(7)(ii) Power shall not be applied to the antenna, nor shall the grounding switch be opened under any circumstances while the tag is affixed.

(m)(7)(iii)(A) Where no grounding switches are provided, grounding sticks shall be used, one on each side of line, and tags shall be placed on the grounding sticks, antenna switch, or plate power switch in a conspicuous place.

(m)(7)(iii)(B) When necessary to further reduce excessive radio frequency pickup, ground sticks or short circuits shall be placed directly on the transmission lines near the transmitter in addition to the regular grounding switches.

(m)(7)(iii)(C) In other cases, the antenna lines may be disconnected from ground and the transmitter to reduce pickup at the point in the field.

(m)(7)(iv) All radio frequency line wires shall be tested for pickup with an insulated probe before they are handled either with bare hands or with metal tools.

(m)(7)(v) The employer shall insure that the transmitting technician warn the riggers about adjacent lines which are, or may become energized.

(m)(7)(vi) The employer shall insure that when antenna work has been completed, the rigger in charge of the job returns to the transmitter, notifies the transmitting technician in charge that work has been completed, and personally removes the tag from the antenna ground switch.

(n) Overhead lines

(n)(1) Handling suspension strand

(n)(1)(i) The employer shall insure that when handling cable suspension strand which is being installed on poles carrying exposed energized power conductors, employees shall wear insulating gloves and shall avoid body contact with the strand until after it has been tensioned, dead-ended and permanently grounded.

(n)(1)(ii) The strand shall be restrained against upward movement during installation:

(n)(1)(ii)(A) On joint-use poles, where there is an upward change in grade at the pole, and

(n)(1)(ii)(B) On non-joint-use poles, where the line croses under energized power conductors.

(n)(2) **Need for testing wood poles** Unless temporary guys or braces are attached, the following poles shall be tested in accordance with paragraph (n)(3) of this Section and determined to be safe before employees are permitted to climb them:

(n)(2)(i) Dead-end poles, except properly braced or guyed "Y" or "T" cable junction poles;

(n)(2)(ii) Straight line poles which are not storm guyed and where adjacent span lengths exceed 165 feet;

(n)(2)(iii) Poles at which there is a downward change in grade and which are not guyed or braced corner poles or cable junction poles;

(n)(2)(iv) Poles which support only telephone drop wire; and

(n)(2)(v) Poles which carry less than ten communication line wires. On joint use poles, one power line wire shall be considered as two communication wires for purposes of this paragraph (n)(2)(v).

(n)(3) **Methods for testing wood poles** One of the following methods or an equivalent method shall be used for testing wood poles:

(n)(3)(i) Rap the pole sharply with a hammer weighing about 3 pounds, starting near the ground line and continuing upwards circumferentially around the pole to a height of approximately 6 feet. The hammer will produce a clear sound and rebound sharply when striking sound wood. Decay pockets will be indicated by a dull sound and/or a less pronounced hammer rebound. When decay pockets are indicated, the pole shall be considered unsafe. Also, prod the pole as near the ground line as possible using a pole prod or a screwdriver with a blade at least 5 inches long. If substantial decay is encountered, the pole shall be considered unsafe.

(n)(3)(ii) Apply a horizontal force to the pole and attempt to rock it back and forth in a direction perpendicular to the line. Caution shall be exercised to avoid causing power wires to swing together. The force may be applied either by pushing with a pike pole or pulling with a rope. If the pole cracks during the test, it shall be considered unsafe.

(n)(4) **Unsafe poles or structures** Poles or structures determined to be unsafe by test or observation may not be climbed until made safe by guying, bracing or other adequate means. Poles determined to be unsafe to climb shall, until they are made safe, be tagged in a conspicuous place to alert and warn all employees of the unsafe condition.

(n)(5) Test requirements for cable suspension strand

(n)(5)(i) Before attaching a splicing platform to a cable suspension strand, the strand shall be tested and determined to have strength sufficient to support the weight of the platform and the employee. Where the strand crosses above power wires or railroad tracks it may not be tested but shall be inspected in accordance with paragraph (n)(6) of this Section.

(n)(5)(ii) The following method or an equivalent method shall be used for testing the strength of the strand: A rope, at least three-eighths inch in diameter, shall be thrown over the strand. On joint lines, the rope shall be passed over the strand using tree pruner handles or a wire raising tool. If two employees are present, both shall grip the double rope and slowly transfer their entire weight to the rope and attempt to raise themselves off the ground. If only one employee is present, one end of the rope which has been passed over the strand shall be tied to the bumper of the truck, or other equally secure anchorage. The employee then shall grasp the other end of the rope and attempt to raise himself off the ground.

(n)(6) **Inspection of strand** Where strand passes over electric power wires or railroad tracks, it shall be inspected from an elevated working position at each pole supporting the span in question. The strand may not be used to support any splicing platform, scaffold or cable car, if any of the following conditions exist:

(n)(6)(i) Corrosion so that no galvanizing can be detected,

(n)(6)(ii) One or more wires of the strand are broken,

(n)(6)(iii) Worn spots, or

(n)(6)(iv) Burn marks such as those caused by contact with electric power wires.

(n)(7) **Outside work platforms** Unless adequate railings are provided, safety straps and body belts shall be used while working on elevated work platforms such as aerial splicing platforms, pole platforms, ladder platforms and terminal balconies.

(n)(8) **Other elevated locations** Safety straps and body belts shall be worn when working at elevated positions on poles, towers or similar structures, which do not have adequately guarded work areas.

(n)(9) **Installing and removing wire and cable** Before installing or removing wire or cable, the pole or structure shall be guyed, braced, or otherwise supported, as necessary, to prevent failure of the pole or structure.

(n)(10) **Avoiding contact with energized power conductors or equipment** When cranes, derricks, or other mechanized equipment are used for setting, moving, or removing poles, all necessary precautions shall be taken to avoid contact with energized power conductors or equipment.

(n)(11) Handling poles near energized power conductors

(n)(11)(i) Joint use poles may not be set, moved, or removed where the nominal voltage of open electrical power conductors exceeds 34.5 kV phase to phase (20 kV to ground).

(n)(11)(ii) Poles that are to be placed, moved or removed during heavy rains, sleet or wet snow in joint lines carrying more than 8.7 kV phase to phase voltage (5 kV to ground) shall be guarded or otherwise prevented from direct cont act with overhead energized power conductors.

(n)(11)(iii)(A) In joint lines where the power voltage is greater than 750 volts but less than 34.5 kV phase to phase (20 kV to ground), wet poles being placed, moved or removed shall be insulated with either a rubber insulating blanket, a fiberglass box guide, or equivalent protective equipment.

(n)(11)(iii)(B) In joint lines where the power voltage is greater than 8.7 kV phase to phase (5 kV to ground) but less than 34.5 kV phase to phase (20 kV to ground), dry poles being placed, moved, or removed shall be insulated with either a rubber insulating blanket, a fiberglass box guide, or equivalent protective equipment.

(n)(11)(iii)(C) Where wet or dry poles are being removed, insulation of the pole is not required if the pole is cut off 2 feet or more below the lowest power wire and also cut off near the ground line.

(n)(11)(iv) Insulating gloves shall be worn when handling the pole with either hands or tools, when there exists a possibility that the pole may contact a power conductor. Where the voltage to ground of the power conductor exceeds 15 kV to ground, Class II gloves (as defined in ANSI J6.6–1971) shall be used. For voltages not exceeding 15 kV to ground, insulating gloves shall have a breakdown voltage of at least 17 kV.

(n)(11)(v) The guard or insulating material used to protect the pole shall meet the appropriate 3 minute proof test voltage requirements contained in the ANSI J6.4–1971.

(n)(11)(vi) When there exists a possibility of contact between the pole or the vehicle-mounted equipment used to handle the pole, and an energized power conductor, the following precautions shall be observed:

(n)(11)(vi)(A) When on the vehicle which carries the derrick, avoid all contact with the ground, with persons standing on the ground, and with all grounded objects such as guys, tree limbs, or metal sign posts. To the extent feasible, remain on the vehicle as long as the possibility of contact exists.

(n)(11)(vi)(B) When it is necessary to leave the vehicle, step onto an insulating blanket and break all contact with the vehicle before stepping off the blanket and onto the ground. As a last resort, if a blanket is not available, the employee may jump cleanly from the vehicle.

(n)(11)(vi)(C) When it is necessary to enter the vehicle, first step onto an insulating blanket and break all contact with the ground, grounded objects and other persons before touching the truck or derrick.

(n)(12) **Working position on poles** Climbing and working are prohibited above the level of the lowest electric power conducter on the pole (exclusive of vertical runs and street light wiring), except:

(n)(12)(i) Where communications facilities are attached above the electric power conductors, and a rigid fixed barrier is installed between the electric power facility and the communications facility, or

(n)(12)(ii) Where the electric power conductors are cabled secondary service drops carrying less than 300 volts to ground and are attached 40 inches or more below the communications conductors or cables.

(n)(13) **Metal tapes and ropes**

(n)(13)(i) Metal measuring tapes, metal measuring ropes, or tapes containing conductive strands may not be used when working near exposed energized parts.

(n)(13)(ii) Where it is necessary to measure clearances from energized parts, only nonconductive devices shall be used.

(o) **Underground lines** The provisions of this paragraph apply to the guarding of manholes and street openings, and to the ventilation and testing for gas in manholes and unvented vaults, where telecommunications field work is performed on or with underground lines.

(o)(1) **Guarding manholes and street openings**

(o)(1)(i) When covers of manholes or vaults are removed, the opening shall be promptly guarded by a railing, temporary cover, or other suitable temporary barrier which is appropriate to prevent an accidental fall through the opening and to protect employees working in the manhole from foreign objects entering the manhole.

(o)(1)(ii) While work is being performed in the manhole, a person with basic first aid training shall be immediately available to render assistance if there is cause for believing that a safety hazard exists, and if the requirements contained in paragraphs (d)(1) and (o)(1)(i) of this Section do not adequately protect the employee(s). Examples of manhole worksite hazards which shall be considered to constitute a safety hazard include, but are not limited to:

(o)(1)(ii)(A) Manhole worksites where safety hazards are created by traffic patterns that cannot be corrected by provisions of paragraph (d)(1) of this Section.

(o)(1)(ii)(B) Manhole worksites that are subject to unusual water hazards that cannot be abated by conventional means.

(o)(1)(ii)(C) Manhole worksites that are occupied jointly with power utilities as described in paragraph (o)(3) of this Section.

(o)(2) **Requirements prior to entering manholes and unvented vaults**

(o)(2)(i) Before an employee enters a manhole, the following steps shall be taken:

(o)(2)(i)(A) The internal atmosphere shall be tested for combustible gas and, except when continuous forced ventilation is provided, the atmosphere shall also be tested for oxygen deficiency.

(o)(2)(i)(B) When unsafe conditions are detected by testing or other means, the work area shall be ventilated and otherwise made safe before entry.

(o)(2)(ii) An adequate continuous supply of air shall be provided while work is performed in manholes under any of the following conditions:

(o)(2)(ii)(A) Where combustible or explosive gas vapors have been initially detected and subsequently reduced to a safe level by ventilation,

(o)(2)(ii)(B) Where organic solvents are used in the work procedure,

(o)(2)(ii)(C) Where open flame torches are used in the work procedure,

(o)(2)(ii)(D) Where the manhole is located in that portion of a public right of way open to vehicular traffic and/or exposed to a seepage of gas or gases, or

(o)(2)(ii)(E) Where a toxic gas or oxygen deficiency is found.

(o)(2)(iii)(A) The requirements of paragraphs (o)(2)(i) and (ii) of this Section do not apply to work in central office cable vaults that are adequately ventilated.

(o)(2)(iii)(B) The requirements of paragraphs (o)(2)(i) and (ii) of this Section apply to work in unvented vaults.

(o)(3) **Joint power and telecommunication manholes** While work is being performed in a manhole occupied jointly by an electric utility and a telecommunication utility, an employee with basic first aid training shall be available in the immediate vicinity to render emergency assistance as may be required. The employee whose presence is required in the immediate vicinity for the purposes of rendering emergency assistance is not to be precluded from occasionally entering a manhole to provide assistance other than in an emergency. The requirement of this paragraph (o)(3) does not preclude a qualified employee, working alone, from entering for brief periods of time, a manhole where energized cables or equipment are in service, for the purpose of inspection, housekeeping, taking readings, or similar work if such work can be performed safely.

(o)(4) **Ladders** Ladders shall be used to enter and exit manholes exceeding 4 feet in depth.

(o)(5) **Flames** When open flames are used in manholes, the following precautions shall be taken to protect against the accumulation of combustible gas:

(o)(5)(i) A test for combustible gas shall be made immediately before using the open flame device, and at least once per hour while using the device; and

(o)(5)(ii) A fuel tank (e.g., acetylene) may not be in the manhole unless in actual use.

(p) **Microwave transmission**

(p)(1) **Eye protection** Employers shall insure that employees do not look into an open waveguide which is connected to an energized source of microwave radiation.

(p)(2) **Hazardous area** Accessible areas associated with microwave communication systems where the electromagnetic radiation level exceeds the radiation protection guide given in §1910.97 shall be posted as described in that Section. The lower half of the warning symbol shall include the following:

Radiation in this area may exceed hazard limitations and special precautions are required. Obtain specific instruction before entering.

(p)(3) **Protective measures** When an employee works in an area where the electromagnetic radiation exceeds the radiation protection guide, the employer shall institute measures that insure that the employee's exposure is not greater than that permitted by the radiation guide. Such measures shall include, but not be limited to those of an administrative or engineering nature or those involving personal protective equipment.

(q) **Tree trimming—electrical hazards**

(q)(1) **General**

(q)(1)(i) Employees engaged in pruning, trimming, removing, or clearing trees from lines shall be required to consider all overhead and underground electrical power conductors to be energized with potentially fatal voltages, never to be touched (contacted) either directly or indirectly.

(q)(1)(ii) Employees engaged in line-clearing operations shall be instructed that:

(q)(1)(ii)(A) A direct contact is made when any part of the body touches or contacts an energized conductor, or other energized electrical fixture or apparatus.

(q)(1)(ii)(B) An indirect contact is made when any part of the body touches any object in contact with an energized electrical conductor, or other energized fixture or apparatus.

(q)(1)(ii)(C) An indirect contact can be made through conductive tools, tree branches, trucks, equipment, or other objects, or as a result of communications wires, cables, fences, or guy wires being accidentally energized.

(q)(1)(ii)(D) Electric shock will occur when an employee, by either direct or indirect contact with an energized conductor, energized tree limb, tool, equipment, or other object, provides a path for the flow of electricity to a grounded object or to the ground itself. Simultaneous contact with two energized conductors will also cause electric shock which may result in serious or fatal injury.

(q)(1)(iii) Before any work is performed in proximity to energized conductors, the system operator/owner of the energized conductors shall be contacted to ascertain if he knows of any hazards associated with the conductors which may not be readily apparent. This rule does not apply when operations are performed by or on behalf of, the system operator/owner.

(q)(2) **Working in proximity to electrical hazards**

(q)(2)(i) Employers shall ensure that a close inspection is made by the employee and by the foremen or supervisor in charge before climbing, entering, or working around any tree, to determine whether an electrical power conductor passes through the tree, or passes within reaching distance of an employee working in the tree. If any of these conditions exist either directly or indirectly, an electrical hazard shall be considered to exist unless the system operator/owner has caused the hazard to be removed by deenergizing the lines, or installing protective equipment.

(q)(2)(ii) Only qualified employees or trainees, familiar with the special techniques and hazards involved in line clearance, shall be permitted to perform the work if it is found that an electrical hazard exists.

(q)(2)(iii) During all tree working operations aloft where an electrical hazard of more than 750V exists, there shall be a second employee or trainee qualified in line clearance tree trimming within normal voice communication.

(q)(2)(iv) Where tree work is performed by employees qualified in line-clearance tree trimming and trainees qualified in line-clearance tree trimming, the clearances from energized conductors given in Table R–3 shall apply.

Table R–3

Minimum Working Distances From Energized Conductors for Line-Clearance Tree Trimmers and Line-Clearance Tree-Trimmer Trainees

Voltage range (phase to phase) (kilovolts)	Minimum working distance
2.1 to 15.0	2 ft. 0 in.
15.1 to 35.0	2 ft. 4 in.
35.1 to 46.0	2 ft. 6 in.

Telecommunications

R

Special Industries

Voltage range (phase to phase) (kilovolts)	Minimum working distance
46.1 to 72.5	3 ft. 0 in.
72.6 to 121.0	3 ft. 4 in.
138.0 to 145.0	3 ft. 6 in.
161.0 to 169.0	3 ft. 8 in.
230.0 to 242.0	5 ft. 0 in.
345.0 to 362.0	7 ft. 0 in.
500.0 to 552.0	11 ft. 0 in.
700.0 to 765.0	15 ft. 0 in.

(q)(2)(v) Branches hanging on an energized conductor may only be removed using appropriately insulated equipment.

(q)(2)(vi) Rubber footwear, including lineman's overshoes, shall not be considered as providing any measure of safety from electrical hazards.

(q)(2)(vii) Ladders, platforms, and aerial devices, including insulated aerial devices, may not be brought in contact with an electrical conductor. Reliance shall not be placed on their dielectric capabilities.

(q)(2)(viii) When an aerial lift device contacts an electrical conductor, the truck supporting the aerial lift device shall be considered as energized.

(q)(3) **Storm work and emergency conditions**

(q)(3)(i) Since storm work and emergency conditions create special hazards, only authorized representatives of the electric utility system operator/owner and not telecommunication workers may perform tree work in these situations where energized electrical power conductors are involved.

(q)(3)(ii) When an emergency condition develops due to tree operations, work shall be suspended and the system operator/owner shall be notified immediately.

(r) **Buried facilities** Communications lines and power lines in the same trench. [Reserved]

(s) **Definitions**

(s)(1) **Aerial lifts** Aerial lifts include the following types of vehicle-mounted aerial devices used to elevate personnel to jobsites above ground:

(s)(1)(i) Extensible boom platforms;
(s)(1)(ii) Aerial ladders;
(s)(1)(iii) Articulating boom platforms;
(s)(1)(iv) Vertical towers;
(s)(1)(v) A combination of any of the above defined in ANSI A92.2–1969, which is incorporated by reference as specified in §1910.6. These devices are made of metal, wood, fiberglass reinforced plastic (FRP), or other material; are powered or manually operated; and are deemed to be aerial lifts whether or not they are capable of rotating about a substantially vertical axis.

(s)(2) **Aerial splicing platform** This consists of a platform, approximately 3 ft. × 4 ft., used to perform aerial cable work. It is furnished with fiber or synthetic ropes for supporting the platform from aerial strand, detachable guy ropes for anchoring it, and a device for raising and lowering it with a handline.

(s)(3) **Aerial tent** A small tent usually constructed of vinyl coated canvas which is usually supported by light metal or plastic tubing. It is designed to protect employees in inclement weather while working on ladders, aerial splicing platforms, or aerial devices.

(s)(4) **Alive or live (energized)** Electrically connected to a source of potential difference, or electrically charged so as to have a potential significantly different from that of the earth in the vicinity. The term live is sometimes used in the place of the term current-carrying, where the intent is clear, to avoid repetition of the longer term.

(s)(5) **Barricade.** A physical obstruction such as tapes, cones, or "A" frame type wood and/or metal structure intended to warn and limit access to a work area.

(s)(6) **Barrier** A physical obstruction which is intended to prevent contact with energized lines or equipment, or to prevent unauthorized access to work area.

(s)(7) **Bond** An electrical connection from one conductive element to another for the purpose of minimizing potential differences or providing suitable conductivity for fault current or for mitigation of leakage current and electrolytic action.

(s)(8) **Cable** A conductor with insulation, or a stranded conductor with or without insulation and other coverings (single-conductor cable), or a combination of conductors insulated from one another (multiple-conductor cable).

(s)(9) **Cable sheath** A protective covering applied to cables.

Note: A cable sheath may consist of multiple layers of which one or more is conductive.

(s)(10) **Circuit** A conductor or system of conductors through which an electric current is intended to flow.

(s)(11) **Communication lines** The conductors and their supporting or containing structures for telephone, telegraph, railroad signal, data, clock, fire, police-alarm, community television antenna and other systems which are used for public or private signal or communication service, and which operate at potentials not exceeding 400 volts to ground or 750 volts between any two points of the circuit, and the transmitted power of which does not exceed 150 watts. When communications lines operate at less than 150 volts to ground, no limit is placed on the capacity of the system. Specifically designed communications cables may include communication circuits not complying with the preceding limitations, where such circuits are also used incidentally to supply power to communication equipment.

(s)(12) **Conductor** A material, usually in the form of a wire, cable, or bus bar, suitable for carrying an electric current.

(s)(13) **Effectively grounded** Intentionally connected to earth through a ground connection or connections of sufficiently low impedance and having sufficient current-carrying capacity to prevent the build-up of voltages which may result in undue hazard to connected equipment or to persons.

(s)(14) **Equipment** A general term which includes materials, fittings, devices, appliances, fixtures, apparatus, and similar items used as part of, or in connection with, a supply or communications installation.

(s)(15) **Ground (reference)** That conductive body, usually earth, to which an electric potential is referenced.

(s)(16) **Ground (as a noun)** A conductive connection, whether intentional or accidental, by which an electric circuit or equipment is connected to reference ground.

(s)(17) **Ground (as a verb)** The connecting or establishment of a connection, whether by intention or accident, of an electric circuit or equipment to reference ground.

(s)(18) **Ground tent** A small tent usually constructed of vinyl coated canvas supported by a metal or plastic frame. Its purpose is to protect employees from inclement weather while working at buried cable pedestal sites or similar locations.

(s)(19) **Grounded conductor** A system or circuit conductor which is intentionally grounded.

(s)(20) **Grounded systems** A system of conductors in which at least one conductor or point (usually the middle wire, or the neutral point of transformer or generator windings) is intentionally grounded, either solidly or through a current-limiting device (not a current-interrupting device).

(s)(21) **Grounding electrode conductor** (Grounding conductor). A conductor used to connect equipment or the grounded circuit of a wiring system to a grounding electrode.

(s)(22) **Insulated** Separated from other conducting surfaces by a dielectric substance (including air space) offering a high resistance to the passage of current.

Note: When any object is said to be insulated, it is understood to be insulated in suitable manner for the conditions to which it is subjected. Otherwise, it is, within the purpose of these rules, uninsulated. Insulating coverings of conductors in one means of making the conductor insulated.

(s)(23) **Insulation (as applied to cable)** That which is relied upon to insulate the conductor from other conductors or conducting parts or from ground.

(s)(24) **Joint use** The sharing of a common facility, such as a manhole, trench or pole, by two or more different kinds of utilities (e.g., power and telecommunications).

(s)(25) **Ladder platform** A device designed to facilitate working aloft from an extension ladder. A typical device consists of a platform (approximately 9" × 18") hinged to a welded pipe frame. The rear edge of the platform and the bottom cross-member of the frame are equipped with latches to lock the platform to ladder rungs.

(s)(26) **Ladder seat** A removable seat used to facilitate work at an elevated position on rolling ladders in telecommunication centers.

(s)(27) **Manhole** A subsurface enclosure which personnel may enter and which is used for the purpose of installing, operating, and maintaining submersible equipment and/or cable.

(s)(28) **Manhole platform** A platform consisting of separate planks which are laid across steel platform supports. The ends of the supports are engaged in the manhole cable racks.

(s)(29) **Microwave transmission** The act of communicating or signaling utilizing a frequency between 1 GHz(gigahertz) and 300 GHz inclusively.

(s)(30) **Nominal voltage** The nominal voltage of a system or circuit is the value assigned to a system or circuit of a given voltage class for the purpose of convenient designation. The actual voltage may vary above or below this value.

(s)(31) **Pole balcony or seat** A balcony or seat used as a support for workmen at pole-mounted equipment or terminal boxes. A typical device consists of a bolted assembly of steel details and a wooden platform. Steel braces run from the pole to the underside of the balcony. A guard rail (approximately 30-inchs high) may be provided.

(s)(32) Pole platform A platform intended for use by a workman in splicing and maintenance operations in an elevated position adjacent to a pole. It consists of a platform equipped at one end with a hinged chain binder for securing the platform to a pole. A brace from the pole to the underside of the platform is also provided.

(s)(33) Qualified employee Any worker who by reason of his training and experience has demonstrated his ability to safely perform his duties.

(s)(34) Qualified line-clearance tree trimmer A tree worker who through related training and on-the-job experience is familiar with the special techniques and hazards involved in line clearance.

(s)(35) Qualified line-clearance tree-trimmer trainee Any worker regularly assigned to a line-clearance tree-trimming crew and undergoing on-the-job training who, in the course of such training, has demonstrated his ability to perform his duties safely at his level of training.

(s)(36) System operator/owner The person or organization that operates or controls the electrical conductors involved.

(s)(37) Telecommunications center An installation of communication equipment under the exclusive control of an organization providing telecommunications service, that is located outdoors or in a vault, chamber, or a building space used primarily for such installations.

Note: Telecommunication centers are facilities established, equipped and arranged in accordance with engineered plans for the purpose of providing telecommunications service. They may be located on premises owned or leased by the organization providing telecommunication service, or on the premises owned or leased by others. This definition includes switch rooms (whether electromechanical, electronic, or computer controlled), terminal rooms, power rooms, repeater rooms, transmitter and receiver rooms, switchboard operating rooms, cable vaults, and miscellaneous communications equipment rooms. Simulation rooms of telecommunication centers for training or developmental purposes are also included.

(s)(38) Telecommunications derricks Rotating or nonrotating derrick structures permanently mounted on vehicles for the purpose of lifting, lowering, or positioning hardware and materials used in telecommunications work.

(s)(39) Telecommunication line truck A truck used to transport men, tools, and material, and to serve as a traveling workshop for telecommunication installation and maintenance work. It is sometimes equipped with a boom and auxiliary equipment for setting poles, digging holes, and elevating material or men.

(s)(40) Telecommunication service The furnishing of a capability to signal or communicate at a distance by means such as telephone, telegraph, police and firealarm, community antenna television, or similar system, using wire, conventional cable, coaxial cable, wave guides, microwave transmission, or other similar means.

(s)(41) Unvented vault An enclosed vault in which the only openings are access openings.

(s)(42) Vault An enclosure above or below ground which personnel may enter, and which is used for the purpose of installing, operating, and/or maintaining equipment and/or cable which need not be of submersible design.

(s)(43) Vented vault An enclosure as described in paragraph(s) (42) of this Section, with provision for air changes using exhaust flue stack(s) and low level air intake(s), operating on differentials of pressure and temperature providing for air flow.

(s)(44) Voltage of an effectively grounded circuit The voltage between any conductor and ground unless otherwise indicated.

(s)(45) Voltage of a circuit not effectively grounded The voltage between any two conductors. If one circuit is directly connected to and supplied from another circuit of higher voltage (as in the case of an autotransformer), both are considered as of the higher voltage, unless the circuit of lower voltage is effectively grounded, in which case its voltage is not determined by the circuit of higher voltage. Direct connection implies electric connection as distinguished from connection merely through electromagnetic or electrostatic induction.

[40 FR 13441, Mar. 26, 1975, as amended at 43 FR 49751, Oct. 24, 1978; 47 FR 14706, Apr. 6, 1982; 52 FR 36387, Sept. 28, 1987; 54 FR 24334, June 7, 1989; 61 FR 9242, Mar. 7, 1996; 63 FR 33467, June 18, 1998; 67 FR 67965, Nov. 7, 2002; 69 FR 31882, June 8, 2004; 70 FR 1141, Jan. 5, 2005]

§1910.269 Electric power generation, transmission, and distribution

(a) General

(a)(1) Application

(a)(1)(i) This Section covers the operation and maintenance of electric power generation, control, transformation, transmission, and distribution lines and equipment. These provisions apply to:

(a)(1)(i)(A) Power generation, transmission, and distribution installations, including related equipment for the purpose of communication or metering that are accessible only to qualified employees;

Note: The types of installations covered by this paragraph include the generation, transmission, and distribution installations of electric utilities, as well as equivalent installations of industrial establishments. Subpart S of this Part covers supplementary electric generating equipment that is used to supply a workplace for emergency, standby, or similar purposes only. (See paragraph (a)(1)(i)(B) of this Section.)

(a)(1)(i)(B) Other installations at an electric power generating station, as follows:

(a)(1)(i)(B)(1) Fuel and ash handling and processing installations, such as coal conveyors,

(a)(1)(i)(B)(2) Water and steam installations, such as penstocks, pipelines, and tanks, providing a source of energy for electric generators, and

(a)(1)(i)(B)(3) Chlorine and hydrogen systems.

(a)(1)(i)(C) Test sites where employees perform electrical testing involving temporary measurements associated with electric power generation, transmission, and distribution in laboratories, in the field, in substations, and on lines, as opposed to metering, relaying, and routine line work;

(a)(1)(i)(D) Work on, or directly associated with, the installations covered in paragraphs (a)(1)(i)(A) through (a)(1)(i)(C) of this Section; and

(a)(1)(i)(E) Line-clearance tree trimming performed for the purpose of clearing space around electric power generation, transmission, or distribution lines or equipment and on behalf of an organization that operates, or that controls the operating procedures for, those lines or equipment, as follows:

(a)(1)(i)(E)(1) Entire §1910.269, except paragraph (r)(1) of this Section, applies to line-clearance tree trimming covered by the introductory text to paragraph (a)(1)(i)(E) of the Section when performed by qualified employees (those who are knowledgeable in the construction and operation of the electric power generation, transmission, or distribution equipment involved, along with the associated hazards).

(a)(1)(i)(E)(2) Paragraphs (a)(2), (a)(3), (b), (c), (g), (k), (p), and (r) of this Section apply to line-clearance tree trimming covered by the introductory text to paragraph (a)(1)(i)(E) of this Section when performed by line-clearance tree trimmers who are not qualified employees.

(a)(1)(ii) Notwithstanding paragraph (a)(1)(i) of this Section, §1910.269 of this Part does not apply:

(a)(1)(ii)(A) To construction work, as defined in §1910.12 of this Part, except for line-clearance tree-trimming involving electric power generation installations as specified in §1926.950(a)(3) of this chapter; or

(a)(1)(ii)(B) To electrical installations, electrical safety-related work practices, or electrical maintenance considerations covered by Subpart S of this Part.

Note 1: The Occupational Safety and Health Administration considers work practices conforming to §1910.332 through §1910.335 as complying with the electrical safety-related work-practice requirements of §1910.269 identified in Table 1 of Appendix A-2 to this Section, provided that employers are performing the work on a generation or distribution installation meeting §1910.303 through §1910.308. This table also identifies provisions in §1910.269 that apply to work by qualified persons directly on, or associated with, installations of electric power generation, transmission, and distribution lines or equipment, regardless of compliance with §1910.332 through §1910.335.

Note 2: The Occupational Safety and Health Administration considers work practices performed by qualified persons and conforming to §1910.269 as complying with §1910.333(c) and §1910.335.

(a)(1)(iii) This Section applies in addition to all other applicable standards contained in this Part 1910. Employers covered under this Section are not exempt from complying with other applicable provisions in Part 1910 by the operation of §1910.5(c). Specific references in this Section to other Sections of Part 1910 are for emphasis only.

(a)(2) Training

(a)(2)(i) All employees performing work covered by this Section shall be trained as follows:

(a)(2)(ii)(A) Each employee shall be trained in, and familiar with, the safety-related work practices, safety procedures, and other safety requirements in this Section that pertain to his or her job assignments.

(a)(2)(ii)(B) Each employee shall also be trained in and familiar with any other safety practices, including applicable emergency procedures (such as pole-top and manhole rescue), that are not specifically addressed by this Section but that are related to his or her work and are necessary for his or her safety.

(a)(2)(ii)(C) The degree of training shall be determined by the risk to the employee for the hazard involved.

(a)(2)(ii) Each qualified employees shall also be trained and competent in:

(a)(2)(ii)(A) The skills and techniques necessary to distinguish exposed live parts from other parts of electric equipment,

(a)(2)(ii)(B) The skills and techniques necessary to determine the nominal voltage of exposed live parts,

(a)(2)(ii)(C) The minimum approach distances specified in this Section corresponding to the voltages to which the qualified employee will be exposed and the skills and techniques necessary to maintain those distances,

(a)(2)(ii)(D) The proper use of the special precautionary techniques, personal protective equipment, insulating and shielding materials, and insulated tools for working on or near exposed energized parts of electric equipment, and

(a)(2)(ii)(E) The recognition of electrical hazards to which the employee may be exposed and the skills and techniques necessary to control or avoid these hazards.

Note: For the purposes of this Section, a person must have the training required by paragraph (a)(2)(ii) of this Section to be considered a qualified person.

(a)(2)(iii) Each line-clearance tree trimmer who is not a qualified employee shall also be trained and competent in:

(a)(2)(ii)(A) The skills and techniques necessary to distinguish exposed live parts from other parts of electric equipment,

(a)(2)(ii)(B) The skills and techniques necessary to determine the nominal voltage of exposed live parts, and

(a)(2)(ii)(C) The minimum approach distances specified in this Section corresponding to the voltages to which the employee will be exposed and the skills and techniques necessary to maintain those distances.

(a)(2)(iv) The employer shall determine, through regular supervision and through inspections conducted on at least an annual basis, that each employee is complying with the safety-related work practices required by this Section.

(a)(2)(v) An employee shall receive additional training (or retraining) under any of the following conditions:

(a)(2)(v)(A) If the supervision or annual inspections required by paragraph (a)(2)(iv) of this Section indicate that the employee is not complying with the safety-related work practices required by this Section, or

(a)(2)(v)(B) If new technology, new types of equipment, or changes in procedures necessitate the use of safety-related work practices that are different from those which the employee would normally use, or

(a)(2)(v)(C) If he or she must employ safety-related work practices that are not normally used during his or her regular job duties.

Note: The Occupational Safety and Health Administration considers tasks that are performed less often than once per year to necessitate retraining before the performance of the work practices involved.

(a)(2)(vi) The training required by paragraph (a)(2) of this Section shall be of the classroom or on-the-job type.

(a)(2)(vii) The training shall establish employee proficiency in the work practices required by this Section and shall introduce the procedures necessary for compliance with this Section.

(a)(2)(viii) The employer shall ensure that each employee has demonstrated proficiency in the work practices involved before that employee is considered as having completed the training required by paragraph (a)(2) of this Section.

Note 1: Though they are not required by this paragraph, employment records that indicate that an employee has successfully completed the required training are one way of keeping track of when an employee has demonstrated proficiency.

Note 2: For an employee with previous training, an employer may determine that that employee has demonstrated the proficiency required by this paragraph using the following process:

(1) Confirm that the employee has the training required by paragraph (a)(2) of this Section,

(2) Use an examination or interview to make an initial determination that the employee understands the relevant safety-related work practices before he or she performs any work covered by this Section, and

(3) Supervise the employee closely until that employee has demonstrated proficiency as required by this paragraph.

(a)(3) **Information transfer**

(a)(3)(i) Before work begins, the host employer shall inform contract employers of:

(a)(3)(i)(A) The characteristics of the host employer's installation that are related to the safety of the work to be performed and are listed in paragraphs (a)(4)(i) through (a)(4)(v) of this Section;

Note: This paragraph requires the host employer to obtain information listed in paragraphs (a)(4)(i) through (a)(4)(v) of this Section if it does not have this information in existing records.

(a)(3)(i)(B) Conditions that are related to the safety of the work to be performed, that are listed in paragraphs (a)(4)(vi) through (a)(4)(viii) of this Section, and that are known to the host employer;

Note: For the purposes of this paragraph, the host employer need only provide information to contract employers that the host employer can obtain from its existing records through the exercise of reasonable diligence. This paragraph does not require the host employer to make inspections of worksite conditions to obtain this information.

(a)(3)(i)(C) Information about the design and operation of the host employer's installation that the contract employer needs to make the assessments required by this Section; and

Note: This paragraph requires the host employer to obtain information about the design and operation of its installation that contract employers need to make required assessments if it does not have this information in existing records.

(a)(3)(i)(D) Any other information about the design and operation of the host employer's installation that is known by the host employer, that the contract employer requests, and that is related to the protection of the contract employer's employees.

Note: For the purposes of this paragraph, the host employer need only provide information to contract employers that the host employer can obtain from its existing records through the exercise of reasonable diligence. This paragraph does not require the host employer to make inspections of worksite conditions to obtain this information.

(a)(3)(ii) Contract employers shall comply with the following requirements:

(a)(3)(ii)(A) The contract employer shall ensure that each of its employees is instructed in the hazardous conditions relevant to the employee's work that the contract employer is aware of as a result of information communicated to the contract employer by the host employer under paragraph (a)(3)(i) of this Section.

(a)(3)(ii)(B) Before work begins, the contract employer shall advise the host employer of any unique hazardous conditions presented by the contract employer's work.

(a)(3)(ii)(C) The contract employer shall advise the host employer of any unanticipated hazardous conditions found during the contract employer's work that the host employer did not mention under paragraph (a)(3)(i) of this Section. The contract employer shall provide this information to the host employer within 2 working days after discovering the hazardous condition.

(a)(3)(iii) The contract employer and the host employer shall coordinate their work rules and procedures so that each employee of the contract employer and the host employer is protected as required by this Section.

(a)(4) **Existing characteristics and conditions** Existing characteristics and conditions of electric lines and equipment that are related to the safety of the work to be performed shall be determined before work on or near the lines or equipment is started. Such characteristics and conditions include, but are not limited to:

(a)(4)(i) The nominal voltages of lines and equipment,

(a)(4)(ii) The maximum switching-transient voltages,

(a)(4)(iii) The presence of hazardous induced voltages,

(a)(4)(iv) The presence of protective grounds and equipment grounding conductors,

(a)(4)(v) The locations of circuits and equipment, including electric supply lines, communication lines, and fire-protective signaling circuits,

(a)(4)(vi) The condition of protective grounds and equipment grounding conductors,

(a)(4)(vii) The condition of poles, and

(a)(4)(viii) Environmental conditions relating to safety.

(b) **Medical services and first aid** The employer shall provide medical services and first aid as required in §1910.151. In addition to the requirements of §1910.151, the following requirements also apply:

(b)(1) **First-aid training** When employees are performing work on, or associated with, exposed lines or equipment energized at 50 volts or more, persons with first-aid training shall be available as follows:

(b)(1)(i) For field work involving two or more employees at a work location, at least two trained persons shall be available. However, for line-clearance tree trimming performed by line-clearance tree trimmers who are not qualified employees, only one trained person need be available if all new employees are trained in first aid within 3 months of their hiring dates.

(b)(1)(ii) For fixed work locations such as substations, the number of trained persons available shall be sufficient to ensure that each employee exposed to electric shock can be reached within 4 minutes by a trained person. However, where the existing number of employees is insufficient to meet this requirement (at a remote substation, for example), each employee at the work location shall be a trained employee.

(b)(2) **First aid supplies** First-aid supplies required by §1910.151(b) shall be placed in weatherproof containers if the supplies could be exposed to the weather.

(b)(3) **First aid kits** The employer shall maintain each first-aid kit, shall ensure that it is readily available for use, and shall inspect it frequently enough to ensure that expended items are replaced. The employer also shall inspect each first aid kit at least once per year.

(c) [OI] **Job briefing**

(c)(1) **Before each job**

(c)(1)(i) In assigning an employee or a group of employees to perform a job, the employer shall provide the employee in charge of the job with all available information that relates to the determination of existing characteristics and conditions required by paragraph (a)(4) of this Section.

(c)(1)(ii) The employer shall ensure that the employee in charge conducts a job briefing that meets paragraphs (c)(2), (c)(3), and (c)(4) of this Section with the employees involved before they start each job.

(c)(2) **Subjects to be covered** The briefing shall cover at least the following subjects: hazards associated with the job, work procedures involved, special precautions, energy-source controls, and personal protective equipment requirements.

(c)(3) **Number of briefings**

(c)(3)(i) If the work or operations to be performed during the work day or shift are repetitive and similar, at least one job briefing shall be conducted before the start of the first job of each day or shift.

(c)(3)(ii) Additional job briefings shall be held if significant changes, which might affect the safety of the employees, occur during the course of the work.

(c)(4) **Extent of briefing**

(c)(4)(i) A brief discussion is satisfactory if the work involved is routine and if the employees, by virtue of training and experience, can reasonably be expected to recognize and avoid the hazards involved in the job.

(c)(4)(ii) A more extensive discussion shall be conducted:

(c)(4)(ii)(A) If the work is complicated or particularly hazardous, or

(c)(4)(ii)(B) If the employee cannot be expected to recognize and avoid the hazards involved in the job.

Note: The briefing must address all the subjects listed in paragraph (c)(2) of this Section.

(c)(5) **Working alone** An employee working alone need not conduct a job briefing. However, the employer shall ensure that the tasks to be performed are planned as if a briefing were required.

(d) [OI] **Hazardous energy control (lockout/tagout) procedures**

(d)(1) **Application** The provisions of paragraph (d) of this Section apply to the use of lockout/tagout procedures for the control of energy sources in installations for the purpose of electric power generation, including related equipment for communication or metering. Locking and tagging procedures for the deenergizing of electric energy sources which are used exclusively for purposes of transmission and distribution are addressed by paragraph (m) of this Section.

Note 1: Installations in electric power generation facilities that are not an integral part of, or inextricably commingled with, power generation processes or equipment are covered under §1910.147 and Subpart S of this Part.

(d)(2) **General**

(d)(2)(i) The employer shall establish a program consisting of energy control procedures, employee training, and periodic inspections to ensure that, before any employee performs any servicing or maintenance on a machine or equipment where the unexpected energizing, start up, or release of stored energy could occur and cause injury, the machine or equipment is isolated from the energy source and rendered inoperative.

(d)(2)(ii) The employer's energy control program under paragraph (d)(2) of this Section shall meet the following requirements:

(d)(2)(ii)(A) If an energy isolating device is not capable of being locked out, the employer's program shall use a tagout system.

(d)(2)(ii)(B) If an energy isolating device is capable of being locked out, the employer's program shall use lockout, unless the employer can demonstrate that the use of a tagout system will provide full employee protection as follows:

(d)(2)(ii)(B)(1) When a tagout device is used on an energy isolating device which is capable of being locked out, the tagout device shall be attached at the same location that the lockout device would have been attached, and the employer shall demonstrate that the tagout program will provide a level of safety equivalent to that obtained by the use of a lockout program.

(d)(2)(ii)(B)(2) In demonstrating that a level of safety is achieved in the tagout program equivalent to the level of safety obtained by the use of a lockout program, the employer shall demonstrate full compliance with all tagout-related provisions of this standard together with such additional elements as are necessary to provide the equivalent safety available from the use of a lockout device. Additional means to be considered as part of the demonstration of full employee protection shall include the implementation of additional safety measures such as the removal of an isolating circuit element, blocking of a controlling switch, opening of an extra disconnecting device, or the removal of a valve handle to reduce the likelihood of inadvertent energizing.

(d)(2)(ii)(C) After November 1, 1994, whenever replacement or major repair, renovation, or modification of a machine or equipment is performed, and whenever new machines or equipment are installed, energy isolating devices for such machines or equipment shall be designed to accept a lockout device.

(d)(2)(iii) Procedures shall be developed, documented, and used for the control of potentially hazardous energy covered by paragraph (d) of this Section.

(d)(2)(iv) The procedure shall clearly and specifically outline the scope, purpose, responsibility, authorization, rules, and techniques to be applied to the control of hazardous energy, and the measures to enforce compliance including, but not limited to, the following:

(d)(2)(iv)(A) A specific statement of the intended use of this procedure;

(d)(2)(iv)(B) Specific procedural steps for shutting down, isolating, blocking and securing machines or equipment to control hazardous energy;

(d)(2)(iv)(C) Specific procedural steps for the placement, removal, and transfer of lockout devices or tagout devices and the responsibility for them; and

(d)(2)(iv)(D) Specific requirements for testing a machine or equipment to determine and verify the effectiveness of lockout devices, tagout devices, and other energy control measures.

(d)(2)(v) The employer shall conduct a periodic inspection of the energy control procedure at least annually to ensure that the procedure and the provisions of paragraph (d) of this Section are being followed.

(d)(2)(v)(A) The periodic inspection shall be performed by an authorized employee who is not using the energy control procedure being inspected.

(d)(2)(v)(B) The periodic inspection shall be designed to identify and correct any deviations or inadequacies.

(d)(2)(v)(C) If lockout is used for energy control, the periodic inspection shall include a review, between the inspector and each authorized employee, of that employee's responsibilities under the energy control procedure being inspected.

(d)(2)(v)(D) Where tagout is used for energy control, the periodic inspection shall include a review, between the inspector and each authorized and affected employee, of that employee's responsibilities under the energy control procedure being inspected, and the elements set forth in paragraph (d)(2)(vii) of this Section.

(d)(2)(v)(E) The employer shall certify that the inspections required by paragraph (d)(2)(v) of this Section have been accomplished. The certification shall identify the machine or equipment on which the energy control procedure was being used, the date of the inspection, the employees included in the inspection, and the person performing the inspection.

Note: If normal work schedule and operation records demonstrate adequate inspection activity and contain the required information, no additional certification is required.

(d)(2)(vi) The employer shall provide training to ensure that the purpose and function of the energy control program are understood by employees and that the knowledge and skills required for the safe application, usage, and removal of energy controls are acquired by employees. The training shall include the following:

(d)(2)(vi)(A) Each authorized employee shall receive training in the recognition of applicable hazardous energy sources, the type and magnitude of energy available in the workplace, and in the methods and means necessary for energy isolation and control.

(d)(2)(vi)(B) Each affected employee shall be instructed in the purpose and use of the energy control procedure.

(d)(2)(vi)(C) All other employees whose work operations are or may be in an area where energy control procedures may be used shall be instructed about the procedures and about the prohibition relating to attempts to restart or reenergize machines or equipment that are locked out or tagged out.

(d)(2)(vii) When tagout systems are used, employees shall also be trained in the following limitations of tags:

(d)(2)(vii)(A) Tags are essentially warning devices affixed to energy isolating devices and do not provide the physical restraint on those devices that is provided by a lock.

(d)(2)(vii)(B) When a tag is attached to an energy isolating means, it is not to be removed without authorization of the authorized person responsible for it, and it is never to be bypassed, ignored, or otherwise defeated.

(d)(2)(vii)(C) Tags must be legible and understandable by all authorized employees, affected employees, and all other employees whose work operations are or may be in the area, in order to be effective.

(d)(2)(vii)(D) Tags and their means of attachment must be made of materials which will withstand the environmental conditions encountered in the workplace.

(d)(2)(vii)(E) Tags may evoke a false sense of security, and their meaning needs to be understood as part of the overall energy control program.

(d)(2)(vii)(F) Tags must be securely attached to energy isolating devices so that they cannot be inadvertently or accidentally detached during use.

(d)(2)(viii) Retraining shall be provided by the employer as follows:

(d)(2)(viii)(A) Retraining shall be provided for all authorized and affected employees whenever there is a change in their job assignments, a change in machines, equipment, or processes that present a new hazard or whenever there is a change in the energy control procedures.

(d)(2)(viii)(B) Retraining shall also be conducted whenever a periodic inspection under paragraph (d)(2)(v) of this Section reveals, or whenever the employer has reason to believe, that there are deviations from or inadequacies in an employee's knowledge or use of the energy control procedures.

(d)(2)(viii)(C) The retraining shall reestablish employee proficiency and shall introduce new or revised control methods and procedures, as necessary.

(d)(2)(ix) The employer shall certify that employee training has been accomplished and is being kept up to date. The certification shall contain each employee's name and dates of training.

(d)(3) **Protective materials and hardware**

(d)(3)(i) Locks, tags, chains, wedges, key blocks, adapter pins, self-locking fasteners, or other hardware shall be provided by the employer for isolating, securing, or blocking of machines or equipment from energy sources.

(d)(3)(ii) Lockout devices and tagout devices shall be singularly identified; shall be the only devices used for controlling energy; may not be used for other purposes; and shall meet the following requirements:

(d)(3)(ii)(A) Lockout devices and tagout devices shall be capable of withstanding the environment to which they are exposed for the maximum period of time that exposure is expected.

(d)(3)(ii)(A)(1) Tagout devices shall be constructed and printed so that exposure to weather conditions or wet and damp locations will not cause the tag to deteriorate or the message on the tag to become illegible.

(d)(3)(ii)(A)(2) Tagout devices shall be so constructed as not to deteriorate when used in corrosive environments.

(d)(3)(ii)(B) Lockout devices and tagout devices shall be standardized within the facility in at least one of the following criteria: color, shape, size. Additionally, in the case of tagout devices, print and format shall be standardized.

(d)(3)(ii)(C) Lockout devices shall be substantial enough to prevent removal without the use of excessive force or unusual techniques, such as with the use of bolt cutters or metal cutting tools.

(d)(3)(ii)(D) Tagout devices, including their means of attachment, shall be substantial enough to prevent inadvertent or accidental removal. Tagout device attachment means shall be of a non-reusable type, attachable by hand, self-locking, and nonreleasable with a minimum unlocking strength of no less than 50 pounds and shall have the general design and basic characteristics of being at least equivalent to a one-piece, all-environment-tolerant nylon cable tie.

(d)(3)(ii)(E) Each lockout device or tagout device shall include provisions for the identification of the employee applying the device.

(d)(3)(ii)(F) Tagout devices shall warn against hazardous conditions if the machine or equipment is energized and shall include a legend such as the following: Do Not Start, Do Not Open, Do Not Close, Do Not Energize, Do Not Operate.

Note: For specific provisions covering accident prevention tags, see §1910.145.

(d)(4) **Energy isolation** Lockout and tagout device application and removal may only be performed by the authorized employees who are performing the servicing or maintenance.

(d)(5) **Notification** Affected employees shall be notified by the employer or authorized employee of the application and removal of lockout or tagout devices. Notification shall be given before the controls are applied and after they are removed from the machine or equipment.

Note: See also paragraph (d)(7) of this Section, which requires that the second notification take place before the machine or equipment is reenergized.

(d)(6) **Lockout/tagout application** The established procedures for the application of energy control (the lockout or tagout procedures) shall include the following elements and actions, and these procedures shall be performed in the following sequence:

(d)(6)(i) Before an authorized or affected employee turns off a machine or equipment, the authorized employee shall have knowledge of the type and magnitude of the energy, the hazards of the energy to be controlled, and the method or means to control the energy.

(d)(6)(ii) The machine or equipment shall be turned off or shut down using the procedures established for the machine or equipment. An orderly shutdown shall be used to avoid any additional or increased hazards to employees as a result of the equipment stoppage.

(d)(6)(iii) All energy isolating devices that are needed to control the energy to the machine or equipment shall be physically located and operated in such a manner as to isolate the machine or equipment from energy sources.

(d)(6)(iv) Lockout or tagout devices shall be affixed to each energy isolating device by authorized employees.

(d)(6)(iv)(A) Lockout devices shall be attached in a manner that will hold the energy isolating devices in a "safe" or "off" position.

(d)(6)(iv)(B) Tagout devices shall be affixed in such a manner as will clearly indicate that the operation or movement of energy isolating devices from the "safe" or "off" position is prohibited.

(d)(6)(iv)(B)(1) Where tagout devices are used with energy isolating devices designed with the capability of being locked out, the tag attachment shall be fastened at the same point at which the lock would have been attached.

(d)(6)(iv)(B)(2) Where a tag cannot be affixed directly to the energy isolating device, the tag shall be located as close as safely possible to the device, in a position that will be immediately obvious to anyone attempting to operate the device.

(d)(6)(v) Following the application of lockout or tagout devices to energy isolating devices, all potentially hazardous stored or residual energy shall be relieved, disconnected, restrained, or otherwise rendered safe.

(d)(6)(vi) If there is a possibility of reaccumulation of stored energy to a hazardous level, verification of isolation shall be continued until the servicing or maintenance is completed or until the possibility of such accumulation no longer exists.

(d)(6)(vii) Before starting work on machines or equipment that have been locked out or tagged out, the authorized employee shall verify that isolation and deenergizing of the machine or equipment have been accomplished. If normally energized parts will be exposed to contact by an employee while the machine or equipment is deenergized, a test shall be performed to ensure that these parts are deenergized.

(d)(7) **Release from lockout/tagout** Before lockout or tagout devices are removed and energy is restored to the machine or equipment, procedures shall be followed and actions taken by the authorized employees to ensure the following:

(d)(7)(i) The work area shall be inspected to ensure that nonessential items have been removed and that machine or equipment components are operationally intac.

(d)(7)(ii) The work area shall be checked to ensure that all employees have been safely positioned or removed.

(d)(7)(iii) After lockout or tagout devices have been removed and before a machine or equipment is started, affected employees shall be notified that the lockout or tagout devices have been removed.

(d)(7)(iv) Each lockout or tagout device shall be removed from each energy isolating device by the authorized employee who applied the lockout or tagout device. However, if that employee is not available to remove it, the device may be removed under the direction of the employer, provided that specific procedures and training for such removal have been developed, documented, and incorporated into the employer's energy control program. The employer shall demonstrate that the specific procedure provides a degree of safety equivalent to that provided by the removal of the device by the authorized employee who applied it. The specific procedure shall include at least the following elements:

(d)(7)(iv)(A) Verification by the employer that the authorized employee who applied the device is not at the facility;

(d)(7)(iv)(B) Making all reasonable efforts to contact the authorized employee to inform him or her that his or her lockout or tagout device has been removed; and

(d)(7)(iv)(C) Ensuring that the authorized employee has this knowledge before he or she resumes work at that facility.

(d)(8) Additional requirements

(d)(8)(i) If the lockout or tagout devices must be temporarily removed from energy isolating devices and the machine or equipment must be energized to test or position the machine, equipment, or component thereof, the following sequence of actions shall be followed:

(d)(8)(i)(A) Clear the machine or equipment of tools and materials in accordance with paragraph (d)(7)(i) of this Section;

(d)(8)(i)(B) Remove employees from the machine or equipment area in accordance with paragraphs (d)(7)(ii) and (d)(7)(iii) of this Section;

(d)(8)(i)(C) Remove the lockout or tagout devices as specified in paragraph (d)(7)(iv) of this Section;

(d)(8)(i)(D) Energize and proceed with the testing or positioning; and

(d)(8)(i)(E) Deenergize all systems and reapply energy control measures in accordance with paragraph (d)(6) of this Section to continue the servicing or maintenance.

(d)(8)(ii) When servicing or maintenance is performed by a crew, craft, department, or other group, they shall use a procedure which affords the employees a level of protection equivalent to that provided by the implementation of a personal lockout or tagout device. Group lockout or tagout devices shall be used in accordance with the procedures required by paragraphs (d)(2)(iii) and (d)(2)(iv) of this Section including, but not limited to, the following specific requirements:

(d)(8)(ii)(A) Primary responsibility shall be vested in an authorized employee for a set number of employees working under the protection of a group lockout or tagout device (such as an operations lock);

(d)(8)(ii)(B) Provision shall be made for the authorized employee to ascertain the exposure status of all individual group members with regard to the lockout or tagout of the machine or equipment;

(d)(8)(ii)(C) When more than one crew, craft, department, or other group is involved, assignment of overall job-associated lockout or tagout control responsibility shall be given to an authorized employee designated to coordinate affected work forces and ensure continuity of protection; and

(d)(8)(ii)(D) Each authorized employee shall affix a personal lockout or tagout device to the group lockout device, group lockbox, or comparable mechanism when he or she begins work and shall remove those devices when he or she stops working on the machine or equipment being serviced or maintained.

(d)(8)(iii) Procedures shall be used during shift or personnel changes to ensure the continuity of lockout or tagout protection, including provision for the orderly transfer of lockout or tagout device protection between off-going and on-coming employees, to minimize their exposure to hazards from the unexpected energizing or start-up of the machine or equipment or from the release of stored energy.

(d)(8)(iv) Whenever outside servicing personnel are to be engaged in activities covered by paragraph (d) of this Section, the on-site employer and the outside employer shall inform each other of their respective lockout or tagout procedures, and each employer shall ensure that his or her personnel understand and comply with restrictions and prohibitions of the energy control procedures being used.

(d)(8)(v) If energy isolating devices are installed in a central location and are under the exclusive control of a system operator, the following requirements apply:

(d)(8)(v)(A) The employer shall use a procedure that affords employees a level of protection equivalent to that provided by the implementation of a personal lockout or tagout device.

(d)(8)(v)(B) The system operator shall place and remove lockout and tagout devices in place of the authorized employee under paragraphs (d)(4), (d)(6)(iv), and (d)(7)(iv) of this Section.

(d)(8)(v)(C) Provisions shall be made to identify the authorized employee who is responsible for (that is, being protected by) the lockout or tagout device, to transfer responsibility for lockout and tagout devices, and to ensure that an authorized employee requesting removal or transfer of a lockout or tagout device is the one responsible for it before the device is removed or transferred.

Note: Lockout and tagging procedures that comply with paragraphs (c) through (f) of §1910.147 will also be deemed to comply with paragraph (d) of this Section if the procedures address the hazards covered by paragraph (d) of this Section.

(e) Enclosed spaces This paragraph covers enclosed spaces that may be entered by employees. It does not apply to vented vaults if the employer makes a determination that the ventilation system is operating to protect employees before they enter the space. This paragraph applies to routine entry into enclosed spaces in lieu of the permit-space entry requirements contained in paragraphs (d) through (k) of §1910.146. If, after the employer takes the precautions given in paragraphs (e) and (t) of this Section, the hazards remaining in the enclosed space endanger the life of an entrant or could interfere with an entrant's escape from the space, then entry into the enclosed space shall meet the permit-space entry requirements of paragraphs (d) through (k) of §1910.146.

(e)(1) Safe work practices The employer shall ensure the use of safe work practices for entry into, and work in, enclosed spaces and for rescue of employees from such spaces.

(e)(2) Training Each employee who enters an enclosed space or who serves as an attendant shall be trained in the hazards of enclosed-space entry, in enclosed-space entry procedures, and in enclosed-space rescue procedures.

(e)(3) Rescue equipment Employers shall provide equipment to ensure the prompt and safe rescue of employees from the enclosed space.

(e)(4) Evaluation of potential hazards Before any entrance cover to an enclosed space is removed, the employer shall determine whether it is safe to do so by checking for the presence of any atmospheric pressure or temperature differences and by evaluating whether there might be a hazardous atmosphere in the space. Any conditions making it unsafe to remove the cover shall be eliminated before the cover is removed.

Note: The determination called for in this paragraph may consist of a check of the conditions that might foreseeably be in the enclosed space. For example, the cover could be checked to see if it is hot and, if it is fastened in place, could be loosened gradually to release any residual pressure. An evaluation also needs to be made of whether conditions at the site could cause a hazardous atmosphere, such as an oxygen-deficient or flammable atmosphere, to develop within the space.

(e)(5) Removal of covers When covers are removed from enclosed spaces, the opening shall be promptly guarded by a railing, temporary cover, or other barrier designed to prevent an accidental fall through the opening and to protect employees working in the space from objects entering the space.

(e)(6) Hazardous atmosphere Employees may not enter any enclosed space while it contains a hazardous atmosphere, unless the entry conforms to the permit-required confined spaces standard in §1910.146.

(e)(7) Attendants While work is being performed in the enclosed space, an attendant with first-aid training shall be immediately available outside the enclosed space to provide assistance if a hazard exists because of traffic patterns in the area of the opening used for entry. The attendant is not precluded from performing other duties outside the enclosed space if these duties do not distract the attendant from: monitoring employees within the space or ensuring that it is safe for employees to enter and exit the space.

Note: See paragraph (t) of this Section for additional requirements on attendants for work in manholes and vaults.

(e)(8) Calibration of test instruments Test instruments used to monitor atmospheres in enclosed spaces shall be kept in calibration and shall have a minimum accuracy of ±10 percent.

(e)(9) Testing for oxygen deficiency Before an employee enters an enclosed space, the atmosphere in the enclosed space shall be tested for oxygen deficiency with a direct-reading meter or similar instrument, capable of collection and immediate analysis of data samples without the need for off-site evaluation. If continuous forced-air ventilation is provided, testing is not required provided that the procedures used ensure that employees are not exposed to the hazards posed by oxygen deficiency.

(e)(10) Testing for flammable gases and vapors Before an employee enters an enclosed space, the internal atmosphere shall be tested for flammable gases and vapors with a direct-reading meter or similar instrument capable of collection and immediate analysis of data samples without the need for off-site evaluation. This test shall be performed after the oxygen testing and ventilation required by paragraph (e)(9) of this Section demonstrate that there is sufficient oxygen to ensure the accuracy of the test for flammability.

(e)(11) Ventilation, and monitoring for flammable gases or vapors If flammable gases or vapors are detected or if an oxygen deficiency is found, forced-air ventilation shall be used to maintain oxygen at a safe level and to prevent a hazardous concentration of flammable gases and vapors from accumulating. A continuous monitoring program to ensure that no increase in flammable gas or vapor concentration above safe levels occurs may be followed in lieu of ventilation if flammable gases or vapors are initially detected at safe levels.

Note: See the definition of "hazardous atmosphere" for guidance in determining whether a specific concentration of a substance is hazardous.

(e)(12) Specific ventilation requirements If continuous forced-air ventilation is used, it shall begin before entry is made and shall be maintained long enough for the employer to be able to demonstrate that a safe atmosphere exists before employees are allowed to enter the work area. The forced-air ventilation shall be so directed as to ventilate the immediate area where employees are present within the enclosed space and shall continue until all employees leave the enclosed space.

(e)(13) Air supply The air supply for the continuous forced-air ventilation shall be from a clean source and may not increase the hazards in the enclosed space.

(e)(14) Open flames If open flames are used in enclosed spaces, a test for flammable gases and vapors shall be made immediately before the open flame device is used and at least once per hour while the device is used in the space. Testing shall be conducted more frequently if conditions present in the enclosed space indicate that once per hour is insufficient to detect hazardous accumulations of flammable gases or vapors.

Note: See the definition of "hazardous atmosphere" for guidance in determining whether a specific concentration of a substance is hazardous.

Note: Entries into enclosed spaces conducted in accordance with the permit-space entry requirements of paragraphs (d) through (k) of §1910.146 are considered as complying with paragraph (e) of this Section.

(f) Excavations Excavation operations shall comply with Subpart P of Part 1926 of this Chapter.

(g) [OI] **Personal protective equipment**

(g)(1) General Personal protective equipment shall meet the requirements of Subpart I of this Part.

Note: Paragraph (h) of §1910.132 sets employer payment obligations for the personal protective equipment required by this Section, including, but not limited to, the fall protection equipment required by paragraph (g)(2) of this Section, the electrical protective equipment required by paragraph (l)(3) of this Section, and the flame-resistant and arc-rated clothing and other protective equipment required by paragraph (l)(8) of this Section.

(g)(2) [OI] **Fall protection**

(g)(2)(i) Personal fall arrest systems shall meet the requirements of Subpart I of this Part.

(g)(2)(ii) Personal fall arrest equipment used by employees who are exposed to hazards from flames or electric arcs, as determined by the employer under paragraph (l)(8)(i) of this Section, shall be capable of passing a drop test equivalent to that required by paragraph (g)(2)(iii)(L) of this Section after exposure to an electric arc with a heat energy o 40±5 cal/cm^2.

(g)(2)(iii) Body belts and positioning straps for work-positioning equipment shall meet the following requirements:

(g)(2)(iii)(A) Hardware for body belts and positioning straps shall meet the following requirements:

(g)(2)(iii)(A)(1) Hardware shall be made of drop-forged steel, pressed steel, formed steel, or equivalent material.

(g)(2)(iii)(A)(2) Hardware shall have a corrosion-resistant finish.

(g)(2)(iii)(A)(3) Hardware surfaces shall be smooth and free of sharp edges.

(g)(2)(iii)(B) Buckles shall be capable of withstanding an 8.9-kilonewton (2,000-pound-force) tension test with a maximum permanent deformation no greater than 0.4 millimeters (0.0156 inches).

(g)(2)(iii)(C) D rings shall be capable of withstanding a 22-kilonewton (5,000-pound-force) tensile test without cracking or breaking.

(g)(2)(iii)(D) Snaphooks shall be capable of withstanding a 22-kilonewton (5,000-pound-force) tension test without failure.

Note: Distortion of the snaphook sufficient to release the keeper is considered to be tensile failure of a snaphook.

(g)(2)(iii)(E) Top grain leather or leather substitute may be used in the manufacture of body belts and positioning straps; however, leather and leather substitutes may not be used alone as a load-bearing component of the assembly.

(g)(2)(iii)(F) Plied fabric used in positioning straps and in load-bearing parts of body belts shall be constructed in such a way that no raw edges are exposed and the plies do not separate.

(g)(2)(iii)(G) Positioning straps shall be capable of withstanding the following tests:

(g)(2)(iii)(G)(1) A dielectric test of 819.7 volts, AC, per centimeter (25,000 volts per foot) for 3 minutes without visible deterioration;

(g)(2)(iii)(G)(2) A leakage test of 98.4 volts, AC, per centimeter (3,000 volts per foot) with a leakage current of no more than 1 mA;

Note: Positioning straps that pass direct-current tests at equivalent voltages are considered as meeting this requirement.

(g)(2)(iii)(G)(3) Tension tests of 20 kilonewtons (4,500 pounds-force) for sections free of buckle holes and of 15 kilonewtons (3,500 pounds-force) for sections with buckle holes;

(g)(2)(iii)(G)(4) A buckle-tear test with a load of 4.4 kilonewtons (1,000 pounds-force); and

(g)(2)(iii)(G)(5) A flammability test in accordance with Table R-2.

Table R-2
Flammability Test

Test method	Criteria for passing the test
Vertically suspend a 500-mm (19.7-inch length of strapping supporting a 100-kg (220.5-lb) weight.	Any flames on the positioning strap shall self extinguish.
Use a butane or propane burner with a 76-mm (3-inch) flame.	The positioning strap shall continue to support the 100-kg (220.5-lb) mass.
Direct the flame to an edge of the strapping at a distance of 25 mm (1 inch).	
Remove the flame after 5 seconds.	
Wait for any flames on the positioning strap to stop burning.	

(g)(2)(iii)(H) The cushion part of the body belt shall contain no exposed rivets on the inside and shall be at least 76 millimeters (3 inches) in width.

(g)(2)(iii)(I) Tool loops shall be situated on the body of a body belt so that the 100 millimeters (4 inches) of the body belt that is in the center of the back, measuring from D ring to D ring, is free of tool loops and any other attachments.

(g)(2)(iii)(J) Copper, steel, or equivalent liners shall be used around the bars of D rings to prevent wear between these members and the leather or fabric enclosing them.

(g)(2)(iii)(K) Snaphooks shall be of the locking type meeting the following requirements:

(g)(2)(iii)(K)(1) The locking mechanism shall first be released, or a destructive force shall be placed on the keeper, before the keeper will open.

(g)(2)(iii)(K)(2) A force in the range of 6.7 N (1.5 lbf) to 17.8 N (4 lbf) shall be required to release the locking mechanism.

(g)(2)(iii)(K)(3) With the locking mechanism released and with a force applied on the keeper against the face of the nose, the keeper may not begin to open with a force of 11.2 N (2.5 lbf) or less and shall begin to open with a maximum force of 17.8 N (4 lbf).

(g)(2)(iii)(L) Body belts and positioning straps shall be capable of withstanding a drop test as follows:

(g)(2)(iii)(L)(1) The test mass shall be rigidly constructed of steel or equivalent material with a mass of 100 kg (220.5 lbm). For work-positioning equipment used by employees weighing more than 140 kg (310 lbm) fully equipped, the test mass shall be increased proportionately (that is, the test mass must equal the mass of the equipped worker divided by 1.4).

(g)(2)(iii)(L)(2) For body belts, the body belt shall be fitted snugly around the test mass and shall be attached to the test-structure anchorage point by means of a wire rope.

(g)(2)(iii)(L)(3) For positioning straps, the strap shall be adjusted to its shortest length possible to accommodate the test and connected to the test-structure anchorage point at one end and to the test mass on the other end.

(g)(2)(iii)(L)(4) The test mass shall be dropped an unobstructed distance of 1 meter (39.4 inches) from a supporting structure that will sustain minimal deflection during the test.

(g)(2)(iii)(L)(5) Body belts shall successfully arrest the fall of the test mass and shall be capable of supporting the mass after the test.

(g)(2)(iii)(L)(6) Positioning straps shall successfully arrest the fall of the test mass without breaking, and the arrest force may not exceed 17.8 kilonewtons (4,000 pounds-force). Additionally, snaphooks on positioning straps may not distort to such an extent that the keeper would release.

Note: When used by employees weighing no more than 140 kg (310 lbm) fully equipped, body belts and positioning straps that conform to American Society of Testing and Materials Standard Specifications for Personal Climbing Equipment, ASTM F887-12^{e1}, are deemed to be in compliance with paragraph (g)(2)(iii) of this Section.

(g)(2)(iv) The following requirements apply to the care and use of personal fall protection equipment.

(g)(2)(iv)(A) Work-positioning equipment shall be inspected before use each day to determine that the equipment is in safe working condition. Work-positioning equipment that is not in safe working condition may not be used.

Note: Appendix F to this Section contains guidelines for inspecting work-positioning equipment.

(g)(2)(iv)(B) Personal fall arrest systems shall be used in accordance with Subpart I of this Part.

Note: Fall protection equipment rigged to arrest falls is considered a fall arrest system and must meet the applicable requirements for the design and use of those systems. Fall protection equipment rigged for work positioning is considered work-positioning equipment and must meet the applicable requirements for the design and use of that equipment.

(g)(2)(iv)(C) The employer shall ensure that employees use fall protection systems as follows:

(g)(2)(iv)(C)(1) Each employee working from an aerial lift shall use a travel restraint system or a personal fall arrest system.

(g)(2)(iv)(C)(2) Except as provided in paragraph (g)(2)(iv)(C)(3) of this Section, each employee in elevated locations more than 1.2 meters (4 feet) above the ground on poles, towers, or similar structures shall use a personal fall arrest system, work-positioning equipment, or fall restraint system, as appropriate, if the employer has not provided other fall protection meeting Subpart D of this Part.

(g)(2)(iv)(C)(3) Until March 31, 2015, a qualified employee climbing or changing location on poles, towers, or similar structures need not use fall protection equipment, unless conditions, such as, but not limited to, ice, high winds, the design of the structure (for example, no provision for holding on with hands), or the presence of contaminants on the structure, could cause the employee to lose his or her grip or footing. On and after April 1, 2015, each qualified employee climbing or changing location on poles, towers, or similar structures must use fall protection equipment unless the employer can demonstrate that climbing or changing location with fall protection is infeasible or creates a greater hazard than climbing or changing location without it.

Note: These paragraphs apply to structures that support overhead electric power transmission and distribution lines and equipment. They do not apply to portions of buildings, such as loading docks, or to electric equipment, such as transformers and capacitors. Subpart D of this Part contains the duty to provide fall protection associated with walking and working surfaces.

Note: Until the employer ensures that employees are proficient in climbing and the use of fall protection under paragraph (a)(2)(viii) of this Section, the employees are not considered "qualified employees" for the purposes of paragraphs (g)(2)(iv)(C)(2) and (g)(2)(iv)(C)(3) of this Section. These paragraphs require unqualified employees (including trainees) to use fall protection any time they are more than 1.2 meters (4 feet) above the ground.

(g)(2)(iv)(D) On and after April 1, 2015, work-positioning systems shall be rigged so that an employee can free fall no more than 0.6 meters (2 feet).

(g)(2)(iv)(E) Anchorages for work-positioning equipment shall be capable of supporting at least twice the potential impact load of an employee's fall, or 13.3 kilonewtons (3,000 pounds-force), whichever is greater.

Note: Wood-pole fall-restriction devices meeting American Society of Testing and Materials Standard Specifications for Personal Climbing Equipment, ASTM F887-12e1, are deemed to meet the anchorage-strength requirement when they are used in accordance with manufacturers' instructions.

(g)(2)(iv)(F) Unless the snaphook is a locking type and designed specifically for the following connections, snaphooks on work-positioning equipment may not be engaged:

(g)(2)(iv)(F)(1) Directly to webbing, rope, or wire rope;

(g)(2)(iv)(F)(2) To each other;

(g)(2)(iv)(F)(3) To a D ring to which another snaphook or other connector is attached;

(g)(2)(iv)(F)(4) To a horizontal lifeline; or

(g)(2)(iv)(F)(5) To any object that is incompatibly shaped or dimensioned in relation to the snaphook such that accidental disengagement could occur should the connected object sufficiently depress the snaphook keeper to allow release of the object.

(h) [OI] Portable ladders and platforms

(h)(1) General Requirements for portable ladders contained in Subpart D of this Part apply in addition to the requirements of paragraph (h) of this Section, except as specifically noted in paragraph (h)(2) of this Section.

(h)(2) Special ladders and platforms Portable ladders used on structures or conductors in conjunction with overhead line work need not meet §1910.25(d)(2)(i) and (d)(2)(iii) or §1910.26(c)(3)(iii). Portable ladders and platforms used on structures or conductors in conjunction with overhead line work shall meet the following requirements:

(h)(2)(i) In the configurations in which they are used, portable ladders and platforms shall be capable of supporting without failure at least 2.5 times the maximum intended load.

(h)(2)(ii) Portable ladders and platforms may not be loaded in excess of the working loads for which they are designed.

(h)(2)(iii) Portable ladders and platforms shall be secured to prevent them from becoming dislodged.

(h)(2)(iv) [OI] Portable ladders and platforms may be used only in applications for which they are designed.

(h)(3) Conductive ladders Portable metal ladders and other portable conductive ladders may not be used near exposed energized lines or equipment. However, in specialized high-voltage work, conductive ladders shall be used when the employer demonstrates that nonconductive ladders would present a greater hazard to employees than conductive ladders.

(i) Hand and portable power equipment

(i)(1) General Paragraph (i)(2) of this Section applies to electric equipment connected by cord and plug. Paragraph (i)(3) of this Section applies to portable and vehicle-mounted generators used to supply cord- and plug-connected equipment. Paragraph (i)(4) of this Section applies to hydraulic and pneumatic tools.

(i)(2) Cord–and plug-connected equipment Cord- and plug-connected equipment not covered by Subpart S of this Part shall comply with one of the following instead of §1910.243(a)(5):

(i)(2)(i) The equipment shall be equipped with a cord containing an equipment grounding conductor connected to the equipment frame and to a means for grounding the other end of the conductor (however, this option may not be used where the introduction of the ground into the work environment increases the hazard to an employee); or

(i)(2)(ii) The equipment shall be of the double-insulated type conforming to Subpart S of this Part; or

(i)(2)(ii) The equipment shall be connected to the power supply through an isolating transformer with an ungrounded secondary of not more than 50 volts.

(i)(3) Portable and vehicle-mounted generators Portable and vehicle-mounted generators used to supply cord- and plug-connected equipment covered by paragraph (i)(2) of this Section shall meet the following requirements:

(i)(3)(i) The generator may only supply equipment located on the generator or the vehicle and cord- and plug-connected equipment through receptacles mounted on the generator or the vehicle.

(i)(3)(ii) The non-current-carrying metal parts of equipment and the equipment grounding conductor terminals of the receptacles shall be bonded to the generator frame.

(i)(3)(iii) For vehicle-mounted generators, the frame of the generator shall be bonded to the vehicle frame.

(i)(3)(iv) Any neutral conductor shall be bonded to the generator frame.

(i)(4) Hydraulic and pneumatic tools

(i)(4)(i) Safe operating pressures for hydraulic and pneumatic tools, hoses, valves, pipes, filters, and fittings may not be exceeded.

Note: If any hazardous defects are present, no operating pressure is safe, and the hydraulic or pneumatic equipment involved may not be used. In the absence of defects, the maximum rated operating pressure is the maximum safe pressure.

(i)(4)(ii) A hydraulic or pneumatic tool used where it may contact exposed energized parts shall be designed and maintained for such use.

(i)(4)(iii) The hydraulic system supplying a hydraulic tool used where it may contact exposed live parts shall provide protection against loss of insulating value, for the voltage involved, due to the formation of a partial vacuum in the hydraulic line.

Note: Use of hydraulic lines that do not have check valves and that have a separation of more than 10.7 meters (35 feet) between the oil reservoir and the upper end of the hydraulic system promotes the formation of a partial vacuum.

(i)(4)(iv) A pneumatic tool used on energized electric lines or equipment, or used where it may contact exposed live parts, shall provide protection against the accumulation of moisture in the air supply.

(i)(4)(v) Pressure shall be released before connections are broken, unless quick-acting, self-closing connectors are used.

(i)(4)(vi) Employers must ensure that employees do not use any part of their bodies to locate, or attempt to stop, a hydraulic leak.

(i)(4)(vii) Hoses may not be kinked.

(j) [OI] Live–line tools

(j)(1) [OI] Design of tools Live-line tool rods, tubes, and poles shall be designed and constructed to withstand the following minimum tests:

(j)(1)(i) If the tool is made of fiberglass-reinforced plastic (FRP), it shall withstand 328,100 volts per meter (100,000 volts per foot) of length for 5 minutes, or

Note: Live-line tools using rod and tube that meet ASTM F711-02 (2007), Standard Specification for Fiberglass-Reinforced Plastic (FRP) Rod and Tube Used in Live Line Tools, are deemed to comply with paragraph (j)(1) of this Section.

(j)(1)(ii) If the tool is made of wood, it shall withstand 246,100 volts per meter (75,000 volts per foot) of length for 3 minutes, or

(j)(1)(iii) [OI] The tool shall withstand other tests that the employer can demonstrate are equivalent.

(j)(2) Condition of tools

(j)(2)(i) Each live-line tool shall be wiped clean and visually inspected for defects before use each day.

(j)(2)(ii) If any defect or contamination that could adversely affect the insulating qualities or mechanical integrity of the live-line tool is present after wiping, the tool shall be removed from service and examined and tested according to paragraph (j)(2)(iii) of this Section before being returned to service.

(j)(2)(iii) Live-line tools used for primary employee protection shall be removed from service every 2 years, and whenever required under paragraph (j)(2)(ii) of this Section, for examination, cleaning, repair, and testing as follows:

(j)(2)(iii)(A) Each tool shall be thoroughly examined for defects.

(j)(2)(iii)(B) If a defect or contamination that could adversely affect the insulating qualities or mechanical integrity of the live-line tool is found, the tool shall be repaired and refinished or shall be permanently removed from service. If no such defect or contamination is found, the tool shall be cleaned and waxed.

(j)(2)(iii)(C) The tool shall be tested in accordance with paragraphs (j)(2)(iii)(D) and (j)(2)(iii)(E) of this Section under the following conditions:

(j)(2)(iii)(C)(1) After the tool has been repaired or refinished; and

(j)(2)(iii)(C)(2) After the examination if repair or refinishing is not performed, unless the tool is made of FRP rod or foam-filled FRP tube and the employer can demonstrate that the tool has no defects that could cause it to fail during use.

(j)(2)(iii)(D) The test method used shall be designed to verify the tool's integrity along its entire working length and, if the tool is made of fiberglass-reinforced plastic, its integrity under wet conditions.

(j)(2)(iii)(E) The voltage applied during the tests shall be as follows:

(j)(2)(iii)(E)(1) 246,100 volts per meter (75,000 volts per foot) of length for 1 minute if the tool is made of fiberglass, or

(j)(2)(iii)(E)(2) 164,000 volts per meter (50,000 volts per foot) of length for 1 minute if the tool is made of wood, or

(j)(2)(iii)(E)(3) Other tests that the employer can demonstrate are equivalent.

Note: Guidelines for the examination, cleaning, repairing, and in-service testing of live-line tools are specified in the Institute of Electrical and Electronics Engineers' IEEE Guide for Maintenance Methods on Energized Power Lines, IEEE Std 516-2009.

(k) Materials handling and storage

(k)(1) General Materials handling and storage shall comply with applicable material-handling and material-storage requirements in this Part, including those in Subpart N of this Part.

(k)(2) Materials storage near energized lines or equipment

(k)(2)(i) In areas to which access is not restricted to qualified persons only, materials or equipment may not be stored closer to energized lines or exposed energized parts of equipment than the following distances, plus a distance that provides for the maximum sag and side swing of all conductors and for the height and movement of material-handling equipment:

(k)(2)(i)(A) For lines and equipment energized at 50 kilovolts or less, the distance is 3.05 meters (10 feet).

(k)(2)(i)(B) For lines and equipment energized at more than 50 kilovolts, the distance is 3.05 meters (10 feet) plus 0.10 meter (4 inches) for every 10 kilovolts over 50 kilovolts.

(k)(2)(ii) In areas restricted to qualified employees, materials may not be stored within the working space about energized lines or equipment.

Note: Paragraphs (u)(1) and (v)(3) of this Section specify the size of the working space.

(l) [OI] Working on or near exposed energized parts This paragraph applies to work on exposed live parts, or near enough to them to expose the employee to any hazard they present.

(l)(1) [OI] General

(l)(1)(i) [OI] Only qualified employees may work on or with exposed energized lines or parts of equipment.

(l)(1)(ii) [OI] Only qualified employees may work in areas containing unguarded, uninsulated energized lines or parts of equipment operating at 50 volts or more.

(l)(1)(iii) Electric lines and equipment shall be considered and treated as energized unless they have been deenergized in accordance with paragraph (d) or (m) of this Section.

(l)(2) [OI] At least two employees

(l)(2)(i) [OI] Except as provided in paragraph (l)(2)(ii) of this Section, at least two employees shall be present while any employees perform the following types of work:

(l)(2)(i)(A) Installation, removal, or repair of lines energized at more than 600 volts,

(l)(2)(i)(B) Installation, removal, or repair of deenergized lines if an employee is exposed to contact with other parts energized at more than 600 volts,

(l)(2)(i)(C) Installation, removal, or repair of equipment, such as transformers, capacitors, and regulators, if an employee is exposed to contact with parts energized at more than 600 volts,

(l)(2)(i)(D) Work involving the use of mechanical equipment, other than insulated aerial lifts, near parts energized at more than 600 volts, and

(l)(2)(i)(E) Other work that exposes an employee to electrical hazards greater than, or equal to, the electrical hazards posed by operations listed specifically in paragraphs (l)(2)(i)(A) through (l)(2)(i)(D) of this Section.

(l)(2)(ii) Paragraph (l)(2)(i) of this Section does not apply to the following operations:

(l)(2)(ii)(A) Routine circuit switching, when the employer can demonstrate that conditions at the site allow safe performance of this work,

(l)(2)(ii)(B) Work performed with live-line tools when the position of the employee is such that he or she is neither within reach of, nor otherwise exposed to contact with, energized parts, and

(l)(2)(ii)(C) Emergency repairs to the extent necessary to safeguard the general public.

(l)(3) [OI] Minimum approach distances

(l)(3)(i) [OI] The employer shall establish minimum approach distances no less than the distances computed by Table R-3 for ac systems or Table R-8 for dc systems.

(l)(3)(ii) [OI] No later than April 1, 2015, for voltages over 72.5 kilovolts, the employer shall determine the maximum anticipated per-unit transient overvoltage, phase-to-ground, through an engineering analysis or assume a maximum anticipated per-unit transient overvoltage, phase-to-ground, in accordance with Table R-9. When the employer uses portable protective gaps to control the maximum transient overvoltage, the value of the maximum anticipated per-unit transient overvoltage, phase-to-ground, must provide for five standard deviations between the statistical sparkover voltage of the gap and the statistical withstand voltage corresponding to the electrical component of the minimum approach distance. The employer shall make any engineering analysis conducted to determine maximum anticipated per-unit transient overvoltage available upon request to employees and to the Assistant Secretary or designee for examination and copying.

Note: See Appendix B to this Section for information on how to calculate the maximum anticipated per-unit transient overvoltage, phase-to-ground, when the employer uses portable protective gaps to reduce maximum transient overvoltages.

(l)(3)(iii) The employer shall ensure that no employee approaches or takes any conductive object closer to exposed energized parts than the employer's established minimum approach distance, unless:

(l)(3)(iii)(A) The employee is insulated from the energized part (rubber insulating gloves or rubber insulating gloves and sleeves worn in accordance with paragraph (l)(4) of this Section constitutes insulation of the employee from the energized part upon which the employee is working provided that the employee has control of the part in a manner sufficient to prevent exposure to uninsulated portions of the employee's body), or

(l)(3)(iii)(B) The energized part is insulated from the employee and from any other conductive object at a different potential, or

(l)(3)(iii)(C) The employee is insulated from any other exposed conductive object in accordance with the requirements for live-line barehand work in paragraph (q)(3) of this Section.

(l)(4) [OI] Type of insulation

(l)(4)(i) When an employee uses rubber insulating gloves as insulation from energized parts (under paragraph (l)(3)(iii)(A) of this Section), the employer shall ensure that the employee also uses rubber insulating sleeves. However, an employee need not use rubber insulating sleeves if:

(l)(4)(i)(A) Exposed energized parts on which the employee is not working are insulated from the employee; and

(l)(4)(i)(B) When installing insulation for purposes of paragraph (l)(4)(i)(A) of this Section, the employee installs the insulation from a position that does not expose his or her upper arm to contact with other energized parts.

(l)(4)(ii) When an employee uses rubber insulating gloves or rubber insulating gloves and sleeves as insulation from energized parts (under paragraph (l)(3)(iii)(A) of this Section), the employer shall ensure that the employee:

(l)(4)(ii)(A) Puts on the rubber insulating gloves and sleeves in a position where he or she cannot reach into the minimum approach distance, established by the employer under paragraph (l)(3)(i) of this Section; and (l)(4)(ii)(B) Does not remove the rubber insulating gloves and sleeves until he or she is in a position where he or she cannot reach into the minimum approach distance, established by the employer under paragraph (l)(3)(i) of this Section.

(l)(5) **Working position**

(l)(5)(i) The employer shall ensure that each employee, to the extent that other safety-related conditions at the worksite permit, works in a position from which a slip or shock will not bring the employee's body into contact with exposed, uninsulated parts energized at a potential different from the employee's.

(l)(5)(ii) When an employee performs work near exposed parts energized at more than 600 volts, but not more than 72.5 kilovolts, and is not wearing rubber insulating gloves, being protected by insulating equipment covering the energized parts, performing work using live-line tools, or performing live-line barehand work under paragraph (q)(3) of this Section, the employee shall work from a position where he or she cannot reach into the minimum approach distance, established by the employer under paragraph (l)(3)(i) of this Section.

(l)(6) **Making connections** The employer shall ensure that connections are made as follows:

(l)(6)(i) In connecting deenergized equipment or lines to an energized circuit by means of a conducting wire or device, an employee shall first attach the wire to the deenergized part;

(l)(6)(ii) When disconnecting equipment or lines from an energized circuit by means of a conducting wire or device, an employee shall remove the source end first; and

(l)(6)(iii) [OI] When lines or equipment are connected to or disconnected from energized circuits, an employee shall keep loose conductors away from exposed energized parts.

(l)(7) **Conductive articles** When an employee performs work within reaching distance of exposed energized parts of equipment, the employer shall ensure that the employee removes or renders nonconductive all exposed conductive articles, such as keychains or watch chains, rings, or wrist watches or bands, unless such articles do not increase the hazards associated with contact with the energized parts.

(l)(8) **Protection from flames and electric arcs**

(l)(8)(i) The employer shall assess the workplace to identify employees exposed to hazards from flames or from electric arcs.

(l)(8)(ii) For each employee exposed to hazards from electric arcs, the employer shall make a reasonable estimate of the incident heat energy to which the employee would be exposed.

Note: Appendix E to this Section provides guidance on estimating available heat energy. The Occupational Safety and Health Administration will deem employers following the guidance in Appendix E to this Section to be in compliance with paragraph (l)(8)(ii) of this Section. An employer may choose a method of calculating incident heat energy not included in Appendix E to this Section if the chosen method reasonably predicts the incident energy to which the employee would be exposed.

Note: This paragraph does not require the employer to estimate the incident heat energy exposure for every job task performed by each employee. The employer may make broad estimates that cover multiple system areas provided the employer uses reasonable assumptions about the energy-exposure distribution throughout the system and provided the estimates represent the maximum employee exposure for those areas. For example, the employer could estimate the heat energy just outside a substation feeding a radial distribution system and use that estimate for all jobs performed on that radial system.

(l)(8)(iii) The employer shall ensure that each employee who is exposed to hazards from flames or electric arcs does not wear clothing that could melt onto his or her skin or that could ignite and continue to burn when exposed to flames or the heat energy estimated under paragraph (l)(8)(ii) of this Section.

Note: This paragraph prohibits clothing made from acetate, nylon, polyester, rayon and polypropylene, either alone or in blends, unless the employer demonstrates that the fabric has been treated to withstand the conditions that may be encountered by the employee or that the employee wears the clothing in such a manner as to eliminate the hazard involved.

(l)(8)(iv) The employer shall ensure that the outer layer of clothing worn by an employee, except for clothing not required to be arc rated under paragraphs (l)(8)(v)(A) through (l)(8)(v)(E) of this Section, is flame resistant under any of the following conditions:

(l)(8)(iv)(A) The employee is exposed to contact with energized circuit parts operating at more than 600 volts,

(l)(8)(iv)(B) An electric arc could ignite flammable material in the work area that, in turn, could ignite the employee's clothing,

(l)(8)(iv)(C) Molten metal or electric arcs from faulted conductors in the work area could ignite the employee's clothing, or

Note: This paragraph does not apply to conductors that are capable of carrying, without failure, the maximum available fault current for the time the circuit protective devices take to interrupt the fault.

(l)(8)(iv)(D) The incident heat energy estimated under paragraph (l)(8)(ii) of this Section exceeds 2.0 cal/cm^2.

(l)(8)(v) The employer shall ensure that each employee exposed to hazards from electric arcs wears protective clothing and other protective equipment with an arc rating greater than or equal to the heat energy estimated under paragraph (l)(8)(ii) of this Section whenever that estimate exceeds 2.0 cal/cm^2. This protective equipment shall cover the employee's entire body, except as follows:

(l)(8)(v)(A) Arc-rated protection is not necessary for the employee's hands when the employee is wearing rubber insulating gloves with protectors or, if the estimated incident energy is no more than 14 cal/cm^2, heavy-duty leather work gloves with a weight of at least 407 gm/m^2 (12 oz/yd^2),

(l)(8)(v)(B) Arc-rated protection is not necessary for the employee's feet when the employee is wearing heavy-duty work shoes or boots,

(l)(8)(v)(C) Arc-rated protection is not necessary for the employee's head when the employee is wearing head protection meeting §1910.135 if the estimated incident energy is less than 9 cal/cm^2 for exposures involving single-phase arcs in open air or 5 cal/cm^2 for other exposures,

(l)(8)(v)(D) The protection for the employee's head may consist of head protection meeting §1910.135 and a faceshield with a minimum arc rating of 8 cal/cm^2 if the estimated incident-energy exposure is less than 13 cal/cm^2 for exposures involving single-phase arcs in open air or 9 cal/cm^2 for other exposures, and

(l)(8)(v)(E) For exposures involving single-phase arcs in open air, the arc rating for the employee's head and face protection may be 4 cal/cm^2 less than the estimated incident energy.

Note: See Appendix E to this Section for further information on the selection of appropriate protection.

(l)(8)(vi) **Dates**

(l)(8)(vi)(A) The obligation in paragraph (l)(8)(ii) of this Section for the employer to make reasonable estimates of incident energy commences January 1, 2015.

(l)(8)(vi)(B) The obligation in paragraph (l)(8)(iv)(D) of this Section for the employer to ensure that the outer layer of clothing worn by an employee is flame-resistant when the estimated incident heat energy exceeds 2.0 cal/cm^2 commences April 1, 2015.

(l)(8)(vi)(C) The obligation in paragraph (l)(8)(v) of this Section for the employer to ensure that each employee exposed to hazards from electric arcs wears the required arc-rated protective equipment commences April 1, 2015.

(l)(9) **Fuse handling** When an employee must install or remove fuses with one or both terminals energized at more than 300 volts, or with exposed parts energized at more than 50 volts, the employer shall ensure that the employee uses tools or gloves rated for the voltage. When an employee installs or removes expulsion-type fuses with one or both terminals energized at more than 300 volts, the employer shall ensure that the employee wears eye protection meeting the requirements of Subpart I of this Part, uses a tool rated for the voltage, and is clear of the exhaust path of the fuse barrel.

(l)(10) **Covered (noninsulated) conductors** The requirements of this Section that pertain to the hazards of exposed live parts also apply when an employee performs work in proximity to covered (noninsulated) wires.

(l)(11) **Non-current-carrying metal parts** Non-current-carrying metal parts of equipment or devices, such as transformer cases and circuit-breaker housings, shall be treated as energized at the highest voltage to which these parts are exposed, unless the employer inspects the installation and determines that these parts are grounded before employees begin performing the work.

(l)(12) **Opening and closing circuits under load**

(l)(12)(i) The employer shall ensure that devices used by employees to open circuits under load conditions are designed to interrupt the current involved.

(l)(12)(ii) The employer shall ensure that devices used by employees to close circuits under load conditions are designed to safely carry the current involved.

Table R-3
AC Live-Line Work Minimum Approach Distance
[The minimum approach distance (MAD; in meters) shall conform to the following equations.]

For phase-to-phase system voltages of 50 V to 300 V:[1]
MAD = avoid contact

For phase-to-phase system voltages of 301 V to 5 kV:[1]
MAD = *M* + *D*, where
D = 0.02 m .... the electrical component of the minimum approach distance.
M = 0.31 m for voltages up to 750 V and 0.61 m otherwise. .... the inadvertent movement factor.

For phase-to-phase system voltages of 5.1 kV to 72.5 kV:[1, 4]
MAD = *M* + *AD*, where
M = 0.61 m .... the inadvertent movement factor.
A = the applicable value from Table R-5........ the altitude correction factor.
D = the value from Table R-4 corresponding to the voltage and exposure .. or the value of the electrical component of the minimum approach distance calculated using the method provided in Appendix B to this Section. .... the electrical component of the minimum approach distance.

For phase-to-phase system voltages of more than 72.5 kV, nominal:[2, 4]
$MAD = 0.3048(C + a)V_{L\text{-}G}TA + M$, where
C = 0.01 for phase-to-ground exposures that the employer can demonstrate consist only of air across the approach distance (gap),
0.01 for phase-to-phase exposures if the employer can demonstrate that no insulated tool spans the gap and that no large conductive object is in the gap, or.
0.011 otherwise
$V_{L\text{-}G}$ = phase-to-ground rms voltage, in kV
T = maximum anticipated per-unit transient overvoltage; for phase-to-ground exposures, *T* equals $T_{L\text{-}G}$, the maximum per-unit transient overvoltage, phase-to-ground, determined by the employer under paragraph (l)(3)(ii) of this Section; for phase-to-phase exposures, *T* equals $1.35T_{L\text{-}G} + 0.45$.
A = altitude correction factor from Table R-5.
M = 0.31 m, the inadvertent movement factor.
a = saturation factor, as follows:

Phase-to-Ground Exposures

$V_{Peak} = T_{L\text{-}G}V_{L\text{-}G}\sqrt{2}$	635 kV or less	635.1 to 915 kV	915.1 to 1,050 kV	More than 1,050 kV
a	0	$(V_{Peak}-635)/140{,}000$	$(V_{Peak}-645)/135{,}000$	$(V_{Peak}-675)/125{,}000$

Phase-to-Phase Exposures[3]

$V_{Peak} = (1.35T_{L\text{-}G} + 0.45)V_{L\text{-}G}\sqrt{2}$	630 kV or less	630.1 to 848 kV	848.1 to 1,131 kV	1,131.1 to 1,485 kV	More than 1,485 kV
a	0	$(V_{Peak}-630)/155{,}000$	$(V_{Peak}-633.6)/152{,}207$	$(V_{Peak}-628)/153{,}846$	$(V_{Peak}-350.5)/203{,}666$

[1] Employers may use the minimum approach distances in Table R-6. If the worksite is at an elevation of more than 900 meters (3,000 feet), see footnote 1 to Table R-6.
[2] Employers may use the minimum approach distances in Table R-7, except that the employer may not use the minimum approach distances in Table R-7 for phase-to-phase exposures if an insulated tool spans the gap or if any large conductive object is in the gap. If the worksite is at an elevation of more than 900 meters (3,000 feet), see footnote 1 to Table R-7. Employers may use the minimum approach distances in Table 14 through Table 21 in Appendix B to this Section, which calculated MAD for various values of *T*, provided the employer follows the notes to those tables.
[3] Use the equations for phase-to-ground exposures (with V_{Peak} for phase-to-phase exposures) unless the employer can demonstrate that no insulated tool spans the gap and that no large conductive object is in the gap.
[4] Until March 31, 2015, employers may use the minimum approach distances in Table 6 through Table 13 in Appendix B to this Section.

Table R-4
Electrical Component of the Minimum Approach Distance at 5.1 to 72.5 kV
[D; In meters]

Nominal voltage (kV) phase-to-phase	Phase-to-ground exposure D (m)	Phase-to-phase exposure D (m)
5.1 to 15.0	0.04	0.07
15.1 to 36.0	0.16	0.28
36.1 to 46.0	0.23	0.37
46.1 to 72.5	0.3	0.59

Table R-5
Altitude Correction Factor

Altitude above sea level (m)	A
0 to 900	1.00
901 to 1,200	1.02
1,201 to 1,500	1.05
1,501 to 1,800	1.08
1,801 to 2,100	1.11
2,101 to 2,400	1.14
2,401 to 2,700	1.17
2,701 to 3,000	1.20
3,001 to 3,600	1.25
3,601 to 4,200	1.30
4,201 to 4,800	1.35
4,801 to 5,400	1.39
5,401 to 6,000	1.44

Table R-6
Alternative Minimum Approach Distances for Voltages of 72.5 kV and Less[1]

Nominal voltage (kV) phase-to-phase	Distance			
	Phase-to-ground exposure		Phase-to-phase exposure	
	m	ft	m	ft
0.050 to 0.300[2]	Avoid Contact		Avoid Contact	
0.301 to 0.750[2]	0.33	1.09	0.33	1.09
0.751 to 5.0	0.63	2.07	0.63	2.07
5.1 to 15.0	0.65	2.14	0.68	2.24
15.1 to 36.0	0.77	2.53	0.89	2.92
36.1 to 46.0	0.84	2.76	0.98	3.22
46.1 to 72.5	1.00	3.29	1.20	3.94

[1] Employers may use the minimum approach distances in this table provided the worksite is at an elevation of 900 meters (3,000 feet) or less. If employees will be working at elevations greater than 900 meters (3,000 feet) above mean sea level, the employer shall determine minimum approach distances by multiplying the distances in this table by the correction factor in Table R-5 corresponding to the altitude of the work.
[2] For single-phase systems, use voltage-to-ground.

Table R-7
Alternative Minimum Approach Distances for Voltages of More Than 72.5 kV[1, 2, 3]

Voltage range voltage phase-to-phase (kV)	Distance			
	Phase-to-ground exposure		Phase-to-phase exposure	
	m	ft	m	ft
72.6 to 121.0	1.13	3.71	1.42	4.66
121.1 to 145.0	1.30	4.27	1.64	5.38
145.1 to 169.0	1.46	4.79	1.94	6.36
169.1 to 242.0	2.01	6.59	3.08	10.10
242.1 to 362.0	3.41	11.19	5.52	18.11
362.1 to 420.0	4.25	13.94	6.81	22.34
420.1 to 550.0	5.07	16.63	8.24	27.03
550.1 to 800.0	6.88	22.57	11.38	37.34

[1] Employers may use the minimum approach distances in this table provided the worksite is at an elevation of 900 meters (3,000 feet) or less. If employees will be working at elevations greater than 900 meters (3,000 feet) above mean sea level, the employer shall determine minimum approach distances by multiplying the distances in this table by the correction factor in Table R-5 corresponding to the altitude of the work.
[2] Employers may use the phase-to-phase minimum approach distances in this table provided that no insulated tool spans the gap and no large conductive object is in the gap.
[3] The clear live-line tool distance shall equal or exceed the values for the indicated voltage ranges.

Table R-8
DC Live-Line Minimum Approach Distance with Overvoltage Factor[1]
[In meters]

Maximum anticipated per-unit transient overvoltage	Distance (m) maximum line-to-ground voltage (kV)				
	250	400	500	600	750
1.5 or less	1.12	1.60	2.06	2.62	3.61
1.6	1.17	1.69	2.24	2.86	3.98
1.7	1.23	1.82	2.42	3.12	4.37
1.8	1.28	1.95	2.62	3.39	4.79

[1] The distances specified in this table are for air, bare-hand, and live-line tool conditions. If employees will be working at elevations greater than 900 meters (3,000 feet) above mean sea level, the employer shall determine minimum approach distances by multiplying the distances in this table by the correction factor in Table R-5 corresponding to the altitude of the work.

Table R-9
Assumed Maximum Per-Unit Transient Overvoltage

Voltage range (kV)	Type of current (ac or dc)	Assumed maximum per-unit transient overvoltage
72.6 to 420.0	ac	3.5
420.1 to 550.0	ac	3.0
550.1 to 800.0	ac	2.5
250 to 750	dc	1.8

(m) **Deenergizing lines and equipment for employee protection**

(m)(1) **Application** Paragraph (m) of this Section applies to the deenergizing of transmission and distribution lines and equipment for the purpose of protecting employees. See paragraph (d) of this Section for requirements on the control of hazardous energy sources used in the generation of electric energy. Conductors and parts of electric equipment that have been deenergized under procedures other than those required by paragraph (d) or (m) of this Section, as applicable, shall be treated as energized.

(m)(2) **General**

(m)(2)(i) If a system operator is in charge of the lines or equipment and their means of disconnection, the employer shall designate one employee in the crew to be in charge of the clearance and shall comply with all of the requirements of paragraph (m)(3) of this Section in the order specified.

(m)(2)(ii) If no system operator is in charge of the lines or equipment and their means of disconnection, the employer shall designate one employee in the crew to be in charge of the clearance and to perform the functions that the system operator would otherwise perform under paragraph (m) of this Section. All of the requirements of paragraph (m)(3) of this Section apply, in the order specified, except as provided in paragraph (m)(2)(iii) of this Section.

(m)(2)(iii) If only one crew will be working on the lines or equipment and if the means of disconnection is accessible and visible to, and under the sole control of, the employee in charge of the clearance, paragraphs (m)(3)(i), (m)(3)(iii), and (m)(3)(v) of this Section do not apply. Additionally, the employer does not need to use the tags required by the remaining provisions of paragraph (m)(3) of this Section.

(m)(2)(iv) If two or more crews will be working on the same lines or equipment, then:

(m)(2)(iv)(A) The crews shall coordinate their activities under paragraph (m) of this Section with a single employee in charge of the clearance for all of the crews and follow the requirements of paragraph (m) of this Section as if all of the employees formed a single crew, or

(m)(2)(iv)(B) Each crew shall independently comply with paragraph (m) of this Section and, if there is no system operator in charge of the lines or equipment, shall have separate tags and coordinate deenergizing and reenergizing the lines and equipment with the other crews.

(m)(2)(v) The employer shall render any disconnecting means that are accessible to individuals outside the employer's control (for example, the general public) inoperable while the disconnecting means are open for the purpose of protecting employees.

(m)(3) **Deenergizing lines and equipment**

(m)(3)(i) The employee that the employer designates pursuant to paragraph (m)(2) of this Section as being in charge of the clearance shall make a request of the system operator to deenergize the particular section of line or equipment. The designated employee becomes the employee in charge (as this term is used in paragraph (m)(3) of this Section) and is responsible for the clearance.

(m)(3)(ii) The employer shall ensure that all switches, disconnectors, jumpers, taps, and other means through which known sources of electric energy may be supplied to the particular lines and equipment to be deenergized are open. The employer shall render such means inoperable, unless its design does not so permit, and then ensure that such means are tagged to indicate that employees are at work.

(m)(3)(iii) The employer shall ensure that automatically and remotely controlled switches that could cause the opened disconnecting means to close are also tagged at the points of control. The employer shall render the automatic or remote control feature inoperable, unless its design does not so permit.

(m)(3)(iv) The employer need not use the tags mentioned in paragraphs (m)(3)(ii) and (m)(3)(iii) of this Section on a network protector for work on the primary feeder for the network protector's associated network transformer when the employer can demonstrate all of the following conditions:

(m)(3)(iv)(A) Every network protector is maintained so that it will immediately trip open if closed when a primary conductor is deenergized;

(m)(3)(iv)(B) Employees cannot manually place any network protector in a closed position without the use of tools, and any manual override position is blocked, locked, or otherwise disabled; and

(m)(3)(iv)(C) The employer has procedures for manually overriding any network protector that incorporate provisions for determining, before anyone places a network protector in a closed position, that: The line connected to the network protector is not deenergized for the protection of any employee working on the line; and (if the line connected to the network protector is not deenergized for the protection of any employee working on the line) the primary conductors for the network protector are energized.

(m)(3)(v) Tags shall prohibit operation of the disconnecting means and shall indicate that employees are at work.

(m)(3)(vi) After the applicable requirements in paragraphs (m)(3)(i) through (m)(3)(v) of this Section have been followed and the system operator gives a clearance to the employee in charge, the employer shall ensure that the lines and equipment are deenergized by testing the lines and equipment to be worked with a device designed to detect voltage.

(m)(3)(vii) The employer shall ensure the installation of protective grounds as required by paragraph (n) of this Section.

(m)(3)(viii) After the applicable requirements of paragraphs (m)(3)(i) through (m)(3)(vii) of this Section have been followed, the lines and equipment involved may be considered deenergized.

(m)(3)(ix) To transfer the clearance, the employee in charge (or the employee's supervisor if the employee in charge must leave the worksite due to illness or other emergency) shall inform the system operator and employees in the crew; and the new employee in charge shall be responsible for the clearance.

(m)(3)(x) To release a clearance, the employee in charge shall:

indicates an OSHA Letter of Interpretation exists for this specific reference. Please see www.oshainterpretation.us for details.

(m)(3)(x)(A) Notify each employee under that clearance of the pending release of the clearance;

(m)(3)(x)(B) Ensure that all employees under that clearance are clear of the lines and equipment;

(m)(3)(x)(C) Ensure that all protective grounds protecting employees under that clearance have been removed; and

(m)(3)(x)(D) Report this information to the system operator and then release the clearance.

(m)(3)(xi) Only the employee in charge who requested the clearance may release the clearance, unless the employer transfers responsibility under paragraph (m)(3)(ix) of this Section.

(m)(3)(xii) No one may remove tags without the release of the associated clearance as specified under paragraphs (m)(3)(x) and (m)(3)(xi) of this Section.

(m)(3)(xiii) The employer shall ensure that no one initiates action to reenergize the lines or equipment at a point of disconnection until all protective grounds have been removed, all crews working on the lines or equipment release their clearances, all employees are clear of the lines and equipment, and all protective tags are removed from that point of disconnection.

(n) [OI] Grounding for the protection of employees

(n)(1) **Application** Paragraph (n) of this Section applies to grounding of generation, transmission, and distribution lines and equipment for the purpose of protecting employees. Paragraph (n)(4) of this Section also applies to protective grounding of other equipment as required elsewhere in this Section.

Note: This paragraph covers grounding of generation, transmission, and distribution lines and equipment when this Section requires protective grounding and whenever the employer chooses to ground such lines and equipment for the protection of employees.

(n)(2) [OI] **General** For any employee to work transmission and distribution lines or equipment as deenergized, the employer shall ensure that the lines or equipment are deenergized under the provisions of paragraph (m) of this Section and shall ensure proper grounding of the lines or equipment as specified in paragraphs (n)(3) through (n)(8) of this Section. However, if the employer can demonstrate that installation of a ground is impracticable or that the conditions resulting from the installation of a ground would present greater hazards to employees than working without grounds, the lines and equipment may be treated as deenergized provided that the employer establishes that all of the following conditions apply:

(n)(2)(i) The employer ensures that the lines and equipment are deenergized under the provisions of paragraph (m) of this Section.

(n)(2)(ii) There is no possibility of contact with another energized source.

(n)(2)(iii) The hazard of induced voltage is not present.

(n)(3) **Equipotential zone** Temporary protective grounds shall be placed at such locations and arranged in such a manner that the employer can demonstrate will prevent each employee from being exposed to hazardous differences in electric potential.

Note: Appendix C to this Section contains guidelines for establishing the equipotential zone required by this paragraph. The Occupational Safety and Health Administration will deem grounding practices meeting these guidelines as complying with paragraph (n)(3) of this Section.

(n)(4) **Protective grounding equipment**

(n)(4)(i) Protective grounding equipment shall be capable of conducting the maximum fault current that could flow at the point of grounding for the time necessary to clear the fault.

(n)(4)(ii) Protective grounding equipment shall have an ampacity greater than or equal to that of No. 2 AWG copper.

(n)(4)(iii) Protective grounds shall have an impedance low enough so that they do not delay the operation of protective devices in case of accidental energizing of the lines or equipment.

Note: American Society for Testing and Materials Standard Specifications for Temporary Protective Grounds to Be Used on De-Energized Electric Power Lines and Equipment, ASTM F855-09, contains guidelines for protective grounding equipment. The Institute of Electrical Engineers Guide for Protective Grounding of Power Lines, IEEE Std 1048-2003, contains guidelines for selecting and installing protective grounding equipment.

(n)(5) **Testing** The employer shall ensure that, unless a previously installed ground is present, employees test lines and equipment and verify the absence of nominal voltage before employees install any ground on those lines or that equipment.

(n)(6) [OI] **Connecting and removing grounds**

(n)(6)(i) The employer shall ensure that, when an employee attaches a ground to a line or to equipment, the employee attaches the ground-end connection first and then attaches the other end by means of a live-line tool. For lines or equipment operating at 600 volts or less, the employer may permit the employee to use insulating equipment other than a live-line tool if the employer ensures that the line or equipment is not energized at the time the ground is connected or if the employer can demonstrate that each employee is protected from hazards that may develop if the line or equipment is energized.

(n)(6)(ii) The employer shall ensure that, when an employee removes a ground, the employee removes the grounding device from the line or equipment using a live-line tool before he or she removes the ground-end connection. For lines or equipment operating at 600 volts or less, the employer may permit the employee to use insulating equipment other than a live-line tool if the employer ensures that the line or equipment is not energized at the time the ground is disconnected or if the employer can demonstrate that each employee is protected from hazards that may develop if the line or equipment is energized.

(n)(7) [OI] **Additional precautions** The employer shall ensure that, when an employee performs work on a cable at a location remote from the cable terminal, the cable is not grounded at the cable terminal if there is a possibility of hazardous transfer of potential should a fault occur.

(n)(8) **Removal of grounds for test** The employer may permit employees to remove grounds temporarily during tests. During the test procedure, the employer shall ensure that each employee uses insulating equipment, shall isolate each employee from any hazards involved, and shall implement any additional measures necessary to protect each exposed employee in case the previously grounded lines and equipment become energized.

(o) Testing and test facilities

(o)(1) **Application** Paragraph (o) of this Section provides for safe work practices for high-voltage and high-power testing performed in laboratories, shops, and substations, and in the field and on electric transmission and distribution lines and equipment. It applies only to testing involving interim measurements using high voltage, high power, or combinations of high voltage and high power, and not to testing involving continuous measurements as in routine metering, relaying, and normal line work.

Note: OSHA considers routine inspection and maintenance measurements made by qualified employees to be routine line work not included in the scope of paragraph (o) of this Section, provided that the hazards related to the use of intrinsic high-voltage or high-power sources require only the normal precautions associated with routine work specified in the other paragraphs of this Section. Two typical examples of such excluded test work procedures are "phasing-out" testing and testing for a "no-voltage" condition.

(o)(2) **General requirements**

(o)(2)(i) The employer shall establish and enforce work practices for the protection of each worker from the hazards of high-voltage or high-power testing at all test areas, temporary and permanent. Such work practices shall include, as a minimum, test area safeguarding, grounding, the safe use of measuring and control circuits, and a means providing for periodic safety checks of field test areas.

(o)(2)(ii) The employer shall ensure that each employee, upon initial assignment to the test area, receives training in safe work practices, with retraining provided as required by paragraph (a)(2) of this Section.

(o)(3) **Safeguarding of test areas**

(o)(3)(i) The employer shall provide safeguarding within test areas to control access to test equipment or to apparatus under test that could become energized as part of the testing by either direct or inductive coupling and to prevent accidental employee contact with energized parts.

(o)(3)(ii) The employer shall guard permanent test areas with walls, fences, or other barriers designed to keep employees out of the test areas.

(o)(3)(iii) In field testing, or at a temporary test site not guarded by permanent fences and gates, the employer shall ensure the use of one of the following means to prevent employees without authorization from entering:

(o)(3)(iii)(A) Distinctively colored safety tape supported approximately waist high with safety signs attached to it,

(o)(3)(iii)(B) A barrier or barricade that limits access to the test area to a degree equivalent, physically and visually, to the barricade specified in paragraph (o)(3)(iii)(A) of this Section, or

(o)(3)(iii)(C) One or more test observers stationed so that they can monitor the entire area.

(o)(3)(iv) The employer shall ensure the removal of the safeguards required by paragraph (o)(3)(iii) of this Section when employees no longer need the protection afforded by the safeguards.

(o)(4) **Grounding practices**

(o)(4)(i) The employer shall establish and implement safe grounding practices for the test facility.

(o)(4)(i)(A) The employer shall maintain at ground potential all conductive parts accessible to the test operator while the equipment is operating at high voltage.

(o)(4)(i)(B) Wherever ungrounded terminals of test equipment or apparatus under test may be present, they shall be treated as energized until tests demonstrate that they are deenergized.

(o)(4)(ii) The employer shall ensure either that visible grounds are applied automatically, or that employees using properly insulated tools manually apply visible grounds, to the high-voltage circuits after they are deenergized and before any employee performs work on the circuit or on the item or apparatus under test. Common ground connections shall be solidly connected to the test equipment and the apparatus under test.

(o)(4)(iii) In high-power testing, the employer shall provide an isolated ground-return conductor system designed to prevent the intentional passage of current, with its attendant voltage rise, from occurring in the ground grid or in the earth. However, the employer need not provide an isolated ground-return conductor if the employer can demonstrate that both of the following conditions exist:

(o)(4)(iii)(A) The employer cannot provide an isolated ground-return conductor due to the distance of the test site from the electric energy source, and

(o)(4)(iii)(B) The employer protects employees from any hazardous step and touch potentials that may develop during the test.

Note: See Appendix C to this Section for information on measures that employers can take to protect employees from hazardous step and touch potentials.

(o)(4)(iv) For tests in which using the equipment grounding conductor in the equipment power cord to ground the test equipment would result in greater hazards to test personnel or prevent the taking of satisfactory measurements, the employer may use a ground clearly indicated in the test set-up if the employer can demonstrate that this ground affords protection for employees equivalent to the protection afforded by an equipment grounding conductor in the power supply cord.

(o)(4)(v) The employer shall ensure that, when any employee enters the test area after equipment is deenergized, a ground is placed on the high-voltage terminal and any other exposed terminals.

(o)(4)(v)(A) Before any employee applies a direct ground, the employer shall discharge high capacitance equipment through a resistor rated for the available energy.

(o)(4)(v)(B) A direct ground shall be applied to the exposed terminals after the stored energy drops to a level at which it is safe to do so.

(o)(4)(vi) If the employer uses a test trailer or test vehicle in field testing, its chassis shall be grounded. The employer shall protect each employee against hazardous touch potentials with respect to the vehicle, instrument panels, and other conductive parts accessible to employees with bonding, insulation, or isolation.

(o)(5) Control and measuring circuits

(o)(5)(i) The employer may not run control wiring, meter connections, test leads, or cables from a test area unless contained in a grounded metallic sheath and terminated in a grounded metallic enclosure or unless the employer takes other precautions that it can demonstrate will provide employees with equivalent safety.

(o)(5)(ii) The employer shall isolate meters and other instruments with accessible terminals or parts from test personnel to protect against hazards that could arise should such terminals and parts become energized during testing. If the employer provides this isolation by locating test equipment in metal compartments with viewing windows, the employer shall provide interlocks to interrupt the power supply when someone opens the compartment cover.

(o)(5)(iii) The employer shall protect temporary wiring and its connections against damage, accidental interruptions, and other hazards. To the maximum extent possible, the employer shall keep signal, control, ground, and power cables separate from each other.

(o)(5)(iv) If any employee will be present in the test area during testing, a test observer shall be present. The test observer shall be capable of implementing the immediate deenergizing of test circuits for safety purposes.

(o)(6) Safety check

(o)(6)(i) Safety practices governing employee work at temporary or field test areas shall provide, at the beginning of each series of tests, for a routine safety check of such test areas.

(o)(6)(ii) The test operator in charge shall conduct these routine safety checks before each series of tests and shall verify at least the following conditions:

(o)(6)(ii)(A) Barriers and safeguards are in workable condition and placed properly to isolate hazardous areas;

(o)(6)(ii)(B) System test status signals, if used, are in operable condition;

(o)(6)(ii)(C) Clearly marked test-power disconnects are readily available in an emergency;

(o)(6)(ii)(D) Ground connections are clearly identifiable;

(o)(6)(ii)(E) Personal protective equipment is provided and used as required by Subpart I of this Part and by this Section; and

(o)(6)(ii)(F) Proper separation between signal, ground, and power cables.

(p) Mechanical equipment

(p)(1) General requirements

(p)(1)(i) OI The critical safety components of mechanical elevating and rotating equipment shall receive a thorough visual inspection before use on each shift.

Note: Critical safety components of mechanical elevating and rotating equipment are components for which failure would result in free fall or free rotation of the boom.

(p)(1)(ii) No motor vehicle or earthmoving or compacting equipment having an obstructed view to the rear may be operated on off-highway jobsites where any employee is exposed to the hazards created by the moving vehicle, unless:

(p)(1)(ii)(A) OI The vehicle has a reverse signal alarm audible above the surrounding noise level, or

(p)(1)(ii)(B) OI The vehicle is backed up only when a designated employee signals that it is safe to do so.

(p)(1)(iii) OI Rubber-tired self-propelled scrapers, rubber-tired front-end loaders, rubber-tired dozers, wheel-type agricultural and industrial tractors, crawler-type tractors, crawler-type loaders, and motor graders, with or without attachments, shall have rollover protective structures that meet the requirements of Subpart W of Part 1926 of this chapter.

(p)(1)(iv) The operator of an electric line truck may not leave his or her position at the controls while a load is suspended, unless the employer can demonstrate that no employee (including the operator) is endangered.

(p)(2) Outriggers

(p)(2)(i) Mobile equipment, if provided with outriggers, shall be operated with the outriggers extended and firmly set, except as provided in paragraph (p)(2)(iii) of this Section.

(p)(2)(ii) Outriggers may not be extended or retracted outside of the clear view of the operator unless all employees are outside the range of possible equipment motion.

(p)(2)(iii) If the work area or the terrain precludes the use of outriggers, the equipment may be operated only within its maximum load ratings specified by the equipment manufacturer for the particular configuration of the equipment without outriggers.

(p)(3) Applied loads Mechanical equipment used to lift or move lines or other material shall be used within its maximum load rating and other design limitations for the conditions under which the mechanical equipment is being used.

(p)(4) OI Operations near energized lines or equipment

(p)(4)(i) Mechanical equipment shall be operated so that the minimum approach distances, established by the employer under paragraph (l)(3)(i) of this Section, are maintained from exposed energized lines and equipment. However, the insulated portion of an aerial lift operated by a qualified employee in the lift is exempt from this requirement if the applicable minimum approach distance is maintained between the uninsulated portions of the aerial lift and exposed objects having a different electrical potential.

(p)(4)(ii) A designated employee other than the equipment operator shall observe the approach distance to exposed lines and equipment and provide timely warnings before the minimum approach distance required by paragraph (p)(4)(i) of this Section is reached, unless the employer can demonstrate that the operator can accurately determine that the minimum approach distance is being maintained.

(p)(4)(iii) If, during operation of the mechanical equipment, that equipment could become energized, the operation also shall comply with at least one of paragraphs (p)(4)(iii)(A) through (p)(4)(iii)(C) of this Section.

(p)(4)(iii)(A) The energized lines or equipment exposed to contact shall be covered with insulating protective material that will withstand the type of contact that could be made during the operation.

(p)(4)(iii)(B) The mechanical equipment shall be insulated for the voltage involved. The mechanical equipment shall be positioned so that its uninsulated portions cannot approach the energized lines or equipment any closer than the minimum approach distances, established by the employer under paragraph (l)(3)(i) of this Section.

(p)(4)(iii)(C) Each employee shall be protected from hazards that could arise from mechanical equipment contact with energized lines or equipment. The measures used shall ensure that employees will not be exposed to hazardous differences in electric potential. Unless the employer can demonstrate that the methods in use protect each employee from the hazards that could arise if the mechanical equipment contacts the energized line or equipment, the measures used shall include all of the following techniques:

(p)(4)(iii)(C)(1) Using the best available ground to minimize the time the lines or electric equipment remain energized,

(p)(4)(iii)(C)(2) Bonding mechanical equipment together to minimize potential differences, (p)(4)(iii)(C)(3) Providing ground mats to extend areas of equipotential, and

(p)(4)(iii)(C)(4) Employing insulating protective equipment or barricades to guard against any remaining hazardous electrical potential differences.

Note: Appendix C to this Section contains information on hazardous step and touch potentials and on methods of protecting employees from hazards resulting from such potentials.

(q) **Overhead lines and live-line barehand work** This paragraph provides additional requirements for work performed on or near overhead lines and equipment and for live-line barehand work.

(q)(1) **General**

(q)(1)(i) Before allowing employees to subject elevated structures, such as poles or towers, to such stresses as climbing or the installation or removal of equipment may impose, the employer shall ascertain that the structures are capable of sustaining the additional or unbalanced stresses. If the pole or other structure cannot withstand the expected loads, the employer shall brace or otherwise support the pole or structure so as to prevent failure.

Note: Appendix D to this Section contains test methods that employers can use in ascertaining whether a wood pole is capable of sustaining the forces imposed by an employee climbing the pole. This paragraph also requires the employer to ascertain that the pole can sustain all other forces imposed by the work employees will perform.

(q)(1)(ii) When a pole is set, moved, or removed near an exposed energized overhead conductor, the pole may not contact the conductor.

(q)(1)(iii) When a pole is set, moved, or removed near an exposed energized overhead conductor, the employer shall ensure that each employee wears electrical protective equipment or uses insulated devices when handling the pole and that no employee contacts the pole with uninsulated parts of his or her body.

(q)(1)(iv) To protect employees from falling into holes used for placing poles, the employer shall physically guard the holes, or ensure that employees attend the holes, whenever anyone is working nearby.

(q)(2) **Installing and removing overhead lines** The following provisions apply to the installation and removal of overhead conductors or cable (overhead lines).

(q)(2)(i) When lines that employees are installing or removing can contact energized parts, the employer shall use the tension-stringing method, barriers, or other equivalent measures to minimize the possibility that conductors and cables the employees are installing or removing will contact energized power lines or equipment.

(q)(2)(ii) For conductors, cables, and pulling and tensioning equipment, the employer shall provide the protective measures required by paragraph (p)(4)(iii) of this Section when employees are installing or removing a conductor or cable close enough to energized conductors that any of the following failures could energize the pulling or tensioning equipment or the conductor or cable being installed or removed:

(q)(2)(ii)(A) Failure of the pulling or tensioning equipment,

(q)(2)(ii)(B) Failure of the conductor or cable being pulled, or

(q)(2)(ii)(C) Failure of the previously installed lines or equipment.

(q)(2)(iii) If the conductors that employees are installing or removing cross over energized conductors in excess of 600 volts and if the design of the circuit-interrupting devices protecting the lines so permits, the employer shall render inoperable the automatic-reclosing feature of these devices.

(q)(2)(iv) Before employees install lines parallel to existing energized lines, the employer shall make a determination of the approximate voltage to be induced in the new lines, or work shall proceed on the assumption that the induced voltage is hazardous. Unless the employer can demonstrate that the lines that employees are installing are not subject to the induction of a hazardous voltage or unless the lines are treated as energized, temporary protective grounds shall be placed at such locations and arranged in such a manner that the employer can demonstrate will prevent exposure of each employee to hazardous differences in electric potential.

Note: If the employer takes no precautions to protect employees from hazards associated with involuntary reactions from electric shock, a hazard exists if the induced voltage is sufficient to pass a current of 1 milliampere through a 500-ohm resistor. If the employer protects employees from injury due to involuntary reactions from electric shock, a hazard exists if the resultant current would be more than 6 milliamperes.

Note: Appendix C to this Section contains guidelines for protecting employees from hazardous differences in electric potential as required by this paragraph.

(q)(2)(v) Reel-handling equipment, including pulling and tensioning devices, shall be in safe operating condition and shall be leveled and aligned.

(q)(2)(vi) The employer shall ensure that employees do not exceed load ratings of stringing lines, pulling lines, conductor grips, load-bearing hardware and accessories, rigging, and hoists.

(q)(2)(vii) The employer shall repair or replace defective pulling lines and accessories.

(q)(2)(viii) The employer shall ensure that employees do not use conductor grips on wire rope unless the manufacturer specifically designed the grip for this application.

(q)(2)(ix) The employer shall ensure that employees maintain reliable communications, through two-way radios or other equivalent means, between the reel tender and the pulling-rig operator.

(q)(2)(x) Employees may operate the pulling rig only when it is safe to do so.

Note: Examples of unsafe conditions include: employees in locations prohibited by paragraph (q)(2)(xi) of this Section, conductor and pulling line hang-ups, and slipping of the conductor grip.

(q)(2)(xi) While a power-driven device is pulling the conductor or pulling line and the conductor or pulling line is in motion, the employer shall ensure that employees are not directly under overhead operations or on the crossarm, except as necessary for the employees to guide the stringing sock or board over or through the stringing sheave.

(q)(3) **Live-line barehand work** In addition to other applicable provisions contained in this Section, the following requirements apply to live-line barehand work:

(q)(3)(i) Before an employee uses or supervises the use of the live-line barehand technique on energized circuits, the employer shall ensure that the employee completes training conforming to paragraph (a)(2) of this Section in the technique and in the safety requirements of paragraph (q)(3) of this Section.

(q)(3)(ii) Before any employee uses the live-line barehand technique on energized high-voltage conductors or parts, the employer shall ascertain the following information in addition to information about other existing conditions required by paragraph (a)(4) of this Section:

(q)(3)(ii)(A) The nominal voltage rating of the circuit on which employees will perform the work,

(q)(3)(ii)(B) The clearances to ground of lines and other energized parts on which employees will perform the work, and

(q)(3)(ii)(C) The voltage limitations of equipment employees will use.

(q)(3)(iii) The employer shall ensure that the insulated equipment, insulated tools, and aerial devices and platforms used by employees are designed, tested, and made for live-line barehand work.

(q)(3)(iv) The employer shall ensure that employees keep tools and equipment clean and dry while they are in use.

(q)(3)(v) The employer shall render inoperable the automatic-reclosing feature of circuit-interrupting devices protecting the lines if the design of the devices permits.

(q)(3)(vi) The employer shall ensure that employees do not perform work when adverse weather conditions would make the work hazardous even after the employer implements the work practices required by this Section. Additionally, employees may not perform work when winds reduce the phase-to-phase or phase-to-ground clearances at the work location below the minimum approach distances specified in paragraph (q)(3)(xiv) of this Section, unless insulating guards cover the grounded objects and other lines and equipment.

Note: Thunderstorms in the vicinity, high winds, snow storms, and ice storms are examples of adverse weather conditions that make live-line barehand work too hazardous to perform safely even after the employer implements the work practices required by this Section.

(q)(3)(vii) The employer shall provide and ensure that employees use a conductive bucket liner or other conductive device for bonding the insulated aerial device to the energized line or equipment.

(q)(3)(vii)(A) The employee shall be connected to the bucket liner or other conductive device by the use of conductive shoes, leg clips, or other means.

(q)(3)(vii)(B) Where differences in potentials at the worksite pose a hazard to employees, the employer shall provide electrostatic shielding designed for the voltage being worked.

(q)(3)(viii) The employer shall ensure that, before the employee contacts the energized part, the employee bonds the conductive bucket liner or other conductive device to the energized conductor by means of a positive connection. This connection shall remain attached to the energized conductor until the employee completes the work on the energized circuit.

(q)(3)(ix) Aerial lifts used for live-line barehand work shall have dual controls (lower and upper) as follows:

(q)(3)(ix)(A) The upper controls shall be within easy reach of the employee in the bucket. On a two-bucket-type lift, access to the controls shall be within easy reach of both buckets.

(q)(3)(ix)(B) The lower set of controls shall be near the base of the boom and shall be designed so that they can override operation of the equipment at any time.

(q)(3)(x) Lower (ground-level) lift controls may not be operated with an employee in the lift except in case of emergency.

(q)(3)(xi) The employer shall ensure that, before employees elevate an aerial lift into the work position, the employees check all controls (ground level and bucket) to determine that they are in proper working condition.

(q)(3)(xii) The employer shall ensure that, before employees elevate the boom of an aerial lift, the employees ground the body of the truck or barricade the body of the truck and treat it as energized.

(q)(3)(xiii) The employer shall ensure that employees perform a boom-current test before starting work each day, each time during the day when they encounter a higher voltage, and when changed conditions indicate a need for an additional test.

(q)(3)(xiii)(A) This test shall consist of placing the bucket in contact with an energized source equal to the voltage to be encountered for a minimum of 3 minutes.

(q)(3)(xiii)(B) The leakage current may not exceed 1 microampere per kilovolt of nominal phase-to-ground voltage.

(q)(3)(xiii)(C) The employer shall immediately suspend work from the aerial lift when there is any indication of a malfunction in the equipment.

(q)(3)(xiv) The employer shall ensure that employees maintain the minimum approach distances, established by the employer under paragraph (l)(3)(i) of this Section, from all grounded objects and from lines and equipment at a potential different from that to which the live-line barehand equipment is bonded, unless insulating guards cover such grounded objects and other lines and equipment.

(q)(3)(xv) The employer shall ensure that, while an employee is approaching, leaving, or bonding to an energized circuit, the employee maintains the minimum approach distances, established by the employer under paragraph (l)(3)(i) of this Section, between the employee and any grounded parts, including the lower boom and portions of the truck and between the employee and conductive objects energized at different potentials.

(q)(3)(xvi) While the bucket is alongside an energized bushing or insulator string, the employer shall ensure that employees maintain the phase-to-ground minimum approach distances, established by the employer under paragraph (l)(3)(i) of this Section, between all parts of the bucket and the grounded end of the bushing or insulator string or any other grounded surface.

(q)(3)(xvii) The employer shall ensure that employees do not use handlines between the bucket and the boom or between the bucket and the ground. However, employees may use nonconductive-type handlines from conductor to ground if not supported from the bucket. The employer shall ensure that no one uses ropes used for live-line barehand work for other purposes.

(q)(3)(xviii) The employer shall ensure that employees do not pass uninsulated equipment or material between a pole or structure and an aerial lift while an employee working from the bucket is bonded to an energized part.

(q)(3)(xix) A nonconductive measuring device shall be readily accessible to employees performing live-line barehand work to assist them in maintaining the required minimum approach distance.

(q)(4) **Towers and structures** The following requirements apply to work performed on towers or other structures that support overhead lines.

(q)(4)(i) The employer shall ensure that no employee is under a tower or structure while work is in progress, except when the employer can demonstrate that such a working position is necessary to assist employees working above.

(q)(4)(ii) The employer shall ensure that employees use tag lines or other similar devices to maintain control of tower sections being raised or positioned, unless the employer can demonstrate that the use of such devices would create a greater hazard to employees.

(q)(4)(iii) The employer shall ensure that employees do not detach the loadline from a member or section until they safely secure the load.

(q)(4)(iv) The employer shall ensure that, except during emergency restoration procedures, employees discontinue work when adverse weather conditions would make the work hazardous in spite of the work practices required by this Section.

Note: Thunderstorms in the vicinity, high winds, snow storms, and ice storms are examples of adverse weather conditions that make this work too hazardous to perform even after the employer implements the work practices required by this Section.

(r) [OI] **Line-clearance tree trimming** This paragraph provides additional requirements for line-clearance tree trimming and for equipment used in this type of work.

(r)(1) **Electrical hazards** This paragraph does not apply to qualified employees.

(r)(1)(i) Before an employee climbs, enters, or works around any tree, a determination shall be made of the nominal voltage of electric power lines posing a hazard to employees. However, a determination of the maximum nominal voltage to which an employee will be exposed may be made instead, if all lines are considered as energized at this maximum voltage.

(r)(1)(ii) There shall be a second line-clearance tree trimmer within normal (that is, unassisted) voice communication under any of the following conditions:

(r)(1)(ii)(A) If a line-clearance tree trimmer is to approach more closely than 3.05 meters (10 feet) to any conductor or electric apparatus energized at more than 750 volts or

(r)(1)(ii)(B) If branches or limbs being removed are closer to lines energized at more than 750 volts than the distances listed in Table R-5, Table R-6, Table R-7, and Table R-8 or

(r)(1)(ii)(C) If roping is necessary to remove branches or limbs from such conductors or apparatus.

(r)(1)(iii) Line-clearance tree trimmers shall maintain the minimum approach distances from energized conductors given in Table R-5, Table R-6, Table R-7, and Table R-8.

(r)(1)(iv) [OI] Branches that are contacting exposed energized conductors or equipment or that are within the distances specified in Table R-5, Table R-6, Table R-7, and Table R-8 may be removed only through the use of insulating equipment.

Note: A tool constructed of a material that the employer can demonstrate has insulating qualities meeting paragraph (j)(1) of this Section is considered as insulated under paragraph (r)(1)(iv) of this Section if the tool is clean and dry.

(r)(1)(v) Ladders, platforms, and aerial devices may not be brought closer to an energized part than the distances listed in Table R-5, Table R-6, Table R-7, and Table R-8.

(r)(1)(vi) Line-clearance tree-trimming may not be performed when adverse weather conditions make the work hazardous in spite of the work practices required by this Section. Each employee performing line-clearance tree trimming work in the aftermath of a storm or under similar emergency conditions shall be trained in the special hazards related to this type of work.

Note: Thunderstorms in the immediate vicinity, high winds, snow storms, and ice storms are examples of adverse weather conditions that are presumed to make line-clearance tree trimming too hazardous to perform safely.

(r)(2) **Brush chippers**

(r)(2)(i) Brush chippers shall be equipped with a locking device in the ignition system.

(r)(2)(ii) Access panels for maintenance and adjustment of the chipper blades and associated drive train shall be in place and secure during operation of the equipment.

(r)(2)(iii) Brush chippers not equipped with a mechanical infeed system shall be equipped with an infeed hopper of length sufficient to prevent employees from contacting the blades or knives of the machine during operation.

(r)(2)(iv) Trailer chippers detached from trucks shall be chocked or otherwise secured.

(r)(2)(v) Each employee in the immediate area of an operating chipper feed table shall wear personal protective equipment as required by Subpart I of this Part.

(r)(3) **Sprayers and related equipment**

(r)(3)(i) Walking and working surfaces of sprayers and related equipment shall be covered with slip-resistant material. If slipping hazards cannot be eliminated, slip-resistant footwear or handrails and stair rails meeting the requirements of Subpart D of this Part may be used instead of slip-resistant material.

(r)(3)(ii) Equipment on which employees stand to spray while the vehicle is in motion shall be equipped with guardrails around the working area. The guardrail shall be constructed in accordance with Subpart D of this Part.

(r)(4) **Stump cutters**

(r)(4)(i) Stump cutters shall be equipped with enclosures or guards to protect employees.

(r)(4)(ii) Each employee in the immediate area of stump grinding operations (including the stump cutter operator) shall wear personal protective equipment as required by Subpart I of this Part.

(r)(5) **Gasoline-engine power saws** Gasoline-engine power saw operations shall meet the requirements of §1910.266(e) and the following:

(r)(5)(i) Each power saw weighing more than 6.8 kilograms (15 pounds, service weight) that is used in trees shall be supported by a separate line, except when work is performed from an aerial lift and except during topping or removing operations where no supporting limb will be available.

(r)(5)(ii) Each power saw shall be equipped with a control that will return the saw to idling speed when released.

(r)(5)(iii) Each power saw shall be equipped with a clutch and shall be so adjusted that the clutch will not engage the chain drive at idling speed.

(r)(5)(iv) A power saw shall be started on the ground or where it is otherwise firmly supported. Drop starting of saws over 6.8 kilograms (15 pounds), other than chain saws, is permitted outside of the bucket of an aerial lift only if the area below the lift is clear of personnel.

Note: Paragraph (e)(2)(vi) of §1910.266 prohibits drop starting of chain saws.

(r)(5)(v) A power saw engine may be started and operated only when all employees other than the operator are clear of the saw.

(r)(5)(vi) A power saw may not be running when the saw is being carried up into a tree by an employee.

(r)(5)(vii) Power saw engines shall be stopped for all cleaning, refueling, adjustments, and repairs to the saw or motor, except as the manufacturer's servicing procedures require otherwise.

(r)(6) Backpack power units for use in pruning and clearing

(r)(6)(i) While a backpack power unit is running, no one other than the operator may be within 3.05 meters (10 feet) of the cutting head of a brush saw.

(r)(6)(ii) A backpack power unit shall be equipped with a quick shutoff switch readily accessible to the operator.

(r)(6)(iii) Backpack power unit engines shall be stopped for all cleaning, refueling, adjustments, and repairs to the saw or motor, except as the manufacturer's servicing procedures require otherwise.

(r)(7) Rope

(r)(7)(i) Climbing ropes shall be used by employees working aloft in trees. These ropes shall have a minimum diameter of 12 millimeters (0.5 inch) with a minimum breaking strength of 10.2 kilonewtons (2,300 pounds). Synthetic rope shall have elasticity of not more than 7 percent.

(r)(7)(ii) Rope shall be inspected before each use and, if unsafe (for example, because of damage or defect), may not be used.

(r)(7)(iii) Rope shall be stored away from cutting edges and sharp tools. Rope contact with corrosive chemicals, gas, and oil shall be avoided.

(r)(7)(iv) When stored, rope shall be coiled and piled, or shall be suspended, so that air can circulate through the coils.

(r)(7)(v) Rope ends shall be secured to prevent their unraveling.

(r)(7)(vi) Climbing rope may not be spliced to effect repair.

(r)(7)(vii) A rope that is wet, that is contaminated to the extent that its insulating capacity is impaired, or that is otherwise not considered to be insulated for the voltage involved may not be used near exposed energized lines.

(r)(8) **Fall protection** Each employee shall be tied in with a climbing rope and safety saddle when the employee is working above the ground in a tree, unless he or she is ascending into the tree.

(s) Communication facilities

(s)(1) Microwave transmission

(s)(1)(i) The employer shall ensure that no employee looks into an open waveguide or antenna connected to an energized microwave source.

(s)(1)(ii) If the electromagnetic-radiation level within an accessible area associated with microwave communications systems exceeds the radiation-protection guide specified by §1910.97(a)(2), the employer shall post the area with warning signs containing the warning symbol described in §1910.97(a)(3). The lower half of the warning symbol shall include the following statements, or ones that the employer can demonstrate are equivalent: "Radiation in this area may exceed hazard limitations and special precautions are required. Obtain specific instruction before entering."

(s)(1)(iii) When an employee works in an area where the electromagnetic radiation could exceed the radiation-protection guide, the employer shall institute measures that ensure that the employee's exposure is not greater than that permitted by that guide. Such measures may include administrative and engineering controls and personal protective equipment.

(s)(2) **Power-line carrier** The employer shall ensure that employees perform power-line carrier work, including work on equipment used for coupling carrier current to power line conductors, in accordance with the requirements of this Section pertaining to work on energized lines.

(t) **Underground electrical installations** This paragraph provides additional requirements for work on underground electrical installations.

(t)(1) **Access** The employer shall ensure that employees use a ladder or other climbing device to enter and exit a manhole or subsurface vault exceeding 1.22 meters (4 feet) in depth. No employee may climb into or out of a manhole or vault by stepping on cables or hangers.

(t)(2) Lowering equipment into manholes

(t)(2)(i) Equipment used to lower materials and tools into manholes or vaults shall be capable of supporting the weight to be lowered and shall be checked for defects before use.

(t)(2)(ii) Before anyone lowers tools or material into the opening for a manhole or vault, each employee working in the manhole or vault shall be clear of the area directly under the opening.

(t)(3) Attendants for manholes and vaults

(t)(3)(i) While work is being performed in a manhole or vault containing energized electric equipment, an employee with first-aid training shall be available on the surface in the immediate vicinity of the manhole or vault entrance to render emergency assistance.

(t)(3)(ii) Occasionally, the employee on the surface may briefly enter a manhole or vault to provide nonemergency assistance.

Note: Paragraph (e)(7) of this Section may also require an attendant and does not permit this attendant to enter the manhole or vault.

Note: Paragraph (l)(1)(ii) of this Section requires employees entering manholes or vaults containing unguarded, uninsulated energized lines or parts of electric equipment operating at 50 volts or more to be qualified.

(t)(3)(iii) For the purpose of inspection, housekeeping, taking readings, or similar work, an employee working alone may enter, for brief periods of time, a manhole or vault where energized cables or equipment are in service if the employer can demonstrate that the employee will be protected from all electrical hazards.

(t)(3)(iv) The employer shall ensure that employees maintain reliable communications, through two-way radios or other equivalent means, among all employees involved in the job.

(t)(4) **Duct rods** The employer shall ensure that, if employees use duct rods, the employees install the duct rods in the direction presenting the least hazard to employees. The employer shall station an employee at the far end of the duct line being rodded to ensure that the employees maintain the required minimum approach distances.

(t)(5) **Multiple cables** When multiple cables are present in a work area, the employer shall identify the cable to be worked by electrical means, unless its identity is obvious by reason of distinctive appearance or location or by other readily apparent means of identification. The employer shall protect cables other than the one being worked from damage.

(t)(6) **Moving cables** Except when paragraph (t)(7)(ii) of this Section permits employees to perform work that could cause a fault in an energized cable in a manhole or vault, the employer shall ensure that employees inspect energized cables to be moved for abnormalities.

(t)(7) Protection against faults

(t)(7)(i) Where a cable in a manhole or vault has one or more abnormalities that could lead to a fault or be an indication of an impending fault, the employer shall deenergize the cable with the abnormality before any employee may work in the manhole or vault, except when service-load conditions and a lack of feasible alternatives require that the cable remain energized. In that case, employees may enter the manhole or vault provided the employer protects them from the possible effects of a failure using shields or other devices that are capable of containing the adverse effects of a fault. The employer shall treat the following abnormalities as indications of impending faults unless the employer can demonstrate that the conditions could not lead to a fault: Oil or compound leaking from cable or joints, broken cable sheaths or joint sleeves, hot localized surface temperatures of cables or joints, or joints swollen beyond normal tolerance.

(t)(7)(ii) If the work employees will perform in a manhole or vault could cause a fault in a cable, the employer shall deenergize that cable before any employee works in the manhole or vault, except when service-load conditions and a lack of feasible alternatives require that the cable remain energized. In that case, employees may enter the manhole or vault provided the employer protects them from the possible effects of a failure using shields or other devices that are capable of containing the adverse effects of a fault.

(t)(8) **Sheath continuity** When employees perform work on buried cable or on cable in a manhole or vault, the employer shall maintain metallic-sheath continuity, or the cable sheath shall be treated as energized.

(u) **Substations** This paragraph provides additional requirements for substations and for work performed in them.

(u)(1) **Access and working space** The employer shall provide and maintain sufficient access and working space about electric equipment to permit ready and safe operation and maintenance of such equipment by employees.

Note: American National Standard National Electrical Safety Code, ANSI/IEEE C2-2012 contains guidelines for the dimensions of access and working space about electric equipment in substations. Installations meeting the ANSI provisions comply with paragraph (u)(1) of this Section. The Occupational Safety and Health Administration will determine whether an installation that does not conform to this ANSI standard complies with paragraph (u)(1) of this Section based on the following criteria:

(1) Whether the installation conforms to the edition of ANSI C2 that was in effect when the installation was made,

(2) Whether the configuration of the installation enables employees to maintain the minimum approach distances, established by the employer under paragraph (l)(3)(i) of this Section, while the employees are working on exposed, energized parts, and

(3) Whether the precautions taken when employees perform work on the installation provide protection equivalent to the protection provided by access and working space meeting ANSI/IEEE C2-2012.

(u)(2) **Draw-out-type circuit breakers** The employer shall ensure that, when employees remove or insert draw-out-type circuit breakers, the breaker is in the open position. The employer shall also render the control circuit inoperable if the design of the equipment permits.

(u)(3) **Substation fences** Conductive fences around substations shall be grounded. When a substation fence is expanded or a section is removed, fence sections shall be isolated, grounded, or bonded as necessary to protect employees from hazardous differences in electric potential.

Note: IEEE Std 80-2000, IEEE Guide for Safety in AC Substation Grounding, contains guidelines for protection against hazardous differences in electric potential.

(u)(4) OI **Guarding of rooms and other spaces containing electric supply equipment**

(u)(4)(i) Rooms and other spaces in which electric supply lines or equipment are installed shall meet the requirements of paragraphs (u)(4)(ii) through (u)(4)(v) of this Section under the following conditions:

(u)(4)(i)(A) If exposed live parts operating at 50 to 150 volts to ground are within 2.4 meters (8 feet) of the ground or other working surface inside the room or other space,

(u)(4)(i)(B) If live parts operating at 151 to 600 volts to ground and located within 2.4 meters (8 feet) of the ground or other working surface inside the room or other space are guarded only by location, as permitted under paragraph (u)(5)(i) of this Section, or

(u)(4)(i)(C) If live parts operating at more than 600 volts to ground are within the room or other space, unless:

(u)(4)(i)(C)(1) The live parts are enclosed within grounded, metal-enclosed equipment whose only openings are designed so that foreign objects inserted in these openings will be deflected from energized parts, or

(u)(4)(i)(C)(2) The live parts are installed at a height, above ground and any other working surface, that provides protection at the voltage on the live parts corresponding to the protection provided by a 2.4-meter (8-foot) height at 50 volts.

(u)(4)(ii) Fences, screens, partitions, or walls shall enclose the rooms and other spaces so as to minimize the possibility that unqualified persons will enter.

(u)(4)(iii) Unqualified persons may not enter the rooms or other spaces while the electric supply lines or equipment are energized.

(u)(4)(iv) The employer shall display signs at entrances to the rooms and other spaces warning unqualified persons to keep out.

(u)(4)(v) The employer shall keep each entrance to a room or other space locked, unless the entrance is under the observation of a person who is attending the room or other space for the purpose of preventing unqualified employees from entering.

(u)(5) OI **Guarding of energized parts**

(u)(5)(i) The employer shall provide guards around all live parts operating at more than 150 volts to ground without an insulating covering unless the location of the live parts gives sufficient clearance (horizontal, vertical, or both) to minimize the possibility of accidental employee contact.

Note: American National Standard National Electrical Safety Code, ANSI/IEEE C2-2002 contains guidelines for the dimensions of clearance distances about electric equipment in substations. Installations meeting the ANSI provisions comply with paragraph (u)(5)(i) of this Section. The Occupational Safety and Health Administration will determine whether an installation that does not conform to this ANSI standard complies with paragraph (u)(5)(i) of this Section based on the following criteria:
(1) Whether the installation conforms to the edition of ANSI C2 that was in effect when the installation was made,
(2) Whether each employee is isolated from energized parts at the point of closest approach; and
(3) Whether the precautions taken when employees perform work on the installation provide protection equivalent to the protection provided by horizontal and vertical clearances meeting ANSI/IEEE C2-2002.

(u)(5)(ii) Except for fuse replacement and other necessary access by qualified persons, the employer shall maintain guarding of energized parts within a compartment during operation and maintenance functions to prevent accidental contact with energized parts and to prevent dropped tools or other equipment from contacting energized parts.

(u)(5)(iii) Before guards are removed from energized equipment, the employer shall install barriers around the work area to prevent employees who are not working on the equipment, but who are in the area, from contacting the exposed live parts.

(u)(6) **Substation entry**

(u)(6)(i) Upon entering an attended substation, each employee, other than employees regularly working in the station, shall report his or her presence to the employee in charge of substation activities to receive information on special system conditions affecting employee safety.

(u)(6)(ii) The job briefing required by paragraph (c) of this Section shall cover information on special system conditions affecting employee safety, including the location of energized equipment in or adjacent to the work area and the limits of any deenergized work area.

(v) OI **Power generation** This paragraph provides additional requirements and related work practices for power generating plants.

(v)(1) **Interlocks and other safety devices**

(v)(1)(i) Interlocks and other safety devices shall be maintained in a safe, operable condition.

(v)(1)(ii) No interlock or other safety device may be modified to defeat its function, except for test, repair, or adjustment of the device.

(v)(2) **Changing brushes** Before exciter or generator brushes are changed while the generator is in service, the exciter or generator field shall be checked to determine whether a ground condition exists. The brushes may not be changed while the generator is energized if a ground condition exists.

(v)(3) **Access and working space** The employer shall provide and maintain sufficient access and working space about electric equipment to permit ready and safe operation and maintenance of such equipment by employees.

Note: American National Standard National Electrical Safety Code, ANSI/IEEE C2-2012 contains guidelines for the dimensions of access and working space about electric equipment in substations. Installations meeting the ANSI provisions comply with paragraph (v)(3) of this Section. The Occupational Safety and Health Administration will determine whether an installation that does not conform to this ANSI standard complies with paragraph (v)(3) of this Section based on the following criteria:
(1) Whether the installation conforms to the edition of ANSI C2 that was in effect when the installation was made;
(2) Whether the configuration of the installation enables employees to maintain the minimum approach distances, established by the employer under paragraph (l)(3)(i) of this Section, while the employees are working on exposed, energized parts, and;
(3) Whether the precautions taken when employees perform work on the installation provide protection equivalent to the protection provided by access and working space meeting ANSI/IEEE C2-2012.

(v)(4) OI **Guarding of rooms and other spaces containing electric supply equipment**

(v)(4)(i) Rooms and other spaces in which electric supply lines or equipment are installed shall meet the requirements of paragraphs (v)(4)(ii) through (v)(4)(v) of this Section under the following conditions:

(v)(4)(i)(A) If exposed live parts operating at 50 to 150 volts to ground are within 2.4 meters (8 feet) of the ground or other working surface inside the room or other space,

(v)(4)(i)(B) If live parts operating at 151 to 600 volts to ground and located within 2.4 meters (8 feet) of the ground or other working surface inside the room or other space are guarded only by location, as permitted under paragraph (v)(5)(i) of this Section, or

(v)(4)(i)(C) If live parts operating at more than 600 volts to ground are within the room or other space, unless:

(v)(4)(i)(C)(1) The live parts are enclosed within grounded, metal-enclosed equipment whose only openings are designed so that foreign objects inserted in these openings will be deflected from energized parts, or

(v)(4)(i)(C)(2) The live parts are installed at a height, above ground and any other working surface, that provides protection at the voltage on the live parts corresponding to the protection provided by a 2.4-meter (8-foot) height at 50 volts.

(v)(4)(ii) Fences, screens, partitions, or walls shall enclose the rooms and other spaces so as to minimize the possibility that unqualified persons will enter.

(v)(4)(iii) Unqualified persons may not enter the rooms or other spaces while the electric supply lines or equipment are energized.

(v)(4)(iv) The employer shall display signs at entrances to the rooms and other spaces warning unqualified persons to keep out.

(v)(4)(v) The employer shall keep each entrance to a room or other space locked, unless the entrance is under the observation of a person who is attending the room or other space for the purpose of preventing unqualified employees from entering.

(v)(5) OI **Guarding of energized parts**

(v)(5)(i) The employer shall provide guards around all live parts operating at more than 150 volts to ground without an insulating covering unless the location of the live parts gives sufficient clearance (horizontal, vertical, or both) to minimize the possibility of accidental employee contact.

Note: American National Standard National Electrical Safety Code, ANSI/IEEE C2-2002 contains guidelines for the dimensions of clearance distances about electric equipment in substations. Installations meeting the ANSI provisions comply with paragraph (v)(5)(i) of this Section. The Occupational Safety and Health Administration will determine whether an installation that does not conform to this ANSI standard complies with paragraph (v)(5)(i) of this Section based on the following criteria:

(1) Whether the installation conforms to the edition of ANSI C2 that was in effect when the installation was made;

(2) Whether each employee is isolated from energized parts at the point of closest approach; and

(3) Whether the precautions taken when employees perform work on the installation provide protection equivalent to the protection provided by horizontal and vertical clearances meeting ANSI/IEEE C2-2002.

(v)(5)(ii) Except for fuse replacement and other necessary access by qualified persons, the employer shall maintain guarding of energized parts within a compartment during operation and maintenance functions to prevent accidental contact with energized parts and to prevent dropped tools or other equipment from contacting energized parts.

(v)(5)(iii) Before guards are removed from energized equipment, the employer shall install barriers around the work area to prevent employees who are not working on the equipment, but who are in the area, from contacting the exposed live parts.

(v)(6) Water or steam spaces The following requirements apply to work in water and steam spaces associated with boilers:

(v)(6)(i) A designated employee shall inspect conditions before work is permitted and after its completion. Eye protection, or full face protection if necessary, shall be worn at all times when condenser, heater, or boiler tubes are being cleaned.

(v)(6)(ii) Where it is necessary for employees to work near tube ends during cleaning, shielding shall be installed at the tube ends.

(v)(7) Chemical cleaning of boilers and pressure vessels The following requirements apply to chemical cleaning of boilers and pressure vessels:

(v)(7)(i) Areas where chemical cleaning is in progress shall be cordoned off to restrict access during cleaning. If flammable liquids, gases, or vapors or combustible materials will be used or might be produced during the cleaning process, the following requirements also apply:

(v)(7)(i)(A) The area shall be posted with signs restricting entry and warning of the hazards of fire and explosion; and

(v)(7)(i)(B) Smoking, welding, and other possible ignition sources are prohibited in these restricted areas.

(v)(7)(ii) The number of personnel in the restricted area shall be limited to those necessary to accomplish the task safely.

(v)(7)(iii) There shall be ready access to water or showers for emergency use.

Note: See §1910.141 for requirements that apply to the water supply and to washing facilities.

(v)(7)(iv) Employees in restricted areas shall wear protective equipment meeting the requirements of Subpart I of this Part and including, but not limited to, protective clothing, boots, goggles, and gloves.

(v)(8) Chlorine systems

(v)(8)(i) Chlorine system enclosures shall be posted with signs restricting entry and warning of the hazard to health and the hazards of fire and explosion.

Note: See Subpart Z of this Part for requirements necessary to protect the health of employees from the effects of chlorine.

(v)(8)(ii) Only designated employees may enter the restricted area. Additionally, the number of personnel shall be limited to those necessary to accomplish the task safely.

(v)(8)(iii) Emergency repair kits shall be available near the shelter or enclosure to allow for the prompt repair of leaks in chlorine lines, equipment, or containers.

(v)(8)(iv) Before repair procedures are started, chlorine tanks, pipes, and equipment shall be purged with dry air and isolated from other sources of chlorine.

(v)(8)(v) The employer shall ensure that chlorine is not mixed with materials that would react with the chlorine in a dangerously exothermic or other hazardous manner.

(v)(9) Boilers

(v)(9)(i) Before internal furnace or ash hopper repair work is started, overhead areas shall be inspected for possible falling objects. If the hazard of falling objects exists, overhead protection such as planking or nets shall be provided.

(v)(9)(ii) When opening an operating boiler door, employees shall stand clear of the opening of the door to avoid the heat blast and gases which may escape from the boiler.

(v)(10) Turbine generators

(v)(10)(i) Smoking and other ignition sources are prohibited near hydrogen or hydrogen sealing systems, and signs warning of the danger of explosion and fire shall be posted.

(v)(10)(ii) Excessive hydrogen makeup or abnormal loss of pressure shall be considered as an emergency and shall be corrected immediately.

(v)(10)(iii) A sufficient quantity of inert gas shall be available to purge the hydrogen from the largest generator.

(v)(11) Coal and ash handling

(v)(11)(i) Only designated persons may operate railroad equipment.

(v)(11)(ii) Before a locomotive or locomotive crane is moved, a warning shall be given to employees in the area.

(v)(11)(iii) Employees engaged in switching or dumping cars may not use their feet to line up drawheads.

(v)(11)(iv) Drawheads and knuckles may not be shifted while locomotives or cars are in motion.

(v)(11)(v) When a railroad car is stopped for unloading, the car shall be secured from displacement that could endanger employees.

(v)(11)(vi) An emergency means of stopping dump operations shall be provided at railcar dumps.

(v)(11)(vii) The employer shall ensure that employees who work in coal- or ash-handling conveyor areas are trained and knowledgeable in conveyor operation and in the requirements of paragraphs (v)(11)(viii) through (v)(11)(xii) of this Section.

(v)(11)(viii) Employees may not ride a coal- or ash-handling conveyor belt at any time. Employees may not cross over the conveyor belt, except at walkways, unless the conveyor's energy source has been deenergized and has been locked out or tagged in accordance with paragraph (d) of this Section.

(v)(11)(ix) A conveyor that could cause injury when started may not be started until personnel in the area are alerted by a signal or by a designated person that the conveyor is about to start.

(v)(11)(x) If a conveyor that could cause injury when started is automatically controlled or is controlled from a remote location, an audible device shall be provided that sounds an alarm that will be recognized by each employee as a warning that the conveyor will start and that can be clearly heard at all points along the conveyor where personnel may be present. The warning device shall be actuated by the device starting the conveyor and shall continue for a period of time before the conveyor starts that is long enough to allow employees to move clear of the conveyor system. A visual warning may be used in place of the audible device if the employer can demonstrate that it will provide an equally effective warning in the particular circumstances involved. However if the employer can demonstrate that the system's function would be seriously hindered by the required time delay, warning signs may be provided in place of the audible warning device. If the system was installed before January 31, 1995, warning signs may be provided in place of the audible warning device until such time as the conveyor or its control system is rebuilt or rewired. These warning signs shall be clear, concise, and legible and shall indicate that conveyors and allied equipment may be started at any time, that danger exists, and that personnel must keep clear. These warning signs shall be provided along the conveyor at areas not guarded by position or location.

(v)(11)(xi) Remotely and automatically controlled conveyors, and conveyors that have operating stations which are not manned or which are beyond voice and visual contact from drive areas, loading areas, transfer points, and other locations on the conveyor path not guarded by location, position, or guards shall be furnished with emergency stop buttons, pull cords, limit switches, or similar emergency stop devices. However, if the employer can demonstrate that the design, function, and operation of the conveyor do not expose an employee to hazards, an emergency stop device is not required.

(v)(11)(xi)(A) Emergency stop devices shall be easily identifiable in the immediate vicinity of such locations.

(v)(11)(xi)(B) An emergency stop device shall act directly on the control of the conveyor involved and may not depend on the stopping of any other equipment.

(v)(11)(xi)(C) Emergency stop devices shall be installed so that they cannot be overridden from other locations.

(v)(11)(xii) Where coal-handling operations may produce a combustible atmosphere from fuel sources or from flammable gases or dust, sources of ignition shall be eliminated or safely controlled to prevent ignition of the combustible atmosphere.

Note: Locations that are hazardous because of the presence of combustible dust are classified as Class II hazardous locations. See §1910.307.

(v)(11)(xiii) An employee may not work on or beneath overhanging coal in coal bunkers, coal silos, or coal storage areas, unless the employee is protected from all hazards posed by shifting coal.

(v)(11)(xiv) An employee entering a bunker or silo to dislodge the contents shall wear a body harness with lifeline attached. The lifeline shall be secured to a fixed support outside the bunker and shall be attended at all times by an employee located outside the bunker or facility.

(v)(12) Hydroplants and equipment Employees working on or close to water gates, valves, intakes, forebays, flumes, or other locations where increased or decreased water flow or levels may pose a significant hazard shall be warned and shall vacate such dangerous areas before water flow changes are made.

(w) **Special conditions**

(w)(1) **Capacitors** The following additional requirements apply to work on capacitors and on lines connected to capacitors.

Note: See paragraphs (m) and (n) of this Section for requirements pertaining to the deenergizing and grounding of capacitor installations.

(w)(1)(i) Before employees work on capacitors, the employer shall disconnect the capacitors from energized sources and short circuit the capacitors. The employer shall ensure that the employee short circuiting the capacitors waits at least 5 minutes from the time of disconnection before applying the short circuit.

(w)(1)(ii) Before employees handle the units, the employer shall short circuit each unit in series-parallel capacitor banks between all terminals and the capacitor case or its rack. If the cases of capacitors are on ungrounded substation racks, the employer shall bond the racks to ground.

(w)(1)(iii) The employer shall short circuit any line connected to capacitors before the line is treated as deenergized.

(w)(2) **Current transformer secondaries** The employer shall ensure that employees do not open the secondary of a current transformer while the transformer is energized. If the employer cannot deenergize the primary of the current transformer before employees perform work on an instrument, a relay, or other section of a current transformer secondary circuit, the employer shall bridge the circuit so that the current transformer secondary does not experience an open-circuit condition.

(w)(3) **Series streetlighting**

(w)(3)(i) If the open-circuit voltage exceeds 600 volts, the employer shall ensure that employees work on series streetlighting circuits in accordance with paragraph (q) or (t) of this Section, as appropriate.

(w)(3)(ii) Before any employee opens a series loop, the employer shall deenergize the streetlighting transformer and isolate it from the source of supply or shall bridge the loop to avoid an open-circuit condition.

(w)(4) **Illumination** The employer shall provide sufficient illumination to enable the employee to perform the work safely.

(w)(5) **Protection against drowning**

(w)(5)(i) Whenever an employee may be pulled or pushed, or might fall, into water where the danger of drowning exists, the employer shall provide the employee with, and shall ensure that the employee uses, a U.S. Coast Guard-approved personal flotation device.

(w)(5)(ii) The employer shall maintain each personal flotation device in safe condition and shall inspect each personal flotation device frequently enough to ensure that it does not have rot, mildew, water saturation, or any other condition that could render the device unsuitable for use.

(w)(5)(iii) An employee may cross streams or other bodies of water only if a safe means of passage, such as a bridge, is available.

(w)(6) **Employee protection in public work areas**

(w)(6)(i) Traffic-control signs and traffic-control devices used for the protection of employees shall meet §1926.200(g)(2) of this chapter.

(w)(6)(ii) Before employees begin work in the vicinity of vehicular or pedestrian traffic that may endanger them, the employer shall place warning signs or flags and other traffic-control devices in conspicuous locations to alert and channel approaching traffic.

(w)(6)(iii) The employer shall use barricades where additional employee protection is necessary.

(w)(6)(iv) The employer shall protect excavated areas with barricades.

(w)(6)(v) The employer shall display warning lights prominently at night.

(w)(7) **Backfeed** When there is a possibility of voltage backfeed from sources of cogeneration or from the secondary system (for example, backfeed from more than one energized phase feeding a common load), the requirements of paragraph (l) of this Section apply if employees will work the lines or equipment as energized, and the requirements of paragraphs (m) and (n) of this Section apply if employees will work the lines or equipment as deenergized.

(w)(8) **Lasers** The employer shall install, adjust, and operate laser equipment in accordance with §1926.54 of this chapter.

(w)(9) **Hydraulic fluids** Hydraulic fluids used for the insulated sections of equipment shall provide insulation for the voltage involved.

(x) [OI] **Definitions**

Affected employee An employee whose job requires him or her to operate or use a machine or equipment on which servicing or maintenance is being performed under lockout or tagout, or whose job requires him or her to work in an area in which such servicing or maintenance is being performed.

Attendant An employee assigned to remain immediately outside the entrance to an enclosed or other space to render assistance as needed to employees inside the space.

Authorized employee An employee who locks out or tags out machines or equipment in order to perform servicing or maintenance on that machine or equipment. An affected employee becomes an authorized employee when that employee's duties include performing servicing or maintenance covered under this Section.

Automatic circuit recloser A self-controlled device for automatically interrupting and reclosing an alternating-current circuit, with a predetermined sequence of opening and reclosing followed by resetting, hold closed, or lockout.

Barricade A physical obstruction such as tapes, cones, or A-frame type wood or metal structures that provides a warning about, and limits access to, a hazardous area.

Barrier A physical obstruction that prevents contact with energized lines or equipment or prevents unauthorized access to a work area.

Bond The electrical interconnection of conductive parts designed to maintain a common electric potential.

Bus A conductor or a group of conductors that serve as a common connection for two or more circuits.

Bushing An insulating structure that includes a through conductor or that provides a passageway for such a conductor, and that, when mounted on a barrier, insulates the conductor from the barrier for the purpose of conducting current from one side of the barrier to the other.

Cable A conductor with insulation, or a stranded conductor with or without insulation and other coverings (single-conductor cable), or a combination of conductors insulated from one another (multiple-conductor cable).

Cable sheath A conductive protective covering applied to cables.

Note: A cable sheath may consist of multiple layers one or more of which is conductive.

Circuit A conductor or system of conductors through which an electric current is intended to flow.

Clearance (between objects) The clear distance between two objects measured surface to surface.

Clearance (for work) Authorization to perform specified work or permission to enter a restricted area.

Communication lines (See Lines, Communication lines)

Conductor A material, usually in the form of a wire, cable, or bus bar, used for carrying an electric current.

Contract employer An employer, other than a host employer, that performs work covered by this Section under contract.

Covered conductor A conductor covered with a dielectric having no rated insulating strength or having a rated insulating strength less than the voltage of the circuit in which the conductor is used.

Current-carrying part A conducting part intended to be connected in an electric circuit to a source of voltage. Non-current-carrying parts are those not intended to be so connected.

Deenergized Free from any electrical connection to a source of potential difference and from electric charge; not having a potential that is different from the potential of the earth.

Note: The term applies only to current-carrying parts, which are sometimes energized (alive).

Designated employee (designated person) An employee (or person) who is assigned by the employer to perform specific duties under the terms of this Section and who has sufficient knowledge of the construction and operation of the equipment, and the hazards involved, to perform his or her duties safely.

Electric line truck A truck used to transport personnel, tools, and material for electric supply line work.

Electric supply equipment Equipment that produces, modifies, regulates, controls, or safeguards a supply of electric energy.

Electric supply lines (See Lines, Electric supply)

Electric utility An organization responsible for the installation, operation, or maintenance of an electric supply system.

Enclosed space A working space, such as a manhole, vault, tunnel, or shaft, that has a limited means of egress or entry, that is designed for periodic employee entry under normal operating conditions, and that, under normal conditions, does not contain a hazardous atmosphere, but may contain a hazardous atmosphere under abnormal conditions.

Note: The Occupational Safety and Health Administration does not consider spaces that are enclosed but not designed for employee entry under normal operating conditions to be enclosed spaces for the purposes of this Section. Similarly, the Occupational Safety and Health Administration does not consider spaces that are enclosed and that are expected to contain a hazardous atmosphere to be enclosed spaces for the purposes of this Section. Such spaces meet the definition of permit spaces in §1910.146, and entry into them must conform to that standard.

Energized (alive, live) Electrically connected to a source of potential difference, or electrically charged so as to have a potential significantly different from that of earth in the vicinity.

Energy isolating device A physical device that prevents the transmission or release of energy, including, but not limited to, the following: a manually operated electric circuit breaker, a disconnect switch, a manually operated switch, a slide gate, a slip blind, a line valve, blocks, and any similar device with a visible indication of the position of the device. (Push buttons, selector switches, and other control-circuit-type devices are not energy isolating devices.)

Energy source Any electrical, mechanical, hydraulic, pneumatic, chemical, nuclear, thermal, or other energy source that could cause injury to employees.

Entry (as used in paragraph (e) of this Section) The action by which a person passes through an opening into an enclosed space. Entry includes ensuing work activities in that space and is considered to have occurred as soon as any part of the entrant's body breaks the plane of an opening into the space.

Equipment (electric) A general term including material, fittings, devices, appliances, fixtures, apparatus, and the like used as part of or in connection with an electrical installation.

Exposed, Exposed to contact (as applied to energized parts) Not isolated or guarded.

Fall restraint system A fall protection system that prevents the user from falling any distance.

First-aid training Training in the initial care, including cardiopulmonary resuscitation (which includes chest compressions, rescue breathing, and, as appropriate, other heart and lung resuscitation techniques), performed by a person who is not a medical practitioner, of a sick or injured person until definitive medical treatment can be administered.

Ground A conducting connection, whether planned or unplanned, between an electric circuit or equipment and the earth, or to some conducting body that serves in place of the earth.

Grounded Connected to earth or to some conducting body that serves in place of the earth.

Guarded Covered, fenced, enclosed, or otherwise protected, by means of suitable covers or casings, barrier rails or screens, mats, or platforms, designed to minimize the possibility, under normal conditions, of dangerous approach or inadvertent contact by persons or objects.

Note: Wires that are insulated, but not otherwise protected, are not guarded.

Hazardous atmosphere An atmosphere that may expose employees to the risk of death, incapacitation, impairment of ability to self-rescue (that is, escape unaided from an enclosed space), injury, or acute illness from one or more of the following causes:

(1) Flammable gas, vapor, or mist in excess of 10 percent of its lower flammable limit (LFL);

(2) Airborne combustible dust at a concentration that meets or exceeds its LFL;

Note: This concentration may be approximated as a condition in which the dust obscures vision at a distance of 1.52 meters (5 feet) or less.

(3) Atmospheric oxygen concentration below 19.5 percent or above 23.5 percent;

(4) Atmospheric concentration of any substance for which a dose or a permissible exposure limit is published in Subpart G, Occupational Health and Environmental Control, or in Subpart Z, Toxic and Hazardous Substances, of this part and which could result in employee exposure in excess of its dose or permissible exposure limit;

Note: An atmospheric concentration of any substance that is not capable of causing death, incapacitation, impairment of ability to self-rescue, injury, or acute illness due to its health effects is not covered by this provision.

(5) Any other atmospheric condition that is immediately dangerous to life or health.

Note: For air contaminants for which the Occupational Safety and Health Administration has not determined a dose or permissible exposure limit, other sources of information, such as Material Safety Data Sheets that comply with the Hazard Communication Standard, §1910.1200, published information, and internal documents can provide guidance in establishing acceptable atmospheric conditions.

High-power tests Tests in which the employer uses fault currents, load currents, magnetizing currents, and line-dropping currents to test equipment, either at the equipment's rated voltage or at lower voltages.

High-voltage tests Tests in which the employer uses voltages of approximately 1,000 volts as a practical minimum and in which the voltage source has sufficient energy to cause injury.

High wind A wind of such velocity that one or more of the following hazards would be present:

(1) The wind could blow an employee from an elevated location,

(2) The wind could cause an employee or equipment handling material to lose control of the material, or

(3) The wind would expose an employee to other hazards not controlled by the standard involved.

Note: The Occupational Safety and Health Administration normally considers winds exceeding 64.4 kilometers per hour (40 miles per hour), or 48.3 kilometers per hour (30 miles per hour) if the work involves material handling, as meeting this criteria, unless the employer takes precautions to protect employees from the hazardous effects of the wind.

Host employer An employer that operates, or that controls the operating procedures for, an electric power generation, transmission, or distribution installation on which a contract employer is performing work covered by this Section.

Note: The Occupational Safety and Health Administration will treat the electric utility or the owner of the installation as the host employer if it operates or controls operating procedures for the installation. If the electric utility or installation owner neither operates nor controls operating procedures for the installation, the Occupational Safety and Health Administration will treat the employer that the utility or owner has contracted with to operate or control the operating procedures for the installation as the host employer. In no case will there be more than one host employer.

Immediately dangerous to life or health (IDLH) Any condition that poses an immediate or delayed threat to life or that would cause irreversible adverse health effects or that would interfere with an individual's ability to escape unaided from a permit space.

Note: Some materials—hydrogen fluoride gas and cadmium vapor, for example—may produce immediate transient effects that, even if severe, may pass without medical attention, but are followed by sudden, possibly fatal collapse 12-72 hours after exposure. The victim "feels normal" from recovery from transient effects until collapse. Such materials in hazardous quantities are considered to be "immediately" dangerous to life or health.

Insulated Separated from other conducting surfaces by a dielectric (including air space) offering a high resistance to the passage of current.

Note: When any object is said to be insulated, it is understood to be insulated for the conditions to which it normally is subjected. Otherwise, it is, for the purpose of this Section, uninsulated.

Insulation (cable) Material relied upon to insulate the conductor from other conductors or conducting parts or from ground.

Isolated Not readily accessible to persons unless special means for access are used.

Line-clearance tree trimmer An employee who, through related training or on-the-job experience or both, is familiar with the special techniques and hazards involved in line-clearance tree trimming.

Note: An employee who is regularly assigned to a line-clearance tree-trimming crew and who is undergoing on-the-job training and who, in the course of such training, has demonstrated an ability to perform duties safely at his or her level of training and who is under the direct supervision of a line-clearance tree trimmer is considered to be a line-clearance tree trimmer for the performance of those duties.

Note: A line-clearance tree trimmer is not considered to be a "qualified employee" under this Section unless he or she has the training required for a qualified employee under paragraph (a)(2)(ii) of this Section. However, under the electrical safety-related work practices Standard in Subpart S of this Part, a line-clearance tree trimmer is considered to be a "qualified employee." Tree trimming performed by such "qualified employees" is not subject to the electrical safety-related work practice requirements contained in §1910.331 through §1910.335 when it is directly associated with electric power generation, transmission, or distribution lines or equipment. (See §1910.331 for requirements on the applicability of the electrical safety-related work practice requirements contained in §1910.331 through §1910.335 to line-clearance tree trimming performed by such "qualified employees," and see the note following §1910.332(b)(3) for information regarding the training an employee must have to be considered a qualified employee under §1910.331 through §1910.335.)

Line-clearance tree trimming The pruning, trimming, repairing, maintaining, removing, or clearing of trees, or the cutting of brush, that is within the following distance of electric supply lines and equipment:

(1) For voltages to ground of 50 kilovolts or less—3.05 meters (10 feet);

(2) For voltages to ground of more than 50 kilovolts—3.05 meters (10 feet) plus 0.10 meters (4 inches) for every 10 kilovolts over 50 kilovolts.

Note: This Section applies only to line-clearance tree trimming performed for the purpose of clearing space around electric power generation, transmission, or distribution lines or equipment and on behalf of an organization that operates, or that controls the operating procedures for, those lines or equipment. See paragraph (a)(1) of this Section. Tree trimming performed on behalf of a homeowner or commercial entity other than an organization that operates, or that controls the operating procedures for, electric power generation, transmission, or distribution lines or equipment is not directly associated with an electric power generation, transmission, or distribution installation and is outside the scope of this Section. In addition, tree trimming that is not for the purpose of clearing space around electric power generation, transmission, or distribution lines or equipment is not directly associated with an electric power generation, transmission, or distribution installation and is outside the scope of this Section. Such tree trimming may be covered by other applicable Standards. See, for example, §1910.268 and §1910.331 through §1910.335.

Lines

(1) Communication lines The conductors and their supporting or containing structures which are used for public or private signal or communication service, and which operate at potentials not exceeding 400 volts to ground or 750 volts between any two points of the circuit, and the transmitted power of which does not exceed 150 watts. If the lines are operating at less than 150 volts, no limit is placed on the transmitted power of the system. Under certain conditions, communication cables may include communication circuits exceeding these limitations where such circuits are also used to supply power solely to communication equipment.

Note: Telephone, telegraph, railroad signal, data, clock, fire, police alarm, cable television, and other systems conforming to this definition are included. Lines used for signaling purposes, but not included under this definition, are considered as electric supply lines of the same voltage.

(2) Electric supply lines Conductors used to transmit electric energy and their necessary supporting or containing structures. Signal lines of more than 400 volts are always supply lines within this Section, and those of less than 400 volts are considered as supply lines, if so run and operated throughout.

Manhole A subsurface enclosure that personnel may enter and that is used for installing, operating, and maintaining submersible equipment or cable.

Minimum approach distance The closest distance an employee may approach an energized or a grounded object.

Note: Paragraph (l)(3)(i) of this Section requires employers to establish minimum approach distances.

Personal fall arrest system A system used to arrest an employee in a fall from a working level.

Qualified employee (qualified person) An employee (person) knowledgeable in the construction and operation of the electric power generation, transmission, and distribution equipment involved, along with the associated hazards.

Note: An employee must have the training required by (a)(2)(ii) of this Section to be a qualified employee.

Note: Except under (g)(2)(iv)(C)(2) and (g)(2)(iv)(C)(3) of this Section, an employee who is undergoing on-the-job training and who has demonstrated, in the course of such training, an ability to perform duties safely at his or her level of training and who is under the direct supervision of a qualified person is a qualified person for the performance of those duties.

Statistical sparkover voltage A transient overvoltage level that produces a 97.72-percent probability of sparkover (that is, two standard deviations above the voltage at which there is a 50-percent probability of sparkover).

Statistical withstand voltage A transient overvoltage level that produces a 0.14-percent probability of sparkover (that is, three standard deviations below the voltage at which there is a 50-percent probability of sparkover).

Switch A device for opening and closing or for changing the connection of a circuit. In this Section, a switch is manually operable, unless otherwise stated.

System operator A qualified person designated to operate the system or its parts.

Vault An enclosure, above or below ground, that personnel may enter and that is used for installing, operating, or maintaining equipment or cable.

Vented vault. A vault that has provision for air changes using exhaust-flue stacks and low-level air intakes operating on pressure and temperature differentials that provide for airflow that precludes a hazardous atmosphere from developing.

Voltage The effective (root mean square, or rms) potential difference between any two conductors or between a conductor and ground. This Section expresses voltages in nominal values, unless otherwise indicated. The nominal voltage of a system or circuit is the value assigned to a system or circuit of a given voltage class for the purpose of convenient designation. The operating voltage of the system may vary above or below this value.

Work-positioning equipment A body belt or body harness system rigged to allow an employee to be supported on an elevated vertical surface, such as a utility pole or tower leg, and work with both hands free while leaning.

§1910.269 Appendix A Flow Charts

This Appendix presents information, in the form of flow charts, that illustrates the scope and application of §1910.269. This Appendix addresses the interface between §1910.269 and Subpart S of this Part (Electrical), between §1910.269 and §1910.146 (Permit-required confined spaces), and between §1910.269 and §1910.147 (The control of hazardous energy (lockout/tagout)). These flow charts provide guidance for employers trying to implement the requirements of §1910.269 in combination with other General Industry Standards contained in Part 1910. Employers should always consult the relevant Standards, in conjunction with this Appendix, to ensure compliance with all applicable requirements.

§1910.269 Appendix A–1 Application of §1910.269 and Subpart S of this Part to the design of electrical installations

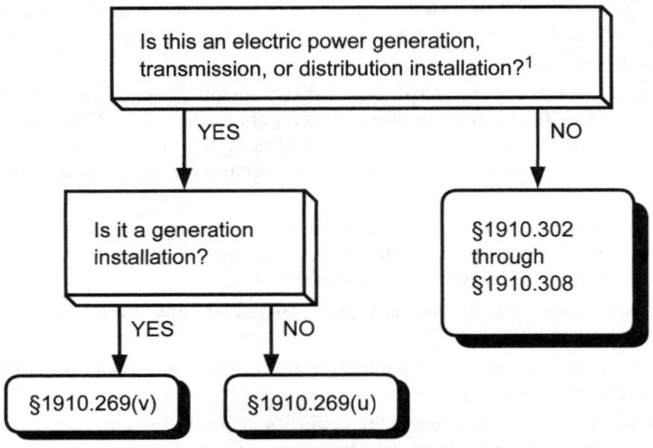

1 This chart applies to electrical installation design requirements only. See Appendix A-2 for electrical safety-related work practices. Supplementary electric generating equipment that is used to supply a workplace for emergency, standby, or similar purposes only is not considered an electric power generation installation

§1910.269 Appendix A–2 Application of §1910.269 and Subpart S of this Part to electrical safety–related work practices[1]

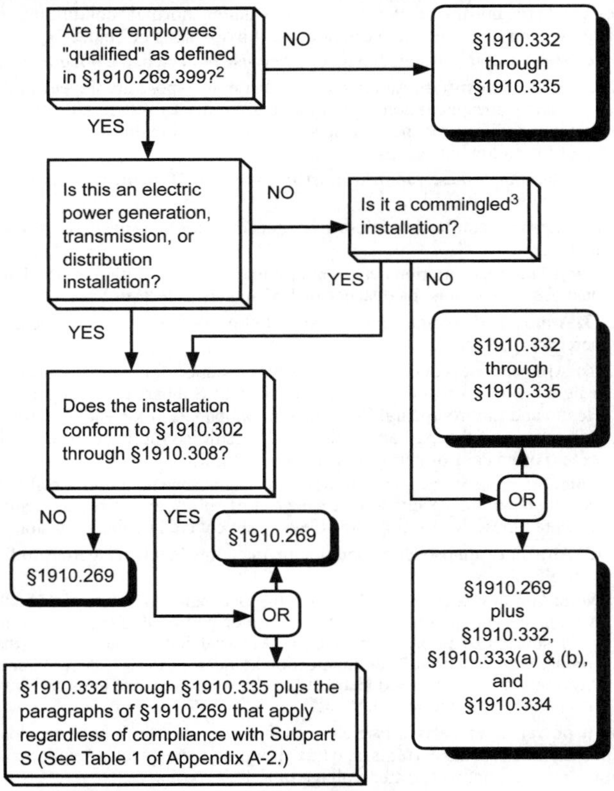

1 This flowchart applies only to the electrical safety-related work practice and training requirements in §1910.269 and §1910.332 through §1910.335

2 See §1910.269(a)(1)(ii)(B) and §1910.331(b) and (c)(1).

3 This means commingled to the extent that the electric power generation, transmission, or distribution installation poses the greater hazard.

Table 1
Electrical Safety Requirements in §1910.269

Compliance with Subpart S will comply with these paragraphs of §1910.269[1]	Paragraphs that apply regardless of compliance with Subpart S[2]
(d), electric shock hazards only	(a)(2), (a)(3) and (a)(4)
(h)(3)	(b)
(i)(2) and (i)(3)	(c)
(k)	(d), for other than electric shock hazards
(l)(1) through (l)(5), (l)(7), and (l)(10) through (l)(12)	(e)
(m)	(f)
(p)(4)	(g)
(s)(2)	(h)(1) and (h)(2)
(u)(1) and (u)(3) through (u)(5)	(i)(4)
(v)(3) through (v)(5)	(j)
(w)(1) and (w)(7)	(l)(6), (l)(8) and (l)(9)
	(n)
	(o)
	(p)(1) through (p)(3)
	(q)
	(r)
	(s)(1)
	(t)
	(u)(2) and (u)(6)
	(v)(1), (v)(2), and (v)(6) through (v)(12)
	(w)(2) through (w)(6), (w)(8), and (w)(9)

[1] If the electrical installation meets the requirements of §1910.303 through §1910.308 of this Part, then the electrical installation and any associated electrical safety-related work practices conforming to §1910.332 through §1910.335 of this Part are considered to comply with these provisions of §1910.269 of this Part.
[2] These provisions include electrical safety and other requirements that must be met regardless of compliance with Subpart S of this Part.

§1910.269 Appendix A–3 Application of §1910.269 and Subpart S of this Part to tree–trimming

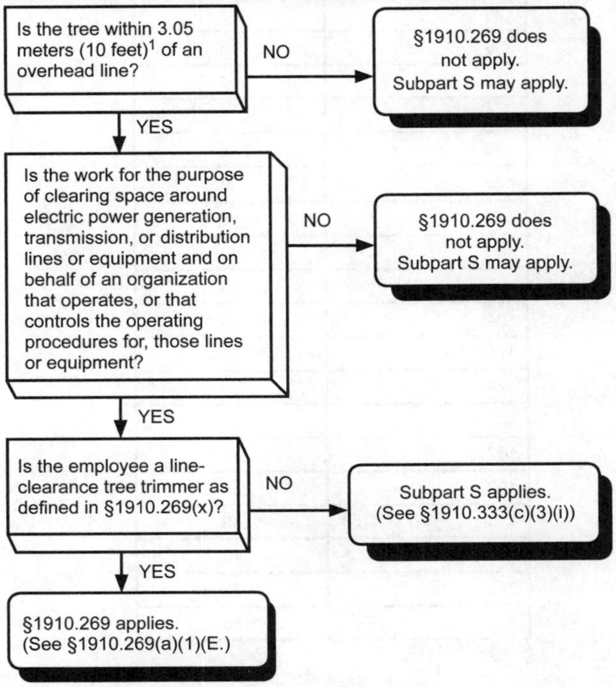

[1] 3.05 meters (10 feet) plus 0.1 meters (4 inches) for every 10 kilovolts over 50 kilovolts
Note: Paragraph (t) of §1910.269 contains additional requirements for work in manholes and underground vaults.

§1910.269 Appendix A–4 Application of §1910.147, §1910.269 and §1910.333 to hazardous energy control procedures (Lockout/Tagout)

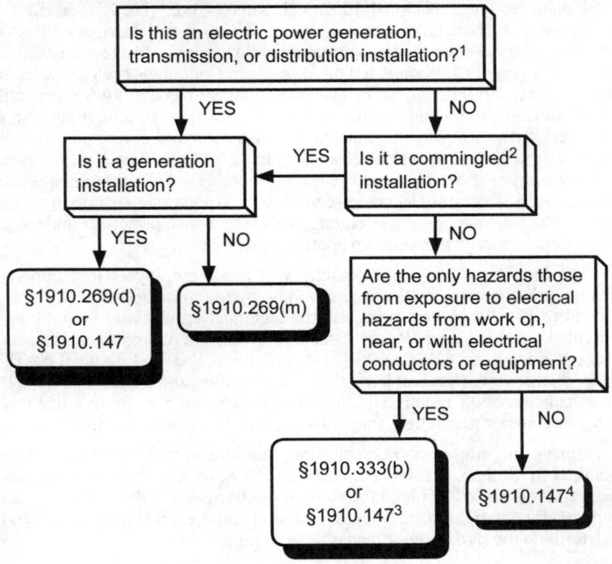

[1] If a generation, transmission, or distribution installation conforms to §1910.302 through §1910.308, the lockout and tagging procedures of §1910.333(b) may be followed.
[2] This means commingled to the extent that the electric power generation, transmission, or distribution installation poses the greater hazard.
[3] Paragraphs (b)(2)(iii)(D) and (b)(2)(iv)(B) of §1910.333 still apply.
[4] §1910 Paragraph (b) of §1910.333 applies to any electrical hazards from work on, near or with electric conductors and equipment.

§1910.269 Appendix A–5 Application of §1910.146 and §1910.269 to permit–required confined spaces

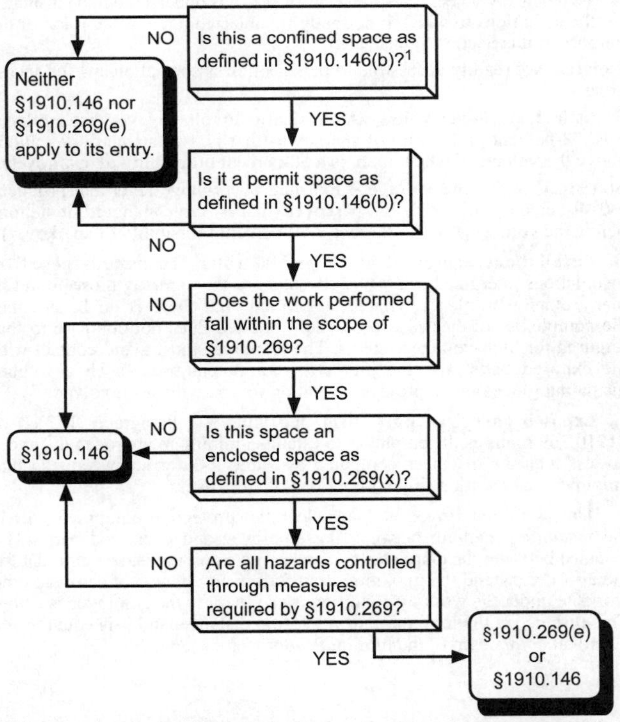

[1] See §1910.146(c) for general non-entry requirements that apply to all confined spaces.
Note: Paragraph (t) of §1910.269 contains additional requirements for work in manholes and underground vaults.

§1910.269 Appendix B
Working on exposed energized parts

I. Introduction

Electric utilities design electric power generation, transmission, and distribution installations to meet National Electrical Safety Code (NESC), ANSI C2, requirements. Electric utilities also design transmission and distribution lines to limit line outages as required by system reliability criteria[1] and to withstand the maximum overvoltages impressed on the system. Conditions such as switching surges, faults, and lightning can cause overvoltages. Electric utilities generally select insulator design and lengths and the clearances to structural parts so as to prevent outages from contaminated line insulation and during storms. Line insulator lengths and structural clearances have, over the years, come closer to the minimum approach distances used by workers. As minimum approach distances and structural clearances converge, it is increasingly important that system designers and system operating and maintenance personnel understand the concepts underlying minimum approach distances.

The information in this Appendix will assist employers in complying with the minimum approach-distance requirements contained in §1910.269(l)(3) and (q)(3). Employers must use the technical criteria and methodology presented in this Appendix in establishing minimum approach distances in accordance with §1910.269(l)(3)(i) and Table R-3 and Table R-8. This Appendix provides essential background information and technical criteria for the calculation of the required minimum approach distances for live-line work on electric power generation, transmission, and distribution installations.

Unless an employer is using the maximum transient overvoltages specified in Table R-9 for voltages over 72.5 kilovolts, the employer must use persons knowledgeable in the techniques discussed in this Appendix, and competent in the field of electric transmission and distribution system design, to determine the maximum transient overvoltage

II. General

A. Definitions The following definitions from §1910.269(x) relate to work on or near electric power generation, transmission, and distribution lines and equipment and the electrical hazards they present.

Exposed Not isolated or guarded.

Guarded Covered, fenced, enclosed, or otherwise protected, by means of suitable covers or casings, barrier rails or screens, mats, or platforms, designed to minimize the possibility, under normal conditions, of dangerous approach or inadvertent contact by persons or objects.
Note: Wires that are insulated, but not otherwise protected, are not guarded.

Insulated Separated from other conducting surfaces by a dielectric (including air space) offering a high resistance to the passage of current.
Note: When any object is said to be insulated, it is understood to be insulated for the conditions to which it normally is subjected. Otherwise, it is, for the purpose of this Section, uninsulated.

Isolated Not readily accessible to persons unless special means for access are used.

Statistical sparkover voltage A transient overvoltage level that produces a 97.72-percent probability of sparkover (that is, two standard deviations above the voltage at which there is a 50-percent probability of sparkover).

Statistical withstand voltage A transient overvoltage level that produces a 0.14-percent probability of sparkover (that is, three standard deviations below the voltage at which there is a 50-percent probability of sparkover).

B. Installations energized at 50 to 300 volts The hazards posed by installations energized at 50 to 300 volts are the same as those found in many other workplaces. That is not to say that there is no hazard, but the complexity of electrical protection required does not compare to that required for high-voltage systems. The employee must avoid contact with the exposed parts, and the protective equipment used (such as rubber insulating gloves) must provide insulation for the voltages involved.

C. Exposed energized parts over 300 volts AC Paragraph (l)(3)(i) of §1910.269 requires the employer to establish minimum approach distances no less than the distances computed by Table R-3 for ac systems so that employees can work safely without risk of sparkover.[2]

Unless the employee is using electrical protective equipment, air is the insulating medium between the employee and energized parts. The distance between the employee and an energized part must be sufficient for the air to withstand the maximum transient overvoltage that can reach the worksite under the working conditions and practices the employee is using. This distance is the minimum air insulation distance, and it is equal to the electrical component of the minimum approach distance.

Normal system design may provide or include a means (such as lightning arrestors) to control maximum anticipated transient overvoltages, or the employer may use temporary devices (portable protective gaps) or measures (such as preventing automatic circuit breaker reclosing) to achieve the same result. Paragraph (l)(3)(ii) of §1910.269 requires the employer to determine the maximum anticipated per-unit transient overvoltage, phase-to-ground, through an engineering analysis or assume a maximum anticipated per-unit transient overvoltage, phase-to-ground, in accordance with Table R-9, which specifies the following maximums for ac systems:

72.6 to 420.0 kilovolts—3.5 per unit
420.1 to 550.0 kilovolts—3.0 per unit
550.1 to 800.0 kilovolts—2.5 per unit

See paragraph IV.A.2, later in this Appendix, for additional discussion of maximum transient overvoltages.

D. Types of exposures Employees working on or near energized electric power generation, transmission, and distribution systems face two kinds of exposures: Phase-to-ground and phase-to-phase. The exposure is phase-to-ground: (1) With respect to an energized part, when the employee is at ground potential or (2) with respect to ground, when an employee is at the potential of the energized part during live-line barehand work. The exposure is phase-to-phase, with respect to an energized part, when an employee is at the potential of another energized part (at a different potential) during live-line barehand work.

III. Determination of Minimum Approach Distances for AC Voltages Greater Than 300 Volts

A. Voltages of 301 to 5,000 volts

Test data generally forms the basis of minimum air insulation distances. The lowest voltage for which sufficient test data exists is 5,000 volts, and these data indicate that the minimum air insulation distance at that voltage is 20, millimeters (1 inch). Because the minimum air insulation distance increases with increasing voltage, and, conversely, decreases with decreasing voltage, an assumed minimum air insulation distance of 20 millimeters will protect against sparkover at voltages of 301 to 5,000 volts. Thus, 20 millimeters is the electrical component of the minimum approach distance for these voltages.

B. Voltages of 5.1 to 72.5 kilovolts For voltages from 5.1 to 72.5 kilovolts, the Occupational Safety and Health Administration bases the methodology for calculating the electrical component of the minimum approach distance on Institute of Electrical and Electronic Engineers (IEEE) Standard 4-1995, Standard Techniques for High-Voltage Testing. Table 1 lists the critical sparkover distances from that standard as listed in IEEE Std 516-2009, IEEE Guide for Maintenance Methods on Energized Power Lines.

Table 1
Sparkover Distance for Rod-to-Rod Gap

60 Hz Rod-to-Rod sparkover (kV peak)	Gap spacing from IEEE Std 4-1995 (cm)
25	2
36	3
46	4
53	5
60	6
70	8
79	10
86	12
95	14
104	16
112	18
120	20
143	25
167	30
192	35
218	40
243	45
270	50
322	60

Source: IEEE Std 516-2009

[1] Federal, State, and local regulatory bodies and electric utilities set reliability requirements that limit the number and duration of system outages.
[2] Sparkover is a disruptive electric discharge in which an electric arc forms and electric current passes through air.

To use this table to determine the electrical component of the minimum approach distance, the employer must determine the peak phase-to-ground transient overvoltage and select a gap from the table that corresponds to that voltage as a withstand voltage rather than a critical sparkover voltage. To calculate the electrical component of the minimum approach distance for voltages between 5 and 72.5 kilovolts, use the following procedure:

1. Divide the phase-to-phase voltage by the square root of 3 to convert it to a phase-to-ground voltage.
2. Multiply the phase-to-ground voltage by the square root of 2 to convert the rms value of the voltage to the peak phase-to-ground voltage.
3. Multiply the peak phase-to-ground voltage by the maximum per-unit transient overvoltage, which, for this voltage range, is 3.0, as discussed later in this Appendix. This is the maximum phase-to-ground transient overvoltage, which corresponds to the withstand voltage for the relevant exposure.[3]
4. Divide the maximum phase-to-ground transient overvoltage by 0.85 to determine the corresponding critical sparkover voltage. (The critical sparkover voltage is 3 standard deviations (or 15 percent) greater than the withstand voltage.)
5. Determine the electrical component of the minimum approach distance from Table 1 through interpolation.

Table 2 illustrates how to derive the electrical component of the minimum approach distance for voltages from 5.1 to 72.5 kilovolts, before the application of any altitude correction factor, as explained later.

Table 2
Calculating the Electrical Component of MAD 751 V to 72.5 kV

Step	Maximum system phase-to-phase voltage (kV)			
	15	36	46	72.5
1. Divide by 3	8.7	20.8	26.6	41.9
2. Multiply by 2	12.2	29.4	37.6	59.2
3. Multiply by 3.0	36.7	88.2	112.7	117.6
4. Divide by 0.85	46.2	103.7	132.6	208.9
5. Interpolate from Table 1	3+ (7.2/10)+1	14+ (8.7/9)*2	20+ (12.6/23)*5	35+ (16.9/26)*5
Electrical component of MAD (cm)	3.72	15.93	22.74	38.25

C. Voltages of 72.6 to 800 kilovolts For voltages of 72.6 kilovolts to 800 kilovolts, this Section bases the electrical component of minimum approach distances, before the application of any altitude correction factor, on the following formula:

Equation 1
For Voltages of 72.6 kV to 800 kV

$$D = 0.3048(C + a)\, V_{L\text{-}G} T$$

Where:

D = Electrical component of the minimum approach distance in air in meters;

C = a correction factor associated with the variation of gap sparkover with voltage;

a = A factor relating to the saturation of air at system voltages of 345 kilovolts or higher;[4]

$V_{L\text{-}G}$ = Maximum system line-to-ground rms voltage in kilovolts—it should be the "actual" maximum, or the normal highest voltage for the range (for example, 10 percent above the nominal voltage); and

T = Maximum transient overvoltage factor in per unit.

In Equation 1, C is 0.01: (1) For phase-to-ground exposures that the employer can demonstrate consist only of air across the approach distance (gap) and (2) for phase-to-phase exposures if the employer can demonstrate that no insulated tool spans the gap and that no large conductive object is in the gap. Otherwise, C is 0.011.

In Equation 1, the term a varies depending on whether the employee's exposure is phase-to-ground or phase-to-phase and on whether objects are in the gap. The employer must use the equations in Table 3 to calculate a. Sparkover test data with insulation spanning the gap form the basis for the equations for phase-to-ground exposures, and sparkover test data with only air in the gap form the basis for the equations for phase-to-phase exposures. The phase-to-ground equations result in slightly higher values of a, and, consequently, produce larger minimum approach distances, than the phase-to-phase equations for the same value of V_{Peak}.

Table 3
Equations for Calculating the Surge Factor, a

Phase-to-ground exposures			
$V_{Peak} = T_{L\text{-}G} V_{L\text{-}G} \sqrt{2}$ a	635 kV or less 0	635.1 to 915 kV (V_{Peak}- 635)/140,000	915.1 to 1,050 kV (V_{Peak}-645)/135,000
$V_{Peak} = T_{L\text{-}G} V_{L\text{-}G} \sqrt{2}$ a	More than 1,050 kV (V_{Peak}-675)/125,000		
Phase-to-ground exposures[1]			
$V_{Peak} = (1.35 T_{L\text{-}G} + 0.45) V_{L\text{-}G} \sqrt{2}$ a	630 kV or less 0	630.1 to 848 kV (V_{Peak}-630)/155,000	848.1 to 1,131 kV (V_{Peak}-633.6)/152,207
$V_{Peak} = (1.35 T_{L\text{-}G} + 0.45) V_{L\text{-}G} \sqrt{2}$ a	1,131.1 to 1,485 kV (V_{Peak}-628)/153,846	More than 1,485 kV (V_{Peak}-350.5)/203,666	

[1] Use the equations for phase-to-ground exposures (with *VPeak* for phase-to-phase exposures) unless the employer can demonstrate that no insulated tool spans the gap and that no large conductive object is in the gap.

In Equation 1, T is the maximum transient overvoltage factor in per unit. As noted earlier, §1910.269(l)(3)(ii) requires the employer to determine the maximum anticipated per-unit transient overvoltage, phase-to-ground, through an engineering analysis or assume a maximum anticipated per-unit transient overvoltage, phase-to-ground, in accordance with Table R-9. For phase-to-ground exposures, the employer uses this value, called $T_{L\text{-}G}$, as T in Equation 1. IEEE Std 516-2009 provides the following formula to calculate the phase-to-phase maximum transient overvoltage, $T_{L\text{-}L}$, from $T_{L\text{-}G}$:

$$T_{L\text{-}L} = 1.35 T_{L\text{-}G} + 0.45$$

For phase-to-phase exposures, the employer uses this value as T in Equation 1.

D. Provisions for inadvertent movement The minimum approach distance must include an "adder" to compensate for the inadvertent movement of the worker relative to an energized part or the movement of the part relative to the worker. This "adder" must account for this possible inadvertent movement and provide the worker with a comfortable and safe zone in which to work. Employers must add the distance for inadvertent movement (called the "ergonomic component of the minimum approach distance") to the electrical component to determine the total safe minimum approach distances used in live-line work.

The Occupational Safety and Health Administration based the ergonomic component of the minimum approach distance on response time-distance analysis. This technique uses an estimate of the total response

[3] The withstand voltage is the voltage at which sparkover is not likely to occur across a specified distance. It is the voltage taken at the 3σ point below the sparkover voltage, assuming that the sparkover curve follows a normal distribution.

[4] Test data demonstrates that the saturation factor is greater than 0 at peak voltages of about 630 kilovolts. Systems operating at 345 kilovolts (or maximum system voltages of 362 kilovolts) can have peak maximum transient overvoltages exceeding 630 kilovolts. Table R-3 sets equations for calculating a based on peak voltage.

time to a hazardous incident and converts that time to the distance traveled. For example, the driver of a car takes a given amount of time to respond to a "stimulus" and stop the vehicle. The elapsed time involved results in the car's traveling some distance before coming to a complete stop. This distance depends on the speed of the car at the time the stimulus appears and the reaction time of the driver.

In the case of live-line work, the employee must first perceive that he or she is approaching the danger zone. Then, the worker responds to the danger and must decelerate and stop all motion toward the energized part. During the time it takes to stop, the employee will travel some distance. This is the distance the employer must add to the electrical component of the minimum approach distance to obtain the total safe minimum approach distance.

At voltages from 751 volts to 72.5 kilovolts,[5] the electrical component of the minimum approach distance is smaller than the ergonomic component. At 72.5 kilovolts, the electrical component is only a little more than 0.3 meters (1 foot). An ergonomic component of the minimum approach distance must provide for all the worker's unanticipated movements. At these voltages, workers generally use rubber insulating gloves; however, these gloves protect only a worker's hands and arms. Therefore, the energized object must be at a safe approach distance to protect the worker's face. In this case, 0.61 meters (2 feet) is a sufficient and practical ergonomic component of the minimum approach distance.

For voltages between 72.6 and 800 kilovolts, employees must use different work practices during energized line work. Generally, employees use live-line tools (hot sticks) to perform work on energized equipment. These tools, by design, keep the energized part at a constant distance from the employee and, thus, maintain the appropriate minimum approach distance automatically.

The location of the worker and the type of work methods the worker is using also influence the length of the ergonomic component of the minimum approach distance. In this higher voltage range, the employees use work methods that more tightly control their movements than when the workers perform work using rubber insulating gloves. The worker, therefore, is farther from the energized line or equipment and must be more precise in his or her movements just to perform the work. For these reasons, this Section adopts an ergonomic component of the minimum approach distance of 0.31 m (1 foot) for voltages between 72.6 and 800 kilovolts.

Table 4 summarizes the ergonomic component of the minimum approach distance for various voltage ranges.

Table 4
Ergonomic Component of Minimum Approach Distance

Voltage range (kV)	Distance	
	m	ft
0.301 to 0.750	0.31	1.0
0.751 to 72.5	0.61	2.0
72.6 to 800	0.31	1.0

Note: The employer must add this distance to the electrical component of the minimum approach distance to obtain the full minimum approach distance.

The ergonomic component of the minimum approach distance accounts for errors in maintaining the minimum approach distance (which might occur, for example, if an employee misjudges the length of a conductive object he or she is holding), and for errors in judging the minimum approach distance. The ergonomic component also accounts for inadvertent movements by the employee, such as slipping. In contrast, the working position selected to properly maintain the minimum approach distance must account for all of an employee's reasonably likely movements and still permit the employee to adhere to the applicable minimum approach distance. (See Figure 1.) Reasonably likely movements include an employee's adjustments to tools, equipment, and working positions and all movements needed to perform the work. For example, the employee should be able to perform all of the following actions without straying into the minimum approach distance:

- Adjust his or her hardhat,
- maneuver a tool onto an energized part with a reasonable amount of overreaching or underreaching,
- reach for and handle tools, material, and equipment passed to him or her, and
- adjust tools, and replace components on them, when necessary during the work procedure.

The training of qualified employees required under §1910.269(a)(2), and the job planning and briefing required under §1910.269(c), must address selection of a proper working position.

[5] For voltages of 50 to 300 volts, Table R-3 specifies a minimum approach distance of "avoid contact." The minimum approach distance for this voltage range contains neither an electrical component nor an ergonomic component.

Figure 1
Maintaining the Minimum Approach Distance

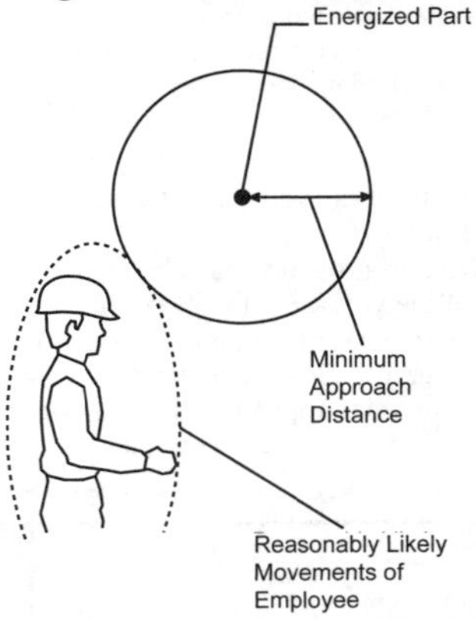

E. Miscellaneous correction factors Changes in the air medium that forms the insulation influences the strength of an air gap. A brief discussion of each factor follows.

1. Dielectric strength of air The dielectric strength of air in a uniform electric field at standard atmospheric conditions is approximately 3 kilovolts per millimeter.[6] The pressure, temperature, and humidity of the air, the shape, dimensions, and separation of the electrodes, and the characteristics of the applied voltage (wave shape) affect the disruptive gradient.

2. Atmospheric effect The empirically determined electrical strength of a given gap is normally applicable at standard atmospheric conditions (20 °C, 101.3 kilopascals, 11 grams/cubic centimeter humidity). An increase in the density (humidity) of the air inhibits sparkover for a given air gap. The combination of temperature and air pressure that results in the lowest gap sparkover voltage is high temperature and low pressure. This combination of conditions is not likely to occur. Low air pressure, generally associated with high humidity, causes increased electrical strength. An average air pressure generally correlates with low humidity. Hot and dry working conditions normally result in reduced electrical strength. The equations for minimum approach distances in Table R-3 assume standard atmospheric conditions.

3. Altitude The reduced air pressure at high altitudes causes a reduction in the electrical strength of an air gap. An employer must increase the minimum approach distance by about 3 percent per 300 meters (1,000 feet) of increased altitude for altitudes above 900 meters (3,000 feet). Table R-5 specifies the altitude correction factor that the employer must use in calculating minimum approach distances.

IV. Determining Minimum Approach Distances

A. Factors Affecting Voltage Stress at the Worksite

1. System voltage (nominal) The nominal system voltage range determines the voltage for purposes of calculating minimum approach distances. The employer selects the range in which the nominal system voltage falls, as given in the relevant table, and uses the highest value within that range in per-unit calculations.

2. Transient overvoltages Operation of switches or circuit breakers, a fault on a line or circuit or on an adjacent circuit, and similar activities may generate transient overvoltages on an electrical system. Each overvoltage has an associated transient voltage wave shape. The wave shape arriving at the site and its magnitude vary considerably.

In developing requirements for minimum approach distances, the Occupational Safety and Health Administration considered the most common wave shapes and the magnitude of transient overvoltages found on electric power generation, transmission, and distribution systems. The equations in Table R-3 for minimum approach distances use per-unit maximum transient overvoltages, which are relative to the nominal maximum voltage of the system. For example, a maximum transient overvoltage value of 3.0 per unit indicates that the highest transient overvoltage is 3.0 times the nominal maximum system voltage.

3. Typical magnitude of overvoltages Table 5 lists the magnitude of typical transient overvoltages.

[6] For the purposes of estimating arc length, §1910.269 generally assumes a more conservative dielectric strength of 10 kilovolts per 25.4 millimeters, consistent with assumptions made in consensus standards such as the National Electrical Safety Code (IEEE C2-2012). The more conservative value accounts for variables such as electrode shape, wave shape, and a certain amount of overvoltage.

Table 5
Magnitude of Typical Transient Overvoltages

Cause	Magnitude (per unit)
Energized 200-mile line without closing resistors	3.5
Energized 200-mile line with one-step closing resistor	2.1
Energized 200-mile line with multistep resistor	2.5
Reclosing with trapped charge one-step resistor	2.2
Opening surge with single restrike	3.0
Fault initiation unfaulted phase	2.1
Fault initiation adjacent circuit	2.5
Fault clearing	1.7 to 1.9

4. Standard deviation—air-gap withstand For each air gap length under the same atmospheric conditions, there is a statistical variation in the breakdown voltage. The probability of breakdown against voltage has a normal (Gaussian) distribution. The standard deviation of this distribution varies with the wave shape, gap geometry, and atmospheric conditions. The withstand voltage of the air gap is three standard deviations (3σ) below the critical sparkover voltage. (The critical sparkover voltage is the crest value of the impulse wave that, under specified conditions, causes sparkover 50 percent of the time. An impulse wave of three standard deviations below this value, that is, the withstand voltage, has a probability of sparkover of approximately 1 in 1,000.)

5. Broken Insulators Tests show reductions in the insulation strength of insulator strings with broken skirts. Broken units may lose up to 70 percent of their withstand capacity. Because an employer cannot determine the insulating capability of a broken unit without testing it, the employer must consider damaged units in an insulator to have no insulating value. Additionally, the presence of a live-line tool alongside an insulator string with broken units may further reduce the overall insulating strength. The number of good units that must be present in a string for it to be "insulated" as defined by §1910.269(x) depends on the maximum overvoltage possible at the worksite.

B. Minimum Approach Distances Based on Known, Maximum-Anticipated Per-Unit Transient Overvoltages

1. Determining the minimum approach distance for AC systems Under §1910.269(l)(3)(ii), the employer must determine the maximum anticipated per-unit transient overvoltage, phase-to-ground, through an engineering analysis or must assume a maximum anticipated per-unit transient overvoltage, phase-to-ground, in accordance with Table R-9. When the employer conducts an engineering analysis of the system and determines that the maximum transient overvoltage is lower than specified by Table R-9, the employer must ensure that any conditions assumed in the analysis, for example, that employees block reclosing on a circuit or install portable protective gaps, are present during energized work. To ensure that these conditions are present, the employer may need to institute new live-work procedures reflecting the conditions and limitations set by the engineering analysis.

2. Calculation of reduced approach distance values An employer may take the following steps to reduce minimum approach distances when the maximum transient overvoltage on the system (that is, the maximum transient overvoltage without additional steps to control overvoltages) produces unacceptably large minimum approach distances:

Step 1. Determine the maximum voltage (with respect to a given nominal voltage range) for the energized part.

Step 2. Determine the technique to use to control the maximum transient overvoltage. (See paragraphs IV.C and IV.D of this Appendix.) Determine the maximum transient overvoltage that can exist at the worksite with that form of control in place and with a confidence level of 3σ. This voltage is the withstand voltage for the purpose of calculating the appropriate minimum approach distance.

Step 3. Direct employees to implement procedures to ensure that the control technique is in effect during the course of the work.

Step 4. Using the new value of transient overvoltage in per unit, calculate the required minimum approach distance from Table R-3.

C. Methods of Controlling Possible Transient Overvoltage Stress Found on a System

1. Introduction There are several means of controlling overvoltages that occur on transmission systems. For example, the employer can modify the operation of circuit breakers or other switching devices to reduce switching transient overvoltages. Alternatively, the employer can hold the overvoltage to an acceptable level by installing surge arresters or portable protective gaps on the system. In addition, the employer can change the transmission system to minimize the effect of switching operations. Section 4.8 of IEEE Std 516-2009 describes various ways of controlling, and thereby reducing, maximum transient overvoltages.

2. Operation of circuit breakers[7] The maximum transient overvoltage that can reach the worksite is often the result of switching on the line on which employees are working. Disabling automatic reclosing during energized line work, so that the line will not be reenergized after being opened for any reason, limits the maximum switching surge overvoltage to the larger of the opening surge or the greatest possible fault-generated surge, provided that the devices (for example, insertion resistors) are operable and will function to limit the transient overvoltage and that circuit breaker restrikes do not occur. The employer must ensure the proper functioning of insertion resistors and other overvoltage-limiting devices when the employer's engineering analysis assumes their proper operation to limit the overvoltage level. If the employer cannot disable the reclosing feature (because of system operating conditions), other methods of controlling the switching surge level may be necessary.

Transient surges on an adjacent line, particularly for double circuit construction, may cause a significant overvoltage on the line on which employees are working. The employer's engineering analysis must account for coupling to adjacent lines.

3. Surge arresters The use of modern surge arresters allows a reduction in the basic impulse-insulation levels of much transmission system equipment. The primary function of early arresters was to protect the system insulation from the effects of lightning. Modern arresters not only dissipate lightning-caused transients, but may also control many other system transients caused by switching or faults.

The employer may use properly designed arresters to control transient overvoltages along a transmission line and thereby reduce the requisite length of the insulator string and possibly the maximum transient overvoltage on the line.[8]

4. Switching Restrictions Another form of overvoltage control involves establishing switching restrictions, whereby the employer prohibits the operation of circuit breakers until certain system conditions are present. The employer restricts switching by using a tagging system, similar to that used for a permit, except that the common term used for this activity is a "hold-off" or "restriction." These terms indicate that the restriction does not prevent operation, but only modifies the operation during the live-work activity.

D. Minimum Approach Distance Based on Control of Maximum Transient Overvoltage at the Worksite

When the employer institutes control of maximum transient overvoltage at the worksite by installing portable protective gaps, the employer may calculate the minimum approach distance as follows:

Step 1. Select the appropriate withstand voltage for the protective gap based on system requirements and an acceptable probability of gap sparkover.[9]

Step 2. Determine a gap distance that provides a withstand voltage[10] greater than or equal to the one selected in the first step.[11]

Step 3. Use 110 percent of the gap's critical sparkover voltage to determine the phase-to-ground peak voltage at gap sparkover ($V_{PPG\ Peak}$).

Step 4. Determine the maximum transient overvoltage, phase-to-ground, at the worksite from the following formula:

$$T = \frac{V_{ppGPeak}}{V_{L\text{-}G}\sqrt{2}}$$

Step 5. Use this value of T[12] in the equation in Table R-3 to obtain the minimum approach distance. If the worksite is no more than 900 meters (3,000 feet) above sea level, the employer may use this value of T to determine the minimum approach distance from Table 14 through Table 21.

Note: All rounding must be to the next higher value (that is, always round up).

[7] The detailed design of a circuit interrupter, such as the design of the contacts, resistor insertion, and breaker timing control, are beyond the scope of this Appendix. The design of the system generally accounts for these features. This Appendix only discusses features that can limit the maximum switching transient overvoltage on a system.

[8] Surge arrester application is beyond the scope of this Appendix. However, if the employer installs the arrester near the work site, the application would be similar to the protective gaps discussed in paragraph IV.D of this Appendix.

[9] The employer should check the withstand voltage to ensure that it results in a probability of gap flashover that is acceptable from a system outage perspective. (In other words, a gap sparkover will produce a system outage. The employer should determine whether such an outage will impact overall system performance to an acceptable degree.) In general, the withstand voltage should be at least 1.25 times the maximum crest operating voltage.

[10] The manufacturer of the gap provides, based on test data, the critical sparkover voltage for each gap spacing (for example, a critical sparkover voltage of 665 kilovolts for a gap spacing of 1.2 meters). The withstand voltage for the gap is equal to 85 percent of its critical sparkover voltage.

[11] Switch steps 1 and 2 if the length of the protective gap is known.

[12] IEEE Std 516-2009 states that most employers add 0.2 to the calculated value of T as an additional safety factor.

Sample protective gap calculations.

Problem: Employees are to perform work on a 500-kilovolt transmission line at sea level that is subject to transient overvoltages of 2.4 p.u. The maximum operating voltage of the line is 550 kilovolts. Determine the length of the protective gap that will provide the minimum practical safe approach distance. Also, determine what that minimum approach distance is.

Step 1. Calculate the smallest practical maximum transient overvoltage (1.25 times the crest phase-to-ground voltage):[13]

$$550\text{ kV} \times \frac{\sqrt{2}}{\sqrt{3}} \times 1.25 = 561\text{ kV}$$

This value equals the withstand voltage of the protective gap.

Step 2. Using test data for a particular protective gap, select a gap that has a critical sparkover voltage greater than or equal to:

$$\frac{561\text{ kV}}{0.85} = 660\text{ kV}$$

For example, if a protective gap with a 1.22-m (4.0-foot) spacing tested to a critical sparkover voltage of 665 kilovolts (crest), select this gap spacing.

Step 3. The phase-to-ground peak voltage at gap sparkover ($V_{PPG\ Peak}$) is 110 percent of the value from the previous step:

$$665\text{kV} \times 1.10 = 732\text{kV}$$

This value corresponds to the withstand voltage of the electrical component of the minimum approach distance.

Step 4. Use this voltage to determine the worksite value of *T*:

$$T = \frac{732}{564} = 1.7\text{ p.u.}$$

Step 5. Use this value of *T* in the equation in Table R-3 to obtain the minimum approach distance, or look up the minimum approach distance in Table 14 through Table 21:

$$MAD = 2.29\text{m } (7.6\text{ ft})$$

E. Location of Protective Gaps

1. Adjacent structures The employer may install the protective gap on a structure adjacent to the worksite, as this practice does not significantly reduce the protection afforded by the gap.

2. Terminal stations Gaps installed at terminal stations of lines or circuits provide a level of protection; however, that level of protection may not extend throughout the length of the line to the worksite. The use of substation terminal gaps raises the possibility that separate surges could enter the line at opposite ends, each with low enough magnitude to pass the terminal gaps without sparkover. When voltage surges occur simultaneously at each end of a line and travel toward each other, the total voltage on the line at the point where they meet is the arithmetic sum of the two surges. A gap installed within 0.8 km (0.5 mile) of the worksite will protect against such intersecting waves. Engineering studies of a particular line or system may indicate that employers can adequately protect employees by installing gaps at even more distant locations. In any event, unless using the default values for *T* from Table R-9, the employer must determine *T* at the worksite.

3. Worksite If the employer installs protective gaps at the worksite, the gap setting establishes the worksite impulse insulation strength. Lightning strikes as far as 6 miles from the worksite can cause a voltage surge greater than the gap withstand voltage, and a gap sparkover can occur. In addition, the gap can sparkover from overvoltages on the line that exceed the withstand voltage of the gap. Consequently, the employer must protect employees from hazards resulting from any sparkover that could occur.

F. Disabling automatic reclosing There are two reasons to disable the automatic-reclosing feature of circuit-interrupting devices while employees are performing live-line work:

- To prevent reenergization of a circuit faulted during the work, which could create a hazard or result in more serious injuries or damage than the injuries or damage produced by the original fault;
- To prevent any transient overvoltage caused by the switching surge that would result if the circuit were reenergized.

However, due to system stability considerations, it may not always be feasible to disable the automatic-reclosing feature.

V. Minimum Approach-Distance Tables

A. Legacy tables Employers may use the minimum approach distances in Table 6 through Table 13 until March 31, 2015.

[13] To eliminate sparkovers due to minor system disturbances, the employer should use a withstand voltage no lower than 1.25 p.u. Note that this is a practical, or operational, consideration only. It may be feasible for the employer to use lower values of withstand voltage.

Table 6
Minimum Approach Distances Until December 31, 2014

Voltage range phase to phase (kV)	Phase-to-ground exposure		Phase-to-phase exposure	
	m	ft	m	ft
0.05 to 1.0	Avoid Contact		Avoid Contact	
1.1 to 15.0	0.64	2.10	0.66	2.20
15.1 to 36.0	0.72	2.30	0.77	2.60
36.1 to 46.0	0.77	2.60	0.85	2.80
46.1 to 72.5	0.90	3.00	1.05	3.50
72.6 to 121	0.95	3.20	1.29	4.30
138 to 145	1.09	3.60	1.50	4.90
161 to 169	1.22	4.00	1.71	5.70
230 to 242	1.59	5.30	2.27	7.50
345 to 362	2.59	8.50	3.80	12.50
500 to 550	3.42	11.30	5.50	18.10
765 to 800	4.53	14.90	7.91	26.00

NOTE: The clear live-line tool distance must equal or exceed the values for the indicated voltage ranges.

Table 7
Minimum Approach Distances Until March 31, 2015
72.6 to 121.0 kV With Overvoltage Factor

T (p.u.)	Phase-to-ground exposure		Phase-to-phase exposure	
	m	ft	m	ft
2.0	0.74	2.42	1.09	3.58
2.1	0.76	2.50	1.09	3.58
2.2	0.79	2.58	1.12	3.67
2.3	0.81	2.67	1.14	3.75
2.4	0.84	5.75	1.17	3.83
2.5	0.84	2.75	1.19	3.92
2.6	0.86	2.83	1.22	4.00
2.7	0.89	2.92	1.24	4.08
2.8	0.91	3.00	1.24	4.08
2.9	0.94	3.08	1.27	4.17
3.0	0.97	3.17	1.30	4.25

NOTE: The employer may apply the distance specified in this table only where the employer determines the maximum anticipated per-unit transient overvoltage by engineering analysis. (Table 6 applies otherwise.)

NOTE: The distances specified in this table are the air, bare-hand, and live-line tool distances.

Table 8
Minimum Approach Distances Until March 31, 2015
121.1 to 145.0 kV With Overvoltage Factor

T (p.u.)	Phase-to-ground exposure		Phase-to-phase exposure	
	m	ft	m	ft
2.0	0.84	2.75	1.24	4.08
2.1	0.86	2.83	1.27	4.17
2.2	0.89	2.92	1.30	4.25
2.3	0.91	3.00	1.32	4.33
2.4	0.94	3.08	1.35	4.42
2.5	0.97	3.17	1.37	4.50
2.6	0.99	3.25	1.40	4.58
2.7	1.02	3.33	1.42	4.67
2.8	1.04	3.42	1.45	4.75
2.9	1.07	3.50	1.47	4.83
3.0	1.09	3.58	1.50	4.92

T (p.u.)	Phase-to-ground exposure		Phase-to-phase exposure	
	m	ft	m	ft

NOTE: The employer may apply the distance specified in this table only where the employer determines the maximum anticipated per-unit transient overvoltage by engineering analysis. (Table 6 applies otherwise.)
NOTE: The distances specified in this table are the air, bare-hand, and live-line tool distances.

Table 9
Minimum Approach Distances Until March 31, 2015 145.1 to 169.0 kV With Overvoltage Factor

T (p.u.)	Phase-to-ground exposure		Phase-to-phase exposure	
	m	ft	m	ft
2.0	0.91	3.00	1.42	4.67
2.1	0.97	3.17	1.45	4.75
2.2	0.99	3.25	1.47	4.83
2.3	1.02	3.33	1.50	4.92
2.4	1.04	3.42	1.52	5.00
2.5	1.07	3.50	1.57	5.17
2.6	1.12	3.67	1.60	5.25
2.7	1.14	3.75	1.63	5.33
2.8	1.17	3.83	1.65	5.42
2.9	1.19	3.92	1.68	5.50
3.0	1.22	4.00	1.73	5.67

NOTE: The employer may apply the distance specified in this table only where the employer determines the maximum anticipated per-unit transient overvoltage by engineering analysis. (Table 6 applies otherwise.)
NOTE: The distances specified in this table are the air, bare-hand, and live-line tool distances.

Table 10
Minimum Approach Distances Until March 31, 2015 169.1 to 242.0 kV With Overvoltage Factor

T (p.u.)	Phase-to-ground exposure		Phase-to-phase exposure	
	m	ft	m	ft
2.0	1.17	3.83	1.85	6.08
2.1	1.22	4.00	1.91	63.25
2.2	1.24	4.08	1.93	6.33
2.3	1.30	4.25	1.98	6.50
2.4	1.35	4.42	2.01	6.58
2.5	1.37	4.50	2.06	6.75
2.6	1.42	4.67	2.11	6.92
2.7	1.47	4.83	2.13	7.00
2.8	1.50	4.92	2.18	7.17
2.9	1.55	5.08	2.24	7.33
3.0	1.60	5.25	2.29	7.50

NOTE: The employer may apply the distance specified in this table only where the employer determines the maximum anticipated per-unit transient overvoltage by engineering analysis. (Table 6 applies otherwise.)
NOTE: The distances specified in this table are the air, bare-hand, and live-line tool distances.

Table 11
Minimum Approach Distances Until March 31, 2015 242.1 to 362.0 kV With Overvoltage Factor

T (p.u.)	Phase-to-ground exposure		Phase-to-phase exposure	
	m	ft	m	ft
2.0	1.60	5.25	2.62	8.58
2.1	1.65	5.42	2.69	8.83
2.2	1.75	5.75	2.79	9.17
2.3	1.85	6.08	2.90	9.50
2.4	1.93	6.33	3.02	9.92
2.5	2.03	6.67	3.15	10.33
2.6	2.16	7.08	3.28	10.75
2.7	2.26	7.42	3.40	11.17
2.8	2.36	7.75	3.53	11.58
2.9	2.49	8.17	3.68	12.08
3.0	2.59	8.50	3.81	12.50

NOTE: The employer may apply the distance specified in this table only where the employer determines the maximum anticipated per-unit transient overvoltage by engineering analysis. (Table 6 applies otherwise.)
NOTE: The distances specified in this table are the air, bare-hand, and live-line tool distances.

Table 12
Minimum Approach Distances Until March 31, 2015 362.1 to 552.0 kV With Overvoltage Factor

T (p.u.)	Phase-to-ground exposure		Phase-to-phase exposure	
	m	ft	m	ft
1.5	1.83	6.00	2.24	7.33
1.6	1.98	6.50	2.67	8.75
1.7	2.13	7.00	3.10	10.17
1.8	2.31	7.58	3.53	11.58
1.9	2.46	8.08	4.01	13.17
2.0	2.67	8.75	4.52	14.83
2.1	2.84	9.33	4.75	15.58
2.2	3.02	9.92	4.98	16.33
2.3	3.20	10.50	5.23	1717
2.4	3.43	11.25	5.51	18.08

NOTE: The employer may apply the distance specified in this table only where the employer determines the maximum anticipated per-unit transient overvoltage by engineering analysis. (Table 6 applies otherwise.)
NOTE: The distances specified in this table are the air, bare-hand, and live-line tool distances.

Table 13
Minimum Approach Distances Until March 31, 2015 552.1 to 800.0 kV With Overvoltage Factor

T (p.u.)	Phase-to-ground exposure		Phase-to-phase exposure	
	m	ft	m	ft
1.5	2.95	9.67	3.68	12.08
1.6	3.25	10.67	4.42	14.50
1.7	3.56	11.67	5.23	17.17
1.8	3.86	12.67	6.07	19.92
1.9	4.19	13.75	6.99	22.92
2.0	4.55	14.92	7.92	26.00

NOTE: The employer may apply the distance specified in this table only where the employer determines the maximum anticipated per-unit transient overvoltage by engineering analysis. (Table 6 applies otherwise.)
NOTE: The distances specified in this table are the air, bare-hand, and live-line tool distances.

B. Alternative minimum approach distances Employers may use the minimum approach distances in Table 14 through Table 21 provided that the employer follows the notes to those tables.

Table 14
AC Minimum Approach Distances 72.6 to 121.0 kV

T (p.u.)	Phase-to-ground exposure		Phase-to-phase exposure	
	m	ft	m	ft
1.5	0.67	2.2	.84	2.8
1.6	0.69	2.3	.87	2.9
1.7	0.71	2.3	.90	3.0
Note: Table data continues on next page.				

T (p.u.)	Phase-to-ground exposure		Phase-to-phase exposure	
	m	ft	m	ft
1.8	0.74	2.4	.93	3.1
1.9	0.76	2.5	.96	3.1
2.0	0.78	2.6	.99	3.2
2.1	0.81	2.7	1.01	3.3
2.2	0.83	2.7	1.04	3.4
2.3	0.85	2.8	1.07	3.5
2.4	0.88	2.9	1.10	3.6
2.5	0..90	3.0	1.13	3.7
2.6	0.92	3.0	1.16	3.8
2.7	0.95	.\3.1	1.19	3.9
2.8	0.97	3.2	1.22	4.0
2.9	0.99	3.2	1.24	4.1
3.0	1.02	3.3	1.27	4.2
3.1	1.04	3.4	1.30	4.3
3.2	1.06	3.5	1.33	4.4
3.3	1.09	3.6	1.36	4.5
3.4	1.11	3.6	1.39	4.6
3.5	1.13	3.7	1.42	4.7

Table 15
AC Minimum Approach Distances
121.1 to 145.0 kV

T (p.u.)	Phase-to-ground exposure		Phase-to-phase exposure	
	m	ft	m	ft
1.5	0.81	2.7	1.05	3.4
1.6	0.84	2.8	1.09	3.6
1.7	0.87	2.9	1.13	3.7
1.8	0.90	3.0	1.17	3.8
1.9	0.94	3.1	1.21	4.0
2.0	0.97	3.2	1.25	4.1
2.1	1.00	3.3	1.29	4.2
2.2	1.03	3.4	1.33	4.4
2.3	1.07	3.5	1.37	4.5
2.4	1.10	3.6	1.41	4.6
2.5	1.13	3.7	1.45	4.8
2.6	1.17	3.8	1.49	4.9
2.7	1.20	3.9	1.53	5.0
2.8	1.23	1.0	1.57	5.2
2.9	1.26	1.1	1.61	5.3
3.0	1.30	4.3	1.65	5.4
3.1	1.33	4.4	1.70	5.6
3.2	1.36	4.5	1.76	5.8
3.3	1.69	4.6	1.82	6.0
3.4	1.43	4.7	1.88	6.2
3.5	1.46	4.8	1.94	6.4

Table 17
AC Minimum Approach Distances
169.1 to 242.0 kV

T (p.u.)	Phase-to-ground exposure		Phase-to-phase exposure	
	m	ft	m	ft
1.5	1.02	3.3	1.37	4.5
1.6	1.06	3.5	1.43	4.7
1.7	1.11	3.6	1.48	4.9
1.8	1.16	3.8	1.54	5.1
1.9	1.21	4.0	1.60	5.2
2.0	1.25	4.1	1.66	5.4
2.1	1.30	4.3	1.73	5.7
2.2	1.35	4.4	1.81	5.9
2.3	1.39	4.6	1.90	6.2
2.4	1.44	4.7	1399	6.5
2.5	1.49	4.9	2.08	6.8
2.6	1.53	5.0	2.17	7.1
2.7	1.58	5.2	2.26	7.4
2.8	1.63	5.3	2.36	7.7
2.9	1.67	5.5	2.45	8.0
3.0	1.72	5.6	2.55	8.4
3.1	1.77	5.8	2.65	8.7
3.2	1.81	5.9	2.76	9.1
3.3	1.88	6.2	2.86	9.4
3.4	1.95	6.4	2.97	9.7
3.5	2.01	6.6	3.08	10.1

Table 18
AC Minimum Approach Distances
242.1 to 362.0 kV

T (p.u.)	Phase-to-ground exposure		Phase-to-phase exposure	
	m	ft	m	ft
1.5	1.37	4.5	1.99	6.5
1.6	1.44	4.7	2.13	7.0
1.7	1.51	5.0	2.27	7.4
1.8	1.58	5.2	2.41	7.9
1.9	1.65	5.4	2.56	8.4
2.0	1.72	5.6	2.71	8.9
2.1	1.79	5.9	2.87	9.4
2.2	1.87	6.1	3.03	9.9
2.3	1.97	6.5	3.20	10.5
2.4	2.08	6.8	3.37	11.1
2.5	2.19	7.2	3.55	11.6
2.6	2.29	7.5	3.73	12.2
2.7	2.41	7.9	3.91	12.8
2.8	2.52	8.3	4.10	13.5
2.9	2.64	8.7	4.29	14.1
3.0	2.76	9.1	4.49	14.7
3.1	2.88	9.4	4.69	15.4
3.2	3.01	9.9	4.90	16.1
3.3	3.14	10.3	5.11	16.8
3.4	3.27	10.7	5.32	17.5
3.5	3.41	11.2	5.52	18.1

Table 19
AC Minimum Approach Distances
362.1 to 420.0 kV

T (p.u.)	Phase-to-ground exposure		Phase-to-phase exposure	
	m	ft	m	ft
1.5	1.53	5.0	2.4	7.9
1.6	1.62	5.3	2.58	8.5
1.7	1.70	5.6	2.75	9.0
1.8	1.78	5.8	2.94	9.6
1.9	1.88	6.2	3.13	10.3
2.0	1.99	6.5	3.33	10.9
2.1	2.12	7.0	3.53	11.6
2.2	2.24	7.3	3.74	12.3
2.3	2.37	7.8	3.95	13.0
2.4	2.50	8.2	4.17	13.7
2.5	2.64	8.7	4.40	14.4
2.6	2.78	9.1	4.63	15.2
2.7	2.93	9.6	4.87	16.0
2.8	3.07	10.1	5.11	16.8
2.9	3.23	10.6	5.36	17.6
3.0	3.38	11.1	5.59	18.3
3.1	3.55	11.6	5.82	19.1
3.2	3.72	12.2	6.07	19.9
3.3	3.89	12.8	6.31	20.7
3.4	4.07	13.4	6.56	21.5
3.5	4.25	13.9	6.81	22.3

Table 20
AC Minimum Approach Distances
420.1 to 550.0 kV

T (p.u.)	Phase-to-ground exposure		Phase-to-phase exposure	
	m	ft	m	ft
1.5	1.95	6.4	3.46	11.4
1.6	2.11	6.9	3.73	12.2
1.7	2.25	7.5	4.02	13.2
1.8	2.45	8.0	4.31	14.1
1.9	2.62	8.6	4.61	15.1
2.0	2.81	9.2	4.92	16.1
2.1	3.00	9.8	5.25	17.2
2.2	3.20	10.5	5.55	18.2
2.3	3.40	11.2	5.86	19.2
2.4	3.62	11.9	6.18	20.3
2.5	3.84	12.6	6.50	21.3
2.6	4.07	13.4	6.83	22.4
2.7	4.31	14.1	7.18	23.6
2.8	4.56	15.0	7.52	24.7
2.9	4.81	15.8	7.88	25.9
3.0	5.07	16.6	8.24	27.0

Table 21
AC Minimum Approach Distances
550.1 to 800.0 kV

T (p.u.)	Phase-to-ground exposure		Phase-to-phase exposure	
	m	ft	m	ft
1.5	3.16	10.4	5.97	19.6
1.6	3.46	11.4	6.43	21.1
1.7	3.78	12.4	6.92	22.7
1.8	4.12	13.5	7.42	24.3
1.9	4.47	14.7	7.93	26.0
2.0	4.83	15.8	8.47	27.8
2.1	5.21	17.1	9.02	29.6
2.2	5.61	18.4	9.58	31.4
2.3	6.02	19.8	10.16	33.3
2.4	6.44	21.1	10.76	35.3
2.5	6.88	22.6	11.38	37.3

Notes to Table 14 through Table 21:

1. The employer must determine the maximum anticipated per-unit transient overvoltage, phase-to-ground, through an engineering analysis, as required by §1910.269(l)(3)(ii), or assume a maximum anticipated per-unit transient overvoltage, phase-to-ground, in accordance with Table R-9.
2. For phase-to-phase exposures, the employer must demonstrate that no insulated tool spans the gap and that no large conductive object is in the gap.
3. The worksite must be at an elevation of 900 meters (3,000 feet) or less above sea level.

§1910.269 Appendix C Protection from hazardous differences in electric potential

I. Introduction

Current passing through an impedance impresses voltage across that impedance. Even conductors have some, albeit low, value of impedance. Therefore, if a "grounded"[1] object, such as a crane or deenergized and grounded power line, results in a ground fault on a power line, voltage is impressed on that grounded object. The voltage impressed on the grounded object depends largely on the voltage on the line, on the impedance of the faulted conductor, and on the impedance to "true," or "absolute," ground represented by the object. If the impedance of the object causing the fault is relatively large, the voltage impressed on the object is essentially the phase-to-ground system voltage. However, even faults to grounded power lines or to well grounded transmission towers or substation structures (which have relatively low values of impedance to ground) can result in hazardous voltages.[2] In all cases, the degree of the hazard depends on the magnitude of the current through the employee and the time of exposure. This Appendix discusses methods of protecting workers against the possibility that grounded objects, such as cranes and other mechanical equipment, will contact energized power lines and that deenergized and grounded power lines will become accidentally energized.

II. Voltage-Gradient Distribution

A. Voltage-gradient distribution curve

Absolute, or true, ground serves as a reference and always has a voltage of 0 volts above ground potential. Because there is an impedance between a grounding electrode and absolute ground, there will be a voltage difference between the grounding electrode and absolute ground under ground-fault conditions. Voltage dissipates from the grounding electrode (or from the grounding point) and creates a ground potential gradient. The voltage decreases rapidly with increasing distance from the grounding electrode. A voltage drop associated with this dissipation of voltage is a ground potential. Figure 1 is a typical voltage-gradient distribution curve (assuming a uniform soil texture).

---

1 This Appendix generally uses the term "grounded" only with respect to grounding that the employer intentionally installs, for example, the grounding an employer installs on a deenergized conductor. However, in this case, the term "grounded" means connected to earth, regardless of whether or not that connection is intentional.

2 Thus, grounding systems for transmission towers and substation structures should be designed to minimize the step and touch potentials involved.

Figure 1
Typical Voltage-Gradient Distribution Curve

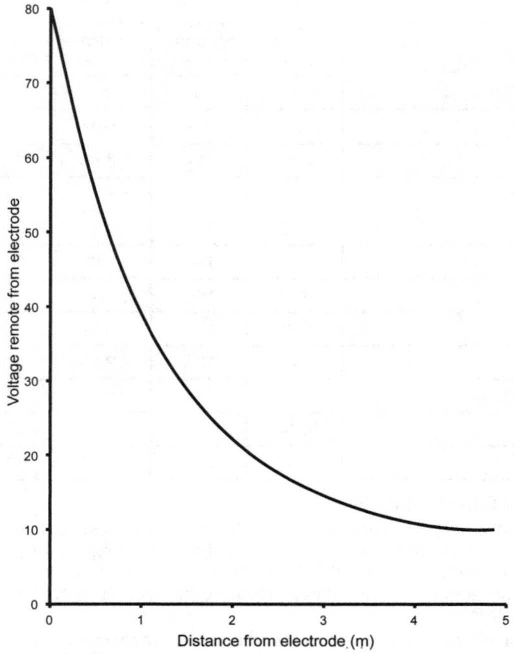

B. Step and touch potentials

Figure 1 also shows that workers are at risk from step and touch potentials. Step potential is the voltage between the feet of a person standing near an energized grounded object (the electrode). In Figure 1, the step potential is equal to the difference in voltage between two points at different distances from the electrode (where the points represent the location of each foot in relation to the electrode). A person could be at risk of injury during a fault simply by standing near the object.

Touch potential is the voltage between the energized grounded object (again, the electrode) and the feet of a person in contact with the object. In Figure 1, the touch potential is equal to the difference in voltage between the electrode (which is at a distance of 0 meters) and a point some distance away from the electrode (where the point represents the location of the feet of the person in contact with the object). The touch potential could be nearly the full voltage across the grounded object if that object is grounded at a point remote from the place where the person is in contact with it. For example, a crane grounded to the system neutral and that contacts an energized line would expose any person in contact with the crane or its uninsulated load line to a touch potential nearly equal to the full fault voltage.

Figure 2 illustrates step and touch potentials.

Figure 2
Step and Touch Potentials

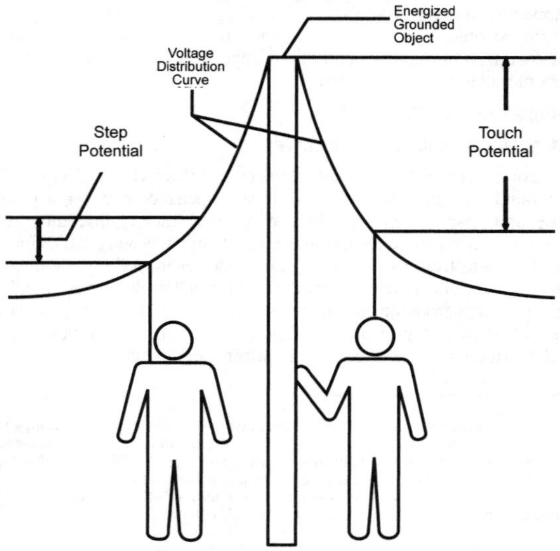

III. Protecting Workers From Hazardous Differences in Electrical Potential

A. Definitions

The following definitions apply to Section III of this Appendix:

Bond The electrical interconnection of conductive parts designed to maintain a common electric potential.

Bonding cable (bonding jumper) A cable connected to two conductive parts to bond the parts together.

Cluster bar A terminal temporarily attached to a structure that provides a means for the attachment and bonding of grounding and bonding cables to the structure.

Ground A conducting connection between an electric circuit or equipment and the earth, or to some conducting body that serves in place of the earth.

Grounding cable (grounding jumper) A cable connected between a deenergized part and ground. Note that grounding cables carry fault current and bonding cables generally do not. A cable that bonds two conductive parts but carries substantial fault current (for example, a jumper connected between one phase and a grounded phase) is a grounding cable.

Ground mat (grounding grid) A temporarily or permanently installed metallic mat or grating that establishes an equipotential surface and provides connection points for attaching grounds.

B. Analyzing the hazard

The employer can use an engineering analysis of the power system under fault conditions to determine whether hazardous step and touch voltages will develop. The analysis should determine the voltage on all conductive objects in the work area and the amount of time the voltage will be present. Based on the this analysis, the employer can select appropriate measures and protective equipment, including the measures and protective equipment outlined in Section III of this Appendix, to protect each employee from hazardous differences in electric potential. For example, from the analysis, the employer will know the voltage remaining on conductive objects after employees install bonding and grounding equipment and will be able to select insulating equipment with an appropriate rating, as described in paragraph III.C.2 of this Appendix.

C. Protecting workers on the ground

The employer may use several methods, including equipotential zones, insulating equipment, and restricted work areas, to protect employees on the ground from hazardous differences in electrical potential.

1. An equipotential zone will protect workers within it from hazardous step and touch potentials. (See Figure 3.) Equipotential zones will not, however, protect employees located either wholly or partially outside the protected area. The employer can establish an equipotential zone for workers on the ground, with respect to a grounded object, through the use of a metal mat connected to the grounded object. The employer can use a grounding grid to equalize the voltage within the grid or bond conductive objects in the immediate work area to minimize the potential between the objects and between each object and ground. (Bonding an object outside the work area can increase the touch potential to that object, however.) Section III.D of this Appendix discusses equipotential zones for employees working on deenergized and grounded power lines.

2. Insulating equipment, such as rubber gloves, can protect employees handling grounded equipment and conductors from hazardous touch potentials. The insulating equipment must be rated for the highest voltage that can be impressed on the grounded objects under fault conditions (rather than for the full system voltage).

3. Restricting employees from areas where hazardous step or touch potentials could arise can protect employees not directly involved in performing the operation. The employer must ensure that employees on the ground in the vicinity of transmission structures are at a distance where step voltages would be insufficient to cause injury. Employees must not handle grounded conductors or equipment likely to become energized to hazardous voltages unless the employees are within an equipotential zone or protected by insulating equipment.

Figure 3
Protection from Ground-Potenttial Gradients

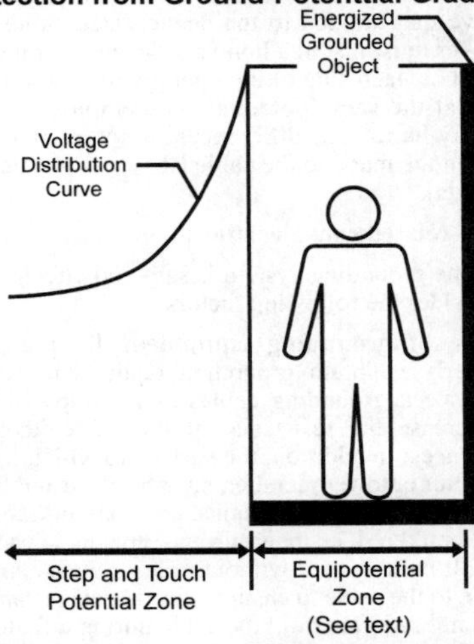

D. Protecting employees working on deenergized and grounded power lines.

This Section III.D of Appendix C establishes guidelines to help employers comply with requirements in §1910.269(n) for using protective grounding to protect employees working on deenergized power lines. Paragraph (n) of §1910.269 applies to grounding of transmission and distribution lines and equipment for the purpose of protecting workers. Paragraph (n)(3) of §1910.269 requires temporary protective grounds to be placed at such locations and arranged in such a manner that the employer can demonstrate will prevent exposure of each employee to hazardous differences in electric potential.[3] Sections III.D.1 and III.D.2 of this Appendix provide guidelines that employers can use in making the demonstration required by §1910.269(n)(3). Section III.D.1 of this Appendix provides guidelines on how the employer can determine whether particular grounding practices expose employees to hazardous differences in electric potential. Section III.D.2 of this Appendix describes grounding methods that the employer can use in lieu of an engineering analysis to make the demonstration required by §1910.269(n)(3). The Occupational Safety and Health Administration will consider employers that comply with the criteria in this Appendix as meeting §1910.269(n)(3).

Finally, Section III.D.3 of this Appendix discusses other safety considerations that will help the employer comply with other requirements in §1910.269(n). Following these guidelines will protect workers from hazards that can occur when a deenergized and grounded line becomes energized.

1. Determining safe body current limits This Section III.D.1 of Appendix C provides guidelines on how an employer can determine whether any differences in electric potential to which workers could be exposed are hazardous as part of the demonstration required by §1910.269(n)(3).

Institute of Electrical and Electronic Engineers (IEEE) Standard 1048-2003, IEEE Guide for Protective Grounding of Power Lines, provides the following equation for determining the threshold of ventricular fibrillation when the duration of the electric shock is limited:

$$I = \frac{116}{\sqrt{t}}$$

where I is the current through the worker's body, and t is the duration of the current in seconds. This equation represents the ventricular fibrillation threshold for 95.5 percent of the adult population with a mass of 50 kilograms (110 pounds) or more. The equation is valid for current durations between 0.0083 to 3.0 seconds.

To use this equation to set safe voltage limits in an equipotential zone around the worker, the employer will need to assume a value for the resistance of the worker's body. IEEE Std 1048-2003 states that "total body resistance is usually taken as 1000 Ω for determining . . . body current limits."

However, employers should be aware that the impedance of a worker's worker's body can be substantially less than that value. For instance, IEEE Std 1048-2003 reports a minimum hand-to-hand resistance of 610 ohms and an internal body resistance of 500 ohms. The internal resistance of the body better represents the minimum resistance of a worker's body when the skin resistance drops near zero, which occurs, for example, when there are breaks in the worker's skin, for instance, from cuts or from blisters formed as a result of the current from an electric shock, or when the worker is wet at the points of contact.

Employers may use the IEEE Std 1048-2003 equation to determine safe body current limits only if the employer protects workers from hazards associated with involuntary muscle reactions from electric shock (for example, the hazard to a worker from falling as a result of an electric shock). Moreover, the equation applies only when the duration of the electric shock is limited. If the precautions the employer takes, including those required by applicable standards, do not adequately protect employees from hazards associated with involuntary reactions from electric shock, a hazard exists if the induced voltage is sufficient to pass a current of 1 milliampere through a 500-ohm resistor. (The 500-ohm resistor represents the resistance of an employee. The 1-milliampere current is the threshold of perception.) Finally, if the employer protects employees from injury due to involuntary reactions from electric shock, but the duration of the electric shock is unlimited (that is, when the fault current at the work location will be insufficient to trip the devices protecting the circuit), a hazard exists if the resultant current would be more than 6 milliamperes (the recognized let-go threshold for workers[4]).

2. Acceptable methods of grounding for employers that do not perform an engineering determination The grounding methods presented in this section of this Appendix ensure that differences in electric potential are as low as possible and, therefore, meet §1910.269(n)(3) without an engineering determination of the potential differences. These methods follow two principles: (i) The grounding method must ensure that the circuit opens in the fastest available clearing time, and (ii) the grounding method must ensure that the potential differences between conductive objects in the employee's work area are as low as possible.

Paragraph (n)(3) of §1910.269 does not require grounding methods to meet the criteria embodied in these principles. Instead, the paragraph requires that protective grounds be "placed at such locations and arranged in such a manner that the employer can demonstrate will prevent exposure of each employee to hazardous differences in electric potential." However, when the employer's grounding practices do not follow these two principles, the employer will need to perform an engineering analysis to make the demonstration required by §1910.269(n)(3).

i. Ensuring that the circuit opens in the fastest available clearing time Generally, the higher the fault current, the shorter the clearing times for the same type of fault. Therefore, to ensure the fastest available clearing time, the grounding method must maximize the fault current with a low impedance connection to ground. The employer accomplishes this objective by grounding the circuit conductors to the best ground available at the worksite. Thus, the employer must ground to a grounded system neutral conductor, if one is present. A grounded system neutral has a direct connection to the system ground at the source, resulting in an extremely low impedance to ground. In a substation, the employer may instead ground to the substation grid, which also has an extremely low impedance to the system ground and, typically, is connected to a grounded system neutral when one is present. Remote system grounds, such as pole and tower grounds, have a higher impedance to the system ground than grounded system neutrals and substation grounding grids; however, the employer may use a remote ground when lower impedance grounds are not available. In the absence of a grounded system neutral, substation grid, and remote ground, the employer may use a temporary driven ground at the worksite.

In addition, if employees are working on a three-phase system, the grounding method must short circuit all three phases. Short circuiting all phases will ensure faster clearing and lower the current through the grounding cable connecting the deenergized line to ground, thereby lowering the voltage across that cable. The short circuit need not be at the worksite; however, the employer must treat any conductor that is not grounded at the worksite as energized because the ungrounded conductors will be energized at fault voltage during a fault.

ii. Ensuring that the potential differences between conductive objects in the employee's work area are as low as possible. To achieve as low a voltage as possible across any two conductive objects in the work area, the employer must bond all conductive objects in the work area. This section of this Appendix discusses how to create a zone that minimizes differences in electric potential between conductive objects in the work area.

The employer must use bonding cables to bond conductive objects, except for metallic objects bonded through metal-to-metal contact. The employer must ensure that metal-to-metal contacts are tight and free of contamination, such as oxidation, that can increase the impedance across the connection. For example, a bolted connection between metal lattice tower members is acceptable if the connection is tight and free of corrosion and other contamination. Figure 4 shows how to create an equipotential zone for metal lattice towers.

[3] The protective grounding required by §1910.269(n) limits to safe values the potential differences between accessible objects in each employee's work environment. Ideally, a protective grounding system would create a true equipotential zone in which every point is at the same electric potential. In practice, current passing through the grounding and bonding elements creates potential differences. If these potential differences are hazardous, the employer may not treat the zone as an equipotential zone.

[4] Electric current passing through the body has varying effects depending on the amount of the current. At the let-go threshold, the current overrides a person's control over his or her muscles. At that level, an employee grasping an object will not be able to let go of the object. The let-go threshold varies from person to person; however, the recognized value for workers is 6 milliamperes.

Wood poles are conductive objects. The poles can absorb moisture and conduct electricity, particularly at distribution and transmission voltages. Consequently, the employer must either: (1) Provide a conductive platform, bonded to a grounding cable, on which the worker stands or (2) use cluster bars to bond wood poles to the grounding cable. The employer must ensure that employees install the cluster bar below, and close to, the worker's feet. The inner portion of the wood pole is more conductive than the outer shell, so it is important that the cluster bar be in conductive contact with a metal spike or nail that penetrates the wood to a depth greater than or equal to the depth the worker's climbing gaffs will penetrate the wood. For example, the employer could mount the cluster bar on a bare pole ground wire fastened to the pole with nails or staples that penetrate to the required depth. Alternatively, the employer may temporarily nail a conductive strap to the pole and connect the strap to the cluster bar. Figure 5 shows how to create an equipotential zone for wood poles.

Figure 4
Equipotential Zone for Metal Lattice Tower

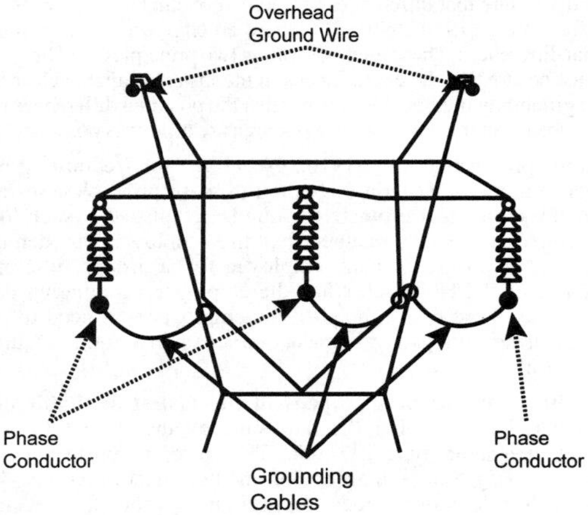

Notes:
1. Employers must ground overhead ground wires that are within reach of the employee.
2. The grounding cable must be as short as practicable; therefore, the attachment points between the grounding cable and the tower may be different from that shown in the figure.

Figure 5 5
Equipotential Grounding for Wood Poles

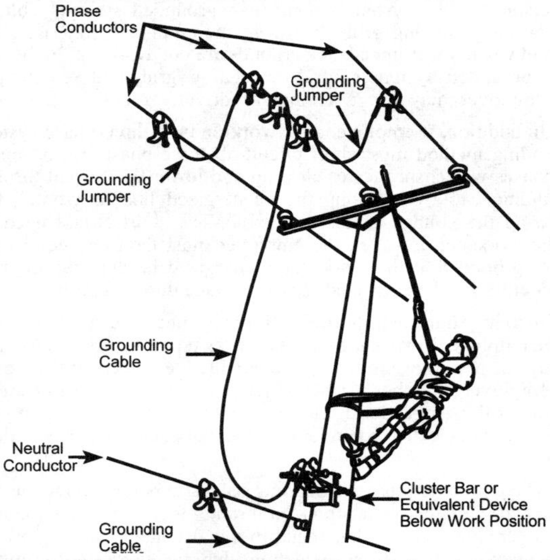

Figure reprinted with permission from Hubbell Power Systems, Inc. (Hubbell). OSHA revised the figure from Hubbell's original.

For underground systems, employers commonly install grounds at the points of disconnection of the underground cables. These grounding points are typically remote from the manhole or underground vault where employees will be working on the cable. Workers in contact with a cable grounded at a remote location can experience hazardous potential differences if the cable becomes energized or if a fault occurs on a different, but nearby, energized cable. The fault current causes potential gradients in the earth, and a potential difference will exist between the earth where the worker is standing and the earth where the cable is grounded. Consequently, to create an equipotential zone for the worker, the employer must provide a means of connecting the deenergized cable to ground at the worksite by having the worker stand on a conductive mat bonded to the deenergized cable. If the cable is cut, the employer must install a bond across the opening in the cable or install one bond on each side of the opening to ensure that the separate cable ends are at the same potential. The employer must protect the worker from any hazardous differences in potential any time there is no bond between the mat and the cable (for example, before the worker installs the bonds).[5]

3. Other safety-related considerations

To ensure that the grounding system is safe and effective, the employer should also consider the following factors:[5]

i. Maintenance of grounding equipment It is essential that the employer properly maintain grounding equipment. Corrosion in the connections between grounding cables and clamps and on the clamp surface can increase the resistance of the cable, thereby increasing potential differences. In addition, the surface to which a clamp attaches, such as a conductor or tower member, must be clean and free of corrosion and oxidation to ensure a low-resistance connection. Cables must be free of damage that could reduce their current-carrying capacity so that they can carry the full fault current without failure. Each clamp must have a tight connection to the cable to ensure a low resistance and to ensure that the clamp does not separate from the cable during a fault.

ii. Grounding cable length and movement The electromagnetic forces on grounding cables during a fault increase with increasing cable length. These forces can cause the cable to move violently during a fault and can be high enough to damage the cable or clamps and cause the cable to fail. In addition, flying cables can injure workers. Consequently, cable lengths should be as short as possible, and grounding cables that might carry high fault current should be in positions where the cables will not injure workers during a fault.

§1910.269 Appendix D Methods of inspecting and testing wood poles

I. Introduction

When employees are to perform work on a wood pole, it is important to determine the condition of the pole before employees climb it. The weight of the employee, the weight of equipment to be installed, and other working stresses (such as the removal or retensioning of conductors) can lead to the failure of a defective pole or a pole that is not designed to handle the additional stresses.[1] For these reasons, it is essential that, before an employee climbs a wood pole, the employer ascertain that the pole is capable of sustaining the stresses of the work. The determination that the pole is capable of sustaining these stresses includes an inspection of the condition of the pole.

If the employer finds the pole to be unsafe to climb or to work from, the employer must secure the pole so that it does not fail while an employee is on it. The employer can secure the pole by a line truck boom, by ropes or guys, or by lashing a new pole alongside it. If a new one is lashed alongside the defective pole, employees should work from the new one.

II. Inspecting Wood Poles

A qualified employee should inspect wood poles for the following conditions:[2]

A. General condition

Buckling at the ground line or an unusual angle with respect to the ground may indicate that the pole has rotted or is broken.

B. Cracks

Horizontal cracks perpendicular to the grain of the wood may weaken the pole. Vertical cracks, although not normally considered to be a sign of a defective pole, can pose a hazard to the climber, and the employee should keep his or her gaffs away from them while climbing.

---

[5] This Appendix only discusses factors that relate to ensuring an equipotential zone for employees. The employer must consider other factors in selecting a grounding system that is capable of conducting the maximum fault current that could flow at the point of grounding for the time necessary to clear the fault, as required by §1910.269(n)(4)(i). IEEE Std 1048-2003 contains guidelines for selecting and installing grounding equipment that will meet §1910.269(n)(4)(i).

Appendix D

[1] A properly guyed pole in good condition should, at a minimum, be able to handle the weight of an employee climbing it.

[2] The presence of any of these conditions is an indication that the pole may not be safe to climb or to work from. The employee performing the inspection must be qualified to make a determination as to whether it is safe to perform the work without taking additional precautions.

C. Holes

Hollow spots and woodpecker holes can reduce the strength of a wood pole.

D. Shell rot and decay

Rotting and decay are cutout hazards and possible indications of the age and internal condition of the pole.

E. Knots

One large knot or several smaller ones at the same height on the pole may be evidence of a weak point on the pole.

F. Depth of setting

Evidence of the existence of a former ground line substantially above the existing ground level may be an indication that the pole is no longer buried to a sufficient depth.

G. Soil conditions

Soft, wet, or loose soil around the base of the pole may indicate that the pole will not support any change in stress.

H. Burn marks

Burning from transformer failures or conductor faults could damage the pole so that it cannot withstand changes in mechanical stress.

III. Testing Wood Poles

The following tests, which are from §1910.268(n)(3), are acceptable methods of testing wood poles:

A. Hammer test

Rap the pole sharply with a hammer weighing about 1.4 kg (3 pounds), starting near the ground line and continuing upwards circumferentially around the pole to a height of approximately 1.8 meters (6 feet). The hammer will produce a clear sound and rebound sharply when striking sound wood. Decay pockets will be indicated by a dull sound or a less pronounced hammer rebound. Also, prod the pole as near the ground line as possible using a pole prod or a screwdriver with a blade at least 127 millimeters (5 inches) long. If substantial decay is present, the pole is unsafe.

§1910.269 Appendix E Protection from flames and electric arcs

I. Introduction

Paragraph (l)(8) of §1910.269 addresses protecting employees from flames and electric arcs. This paragraph requires employers to: (1) Assess the workplace for flame and electric-arc hazards (paragraph (l)(8)(i)); (2) estimate the available heat energy from electric arcs to which employees would be exposed (paragraph (l)(8)(ii)); (3) ensure that employees wear clothing that will not melt, or ignite and continue to burn, when exposed to flames or the estimated heat energy (paragraph (l)(8)(iii)); and (4) ensure that employees wear flame-resistant clothing[1] and protective clothing and other protective equipment that has an arc rating greater than or equal to the available heat energy under certain conditions (paragraphs (l)(8)(iv) and (l)(8)(v)). This Appendix contains information to help employers estimate available heat energy as required by §1910.269(l)(8)(ii), select protective clothing and other protective equipment with an arc rating suitable for the available heat energy as required by §1910.269(l)(8)(v), and ensure that employees do not wear flammable clothing that could lead to burn injury as addressed by §1910.269(l)(8)(iii) and (l)(8)(iv).

[1] Flame-resistant clothing includes clothing that is inherently flame resistant and clothing chemically treated with a flame retardant. (See ASTM F1506-10a, Standard Performance Specification for Flame Resistant Textile Materials for Wearing Apparel for Use by Electrical Workers Exposed to Momentary Electric Arc and Related Thermal Hazards, and ASTM F1891-12 Standard Specification for Arc and Flame Resistant Rainwear.)

II. Assessing the Workplace for Flame and Electric-Arc Hazards

Paragraph (l)(8)(i) of §1910.269 requires the employer to assess the workplace to identify employees exposed to hazards from flames or from electric arcs. This provision ensures that the employer evaluates employee exposure to flames and electric arcs so that employees who face such exposures receive the required protection. The employer must conduct an assessment for each employee who performs work on or near exposed, energized parts of electric circuits.

A. Assessment Guidelines

Sources electric arcs. Consider possible sources of electric arcs, including:
- Energized circuit parts not guarded or insulated,
- Switching devices that produce electric arcs in normal operation,
- Sliding parts that could fault during operation (for example, rack-mounted circuit breakers), and
- Energized electric equipment that could fail (for example, electric equipment with damaged insulation or with evidence of arcing or overheating).

Exposure to flames. Identify employees exposed to hazards from flames. Factors to consider include:
- The proximity of employees to open flames, and
- For flammable material in the work area, whether there is a reasonable likelihood that an electric arc or an open flame can ignite the material.

Probability that an electric arc will occur. Identify employees exposed to electric-arc hazards. The Occupational Safety and Health Administration will consider an employee exposed to electric-arc hazards if there is a reasonable likelihood that an electric arc will occur in the employee's work area, in other words, if the probability of such an event is higher than it is for the normal operation of enclosed equipment. Factors to consider include:
- For energized circuit parts not guarded or insulated, whether conductive objects can come too close to or fall onto the energized parts,
- For exposed, energized circuit parts, whether the employee is closer to the part than the minimum approach distance established by the employer (as permitted by §1910.269(l)(3)(iii)).
- Whether the operation of electric equipment with sliding parts that could fault during operation is part of the normal operation of the equipment or occurs during servicing or maintenance, and
- For energized electric equipment, whether there is evidence of impending failure, such as evidence of arcing or overheating.

B. Rocking test

Apply a horizontal force to the pole and attempt to rock it back and forth in a direction perpendicular to the line. Exercise caution to avoid causing power lines to swing together. Apply the force to the pole either by pushing it with a pike pole or pulling the pole with a rope. If the pole cracks during the test, it is unsafe.

B. Examples

Table 1 provides task-based examples of exposure assessments.

Table 1
Example Assessments for Various Tasks

Task		Is employee exposed to flame or electric-arc hazard?
Normal operation of enclosed equipment, such as closing or opening a switch.	The employer properly installs and maintains enclosed equipment, and there is no evidence of impending failure..	No
	There is evidence of arching or overheating	Yes
	Parts of the equipment are loose or sticking, or the equipment otherwise exhibits signs of lack of maintenance.	Yes
Servicing electric equipment, such as racking in a circuit breaker of replacing a switch		Yes
Inspection of electric equipment with exposed energized parts.	The employee is not holding conductive objects and remains outside the minimum approach distance established by the employer.	No
	The employee is holding a conductive object, such as a flashlight, that could fall or otherwise contact energized parts (irrespective of whether the employee maintains the minimum approach distance).	Yes
	The employee is closer than the minimum approach distance established by the employer (for example, when wearing rubber insulating gloves or rubber insulating gloves and sleeves).	Yes
Using open flames, for example, in wiping cable splice sleeves		Yes

III. Protection Against Burn Injury

A. Estimating Available Heat Energy

Calculation methods Paragraph (l)(8)(ii) of §1910.269 provides that, for each employee exposed to an electric-arc hazard, the employer must make a reasonable estimate of the heat energy to which the employee would be exposed if an arc occurs. Table 2 lists various methods of calculating values of available heat energy from an electric circuit. The Occupational Safety and Health Administration does not endorse any of these specific methods. Each method requires the input of various parameters, such as fault current, the expected length of the electric arc, the distance from the arc to the employee, and the clearing time for the fault (that is, the time the circuit protective devices take to open the circuit and clear the fault). The employer can precisely determine some of these parameters, such as the fault current and the clearing time, for a given system. The employer will need to estimate other parameters, such as the length of the arc and the distance between the arc and the employee, because such parameters vary widely.

Table 2
Methods of Calculating Incident Heat Energy From an Electric Arc

1. Standard for Electrical Safety Requirements for Employee Workplaces, NFPA 70E-2012, Annex D, ``Sample Calculation of Flash Protection Boundary.''
2. Doughty, T.E., Neal, T.E., and Floyd II, H.L., ``Predicting Incident Energy to Better Manage the Electric Arc Hazard on 600 V Power Distribution Systems,'' Record of Conference Papers IEEE IAS 45th Annual Petroleum and Chemical Industry Conference, September 28-30, 1998.
3. Guide for Performing Arc-Flash Hazard Calculations, IEEE Std 1584- 2002, 1584a-2004 (Amendment 1 to IEEE Std 1584-2002), and 1584b-2011 (Amendment 2: Changes to Clause 4 of IEEE Std 1584-2002).*
4. ARCPRO, a commercially available software program developed by Kinectrics, Toronto, ON, CA.

* This Appendix refers to IEEE Std 1584-2002 with both amendments as IEEE Std 1584b-2011

The amount of heat energy calculated by any of the methods is approximately inversely proportional to the square of the distance between the employee and the arc. In other words, if the employee is very close to the arc, the heat energy is very high; but if the employee is just a few more centimeters away, the heat energy drops substantially. Thus, estimating the distance from the arc to the employee is key to protecting employees.

The employer must select a method of estimating incident heat energy that provides a reasonable estimate of incident heat energy for the exposure involved. Table 3 shows which methods provide reasonable estimates for various exposures.

Table 3
Selecting a Reasonable Incident-Energy Calculation Method[1]

Incident-energy calculation method	600 V and Less[2]			601 V to 15 kV[2]			More than 15 kV		
	1Φ	3Φa	3Φb	1Φ	3Φa	3Φb	1Φ	3Φa	3Φb
NFPA 70E-2012 Annex D (Lee Equation)	Y-C	Y	N	Y-C	Y-C	N	N3	N3	N3
Doughty, Neal, and Floyd	Y-C	Y	Y	N	N	N	N	N	N
IEEE Std 1584b-2011	Y	Y	Y	Y	Y	Y	N	N	N
ARCPRO	Y	N	N	Y	N	N	Y	Y4	Y4

Key:
1Φ: Single-phase arc in open air.
3Φa: Three-phase arc in open air.
3Φb: Three-phase arc in an enclosure (box).
Y: Acceptable; produces a reasonable estimate of incident heat energy from this type of electric arc.
N: Not acceptable; does not produce a reasonable estimate of incident heat energy from this type of electric arc.
Y-C: Acceptable; produces a reasonable, but conservative, estimate of incident heat energy from this type of electric arc.

Notes:
[1] Although the Occupational Safety and Health Administration will consider these methods reasonable for enforcement purposes when employers use the methods in accordance with this table, employers should be aware that the listed methods do not necessarily result in estimates that will provide full protection from internal faults in transformers and similar equipment or from arcs in underground manholes or vaults.
[2] At these voltages, the presumption is that the arc is three-phase unless the employer can demonstrate that only one phase is present or that the spacing of the phases is sufficient to prevent a multiphase arc from occurring.
[3] Although the Occupational Safety and Health Administration will consider this method acceptable for purposes of assessing whether incident energy exceeds 2.0 cal/cm^2, the results at voltages of more than 15 kilovolts are extremely conservative and unrealistic.
[4] The Occupational Safety and Health Administration will deem the results of this method reasonable when the employer adjusts them using the conversion factors for three-phase arcs in open air or in an enclosure, as indicated in the program's instructions.

Selecting a reasonable distance from the employee to the arc. In estimating available heat energy, the employer must make some reasonable assumptions about how far the employee will be from the electric arc. Table 4 lists reasonable distances from the employee to the electric arc. The distances in Table 4 are consistent with national consensus standards, such as the Institute of Electrical and Electronic Engineers' National Electrical Safety Code, ANSI/IEEE C2-2012, and IEEE Guide for Performing Arc-Flash Hazard Calculations, IEEE Std 1584b-2011. The employer is free to use other reasonable distances, but must consider equipment enclosure size and the working distance to the employee in selecting a distance from the employee to the arc. The Occupational Safety and Health Administration will consider a distance reasonable when the employer bases it on equipment size and working distance.

Table 4
Selecting a Reasonable Distance From the Employee to the Electric Arc

Class of equipment	Single-Phase arc mm (inches)	Three-phase arc (inches)
Cable	* NA	455 (18)
Low voltage MCCs and panelboards	NA	455 (18)
Low-voltage switchgear	NA	610 (24)
5-kV switchgear	NA	910 (36)
15-kV switchgear	NA	910 (36)
Single conductors in air (up to 46 kilovolts), work with rubber insulating gloves	380 (15)	
Single conductors in air, work with live-line tools and live-line barehand work	*MAD* - (2 x kV x2.54) (*MAD* - (2 x kV/10)) †	NA

* NA = not applicable.
† The terms in this equation are:
MAD = The applicable minimum approach distance, and
kV = The system voltage in kilovolts.

Selecting a reasonable arc gap. For a single-phase arc in air, the electric arc will almost always occur when an energized conductor approaches too close to ground. Thus, an employer can determine the arc gap, or arc length, for these exposures by the dielectric strength of air and the voltage on the line. The dielectric strength of air is approximately 10 kilovolts for every 25.4 millimeters (1 inch). For example, at 50 kilovolts, the arc gap would be 50 ÷ 10 × 25.4 (or 50 × 2.54), which equals 127 millimeters (5 inches).

For three-phase arcs in open air and in enclosures, the arc gap will generally be dependent on the spacing between parts energized at different electrical potentials. Documents such as IEEE Std 1584b-2011 provide information on these distances. Employers may select a reasonable arc gap from Table 5, or they may select any other reasonable arc gap based on sparkover distance or on the spacing between (1) live parts at different potentials or (2) live parts and grounded parts (for example, bus or conductor spacings in equipment). In any event, the employer must use an estimate that reasonably resembles the actual exposures faced by the employee.

Table 5
Selecting a Reasonable Arc Gap

Class of equipment	Single-phase arc mm (inches)	Three-phase arc mm[1] (inches)
Cable	NA\2	13 (0.5)
Low voltage MCCs and panelboards	NA	25 (1.0)
Low-voltage switchgear	NA	32 (1.25)
5-kV switchgear	NA	104 (4.0)
15-kV switchgear	NA	152 (6.0)
Single conductors in air, 15 kV and less	51 (2.0)	Phase conductor spacing
Single conductor in air, more than 15 kV	Voltage in kV x 2.54 (Voltage in kV x 0.1), but no less than 51 mm (2 inches)	Phase conductor spacing

[1] Source: IEEE Std 1584b-2011.
[2] NA = not applicable

Making estimates over multiple system areas. The employer need not estimate the heat-energy exposure for every job task performed by each employee. Paragraph (l)(8)(ii) of §1910.269 permits the employer to make broad estimates that cover multiple system areas provided that: (1) The employer uses reasonable assumptions about the energy-exposure distribution throughout the system, and (2) the estimates represent the maximum exposure for those areas. For example, the employer can use the maximum fault current and clearing time to cover several system areas at once.

Incident heat energy for single-phase-to-ground exposures. Table 6 and Table 7 provide incident heat energy levels for open-air, phase-to-ground electric-arc exposures typical for overhead systems.[2] Table 6 presents estimates of available energy for employees using rubber insulating gloves to perform work on overhead systems operating at 4 to 46 kilovolts. The table assumes that the employee will be 380 millimeters (15 inches) from the electric arc, which is a reasonable estimate for rubber insulating glove work. Table 6 also assumes that the arc length equals the sparkover distance for the maximum transient overvoltage of each voltage range.[3] To use the table, an employer would use the voltage, maximum fault current, and maximum clearing time for a system area and, using the appropriate voltage range and fault-current and clearing-time values corresponding to the next higher values listed in the table, select the appropriate heat energy (4, 5, 8, or 12 cal/cm^2) from the table. For example, an employer might have a 12,470-volt power line supplying a system area. The power line can supply a maximum fault current of 8 kiloamperes with a maximum clearing time of 10 cycles. For rubber glove work, this system falls in the 4.0-to-15.0-kilovolt range; the next-higher fault current is 10 kA (the second row in that voltage range); and the clearing time is under 18 cycles (the first column to the right of the fault current column). Thus, the available heat energy for this part of the system will be 4 cal/cm^2 or less (from the column heading), and the employer could select protection with a 5-cal/cm^2 rating to meet §1910.269(l)(8)(v). Alternatively, an employer could select a base incident-energy value and ensure that the clearing times for each voltage range and fault current listed in the table do not exceed the corresponding clearing time specified in the table. For example, an employer that provides employees with arc-flash protective equipment rated at 8 cal/cm^2 can use the table to determine if any system area exceeds 8 cal/cm^2 by checking the clearing time for the highest fault current for each voltage range and ensuring that the clearing times do not exceed the values specified in the 8-cal/cm^2 column in the table.

Table 7 presents similar estimates for employees using live-line tools to perform work on overhead systems operating at voltages of 4 to 800 kilovolts. The table assumes that the arc length will be equal to the sparkover distance[4] and that the employee will be a distance from the arc equal to the minimum approach distance minus twice the sparkover distance.

The employer will need to use other methods for estimating available heat energy in situations not addressed by Table 6 or Table 7. The calculation methods listed in Table 2 and the guidance provided in Table 3 will help employers do this. For example, employers can use IEEE Std 1584b-2011 to estimate the available heat energy (and to select appropriate protective equipment) for many specific conditions, including lower-voltage, phase-to-phase arc, and enclosed arc exposures.

Table 6
Incident Heat Energy for Various Fault Currents, Clearing Times, and Voltages of 4.0 to 46.0 kV: Rubber Insulating Glove Exposures Involving Phase-to-Ground Arcs in Open Air Only* † ‡

Voltage range (kV) **	Fault current (kA)	Maximum clearing time (cycles)			
		4 cal/cm^2	5 cal/cm^2	8 cal/cm^2	12 cal/cm^2
4.0 to 15.0	5	46	58	92	138
	10	18	22	36	54
	15	10	12	20	30
	20	6	8	13	19
15.1 to 25.0	5	28	34	55	83
	10	11	14	23	34
	15	7	8	13	20
	20	4	5	9	13

Note: Table data continues on next page.

[2] The Occupational Safety and Health Administration used metric values to calculate the clearing times in Table 6 and Table 7. An employer may use English units to calculate clearing times instead even though the results will differ slightly.
[3] The Occupational Safety and Health Administration based this assumption, which is more conservative than the arc length specified in Table 5, on Table 410-2 of the 2012 NESC.

[4] The dielectric strength of air is about 10 kilovolts for every 25.4 millimeters (1 inch). Thus, the employer can estimate the arc length in millimeters to be the phase-to-ground voltage in kilovolts multiplied by 2.54 (or voltage (in kilovolts) × 2.54).

Voltage range (kV) **	Fault current (kA)	Maximum clearing time (cycles)			
		4 cal/cm²	5 cal/cm²	8 cal/cm²	12 cal/cm²
25.1 to 36.0	5	21	26	42	62
	10	9	11	18	26
	15	5	6	10	16
	20	4	4	7	11
36.1 to 46.0	5	16	20	32	48
	10	7	9	14	21
	15	4	5	8	13
	20	3	4	6	9

Notes:
* This table is for open-air, phase-to-ground electric-arc exposures. It is not for phase-to-phase arcs or enclosed arcs (arc in a box).
† The table assumes that the employee will be 380 mm (15 in.) from the electric arc. The table also assumes the arc length to be the sparkover distance for the maximum transient overvoltage of each voltage range (see Appendix B to §1910.269), as follows:
4.0 to 15.0 kV 51 mm (2 in.)
15.1 to 25.0 kV 102 mm (4 in.)
25.1 to 36.0 kV 152 mm (6 in.)
36.1 to 46.0 kV 229 mm (9 in.)
‡ The Occupational Safety and Health Administration calculated the values in this table using the ARCPRO method listed in Table 2.
** The voltage range is the phase-to-phase system voltage.

Table 7
Incident Heat Energy for Various Fault Currents, Clearing Times, and Voltages: Live-Line Tool Exposures Involving Phase-to-Ground Arcs in Open Air Only* † ‡

Voltage range (kV)**	Fault current (kA)	Maximum clearing time (cycles)			
		4 cal/cm²	5 cal/cm²	8 cal/cm²	12 cal/cm²
4.0 to 15.0	5	197	246	394	591
	10	73	92	147	220
	15	39	49	78	117
	20	24	31	49	73
15.1 to 25.0	5	197	246	394	591
	10	75	94	150	225
	15	41	51	82	122
	20	26	33	52	78
25.1 to 36.0	5	138	172	275	413
	10	53	66	106	159
	15	30	37	59	89
	20	19	24	38	58
36.1 to 46.0	5	129	161	257	386
	10	51	64	102	154
	15	29	36	58	87
	20	19	24	38	57
46.1 to 72.5	20	18	23	36	55
	30	10	13	20	30
	40	6	8	13	19
	50	4	6	9	13
72.6 to 121.0	20	10	12	20	30
	30	6	7	11	17
	40	4	5	7	11
	50	3	3	5	8
121.1 to 145.0	20	12	15	24	35
	30	7	9	15	22
	40	5	6	10	15
	50	4	5	8	11
145.1 to 169.0	20	12	15	24	36
	30	7	9	15	22
	40	5	7	10	16
	50	4	5	8	12
169.1 to 242.0	20	13	17	27	40
	30	8	10	17	25
	40	6	7	12	17
	50	4	5	9	13
242.1 to 362.0	20	25	32	51	76
	30	16	19	31	47
	40	11	14	22	35
	50	8	10	16	25
362.1 to 420.0	20	12	15	25	37
	30	8	10	15	23
	40	5	7	11	16
	50	4	5	8	12
420.1 to 550.0	20	23	29	47	70
	30	14	18	29	43
	40	10	13	20	30
	50	8	9	15	23

Voltage range (kV)**	Fault current (kA)	Maximum clearing time (cycles)			
		4 cal/cm^2	5 cal/cm^2	8 cal/cm^2	12 cal/cm^2
550.1 to 800.0	20	25	31	50	75
	30	15	19	31	46
	40	11	13	21	32
	50	8	10	16	24

Notes:
* This table is for open-air, phase-to-ground electric-arc exposures. It is not for phase-to-phase arcs or enclosed arcs (arc in a box).
† The table assumes the arc length to be the sparkover distance for the maximum phase-to-ground voltage of each voltage range (see Appendix B to this Section). The table also assumes that the employee will be the minimum approach distance minus twice the arc length from the electric arc.
‡ The Occupational Safety and Health Administration calculated the values in this table using the ARCPRO method listed in Table 2.
# For voltages of more than 72.6 kV, employers may use this table only when the minimum approach distance established under §1910.269(l)(3)(i) is greater than or equal to the following values:
72.6 to 121.0 kV 1.02 m.
121.1 to 145.0 kV 1.16 m.
145.1 to 169.0 kV 1.30 m.
169.1 to 242.0 kV 1.72 m.
242.1 to 362.0 kV 2.76 m.
362.1 to 420.0 kV 2.50 m.
420.1 to 550.0 kV 3.62 m.
550.1 to 800.0 kV 4.83 m.
** The voltage range is the phase-to-phase system voltage.

B. Selecting Protective Clothing and Other Protective Equipment

Paragraph (l)(8)(v) of §1910.269 requires employers, in certain situations, to select protective clothing and other protective equipment with an arc rating that is greater than or equal to the incident heat energy estimated under §1910.269(l)(8)(ii). Based on laboratory testing required by ASTM F1506-10a, the expectation is that protective clothing with an arc rating equal to the estimated incident heat energy will be capable of preventing second-degree burn injury to an employee exposed to that incident heat energy from an electric arc. Note that actual electric-arc exposures may be more or less severe than the estimated value because of factors such as arc movement, arc length, arcing from reclosing of the system, secondary fires or explosions, and weather conditions. Additionally, for arc rating based on the fabric's arc thermal performance value[5] (ATPV), a worker exposed to incident energy at the arc rating has a 50-percent chance of just barely receiving a second-degree burn. Therefore, it is possible (although not likely) that an employee will sustain a second-degree (or worse) burn wearing clothing conforming to §1910.269(l)(8)(v) under certain circumstances. However, reasonable employer estimates and maintaining appropriate minimum approach distances for employees should limit burns to relatively small burns that just barely extend beyond the epidermis (that is, just barely a second-degree burn). Consequently, protective clothing and clothing and other protective equipment meeting §1910.269(l)(8)(v) will provide an appropriate degree of protection for an employee exposed to electric-arc hazards.

Paragraph (l)(8)(v) of §1910.269 does not require arc-rated protection for exposures of 2 cal/cm2 or less. Untreated cotton clothing will reduce a 2-cal/cm2 exposure below the 1.2- to 1.5-cal/cm2 level necessary to cause burn injury, and this material should not ignite at such low heat energy levels. Although §1910.269(l)(8)(v) does not require clothing to have an arc rating when exposures are 2 cal/cm2 or less, §1910.269(l)(8)(iv) requires the outer layer of clothing to be flame resistant under certain conditions, even when the estimated incident heat energy is less than 2 cal/cm2, as discussed later in this Appendix. Additionally, it is especially important to ensure that employees do not wear undergarments made from fabrics listed in the note to §1910.269(l)(8)(iii) even when the outer layer is flame resistant or arc rated. These fabrics can melt or ignite easily when an electric arc occurs. Logos and name tags made from non-flame-resistant material can adversely affect the arc rating or the flame-resistant characteristics of arc-rated or flame-resistant clothing. Such logos and name tags may violate §1910.269(l)(8)(iii), (l)(8)(iv), or (l)(8)(v).

Paragraph (l)(8)(v) of §1910.269 requires that arc-rated protection cover the employee's entire body, with limited exceptions for the employee's hands, feet, face, and head. Paragraph (l)(8)(v)(A) of §1910.269 provides that arc-rated protection is not necessary for the employee's hands under the following conditions:

For any estimated incident heat energy.	When the employee is wearing rubber insulating gloves with protectors.
If the estimated incident heat energy does not exceed 14 cal/cm ^{2}.	When the employee is wearing heavy-duty leather work gloves with a weight of at least 407 gm/m^2 (12 oz/yd^2).

Paragraph (l)(8)(v)(B) of §1910.269 provides that arc-rated protection is not necessary for the employee's feet when the employee is wearing heavy-duty work shoes or boots. Finally, §1910.269(l)(8)(v)(C), (l)(8)(v)(D), and (l)(8)(v)(E) require arc-rated head and face protection as follows:

Exposure	Minimum head and face protection		
	None *	Arc-rated faceshield with a minimum rating of 8 cal/cm^2*	Arc-rated hood or faceshield with balaclava
Single-phase, open air	2-8 cal/cm^2	9-12 cal/cm^2	13 cal/cm^2 or higher†
Three-phase	2-4 cal/cm^2	5-8 cal/cm^2	9 cal/cm^2 or higher‡

* These ranges assume that employees are wearing hardhats meeting the specifications in §1910.135 or §1926.100(b)(2), as applicable.
† The arc rating must be a minimum of 4 cal/cm^2 less than the estimated incident energy. Note that §1910.269(l)(8)(v)(E) permits this type of head and face protection, with a minimum arc rating of 4 cal/ cm\2\ less than the estimated incident energy, at any incident energy level.
‡ Note that §1910.269(l)(8)(v) permits this type of head and face protection at any incident energy level.

IV. Protection Against Ignition

Paragraph (l)(8)(iii) of §1910.269 prohibits clothing that could melt onto an employee's skin or that could ignite and continue to burn when exposed to flames or to the available heat energy estimated by the employer under §1910.269(l)(8)(ii). Meltable fabrics, such as acetate, nylon, polyester, and polypropylene, even in blends, must be avoided. When these fibers melt, they can adhere to the skin, thereby transferring heat rapidly, exacerbating burns, and complicating treatment. These outcomes can result even if the the meltable fabric is not directly next to the skin. The remainder of this section focuses on the prevention of ignition.

Paragraph (l)(8)(v) of §1910.269 generally requires protective clothing and other protective equipment with an arc rating greater than or equal to the employer's estimate of available heat energy. As explained earlier in this Appendix, untreated cotton is usually acceptable for exposures of 2 cal/cm^2 or less.[6] If the exposure is greater than that, the employee generally must wear flame-resistant clothing with a suitable arc rating in accordance with §1910.269(l)(8)(iv) and (l)(8)(v). However, even if an employee is wearing a layer of flame-resistant clothing, there are circumstances under which flammable layers of clothing would be uncovered, and an electric arc could ignite them. For example, clothing ignition is possible if the employee is wearing flammable clothing under the flame-resistant clothing and the underlayer is uncovered because of an opening in the flame-resistant clothing. Thus, for purposes of §1910.269(l)(8)(iii), it is important for the employer to consider the possibility of clothing ignition even when an employee is wearing flame-resistant clothing with a suitable arc rating.

5 ASTM F1506-10a defines "arc thermal performance value" as "the incident energy on a material or a multilayer system of materials that results in a 50% probability that sufficient heat transfer through the tested specimen is predicted to cause the onset of a second-degree skin burn injury based on the Stoll [footnote] curve, cal/cm^2." The footnote to this definition reads: "Derived from: Stoll, A. M., and Chianta, M. A., 'Method and Rating System for Evaluations of Thermal Protection,' Aerospace Medicine, Vol 40, 1969, pp. 1232-1238 and Stoll, A. M., and Chianta, M. A., 'Heat Transfer through Fabrics as Related to Thermal Injury,' Transactions—New York Academy of Sciences, Vol 33(7), Nov. 1971, pp. 649-670."

6 See §1910.269(l)(8)(iv)(A), (l)(8)(iv)(B), and (l)(8)(iv)(C) for conditions under which employees must wear flame-resistant clothing as the outer layer of clothing even when the incident heat energy does not exceed 2 cal/cm2.

Under §1910.269(l)(8)(iii), employees may not wear flammable clothing in conjunction with flame-resistant clothing if the flammable clothing poses an ignition hazard.[7] Although outer flame-resistant layers may not have openings that expose flammable inner layers, when an outer flame-resistant layer would be unable to resist breakopen,[8] the next (inner) layer must be flame-resistant if it could ignite.

Non-flame-resistant clothing can ignite even when the heat energy from an electric arc is insufficient to ignite the clothing. For example, nearby flames can ignite an employee's clothing; and, even in the absence of flames, electric arcs pose ignition hazards beyond the hazard of ignition from incident energy under certain conditions. In addition to requiring flame-resistant clothing when the estimated incident energy exceeds 2.0 cal/cm^2, §1910.269(l)(8)(iv) requires flame-resistant clothing when: The employee is exposed to contact with energized circuit parts operating at more than 600 volts (§1910.269(l)(8)(iv)(A)), an electric arc could ignite flammable material in the work area that, in turn, could ignite the employee's clothing (§1910.269(l)(8)(iv)(B)), and molten metal or electric arcs from faulted conductors in the work area could ignite the employee's clothing (§1910.269(l)(8)(iv)(C)). For example, grounding conductors can become a source of heat energy if they cannot carry fault current without failure. The employer must consider these possible sources of electric arcs[9] in determining whether the employee's clothing could ignite under §1910.269(l)(8)(iv)(C).

§1910.269 Appendix F Work-positioning equipment inspection guidelines

I. Body Belts

Inspect body belts to ensure that:

A. The hardware has no cracks, nicks, distortion, or corrosion;

B. No loose or worn rivets are present;

C. The waist strap has no loose grommets;

D. The fastening straps are not 100-percent leather; and

E. No worn materials that could affect the safety of the user are present.

II. Positioning Straps

Inspect positioning straps to ensure that:

A. The warning center of the strap material is not exposed;

B. No cuts, burns, extra holes, or fraying of strap material is present;

C. Rivets are properly secured;

D. Straps are not 100-percent leather; and

E. Snaphooks do not have cracks, burns, or corrosion.

III. Climbers

Inspect pole and tree climbers to ensure that:

A. Gaffs are at least as long as the manufacturer's recommended minimums (generally 32 and 51 millimeters (1.25 and 2.0 inches) for pole and tree climbers, respectively, measured on the underside of the gaff);

Note: Gauges are available to assist in determining whether gaffs are long enough and shaped to easily penetrate poles or trees.

B. Gaffs and leg irons are not fractured or cracked;

C. Stirrups and leg irons are free of excessive wear;

D. Gaffs are not loose;

E. Gaffs are free of deformation that could adversely affect use;

F. Gaffs are properly sharpened; and

G. There are no broken straps or buckles.

§1910.269 Appendix G Reference documents

The references contained in this Appendix provide information that can be helpful in understanding and complying with the requirements contained in §1910.269. The national consensus standards referenced in this Appendix contain detailed specifications that employers may follow in complying with the more performance-based requirements of §1910.269. Except as specifically noted in §1910.269, however, the Occupational Safety and Health Administration will not necessarily deem compliance with the national consensus standards to be compliance with the provisions of §1910.269.

7 Paragraph (l)(8)(iii) of §1910.269 prohibits clothing that could ignite and continue to burn when exposed to the heat energy estimated under paragraph (l)(8)(ii) of that Section.

8 Breakopen occurs when a hole, tear, or crack develops in the exposed fabric such that the fabric no longer effectively blocks incident heat energy.

9 Static wires and pole grounds are examples of grounding conductors that might not be capable of carrying fault current without failure. Grounds that can carry the maximum available fault current are not a concern, and employers need not consider such grounds a possible electric arc source.

ANSI/SIA A92.2-2009, American National Standard for Vehicle-Mounted Elevating and Rotating Aerial Devices.

ANSI Z133-2012, American National Standard Safety Requirements for Arboricultural Operations—Pruning, Trimming, Repairing, Maintaining, and Removing Trees, and Cutting Brush.

ANSI/IEEE Std 935-1989, IEEE Guide on Terminology for Tools and Equipment to Be Used in Live Line Working.

ASME B20.1-2012, Safety Standard for Conveyors and Related Equipment.

ASTM D120-09, Standard Specification for Rubber Insulating Gloves.

ASTM D149-09 (2013), Standard Test Method for Dielectric Breakdown Voltage and Dielectric Strength of Solid Electrical Insulating Materials at Commercial Power Frequencies.

ASTM D178-01 (2010), Standard Specification for Rubber Insulating Matting.

ASTM D1048-12, Standard Specification for Rubber Insulating Blankets.

ASTM D1049-98 (2010), Standard Specification for Rubber Insulating Covers.

ASTM D1050-05 (2011), Standard Specification for Rubber Insulating Line Hose.

ASTM D1051-08, Standard Specification for Rubber Insulating Sleeves.

ASTM F478-09, Standard Specification for In-Service Care of Insulating Line Hose and Covers.

ASTM F479-06 (2011), Standard Specification for In-Service Care of Insulating Blankets.

ASTM F496-08, Standard Specification for In-Service Care of Insulating Gloves and Sleeves.

ASTM F711-02 (2007), Standard Specification for Fiberglass-Reinforced Plastic (FRP) Rod and Tube Used in Live Line Tools.

ASTM F712-06 (2011), Standard Test Methods and Specifications for Electrically Insulating Plastic Guard Equipment for Protection of Workers.

ASTM F819-10, Standard Terminology Relating to Electrical Protective Equipment for Workers.

ASTM F855-09, Standard Specifications for Temporary Protective Grounds to Be Used on De-energized Electric Power Lines and Equipment.

ASTM F887-12e1, Standard Specifications for Personal Climbing Equipment.

ASTM F914/F914M-10, Standard Test Method for Acoustic Emission for Aerial Personnel Devices Without Supplemental Load Handling Attachments.

ASTM F1116-03 (2008), Standard Test Method for Determining Dielectric Strength of Dielectric Footwear.

ASTM F1117-03 (2008), Standard Specification for Dielectric Footwear.

ASTM F1236-96 (2012), Standard Guide for Visual Inspection of Electrical Protective Rubber Products.

ASTM F1430/F1430M-10, Standard Test Method for Acoustic Emission Testing of Insulated and Non-Insulated Aerial Personnel Devices with Supplemental Load Handling Attachments.

ASTM F1505-10, Standard Specification for Insulated and Insulating Hand Tools.

ASTM F1506-10a, Standard Performance Specification for Flame Resistant and Arc Rated Textile Materials for Wearing Apparel for Use by Electrical Workers Exposed to Momentary Electric Arc and Related Thermal Hazards.

ASTM F1564-13, Standard Specification for Structure-Mounted Insulating Work Platforms for Electrical Workers.

ASTM F1701-12, Standard Specification for Unused Polypropylene Rope with Special Electrical Properties.

ASTM F1742-03 (2011), Standard Specification for PVC Insulating Sheeting.

ASTM F1796-09, Standard Specification for High Voltage Detectors—Part 1 Capacitive Type to be Used for Voltages Exceeding 600 Volts AC.

ASTM F1797-09ε1, Standard Test Method for Acoustic Emission Testing of Insulated and Non-Insulated Digger Derricks.

ASTM F1825-03 (2007), Standard Specification for Clampstick Type Live Line Tools.

ASTM F1826-00 (2011), Standard Specification for Live Line and Measuring Telescoping Tools.

ASTM F1891-12, Standard Specification for Arc and Flame Resistant Rainwear.

ASTM F1958/F1958M-12, Standard Test Method for Determining the Ignitability of Non-flame-Resistant Materials for Clothing by Electric Arc Exposure Method Using Mannequins.

ASTM F1959/F1959M-12, Standard Test Method for Determining the Arc Rating of Materials for Clothing.

IEEE Stds 4-1995, 4a-2001 (Amendment to IEEE Standard Techniques for High-Voltage Testing), IEEE Standard Techniques for High-Voltage Testing.

IEEE Std 62-1995, IEEE Guide for Diagnostic Field Testing of Electric Power Apparatus—Part 1: Oil Filled Power Transformers, Regulators, and Reactors.

IEEE Std 80-2000, Guide for Safety in AC Substation Grounding.

IEEE Std 100-2000, The Authoritative Dictionary of IEEE Standards Terms Seventh Edition.

IEEE Std 516-2009, IEEE Guide for Maintenance Methods on Energized Power Lines.

IEEE Std 524-2003, IEEE Guide to the Installation of Overhead Transmission Line Conductors .

IEEE Std 957-2005, IEEE Guide for Cleaning Insulators.

IEEE Std 1048-2003, IEEE Guide for Protective Grounding of Power Lines.

IEEE Std 1067-2005, IEEE Guide for In-Service Use, Care, Maintenance, and Testing of Conductive Clothing for Use on Voltages up to 765 kV AC and ±750 kV DC.

IEEE Std 1307-2004, IEEE Standard for Fall Protection for Utility Work.

IEEE Stds 1584-2002, 1584a-2004 (Amendment 1 to IEEE Std 1584-2002), and 1584b-2011 (Amendment 2: Changes to Clause 4 of IEEE Std 1584-2002), IEEE Guide for Performing Arc-Flash Hazard Calculations.

IEEE C2-2012, National Electrical Safety Code.

NFPA 70E-2012, Standard for Electrical Safety in the Workplace.

§1910.272 [OI]
Grain handling facilities

(a) **Scope** This Section contains requirements for the control of grain dust fires and explosions, and certain other safety hazards associated with grain handling facilities. It applies in addition to all other relevant provisions of Part 1910 (or Part 1917 at marine terminals).

(b) **Application**

(b)(1) Paragraphs (a) through (n) of this Section apply to grain elevators, feed mills, flour mills, rice mills, dust pelletizing plants, dry corn mills, soybean flaking operations, and the dry grinding operations of soycake.

(b)(2) Paragraphs (o), (p), and (q) of this Section apply only to grain elevators.

(c) **Definitions**

Choked leg means a condition of material buildup in the bucket elevator that results in the stoppage of material flow and bucket movement. A bucket elevator is not considered choked that has the up-leg partially or fully loaded and has the boot and discharge cleared allowing bucket movement.

Flat storage structure means a grain storage building or structure that will not empty completely by gravity, has an unrestricted ground level opening for entry, and must be entered to reclaim the residual grain using powered equipment or manual means.

Fugitive grain dust means combustible dust particles, emitted from the stock handling system, of such size as will pass through a U.S. Standard 40 mesh sieve (425 microns or less).

Grain elevator means a facility engaged in the receipt, handling, storage, and shipment of bulk raw agricultural commodities such as corn, wheat, oats, barley, sunflower seeds, and soybeans.

Hot work means work involving electric or gas welding, cutting, brazing, or similar flame producing operations.

Inside bucket elevator means a bucket elevator that has the boot and more than 20 percent of the total leg height (above grade or ground level) inside the grain elevator structure. Bucket elevators with leg casings that are inside (and pass through the roofs) of rail or truck dump sheds with the remainder of the leg outside of the grain elevator structure, are not considered inside bucket elevators.

Jogging means repeated starting and stopping of drive motors in an attempt to clear choked legs.

Lagging means a covering on drive pulleys used to increase the coefficient of friction between the pulley and the belt.

Permit means the written certification by the employer authorizing employees to perform identified work operations subject to specified precautions.

(d) **Emergency action plan** The employer shall develop and implement an emergency action plan meeting the requirements contained in 29 CFR §1910.38.

(e) **Training**

(e)(1) The employer shall provide training to employees at least annually and when changes in job assignment will expose them to new hazards. Current employees, and new employees prior to starting work, shall be trained in at least the following:

(e)(1)(i) [OI] General safety precautions associated with the facility, including recognition and preventive measures for the hazards related to dust accumulations and common ignition sources such as smoking; and,

(e)(1)(ii) Specific procedures and safety practices applicable to their job tasks including but not limited to, cleaning procedures for grinding equipment, clearing procedures for choked legs, housekeeping procedures, hot work procedures, preventive maintenance procedures and lock-out/tag-out procedures.

(e)(2) [OI] Employees assigned special tasks, such as bin entry and handling of flammable or toxic substances, shall be provided training to perform these tasks safely.

Note to paragraph (e)(2): Training for an employee who enters grain storage structures includes training about engulfment and mechanical hazards and how to avoid them.

(f) **Hot work permit**

(f)(1) The employer shall issue a permit for all hot work, with the following exceptions:

(f)(1)(i) Where the employer or the employer's representative (who would otherwise authorize the permit) is present while the hot work is being performed;

(f)(1)(ii) In welding shops authorized by the employer;

(f)(1)(iii) In hot work areas authorized by the employer which are located outside of the grain handling structure.

(f)(2) The permit shall certify that the requirements contained in §1910.252(a) have been implemented prior to beginning the hot work operations. The permit shall be kept on file until completion of the hot work operations.

(g) [OI] **Entry into grain storage structures** This paragraph applies to employee entry into bins, silos , tanks, and other grain storage structures. Exception: Entry through unrestricted ground level openings into flat storage structures in which there are no toxicity, flammability, oxygen-deficiency, or other atmospheric hazards is covered by paragraph (h) of this Section. For the purposes of this paragraph (g), the term "grain" includes raw and processed grain and grain products in facilities within the scope of paragraph (b)(1) of this Section.

(g)(1) The following actions shall be taken before employees enter bins, silos, or tanks:

(g)(1)(i) The employer shall issue a permit for entering bins, silos, or tanks unless the employer or the employer's representative (who would otherwise authorize the permit) is present during the entire operation. The permit shall certify that the precautions contained in this paragraph (§1910.272(g)) have been implemented prior to employees entering bins, silos or tanks. The permit shall be kept on file until completion of the entry operations.

(g)(1)(ii) [OI] All mechanical, electrical, hydraulic, and pneumatic equipment which presents a danger to employees inside grain storage structures shall be deenergized and shall be disconnected, locked-out and tagged, blocked-off, or otherwise prevented from operating by other equally effective means or methods.

(g)(1)(iii) The atmosphere within a bin, silo, or tank shall be tested for the presence of combustible gases, vapors, and toxic agents when the employer has reason to believe they may be present. Additionally, the atmosphere within a bin, silo, or tank shall be tested for oxygen content unless there is continuous natural air movement or continuous forced-air ventilation before and during the period employees are inside. If the oxygen level is less than 19.5%, or if combustible gas or vapor is detected in excess of 10% of the lower flammable limit, or if toxic agents are present in excess of the ceiling values listed in Subpart Z of 29 CFR Part 1910, or if toxic agents are present in concentrations that will cause health effects which prevent employees from effecting self-rescue or communication to obtain assistance, the following provisions apply.

(g)(1)(iii)(A) Ventilation shall be provided until the unsafe condition or conditions are eliminated, and the ventilation shall be continued as long as there is a possibility of recurrence of the unsafe condition while the bin, silo, or tank is occupied by employees.

(g)(1)(iii)(B) If toxicity or oxygen deficiency cannot be eliminated by ventilation, employees entering the bin, silo, or tank shall wear an appropriate respirator. Respirator use shall be in accordance with the requirements of §1910.134.

(g)(1)(iv) "Walking down grain" and similar practices where an employee walks on grain to make it flow within or out from a grain storage structure, or where an employee is on moving grain, are prohibited.

(g)(2) [OI] Whenever an employee enters a grain storage structure from a level at or above the level of the stored grain or grain products, or whenever an employee walks or stands on or in stored grain of a depth which poses an engulfment hazard, the employer shall equip the employee with a body harness with lifeline, or a boatswain's chair that meets the requirements of Subpart D of this Part. The lifeline shall be so positioned, and of sufficient length, to prevent the employee from sinking further than waist-deep in the grain. Exception: Where the employer can demonstrate that the protection required by this paragraph is not feasible or creates a greater hazard, the employer shall provide an alternative means of protection which is demonstrated to prevent the employee from sinking further than waist-deep in the grain.

Note to paragraph (g)(2): When the employee is standing or walking on a surface which the employer demonstrates is free from engulfment hazards, the lifeline or alternative means may be disconnected or removed.

(g)(3) An observer, equipped to provide assistance, shall be stationed outside the bin, silo, or tank being entered by an employee. Communications (visual, voice, or signal line) shall be maintained between the observer and employee entering the bin, silo, or tank.

(g)(4) The employer shall provide equipment for rescue operations which is specifically suited for the bin, silo, or tank being entered.

(g)(5) The employee acting as observer shall be trained in rescue procedures, including notification methods for obtaining additional assistance.

(g)(6) Employees shall not enter bins, silos, or tanks underneath a bridging condition, or where a buildup of grain products on the sides could fall and bury them.

(h) **Entry into flat storage structures** For the purposes of this paragraph (h), the term "grain" means raw and processed grain and grain products in facilities within the scope of paragraph (b)(1) of this Section.

(h)(1) Each employee who walks or stands on or in stored grain, where the depth of the grain poses an engulfment hazard, shall be equipped with a lifeline or alternative means which the employer demonstrates will prevent the employee from sinking further than waist-deep into the grain.

Note to paragraph (h)(1): When the employee is standing or walking on a surface which the employer demonstrates is free from engulfment hazards, the lifeline or alternative means may be disconnected or removed.

(h)(2)(i) Whenever an employee walks or stands on or in stored grain or grain products of a depth which poses an engulfment hazard, all equipment which presents a danger to that employee (such as an auger or other grain transport equipment) shall be deenergized, and shall be disconnected, locked-out and tagged, blocked-off, or otherwise prevented from operating by other equally effective means or methods.

(h)(2)(ii) "Walking down grain" and similar practices where an employee walks on grain to make it flow within or out from a grain storage structure, or where an employee is on moving grain, are prohibited.

(h)(3) No employee shall be permitted to be either underneath a bridging condition, or in any other location where an accumulation of grain on the sides or elsewhere could fall and engulf that employee.

(i) **Contractors**

(i)(1) The employer shall inform contractors performing work at the grain handling facility of known potential fire and explosion hazards related to the contractor's work and work area. The employer shall also inform contractors of the applicable safety rules of the facility.

(i)(2) The employer shall explain the applicable provisions of the emergency action plan to contractors.

(j) **Housekeeping**

(j)(1) The employer shall develop and implement a written housekeeping program that establishes the frequency and method(s) determined best to reduce accumulations of fugitive grain dust on ledges, floors, equipment, and other exposed surfaces.

(j)(2) In addition, the housekeeping program for grain elevators shall address fugitive grain dust accumulations at priority housekeeping areas.

(j)(2)(i) Priority housekeeping areas shall include at least the following:

(j)(2)(i)(A) Floor areas within 35 feet (10.7 m) of inside bucket elevators;

(j)(2)(i)(B) Floors of enclosed areas containing grinding equipment;

(j)(2)(i)(C) Floors of enclosed areas containing grain dryers located inside the facility.

(j)(2)(ii) The employer shall immediately remove any fugitive grain dust accumulations whenever they exceed ⅛ inch (.32 cm) at priority housekeeping areas, pursuant to the housekeeping program, or shall demonstrate and assure, through the development and implementation of the housekeeping program, that equivalent protection is provided.

(j)(3) The use of compressed air to blow dust from ledges, walls, and other areas shall only be permitted when all machinery that presents an ignition source in the area is shut-down, and all other known potential ignition sources in the area are removed or controlled.

(j)(4) Grain and product spills shall not be considered fugitive grain dust accumulations. However, the housekeeping program shall address the procedures for removing such spills from the work area.

(k) **Grate openings** Receiving-pit feed openings, such as truck or railcar receiving-pits, shall be covered by grates. The width of openings in the grates shall be a maximum of 2 ½" (6.35 cm).

(l) **Filter collectors**

(l)(1) All fabric dust filter collectors which are a part of a pneumatic dust collection system shall be equipped with a monitoring device that will indicate a pressure drop across the surface of the filter.

(l)(2) Filter collectors installed after March 30, 1988 shall be:

(l)(2)(i) Located outside the facility; or

(l)(2)(ii) Located in an area inside the facility protected by an explosion suppression system; or

(l)(2)(iii) Located in an area inside the facility that is separated from other areas of the facility by construction having at least a one hour fire-resistance rating, and which is adjacent to an exterior wall and vented to the outside. The vent and ductwork shall be designed to resist rupture due to deflagration.

(m) **Preventive maintenance**

(m)(1) The employer shall implement preventive maintenance procedures consisting of:

(m)(1)(i) Regularly scheduled inspections of at least the mechanical and safety control equipment associated with dryers, grain stream processing equipment, dust collection equipment including filter collectors, and bucket elevators;

(m)(1)(ii) Lubrication and other appropriate maintenance in accordance with manufacturers' recommendations, or as determined necessary by prior operating records.

(m)(2) The employer shall promptly correct dust collection systems which are malfunctioning or which are operating below designed efficiency. Additionally, the employer shall promptly correct, or remove from service, overheated bearings and slipping or misaligned belts associated with inside bucket elevators.

(m)(3) A certification record shall be maintained of each inspection, performed in accordance with this paragraph (m), containing the date of the inspection, the name of the person who performed the inspection and the serial number, or other identifier, of the equipment specified in paragraph (m)(1)(i) of this Section that was inspected.

(m)(4) The employer shall implement procedures for the use of tags and locks which will prevent the inadvertent application of energy or motion to equipment being repaired, serviced, or adjusted, which could result in employee injury. Such locks and tags shall be removed in accordance with established procedures only by the employee installing them or, if unavailable, by his or her supervisor.

(n) **Grain stream processing equipment** The employer shall equip grain stream processing equipment (such as hammer mills, grinders, and pulverizers) with an effective means of removing ferrous material from the incoming grain stream.

(o) **Emergency escape**

(o)(1) The employer shall provide at least two means of emergency escape from galleries (bin decks).

(o)(2) The employer shall provide at least one means of emergency escape in tunnels of existing grain elevators. Tunnels in grain elevators constructed after the effective date of this standard shall be provided with at least two means of emergency escape.

(p) **Continuous-flow bulk raw grain dryers**

(p)(1) All direct-heat grain dryers shall be equipped with automatic controls that:

(p)(1)(i) Will shut-off the fuel supply in case of power or flame failure or interruption of air movement through the exhaust fan; and,

(p)(1)(ii) Will stop the grain from being fed into the dryer if excessive temperature occurs in the exhaust of the drying section.

(p)(2) Direct-heat grain dryers installed after March 30, 1988 shall be:

(p)(2)(i) Located outside the grain elevator; or

(p)(2)(ii) Located in an area inside the grain elevator protected by a fire or explosion suppression system; or

(p)(2)(iii) Located in an area inside the grain elevator which is separated from other areas of the facility by construction having at least a one hour fire-resistance rating.

(q) **Inside bucket elevators**

(q)(1) Bucket elevators shall not be jogged to free a choked leg.

(q)(2) All belts and lagging purchased after March 30, 1988 shall be conductive. Such belts shall have a surface electrical resistance not to exceed 300 megohms.

(q)(3) All bucket elevators shall be equipped with a means of access to the head pulley section to allow inspection of the head pulley, lagging, belt, and discharge throat of the elevator head. The boot section shall also be provided with a means of access for clean-out of the boot and for inspection of the boot, pulley, and belt.

(q)(4) All the employer shall:

(q)(4)(i) Mount bearings externally to the leg casing; or,

(q)(4)(ii) Provide vibration monitoring, temperature monitoring, or other means to monitor the condition of those bearings mounted inside or partially-inside the leg casing.

(q)(5) All the employer shall equip bucket elevators with a motion detection device which will shut-down the bucket elevator when the belt speed is reduced by no more than 20% of the normal operating speed.

(q)(6) All the employer shall:

(q)(6)(i) Equip bucket elevators with a belt alignment monitoring device which will initiate an alarm to employees when the belt is not tracking properly; or,

(q)(6)(ii) Provide a means to keep the belt tracking properly, such as a system that provides constant alignment adjustment of belts.

(q)(7) Paragraphs (q)(5) and (q)(6) of this Section do not apply to grain elevators having a permanent storage capacity of less than one million bushels, provided that daily visual inspection is made of bucket movement and tracking of the belt.

(q)(8) Paragraphs (q)(4), (q)(5), and (q)(6) of this Section do not apply to the following:

(q)(8)(i) Bucket elevators which are equipped with an operational fire and explosion suppression system capable of protecting at least the head and boot section of the bucket elevator; or,

(q)(8)(ii) Bucket elevators which are equipped with pneumatic or other dust control systems or methods that keep the dust concentration inside the bucket elevator at least 25% below the lower explosive limit at all times during operations.

Note: The following Appendices to §1910.272 serve as nonmandatory guidelines to assist employers and employees in complying with the requirements of this Section, as well as to provide other helpful information. No additional burdens are imposed through these Appendices.

§1910.272 [O1] Appendix A Grain handling facilities

Examples presented in this Appendix may not be the only means of achieving the performance goals in the standard.

1. Scope and Application

The provisions of this standard apply in addition to any other applicable requirements of this Part 1910 (or Part 1917 at marine terminals). The standard contains requirements for new and existing grain handling facilities. The standard does not apply to seed plants which handle and prepare seeds for planting of future crops, nor to on-farm storage or feed lots.

2. Emergency Action Plan

The standard requires the employer to develop and implement an emergency action plan. The emergency action plan (§1910.38) covers those designated actions employers and employees are to take to ensure employee safety from fire and other emergencies. The plan specifies certain minimum elements which are to be addressed. These elements include the establishment of an employee alarm system, the development of evacuation procedures, and training employees in those actions they are to take during an emergency.

The standard does not specify a particular method for notifying employees of an emergency. Public announcement systems, air horns, steam whistles, a standard fire alarm system, or other types of employee alarm may be used. However, employers should be aware that employees in a grain facility may have difficulty hearing an emergency alarm, or distinguishing an emergency alarm from other audible signals at the facility, or both. Therefore, it is important that the type of employee alarm used be distinguishable and distinct.

The use of floor plans or workplace maps which clearly show the emergency escape routes should be included in the emergency action plan; color coding will aid employees in determining their route assignments. The employer should designate a safe area, outside the facility, where employees can congregate after evacuation, and implement procedures to account for all employees after emergency evacuation has been completed.

It is also recommended that employers seek the assistance of the local fire department for the purpose of preplanning for emergencies. Preplanning is encouraged to facilitate coordination and cooperation between facility personnel and those who may be called upon for assistance during an emergency. It is important for emergency service units to be aware of the usual work locations of employees at the facility.

3. Training

It is important that employees be trained in the recognition and prevention of hazards associated with grain facilities, especially those hazards associated with their own work tasks. Employees should understand the factors which are necessary to produce a fire or explosion, i.e., fuel (such as grain dust), oxygen, ignition source, and (in the case of explosions) confinement. Employees should be made aware that any efforts they make to keep these factors from occurring simultaneously will be an important step in reducing the potential for fires and explosions.

The standard provides flexibility for the employer to design a training program which fulfills the needs of a facility. The type, amount, and frequency of training will need to reflect the tasks that employees are expected to perform. Although training is to be provided to employees at least annually, it is recommended that safety meetings or discussions and drills be conducted at more frequent intervals.

The training program should include those topics applicable to the particular facility, as well as topics such as: Hot work procedures; lock-out/tag-out procedures; bin entry procedures; bin cleaning procedures; grain dust explosions; fire prevention; procedures for handling "hot grain"; housekeeping procedures, including methods and frequency of dust removal; pesticide and fumigant usage; proper use and maintenance of personal protective equipment; and, preventive maintenance. The types of work clothing should also be considered in the program at least to caution against using polyester clothing that easily melts and increases the severity of burns, as compared to wool or fire retardant cotton.

In implementing the training program, it is recommended that the employer utilize films, slide-tape presentations, pamphlets, and other information which can be obtained from such sources as the Grain Elevator and Processing Society, the Cooperative Extension Service of the U.S. Department of Agriculture, Kansas State University's Extension Grain Science and Industry, and other state agriculture schools, industry associations, union organizations, and insurance groups.

4. Hot Work Permit

The implementation of a permit system for hot work is intended to assure that employers maintain control over operations involving hot work and to assure that employees are aware of and utilize appropriate safeguards when conducting these activities.

Precautions for hot work operations are specified in 29 CFR §1910.252(a), and include such safeguards as relocating the hot work operation to a safe location if possible, relocating or covering combustible material in the vicinity, providing fire extinguishers, and provisions for establishing a fire watch. Permits are not required for hot work operations conducted in the presence of the employer or the employer's authorized representative who would otherwise issue the permit, or in an employer authorized welding shop or when work is conducted outside and away from the facility.

It should be noted that the permit is not a record, but is an authorization of the employer certifying that certain safety precautions have been implemented prior to the beginning of work operations.

5. Entry Into Bins, Silos, And Tanks

In order to assure that employers maintain control over employee entry into bins, silos, and tanks, OSHA is requiring that the employer issue a permit for entry into bins, silos, and tanks unless the employer (or the employer's representative who would otherwise authorize the permit) is present at the entry and during the entire operation.

Employees should have a thorough understanding of the hazards associated with entry into bins, silos, and tanks. Employees are not to be permitted to enter these spaces from the bottom when grain or other agricultural products are hung up or sticking to the sides which might fall and injure or kill an employee. Employees should be made aware that the atmosphere in bins, silos, and tanks can be oxygen deficient or toxic. Employees should be trained in the proper methods of testing the atmosphere, as well as in the appropriate procedures to be taken if the atmosphere is found to be oxygen deficient or toxic. When a fumigant has been recently applied in these areas and entry must be made, aeration fans should be running continuously to assure a safe atmosphere for those inside. Periodic monitoring of toxic levels should be done by direct reading instruments to measure the levels, and, if there is an increase in these readings, appropriate actions should be promptly taken.

Employees have been buried and suffocated in grain or other agricultural products because they sank into the material. Therefore, it is suggested that employees not be permitted to walk or stand on the grain or other grain product where the depth is greater than waist high. In this regard, employees must use a full body harness or boatswain's chair with a lifeline when entering from the top. A winch system with mechanical advantage (either powered or manual) would allow better control of the employee than just using a hand held hoist line, and such a system would allow the observer to remove the employee easily without having to enter the space.

It is important that employees be trained in the proper selection and use of any personal protective equipment which is to be worn. Equally important is the training of employees in the planned emergency rescue procedures. Employers should carefully read §1910.134(e)(3) and assure that their procedures follow these requirements. The employee acting as observer is to be equipped to provide assistance and is to know procedures for obtaining additional assistance. The observer should not enter a space until adequate assistance is available. It is recommended that an employee trained in CPR be readily available to provide assistance to those employees entering bins, silos, or tanks.

6. Contractors

These provisions of the standard are intended to ensure that outside contractors are cognizant of the hazards associated with grain handling facilities, particularly in relation to the work they are to perform for the employer. Also, in the event of an emergency, contractors should be able to take appropriate action as a part of the overall facility emergency action plan. Contractors should also be aware of the employer's permit systems. Contractors should develop specified procedures for performing hot work and for entry into bins, silos, and tanks and these activities should be coordinated with the employer. Contractors are responsible for informing their own employees.

This coordination will help to ensure that employers know what work is being performed at the facility by contractors; where it is being performed; and, that it is being performed in a manner that will not endanger employees.

7. Housekeeping.

The housekeeping program is to be designed to keep dust accumulations and emissions under control inside grain facilities. The housekeeping program, which is to be written, is to specify the frequency and method(s) used to best reduce dust accumulations.

Ship, barge, and rail loadout and receiving areas which are located outside the facility need not be addressed in the housekeeping program. Additionally, truck dumps which are open on two or more sides need not be addressed by the housekeeping program. Other truck dumps should be addressed in the housekeeping program to provide for regular cleaning during periods of receiving grain or agricultural products. The housekeeping program should provide coverage for all workspaces in the facility and include walls, beams, etc., especially in relation to the extent that dust could accumulate.

Dust Accumulations

Almost all facilities will require some level of manual housekeeping. Manual housekeeping methods, such as vacuuming or sweeping with soft bristle brooms, should be used which will minimize the possibility of layered dust being suspended in the air when it is being removed.

The housekeeping program should include a contingency plan to respond to situations where dust accumulates rapidly due to a failure of a dust enclosure hood, an unexpected breakdown of the dust control system, a dust-tight connection inadvertently knocked open, etc.

The housekeeping program should also specify the manner of handling spills. Grain spills are not considered to be dust accumulations.

A fully enclosed horizontal belt conveying system where the return belt is inside the enclosure should have inspection access such as sliding panels or doors to permit checking of equipment, checking for dust accumulations and facilitate cleaning if needed.

Dust Emissions

Employers should analyze the entire stock handling system to determine the location of dust emissions and effective methods to control or to eliminate them. The employer should make sure that holes in spouting, casings of bucket elevators, pneumatic conveying pipes, screw augers, or drag conveyor casings, are patched or otherwise properly repaired to prevent leakage. Minimizing free falls of grain or grain products by using choke feeding techniques, and utilization of dust-tight enclosures at transfer points, can be effective in reducing dust emissions.

Each housekeeping program should specify the schedules and control measures which will be used to control dust emitted from the stock handling system. The housekeeping program should address the schedules to be used for cleaning dust accumulations from motors, critical bearings and other potential ignition sources in the working areas. Also, the areas around bucket elevator legs, milling machinery and similar equipment should be given priority in the cleaning schedule. The method of disposal of the dust which is swept or vacuumed should also be planned.

Dust may accumulate in somewhat inaccessible areas, such as those areas where ladders or scaffolds might be necessary to reach them. The employer may want to consider the use of compressed air and long lances to blow down these areas frequently. The employer may also want to consider the periodic use of water and hoselines to wash down these areas. If these methods are used, they are to be specified in the housekeeping program along with the appropriate safety precautions, including the use of personal protective equipment such as eyewear and dust respirators.

Several methods have been effective in controlling dust emissions. A frequently used method of controlling dust emissions is a pneumatic dust collection system. However, the installation of a poorly designed pneumatic dust collection system has fostered a false sense of security and has often led to an inappropriate reduction in manual housekeeping. Therefore, it is imperative that the system be designed properly and installed by a competent contractor. Those employers who have a pneumatic dust control system that is not working according to expectations should request the engineering design firm, or the manufacturer of the filter and related equipment, to conduct an evaluation of the system to determine the corrections necessary for proper operation of the system. If the design firm or manufacturer of the equipment is not known, employers should contact their trade association for recommendations of competent designers of pneumatic dust control systems who could provide assistance.

When installing a new or upgraded pneumatic control system, the employer should insist on an acceptance test period of 30 to 45 days of operation to ensure that the system is operating as intended and designed. The employer should also obtain maintenance, testing, and inspection information from the manufacturer to ensure that the system will continue to operate as designed.

Aspiration of the leg, as part of a pneumatic dust collection system, is another effective method of controlling dust emissions. Aspiration of the leg consists of a flow of air across the entire boot, which entrains the liberated dust and carries it up the up-leg to take-off points. With proper aspiration, dust concentrations in the leg can be lowered below the lower explosive limit. Where a prototype leg installation has been instrumented and shown to be effective in keeping the dust level 25% below the lower explosive limit during normal operations for the various products handled, then other legs of similar size, capacity and products being handled which have the same design criteria for the air aspiration would be acceptable to OSHA, provided the prototype test report is available on site.

Another method of controlling dust emissions is enclosing the conveying system, pressurizing the general work area, and providing a lower pressure inside the enclosed conveying system. Although this method is effective in controlling dust emissions from the conveying system, adequate access to the inside of the enclosure is necessary to facilitate frequent removal of dust accumulations. This is also necessary for those systems called "self-cleaning."

The use of edible oil sprayed on or into a moving stream of grain is another method which has been used to control dust emissions. Tests performed using this method have shown that the oil treatment can reduce dust emissions. Repeated handling of the grain may necessitate additional oil treatment to prevent liberation of dust. However, before using this method, operators of grain handling facilities should be aware that the Food and Drug Administration must approve the specific oil treatment used on products for food or feed.

As a part of the housekeeping program, grain elevators are required to address accumulations of dust at priority areas using the action level. The standard specifies a maximum accumulation of ⅛ inch dust, measurable by a ruler or other measuring device, anywhere within a priority area as the upper limit at which time employers must initiate action to remove the accumulations using designated means or methods. Any accumulation in excess of this amount and where no action has been initiated to implement cleaning would constitute a violation of the standard, unless the employer can demonstrate equivalent protection. Employers should make every effort to minimize dust accumulations on exposed surfaces since dust is the fuel for a fire or explosion, and it is recognized that a ⅛" dust accumulation is more than enough to fuel such occurrences.

8. Filter Collectors

Proper sizing of filter collectors for the pneumatic dust control system they serve is very important for the overall effectiveness of the system. The air to cloth ratio of the system should be in accordance with the manufacturer's recommendations. If higher ratios are used, they can result in more maintenance on the filter, shorter bag or sock life, increased differential pressure resulting in higher energy costs, and an increase in operational problems.

A photohelic gauge, magnehelic gauge, or manometer, may be used to indicate the pressure rise across the inlet and outlet of the filter. When the pressure exceeds the design value for the filter, the air volume will start to drop, and maintenance will be required. Any of these three monitoring devices is acceptable as meeting paragraph (l)(1) of the standard.

The employer should establish a level or target reading on the instrument which is consistent with the manufacturer's recommendations that will indicate when the filter should be serviced. This target reading on the instrument and the accompanying procedures should be in the preventive maintenance program. These efforts would minimize the blinding of the filter and the subsequent failure of the pneumatic dust control system.

There are other instruments that the employer may want to consider using to monitor the operation of the filter. One instrument is a zero motion switch for detecting a failure of motion by the rotary discharge valve on the hopper. If the rotary discharge valve stops turning, the dust released by the bag or sock will accumulate in the filter hopper until the filter becomes clogged. Another instrument is a level indicator which is installed in the hopper of the filter to detect the buildup of dust that would otherwise cause the filter hopper to be plugged. The installation of these instruments should be in accordance with manufacturer's recommendations.

All of these monitoring devices and instruments are to be capable of being read at an accessible location and checked as frequently as specified in the preventive maintenance program.

Filter collectors on portable vacuum cleaners, and those used where fans are not part of the system, are not covered by requirements of paragraph (l) of the standard.

9. Preventive Maintenance

The control of dust and the control of ignition sources are the most effective means for reducing explosion hazards. Preventive maintenance is related to ignition sources in the same manner as housekeeping is related to dust control and should be treated as a major function in a facility. Equipment such as critical bearings, belts, buckets, pulleys, and milling machinery are potential ignition sources, and periodic inspection and lubrication of such equipment through a scheduled preventive maintenance program is an effective method for keeping equipment functioning properly and safely. The use of vibration detection methods, heat sensitive tape or other heat detection methods that can be seen by the inspector or maintenance person will allow for a quick, accurate, and consistent evaluation of bearings and will help in the implementation of the program.

The standard does not require a specific frequency for preventive maintenance. The employer is permitted flexibility in determining the appropriate interval for maintenance provided that the effectiveness of the maintenance program can be demonstrated. Scheduling of preventive maintenance should be based on manufacturer's recommendations for effective operation, as well as from the employer's previous experience with the equipment. However, the employer's schedule for preventive maintenance should be frequent enough to allow for both prompt identification and correction of any problems concerning the failure or malfunction of the mechanical and safety control equipment associated with bucket elevators, dryers, filter collectors and magnets. The pressure-drop monitoring device for a filter collector, and the condition of the lagging on the head pulley, are examples of items that require regularly scheduled inspections. A system of identifying the date, the equipment inspected and the maintenance performed, if any, will assist employers in continually refining their preventive maintenance schedules and identifying equipment problem areas. Open work orders where repair work or replacement is to be done at a designated future date as scheduled, would be an indication of an effective preventive maintenance program.

It is imperative that the prearranged schedule of maintenance be adhered to regardless of other facility constraints. The employer should give priority to the maintenance or repair work associated with safety control equipment, such as that on dryers, magnets, alarm and shut-down systems on bucket elevators, bearings on bucket elevators, and the filter collectors in the dust control system. Benefits of a strict preventive maintenance program can be a reduction of unplanned downtime, improved equipment performance, planned use of resources, more efficient operations, and, most importantly, safer operations.

The standard also requires the employer to develop and implement procedures consisting of locking out and tagging equipment to prevent the inadvertent application of energy or motion to equipment being repaired, serviced, or adjusted, which could result in employee injury. All employees who have responsibility for repairing or servicing equipment, as well as those who operate the equipment, are to be familiar with the employer's lock and tag procedures. A lock is to be used as the positive means to prevent operation of the disconnected equipment. Tags are to be used to inform employees why equipment is locked out. Tags are to meet requirements in §1910.145(f). Locks and tags may only be removed by employees that placed them, or by their supervisor, to ensure the safety of the operation.

10. Grain Stream Processing Equipment

The standard requires an effective means of removing ferrous material from grain streams so that such material does not enter equipment such as hammer mills, grinders and pulverizers. Large foreign objects, such as stones, should have been removed at the receiving pit. Introduction of foreign objects and ferrous material into such equipment can produce sparks which can create an explosion hazard. Acceptable means for removal of ferrous materials include the use of permanent or electromagnets. Means used to separate foreign objects and ferrous material should be cleaned regularly and kept in good repair as part of the preventive maintenance program in order to maximize their effectiveness.

11. Emergency Escape

The standard specifies that at least two means of escape must be provided from galleries (bin decks). Means of emergency escape may include any available means of egress (consisting of three components, exit access, exit, and exit discharge as defined in §1910.35), the use of controlled descent devices with landing velocities not to exceed 15 ft/sec., or emergency escape ladders from galleries. Importantly, the means of emergency escape are to be addressed in the facility emergency action plan. Employees are to know the location of the nearest means of emergency escape and the action they must take during an emergency.

12. Dryers

Liquefied petroleum gas fired dryers should have the vaporizers installed at least ten feet from the dryer. The gas piping system should be protected from mechanical damage. The employer should establish procedures for locating and repairing leaks when there is a strong odor of gas or other signs of a leak.

13. Inside Bucket Elevators

Hazards associated with inside bucket elevator legs are the source of many grain elevator fires and explosions. Therefore, to mitigate these hazards, the standard requires the implementation of special safety precautions and procedures, as well as the installation of safety control devices. The standard provides for a phase-in period for many of the requirements to provide the employer time for planning the implementation of the requirements. Additionally, for elevators with a permanent storage capacity of less than one million bushels, daily visual inspection of belt alignment and bucket movement can be substituted for alignment monitoring devices and motion detection devices.

The standard requires that belts (purchased after the effective date of the standard) have surface electrical resistance not to exceed 300 megohms. Test methods available regarding electrical resistance of belts are: The American Society for Testing and Materials D257–76, "Standard Test Methods for D-C Resistance or Conductance of Insulating Materials"; and, the International Standards Organization's #284, "Conveyor Belts-Electrical Conductivity-Specification and Method of Test." When an employer has a written certification from the manufacturer that a belt has been tested using one of the above test methods, and meets the 300 megohm criteria, the belt is acceptable as meeting this standard. When using conductive belts, the employer should make certain that the head pulley and shaft are grounded through the drive motor ground or by some other equally effective means. When V-type belts are used to transmit power to the head pulley assembly from the motor drive shaft, it will be necessary to provide electrical continuity from the head pulley assembly to ground, e.g., motor grounds.

Employers should also consider purchasing new belts that are flame retardant or fire resistive. A flame resistance test for belts is contained in 30 CFR 18.65.

§1910.272 Appendix B
Grain handling facilities–
National consensus standards

The following table contains a cross-reference listing of current national consensus standards which provide information that may be of assistance to grain handling operations. Employers who comply with provisions in these national consensus standards that provide equal or greater protection than those in §1910.272 will be considered in compliance with the corresponding requirements in §1910.272.

Subject	National consensus standards
Grain elevators and facilities handling bulk raw agricultural commodities	ANSI/NFPA 61B
Feed mills	ANSI/NFPA 61C
Facilities handling agricultural commodities for human consumption	ANSI/NFPA 61D
Pneumatic conveying systems for agricultural commodities	ANSI/NFPA 66
Guide for explosion venting	ANSI/NFPA 68
Explosion prevention systems	ANSI/NFPA 69
Dust removal and exhaust systems	ANSI/NFPA 91

§1910.272 Appendix C
Grain handling facilities–
References for further information

The following references provide information which can be helpful in understanding the requirements contained in various provisions of the standard, as well as provide other helpful information.

1. Accident Prevention Manual for Industrial Operations; National Safety Council, 425 North Michigan Avenue, Chicago, Illinois 60611.
2. Practical Guide to Elevator Design; National Grain and Feed Association, P.O. Box 28328, Washington, DC 20005.
3. Dust Control for Grain Elevators; National Grain and Feed Association, P.O. Box 28328, Washington, DC 20005.
4. Prevention of Grain Elevator and Mill Explosions; National Academy of Sciences, Washington, DC (Available from National Technical Information Service, Springfield, Virginia 22151.).
5. Standard for the Prevention of Fires and Explosions in Grain Elevators and Facilities Handling Bulk Raw Agricultural

Commodities, NFPA 61B; National Fire Protection Association, Batterymarch Park, Quincy, Massachusetts 02269.

6. Standard for the Prevention of Fire and Dust Explosions in Feed Mills, NFPA 61C; National Fire Protection Association, Batterymarch Park, Quincy, Massachusetts 02269.
7. Standard for the Prevention of Fire and Dust Explosions in the Milling of Agricultural Commodities for Human Consumption, NFPA 61D; National Fire Protection Association, Batterymarch Park, Quincy, Massachusetts 02269.
8. Standard for Pneumatic Conveying Systems for Handling Feed, Flour, Grain and Other Agricultural Dusts, NFPA 66; National Fire Protection Association, Batterymarch Park, Quincy, Massachusetts 02269.
9. Guide for Explosion Venting, NFPA 68; National Fire Protection Association, Batterymarch Park, Quincy, Massachusetts 02269.
10. Standard on Explosion Prevention Systems, NFPA 69; National Fire Protection Association, Batterymarch Park, Quincy, Massachusetts 02269.
11. Safety-Operations Plans; U.S. Department of Agriculture, Washington, DC 20250.
12. Inplant Fire Prevention Control Programs; Mill Mutual Fire Prevention Mutual Fire Prevention Bureau, 1 Pierce Place, Suite 1260 West, Itasca, Illinois 60143–1269.
13. Guidelines for Terminal Elevators; Mill Mutual Fire Prevention Bureau, 1 Pierce Place, Suite 1260 West, Itasca, Illinois 60143–1269.
14. Standards for Preventing the Horizontal and Vertical Spread of Fires in Grain Handling Properties; Mill Mutual Fire Mutual Fire Prevention Bureau, 1 Pierce Place, Suite 1260 West, Itasca, Illinois 60143–1269.
15. Belt Conveyors for Bulk Materials, Part I and Part II, Data Sheet 570, Revision A; National Safety Council, 425 North Michigan Avenue, Chicago, Illinois 60611.
16. Suggestions for Precautions and Safety Practices in Welding and Cutting; Mill Mutual Fire Prevention Bureau, 1 Pierce Place, Suite 1260 West, Itasca, Illinois 60143–1269.
17. Food Bins and Tanks, Data Sheet 524; National Safety Council, 425 North Michigan Avenue, Chicago, Illinois 60611.
18. Pneumatic Dust Control in Grain Elevators; National Academy of Sciences, Washington, DC (Available from National Technical Information Service, Springfield, Virginia 22151.).
19. Dust Control Analysis and Layout Procedures for Grain Storage and Processing Plants ; Mill Mutual Fire Prevention Bureau, 1 Pierce Place, Suite 1260 West, Itasca, Illinois 60143–1269.
20. Standard for the Installation of Blower and Exhaust Systems for Dust, Stock and Vapor Removal, NFPA 91; National Fire Protection Association, Batterymarch Park, Quincy, Massachusetts 02269.
21. Standards for the Installation of Direct Heat Grain Driers in Grain and Milling Properties; Mill Mutual Fire Prevention Bureau, 1 Pierce Place, Suite 1260 West, Itasca, Illinois 60143–1269.
22. Guidelines for Lubrication and Bearing Maintenance; Mill Mutual Fire Prevention Bureau, 1 Pierce Place, Suite 1260 West, Itasca, Illinois 60143–1269.
23. Organized Maintenance in Grain and Milling Properties; Mill Mutual Fire Prevention Bureau, 1 Pierce Place, Suite 1260 West, Itasca, Illinois 60143–1269.
24. Safe and Efficient Elevator Legs for Grain and Milling Properties; Mill Mutual Fire Prevention Bureau, 1 Pierce Place, Suite 1260 West, Itasca, Illinois 60143–1269.
25. Explosion Venting and Supression of Bucket Elevators; National Grain and Feed Association, P.O. Box 28328, Washington, DC 20005.
26. Lightning Protection Code, NFPA 78; National Fire Protection Association, Batterymarch Park, Quincy, Massachusetts 02269.
27. Occupational Safety in Grain Elevators, DHHS (NIOSH) Publication No. 83–126); National Institute for Occupational Safety and Health, Morgantown, West Virginia 26505.
28. Retrofitting and Constructing Grain Elevators; National Grain and Feed Association, P.O. Box 28328, Washington, DC 20005.
29. Grain Industry Safety and Health Center—Training Series (Preventing grain dust explosions, operations maintenance safety, transportation safety, occupational safety and health); Grain Elevator and Processing Society, P.O. Box 15026, Commerce Station, Minneapolis, Minnesota 55415–0026.
30. Suggestions for Organized Maintenance; The Mill Mutuals Loss Control Department, 1 Pierce Place, Suite 1260 West, Itasca, Illinois 60143–1269.
31. Safety—The First Step to Success; The Mill Mutual Loss Control Department, 1 Pierce Place, Suite 1260 West, Itasca, Illinois 60143–1269.
32. Emergency Plan Notebook; Schoeff, Robert W. and James L. Balding, Kansas State University, Cooperative Extension Service, Extension Grain Science and Industry, Shellenberger Hall, Manhattan, Kansas 66506.

[52 FR 49625, Dec. 31, 1987, as amended at 53 FR 17696, May 18, 1988; 54 FR 24334, June 7, 1989; 55 FR 25094, June 20, 1990; 61 FR 9242, Mar. 7, 1996; 61 FR 9584, Mar. 8, 1996; 67 FR 67965, Nov. 7, 2002]

29 CFR PART 1910 Subpart S
Electrical

Section Contents

Authority: 29 U.S.C. 653, 655, 657; Secretary of Labor's Order No. 8-76 (41 FR 25059), 1-90 (55 FR 9033), 5-2002 (67 FR 65008), 5-2007 (72 FR 31160), or 1-2012 (77 FR 3912), as applicable; and 29 CFR Part §1911.

Source: 46 FR 4056, Jan. 16, 1981, unless otherwise noted.

General

§1910.301 Introduction

This Subpart addresses electrical safety requirements that are necessary for the practical safeguarding of employees in their workplaces and is divided into four major divisions as follows:

(a) **Design safety standards for electrical systems** These regulations are contained in §1910.302 through §1910.330. §1910.302 through §1910.308 contain design safety standards for electric utilization systems. Included in this category are all electric equipment and installations used to provide electric power and light for employee workplaces. §1910.309 through §1910.330 are reserved for possible future design safety standards for other electrical systems.

(b) **Safety-related work practices** These regulations will be contained in §1910.331 through §1910.360.

(c) **Safety-related maintenance requirements** These regulations will be contained in §1910.361 through §1910.380.

(d) **Safety requirements for special equipment** These regulations will be contained in §1910.381 through §1910.398.

(e) **Definitions** Definitions applicable to each division are contained in §1910.399.

[46 FR 4056, Jan. 16, 1982; 46 FR 40185, Aug. 7, 1981]

Design Safety Standards for Electrical Systems

§1910.302 Electrical utilization systems

§1910.302 through §1910.308 contain design safety standards for electric utilization systems.

(a) **Scope**

(a)(1) **Covered** The provisions of §1910.302 through §1910.308 cover electrical installations and utilization equipment installed or used within or on buildings, structures, and other premises, including:

(a)(1)(i) Yards;

(a)(1)(ii) Carnivals;

(a)(1)(iii) Parking and other lots;

(a)(1)(iv) Mobile homes;

(a)(1)(v) Recreational vehicles;

(a)(1)(vi) Industrial substations;

(a)(1)(vii) Conductors that connect the installations to a supply of electricity; and

(a)(1)(viii) Other outside conductors on the premises.

(a)(2) **Not covered** The provisions of §1910.302 through §1910.308 do not cover:

(a)(2)(i) Installations in ships, watercraft, railway rolling stock, aircraft, or automotive vehicles other than mobile homes and recreational vehicles;

(a)(2)(ii) Installations underground in mines;

(a)(2)(iii) Installations of railways for generation, transformation, transmission, or distribution of power used exclusively for operation of rolling stock or installations used exclusively for signaling and communication purposes;

(a)(2)(iv) Installations of communication equipment under the exclusive control of communication utilities, located outdoors or in building spaces used exclusively for such installations; or

(a)(2)(v) Installations under the exclusive control of electric utilities for the purpose of communication or metering; or for the generation, control, transformation, transmission, and distribution of electric energy located in buildings used exclusively by utilities for such purposes or located outdoors on property owned or leased by the utility or on public highways, streets, roads, etc., or outdoors by established rights on private property.

(b) **Extent of application**

(b)(1) **Requirements applicable to all installations** The following requirements apply to all electrical installations and utilization equipment, regardless of when they were designed or installed:

- §1910.303(b)—Examination, installation, and use of equipment
- §1910.303(c)(3)—Electrical connections—Splices
- §1910.303(d)—Arcing parts
- §1910.303(e)—Marking
- §1910.303(f), except (f)(4) and (f)(5)—Disconnecting means and circuits
- §1910.303(g)(2)—600 volts or less—Guarding of live parts
- §1910.304(a)(3)—Use of grounding terminals and devices
- §1910.304(f)(1)(i), (f)(1)(iv), and (f)(1)(v)—Overcurrent protection—600 volts, nominal, or less
- §1910.304(g)(1)(ii), (g)(1)(iii), (g)(1)(iv), and (g)(1)(v)—Grounding—Systems to be grounded
- §1910.304(g)(4)—Grounding—Grounding connections
- §1910.304(g)(5)—Grounding—Grounding path
- §1910.304(g)(6)(iv)(A) through (g)(6)(iv)(D), and (g)(6)(vi)—Grounding—Supports, enclosures, and equipment to be grounded
- §1910.304(g)(7)—Grounding—Nonelectrical equipment
- §1910.304(g)(8)(i)—Grounding—Methods of grounding fixed equipment
- §1910.305(g)(1)—Flexible cords and cables—Use of flexible cords and cables
- §1910.305(g)(2)(ii) and (g)(2)(iii)—Flexible cords and cables—Identification, splices, and terminations
- §1910.307, except as specified in §1910.307(b)—Hazardous (classified) locations

(b)(2) **Requirements applicable to installations made after March 15, 1972** Every electrical installation and all utilization equipment installed or overhauled after March 15, 1972, shall comply with the provisions of §1910.302 through §1910.308, except as noted in paragraphs (b)(3) and (b)(4) of this section.

(b)(3) **Requirements applicable only to installations made after April 16, 1981** The following requirements apply only to electrical installations and utilization equipment installed after April 16, 1981:

§1910.303(h)(4)—Over 600 volts, nominal—Entrance and access to work space
§1910.304(f)(1)(vii) and (f)(1)(viii)—Overcurrent protection—600 volts, nominal, or less
§1910.304(g)(9)(i)—Grounding—Grounding of systems and circuits of 1000 volts and over (high voltage)
§1910.305(j)(6)(ii)(D)—Equipment for general use—Capacitors
§1910.306(c)(9)—Elevators, dumbwaiters, escalators, moving walks, wheelchair lifts, and stairway chair lifts—Interconnection between multicar controllers
§1910.306(i)—Electrically driven or controlled irrigation machines
§1910.306(j)(5)—Swimming pools, fountains, and similar installations—Fountains
§1910.308(a)(1)(ii)—Systems over 600 volts, nominal—Aboveground wiring methods
§1910.308(c)(2)—Class 1, Class 2, and Class 3 remote control, signaling, and power-limited circuits—Marking
§1910.308(d)—Fire alarm systems

(b)(4) **Requirements applicable only to installations made after August 13, 2007** The following requirements apply only to electrical installations and utilization equipment installed after August 13, 2007:

§1910.303(f)(4)—Disconnecting means and circuits—Capable of accepting a lock
§1910.303(f)(5)—Disconnecting means and circuits—Marking for series combination ratings
§1910.303(g)(1)(iv) and (g)(1)(vii)—600 Volts, nominal, or less—Space about electric equipment
§1910.303(h)(5)(vi)—Over 600 volts, nominal—Working space and guarding
§1910.304(b)(1)—Branch circuits—Identification of multiwire branch circuits
§1910.304(b)(3)(i)—Branch circuits—Ground-fault circuit interrupter protection for personnel
§1910.304(f)(2)(i)(A), (f)(2)(i)(B) (but not the introductory text to §1910.304(f)(2)(i)), and (f)(2)(iv)(A)—Overcurrent protection—Feeders and branch circuits over 600 volts, nominal
§1910.305(c)(3)(ii)—Switches—Connection of switches
§1910.305(c)(5)—Switches—Grounding
§1910.306(a)(1)(ii)—Electric signs and outline lighting—Disconnecting means
§1910.306(c)(4)—Elevators, dumbwaiters, escalators, moving walks, wheelchair lifts, and stairway chair lifts—Operation
§1910.306(c)(5)—Elevators, dumbwaiters, escalators, moving walks, wheelchair lifts, and stairway chair lifts—Location
§1910.306(c)(6)—Elevators, dumbwaiters, escalators, moving walks, wheelchair lifts, and stairway chair lifts—Identification and signs
§1910.306(c)(7)—Elevators, dumbwaiters, escalators, moving walks, wheelchair lifts, and stairway chair lifts—Single-car and multicar installations
§1910.306(j)(1)(iii)—Swimming pools, fountains, and similar installations—Receptacles
§1910.306(k)—Carnivals, circuses, fairs, and similar events
§1910.308(a)(5)(v) and (a)(5)(vi)(B)—Systems over 600 volts, nominal—Interrupting and isolating devices
§1910.308(a)(7)(vi)—Systems over 600 volts, nominal—Tunnel installations
§1910.308(b)(3)—Emergency power systems—Signs
§1910.308(c)(3)—Class 1, Class 2, and Class 3 remote control, signaling, and power-limited circuits—Separation from conductors of other circuits
§1910.308(f)—Solar photovoltaic systems

(c) **Applicability of requirements for disconnecting means** The requirement in §1910.147(c)(2)(iii) that energy isolating devices be capable of accepting a lockout device whenever replacement or major repair, renovation or modification of a machine or equipment is performed, and whenever new machines or equipment are installed after January 2, 1990, applies in addition to any requirements in §1910.303 through §1910.308 that disconnecting means be capable of being locked in the open position under certain conditions.

§1910.303 OI General

(a) OI **Approval** The conductors and equipment required or permitted by this Subpart shall be acceptable only if approved, as defined in §1910.399.

(b) OI **Examination, installation, and use of equipment**

(b)(1) OI **Examination** Electric equipment shall be free from recognized hazards that are likely to cause death or serious physical harm to employees. Safety of equipment shall be determined using the following considerations:

(b)(1)(i) OI Suitability for installation and use in conformity with the provisions of this Subpart;

Note to paragraph (b)(1)(i) of this section: Suitability of equipment for an identified purpose may be evidenced by listing or labeling for that identified purpose.

(b)(1)(ii) Mechanical strength and durability, including, for parts designed to enclose and protect other equipment, the adequacy of the protection thus provided;

(b)(1)(iii) Wire-bending and connection space;

(b)(1)(iv) Electrical insulation;

(b)(1)(v) Heating effects under all conditions of use;

(b)(1)(vi) Arcing effects;

(b)(1)(vii) Classification by type, size, voltage, current capacity, and specific use; and

(b)(1)(viii) Other factors that contribute to the practical safeguarding of persons using or likely to come in contact with the equipment.

(b)(2) OI **Installation and use** Listed or labeled equipment shall be installed and used in accordance with any instructions included in the listing or labeling.

(b)(3) **Insulation integrity** Completed wiring installations shall be free from short circuits and from grounds other than those required or permitted by this Subpart.

(b)(4) **Interrupting rating** Equipment intended to interrupt current at fault levels shall have an interrupting rating sufficient for the nominal circuit voltage and the current that is available at the line terminals of the equipment. Equipment intended to interrupt current at other than fault levels shall have an interrupting rating at nominal circuit voltage sufficient for the current that must be interrupted.

(b)(5) **Circuit impedance and other characteristics** The overcurrent protective devices, the total impedance, the component short-circuit current ratings, and other characteristics of the circuit to be protected shall be selected and coordinated to permit the circuit protective devices used to clear a fault to do so without the occurrence of extensive damage to the electrical components of the circuit. This fault shall be assumed to be either between two or more of the circuit conductors, or between any circuit conductor and the grounding conductor or enclosing metal raceway.

(b)(6) **Deteriorating agents** Unless identified for use in the operating environment, no conductors or equipment shall be located in damp or wet locations; where exposed to gases, fumes, vapors, liquids, or other agents that have a deteriorating effect on the conductors or equipment; or where exposed to excessive temperatures.

(b)(7) **Mechanical execution of work** Electric equipment shall be installed in a neat and workmanlike manner.

(b)(7)(i) Unused openings in boxes, raceways, auxiliary gutters, cabinets, equipment cases, or housings shall be effectively closed to afford protection substantially equivalent to the wall of the equipment.

(b)(7)(ii) Conductors shall be racked to provide ready and safe access in underground and subsurface enclosures that persons enter for installation and maintenance.

(b)(7)(iii) Internal parts of electrical equipment, including busbars, wiring terminals, insulators, and other surfaces, may not be damaged or contaminated by foreign materials such as paint, plaster, cleaners, abrasives, or corrosive residues.

(b)(7)(iv) There shall be no damaged parts that may adversely affect safe operation or mechanical strength of the equipment, such as parts that are broken, bent, cut, or deteriorated by corrosion, chemical action, or overheating.

(b)(8) **Mounting and cooling of equipment**

(b)(8)(i) Electric equipment shall be firmly secured to the surface on which it is mounted.

Note to paragraph (b)(8)(i) of this section: Wooden plugs driven into holes in masonry, concrete, plaster, or similar materials are not considered secure means of fastening electric equipment.

(b)(8)(ii) Electric equipment that depends on the natural circulation of air and convection principles for cooling of exposed surfaces shall be installed so that room airflow over such surfaces is not prevented by walls or by adjacent installed equipment. For equipment designed for floor mounting, clearance between top surfaces and adjacent surfaces shall be provided to dissipate rising warm air.

(b)(8)(iii) Electric equipment provided with ventilating openings shall be installed so that walls or other obstructions do not prevent the free circulation of air through the equipment.

(c) **Electrical connections**

(c)(1) **General** Because of different characteristics of dissimilar metals:

(c)(1)(i) Devices such as pressure terminal or pressure splicing connectors and soldering lugs shall be identified for the material of the conductor and shall be properly installed and used;

(c)(1)(ii) Conductors of dissimilar metals may not be intermixed in a terminal or splicing connector where physical contact occurs between dissimilar conductors (such as copper and aluminum, copper and copper-clad aluminum, or aluminum and copper-clad aluminum) unless the device is identified for the purpose and conditions of use; and

(c)(1)(iii) Materials such as solder, fluxes, inhibitors, and compounds, where employed, shall be suitable for the use and shall be of a type that will not adversely affect the conductors, installation, or equipment.

(c)(2) **Terminals**

(c)(2)(i) Connection of conductors to terminal parts shall ensure a good connection without damaging the conductors and shall be made by means of pressure connectors (including set-screw type), solder lugs, or splices to flexible leads. However, No. 10 or smaller conductors may be connected by means of wire binding screws or studs and nuts having upturned lugs or equivalent.

(c)(2)(ii) Terminals for more than one conductor and terminals used to connect aluminum shall be so identified.

(c)(3) **Splices**

(c)(3)(i) Conductors shall be spliced or joined with splicing devices identified for the use or by brazing, welding, or soldering with a fusible metal or alloy. Soldered splices shall first be spliced or joined to be mechanically and electrically secure without solder and then soldered. All splices and joints and the free ends of conductors shall be covered with an insulation equivalent to that of the conductors or with an insulating device identified for the purpose.

(c)(3)(ii) Wire connectors or splicing means installed on conductors for direct burial shall be listed for such use.

(d) **Arcing parts** Parts of electric equipment that in ordinary operation produce arcs, sparks, flames, or molten metal shall be enclosed or separated and isolated from all combustible material.

(e) [OI] **Marking**

(e)(1) **Identification of manufacturer and ratings** Electric equipment may not be used unless the following markings have been placed on the equipment:

(e)(1)(i) The manufacturer's name, trademark, or other descriptive marking by which the organization responsible for the product may be identified; and

(e)(1)(ii) Other markings giving voltage, current, wattage, or other ratings as necessary.

(e)(2) **Durability** The marking shall be of sufficient durability to withstand the environment involved.

(f) **Disconnecting means and circuits**

(f)(1) **Motors and appliances** Each disconnecting means required by this Subpart for motors and appliances shall be legibly marked to indicate its purpose, unless located and arranged so the purpose is evident.

(f)(2) **Services, feeders, and branch circuits** Each service, feeder, and branch circuit, at its disconnecting means or overcurrent device, shall be legibly marked to indicate its purpose, unless located and arranged so the purpose is evident.

(f)(3) **Durability of markings** The markings required by paragraphs (f)(1) and (f)(2) of this section shall be of sufficient durability to withstand the environment involved.

(f)(4) **Capable of accepting a lock** Disconnecting means required by this Subpart shall be capable of being locked in the open position.

(f)(5) **Marking for series combination ratings**

(f)(5)(i) Where circuit breakers or fuses are applied in compliance with the series combination ratings marked on the equipment by the manufacturer, the equipment enclosures shall be legibly marked in the field to indicate that the equipment has been applied with a series combination rating.

(f)(5)(ii) The marking required by paragraph (f)(5)(i) of this section shall be readily visible and shall state "Caution—Series Combination System Rated __ Amperes. Identified Replacement Component Required."

(g) [OI] **600 Volts, nominal, or less** This paragraph applies to electric equipment operating at 600 volts, nominal, or less to ground.

(g)(1) [OI] **Space about electric equipment** Sufficient access and working space shall be provided and maintained about all electric equipment to permit ready and safe operation and maintenance of such equipment.

(g)(1)(i) [OI] Working space for equipment likely to require examination, adjustment, servicing, or maintenance while energized shall comply with the following dimensions, except as required or permitted elsewhere in this Subpart:

(g)(1)(i)(A) The depth of the working space in the direction of access to live parts may not be less than indicated in Table S–1. Distances shall be measured from the live parts if they are exposed or from the enclosure front or opening if they are enclosed;

(g)(1)(i)(B) The width of working space in front of the electric equipment shall be the width of the equipment or 762 mm (30 in.), whichever is greater. In all cases, the working space shall permit at least a 90-degree opening of equipment doors or hinged panels; and

(g)(1)(i)(C) The work space shall be clear and extend from the grade, floor, or platform to the height required by paragraph (g)(1)(vi) of this section. However, other equipment associated with the electrical installation and located above or below the electric equipment may extend not more than 153 mm (6 in.) beyond the front of the electric equipment.

(g)(1)(ii) Working space required by this standard may not be used for storage. When normally enclosed live parts are exposed for inspection or servicing, the working space, if in a passageway or general open space, shall be suitably guarded.

(g)(1)(iii) At least one entrance of sufficient area shall be provided to give access to the working space about electric equipment.

(g)(1)(iv) For equipment rated 1200 amperes or more and over 1.83 m (6.0 ft) wide, containing overcurrent devices, switching devices, or control devices, there shall be one entrance not less than 610 mm (24 in.) wide and 1.98 m (6.5 ft) high at each end of the working space, except that:

(g)(1)(iv)(A) Where the location permits a continuous and unobstructed way of exit travel, one means of exit is permitted; or

(g)(1)(iv)(B) Where the working space required by paragraph (g)(1)(i) of this section is doubled, only one entrance to the working space is required; however, the entrance shall be located so that the edge of the entrance nearest the equipment is the minimum clear distance given in Table S–1 away from such equipment.

(g)(1)(v) Illumination shall be provided for all working spaces about service equipment, switchboards, panelboards, and motor control centers installed indoors. Additional lighting fixtures are not required where the working space is illuminated by an adjacent light source. In electric equipment rooms, the illumination may not be controlled by automatic means only.

(g)(1)(vi) The minimum headroom of working spaces about service equipment, switchboards, panelboards, or motor control centers shall be as follows:

(g)(1)(vi)(A) For installations built before August 13, 2007, 1.91 m (6.25 ft); and

(g)(1)(vi)(B) For installations built on or after August 13, 2007, 1.98 m (6.5 ft), except that where the electrical equipment exceeds 1.98 m (6.5 ft) in height, the minimum headroom may not be less than the height of the equipment.

Table S–1
Minimum Depth of Clear Working Space at Electric Equipment, 600 V or Less

Nominal voltage to ground	Minimum clear distance for condition[2,3]					
	Condition A		Condition B		Condition C	
	m	ft	m	ft	m	ft
0-150	[1]0.9	[1]3.0	[1]0.9	[1]3.0	0.9	3.0
150-600	[1]0.9	[1]3.0	1.0	3.5	1.2	4.0

Notes to Table S–1:

[1] Minimum clear distances may be 0.7 m (2.5 ft) for installations built before April 16, 1981.

[2] Conditions A, B, and C are as follows:
Condition A—Exposed live parts on one side and no live or grounded parts on the other side of the working space, or exposed live parts on both sides effectively guarded by suitable wood or other insulating material. Insulated wire or insulated busbars operating at not over 300 volts are not considered live parts.
Condition B—Exposed live parts on one side and grounded parts on the other side.
Condition C—Exposed live parts on both sides of the work space (not guarded as provided in Condition A) with the operator between.

[3] Working space is not required in back of assemblies such as dead-front switchboards or motor control centers where there are no renewable or adjustable parts (such as fuses or switches) on the back and where all connections are accessible from locations other than the back. Where rear access is required to work on deenergized parts on the back of enclosed equipment, a minimum working space of 762 mm (30 in.) horizontally shall be provided.

(g)(1)(vii) Switchboards, panelboards, and distribution boards installed for the control of light and power circuits, and motor control centers shall be located in dedicated spaces and protected from damage.

(g)(1)(vii)(A) For indoor installation, the dedicated space shall comply with the following:

(g)(1)(vii)(A)(1) The space equal to the width and depth of the equipment and extending from the floor to a height of 1.83 m (6.0 ft) above the equipment or to the structural ceiling, whichever is lower, shall be dedicated to the electrical installation. Unless isolated from equipment by height or physical enclosures or covers that will afford adequate mechanical protection from vehicular traffic or accidental contact by unauthorized personnel or that complies with paragraph (g)(1)(vii)(A)(2) of this section, piping, ducts, or equipment foreign to the electrical installation may not be located in this area;

(g)(1)(vii)(A)(2) The space equal to the width and depth of the equipment shall be kept clear of foreign systems unless protection is provided to avoid damage from condensation, leaks, or breaks in such foreign systems. This area shall extend from the top of the electric equipment to the structural ceiling;

(g)(1)(vii)(A)(3) Sprinkler protection is permitted for the dedicated space where the piping complies with this section; and

(g)(1)(vii)(A)(4) Control equipment that by its very nature or because of other requirements in this Subpart must be adjacent to or within sight of its operating machinery is permitted in the dedicated space.

Note to paragraph (g)(1)(vii)(A) of this section: A dropped, suspended, or similar ceiling that does not add strength to the building structure is not considered a structural ceiling.

(g)(1)(vii)(B) Outdoor electric equipment shall be installed in suitable enclosures and shall be protected from accidental contact by unauthorized personnel, or by vehicular traffic, or by accidental spillage or leakage from piping systems. No architectural appurtenance or other equipment may be located in the working space required by paragraph (g)(1)(i) of this section.

(g)(2) OI **Guarding of live parts**

(g)(2)(i) OI Except as elsewhere required or permitted by this standard, live parts of electric equipment operating at 50 volts or more shall be guarded against accidental contact by use of approved cabinets or other forms of approved enclosures or by any of the following means:

(g)(2)(i)(A) By location in a room, vault, or similar enclosure that is accessible only to qualified persons;

(g)(2)(i)(B) By suitable permanent, substantial partitions or screens so arranged so that only qualified persons will have access to the space within reach of the live parts. Any openings in such partitions or screens shall be so sized and located that persons are not likely to come into accidental contact with the live parts or to bring conducting objects into contact with them;

(g)(2)(i)(C) By placement on a suitable balcony, gallery, or platform so elevated and otherwise located as to prevent access by unqualified persons; or

(g)(2)(i)(D) By elevation of 2.44 m (8.0 ft) or more above the floor or other working surface.

(g)(2)(ii) OI In locations where electric equipment is likely to be exposed to physical damage, enclosures or guards shall be so arranged and of such strength as to prevent such damage.

(g)(2)(iii) Entrances to rooms and other guarded locations containing exposed live parts shall be marked with conspicuous warning signs forbidding unqualified persons to enter.

(h) OI **Over 600 volts, nominal**

(h)(1) **General** Conductors and equipment used on circuits exceeding 600 volts, nominal, shall comply with all applicable provisions of the paragraphs (a) through (g) of this section and with the following provisions, which supplement or modify the preceding requirements. However, paragraphs (h)(2), (h)(3), and (h)(4) of this section do not apply to the equipment on the supply side of the service point.

(h)(2) OI **Enclosure for electrical installations**

(h)(2)(i) Electrical installations in a vault, room, or closet or in an area surrounded by a wall, screen, or fence, access to which is controlled by lock and key or other approved means, are considered to be accessible to qualified persons only. The type of enclosure used in a given case shall be designed and constructed according to the hazards associated with the installation.

(h)(2)(ii) OI For installations other than equipment described in paragraph (h)(2)(v) of this section, a wall, screen, or fence shall be used to enclose an outdoor electrical installation to deter access by persons who are not qualified. A fence may not be less than 2.13 m (7.0 ft) in height or a combination of 1.80 m (6.0 ft) or more of fence fabric and a 305-mm (1-ft) or more extension utilizing three or more strands of barbed wire or equivalent.

(h)(2)(iii) The following requirements apply to indoor installations that are accessible to other than qualified persons:

(h)(2)(iii)(A) The installations shall be made with metal-enclosed equipment or shall be enclosed in a vault or in an area to which access is controlled by a lock;

(h)(2)(iii)(B) Metal-enclosed switchgear, unit substations, transformers, pull boxes, connection boxes, and other similar associated equipment shall be marked with appropriate caution signs; and

(h)(2)(iii)(C) Openings in ventilated dry-type transformers and similar openings in other equipment shall be designed so that foreign objects inserted through these openings will be deflected from energized parts.

(h)(2)(iv) Outdoor electrical installations having exposed live parts shall be accessible to qualified persons only.

(h)(2)(v) The following requirements apply to outdoor enclosed equipment accessible to unqualified employees:

(h)(2)(v)(A) Ventilating or similar openings in equipment shall be so designed that foreign objects inserted through these openings will be deflected from energized parts;

(h)(2)(v)(B) Where exposed to physical damage from vehicular traffic, suitable guards shall be provided;

(h)(2)(v)(C) Nonmetallic or metal-enclosed equipment located outdoors and accessible to the general public shall be designed so that exposed nuts or bolts cannot be readily removed, permitting access to live parts;

(h)(2)(v)(D) Where nonmetallic or metal-enclosed equipment is accessible to the general public and the bottom of the enclosure is less than 2.44 m (8.0 ft) above the floor or grade level, the enclosure door or hinged cover shall be kept locked; and

(h)(2)(v)(E) Except for underground box covers that weigh over 45.4 kg (100 lb), doors and covers of enclosures used solely as pull boxes, splice boxes, or junction boxes shall be locked, bolted, or screwed on.

(h)(3) **Work space about equipment** Sufficient space shall be provided and maintained about electric equipment to permit ready and safe operation and maintenance of such equipment. Where energized parts are exposed, the minimum clear work space may not be less than 1.98 m (6.5 ft) high (measured vertically from the floor or platform) or less than 914 mm (3.0 ft) wide (measured parallel to the equipment). The depth shall be as required in paragraph (h)(5)(i) of this section. In all cases, the work space shall be adequate to permit at least a 90-degree opening of doors or hinged panels.

(h)(4) **Entrance and access to work space**

(h)(4)(i) At least one entrance not less than 610 mm (24 in.) wide and 1.98 m (6.5 ft) high shall be provided to give access to the working space about electric equipment.

(h)(4)(i)(A) On switchboard and control panels exceeding 1.83 m (6.0 ft) in width, there shall be one entrance at each end of such boards unless the location of the switchboards and control panels permits a continuous and unobstructed way of exit travel, or unless the work space required in paragraph (h)(5)(i) of this section is doubled.

(h)(4)(i)(B) Where one entrance to the working space is permitted under the conditions described in paragraph (h)(4)(i)(A) of this section, the entrance shall be located so that the edge of the entrance nearest the switchboards and control panels is at least the minimum clear distance given in Table S–2 away from such equipment.

(h)(4)(i)(C) Where bare energized parts at any voltage or insulated energized parts above 600 volts, nominal, to ground are located adjacent to such entrance, they shall be suitably guarded.

(h)(4)(ii) Permanent ladders or stairways shall be provided to give safe access to the working space around electric equipment installed on platforms, balconies, mezzanine floors, or in attic or roof rooms or spaces.

(h)(5) **Working space and guarding**

(h)(5)(i) Except as elsewhere required or permitted in this Subpart, the minimum clear working space in the direction of access to live parts of electric equipment may not be less than specified in Table S–2. Distances shall be measured from the live parts, if they are exposed, or from the enclosure front or opening, if they are enclosed.

(h)(5)(ii) If switches, cutouts, or other equipment operating at 600 volts, nominal, or less, are installed in a room or enclosure where there are exposed live parts or exposed wiring operating at over 600 volts, nominal, the high-voltage equipment shall be effectively separated from the space occupied by the low-voltage equipment by a suitable partition, fence, or screen. However, switches or other equipment operating at 600 volts, nominal, or less, and serving only equipment within the high-voltage vault, room, or enclosure may be installed in the high-voltage enclosure, room, or vault if accessible to qualified persons only.

(h)(5)(iii) The following requirements apply to the entrances to all buildings, rooms, or enclosures containing exposed live parts or exposed conductors operating at over 600 volts, nominal:

(h)(5)(iii)(A) The entrances shall be kept locked unless they are under the observation of a qualified person at all times; and

(h)(5)(iii)(B) Permanent and conspicuous warning signs shall be provided, reading substantially as follows:

"DANGER—HIGH VOLTAGE—KEEP OUT"

(h)(5)(iv) Illumination shall be provided for all working spaces about electric equipment.

(h)(5)(iv)(A) The lighting outlets shall be arranged so that persons changing lamps or making repairs on the lighting system will not be endangered by live parts or other equipment.

(h)(5)(iv)(B) The points of control shall be located so that persons are prevented from contacting any live part or moving part of the equipment while turning on the lights.

(h)(5)(v) Unguarded live parts above working space shall be maintained at elevations not less than specified in Table S–3.

(h)(5)(vi) Pipes or ducts that are foreign to the electrical installation and that require periodic maintenance or whose malfunction would endanger the operation of the electrical system may not be located in the vicinity of service equipment, metal-enclosed power switchgear, or industrial control assemblies. Protection shall be provided where necessary to avoid damage from condensation leaks and breaks in such foreign systems.

Note to paragraph (h)(5)(vi) of this section: Piping and other facilities are not considered foreign if provided for fire protection of the electrical installation.

Table S–2
Minimum Depth of Clear Working Space at Electric Equipment, Over 600 V

Nominal voltage to ground	Minimum clear distance for condition[2,3]					
	Condition A		Condition B		Condition C	
	m	ft	m	ft	m	ft
601–2500 V	0.9	3.0	1.2	4.0	1.5	5.0
2501–9000 V	1.2	4.0	1.5	5.0	1.8	6.0
9001 V–25 kV	1.5	5.0	1.8	6.0	2.8	9.0
Over 25–75 kV[1]	1.8	6.0	2.5	8.0	3.0	10.0
Above 75 kV[1]	2.5	8.0	3.0	10.0	3.7	12.0

Notes to Table S–2:

[1] Minimum depth of clear working space in front of electric equipment with a nominal voltage to ground above 25,000 volts may be the same as that for 25,000 volts under Conditions A, B, and C for installations built before April 16, 1981.

[2] Conditions A, B, and C are as follows:
Condition A—Exposed live parts on one side and no live or grounded parts on the other side of the working space, or exposed live parts on both sides effectively guarded by suitable wood or other insulating material. Insulated wire or insulated busbars operating at not over 300 volts are not considered live parts.
Condition B—Exposed live parts on one side and grounded parts on the other side. Concrete, brick, and tile walls are considered as grounded surfaces.
Condition C—Exposed live parts on both sides of the work space (not guarded as provided in Condition A) with the operator between.

[3] Working space is not required in back of equipment such as dead-front switchboards or control assemblies that has no renewable or adjustable parts (such as fuses or switches) on the back and where all connections are accessible from locations other than the back. Where rear access is required to work on the deenergized parts on the back of enclosed equipment, a minimum working space 762 mm (30 in.) horizontally shall be provided.

Table S–3
Elevation of Unguarded Live Parts Above Working Space

Nominal voltage between phases	Elevation	
	m	ft
601–7500 V	[1]2.8	[1]9.0
7501 V–35 kV	2.8	9.0
Over 35 kV	2.8 + 9.5 mm/kV over 35 kV	9/0 + 0.37 in/kV over 35 kV.

[1] The minimum elevation may be 2.6 m (8.5 ft) for installations built before August 13, 2007. The minimum elevation may be 2.4 m (8.0 ft) for installations built before April 16, 1981, if the nominal voltage between phases is in the range of 601–6600 volts.

[46 FR 4056, Jan. 16, 1981, as amended at 73 FR 64205, Oct. 29, 2008]

§1910.304 Wiring design and protection

(a) Use and identification of grounded and grounding conductors

(a)(1) Identification of conductors

(a)(1)(i) A conductor used as a grounded conductor shall be identifiable and distinguishable from all other conductors.

(a)(1)(ii) A conductor used as an equipment grounding conductor shall be identifiable and distinguishable from all other conductors.

(a)(2) **Polarity of connections** No grounded conductor may be attached to any terminal or lead so as to reverse designated polarity.

(a)(3) **Use of grounding terminals and devices** A grounding terminal or grounding-type device on a receptacle, cord connector, or attachment plug may not be used for purposes other than grounding.

(b) Branch circuits

(b)(1) **Identification of multiwire branch circuits** Where more than one nominal voltage system exists in a building containing multiwire branch circuits, each ungrounded conductor of a multiwire branch circuit, where accessible, shall be identified by phase and system. The means of identification shall be permanently posted at each branch-circuit panelboard.

(b)(2) **Receptacles and cord connectors**

(b)(2)(i) Receptacles installed on 15- and 20-ampere branch circuits shall be of the grounding type except as permitted for replacement receptacles in paragraph (b)(2)(iv) of this section. Grounding-type receptacles shall be installed only on circuits of the voltage class and current for which they are rated, except as provided in Table S–4 and Table S–5.

(b)(2)(ii) Receptacles and cord connectors having grounding contacts shall have those contacts effectively grounded except for receptacles mounted on portable and vehicle-mounted generators in accordance with paragraph (g)(3) of this section and replacement receptacles installed in accordance with paragraph (b)(2)(iv) of this section.

(b)(2)(iii) The grounding contacts of receptacles and cord connectors shall be grounded by connection to the equipment grounding conductor of the circuit supplying the receptacle or cord connector. The branch circuit wiring method shall include or provide an equipment grounding conductor to which the grounding contacts of the receptacle or cord connector shall be connected.

(b)(2)(iv) Replacement of receptacles shall comply with the following requirements:

(b)(2)(iv)(A) Where a grounding means exists in the receptacle enclosure or a grounding conductor is installed, grounding-type receptacles shall be used and shall be connected to the grounding means or conductor;

(b)(2)(iv)(B) Ground-fault circuit-interrupter protected receptacles shall be provided where replacements are made at receptacle outlets that are required to be so protected elsewhere in this Subpart; and

(b)(2)(iv)(C) Where a grounding means does not exist in the receptacle enclosure, the installation shall comply with one of the following provisions:

(b)(2)(iv)(C)(1) A nongrounding-type receptacle may be replaced with another nongrounding-type receptacle; or

(b)(2)(iv)(C)(2) A nongrounding-type receptacle may be replaced with a ground-fault circuit-interrupter-type of receptacle that is marked "No Equipment Ground"; an equipment grounding conductor may not be connected from the ground-fault circuit-interrupter-type receptacle to any outlet supplied from the ground-fault circuit-interrupter receptacle; or

(b)(2)(iv)(C)(3) A nongrounding-type receptacle may be replaced with a grounding-type receptacle where supplied through a ground-fault circuit-interrupter; the replacement receptacle shall be marked "GFCI Protected" and "No Equipment Ground;" an equipment grounding conductor may not be connected to such grounding-type receptacles.

(b)(2)(v) Receptacles connected to circuits having different voltages frequencies, or types of current (AC or DC) on the same premises shall be of such design that the attachment plugs used on these circuits are not interchangeable.

(b)(3) Ground-fault circuit interrupter protection for personnel

(b)(3)(i) All 125-volt, single-phase, 15- and 20-ampere receptacles installed in bathrooms or on rooftops shall have ground-fault circuit-interrupter protection for personnel.

(b)(3)(ii) The following requirements apply to temporary wiring installations that are used during construction-like activities, including certain maintenance, remodeling, or repair activities, involving buildings, structures or equipment.

(b)(3)(ii)(A) All 125-volt, single-phase,15-,20-, and 30-ampere receptacle outlets that are not part of the permanent wiring of the building or structure and that are in use by personnel shall have ground-fault circuit-interrupter protection for personnel.

Note 1 to paragraph (b)(3)(ii)(A) of this section: A cord connector on an extension cord set is considered to be a receptacle outlet if the cord set is used for temporary electric power.

Note 2 to paragraph (b)(3)(ii)(A) of this section: Cord sets and devices incorporating the required ground-fault circuit-interrupter that are connected to the receptacle closest to the source of power are acceptable forms of protection.

(b)(3)(ii)(B) Receptacles other than 125 volt, single-phase, 15-, 20-, and 30-ampere receptacles that are not part of the permanent wiring of the building or structure and that are in use by personnel shall have ground-fault circuit-interrupter protection for personnel.

(b)(3)(ii)(C) Where the ground-fault circuit-interrupter protection required by paragraph (b)(3)(ii)(B) of this section is not available for receptacles other than 125-volt, single-phase, 15-, 20-, and 30-ampere, the employer shall establish and implement an assured equipment grounding conductor program covering cord sets, receptacles that are not a part of the building or structure, and equipment connected by cord and plug that are available for use or used by employees on those receptacles. This program shall comply with the following requirements:

(b)(3)(ii)(C)(1) A written description of the program, including the specific procedures adopted by the employer, shall be available at the jobsite for inspection and copying by the Assistant Secretary of Labor and any affected employee;

(b)(3)(ii)(C)(2) The employer shall designate one or more competent persons to implement the program;

(b)(3)(ii)(C)(3) Each cord set, attachment cap, plug, and receptacle of cord sets, and any equipment connected by cord and plug, except cord sets and receptacles which are fixed and not exposed to damage, shall be visually inspected before each day's use for external defects, such as deformed or missing pins or insulation damage, and for indications of possible internal damage. Equipment found damaged or defective shall not be used until repaired;

(b)(3)(ii)(C)(4) The following tests shall be performed on all cord sets and receptacles which are not a part of the permanent wiring of the building or structure, and cord- and plug-connected equipment required to be grounded:

(b)(3)(ii)(C)(4)(i) All equipment grounding conductors shall be tested for continuity and shall be electrically continuous;

(b)(3)(ii)(C)(4)(ii) Each receptacle and attachment cap or plug shall be tested for correct attachment of the equipment grounding conductor. The equipment grounding conductor shall be connected to its proper terminal; and

(b)(3)(ii)(C)(4)(iii) All required tests shall be performed before first use; before equipment is returned to service following any repairs; before equipment is used after any incident which can be reasonably suspected to have caused damage (for example, when a cord set is run over); and at intervals not to exceed 3 months, except that cord sets and receptacles which are fixed and not exposed to damage shall be tested at intervals not exceeding 6 months;

(b)(3)(ii)(C)(5) The employer shall not make available or permit the use by employees of any equipment which has not met the requirements of paragraph (b)(3)(ii)(C) of this section; and

(b)(3)(ii)(C)(6) Tests performed as required in paragraph (b)(3)(ii)(C) of this section shall be recorded. This test record shall identify each receptacle, cord set, and cord- and plug-connected equipment that passed the test and shall indicate the last date it was tested or the interval for which it was tested. This record shall be kept by means of logs, color coding, or other effective means and shall be maintained until replaced by a more current record. The record shall be made available on the jobsite for inspection by the Assistant Secretary and any affected employee.

(b)(4) **Outlet devices** Outlet devices shall have an ampere rating not less than the load to be served and shall comply with the following provisions:

(b)(4)(i) Where connected to a branch circuit having a rating in excess of 20 amperes, lampholders shall be of the heavy-duty type. A heavy-duty lampholder shall have a rating of not less than 660 watts if of the admedium type and not less than 750 watts if of any other type; and

(b)(4)(ii) Receptacle outlets shall comply with the following provisions:

(b)(4)(ii)(A) A single receptacle installed on an individual branch circuit shall have an ampere rating of not less than that of the branch circuit;

(b)(4)(ii)(B) Where connected to a branch circuit supplying two or more receptacles or outlets, a receptacle may not supply a total cord- and plug-connected load in excess of the maximum specified in Table S–4; and

(b)(4)(ii)(C) Where connected to a branch circuit supplying two or more receptacles or outlets, receptacle ratings shall conform to the values listed in Table S–5; or, where larger than 50 amperes, the receptacle rating may not be less than the branch-circuit rating. However, receptacles of cord- and plug-connected arc welders may have ampere ratings not less than the minimum branch-circuit conductor ampacity.

(b)(5) **Cord connections** A receptacle outlet shall be installed wherever flexible cords with attachment plugs are used. Where flexible cords are permitted to be permanently connected, receptacles may be omitted.

Table S–4
Maximum Cord- and Plug-Connected Load to Receptacle

Circuit rating (amperes)	Receptacle rating (amperes)	Maximum load (amperes)
15 or 20	15	12
20	20	16
30	30	24

Table S–5
Receptacle Ratings for Various Size Circuits

Circuit rating (amperes)	Receptacle rating (amperes)
15	Not over 15
20	15 or 20
30	30
40	40 or 50
50	50

(c) **Outside conductors, 600 volts, nominal, or less** The following requirements apply to branch-circuit, feeder, and service conductors rated 600 volts, nominal, or less and run outdoors as open conductors.

(c)(1) Conductors on poles. Conductors on poles shall have a separation of not less than 305 mm (1.0 ft) where not placed on racks or brackets. Conductors supported on poles shall provide a horizontal climbing space not less than the following:

(c)(1)(i) Power conductors below communication conductors—762 mm (30 in.);

(c)(1)(ii) Power conductors alone or above communication conductors:

(c)(1)(ii)(A) 300 volts or less—610 mm (24 in.);

(c)(1)(ii)(B) Over 300 volts—762 mm (30 in.);

(c)(1)(iii) Communication conductors below power conductors—same as power conductors; and

(c)(1)(iv) Communications conductors alone—no requirement.

(c)(2) **Clearance from ground** Open conductors, open multiconductor cables, and service-drop conductors of not over 600 volts, nominal, shall conform to the minimum clearances specified in Table S–6.

Table S–6
Clearances From Ground

Distance	Installations built before August 13, 2007		Installations built on or after August 13, 2007	
	Maximum voltage	Conditions	Voltage to ground	Conditions
3.05 m (10.0 ft)	< 600 V	Above finished grade or sidewalks, or from any platform or projection from which they might be reached. (If these areas are accessible to other than pedestrian traffic, then one of the other conditions applies)	< 150 V	Above finished grade or sidewalks, or from any platform or projection from which they might be reached. (If these areas are accessible to other than pedestrian traffic, then one of the other conditions applies.)
3.66 m (12.0 ft)	< 600 V	Over areas, other than public streets, alleys, roads, and driveways, subject to vehicular traffic other than truck traffic	< 300 V	Over residential property and driveways. Over commercial areas subject to pedestrian traffic or to vehicular traffic other than truck traffic. (This category includes conditions covered under the 3.05-m (10.0-ft) category where the voltage exceeds 150 V.)

Distance	Installations built before August 13, 2007		Installations built on or after August 13, 2007	
	Maximum voltage	Conditions	Voltage to ground	Conditions
4.57 m (15.0 ft)	< 600 V	Over areas, other than public streets, alleys, roads, and driveways, subject to truck traffic	301 to 600 V	Over residential property and driveways. Over commercial areas subject to pedestrian traffic or to vehicular traffic other than truck traffic. (This category includes conditions covered under the 3.05-m (10.0-ft) category where the voltage exceeds 300 V.)
5.49 m (18.0 ft)	< 600 V	Over public streets, alleys, roads, and driveways	< 600 V	Over public streets, alleys, roads, and driveways. Over commercial areas subject to truck traffic. Other land traversed by vehicles, including land used for cultivating or grazing and forests and orchards.

(c)(3) **Clearance from building openings**

(c)(3)(i) Service conductors installed as open conductors or multiconductor cable without an overall outer jacket shall have a clearance of not less than 914 mm (3.0 ft) from windows that are designed to be opened, doors, porches, balconies, ladders, stairs, fire escapes, and similar locations. However, conductors that run above the top level of a window may be less than 914 mm (3.0 ft) from the window. Vertical clearance of final spans above, or within 914 mm (3.0 ft) measured horizontally of, platforms, projections, or surfaces from which they might be reached shall be maintained in accordance with paragraph (c)(2) of this section.

(c)(3)(ii) Overhead service conductors may not be installed beneath openings through which materials may be moved, such as openings in farm and commercial buildings, and may not be installed where they will obstruct entrance to these building openings.

(c)(4) **Above roofs** Overhead spans of open conductors and open multiconductor cables shall have a vertical clearance of not less than 2.44 m (8.0 ft) above the roof surface. The vertical clearance above the roof level shall be maintained for a distance not less than 914 mm (3.0 ft) in all directions from the edge of the roof.

(c)(4)(i) The area above a roof surface subject to pedestrian or vehicular traffic shall have a vertical clearance from the roof surface in accordance with the clearance requirements of paragraph (c)(2) of this section.

(c)(4)(ii) A reduction in clearance to 914 mm (3.0 ft) is permitted where the voltage between conductors does not exceed 300 and the roof has a slope of 102 mm (4 in.) in 305 mm (12 in.) or greater.

(c)(4)(iii) A reduction in clearance above only the overhanging portion of the roof to not less than 457 mm (18 in.) is permitted where the voltage between conductors does not exceed 300 if:

(c)(4)(iii)(A) The conductors do not pass above the roof overhang for a distance of more than 1.83 m (6.0 ft), 1.22 m (4.0 ft) horizontally, and

(c)(4)(iii)(B) The conductors are terminated at a through-the-roof raceway or approved support.

(c)(4)(iv) The requirement for maintaining a vertical clearance of 914 mm (3.0 ft) from the edge of the roof does not apply to the final conductor span, where the conductors are attached to the side of a building.

(d) **Location of outdoor lamps** Lamps for outdoor lighting shall be located below all energized conductors, transformers, or other electric equipment, unless such equipment is controlled by a disconnecting means that can be locked in the open position, or unless adequate clearances or other safeguards are provided for relamping operations.

(e) **Services**

(e)(1) **Disconnecting means**

(e)(1)(i) Means shall be provided to disconnect all conductors in a building or other structure from the service-entrance conductors. The service disconnecting means shall plainly indicate whether it is in the open or closed position and shall be installed at a readily accessible location nearest the point of entrance of the service-entrance conductors.

(e)(1)(ii) Each service disconnecting means shall simultaneously disconnect all ungrounded conductors.

(e)(1)(iii) Each service disconnecting means shall be suitable for the prevailing conditions.

(e)(2) **Services over 600 volts, nominal** The following additional requirements apply to services over 600 volts, nominal.

(e)(2)(i) Service-entrance conductors installed as open wires shall be guarded to make them accessible only to qualified persons.

(e)(2)(ii) Signs warning of high voltage shall be posted where unqualified employees might come in contact with live parts.

(f) [OI] **Overcurrent protection**

(f)(1) **600 volts, nominal, or less** The following requirements apply to overcurrent protection of circuits rated 600 volts, nominal, or less.

(f)(1)(i) Conductors and equipment shall be protected from overcurrent in accordance with their ability to safely conduct current.

(f)(1)(ii) Except for motor running overload protection, overcurrent devices may not interrupt the continuity of the grounded conductor unless all conductors of the circuit are opened simultaneously.

(f)(1)(iii) A disconnecting means shall be provided on the supply side of all fuses in circuits over 150 volts to ground and cartridge fuses in circuits of any voltage where accessible to other than qualified persons so that each individual circuit containing fuses can be independently disconnected from the source of power. However, a current-limiting device without a disconnecting means is permitted on the supply side of the service disconnecting means. In addition, a single disconnecting means is permitted on the supply side of more than one set of fuses as permitted by the exception in §1910.305(j)(4)(vi) for group operation of motors, and a single disconnecting means is permitted for fixed electric space-heating equipment.

(f)(1)(iv) Overcurrent devices shall be readily accessible to each employee or authorized building management personnel. These overcurrent devices may not be located where they will be exposed to physical damage or in the vicinity of easily ignitable material.

(f)(1)(v) Fuses and circuit breakers shall be so located or shielded that employees will not be burned or otherwise injured by their operation. Handles or levers of circuit breakers, and similar parts that may move suddenly in such a way that persons in the vicinity are likely to be injured by being struck by them, shall be guarded or isolated.

(f)(1)(vi) Circuit breakers shall clearly indicate whether they are in the open (off) or closed (on) position.

(f)(1)(vii) Where circuit breaker handles on switchboards are operated vertically rather than horizontally or rotationally, the up position of the handle shall be the closed (on) position.

(f)(1)(viii) Circuit breakers used as switches in 120-volt and 277-volt, fluorescent lighting circuits shall be listed and marked "SWD."

(f)(1)(ix) A circuit breaker with a straight voltage rating, such as 240 V or 480 V, may only be installed in a circuit in which the nominal voltage between any two conductors does not exceed the circuit breaker's voltage rating. A two-pole circuit breaker may not be used for protecting a 3-phase, corner-grounded delta circuit unless the circuit breaker is marked 1Φ—3Φ to indicate such suitability. A circuit breaker with a slash rating, such as 120/240 V or 480Y/277 V, may only be installed in a circuit where the nominal voltage of any conductor to ground does not exceed the lower of the two values of the circuit breaker's voltage rating and the nominal voltage between any two conductors does not exceed the higher value of the circuit breaker's voltage rating.

(f)(2) **Feeders and branch circuits over 600 volts, nominal** The following requirements apply to feeders and branch circuits energized at more than 600 volts, nominal:

(f)(2)(i) Feeder and branch-circuit conductors shall have overcurrent protection in each ungrounded conductor located at the point where the conductor receives its supply or at a location in the circuit determined under engineering supervision;

(f)(2)(i)(A) Circuit breakers used for overcurrent protection of three-phase circuits shall have a minimum of three overcurrent relays operated from three current transformers. On three-phase, three-wire circuits, an overcurrent relay in the residual circuit of the current transformers may replace one of the phase relays. An overcurrent relay, operated from a current transformer that links all phases of a three-phase, three-wire circuit, may replace the residual relay and one other phase-conductor current transformer. Where the neutral is not grounded on the load side of the circuit, the current transformer may link all three phase conductors and the grounded circuit conductor (neutral); and

(f)(2)(i)(B) If fuses are used for overcurrent protection, a fuse shall be connected in series with each ungrounded conductor;

(f)(2)(ii) Each protective device shall be capable of detecting and interrupting all values of current that can occur at its location in excess of its trip setting or melting point;

(f)(2)(iii) The operating time of the protective device, the available short-circuit current, and the conductor used shall be coordinated to prevent damaging or dangerous temperatures in conductors or conductor insulation under short-circuit conditions; and

(f)(2)(iv) The following additional requirements apply to feeders only:

(f)(2)(iv)(A) The continuous ampere rating of a fuse may not exceed three times the ampacity of the conductors. The long-time trip element setting of a breaker or the minimum trip setting of an electronically actuated fuse may not exceed six times the ampacity of the conductor. For fire pumps, conductors may be protected for short circuit only; and

(f)(2)(iv)(B) Conductors tapped to a feeder may be protected by the feeder overcurrent device where that overcurrent device also protects the tap conductor.

(g) **Grounding** Paragraphs (g)(1) through (g)(9) of this section contain grounding requirements for systems, circuits, and equipment.

(g)(1) **Systems to be grounded** Systems that supply premises wiring shall be grounded as follows:

(g)(1)(i) All 3-wire dc systems shall have their neutral conductor grounded;

(g)(1)(ii) Two-wire DC systems operating at over 50 volts through 300 volts between conductors shall be grounded unless:

(g)(1)(ii)(A) They supply only industrial equipment in limited areas and are equipped with a ground detector;

(g)(1)(ii)(B) They are rectifier-derived from an ac system complying with paragraphs (g)(1)(iii), (g)(1)(iv), and (g)(1)(v) of this section; or

(g)(1)(ii)(C) They are fire-alarm circuits having a maximum current of 0.030 amperes;

(g)(1)(iii) AC circuits of less than 50 volts shall be grounded if they are installed as overhead conductors outside of buildings or if they are supplied by transformers and the transformer primary supply system is ungrounded or exceeds 150 volts to ground;

(g)(1)(iv) AC systems of 50 volts to 1000 volts shall be grounded under any of the following conditions, unless exempted by paragraph (g)(1)(v) of this section:

(g)(1)(iv)(A) If the system can be so grounded that the maximum voltage to ground on the ungrounded conductors does not exceed 150 volts;

(g)(1)(iv)(B) If the system is nominally rated three-phase, four-wire wye connected in which the neutral is used as a circuit conductor;

(g)(1)(iv)(C) If the system is nominally rated three-phase, four-wire delta connected in which the midpoint of one phase is used as a circuit conductor; or

(g)(1)(iv)(D) If a service conductor is uninsulated;

(g)(1)(v) AC systems of 50 volts to 1000 volts are not required to be grounded under any of the following conditions:

(g)(1)(v)(A) If the system is used exclusively to supply industrial electric furnaces for melting, refining, tempering, and the like;

(g)(1)(v)(B) If the system is separately derived and is used exclusively for rectifiers supplying only adjustable speed industrial drives;

(g)(1)(v)(C) If the system is separately derived and is supplied by a transformer that has a primary voltage rating less than 1000 volts, provided all of the following conditions are met:

(g)(1)(v)(C)(1) The system is used exclusively for control circuits;

(g)(1)(v)(C)(2) The conditions of maintenance and supervision ensure that only qualified persons will service the installation;

(g)(1)(v)(C)(3) Continuity of control power is required; and

(g)(1)(v)(C)(4) Ground detectors are installed on the control system;

(g)(1)(v)(D) If the system is an isolated power system that supplies circuits in health care facilities; or

(g)(1)(v)(E) If the system is a high-impedance grounded neutral system in which a grounding impedance, usually a resistor, limits the ground-fault current to a low value for 3-phase ac systems of 480 volts to 1000 volts provided all of the following conditions are met:

(g)(1)(v)(E)(1) The conditions of maintenance and supervision ensure that only qualified persons will service the installation;

(g)(1)(v)(E)(2) Continuity of power is required;

(g)(1)(v)(E)(3) Ground detectors are installed on the system; and

(g)(1)(v)(E)(4) Line-to-neutral loads are not served.

(g)(2) **Conductor to be grounded** The conductor to be grounded for ac premises wiring systems required to be grounded by paragraph (g)(1) of this section shall be as follows:

(g)(2)(i) One conductor of a single-phase, two-wire system shall be grounded;

(g)(2)(ii) The neutral conductor of a single-phase, three-wire system shall be grounded;

(g)(2)(iii) The common conductor of a multiphase system having one wire common to all phases shall be grounded;

(g)(2)(iv) One phase conductor of a multiphase system where one phase is grounded shall be grounded; and

(g)(2)(v) The neutral conductor of a multiphase system in which one phase is used as a neutral conductor shall be grounded.

(g)(3) **Portable and vehicle-mounted generators**

(g)(3)(i) The frame of a portable generator need not be grounded and may serve as the grounding electrode for a system supplied by the generator under the following conditions:

(g)(3)(i)(A) The generator supplies only equipment mounted on the generator or cord- and plug-connected equipment through receptacles mounted on the generator, or both; and

(g)(3)(i)(B) The noncurrent-carrying metal parts of equipment and the equipment grounding conductor terminals of the receptacles are bonded to the generator frame.

(g)(3)(ii) The frame of a vehicle need not be grounded and may serve as the grounding electrode for a system supplied by a generator located on the vehicle under the following conditions:

(g)(3)(ii)(A) The frame of the generator is bonded to the vehicle frame;

(g)(3)(ii)(B) The generator supplies only equipment located on the vehicle and cord- and plug-connected equipment through receptacles mounted on the vehicle;

(g)(3)(ii)(C) The noncurrent-carrying metal parts of equipment and the equipment grounding conductor terminals of the receptacles are bonded to the generator frame; and

(g)(3)(ii)(D) The system complies with all other provisions of paragraph (g) of this section.

(g)(3)(iii) A system conductor that is required to be grounded by the provisions of paragraph (g)(2) of this section shall be bonded to the generator frame where the generator is a component of a separately derived system.

(g)(4) **Grounding connections**

(g)(4)(i) For a grounded system, a grounding electrode conductor shall be used to connect both the equipment grounding conductor and the grounded circuit conductor to the grounding electrode. Both the equipment grounding conductor and the grounding electrode conductor shall be connected to the grounded circuit conductor on the supply side of the service disconnecting means or on the supply side of the system disconnecting means or overcurrent devices if the system is separately derived.

(g)(4)(ii) For an ungrounded service-supplied system, the equipment grounding conductor shall be connected to the grounding electrode conductor at the service equipment. For an ungrounded separately derived system, the equipment grounding conductor shall be connected to the grounding electrode conductor at, or ahead of, the system disconnecting means or overcurrent devices.

(g)(4)(iii) On extensions of existing branch circuits that do not have an equipment grounding conductor, grounding-type receptacles may be grounded to a grounded cold water pipe near the equipment if the extension was installed before August 13, 2007. When any element of this branch circuit is replaced, the entire branch circuit shall use an equipment grounding conductor that complies with all other provisions of paragraph (g) of this section.

(g)(5) **Grounding path** The path to ground from circuits, equipment, and enclosures shall be permanent, continuous, and effective.

(g)(6) **Supports, enclosures, and equipment to be grounded**

(g)(6)(i) Metal cable trays, metal raceways, and metal enclosures for conductors shall be grounded, except that:

(g)(6)(i)(A) Metal enclosures such as sleeves that are used to protect cable assemblies from physical damage need not be grounded; and

(g)(6)(i)(B) Metal enclosures for conductors added to existing installations of open wire, knob-and-tube wiring, and nonmetallic-sheathed cable need not be grounded if all of the following conditions are met:

(g)(6)(i)(B)(1) Runs are less than 7.62 meters (25.0 ft);

(g)(6)(i)(B)(2) Enclosures are free from probable contact with ground, grounded metal, metal laths, or other conductive materials; and

(g)(6)(i)(B)(3) Enclosures are guarded against employee contact.

(g)(6)(ii) Metal enclosures for service equipment shall be grounded.

(g)(6)(iii) Frames of electric ranges, wall-mounted ovens, counter-mounted cooking units, clothes dryers, and metal outlet or junction boxes that are part of the circuit for these appliances shall be grounded.

(g)(6)(iv) Exposed noncurrent-carrying metal parts of fixed equipment that may become energized shall be grounded under any of the following conditions:

(g)(6)(iv)(A) If within 2.44 m (8 ft) vertically or 1.52 m (5 ft) horizontally of ground or grounded metal objects and subject to employee contact;

(g)(6)(iv)(B) If located in a wet or damp location and not isolated;

(g)(6)(iv)(C) If in electrical contact with metal;

(g)(6)(iv)(D) If in a hazardous (classified) location;

(g)(6)(iv)(E) If supplied by a metal-clad, metal-sheathed, or grounded metal raceway wiring method; or

(g)(6)(iv)(F) If equipment operates with any terminal at over 150 volts to ground.

(g)(6)(v) Notwithstanding the provisions of paragraph (g)(6)(iv) of this section, exposed noncurrent-carrying metal parts of the following types of fixed equipment need not be grounded:

(g)(6)(v)(A) Enclosures for switches or circuit breakers used for other than service equipment and accessible to qualified persons only;

(g)(6)(v)(B) Electrically heated appliances that are permanently and effectively insulated from ground;

(g)(6)(v)(C) Distribution apparatus, such as transformer and capacitor cases, mounted on wooden poles, at a height exceeding 2.44 m (8.0 ft) above ground or grade level; and

(g)(6)(v)(D) Listed equipment protected by a system of double insulation, or its equivalent, and distinctively marked as such.

(g)(6)(vi) Exposed noncurrent-carrying metal parts of cord- and plug-connected equipment that may become energized shall be grounded under any of the following conditions:

(g)(6)(vi)(A) If in hazardous (classified) locations (see §1910.307);

(g)(6)(vi)(B) If operated at over 150 volts to ground, except for guarded motors and metal frames of electrically heated appliances if the appliance frames are permanently and effectively insulated from ground;

(g)(6)(vi)(C) If the equipment is of the following types:

(g)(6)(vi)(C)(1) Refrigerators, freezers, and air conditioners;

(g)(6)(vi)(C)(2) Clothes-washing, clothes-drying, and dishwashing machines, sump pumps, and electric aquarium equipment;

(g)(6)(vi)(C)(3) Hand-held motor-operated tools, stationary and fixed motor-operated tools, and light industrial motor-operated tools;

(g)(6)(vi)(C)(4) Motor-operated appliances of the following types: hedge clippers, lawn mowers, snow blowers, and wet scrubbers;

(g)(6)(vi)(C)(5) Cord- and plug-connected appliances used in damp or wet locations, or by employees standing on the ground or on metal floors or working inside of metal tanks or boilers;

(g)(6)(vi)(C)(6) Portable and mobile X-ray and associated equipment;

(g)(6)(vi)(C)(7) Tools likely to be used in wet and conductive locations; and

(g)(6)(vi)(C)(8) Portable hand lamps.

(g)(6)(vii) Notwithstanding the provisions of paragraph (g)(6)(vi) of this section, the following equipment need not be grounded:

(g)(6)(vii)(A) Tools likely to be used in wet and conductive locations if supplied through an isolating transformer with an ungrounded secondary of not over 50 volts; and

(g)(6)(vii)(B) Listed or labeled portable tools and appliances if protected by an approved system of double insulation, or its equivalent, and distinctively marked.

(g)(7) **Nonelectrical equipment** The metal parts of the following nonelectrical equipment shall be grounded: frames and tracks of electrically operated cranes and hoists; frames of nonelectrically driven elevator cars to which electric conductors are attached; hand-operated metal shifting ropes or cables of electric elevators; and metal partitions, grill work, and similar metal enclosures around equipment of over 750 volts between conductors.

(g)(8) **Methods of grounding fixed equipment**

(g)(8)(i) Noncurrent-carrying metal parts of fixed equipment, if required to be grounded by this Subpart, shall be grounded by an equipment grounding conductor that is contained within the same raceway, cable, or cord, or runs with or encloses the circuit conductors. For dc circuits only, the equipment grounding conductor may be run separately from the circuit conductors.

(g)(8)(ii) Electric equipment is considered to be effectively grounded if it is secured to, and in electrical contact with, a metal rack or structure that is provided for its support and the metal rack or structure is grounded by the method specified for the noncurrent-carrying metal parts of fixed equipment in paragraph (g)(8)(i) of this section. Metal car frames supported by metal hoisting cables attached to or running over metal sheaves or drums of grounded elevator machines are also considered to be effectively grounded.

(g)(8)(iii) For installations made before April 16, 1981, electric equipment is also considered to be effectively grounded if it is secured to, and in metallic contact with, the grounded structural metal frame of a building. When any element of this branch circuit is replaced, the entire branch circuit shall use an equipment grounding conductor that complies with all other provisions of paragraph (g) of this section.

(g)(9) **Grounding of systems and circuits of 1000 volts and over (high voltage)** If high voltage systems are grounded, they shall comply with all applicable provisions of paragraphs (g)(1) through (g)(8) of this section as supplemented and modified by the following requirements:

(g)(9)(i) Systems supplying portable or mobile high voltage equipment, other than substations installed on a temporary basis, shall comply with the following:

(g)(9)(i)(A) The system shall have its neutral grounded through an impedance. If a delta-connected high voltage system is used to supply the equipment, a system neutral shall be derived.

(g)(9)(i)(B) Exposed noncurrent-carrying metal parts of portable and mobile equipment shall be connected by an equipment grounding conductor to the point at which the system neutral impedance is grounded.

(g)(9)(i)(C) Ground-fault detection and relaying shall be provided to automatically deenergize any high voltage system component that has developed a ground fault. The continuity of the equipment grounding conductor shall be continuously monitored so as to deenergize automatically the high voltage feeder to the portable equipment upon loss of continuity of the equipment grounding conductor.

(g)(9)(i)(D) The grounding electrode to which the portable equipment system neutral impedance is connected shall be isolated from and separated in the ground by at least 6.1 m (20.0 ft) from any other system or equipment grounding electrode, and there shall be no direct connection between the grounding electrodes, such as buried pipe, fence, and so forth.

(g)(9)(ii) All noncurrent-carrying metal parts of portable equipment and fixed equipment, including their associated fences, housings, enclosures, and supporting structures, shall be grounded. However, equipment that is guarded by location and isolated from ground need not be grounded. Additionally, pole-mounted distribution apparatus at a height exceeding 2.44 m (8.0 ft) above ground or grade level need not be grounded.

[46 FR 4056, Jan. 16, 1981, as amended at 73 FR 64205, Oct. 29, 2008]

§1910.305 Wiring methods, components, and equipment for general use

(a) **Wiring methods** The provisions of this section do not apply to conductors that are an integral part of factory-assembled equipment.

(a)(1) **General requirements**

(a)(1)(i) Metal raceways, cable trays, cable armor, cable sheath, enclosures, frames, fittings, and other metal noncurrent-carrying parts that are to serve as grounding conductors, with or without the use of supplementary equipment grounding conductors, shall be effectively bonded where necessary to ensure electrical continuity and the capacity to conduct safely any fault current likely to be imposed on them. Any nonconductive paint, enamel, or similar coating shall be removed at threads, contact points, and contact surfaces or be connected by means of fittings designed so as to make such removal unnecessary.

(a)(1)(ii) Where necessary for the reduction of electrical noise (electromagnetic interference) of the grounding circuit, an equipment enclosure supplied by a branch circuit may be isolated from a raceway containing circuits supplying only that equipment by one or more listed nonmetallic raceway fittings located at the point of attachment of the raceway to the equipment enclosure. The metal raceway shall be supplemented by an internal insulated equipment grounding conductor installed to ground the equipment enclosure.

(a)(1)(iii) No wiring systems of any type may be installed in ducts used to transport dust, loose stock, or flammable vapors. No wiring system of any type may be installed in any duct used for vapor removal or for ventilation of commercial-type cooking equipment, or in any shaft containing only such ducts.

(a)(2) **Temporary wiring** Except as specifically modified in this paragraph, all other requirements of this Subpart for permanent wiring shall also apply to temporary wiring installations.

(a)(2)(i) Temporary electrical power and lighting installations of 600 volts, nominal, or less may be used only as follows:

(a)(2)(i)(A) During and for remodeling, maintenance, or repair of buildings, structures, or equipment, and similar activities;

(a)(2)(i)(B) For a period not to exceed 90 days for Christmas decorative lighting, carnivals, and similar purposes; or

(a)(2)(i)(C) For experimental or development work, and during emergencies.

(a)(2)(ii) Temporary wiring shall be removed immediately upon completion of the project or purpose for which the wiring was installed.

(a)(2)(iii) Temporary electrical installations of more than 600 volts may be used only during periods of tests, experiments, emergencies, or construction-like activities.

(a)(2)(iv) The following requirements apply to feeders:

(a)(2)(iv)(A) Feeders shall originate in an approved distribution center.

(a)(2)(iv)(B) Conductors shall be run as multiconductor cord or cable assemblies. However, if installed as permitted in paragraph (a)(2)(i)(C) of this section, and if accessible only to qualified persons, feeders may be run as single insulated conductors.

(a)(2)(v) The following requirements apply to branch circuits:

(a)(2)(v)(A) Branch circuits shall originate in an approved power outlet or panelboard.

(a)(2)(v)(B) Conductors shall be multiconductor cord or cable assemblies or open conductors. If run as open conductors, they shall be fastened at ceiling height every 3.05 m (10.0 ft).

(a)(2)(v)(C) No branch-circuit conductor may be laid on the floor.

(a)(2)(v)(D) Each branch circuit that supplies receptacles or fixed equipment shall contain a separate equipment grounding conductor if run as open conductors.

(a)(2)(vi) Receptacles shall be of the grounding type. Unless installed in a continuous grounded metallic raceway or metallic covered cable, each branch circuit shall contain a separate equipment grounding conductor and all receptacles shall be electrically connected to the grounding conductor.

(a)(2)(vii) No bare conductors nor earth returns may be used for the wiring of any temporary circuit.

(a)(2)(viii) Suitable disconnecting switches or plug connectors shall be installed to permit the disconnection of all ungrounded conductors of each temporary circuit. Multiwire branch circuits shall be provided with a means to disconnect simultaneously all ungrounded conductors at the power outlet or panelboard where the branch circuit originated.

Note to paragraph (a)(2)(viii) of this section Circuit breakers with their handles connected by approved handle ties are considered a single disconnecting means for the purpose of this requirement.

(a)(2)(ix) All lamps for general illumination shall be protected from accidental contact or breakage by a suitable fixture or lampholder with a guard. Brass shell, paper-lined sockets, or other metal-cased sockets may not be used unless the shell is grounded.

(a)(2)(x) Flexible cords and cables shall be protected from accidental damage, as might be caused, for example, by sharp corners, projections, and doorways or other pinch points.

(a)(2)(xi) Cable assemblies and flexible cords and cables shall be supported in place at intervals that ensure that they will be protected from physical damage. Support shall be in the form of staples, cables ties, straps, or similar type fittings installed so as not to cause damage.

(a)(3) Cable trays

(a)(3)(i) Only the following wiring methods may be installed in cable tray systems: armored cable; electrical metallic tubing; electrical nonmetallic tubing; fire alarm cables; flexible metal conduit; flexible metallic tubing; instrumentation tray cable; intermediate metal conduit; liquidtight flexible metal conduit; liquidtight flexible nonmetallic conduit; metal-clad cable; mineral-insulated, metal-sheathed cable; multiconductor service-entrance cable; multiconductor underground feeder and branch-circuit cable; multipurpose and communications cables; nonmetallic-sheathed cable; power and control tray cable; power-limited tray cable; optical fiber cables; and other factory-assembled, multiconductor control, signal, or power cables that are specifically approved for installation in cable trays, rigid metal conduit, and rigid nonmetallic conduit.

(a)(3)(ii) In industrial establishments where conditions of maintenance and supervision assure that only qualified persons will service the installed cable tray system, the following cables may also be installed in ladder, ventilated-trough, or ventilated-channel cable trays:

(a)(3)(ii)(A) Single conductor cable; the cable shall be No. 1/0 or larger and shall be of a type listed and marked on the surface for use in cable trays; where Nos. 1/0 through 4/0 single conductor cables are installed in ladder cable tray, the maximum allowable rung spacing for the ladder cable tray shall be 229 mm (9 in.); where exposed to direct rays of the sun, cables shall be identified as being sunlight resistant;

(a)(3)(ii)(B) Welding cables installed in dedicated cable trays;

(a)(3)(ii)(C) Single conductors used as equipment grounding conductors; these conductors, which may be insulated, covered, or bare, shall be No. 4 or larger; and

(a)(3)(ii)(D) Multiconductor cable, Type MV; where exposed to direct rays of the sun, the cable shall be identified as being sunlight resistant.

(a)(3)(iii) Metallic cable trays may be used as equipment grounding conductors only where continuous maintenance and supervision ensure that qualified persons will service the installed cable tray system.

(a)(3)(iv) Cable trays in hazardous (classified) locations may contain only the cable types permitted in such locations. (See §1910.307.)

(a)(3)(v) Cable tray systems may not be used in hoistways or where subjected to severe physical damage.

(a)(4) Open wiring on insulators

(a)(4)(i) Open wiring on insulators is only permitted on systems of 600 volts, nominal, or less for industrial or agricultural establishments, indoors or outdoors, in wet or dry locations, where subject to corrosive vapors, and for services.

(a)(4)(ii) Conductors smaller than No. 8 shall be rigidly supported on noncombustible, nonabsorbent insulating materials and may not contact any other objects. Supports shall be installed as follows:

(a)(4)(ii)(A) Within 152 mm (6 in.) from a tap or splice;

(a)(4)(ii)(B) Within 305 mm (12 in.) of a dead-end connection to a lampholder or receptacle; and

(a)(4)(ii)(C) At intervals not exceeding 1.37 m (4.5 ft), and at closer intervals sufficient to provide adequate support where likely to be disturbed.

(a)(4)(iii) In dry locations, where not exposed to severe physical damage, conductors may be separately enclosed in flexible nonmetallic tubing. The tubing shall be in continuous lengths not exceeding 4.57 m (15.0 ft) and secured to the surface by straps at intervals not exceeding 1.37 m (4.5 ft).

(a)(4)(iv) Open conductors shall be separated from contact with walls, floors, wood cross members, or partitions through which they pass by tubes or bushings of noncombustible, nonabsorbent insulating material. If the bushing is shorter than the hole, a waterproof sleeve of nonconductive material shall be inserted in the hole and an insulating bushing slipped into the sleeve at each end in such a manner as to keep the conductors absolutely out of contact with the sleeve. Each conductor shall be carried through a separate tube or sleeve.

(a)(4)(v) Where open conductors cross ceiling joints and wall studs and are exposed to physical damage (for example, located within 2.13 m (7.0 ft) of the floor), they shall be protected.

(b) Cabinets, boxes, and fittings

(b)(1) Conductors entering boxes, cabinets, or fittings

(b)(1)(i) Conductors entering cutout boxes, cabinets, or fittings shall be protected from abrasion, and openings through which conductors enter shall be effectively closed.

(b)(1)(ii) Unused openings in cabinets, boxes, and fittings shall be effectively closed.

(b)(1)(iii) Where cable is used, each cable shall be secured to the cabinet, cutout box, or meter socket enclosure. However, where cable with an entirely nonmetallic sheath enters the top of a surface-mounted enclosure through one or more nonflexible raceways not less than 457 mm (18 in.) or more than 3.05 m (10.0 ft) in length, the cable need not be secured to the cabinet, box, or enclosure provided all of the following conditions are met:

(b)(1)(iii)(A) Each cable is fastened within 305 mm (12 in.) of the outer end of the raceway, measured along the sheath;

(b)(1)(iii)(B) The raceway extends directly above the enclosure and does not penetrate a structural ceiling;

(b)(1)(iii)(C) A fitting is provided on each end of the raceway to protect the cable from abrasion, and the fittings remain accessible after installation;

(b)(1)(iii)(D) The raceway is sealed or plugged at the outer end using approved means so as to prevent access to the enclosure through the raceway;

(b)(1)(iii)(E) The cable sheath is continuous through the raceway and extends into the enclosure not less than 6.35 mm (0.25 in.) beyond the fitting;

(b)(1)(iii)(F) The raceway is fastened at its outer end and at other points as necessary; and

(b)(1)(iii)(G) Where installed as conduit or tubing, the allowable cable fill does not exceed that permitted for complete conduit or tubing systems.

(b)(2) Covers and canopies

(b)(2)(i) All pull boxes, junction boxes, and fittings shall be provided with covers identified for the purpose. If metal covers are used, they shall be grounded. In completed installations, each outlet box shall have a cover, faceplate, or fixture canopy. Covers of outlet boxes having holes through which flexible cord pendants pass shall be provided with bushings designed for the purpose or shall have smooth, well-rounded surfaces on which the cords may bear.

(b)(2)(ii) Where a fixture canopy or pan is used, any combustible wall or ceiling finish exposed between the edge of the canopy or pan and the outlet box shall be covered with noncombustible material.

(b)(3) Pull and junction boxes for systems over 600 volts, nominal. In addition to other requirements in this section, the following requirements apply to pull and junction boxes for systems over 600 volts, nominal:

(b)(3)(i) Boxes shall provide a complete enclosure for the contained conductors or cables.

(b)(3)(ii) Boxes shall be closed by suitable covers securely fastened in place.

Note to paragraph (b)(3)(ii) of this section: Underground box covers that weigh over 45.4 kg (100 lbs) meet this requirement.

(b)(3)(iii) Covers for boxes shall be permanently marked "HIGH VOLTAGE." The marking shall be on the outside of the box cover and shall be readily visible and legible.

(c) Switches

(c)(1) **Single-throw knife switches** Single-throw knife switches shall be so placed that gravity will not tend to close them. Single-throw knife switches approved for use in the inverted position shall be provided with a locking device that will ensure that the blades remain in the open position when so set.

(c)(2) **Double-throw knife switches** Double-throw knife switches may be mounted so that the throw will be either vertical or horizontal. However, if the throw is vertical, a locking device shall be provided to ensure that the blades remain in the open position when so set.

(c)(3) **Connection of switches**

(c)(3)(i) Single-throw knife switches and switches with butt contacts shall be connected so that the blades are deenergized when the switch is in the open position.

(c)(3)(ii) Single-throw knife switches, molded-case switches, switches with butt contacts, and circuit breakers used as switches shall be connected so that the terminals supplying the load are deenergized when the switch is in the open position. However, blades and terminals supplying the load of a switch may be energized when the switch is in the open position where the switch is connected to circuits or equipment inherently capable of providing a backfeed source of power. For such installations, a permanent sign shall be installed on the switch enclosure or immediately adjacent to open switches that read, **"WARNING—LOAD SIDE TERMINALS MAY BE ENERGIZED BY BACKFEED."**

(c)(4) **Faceplates for flush-mounted snap switches** Snap switches mounted in boxes shall have faceplates installed so as to completely cover the opening and seat against the finished surface.

(c)(5) **Grounding** Snap switches, including dimmer switches, shall be effectively grounded and shall provide a means to ground metal faceplates, whether or not a metal faceplate is installed. However, if no grounding means exists within the snap-switch enclosure, or where the wiring method does not include or provide an equipment ground, a snap switch without a grounding connection is permitted for replacement purposes only. Such snap switches shall be provided with a faceplate of nonconducting, noncombustible material if they are located within reach of conducting floors or other conducting surfaces.

(d) Switchboards and panelboards

(d)(1) **Switchboards with exposed live parts** Switchboards that have any exposed live parts shall be located in permanently dry locations and shall be accessible only to qualified persons.

(d)(2) **Panelboard enclosures** Panelboards shall be mounted in cabinets, cutout boxes, or enclosures designed for the purpose and shall be dead front. However, panelboards other than the dead front externally-operable type are permitted where accessible only to qualified persons.

(d)(3) **Knife switches mounted in switchboards or panelboards** Exposed blades of knife switches mounted in switchboards or panelboards shall be dead when open.

(e) Enclosures for damp or wet locations

(e)(1) **Cabinets, cutout boxes, fittings, boxes, and panelboard enclosures** Cabinets, cutout boxes, fittings, boxes, and panelboard enclosures in damp or wet locations shall be installed so as to prevent moisture or water from entering and accumulating within the enclosures and shall be mounted so there is at least 6.35 mm (0.25 in.) airspace between the enclosure and the wall or other supporting surface. However, nonmetallic enclosures may be installed without the airspace on a concrete, masonry, tile, or similar surface. The enclosures shall be weatherproof in wet locations.

(e)(2) **Switches, circuit breakers, and switchboards** Switches, circuit breakers, and switchboards installed in wet locations shall be enclosed in weatherproof enclosures.

(f) Conductors for general wiring

(f)(1) **Insulation** All conductors used for general wiring shall be insulated unless otherwise permitted in this Subpart.

(f)(2) **Type** The conductor insulation shall be of a type that is approved for the voltage, operating temperature, and location of use.

(f)(3) **Distinguishable** Insulated conductors shall be distinguishable by appropriate color or other suitable means as being grounded conductors, ungrounded conductors, or equipment grounding conductors.

(g) Flexible cords and cables

(g)(1) **Use of flexible cords and cables**

(g)(1)(i) Flexible cords and cables shall be approved for conditions of use and location.

(g)(1)(ii) Flexible cords and cables may be used only for:

(g)(1)(ii)(A) Pendants;
(g)(1)(ii)(B) Wiring of fixtures;
(g)(1)(ii)(C) Connection of portable lamps or appliances;
(g)(1)(ii)(D) Portable and mobile signs;
(g)(1)(ii)(E) Elevator cables;
(g)(1)(ii)(F) Wiring of cranes and hoists;
(g)(1)(ii)(G) Connection of stationary equipment to facilitate their frequent interchange;
(g)(1)(ii)(H) Prevention of the transmission of noise or vibration;
(g)(1)(ii)(I) Appliances where the fastening means and mechanical connections are designed to permit removal for maintenance and repair;
(g)(1)(ii)(J) Data processing cables approved as a part of the data processing system;
(g)(1)(ii)(K) Connection of moving parts; and
(g)(1)(ii)(L) Temporary wiring as permitted in paragraph (a)(2) of this section.

(g)(1)(iii) If used as permitted in paragraphs (g)(1)(ii)(C), (g)(1)(ii)(G), or (g)(1)(ii)(I) of this section, the flexible cord shall be equipped with an attachment plug and shall be energized from an approved receptacle outlet.

(g)(1)(iv) Unless specifically permitted otherwise in paragraph (g)(1)(ii) of this section, flexible cords and cables may not be used:

(g)(1)(iv)(A) As a substitute for the fixed wiring of a structure;
(g)(1)(iv)(B) Where run through holes in walls, ceilings, or floors;
(g)(1)(iv)(C) Where run through doorways, windows, or similar openings;
(g)(1)(iv)(D) Where attached to building surfaces;
(g)(1)(iv)(E) Where concealed behind building walls, ceilings, or floors; or
(g)(1)(iv)(F) Where installed in raceways, except as otherwise permitted in this Subpart.

(g)(1)(v) Flexible cords used in show windows and showcases shall be Type S, SE, SEO, SEOO, SJ, SJE, SJEO, SJEOO, SJO, SJOO, SJT, SJTO, SJTOO, SO, SOO, ST, STO, or STOO, except for the wiring of chain-supported lighting fixtures and supply cords for portable lamps and other merchandise being displayed or exhibited.

(g)(2) **Identification, splices, and terminations**

(g)(2)(i) A conductor of a flexible cord or cable that is used as a grounded conductor or an equipment grounding conductor shall be distinguishable from other conductors. Types S, SC, SCE, SCT, SE, SEO, SEOO, SJ, SJE, SJEO, SJEOO, SJO, SJT, SJTO, SJTOO, SO, SOO, ST, STO, and STOO flexible cords and Types G, G–GC, PPE, and W flexible cables shall be durably marked on the surface at intervals not exceeding 610 mm (24 in.) with the type designation, size, and number of conductors.

(g)(2)(ii) Flexible cords may be used only in continuous lengths without splice or tap. Hard-service cord and junior hard-service cord No. 14 and larger may be repaired if spliced so that the splice retains the insulation, outer sheath properties, and usage characteristics of the cord being spliced.

(g)(2)(iii) Flexible cords and cables shall be connected to devices and fittings so that strain relief is provided that will prevent pull from being directly transmitted to joints or terminal screws.

(h) **Portable cables over 600 volts, nominal** This paragraph applies to portable cables used at more than 600 volts, nominal.

(h)(1) **Conductor construction** Multiconductor portable cable for use in supplying power to portable or mobile equipment at over 600 volts, nominal, shall consist of No. 8 or larger conductors employing flexible stranding. However, the minimum size of the insulated ground-check conductor of Type G–GC cables shall be No. 10.

(h)(2) **Shielding** Cables operated at over 2,000 volts shall be shielded for the purpose of confining the voltage stresses to the insulation.

(h)(3) **Equipment grounding conductors** Grounding conductors shall be provided.

(h)(4) **Grounding shields** All shields shall be grounded.

(h)(5) **Minimum bending radii** The minimum bending radii for portable cables during installation and handling in service shall be adequate to prevent damage to the cable.

(h)(6) **Fittings** Connectors used to connect lengths of cable in a run shall be of a type that lock firmly together. Provisions shall be made to prevent opening or closing these connectors while energized. Strain relief shall be provided at connections and terminations.

(h)(7) **Splices** Portable cables may not be operated with splices unless the splices are of the permanent molded, vulcanized, or other approved type.

(h)(8) **Terminations** Termination enclosures shall be suitably marked with a high voltage hazard warning, and terminations shall be accessible only to authorized and qualified employees.

(i) **Fixture wires**

(i)(1) **General** Fixture wires shall be approved for the voltage, temperature, and location of use. A fixture wire which is used as a grounded conductor shall be identified.

(i)(2) **Uses permitted** Fixture wires may be used only:

(i)(2)(i) For installation in lighting fixtures and in similar equipment where enclosed or protected and not subject to bending or twisting in use; or

(i)(2)(ii) For connecting lighting fixtures to the branch-circuit conductors supplying the fixtures.

(i)(3) **Uses not permitted** Fixture wires may not be used as branch-circuit conductors except as permitted for Class 1 power limited circuits and for fire alarm circuits.

(j) **Equipment for general use**

(j)(1) **Lighting fixtures, lampholders, lamps, and receptacles**

(j)(1)(i) Fixtures, lampholders, lamps, rosettes, and receptacles may have no live parts normally exposed to employee contact. However, rosettes and cleat-type lampholders and receptacles located at least 2.44 m (8.0 ft) above the floor may have exposed terminals.

(j)(1)(ii) Handlamps of the portable type supplied through flexible cords shall be equipped with a handle of molded composition or other material identified for the purpose, and a substantial guard shall be attached to the lampholder or the handle. Metal shell, paper-lined lampholders may not be used.

(j)(1)(iii) Lampholders of the screw-shell type shall be installed for use as lampholders only. Where supplied by a circuit having a grounded conductor, the grounded conductor shall be connected to the screw shell. Lampholders installed in wet or damp locations shall be of the weatherproof type.

(j)(1)(iv) Fixtures installed in wet or damp locations shall be identified for the purpose and shall be so constructed or installed that water cannot enter or accumulate in wireways, lampholders, or other electrical parts.

(j)(2) **Receptacles, cord connectors, and attachment plugs (caps)**

(j)(2)(i) All 15- and 20-ampere attachment plugs and connectors shall be constructed so that there are no exposed current-carrying parts except the prongs, blades, or pins. The cover for wire terminations shall be a part that is essential for the operation of an attachment plug or connector (dead-front construction). Attachment plugs shall be installed so that their prongs, blades, or pins are not energized unless inserted into an energized receptacle. No receptacles may be installed so as to require an energized attachment plug as its source of supply.

(j)(2)(ii) Receptacles, cord connectors, and attachment plugs shall be constructed so that no receptacle or cord connector will accept an attachment plug with a different voltage or current rating than that for which the device is intended. However, a 20-ampere T-slot receptacle or cord connector may accept a 15-ampere attachment plug of the same voltage rating.

(j)(2)(iii) Nongrounding-type receptacles and connectors may not be used for grounding-type attachment plugs.

(j)(2)(iv) A receptacle installed in a wet or damp location shall be suitable for the location.

(j)(2)(v) A receptacle installed outdoors in a location protected from the weather or in other damp locations shall have an enclosure for the receptacle that is weatherproof when the receptacle is covered (attachment plug cap not inserted and receptacle covers closed).

Note to paragraph (j)(2)(v) of this section. A receptacle is considered to be in a location protected from the weather when it is located under roofed open porches, canopies, marquees, or the like and where it will not be subjected to a beating rain or water runoff.

(j)(2)(vi) A receptacle installed in a wet location where the product intended to be plugged into it is not attended while in use (for example, sprinkler system controllers, landscape lighting, and holiday lights) shall have an enclosure that is weatherproof with the attachment plug cap inserted or removed.

(j)(2)(vii) A receptacle installed in a wet location where the product intended to be plugged into it will be attended while in use (for example, portable tools) shall have an enclosure that is weatherproof when the attachment plug cap is removed.

(j)(3) **Appliances**

(j)(3)(i) Appliances may have no live parts normally exposed to contact other than parts functioning as open-resistance heating elements, such as the heating elements of a toaster, which are necessarily exposed.

(j)(3)(ii) Each appliance shall have a means to disconnect it from all ungrounded conductors. If an appliance is supplied by more than one source, the disconnecting means shall be grouped and identified.

(j)(3)(iii) Each electric appliance shall be provided with a nameplate giving the identifying name and the rating in volts and amperes, or in volts and watts. If the appliance is to be used on a specific frequency or frequencies, it shall be so marked. Where motor overload protection external to the appliance is required, the appliance shall be so marked.

(j)(3)(iv) Marking shall be located so as to be visible or easily accessible after installation.

(j)(4) **Motors** This paragraph applies to motors, motor circuits, and controllers.

(j)(4)(i) If specified in paragraph (j)(4) of this section that one piece of equipment shall be "within sight of" another piece of equipment, the piece of equipment shall be visible and not more than 15.24 m (50.0 ft) from the other.

(j)(4)(ii) An individual disconnecting means shall be provided for each controller. A disconnecting means shall be located within sight of the controller location. However, a single disconnecting means may be located adjacent to a group of coordinated controllers mounted adjacent to each other on a multi-motor continuous process machine. The controller disconnecting means for motor branch circuits over 600 volts, nominal, may be out of sight of the controller, if the controller is marked with a warning label giving the location and identification of the disconnecting means that is to be locked in the open position.

(j)(4)(iii) The disconnecting means shall disconnect the motor and the controller from all ungrounded supply conductors and shall be so designed that no pole can be operated independently.

(j)(4)(iv) The disconnecting means shall plainly indicate whether it is in the open (off) or closed (on) position.

(j)(4)(v) The disconnecting means shall be readily accessible. If more than one disconnect is provided for the same equipment, only one need be readily accessible.

(j)(4)(vi) An individual disconnecting means shall be provided for each motor, but a single disconnecting means may be used for a group of motors under any one of the following conditions:

(j)(4)(vi)(A) If a number of motors drive several parts of a single machine or piece of apparatus, such as a metal or woodworking machine, crane, or hoist;

(j)(4)(vi)(B) If a group of motors is under the protection of one set of branch-circuit protective devices; or

(j)(4)(vi)(C) If a group of motors is in a single room within sight of the location of the disconnecting means.

(j)(4)(vii) Motors, motor-control apparatus, and motor branch-circuit conductors shall be protected against overheating due to motor overloads or failure to start, and against short-circuits or ground faults. These provisions do not require overload protection that will stop a motor where a shutdown is likely to introduce additional or increased hazards, as in the case of fire pumps, or where continued operation of a motor is necessary for a safe shutdown of equipment or process and motor overload sensing devices are connected to a supervised alarm.

(j)(4)(viii) Where live parts of motors or controllers operating at over 150 volts to ground are guarded against accidental contact only by location, and where adjustment or other attendance may be necessary during the operation of the apparatus, suitable insulating mats or platforms shall be provided so that the attendant cannot readily touch live parts unless standing on the mats or platforms.

(j)(5) **Transformers**

(j)(5)(i) Paragraph (j)(5) of this section covers the installation of all transformers except the following:

(j)(5)(i)(A) Current transformers;

(j)(5)(i)(B) Dry-type transformers installed as a component part of other apparatus;

(j)(5)(i)(C) Transformers that are an integral part of an X-ray, high frequency, or electrostatic-coating apparatus;

(j)(5)(i)(D) Transformers used with Class 2 and Class 3 circuits, sign and outline lighting, electric discharge lighting, and power-limited fire-alarm circuits; and (j)(5)(i)(E) Liquid-filled or dry-type transformers used for research, development, or testing, where effective safeguard arrangements are provided.

(j)(5)(ii) The operating voltage of exposed live parts of transformer installations shall be indicated by signs or visible markings on the equipment or structure.

(j)(5)(iii) Dry-type, high fire point liquid-insulated, and askarel-insulated transformers installed indoors and rated over 35kV shall be in a vault.

(j)(5)(iv) Oil-insulated transformers installed indoors shall be installed in a vault.

(j)(5)(v) Combustible material, combustible buildings and parts of buildings, fire escapes, and door and window openings shall be safeguarded from fires that may originate in oil-insulated transformers attached to or adjacent to a building or combustible material.

(j)(5)(vi) Transformer vaults shall be constructed so as to contain fire and combustible liquids within the vault and to prevent unauthorized access. Locks and latches shall be so arranged that a vault door can be readily opened from the inside.

(j)(5)(vii) Any pipe or duct system foreign to the electrical installation may not enter or pass through a transformer vault.

Note to paragraph (j)(5)(vii) of this section. Piping or other facilities provided for vault fire protection, or for transformer cooling, are not considered foreign to the electrical installation.

(j)(5)(viii) Material may not be stored in transformer vaults.

(j)(6) Capacitors

(j)(6)(i) All capacitors, except surge capacitors or capacitors included as a component part of other apparatus, shall be provided with an automatic means of draining the stored charge after the capacitor is disconnected from its source of supply.

(j)(6)(ii) The following requirements apply to capacitors installed on circuits operating at more than 600 volts, nominal:

(j)(6)(ii)(A) Group-operated switches shall be used for capacitor switching and shall be capable of the following:

(j)(6)(ii)(A)(1) Carrying continuously not less than 135 percent of the rated current of the capacitor installation;

(j)(6)(ii)(A)(2) Interrupting the maximum continuous load current of each capacitor, capacitor bank, or capacitor installation that will be switched as a unit;

(j)(6)(ii)(A)(3) Withstanding the maximum inrush current, including contributions from adjacent capacitor installations; and

(j)(6)(ii)(A)(4) Carrying currents due to faults on the capacitor side of the switch;

(j)(6)(ii)(B) A means shall be installed to isolate from all sources of voltage each capacitor, capacitor bank, or capacitor installation that will be removed from service as a unit. The isolating means shall provide a visible gap in the electric circuit adequate for the operating voltage;

(j)(6)(ii)(C) Isolating or disconnecting switches (with no interrupting rating) shall be interlocked with the load interrupting device or shall be provided with prominently displayed caution signs to prevent switching load current; and

(j)(6)(ii)(D) For series capacitors, the proper switching shall be assured by use of at least one of the following:

(j)(6)(ii)(D)(1) Mechanically sequenced isolating and bypass switches;

(j)(6)(ii)(D)(2) Interlocks; or

(j)(6)(ii)(D)(3) Switching procedure prominently displayed at the switching location.

(j)(7) [OI] **Storage Batteries** Provisions shall be made for sufficient diffusion and ventilation of gases from storage batteries to prevent the accumulation of explosive mixtures.

§1910.306 Specific purpose equipment and installations

(a) Electric signs and outline lighting

(a)(1) Disconnecting means

(a)(1)(i) Each sign and outline lighting system, or feeder circuit or branch circuit supplying a sign or outline lighting system, shall be controlled by an externally operable switch or circuit breaker that will open all ungrounded conductors. However, a disconnecting means is not required for an exit directional sign located within a building or for cord-connected signs with an attachment plug.

(a)(1)(ii) Signs and outline lighting systems located within fountains shall have the disconnect located at least 1.52 m (5.0 ft) from the inside walls of the fountain.

(a)(2) Location

(a)(2)(i) The disconnecting means shall be within sight of the sign or outline lighting system that it controls. Where the disconnecting means is out of the line of sight from any section that may be energized, the disconnecting means shall be capable of being locked in the open position.

(a)(2)(ii) Signs or outline lighting systems operated by electronic or electromechanical controllers located external to the sign or outline lighting system may have a disconnecting means located within sight of the controller or in the same enclosure with the controller. The disconnecting means shall disconnect the sign or outline lighting system and the controller from all ungrounded supply conductors. It shall be designed so no pole can be operated independently and shall be capable of being locked in the open position.

(a)(2)(iii) Doors or covers giving access to uninsulated parts of indoor signs or outline lighting exceeding 600 volts and accessible to other than qualified persons shall either be provided with interlock switches to disconnect the primary circuit or shall be so fastened that the use of other than ordinary tools will be necessary to open them.

(b) Cranes and hoists This paragraph applies to the installation of electric equipment and wiring used in connection with cranes, monorail hoists, hoists, and all runways.

(b)(1) Disconnecting means for runway conductors A disconnecting means shall be provided between the runway contact conductors and the power supply. Such disconnecting means shall consist of a motor-circuit switch, circuit breaker, or molded case switch. The disconnecting means shall open all ungrounded conductors simultaneously and shall be:

(b)(1)(i) Readily accessible and operable from the ground or floor level;

(b)(1)(ii) Arranged to be locked in the open position; and

(b)(1)(iii) Placed within view of the runway contact conductors.

(b)(2) Disconnecting means for cranes and monorail hoists

(b)(2)(i) Except as provided in paragraph (b)(2)(iv) of this section, a motor-circuit switch, molded case switch, or circuit breaker shall be provided in the leads from the runway contact conductors or other power supply on all cranes and monorail hoists.

(b)(2)(ii) The disconnecting means shall be capable of being locked in the open position.

(b)(2)(iii) Means shall be provided at the operating station to open the power circuit to all motors of the crane or monorail hoist where the disconnecting means is not readily accessible from the crane or monorail hoist operating station.

(b)(2)(iv) The disconnecting means may be omitted where a monorail hoist or hand-propelled crane bridge installation meets all of the following conditions:

(b)(2)(iv)(A) The unit is controlled from the ground or floor level;

(b)(2)(iv)(B) The unit is within view of the power supply disconnecting means; and

(b)(2)(iv)(C) No fixed work platform has been provided for servicing the unit.

(b)(3) Limit switch A limit switch or other device shall be provided to prevent the load block from passing the safe upper limit of travel of any hoisting mechanism.

(b)(4) Clearance The dimension of the working space in the direction of access to live parts that may require examination, adjustment, servicing, or maintenance while alive shall be a minimum of 762 mm (2.5 ft). Where controls are enclosed in cabinets, the doors shall either open at least 90 degrees or be removable.

(c) Elevators, dumbwaiters, escalators, moving walks, wheelchair lifts, and stairway chair lifts The following requirements apply to elevators, dumbwaiters, escalators, moving walks, wheelchair lifts, and stairway chair lifts.

(c)(1) Disconnecting means Elevators, dumbwaiters, escalators, moving walks, wheelchair lifts, and stairway chair lifts shall have a single means for disconnecting all ungrounded main power supply conductors for each unit.

(c)(2) Control panels Control panels not located in the same space as the drive machine shall be located in cabinets with doors or panels capable of being locked closed.

(c)(3) Type The disconnecting means shall be an enclosed externally operable fused motor circuit switch or circuit breaker capable of being locked in the open position. The disconnecting means shall be a listed device.

(c)(4) Operation No provision may be made to open or close this disconnecting means from any other part of the premises. If sprinklers are installed in hoistways, machine rooms, or machinery spaces, the disconnecting means may automatically open the power supply to the affected elevators prior to the application of water. No provision may be made to close this disconnecting means automatically (that is, power may only be restored by manual means).

(c)(5) **Location** The disconnecting means shall be located where it is readily accessible to qualified persons.

(c)(5)(i) On elevators without generator field control, the disconnecting means shall be located within sight of the motor controller. Driving machines or motion and operation controllers not within sight of the disconnecting means shall be provided with a manually operated switch installed in the control circuit adjacent to the equipment in order to prevent starting. Where the driving machine is located in a remote machinery space, a single disconnecting means for disconnecting all ungrounded main power supply conductors shall be provided and be capable of being locked in the open position.

(c)(5)(ii) On elevators with generator field control, the disconnecting means shall be located within sight of the motor controller for the driving motor of the motor-generator set. Driving machines, motor-generator sets, or motion and operation controllers not within sight of the disconnecting means shall be provided with a manually operated switch installed in the control circuit to prevent starting. The manually operated switch shall be installed adjacent to this equipment. Where the driving machine or the motor-generator set is located in a remote machinery space, a single means for disconnecting all ungrounded main power supply conductors shall be provided and be capable of being locked in the open position.

(c)(5)(iii) On escalators and moving walks, the disconnecting means shall be installed in the space where the controller is located.

(c)(5)(iv) On wheelchair lifts and stairway chair lifts, the disconnecting means shall be located within sight of the motor controller.

(c)(6) **Identification and signs**

(c)(6)(i) Where there is more than one driving machine in a machine room, the disconnecting means shall be numbered to correspond to the identifying number of the driving machine that they control.

(c)(6)(ii) The disconnecting means shall be provided with a sign to identify the location of the supply-side overcurrent protective device.

(c)(7) **Single-car and multicar installations** On single-car and multicar installations, equipment receiving electrical power from more than one source shall be provided with a disconnecting means for each source of electrical power. The disconnecting means shall be within sight of the equipment served.

(c)(8) **Warning sign for multiple disconnecting means** A warning sign shall be mounted on or next to the disconnecting means where multiple disconnecting means are used and parts of the controllers remain energized from a source other than the one disconnected. The sign shall be clearly legible and shall read **"WARNING—PARTS OF THE CONTROLLER ARE NOT DEENERGIZED BY THIS SWITCH**."

(c)(9) **Interconnection between multicar controllers** A warning sign worded as required in paragraph (c)(8) of this section shall be mounted on or next to the disconnecting means where interconnections between controllers are necessary for the operation of the system on multicar installations that remain energized from a source other than the one disconnected.

(c)(10) **Motor controllers** Motor controllers may be located outside the spaces otherwise required by paragraph (c) of this section, provided they are in enclosures with doors or removable panels capable of being locked closed and the disconnecting means is located adjacent to or is an integral part of the motor controller. Motor controller enclosures for escalators or moving walks may be located in the balustrade on the side located away from the moving steps or moving treadway. If the disconnecting means is an integral part of the motor controller, it shall be operable without opening the enclosure.

(d) **Electric welders—disconnecting means**

(d)(1) **Arc welders** A disconnecting means shall be provided in the supply circuit for each arc welder that is not equipped with a disconnect mounted as an integral part of the welder. The disconnecting means shall be a switch or circuit breaker, and its rating may not be less than that necessary to accommodate overcurrent protection.

(d)(2) **Resistance welders** A switch or circuit breaker shall be provided by which each resistance welder and its control equipment can be disconnected from the supply circuit. The ampere rating of this disconnecting means may not be less than the supply conductor ampacity. The supply circuit switch may be used as the welder disconnecting means where the circuit supplies only one welder.

(e) **Information technology equipment**

(e)(1) **Disconnecting means** A means shall be provided to disconnect power to all electronic equipment in an information technology equipment room. There shall also be a similar means to disconnect the power to all dedicated heating, ventilating, and air-conditioning (HVAC) systems serving the room and to cause all required fire/smoke dampers to close.

(e)(2) **Grouping** The control for these disconnecting means shall be grouped and identified and shall be readily accessible at the principal exit doors. A single means to control both the electronic equipment and HVAC system is permitted.

(e)(3) **Exception** Integrated electrical systems covered by §1910.308(g) need not have the disconnecting means required by paragraph (e)(1) of this section.

(f) **X-Ray equipment** This paragraph applies to X-ray equipment.

(f)(1) **Disconnecting means**

(f)(1)(i) A disconnecting means shall be provided in the supply circuit. The disconnecting means shall be operable from a location readily accessible from the X-ray control. For equipment connected to a 120-volt branch circuit of 30 amperes or less, a grounding-type attachment plug cap and receptacle of proper rating may serve as a disconnecting means.

(f)(1)(ii) If more than one piece of equipment is operated from the same high-voltage circuit, each piece or each group of equipment as a unit shall be provided with a high-voltage switch or equivalent disconnecting means. The disconnecting means shall be constructed, enclosed, or located so as to avoid contact by employees with its live parts.

(f)(2) **Control** The following requirements apply to industrial and commercial laboratory equipment.

(f)(2)(i) Radiographic and fluoroscopic-type equipment shall be effectively enclosed or shall have interlocks that deenergize the equipment automatically to prevent ready access to live current-carrying parts.

(f)(2)(ii) Diffraction- and irradiation-type equipment shall have a pilot light, readable meter deflection, or equivalent means to indicate when the equipment is energized, unless the equipment or installation is effectively enclosed or is provided with interlocks to prevent access to live current-carrying parts during operation.

(g) **Induction and dielectric heating equipment** This paragraph applies to induction and dielectric heating equipment and accessories for industrial and scientific applications, but not for medical or dental applications or for appliances.

(g)(1) **Guarding and grounding**

(g)(1)(i) The converting apparatus (including the dc line) and high-frequency electric circuits (excluding the output circuits and remote-control circuits) shall be completely contained within enclosures of noncombustible material.

(g)(1)(ii) All panel controls shall be of dead-front construction.

(g)(1)(iii) Doors or detachable panels shall be employed for internal access. Where doors are used giving access to voltages from 500 to 1000 volts ac or dc, either door locks shall be provided or interlocks shall be installed. Where doors are used giving access to voltages of over 1000 volts ac or dc, either mechanical lockouts with a disconnecting means to prevent access until circuit parts within the cubicle are deenergized, or both door interlocking and mechanical door locks, shall be provided. Detachable panels not normally used for access to such parts shall be fastened in a manner that will make them difficult to remove (for example, by requiring the use of tools).

(g)(1)(iv) Warning labels or signs that read **"DANGER—HIGH VOLTAGE—KEEP OUT"** shall be attached to the equipment and shall be plainly visible where persons might contact energized parts when doors are opened or closed or when panels are removed from compartments containing over 250 volts AC or DC.

(g)(1)(v) Induction and dielectric heating equipment shall be protected as follows:

(g)(1)(v)(A) Protective cages or adequate shielding shall be used to guard work applicators other than induction heating coils.

(g)(1)(v)(B) Induction heating coils shall be protected by insulation or refractory materials or both.

(g)(1)(v)(C) Interlock switches shall be used on all hinged access doors, sliding panels, or other such means of access to the applicator, unless the applicator is an induction heating coil at dc ground potential or operating at less than 150 volts AC.

(g)(1)(v)(D) Interlock switches shall be connected in such a manner as to remove all power from the applicator when any one of the access doors or panels is open.

(g)(1)(vi) A readily accessible disconnecting means shall be provided by which each heating equipment can be isolated from its supply circuit. The ampere rating of this disconnecting means may not be less than the nameplate current rating of the equipment. The supply circuit disconnecting means is permitted as a heating equipment disconnecting means where the circuit supplies only one piece of equipment.

(g)(2) **Remote control**

(g)(2)(i) If remote controls are used for applying power, a selector switch shall be provided and interlocked to provide power from only one control point at a time.

(g)(2)(ii) Switches operated by foot pressure shall be provided with a shield over the contact button to avoid accidental closing of the switch.

(h) Electrolytic cells This paragraph applies to the installation of the electrical components and accessory equipment of electrolytic cells, electrolytic cell lines, and process power supply for the production of aluminum, cadmium, chlorine, copper, fluorine, hydrogen peroxide, magnesium, sodium, sodium chlorate, and zinc. Cells used as a source of electric energy and for electroplating processes and cells used for production of hydrogen are not covered by this paragraph.

(h)(1) Application Installations covered by paragraph (h) of this section shall comply with all applicable provisions of this Subpart, except as follows:

(h)(1)(i) Overcurrent protection of electrolytic cell dc process power circuits need not comply with the requirements of §1910.304(f);

(h)(1)(ii) Equipment located or used within the cell line working zone or associated with the cell line dc power circuits need not comply with the provisions of §1910.304(g); and

(h)(1)(iii) Electrolytic cells, cell line conductors, cell line attachments, and the wiring of auxiliary equipment and devices within the cell line working zone need not comply with the provisions of §1910.303 or §1910.304(b) and (c).

(h)(2) Disconnecting means If more than one dc cell line process power supply serves the same cell line, a disconnecting means shall be provided on the cell line circuit side of each power supply to disconnect it from the cell line circuit. Removable links or removable conductors may be used as the disconnecting means.

(h)(3) Portable electric equipment

(h)(3)(i) The frames and enclosures of portable electric equipment used within the cell line working zone may not be grounded, unless the cell line circuit voltage does not exceed 200 volts DC or the frames are guarded.

(h)(3)(ii) Ungrounded portable electric equipment shall be distinctively marked and shall employ plugs and receptacles of a configuration that prevents connection of this equipment to grounding receptacles and that prevents inadvertent interchange of ungrounded and grounded portable electric equipment.

(h)(4) Power supply circuits and receptacles for portable electric equipment

(h)(4)(i) Circuits supplying power to ungrounded receptacles for hand-held, cord- and plug-connected equipment shall meet the following requirements:

(h)(4)(i)(A) The circuits shall be electrically isolated from any distribution system supplying areas other than the cell line working zone and shall be ungrounded;

(h)(4)(i)(B) The circuits shall be supplied through isolating transformers with primaries operating at not more than 600 volts between conductors and protected with proper overcurrent protection;

(h)(4)(i)(C) The secondary voltage of the isolating transformers may not exceed 300 volts between conductors; and

(h)(4)(i)(D) All circuits supplied from the secondaries shall be ungrounded and shall have an approved overcurrent device of proper rating in each conductor.

(h)(4)(ii) Receptacles and their mating plugs for ungrounded equipment may not have provision for a grounding conductor and shall be of a configuration that prevents their use for equipment required to be grounded.

(h)(4)(iii) Receptacles on circuits supplied by an isolating transformer with an ungrounded secondary:

(h)(4)(iii)(A) Shall have a distinctive configuration;

(h)(4)(iii)(B) Shall be distinctively marked; and

(h)(4)(iii)(C) May not be used in any other location in the facility.

(h)(5) Fixed and portable electric equipment

(h)(5)(i) The following need not be grounded:

(h)(5)(i)(A) AC systems supplying fixed and portable electric equipment within the cell line working zone; and

(h)(5)(i)(B) Exposed conductive surfaces, such as electric equipment housings, cabinets, boxes, motors, raceways and the like that are within the cell line working zone.

(h)(5)(ii) Auxiliary electric equipment, such as motors, transducers, sensors, control devices, and alarms, mounted on an electrolytic cell or other energized surface shall be connected to the premises wiring systems by any of the following means:

(h)(5)(ii)(A) Multiconductor hard usage or extra hard usage flexible cord;

(h)(5)(ii)(B) Wire or cable in suitable nonmetallic raceways or cable trays; or

(h)(5)(ii)(C) Wire or cable in suitable metal raceways or metal cable trays installed with insulating breaks such that they will not cause a potentially hazardous electrical condition.

(h)(5)(iii) Fixed electric equipment may be bonded to the energized conductive surfaces of the cell line, its attachments, or auxiliaries. If fixed electric equipment is mounted on an energized conductive surface, it shall be bonded to that surface.

(h)(6) Auxiliary nonelectrical connections Auxiliary nonelectrical connections such as air hoses, water hoses, and the like, to an electrolytic cell, its attachments, or auxiliary equipment may not have continuous conductive reinforcing wire, armor, braids, or the like. Hoses shall be of a nonconductive material.

(h)(7) Cranes and hoists

(h)(7)(i) The conductive surfaces of cranes and hoists that enter the cell line working zone need not be grounded. The portion of an overhead crane or hoist that contacts an energized electrolytic cell or energized attachments shall be insulated from ground.

(h)(7)(ii) Remote crane or hoist controls that may introduce hazardous electrical conditions into the cell line working zone shall employ one or more of the following systems:

(h)(7)(ii)(A) Isolated and ungrounded control circuit;

(h)(7)(ii)(B) Nonconductive rope operator;

(h)(7)(ii)(C) Pendant pushbutton with nonconductive supporting means and with nonconductive surfaces or ungrounded exposed conductive surfaces; or

(h)(7)(ii)(D) Radio.

(i) Electrically driven or controlled irrigation machines

(i)(1) Lightning protection If an irrigation machine has a stationary point, a grounding electrode system shall be connected to the machine at the stationary point for lightning protection.

(i)(2) Disconnecting means

(i)(2)(i) The main disconnecting means for a center pivot irrigation machine shall be located at the point of connection of electrical power to the machine or shall be visible and not more than 15.2 m (50 ft) from the machine.

(i)(2)(ii) The disconnecting means shall be readily accessible and capable of being locked in the open position.

(i)(2)(iii) A disconnecting means shall be provided for each motor and controller.

(j) Swimming pools, fountains, and similar installations This paragraph applies to electric wiring for and equipment in or adjacent to all swimming, wading, therapeutic, and decorative pools and fountains; hydro-massage bathtubs, whether permanently installed or storable; and metallic auxiliary equipment, such as pumps, filters, and similar equipment. Therapeutic pools in health care facilities are exempt from these provisions.

(j)(1) Receptacles

(j)(1)(i) A single receptacle of the locking and grounding type that provides power for a permanently installed swimming pool recirculating pump motor may be located not less than 1.52 m (5 ft) from the inside walls of a pool. All other receptacles on the property shall be located at least 3.05 m (10 ft) from the inside walls of a pool.

(j)(1)(ii) Receptacles that are located within 4.57 m (15 ft), or 6.08 m (20 ft) if the installation was built after August 13, 2007, of the inside walls of the pool shall be protected by ground-fault circuit interrupters.

(j)(1)(iii) Where a pool is installed permanently at a dwelling unit, at least one 125-volt, 15- or 20-ampere receptacle on a general-purpose branch circuit shall be located a minimum of 3.05 m (10 ft) and not more than 6.08 m (20 ft) from the inside wall of the pool. This receptacle shall be located not more than 1.98 m (6.5 ft) above the floor, platform, or grade level serving the pool.

Note to paragraph (j)(1) of this section: In determining these dimensions, the distance to be measured is the shortest path the supply cord of an appliance connected to the receptacle would follow without piercing a floor, wall, or ceiling of a building or other effective permanent barrier.

(j)(2) Lighting fixtures, lighting outlets, and ceiling suspended (paddle) fans

(j)(2)(i) In outdoor pool areas, lighting fixtures, lighting outlets, and ceiling-suspended (paddle) fans may not be installed over the pool or over the area extending 1.52 m (5 ft) horizontally from the inside walls of a pool unless no part of the lighting fixture of a ceiling-suspended (paddle) fan is less than 3.66 m (12 ft) above the maximum water level. However, a lighting fixture or lighting outlet that was installed before April 16, 1981, may be located less than 1.52 m (5 ft) measured horizontally from the inside walls of a pool if it is at least 1.52 m (5 ft) above the surface of the maximum water level and is rigidly attached to the existing structure. It shall also be protected by a ground-fault circuit interrupter installed in the branch circuit supplying the fixture.

(j)(2)(ii) Lighting fixtures and lighting outlets installed in the area extending between 1.52 m (5 ft) and 3.05 m (10 ft) horizontally from the inside walls of a pool shall be protected by a ground-fault circuit interrupter unless installed 1.52 m (5 ft) above the maximum water level and rigidly attached to the structure adjacent to or enclosing the pool.

(j)(3) Cord- and plug-connected equipment Flexible cords used with the following equipment may not exceed 0.9 m (3 ft) in length and shall have a copper equipment grounding conductor with a grounding-type attachment plug:

(j)(3)(i) Cord- and plug-connected lighting fixtures installed within 4.88 m (16 ft) of the water surface of permanently installed pools; and

(j)(3)(ii) Other cord- and plug-connected, fixed or stationary equipment used with permanently installed pools.

(j)(4) Underwater equipment

(j)(4)(i) A ground-fault circuit interrupter shall be installed in the branch circuit supplying underwater fixtures operating at more than 15 volts. Equipment installed underwater shall be identified for the purpose.

(j)(4)(ii) No underwater lighting fixtures may be installed for operation at over 150 volts between conductors.

(j)(4)(iii) A lighting fixture facing upward shall have the lens adequately guarded to prevent contact by any person.

(j)(5) Fountains All electric equipment, including power supply cords, operating at more than 15 volts and used with fountains shall be protected by ground-fault circuit interrupters.

(k) Carnivals, circuses, fairs, and similar events This paragraph covers the installation of portable wiring and equipment, including wiring in or on all structures, for carnivals, circuses, exhibitions, fairs, traveling attractions, and similar events.

(k)(1) Protection of electric equipment Electric equipment and wiring methods in or on rides, concessions, or other units shall be provided with mechanical protection where such equipment or wiring methods are subject to physical damage.

(k)(2) Installation

(k)(2)(i) Services shall be installed in accordance with applicable requirements of this Subpart, and, in addition, shall comply with the following:

(k)(2)(i)(A) Service equipment may not be installed in a location that is accessible to unqualified persons, unless the equipment is lockable; and

(k)(2)(i)(B) Service equipment shall be mounted on solid backing and installed so as to be protected from the weather, unless the equipment is of weatherproof construction.

(k)(2)(ii) Amusement rides and amusement attractions shall be maintained not less than 4.57 m (15 ft) in any direction from overhead conductors operating at 600 volts or less, except for the conductors supplying the amusement ride or attraction. Amusement rides or attractions may not be located under or within 4.57 m (15 ft) horizontally of conductors operating in excess of 600 volts.

(k)(2)(iii) Flexible cords and cables shall be listed for extra-hard usage. When used outdoors, flexible cords and cables shall also be listed for wet locations and shall be sunlight resistant.

(k)(2)(iv) Single conductor cable shall be size No. 2 or larger.

(k)(2)(v) Open conductors are prohibited except as part of a listed assembly or festoon lighting installed in accordance with §1910.304(c).

(k)(2)(vi) Flexible cords and cables shall be continuous without splice or tap between boxes or fittings. Cord connectors may not be laid on the ground unless listed for wet locations. Connectors and cable connections may not be placed in audience traffic paths or within areas accessible to the public unless guarded.

(k)(2)(vii) Wiring for an amusement ride, attraction, tent, or similar structure may not be supported by another ride or structure unless specifically identified for the purpose.

(k)(2)(viii) Flexible cords and cables run on the ground, where accessible to the public, shall be covered with approved nonconductive mats. Cables and mats shall be arranged so as not to present a tripping hazard.

(k)(2)(ix) A box or fitting shall be installed at each connection point, outlet, switch point, or junction point.

(k)(3) Inside tents and concessions Electrical wiring for temporary lighting, where installed inside of tents and concessions, shall be securely installed, and, where subject to physical damage, shall be provided with mechanical protection. All temporary lamps for general illumination shall be protected from accidental breakage by a suitable fixture or lampholder with a guard.

(k)(4) Portable distribution and termination boxes Employers may only use portable distribution and termination boxes that meet the following requirements:

(k)(4)(i) Boxes shall be designed so that no live parts are exposed to accidental contact. Where installed outdoors, the box shall be of weatherproof construction and mounted so that the bottom of the enclosure is not less than 152 mm (6 in.) above the ground;

(k)(4)(ii) Busbars shall have an ampere rating not less than the overcurrent device supplying the feeder supplying the box. Busbar connectors shall be provided where conductors terminate directly on busbars;

(k)(4)(iii) Receptacles shall have overcurrent protection installed within the box. The overcurrent protection may not exceed the ampere rating of the receptacle, except as permitted in §1910.305(j)(4) for motor loads;

(k)(4)(iv) Where single-pole connectors are used, they shall comply with the following:

(k)(4)(iv)(A) Where AC single-pole portable cable connectors are used, they shall be listed and of the locking type. Where paralleled sets of current-carrying single-pole separable connectors are provided as input devices, they shall be prominently labeled with a warning indicating the presence of internal parallel connections. The use of single-pole separable connectors shall comply with at least one of the following conditions:

(k)(4)(iv)(A)(1) Connection and disconnection of connectors are only possible where the supply connectors are interlocked to the source and it is not possible to connect or disconnect connectors when the supply is energized; or

(k)(4)(iv)(A)(2) Line connectors are of the listed sequential-interlocking type so that load connectors are connected in the following sequence:

(k)(4)(iv)(A)(2)(i) Equipment grounding conductor connection;

(k)(4)(iv)(A)(2)(ii) Grounded circuit-conductor connection, if provided; and

(k)(4)(iv)(A)(2)(iii) Ungrounded conductor connection; and so that disconnection is in the reverse order; or

(k)(4)(iv)(A)(3) A caution notice is provided adjacent to the line connectors indicating that plug connection must be in the following sequence:

(k)(4)(iv)(A)(3)(i) Equipment grounding conductor connection;

(k)(4)(iv)(A)(3)(ii) Grounded circuit-conductor connection, if provided; and

(k)(4)(iv)(A)(3)(iii) Ungrounded conductor connection; and indicating that disconnection is in the reverse order; and

(k)(4)(iv)(B) Single-pole separable connectors used in portable professional motion picture and television equipment may be interchangeable for ac or dc use or for different current ratings on the same premises only if they are listed for ac/dc use and marked to identify the system to which they are connected;

(k)(4)(v) Overcurrent protection of equipment and conductors shall be provided; and

(k)(4)(vi) The following equipment connected to the same source shall be bonded:

(k)(4)(vi)(A) Metal raceways and metal sheathed cable;

(k)(4)(vi)(B) Metal enclosures of electrical equipment; and

(k)(4)(vi)(C) Metal frames and metal parts of rides, concessions, trailers, trucks, or other equipment that contain or support electrical equipment.

(k)(5) Disconnecting means

(k)(5)(i) Each ride and concession shall be provided with a fused disconnect switch or circuit breaker located within sight and within 1.83 m (6 ft) of the operator's station.

(k)(5)(ii) The disconnecting means shall be readily accessible to the operator, including when the ride is in operation.

(k)(5)(iii) Where accessible to unqualified persons, the enclosure for the switch or circuit breaker shall be of the lockable type.

(k)(5)(iv) A shunt trip device that opens the fused disconnect or circuit breaker when a switch located in the ride operator's console is closed is a permissible method of opening the circuit.

§1910.307 OI
Hazardous (classified) locations

(a) Scope

(a)(1) Applicability This section covers the requirements for electric equipment and wiring in locations that are classified depending on the properties of the flammable vapors, liquids or gases, or combustible dusts or fibers that may be present therein and the likelihood that a flammable or combustible concentration or quantity is present. Hazardous (classified) locations may be found in occupancies such as, but not limited to, the following: aircraft hangars, gasoline dispensing and service stations, bulk storage plants for gasoline or other volatile flammable liquids, paint-finishing process plants, health care facilities, agricultural or other facilities where excessive combustible dusts may be present, marinas, boat yards, and petroleum and chemical processing plants. Each room, section or area shall be considered individually in determining its classification.

(a)(2) Classifications

(a)(2)(i) These hazardous (classified) locations are assigned the following designations:

(a)(2)(i)(A) Class I, Division 1;

(a)(2)(i)(B) Class I, Division 2;

(a)(2)(i)(C) Class I, Zone 0;
(a)(2)(i)(D) Class I, Zone 1;
(a)(2)(i)(E) Class I, Zone 2;
(a)(2)(i)(F) Class II, Division 1;
(a)(2)(i)(G) Class II, Division 2;
(a)(2)(i)(H) Class III, Division 1;
(a)(2)(i)(I) Class III, Division 2;

(a)(2)(ii) For definitions of these locations, see §1910.399.

(a)(3) **Other sections of this Subpart** All applicable requirements in this Subpart apply to hazardous (classified) locations unless modified by provisions of this section.

(a)(4) **Division and zone classification** In Class I locations, an installation must be classified as using the division classification system meeting paragraphs (c), (d), (e), and (f) of this section or using the zone classification system meeting paragraph (g) of this section. In Class II and Class III locations, an installation must be classified using the division classification system meeting paragraphs (c), (d), (e), and (f) of this section.

(b) **Documentation** All areas designated as hazardous (classified) locations under the Class and Zone system and areas designated under the Class and Division system established after August 13, 2007 shall be properly documented. This documentation shall be available to those authorized to design, install, inspect, maintain, or operate electric equipment at the location.

(c) **Electrical installations** Equipment, wiring methods, and installations of equipment in hazardous (classified) locations shall be intrinsically safe, approved for the hazardous (classified) location, or safe for the hazardous (classified) location. Requirements for each of these options are as follows:

(c)(1) **Intrinsically safe** Equipment and associated wiring approved as intrinsically safe is permitted in any hazardous (classified) location for which it is approved;

(c)(2) **Approved for the hazardous (classified) location**

(c)(2)(i) Equipment shall be approved not only for the class of location, but also for the ignitable or combustible properties of the specific gas, vapor, dust, or fiber that will be present.

Note to paragraph (c)(2)(i) of this section: NFPA 70, the National Electrical Code, lists or defines hazardous gases, vapors, and dusts by "Groups" characterized by their ignitable or combustible properties.

(c)(2)(ii) Equipment shall be marked to show the class, group, and operating temperature or temperature range, based on operation in a 40-degree C ambient, for which it is approved. The temperature marking may not exceed the ignition temperature of the specific gas or vapor to be encountered. However, the following provisions modify this marking requirement for specific equipment:

(c)(2)(ii)(A) Equipment of the nonheat-producing type, such as junction boxes, conduit, and fittings, and equipment of the heat-producing type having a maximum temperature not more than 100 °C (212 °F) need not have a marked operating temperature or temperature range;

(c)(2)(ii)(B) Fixed lighting fixtures marked for use in Class I, Division 2 or Class II, Division 2 locations only need not be marked to indicate the group;

(c)(2)(ii)(C) Fixed general-purpose equipment in Class I locations, other than lighting fixtures, that is acceptable for use in Class I, Division 2 locations need not be marked with the class, group, division, or operating temperature;

(c)(2)(ii)(D) Fixed dust-tight equipment, other than lighting fixtures, that is acceptable for use in Class II, Division 2 and Class III locations need not be marked with the class, group, division, or operating temperature; and

(c)(2)(ii)(E) Electric equipment suitable for ambient temperatures exceeding 40 °C (104 °F) shall be marked with both the maximum ambient temperature and the operating temperature or temperature range at that ambient temperature; and

(c)(3) **Safe for the hazardous (classified) location** Equipment that is safe for the location shall be of a type and design that the employer demonstrates will provide protection from the hazards arising from the combustibility and flammability of vapors, liquids, gases, dusts, or fibers involved.

Note to paragraph (c)(3) of this section: The National Electrical Code, NFPA 70, contains guidelines for determining the type and design of equipment and installations that will meet this requirement. Those guidelines address electric wiring, equipment, and systems installed in hazardous (classified) locations and contain specific provisions for the following: wiring methods, wiring connections; conductor insulation, flexible cords, sealing and drainage, transformers, capacitors, switches, circuit breakers, fuses, motor controllers, receptacles, attachment plugs, meters, relays, instruments, resistors, generators, motors, lighting fixtures, storage battery charging equipment, electric cranes, electric hoists and similar equipment, utilization equipment, signaling systems, alarm systems, remote control systems, local loud speaker and communication systems, ventilation piping, live parts, lightning surge protection, and grounding.

(d) **Conduits** All conduits shall be threaded and shall be made wrench-tight. Where it is impractical to make a threaded joint tight, a bonding jumper shall be utilized.

(e) **Equipment in Division 2 locations** Equipment that has been approved for a Division 1 location may be installed in a Division 2 location of the same class and group. General-purpose equipment or equipment in general-purpose enclosures may be installed in Division 2 locations if the employer can demonstrate that the equipment does not constitute a source of ignition under normal operating conditions.

(f) **Protection techniques** The following are acceptable protection techniques for electric and electronic equipment in hazardous (classified) locations.

(f)(1) **Explosionproof apparatus** This protection technique is permitted for equipment in the Class I, Division 1 and 2 locations for which it is approved.

(f)(2) **Dust ignitionproof** This protection technique is permitted for equipment in the Class II, Division 1 and 2 locations for which it is approved.

(f)(3) **Dust-tight** This protection technique is permitted for equipment in the Class II, Division 2 and Class III locations for which it is approved.

(f)(4) **Purged and pressurized** This protection technique is permitted for equipment in any hazardous (classified) location for which it is approved.

(f)(5) **Nonincendive circuit** This protection technique is permitted for equipment in Class I, Division 2; Class II, Division 2; or Class III, Division 1or 2 locations.

(f)(6) **Nonincendive equipment** This protection technique is permitted for equipment in Class I, Division 2; Class II, Division 2; or Class III, Division 1 or 2 locations.

(f)(7) **Nonincendive component** This protection technique is permitted for equipment in Class I, Division 2; Class II, Division 2; or Class III, Division 1 or 2 locations.

(f)(8) **Oil immersion** This protection technique is permitted for current-interrupting contacts in Class I, Division 2 locations as described in the Subpart.

(f)(9) **Hermetically sealed** This protection technique is permitted for equipment in Class I, Division 2; Class II, Division 2; and Class III, Division 1 or 2 locations.

(f)(10) **Other protection techniques** Any other protection technique that meets paragraph (c) of this section is acceptable in any hazardous (classified) location.

(g) **Class I, Zone 0, 1, and 2 locations**

(g)(1) **Scope** Employers may use the zone classification system as an alternative to the division classification system for electric and electronic equipment and wiring for all voltage in Class I, Zone 0, Zone 1, and Zone 2 hazardous (classified) locations where fire or explosion hazards may exist due to flammable gases, vapors, or liquids.

(g)(2) **Location and general requirements**

(g)(2)(i) Locations shall be classified depending on the properties of the flammable vapors, liquids, or gases that may be present and the likelihood that a flammable or combustible concentration or quantity is present. Where pyrophoric materials are the only materials used or handled, these locations need not be classified.

(g)(2)(ii) Each room, section, or area shall be considered individually in determining its classification.

(g)(2)(iii) All threaded conduit shall be threaded with an NPT (National (American) Standard Pipe Taper) standard conduit cutting die that provides ¾-in. taper per foot. The conduit shall be made wrench tight to prevent sparking when fault current flows through the conduit system and to ensure the explosionproof or flameproof integrity of the conduit system where applicable.

(g)(2)(iv) Equipment provided with threaded entries for field wiring connection shall be installed in accordance with paragraph (g)(2)(iv)(A) or (g)(2)(iv)(B) of this section.

(g)(2)(iv)(A) For equipment provided with threaded entries for NPT threaded conduit or fittings, listed conduit, conduit fittings, or cable fittings shall be used.

(g)(2)(iv)(B) For equipment with metric threaded entries, such entries shall be identified as being metric, or listed adaptors to permit connection to conduit of NPT-threaded fittings shall be provided with the equipment. Adapters shall be used for connection to conduit or NPT-threaded fittings.

(g)(3) Protection techniques One or more of the following protection techniques shall be used for electric and electronic equipment in hazardous (classified) locations classified under the zone classification system.

(g)(3)(i) Flameproof "d" — This protection technique is permitted for equipment in the Class I, Zone 1 locations for which it is approved.

(g)(3)(ii) Purged and pressurized — This protection technique is permitted for equipment in the Class I, Zone 1 or Zone 2 locations for which it is approved.

(g)(3)(iii) Intrinsic safety — This protection technique is permitted for equipment in the Class I, Zone 0 or Zone 1 locations for which it is approved.

(g)(3)(iv) Type of protection "n" — This protection technique is permitted for equipment in the Class I, Zone 2 locations for which it is approved. Type of protection "n" is further subdivided into nA, nC, and nR.

(g)(3)(v) Oil Immersion "o" — This protection technique is permitted for equipment in the Class I, Zone 1 locations for which it is approved.

(g)(3)(vi) Increased safety "e" — This protection technique is permitted for equipment in the Class I, Zone 1 locations for which it is approved.

(g)(3)(vii) Encapsulation "m" — This protection technique is permitted for equipment in the Class I, Zone 1 locations for which it is approved.

(g)(3)(viii) Powder Filling "q" — This protection technique is permitted for equipment in the Class I, Zone 1 locations for which it is approved.

(g)(4) **Special precaution** Paragraph (g) of this section requires equipment construction and installation that will ensure safe performance under conditions of proper use and maintenance.

(g)(4)(i) Classification of areas and selection of equipment and wiring methods shall be under the supervision of a qualified registered professional engineer.

(g)(4)(ii) In instances of areas within the same facility classified separately, Class I, Zone 2 locations may abut, but not overlap, Class I, Division 2 locations. Class I, Zone 0 or Zone 1 locations may not abut Class I, Division 1 or Division 2 locations.

(g)(4)(iii) A Class I, Division 1 or Division 2 location may be reclassified as a Class I, Zone 0, Zone 1, or Zone 2 location only if all of the space that is classified because of a single flammable gas or vapor source is reclassified.

Note to paragraph (g)(4) of this section: Low ambient conditions require special consideration. Electric equipment depending on the protection techniques described by paragraph (g)(3)(i) of this section may not be suitable for use at temperatures lower than −20°C (−4°F) unless they are approved for use at lower temperatures. However, at low ambient temperatures, flammable concentrations of vapors may not exist in a location classified Class I, Zone 0, 1, or 2 at normal ambient temperature.

(g)(5) **Listing and marking**

(g)(5)(i) Equipment that is listed for a Zone 0 location may be installed in a Zone 1 or Zone 2 location of the same gas or vapor. Equipment that is listed for a Zone 1 location may be installed in a Zone 2 location of the same gas or vapor.

(g)(5)(ii) Equipment shall be marked in accordance with paragraph (g)(5)(ii)(A) and (g)(5)(ii)(B) of this section, except as provided in (g)(5)(ii)(C).

(g)(5)(ii)(A) Equipment approved for Class I, Division 1 or Class 1, Division 2 shall, in addition to being marked in accordance with (c)(2)(ii), be marked with the following:

(g)(5)(ii)(A)(1) Class I, Zone 1 or Class I, Zone 2 (as applicable);

(g)(5)(ii)(A)(2) Applicable gas classification groups; and

(g)(5)(ii)(A)(3) Temperature classification; or

(g)(5)(ii)(B) Equipment meeting one or more of the protection techniques described in paragraph (g)(3) of this section shall be marked with the following in the order shown:

(g)(5)(ii)(B)(1) Class, except for intrinsically safe apparatus;

(g)(5)(ii)(B)(2) Zone, except for intrinsically safe apparatus;

(g)(5)(ii)(B)(3) Symbol "AEx;"

(g)(5)(ii)(B)(4) Protection techniques;

(g)(5)(ii)(B)(5) Applicable gas classification groups; and

(g)(5)(ii)(B)(6) Temperature classification, except for intrinsically safe apparatus.

Note to paragraph (g)(5)(ii)(B) of this Section: An example of such a required marking is "Class I, Zone 0, AEx ia IIC T6." See Figure S–1 for an explanation of this marking.

(g)(5)(ii)(C) Equipment that the employer demonstrates will provide protection from the hazards arising from the flammability of the gas or vapor and the zone of location involved and will be recognized as providing such protection by employees need not be marked.

Note to paragraph (g)(5)(ii)(C) of this Section: The National Electrical Code, NFPA 70, contains guidelines for determining the type and design of equipment and installations that will meet this provision.

Figure S-1
Example Marking for Class I, Zone 0, AEx ia IIC T6

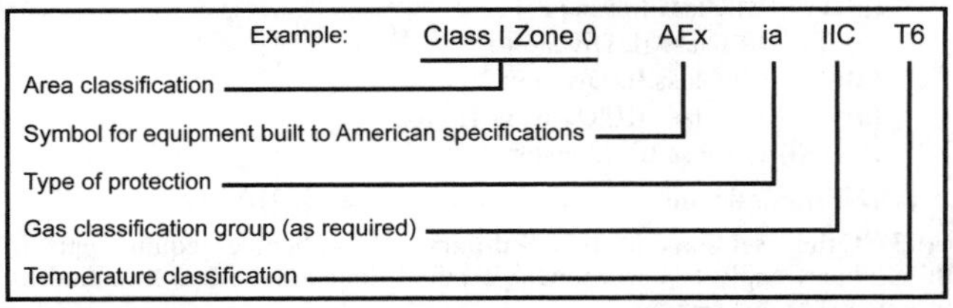

§1910.308
Special systems

(a) **Systems over 600 volts, nominal** This paragraph covers the general requirements for all circuits and equipment operated at over 600 volts.

(a)(1) **Aboveground wiring methods**

(a)(1)(i) Aboveground conductors shall be installed in rigid metal conduit, in intermediate metal conduit, in electrical metallic tubing, in rigid nonmetallic conduit, in cable trays, as busways, as cablebus, in other identified raceways, or as open runs of metal-clad cable suitable for the use and purpose. In locations accessible to qualified persons only, open runs of Type MV cables, bare conductors, and bare busbars are also permitted. Busbars shall be either copper or aluminum. Open runs of insulated wires and cables having a bare lead sheath or a braided outer covering shall be supported in a manner designed to prevent physical damage to the braid or sheath.

(a)(1)(ii) Conductors emerging from the ground shall be enclosed in approved raceways.

(a)(2) **Braid-covered insulated conductors—open installations** The braid on open runs of braid-covered insulated conductors shall be flame retardant or shall have a flame-retardant saturant applied after installation. This treated braid covering shall be stripped back a safe distance at conductor terminals, according to the operating voltage.

(a)(3) **Insulation shielding**

(a)(3)(i) Metallic and semiconductor insulation shielding components of shielded cables shall be removed for a distance dependent on the circuit voltage and insulation. Stress reduction means shall be provided at all terminations of factory-applied shielding.

(a)(3)(ii) Metallic shielding components such as tapes, wires, or braids, or combinations thereof, and their associated conducting and semiconducting components shall be grounded.

(a)(4) **Moisture or mechanical protection for metal-sheathed cables** Where cable conductors emerge from a metal sheath and where protection against moisture or physical damage is necessary, the insulation of the conductors shall be protected by a cable sheath terminating device.

(a)(5) **Interrupting and isolating devices**

(a)(5)(i) Circuit breaker installations located indoors shall consist of metal-enclosed units or fire-resistant cell-mounted units. In locations accessible only to qualified employees, open mounting of circuit breakers is permitted. A means of indicating the open and closed position of circuit breakers shall be provided.

(a)(5)(ii) Where fuses are used to protect conductors and equipment, a fuse shall be placed in each ungrounded conductor. Two power fuses may be used in parallel to protect the same load, if both fuses have identical ratings, and if both fuses are installed in an identified common mounting with electrical connections that will divide the current equally. Power fuses of the vented type may not be used indoors, underground, or in metal enclosures unless identified for the use.

(a)(5)(iii) Fused cutouts installed in buildings or transformer vaults shall be of a type identified for the purpose. Distribution cutouts may not be used indoors, underground, or in metal enclosures. They shall be readily accessible for fuse replacement.

(a)(5)(iv) Where fused cutouts are not suitable to interrupt the circuit manually while carrying full load, an approved means shall be installed to interrupt the entire load. Unless the fused cutouts are interlocked with the switch to prevent opening of the cutouts under load, a conspicuous sign shall be placed at such cutouts reading: **"WARNING—DO NOT OPERATE UNDER LOAD."**

(a)(5)(v) Suitable barriers or enclosures shall be provided to prevent contact with nonshielded cables or energized parts of oil-filled cutouts.

(a)(5)(vi) Load interrupter switches may be used only if suitable fuses or circuits are used in conjunction with these devices to interrupt fault currents.

(a)(5)(vi)(A) Where these devices are used in combination, they shall be coordinated electrically so that they will safely withstand the effects of closing, carrying, or interrupting all possible currents up to the assigned maximum short-circuit rating.

(a)(5)(vi)(B) Where more than one switch is installed with interconnected load terminals to provide for alternate connection to different supply conductors, each switch shall be provided with a conspicuous sign reading: **"WARNING—SWITCH MAY BE ENERGIZED BY BACKFEED."**

(a)(5)(vii) A means (for example, a fuseholder and fuse designed for the purpose) shall be provided to completely isolate equipment for inspection and repairs. Isolating means that are not designed to interrupt the load current of the circuit shall be either interlocked with an approved circuit interrupter or provided with a sign warning against opening them under load.

(a)(6) Mobile and portable equipment

(a)(6)(i) A metallic enclosure shall be provided on the mobile machine for enclosing the terminals of the power cable. The enclosure shall include provisions for a solid connection for the grounding terminal to effectively ground the machine frame. The method of cable termination used shall prevent any strain or pull on the cable from stressing the electrical connections. The enclosure shall have provision for locking so only authorized qualified persons may open it and shall be marked with a sign warning of the presence of energized parts.

(a)(6)(ii) All energized switching and control parts shall be enclosed in effectively grounded metal cabinets or enclosures. Circuit breakers and protective equipment shall have the operating means projecting through the metal cabinet or enclosure so these units can be reset without locked doors being opened. Enclosures and metal cabinets shall be locked so that only authorized qualified persons have access and shall be marked with a sign warning of the presence of energized parts. Collector ring assemblies on revolving-type machines (shovels, draglines, etc.) shall be guarded.

(a)(7) Tunnel installations This paragraph applies to installation and use of high-voltage power distribution and utilization equipment that is portable or mobile, such as substations, trailers, cars, mobile shovels, draglines, hoists, drills, dredges, compressors, pumps, conveyors, and underground excavators.

(a)(7)(i) Conductors in tunnels shall be installed in one or more of the following:

(a)(7)(i)(A) Metal conduit or other metal raceway;

(a)(7)(i)(B) Type MC cable; or

(a)(7)(i)(C) Other approved multiconductor cable.

(a)(7)(ii) Multiconductor portable cable may supply mobile equipment.

(a)(7)(iii) Conductors and cables shall also be so located or guarded as to protect them from physical damage. An equipment grounding conductor shall be run with circuit conductors inside the metal raceway or inside the multiconductor cable jacket. The equipment grounding conductor may be insulated or bare.

(a)(7)(iv) Bare terminals of transformers, switches, motor controllers, and other equipment shall be enclosed to prevent accidental contact with energized parts.

(a)(7)(v) Enclosures for use in tunnels shall be drip-proof, weatherproof, or submersible as required by the environmental conditions.

(a)(7)(vi) Switch or contactor enclosures may not be used as junction boxes or raceways for conductors feeding through or tapping off to other switches, unless special designs are used to provide adequate space for this purpose.

(a)(7)(vii) A disconnecting means that simultaneously opens all ungrounded conductors shall be installed at each transformer or motor location.

(a)(7)(viii) All nonenergized metal parts of electric equipment and metal raceways and cable sheaths shall be effectively grounded and bonded to all metal pipes and rails at the portal and at intervals not exceeding 305 m (1000 ft) throughout the tunnel.

(b) Emergency power systems This paragraph applies to circuits, systems, and equipment intended to supply power for illumination and special loads in the event of failure of the normal supply.

(b)(1) Wiring methods Emergency circuit wiring shall be kept entirely independent of all other wiring and equipment and may not enter the same raceway, cable, box, or cabinet or other wiring except either where common circuit elements suitable for the purpose are required, or for transferring power from the normal to the emergency source.

(b)(2) Emergency illumination Emergency illumination shall include all required means of egress lighting, illuminated exit signs, and all other lights necessary to provide illumination. Where emergency lighting is necessary, the system shall be so arranged that the failure of any individual lighting element, such as the burning out of a light bulb, cannot leave any space in total darkness.

(b)(3) Signs

(b)(3)(i) A sign shall be placed at the service entrance equipment indicating the type and location of on-site emergency power sources. However, a sign is not required for individual unit equipment.

(b)(3)(ii) Where the grounded circuit conductor connected to the emergency source is connected to a grounding electrode conductor at a location remote from the emergency source, there shall be a sign at the grounding location that shall identify all emergency and normal sources connected at that location.

(c) Class 1, Class 2, and Class 3 remote control, signaling, and power-limited circuits

(c)(1) Classification Class 1, Class 2, and Class 3 remote control, signaling, or power-limited circuits are characterized by their usage and electrical power limitation that differentiates them from light and power circuits. These circuits are classified in accordance with their respective voltage and power limitations as summarized in paragraphs (c)(1)(i) through (c)(1)(iii) of this section.

(c)(1)(i) A Class 1 power-limited circuit shall be supplied from a source having a rated output of not more than 30 volts and 1000 volt-amperes.

(c)(1)(ii) A Class 1 remote control circuit or a Class 1 signaling circuit shall have a voltage not exceeding 600 volts; however, the power output of the source need not be limited.

(c)(1)(iii) The power source for a Class 2 or Class 3 circuit shall be listed equipment marked as a Class 2 or Class 3 power source, except as follows:

(c)(1)(iii)(A) Thermocouples do not require listing as a Class 2 power source; and

(c)(1)(iii)(B) A dry cell battery is considered an inherently limited Class 2 power source, provided the voltage is 30 volts or less and the capacity is less than or equal to that available from series-connected No. 6 carbon zinc cells.

(c)(2) Marking A Class 2 or Class 3 power supply unit shall be durably marked where plainly visible to indicate the class of supply and its electrical rating.

(c)(3) Separation from conductors of other circuits Cables and conductors of Class 2 and Class 3 circuits may not be placed in any cable, cable tray, compartment, enclosure, manhole, outlet box, device box, raceway, or similar fitting with conductors of electric light, power, Class 1, nonpower-limited fire alarm circuits, and medium power network-powered broadband communications cables unless a barrier or other equivalent form of protection against contact is employed.

(d) Fire alarm systems

(d)(1) Classifications Fire alarm circuits shall be classified either as nonpower limited or power limited.

(d)(2) Power sources The power sources for use with fire alarm circuits shall be either power limited or nonpower limited as follows:

(d)(2)(i) The power source of nonpower-limited fire alarm (NPLFA) circuits shall have an output voltage of not more than 600 volts, nominal; and

(d)(2)(ii) The power source for a power-limited fire alarm (PLFA) circuit shall be listed equipment marked as a PLFA power source.

(d)(3) Separation from conductors of other circuits

(d)(3)(i) Nonpower-limited fire alarm circuits and Class 1 circuits may occupy the same enclosure, cable, or raceway provided all conductors are insulated for maximum voltage of any conductor within the enclosure, cable, or raceway. Power supply and fire alarm circuit conductors are permitted in the same enclosure, cable, or raceway only if connected to the same equipment.

(d)(3)(ii) Power-limited circuit cables and conductors may not be placed in any cable, cable tray, compartment, enclosure, outlet box, raceway, or similar fitting with conductors of electric light, power, Class 1, nonpower-limited fire alarm circuit conductors, or medium power network-powered broadband communications circuits.

(d)(3)(iii) Power-limited fire alarm circuit conductors shall be separated at least 50.8 mm (2 in.) from conductors of any electric light, power, Class 1, nonpower-limited fire alarm, or medium power network-powered broadband communications circuits unless a special and equally protective method of conductor separation is employed.

(d)(3)(iv) Conductors of one or more Class 2 circuits are permitted within the same cable, enclosure, or raceway with conductors of power-limited fire alarm circuits provided that the insulation of Class 2 circuit conductors in the cable, enclosure, or raceway is at least that needed for the power-limited fire alarm circuits.

(d)(4) Identification Fire alarm circuits shall be identified at terminal and junction locations in a manner that will prevent unintentional interference with the signaling circuit during testing and servicing. Power-limited fire alarm circuits shall be durably marked as such where plainly visible at terminations.

(e) Communications systems This paragraph applies to central-station-connected and non-central-station-connected telephone circuits, radio and television receiving and transmitting equipment, including community antenna television and radio distribution systems, telegraph, district messenger, and outside wiring for fire and burglar alarm, and similar central station systems. These installations need not comply with the provisions of §1910.303 through §1910.308(d), except for §1910.304(c)(1) and §1910.307.

(e)(1) **Protective devices**

(e)(1)(i) A listed primary protector shall be provided on each circuit run partly or entirely in aerial wire or aerial cable not confined within a block.

(e)(1)(ii) A listed primary protector shall be also provided on each aerial or underground circuit when the location of the circuit within the block containing the building served allows the circuit to be exposed to accidental contact with electric light or power conductors operating at over 300 volts to ground.

(d)(1)(iii) In addition, where there exists a lightning exposure, each interbuilding circuit on premises shall be protected by a listed primary protector at each end of the interbuilding circuit.

(e)(2) **Conductor location**

(e)(2)(i) Lead-in or aerial-drop cables from a pole or other support, including the point of initial attachment to a building or structure, shall be kept away from electric light, power, Class 1, or nonpower-limited fire alarm circuit conductors so as to avoid the possibility of accidental contact.

(e)(2)(ii) A separation of at least 1.83 m (6 ft) shall be maintained between communications wires and cables on buildings and lightning conductors.

(e)(2)(iii) Where communications wires and cables and electric light or power conductors are supported by the same pole or run parallel to each other in-span, the following conditions shall be met:

(e)(2)(iii)(A) Where practicable, communication wires and cables on poles shall be located below the electric light or power conductors; and

(e)(2)(iii)(B) Communications wires and cables may not be attached to a crossarm that carries electric light or power conductors.

(e)(2)(iv) Indoor communications wires and cables shall be separated at least 50.8 mm (2 in.) from conductors of any electric light, power, Class 1, nonpower-limited fire alarm, or medium power network-powered broadband communications circuits, unless a special and equally protective method of conductor separation, identified for the purpose, is employed.

(e)(3) **Equipment location** Outdoor metal structures supporting antennas, as well as self-supporting antennas such as vertical rods or dipole structures, shall be located as far away from overhead conductors of electric light and power circuits of over 150 volts to ground as necessary to prevent the antenna or structure from falling into or making accidental contact with such circuits.

(e)(4) **Grounding**

(e)(4)(i) If exposed to contact with electric light and power conductors, the metal sheath of aerial cables entering buildings shall be grounded or shall be interrupted close to the entrance to the building by an insulating joint or equivalent device. Where protective devices are used, they shall be grounded in an approved manner.

(e)(4)(ii) Masts and metal structures supporting antennas shall be permanently and effectively grounded without splice or connection in the grounding conductor.

(e)(4)(iii) Transmitters shall be enclosed in a metal frame or grill or separated from the operating space by a barrier, all metallic parts of which are effectively connected to ground. All external metal handles and controls accessible to the operating personnel shall be effectively grounded. Unpowered equipment and enclosures are considered to be grounded where connected to an attached coaxial cable with an effectively grounded metallic shield.

(f) **Solar photovoltaic systems** This paragraph covers solar photovoltaic systems that can be interactive with other electric power production sources or can stand alone with or without electrical energy storage such as batteries. These systems may have AC or DC output for utilization.

(f)(1) **Conductors of different systems** Photovoltaic source circuits and photovoltaic output circuits may not be contained in the same raceway, cable tray, cable, outlet box, junction box, or similar fitting as feeders or branch circuits of other systems, unless the conductors of the different systems are separated by a partition or are connected together.

(f)(2) **Disconnecting means** Means shall be provided to disconnect all current-carrying conductors of a photovoltaic power source from all other conductors in a building or other structure. Where a circuit grounding connection is not designed to be automatically interrupted as part of the ground-fault protection system, a switch or circuit breaker used as disconnecting means may not have a pole in the grounded conductor.

(g) **Integrated electrical systems**

(g)(1) **Scope** Paragraph (g) of this section covers integrated electrical systems, other than unit equipment, in which orderly shutdown is necessary to ensure safe operation. An integrated electrical system as used in this section shall be a unitized segment of an industrial wiring system where all of the following conditions are met:

(g)(1)(i) An orderly shutdown process minimizes employee hazard and equipment damage;

(g)(1)(ii) The conditions of maintenance and supervision ensure that only qualified persons will service the system; and

(g)(1)(iii) Effective safeguards are established and maintained.

(g)(2) **Location of overcurrent devices in or on premises** Overcurrent devices that are critical to integrated electrical systems need not be readily accessible to employees as required by §1910.304(f)(1)(iv) if they are located with mounting heights to ensure security from operation by nonqualified persons.

§1910.309–§1910.330 [Reserved]

[Safety–Related Work Practices]

§1910.331 [OI] Scope

(a) [OI] **Covered work by both qualified and unqualified persons** The provisions of §1910.331 through §1910.335 cover electrical safety-related work practices for both qualified persons (those who have training in avoiding the electrical hazards of working on or near exposed energized parts) and unqualified persons (those with little or no such training) working on, near, or with the following installations:

(a)(1) **Premises wiring** Installations of electric conductors and equipment within or on buildings or other structures, and on other premises such as yards, carnival, parking, and other lots, and industrial substations;

(a)(2) **Wiring for connection to supply** Installations of conductors that connect to the supply of electricity; and

(a)(3) **Other wiring** Installations of other outside conductors on the premises.

(a)(4) **Optical fiber cable** Installations of optical fiber cable where such installations are made along with electric conductors.

Note: See §1910.399 for the definition of "qualified person." See §1910.332 for training requirements that apply to qualified and unqualified persons.

(b) [OI] **Other covered work** The provisions of §1910.331 through §1910.335 also cover:

(b)(1) Work performed by unqualified persons on, near, or with the installations listed in paragraphs (c)(1) through (c)(4) of this Section; and

(b)(2) Work performed by qualified persons near the installations listed in paragraphs (c)(1) through (c)(4) of this Section when that work is not on or directly associated with those installations.

(c) **Excluded work by qualified persons** The provisions of §1910.331 through §1910.335 do not apply to work performed by qualified persons on or directly associated with the following installations:

(c)(1) [OI] **Generation, transmission, and distribution installations** Installations for the generation, control, transformation, transmission, and distribution of electric energy (including communication and metering) located in buildings used for such purposes or located outdoors.

Note 1: Work on or directly associated with installations of utilization equipment used for purposes other than generating, transmitting, or distributing electric energy (such as installations which are in office buildings, warehouses, garages, machine shops, or recreational buildings, or other utilization installations which are not an integral part of a generating installation, substation, or control center) is covered under paragraph (a)(1) of this section.

Note 2: For work on or directly associated with utilization installations, an employer who complies with the work practices of §1910.269 (electric power generation, transmission, and distribution) will be deemed to be in compliance with §1910.333(c) and §1910.335. However, the requirements of §1910.332, §1910.333(a), §1910.333(b), and §1910.334 apply to all work on or directly associated with utilization installations, regardless of whether the work is performed by qualified or unqualified persons.

Note 3: Work on or directly associated with generation, transmission, or distribution installations includes:

(1) Work performed directly on such installations, such as repairing overhead or underground distribution lines or repairing a feed-water pump for the boiler in a generating plant.

(2) Work directly associated with such installations, such as line-clearance tree trimming and replacing utility poles, when that work is covered by

§1910.269 (see §1910.269(a)(1)(i)(D) and (E) and the definition of "line-clearance tree trimming" in §1910.269(x)).

(3) Work on electric utilization circuits in a generating plant provided that:

(A) Such circuits are commingled with installations of power generation equipment or circuits, and

(B) The generation equipment or circuits present greater electrical hazards than those posed by the utilization equipment or circuits (such as exposure to higher voltages or lack of overcurrent protection).

This work is covered by §1910.269.

(c)(2) Communications installations Installations of communication equipment to the extent that the work is covered under §1910.268.

(c)(3) Installations in vehicles Installations in ships, watercraft, railway rolling stock, aircraft, or automotive vehicles other than mobile homes and recreational vehicles.

(c)(4) Railway installations Installations of railways for generation, transformation, transmission, or distribution of power used exclusively for operation of rolling stock or installations of railways used exclusively for signaling and communication purposes.

[55 FR 32016, Aug. 6, 1990, as amended at 59 FR 4476, Jan. 31, 1994]

§1910.332 O/I Training

(a) O/I Scope The training requirements contained in this section apply to employees who face a risk of electric shock that is not reduced to a safe level by the electrical installation requirements of §1910.303 through §1910.308.

Note: Employees in occupations listed in Table S–4 face such a risk and are required to be trained. Other employees who also may reasonably be expected to face a comparable risk of injury due to electric shock or other electrical hazards must also be trained.

(b) Content of training

(b)(1) Practices addressed in this standard. Employees shall be trained in and familiar with the safety-related work practices required by §1910.331 through §1910.335 that pertain to their respective job assignments.

(b)(2) Additional requirements for unqualified persons Employees who are covered by paragraph (a) of this section but who are not qualified persons shall also be trained in and familiar with any electrically related safety practices not specifically addressed by §1910.331 through §1910.335 but which are necessary for their safety.

(b)(3) Additional requirements for qualified persons Qualified persons (i.e., those permitted to work on or near exposed energized parts) shall, at a minimum, be trained in and familiar with the following:

(b)(3)(i) The skills and techniques necessary to distinguish exposed live parts from other parts of electric equipment,

(b)(3)(ii) The skills and techniques necessary to determine the nominal voltage of exposed live parts, and

(b)(3)(iii) The clearance distances specified in §1910.333(c) and the corresponding voltages to which the qualified person will be exposed.

Note 1: For the purposes of §1910.331 through §1910.335, a person must have the training required by paragraph (b)(3) of this section in order to be considered a qualified person.

Note 2: Qualified persons whose work on energized equipment involves either direct contact or contact by means of tools or materials must also have the training needed to meet §1910.333(c)(2).

(c) Type of training The training required by this section shall be of the classroom or on-the-job type. The degree of training provided shall be determined by the risk to the employee.

Table S–4
Typical Occupational Categories of Employees Facing a Higher Than Normal Risk of Electrical Accident

Occupation
Blue collar supervisors[1]
Electrical and electronic engineers[1]
Electrical and electronic equipment assemblers[1]
Electrical and electronic technicians[1]
Electricians
Industrial machine operators[1]
Material handling equipment operators[1]
Mechanics and repairers[1]
Painters[1]
Riggers and roustabouts[1]
Stationary engineers[1]
Welders

[1] Workers in these groups do not need to be trained if their work or the work of those they supervise does not bring them or the employees they supervise close enough to exposed parts of electric circuits operating at 50 volts or more to ground for a hazard to exist.

[55 FR 32016, Aug. 6, 1990]

§1910.333 O/I Selection and use of work practices

(a) General Safety-related work practices shall be employed to prevent electric shock or other injuries resulting from either direct or indirect electrical contacts, when work is performed near or on equipment or circuits which are or may be energized. The specific safety-related work practices shall be consistent with the nature and extent of the associated electrical hazards.

(a)(1) O/I Deenergized parts Live parts to which an employee may be exposed shall be deenergized before the employee works on or near them, unless the employer can demonstrate that deenergizing introduces additional or increased hazards or is infeasible due to equipment design or operational limitations. Live parts that operate at less than 50 volts to ground need not be deenergized if there will be no increased exposure to electrical burns or to explosion due to electric arcs.

Note 1: Examples of increased or additional hazards include interruption of life support equipment, deactivation of emergency alarm systems, shutdown of hazardous location ventilation equipment, or removal of illumination for an area.

Note 2: Examples of work that may be performed on or near energized circuit parts because of infeasibility due to equipment design or operational limitations include testing of electric circuits that can only be performed with the circuit energized and work on circuits that form an integral part of a continuous industrial process in a chemical plant that would otherwise need to be completely shut down in order to permit work on one circuit or piece of equipment.

Note 3: Work on or near deenergized parts is covered by paragraph (b) of this Section.

(a)(2) O/I Energized parts If the exposed live parts are not deenergized (i.e., for reasons of increased or additional hazards or infeasibility), other safety-related work practices shall be used to protect employees who may be exposed to the electrical hazards involved. Such work practices shall protect employees against contact with energized circuit parts directly with any part of their body or indirectly through some other conductive object. The work practices that are used shall be suitable for the conditions under which the work is to be performed and for the voltage level of the exposed electric conductors or circuit parts. Specific work practice requirements are detailed in paragraph (c) of this section.

(b) O/I Working on or near exposed deenergized parts

(b)(1) O/I Application This paragraph applies to work on exposed deenergized parts or near enough to them to expose the employee to any electrical hazard they present. Conductors and parts of electric equipment that have been deenergized but have not been locked out or tagged in accordance with paragraph (b) of this section shall be treated as energized parts, and paragraph (c) of this section applies to work on or near them.

(b)(2) O/I Lockout and tagging While any employee is exposed to contact with parts of fixed electric equipment or circuits which have been deenergized, the circuits energizing the parts shall be locked out or tagged or both in accordance with the requirements of this paragraph. The requirements shall be followed in the order in which they are presented (i.e., paragraph (b)(2)(i) first, then paragraph (b)(2)(ii), etc.).

Note 1: As used in this section, fixed equipment refers to equipment fastened in place or connected by permanent wiring methods.

Note 2: Lockout and tagging procedures that comply with paragraphs (c) through (f) of §1910.147 will also be deemed to comply with paragraph (b)(2) of this section provided that:

(1) The procedures address the electrical safety hazards covered by this Subpart; and

(2) The procedures also incorporate the requirements of paragraphs (b)(2)(iii)(D) and (b)(2)(iv)(B) of this section.

(b)(2)(i) Procedures The employer shall maintain a written copy of the procedures outlined in paragraph (b)(2) and shall make it available for inspection by employees and by the Assistant Secretary of Labor and his or her authorized representatives.

Note: The written procedures may be in the form of a copy of paragraph (b) of this section.

(b)(2)(ii) Deenergizing equipment

(b)(2)(ii)(A) Safe procedures for deenergizing circuits and equipment shall be determined before circuits or equipment are deenergized.

(b)(2)(ii)(B) The circuits and equipment to be worked on shall be disconnected from all electric energy sources. Control circuit devices, such as push buttons, selector switches, and interlocks, may not be used as the sole means for deenergizing circuits or equipment. Interlocks for electric equipment may not be used as a substitute for lockout and tagging procedures.

(b)(2)(ii)(C) Stored electric energy which might endanger personnel shall be released. Capacitors shall be discharged and high capacitance elements shall be short-circuited and grounded, if the stored electric energy might endanger personnel.

Note: If the capacitors or associated equipment are handled in meeting this requirement, they shall be treated as energized.

(b)(2)(ii)(D) Stored non-electrical energy in devices that could reenergize electric circuit parts shall be blocked or relieved to the extent that the circuit parts could not be accidentally energized by the device.

(b)(2)(iii) Application of locks and tags

(b)(2)(iii)(A) A lock and a tag shall be placed on each disconnecting means used to deenergize circuits and equipment on which work is to be performed, except as provided in paragraphs (b)(2)(iii)(C) and (b)(2)(iii)(E) of this section. The lock shall be attached so as to prevent persons from operating the disconnecting means unless they resort to undue force or the use of tools.

(b)(2)(iii)(B) Each tag shall contain a statement prohibiting unauthorized operation of the disconnecting means and removal of the tag.

(b)(2)(iii)(C) If a lock cannot be applied, or if the employer can demonstrate that tagging procedures will provide a level of safety equivalent to that obtained by the use of a lock, a tag may be used without a lock.

(b)(2)(iii)(D) A tag used without a lock, as permitted by paragraph (b)(2)(iii)(C) of this section, shall be supplemented by at least one additional safety measure that provides a level of safety equivalent to that obtained by the use of a lock. Examples of additional safety measures include the removal of an isolating circuit element, blocking of a controlling switch, or opening of an extra disconnecting device.

(b)(2)(iii)(E) [OI] A lock may be placed without a tag only under the following conditions:

(b)(2)(iii)(E)(1) Only one circuit or piece of equipment is deenergized, and

(b)(2)(iii)(E)(2) The lockout period does not extend beyond the work shift, and

(b)(2)(iii)(E)(3) Employees exposed to the hazards associated with reenergizing the circuit or equipment are familiar with this procedure.

(b)(2)(iv) Verification of deenergized condition The requirements of this paragraph shall be met before any circuits or equipment can be considered and worked as deenergized.

(b)(2)(iv)(A) A qualified person shall operate the equipment operating controls or otherwise verify that the equipment cannot be restarted.

(b)(2)(iv)(B) A qualified person shall use test equipment to test the circuit elements and electrical parts of equipment to which employees will be exposed and shall verify that the circuit elements and equipment parts are deenergized. The test shall also determine if any energized condition exists as a result of inadvertently induced voltage or unrelated voltage backfeed even though specific parts of the circuit have been deenergized and presumed to be safe. If the circuit to be tested is over 600 volts, nominal, the test equipment shall be checked for proper operation immediately before and immediately after this test.

(b)(2)(v) Reenergizing equipment These requirements shall be met, in the order given, before circuits or equipment are reenergized, even temporarily.

(b)(2)(v)(A) A qualified person shall conduct tests and visual inspections, as necessary, to verify that all tools, electrical jumpers, shorts, grounds, and other such devices have been removed, so that the circuits and equipment can be safely energized.

(b)(2)(v)(B) Employees exposed to the hazards associated with reenergizing the circuit or equipment shall be warned to stay clear of circuits and equipment.

(b)(2)(v)(C) [OI] Each lock and tag shall be removed by the employee who applied it or under his or her direct supervision. However, if this employee is absent from the workplace, then the lock or tag may be removed by a qualified person designated to perform this task provided that:

(b)(2)(v)(C)(1) The employer ensures that the employee who applied the lock or tag is not available at the workplace, and

(b)(2)(v)(C)(2) The employer ensures that the employee is aware that the lock or tag has been removed before he or she resumes work at that workplace.

(b)(2)(v)(D) There shall be a visual determination that all employees are clear of the circuits and equipment.

(c) Working on or near exposed energized parts

(c)(1) Application This paragraph applies to work performed on exposed live parts (involving either direct contact or contact by means of tools or materials) or near enough to them for employees to be exposed to any hazard they present.

(c)(2) [OI] **Work on energized equipment** Only qualified persons may work on electric circuit parts or equipment that have not been deenergized under the procedures of paragraph (b) of this section. Such persons shall be capable of working safely on energized circuits and shall be familiar with the proper use of special precautionary techniques, personal protective equipment, insulating and shielding materials, and insulated tools.

(c)(3) Overhead lines If work is to be performed near overhead lines, the lines shall be deenergized and grounded, or other protective measures shall be provided before work is started. If the lines are to be deenergized, arrangements shall be made with the person or organization that operates or controls the electric circuits involved to deenergize and ground them. If protective measures, such as guarding, isolating, or insulating are provided, these precautions shall prevent employees from contacting such lines directly with any part of their body or indirectly through conductive materials, tools, or equipment.

Note: The work practices used by qualified persons installing insulating devices on overhead power transmission or distribution lines are covered by §1910.269 of this Part, not by §1910.332 through §1910.335 of this Part. Under paragraph (c)(2) of this section, unqualified persons are prohibited from performing this type of work.

(c)(3)(i) Unqualified persons

(c)(3)(i)(A) When an unqualified person is working in an elevated position near overhead lines, the location shall be such that the person and the longest conductive object he or she may contact cannot come closer to any unguarded, energized overhead line than the following distances:

(c)(3)(i)(A)(1) For voltages to ground 50kV or below—10 ft. (305 cm);

(c)(3)(i)(A)(2) For voltages to ground over 50kV — 10 ft. (305 cm) plus 4 in. (10 cm) for every 10kV over 50kV.

(c)(3)(i)(B) When an unqualified person is working on the ground in the vicinity of overhead lines, the person may not bring any conductive object closer to unguarded, energized overhead lines than the distances given in paragraph (c)(3)(i)(A) of this section.

Note: For voltages normally encountered with overhead power lines, objects which do not have an insulating rating for the voltage involved are considered to be conductive.

(c)(3)(ii) Qualified persons When a qualified person is working in the vicinity of overhead lines, whether in an elevated position or on the ground, the person may not approach or take any conductive object without an approved insulating handle closer to exposed energized parts than shown in Table S–5 unless:

(c)(3)(ii)(A) The person is insulated from the energized part (gloves, with sleeves if necessary, rated for the voltage involved are considered to be insulation of the person from the energized part on which work is performed), or

(c)(3)(ii)(B) The energized part is insulated both from all other conductive objects at a different potential and from the person, or

(c)(3)(ii)(C) The person is insulated from all conductive objects at a potential different from that of the energized part.

Table S–5
Approach Distances for Qualified Employees —Alternating Current

Voltage range (phase to phase)	Minimum approach distance
300V and less	Avoid contact.
Over 300V, not over 750V	1 ft. 0 in. (30.5 cm)
Over 750V, not over 2kV	1 ft. 6 in. (46 cm)
Over 2kV, not over 15kV	2 ft. 0 in. (61 cm)
Over 15kV, not over 37kV	3 ft. 0 in. (91 cm)
Over 37kV, not over 87.5kV	3 ft. 6 in. (107 cm)
Over 87.5kV, not over 121kV	4 ft. 0 in. (122 cm)
Over 121kV, not over 140kV	4 ft. 6 in. (137 cm)

(c)(3)(iii) Vehicular and mechanical equipment

(c)(3)(iii)(A) Any vehicle or mechanical equipment capable of having parts of its structure elevated near energized overhead lines shall be operated so that a clearance of 10 ft. (305 cm) is maintained. If the voltage is higher than 50kV, the clearance shall be increased 4 in. (10 cm) for every 10kV over that voltage. However, under any of the following conditions, the clearance may be reduced:

(c)(3)(iii)(A)(1) If the vehicle is in transit with its structure lowered, the clearance may be reduced to 4 ft. (122 cm). If the voltage is higher than 50kV, the clearance shall be increased 4 in. (10 cm) for every 10kV over that voltage.

(c)(3)(iii)(A)(2) If insulating barriers are installed to prevent contact with the lines, and if the barriers are rated for the voltage of the line being guarded and are not a part of or an attachment to the vehicle or its raised structure, the clearance may be reduced to a distance within the designed working dimensions of the insulating barrier.

(c)(3)(iii)(A)(3) If the equipment is an aerial lift insulated for the voltage involved, and if the work is performed by a qualified person, the clearance (between the uninsulated portion of the aerial lift and the power line) may be reduced to the distance given in Table S–5.

(c)(3)(iii)(B) Employees standing on the ground may not contact the vehicle or mechanical equipment or any of its attachments, unless:

(c)(3)(iii)(B)(1) The employee is using protective equipment rated for the voltage; or

(c)(3)(iii)(B)(2) The equipment is located so that no uninsulated part of its structure (that portion of the structure that provides a conductive path to employees on the ground) can come closer to the line than permitted in paragraph (c)(3)(iii) of this section.

(c)(3)(iii)(C) If any vehicle or mechanical equipment capable of having parts of its structure elevated near energized overhead lines is intentionally grounded, employees working on the ground near the point of grounding may not stand at the grounding location whenever there is a possibility of overhead line contact. Additional precautions, such as the use of barricades or insulation, shall be taken to protect employees from hazardous ground potentials, depending on earth resistivity and fault currents, which can develop within the first few feet or more outward from the grounding point.

(c)(4) **Illumination**

(c)(4)(i) Employees may not enter spaces containing exposed energized parts, unless illumination is provided that enables the employees to perform the work safely.

(c)(4)(ii) Where lack of illumination or an obstruction precludes observation of the work to be performed, employees may not perform tasks near exposed energized parts. Employees may not reach blindly into areas which may contain energized parts.

(c)(5) **Confined or enclosed work spaces** When an employee works in a confined or enclosed space (such as a manhole or vault) that contains exposed energized parts, the employer shall provide, and the employee shall use, protective shields, protective barriers, or insulating materials as necessary to avoid inadvertent contact with these parts. Doors, hinged panels, and the like shall be secured to prevent their swinging into an employee and causing the employee to contact exposed energized parts.

(c)(6) **Conductive materials and equipment** Conductive materials and equipment that are in contact with any part of an employee's body shall be handled in a manner that will prevent them from contacting exposed energized conductors or circuit parts. If an employee must handle long dimensional conductive objects (such as ducts and pipes) in areas with exposed live parts, the employer shall institute work practices (such as the use of insulation, guarding, and material handling techniques) which will minimize the hazard.

(c)(7) **Portable ladders** Portable ladders shall have nonconductive siderails if they are used where the employee or the ladder could contact exposed energized parts.

(c)(8) **Conductive apparel** Conductive articles of jewelry and clothing (such as watch bands, bracelets, rings, key chains, necklaces, metalized aprons, cloth with conductive thread, or metal headgear) may not be worn if they might contact exposed energized parts. However, such articles may be worn if they are rendered nonconductive by covering, wrapping, or other insulating means.

(c)(9) **Housekeeping duties** Where live parts present an electrical contact hazard, employees may not perform housekeeping duties at such close distances to the parts that there is a possibility of contact, unless adequate safeguards (such as insulating equipment or barriers) are provided. Electrically conductive cleaning materials (including conductive solids such as steel wool, metalized cloth, and silicon carbide, as well as conductive liquid solutions) may not be used in proximity to energized parts unless procedures are followed which will prevent electrical contact.

(c)(10) **Interlocks** Only a qualified person following the requirements of paragraph (c) of this section may defeat an electrical safety interlock, and then only temporarily while he or she is working on the equipment. The interlock system shall be returned to its operable condition when this work is completed.

[55 FR 32016, Aug. 6, 1990; 55 FR 42053, Nov. 1, 1990, as amended at 59 FR 4476, Jan. 31, 1994]

§1910.334 OI Use of equipment

(a) **Portable electric equipment** This paragraph applies to the use of cord- and plug-connected equipment, including flexible cord sets (extension cords).

(a)(1) **Handling** Portable equipment shall be handled in a manner which will not cause damage. Flexible electric cords connected to equipment may not be used for raising or lowering the equipment. Flexible cords may not be fastened with staples or otherwise hung in such a fashion as could damage the outer jacket or insulation.

(a)(2) OI **Visual inspection**

(a)(2)(i) Portable cord- and plug-connected equipment and flexible cord sets (extension cords) shall be visually inspected before use on any shift for external defects (such as loose parts, deformed and missing pins, or damage to outer jacket or insulation) and for evidence of possible internal damage (such as pinched or crushed outer jacket). Cord- and plug-connected equipment and flexible cord sets (extension cords) which remain connected once they are put in place and are not exposed to damage need not be visually inspected until they are relocated.

(a)(2)(ii) If there is a defect or evidence of damage that might expose an employee to injury, the defective or damaged item shall be removed from service, and no employee may use it until repairs and tests necessary to render the equipment safe have been made.

(a)(2)(iii) When an attachment plug is to be connected to a receptacle (including any on a cord set), the relationship of the plug and receptacle contacts shall first be checked to ensure that they are of proper mating configurations.

(a)(3) **Grounding-type equipment**

(a)(3)(i) A flexible cord used with grounding-type equipment shall contain an equipment grounding conductor.

(a)(3)(ii) Attachment plugs and receptacles may not be connected or altered in a manner which would prevent proper continuity of the equipment grounding conductor at the point where plugs are attached to receptacles. Additionally, these devices may not be altered to allow the grounding pole of a plug to be inserted into slots intended for connection to the current-carrying conductors.

(a)(3)(iii) Adapters which interrupt the continuity of the equipment grounding connection may not be used.

(a)(4) **Conductive work locations** Portable electric equipment and flexible cords used in highly conductive work locations (such as those inundated with water or other conductive liquids), or in job locations where employees are likely to contact water or conductive liquids, shall be approved for those locations.

(a)(5) **Connecting attachment plugs**

(a)(5)(i) Employees' hands may not be wet when plugging and unplugging flexible cords and cord- and plug-connected equipment, if energized equipment is involved.

(a)(5)(ii) Energized plug and receptacle connections may be handled only with insulating protective equipment if the condition of the connection could provide a conducting path to the employee's hand (if, for example, a cord connector is wet from being immersed in water).

(a)(5)(iii) Locking-type connectors shall be properly secured after connection.

(b) **Electric power and lighting circuits**

(b)(1) **Routine opening and closing of circuits** Load rated switches, circuit breakers, or other devices specifically designed as disconnecting means shall be used for the opening, reversing, or closing of circuits under load conditions. Cable connectors not of the load-break type, fuses, terminal lugs, and cable splice connections may not be used for such purposes, except in an emergency.

(b)(2) OI **Reclosing circuits after protective device operation** After a circuit is deenergized by a circuit protective device, the circuit may not be manually reenergized until it has been determined that the equipment and circuit can be safely energized. The repetitive manual reclosing of circuit breakers or reenergizing circuits through replaced fuses is prohibited.

Note: When it can be determined from the design of the circuit and the overcurrent devices involved that the automatic operation of a device was caused by an overload rather than a fault condition, no examination of the circuit or connected equipment is needed before the circuit is reenergized.

(b)(3) Overcurrent protection modification Overcurrent protection of circuits and conductors may not be modified, even on a temporary basis, beyond that allowed by §1910.304(e), the installation safety requirements for overcurrent protection.

(c) Test instruments and equipment

(c)(1) [OI] **Use** Only qualified persons may perform testing work on electric circuits or equipment.

(c)(2) Visual inspection Test instruments and equipment and all associated test leads, cables, power cords, probes, and connectors shall be visually inspected for external defects and damage before the equipment is used. If there is a defect or evidence of damage that might expose an employee to injury, the defective or damaged item shall be removed from service, and no employee may use it until repairs and tests necessary to render the equipment safe have been made.

(c)(3) Rating of equipment Test instruments and equipment and their accessories shall be rated for the circuits and equipment to which they will be connected and shall be designed for the environment in which they will be used.

(d) Occasional use of flammable or ignitible materials Where flammable materials are present only occasionally, electric equipment capable of igniting them shall not be used, unless measures are taken to prevent hazardous conditions from developing. Such materials include, but are not limited to: flammable gases, vapors, or liquids; combustible dust; and ignitible fibers or flyings.

Note: Electrical installation requirements for locations where flammable materials are present on a regular basis are contained in §1910.307.

[55 FR 32019, Aug. 6, 1990]

§1910.335 [OI] Safeguards for personnel protection

(a) [OI] **Use of protective equipment**

(a)(1) Personal protective equipment

(a)(1)(i) Employees working in areas where there are potential electrical hazards shall be provided with, and shall use, electrical protective equipment that is appropriate for the specific parts of the body to be protected and for the work to be performed.

Note: Personal protective equipment requirements are contained in Subpart I of this Part.

(a)(1)(ii) Protective equipment shall be maintained in a safe, reliable condition and shall be periodically inspected or tested, as required by §1910.137.

(a)(1)(iii) If the insulating capability of protective equipment may be subject to damage during use, the insulating material shall be protected. (For example, an outer covering of leather is sometimes used for the protection of rubber insulating material.)

(a)(1)(iv) [OI] Employees shall wear nonconductive head protection wherever there is a danger of head injury from electric shock or burns due to contact with exposed energized parts.

(a)(1)(v) [OI] Employees shall wear protective equipment for the eyes or face wherever there is danger of injury to the eyes or face from electric arcs or flashes or from flying objects resulting from electrical explosion.

(a)(2) General protective equipment and tools

(a)(2)(i) [OI] When working near exposed energized conductors or circuit parts, each employee shall use insulated tools or handling equipment if the tools or handling equipment might make contact with such conductors or parts. If the insulating capability of insulated tools or handling equipment is subject to damage, the insulating material shall be protected.

(a)(2)(i)(A) Fuse handling equipment, insulated for the circuit voltage, shall be used to remove or install fuses when the fuse terminals are energized.

(a)(2)(i)(B) Ropes and handlines used near exposed energized parts shall be nonconductive.

(a)(2)(ii) [OI] Protective shields, protective barriers, or insulating materials shall be used to protect each employee from shock, burns, or other electrically related injuries while that employee is working near exposed energized parts which might be accidentally contacted or where dangerous electric heating or arcing might occur. When normally enclosed live parts are exposed for maintenance or repair, they shall be guarded to protect unqualified persons from contact with the live parts.

(b) [OI] **Alerting techniques** The following alerting techniques shall be used to warn and protect employees from hazards which could cause injury due to electric shock, burns, or failure of electric equipment parts:

(b)(1) [OI] **Safety signs and tags** Safety signs, safety symbols, or accident prevention tags shall be used where necessary to warn employees about electrical hazards which may endanger them, as required by §1910.145.

(b)(2) Barricades Barricades shall be used in conjunction with safety signs where it is necessary to prevent or limit employee access to work areas exposing employees to uninsulated energized conductors or circuit parts. Conductive barricades may not be used where they might cause an electrical contact hazard.

(b)(3) Attendants If signs and barricades do not provide sufficient warning and protection from electrical hazards, an attendant shall be stationed to warn and protect employees.

[55 FR 32020, Aug. 6, 1990]

§1910.336–§1910.360 [Reserved]

Safety–Related Maintenance Requirements

§1910.361–§1910.380 [Reserved]

Safety Requirements for Special Equipment

§1910.381–§1910.398 Reserved]

Definitions

§1910.399 [OI] Definitions applicable to this Subpart

Acceptable An installation or equipment is acceptable to the Assistant Secretary of Labor, and approved within the meaning of this Subpart S:

(1) If it is accepted, or certified, or listed, or labeled, or otherwise determined to be safe by a nationally recognized testing laboratory recognized pursuant to §1910.7; or

(2) With respect to an installation or equipment of a kind that no nationally recognized testing laboratory accepts, certifies, lists, labels, or determines to be safe, if it is inspected or tested by another Federal agency, or by a State, municipal, or other local authority responsible for enforcing occupational safety provisions of the National Electrical Code, and found in compliance with the provisions of the National Electrical Code as applied in this Subpart; or

(3) With respect to custom-made equipment or related installations that are designed, fabricated for, and intended for use by a particular customer, if it is determined to be safe for its intended use by its manufacturer on the basis of test data which the employer keeps and makes available for inspection to the Assistant Secretary and his authorized representatives.

Accepted An installation is "accepted" if it has been inspected and found by a nationally recognized testing laboratory to conform to specified plans or to procedures of applicable codes.

Accessible (As applied to wiring methods.) Capable of being removed or exposed without damaging the building structure or finish, or not permanently closed in by the structure or finish of the building. (See "concealed" and "exposed.")

Accessible (As applied to equipment.) Admitting close approach; not guarded bylocked doors, elevation, or other effective means. (See "Readily accessible.")

Ampacity The current, in amperes, that a conductor can carry continuously under the conditions of use without exceeding its temperature rating.

Appliances Utilization equipment, generally other than industrial, normally built in standardized sizes or types, that is installed or connected as a unit to perform one or more functions.

Approved Acceptable to the authority enforcing this Subpart. The authority enforcing this Subpart is the Assistant Secretary of Labor for Occupational Safety and Health. The definition of "acceptable" indicates what is acceptable to the Assistant Secretary of Labor, and therefore approved within the meaning of this Subpart.

Armored cable (Type AC) A fabricated assembly of insulated conductors in a flexible metallic enclosure.

Askarel A generic term for a group of nonflammable synthetic chlorinated hydrocarbons used as electrical insulating media. Askarels of various compositional types are used. Under arcing conditions, the gases produced, while consisting predominantly of noncombustible hydrogen chloride, can include varying amounts of combustible gases depending upon the askarel type.

Attachment plug (Plug cap)(Cap) A device that, by insertion in a receptacle, establishes a connection between the conductors of the attached flexible cord and the conductors connected permanently to the receptacle.

Automatic Self-acting, operating by its own mechanism when actuated by some impersonal influence, as, for example, a change in current strength, pressure, temperature, or mechanical configuration.

Bare conductor See Conductor.

Barrier A physical obstruction that is intended to prevent contact with equipment or live parts or to prevent unauthorized access to a work area.

Bathroom An area including a basin with one or more of the following: a toilet, a tub, or a shower.

Bonding (Bonded) The permanent joining of metallic parts to form an electrically conductive path that ensures electrical continuity and the capacity to conduct safely any current likely to be imposed.

Bonding jumper A conductor that assures the necessary electrical conductivity between metal parts required to be electrically connected.

Branch circuit The circuit conductors between the final overcurrent device protecting the circuit and the outlets.

Building A structure that stands alone or is cut off from adjoining structures by fire walls with all openings therein protected by approved fire doors.

Cabinet An enclosure designed either for surface or flush mounting, and provide with a frame, mat, or trim in which a swinging door or doors are or can be hung.

Cable tray system A unit or assembly of units or sections and associated fittings forming a riid structural system used to securely fasten or support cables and raceways. Cable tray systems include ladders, troughs, channels, solid bottom trays, and other similar structures.

Cablebus An assembly of insulated conductors with fittings and conductor terminations in a completely enclosed, ventilated, protective metal housing.

Cell line An assembly of electrically interconnected electrolytic cells supplied by a source of direct current power.

Cell line attachments and auxiliary equipment Cell line attachments and auxiliary equipment include, but are not limited to, auxiliary tanks, process piping, ductwork, structural supports, exposed cell line conductors, conduits and other raceways, pumps, positioning equipment, and cell cutout or bypass electrical devices. Auxiliary equipment also includes tools, welding machines, crucibles, and other portable equipment used for operation and maintenance within the electrolytic cell line working zone. In the cell line working zone, auxiliary equipment includes the exposed conductive surfaces of ungrounded cranes and crane-mounted cell-servicing equipment.

Center pivot irrigation machine A multi-motored irrigation machine that revolves around a central pivot and employs alignment switches or similar devices to control individual motors.

Certified Equipment is "certified" if it bears a label, tag, or other record of certification that the equipment:

(1) Has been tested and found by a nationally recognized testing laboratory to meet nationally recognized standards or to be safe for use in a specified manner; or

(2) Is of a kind whose production is periodically inspected by a nationally recognized testing laboratory and is accepted by the laboratory as safe for its intended use.

Circuit breaker A device designed to open and close a circuit by nonautomatic means and to open the circuit automatically on a predetermined overcurrent without damage to itself when properly applied within its rating.

Class I locations Class I locations are those in which flammable gases or vapors are or may be present in the air in quantities sufficient to produce explosive or ignitable mixtures. Class I locations include the following:

(1) Class I, Division 1 A Class I, Division 1 location is a location:

(1)(i) In which ignitable concentrations of flammable gases or vapors may exist under normal operating conditions; or

(1)(ii) In which ignitable concentrations of such gases or vapors may exist frequently because of repair or maintenance operations or because of leakage; or

(1)(iii) In which breakdown or faulty operation of equipment or processes might release ignitable concentrations of flammable gases or vapors, and might also cause simultaneous failure of electric equipment.

Note to the definition of "Class I, Division 1:" This classification usually includes locations where volatile flammable liquids or liquefied flammable gases are transferred from one container to another; interiors of spray booths and areas in the vicinity of spraying and painting operations where volatile flammable solvents are used; locations containing open tanks or vats of volatile flammable liquids; drying rooms or compartments for the evaporation of flammable solvents; locations containing fat and oil extraction equipment using volatile flammable solvents; portions of cleaning and dyeing plants where flammable liquids are used; gas generator rooms and other portions of gas manufacturing plants where flammable gas may escape; inadequately ventilated pump rooms for flammable gas or for volatile flammable liquids; the interiors of refrigerators and freezers in which volatile flammable materials are stored in open, lightly stoppered, or easily ruptured containers; and all other locations where ignitable concentrations of flammable vapors or gases are likely to occur in the course of normal operations.

(2) Class I, Division 2 A Class I, Division 2 location is a location:

(2)(i) In which volatile flammable liquids or flammable gases are handled, processed, or used, but in which the hazardous liquids, vapors, or gases will normally be confined within closed containers or closed systems from which they can escape only in the event of accidental rupture or breakdown of such containers or systems, or as a result of abnormal operation of equipment; or

(2)(ii) In which ignitable concentrations of gases or vapors are normally prevented by positive mechanical ventilation, and which might become hazardous through failure or abnormal operations of the ventilating equipment; or

(2)(iii) That is adjacent to a Class I, Division 1 location, and to which ignitable concentrations of gases or vapors might occasionally be communicated unless such communication is prevented by adequate positive-pressure ventilation from a source of clean air, and effective safeguards against ventilation failure are provided.

Note to the definition of "Class I, Division 2:" This classification usually includes locations where volatile flammable liquids or flammable gases or vapors are used, but which would become hazardous only in case of an accident or of some unusual operating condition. The quantity of flammable material that might escape in case of accident, the adequacy of ventilating equipment, the total area involved, and the record of the industry or business with respect to explosions or fires are all factors that merit consideration in determining the classification and extent of each location.

Piping without valves, checks, meters, and similar devices would not ordinarily introduce a hazardous condition even though used for flammable liquids or gases. Locations used for the storage of flammable liquids or liquefied or compressed gases in sealed containers would not normally be considered hazardous unless also subject to other hazardous conditions.

Electrical conduits and their associated enclosures separated from process fluids by a single seal or barrier are classed as a Division 2 location if the outside of the conduit and enclosures is a nonhazardous location.

(3) Class I, Zone 0 A Class I, Zone 0 location is a location in which one of the following conditions exists:

(3)(i) Ignitable concentrations of flammable gases or vapors are present continuously; or

(3)(ii) Ignitable concentrations of flammable gases or vapors are present for long periods of time.

Note to the definition of "Class I, Zone 0:" As a guide in determining when flammable gases or vapors are present continuously or for long periods of time, refer to Recommended Practice for Classification of Locations for Electrical Installations of Petroleum Facilities Classified as Class I, Zone 0, Zone 1 or Zone 2, API RP 505–1997; Electrical Apparatus for Explosive Gas Atmospheres, Classifications of Hazardous Areas, IEC 79–10–1995; Area Classification Code for Petroleum Installations, Model Code—Part 15, Institute for Petroleum; and Electrical Apparatus for Explosive Gas Atmospheres, Classifications of Hazardous (Classified) Locations, ISA S12.24.01–1997.

(4) Class I, Zone 1 A Class I, Zone 1 location is a location in which one of the following conditions exists:

(4)(i) Ignitable concentrations of flammable gases or vapors are likely to exist under normal operating conditions; or

(4)(ii) Ignitable concentrations of flammable gases or vapors may exist frequently because of repair or maintenance operations or because of leakage; or

(4)(iii) Equipment is operated or processes are carried on of such a nature that equipment breakdown or faulty operations could result in the release of ignitable concentrations of flammable gases or vapors and also cause simultaneous failure of electric equipment in a manner that would cause the electric equipment to become a source of ignition; or

(4)(iv) A location that is adjacent to a Class I, Zone 0 location from which ignitable concentrations of vapors could be communicated, unless communication is prevented by adequate positive pressure ventilation from a source of clean air and effective safeguards against ventilation failure are provided.

(5) Class I, Zone 2 A Class I, Zone 2 location is a location in which one of the following conditions exists:

(5)(i) Ignitable concentrations of flammable gases or vapors are not likely to occur in normal operation and if they do occur will exist only for a short period; or

(5)(ii) Volatile flammable liquids, flammable gases, or flammable vapors are handled, processed, or used, but in which the liquids, gases, or vapors are normally confined within closed containers or closed systems from which they can escape only as a result of accidental rupture or breakdown of the containers or system or as the result of the abnormal operation of the equipment with which the liquids or gases are handled, processed, or used; or

(5)(iii) Ignitable concentrations of flammable gases or vapors normally are prevented by positive mechanical ventilation, but which may become hazardous as the result of failure or abnormal operation of the ventilation equipment; or

(5)(iv) A location that is adjacent to a Class I, Zone 1 location, from which ignitable concentrations of flammable gases or vapors could be communicated, unless such communication is prevented by adequate positive-pressure ventilation from a source of clean air, and effective safeguards against ventilation failure are provided.

Class II locations Class II locations are those that are hazardous because of the presence of combustible dust. Class II locations include the following:

(1) Class II, Division 1 A Class II, Division 1 location is a location:

(1)(i) In which combustible dust is or may be in suspension in the air under normal operating conditions, in quantities sufficient to produce explosive or ignitable mixtures; or

(1)(ii) Where mechanical failure or abnormal operation of machinery or equipment might cause such explosive or ignitable mixtures to be produced, and might also provide a source of ignition through simultaneous failure of electric equipment, through operation of protection devices, or from other causes; or

(1)(iii) In which combustible dusts of an electrically conductive nature may be present.

Note to the definition of "Class II, Division 1:" This classification may include areas of grain handling and processing plants, starch plants, sugar-pulverizing plants, malting plants, hay-grinding plants, coal pulverizing plants, areas where metal dusts and powders are produced or processed, and other similar locations that contain dust producing machinery and equipment (except where the equipment is dust-tight or vented to the outside). These areas would have combustible dust in the air, under normal operating conditions, in quantities sufficient to produce explosive or ignitable mixtures. Combustible dusts that are electrically nonconductive include dusts produced in the handling and processing of grain and grain products, pulverized sugar and cocoa, dried egg and milk powders, pulverized spices, starch and pastes, potato and wood flour, oil meal from beans and seed, dried hay, and other organic materials which may produce combustible dusts when processed or handled. Dusts containing magnesium or aluminum are particularly hazardous, and the use of extreme caution is necessary to avoid ignition and explosion.

(2) Class II, Division 2 A Class II, Division 2 location is a location where:

(2)(i) Combustible dust will not normally be in suspension in the air in quantities sufficient to produce explosive or ignitable mixtures, and dust accumulations will normally be insufficient to interfere with the normal operation of electric equipment or other apparatus, but combustible dust may be in suspension in the air as a result of infrequent malfunctioning of handling or processing equipment; and

(2)(ii) Resulting combustible dust accumulations on, in, or in the vicinity of the electric equipment may be sufficient to interfere with the safe dissipation of heat from electric equipment or may be ignitable by abnormal operation or failure of electric equipment.

Note to the definition of "Class II, Division 2:" This classification includes locations where dangerous concentrations of suspended dust would not be likely, but where dust accumulations might form on or in the vicinity of electric equipment. These areas may contain equipment from which appreciable quantities of dust would escape under abnormal operating conditions or be adjacent to a Class II Division 1 location, as described above, into which an explosive or ignitable concentration of dust may be put into suspension under abnormal operating conditions.

Class III locations Class III locations are those that are hazardous because of the presence of easily ignitable fibers or flyings, but in which such fibers or flyings are not likely to be in suspension in the air in quantities sufficient to produce ignitable mixtures. Class III locations include the following:

(1) Class III, Division 1 A Class III, Division 1 location is a location in which easily ignitable fibers or materials producing combustible flyings are handled, manufactured, or used.

Note to the definition of "Class III, Division 1:" Such locations usually include some parts of rayon, cotton, and other textile mills; combustible fiber manufacturing and processing plants; cotton gins and cotton-seed mills; flax-processing plants; clothing manufacturing plants; woodworking plants, and establishments; and industries involving similar hazardous processes or conditions.

Easily ignitable fibers and flyings include rayon, cotton (including cotton linters and cotton waste), sisal or henequen, istle, jute, hemp, tow, cocoa fiber, oakum, baled waste kapok, Spanish moss, excelsior, and other materials of similar nature.

(2) Class III, Division 2. A Class III, Division 2 location is a location in which easily ignitable fibers are stored or handled, other than in the process of manufacture.

Collector ring An assembly of slip rings for transferring electric energy from a stationary to a rotating member.

Competent Person One who is capable of identifying existing and predictable hazards in the surroundings or working conditions that are unsanitary, hazardous, or dangerous to employees and who has authorization to take prompt corrective measures to eliminate them.

Concealed Rendered inaccessible by the structure or finish of the building. Wires in concealed raceways are considered concealed, even though they may become accessible by withdrawing them. (See Accessible. (As applied to wiring methods.))

Conductor

(1) Bare A conductor having no covering or electrical insulation whatsoever.

(2) Covered A conductor encased within material of composition or thickness that is not recognized by this Subpart as electrical insulation.

(3) Insulated A conductor encased within material of composition and thickness that is recognized by this Subpart as electrical insulation.

Conduit body A separate portion of a conduit or tubing system that provides access through one or more removable covers to the interior of the system at a junction of two or more sections of the system or at a terminal point of the system. Boxes such as FS and FD or larger cast or sheet metal boxes are not classified as conduit bodies.

Controller A device or group of devices that serves to govern, in some predetermined manner, the electric power delivered to the apparatus to which it is connected.

Covered conductor See Conductor.

Cutout (Over 600 volts, nominal.) An assembly of a fuse support with either a fuseholder, fuse carrier, or disconnecting blade. The fuseholder or fuse carrier may include a conducting element (fuse link), or may act as the disconnecting blade by the inclusion of a nonfusible member.

Cutout box An enclosure designed for surface mounting and having swinging doors or covers secured directly to and telescoping with the walls of the box proper. (See Cabinet.)

Damp location See Location.

Dead front Without live parts exposed to a person on the operating side of the equipment

Deenergized Free from any electrical connection to a source of potential difference and from electrical charge; not having a potential different from that of the earth.

Device A unit of an electrical system that is intended to carry but not utilize electric energy.

Dielectric heating The heating of a nominally insulating material due to its own dielectric losses when the material is placed in a varying electric field.

Disconnecting means A device, or group of devices, or other means by which the conductors of a circuit can be disconnected from their source of supply.

Disconnecting (or Isolating) switch. (Over 600 volts, nominal.) A mechanical switching device used for isolating circuit or equipment from a source of power.

Electrolytic cell line working zone The cell line working zone is the space envelope wherein operation or maintenance is normally performed on or in the vicinity of exposed energized surfaces of electrolytic cell lines or their attachments.

Electrolytic cells. A tank or vat in which electrochemical reactions are caused by applying energy for the purpose of refining or producing usable materials.

Enclosed Surrounded by a case, housing, fence, or walls that will prevent persons from accidentally contacting energized parts.

Enclosure The case or housing of apparatus, or the fence or walls surrounding an installation to prevent personnel from accidentally contacting energized parts, or to protect the equipment from physical damage.

Energized Electrically connected to a source of potential difference.

Equipment A general term including material, fittings, devices, appliances, fixtures, apparatus, and the like, used as a part of, or in connection with, an electrical installation.

Equipment grounding conductor See Grounding conductor, equipment.

Explosion-proof apparatus Apparatus enclosed in a case that is capable of withstanding an explosion of a specified gas or vapor that may occur within it and of preventing the ignition of a specified gas or vapor surrounding the enclosure by sparks, flashes, or explosion of the gas or vapor within, and that operates at such an external temperature that it will not ignite a surrounding flammable atmosphere.

Exposed (As applied to live parts.) Capable of being inadvertently touched or approached nearer than a safe distance by a person. It is applied to parts not suitably guarded, isolated, or insulated. (See Accessible and Concealed.)

Exposed (As applied to wiring methods.) On or attached to the surface, or behind panels designed to allow access. (See Accessible. (As applied to wiring methods.))

Exposed (For the purposes of §1910.308(e).) Where the circuit is in such a position that in case of failure of supports or insulation, contact with another circuit may result.

Externally operable Capable of being operated without exposing the operator to contact with live parts.

Feeder All circuit conductors between the service equipment, the source of a separate derived system, or other power supply source and the final branch-circuit overcurrent device.

Fitting An accessory such as a locknut, bushing, or other part of a wiring system that is intended primarily to perform a mechanical rather than an electrical function.

Fountain Fountains, ornamental pools, display pools, and reflection pools.

Note to the definition of "fountain:" This definition does not include drinking fountains.

Fuse (Over 600 volts, nominal.) An overcurrent protective device with a circuit opening fusible part that is heated and severed by the passage of overcurrent through it. A fuse comprises all the parts that form a unit capable of performing the prescribed functions. It may or may not be the complete device necessary to connect it into an electrical circuit.

Ground A conducting connection, whether intentional or accidental, between an electric circuit or equipment and the earth, or to some conducting body that serves in place of the earth.

Grounded Connected to the earth or to some conducting body that serves in place of the earth.

Grounded, effectively Intentionally connected to earth through a ground connection or connections of sufficiently low impedance and having sufficient current-carrying capacity to prevent the buildup of voltages that may result in undue hazards to connected equipment or to persons.

Grounded conductor A system or circuit conductor that is intentionally grounded.

Grounding conductor A conductor used to connect equipment or the grounded circuit of a wiring system to a grounding electrode or electrodes.

Grounding conductor, equipment The conductor used to connect the noncurrent-carrying metal parts of equipment, raceways, and other enclosures to the system grounded conductor, the grounding electrode conductor, or both, at the service equipment or at the source of a separately derived system.

Grounding electrode conductor The conductor used to connect the grounding electrode to the equipment grounding conductor, to the grounded conductor, or to both, of the circuits at the service equipment or at the source of a separately derived system.

Ground-fault circuit-interrupter A device intended for the protection of personnel that functions to deenergize a circuit or a portion of a circuit within an established period of time when a current to ground exceeds some predetermined value that is less than that required to operate the overcurrent protective device of the supply circuit.

Guarded Covered, shielded, fenced, enclosed, or otherwise protected by means of suitable covers, casings, barriers, rails, screens, mats, or platforms to remove the likelihood of approach to a point of danger or contact by persons or objects.

Health care facilities Buildings or portions of buildings in which medical, dental, psychiatric, nursing, obstetrical, or surgical care are provided.

Note to the definition of "health care facilities:" Health care facilities include, but are not limited to, hospitals, nursing homes, limited care facilities, clinics, medical and dental offices, and ambulatory care centers, whether permanent or movable.

Heating equipment For the purposes of §1910.306(g), the term "heating equipment" includes any equipment used for heating purposes if heat is generated by induction or dielectric methods.

Hoistway Any shaftway, hatchway, well hole, or other vertical opening or space that is designed for the operation of an elevator or dumbwaiter.

Identified (as applied to equipment) Approved as suitable for the specific purpose, function, use, environment, or application, where described in a particular requirement.

Note to the definition of "identified:" Some examples of ways to determine suitability of equipment for a specific purpose, environment, or application include investigations by a nationally recognized testing laboratory (through listing and labeling), inspection agency, or other organization recognized under the definition of "acceptable."

Induction heating The heating of a nominally conductive material due to its own I2 R losses when the material is placed in a varying electromagnetic field.

Insulated Separated from other conducting surfaces by a dielectric (including air space) offering a high resistance to the passage of current.

Insulated conductor See Conductor, Insulated.

Interrupter switch. (Over 600 volts, nominal.) A switch capable of making, carrying, an interrupting specified currents.

Irrigation Machine An electrically driven or controlled machine, with one or more motors, not hand portable, and used primarily to transport and distribute water for agricultural purposes.

Isolated (As applied to location) Not readily accessible to persons unless special means for access are used.

Isolated power system A system comprising an isolating transformer or its equivalent, a line isolation monitor, and its ungrounded circuit conductors.

Labeled Equipment is "labeled" if there is attached to it a label, symbol, or other identifying mark of a nationally recognized testing laboratory:

(1) That makes periodic inspections of the production of such equipment, and

(2) Whose labeling indicates compliance with nationally recognized standards or tests to determine safe use in a specified manner.

Lighting outlet An outlet intended for the direct connection of a lampholder, a lighting fixture, or a pendant cord terminating in a lampholder.

Listed Equipment is "listed" if it is of a kind mentioned in a list that:

(1) Is published by a nationally recognized laboratory that makes periodic inspection of the production of such equipment, and

(2) States that such equipment meets nationally recognized standards or has been tested and found safe for use in a specified manner.

Live parts Energized conductive components.

Location

(1) Damp location Partially protected locations under canopies, marquees, roofed open porches, and like locations, and interior locations subject to moderate degrees of moisture, such as some basements, some barns, and some cold-storage warehouses.

(2) Dry location A location not normally subject to dampness or wetness. A location classified as dry may be temporarily subject to dampness or wetness, as in the case of a building under construction.

(3) Wet location Installations underground or in concrete slabs or masonry in direct contact with the earth, and locations subject to saturation with water or other liquids, such as vehicle-washing areas, and locations unprotected and exposed to weather.

Medium voltage cable (Type MV) A single or multiconductor solid dielectric insulated cable rated 2001 volts or higher.

Metal-clad cable (Type MC) A factory assembly of one or more insulated circuit conductors with or without optical fiber members enclosed in an armor of interlocking metal tape, or a smooth or corrugated metallic sheath.

Mineral-insulated metal-sheathed cable (Type MI) Type MI, mineral-insulated metal-sheathed, cable is a factory assembly of one or more conductors insulated with a highly compressed refractory mineral insulation and enclosed in a liquidtight and gastight continuous copper or alloy steel sheath.

Mobile X-ray X-ray equipment mounted on a permanent base with wheels or casters or both for moving while completely assembled.

Motor control center An assembly of one or more enclosed sections having a common power bus and principally containing motor control units.

Nonmetallic-sheathed cable (Types NM, NMC, and NMS) A factory assembly of two or more insulated conductors having an outer sheath of moisture resistant, flame-retardant, nonmetallic material.

Oil (filled) cutout (Over 600 volts, nominal.) A cutout in which all or part of the fuse support and its fuse link or disconnecting blade are mounted in oil with complete immersion of the contacts and the fusible portion of the conducting element (fuse link), so that arc interruption by severing of the fuse link or by opening of the contacts will occur under oil.

Open wiring on insulators Open wiring on insulators is an exposed wiring method using cleats, knobs, tubes, and flexible tubing for the protection and support of single insulated conductors run in or on buildings, and not concealed by the building structure.

Outlet A point on the wiring system at which current is taken to supply utilization equipment.

Outline lighting An arrangement of incandescent lamps or electric discharge lighting to outline or call attention to certain features, such as the shape of a building or the decoration of a window.

Overcurrent Any current in excess of the rated current of equipment or the ampacity of a conductor. It may result from overload, short circuit, or ground fault.

Overhaul means to perform a major replacement, modification, repair, or rehabilitation similar to that involved when a new building or facility is built, a new wing is added, or an entire floor is renovated.

Overload Operation of equipment in excess of normal, full-load rating, or of a conductor in excess of rated ampacity that, when it persists for a sufficient length of time, would cause damage or dangerous overheating. A fault, such as a short circuit or ground fault, is not an overload. (See Overcurrent.)

Panelboard A single panel or group of panel units designed for assembly in the form of a single panel; including buses, automatic overcurrent devices, and with or without switches for the control of light, heat, or power circuits; designed to be placed in a cabinet or cutout box placed in or against a wall or partition and accessible only from the front. (See Switchboard.)

Permanently installed decorative fountains and reflection pools Pools that are constructed in the ground, on the ground, or in a building in such a manner that the fountain or pool cannot be readily disassembled for storage, whether or not served by electrical circuits of any nature. These units are primarily constructed for their aesthetic value and are not intended for swimming or wading.

Permanently installed swimming, wading, and therapeutic pools Pools that are constructed in the ground or partially in the ground, and all other capable of holding water in a depth greater than 1.07 m (42 in.). The definition also applies to all pools installed inside of a building, regardless of water depth, whether or not served by electric circuits of any nature.

Portable X-ray X-ray equipment designed to be hand-carried.

Power and control tray cable (Type TC) A factory assembly of two or more insulated conductors, with or without associated bare or covered grounding conductors under a nonmetallic sheath, approved for installation in cable trays, in raceways, or where supported by a messenger wire.

Power fuse (Over 600 volts, nominal.) See Fuse.

Power-limited tray cable (Type PLTC) A factory assembly of two or more insulated conductors under a nonmetallic jacket.

Power outlet An enclosed assembly, which may include receptacles, circuit breakers, fuseholders, fused switches, buses, and watt-hour meter mounting means, that is intended to supply and control power to mobile homes, recreational vehicles, or boats or to serve as a means for distributing power needed to operate mobile or temporarily installed equipment.

Premises wiring (**Premises wiring system**) The interior and exterior wiring, including power, lighting, control, and signal circuit wiring together with all of their associated hardware, fittings, and wiring devices, both permanently and temporarily installed, that extends from the service point of utility conductors or source of power (such as a battery, a solar photovoltaic system, or a generator, transformer, or converter) to the outlets. Such wiring does not include wiring internal to appliances, fixtures, motors, controllers, motor control centers, and similar equipment.

Qualified person One who has received training in and has demonstrated skills and knowledge in the construction and operation of electric equipment and installations and the hazards involved.

Note 1 to the definition of "qualified person:" Whether an employee is considered to be a "qualified person" will depend upon various circumstances in the workplace. For example, it is possible and, in fact, likely for an individual to be considered "qualified" with regard to certain equipment in the workplace, but "unqualified" as to other equipment. (See §1910.332(b)(3) for training requirements that specifically apply to qualified persons.)

Note 2 to the definition of "qualified person:" An employee who is undergoing on-the-job training and who, in the course of such training, has demonstrated an ability to perform duties safely at his or her level of training and who is under the direct supervision of a qualified person is considered to be a qualified person for the performance of those duties.

Raceway An enclosed channel of metal or nonmetallic materials designed expressly for holding wires, cables, or busbars, with additional functions as permitted in this standard. Raceways include, but are not limited to, rigid metal conduit, rigid nonmetallic conduit, intermediate metal conduit, liquidtight flexible conduit, flexible metallic tubing, flexible metal conduit, electrical metallic tubing, electrical nonmetallic tubing, underfloor raceways, cellular concrete floor raceways, cellular metal floor raceways, surface raceways, wireways, and busways.

Readily accessible Capable of being reached quickly for operation, renewal, or inspections, so that those needing ready access do not have to climb over or remove obstacles or to resort to portable ladders, chairs, etc. (See Accessible.)

Receptacle A receptacle is a contact device installed at the outlet for the connection of an attachment plug. A single receptacle is a single contact device with no other contact device on the same yoke. A multiple receptacle is two or more contact devices on the same yoke.

Receptacle outlet An outlet where one or more receptacles are installed.

Remote-control circuit Any electric circuit that controls any other circuit through a relay or an equivalent device.

Sealable equipment Equipment enclosed in a case or cabinet that is provided with a means of sealing or locking so that live parts cannot be made accessible without opening the enclosure. The equipment may or may not be operable without opening the enclosure.

Separately derived system A premises wiring system whose power is derived from a battery, a solar photovoltaic system, or from a generator, transformer, or converter windings, and that has no direct electrical connection, including a solidly connected grounded circuit conductor, to supply conductors originating in another system.

Service The conductors and equipment for delivering electric energy from the serving utility to the wiring system of the premises served.

Service cable Service conductors made up in the form of a cable.

Service conductors The conductors from the service point to the service disconnecting means.

Service drop The overhead service conductors from the last pole or other aerial support to and including the splices, if any, connecting to the service-entrance conductors at the building or other structure.

Service-entrance cable A single conductor or multiconductor assembly provided with or without an overall covering, primarily used for services, and is of the following types:

(1) Type SE Type SE, having a flame-retardant, moisture resistant covering; and

(2) Type USE Type USE, identified for underground use, having a moisture-resistant covering, but not required to have a flame-retardant covering. Cabled, single-conductor, Type USE constructions recognized for underground use may have a bare copper conductor cabled with the assembly. Type USE single, parallel, or cable conductor assemblies recognized for underground use may have a bare copper concentric conductor applied. These constructions do not require an outer overall covering.

Service-entrance conductors, overhead system The service conductors between the terminals of the service equipment and a point usually outside the building, clear of building walls, where joined by tap or splice to the service drop.

Service entrance conductors, underground system The service conductors between the terminals of the service equipment and the point of connection to the service lateral.

Service equipment The necessary equipment, usually consisting of one or more circuit breakers or switches and fuses, and their accessories, connected to the load end of service conductors to a building or other structure, or an otherwise designated area, and intended to constitute the main control and cutoff of the supply.

Service point The point of connection between the facilities of the serving utility and the premises wiring.

Shielded nonmetallic-sheathed cable (Type SNM) A factory assembly of two or more insulated conductors in an extruded core of moisture-resistant, flame-resistant nonmetallic material, covered with an overlapping spiral metal tape and wire shield and jacketed with an extruded moisture-, flame-, oil-, corrosion-, fungus-, and sunlight-resistant nonmetallic material.

Show window Any window used or designed to be used for the display of goods or advertising material, whether it is fully or partly enclosed or entirely open at the rear and whether or not it has a platform raised higher than the street floor level.

Signaling circuit Any electric circuit that energizes signaling equipment.

Storable swimming or wading pool A pool that is constructed on or above the ground and is capable of holding water to a maximum depth of 1.07 m (42 in.), or a pool with nonmetallic, molded polymeric walls or inflatable fabric walls regardless of dimension.

Switchboard A large single panel, frame, or assembly of panels on which are mounted, on the face or back, or both, switches, overcurrent and other protective devices, buses, and (usually) instruments. Switchboards are generally accessible from the rear as well as from the front and are not intended to be installed in cabinets. (See Panelboard.)

Switch

(1) General-use switch A switch intended for use in general distribution and branch circuits. It is rated in amperes, and it is capable of interrupting its rated current at its rated voltage.

(2) **General-use snap switch** A form of general-use switch constructed so that it can be installed in device boxes or on box covers, or otherwise used in conjunction with wiring systems recognized by this Subpart.

(3) **Isolating switch** A switch intended for isolating an electric circuit from the source of power. It has no interrupting rating, and it is intended to be operated only after the circuit has been opened by some other means.

(4) **Motor-circuit switch** A switch, rated in horsepower, capable of interrupting the maximum operating overload current of a motor of the same horsepower rating as the switch at the rated voltage.

Switching devices (Over 600 volts, nominal.) Devices designed to close and open one or more electric circuits. Included in this category are circuit breakers, cutouts, disconnecting (or isolating) switches, disconnecting means, interrupter switches, and oil (filled) cutouts.

Transportable X-ray X-ray equipment installed in a vehicle or that may readily be disassembled for transport in a vehicle.

Utilization equipment Equipment that utilizes electric energy for electronic, electromechanical, chemical, heating, lighting, or similar purposes.

Ventilated Provided with a means to permit circulation of air sufficient to remove an excess of heat, fumes, or vapors.

Volatile flammable liquid A flammable liquid having a flash point below 38 °C (100 °F), or a flammable liquid whose temperature is above its flash point, or a Class II combustible liquid having a vapor pressure not exceeding 276 kPa (40 psia) at 38 °C (100 °F) and whose temperature is above its flash point.

Voltage (of a circuit) The greatest root-mean-square (rms) (effective) difference of potential between any two conductors of the circuit concerned.

Voltage, nominal A nominal value assigned to a circuit or system for the purpose of conveniently designating its voltage class (as 120/240 volts, 480Y/277 volts, 600 volts). The actual voltage at which a circuit operates can vary from the nominal within a range that permits satisfactory operation of equipment.

Voltage to ground For grounded circuits, the voltage between the given conductor and that point or conductor of the circuit that is grounded; for ungrounded circuits, the greatest voltage between the given conductor and any other conductor of the circuit.

Watertight So constructed that moisture will not enter the enclosure.

Weatherproof So constructed or protected that exposure to the weather will not interfere with successful operation. Rainproof, raintight, or watertight equipment can fulfill the requirements for weatherproof where varying weather conditions other than wetness, such as snow, ice, dust, or temperature extremes, are not a factor.

Wireways Sheet-metal troughs with hinged or removable covers for housing and protecting electric wires and cable and in which conductors are laid in place after the wireway has been installed as a complete system.

[72 FR 7215, Feb. 14, 2007]

Subpart S of §1910 Appendix A References for further information

The references contained in this Appendix provide nonmandatory information that can be helpful in understanding and complying with Subpart S of this Part. However, compliance with these standards is not a substitute for compliance with Subpart S of this Part.

ANSI/API RP 500–1998 (2002) Recommended Practice for Classification of Locations for Electrical Installations at Petroleum Facilities Classified as Class I Division 1 and Division 2

ANSI/API RP 505–1997 (2002) Recommended Practice for Classification of Locations for Electrical Installations at Petroleum Facilities Classified as Class I, Zone 0, Zone 1 and Zone 2

ANSI/ASME A17.1–2004 Safety Code for Elevators and Escalators.

ANSI/ASME B30.2–2005 Overhead and Gantry Cranes (Top Running Bridge, Single or Multiple Girder, Top Running Trolley Hoist)

ANSI/ASME B30.3–2004 Construction Tower Cranes

ANSI/ASME B30.4–2003 Portal, Tower, and Pedestal Cranes

ANSI/ASME B30.5–2004 Mobile And Locomotive Cranes

ANSI/ASME B30.6–2003 Derricks

ANSI/ASME B30.7–2001 Base Mounted Drum Hoists

ANSI/ASME B30.8–2004 Floating Cranes And Floating Derricks

ANSI/ASME B30.11–2004 Monorails And Underhung Cranes

ANSI/ASME B30.12–2001 Handling Loads Suspended from Rotorcraft.

ANSI/ASME B30.13–2003 Storage/Retrieval (S/R) Machines and Associated Equipment

ANSI/ASME B30.16–2003 Overhead Hoists (Underhung)

ANSI/ASME B30.22–2005 Articulating Boom Cranes

ANSI/ASSE Z244.1–2003 Control of Hazardous Energy Lockout/Tagout and Alternative Methods

ANSI/ASSE Z490.1–2001 Criteria for Accepted Practices in Safety, Health, and Environmental Training

ANSI/IEEE C2–2002 National Electrical Safety Code

ANSI K61.1–1999 Safety Requirements for the Storage and Handling of Anhydrous Ammonia

ANSI/UL 913–2003 Intrinsically Safe Apparatus and Associated Apparatus for Use in Class I, II, and III, Division 1, Hazardous (Classified) Locations

ASTM D3176–1989 (2002) Standard Practice for Ultimate Analysis of Coal and Coke

ASTM D3180–1989 (2002) Standard Practice for Calculating Coal and Coke Analyses from As-Determined to Different Bases

NFPA 20–2003 Standard for the Installation of Stationary Pumps for Fire Protection

NFPA 30–2003 Flammable and Combustible Liquids Code

NFPA 32–2004 Standard for Drycleaning Plants

NFPA 33–2003 Standard for Spray Application Using Flammable or Combustible Materials

NFPA 34–2003 Standard for Dipping and Coating Processes Using Flammable or Combustible Liquids

NFPA 35–2005 Standard for the Manufacture of Organic Coatings

NFPA 36–2004 Standard for Solvent Extraction Plants

NFPA 40–2001 Standard for the Storage and Handling of Cellulose Nitrate Film

NFPA 58–2004 Liquefied Petroleum Gas Code

NFPA 59–2004 Utility LP-Gas Plant Code

NFPA 70–2002 National Electrical Code. (See also NFPA 70–2005.)

NFPA 70E–2000 Standard for Electrical Safety Requirements for Employee Workplaces. (See also NFPA 70E–2004.)

NFPA 77–2000 Recommended Practice on Static Electricity

NFPA 80–1999 Standard for Fire Doors and Fire Windows

NFPA 88A–2002 Standard for Parking Structures

NFPA 91–2004 Standard for Exhaust Systems for Air Conveying of Vapors, Gases, Mists, and Noncombustible Particulate Solids

NFPA 101–2006 Life Safety Code

NFPA 496–2003 Standard for Purged and Pressurized Enclosures for Electrical Equipment

NFPA 497–2004 Recommended Practice for the Classification of Flammable Liquids, Gases, or Vapors and of Hazardous (Classified) Locations for Electrical Installations in Chemical Process Areas

NFPA 505–2006 Fire Safety Standard for Powered Industrial Trucks Including Type Designations, Areas of Use, Conversions, Maintenance, and Operation

NFPA 820–2003 Standard for Fire Protection in Wastewater Treatment and Collection Facilities

NMAB 353–1–1979 Matrix of Combustion-Relevant Properties and Classification of Gases, Vapors, and Selected Solids

NMAB 353–2–1979 Test Equipment for Use in Determining Classifications of Combustible Dusts

NMAB 353–3–1980 Classification of Combustible Dust in Accordance with the National Electrical Code

[72 FR 7221, Feb., 14, 2007]

This page intentionally left blank.

29 CFR PART 1910 Subpart T
Commercial Diving Operations

Section Contents

Authority: 29 U.S.C. 653, 655, 657; 40 U.S.C. 333; 33 U.S.C. 941; Secretary of Labor's Order No. 8–76 (41 FR 25059), 9–83 (48 FR 35736), 1–90 (55 FR 9033), 6–96 (62 FR 111), 3–2000 (65 FR 50017), 5–2002 (67 FR 65008), 5–2007 (72 FR 31160), or 4–2010 (75 FR 55355) as applicable, and 29 CFR §1911.

Source: 42 FR 37668, July 22, 1977, unless otherwise noted.

General

§1910.401 Scope and application

(a) Scope

(a)(1) This Subpart (standard) applies to every place of employment within the waters of the United States, or within any State, the District of Columbia, the Commonwealth of Puerto Rico, the Virgin Islands, American Samoa, Guam, the Trust Territory of the Pacific Islands, Wake Island, Johnston Island, the Canal Zone, or within the Outer Continental Shelf lands as defined in the Outer Continental Shelf Lands Act (67 Stat. 462, 43 U.S.C. 1331), where diving and related support operations are performed.

(a)(2) This standard applies to diving and related support operations conducted in connection with all types of work and employments, including general industry, construction, ship repairing, shipbuilding, shipbreaking and longshoring. However, this standard does not apply to any diving operation:

(a)(2)(i) Performed solely for instructional purposes, using open-circuit, compressed-air SCUBA and conducted within the no-decompression limits;

(a)(2)(ii) Performed solely for search, rescue, or related public safety purposes by or under the control of a governmental agency; or

(a)(2)(iii) Governed by 45 CFR part 46 (Protection of Human Subjects, U.S. Department of Health and Human Services) or equivalent rules or regulations established by another federal agency, which regulate research, development, or related purposes involving human subjects.

(a)(2)(iv) Defined as scientific diving and which is under the direction and control of a diving program containing at least the following elements:

(a)(2)(iv)(A) Diving safety manual which includes at a minimum: Procedures covering all diving operations specific to the program; procedures for emergency care, including recompression and evacuation; and criteria for diver training and certification.

(a)(2)(iv)(B) Diving control (safety) board, with the majority of its members being active divers, which shall at a minimum have the authority to: Approve and monitor diving projects; review and revise the diving safety manual; assure compliance with the manual; certify the depths to which a diver has been trained; take disciplinary action for unsafe practices; and, assure adherence to the buddy system (a diver is accompanied by and is in continuous contact with another diver in the water) for SCUBA diving.

(a)(3) Alternative requirements for recreational diving instructors and diving guides Employers of recreational diving instructors and diving guides are not required to comply with the decompression-chamber requirements specified by paragraphs (b)(2) and (c)(3)(iii) of §1910.423 and paragraph (b)(1) of §1910.426 when they meet all of the following conditions:

(a)(3)(i) The instructor or guide is engaging solely in recreational diving instruction or dive-guiding operations;

(a)(3)(ii) The instructor or guide is diving within the no-decompression limits in these operations;

(a)(3)(iii) The instructor or guide is using a nitrox breathing-gas mixture consisting of a high percentage of oxygen (more than 22% by volume) mixed with nitrogen;

(a)(3)(iv) The instructor or guide is using an open-circuit, semi-closed-circuit, or closed-circuit self-contained underwater breathing apparatus (SCUBA); and

(a)(3)(v) The employer of the instructor or guide is complying with all requirements of Appendix C of this Subpart.

(b) Application in emergencies An employer may deviate from the requirements of this standard to the extent necessary to prevent or minimize a situation which is likely to cause death, serious physical harm, or major environmental damage, provided that the employer:

(b)(1) Notifies the Area Director, Occupational Safety and Health Administration within 48 hours of the onset of the emergency situation indicating the nature of the emergency and extent of the deviation from the prescribed regulations; and

(b)(2) Upon request from the Area Director, submits such information in writing.

(c) Employer obligation The employer shall be responsible for compliance with:

(c)(1) All provisions of this standard of general applicability; and

(c)(2) All requirements pertaining to specific diving modes to the extent diving operations in such modes are conducted.

[42 FR 37668, July 22, 1977, as amended at 47 FR 53365, Nov. 26, 1982; 58 FR 35310, June 30, 1993; 69 FR 7363, Feb. 17, 2004]

§1910.402 Definitions

As used in this standard, the listed terms are defined as follows:

Acfm Actual cubic feet per minute.

ASME Code or equivalent ASME (American Society of Mechanical Engineers) Boiler and Pressure Vessel Code, Section VIII, or an equivalent code which the employer can demonstrate to be equally effective.

ATA Atmosphere absolute.

Bell An enclosed compartment, pressurized (closed bell) or unpressurized (open bell), which allows the diver to be transported to and from the underwater work area and which may be used as a temporary refuge during diving operations.

Bottom time The total elapsed time measured in minutes from the time when the diver leaves the surface in descent to the time that the diver begins ascent.

Bursting pressure The pressure at which a pressure containment device would fail structurally.

Cylinder A pressure vessel for the storage of gases.

Decompression chamber A pressure vessel for human occupancy such as a surface decompression chamber, closed bell, or deep diving system used to decompress divers and to treat decompression sickness.

Decompression sickness A condition with a variety of symptoms which may result from gas or bubbles in the tissues of divers after pressure reduction.

Decompression table A profile or set of profiles of depth-time relationships for ascent rates and breathing mixtures to be followed after a specific depth-time exposure or exposures.

Dive-guiding operations means leading groups of sports divers, who use an open-circuit, semi-closed-circuit, or closed-circuit self-contained underwater breathing apparatus, to local undersea diving locations for recreational purposes.

Dive location A surface or vessel from which a diving operation is conducted.

Dive-location reserve breathing gas A supply system of air or mixed-gas (as appropriate) at the dive location which is independent of the primary supply system and sufficient to support divers during the planned decompression.

Dive team Divers and support employees involved in a diving operation, including the designated person-in-charge.

Diver An employee working in water using underwater apparatus which supplies compressed breathing gas at the ambient pressure.

Diver-carried reserve breathing gas A diver-carried supply of air or mixed gas (as appropriate) sufficient under standard operating conditions to allow the diver to reach the surface, or another source of breathing gas, or to be reached by a standby diver.

Diving mode A type of diving requiring specific equipment, procedures and techniques (SCUBA, surface-supplied air, or mixed gas).

Fsw Feet of seawater (or equivalent static pressure head).

Heavy gear Diver-worn deep-sea dress including helmet, breastplate, dry suit, and weighted shoes.

Hyperbaric conditions Pressure conditions in excess of surface pressure.

Inwater stage A suspended underwater platform which supports a diver in the water.

Liveboating The practice of supporting a surfaced-supplied air or mixed gas diver from a vessel which is underway.

Mixed-gas diving A diving mode in which the diver is supplied in the water with a breathing gas other than air.

No-decompression limits The depth-time limits of the "no-decompression limits and repetitive dive group designation table for no-decompression air dives", U.S. Navy Diving Manual or equivalent limits which the employer can demonstrate to be equally effective.

Psi(g) Pounds per square inch (gauge).

Recreational diving instruction means training diving students in the use of recreational diving procedures and the safe operation of diving equipment, including an open-circuit, semi-closed-circuit, or closed-circuit self-contained underwater breathing apparatus, during dives.

Scientific diving means diving performed solely as a necessary part of a scientific, research, or educational activity by employees whose sole purpose for diving is to perform scientific research tasks. Scientific diving does not include performing any tasks usually associated with commercial diving such as: Placing or removing heavy objects underwater; inspection of pipelines and similar objects; construction; demolition; cutting or welding; or the use of explosives.

SCUBA diving A diving mode independent of surface supply in which the diver uses open circuit self-contained underwater breathing apparatus.

Standby diver A diver at the dive location available to assist a diver in the water.

Surface-supplied air diving A diving mode in which the diver in the water is supplied from the dive location with compressed air for breathing.

Treatment table A depth-time and breathing gas profile designed to treat decompression sickness.

Umbilical The composite hose bundle between a dive location and a diver or bell, or between a diver and a bell, which supplies the diver or bell with breathing gas, communications, power, or heat as appropriate to the diving mode or conditions, and includes a safety line between the diver and the dive location.

Volume tank A pressure vessel connected to the outlet of a compressor and used as an air reservoir.

Working pressure The maximum pressure to which a pressure containment device may be exposed under standard operating conditions.

[42 FR 37668, July 22, 1977, as amended at 47 FR 53365, Nov. 26, 1982; 69 FR 7363, Feb. 17, 2004]

Personnel Requirements

§1910.410 Qualifications of dive team

(a) **General**

(a)(1) Each dive team member shall have the experience or training necessary to perform assigned tasks in a safe and healthful manner.

(a)(2) Each dive team member shall have experience or training in the following:

- (a)(2)(i) The use of tools, equipment and systems relevant to assigned tasks;
- (a)(2)(ii) Techniques of the assigned diving mode: and
- (a)(2)(iii) Diving operations and emergency procedures.

(a)(3) All dive team members shall be trained in cardiopulmonary resuscitation and first aid (American Red Cross standard course or equivalent).

(a)(4) Dive team members who are exposed to or control the exposure of others to hyperbaric conditions shall be trained in diving-related physics and physiology.

(b) **Assignments**

(b)(1) Each dive team member shall be assigned tasks in accordance with the employee's experience or training, except that limited additional tasks may be assigned to an employee undergoing training provided that these tasks are performed under the direct supervision of an experienced dive team member.

(b)(2) The employer shall not require a dive team member to be exposed to hyperbaric conditions against the employee's will, except when necessary to complete decompression or treatment procedures.

(b)(3) The employer shall not permit a dive team member to dive or be otherwise exposed to hyperbaric conditions for the duration of any temporary physical impairment or condition which is known to the employer and is likely to affect adversely the safety or health of a dive team member.

(c) **Designated person-in-charge**

(c)(1) The employer or an employee designated by the employer shall be at the dive location in charge of all aspects of the diving operation affecting the safety and health of dive team members.

(c)(2) The designated person-in-charge shall have experience and training in the conduct of the assigned diving operation.

General Operations Procedures

§1910.420 Safe practices manual

(a) **General** The employer shall develop and maintain a safe practices manual which shall be made available at the dive location to each dive team member.

(b) **Contents**

(b)(1) The safe practices manual shall contain a copy of this standard and the employer's policies for implementing the requirements of this standard.

(b)(2) For each diving mode engaged in, the safe practices manual shall include:

- (b)(2)(i) Safety procedures and checklists for diving operations;
- (b)(2)(ii) Assignments and responsibilities of the dive team members;
- (b)(2)(iii) Equipment procedures and checklists; and
- (b)(2)(iv) Emergency procedures for fire, equipment failure, adverse environmental conditions, and medical illness and injury.

[42 FR 37668, July 22, 1977, as amended at 49 FR 18295, Apr. 30, 1984]

§1910.421 Pre–dive procedures

(a) **General** The employer shall comply with the following requirements prior to each diving operation, unless otherwise specified.

(b) **Emergency aid** A list shall be kept at the dive location of the telephone or call numbers of the following:

(b)(1) An operational decompression chamber (if not at the dive location);
(b)(2) Accessible hospitals;
(b)(3) Available physicians;
(b)(4) Available means of transportation; and
(b)(5) The nearest U.S. Coast Guard Rescue Coordination Center.

(c) **First aid supplies**

(c)(1) A first aid kit appropriate for the diving operation and approved by a physician shall be available at the dive location.

(c)(2) When used in a decompression chamber or bell, the first aid kit shall be suitable for use under hyperbaric conditions.

(c)(3) In addition to any other first aid supplies, an American Red Cross standard first aid handbook or equivalent, and a bag-type manual resuscitator with transparent mask and tubing shall be available at the dive location.

(d) **Planning and assessment** Planning of a diving operation shall include an assessment of the safety and health aspects of the following:
(d)(1) Diving mode;
(d)(2) Surface and underwater conditions and hazards;
(d)(3) Breathing gas supply (including reserves);
(d)(4) Thermal protection;
(d)(5) Diving equipment and systems;
(d)(6) Dive team assignments and physical fitness of dive team members (including any impairment known to the employer);
(d)(7) Repetitive dive designation or residual inert gas status of dive team members;

(d)(8) Decompression and treatment procedures (including altitude corrections); and

(d)(9) Emergency procedures.

(e) **Hazardous activities** To minimize hazards to the dive team, diving operations shall be coordinated with other activities in the vicinity which are likely to interfere with the diving operation.

(f) **Employee briefing**

(f)(1) Dive team members shall be briefed on:

- (f)(1)(i) The tasks to be undertaken;
- (f)(1)(ii) Safety procedures for the diving mode;
- (f)(1)(iii) Any unusual hazards or environmental conditions likely to affect the safety of the diving operation; and
- (f)(1)(iv) Any modifications to operating procedures necessitated by the specific diving operation.

(f)(2) Prior to making individual dive team member assignments, the employer shall inquire into the dive team member's current state of physical fitness, and indicate to the dive team member the procedure for reporting physical problems or adverse physiological effects during and after the dive.

(g) **Equipment inspection** The breathing gas supply system including reserve breathing gas supplies, masks, helmets, thermal protection, and bell handling mechanism (when appropriate) shall be inspected prior to each dive.

(h) **Warning signal** When diving from surfaces other than vessels in areas capable of supporting marine traffic, a rigid replica of the international code flag "A" at least one meter in height shall be displayed at the dive location in a manner which allows all-round visibility, and shall be illuminated during night diving operations.

[42 FR 37668, July 22, 1977, as amended at 47 FR 14706, Apr. 6, 1982; 54 FR 24334, June 7, 1989]

§1910.422 Procedures during dive

(a) **General** The employer shall comply with the following requirements which are applicable to each diving operation unless otherwise specified.

(b) **Water entry and exit**

(b)(1) A means capable of supporting the diver shall be provided for entering and exiting the water.

(b)(2) The means provided for exiting the water shall extend below the water surface.

(b)(3) A means shall be provided to assist an injured diver from the water or into a bell.

(c) **Communications**

(c)(1) An operational two-way voice communication system shall be used between:

- (c)(1)(i) Each surface-supplied air or mixed-gas diver and a dive team member at the dive location or bell (when provided or required); and
- (c)(1)(ii) The bell and the dive location.

(c)(2) An operational, two-way communication system shall be available at the dive location to obtain emergency assistance.

(d) **Decompression tables** Decompression, repetitive, and no-decompression tables (as appropriate) shall be at the dive location.

(e) **Dive profiles** A depth-time profile, including when appropriate any breathing gas changes, shall be maintained for each diver during the dive including decompression.

(f) **Hand-held power tools and equipment**

(f)(1) Hand-held electrical tools and equipment shall be de-energized before being placed into or retrieved from the water.

(f)(2) Hand-held power tools shall not be supplied with power from the dive location until requested by the diver.

(g) **Welding and burning**

(g)(1) A current supply switch to interrupt the current flow to the welding or burning electrode shall be:

- (g)(1)(i) Tended by a dive team member in voice communication with the diver performing the welding or burning; and
- (g)(1)(ii) Kept in the open position except when the diver is welding or burning.

(g)(2) The welding machine frame shall be grounded.

(g)(3) Welding and burning cables, electrode holders, and connections shall be capable of carrying the maximum current required by the work, and shall be properly insulated.

(g)(4) Insulated gloves shall be provided to divers performing welding and burning operations.

(g)(5) Prior to welding or burning on closed compartments, structures or pipes, which contain a flammable vapor or in which a flammable vapor may be generated by the work, they shall be vented, flooded, or purged with a mixture of gases which will not support combustion.

(h) **Explosives**

(h)(1) Employers shall transport, store, and use explosives in accordance with this section and the applicable provisions of §1910.109 and §1926.912 of Title 29 of the Code of Federal Regulations.

(h)(2) Electrical continuity of explosive circuits shall not be tested until the diver is out of the water.

(h)(3) Explosives shall not be detonated while the diver is in the water.

(i) **Termination of dive** The working interval of a dive shall be terminated when:

(i)(1) A diver requests termination;

(i)(2) A diver fails to respond correctly to communications or signals from a dive team member;

(i)(3) Communications are lost and can not be quickly re-established between the diver and a dive team member at the dive location, and between the designated person-in-charge and the person controlling the vessel in liveboating operations; or

(i)(4) A diver begins to use diver-carried reserve breathing gas or the dive-location reserve breathing gas.

§1910.423 Post–dive procedures

(a) **General** The employer shall comply with the following requirements which are applicable after each diving operation, unless otherwise specified.

(b) **Precautions**

(b)(1) After the completion of any dive, the employer shall:

- (b)(1)(i) Check the physical condition of the diver;
- (b)(1)(ii) Instruct the diver to report any physical problems or adverse physiological effects including symptoms of decompression sickness;
- (b)(1)(iii) Advise the diver of the location of a decompression chamber which is ready for use; and
- (b)(1)(iv) Alert the diver to the potential hazards of flying after diving.

(b)(2) For any dive outside the no-decompression limits, deeper than 100 fsw or using mixed gas as a breathing mixture, the employer shall instruct the diver to remain awake and in the vicinity of the decompression chamber which is at the dive location for at least one hour after the dive (including decompression or treatment as appropriate).

(c) **Recompression capability**

(c)(1) A decompression chamber capable of recompressing the diver at the surface to a minimum of 165 fsw (6 ATA) shall be available at the dive location for:

- (c)(1)(i) Surface-supplied air diving to depths deeper than 100 fsw and shallower than 220 fsw;
- (c)(1)(ii) Mixed gas diving shallower than 300 fsw; or
- (c)(1)(iii) Diving outside the no-decompression limits shallower than 300 fsw.

(c)(2) A decompression chamber capable of recompressing the diver at the surface to the maximum depth of the dive shall be available at the dive location for dives deeper than 300 fsw.

(c)(3) The decompression chamber shall be:

- (c)(3)(i) Dual-lock;
- (c)(3)(ii) Multiplace; and
- (c)(3)(iii) Located within 5 minutes of the dive location.

(c)(4) The decompression chamber shall be equipped with:

- (c)(4)(i) A pressure gauge for each pressurized compartment designed for human occupancy;
- (c)(4)(ii) A built-in-breathing-system with a minimum of one mask per occupant;
- (c)(4)(iii) A two-way voice communication system between occupants and a dive team member at the dive location;
- (c)(4)(iv) A viewport; and
- (c)(4)(v) Illumination capability to light the interior.

(c)(5) **Treatment tables** treatment gas appropriate to the diving mode, and sufficient gas to conduct treatment shall be available at the dive location.

(c)(6) A dive team member shall be available at the dive location during and for at least one hour after the dive to operate the decompression chamber (when required or provided).

(d) **Record of dive**

(d)(1) The following information shall be recorded and maintained for each diving operation:

(d)(1)(i) Names of dive team members including designated person-in-charge;
(d)(1)(ii) Date, time, and location;
(d)(1)(iii) Diving modes used;
(d)(1)(iv) General nature of work performed;
(d)(1)(v) Approximate underwater and surface conditions (visibility, water temperature and current); and
(d)(1)(vi) Maximum depth and bottom time for each diver.

(d)(2) For each dive outside the no-decompression limits, deeper than 100 fsw or using mixed gas, the following additional information shall be recorded and maintained:
(d)(2)(i) Depth-time and breathing gas profiles;
(d)(2)(ii) Decompression table designation (including modification); and
(d)(2)(iii) Elapsed time since last pressure exposure if less than 24 hours or repetitive dive designation for each diver.

(d)(3) For each dive in which decompression sickness is suspected or symptoms are evident, the following additional information shall be recorded and maintained:
(d)(3)(i) Description of decompression sickness symptoms (including depth and time of onset); and
(d)(3)(ii) Description and results of treatment.

(e) **Decompression procedure assessment** The employer shall:
(e)(1) Investigate and evaluate each incident of decompression sickness based on the recorded information, consideration of the past performance of decompression table used, and individual susceptibility;
(e)(2) Take appropriate corrective action to reduce the probability of recurrence of decompression sickness; and
(e)(3) Prepare a written evaluation of the decompression procedure assessment, including any corrective action taken, within 45 days of the incident of decompression sickness.

[42 FR 37668, July 22, 1977, as amended at 49 FR 18295, Apr. 30, 1984]

Specific Operations Procedures

§1910.424 OI SCUBA diving

(a) **General** Employers engaged in SCUBA diving shall comply with the following requirements, unless otherwise specified.

(b) **Limits** SCUBA diving shall not be conducted:
(b)(1) At depths deeper than 130 fsw;
(b)(2) At depths deeper than 100 fsw or outside the no-decompression limits unless a decompression chamber is ready for use;
(b)(3) Against currents exceeding one (1) knot unless line-tended; or
(b)(4) In enclosed or physically confining spaces unless line-tended.

(c) **Procedures**

(c)(1) A standby diver shall be available while a diver is in the water.

(c)(2) A diver shall be line-tended from the surface, or accompanied by another diver in the water in continuous visual contact during the diving operations.

(c)(3) A diver shall be stationed at the underwater point of entry when diving is conducted in enclosed or physically confining spaces.

(c)(4) A diver-carried reserve breathing gas supply shall be provided for each diver consisting of:
(c)(4)(i) A manual reserve (J valve); or
(c)(4)(ii) An independent reserve cylinder with a separate regulator or connected to the underwater breathing apparatus.

(c)(5) The valve of the reserve breathing gas supply shall be in the closed position prior to the dive.

§1910.425 Surface–supplied air diving

(a) **General** Employers engaged in surface-supplied air diving shall comply with the following requirements, unless otherwise specified.

(b) **Limits**

(b)(1) Surface-supplied air diving shall not be conducted at depths deeper than 190 fsw, except that dives with bottom times of 30 minutes or less may be conducted to depths of 220 fsw.

(b)(2) A decompression chamber shall be ready for use at the dive location for any dive outside the no-decompression limits or deeper than 100 fsw.

(b)(3) A bell shall be used for dives with an inwater decompression time greater than 120 minutes, except when heavy gear is worn or diving is conducted in physically confining spaces.

(c) **Procedures**

(c)(1) Each diver shall be continuously tended while in the water.

(c)(2) A diver shall be stationed at the underwater point of entry when diving is conducted in enclosed or physically confining spaces.

(c)(3) Each diving operation shall have a primary breathing gas supply sufficient to support divers for the duration of the planned dive including decompression.

(c)(4) For dives deeper than 100 fsw or outside the no-decompression limits:
(c)(4)(i) A separate dive team member shall tend each diver in the water;
(c)(4)(ii) A standby diver shall be available while a diver is in the water;
(c)(4)(iii) A diver-carried reserve breathing gas supply shall be provided for each diver except when heavy gear is worn; and
(c)(4)(iv) A dive-location reserve breathing gas supply shall be provided.

(c)(5) For heavy-gear diving deeper than 100 fsw or outside the no-decompression limits:
(c)(5)(i) An extra breathing gas hose capable of supplying breathing gas to the diver in the water shall be available to the standby diver.
(c)(5)(ii) An inwater stage shall be provided to divers in the water.

(c)(6) Except when heavy gear is worn or where physical space does not permit, a diver-carried reserve breathing gas supply shall be provided whenever the diver is prevented by the configuration of the dive area from ascending directly to the surface.

§1910.426 Mixed–gas diving

(a) **General** Employers engaged in mixed-gas diving shall comply with the following requirements, unless otherwise specified.

(b) **Limits** Mixed-gas diving shall be conducted only when:
(b)(1) A decompression chamber is ready for use at the dive location; and

(b)(1)(i) A bell is used at depths greater than 220 fsw or when the dive involves inwater decompression time of greater than 120 minutes, except when heavy gear is worn or when diving in physically confining spaces; or

(b)(1)(ii) A closed bell is used at depths greater than 300 fsw, except when diving is conducted in physically confining spaces.

(c) **Procedures**

(c)(1) A separate dive team member shall tend each diver in the water.

(c)(2) A standby diver shall be available while a diver is in the water.

(c)(3) A diver shall be stationed at the underwater point of entry when diving is (c)conducted in enclosed or physically confining spaces.

(c)(4) Each diving operation shall have a primary breathing gas supply sufficient to support divers for the duration of the planned dive including decompression.

(c)(5) Each diving operation shall have a dive-location reserve breathing gas supply.

(c)(6) When heavy gear is worn:
(c)(6)(i) An extra breathing gas hose capable of supplying breathing gas to the diver in the water shall be available to the standby diver; and
(c)(6)(ii) An inwater stage shall be provided to divers in the water.

(c)(7) An inwater stage shall be provided for divers without access to a bell for dives deeper than 100 fsw or outside the no-decompression limits.

(c)(8) When a closed bell is used, one dive team member in the bell shall be available and tend the diver in the water.

(c)(9) Except when heavy gear is worn or where physical space does not permit, a diver-carried reserve breathing gas supply shall be provided for each diver:
(c)(9)(i) Diving deeper than 100 fsw or outside the no-decompression limits; or
(c)(9)(ii) Prevented by the configuration of the dive area from directly ascending to the surface.

§1910.427 Liveboating

(a) **General** Employers engaged in diving operations involving liveboating shall comply with the following requirements.

(b) **Limits** Diving operations involving liveboating shall not be conducted:

(b)(1) With an inwater decompression time of greater than 120 minutes;

(b)(2) Using surface-supplied air at depths deeper than 190 fsw, except that dives with bottom times of 30 minutes or less may be conducted to depths of 220 fsw;

(b)(3) Using mixed gas at depths greater than 220 fsw;

(b)(4) In rough seas which significantly impede diver mobility or work function; or

(b)(5) In other than daylight hours.

(c) **Procedures**

(c)(1) The propeller of the vessel shall be stopped before the diver enters or exits the water.

(c)(2) A device shall be used which minimizes the possibility of entanglement of the diver's hose in the propeller of the vessel.

(c)(3) Two-way voice communication between the designated person-in-charge and the person controlling the vessel shall be available while the diver is in the water.

(c)(4) A standby diver shall be available while a diver is in the water.

(c)(5) A diver-carried reserve breathing gas supply shall be carried by each diver engaged in liveboating operations.

Equipment Procedures and Requirements

§1910.430 Equipment

(a) **General**

(a)(1) All employers shall comply with the following requirements, unless otherwise specified.

(a)(2) Each equipment modification, repair, test, calibration or maintenance service shall be recorded by means of a tagging or logging system, and include the date and nature of work performed, and the name or initials of the person performing the work.

(b) **Air compressor system**

(b)(1) Compressors used to supply air to the diver shall be equipped with a volume tank with a check valve on the inlet side, a pressure gauge, a relief valve, and a drain valve.

(b)(2) Air compressor intakes shall be located away from areas containing exhaust or other contaminants.

(b)(3) Respirable air supplied to a diver shall not contain:

(b)(3)(i) A level of carbon monoxide (CO) greater than 20 p/m;

(b)(3)(ii) A level of carbon dioxide (CO2) greater than 1,000 p/m;

(b)(3)(iii) A level of oil mist greater than 5 milligrams per cubic meter; or

(b)(3)(iv) A noxious or pronounced odor.

(b)(4) [OI] The output of air compressor systems shall be tested for air purity every 6 months by means of samples taken at the connection to the distribution system, except that non-oil lubricated compressors need not be tested for oil mist.

(c) **Breathing gas supply hoses**

(c)(1) **Breathing gas supply hoses shall:**

(c)(1)(i) Have a working pressure at least equal to the working pressure of the total breathing gas system;

(c)(1)(ii) Have a rated bursting pressure at least equal to 4 times the working pressure;

(c)(1)(iii) Be tested at least annually to 1.5 times their working pressure; and

(c)(1)(iv) Have their open ends taped, capped or plugged when not in use.

(c)(2) **Breathing gas supply hose connectors shall:**

(c)(2)(i) Be made of corrosion-resistant materials;

(c)(2)(ii) Have a working pressure at least equal to the working pressure of the hose to which they are attached; and

(c)(2)(iii) Be resistant to accidental disengagement.

(c)(3) **Umbilicals shall:**

(c)(3)(i) Be marked in 10-ft. increments to 100 feet beginning at the diver's end, and in 50 ft. increments thereafter;

(c)(3)(ii) Be made of kink-resistant materials; and

(c)(3)(iii) Have a working pressure greater than the pressure equivalent to the maximum depth of the dive (relative to the supply source) plus 100 psi.

(d) **Buoyancy control**

(d)(1) Helmets or masks connected directly to the dry suit or other buoyancy-changing equipment shall be equipped with an exhaust valve.

(d)(2) A dry suit or other buoyancy-changing connected to the helmet or mask shall be equipped

(d)(3) When used for SCUBA diving, a buoyancy con an inflation source separate from the breathing gas suppl

(d)(4) An inflatable flotation device capable of maintaining surface in a face-up position, having a manually activated infl independent of the breathing supply, an oral inflation device, and a valve shall be used for SCUBA diving.

(e) **Compressed gas cylinders** Compressed gas cylinders shall:

(e)(1) Be designed, constructed and maintained in accordance with th applicable provisions of 29 CFR §1910.101 and §1910.169 through §1910.171.

(e)(2) Be stored in a ventilated area and protected from excessive heat;

(e)(3) Be secured from falling; and

(e)(4) Have shut-off valves recessed into the cylinder or protected by a cap, except when in use or manifolded, or when used for SCUBA diving.

(f) **Decompression chambers**

(f)(1) Each decompression chamber manufactured after the effective date of this standard, shall be built and maintained in accordance with the ASME Code or equivalent.

(f)(2) Each decompression chamber manufactured prior to the effective date of this standard shall be maintained in conformity with the code requirements to which it was built, or equivalent.

(f)(3) Each decompression chamber shall be equipped with:

(f)(3)(i) Means to maintain the atmosphere below a level of 25 percent oxygen by volume;

(f)(3)(ii) Mufflers on intake and exhaust lines, which shall be regularly inspected and maintained;

(f)(3)(iii) Suction guards on exhaust line openings; and

(f)(3)(iv) A means for extinguishing fire, and shall be maintained to minimize sources of ignition and combustible material.

(g) **Gauges and timekeeping devices**

(g)(1) Gauges indicating diver depth which can be read at the dive location shall be used for all dives except SCUBA.

(g)(2) Each depth gauge shall be deadweight tested or calibrated against a master reference gauge every 6 months, and when there is a discrepancy greater than two percent (2 percent) of full scale between any two equivalent gauges.

(g)(3) A cylinder pressure gauge capable of being monitored by the diver during the dive shall be worn by each SCUBA diver.

(g)(4) A timekeeping device shall be available at each dive location.

(h) **Masks and helmets**

(h)(1) Surface-supplied air and mixed-gas masks and helmets shall have:

(h)(1)(i) A non-return valve at the attachment point between helmet or mask and hose which shall close readily and positively; and

(h)(1)(ii) An exhaust valve.

(h)(2) Surface-supplied air masks and helmets shall have a minimum ventilation rate capability of 4.5 acfm at any depth at which they are operated or the capability of maintaining the diver's inspired carbon dioxide partial pressure below 0.02 ATA when the diver is producing carbon dioxide at the rate of 1.6 standard liters per minute.

(i) **Oxygen safety**

(i)(1) Equipment used with oxygen or mixtures containing over forty percent (40%) by volume oxygen shall be designed for oxygen service.

(i)(2) Components (except umbilicals) exposed to oxygen or mixtures containing over forty percent (40%) by volume oxygen shall be cleaned of flammable materials before use.

(i)(3) Oxygen systems over 125 psig and compressed air systems over 500 psig shall have slow-opening shut-off valves.

(j) **Weights and harnesses**

(j)(1) Except when heavy gear is worn, divers shall be equipped with a weight belt or assembly capable of quick release.

(j)(2) Except when heavy gear is worn or in SCUBA diving, each diver shall wear a safety harness with:

(j)(2)(i) A positive buckling device;

(j)(2)(ii) An attachment point for the umbilical to prevent strain on the mask or helmet; and

(j)(2)(iii) A lifting point to distribute the pull force of the line over the diver's body.

[39 FR 23502, June 27, 1974, as amended at 49 FR 18295, Apr. 30, 1984; 51 FR 33033, Sept. 18, 1986]

Recordkeeping

§1910.440 Recordkeeping requirements

(a)(1) [Reserved]

(a)(2) The employer shall record the occurrence of any diving-related injury or illness which requires any dive team member to be hospitalized for 24 hours or more, specifying the circumstances of the incident and the extent of any injuries or illnesses.

(b) **Availability of records**

(b)(1) Upon the request of the Assistant Secretary of Labor for Occupational Safety and Health, or the Director, National Institute for Occupational Safety and Health, Department of Health and Human Services of their designees, the employer shall make available for inspection and copying any record or document required by this standard.

(b)(2) Records and documents required by this standard shall be provided upon request to employees, designated representatives, and the Assistant Secretary in accordance with 29 CFR §1910.1020 (a)–(e) and (g)–(i). Safe practices manuals (§1910.420), depth-time profiles (§1910.422), recordings of dives (§1910.423), decompression procedure assessment evaluations (§1910.423), and records of hospitalizations (§1910.440) shall be provided in the same manner as employee exposure records or analyses using exposure or medical records. Equipment inspections and testing records which pertain to employees (§1910.430) shall also be provided upon request to employees and their designated representatives.

(b)(3) Records and documents required by this standard shall be retained by the employer for the following period:

(b)(3)(i) [Reserved]

(b)(3)(ii) Safe practices manual (§1910.420)—current document only;

(b)(3)(iii) Depth-time profile (§1910.422)—until completion of the recording of dive, or until completion of decompression procedure assessment where there has been an incident of decompression sickness;

(b)(3)(iv) Recording of dive (§1910.423)—1 year, except 5 years where there has been an incident of decompression sickness;

(b)(3)(v) Decompression procedure assessment evaluations (§1910.423)—5 years;

(b)(3)(vi) Equipment inspections and testing records (§1910.430)—current entry or tag, or until equipment is withdrawn from service;

(b)(3)(vii) Records of hospitalizations (§1910.440)—5 years.

(b)(4) After the expiration of the retention period of any record required to be kept for five (5) years, the employer shall forward such records to the National Institute for Occupational Safety and Health, Department of Health and Human Services. The employer shall also comply with any additional requirements set forth at 29 CFR §1910.20(h).

(b)(5) [Reserved]

[42 FR 37668, July 22, 1977, as amended at 45 FR 35281, May 23, 1980; 47 FR 14706, Apr. 6, 1982; 51 FR 34562, Sept. 29, 1986; 61 FR 9242, Mar. 7, 1996; 71 FR 16672, Apr. 3, 2006; 76 FR 33607, June 8, 2011]

Subpart T to §1910 Appendix A Examples of conditions which may restrict or limit exposure to hyperbaric conditions

The following disorders may restrict or limit occupational exposure to hyperbaric conditions depending on severity, presence of residual effects, response to therapy, number of occurrences, diving mode, or degree and duration of isolation.

History of seizure disorder other than early febrile convulsions.
Malignancies (active) unless treated and without recurrence for 5 yrs.
Chronic inability to equalize sinus and/or middle ear pressure.
Cystic or cavitary disease of the lungs.
Impaired organ function caused by alcohol or drug use.
Conditions requiring continuous medication for control (e.g., antihistamines, steroids, barbiturates, moodaltering drugs, or insulin).
Meniere's disease.
Hemoglobinopathies.
Obstructive or restrictive lung disease.
Vestibular end organ destruction.
Pneumothorax.
Cardiac abnormalities (e.g., pathological heart block, valvular disease, intraventricular conduction defects other than isolated right bundle branch block, angina pectoris, arrhythmia, coronary artery disease).
Juxta-articular osteonecrosis.

Subpart T to §1910 Appendix B Guidelines for scientific diving

This Appendix contains guidelines that will be used in conjunction with §1910.401(a)(2)(iv) to determine those scientific diving programs which are exempt from the requirements for commercial diving. The guidelines are as follows:

1. The Diving Control Board consists of a majority of active scientific divers and has autonomous and absolute authority over the scientific diving program's operations.
2. The purpose of the project using scientific diving is the advancement of science; therefore, information and data resulting from the project are non-proprietary.
3. The tasks of a scientific diver are those of an observer and data gatherer. Construction and trouble-shooting tasks traditionally associated with commercial diving are not included within scientific diving.
4. Scientific divers, based on the nature of their activities, must use scientific expertise in studying the underwater environment and, therefore, are scientists or scientists in training.

Subpart T to §1910 Appendix C Alternative conditions under §1910.401(a)(3) for recreational diving instructors and diving guides

(Mandatory)

Paragraph (a)(3) of §1910.401 specifies that an employer of recreational diving instructors and diving guides (hereafter, "divers" or "employees") who complies with all of the conditions of this Appendix need not provide a decompression chamber for these divers as required under §1910.423(b)(2) or (c)(3) or §1910.426(b)(1).

1. Equipment Requirements for Rebreathers

(a) The employer must ensure that each employee operates the rebreather (i.e., semi-closed-circuit and closed-circuit self-contained underwater breathing apparatuses (hereafter, "SCUBAs")) according to the rebreather manufacturer's instructions.

(b) The employer must ensure that each rebreather has a counterlung that supplies a sufficient volume of breathing gas to their divers to sustain the divers' respiration rates, and contains a baffle system and/or other moisture separating system that keeps moisture from entering the scrubber.

(c) The employer must place a moisture trap in the breathing loop of the rebreather, and ensure that:

(i) The rebreather manufacturer approves both the moisture trap and its location in the breathing loop; and
(ii) Each employee uses the moisture trap according to the rebreather manufacturer's instructions.

(d) The employer must ensure that each rebreather has a continuously functioning moisture sensor, and that:

(i) The moisture sensor connects to a visual (e.g., digital, graphic, analog) or auditory (e.g., voice, pure tone) alarm that is readily detectable by the diver under the diving conditions in which the diver operates, and warns the diver of moisture in the breathing loop in sufficient time to terminate the dive and return safely to the surface; and
(ii) Each diver uses the moisture sensor according to the rebreather manufacturer's instructions.

(e) The employer must ensure that each rebreather contains a continuously functioning CO_2 sensor in the breathing loop, and that:

(i) The rebreather manufacturer approves the location of the CO_2 sensor in the breathing loop;
(ii) The CO_2 sensor is integrated with an alarm that operates in a visual (e.g., digital, graphic, analog) or auditory (e.g., voice, pure tone) mode that is readily detectable by each diver under the diving conditions in which the diver operates; and
(iii) The CO_2 alarm remains continuously activated when the inhaled CO_2 level reaches and exceeds 0.005 atmospheres absolute (ATA).

(f) Before each day's diving operations, and more often when necessary, the employer must calibrate the CO_2 sensor according to the sensor manufacturer's instructions, and ensure that:

(i) The equipment and procedures used to perform this calibration are accurate to within 10% of a CO_2 concentration of 0.005 ATA or less;
(ii) The equipment and procedures maintain this accuracy as required by the sensor manufacturer's instructions; and
(iii) The calibration of the CO_2 sensor is accurate to within 10% of a CO_2 concentration of 0.005 ATA or less.

(g) The employer must replace the CO_2 sensor when it fails to meet the accuracy requirements specified in paragraph 1(f)(iii) of this Appendix, and ensure that the replacement CO_2 sensor meets the accuracy requirements specified in paragraph 1(f)(iii) of this Appendix before placing the rebreather in operation.

(h) As an alternative to using a continuously functioning CO_2 sensor, the employer may use a schedule for replacing CO_2-sorbent material provided by the rebreather manufacturer. The employer may use such a schedule only when the rebreather manufacturer has developed it according to the canister-testing protocol specified below in Condition 11, and must use the canister within the temperature range for which the manufacturer conducted its scrubber canister tests following that protocol. Variations above or below the range are acceptable only after the manufacturer adds that lower or higher temperature to the protocol.

(i) When using CO_2-sorbent replacement schedules, the employer must ensure that each rebreather uses a manufactured (i.e., commercially pre-packed), disposable scrubber cartridge containing a CO_2-sorbent material that:

(i) Is approved by the rebreather manufacturer;
(ii) Removes CO_2 from the diver's exhaled gas; and
(iii) Maintains the CO_2 level in the breathable gas (i.e., the gas that a diver inhales directly from the regulator) below a partial pressure of 0.01 ATA.

(j) As an alternative to manufactured, disposable scrubber cartridges, the employer may fill CO_2 scrubber cartridges manually with CO_2-sorbent material when:

(i) The rebreather manufacturer permits manual filling of scrubber cartridges;
(ii) The employer fills the scrubber cartridges according to the rebreather manufacturer's instructions;
(iii) The employer replaces the CO_2-sorbent material using a replacement schedule developed under paragraph 1(h) of this Appendix; and
(iv) The employer demonstrates that manual filling meets the requirements specified in paragraph 1(i) of this Appendix.

(k) The employer must ensure that each rebreather has an information module that provides:

(i) A visual (e.g., digital, graphic, analog) or auditory (e.g., voice, pure tone) display that effectively warns the diver of solenoid failure (when the rebreather uses solenoids) and other electrical weaknesses or failures (e.g., low battery voltage);
(ii) For a semi-closed circuit rebreather, a visual display for the partial pressure of CO_2, or deviations above and below a preset CO_2 partial pressure of 0.005 ATA; and
(iii) For a closed-circuit rebreather, a visual display for: partial pressures of O_2 and CO_2, or deviations above and below a preset CO_2 partial pressure of 0.005 ATA and a preset O_2 partial pressure of 1.40 ATA or lower; gas temperature in the breathing loop; and water temperature.

(l) Before each day's diving operations, and more often when necessary, the employer must ensure that the electrical power supply and electrical and electronic circuits in each rebreather are operating as required by the rebreather manufacturer's instructions.

2. Special Requirements for Closed-Circuit Rebreathers

(a) The employer must ensure that each closed-circuit rebreather uses supply-pressure sensors for the O_2 and diluent (i.e., air or nitrogen) gases and continuously functioning sensors for detecting temperature in the inhalation side of the gas-loop and the ambient water.

(b) The employer must ensure that:

(i) At least two O_2 sensors are located in the inhalation side of the breathing loop; and
(ii) The O_2 sensors are: functioning continuously; temperature compensated; and approved by the rebreather manufacturer.

(c) Before each day's diving operations, and more often when necessary, the employer must calibrate O_2 sensors as required by the sensor manufacturer's instructions. In doing so, the employer must:

(i) Ensure that the equipment and procedures used to perform the calibration are accurate to within 1% of the O_2 fraction by volume;
(ii) Maintain this accuracy as required by the manufacturer of the calibration equipment;
(iii) Ensure that the sensors are accurate to within 1% of the O_2 fraction by volume;
(iv) Replace O_2 sensors when they fail to meet the accuracy requirements specified in paragraph 2(c)(iii) of this Appendix; and
(v) Ensure that the replacement O_2 sensors meet the accuracy requirements specified in paragraph 2(c)(iii) of this Appendix before placing a rebreather in operation.

(d) The employer must ensure that each closed-circuit rebreather has:

(i) A gas-controller package with electrically operated solenoid O_2-supply valves;
(ii) A pressure-activated regulator with a second-stage diluent-gas addition valve;
(iii) A manually operated gas-supply bypass valve to add O_2 or diluent gas to the breathing loop; and
(iv) Separate O_2 and diluent-gas cylinders to supply the breathing-gas mixture.

3. O_2 Concentration in the Breathing Gas

The employer must ensure that the fraction of O_2 in the nitrox breathing-gas mixture:

(a) Is greater than the fraction of O_2 in compressed air (i.e., exceeds 22% by volume);

(b) For open-circuit SCUBA, never exceeds a maximum fraction of breathable O_2 of 40% by volume or a maximum O_2 partial pressure of 1.40 ATA, whichever exposes divers to less O_2; and

(c) For a rebreather, never exceeds a maximum O_2 partial pressure of 1.40 ATA.

4. Regulating O_2 Exposures and Diving Depth

(a) Regarding O_2 exposure, the employer must:

(i) Ensure that the exposure of each diver to partial pressures of O_2 between 0.60 and 1.40 ATA does not exceed the 24-hour single-exposure time limits specified either by the 2001 National Oceanic and Atmospheric Administration Diving Manual (the "2001 NOAA Diving Manual"), or by the report entitled "Enriched Air Operations and Resource Guide" published in 1995 by the Professional Association of Diving Instructors (known commonly as the "1995 DSAT Oxygen Exposure Table"); and
(ii) Determine a diver's O_2 exposure duration using the diver's maximum O_2 exposure (partial pressure of O_2) during the dive and the total dive time (i.e., from the time the diver leaves the surface until the diver returns to the surface).

(b) Regardless of the diving equipment used, the employer must ensure that no diver exceeds a depth of 130 feet of sea water ("fsw") or a maximum O_2 partial pressure of 1.40 ATA, whichever exposes the diver to less O_2.

5. Use of No-Decompression Limits

(a) For diving conducted while using nitrox breathing-gas mixtures, the employer must ensure that each diver remains within the no-decompression limits specified for single and repetitive air diving and published in the 2001 NOAA Diving Manual or the report entitled "Development and Validation of No-Stop Decompression Procedures for Recreational Diving: The DSAT Recreational Dive Planner," published in 1994 by Hamilton Research Ltd. (known commonly as the "1994 DSAT No-Decompression Tables").

(b) An employer may permit a diver to use a dive-decompression computer designed to regulate decompression when the dive-decompression computer uses the no-decompression limits specified in paragraph 5(a) of this Appendix, and provides output that reliably represents those limits.

6. Mixing and Analyzing the Breathing Gas

(a) The employer must ensure that:

(i) Properly trained personnel mix nitrox-breathing gases, and that nitrogen is the only inert gas used in the breathing-gas mixture; and
(ii) When mixing nitrox-breathing gases, they mix the appropriate breathing gas before delivering the mixture to the breathing-gas cylinders, using the continuous-flow or partial-pressure mixing techniques specified in the 2001 NOAA Diving Manual, or using a filter-membrane system.

(b) Before the start of each day's diving operations, the employer must determine the O_2 fraction of the breathing-gas mixture using an O_2 analyzer. In doing so, the employer must:

(i) Ensure that the O_2 analyzer is accurate to within 1% of the O_2 fraction by volume.
(ii) Maintain this accuracy as required by the manufacturer of the analyzer.

(c) When the breathing gas is a commercially supplied nitrox breathing-gas mixture, the employer must ensure that the O_2 meets the medical USP specifications (Type I, Quality Verification Level A) or aviator's breathing-oxygen specifications (Type I, Quality Verification Level E) of CGA G–4.3–2000 ("Commodity Specification for Oxygen"). In addition, the commercial supplier must:

(i) Determine the O_2 fraction in the breathing-gas mixture using an analytic method that is accurate to within 1% of the O_2 fraction by volume;
(ii) Make this determination when the mixture is in the charged tank and after disconnecting the charged tank from the charging apparatus;
(iii) Include documentation of the O_2-analysis procedures and the O_2 fraction when delivering the charged tanks to the employer.

(d) Before producing nitrox breathing-gas mixtures using a compressor in which the gas pressure in any system component exceeds 125 pounds per square inch (psi), the:

(i) Compressor manufacturer must provide the employer with documentation that the compressor is suitable for mixing high-pressure air with the highest O_2 fraction used in the nitrox breathing-gas mixture when operated according to the manufacturer's operating and maintenance specifications;

(ii) Employer must comply with paragraph 6(e) of this Appendix, unless the compressor is rated for O_2 service and is oil-less or oil-free; and

(iii) Employer must ensure that the compressor meets the requirements specified in paragraphs (i)(1) and (i)(2) of §1910.430 whenever the highest O_2 fraction used in the mixing process exceeds 40%.

(e) Before producing nitrox breathing-gas mixtures using an oil-lubricated compressor to mix high-pressure air with O_2, and regardless of the gas pressure in any system component, the:

(i) Employer must use only uncontaminated air (i.e., air containing no hydrocarbon particulates) for the nitrox breathing-gas mixture;

(ii) Compressor manufacturer must provide the employer with documentation that the compressor is suitable for mixing the high-pressure air with the highest O_2 fraction used in the nitrox breathing-gas mixture when operated according to the manufacturer's operating and maintenance specifications;

(iii) Employer must filter the high-pressure air to produce O_2-compatible air;

(iv) The filter-system manufacturer must provide the employer with documentation that the filter system used for this purpose is suitable for producing O_2-compatible air when operated according to the manufacturer's operating and maintenance specifications; and

(v) Employer must continuously monitor the air downstream from the filter for hydrocarbon contamination.

(f) The employer must ensure that diving equipment using nitrox breathing-gas mixtures or pure O_2 under high pressure (i.e., exceeding 125 psi) conforms to the O_2-service requirements specified in paragraphs (i)(1) and (i)(2) of §1910.430.

7. Emergency Egress

(a) Regardless of the type of diving equipment used by a diver (i.e., open-circuit SCUBA or rebreathers), the employer must ensure that the equipment contains (or incorporates) an open-circuit emergency-egress system (a "bail-out" system) in which the second stage of the regulator connects to a separate supply of emergency breathing gas, and the emergency breathing gas consists of air or the same nitrox breathing-gas mixture used during the dive.

(b) As an alternative to the "bail-out" system specified in paragraph 7(a) of this Appendix, the employer may use:

(i) For open-circuit SCUBA, an emergency-egress system as specified in §1910.424(c)(4); or

(ii) For a semi-closed-circuit and closed-circuit rebreather, a system configured so that the second stage of the regulator connects to a reserve supply of emergency breathing gas.

(c) The employer must obtain from the rebreather manufacturer sufficient information to ensure that the bail-out system performs reliably and has sufficient capacity to enable the diver to terminate the dive and return safely to the surface.

8. Treating Diving-Related Medical Emergencies

(a) Before each day's diving operations, the employer must:

(i) Verify that a hospital, qualified health-care professionals, and the nearest Coast Guard Coordination Center (or an equivalent rescue service operated by a state, county, or municipal agency) are available to treat diving-related medical emergencies;

(ii) Ensure that each dive site has a means to alert these treatment resources in a timely manner when a diving-related medical emergency occurs; and

(iii) Ensure that transportation to a suitable decompression chamber is readily available when no decompression chamber is at the dive site, and that this transportation can deliver the injured diver to the decompression chamber within four (4) hours travel time from the dive site.

(b) The employer must ensure that portable O_2 equipment is available at the dive site to treat injured divers. In doing so, the employer must ensure that:

(i) The equipment delivers medical-grade O_2 that meets the requirements for medical USP oxygen (Type I, Quality Verification Level A) of CGA G-4.3-2000 ("Commodity Specification for Oxygen");

(ii) The equipment delivers this O_2 to a transparent mask that covers the injured diver's nose and mouth; and

(iii) Sufficient O_2 is available for administration to the injured diver from the time the employer recognizes the symptoms of a diving-related medical emergency until the injured diver reaches a decompression chamber for treatment.

(c) Before each day's diving operations, the employer must:

(i) Ensure that at least two attendants, either employees or non-employees, qualified in first-aid and administering O_2 treatment, are available at the dive site to treat diving-related medical emergencies; and

(ii) Verify their qualifications for this task.

9. Diving Logs and No-Decompression Tables

(a) Before starting each day's diving operations, the employer must:

(i) Designate an employee or a non-employee to make entries in a diving log; and

(ii) Verify that this designee understands the diving and medical terminology, and proper procedures, for making correct entries in the diving log.

(b) The employer must:

(i) Ensure that the diving log conforms to the requirements specified by paragraph (d) ("Record of dive") of §1910.423; and

(ii) Maintain a record of the dive according to §1910.440 ("Recordkeeping requirements").

(c) The employer must ensure that a hard-copy of the no-decompression tables used for the dives (as specified in paragraph 6(a) of this Appendix) is readily available at the dive site, whether or not the divers use dive-decompression computers.

10. Diver Training

The employer must ensure that each diver receives training that enables the diver to perform work safely and effectively while using open-circuit SCUBAs or rebreathers supplied with nitrox breathing-gas mixtures. Accordingly, each diver must be able to demonstrate the ability to perform critical tasks safely and effectively, including, but not limited to: recognizing the effects of breathing excessive CO_2 and O_2; taking appropriate action after detecting excessive levels of CO_2 and O_2; and properly evaluating, operating, and maintaining their diving equipment under the diving conditions they encounter.

11. Testing Protocol for Determining the CO_2 Limits of Rebreather Canisters

(a) The employer must ensure that the rebreather manufacturer has used the following procedures for determining that the CO_2-sorbent material meets the specifications of the sorbent material's manufacturer:

(i) The North Atlantic Treating Organization CO_2 absorbent-activity test;

(ii) The RoTap shaker and nested-sieves test;

(iii) The Navy Experimental Diving Unit ("NEDU")-derived Schlegel test; and

(iv) The NEDU MeshFit software.

(b) The employer must ensure that the rebreather manufacturer has applied the following canister-testing materials, methods, procedures, and statistical analyses:

(i) Use of a nitrox breathing-gas mixture that has an O_2 fraction maintained at 0.28 (equivalent to 1.4 ATA of O_2 at 130 fsw, the maximum O_2 concentration permitted at this depth);

(ii) While operating the rebreather at a maximum depth of 130 fsw, use of a breathing machine to continuously ventilate the rebreather with breathing gas that is at 100% humidity and warmed to a temperature of 98.6 degrees F (37 degrees C) in the heating-humidification chamber;

(iii) Measurement of the O_2 concentration of the inhalation breathing gas delivered to the mouthpiece;

(iv) Testing of the canisters using the three ventilation rates listed in Table I below (with the required breathing-machine tidal volumes and frequencies, and CO_2-injection rates, provided for each ventilation rate):

Table I—Canister Testing Parameters

Ventilation rates (Lpm, ATPS[1])	Breathing machine tidal volumes (L)	Breathing machine frequencies (breaths per min.)	CO_2 injection rates (Lpm, STPD[2])
22.5	1.5	15	0.90
40.0	2.0	20	1.35
62.5	2.5	25	2.25

[1] ATPS means ambient temperature and pressure, saturated with water.

[2] STPD means standard temperature and pressure, dry; the standard temperature is 32 degrees F (0 degrees C).

(v) When using a work rate (i.e., breathing-machine tidal volume and frequency) other than the work rates listed in the table above, addition of the appropriate combinations of ventilation rates and CO_2-injection rates;

(vi) Performance of the CO_2 injection at a constant (steady) and continuous rate during each testing trial;
(vii) Determination of canister duration using a minimum of four (4) water temperatures, including 40, 50, 70, and 90 °F (4.4, 10.0, 21.1, and 32.2 °C, respectively);
(viii) Monitoring of the breathing-gas temperature at the rebreather mouthpiece (at the "chrome T" connector), and ensuring that this temperature conforms to the temperature of a diver's exhaled breath at the water temperature and ventilation rate used during the testing trial;[1]
(ix) Implementation of at least eight (8) testing trials for each combination of temperature and ventilation-CO_2-injection rates (for example, eight testing trials at 40 degrees F using a ventilation rate of 22.5 Lpm at a CO_2-injection rate of 0.90 Lpm);
(x) Allowing the water temperature to vary no more than ± 2.0 °F (± 1.0 °C) between each of the eight testing trials, and no more than ± 1.0 °F (± 0.5 °C) within each testing trial;
(xi) Use of the average temperature for each set of eight testing tria... the statistical analysis of the testing-trial results, with the testing-trial results being the time taken for the inhaled breathing gas to reach 0.005 ATA of CO_2 (i.e., the canister-duration results);
(xii) Analysis of the canister-duration results using the repeated-measures statistics described in NEDU Report 2–99;
(xiii) Specification of the replacement schedule for the CO_2-sorbent materials in terms of the lower prediction line (or limit) of the 95 % confidence interval; and
(xiv) Derivation of replacement schedules only by interpolating among, but not by extrapolating beyond, the depth, water temperatures, and exercise levels used during canister testing.

[69 FR 7363, Feb. 17, 2004]

---

[1] NEDU can provide the manufacturer with information on the temperature of a diver's exhaled breath at various water temperatures and ventilation rates, as well as techniques and procedures used to maintain these temperatures during the testing trials.

29 CFR PART 1910 Subpart U–Y
[Reserved]

§191.901–§1910.999
[Reserved]

This page intentionally left blank.

29 CFR PART 1910 Subpart Z
Toxic and Hazardous Substances

Section Contents

Subpart Z—Toxic and Hazardous Substances

Authority: Secs. 4, 6, 8 of the Occupational Safety and Health Act of 1970 (29 U.S.C. 653, 655, 657); Secretary of Labor's Order No. 12-71 (36 FR 8754), 8-76 (41 FR 25059), 9-83 (48 FR 35736), 1-90 (55 FR 9033), 6-96 (62 FR 111), 3-2000 (65 FR 50017), 5-2002 (67 FR 65008), 5-2007 (72 FR 31160), 4-2010 (75 FR 55355), or 1-2012 (77 FR 3912), as applicable; and 29 CFR part 1911. All of subpart Z issued under section 6(b) of the Occupational Safety and Health Act of 1970, except those substances that have exposure limits listed in Tables Z-1, Z-2, and Z-3 of 29 CFR 1910.1000. The latter were issued under section 6(a) (29 U.S.C. 655(a)).
Section 1910.1000, Tables Z-1, Z-2 and Z-3 also issued under 5 U.S.C. 553, but not under 29 CFR part 1911 except for the arsenic (organic compounds), benzene, cotton dust, and chromium (VI) listings.
Section 1910.1001 also issued under section 107 of the Contract Work Hours and Safety Standards Act (40 U.S.C. 3704) and 5 U.S.C. 553.
Section 1910.1002 also issued under 5 U.S.C. 553, but not under 29 U.S.C. 655 or 29 CFR part 1911.
Sections 1910.1018, 1910.1029, and 1910.1200 also issued under 29 U.S.C. 653.
Section 1910.1030 also issued under Pub. L. 106-430, 114 Stat. 1901.
Section 1910.1201 also issued under 49 U.S.C. 1801-1819 and 5 U.S.C. 553.

§1910.1000
Air contaminants

An employee's exposure to any substance listed in Tables Z–1, Z–2, or Z–3 of this Section shall be limited in accordance with the requirements of the following paragraphs of this Section.

(a) **Table Z–1**

(a)(1) **Substances with limits preceded by "C"—Ceiling Values** An employee's exposure to any substance in Table Z–1, the exposure limit of which is preceded by a "C", shall at no time exceed the exposure limit given for that substance. If instantaneous monitoring is not feasible, then the ceiling shall be assessed as a 15-minute time weighted average exposure which shall not be exceeded at any time during the working day.

(a)(2) **Other substances–8-hour Time Weighted Averages** An employee's exposure to any substance in Table Z–1, the exposure limit of which is not preceded by a "C", shall not exceed the 8-hour Time Weighted Average given for that substance in any 8-hour work shift of a 40-hour work week.

(b) **Table Z–2** An employee's exposure to any substance listed in Table Z–2 shall not exceed the exposure limits specified as follows:

(b)(1) **8-hour time weighted averages** An employee's exposure to any substance listed in Table Z–2, in any 8-hour work shift of a 40-hour work week, shall not exceed the 8-hour time weighted average limit given for that substance in Table Z–2.

(b)(2) **Acceptable ceiling concentrations** An employee's exposure to a substance listed in Table Z–2 shall not exceed at any time during an 8-hour shift the acceptable ceiling concentration limit given for the substance in the table, except for a time period, and up to a concentration not exceeding the maximum duration and concentration allowed in the column under "acceptable maximum peak above the acceptable ceiling concentration for an 8-hour shift."

(b)(3) **Example** During an 8-hour work shift, an employee may be exposed to a concentration of Substance A (with a 10 ppm TWA, 25 ppm ceiling and 50 ppm peak) above 25 ppm (but never above 50 ppm) only for a maximum period of 10 minutes. Such exposure must be compensated by exposures to concentrations less than 10 ppm so that the cumulative exposure for the entire 8-hour work shift does not exceed a weighted average of 10 ppm.

(c) **Table Z–3** An employee's exposure to any substance listed in Table Z–3, in any 8-hour work shift of a 40-hour work week, shall not exceed the 8-hour time weighted average limit given for that substance in the table.

(d) **Computation formula** The computation formula which shall apply to employee exposure to more than one substance for which 8-hour time weighted averages are listed in Subpart Z of 29 CFR Part 1910 in order to determine whether an employee is exposed over the regulatory limit is as follows:

(d)(1)(i) The cumulative exposure for an 8-hour work shift shall be computed as follows:

$$E = (C_aT_a+C_bT_b+...C_nT_n) \div 8$$

Where:

E is the equivalent exposure for the working shift;

C is the concentration during any period of time T where the concentration remains constant;

T is the duration in hours of the exposure at the concentration C.

The value of E shall not exceed the 8-hour time weighted average specified in Subpart Z of 29 CFR Part 1910 for the substance involved.

(d)(1)(ii) To illustrate the formula prescribed in paragraph (d)(1)(i) of this Section, assume that Substance A has an 8-hour time weighted average limit of 100 ppm noted in Table Z–1. Assume that an employee is subject to the following exposure:

Two hours exposure at 150 ppm

Two hours exposure at 75 ppm

Four hours exposure at 50 ppm

Substituting this information in the formula, we have

$$(2 \times 150 + 2 \times 75 + 4 \times 50) \div 8 = 81.25 \text{ ppm}$$

Since 81.25 ppm is less than 100 ppm, the 8-hour time weighted average limit, the exposure is acceptable.

(d)(2)(i) In case of a mixture of air contaminants an employer shall compute the equivalent exposure as follows:

$$E_m = (C_1 \div L_1 + C_2 \div L_2) +...(C_n \div L_n)$$

Where:

E_m is the equivalent exposure for the mixture.

C is the concentration of a particular contaminant.

L is the exposure limit for that substance specified in Subpart Z of 29 CFR Part §1910.

The value of E_m shall not exceed unity (1).

(d)(2)(ii) To illustrate the formula prescribed in paragraph (d)(2)(i) of this Section, consider the following exposures:

Air contaminants

Z

Toxic and Hazardous Substances

Substance	Actual concentration of 8-hour exposure (ppm)	8-hour TWA PEL (ppm)
B	500	1,000
C	45	200
D	40	200

Substituting in the formula, we have:

$E_m = 500 \div 1{,}000 + 45 \div 200 + 40 \div 200$

$E_m = 0.500 + 0.225 + 0.200$

$E_m = 0.925$

Since E_m is less than unity (1), the exposure combination is within acceptable limits.

(e) To achieve compliance with paragraphs (a) through (d) of this Section, administrative or engineering controls must first be determined and implemented whenever feasible. When such controls are not feasible to achieve full compliance, protective equipment or any other protective measures shall be used to keep the exposure of employees to air contaminants within the limits prescribed in this Section. Any equipment and/or technical measures used for this purpose must be approved for each particular use by a competent industrial hygienist or other technically qualified person. Whenever respirators are used, their use shall comply with §1910.134.

Table Z–1 [OI]
Limits for Air Contaminants

Substance	CAS No. (c)	ppm (a)[1]	mg/m³(b)[1]	Skin designation
Acetaldehyde	75–07–0	200	360	
Acetic acid	64–19–7	10	25	
Acetic anhydride	108–24–7	5	20	
Acetone	67–64–1	1000	2400	
Acetonitrile	75–05–8	40	70	
2-Acetylaminofluorine; see §1910.1014	53–96–3			
Acetylene dichloride; see 1,2-Dichloroethylene				
Acetylene tetrabromide	79–27–6	1	14	
Acrolein	107–02–8	0.1	0.25	
Acrylamide	79–06–1		0.3	X
Acrylonitrile; see §1910.1045	107–13–1			
Aldrin	309–00–2		0.25	X
Allyl alcohol	107–18–6	2	5	X
Allyl chloride	107–05–1	1	3	
Allyl glycidyl ether (AGE)	106–92–3	(C)10	(C)45	
Allyl propyl disulfide	2179–59–1	2	12	
alpha-Alumina Total dust Respirable fraction	1344–28–1		 15 5	
Aluminum, metal (as Al) Total dust Respirable fraction	7429–90–5		 15 5	
4-Aminodiphenyl; see §1910.1011	92–67–1			
2-Aminoethanol; see Ethanolamine				
2-Aminopyridine	504–29–0	0.5	2	
Ammonia	7664–41–7	50	35	
Ammonium sulfamate Total dust Respirable fraction	7773–06–0		 15 5	
n-Amyl acetate	628–63–7	100	525	
sec-Amyl acetate	626–38–0	125	650	
Aniline and homologs	62–53–3	5	19	X
Anisidine (o-, p-isomers)	29191–52–4		0.5	X
Antimony and compounds (as Sb)	7440–36–0		0.5	
ANTU (alpha Naphthylthiourea)	86–88–4		0.3	
Arsenic, inorganic compounds (as As); see §1910.1018	7440–38–2			
Arsenic, organic compounds (as As)	7440–38–2		0.5	
Arsine	7784–42–1	0.05	0.2	
Asbestos; see §1910.1001	([4])			
Azinphos-methyl	86–50–0		0.2	X
Barium, soluble compounds (as Ba)	7440–39–3		0.5	
Barium sulfate Total dust Respirable fraction	7727–43–7		 15 5	
Benomyl Total dust Respirable fraction	17804–35–2		 15 5	

[OI] indicates an OSHA Letter of Interpretation exists for this specific reference. Please see www.oshainterpretation.us for details.

Substance	CAS No. (c)	ppm (a)[1]	mg/m³(b)[1]	Skin designation
Benzene; see §1910.1028 See Table Z–2 for the limits applicable in the operations or sectors excluded in §1910.1028[d]	71–43–2			
Benzidine; see §1910.1010	92–87–5			
p-Benzoquinone; see Quinone				
Benzo(a)pyrene; see Coal tar pitch volatiles				
Benzoyl peroxide	94–36–0		5	
Benzyl chloride	100–44–7	1	5	
Beryllium and beryllium compounds (as Be)	7440–41–7		([2])	
Biphenyl; see Diphenyl				
Bismuth telluride, Undoped Total dust Respirable fraction	1304–82–1		 15 5	
Boron oxide Total dust	1303–86–2		 15	
Boron trifluoride	7637–07–2	(C)1	(C)3	
Bromine	7726–95–6	0.1	0.7	
Bromoform	75–25–2	0.5	5	X
Butadiene (1,3-Butadiene); See 29 CFR §1910.1051; 29 CFR §1910.19(l)	106–99–0	1 ppm/ 5 ppmSTEL		
Butanethiol; see Butyl mercaptan				
2-Butanone (Methyl ethyl ketone)	78–93–3	200	590	
2-Butoxyethanol	111–76–2	50	240	X
n-Butyl-acetate	123–86–4	150	710	
sec-Butyl acetate	105–45–4	200	950	
tert-Butyl acetate	540–88–5	200	950	
n-Butyl alcohol	71–36–3	100	300	
sec-Butyl alcohol	78–92–2	150	450	
tert-Butyl alcohol	75–65–0	100	300	
Butylamine	109–73–9	(C)5	(C)15	X
tert-Butyl chromate (as CrO_3); see §1910.1026[6]	1189–85–1			
n-Butyl glycidyl ether (BGE)	2426–08–6	50	270	
Butyl mercaptan	109–79–5	10	35	
p-tert-Butyltoluene	98–51–1	10	60	
Cadmium (as Cd); see §1910.1027	7440–43–9			
Calcium carbonate Total dust Total dust	1317–65–3		 15 5	
Calcium hydroxide Total dust Respirable fraction	1305–62–0		 15 5	
Calcium oxide	1305–78–8		5	
Calcium silicate Total dust Respirable fraction	1344–95–2		 15 5	
Calcium sulfate Total dust Respirable fraction	7778–18–9		 15 5	
Camphor, synthetic	76–22–2		2	
Carbaryl (Sevin)	63–25–2		5	
Carbon black	1333–86–4		3.5	
Carbon dioxide	124–38–9	5000	9000	
Carbon disulfide	75–15–0		([2])	
Carbon monoxide	630–08–0	50	55	
Carbon tetrachloride	56–23–5		([2])	
Cellulose Total dust Respirable fraction	9004–34–6		 15 5	
Note: Table data continues on next page.				

Substance	CAS No. (c)	ppm (a)[1]	mg/m3(b)[1]	Skin designation
Chlordane	57–74–9		0.5	X
Chlorinated camphene	8001–35–2		0.5	X
Chlorinated diphenyl oxide	55720–99–5		0.5	
Chlorine	7782–50–5	(c)1	(c)3	
Chlorine dioxide	10049–04–4	0.1	0.3	
Chlorine trifluoride	7790–91–2	(C)0.1	(C)0.4	
Chloroacetaldehyde	107–20–0	(C)1	(C)3	
a-Chloroacetophenone (Phenacyl chloride)	532–27–4	0.05	0.3	
Chlorobenzene	108–90–7	75	350	
o-Chlorobenzylidene malononitrile	2698–41–1	0.05	0.4	
Chlorobromomethane	74–97–5	200	1050	
2-Chloro-1,3-butadiene; see beta-Chloroprene				
Chlorodiphenyl (42% Chlorine) (PCB)	53469–21–9		1	X
Chlorodiphenyl (54% Chlorine) (PCB)	11097–69–1		0.5	X
1-Chloro-2,3-epoxypropane; see Epichlorohydrin				
2-Chloroethanol; see Ethylene chlorohydrin				
Chloroethylene; see Vinyl chloride				
Chloroform (Trichloromethane)	67–66–3	(C)50	(C)240	
bis(Chloromethyl) ether; see §1910.1008	542–88–1			
Chloromethyl methyl ether; see §1910.1006	107–30–2			
1-Chloro-1-nitropropane	600–25–9	20	100	
Chloropicrin	76–06–2	0.1	0.7	
beta-Chloroprene	126–99–8	25	90	X
2-Chloro-6-(trichloromethyl) pyridine Total dust Respirable fraction	1929–82–4		 15 5	
Chromium (II) compounds (as Cr)	7440–47–3		0.5	
Chromium (III) compounds (as Cr)	7440–47–3		0.5	
Chromium (VI) compounds; See §1910.1026[5]				
Chromium metal and insol. salts (as Cr)	7440–47–3		1	
Chrysene; see Coal tar pitch volatiles				
Clopidol Total dust Respirable fraction	2971–90–6		 15 5	
Coal dust (less than 5% SiO_2), respirable fraction			([3])	
Coal dust (greater than or equal to 5% SiO_2), respirable fraction			([3])	
Coal tar pitch volatiles (benzene soluble fraction), anthracene, BaP, phenanthrene, acridine, chrysene, pyrene	65966–93–2		0.2	
Cobalt metal, dust, and fume (as Co)	7440–48–4		0.1	
Coke oven emissions; see §1910.1029				
Copper Fume (as Cu) Dusts and mists (as Cu)	7440–50–8		 0.1 1	
Cotton dust[e]; see §1910.1043			1	
Crag herbicide (Sesone) Total dust Respirable fraction	136–78–7		 15 5	
Cresol, all isomers	1319–77–3	5	22	X
Crotonaldehyde	123–73–9; 4170–30–3	2	6	
Cumene	98–82–8	50	245	X
Cyanides (as CN)	([4])		5	X
Cyclohexane	110–82–7	300	1050	
Cyclohexanol	108–93–0	50	200	
Cyclohexanone	108–94–1	50	200	
Cyclohexene	110–83–8	300	1015	

Substance	CAS No. (c)	ppm (a)[1]	mg/m^3(b)[1]	Skin designation
Cyclopentadiene	542–92–7	75	200	
2,4-D (Dichlorophenoxyacetic acid)	94–75–7		10	
Decaborane	17702–41–9	0.05	0.3	X
Demeton (Systox)	8065–48–3		0.1	X
Diacetone alcohol (4-Hydroxy-4-methyl-2-pentanone)	123–42–2	50	240	
1,2-Diaminoethane; see Ethylenediamine				
Diazomethane	334–88–3	0.2	0.4	
Diborane	19287–45–7	0.1	0.1	
1,2-Dibromo-3-chloropropane (DBCP); see §1910.1044	96–12–8			
1,2-Dibromoethane; see Ethylene dibromide				
Dibutyl phosphate	107–66–4	1	5	
Dibutyl phthalate	84–74–2		5	
o-Dichlorobenzene	95–50–1	(C)50	(C)300	
p-Dichlorobenzene	106–46–7	75	450	
3,'-Dichlorobenzidine; see §1910.1007	91–94–1			
Dichlorodifluoromethane	75–71–8	1000	4950	
1,3-Dichloro-5,5-dimethyl hydantoin	118–52–5		0.2	
Dichlorodiphenyltrichloroethane (DDT)	50–29–3		1	X
1,1-Dichloroethane	75–34–3	100	400	
1,2-Dichloroethane; see Ethylene dichloride				
1,2-Dichloroethylene	540–59–0	200	790	
Dichloroethyl ether	111–44–4	(C)15	(C)90	X
Dichloromethane; see Methylene chloride				
Dichloromonofluoromethane	75–43–4	1000	4200	
1,1-Dichloro-1-nitroethane	594–72–9	(C)10	(C)60	
1,2-Dichloropropane; see Propylene dichloride				
Dichlorotetrafluoroethane	76–14–2	1000	7000	
Dichlorvos (DDVP)	62–73–7		1	X
Dicyclopentadienyl iron Total dust Respirable fraction	102–54–5		 15 5	
Dieldrin	60–57–1		0.25	X
Diethylamine	109–89–7	25	75	
2-Diethylaminoethanol	100–37–8	10	50	X
Diethyl ether; see Ethyl ether				
Difluorodibromomethane	75–61–6	100	860	
Diglycidyl ether (DGE)	2238–07–5	(C)0.5	(C)2.8	
Dihydroxybenzene; see Hydroquinone				
Diisobutyl ketone	108–83–8	50	290	
Diisopropylamine	108–18–9	5	20	X
4-Dimethylaminoazobenzene; see §1910.1015	60–11–7			
Dimethoxymethane; see Methylal				
Dimethyl acetamide	127–19–5	10	35	X
Dimethylamine	124–40–3	10	18	
Dimethylaminobenzene; see Xylidine				
Dimethylaniline (N,N-Dimethylaniline)	121–69–7	5	25	X
Dimethylbenzene; see Xylene				
Dimethyl-1,2-dibromo-2,2-dichloroethyl phosphate	300–76–5		3	
Dimethylformamide	68–12–2	10	30	X
2,6-Dimethyl-4-heptanone; see Diisobutyl ketone				
1,1-Dimethylhydrazine	57–14–7	0.5	1	X
Dimethylphthalate	131–11–3		5	

Note: Table data continues on next page.

Air contaminants

Z

Toxic and Hazardous Substances

Substance	CAS No. (c)	ppm (a)[1]	mg/m³(b)[1]	Skin designation
Dimethyl sulfate	77–78–1	1	5	X
Dinitrobenzene (all isomers) (ortho) (meta) (para)	 528–29–0 99–65–0 100–25–4		1	X
Dinitro-o-cresol	534–52–1		0.2	X
Dinitrotoluene	25321–14–6		1.5	X
Dioxane (Diethylene dioxide)	123–91–1	100	360	X
Diphenyl (Biphenyl)	92–52–4	0.2	1	
Diphenylmethane diisocyanate; see Methylene bisphenyl isocyanate				
Dipropylene glycol methyl ether	34590–94–8	100	600	X
Di-sec octyl phthalate (Di-(2-ethylhexyl) phthalate)	117–81–7		5	
Emery	12415–34–8			
Total dust			15	
Respirable fraction			5	
Endrin	72–20–8		0.1	X
Epichlorohydrin	106–89–8	5	19	X
EPN	2104–64–5		0.5	X
1,2-Epoxypropane; see Propylene oxide				
2,3-Epoxy-1-propanol; see Glycidol				
Ethanethiol; see Ethyl mercaptan				
Ethanolamine	141–43–5	3	6	
2-Ethoxyethanol (Cellosolve)	110–80–5	200	740	X
2-Ethoxyethyl acetate (Cellosolve acetate)	111–15–9	100	540	X
Ethyl acetate	141–78–6	400	1400	
Ethyl acrylate	140–88–5	25	100	X
Ethyl alcohol (Ethanol)	64–17–5	1000	1900	
Ethylamine	75–04–7	10	18	
Ethyl amyl ketone (5-Methyl-3-heptanone)	541–85–5	25	130	
Ethyl benzene	100–41–4	100	435	
Ethyl bromide	74–96–4	200	890	
Ethyl butyl ketone (3-Heptanone)	106–35–4	50	230	
Ethyl chloride	75–00–3	1000	2600	
Ethyl ether	60–29–7	400	1200	
Ethyl formate	109–94–4	100	300	
Ethyl mercaptan	75–08–1	(C)10	(C)25	
Ethyl silicate	78–10–4	100	850	
Ethylene chlorohydrin	107–07–3	5	16	X
Ethylenediamine	107–15–3	10	25	
Ethylene dibromide	106–93–4		([2])	
Ethylene dichloride (1,2-Dichloroethane)	107–06–2		([2])	
Ethylene glycol dinitrate	628–96–6	(C)0.2	(C)1	X
Ethylene glycol methyl acetate; see Methyl cellosolve acetate				
Ethyleneimine; see §1910.1012	151–56–4			
Ethylene oxide; see §1910.1047	75–21–8			
Ethylidene chloride; see 1,1-Dichloroethane				
N-Ethylmorpholine	100–74–3	20	94	X
Ferbam Total dust	14484–64–1		 15	
Ferrovanadium dust	12604–58–9		1	
Fluorides (as F)	([4])		2.5	
Fluorine	7782–41–4	0.1	0.2	
Fluorotrichloromethane (Trichlorofluoromethane)	75–69–4	1000	5600	
Formaldehyde; see §1910.1048	50–00–0			

Substance	CAS No. (c)	ppm (a)[1]	mg/m³(b)[1]	Skin designation
Formic acid	64–18–6	5	9	
Furfural	98–01–1	5	20	X
Furfuryl alcohol	98–00–0	50	200	
Grain dust (oat, wheat, barley)			10	
Glycerin (mist) Total dust Respirable fraction	56–81–5		 15 5	
Glycidol	556–52–5	50	150	
Glycol monoethyl ether; see 2-Ethoxyethanol				
Graphite, natural, respirable dust	7782–42–5		([3])	
Graphite, synthetic Total dust Respirable fraction			 15 5	
Guthion; see Azinphos methyl				
Gypsum Total dust Respirable fraction	13397–24–5		 15 5	
Hafnium	7440–58–6		0.5	
Heptachlor	76–44–8		0.5	X
Heptane (n-Heptane)	142–82–5	500	2000	
Hexachloroethane	67–72–1	1	10	X
Hexachloronaphthalene	1335–87–1		0.2	X
n-Hexane	110–54–3	500	1800	
2-Hexanone (Methyl n-butyl ketone)	591–78–6	100	410	
Hexone (Methyl isobutyl ketone)	108–10–1	100	410	
sec-Hexyl acetate	108–84–9	50	300	
Hydrazine	302–01–2	1	1.3	X
Hydrogen bromide	10035–10–6	3	10	
Hydrogen chloride	7647–01–0	(C)5	(C)7	
Hydrogen cyanide	74–90–8	10	11	X
Hydrogen fluoride (as F)	7664–39–3		([2])	
Hydrogen peroxide	7722–84–1	1	1.4	
Hydrogen selenide (as Se)	7783–07–5	0.05	0.2	
Hydrogen sulfide	7783–06–4		([2])	
Hydroquinone	123–31–9		2	
Iodine	7553–56–2	(C)0.1	(C)1	
Iron oxide fume	1309–37–1		10	
Isoamyl acetate	123–92–2	100	525	
Isoamyl alcohol (primary and secondary)	123–51–3	100	360	
Isobutyl acetate	110–19–0	150	700	
Isobutyl alcohol	78–83–1	100	300	
Isophorone	78–59–1	25	140	
Isopropyl acetate	108–21–4	250	950	
Isopropyl alcohol	67–63–0	400	980	
Isopropylamine	75–31–0	5	12	
Isopropyl ether	108–20–3	500	2100	
Isopropyl glycidyl ether (IGE)	4016–14–2	50	240	
Kaolin Total dust Respirable fraction	1332–58–7		 15 5	
Ketene	463–51–4	0.5	0.9	
Lead, inorganic (as Pb); see §1910.1025	7439–92–1			
Limestone Total dust Respirable fraction	1317–65–3		 15 5	

Note: Table data continues on next page.

Air contaminants

Z

Toxic and Hazardous Substances

Substance	CAS No. (c)	ppm (a)[1]	mg/m³(b)[1]	Skin designation
Lindane	58–89–9		0.5	X
Lithium hydride	7580–67–8		0.025	
L.P.G. (Liquefied petroleum gas)	68476–85–7	1000	1800	
Magnesite Total dust Respirable fraction	546–93–0		 15 5	
Magnesium oxide fume Total particulate	1309–48–4		 15	
Malathion Total dust	121–75–5		 15	 X
Maleic anhydride	108–31–6	0.25	1	
Manganese compounds (as Mn)	7439–96–5		(C)5	
Manganese fume (as Mn)	7439–96–5		(C)5	
Marble Total dust Respirable fraction	1317–65–3		 15 5	
Mercury (aryl and inorganic) (as Hg)	7439–97–6		([2])	
Mercury (organo) alkyl compounds (as Hg)	7439–97–6		([2])	
Mercury (vapor) (as Hg)	7439–97–6		([2])	
Mesityl oxide	141–79–7	25	100	
Methanethiol; see Methyl mercaptan				
Methoxychlor Total dust	72–43–5		 15	
2-Methoxyethanol (Methyl cellosolve)	109–86–4	25	80	X
2-Methoxyethyl acetate (Methyl cellosolve acetate)	110–49–6	25	120	X
Methyl acetate	79–20–9	200	610	
Methyl acetylene (Propyne)	74–99–7	1000	1650	
Methyl acetylene-propadiene mixture (MAPP)		1000	1800	
Methyl acrylate	96–33–3	10	35	X
Methylal (Dimethoxy-methane)	109–87–5	1000	3100	
Methyl alcohol	67–56–1	200	260	
Methylamine	74–89–5	10	12	
Methyl amyl alcohol; see Methyl isobutyl carbinol				
Methyl n-amyl ketone	110–43–0	100	465	
Methyl bromide	74–83–9	(C)20	(C)80	X
Methyl butyl ketone; see 2-Hexanone				
Methyl cellosolve; see 2-Methoxyethanol				
Methyl cellosolve acetate; see 2-Methoxyethyl acetate				
Methyl chloride	74–87–3		([2])	
Methyl chloroform (1,1,1-Trichloroethane)	71–55–6	350	1900	
Methylcyclohexane	108–87–2	500	2000	
Methylcyclohexanol	25639–42–3	100	470	
o-Methylcyclohexanone	583–60–8	100	460	X
Methylene chloride	75–09–2		([2])	
Methyl ethyl ketone (MEK); see 2-Butanone				
Methyl formate	107–31–3	100	250	
Methyl hydrazine (Monomethyl hydrazine)	60–34–4	(C)0.2	(C)0.35	X
Methyl iodide	74–88–4	5	28	X
Methyl isoamyl ketone	110–12–3	100	475	
Methyl isobutyl carbinol	108–11–2	25	100	X
Methyl isobutyl ketone; see Hexone				
Methyl isocyanate	624–83–9	0.02	0.05	X
Methyl mercaptan	74–93–1	(C)10	(C)20	
Methyl methacrylate	80–62–6	100	410	
Methyl propyl ketone; see 2-Pentanone				

Substance	CAS No. (c)	ppm (a)[1]	mg/m³(b)[1]	Skin designation
alpha-Methyl styrene	98–83–9	(C)100	(C)480	
Methylene bisphenyl isocyanate (MDI)	101–68–8	(C)0.02	(C)0.2	
Mica; see Silicates				
Molybdenum (as Mo) Soluble compounds Insoluble compounds Total dust	7439–98–7		 5 15	
Monomethyl aniline	100–61–8	2	9	X
Monomethyl hydrazine; see Methyl hydrazine				
Morpholine	110–91–8	20	70	X
Naphtha (Coal tar)	8030–30–6	100	400	
Naphthalene	91–20–3	10	50	
alpha-Naphthylamine; see §1910.1004	134–32–7			
beta-Naphthylamine; see §1910.1009	91–59–8			
Nickel carbonyl (as Ni)	13463–39–3	0.001	0.007	
Nickel, metal and insoluble compounds (as Ni)	7440–02–0		1	
Nickel, soluble compounds (as Ni)	7440–02–0		1	
Nicotine	54–11–5		0.5	X
Nitric acid	7697–37–2	2	5	
Nitric oxide	10102–43–9	25	30	
p-Nitroaniline	100–01–6	1	6	X
Nitrobenzene	98–95–3	1	5	X
p-Nitrochlorobenzene	100–00–5		1	X
4-Nitrodiphenyl; see §1910.1003	92–93–3			
Nitroethane	79–24–3	100	310	
Nitrogen dioxide	10102–44–0	(C)5	(C)9	
Nitrogen trifluoride	7783–54–2	10	29	
Nitroglycerin	55–63–0	(C)0.2	(C)2	X
Nitromethane	75–52–5	100	250	
1-Nitropropane	108–03–2	25	90	
2-Nitropropane	79–46–9	25	90	
N-Nitrosodimethylamine; see §1910.1016				
Nitrotoluene (all isomers) o-isomer m-isomer p-isomer	 88–72–2 99–08–1 99–99–0	5	30	X
Nitrotrichloromethane; see Chloropicrin				
Octachloronaphthalene	2234–13–1		0.1	X
Octane	111–65–9	500	2350	
Oil mist, mineral	8012–95–1		5	
Osmium tetroxide (as Os)	20816–12–0		0.002	
Oxalic acid	144–62–7		1	
Oxygen difluoride	7783–41–7	0.05	0.1	
Ozone	10028–15–6	0.1	0.2	
Paraquat, respirable dust	4685–14–7; 1910–42–5; 2074–50–2		0.5	X
Parathion	56–38–2		0.1	X
Particulates not otherwise regulated (PNOR)[f] Total dust Respirable fraction			 15 5	
PCB; see Chlorodiphenyl (42% and 54% chlorine)				
Pentaborane	19624–22–7	0.005	0.01	
Pentachloronaphthalene	1321–64–8		0.5	X
Pentachlorophenol	87–86–5		0.5	X

Note: Table data continues on next page.

Substance	CAS No. (c)	ppm (a)[1]	mg/m³(b)[1]	Skin designation
Pentaerythritol Total dust Respirable fraction	115–77–5		 15 5	
Pentane	109–66–0	1000	2950	
2-Pentanone (Methyl propyl ketone)	107–87–9	200	700	
Perchloroethylene (Tetrachloroethylene)	127–18–4		(2)	
Perchloromethyl mercaptan	594–42–3	0.1	0.8	
Perchloryl fluoride	7616–94–6	3	13.5	
Petroleum distillates (Naphtha) (Rubber Solvent)		500	2000	
Phenol	108–95–2	5	19	X
p-Phenylene diamine	106–50–3		0.1	X
Phenyl ether, vapor	101–84–8	1	7	
Phenyl ether-biphenyl mixture, vapor		1	7	
Phenylethylene; see Styrene				
Phenyl glycidyl ether (PGE)	122–60–1	10	60	
Phenylhydrazine	100–63–0	5	22	X
Phosdrin (Mevinphos)	7786–34–7		0.1	X
Phosgene (Carbonyl chloride)	75–44–5	0.1	0.4	
Phosphine	7803–51–2	0.3	0.4	
Phosphoric acid	7664–38–2		1	
Phosphorus (yellow)	7723–14–0		0.1	
Phosphorus pentachloride	10026–13–8		1	
Phosphorus pentasulfide	1314–80–3		1	
Phosphorus trichloride	7719–12–2	0.5	3	
Phthalic anhydride	85–44–9	2	12	
Picloram Total dust Respirable fraction	1918–02–1		 15 5	
Picric acid	88–89–1		0.1	X
Pindone (2-Pivalyl-1,3-indandione)	83–26–1		0.1	
Plaster of Paris Total dust Respirable fraction	26499–65–0		 15 5	
Platinum (as Pt) Metal Soluble salts	7440–06–4		 0.002	
Portland cement Total dust Respirable fraction	65997–15–1		 15 5	
Propane	74–98–6	1000	1800	
beta-Propriolactone; see §1910.1013	57–57–8			
n-Propyl acetate	109–60–4	200	840	
n-Propyl alcohol	71–23–8	200	500	
n-Propyl nitrate	627–13–4	25	110	
Propylene dichloride	78–87–5	75	350	
Propylene imine	75–55–8	2	5	X
Propylene oxide	75–56–9	100	240	
Propyne; see Methyl acetylene				
Pyrethrum	8003–34–7		5	
Pyridine	110–86–1	5	15	
Quinone	106–51–4	0.1	0.4	
RDX; see Cyclonite				
Rhodium (as Rh), metal fume and insoluble compounds	7440–16–6		0.1	
Rhodium (as Rh), soluble compounds	7440–16–6		0.001	
Ronnel	299–84–3		15	
Rotenone	83–79–4		5	

Substance	CAS No. (c)	ppm (a)[1]	mg/m³(b)[1]	Skin designation
Rouge Total dust Respirable fraction			 15 5	
Selenium compounds (as Se)	7782–49–2		0.2	
Selenium hexafluoride (as Se)	7783–79–1	0.05	0.4	
Silica, amorphous, precipitated and gel	112926–00–8		(3)	
Silica, amorphous, diatomaceous earth, containing less than 1% crystalline silica	61790–53–2		(3)	
Silica, crystalline, respirable dust Cristobalite: Use ½ the value calculated from the count or formulae for quartz[f] Quartz; see 1910.1053[7] Tripoli (as quartz); see 1910.1053[7] Tridymite: Use ½ the value calculated from the formulae for quartz[f]	 14464–46–1 14808–60–7 1317–95–9 15468–32–3			
Silica, fused, respirable dust	60676–86–0		(3)	
Silicates (less than 1% crystalline silica) Mica (respirable dust) Soapstone, total dust Soapstone, respirable dust Talc (containing asbestos); use asbestos limit; see 29 CFR §1910.1001 Talc (containing no asbestos), respirable dust Tremolite, asbestiform; see §1910.1001	 12001–26–2 14807–96–6		 (3) (3) (3) (3) (3)	
Silicon Total dust Respirable fraction	7440–21–3		 15 5	
Silicon carbide Total dust Respirable fraction	409–21–2		 15 5	
Silver, metal and soluble compounds (as Ag)	7440–22–4		0.01	
Soapstone; see Silicates				
Sodium fluoroacetate	62–74–8		0.05	X
Sodium hydroxide	1310–73–2		2	
Starch Total dust Respirable fraction	9005–25–8		 15 5	
Stibine	7803–52–3	0.1	0.5	
Stoddard solvent	8052–41–3	500	2900	
Strychnine	57–24–9		0.15	
Styrene	100–42–5		(2)	
Sucrose Total dust Respirable fraction	57–50–1		 15 5	
Sulfur dioxide	7446–09–5	5	13	
Sulfur hexafluoride	2551–62–4	1000	6000	
Sulfuric acid	7664–93–9		1	
Sulfur monochloride	10025–67–9	1	6	
Sulfur pentafluoride	5714–22–7	0.025	0.25	
Sulfuryl fluoride	2699–79–8	5	20	
Systox; see Demeton				
2,4,5-T (2,4,5-trichlorophenoxyacetic acid)	93–76–5		10	
Talc; see Silicates				
Tantalum, metal and oxide dust	7440–25–7		5	
TEDP (Sulfotep)	3689–24–5		0.2	X
Tellurium and compounds (as Te)	13494–80–9		0.1	
Tellurium hexafluoride (as Te)	7783–80–4	0.02	0.2	
Temephos Total dust Respirable fraction	3383–96–8		 15 5	
TEPP (Tetraethyl pyrophosphate)	107–49–3		0.05	X
Terphenyls	26140–60–3	(C)1	(C)9	
1,1,1,2-Tetrachloro-2,2-difluoroethane	76–11–9	500	4170	

Note: Table data continues on next page.

Substance	CAS No. (c)	ppm (a)[1]	mg/m^3(b)[1]	Skin designation
1,1,2,2-Tetrachloro-1,2-difluoroethane	76–12–0	500	4170	
1,1,2,2-Tetrachloroethane	79–34–5	5	35	X
Tetrachloroethylene; see Perchloroethylene				
Tetrachloromethane; see Carbon tetrachloride				
Tetrachloronaphthalene	1335–88–2		2	X
Tetraethyl lead (as Pb)	78–00–2		0.075	X
Tetrahydrofuran	109–99–9	200	590	
Tetramethyl lead (as Pb)	75–74–1		0.075	X
Tetramethyl succinonitrile	3333–52–6	0.5	3	X
Tetranitromethane	509–14–8	1	8	
Tetryl (2,4,6-Trinitrophenylmethylnitramine)	479–45–8		1.5	X
Thallium, soluble compounds (as Tl)	7440–28–0		0.1	X
4,4′-Thiobis (6-tert, Butyl-m-cresol) Total dust Respirable fraction	96–69–5		 15 5	
Thiram	137–26–8		5	
Tin, inorganic compounds (except oxides) (as Sn)	7440–31–5		2	
Tin, organic compounds (as Sn)	7440–31–5		0.1	
Titanium dioxide Total dust	13463–67–7		 15	
Toluene	108–88–3		([2])	
Toluene-2,4-diisocyanate (TDI)	584–84–9	(C)0.02	(C)0.14	
o-Toluidine	95–53–4	5	22	X
Toxaphene; see Chlorinated camphene				
Tremolite; see Silicates				
Tributyl phosphate	126–73–8		5	
1,1,1-Trichloroethane; see Methyl chloroform				
1,1,2-Trichloroethane	79–00–5	10	45	X
Trichloroethylene	79–01–6		([2])	
Trichloromethane; see Chloroform				
Trichloronaphthalene	1321–65–9		5	X
1,2,3-Trichloropropane	96–18–4	50	300	
1,1,2-Trichloro-1,2,2-trifluoroethane	76–13–1	1000	7600	
Triethylamine	121–44–8	25	100	
Trifluorobromomethane	75–63–8	1000	6100	
2,4,6-Trinitrophenol; see Picric acid				
2,4,6-Trinitrophenylmethylnitramine; see Tetryl				
2,4,6-Trinitrotoluene (TNT)	118–96–7		1.5	X
Triorthocresyl phosphate	78–30–8		0.1	
Triphenyl phosphate	115–86–6		3	
Turpentine	8006–64–2	100	560	
Uranium (as U) Soluble compounds Insoluble compounds	7440–61–1		 0.05 0.25	
Vanadium Respirable dust (as V_2O_5) Fume (as V_2O_5)	1314–62–1		 (C)0.5 (C)0.1	
Vegetable oil mist Total dust Respirable fraction			 15 5	
Vinyl benzene; see Styrene				
Vinyl chloride; see §1910.1017	75–01–4			
Vinyl cyanide; see Acrylonitrile				
Vinyl toluene	25013–15–4	100	480	
Warfarin	81–81–2		0.1	
Xylenes (o-, m-, p-isomers)	1330–20–7	100	435	

Substance	CAS No. (c)	ppm (a)[1]	mg/m³(b)[1]	Skin designation
Xylidine	1300–73–8	5	25	X
Yttrium	7440–65–5		1	
Zinc chloride fume	7646–85–7		1	
Zinc oxide fume	1314–13–2		5	
Zinc oxide Total dust Respirable fraction	1314–13–2		 15 5	
Zinc stearate Total dust Respirable fraction	557–05–1		 15 5	
Zirconium compounds (as Zr)	7440–67–7		5	

1 The PELs are 8-hour TWAs unless otherwise noted; a (C) designation denotes a ceiling limit. They are to be determined from breathing-zone air samples.
(a) Parts of vapor or gas per million parts of contaminated air by volume at 25 °C and 760 torr.
(b) Milligrams of substance per cubic meter of air. When entry is in this column only, the value is exact; when listed with a ppm entry, it is approximate.
(c) The CAS number is for information only. Enforcement is based on the substance name. For an entry covering more than one metal compound, measured as the metal, the CAS number for the metal is given—not CAS numbers for the individual compounds.
(d) The final benzene Standard in §1910.1028 applies to all occupational exposures to benzene except in some circumstances the distribution and sale of fuels, sealed containers and pipelines, coke production, oil and gas drilling and production, natural gas processing, and the percentage exclusion for liquid mixtures; for the excepted subsegments, the benzene limits in Table Z–2 apply. See §1910.1028 for specific circumstances.
(e) This 8-hour TWA applies to respirable dust as measured by a vertical elutriator cotton dust sampler or equivalent instrument. The time-weighted average applies to the cottom waste processing operations of waste recycling (sorting, blending, cleaning and willowing) and garnetting. See also §1910.1043 for cotton dust limits applicable to other sectors.
(f) All inert or nuisance dusts, whether mineral, inorganic, or organic, not listed specifically by substance name are covered by the Particulates Not Otherwise Regulated (PNOR) limit which is the same as the inert or nuisance dust limit of Table Z–3.
2 See Table Z–2
3 See Table Z–3.
4 Varies with compound.
5 See Table Z–2 for the exposure limit for any operations or sectors where the exposure limit in §1910.1026 is stayed or is otherwise not in effect.
6 If the exposure limit in §1910.1026 is stayed or is otherwise not in effect, the exposure limit is a ceiling of 0.1 mg/m³.
7 See Table Z-3 for the exposure limit for any operations or sectors where the exposure limit in §1910.1053 is stayed or is otherwise not in effect.

Table Z–2 [OI]

Substance	8-hour time weighted average	Acceptable ceiling concentration	Acceptable maximum peak above the acceptable ceiling concentration for an 8-hr shift	
			Concentration	Maximum duration
Benzene[a](Z37.40–1969)	10 ppm	25 ppm	50 ppm	10 minutes
Beryllium and beryllium compounds (Z37.29–1970)	2 μg/m³	5 μg/m³	25 μg/m³	30 minutes
Cadmium fume[b](Z37.5–1970)	0.1 mg/m³	0.3 mg/m³		
Cadmium dust[b](Z37.5–1970)	0.2 mg/m³	0.6 mg/m³		
Carbon disulfide (Z37.3–1968)	20 ppm	30 ppm	100 ppm	30 minutes
Carbon tetrachloride (Z37.17–1967)	10 ppm	25 ppm	200 ppm	5 minutes in any 4 hrs
Chromic acid and chromates (Z37.7–1971) (as CrO_3)[c]		1 mg/10m³		
Ethylene dibromide (Z37.31–1970)	20 ppm	30 ppm	50 ppm	5 minutes
Ethylene dichloride (Z37.21–1969)	50 ppm	100 ppm	200 ppm	5 minutes in any 3 hrs
Fluoride as dust (Z37.28–1969)	2.5 mg/m³			
Formaldehyde; see §1910.1048				
Hydrogen fluoride (Z37.28–1969)	3 ppm			
Hydrogen sulfide (Z37.2–1966)		20 ppm	50 ppm	10 mins. once, only if no other meas. exp. occurs
Mercury (Z37.8–1971)		1 mg/10m³		
Methyl chloride (Z37.18–1969)	100 ppm	200 ppm	300 ppm	5 mins. in any 3 hrs
Methylene Chloride: See §1910.1052.				
Organo (alkyl) mercury (Z37.30–1969)	0.01 mg/m³	0.04 mg/m³		
Styrene (Z37.15–1969)	100 ppm	200 ppm	600 ppm	5 mins. in any 3 hrs
Tetrachloroethylene (Z37.22–1967)	100 ppm	200 ppm	300 ppm	5 mins. in any 3 hrs
Toluene (Z37.12–1967)	200 ppm	300 ppm	500 ppm	10 minutes
Trichloroethylene (Z37.19–1967)	100 ppm	200 ppm	300 ppm	5 mins. in any 2 hrs

a This Standard applies to the industry segments exempt from the 1 ppm 8-hour TWA and 5 ppm STEL of the benzene Standard at §1910.1028.
b This Standard applies to any operations or sectors for which the Cadmium Standard, §1910.1027, is stayed or otherwise not in effect.
c This Standard applies to any operations or sectors for which the exposure limit in the Chromium (VI) Standard, §1910.1026, is stayed or is otherwise not in effect.

Air contaminants

Z

Toxic and Hazardous Substances

Table Z–3
Mineral Dusts

Substance	mppcf[a]	mg/m³
Silica: Crystalline Quartz (Respirable)[f]	250[b] $\%SiO_2 +5$	10 mg/m[3e] $\%SiO_2+2$
Cristobalite: Use ½ the value calculated from the count or mass formulae for quartz[f]		
Tridymite: Use ½ the value calculated from the formulae for quartz[f]		
Amorphous, including natural diatomaceous earth	20	80 mg/m³ $\%SiO_2$
Silicates (less than 1% crystalline silica):		
Mica	20	
Soapstone	20	
Talc (not containing asbestos)	20[c]	
Talc (containing asbestos) Use asbestos limit		
Tremolite, asbestiform (see 29 CFR §1910.1001)		
Portland cement	50	
Graphite (Natural)	15	
Coal Dust:		
Respirable fraction less than 5% SiO_2		2.4 mg/m[3e]
Respirable fraction greater than 5% SiO_2		10 mg/m[3e] $\%SiO_2+2$
Inert or Nuisance Dust:[d]		
Respirable fraction	15	5 mg/m³
Total dust	50	15 mg/m³

Note: Conversion factors - mppcf × 35.3 = million particles per cubic meter = particles per c.c.

[a] Millions of particles per cubic foot of air, based on impinger samples counted by light-field techniques.

[b] The percentage of crystalline silica in the formula is the amount determined from airborne samples, except in those instances in which other methods have been shown to be applicable.

[c] Containing less than 1% quartz; if 1% quartz or more, use quartz limit.

[d] All inert or nuisance dusts, whether mineral, inorganic, or organic, not listed specifically by substance name are covered by this limit, which is the same as the Particulates Not Otherwise Regulated (PNOR) limit in Table Z–1.

[e] Both concentration and percent quartz for the application of this limit are to be determined from the fraction passing a size-selector with the following characteristics:

Aerodynamic diameter (unit density sphere)	Percent passing selector
2	90
2.5	75
3.5	50
5.0	25
10	0

The measurements under this note refer to the use of an AEC (now NRC) instrument. The respirable fraction of coal dust is determined with an MRE; the figure corresponding to that of 2.4 mg/m³ in the table for coal dust is 4.5 mg/m[3K].

[f] This Standard applies to any operations or sectors for which the respirable crystalline silica standard, 1910.1053, is stayed or is otherwise not in effect.

[58 FR 35340, June 30. 1993; 58 FR 40191, July 27, 1993, as amended at 61 FR 56831, Nov. 4, 1996; 62 FR 1600, Jan. 10, 1997; 62 FR 42018, Aug. 4, 1997; 71 FR 10373, Feb. 28, 2006; 71 FR 16673, Apr. 3, 2006; 71 FR 36008, June 23, 2006]

§1910.1001 Asbestos

(a) **Scope and application**

(a)(1) This Section applies to all occupational exposures to asbestos in all industries covered by the Occupational Safety and Health Act, except as provided in paragraph (a)(2) and (3) of this Section.

(a)(2) This Section does not apply to construction work as defined in 29 CFR §1910.12(b). (Exposure to asbestos in construction work is covered by 29 CFR §1926.1101.)

(a)(3) This Section does not apply to ship repairing, shipbuilding and shipbreaking employments and related employments as defined in 29 CFR §1915.4. (Exposure to asbestos in these employments is covered by 29 CFR §1915.1001).

(b) **Definitions**

Asbestos includes chrysotile, amosite, crocidolite, tremolite asbestos, anthophyllite asbestos, actinolite asbestos, and any of these minerals that have been chemically treated and/or altered.

Asbestos-containing material (ACM) means any material containing more than 1% asbestos.

Assistant Secretary means the Assistant Secretary of Labor for Occupational Safety and Health, U.S. Department of Labor, or designee.

Authorized person means any person authorized by the employer and required by work duties to be present in regulated areas.

Building/facility owner is the legal entity, including a lessee, which exercises control over management and record keeping functions relating to a building and/or facility in which activities covered by this Standard take place.

Certified industrial hygienist (CIH) means one certified in the practice of industrial hygiene by the American Board of Industrial Hygiene.

Director means the Director of the National Institute for Occupational Safety and Health, U.S. Department of Health and Human Services, or designee.

Employee exposure means that exposure to airborne asbestos that would occur if the employee were not using respiratory protective equipment.

Fiber means a particulate form of asbestos 5 micrometers or longer,with a length-to-diameter ratio of at least 3 to 1.

High-efficiency particulate air (HEPA) filter means a filter capable of trapping and retaining at least 99.97 percent of 0.3 micrometer diameter mono-disperse particles.

Homogeneous area means an area of surfacing material or thermal system insulation that is uniform in color and texture.

Industrial hygienist means a professional qualified by education, training, and experience to anticipate, recognize, evaluate and develop controls for occupational health hazards.

PACM means "presumed asbestos containing material."

Presumed asbestos containing material means thermal system insulation and surfacing material found in buildings constructed no later than 1980. The designation of a material as "PACM" may be rebutted pursuant to paragraph (j)(8) of this Section.

Regulated area means an area established by the employer to demarcate areas where airborne concentrations of asbestos exceed, or there is a reasonable possibility they may exceed, the permissible exposure limits.

Surfacing ACM means surfacing material which contains more than 1% asbestos.

Surfacing material means material that is sprayed, troweled-on or otherwise applied to surfaces (such as acoustical plaster on ceilings and fireproofing materials on structural members, or other materials on surfaces for acoustical, fireproofing, and other purposes).

Thermal System Insulation (TSI) means ACM applied to pipes, fittings, boilers, breeching, tanks, ducts or other structural components to prevent heat loss or gain.

Thermal System Insulation ACM means thermal system insulation which contains more than 1% asbestos.

(c) **Permissible exposure limit (PELS)**

(c)(1) **Time-weighted average limit (TWA)** The employer shall ensure that no employee is exposed to an airborne concentration of asbestos in excess of 0.1 fiber per cubic centimeter of air as an eight (8)-hour time-weighted average (TWA) as determined by the method prescribed in Appendix A to this Section, or by an equivalent method.

(c)(2) **Excursion limit** The employer shall ensure that no employee is exposed to an airborne concentration of asbestos in excess of 1.0 fiber per cubic centimeter of air (1 f/cc) as averaged over a sampling period of thirty (30) minutes as determined by the method prescribed in Appendix A to this Section, or by an equivalent method.

(d) **Exposure monitoring**

(d)(1) **General**

(d)(1)(i) Determinations of employee exposure shall be made from breathing zone air samples that are representative of the 8-hour TWA and 30-minute short-term exposures of each employee.

(d)(1)(ii) Representative 8-hour TWA employee exposures shall be determined on the basis of one or more samples representing full-shift exposures for each shift for each employee in each job classification in each work area. Representative 30-minute short-term employee exposures shall be determined on the basis of one or more samples representing 30 minute exposures associated with operations that are most likely to produce exposures above the excursion limit for each shift for each job classification in each work area.

(d)(2) **Initial monitoring**

(d)(2)(i) Each employer who has a workplace or work operation covered by this Standard, except as provided for in paragraphs (d)(2)(ii) and (d)(2)(iii) of this Section, shall perform initial monitoring of employees who are, or may reasonably be expected to be exposed to airborne concentrations at or above the TWA permissible exposure limit and/or excursion limit.

(d)(2)(ii) Where the employer has monitored after March 31, 1992, for the TWA permissible exposure limit and/or the excursion limit, and the monitoring satisfies all other requirements of this Section, the employer may rely on such earlier monitoring results to satisfy the requirements of paragraph (d)(2)(i) of this Section.

(d)(2)(iii) Where the employer has relied upon objective data that demonstrate that asbestos is not capable of being released in airborne concentrations at or above the TWA permissible exposure limit and/or excursion limit under the expected conditions of processing, use, or handling, then no initial monitoring is required.

(d)(3) **Monitoring frequency (periodic monitoring) and patterns** After the initial determinations required by paragraph (d)(2)(i) of this Section, samples shall be of such frequency and pattern as to represent with reasonable accuracy the levels of exposure of the employees. In no case shall sampling be at intervals greater than six months for employees whose exposures may reasonably be foreseen to exceed the TWA permissible exposure limit and/or excursion limit.

(d)(4) **Changes in monitoring frequency** If either the initial or the periodic monitoring required by paragraphs (d)(2) and (d)(3) of this Section statistically indicates that employee exposures are below the TWA permissible exposure limit and/or excursion limit, the employer may discontinue the monitoring for those employees whose exposures are represented by such monitoring.

(d)(5) **Additional monitoring** Notwithstanding the provisions of paragraphs (d)(2)(ii) and (d)(4) of this Section, the employer shall institute the exposure monitoring required under paragraphs (d)(2)(i) and (d)(3) of this Section whenever there has been a change in the production, process, control equipment, personnel or work practices that may result in new or additional exposures above the TWA permissible exposure limit and/or excursion limit or when the employer has any reason to suspect that a change may result in new or additional exposures above the PEL and/or excursion limit.

(d)(6) **Method of monitoring**

(d)(6)(i) All samples taken to satisfy the monitoring requirements of paragraph (d) of this Section shall be personal samples collected following the procedures specified in Appendix A.

(d)(6)(ii) All samples taken to satisfy the monitoring requirements of paragraph (d) of this Section shall be evaluated using the OSHA Reference Method (ORM) specified in Appendix A of this Section, or an equivalent counting method.

(d)(6)(iii) If an equivalent method to the ORM is used, the employer shall ensure that the method meets the following criteria:

(d)(6)(iii)(A) Replicate exposure data used to establish equivalency are collected in side-by-side field and laboratory comparisons; and

(d)(6)(iii)(B) The comparison indicates that 90% of the samples collected in the range 0.5 to 2.0 times the permissible limit have an accuracy range of plus or minus 25 percent of the ORM results at a 95% confidence level as demonstrated by a statistically valid protocol; and

(d)(6)(iii)(C) The equivalent method is documented and the results of the comparison testing are maintained.

(d)(6)(iv) To satisfy the monitoring requirements of paragraph (d) of this Section, employers must use the results of monitoring analysis performed by laboratories which have instituted quality assurance programs that include the elements as prescribed in Appendix A of this Section.

(d)(7) **Employee notification of monitoring results**

(d)(7)(i) The employer must, within 15 working days after the receipt of the results of any monitoring performed under this Sections, notify each affected employee of these results either individually in writing or by posting the results in an appropriate location that is accessible to affected employees.

(d)(7)(ii) The written notification required by paragraph (d)(7)(i) of this Section shall contain the corrective action being taken by the employer to reduce employee exposure to or below the TWA and/or excursion limit, wherever monitoring results indicated that the TWA and/or excursion limit had been exceeded.

(e) **Regulated Areas**

(e)(1) **Establishment** The employer shall establish regulated areas wherever airborne concentrations of asbestos and/or PACM are in excess of the TWA and/or excursion limit prescribed in paragraph (c) of this Section.

(e)(2) **Demarcation** Regulated areas shall be demarcated from the rest of the workplace in any manner that minimizes the number of persons who will be exposed to asbestos.

(e)(3) **Access** Access to regulated areas shall be limited to authorized persons or to persons authorized by the Act or regulations issued pursuant thereto.

(e)(4) **Provision of respirators** Each person entering a regulated area shall be supplied with and required to use a respirator, selected in accordance with paragraph (g)(2) of this Section.

(e)(5) **Prohibited activities** The employer shall ensure that employees do not eat, drink, smoke, chew tobacco or gum, or apply cosmetics in the regulated areas.

(f) **Methods of compliance**

(f)(1) **Engineering controls and work practices**

(f)(1)(i) The employer shall institute engineering controls and work practices to reduce and maintain employee exposure to or below the TWA and/or excursion limit prescribed in paragraph (c) of this Section, except to the extent that such controls are not feasible.

(f)(1)(ii) Wherever the feasible engineering controls and work practices that can be instituted are not sufficient to reduce employee exposure to or below the TWA and/or excursion limit prescribed in paragraph (c) of this Section, the employer shall use them to reduce employee exposure to the lowest levels achievable by these controls and shall supplement them by the use of respiratory protection that complies with the requirements of paragraph (g) of this Section.

(f)(1)(iii) For the following operations, wherever feasible engineering controls and work practices that can be instituted are not sufficient to reduce the employee exposure to or below the TWA and/or excursion limit prescribed in paragraph (c) of this Section, the employer shall use them to reduce employee exposure to or below 0.5 fiber per cubic centimeter of air (as an eight-hour time-weighted average) or 2.5 fibers/cc for 30 minutes (short-term exposure) and shall supplement them by the use of any combination of respiratory protection that complies with the requirements of paragraph (g) of this Section, work practices and feasible engineering controls that will reduce employee exposure to or below the TWA and to or below the excursion limit permissible prescribed in paragraph (c) of this Section: Coupling cutoff in primary asbestos cement pipe manufacturing; sanding in primary and secondary asbestos cement sheet manufacturing; grinding in primary and secondary friction product manufacturing; carding and spinning in dry textile processes; and grinding and sanding in primary plastics manufacturing.

(f)(1)(iv) **Local exhaust ventilation** Local exhaust ventilation and dust collection systems shall be designed, constructed, installed, and maintained in accordance with good practices such as those found in the American National Standard Fundamentals Governing the Design and Operation of Local Exhaust Systems, ANSI Z9.2–1979.

(f)(1)(v) **Particular tools** All hand-operated and power-operated tools which would produce or release fibers of asbestos, such as, but not limited to, saws, scorers, abrasive wheels, and drills, shall be provided with local exhaust ventilation systems which comply with paragraph (f)(1)(iv) of this Section.

(f)(1)(vi) **Wet methods** Insofar as practicable, asbestos shall be handled, mixed, applied, removed, cut, scored, or otherwise worked in a wet state sufficient to prevent the emission of airborne fibers so as to expose employees to levels in excess of the TWA and/or excursion limit, prescribed in paragraph (c) of this Section, unless the usefulness of the product would be diminished thereby.

(f)(1)(vii) [Reserved]

(f)(1)(viii) **Particular products and operations** No asbestos cement, mortar, coating, grout, plaster, or similar material containing asbestos, shall be removed from bags, cartons, or other containers in which they are shipped, without being either wetted, or enclosed, or ventilated so as to prevent effectively the release of airborne fibers.

(f)(1)(ix) **Compressed air** Compressed air shall not be used to remove asbestos or materials containing asbestos unless the compressed air is used in conjunction with a ventilation system which effectively captures the dust cloud created by the compressed air.

(f)(1)(x) **Flooring** Sanding of asbestos-containing flooring material is prohibited.

(f)(2) **Compliance program**

(f)(2)(i) Where the TWA and/or excursion limit is exceeded, the employer shall establish and implement a written program to reduce employee exposure to or below the TWA and to or below the excursion limit by means of engineering and work practice controls as required by paragraph (f)(1) of this Section, and by the use of respiratory protection where required or permitted under this Section.

(f)(2)(ii) Such programs shall be reviewed and updated as necessary to reflect significant changes in the status of the employer's compliance program.

(f)(2)(iii) Written programs shall be submitted upon request for examination and copying to the Assistant Secretary, the Director, affected employees and designated employee representatives.

(f)(2)(iv) The employer shall not use employee rotation as a means of compliance with the TWA and/or excursion limit.

(f)(3) **Specific compliance methods for brake and clutch repair:**

(f)(3)(i) Engineering controls and work practices for brake and clutch repair and service. During automotive brake and clutch inspection, disassembly, repair and assembly operations, the employer shall institute engineering controls and work practices to reduce employee exposure to materials containing asbestos using a negative pressure enclosure/ HEPA vacuum system method or low pressure/wet cleaning method, which meets the detailed requirements set out in Appendix F to this Section. The employer may also comply using an equivalent method which follows written procedures which the employer demonstrates can achieve results equivalent to Method A in Appendix F to this Section. For facilities in which no more than 5 pair of brakes or 5 clutches are inspected, disassembled, repaired, or assembled per week, the method set forth in paragraph [D] of Appendix F to this Section may be used.

(f)(3)(ii) The employer may also comply by using an equivalent method which follows written procedures, which the employer demonstrates can achieve equivalent exposure reductions as do the two "preferred methods." Such demonstration must include monitoring data conducted under workplace conditions closely resembling the process, type of asbestos containing materials, control method, work practices and environmental conditions which the equivalent method will be used, or objective data, which document that under all reasonably foreseeable conditions of brake and clutch repair applications, the method results in exposures which are equivalent to the methods set out in Appendix F to this Section.

(g) **Respiratory protection**

(g)(1) **General** For employees who use respirators required by this Section, the employer must provide each employee an appropriate respirator that complies with the requirements of this paragraph. Respirators must be used during:

(g)(1)(i) Periods necessary to install or implement feasible engineering and work-practice controls.

(g)(1)(ii) Work operations, such as maintenance and repair activities, for which engineering and work-practice controls are not feasible.

(g)(1)(iii) Work operations for which feasible engineering and work-practice controls are not yet sufficient to reduce employee exposure to or below the TWA and/or excursion limit.

(g)(1)(iv) Emergencies.

(g)(2) **Respirator program**

(g)(2)(i) The employer must implement a respiratory protection program in accordance with 29 CFR 134 (b) through (d) (except (d)(1)(iii)), and (f) through (m), which covers each employee required by this Section to use a respirator.

(g)(2)(ii) Employers must provide an employee with a tight-fitting, powered air-purifying respirator (PAPR) instead of a negative pressure respirator selected according to paragraph (g)(3) of this Standard when the employee chooses to use a PAPR and it provides adequate protection to the employee.

(g)(2)(iii) No employee must be assigned to tasks requiring the use of respirators if, based on their most recent medical examination, the examining physician determines that the employee will be unable to function normally using a respirator, or that the safety or health of the employee or other employees will be impaired by the use of a respirator. Such employees must be assigned to another job or given the opportunity to transfer to a different position, the duties of which they can perform. If such a transfer position is available, the position must be with the same employer, in the same geographical area, and with the same seniority, status, and rate of pay the employee had just prior to such transfer.

(g)(3) **Respirator selection** Employers must:

(g)(3)(i) Select, and provide to employees, the appropriate respirators specified in paragraph (d)(3)(i)(A) of 29 CFR §1910.134; however, employers must not select or use filtering facepiece respirators for protection against asbestos fibers.

(g)(3)(ii) Provide HEPA filters for powered and non-powered air-purifying respirators.

(h) **Protective work clothing and equipment**

(h)(1) **Provision and use** If an employee is exposed to asbestos above the TWA and/or excursion limit, or where the possibility of eye irritation exists, the employer shall provide at no cost to the employee and ensure that the employee uses appropriate protective work clothing and equipment such as, but not limited to:

(h)(1)(i) Coveralls or similar full-body work clothing;

(h)(1)(ii) Gloves, head coverings, and foot coverings; and

(h)(1)(iii) Face shields, vented goggles, or other appropriate protective equipment which complies with §1910.133 of this Part.

(h)(2) **Removal and storage**

(h)(2)(i) The employer shall ensure that employees remove work clothing contaminated with asbestos only in change rooms provided in accordance with paragraph (i)(1) of this Section.

(h)(2)(ii) The employer shall ensure that no employee takes contaminated work clothing out of the change room, except those employees authorized to do so for the purpose of laundering, maintenance, or disposal.

(h)(2)(iii) Contaminated work clothing shall be placed and stored in closed containers which prevent dispersion of the asbestos outside the container.

(h)(2)(iv) The employer shall ensure that containers of contaminated protective devices or work clothing, which are to be taken out of change rooms or the workplace for cleaning, maintenance or disposal, bear labels in accordance with paragraph (j) of this Section.

(h)(3) **Cleaning and replacement**

(h)(3)(i) The employer shall clean, launder, repair, or replace protective clothing and equipment required by this paragraph to maintain their effectiveness. The employer shall provide clean protective clothing and equipment at least weekly to each affected employee.

(h)(3)(ii) The employer shall prohibit the removal of asbestos from protective clothing and equipment by blowing or shaking.

(h)(3)(iii) Laundering of contaminated clothing shall be done so as to prevent the release of airborne fibers of asbestos in excess of the permissible exposure limits prescribed in paragraph (c) of this Section.

(h)(3)(iv) Any employer who gives contaminated clothing to another person for laundering shall inform such person of the requirement in paragraph (h)(3)(iii) of this Section to effectively prevent the release of airborne fibers of asbestos in excess of the permissible exposure limits.

(h)(3)(v) The employer shall inform any person who launders or cleans protective clothing or equipment contaminated with asbestos of the potentially harmful effects of exposure to asbestos.

(h)(3)(vi) The employer shall ensure that contaminated clothing is transported in sealed impermeable bags, or other closed, impermeable containers, and labeled in accordance with paragraph (j) of this Section.

(i) **Hygiene facilities and practices**

(i)(1) **Change rooms**

(i)(1)(i) The employer shall provide clean change rooms for employees who work in areas where their airborne exposure to asbestos is above the TWA and/or excursion limit.

(i)(1)(ii) The employer shall ensure that change rooms are in accordance with §1910.141(e) of this Part, and are equipped with two separate lockers or storage facilities, so separated as to prevent contamination of the employee's street clothes from his protective work clothing and equipment.

(i)(2) **Showers**

(i)(2)(i) The employer shall ensure that employees who work in areas where their airborne exposure is above the TWA and/or excursion limit, shower at the end of the work shift.

(i)(2)(ii) The employer shall provide shower facilities which comply with §1910.141(d)(3) of this Part.

(i)(2)(iii) The employer shall ensure that employees who are required to shower pursuant to paragraph (i)(2)(i) of this Section do not leave the workplace wearing any clothing or equipment worn during the work shift.

(i)(3) **Lunchrooms**

(i)(3)(i) The employer shall provide lunchroom facilities for employees who work in areas where their airborne exposure is above the TWA and/ or excursion limit.

(i)(3)(ii) The employer shall ensure that lunchroom facilities have a positive pressure, filtered air supply, and are readily accessible to employees.

(i)(3)(iii) The employer shall ensure that employees who work in areas where their airborne exposure is above the PEL and/or excursion limit wash their hands and faces prior to eating, drinking or smoking.

(i)(3)(iv) The employer shall ensure that employees do not enter lunchroom facilities with protective work clothing or equipment unless surface asbestos fibers have been removed from the clothing or equipment by vacuuming or other method that removes dust without causing the asbestos to become airborne.

(i)(4) **Smoking in work areas** The employer shall ensure that employees do not smoke in work areas where they are occupationally exposed to asbestos because of activities in that work area.

(j) **Communication of hazards to employees—Introduction** This Section applies to the communication of information concerning asbestos hazards in general industry to facilitate compliance with this Standard. Asbestos exposure in general industry occurs in a wide variety of industrial and commercial settings. Employees who manufacture asbestos-containing products may be exposed to asbestos fibers. Employees who repair and replace automotive brakes and clutches may be exposed to asbestos fibers. In addition, employees engaged in housekeeping activities in industrial facilities with asbestos product manufacturing operations, and in public and commercial buildings with installed asbestos containing materials may be exposed to asbestos fibers. Most of these workers are covered by this General Industry Standard, with the exception of state or local governmental employees in non-state plan states. It should be noted that employees who perform housekeeping activities during and after construction activities are covered by the asbestos Construction Standard, 29 CFR §1926.1101, formerly §1926.58. However, housekeeping employees, regardless of industry designation, should know whether building components they maintain may expose them to asbestos. The same hazard communication provisions will protect employees who perform housekeeping operations in all three asbestos standards; general industry, construction, and shipyard employment. As noted in the Construction Standard, building owners are often the only and/or best source of information concerning the presence of previously installed asbestos containing building materials. Therefore they, along with employers of potentially exposed employees, are assigned specific information conveying and retention duties under this Section.

(j)(1) **Hazard communication—general**

(j)(1)(i) Chemical manufacturers, importers, distributors and employers shall comply with all requirements of the Hazard Communication Standard (HCS) (§1910.1200) for asbestos.

(j)(1)(ii) In classifying the hazards of asbestos at least the following hazards are to be addressed: Cancer and lung effects.

(j)(1)(iii) Employers shall include asbestos in the hazard communication program established to comply with the HCS (§1910.1200). Employers shall ensure that each employee has access to labels on containers of asbestos and to safety data sheets, and is trained in accordance with the requirements of HCS and paragraph (j)(7) of this Section.

(j)(2) **Installed Asbestos Containing Material** Employers and building owners are required to treat installed TSI and sprayed on and troweled-on surfacing materials as ACM in buildings constructed no later than 1980 for purposes of this Standard. These materials are designated "presumed ACM or PACM", and are defined in paragraph (b) of this Section. Asphalt and vinyl flooring material installed no later than 1980 also must be treated as asbestos-containing. The employer or building owner may demonstrate that PACM and flooring material do not contain asbestos by complying with paragraph (j)(8)(iii) of this Section.

(j)(3) **Duties of employers and building and facility owners**

(j)(3)(i) Building and facility owners shall determine the presence, location, and quantity of ACM and/or PACM at the work site. Employers and building and facility owners shall exercise due diligence in complying with these requirements to inform employers and employees about the presence and location of ACM and PACM.

(j)(3)(ii) Building and facility owners shall maintain records of all information required to be provided pursuant to this Section and/or otherwise known to the building owner concerning the presence, location and quantity of ACM and PACM in the building/facility. Such records shall be kept for the duration of ownership and shall be transferred to successive owners.

(j)(3)(iii) Building and facility owners shall inform employers of employees, and employers shall inform employees who will perform housekeeping activities in areas which contain ACM and/or PACM of the presence and location of ACM and/or PACM in such areas which may be contacted during such activities.

(j)(4) **Warning signs**

(j)(4)(i) **Posting** Warning signs shall be provided and displayed at each regulated area. In addition, warning signs shall be posted at all approaches to regulated areas so that an employee may read the signs and take necessary protective steps before entering the area.

(j)(4)(ii) **Sign specifications**

(j)(4)(ii)(A) The warning signs required by paragraph (j)(4)(i) of this Section shall bear the following legend:

DANGER
ASBESTOS
MAY CAUSE CANCER
CAUSES DAMAGE TO LUNGS
AUTHORIZED PERSONNEL ONLY

(j)(4)(ii)(B) In addition, where the use of respirators and protective clothing is required in the regulated area under this Section, the warning signs shall include the following:

WEAR RESPIRATORY PROTECTION AND
PROTECTIVE CLOTHING IN THIS AREA

(j)(4)(ii)(C) Prior to June 1, 2016, employers may use the following legend in lieu of that specified in paragraph (j)(4)(ii)(A) of this Section:

DANGER
ASBESTOS
CANCER AND LUNG DISEASE HAZARD
AUTHORIZED PERSONNEL ONLY

(j)(4)(ii)(D) Prior to June 1, 2016, employers may use the following legend in lieu of that specified in paragraph (j)(4)(ii)(B) of this Section:

RESPIRATORS AND PROTECTIVE CLOTHING
ARE REQUIRED IN THIS AREA

(j)(4)(iii) The employer shall ensure that employees working in and contiguous to regulated areas comprehend the warning signs required to be posted by paragraph (j)(4)(i) of this Section. Means to ensure employee comprehension may include the use of foreign languages, pictographs and graphics.

(j)(4)(iv) At the entrance to mechanical rooms/areas in which employees reasonably can be expected to enter and which contain ACM and/or PACM, the building owner shall post signs which identify the material which is present, its location, and appropriate work practices which, if followed, will ensure that ACM and/or PACM will not be disturbed. The employer shall ensure, to the extent feasible, that employees who come in contact with these signs can comprehend them. Means to ensure employee comprehension may include the use of foreign languages, pictographs, graphics, and awareness training.

(j)(5) **Warning labels**

(j)(5)(i) **Labeling** Labels shall be affixed to all raw materials, mixtures, scrap, waste, debris, and other products containing asbestos fibers, or to their containers. When a building owner or employer identifies previously installed ACM and/or PACM, labels or signs shall be affixed or posted so that employees will be notified of what materials contain ACM and/or PACM. The employer shall attach such labels in areas where they will clearly be noticed by employees who are likely to be exposed, such as at the entrance to mechanical room/areas. Signs required by paragraph (j) of this Section may be posted in lieu of labels so long as they contain the information required for labeling.

(j)(5)(ii) In addition to the requirements of paragraph (j)(1), the employer shall ensure that labels of bags or containers of protective clothing and equipment, scrap, waste, and debris containing asbestos fibers include the following information:

DANGER
CONTAINS ASBESTOS FIBERS
MAY CAUSE CANCER
CAUSES DAMAGE TO LUNGS
DO NOT BREATHE DUST
AVOID CREATING DUST

(j)(5)(iii) Prior to June 1, 2015, employers may include the following information on raw materials, mixtures or labels of bags or containers of protective clothing and equipment, scrap, waste, and debris containing asbestos fibers in lieu of the labeling requirements in paragraphs (j)(1)(i) and (j)(5)(ii) of this Section:

DANGER
CONTAINS ASBESTOS FIBERS
AVOID CREATING DUST
CANCER AND LUNG DISEASE HAZARD

(j)(6) The provisions for labels and for safety data sheets required by paragraph (j) of this Section do not apply where:

(j)(1)(i) Asbestos fibers have been modified by a bonding agent, coating, binder, or other material provided that the manufacturer can demonstrate that during any reasonably foreseeable use, handling, storage, disposal, processing, or transportation, no airborne concentrations of fibers of asbestos in excess of the TWA permissible exposure level and/or excursion limit will be released or

(j)(1)(ii) Asbestos is present in a product in concentrations less than 1.0%.

(j)(7) **Employee information and training**

(j)(7)(i) The employer shall train each employee who is exposed to airborne concentrations of asbestos at or above the PEL and/or excursion limit in accordance with the requirements of this Section. The employer shall institute a training program and ensure employee participation in the program.

(j)(7)(ii) Training shall be provided prior to or at the time of initial assignment and at least annually thereafter.

(j)(7)(iii) The training program shall be conducted in a manner which the employee is able to understand. The employer shall ensure that each employee is informed of the following:

(j)(7)(iii)(A) The health effects associated with asbestos exposure;

(j)(7)(iii)(B) The relationship between smoking and exposure to asbestos producing lung cancer:

(j)(7)(iii)(C) The quantity, location, manner of use, release, and storage of asbestos, and the specific nature of operations which could result in exposure to asbestos;

(j)(7)(iii)(D) The engineering controls and work practices associated with the employee's job assignment;

(j)(7)(iii)(E) The specific procedures implemented to protect employees from exposure to asbestos, such as appropriate work practices, emergency and clean-up procedures, and personal protective equipment to be used;

(j)(7)(iii)(F) The purpose, proper use, and limitations of respirators and protective clothing, if appropriate;

(j)(7)(iii)(G) The purpose and a description of the medical surveillance program required by paragraph (l) of this Section;

(j)(7)(iii)(H) The content of this Standard, including Appendices.

(j)(7)(iii)(I) The names, addresses and phone numbers of public health organizations which provide information, materials, and/or conduct programs concerning smoking cessation. The employer may distribute the list of such organizations contained in Appendix I to this Section, to comply with this requirement.

(j)(7)(iii)(J) The requirements for posting signs and affixing labels and the meaning of the required legends for such signs and labels.

(j)(7)(iv) [OI] The employer shall also provide, at no cost to employees who perform housekeeping operations in an area which contains ACM or PACM, an asbestos awareness training course, which shall at a minimum contain the following elements: health effects of asbestos, locations of ACM and PACM in the building/facility, recognition of ACM and PACM damage and deterioration, requirements in this Standard relating to housekeeping, and proper response to fiber release episodes, to all employees who perform housekeeping work in areas where ACM and/or PACM is present. Each such employee shall be so trained at least once a year.

(j)(7)(v) **Access to information and training materials**

(j)(7)(v)(A) The employer shall make a copy of this Standard and its Appendices readily available without cost to all affected employees.

(j)(7)(v)(B) The employer shall provide, upon request, all materials relating to the employee information and training program to the Assistant Secretary and the training program to the Assistant Secretary and the Director.

(j)(7)(v)(C) The employer shall inform all employees concerning the availability of self-help smoking cessation program material. Upon employee request, the employer shall distribute such material, consisting of NIH Publication No. 89–1647, or equivalent self-help material, which is approved or published by a public health organization listed in Appendix I to this Section.

(j)(8) **Criteria to rebut the designation of installed material as PACM**

(j)(8)(i) At any time, an employer and/or building owner may demonstrate, for purposes of this Standard, that PACM does not contain asbestos. Building owners and/or employers are not required to communicate information about the presence of building material for which such a demonstration pursuant to the requirements of paragraph (j)(8)(ii) of this Section has been made. However, in all such cases, the information, data and analysis supporting the determination that PACM does not contain asbestos, shall be retained pursuant to paragraph (m) of this Section.

(j)(8)(ii) An employer or owner may demonstrate that PACM does not contain asbestos by the following:

(j)(8)(ii)(A) Having a completed inspection conducted pursuant to the requirements of AHERA (40 CFR 763, Subpart E) which demonstrates that no ACM is present in the material; or

(j)(8)(ii)(B) [OI] Performing tests of the material containing PACM which demonstrate that no ACM is present in the material. Such tests shall include analysis of bulk samples collected in the manner described in 40 CFR 763.86. The tests, evaluation and sample collection shall be conducted by an accredited inspector or by a CIH. Analysis of samples shall be performed by persons or laboratories with proficiency demonstrated by current successful participation in a nationally recognized testing program such as the National Voluntary Laboratory Accreditation Program (NVLAP) or the National Institute for Standards and Technology (NIST) or the Round Robin for bulk samples administered by the American Industrial Hygiene Association (AIHA) or an equivalent nationally-recognized round robin testing program.

(j)(8)(iii) [OI] The employer and/or building owner may demonstrate that flooring material including associated mastic and backing does not contain asbestos, by a determination of an industrial hygienist based upon recognized analytical techniques showing that the material is not ACM.

(k) **Housekeeping**

(k)(1) All surfaces shall be maintained as free as practicable of ACM waste and debris and accompanying dust.

(k)(2) All spills and sudden releases of material containing asbestos shall be cleaned up as soon as possible.

(k)(3) Surfaces contaminated with asbestos may not be cleaned by the use of compressed air.

(k)(4) **Vacuuming** HEPA-filtered vacuuming equipment shall be used for vacuuming asbestos containing waste and debris. The equipment shall be used and emptied in a manner which minimizes the reentry of asbestos into the workplace.

(k)(5) Shoveling, dry sweeping and dry clean-up of asbestos may be used only where vacuuming and/or wet cleaning are not feasible.

(k)(6) [OI] **Waste disposal** Waste, scrap, debris, bags, containers, equipment, and clothing contaminated with asbestos consigned for disposal, shall be collected, recycled and disposed of in sealed impermeable bags, or other closed, impermeable containers.

(k)(7) [OI] **Care of asbestos-containing flooring material**

(k)(7)(i) Sanding of asbestos-containing floor material is prohibited.

(k)(7)(ii) Stripping of finishes shall be conducted using low abrasion pads at speeds lower than 300 rpm and wet methods.

(k)(7)(iii) Burnishing or dry buffing may be performed only on asbestos-containing flooring which has sufficient finish so that the pad cannot contact the asbestos-containing material.

(k)(8) Waste and debris and accompanying dust in an area containing accessible ACM and/or PACM or visibly deteriorated ACM, shall not be dusted or swept dry, or vacuumed without using a HEPA filter.

(l) [OI] **Medical surveillance**

(l)(1) **General**

(l)(1)(i) **Employees covered** The employer shall institute a medical surveillance program for all employees who are or will be exposed to airborne concentrations of fibers of asbestos at or above the TWA and/or excursion limit.

(l)(1)(ii) **Examination by a physician**

(l)(1)(ii)(A) The employer shall ensure that all medical examinations and procedures are performed by or under the supervision of a licensed physician, and shall be provided without cost to the employee and at a reasonable time and place.

(l)(1)(ii)(B) [OI] Persons other than licensed physicians, who administer the pulmonary function testing required by this Section, shall complete a training course in spirometry sponsored by an appropriate academic or professional institution.

(l)(2) **Pre-placement examinations**

(l)(2)(i) Before an employee is assigned to an occupation exposed to airborne concentrations of asbestos fibers at or above the TWA and/or excursion limit, a pre-placement medical examination shall be provided or made available by the employer.

(l)(2)(ii) [OI] Such examination shall include, as a minimum, a medical and work history; a complete physical examination of all systems with emphasis on the respiratory system, the cardiovascular system and digestive tract; completion of the respiratory disease standardized questionnaire in Appendix D to this Section, Part 1; a chest roentgenogram (posterior-anterior 14×17 inches); pulmonary function tests to include forced vital capacity (FVC) and forced expiratory volume at 1 second (FEV(1.0)); and any additional tests deemed appropriate by the examining physician. Interpretation and classification of chest roentgenogram shall be conducted in accordance with Appendix E to this Section.

(l)(3) **Periodic examinations**

(l)(3)(i) Periodic medical examinations shall be made available annually.

(l)(3)(ii) The scope of the medical examination shall be in conformance with the protocol established in paragraph (l)(2)(ii) of this Section, except that the frequency of chest roentgenogram shall be conducted in accordance with Table 1, and the abbreviated standardized questionnaire contained in, Part 2 of Appendix D to this Section shall be administered to the employee.

Table 1
Frequency of Chest Roentgenogram

Years since first exposure	Age of employee		
	15 to 35	35+ to 45	45+
0 to 10	Every 5 years	Every 5 years	Every 5 years
10+	Every 5 years	Every 2 years	Every 1 year

(l)(4) **Termination of employment examinations**

(l)(4)(i) The employer shall provide, or make available, a termination of employment medical examination for any employee who has been exposed to airborne concentrations of fibers of asbestos at or above the TWA and/or excursion limit.

(l)(4)(ii) The medical examination shall be in accordance with the requirements of the periodic examinations stipulated in paragraph (l)(3) of this Section, and shall be given within 30 calendar days before or after the date of termination of employment.

(l)(5) **Recent examinations** No medical examination is required of any employee, if adequate records show that the employee has been examined in accordance with any of paragraphs ((l)(2) through (l)(4)) of this Section within the past 1 year period. A pre- employment medical examination which was required as a condition of employment by the employer, may not be used by that employer to meet the requirements of this paragraph, unless the cost of such examination is borne by the employer.

(l)(6) **Information provided to the physician** The employer shall provide the following information to the examining physician:

(l)(6)(i) A copy of this Standard and Appendices D and E;

(l)(6)(ii) A description of the affected employee's duties as they relate to the employee's exposure;

(l)(6)(iii) The employee's representative exposure level or anticipated exposure level;

(l)(6)(iv) A description of any personal protective and respiratory equipment used or to be used; and

(l)(6)(v) Information from previous medical examinations of the affected employee that is not otherwise available to the examining physician.

(l)(7) **Physician's written opinion**

(l)(7)(i) The employer shall obtain a written opinion from the examining physician. This written opinion shall contain the results of the medical examination and shall include:

(l)(7)(i)(A) The physician's opinion as to whether the employee has any detected medical conditions that would place the employee at an increased risk of material health impairment from exposure to asbestos;

(l)(7)(i)(B) Any recommended limitations on the employee or upon the use of personal protective equipment such as clothing or respirators;

(l)(7)(i)(C) A statement that the employee has been informed by the physician of the results of the medical examination and of any medical conditions resulting from asbestos exposure that require further explanation or treatment; and

(l)(7)(i)(D) A statement that the employee has been informed by the physician of the increased risk of lung cancer attributable to the combined effect of smoking and asbestos exposure.

(l)(7)(ii) OI The employer shall instruct the physician not to reveal in the written opinion given to the employer specific findings or diagnoses unrelated to occupational exposure to asbestos.

(l)(7)(iii) The employer shall provide a copy of the physician's written opinion to the affected employee within 30 days from its receipt.

(m) **Recordkeeping**

(m)(1) **Exposure measurements**

Note: The employer may utilize the services of competent organizations such as industry trade associations and employee associations to maintain the records required by this Section.

(m)(1)(i) The employer shall keep an accurate record of all measurements taken to monitor employee exposure to asbestos as prescribed in paragraph (d) of this Section.

(m)(1)(ii) This record shall include at least the following information:

(m)(1)(ii)(A) The date of measurement;

(m)(1)(ii)(B) The operation involving exposure to asbestos which is being monitored;

(m)(1)(ii)(C) Sampling and analytical methods used and evidence of their accuracy;

(m)(1)(ii)(D) Number, duration, and results of samples taken;

(m)(1)(ii)(E) Type of respiratory protective devices worn, if any; and

(m)(1)(ii)(F) OI Name, social security number and exposure of the employees whose exposure are represented.

(m)(1)(iii) The employer shall maintain this record for at least thirty (30) years, in accordance with 29 CFR §1910.1020.

(m)(2) **Objective data for exempted operations**

(m)(2)(i) Where the processing, use, or handling of products made from or containing asbestos is exempted from other requirements of this Section under paragraph (d)(2)(iii) of this Section, the employer shall establish and maintain an accurate record of objective data reasonably relied upon in support of the exemption.

(m)(2)(ii) The record shall include at least the following:

(m)(2)(ii)(A) The product qualifying for exemption;

(m)(2)(ii)(B) The source of the objective data;

(m)(2)(ii)(C) The testing protocol, results of testing, and/or analysis of the material for the release of asbestos;

(m)(2)(ii)(D) A description of the operation exempted and how the data support the exemption; and

(m)(2)(ii)(E) Other data relevant to the operations, materials, processing, or employee exposures covered by the exemption.

(m)(2)(iii) The employer shall maintain this record for the duration of the employer's reliance upon such objective data.

(m)(3) OI **Medical surveillance**

(m)(3)(i) The employer shall establish and maintain an accurate record for each employee subject to medical surveillance by paragraph (l)(1)(i) of this Section, in accordance with 29 CFR §1910.1020.

(m)(3)(ii) The record shall include at least the following information:

(m)(3)(ii)(A) The name and social security number of the employee;

(m)(3)(ii)(B) Physician's written opinions;

(m)(3)(ii)(C) Any employee medical complaints related to exposure to asbestos; and

(m)(3)(ii)(D) A copy of the information provided to the physician as required by paragraph (l)(6) of this Section.

(m)(3)(iii) The employer shall ensure that this record is maintained for the duration of employment plus thirty (30) years, in accordance with 29 CFR §1910.1020.

(m)(4) **Training** The employer shall maintain all employee training records for one (1) year beyond the last date of employment of that employee.

(m)(5) OI **Availability**

(m)(5)(i) The employer, upon written request, shall make all records required to be maintained by this Section available to the Assistant Secretary and the Director for examination and copying.

(m)(5)(ii) The employer, upon request shall make any exposure records required by paragraph (m)(1) of this Section available for examination and copying to affected employees, former employees, designated representatives and the Assistant Secretary, in accordance with 29 CFR §1910.1020 (a) through (e) and (g) through (i).

(m)(5)(iii) The employer, upon request, shall make employee medical records required by paragraph (m)(3) of this Section available for examination and copying to the subject employee, to anyone having the specific written consent of the subject employee, and the Assistant Secretary, in accordance with 29 CFR §1910.1020.

(m)(6) **Transfer of records** The employer shall comply with the requirements concerning transfer of records set forth in 29 CFR §1910.1020(h).

(n) **Observation of monitoring**

(n)(1) **Employee observation** The employer shall provide affected employees or their designated representatives an opportunity to observe any monitoring of employee exposure to asbestos conducted in accordance with paragraph (d) of this Section.

(n)(2) **Observation procedures** When observation of the monitoring of employee exposure to asbestos requires entry into an area where the use of protective clothing or equipment is required, the observer shall be provided with and be required to use such clothing and equipment and shall comply with all other applicable safety and health procedures.

(o) **Appendices**

(o)(1) Appendices A, C, D, E, and F to this Section are incorporated as part of this Section and the contents of these Appendices are mandatory.

(o)(2) Appendices B, G, H, I, and J to this Section are informational and are not intended to create any additional obligations not otherwise imposed or to detract from any existing obligations.

§1910.1001 Appendix A OI
OSHA reference method
Mandatory

This mandatory Appendix specifies the procedure for analyzing air samples for asbestos and specifies quality control procedures that must be implemented by laboratories performing the analysis. The sampling and analytical methods described below represent the elements of the available monitoring methods (such as Appendix B of their regulation, the most current version of the OSHA method ID–160, or the most current version of the NIOSH Method 7400). All employers who are required to conduct air monitoring under paragraph (d) of the Standard are required to utilize analytical laboratories that use this procedure, or an equivalent method, for collecting and analyzing samples.

Sampling and Analytical Procedure

1. The sampling medium for air samples shall be mixed cellulose ester filter membranes. These shall be designated by the manufacturer as suitable for asbestos counting. See below for rejection of blanks.

2. The preferred collection device shall be the 25-mm diameter cassette with an open-faced 50-mm electrically conductive extension cowl. The 37-mm cassette may be used if necessary but only if written justification for the need to use the 37-mm filter cassette accompanies the sample results in the employee's exposure monitoring record. Do not reuse or reload cassettes for asbestos sample collection.

3. An air flow rate between 0.5 liter/min and 2.5 liters/min shall be selected for the 25-mm cassette. If the 37-mm cassette is used, an air flow rate between 1 liter/min and 2.5 liters/min shall be selected.

4. Where possible, a sufficient air volume for each air sample shall be collected to yield between 100 and 1,300 fibers per square millimeter on the membrane filter. If a filter darkens in appearance or if loose dust is seen on the filter, a second sample shall be started.

5. Ship the samples in a rigid container with sufficient packing material to prevent dislodging the collected fibers. Packing material that has a high electrostatic charge on its surface (e.g., expanded polystyrene) cannot be used because such material can cause loss of fibers to the sides of the cassette.

6. Calibrate each personal sampling pump before and after use with a representative filter cassette installed between the pump and the calibration devices.

7. Personal samples shall be taken in the "breathing zone" of the employee (i.e., attached to or near the collar or lapel near the worker's face).

8. Fiber counts shall be made by positive phase contrast using a microscope with an 8 to 10X eyepiece and a 40 to 45X objective for a total magnification of approximately 400X and a numerical aperture of 0.65 to 0.75. The microscope shall also be fitted with a green or blue filter.

9. The microscope shall be fitted with a Walton-Beckett eyepiece graticule calibrated for a field diameter of 100 micrometers (± 2 micrometers).

10. The phase-shift detection limit of the microscope shall be about 3 degrees measured using the HSE phase shift test slide as outlined below.

a. Place the test slide on the microscope stage and center it under the phase objective.

b. Bring the blocks of grooved lines into focus.

Note: The slide consists of seven sets of grooved lines (ca. 20 grooves to each block) in descending order of visibility from sets 1 to 7, seven being the least visible. The requirements for asbestos counting are that the microscope optics must resolve the grooved lines in set 3 completely, although they may appear somewhat faint, and that the grooved lines in sets 6 and 7 must be invisible. Sets 4 and 5 must be at least partially visible but may vary slightly in visibility between microscopes. A microscope that fails to meet these requirements has either too low or too high a resolution to be used for asbestos counting.

c. If the image deteriorates, clean and adjust the microscope optics. If the problem persists, consult the microscope manufacturer.

11. Each set of samples taken will include 10% field blanks or a minimum of 2 field blanks. These blanks must come from the same lot as the filters used for sample collection. The field blank results shall be averaged and subtracted from the analytical results before reporting. A set consists of any sample or group of samples for which an evaluation for this Standard must be made. Any samples represented by a field blank having a fiber count in excess of the detection limit of the method being used shall be rejected.

12. The samples shall be mounted by the acetone/triacetin method or a method with an equivalent index of refraction and similar clarity.

13. Observe the following counting rules.

a. Count only fibers equal to or longer than 5 micrometers. Measure the length of curved fibers along the curve.

b. In the absence of other information, count all particles as asbesto that have a length-to-width ratio (aspect ratio) of 3:1 or greater.

c. Fibers lying entirely within the boundary of the Walton-Beckett graticule field shall receive a count of 1. Fibers crossing the boundary once, having one end within the circle, shall receive the count of one half (1/2). Do not count any fiber that crosses the graticule boundary more than once. Reject and do not count any other fibers even though they may be visible outside the graticule area.

d. Count bundles of fibers as one fiber unless individual fibers can be identified by observing both ends of an individual fiber.

e. Count enough graticule fields to yield 100 fibers. Count a minimum of 20 fields; stop counting at 100 fields regardless of fiber count.

14. Blind recounts shall be conducted at the rate of 10 percent.

Quality Control Procedures.

1. **Intralaboratory program** Each laboratory and/or each company with more than one microscopist counting slides shall establish a statistically designed quality assurance program involving blind recounts and comparisons between microscopists to monitor the variability of counting by each microscopist and between microscopists. In a company with more than one laboratory, the program shall include all laboratories and shall also evaluate the laboratory-to-laboratory variability.

2.a. **Interlaboratory program** Each laboratory analyzing asbestos samples for compliance determination shall implement an interlaboratory quality assurance program that as a minimum includes participation of at least two other independent laboratories. Each laboratory shall participate in round robin testing at least once every 6 months with at least all the other laboratories in its interlaboratory quality assurance group. Each laboratory shall submit slides typical of its own work load for use in this program. The round robin shall be designed and results analyzed using appropriate statistical methodology.

2.b. All laboratories should also participate in a national sample testing scheme such as the Proficiency Analytical Testing Program (PAT), or the Asbestos Registry sponsored by the American Industrial Hygiene Association (AIHA).

3. All individuals performing asbestos analysis must have taken the NIOSH course for sampling and evaluating airborne asbestos dust or an equalivalent course.

4. When the use of different microscopes contributes to differences between counters and laboratories, the effect of the different microscope shall be evaluated and the microscope shall be replaced, as necessary.

5. Current results of these quality assurance programs shall be posted in each laboratory to keep the microscopists informed.

§1910.1001 Appendix B
Detailed Procedures for Asbestos Sampling and Analysis

Nonmandatory

Matrix Air: OSHA Permissible Exposure Limits: Time Weighted Average Excursion Level (30 minutes)	 0.1 fiber/cc 1.0 fiber/cc
Collection Procedure: A known volume of air is drawn through a 25-mm diameter cassette containing a mixed-cellulose ester filter. The cassette must be equipped with an electrically conductive 50-mm extension cowl. The sampling time and rate are chosen to give a fiber density of between 100 to 1,300 fibers/mm^2 on the filter.	
Recommended Sampling Rate	0.5 to 5.0 liters/minute (L/min)
Recommended Air Volumes: Minimum Maximum	 25 L 2,400 L

Analytical Procedure: A portion of the sample filter is cleared and prepared for asbestos fiber counting by Phase Contrast Microscopy (PCM) at 400X.

Commercial manufacturers and products mentioned in this method are for descriptive use only and do not constitute endorsements by USDOL-OSHA. Similar products from other sources can be substituted.

1. Introduction

This method describes the collection of airborne asbestos fibers using calibrated sampling pumps with mixed-cellulose ester (MCE) filters and analysis by phase contrast microscopy (PCM). Some terms used are unique to this method and are defined below:

Asbestos A term for naturally occurring fibrous minerals. Asbestos includes chrysotile, crocidolite, amosite (cummingtonite-grunerite asbestos), tremolite asbestos, actinolite asbestos, anthophyllite asbestos, and any of these minerals that have been chemically treated and/or altered. The precise chemical formulation of each species will vary with the location from which it was mined. Nominal compositions are listed:

Chrysotile	$Mg_3Si_2O_5(OH)_4$
Crocidolite	$Na_2Fe_3{}^2+ Fe_2{}^3 + Si_8O_{22}(OH)^2$
Amosite	$(Mg,Fe)_7Si8O_{22}(OH)_2$
Tremolite-actinolite	$Ca_2(Mg,Fe)_5Si_8O_{22}(OH)_2$
Anthophyllite	$(Mg,Fe)_7Si_8O_{22}(OH)_2$

Asbestos Fiber A fiber of asbestos which meets the criteria specified below for a fiber.

Aspect Ratio The ratio of the length of a fiber to it's diameter (e.g. 3:1, 5:1 aspect ratios).

Cleavage Fragments Mineral particles formed by comminution of minerals, especially those characterized by parallel sides and a moderate aspect ratio (usually less than 20:1).

Detection Limit The number of fibers necessary to be 95% certain that the result is greater than zero.

Differential Counting The term applied to the practice of excluding certain kinds of fibers from the fiber count because they do not appear to be asbestos.

Fiber A particle that is 5 µm or longer, with a length-to-width ratio of 3 to 1 or longer.

Field The area within the graticule circle that is superimposed on the microscope image.

Set The samples which are taken, submitted to the laboratory, analyzed, and for which, interim or final result reports are generated.

Tremolite, Anthophyllite, and Actinolite The non-asbestos form of these minerals which meet the definition of a fiber. It includes any of these minerals that have been chemically treated and/or altered.

Walton-Beckett Graticule An eyepiece graticule specifically designed for asbestos fiber counting. It consists of a circle with a projected diameter of 100 2 µm (area of about 0.00785 mm^2) with a crosshair having tic-marks at 3-µm intervals in one direction and 5-µm in the orthogonal direction. There are marks around the periphery of the circle to demonstrate the proper sizes and shapes of fibers. This design is reproduced in Figure 1. The disk is placed in one of the microscope eyepieces so that the design is superimposed on the field of view.

1.1. History

Early surveys to determine asbestos exposures were conducted using impinger counts of total dust with the counts expressed as million particles per cubic foot. The British Asbestos Research Council recommended filter membrane counting in 1969. In July 1969, the Bureau of Occupational Safety and Health published a filter membrane method for counting asbestos fibers in the United States. This method was refined by NIOSH and published as PCAM 239. On May 29, 1971, OSHA specified filter membrane sampling with phase contrast counting for evaluation of asbestos exposures at work sites in the United States. The use of this technique was again required by OSHA in 1986. Phase contrast microscopy has continued to be the method of choice for the measurement of occupational exposure to asbestos.

1.2. Principle

Air is drawn through a MCE filter to capture airborne asbestos fibers. A wedge shaped portion of the filter is removed, placed on a glass microscope slide and made transparent. A measured area (field) is viewed by PCM. All the fibers meeting defined criteria for asbestos are counted and considered a measure of the airborne asbestos concentration.

1.3. Advantages and Disadvantages

There are four main advantages of PCM over other methods:

(1) The technique is specific for fibers. Phase contrast is a fiber counting technique which excludes non-fibrous particles from the analysis.

(2) The technique is inexpensive and does not require specialized knowledge to carry out the analysis for total fiber counts.

(3) The analysis is quick and can be performed on-site for rapid determination of air concentrations of asbestos fibers.

(4) The technique has continuity with historical epidemiological studies so that estimates of expected disease can be inferred from long-term determinations of asbestos exposures.

The main disadvantage of PCM is that it does not positively identify asbestos fibers. Other fibers which are not asbestos may be included in the count unless differential counting is performed. This requires a great deal of experience to adequately differentiate asbestos from non-asbestos fibers. Positive identification of asbestos must be performed by polarized light or electron microscopy techniques. A further disadvantage of PCM is that the smallest visible fibers are about 0.2 µm in diameter while the finest asbestos fibers may be as small as 0.02 µm in diameter. For some exposures, substantially more fibers may be present than are actually counted.

1.4. Workplace Exposure

Asbestos is used by the construction industry in such products as shingles, floor tiles, asbestos cement, roofing felts, insulation and acoustical products. Non-construction uses include brakes, clutch facings, paper, paints, plastics, and fabrics. One of the most significant exposures in the workplace is the removal and encapsulation of asbestos in schools, public buildings, and homes. Many workers have the potential to be exposed to asbestos during these operations.

About 95% of the asbestos in commercial use in the United States is chrysotile. Crocidolite and amosite make up most of the remainder. Anthophyllite and tremolite or actinolite are likely to be encountered as contaminants in various industrial products.

1.5. Physical Properties

Asbestos fiber possesses a high tensile strength along its axis, is chemically inert, non-combustible, and heat resistant. It has a high electrical resistance and good sound absorbing properties. It can be weaved into cables, fabrics or other textiles, and also matted into asbestos papers, felts, or mats.

2. Range and Detection Limit

2.1. The ideal counting range on the filter is 100 to 1,300 fibers/mm^2 . With a Walton-Beckett graticule this range is equivalent to 0.8 to 10 fibers/field. Using NIOSH counting statistics, a count of 0.8 fibers/field would give an approximate coefficient of variation (CV) of 0.13.

2.2. The detection limit for this method is 4.0 fibers per 100 fields or 5.5 fibers/mm^2. This was determined using an equation to estimate the maximum CV possible at a specific concentration (95% confidence) and a Lower Control Limit of zero. The CV value was then used to determine a corresponding concentration from historical CV vs. fiber relationships. As an example:

$$\text{Lower Control Limit (95\% Confidence)} = AC - 1.645(CV)(AC)$$

Where:

AC = Estimate of the airborne fiber concentration (fibers/cc) Setting the Lower Control Limit = 0 and solving for CV:

$0 = AC - 1.645(CV)(AC)$

$CV = 0.61$

This value was compared with CV vs. count curves. The count at which CV = 0.61 for Leidel-Busch counting statistics or for an OSHA Salt Lake Technical Center (OSHA-SLTC) CV curve (see Appendix A for further information) was 4.4 fibers or 3.9 fibers per 100 fields, respectively. Although a lower detection limit of 4 fibers per 100 fields is supported by the OSHA-SLTC data, both data sets support the 4.5 fibers per 100 fields value.

3. Method Performance—Precision and Accuracy

Precision is dependent upon the total number of fibers counted and the uniformity of the fiber distribution on the filter. A general rule is to count at least 20 and not more than 100 fields. The count is discontinued when 100 fibers are counted, provided that 20 fields have already been counted. Counting more than 100 fibers results in only a small gain in precision. As the total count drops below 10 fibers, an accelerated loss of precision is noted.

At this time, there is no known method to determine the absolute accuracy of the asbestos analysis. Results of samples prepared through the Proficiency Analytical Testing (PAT) Program and analyzed by the OSHA-SLTC showed no significant bias when compared to PAT reference values. The PAT samples were analyzed from 1987 to 1989 (N=36) and the concentration range was from 120 to 1,300 fibers/mm^2 .

4. Interferences

Fibrous substances, if present, may interfere with asbestos analysis.

Some common fibers are:

- fiberglass
- anhydrite
- plant fibers
- perlite veins
- gypsum
- some synthetic fibers
- membrane structures
- sponge spicules
- diatoms
- microorganisms
- wollastonite

The use of electron microscopy or optical tests such as polarized light, and dispersion staining may be used to differentiate these materials from asbestos when necessary.

5. Sampling

5.1. Equipment

5.1.1. Sample assembly (The assembly is shown in Figure 3). Conductive filter holder consisting of a 25-mm diameter, 3-piece cassette having a 50-mm long electrically conductive extension cowl. Backup pad, 25-mm, cellulose. Membrane filter, mixed-cellulose ester (MCE), 25-mm, plain, white, 0.4 to 1.2-µm pore size.

Notes:

(a) Do not re-use cassettes.

(b) Fully conductive cassettes are required to reduce fiber loss to the sides of the cassette due to electrostatic attraction.

(c) Purchase filters which have been selected by the manufacturer for asbestos counting or analyze representative filters for fiber background before use. Discard the filter lot if more than 4 fibers/100 fields are found.

(d) To decrease the possibility of contamination, the sampling system (filter-backup pad-cassette) for asbestos is usually preassembled by the manufacturer.

(e) Other cassettes, such as the Bell-mouth, may be used within the limits of their validation.

5.1.2. Gel bands for sealing cassettes

5.1.3. Sampling pump

Each pump must be a battery operated, self-contained unit small enough to be placed on the monitored employee and not interfere with the work being performed. The pump must be capable of sampling at the collection rate for the required sampling time.

5.1.4. Flexible tubing, 6-mm bore

5.1.5. Pump calibration

Stopwatch and bubble tube/burette or electronic meter

5.2. Sampling Procedure

5.2.1. Seal the point where the base and cowl of each cassette meet with a gel band or tape.

5.2.2. Charge the pumps completely before beginning.

5.2.3. Connect each pump to a calibration cassette with an appropriate length of 6-mm bore plastic tubing. Do not use luer connectors—the type of cassette specified above has built-in adapters.

5.2.4. Select an appropriate flow rate for the situation being monitored. The sampling flow rate must be between 0.5 and 5.0 L/min for personal sampling and is commonly set between 1 and 2 L/min. Always choose a flow rate that will not produce overloaded filters.

5.2.5. Calibrate each sampling pump before and after sampling with a calibration cassette in-line (**Note:** This calibration cassette should be from the same lot of cassettes used for sampling). Use a primary standard (e.g. bubble burette) to calibrate each pump. If possible, calibrate at the sampling site.

Note: If sampling site calibration is not possible, environmental influences may affect the flow rate. The extent is dependent on the type of pump used. Consult with the pump manufacturer to determine dependence on environmental influences. If the pump is affected by temperature and pressure changes, correct the flow rate using the formula shown in the section "Sampling Pump Flow Rate Corrections" at the end of this Appendix.

5.2.6. Connect each pump to the base of each sampling cassette with flexible tubing. Remove the end cap of each cassette and take each air sample open face. Assure that each sample cassette is held open side down in the employee's breathing zone during sampling. The distance from the nose/mouth of the employee to the cassette should be about 10 cm. Secure the cassette on the collar or lapel of the employee using spring clips or other similar devices.

5.2.7. A suggested minimum air volume when sampling to determine TWA compliance is 25 L. For Excursion Limit (30 min sampling time) evaluations, a minimum air volume of 48 L is recommended.

5.2.8. The most significant problem when sampling for asbestos is overloading the filter with non-asbestos dust. Suggested maximum air sample volumes for specific environments are:

Environment	Air vol. (L)
Asbestos removal operations (visible dust)	100
Asbestos removal operations (little dust)	240
Office environments	400 to 2,400

Caution: Do not overload the filter with dust. High levels of non-fibrous dust particles may obscure fibers on the filter and lower the count or make counting impossible. If more than about 25 to 30% of the field area is obscured with dust, the result may be biased low. Smaller air volumes may be necessary when there is excessive non-asbestos dust in the air.

While sampling, observe the filter with a small flashlight. If there is a visible layer of dust on the filter, stop sampling, remove and seal the cassette, and replace with a new sampling assembly. The total dust loading should not exceed 1 mg.

5.2.9. Blank samples are used to determine if any contamination has occurred during sample handling. Prepare two blanks for the first 1 to 20 samples. For sets containing greater than 20 samples, prepare blanks as 10% of the samples. Handle blank samples in the same manner as air samples with one exception: Do not draw any air through the blank samples. Open the blank cassette in the place where the sample cassettes are mounted on the employee. Hold it open for about 30 seconds. Close and seal the cassette appropriately. Store blanks for shipment with the sample cassettes.

5.2.10. Immediately after sampling, close and seal each cassette with the base and plastic plugs. Do not touch or puncture the filter membrane as this will invalidate the analysis.

5.2.11. Attach and secure a sample seal around each sample cassette in such a way as to assure that the end cap and base plugs cannot be removed without destroying the seal. Tape the ends of the seal together since the seal is not long enough to be wrapped end-to-end. Also wrap tape around the cassette at each joint to keep the seal secure.

5.3. Sample Shipment

5.3.1. Send the samples to the laboratory with paperwork requesting asbestos analysis. List any known fibrous interferences present during sampling on the paperwork. Also, note the workplace operation(s) sampled.

5.3.2. Secure and handle the samples in such that they will not rattle during shipment nor be exposed to static electricity. Do not ship samples in expanded polystyrene peanuts, vermiculite, paper shreds, or excelsior. Tape sample cassettes to sheet bubbles and place in a container that will cushion the samples in such a manner that they will not rattle.

5.3.3. To avoid the possibility of sample contamination, always ship bulk samples in separate mailing containers.

6. Analysis

6.1. Safety Precautions

6.1.1. Acetone is extremely flammable and precautions must be taken not to ignite it. Avoid using large containers or quantities of acetone. Transfer the solvent in a ventilated laboratory hood. Do not use acetone near any open flame. For generation of acetone vapor, use a spark free heat source.

6.1.2. Any asbestos spills should be cleaned up immediately to prevent dispersal of fibers. Prudence should be exercised to avoid contamination of laboratory facilities or exposure of personnel to asbestos. Asbestos spills should be cleaned up with wet methods and/or a High Efficiency Particulate-Air (HEPA) filtered vacuum.

Caution: Do not use a vacuum without a HEPA filter—It will disperse fine asbestos fibers into the air.

6.2. Equipment

6.2.1. Phase contrast microscope with binocular or trinocular head

6.2.2. Widefield or Huygenian 10X eyepieces (**Note:** The eyepiece containing the graticule must be a focusing eyepiece. Use a 40X phase objective with a numerical aperture of 0.65 to 0.75).

6.2.3. Kohler illumination (if possible) with green or blue filter

6.2.4. Walton-Beckett Graticule, type G–22 with 100 ± 2 µm projected diameter

6.2.5. Mechanical stage. A rotating mechanical stage is convenient for use with polarized light

6.2.6. Phase telescope

6.2.7. Stage micrometer with 0.01–mm subdivisions

6.2.8. Phase-shift test slide, mark II (Available from PTR optics Ltd., and also McCrone)

6.2.9. Precleaned glass slides, 25 mm × 75 mm. One end can be frosted for convenience in writing sample numbers, etc., or paste-on labels can be used

6.2.10. Cover glass #1½

6.2.11. Scalpel (#10, curved blade)

6.2.12. Fine tipped forceps

6.2.13. Aluminum block for clearing filter (see Appendix D and Figure 4)

6.2.14. Automatic adjustable pipette, 100- to 500-µL

6.2.15. Micropipette, 5 µL

6.3. Reagents

6.3.1. Acetone (HPLC grade)

6.3.2. Triacetin (glycerol triacetate)

6.3.3. Lacquer or nail polish

6.4. Standard Preparation

A way to prepare standard asbestos samples of known concentration has not been developed. It is possible to prepare replicate samples of nearly equal concentration. This has been performed through the PAT program. These asbestos samples are distributed by the AIHA to participating laboratories.

Since only about one-fourth of a 25–mm sample membrane is required for an asbestos count, any PAT sample can serve as a "standard" for replicate counting.

6.5. Sample Mounting

Note: See Safety Precautions in Section 6.1. before proceeding. The objective is to produce samples with a smooth (non-grainy) background in a medium with a refractive index of approximately 1.46. The technique below collapses the filter for easier focusing and produces permanent mounts which are useful for quality control and interlaboratory comparison.

An aluminum block or similar device is required for sample preparation.

6.5.1. Heat the aluminum block to about 70 °C. The hot block should not be used on any surface that can be damaged by either the heat or from exposure to acetone.

6.5.2. Ensure that the glass slides and cover glasses are free of dust and fibers.

6.5.3. Remove the top plug to prevent a vacuum when the cassette is opened. Clean the outside of the cassette if necessary. Cut the seal and/or tape on the cassette with a razor blade. Very carefully separate the base from the extension cowl, leaving the filter and backup pad in the base.

6.5.4. With a rocking motion cut a triangular wedge from the filter using the scalpel. This wedge should be one-sixth to one-fourth of the filter. Grasp the filter wedge with the forceps on the perimeter of the filter which was clamped between the cassette pieces. DO NOT TOUCH the filter with your finger. Place the filter on the glass slide sample side up. Static electricity will usually keep the filter on the slide until it is cleared.

6.5.5. Place the tip of the micropipette containing about 200 µL acetone into the aluminum block. Insert the glass slide into the receiving slot in the aluminum block. Inject the acetone into the block with slow, steady pressure on the plunger while holding the pipette firmly in place. Wait 3 to 5 seconds for the filter to clear, then remove the pipette and slide from the aluminum block.

6.5.6. Immediately (less than 30 seconds) place 2.5 to 3.5 μL of triacetin on the filter (**Note:** Waiting longer than 30 seconds will result in increased index of refraction and decreased contrast between the fibers and the preparation. This may also lead to separation of the cover slip from the slide).

6.5.7. Lower a cover slip gently onto the filter at a slight angle to reduce the possibility of forming air bubbles. If more than 30 seconds have elapsed between acetone exposure and triacetin application, glue the edges of the cover slip to the slide with lacquer or nail polish.

6.5.8. If clearing is slow, warm the slide for 15 min on a hot plate having a surface temperature of about 50 °C to hasten clearing. The top of the hot block can be used if the slide is not heated too long.

6.5.9. Counting may proceed immediately after clearing and mounting are completed.

6.6. Sample Analysis

Completely align the microscope according to the manufacturer's instructions. Then, align the microscope using the following general alignment routine at the beginning of every counting session and more often if necessary.

6.6.1. Alignment

(1) Clean all optical surfaces. Even a small amount of dirt can significantly degrade the image.

(2) Rough focus the objective on a sample.

(3) Close down the field iris so that it is visible in the field of view. Focus the image of the iris with the condenser focus. Center the image of the iris in the field of view.

(4) Install the phase telescope and focus on the phase rings. Critically center the rings. Misalignment of the rings results in astigmatism which will degrade the image.

(5) Place the phase-shift test slide on the microscope stage and focus on the lines. The analyst must see line set 3 and should see at least parts of 4 and 5 but, not see line set 6 or 6. A microscope/microscopist combination which does not pass this test may not be used.

6.6.2. Counting Fibers

(1) Place the prepared sample slide on the mechanical stage of the microscope. Position the center of the wedge under the objective lens and focus upon the sample.

(2) Start counting from one end of the wedge and progress along a radial line to the other end (count in either direction from perimeter to wedge tip). Select fields randomly, without looking into the eyepieces, by slightly advancing the slide in one direction with the mechanical stage control.

(3) Continually scan over a range of focal planes (generally the upper 10 to 15 μm of the filter surface) with the fine focus control during each field count. Spend at least 5 to 15 seconds per field.

(4) Most samples will contain asbestos fibers with fiber diameters less than 1 μm. Look carefully for faint fiber images. The small diameter fibers will be very hard to see. However, they are an important contribution to the total count.

(5) Count only fibers equal to or longer than 5 μm. Measure the length of curved fibers along the curve.

(6) Count fibers which have a length to width ratio of 3:1 or greater.

(7) Count all the fibers in at least 20 fields. Continue counting until either 100 fibers are counted or 100 fields have been viewed; whichever occurs first. Count all the fibers in the final field.

(8) Fibers lying entirely within the boundary of the Walton-Beckett graticule field shall receive a count of 1. Fibers crossing the boundary once, having one end within the circle shall receive a count of ½. Do not count any fiber that crosses the graticule boundary more than once. Reject and do not count any other fibers even though they may be visible outside the graticule area. If a fiber touches the circle, it is considered to cross the line.

(9) Count bundles of fibers as one fiber unless individual fibers can be clearly identified and each individual fiber is clearly not connected to another counted fiber. See Figure 1 for counting conventions.

(10) Record the number of fibers in each field in a consistent way such that filter non-uniformity can be assessed.

(11) Regularly check phase ring alignment.

(12) When an agglomerate (mass of material) covers more than 25% of the field of view, reject the field and select another. Do not include it in the number of fields counted.

(13) Perform a "blind recount" of 1 in every 10 filter wedges (slides). Re-label the slides using a person other than the original counter.

6.7. Fiber Identification

As previously mentioned in Section 1.3., PCM does not provide positive confirmation of asbestos fibers. Alternate differential counting techniques should be used if discrimination is desirable. Differential counting may include primary discrimination based on morphology, polarized light analysis of fibers, or modification of PCM data by Scanning Electron or Transmission Electron Microscopy.

A great deal of experience is required to routinely and correctly perform differential counting. It is discouraged unless it is legally necessary. Then, only if a fiber is obviously not asbestos should it be excluded from the count. Further discussion of this technique can be found in reference 8.10.

If there is a question whether a fiber is asbestos or not, follow the rule:

"WHEN IN DOUBT, COUNT."

6.8. Analytical Recommendations—Quality Control System

6.8.1. All individuals performing asbestos analysis must have taken the NIOSH course for sampling and evaluating airborne asbestos or an equivalent course.

6.8.2. Each laboratory engaged in asbestos counting shall set up a slide trading arrangement with at least two other laboratories in order to compare performance and eliminate inbreeding of error. The slide exchange occurs at least semiannually. The round robin results shall be posted where all analysts can view individual analyst's results.

6.8.3. Each laboratory engaged in asbestos counting shall participate in the Proficiency Analytical Testing Program, the Asbestos Analyst Registry or equivalent.

6.8.4. Each analyst shall select and count prepared slides from a "slide bank". These are quality assurance counts. The slide bank shall be prepared using uniformly distributed samples taken from the workload. Fiber densities should cover the entire range routinely analyzed by the laboratory. These slides are counted blind by all counters to establish an original standard deviation. This historical distribution is compared with the quality assurance counts. A counter must have 95% of all quality control samples counted within three standard deviations of the historical mean. This count is then integrated into a new historical mean and standard deviation for the slide.

The analyses done by the counters to establish the slide bank may be used for an interim quality control program if the data are treated in a proper statistical fashion.

7. Calculations

7.1. Calculate the estimated airborne asbestos fiber concentration on the filter sample using the following formula:

$$AC = \frac{\left[\left(\frac{FB}{FL}\right) - \left(\frac{BFB}{BFL}\right)\right] \times ECA}{1000 \times FR \times T \times MFA}$$

Where:

AC = Airborne fiber concentration FB = Total number of fibers greater than 5 μm counted

FL = Total number of fields counted on the filter

BFB = Total number of fibers greater than 5 μm counted in the blank

BFL = Total number of fields counted on the blank

ECA = Effective collecting area of filter (385 mm^2 nominal for a 25-mm filter.)

FR = Pump flow rate (L/min)

MFA = Microscope count field area (mm^2). This is 0.00785 mm^2 for a Walton-Beckett Graticule.

T = Sample collection time (min)

1,000 = Conversion of L to cc

Note: The collection area of a filter is seldom equal to 385mm^2 . It is appropriate for laboratories to routinely monitor the exact diameter using an inside micrometer. The collection area is calculated according to the formula:

$$Area = \pi(d/2)^2$$

7.2. Short-cut Calculation

Since a given analyst always has the same interpupillary distance, the number of fields per filter for a particular analyst will remain constant for a given size filter. The field size for that analyst is constant (i.e. the analyst is using an assigned microscope and is not changing the reticle).

For example, if the exposed area of the filter is always 385 mm^2 and the size of the field is always 0.00785 mm^2, the number of fields per filter will always be 49,000. In addition it is necessary to convert liters of air to cc. These three constants can then be combined such that ECA/(1,000 × MFA) = 49. The previous equation simplifies to:

$$AC = \frac{\left[\left(\frac{FB}{FL}\right) - \left(\frac{BFB}{BFL}\right)\right] x\ 49}{FR\ x\ T}$$

7.3. Recount Calculations

As mentioned in step 13 of Section 6.6.2., a "blind recount" of 10% of the slides is performed. In all cases, differences will be observed between the first and second counts of the same filter wedge. Most of these differences will be due to chance alone, that is, due to the random variability (precision) of the count method. Statistical recount criteria enables one to decide whether observed differences can be explained due to chance alone or are probably due to systematic differences between analysts, microscopes, or other biasing factors.

The following recount criterion is for a pair of counts that estimate AC in fibers/cc. The criterion is given at the type-I error level. That is, there is 5% maximum risk that we will reject a pair of counts for the reason that one might be biased, when the large observed difference is really due to chance.

Reject a pair of counts if:

$$\left|\sqrt{AC_2} - \sqrt{AC_1}\right| > 2.78\ x \left(\sqrt{AC_{AVG}}\right) x\ CV_{FB}$$

Where:

AC_1 = lower estimated airborne fiber concentration

AC_2 = higher estimated airborne fiber concentration

AC_{avg} = average of the two concentration estimates

CV_{FB}= CV for the average of the two concentration estimates

If a pair of counts are rejected by this criterion then, recount the rest of the filters in the submitted set. Apply the test and reject any other pairs failing the test. Rejection shall include a memo to the industrial hygienist stating that the sample failed a statistical test for homogeneity and the true air concentration may be significantly different than the reported value.

7.4. Reporting Results

Report results to the industrial hygienist as fibers/cc. Use two significant figures. If multiple analyses are performed on a sample, an average of the results is to be reported unless any of the results can be rejected for cause.

8. References

8.1. Dreesen, W.C., et al, U.S. Public Health Service: A Study of Asbestosis in the Asbestos Textile Industry, (Public Health Bulletin No. 241), US Treasury Dept., Washington, DC, 1938.

8.2. Asbestos Research Council: The Measurement of Airborne Asbestos Dust by the Membrane Filter Method (Technical Note), Asbestos Research Council, Rockdale, Lancashire, Great Britain, 1969.

8.3. Bayer, S.G., Zumwalde, R.D., Brown, T.A., Equipment and Procedure for Mounting Millipore Filters and Counting Asbestos Fibers by Phase Contrast Microscopy, Bureau of Occupational Health, U.S. Dept. of Health, Education and Welfare, Cincinnati, OH, 1969.

8.4. NIOSH Manual of Analytical Methods, 2nd ed., Vol. 1 (DHEW/ NIOSH Pub. No. 77–157–A). National Institute for Occupational Safety and Health, Cincinnati, OH, 1977. pp. 239–1-239–21.

8.5. Asbestos, Code of Federal Regulations 29 CFR §1910.1001. 1971.

8.6. Occupational Exposure to Asbestos, Tremolite, Anthophyllite, and Actinolite. Final Rule, Federal Register 51:119 (20 June 1986). pp.22612–22790.

8.7. Asbestos, Tremolite, Anthophyllite, and Actinolite, Code of Federal Regulations §1910.1001. 1988. pp 711–752.

8.8. Criteria for a Recommended Standard—Occupational Exposure to Asbestos (DHEW/NIOSH Pub. No. HSM 72–10267), National Institute for Occupational Safety and Health NIOSH, Cincinnati,OH, 1972. pp. III–1–III–24.

8.9. Leidel, N.A., Bayer,S.G., Zumwalde, R.D.,Busch, K.A., USPHS/ NIOSH Membrane Filter Method for Evaluating Airborne Asbestos Fibers (DHEW/NIOSH Pub. No. 79–127). National Institute for Occupational Safety and Health, Cincinnati, OH, 1979.

8.10. Dixon, W.C., Applications of Optical Microscopy in Analysis of Asbestos and Quartz, Analytical Techniques in Occupational Health Chemistry, edited by D.D. Dollberg and A.W. Verstuyft. Wash. DC: American Chemical Society, (ACS Symposium Series 120) 1980. pp. 13–41.

Quality Control

The OSHA asbestos regulations require each laboratory to establish a quality control program. The following is presented as an example of how the OSHA-SLTC constructed its internal CV curve as part of meeting this requirement. Data is from 395 samples collected during OSHA compliance inspections and analyzed from October 1980 through April 1986.

Each sample was counted by 2 to 5 different counters independently of one another. The standard deviation and the CV statistic was calculated for each sample. This data was then plotted on a graph of CV vs. fibers/mm^2. A least squares regression was performed using the following equation:

$$CV = antilog1_{10}[A(\log_{10}(x))^2 + B(\log_{10}(x)) + C]$$

Where:

x = the number of fibers/mm^2

Application of least squares gave:

A = 0.182205

B = −0.973343

C = 0.327499

Using these values, the equation becomes:

$$CV = antilog_{10}[0.182205(\log_{10}(x))^2 - 0.973343(\log_{10}(x)) + 0.327499]$$

Sampling Pump Flow Rate Corrections

This correction is used if a difference greater than 5% in ambient temperature and/or pressure is noted between calibration and sampling sites and the pump does not compensate for the differences.

$$Q_{act} = Q_{cal}\ x \sqrt{\left(\frac{P_{cal}}{P_{act}}\right) x \left(\frac{T_{act}}{T_{cal}}\right)}$$

Where:

Q_{act} = actual flow rate

Q_{cal} = calibrated flow rate (if a rotameter was used, the rotameter value)

P_{cal} = uncorrected air pressure at calibration

P_{act} = uncorrected air pressure at sampling site

T_{act} = temperature at sampling site (K)

T_{cal} = temperature at calibration (K)

Walton-Beckett Graticule

When ordering the Graticule for asbestos counting, specify the exact disc diameter needed to fit the ocular of the microscope and the diameter (mm) of the circular counting area. Instructions for measuring the dimensions necessary are listed:

(1) Insert any available graticule into the focusing eyepiece and focus so that the graticule lines are sharp and clear.

(2) Align the microscope.

(3) Place a stage micrometer on the microscope object stage and focus the microscope on the graduated lines.

(4) Measure the magnified grid length, PL (µm), using the stage micrometer.

(5) Remove the graticule from the microscope and measure its actual grid length, AL (mm). This can be accomplished by using a mechanical stage fitted with verniers, or a jeweler's loupe with a direct reading scale.

(6) Let D = 100 µm. Calculate the circle diameter, dc(mm), for the Walton-Beckett graticule and specify the diameter when making a purchase:

$$d_c = \frac{AL\ x\ D}{PL}$$

Example: If PL=108 µm, AL=2.93 mm and D=100 µm, then,

$$d_c = \frac{2.93\ x\ 100}{108}\quad 2.71\ mm$$

(7) Each eyepiece-objective-reticle combination on the microscope must be calibrated. Should any of the three be changed (by zoom adjustment, disassembly, replacement, etc.), the combination must be recalibrated. Calibration may change if interpupillary distance is changed. Measure the field diameter, D (acceptable range: 100 ± 2 µm) with a stage micrometer upon receipt of the graticule from the manufacturer. Determine the field area (mm^2).

$$Field\ Area = \Delta(D/2)^2$$

If D=100 µm=0.1 mm, then

Field Area = $\Delta(0.1\ mm/2)^2 = 0.00785\ mm^2$

The Graticule is available from: Graticules Ltd., Morley Road, Tonbridge TN9 IRN, Kent, England (Telephone 011–44–732–359061). Also available from PTR Optics Ltd., 145 Newton Street, Waltham, MA 02154 [telephone (617) 891–6000] or McCrone Accessories and Components, 2506 S. Michigan Ave., Chicago, IL 60616 [phone (312)-842–7100]. The graticule is custom made for each microscope.

Counts for the Fibers in the Figure

Structure No.	Count	Explanation
1 to 6	1	Single fibers all contained within the circle
7	½	Fiber crosses circle once
8	0	Fiber too short

Structure No.	Count	Explanation
9	2	Two crossing fibers
10	0	Fiber outside graticule
11	0	Fiber crosses graticule twice
12	½	Although split, fiber only crosses once

Figure 1
Walton–Beckett Graticule with some explanatory fibers

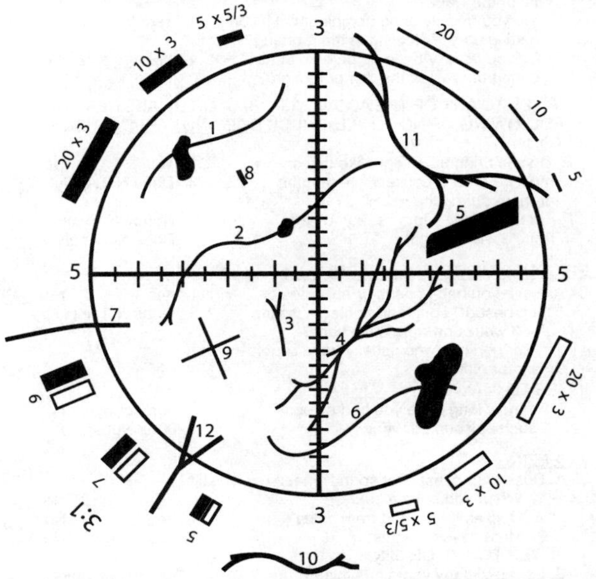

§1910.1001 Appendix C [Reserved]

§1910.1001 Appendix D Medical questionnaires

Mandatory

This mandatory Appendix contains the medical questionnaires that must be administered to all employees who are exposed to asbestos above the permissible exposure limit, and who will therefore be included in their employer's medical surveillance program. Part 1 of the Appendix contains the Initial Medical Questionnaire, which must be obtained for all new hires who will be covered by the medical surveillance requirements. Part 2 includes the abbreviated Periodical Medical Questionnaire, which must be administered to all employees who are provided periodic medical examinations under the medical surveillance provisions of the Standard.

Part 1
INITIAL MEDICAL QUESTIONNAIRE

1. NAME ______
2. SOCIAL SECURITY # ____-____-____
3. CLOCK NUMBER ______
4. PRESENT OCCUPATION ______
5. PLANT ______
6. ADDRESS ______
7. ______ (zip code)
8. TELEPHONE NUMBER ______
9. INTERVIEWER ______
10. DATE ______ Month Day Year
11. Date of Birth ______ Month Day Year
12. Place of Birth ______
13. Sex 1. Male ___ 2. Female ___
14. What is your marital status? 1. Single ___ 2. Married ___ 3. Widowed ___ 4. Separated/Divorced ___
15. Race 1. White ___ 2. Black ___ 3. Asian ___ 4. Hispanic ___ 5. Indian ___ 6. Other ___
16. What is the highest grade completed in school? ______
(For example 12 years is completion of high school.)

OCCUPATIONAL HISTORY

17 A. Have you ever worked full time (30 hours per week or more) for 6 months or more? 1. Yes ___ 2. No ___

IF YES TO 17A:
B. Have you ever worked for a year or more in any dusty job? 1. Yes ___ 2. No ___ 3. Does Not Apply ___

Specify job/industry ______
Total Years Worked ______
What dust exposure: 1. Mild ___ 2. Moderate ___ 3. Severe ___

C. Have you ever been exposed to gas or chemical fumes in your work? 1. Yes ___ 2. No ___
Specify job/industry ______
Total Years Worked ______
What exposure: 1. Mild ___ 2. Moderate ___ 3. Severe ___

D. What has been your usual occupation or job- -the one you have worked at the longest?
1. Job occupation ______
2. Number of years employed in this occupation ______
3. Position/job title ______
4. Business field or industry ______

(Record on lines the years in which you have worked in any of these industries, e.g. 1960-1969)

E. In a mine? 1. Yes ___ 2. No ___ Years: ___
F. In a quarry? 1. Yes ___ 2. No ___ Years: ___
G. In a foundry? 1. Yes ___ 2. No ___ Years: ___
H. In a pottery? 1. Yes ___ 2. No ___ Years: ___
I. In a cotton, flax or hemp mill? 1. Yes ___ 2. No ___ Years: ___
J. With asbestos? 1. Yes ___ 2. No ___ Years: ___

18. PAST MEDICAL HISTORY

A. Do you consider yourself to be in good health? 1. Yes ___ 2. No ___
If "No" state reason ______
B. Have you any defect of vision? 1. Yes ___ 2. No ___
If "YES" state nature of defect ______
C. Have you any hearing defect? 1. Yes ___ 2. No ___ 3. Does Not Apply ___
If "YES" state nature of defect ______

D. Are you suffering from or have you ever suffered from:
a. Epilepsy (fits, seizures, convulsions)? 1. Yes ___ 2. No ___
b. Rheumatic fever? 1. Yes ___ 2. No ___
c. Kidney disease? 1. Yes ___ 2. No ___
d. Bladder disease? 1. Yes ___ 2. No ___
e. Diabetes? 1. Yes ___ 2. No ___
f. Jaundice? 1. Yes ___ 2. No ___

19. CHEST COLDS AND CHEST ILLNESSES

19 A. If you get a cold, does it usually go to your chest? (Usually means more than 1/2 the time) 1. Yes ___ 2. No ___ 3. Don't get colds ___

20 A. During the past 3 years, have you had any chest illnesses that have kept you off work, indoors at home, or in bed? 1. Yes ___ 2. No ___

IF YES TO 20A:
B. Did you produce phlegm with any of these chesk illnesses? 1. Yes ___ 2. No ___ 3. Does Not Apply ___
C. In the last 3 years, how many such illnesses with (increased) phlegm did you have which lasted a week or more? Number of illnesses ___ No such illnesses ___

21. Did you have any lung trouble before the age of 16: 1. Yes ___ 2. No ___

22. Have you ever had any of the following?
1 A. Attacks of bronchitis? 1. Yes ___ 2. No ___
IF YES TO 1A:
B. Was it confirmed by a doctor? 1. Yes ___ 2. No ___ 3. Does Not Apply ___
C. At what age did you first have it? Age in years ___ 2. Does Not Apply ___

2 A. Pneumonia (includes bronchopneumonia)? 1. Yes ___ 2. No ___
IF YES TO 2A:
B. Was it confirmed by a doctor? 1. Yes ___ 2. No ___ 3. Does Not Apply ___
C. At what age did you first have it? Age in years ___ 2. Does Not Apply ___

3 A. Hay Fever? 1. Yes ___ . 2. No ___
IF YES TO 3A:
B. Was it confirmed by a doctor? 1. Yes ___ 2. No ___ 3. Does Not Apply ___
C. At what age did you first have it? Age in years ___ 2. Does Not Apply ___

Note: Questionnaire continues on next page.

23 A. Have you ever had chronic bronchitis? — 1. Yes ___ 2. No ___

IF YES TO 23A:

B. Do you still have it? — 1. Yes ___ 2. No ___ 3. Does Not Apply ___

C. Was it confirmed by a doctor? — 1. Yes ___ 2. No ___ 3. Does Not Apply ___

D. At what age did you first have it? — 1. Yes ___ 2. No ___ 3. Does Not Apply ___

24 A. Have you ever had emphysema? — 1. Yes ___ 2. No ___

IF YES TO 23A:

B. Do you still have it? — 1. Yes ___ 2. No ___ 3. Does Not Apply ___

C. Was it confirmed by a doctor? — 1. Yes ___ 2. No ___ 3. Does Not Apply ___

D. At what age did you first have it? — Age in years ___ 2. Does Not Apply ___

25 A. Have you ever had asthma? — 1. Yes ___ 2. No ___

IF YES TO 23A: — Age in years ___ 2. Does Not Apply ___

B. Do you still have it? — 1. Yes ___ 2. No ___ 3. Does Not Apply ___

C. Was it confirmed by a doctor? — 1. Yes ___ 2. No ___ 3. Does Not Apply ___

D. At what age did you first have it? — Age in years ___ 2. Does Not Apply ___

E. If you no longer have it, at what age did it stop? — Age in years ___ 2. Does Not Apply ___

26. Have you ever had:

A. Any other chest illness? — 1. Yes ___ 2. No ___
If yes, please specify ___

B. Any chest operations? — 1. Yes ___ 2. No ___
If yes, please specify ___

C. Any chest injuries? — 1. Yes ___ 2. No ___
If yes, please specify ___

27 A. Has a doctor ever told you that you had heart trouble? — 1. Yes ___ 2. No ___

IF YES TO 27A:

B. Have you ever had treatment for heart trouble in the past 10 years? — 1. Yes ___ 2. No ___ 3. Does Not Apply ___

28 A. Has a doctor ever told you that you had high blood pressure? — 1. Yes ___ 2. No ___

IF YES TO 28A:

B Have you had any treatment for high blood pressure (hypertension) in the past 10 years? — 1. Yes ___ 2. No ___ 3. Does Not Apply ___

29. When did you last have your chest X-rayed? (Year) ___

30. Where did you last have your chest X-rayed? (if known)? ___

What was the outcome? ___

FAMILY HISTORY

31. Were either of your natural parents ever told by a doctor that they had a chronic lung conditions such as:

	FATHER 1. Yes	FATHER 2. No	FATHER 3. Don't Know	MOTHER 1. Yes	MOTHER 2. No	MOTHER 3. Don't Know
A. Chronic Bronchitis?	___	___	___	___	___	___
B. Emphysema?	___	___	___	___	___	___
C. Asthma?	___	___	___	___	___	___
D. Lung cancer	___	___	___	___	___	___
E. Other chest condition?	___	___	___	___	___	___
F. Is parent currently alive?	___	___	___	___	___	___

G. Please Specify ___ Age if living ___ Age at death ___ Don't know — ___ Age if living ___ Age at death ___ Don't know

H. Please specify cause of death ___

COUGH

32 A. Do you usually have a cough? (Count a cough with first smoke or on first going out of doors. Exclude clearing of throat.) [If no, skip to question 32C.] — 1. Yes ___ 2. No ___

B. Do you usually cough as much as 4 to 6 times a day or 4 or more days out of the week? — 1. Yes ___ 2. No ___

C. Do you usually cough at all on getting up or first thing in the morning? — 1. Yes ___ 2. No ___

D. Do you usually cough at all during the rest of the day or at night — 1. Yes ___ 2. No ___

IF YES TO ANY OF ABOVE (32A, B, C OR D), ANSWER THE FOLLOWING. IF NO TO ALL, CHECK DOES NOT APPLY AND SKIP TO NEXT PAGE.

E. Do you usually cough like this on most days for 3 consecutive months or more during the year? — 1. Yes ___ 2. No ___

F. For how many years have you had the cough? — Number of years ___ Does Not apply ___

33 A. Do you usually bring up phlegm from your chest? (Count phlegm with the first smoke or on first going out of doors. Exclude phlegm from the nose. Count swallowed phlegm.) [If no, skip to 33C.] — 1. Yes ___ 2. No ___

B. Do you usually bring up phlegm like this as much as twice a day 4 or more days out of the week? — 1. Yes ___ 2. No ___

C. Do you usually bring up phlegm at all on getting up or first thing in the morning? — 1. Yes ___ 2. No ___

D. Do you usually bring up phlegm at all during the rest of the day or at night? — 1. Yes ___ 2. No ___

IF YES TO ANY OF THE ABOVE (33A, B, C, OR D), ANSWER THE FOLLOWING. IF NO TO ALL, CHECK DOES NOT APPLY AND SKIP TO 34A.

E. Do you bring up phlegm like this on most days for 3 consecutive months or more during the year? — 1. Yes ___ 2. No ___ 3. Does Not Apply ___

F. For how many years have you had trouble with phlegm — Number of years ___ Does Not Apply ___

EPISODES OF COUGH AND PHLEGM

34 A. Have you had periods or episodes of increased*) cough and phlegm lasting for 3 weeks or more each year? *(For persons who usually have cough and/or phlegm) — 1. Yes ___ 2. No ___ 3. Does Not Apply ___

IF YES TO 34A:

B. For how long have you had at least 1 such episode per year? — Number of years ___ Does Not apply ___

WHEEZING

35 A. Does your chest ever sound wheezy or whistling

1. When you have a cold? — 1. Yes ___ 2. No ___
2. Occasionally apart from colds? — 1. Yes ___ 2. No ___
3. Most days or nights? — 1. Yes ___ 2. No ___

IF YES TO 1, 2, OR 3 IN 35A:

B. For how many years has this been present? — Number of years ___ Does Not apply ___

36 A. Have you ever had an attack of wheezing that has made you feel short of breath? — 1. Yes ___ 2. No ___

IF YES TO 36A:

B. How old were you when your had your first such attack — Number of years ___ Does Not apply ___

C. Have you had 2 or more such episodes? — 1. Yes ___ 2. No ___ 3. Does Not Apply ___

D. Have you ever required medicine or treatment for the(se) attack(s)? — 1. Yes ___ 2. No ___ 3. Does Not Apply ___

BREATHLESSNESS

37. If disabled from walking by any condition other than heart or lung disease, please describe and proceed to question 39A. Nature of condition ___

38. Are you troubled by shortness of breath when hurrying on the level or walking up a slight hill? — 1. Yes ___ 2. No ___

IF YES TO 38A:

B. Do you have to walk lower than people of your age on the level because of breathlessness? — 1. Yes ___ 2. No ___ 3. Does Not Apply ___

C. Do you ever have to stop for breath when walking at your own pace on the level? — 1. Yes ___ 2. No ___ 3. Does Not Apply ___

D. Do you ever have to stop for breath after walking about 100 yards (or after a few minutes) on the level? — 1. Yes ___ 2. No ___ 3. Does Not Apply ___

E. Are you too breathless to leave the house or breathless on dressing or climbing one flight of stairs? — 1. Yes ___ 2. No ___ 3. Does Not Apply ___

TOBACCO SMOKING

39 A. Have you ever smoked cigarettes? (No means less than 20 packs of cigarettes or 12 oz. of tobacco in a lifetime or less than 1 cigarette a day for 1 year.) — 1. Yes ___ 2. No ___

IF YES TO 39A:

B. Do you now smoke cigarettes (as of one month ago) — 1. Yes ___ 2. No ___ 3. Does Not Apply ___

C. How old were you when you first started regular cigarette smoking? — Age in years ___ Does Not Apply ___

D. If you have stopped smoking cigarettes completely, how old were you when you stopped? — Age stopped ___ Check if still smoking ___ Does Not Apply ___

E. How many cigarettes do you smoke per day now? — Cigarettes per day ___ Does Not Apply ___

F. On the average of the entire time you smoked, how many cigarettes did you smoke per day? — Cigarettes per day ___ Does Not Apply ___

G. Do or did you inhale the cigarette smoke? 1. Does Not Apply ___
2. Not at all ___ 3. Slightly ___
4. Moderately ___ 5. Deeply ___

40 A. Have you ever smoked a pipe regularly? (Yes means more than 12 oz. of tobacco in a lifetime.) 1. Yes ___ 2. No ___

IF YES TO 40A:

B. 1. How old were you when you started to smoke a pipe regularly? Age ___

2. If you have stopped smoking a pipe completely, how old were you when you stopped? Age stopped ___ Check if still smoking a pipe ___ Does not apply ___

C. On the average over the entire time you smoked a pipe, how much pipe tobacco did you smoke per week? ___ oz. per week (a standard pouch of tobacco contains 1½ oz.) Does not apply ___

D. How much pipe tobacco are you smoking now? ___ oz. per week Not currently smoking a pipe ___

E. Do you or did you inhale the pipe smoke? 1. Never smoked ___
2. Not at all ___ 3. Slightly ___
4. Moderately ___ 5. Deeply ___

41 A. Have you ever smoked cigars regularly? (Yes means more than 1 cigar a week for a year) 1. Yes ___ 2. No ___

IF YES TO 41A:

B. 1. How old were you when you started to smoke cigars regularly? Age ___

2. If you have stopped smoking cigars completely, how old were you when you stopped Age stopped ___ Check if still smoking cigars ___ Does Not Apply ___

C. On the average over the entire time you smoked cigars, how many cigars did you smoke per week? Cigars per day ___ Does Not Apply ___

D. How many cigars are you smoking now? Cigars per week ___ Check if not smoking cigars currently ___

E. Do you or did you inhale the cigar smoke? 1. Never smoked ___
2. Not at all ___ 3. Slightly ___
4. Moderately ___ 5. Deeply ___

Signature ______________________ Date ___________

Part 1

INITIAL MEDICAL QUESTIONNAIRE

1. NAME ______________________
2. SOCIAL SECURITY # ______-____-______
3. CLOCK NUMBER ______________________
4. PRESENT OCCUPATION ______________________
5. PLANT ______________________
6. ADDRESS ______________________
7. ______________________ (zip code)
8. TELEPHONE NUMBER ______________________
9. INTERVIEWER ______________________
10. DATE ______________________
Month Day Year

11. What is your marital status? 1. Single ___ 2. Married ___
3. Widowed ___
4. Separated/Divorced ___

12. OCCUPATIONAL HISTORY

12 A. In the past year, did you work full time (30 hours per week or more) for 6 months or more? 1. Yes ___ 2. No ___

IF YES TO 12A:

12 B. In the past year, did you work in a dusty job? 1. Yes ___ 2. No ___ 3. Does Not Apply ___

12 C. Was dust exposure: 1. Mild ___ 2. Moderate ___ 3. Severe ___

12 D. In the past year, were you exposed to gas or chemical fumes in your work? 1. Yes ___ 2. No ___

12 E. Was exposure 1. Mild ___ 2. Moderate ___ 3. Severe ___

12 F. In the past year, what was your:
1. Job/occupation? ______________________
2. Position/job title? ______________________

13. RECENT MEDICAL HISTORY

13 A. Do you consider yourself to be in good health? 1. Yes ___ 2. No ___
If NO, state reason ______________________

13 B. In the past year, have you developed:

Epilepsy?	Yes ___	No ___
Rheumatic fever?	Yes ___	No ___
Kidney disease?	Yes ___	No ___
Bladder disease?	Yes ___	No ___
Diabetes?	Yes ___	No ___
Jaundice?	Yes ___	No ___
Cancer?	Yes ___	No ___

14. CHEST COLDS AND CHEST ILLNESSES

14 A. If you get a cold, does it usually go to your chest? (Usually means more than 1/2 the time) 1. Yes ___ 2. No ___ 3. Does Not Apply ___

15 A. During the past year, have you had illnesses that have kept you off work, indoors at home, or in bed? 1. Yes ___ 2. No ___ 3. Does Not Apply ___

IF YES TO 15A

15 B. Did you produce phlegm with any of these chest illnesses? 1. Yes ___ 2. No ___ 3. Does Not Apply ___

15 C. In the past year, how many such illnesses with (increased) phlegm did you have which lasted a week or more? 1. Number of Illnesses ___ 2. No such illnesses ___

16. RESPIRATORY SYSTEM

In the past year have you had:

	Yes or No	Further Comment on Positive Answers
Asthma	___	___
Bronchitis	___	___
Hay Fever	___	___
Other Allergies	___	___
Pneumonia	___	___
Tuberculosis	___	___
Chest Surgery	___	___
Other Lung Problems	___	___
Heart Disease	___	___
Do you have:		
Frequent colds	___	___
Shortness of breath when walking or climbing one flight of stairs	___	___
Do you:		
Wheeze	___	___
Cough up phlegm	___	___
Smoke cigarettes	___	___

Signature ______________________ Date ___________

§1910.1001 Appendix E Interpretation and classification of chest roentgenograms

Mandatory

(a) Chest roentgenograms shall be interpreted and classified in accordance with a professionally accepted Classification system and recorded on an interpretation form following the format of the CDC/NIOSH (M) 2.8 form. As a minimum, the content within the bold lines of this form (items 1 though 4) shall be included. This form is not to be submitted to NIOSH.

(b) Roentgenograms shall be interpreted and classified only by a B-reader, a board eligible/certified radiologist, or an experienced physician with known expertise in pneumoconioses.

(c) All interpreters, whenever interpreting chest roentgenograms made under this Section, shall have immediately available for reference a complete set of the ILO-U/C International Classification of Radiographs for Pneumoconioses, 1980.

§1910.1001 Appendix F Work practices and engineering controls for automotive brake and clutch inspection, disassembly, repair and assembly

Mandatory

This mandatory Appendix specifies engineering controls and work practices that must be implemented by the employer during automotive brake and clutch inspection, disassembly, repair, and assembly operations. Proper use of these engineering controls and work practices by trained employees will reduce employees' asbestos exposure below the permissible exposure level during clutch and brake inspection, disassembly, repair, and assembly operations. The employer shall institute engineering controls and work practices using either the method set forth in paragraph [A] or paragraph [B] of this Appendix, or any other method which the employer can demonstrate to be equivalent in terms of reducing employee exposure to asbestos as defined and which meets the requirements described in paragraph [C] of this Appendix, for those facilities in which no more than 5 pairs of brakes or 5 clutches are inspected, disassembled, reassembled and/or repaired per week, the method set forth in paragraph [D] of this Appendix may be used:

[A] Negative Pressure Enclosure/HEPA Vacuum System Method

(1) The brake and clutch inspection, disassembly, repair, and assembly operations shall be enclosed to cover and contain the clutch or brake assembly and to prevent the release of asbestos fibers into the worker's breathing zone.

(2) The enclosure shall be sealed tightly and thoroughly inspected for leaks before work begins on brake and clutch inspection, disassembly, repair, and assembly.

(3) The enclosure shall be such that the worker can clearly see the operation and shall provide impermeable sleeves through which the worker can handle the brake and clutch inspection, disassembly, repair and assembly. The integrity of the sleeves and ports shall be examined before work begins.

(4) A HEPA-filtered vacuum shall be employed to maintain the enclosure under negative pressure throughout the operation. Compressed-air may be used to remove asbestos fibers or particles from the enclosure.

(5) The HEPA vacuum shall be used first to loosen the asbestos containing residue from the brake and clutch parts and then to evacuate the loosened asbestos containing material from the enclosure and capture the material in the vacuum filter.

(6) The vacuum's filter, when full, shall be first wetted with a fine mist of water, then removed and placed immediately in an impermeable container, labeled according to paragraph (j)(5) of this Section and disposed of according to paragraph (k) of this Section.

(7) Any spills or releases of asbestos containing waste material from inside of the enclosure or vacuum hose or vacuum filter shall be immediately cleaned up and disposed of according to paragraph (k) of this Section.

[B] Low Pressure/Wet Cleaning Method

(1) A catch basin shall be placed under the brake assembly, positioned to avoid splashes and spills.

(2) The reservoir shall contain water containing an organic solvent or wetting agent. The flow of liquid shall be controlled such that the brake assembly is gently flooded to prevent the asbestos-containing brake dust from becoming airborne.

(3) The aqueous solution shall be allowed to flow between the brake drum and brake support before the drum is removed.

(4) After removing the brake drum, the wheel hub and back of the brake assembly shall be thoroughly wetted to suppress dust.

(5) The brake support plate, brake shoes and brake components used to attach the brake shoes shall be thoroughly washed before removing the old shoes.

(6) In systems using filters, the filters, when full, shall be first wetted with a fine mist of water, then removed and placed immediately in an impermeable container, labeled according to paragraph (j)(4) of this Section and disposed of according to paragraph (k) of this Section.

(7) Any spills of asbestos-containing aqueous solution or any asbestos-containing waste material shall be cleaned up immediately and disposed of according to paragraph (k) of this Section.

(8) The use of dry brushing during low pressure/wet cleaning operations is prohibited.

[C] Equivalent Methods

An equivalent method is one which has sufficient written detail so that it can be reproduced and has been demonstrated that the exposures resulting from the equivalent method are equal to or less than the exposures which would result from the use of the method described in paragraph [A] of this Appendix. For purposes of making this comparison, the employer shall assume that exposures resulting from the use of the method described in paragraph [A] of this Appendix shall not exceed 0.016 f/cc, as measured by the OSHA reference method and as averaged over at least 18 personal samples.

[D] Wet Method.

(1) A spray bottle, hose nozzle, or other implement capable of delivering a fine mist of water or amended water or other delivery system capable of delivering water at low pressure, shall be used to first thoroughly wet the brake and clutch parts. Brake and clutch components shall then be wiped clean with a cloth.

(2) The cloth shall be placed in an impermeable container, labelled according to paragraph (j)(4) of this Section and then disposed of according to paragraph (k) of this Section, or the cloth shall be laundered in a way to prevent the release of asbestos fibers in excess of 0.1 fiber per cubic centimeter of air.

(3) Any spills of solvent or any asbestos containing waste material shall be cleaned up immediately according to paragraph (k) of this Section.

(4) The use of dry brushing during the wet method operations is prohibited.

§1910.1001 Appendix G
Substance Technical Information for Asbestos
Nonmandatory

I. Substance Identification

A. Substance: "Asbestos" is the name of a class of magnesium-silicate minerals that occur in fibrous form. Minerals that are included in this group are chrysotile, crocidolite, amosite, tremolite asbestos, anthophyllite asbestos, and actinolite asbestos.

B. Asbestos is used in the manufacture of heat-resistant clothing, automative brake and clutch linings, and a variety of building materials including floor tiles, roofing felts, ceiling tiles, asbestos-cement pipe and sheet, and fire-resistant drywall. Asbestos is also present in pipe and boiler insulation materials, and in sprayed-on materials located on beams, in crawlspaces, and between walls.

C. The potential for a product containing asbestos to release breatheable fibers depends on its degree of friability. Friable means that the material can be crumbled with hand pressure and is therefore likely to emit fibers. The fibrous or fluffy sprayed-on materials used for fireproofing, insulation, or sound proofing are considered to be friable, and they readily release airborne fibers if disturbed. Materials such as vinyl-asbestos floor tile or roofing felts are considered nonfriable and generally do not emit airborne fibers unless subjected to sanding or sawing operations. Asbestos-cement pipe or sheet can emit airborne fibers if the materials are cut or sawed, or if they are broken during demolition operations.

D. Permissible exposure: Exposure to airborne asbestos fibers may not exceed 0.2 fibers per cubic centimeter of air (0.1 f/cc) averaged over the 8-hour workday.

II. Health Hazard Data

A. Asbestos can cause disabling respiratory disease and various types of cancers if the fibers are inhaled. Inhaling or ingesting fibers from contaminated clothing or skin can also result in these diseases. The symptoms of these diseases generally do not appear for 20 or more years after initial exposure.

B. Exposure to asbestos has been shown to cause lung cancer, mesothelioma, and cancer of the stomach and colon. Mesothelioma is a rare cancer of the thin membrane lining of the chest and abdomen. Symptoms of mesothelioma include shortness of breath, pain in the walls of the chest, and/or abdominal pain.

III. Respirators and Protective Clothing

A. Respirators: You are required to wear a respirator when performing tasks that result in asbestos exposure that exceeds the permissible exposure limit (PEL) of 0.1 f/cc. These conditions can occur while your employer is in the process of installing engineering controls to reduce asbestos exposure, or where engineering controls are not feasible to reduce asbestos exposure. Air-purifying respirators equipped with a high-efficiency particulate air (HEPA) filter can be used where airborne asbestos fiber concentrations do not exceed 2 f/cc; otherwise, air-supplied, positive-pressure, full facepiece respirators must be used. Disposable respirators or dust masks are not permitted to be used for asbestos work. For effective protection, respirators must fit your face and head snugly. Your employer is required to conduct fit tests when you are first assigned a respirator and every 6 months thereafter. Respirators should not be loosened or removed in work situations where their use is required.

B. Protective clothing: You are required to wear protective clothing in work areas where asbestos fiber concentrations exceed the permissible exposure limit.

IV. Disposal Procedures and Cleanup

A. Wastes that are generated by processes where asbestos is present include:

1. Empty asbestos shipping containers
2. Process wastes such as cuttings, trimmings, or reject material
3. Housekeeping waste from sweeping or vacuuming
4. Asbestos fireproofing or insulating material that is removed from buildings
5. Building products that contain asbestos removed during building renovation or demolition
6. Contaminated disposable protective clothing

B. Empty shipping bags can be flattened under exhaust hoods and packed into airtight containers for disposal. Empty shipping drums are difficult to clean and should be sealed.

C. Vacuum bags or disposable paper filters should not be cleaned, but should be sprayed with a fine water mist and placed into a labeled waste container.

D. Process waste and housekeeping waste should be wetted with water or a mixture of water and surfactant prior to packaging in disposable containers.

E. Material containing asbestos that is removed from buildings must be disposed of in leak-tight 6-mil thick plastic bags, plastic-lined cardboard containers, or plastic-lined metal containers. These wastes, which are removed while wet, should be sealed in containers before they dry out to minimize the release of asbestos fibers during handling.

V. Access to Information

A. Each year, your employer is required to inform you of the information contained in this Standard and Appendices for asbestos. In addition, your employer must instruct you in the proper work practices for handling materials containing asbestos, and the correct use of protective equipment.

B. Your employer is required to determine whether you are being exposed to asbestos. You or your representative has the right to observe employee measurements and to record the results obtained. Your employer is required to inform you of your exposure, and, if you are exposed above the permissible limit, he or she is required to inform you of the actions that are being taken to reduce your exposure to within the permissible limit.

C. Your employer is required to keep records of your exposures and medical examinations. These exposure records must be kept for at least thirty (30) years. Medical records must be kept for the period of your employment plus thirty (30) years.

D. Your employer is required to release your exposure and medical records to your physician or designated representative upon your written request.

§1910.1001 Appendix H Medical surveillance guidelines for Asbestos

Nonmandatory

I. Route of Entry Inhalation, Ingestion

II. Toxicology

Clinical evidence of the adverse effects associated with exposure to asbestos is present in the form of several well-conducted epidemiological studies of occupationally exposed workers, family contacts of workers, and persons living near asbestos mines. These studies have shown a definite association between exposure to asbestos and an increased incidence of lung cancer, pleural and peritoneal mesothelioma, gastrointestinal cancer, and asbestosis. The latter is a disabling fibrotic lung disease that is caused only by exposure to asbestos. Exposure to asbestos has also been associated with an increased incidence of esophageal, kidney, laryngeal, pharyngeal, and buccal cavity cancers. As with other known chronic occupational diseases, disease associated with asbestos generally appears about 20 years following the first occurrence of exposure: There are no known acute effects associated with exposure to asbestos.

Epidemiological studies indicate that the risk of lung cancer among exposed workers who smoke cigarettes is greatly increased over the risk of lung cancer among non-exposed smokers or exposed nonsmokers. These studies suggest that cessation of smoking will reduce the risk of lung cancer for a person exposed to asbestos but will not reduce it to the same level of risk as that existing for an exposed worker who has never smoked.

III. Signs and Symptoms of Exposure-Related Disease

The signs and symptoms of lung cancer or gastrointestinal cancer induced by exposure to asbestos are not unique, except that a chest X-ray of an exposed patient with lung cancer may show pleural plaques, pleural calcification, or pleural fibrosis. Symptoms characteristic of mesothelioma include shortness of breath, pain in the walls of the chest, or abdominal pain. Mesothelioma has a much longer latency period compared with lung cancer (40 years versus 15–20 years), and mesothelioma is therefore more likely to be found among workers who were first exposed to asbestos at an early age. Mesothelioma is always fatal.

Asbestosis is pulmonary fibrosis caused by the accumulation of asbestos fibers in the lungs. Symptoms include shortness of breath, coughing, fatigue, and vague feelings of sickness. When the fibrosis worsens, shortness of breath occurs even at rest. The diagnosis of asbestosis is based on a history of exposure to asbestos, the presence of characteristic radiologic changes, end-inspiratory crackles (rales), and other clinical features of fibrosing lung disease. Pleural plaques and thickening are observed on X-rays taken during the early stages of the disease. Asbestosis is often a progressive disease even in the absence of continued exposure, although this appears to be a highly individualized characteristic. In severe cases, death may be caused by respiratory or cardiac failure.

IV. Surveillance and Preventive Considerations

As noted above, exposure to asbestos has been linked to an increased risk of lung cancer, mesothelioma, gastrointestinal cancer, and asbestosis among occupationally exposed workers. Adequate screening tests to determine an employee's potential for developing serious chronic diseases, such as cancer, from exposure to asbestos do not presently exist. However, some tests, particularly chest X-rays and pulmonary function tests, may indicate that an employee has been overexposed to asbestos increasing his or her risk of developing exposure-related chronic diseases. It is important for the physician to become familiar with the operating conditions in which occupational exposure to asbestos is likely to occur. This is particularly important in evaluating medical and work histories and in conducting physical examinations. When an active employee has been identified as having been overexposed to asbestos, measures taken by the employer to eliminate or mitigate further exposure should also lower the risk of serious long-term consequences.

The employer is required to institute a medical surveillance program for all employees who are or will be exposed to asbestos at or above the permissible exposure limit (0.1 fiber per cubic centimeter of air). All examinations and procedures must be performed by or under the supervision of a licensed physician, at a reasonable time and place, and at no cost to the employee.

Although broad latitude is given to the physician in prescribing specific tests to be included in the medical surveillance program, OSHA requires inclusion of the following elements in the routine examination:

(i) Medical and work histories with special emphasis directed to symptoms of the respiratory system, cardiovascular system, and digestive tract.

(ii) Completion of the respiratory disease questionnaire contained in Appendix D.

(iii) A physical examination including a chest roentgenogram and pulmonary function test that includes measurement of the employee's forced vital capacity (FVC) and forced expiratory volume at one second (FEV_1).

(iv) Any laboratory or other test that the examining physician deems by sound medical practice to be necessary.

The employer is required to make the prescribed tests available at least annually to those employees covered; more often than specified if recommended by the examining physician; and upon termination of employment.

The employer is required to provide the physician with the following information: A copy of this Standard and Appendices; a description of the mployee's duties as they relate to asbestos exposure; the employee's representative level of exposure to asbestos; a description of any personal protective and respiratory equipment used; and information from previous medical examinations of the affected employee that is not otherwise available to the physician. Making this information available to the physician will aid in the evaluation of the employee's health in relation to assigned duties and fitness to wear personal protective equipment, if required.

The employer is required to obtain a written opinion from the examining physician containing the results of the medical examination; the physician's opinion as to whether the employee has any detected medical conditions that would place the employee at an increased risk of exposure-related disease; any recommended limitations on the employee or on the use of personal protective equipment; and a statement that the employee has been informed by the physician of the results of the medical examination and of any medical conditions related to asbestos exposure that require further explanation or treatment. This written opinion must not reveal specific findings or diagnoses unrelated to exposure to asbestos, and a copy of the opinion must be provided to the affected employee.

§1910.1001 Appendix I Smoking cessation program information for Asbestos

Nonmandatory

The following organizations provide smoking cessation information and program material.

1. The National Cancer Institute operates a toll-free Cancer Information Service (CIS) with trained personnel to help you. Call 1–800–4–CANCER* to reach the CIS office serving your area, or write: Office of Cancer Communications, National Cancer Institute, National Institutes of Health, Building 31, Room 10A24, Bethesda, Maryland 20892.

*In Hawaii, on Oahu call 524–1234 (call collect from neighboring islands), Spanish-speaking staff members are available during daytime hours to callers from the following areas: California, Florida, Georgia, Illinois, New Jersey (area code 210), New York, and Texas. Consult your local telephone directory for listings of local chapters.

2. American Cancer Society, 3340 Peachtree Road, NE., Atlanta, Georgia 30062, (404) 320–3333.

The American Cancer Society (ACS) is a voluntary organization composed of 58 divisions and 3,100 local units. Through "The Great American Smokeout" in November, the annual Cancer Crusade in April, and numerous educational materials, ACS helps people learn about the health hazards of smoking and become successful ex-smokers.

3. American Heart Association, 7320 Greenville Avenue, Dallas, Texas 75231, (214) 750–5300.

The American Heart Association (AHA) is a voluntary organization with 130,000 members (physicians, scientists, and laypersons) in 55 state and regional groups. AHA produces a variety of publications and audiovisual materials about the effects of smoking on the heart. AHA also has developed a guidebook for incorporating a weight-control component into smoking cessation programs.

4. American Lung Association, 1740 Broadway, New York, New York 10019, (212) 245–8000.

A voluntary organization of 7,500 members (physicians, nurses, and laypersons), the American Lung Association (ALA) conducts numerous public information programs about the health effect of smoking. ALA has 59 state and 85 local units. The organization actively supports legislation and information campaigns for non-smokers' rights and provides help for smokers who want to quit, for example, through "Freedom From Smoking," a self-help smoking cessation program.

5. Office on Smoking and Health, U.S. Department of Health and, Human Services, 5600 Fishers Lane, Park Building, Room 110, Rockville, Maryland 20857.

The Office on Smoking and Health (OSH) is the Department of Health and Human Services' lead agency in smoking control. OSH has sponsored distribution of publications on smoking-realted topics, such as free flyers on relapse after initial quitting, helping a friend or family member quit smoking, the health hazards of smoking, and the effects of parental smoking on teenagers.

§1910.1001 Appendix J
Polarized light microscopy of Asbestos
Nonmandatory

Method number: ID–191

Matrix: Bulk

Collection Procedure

Collect approximately 1 to 2 grams of each type of material and place into separate 20 mL scintillation vials.

Analytical Procedure

A portion of each separate phase is analyzed by gross examination, phase-polar examination, and central stop dispersion microscopy.

Commercial manufacturers and products mentioned in this method are for descriptive use only and do not constitute endorsements by USDOL-OSHA. Similar products from other sources may be substituted.

1. Introduction

This method describes the collection and analysis of asbestos bulk materials by light microscopy techniques including phase- polar illumination and central-stop dispersion microscopy. Some terms unique to asbestos analysis are defined below:

Amphibole A family of minerals whose crystals are formed by long, thin units which have two thin ribbons of double chain silicate with a brucite ribbon in between. The shape of each unit is similar to an "I beam". Minerals important in asbestos analysis include cummingtonite-grunerite, crocidolite, tremolite-actinolite and anthophyllite.

Asbestos A term for naturally occurring fibrous minerals. Asbestos includes chrysotile, cummingtonite-grunerite asbestos (amosite), anthophyllite asbestos, tremolite asbestos, crocidolite, actinolite asbestos and any of these minerals which have been chemically treated or altered. The precise chemical formulation of each species varies with the location from which it was mined. Nominal compositions are listed:

Chrysotile	$Mg_3Si_2O_5(OH)_4$
Crocidolite (Riebeckite asbestos)	$Na_2\ Fe_3{}^2 + Fe_2{}^3 + Si_8\ O_{22}\ (OH)_2$
Cummingtonite-Grunerite asbestos (Amosite)	$(Mg,Fe)_7\ Si_8\ O_{22}\ (OH)_2$
Tremolite-Actinolite asbestos	$Ca_2(Mg,Fe)_5\ Si_8\ O_{22}\ (OH)_2$
Anthophyllite asbestos	$(Mg,Fe)_7\ Si_8\ O_{22}\ (OH)_2$

Asbestos Fiber A fiber of asbestos meeting the criteria for a fiber. (See Section 3.5.)

Aspect Ratio The ratio of the length of a fiber to its diameter usually defined as "length : width", e.g. 3:1.

Brucite A sheet mineral with the composition $Mg(OH)_2$.

Central Stop Dispersion Staining (microscope) This is a dark field microscope technique that images particles using only light refracted by the particle, excluding light that travels through the particle unrefracted. This is usually accomplished with a McCrone objective or other arrangement which places a circular stop with apparent aperture equal to the objective aperture in the back focal plane of the microscope.

Cleavage Fragments Mineral particles formed by the comminution of minerals, especially those characterized by relatively parallel sides and moderate aspect ratio.

Differential Counting The term applied to the practice of excluding certain kinds of fibers from a phase contrast asbestos count because they are not asbestos.

Fiber A particle longer than or equal to 5 µm with a length to width ratio greater than or equal to 3:1. This may include cleavage fragments. (see Section 3.5 of this Appendix).

Phase Contrast Contrast obtained in the microscope by causing light scattered by small particles to destructively interfere with unscattered light, thereby enhancing the visibility of very small particles and particles with very low intrinsic contrast.

Phase Contrast Microscope A microscope configured with a phase mask pair to create phase contrast. The technique which uses this is called Phase Contrast Microscopy (PCM).

Phase-Polar Analysis This is the use of polarized light in a phase contrast microscope. It is used to see the same size fibers that are visible in air filter analysis. Although fibers finer than 1 µm are visible, analysis of these is inferred from analysis of larger bundles that are usually present.

Phase-Polar Microscope The phase-polar microscope is a phase contrast microscope which has an analyzer, a polarizer, a first order red plate and a rotating phase condenser all in place so that the polarized light image is enhanced by phase contrast.

Sealing Encapsulant This is a product which can be applied, preferably by spraying, onto an asbestos surface which will seal the surface so that fibers cannot be released.

Serpentine A mineral family consisting of minerals with the general composition $Mg_3(Si_2O_5(OH)_4$ having the magnesium in brucite layer over a silicate layer. Minerals important in asbestos analysis included in this family are chrysotile, lizardite, antigorite.

1.1. History

Light microscopy has been used for well over 100 years for the determination of mineral species. This analysis is carried out using specialized polarizing microscopes as well as bright field microscopes. The identification of minerals is an on-going process with many new minerals described each year. The first recorded use of asbestos was in Finland about 2500 B.C. where the material was used in the mud wattle for the wooden huts the people lived in as well as strengthening for pottery. Adverse health aspects of the mineral were noted nearly 2000 years ago when Pliny the Younger wrote about the poor health of slaves in the asbestos mines. Although known to be injurious for centuries, the first modern references to its toxicity were by the British Labor Inspectorate when it banned asbestos dust from the workplace in 1898. Asbestosis cases were described in the literature after the turn of the century. Cancer was first suspected in the mid 1930's and a causal link to mesothelioma was made in 1965. Because of the public concern for worker and public safety with the use of this material, several different types of analysis were applied to the determination of asbestos content. Light microscopy requires a great deal of experience and craft. Attempts were made to apply less subjective methods to the analysis. X-ray diffraction was partially successful in determining the mineral types but was unable to separate out the fibrous portions from the non-fibrous portions. Also, the minimum detection limit for asbestos analysis by X-ray diffraction (XRD) is about 1%. Differential Thermal Analysis (DTA) was no more successful. These provide useful corroborating information when the presence of asbestos has been shown by microscopy; however, neither can determine the difference between fibrous and non-fibrous minerals when both habits are present. The same is true of Infrared Absorption (IR).

When electron microscopy was applied to asbestos analysis, hundreds of fibers were discovered present too small to be visible in any light microscope. There are two different types of electron microscope used for asbestos analysis: Scanning Electron Microscope (SEM) and Transmission Electron Microscope (TEM). Scanning Electron Microscopy is useful in identifying minerals. The SEM can provide two of the three pieces of information required to identify fibers by electron microscopy: morphology and chemistry. The third is structure as determined by Selected Area Electron Diffraction—SAED which is performed in the TEM. Although the resolution of the SEM is sufficient for very fine fibers to be seen, accuracy of chemical analysis that can be performed on the fibers varies with fiber diameter in fibers of less than 0.2 µm diameter. The TEM is a powerful tool to identify fibers too small to be resolved by light microscopy and should be used in conjunction with this method when necessary. The TEM can provide all three pieces of information required for fiber identification. Most fibers thicker than 1 µm can adequately be defined in the light microscope. The light microscope remains as the best instrument for the determination of mineral type. This is because the minerals under investigation were first described analytically with the light microscope. It is inexpensive and gives positive identification for most samples analyzed. Further, when optical techniques are inadequate, there is ample indication that alternative techniques should be used for complete identification of the sample.

1.2. Principle

Minerals consist of atoms that may be arranged in random order or in a regular arrangement. Amorphous materials have atoms in random order while crystalline materials have long range order. Many materials are transparent to light, at least for small particles or for thin sections. The properties of these materials can be investigated by the effect that the material has on light passing through it. The six asbestos minerals are all crystalline with particular properties that have been identified and cataloged. These six minerals are anisotropic. They have a regular array of atoms, but the arrangement is not the same in all directions. Each major direction of the crystal presents a different regularity. Light photons travelling in each of these main directions will encounter different electrical neighborhoods, affecting the path and time of travel. The techniques outlined in this method use the fact that light traveling through fibers or crystals in different directions will behave differently, but predictably. The behavior of the light as it travels through a crystal can be measured and compared with known or determined values to identify the mineral species. Usually, Polarized Light Microscopy (PLM) is performed with strain-free objectives on a bright-field microscope platform. This would limit the resolution of the microscope to about 0.4 μm. Because OSHA requires the counting and identification of fibers visible in phase contrast, the phase contrast platform is used to visualize the fibers with the polarizing elements added into the light path. Polarized light methods cannot identify fibers finer than about 1 μm in diameter even though they are visible. The finest fibers are usually identified by inference from the presence of larger, identifiable fiber bundles. When fibers are present, but not identifiable by light microscopy, use either SEM or TEM to determine the fiber identity.

1.3. Advantages and Disadvantages

The advantages of light microcopy are:

(a) Basic identification of the materials was first performed by light microscopy and gross analysis. This provides a large base of published information against which to check analysis and analytical technique.
(b) The analysis is specific to fibers. The minerals present can exist in asbestiform, fibrous, prismatic, or massive varieties all at the same time. Therefore, bulk methods of analysis such as X-ray diffraction, IR analysis, DTA, etc. are inappropriate where the material is not known to be fibrous.
(c) The analysis is quick, requires little preparation time, and can be performed on-site if a suitably equipped microscope is available.

The disadvantages are:

(a) Even using phase-polar illumination, not all the fibers present may be seen. This is a problem for very low asbestos concentrations where agglomerations or large bundles of fibers may not be present to allow identification by inference.
(b) The method requires a great degree of sophistication on the part of the microscopist. An analyst is only as useful as his mental catalog of images. Therefore, a microscopist's accuracy is enhanced by experience. The mineralogical training of the analyst is very important. It is the basis on which subjective decisions are made.
(c) The method uses only a tiny amount of material for analysis. This may lead to sampling bias and false results (high or low). This is especially true if the sample is severely inhomogeneous.
(d) Fibers may be bound in a matrix and not distinguishable as fibers so identification cannot be made.

1.4. Method Performance

1.4.1. This method can be used for determination of asbestos content from 0 to 100% asbestos. The detection limit has not been adequately determined, although for selected samples, the limit is very low, depending on the number of particles examined. For mostly homogeneous, finely divided samples, with no difficult fibrous interferences, the detection limit is below 1%. For inhomogeneous samples (most samples), the detection limit remains undefined. NIST has conducted proficiency testing of laboratories on a national scale. Although each round is reported statistically with an average, control limits, etc., the results indicate a difficulty in establishing precision especially in the low concentration range. It is suspected that there is significant bias in the low range especially near 1%. EPA tried to remedy this by requiring a mandatory point counting scheme for samples less than 10%. The point counting procedure is tedious, and may introduce significant biases of its own. It has not been incorporated into this method.

1.4.2. The precision and accuracy of the quantitation tests performed in this method are unknown. Concentrations are easier to determine in commercial products where asbestos was deliberately added because the amount is usually more than a few percent. An analyst's results can be "calibrated" against the known amounts added by the manufacturer. For geological samples, the degree of homogeneity affects the precision.

1.4.3. The performance of the method is analyst dependent. The analyst must choose carefully and not necessarily randomly the portions for analysis to assure that detection of asbestos occurs when it is present. For this reason, the analyst must have adequate training in sample preparation, and experience in the location and identification of asbestos in samples. This is usually accomplished through substantial on-the-job training as well as formal education in mineralogy and microscopy.

1.5. Interferences

Any material which is long, thin, and small enough to be viewed under the microscope can be considered an interference for asbestos. There are literally hundreds of interferences in workplaces. The techniques described in this method are normally sufficient to eliminate the interferences. An analyst's success in eliminating the interferences depends on proper training.

Asbestos minerals belong to two mineral families: the serpentines and the amphiboles. In the serpentine family, the only common fibrous mineral is chrysotile. Occasionally, the mineral antigorite occurs in a fibril habit with morphology similar to the amphiboles. The amphibole minerals consist of a score of different minerals of which only five are regulated by federal standard: amosite, crocidolite, anthophyllite asbestos, tremolite asbestos and actinolite asbestos. These are the only amphibole minerals that have been commercially exploited for their fibrous properties; however, the rest can and do occur occasionally in asbestiform habit.

In addition to the related mineral interferences, other minerals common in building material may present a problem for some microscopists: gypsum, anhydrite, brucite, quartz fibers, talc fibers or ribbons, wollastonite, perlite, attapulgite, etc. Other fibrous materials commonly present in workplaces are: fiberglass, mineral wool, ceramic wool, refractory ceramic fibers, kevlar, nomex, synthetic fibers, graphite or carbon fibers, cellulose (paper or wood) fibers, metal fibers, etc.

Matrix embedding material can sometimes be a negative interference. The analyst may not be able to easily extract the fibers from the matrix in order to use the method. Where possible, remove the matrix before the analysis, taking careful note of the loss of weight. Some common matrix materials are: vinyl, rubber, tar, paint, plant fiber, cement, and epoxy. A further negative interference is that the asbestos fibers themselves may be either too small to be seen in Phase contrast Microscopy (PCM) or of a very low fibrous quality, having the appearance of plant fibers. The analyst's ability to deal with these materials increases with experience.

1.6. Uses and Occupational Exposure

Asbestos is ubiquitous in the environment. More than 40% of the land area of the United States is composed of minerals which may contain asbestos. Fortunately, the actual formation of great amounts of asbestos is relatively rare. Nonetheless, there are locations in which environmental exposure can be severe such as in the Serpentine Hills of California.

There are thousands of uses for asbestos in industry and the home. Asbestos abatement workers are the most current segment of the population to have occupational exposure to great amounts of asbestos. If the material is undisturbed, there is no exposure. Exposure occurs when the asbestos-containing material is abraded or otherwise disturbed during maintenance operations or some other activity. Approximately 95% of the asbestos in place in the United States is chrysotile.

Amosite and crocidolite make up nearly all the difference. Tremolite and anthophyllite make up a very small percentage. Tremolite is found in extremely small amounts in certain chrysotile deposits. Actinolite exposure is probably greatest from environmental sources, but has been identified in vermiculite containing, sprayed-on insulating materials which may have been certified as asbestos-free.

1.7. Physical and Chemical Properties

The nominal chemical compositions for the asbestos minerals were given in Section 1. Compared to cleavage fragments of the same minerals, asbestiform fibers possess a high tensile strength along the fiber axis. They are chemically inert, non- combustible, and heat resistant. Except for chrysotile, they are insoluble in Hydrochloric acid (HCl). Chrysotile is slightly soluble in HCl. Asbestos has high electrical resistance and good sound absorbing characteristics. It can be woven into cables, fabrics or other textiles, or matted into papers, felts, and mats.

1.8. Toxicology (This section is for Information Only and Should Not Be Taken as OSHA Policy)

Possible physiologic results of respiratory exposure to asbestos are mesothelioma of the pleura or peritoneum, interstitial fibrosis, asbestosis, pneumoconiosis, or respiratory cancer. The possible consequences of asbestos exposure are detailed in the NIOSH Criteria Document or in the OSHA Asbestos Standards 29 CFR §1910.1001 and 29 CFR §1926.1101 and 29 CFR §1915.1001.

2. Sampling Procedure

2.1. Equipment for Sampling

(a) Tube or cork borer sampling device
(b) Knife
(c) 20 mL scintillation vial or similar vial
(d) Sealing encapsulant

2.2. Safety Precautions

Asbestos is a known carcinogen. Take care when sampling. While in an asbestos-containing atmosphere, a properly selected and fit-tested respirator should be worn. Take samples in a manner to cause the least amount of dust. Follow these general guidelines:

(a) Do not make unnecessary dust.
(b) Take only a small amount (1 to 2 g).
(c) Tightly close the sample container.
(d) Use encapsulant to seal the spot where the sample was taken, if necessary.

2.3. Sampling Procedure

Samples of any suspect material should be taken from an inconspicuous place. Where the material is to remain, seal the sampling wound with an encapsulant to eliminate the potential for exposure from the sample site. Microscopy requires only a few milligrams of material. The amount that will fill a 20 mL scintillation vial is more than adequate. Be sure to collect samples from all layers and phases of material. If possible, make separate samples of each different phase of the material. This will aid in determining the actual hazard. DO NOT USE ENVELOPES, PLASTIC OR PAPER BAGS OF ANY KIND TO COLLECT SAMPLES. The use of plastic bags presents a contamination hazard to laboratory personnel and to other samples. When these containers are opened, a bellows effect blows fibers out of the container onto everything, including the person opening the container.

If a cork-borer type sampler is available, push the tube through the material all the way, so that all layers of material are sampled. Some samplers are intended to be disposable. These should be capped and sent to the laboratory. If a non-disposable cork borer is used, empty the contents into a scintillation vial and send to the laboratory. Vigorously and completely clean the cork borer between samples.

2.4 Shipment

Samples packed in glass vials must not touch or they might break in shipment.

(a) Seal the samples with a sample seal over the end to guard against tampering and to identify the sample.
(b) Package the bulk samples in separate packages from the air samples. They may cross-contaminate each other and will invalidate the results of the air samples.
(c) Include identifying paperwork with the samples, but not in contact with the suspected asbestos.
(d) To maintain sample accountability, ship the samples by certified mail, overnight express, or hand carry them to the laboratory.

3. Analysis

The analysis of asbestos samples can be divided into two major parts: sample preparation and microscopy. Because of the different asbestos uses that may be encountered by the analyst, each sample may need different preparation steps. The choices are outlined below. There are several different tests that are performed to identify the asbestos species and determine the percentage. They will be explained below.

3.1. Safety

(a) Do not create unnecessary dust. Handle the samples in HEPA-filter equipped hoods. If samples are received in bags, envelopes or other inappropriate container, open them only in a hood having a face velocity at or greater than 100 fpm. Transfer a small amount to a scintillation vial and only handle the smaller amount.
(b) Open samples in a hood, never in the open lab area.
(c) Index of refraction oils can be toxic. Take care not to get this material on the skin. Wash immediately with soap and water if this happens.
(d) Samples that have been heated in the muffle furnace or the drying oven may be hot. Handle them with tongs until they are cool enough to handle.
(e) Some of the solvents used, such as THF (tetrahydrofuran), are toxic and should only be handled in an appropriate fume hood and according to instructions given in the Safety Data Sheet (SDS).

3.2. Equipment

(a) Phase contrast microscope with 10x, 16x and 40x objectives, 10x wide-field eyepieces, G–22 Walton-Beckett graticule, Whipple disk, polarizer, analyzer and first order red or gypsum plate, 100 Watt illuminator, rotating position condenser with oversize phase rings, central stop dispersion objective, Kohler illumination and a rotating mechanical stage.
(b) Stereo microscope with reflected light illumination, transmitted light illumination, polarizer, analyzer and first order red or gypsum plate, and rotating stage.
(c) Negative pressure hood for the stereo microscope
(d) Muffle furnace capable of 600 °C
(e) Drying oven capable of 50–150 °C
(f) Aluminum specimen pans
(g) Tongs for handling samples in the furnace
(h) High dispersion index of refraction oils (Special for dispersion staining.)
n = 1.550
n = 1.585
n = 1.590
n = 1.605
n = 1.620
n = 1.670
n = 1.680
n = 1.690
(i) A set of index of refraction oils from about n = 1.350 to n = 2.000 in n = 0.005 increments. (Standard for Becke line analysis.)
(j) Glass slides with painted or frosted ends 1×3 inches 1mm thick, precleaned.
(k) Cover Slips 22 × 22 mm, #1 ½
(l) Paper clips or dissection needles
(m) Hand grinder
(n) Scalpel with both #10 and #11 blades
(o) 0.1 molar HCl
(p) Decalcifying solution (Baxter Scientific Products) Ethylenediaminetetraacetic Acid,

Tetrasodium 0.7 g/l	Sodium Potassium Tartrate 8.0 mg/liter
Hydrochloric Acid 99.2 g/liter	Sodium Tartrate 0.14 g/liter

(q) Tetrahydrofuran (THF)
(r) Hotplate capable of 60 °C
(s) Balance
(t) Hacksaw blade
(u) Ruby mortar and pestle

3.3. Sample Pre-Preparation

Sample preparation begins with pre-preparation which may include chemical reduction of the matrix, heating the sample to dryness or heating in the muffle furnace. The end result is a sample which has been reduced to a powder that is sufficiently fine to fit under the cover slip. Analyze different phases of samples separately, e.g., tile and the tile mastic should be analyzed separately as the mastic may contain asbestos while the tile may not.

(a) Wet samples

Samples with a high water content will not give the proper dispersion colors and must be dried prior to sample mounting. Remove the lid of the scintillation vial, place the bottle in the drying oven and heat at 100 °C to dryness (usually about 2 h). Samples which are not submitted to the lab in glass must be removed and placed in glass vials or aluminum weighing pans before placing them in the drying oven.

(b) Samples With Organic Interference—Muffle Furnace

These may include samples with tar as a matrix, vinyl asbestos tile, or any other organic that can be reduced by heating. Remove the sample from the vial and weigh in a balance to determine the weight of the submitted portion. Place the sample in a muffle furnace at 500 °C for 1 to 2 h or until all obvious organic material has been removed. Retrieve, cool and weigh again to determine the weight loss on ignition. This is necessary to determine the asbestos content of the submitted sample, because the analyst will be looking at a reduced sample.

Note: Heating above 600 °C will cause the sample to undergo a structural change which, given sufficient time, will convert the chrysotile to forsterite. Heating even at lower temperatures for 1 to 2 h may have a measurable effect on the optical properties of the minerals. If the analyst is unsure of what to expect, a sample of standard asbestos should be heated to the same temperature for the same length of time so that it can be examined for the proper interpretation.

(c) Samples With Organic Interference—THF

Vinyl asbestos tile is the most common material treated with this solvent, although, substances containing tar will sometimes yield to this treatment. Select a portion of the material and then grind it up if possible. Weigh the sample and place it in a test tube. Add sufficient THF to dissolve the organic matrix. This is usually about 4 to 5 mL. Remember, THF is highly flammable. Filter the remaining material through a tared silver membrane, dry and weigh to determine how much is left after the solvent extraction. Further process the sample to remove carbonate or mount directly.

(d) Samples With Carbonate Interference

Carbonate material is often found on fibers and sometimes must be removed in order to perform dispersion microscopy. Weigh out a portion of the material and place it in a test tube. Add a sufficient amount of 0.1 M HCl or decalcifying solution in the tube to react all the carbonate as evidenced by gas formation; i.e., when the gas bubbles stop, add a little more solution. If no more gas forms, the reaction is complete. Filter the material out through a tared silver membrane, dry and weigh to determine the weight lost.

3.4. Sample Preparation

Samples must be prepared so that accurate determination can be made of the asbestos type and amount present. The following steps are carried out in the low-flow hood (a low-flow hood has less than 50 fpm flow):

(1) If the sample has large lumps, is hard, or cannot be made to lie under a cover slip, the grain size must be reduced. Place a small amount between two slides and grind the material between them or grind a small amount in a clean mortar and pestle. The choice of whether to use an alumina, ruby, or diamond mortar depends on the hardness of the material. Impact damage can alter the asbestos mineral if too much mechanical shock occurs. (Freezer mills can completely destroy the observable crystallinity of asbestos and should not be

used). For some samples, a portion of material can be shaved off with a scalpel, ground off with a hand grinder or hacksaw blade.

The preparation tools should either be disposable or cleaned thoroughly. Use vigorous scrubbing to loosen the fibers during the washing. Rinse the implements with copious amounts of water and air-dry in a dust-free environment.

(2) If the sample is powder or has been reduced as in (1) above, it is ready to mount. Place a glass slide on a piece of optical tissue and write the identification on the painted or frosted end. Place two drops of index of refraction medium n = 1.550 on the slide. (The medium n = 1.550 is chosen because it is the matching index for chrysotile. Dip the end of a clean paper-clip or dissecting needle into the droplet of refraction medium on the slide to moisten it. Then dip the probe into the powder sample. Transfer what sticks on the probe to the slide. The material on the end of the probe should have a diameter of about 3 mm for a good mount. If the material is very fine, less sample may be appropriate. For non-powder samples such as fiber mats, forceps should be used to transfer a small amount of material to the slide. Stir the material in the medium on the slide, spreading it out and making the preparation as uniform as possible. Place a cover-slip on the preparation by gently lowering onto the slide and allowing it to fall "trapdoor" fashion on the preparation to push out any bubbles. Press gently on the cover slip to even out the distribution of particulate on the slide. If there is insufficient mounting oil on the slide, one or two drops may be placed near the edge of the coverslip on the slide. Capillary action will draw the necessary amount of liquid into the preparation. Remove excess oil with the point of a laboratory wiper.

Treat at least two different areas of each phase in this fashion. Choose representative areas of the sample. It may be useful to select particular areas or fibers for analysis. This is useful to identify asbestos in severely inhomogeneous samples.

When it is determined that amphiboles may be present, repeat the above process using the appropriate high-dispersion oils until an identification is made or all six asbestos minerals have been ruled out. Note that percent determination must be done in the index medium 1.550 because amphiboles tend to disappear in their matching mediums.

3.5. Analytical Procedure

Note: This method presumes some knowledge of mineralogy and optical petrography.

The analysis consists of three parts: The determination of whether there is asbestos present, what type is present and the determination of how much is present. The general flow of the analysis is:

(1) Gross examination;
(2) Examination under polarized light on the stereo microscope.;
(3) Examination by phase-polar illumination on the compound phase microscope;
(4) Determination of species by dispersion stain; Examination by Becke line analysis may also be used; however, this is usually more cumbersome for asbestos determination;
(5) Difficult samples may need to be analyzed by SEM or TEM, or the results from those techniques combined with light microscopy for a definitive identification. Identification of a particle as asbestos requires that it be asbestiform. Description of particles should follow the suggestion of Campbell. (Figure 1)

Figure 1
Particle definitons showing mineral growth habits From the U.S.Bureau of Mines

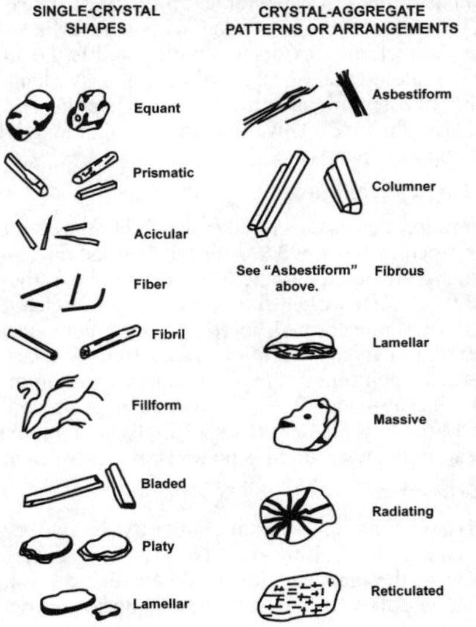

For the purpose of regulation, the mineral must be one of the six minerals covered and must be in the asbestos growth habit. Large specimen samples of asbestos generally have the gross appearance of wood. Fibers are easily parted from it. Asbestos fibers are very long compared with their widths. The fibers have a very high tensile strength as demonstrated by bending without breaking. Asbestos fibers exist in bundles that are easily parted, show longitudinal fine structure and may be tufted at the ends showing "bundle of sticks" morphology. In the microscope some of these properties may not be observable. Amphiboles do not always show striations along their length even when they are asbestos. Neither will they always show tufting. They generally do not show a curved nature except for very long fibers. Asbestos and asbestiform minerals are usually characterized in groups by extremely high aspect ratios (greater than 100:1). While aspect ratio analysis is useful for characterizing populations of fibers, it cannot be used to identify individual fibers of intermediate to short aspect ratio. Observation of many fibers is often necessary to determine whether a sample consists of "cleavage fragments" or of asbestos fibers.

Most cleavage fragments of the asbestos minerals are easily distinguishable from true asbestos fibers. This is because true cleavage fragments usually have larger diameters than 1 µm. Internal structure of particles larger than this usually shows them to have no internal fibrillar structure. In addition, cleavage fragments of the monoclinic amphiboles show inclined extinction under crossed polars with no compensator. Asbestos fibers usually show extinction at zero degrees or ambiguous extinction if any at all. Morphologically, the larger cleavage fragments are obvious by their blunt or stepped ends showing prismatic habit. Also, they tend to be acicular rather than filiform.

Where the particles are less than 1 µm in diameter and have an aspect ratio greater than or equal to 3:1, it is recommended that the sample be analyzed by SEM or TEM if there is any question whether the fibers are cleavage fragments or asbestiform particles.

Care must be taken when analyzing by electron microscopy because the interferences are different from those in light microscopy and may structurally be very similar to asbestos. The classic interference is between anthophyllite and biopyribole or intermediate fiber. Use the same morphological clues for electron microscopy as are used for light microscopy, e.g. fibril splitting, internal longitudinal striation, fraying, curvature, etc.

(1) Gross examination:

Examine the sample, preferably in the glass vial. Determine the presence of any obvious fibrous component. Estimate a percentage based on previous experience and current observation. Determine whether any pre- preparation is necessary. Determine the number of phases present. This step may be carried out or augmented by observation at 6 to 40× under a stereo microscope.

(2) After performing any necessary pre-preparation, prepare slides of each phase as described above. Two preparations of the same phase in the same index medium can be made side-by-side on the same glass for convenience. Examine with the polarizing stereo microscope. Estimate the percentage of asbestos based on the amount of birefringent fiber present.

(3) Examine the slides on the phase-polar microscopes at magnifications of 160 and 400×. Note the morphology of the fibers. Long, thin, very straight fibers with little curvature are indicative of fibers from the amphibole family. Curved, wavy fibers are usually indicative of chrysotile. Estimate the percentage of asbestos on the phase-polar microscope under conditions of crossed polars and a gypsum plate. Fibers smaller than 1.0 µm in thickness must be identified by inference to the presence of larger, identifiable fibers and morphology. If no larger fibers are visible, electron microscopy should be performed. At this point, only a tentative identification can be made. Full identification must be made with dispersion microscopy. Details of the tests are included in the appendices.

(4) Once fibers have been determined to be present, they must be identified. Adjust the microscope for dispersion mode and observe the fibers. The microscope has a rotating stage, one polarizing element, and a system for generating dark-field dispersion microscopy (see Section 4.6. of this Appendix). Align a fiber with its length parallel to the polarizer and note the color of the Becke lines. Rotate the stage to bring the fiber length perpendicular to the polarizer and note the color. Repeat this process for every fiber or fiber bundle examined. The colors must be consistent with the colors generated by standard asbestos reference materials for a positive identification. In n=1.550, amphiboles will generally show a yellow to straw-yellow color indicating that the fiber indices of refraction are higher than the liquid. If long, thin fibers are noted and the colors are yellow, prepare further slides as above in the suggested matching liquids listed below:

Type of asbestos	Index of refraction
Chrysotile	n = 1.550
Amosite	n = 1.670 or 1.680
Crocidolite	n = 1.690
Anthophyllite	n = 1.605 and 1.620
Tremolite	n = 1.605 and 1.620
Actinolite	n = 1.620

Where more than one liquid is suggested, the first is preferred; however, in some cases this liquid will not give good dispersion color. Take care to avoid interferences in the other liquid; e.g., wollastonite in n=1.620 will give the same colors as tremolite. In n=1.605 wollastonite will appear yellow in all directions. Wollastonite may be determined under crossed polars as it will change from blue to yellow as it is rotated along its fiber axis by tapping on the cover slip. Asbestos minerals will not change in this way.

Determination of the angle of extinction may, when present, aid in the determination of anthophyllite from tremolite. True asbestos fibers usually have 0° extinction or ambiguous extinction, while cleavage fragments have more definite extinction.

Continue analysis until both preparations have been examined and all present species of asbestos are identified. If there are no fibers present, or there is less than 0.1% present, end the analysis with the minimum number of slides (2).

(5) Some fibers have a coating on them which makes dispersion microscopy very difficult or impossible. Becke line analysis or electron microscopy may be performed in those cases. Determine the percentage by light microscopy. TEM analysis tends to overestimate the actual percentage present.

(6) Percentage determination is an estimate of occluded area, tempered by gross observation. Gross observation information is used to make sure that the high magnification microscopy does not greatly over- or under- estimate the amount of fiber present. This part of the analysis requires a great deal of experience. Satisfactory models for asbestos content analysis have not yet been developed, although some models based on metallurgical grain-size determination have found some utility. Estimation is more easily handled in situations where the grain sizes visible at about 160× are about the same and the sample is relatively homogeneous.

View all of the area under the cover slip to make the percentage determination. View the fields while moving the stage, paying attention to the clumps of material. These are not usually the best areas to perform dispersion microscopy because of the interference from other materials. But, they are the areas most likely to represent the accurate percentage in the sample. Small amounts of asbestos require slower scanning and more frequent analysis of individual fields.

Report the area occluded by asbestos as the concentration. This estimate does not generally take into consideration the difference in density of the different species present in the sample. For most samples this is adequate. Simulation studies with similar materials must be carried out to apply microvisual estimation for that purpose and is beyond the scope of this procedure.

(7) Where successive concentrations have been made by chemical or physical means, the amount reported is the percentage of the material in the "as submitted" or original state. The percentage determined by microscopy is multiplied by the fractions remaining after pre-preparation steps to give the percentage in the original sample. For example:

Step 1. 60% remains after heating at 550 °C for 1 h.

Step 2. 30% of the residue of step 1 remains after dissolution of carbonate in 0.1 m HCl.

Step 3. Microvisual estimation determines that 5% of the sample is chrysotile asbestos.

The reported result is:

R = (Microvisual result in percent) × (Fraction remaining after step 2) × (Fraction remaining of original sample after step 1)

R = (5) × (.30) × (.60) = 0.9%

(8) Report the percent and type of asbestos present. For samples where asbestos was identified, but is less than 1.0%, report "Asbestos present, less than 1.0%." There must have been at least two observed fibers or fiber bundles in the two preparations to be reported as present. For samples where asbestos was not seen, report as "None Detected."

4. Auxiliary Information

Because of the subjective nature of asbestos analysis, certain concepts and procedures need to be discussed in more depth. This information will help the analyst understand why some of the procedures are carried out the way they are.

4.1. Light

Light is electromagnetic energy. It travels from its source in packets called quanta. It is instructive to consider light as a plane wave. The light has a direction of travel. Perpendicular to this and mutually perpendicular to each other, are two vector components. One is the magnetic vector and the other is the electric vector. We shall only be concerned with the electric vector. In this description, the interaction of the vector and the mineral will describe all the observable phenomena. From a light source such a microscope illuminator, light travels in all different direction from the filament.

In any given direction away from the filament, the electric vector is perpendicular to the direction of travel of a light ray. While perpendicular, its orientation is random about the travel axis. If the electric vectors from all the light rays were lined up by passing the light through a filter that would only let light rays with electric vectors oriented in one direction pass, the light would then be POLARIZED.

Polarized light interacts with matter in the direction of the electric vector. This is the polarization direction. Using this property it is possible to use polarized light to probe different materials and identify them by how they interact with light.

The speed of light in a vacuum is a constant at about 2.99×108 m/s. When light travels in different materials such as air, water, minerals or oil, it does not travel at this speed. It travels slower. This slowing is a function of both the material through which the light is traveling and the wavelength or frequency of the light. In general, the more dense the material, the slower the light travels. Also, generally, the higher the frequency, the slower the light will travel. The ratio of the speed of light in a vacuum to that in a material is called the index of refraction (n). It is usually measured at 589 nm (the sodium D line). If white light (light containing all the visible wavelengths) travels through a material, rays of longer wavelengths will travel faster than those of shorter wavelengths, this separation is called dispersion. Dispersion is used as an identifier of materials as described in Section 4.6.

4.2. Material Properties

Materials are either amorphous or crystalline. The difference between these two descriptions depends on the positions of the atoms in them. The atoms in amorphous materials are randomly arranged with no long range order. An example of an amorphous material is glass. The atoms in crystalline materials, on the other hand, are in regular arrays and have long range order. Most of the atoms can be found in highly predictable locations. Examples of crystalline material are salt, gold and the asbestos minerals.

It is beyond the scope of this method to describe the different types of crystalline materials that can be found, or the full description of the classes into which they can fall. However, some general crystallography is provided below to give a foundation to the procedures described.

With the exception of anthophyllite, all the asbestos minerals belong to the monoclinic crystal type. The unit cell is the basic repeating unit of the crystal and for monoclinic crystals can be described as having three unequal sides, two 90° angles and one angle not equal to 90°. The orthorhombic group, of which anthophyllite is a member has three unequal sides and three 90° angles. The unequal sides are a consequence of the complexity of fitting the different atoms into the unit cell. Although the atoms are in a regular array, that array is not symmetrical in all directions. There is long range order in the three major directions of the crystal. However, the order is different in each of the three directions. This has the effect that the index of refraction is different in each of the three directions. Using polarized light, we can investigate the index of refraction in each of the directions and identify the mineral or material under investigation. The indices α, β, and γ are used to identify the lowest, middle, and highest index of refraction respectively. The x direction, associated with α is called the fast axis. Conversely, the z direction is associated with γ and is the slow direction. Crocidolite has α along the fiber length making it "length-fast". The remainder of the asbestos minerals have the γ axis along the fiber length. They are called "length-slow". This orientation to fiber length is used to aid in the identification of asbestos.

4.3. Polarized Light Technique

Polarized light microscopy as described in this Section uses the phase-polar microscope described in Section 3.2. A phase contrast microscope is fitted with two polarizing elements, one below and one above the sample. The polarizers have their polarization directions at right angles to each other. Depending on the tests performed, there may be a compensator between these two polarizing elements. Light emerging from a polarizing element has its electric vector pointing in the polarization direction of the element. The light will not be subsequently transmitted through a second element set at a right angle to the first element. Unless the light is altered as it passes from one element to the other, there is no transmission of light.

4.4. Angle of Extinction

Crystals which have different crystal regularity in two or three main directions are said to be anisotropic. They have a different index of refraction in each of the main directions. When such a crystal is inserted between the crossed polars, the field of view is no longer dark but shows the crystal in color. The color depends on the properties of the crystal. The light acts as if it travels through the crystal along the optical axes. If a crystal optical axis were lined up along one of the polarizing directions (either the polarizer or the analyzer) the light would appear to travel only in that direction, and it would blink out or go dark. The difference in degrees between the fiber direction and the angle at which it blinks out is called the angle of extinction. When this angle can be measured, it is useful in identifying the mineral. The procedure for measuring the angle of extinction is to first identify the polarization direction in the microscope. A commercial alignment slide can be used to establish the polarization directions or use anthophyllite or another suitable mineral. This mineral has a zero degree angle of extinction and will go dark to extinction as it aligns with the polarization directions. When a fiber of anthophyllite has gone to extinction, align the eyepiece reticle or graticule with the fiber so that there is a visual cue as to the direction of polarization in the field of view. Tape or otherwise secure the eyepiece in this position so it will not shift.

After the polarization direction has been identified in the field of view, move the particle of interest to the center of the field of view and align it with the polarization direction. For fibers, align the fiber along this direction. Note the angular reading of the rotating stage. Looking at the particle, rotate the stage until the fiber goes dark or "blinks out". Again note the reading of the stage. The difference in the first reading and the second is an angle of extinction.

The angle measured may vary as the orientation of the fiber changes about its long axis. Tables of mineralogical data usually report the maximum angle of extinction. Asbestos forming minerals, when they exhibit an angle of extinction, usually do show an angle of extinction close to the reported maximum, or as appropriate depending on the substitution chemistry.

4.5. Crossed Polars with Compensator

When the optical axes of a crystal are not lined up along one of the polarizing directions (either the polarizer or the analyzer) part of the light travels along one axis and part travels along the other visible axis. This is characteristic of birefringent materials.

The color depends on the difference of the two visible indices of refraction and the thickness of the crystal. The maximum difference available is the difference between the α and the γ axes. This maximum difference is usually tabulated as the birefringence of the crystal.

For this test, align the fiber at 45° to the polarization directions in order to maximize the contribution to each of the optical axes. The colors seen are called retardation colors. They arise from the recombination of light which has traveled through the two separate directions of the crystal. One of the rays is retarded behind the other since the light in that direction travels slower. On recombination, some of the colors which make up white light are enhanced by constructive interference and some are suppressed by destructive interference. The result is a color dependent on the difference between the indices and the thickness of the crystal. The proper colors, thicknesses, and retardations are shown on a Michel-Levy chart. The three items, retardation, thickness and birefringence are related by the following relationship:

$R = t(n_\gamma - n_\alpha)$

R = retardation, t = crystal thickness in µm, and

$n_{\alpha,\gamma}$ = indices of refraction.

Examination of the equation for asbestos minerals reveals that the visible colors for almost all common asbestos minerals and fiber sizes are shades of gray and black. The eye is relatively poor at discriminating different shades of gray. It is very good at discriminating different colors. In order to compensate for the low retardation, a compensator is added to the light train between the polarization elements. The compensator used for this test is a gypsum plate of known thickness and birefringence. Such a compensator when oriented at 45° to the polarizer direction, provides a retardation of 530 nm of the 530 nm wavelength color. This enhances the red color and gives the background a characteristic red to red-magenta color. If this "full-wave" compensator is in place when the asbestos preparation is inserted into the light train, the colors seen on the fibers are quite different. Gypsum, like asbestos has a fast axis and a slow axis. When a fiber is aligned with its fast axis in the same direction as the fast axis of the gypsum plate, the ray vibrating in the slow direction is retarded by both the asbestos and the gypsum. This results in a higher retardation than would be present for either of the two minerals. The color seen is a second order blue. When the fiber is rotated 90° using the rotating stage, the slow direction of the fiber is now aligned with the fast direction of the gypsum and the fast direction of the fiber is aligned with the slow direction of the gypsum. Thus, one ray vibrates faster in the fast direction of the gypsum, and slower in the slow direction of the fiber; the other ray will vibrate slower in the slow direction of the gypsum and faster in the fast direction of the fiber. In this case, the effect is subtractive and the color seen is a first order yellow. As long as the fiber thickness does not add appreciably to the color, the same basic colors will be seen for all asbestos types except crocidolite. In crocidolite the colors will be weaker, may be in the opposite directions, and will be altered by the blue absorption color natural to crocidolite. Hundreds of other materials will give the same colors as asbestos, and therefore, this test is not definitive for asbestos. The test is useful in discriminating against fiberglass or other amorphous fibers such as some synthetic fibers. Certain synthetic fibers will show retardation colors different than asbestos; however, there are some forms of polyethylene and aramid which will show morphology and retardation colors similar to asbestos minerals. This test must be supplemented with a positive identification test when birefringent fibers are present which can not be excluded by morphology. This test is relatively ineffective for use on fibers less than 1 µm in diameter. For positive confirmation TEM or SEM should be used if no larger bundles or fibers are visible.

4.6. Dispersion Staining

Dispersion microscopy or dispersion staining is the method of choice for the identification of asbestos in bulk materials. Becke line analysis is used by some laboratories and yields the same results as does dispersion staining for asbestos and can be used in lieu of dispersion staining. Dispersion staining is performed on the same platform as the phase-polar analysis with the analyzer and compensator removed. One polarizing element remains to define the direction of the light so that the different indices of refraction of the fibers may be separately determined. Dispersion microscopy is a dark-field technique when used for asbestos. Particles are imaged with scattered light. Light which is unscattered is blocked from reaching the eye either by the back field image mask in a McCrone objective or a back field image mask in the phase condenser. The most convenient method is to use the rotating phase condenser to move an oversized phase ring into place. The ideal size for this ring is for the central disk to be just larger than the objective entry aperture as viewed in the back focal plane. The larger the disk, the less scattered light reaches the eye. This will have the effect of diminishing the intensity of dispersion color and will shift the actual color seen. The colors seen vary even on microscopes from the same manufacturer. This is due to the different bands of wavelength exclusion by different mask sizes. The mask may either reside in the condenser or in the objective back focal plane. It is imperative that the analyst determine by experimentation with asbestos standards what the appropriate colors should be for each asbestos type. The colors depend also on the temperature of the preparation and the exact chemistry of the asbestos. Therefore, some slight differences from the standards should be allowed. This is not a serious problem for commercial asbestos uses. This technique is used for identification of the indices of refraction for fibers by recognition of color. There is no direct numerical readout of the index of refraction. Correlation of color to actual index of refraction is possible by referral to published conversion tables. This is not necessary for the analysis of asbestos. Recognition of appropriate colors along with the proper morphology are deemed sufficient to identify the commercial asbestos minerals. Other techniques including SEM, TEM, and XRD may be required to provide additional information in order to identify other types of asbestos.

Make a preparation in the suspected matching high dispersion oil, e.g., n = 1.550 for chrysotile. Perform the preliminary tests to determine whether the fibers are birefringent or not. Take note of the morphological character. Wavy fibers are indicative of chrysotile while long, straight, thin, frayed fibers are indicative of amphibole asbestos. This can aid in the selection of the appropriate matching oil. The microscope is set up and the polarization direction is noted as in Section 4.4. Align a fiber with the polarization direction. Note the color. This is the color parallel to the polarizer. Then rotate the fiber rotating the stage 90° so that the polarization direction is across the fiber. This is the perpendicular position. Again note the color. Both colors must be consistent with standard asbestos minerals in the correct direction for a positive identification of asbestos. If only one of the colors is correct while the other is not, the identification is not positive. If the colors in both directions are bluish-white, the analyst has chosen a matching index oil which is higher than the correct matching oil, e.g. the analyst has used n=1.620 where chrysotile is present. The next lower oil (Section 3.5.) should be used to prepare another specimen. If the color in both directions is yellow-white to straw-yellow-white, this indicates that the index of the oil is lower than the index of the fiber, e.g. the preparation is in n=1.550 while anthophyllite is present. Select the next higher oil (Section 3.5.) and prepare another slide. Continue in this fashion until a positive identification of all asbestos species present has been made or all possible asbestos species have been ruled out by negative results in this test. Certain plant fibers can have similar dispersion colors as asbestos. Take care to note and evaluate the morphology of the fibers or remove the plant fibers in pre- preparation. Coating material on the fibers such as carbonate or vinyl may destroy the dispersion color. Usually, there will be some outcropping of fiber which will show the colors sufficient for identification. When this is not the case, treat the sample as described in Section 3.3. and then perform dispersion staining. Some samples will yield to Becke line analysis if they are coated or electron microscopy can be used for identification.

5. References

5.1. Crane, D.T., Asbestos in Air, OSHA method ID160, Revised November 1992.

5.2. Ford, W.E., Dana's Textbook of Mineralogy; Fourth Ed.; John Wiley and Son, New York, 1950, p. vii.

5.3. Selikoff,.I.J., Lee, D.H.K., Asbestos and Disease, Academic Press, New York, 1978, pp. 3, 20.

5.4. Women Inspectors of Factories. Annual Report for 1898, H.M. Statistical Office, London, p. 170 (1898).

5.5. Selikoff, I.J., Lee, D.H.K., Asbestos and Disease, Academic Press, New York, 1978, pp. 26, 30.

5.6. Campbell, W.J., et al, Selected Silicate Minerals and Their Asbestiform Varieties, United States Department of the Interior, Bureau of Mines, Information Circular 8751, 1977.

5.7. Asbestos, Code of Federal Regulations, 29 CFR §1910.1001 and 29 CFR §1926.58.

5.8. National Emission Standards for Hazardous Air Pollutants; Asbestos NESHAP Revision, Federal Register,Vol. 55, No. 224, 20 November 1990, p. 48410.

5.9. Ross, M. The Asbestos Minerals: Definitions, Description, Modes of Formation, Physical and Chemical Properties and Health Risk to the Mining Community, Nation Bureau of Standards Special Publication, Washington, DC, 1977.

5.10. Lilis, R., Fibrous Zeolites and Endemic Mesothelioma in Cappadocia, Turkey, J. Occ Medicine, 1981, 23,(8), 548–550.

5.11. Occupational Exposure to Asbestos—1972, U.S. Department of Health, Education and Welfare, Public Health Service, Center for Disease Control, National Institute for Occupational Safety and Health, HSM–72–10267.

5.12. Campbell, W.J., et al, Relationship of Mineral Habit to Size Characteristics for Tremolite Fragments and Fibers, United States Department of the Interior, Bureau of Mines, Information Circular 8367, 1979.

5.13. Mefford, D., DCM Laboratory, Denver, private communication, July 1987.

5.14. Deer, W.A., Howie, R.A., Zussman, J., Rock Forming Minerals, Longman, Thetford, UK, 1974.

5.15. Kerr, P.F., Optical Mineralogy; Third Ed. McGraw-Hill, New York, 1959.

5.16. Veblen, D.R. (Ed.), Amphiboles and Other Hydrous Pyriboles—Mineralogy, Reviews in Mineralogy, Vol 9A, Michigan, 1982, pp 1–102.

5.17. Dixon, W.C., Applications of Optical Microscopy in the Analysis of Asbestos and Quartz, ACS Symposium Series, No. 120, Analytical Techniques in Occupational Health Chemistry, 1979.

5.18. Polarized Light Microscopy, McCrone Research Institute, Chicago, 1976.

5.19. Asbestos Identification, McCrone Research Institute, G & G printers, Chicago, 1987.

5.20. McCrone, W.C., Calculation of Refractive Indices from Dispersion Staining Data, The Microscope, No 37, Chicago, 1989.

5.21. Levadie, B. (Ed.), Asbestos and Other Health Related Silicates, ASTM Technical Publication 834, ASTM, Philadelphia 1982.

5.22. Steel, E. and Wylie, A., Riordan, P.H. (Ed.), Mineralogical Characteristics of Asbestos, Geology of Asbestos Deposits, pp. 93–101, SME-AIME, 1981.

5.23. Zussman, J., The Mineralogy of Asbestos, Asbestos: Properties, Applications and Hazards, pp. 45–67 Wiley, 1979.

[51 FR 22733, June 20, 1986]

Editorial Note: For Federal Register citations affecting §1910.1001, see the List of CFR Sections Affected, which appears in the Finding Aids section of the printed volume and at www.fdsys.gov.

§1910.1002 Coal tar pitch volatiles; interpretation of term

As used in §1910.1000 (Table Z-1), coal tar pitch volatiles include the fused polycyclic hydrocarbons which volatilize from the distillation residues of coal, petroleum (excluding asphalt), wood, and other organic matter. Asphalt (CAS 8052–42–4, and CAS 64742–93–4) is not covered under the "coal tar pitch volatiles" standard.

[48 FR 2768, Jan. 21, 1983]

§1910.1003 13 Carcinogens

(4-Nitrobiphenyl, etc.)

(a) Scope and application

(a)(1) This Section applies to any area in which the 13 carcinogens addressed by this Section are manufactured, processed, repackaged, released, handled, or stored, but shall not apply to transshipment in sealed containers, except for the labeling requirements under paragraphs (e)(2), (3) and (4) of this Section. The 13 carcinogens are the following:

4-Nitrobiphenyl, Chemical Abstracts Service Register Number (CAS No.) 92933;
alpha-Naphthylamine, CAS No. 134327;
methyl chloromethyl ether, CAS No. 107302;
3,′-Dichlorobenzidine (and its salts) CAS No. 91941;
bis-Chloromethyl ether, CAS No. 542881;
beta-Naphthylamine, CAS No. 91598;
Benzidine, CAS No. 92875;
4-Aminodiphenyl, CAS No. 92671;
Ethyleneimine, CAS No. 151564;
beta-Propiolactone, CAS No. 57578;
2-Acetylaminofluorene, CAS No. 53963;
4-Dimethylaminoazo-benezene, CAS No. 60117; and
N-Nitrosodimethylamine, CAS No. 62759.

(a)(2) This Section shall not apply to the following:

(a)(2)(i) Solid or liquid mixtures containing less than 0.1 percent by weight or volume of 4–Nitrobiphenyl; methyl chloromethyl ether; bis-chloromethyl ether; beta-Naphthylamine; benzidine or 4–Aminodiphenyl; and

(a)(2)(ii) Solid or liquid mixtures containing less than 1.0 percent by weight or volume of alpha-Naphthylamine; 3,′-Dichlorobenzidine (and its salts); Ethyleneimine; beta-Propiolactone; 2-Acetylaminofluorene; 4-Dimethylaminoazobenzene, or N-Nitrosodimethylamine.

(b) Definitions For the purposes of this Section:

Absolute filter is one capable of retaining 99.97 percent of a mono disperse aerosol of 0.3 µm particles.

Authorized employee means an employee whose duties require him to be in the regulated area and who has been specifically assigned by the employer.

Clean change room means a room where employees put on clean clothing and/or protective equipment in an environment free of the 13 carcinogens addressed by this Section. The clean change room shall be contiguous to and have an entry from a shower room, when the shower room facilities are otherwise required in this Section.

Closed system means an operation involving a carcinogen addressed by this Section where containment prevents the release of the material into regulated areas, non-regulated areas, or the external environment.

Decontamination means the inactivation of a carcinogen addressed by this Section or its safe disposal.

Director means the Director, National Institute for Occupational Safety and Health, or any person directed by him or the Secretary of Health and Human Services to act for the Director.

Disposal means the safe removal of the carcinogens addressed by this Section from the work environment.

Emergency means an unforeseen circumstance or set of circumstances resulting in the release of a carcinogen addressed by this Section that may result in exposure to or contact with the material.

External environment means any environment external to regulated and nonregulated areas.

Isolated system means a fully enclosed structure other than the vessel of containment of a carcinogen addressed by this Section that is impervious to the passage of the material and would prevent the entry of the carcinogen addressed by this Section into regulated areas, nonregulated areas, or the external environment, should leakage or spillage from the vessel of containment occur.

Laboratory-type hood is a device enclosed on the three sides and the top and bottom, designed and maintained so as to draw air inward at an average linear face velocity of 150 feet per minute with a minimum of 125 feet per minute; designed, constructed, and maintained in such a way that an operation involving a carcinogen addressed by this Section within the hood does not require the insertion of any portion of any employee's body other than his hands and arms.

Nonregulated area means any area under the control of the employer where entry and exit is neither restricted nor controlled.

Open-vessel system means an operation involving a carcinogen addressed by this Section in an open vessel that is not in an isolated system, a laboratory-type hood, nor in any other system affording equivalent protection against the entry of the material into regulated areas, non-regulated areas, or the external environment.

Protective clothing means clothing designed to protect an employee against contact with or exposure to a carcinogen addressed by this Section.

Regulated area means an area where entry and exit is restricted and controlled.

(c) **Requirements for areas containing a carcinogen addressed by this Section.** A regulated area shall be established by an employer where a carcinogen addressed by this Section is manufactured, processed, used, repackaged, released, handled or stored. All such areas shall be controlled in accordance with the requirements for the following category or categories describing the operation involved:

(c)(1) **Isolated systems** Employees working with a carcinogen addressed by this Section within an isolated system such as a "glove box" shall wash their hands and arms upon completion of the assigned task and before engaging in other activities not associated with the isolated system.

(c)(2) **Closed system operation**

(c)(2)(i) Within regulated areas where the carcinogens addressed by this Section are stored in sealed containers, or contained in a closed system, including piping systems, with any sample ports or openings closed while the carcinogens addressed by this Section are contained within, access shall be restricted to authorized employees only.

(c)(2)(ii) Employees exposed to 4–Nitrobiphenyl; alpha-Naphthylamine; 3,'-Dichlorobenzidine (and its salts); beta-Naphthylamine; benzidine; 4–Aminodiphenyl; 2–Acetylaminofluorene; 4–Dimethylaminoazo-benzene; and N-Nitrosodimethylamine shall be required to wash hands, forearms, face, and neck upon each exit from the regulated areas, close to the point of exit, and before engaging in other activities.

(c)(3) Open-vessel system operations. Open-vessel system operations as defined in paragraph (b)(13) of this Section are prohibited.

(c)(4) Transfer from a closed system, charging or discharging point operations, or otherwise opening a closed system. In operations involving "laboratory-type hoods," or in locations where the carcinogens addressed by this Section are contained in an otherwise "closed system," but is transferred, charged, or discharged into other normally closed containers, the provisions of this paragraph shall apply.

(c)(4)(i) Access shall be restricted to authorized employees only.

(c)(4)(ii) Each operation shall be provided with continuous local exhaust ventilation so that air movement is always from ordinary work areas to the operation. Exhaust air shall not be discharged to regulated areas, nonregulated areas or the external environment unless decontaminated. Clean makeup air shall be introduced in sufficient volume to maintain the correct operation of the local exhaust system.

(c)(4)(iii) Employees shall be provided with, and required to wear, clean, full body protective clothing (smocks, coveralls, or long-sleeved shirt and pants), shoe covers and gloves prior to entering the regulated area.

(c)(4)(iv) Employers must provide each employee engaged in handling operations involving the carcinogens 4-Nitrobiphenyl, alpha-Naphthylamine, 3,3'-Dichlorobenzidine (and its salts), beta-Naphthylamine, Benzidine, 4-Aminodiphenyl, 2-Acetylaminofluorene, 4-Dimethylaminoazo-benzene, and N-Nitrosodimethylamine, addressed by this Section, with, and ensure that each of these employees wears and uses, a NIOSH-certified air-purifying, half-mask respirator with particulate filters. Employers also must provide each employee engaged in handling operations involving the carcinogens methyl chloromethyl ether, bis-Chloromethyl ether, Ethyleneimine, and beta-Propiolactone, addressed by this Section, with, and ensure that each of these employees wears and uses any self-contained breathing apparatus that has a full facepiece and is operated in a pressure-demand or other positive-pressure mode, or any supplied-air respirator that has a full facepiece and is operated in a pressure-demand or other positive-pressure mode in combination with an auxiliary self-contained positive-pressure breathing apparatus. Employers may substitute a respirator affording employees higher levels of protection than these respirators.

(c)(4)(v) Prior to each exit from a regulated area, employees shall be required to remove and leave protective clothing and equipment at the point of exit and at the last exit of the day, to place used clothing and equipment in impervious containers at the point of exit for purposes of decontamination or disposal. The contents of such impervious containers shall be identified, as required under paragraph (e) of this Section.

(c)(4)(vi) Drinking fountains are prohibited in the regulated area.

(c)(4)(vii) Employees shall be required to wash hands, forearms, face, and neck on each exit from the regulated area, close to the point of exit, and before engaging in other activities and employees exposed to 4–Nitrobiphenyl; alpha-Naphthylamine; 3,'-Dichlorobenzidine (and its salts); beta-Naphthylamine; Benzidine; 4–Aminodiphenyl; 2–Acetylaminofluorene; 4–Dimethylaminoazo-benzene; and N-Nitrosodimethylamine shall be required to shower after the last exit of the day.

(c)(5) **Maintenance and decontamination activities** In cleanup of leaks of spills, maintenance, or repair operations on contaminated systems or equipment, or any operations involving work in an area where direct contact with a carcinogen addressed by this Section could result, each authorized employee entering that area shall:

(c)(5)(i) [OI] Be provided with and required to wear clean, impervious garments, including gloves, boots, and continuous-air supplied hood in accordance with §1910.134;

(c)(5)(ii) Be decontaminated before removing the protective garments and hood;

(c)(5)(iii) Be required to shower upon removing the protective garments and hood.

(d) **General regulated area requirements**

(d)(1) **Respiratory program** The employer must implement a respiratory protection program in accordance with §1910.134 (b), (c), (d) (except (d)(1)(iii) and (iv), and (d)(3), and (e) through (m), which covers each employee required by this Section to use a respirator.

(d)(2) **Emergencies** In an emergency, immediate measures including, but not limited to, the requirements of paragraphs (d)(2)(i) through (v) of this Section shall be implemented.

(d)(2)(i) The potentially affected area shall be evacuated as soon as the emergency has been determined.

(d)(2)(ii) Hazardous conditions created by the emergency shall be eliminated and the potentially affected area shall be decontaminated prior to the resumption of normal operations.

(d)(2)(iii) Special medical surveillance by a physician shall be instituted within 24 hours for employees present in the potentially affected area at the time of the emergency. A report of the medical surveillance and any treatment shall be included in the incident report, in accordance with paragraph (f)(2) of this Section.

(d)(2)(iv) Where an employee has a known contact with a carcinogen addressed by this Section, such employee shall be required to shower as soon as possible, unless contraindicated by physical injuries.

(d)(2)(v) An incident report on the emergency shall be reported as provided in paragraph (f)(2) of this Section.

(d)(2)(vi) Emergency deluge showers and eyewash fountains supplied with running potable water shall be located near, within sight of, and on the same level with locations where a direct exposure to Ethyleneimine or beta-Propiolactone only would be most likely as a result of equipment failure or improper work practice.

(d)(3) **Hygiene facilities and practices**

(d)(3)(i) Storage or consumption of food, storage or use of containers of beverages, storage or application of cosmetics, smoking, storage of smoking materials, tobacco products or other products for chewing, or the chewing of such products are prohibited in regulated areas.

(d)(3)(ii) Where employees are required by this Section to wash, washing facilities shall be provided in accordance with §1910.141(d)(1) and (2)(ii) through (vii).

(d)(3)(iii) Where employees are required by this Section to shower, shower facilities shall be provided in accordance with §1910.141(d)(3).

(d)(3)(iv) Where employees wear protective clothing and equipment, clean change rooms shall be provided for the number of such employees required to change clothes, in accordance with §1910.141(e).

(d)(3)(v) Where toilets are in regulated areas, such toilets shall be in a separate room.

(d)(4) **Contamination control**

(d)(4)(i) Except for outdoor systems, regulated areas shall be maintained under pressure negative with respect to nonregulated areas. Local exhaust ventilation may be used to satisfy this requirement. Clean makeup air in equal volume shall replace air removed.

(d)(4)(ii) Any equipment, material, or other item taken into or removed from a regulated area shall be done so in a manner that does not cause contamination in nonregulated areas or the external environment.

(d)(4)(iii) Decontamination procedures shall be established and implemented to remove carcinogens addressed by this Section from the surfaces of materials, equipment, and the decontamination facility.

(d)(4)(iv) Dry sweeping and dry mopping are prohibited for 4–Nitrobiphenyl; alpha-Naphthylamine; 3,'-Dichlorobenzidine (and its salts); beta-Naphthylamine; Benzidine; 4–Aminodiphenyl; 2–Acetylaminofluorene; 4–Dimethylaminoazo-benzene and N-Nitrosodimethylamine.

(e) **Communication of hazards**

(e)(1) **Hazard communication**

(e)(1)(i) Chemical manufacturers, importers, distributors and employers shall comply with all requirements of the Hazard Communication Standard (HCS) (§1910.1200) for each carcinogen listed in paragraph (e)(1)(iv) of this Section.

(e)(1)(ii) In classifying the hazards of carcinogens listed in paragraph (e)(1)(iv) of this Section, at least the hazards listed in paragraph (e)(1)(iv) are to be addressed.

(e)(1)(iii) Employers shall include the carcinogens listed in paragraph (e)(1)(iv) of this Section in the hazard communication program established to comply with the HCS (§1910.1200). Employers shall ensure that each employee has access to labels on containers of the carcinogens listed in paragraph (e)(1)(iv) and to safety data sheets, and is trained in accordance with the requirements of HCS and paragraph (e)(4) of this Section.

(e)(1)(iv) **List of Carcinogens:**

(e)(1)(iv)(A) 4-Nitrobiphenyl: Cancer.

(e)(1)(iv)(B) alpha-Naphthylamine: Cancer; skin irritation; and acute toxicity effects.

(e)(1)(iv)(C) Methyl chloromethyl ether: Cancer; skin, eye and respiratory effects; acute toxicity effects; and flammability.

(e)(1)(iv)(D) 3,3'-Dichlorobenzidine (and its salts): Cancer and skin sensitization.

(e)(1)(iv)(E) bis-Chloromethyl ether: Cancer; skin, eye, and respiratory tract effects; acute toxicity effects; and flammability.

(e)(1)(iv)(F) beta-Naphthylamine: Cancer and acute toxicity effects.

(e)(1)(iv)(G) Benzidine: Cancer and acute toxicity effects.

(e)(1)(iv)(H) 4-Aminodiphenyl: Cancer.

(e)(1)(iv)(I) Ethyleneimine: Cancer; mutagenicity; skin and eye effects; liver effects; kidney effects; acute toxicity effects; and flammability.

(e)(1)(iv)(J) beta-Propiolactone: Cancer; skin irritation; eye effects; and acute toxicity effects.

(e)(1)(iv)(K) 2-Acetylaminofluorene: Cancer.

(e)(1)(iv)(L) 4-Dimethylaminoazo-benzene: Cancer; skin effects; and respiratory tract irritation.

(e)(1)(iv)(M) N-Nitrosodimethylamine: Cancer; liver effects; and acute toxicity effects.

(e)(2) **Signs**

(e)(2)(i) The employer shall post entrances to regulated areas with signs bearing the legend:

DANGER
(CHEMICAL IDENTIFICATION)
MAY CAUSE CANCER
AUTHORIZED PERSONNEL ONLY

(e)(2)(ii) The employer shall post signs at entrances to regulated areas containing operations covered in paragraph (c)(5) of this Section. The signs shall bear the legend:

DANGER
(CHEMICAL IDENTIFICATION)
MAY CAUSE CANCER
WEAR AIR-SUPPLIED HOODS, IMPERVIOUS SUITS, AND PROTECTIVE EQUIPMENT IN THIS AREA
AUTHORIZED PERSONNEL ONLY

(e)(2)(iii) Prior to June 1, 2016, employers may use the following legend in lieu of that specified in paragraph (e)(2)(i) of this Section:

CANCER-SUSPECT AGENT
AUTHORIZED PERSONNEL ONLY

(e)(2)(iv) Prior to June 1, 2016, employers may use the following legend in lieu of that specified in paragraph (e)(2)(ii) of this Section:

CANCER-SUSPECT AGENT EXPOSED IN THIS AREA
IMPERVIOUS SUIT INCLUDING GLOVES, BOOTS, AND AIR-SUPPLIED HOOD REQUIRED AT ALL TIMES
AUTHORIZED PERSONNEL ONLY

(e)(2)(v) Appropriate signs and instructions shall be posted at the entrance to, and exit from, regulated areas, informing employees of the procedures that must be followed in entering and leaving a regulated area.

(e)(3) **Prohibited statements** No statement shall appear on or near any required sign, label, or instruction that contradicts or detracts from the effect of any required warning, information, or instruction.

(e)(4) **Training and indoctrination**

(e)(4)(i) Each employee prior to being authorized to enter a regulated area, shall receive a training and indoctrination program including, but not necessarily limited to:

(e)(4)(i)(A) The nature of the carcinogenic hazards of a carcinogen addressed by this Section, including local and systemic toxicity;

(e)(4)(i)(B) The specific nature of the operation involving a carcinogen addressed by this Section that could result in exposure;

(e)(4)(i)(C) The purpose for and application of the medical surveillance program, including, as appropriate, methods of self-examination;

(e)(4)(i)(D) The purpose for and application of decontamination practices and purposes;

(e)(4)(i)(E) The purpose for and significance of emergency practices and procedures;

(e)(4)(i)(F) The employee's specific role in emergency procedures;

(e)(4)(i)(G) Specific information to aid the employee in recognition and evaluation of conditions and situations which may result in the release of a carcinogen addressed by this Section;

(e)(4)(i)(H) The purpose for and application of specific first aid procedures and practices;

(e)(4)(i)(I) A review of this Section at the employee's first training and indoctrination program and annually thereafter.

(e)(4)(ii) Specific emergency procedures shall be prescribed, and posted, and employees shall be familiarized with their terms, and rehearsed in their application.

(e)(4)(iii) All materials relating to the program shall be provided upon request to authorized representatives of the Assistant Secretary and the Director.

(f) [Reserved]

(g) **Medical surveillance** At no cost to the employee, a program of medical surveillance shall be established and implemented for employees considered for assignment to enter regulated areas, and for authorized employees.

(g)(1) **Examinations**

(g)(1)(i) Before an employee is assigned to enter a regulated area, a preassignment physical examination by a physician shall be provided. The examination shall include the personal history of the employee, family and occupational background, including genetic and environmental factors.

(g)(1)(ii) Authorized employees shall be provided periodic physical examinations, not less often than annually, following the preassignment examination.

(g)(1)(iii) In all physical examinations, the examining physician shall consider whether there exist conditions of increased risk, including reduced immunological competence, those undergoing treatment with steroids or cytotoxic agents, pregnancy, and cigarette smoking.

(g)(2) **Records**

(g)(2)(i) Employers of employees examined pursuant to this paragraph shall cause to be maintained complete and accurate records of all such medical examinations. Records shall be maintained for the duration of the employee's employment.

(g)(2)(ii) Records required by this paragraph shall be provided upon request to employees, designated representatives, and the Assistant Secretary in accordance with 29 CFR §1910.1020 (a) through (e) and (g) through (i). These records shall also be provided upon request to the Director.

(g)(2)(iii) Any physician who conducts a medical examination required by this paragraph shall furnish to the employer a statement of the employee's suitability for employment in the specific exposure.

[61 FR 9242, Mar. 7, 1996, as amended at 63 FR 1286, Jan. 8, 1998; 63 FR 20099, Apr. 23, 1998; 70 FR 1141, Jan. 5, 2005; 71 FR 16672, Apr. 3, 2006; 73 FR 75584, Dec. 2, 2008; 76 FR 33608, June 8, 2011]

§1910.1004 alpha–Naphthylamine

See §1910.1003, 13 carcinogens.

[61 FR 9245, Mar. 7, 1996] 7, 1996]

§1910.1005 [Reserved]

§1910.1006 Methyl chloromethyl ether

See §1910.1003, 13 carcinogens.

[61 FR 9245, Mar. 7, 1996]

§1910.1007 3,'–Dichlorobenzidine (and its salts)

See §1910.1003, 13 carcinogens.

[61 FR 9245, Mar. 7, 1996]

§1910.1008 bis–Chloromethyl ether

See §1910.1003, 13 carcinogens.

[61 FR 9245, Mar. 7, 1996]

§1910.1009 beta–Naphthylamine

See §1910.1003, 13 carcinogens.

[61 FR 9245, Mar. 7, 1996]

§1910.1010 Benzidine

See §1910.1003, 13 carcinogens.

[61 FR 9245, Mar. 7, 1996]

§1910.1011 4–Aminodiphenyl

See §1910.1003, 13 carcinogens.

[61 FR 9245, Mar. 7, 1996]

§1910.1012 Ethyleneimine

See §1910.1003, 13 carcinogens.

[61 FR 9245, Mar. 7, 1996]

§1910.1013 beta–Propiolactone

See §1910.1003, 13 carcinogens.

[61 FR 9245, Mar. 7, 1996]

§1910.1014 2–Acetylaminofluorene

See §1910.1003, 13 carcinogens.

[61 FR 9245, Mar. 7, 1996]

§1910.1015 4–Dimethylaminoazobenzene

See §1910.1003, 13 carcinogens.

[61 FR 9245, Mar. 7, 1996]

§1910.1016 N–Nitrosodimethylamine

See §1910.1003, 13 carcinogens.

[61 FR 9245, Mar. 7, 1996]

§1910.1017 Vinyl chloride

(a) Scope and application

(a)(1) This Section includes requirements for the control of employee exposure to vinyl chloride (chloroethene), Chemical Abstracts Service Registry No. 75014.

(a)(2) This Section applies to the manufacture, reaction, packaging, repackaging, storage, handling or use of vinyl chloride or polyvinyl chloride, but does not apply to the handling or use of fabricated products made of polyvinyl chloride.

(a)(3) This Section applies to the transportation of vinyl chloride or polyvinyl chloride except to the extent that the Department of Transportation may regulate the hazards covered by this Section.

(b) Definitions

(b)(1) **Action level** means a concentration of vinyl chloride of 0.5 ppm averaged over an 8-hour work day.

(b)(2) **Assistant Secretary** means the Assistant Secretary of Labor for Occupational Safety and Health, U.S. Department of Labor, or his designee.

(b)(3) **Authorized person** means any person specifically authorized by the employer whose duties require him to enter a regulated area or any person entering such an area as a designated representative of employees for the purpose of exercising an opportunity to observe monitoring and measuring procedures.

(b)(4) **Director** means the Director, National Institute for Occupational Safety and Health, U.S. Department of Health and Human Services, or his designee.

(b)(5) **Emergency** means any occurrence such as, but not limited to, equipment failure, or operation of a relief device which is likely to, or does, result in massive release of vinyl chloride.

(b)(6) **Fabricated product** means a product made wholly or partly from polyvinyl chloride, and which does not require further processing at temperatures, and for times, sufficient to cause mass melting of the polyvinyl chloride resulting in the release of vinyl chloride.

(b)(7) **Hazardous operation** means any operation, procedure, or activity where a release of either vinyl chloride liquid or gas might be expected as a consequence of the operation or because of an accident in the operation, which would result in an employee exposure in excess of the permissible exposure limit.

(b)(8) **OSHA Area Director** means the Director for the Occupational Safety and Health Administration Area Office having jurisdiction over the geographic area in which the employer's establishment is located.

(b)(9) **Polyvinyl chloride** means polyvinyl chloride homopolymer or copolymer before such is converted to a fabricated product.

(b)(10) **Vinyl chloride** means vinyl chloride monomer.

(c) Permissible exposure limit

(c)(1) No employee may be exposed to vinyl chloride at concentrations greater than 1 ppm averaged over any 8-hour period, and

(c)(2) No employee may be exposed to vinyl chloride at concentrations greater than 5 ppm averaged over any period not exceeding 15 minutes.

(c)(3) No employee may be exposed to vinyl chloride by direct contact with liquid vinyl chloride.

(d) Monitoring

(d)(1) A program of initial monitoring and measurement shall be undertaken in each establishment to determine if there is any employee exposed, without regard to the use of respirators, in excess of the action level.

(d)(2) Where a determination conducted under paragraph (d)(1) of this Section shows any employee exposures, without regard to the use of respirators, in excess of the action level, a program for determining exposures for each such employee shall be established. Such a program:

(d)(2)(i) Must be repeated at least quarterly for any employee exposed, without regard to the use of respirators, in excess of the permissible exposure limit;

(d)(2)(ii) Must be repeated not less than every 6 months for any employee exposed without regard to the use of respirators, at or above the action level;

(d)(2)(iii) May be discontinued for any employee only when at least two consecutive monitoring determinations, made not less than 5 working days apart, show exposures for that employee at or below the action level.

(d)(3) Whenever there has been a production, process or control change which may result in an increase in the release of vinyl chloride, or the employer has any other reason to suspect that any employee may be exposed in excess of the action level, a determination of employee exposure under paragraph (d)(1) of this Section shall be performed.

(d)(4) The method of monitoring and measurement shall have an accuracy (with a confidence level of 95 percent) of not less than plus or minus 50 percent from 0.25 through 0.5 ppm, plus or minus 35 percent from over 0.5 ppm through 1.0 ppm, and plus or minus 25 percent over 1.0 ppm. (Methods meeting these accuracy requirements are available in the "NIOSH Manual of Analytical Methods".)

(d)(5) Employees or their designated representatives shall be afforded reasonable opportunity to observe the monitoring and measuring required by this paragraph.

(e) Regulated area

(e)(1) A regulated area shall be established where:

(e)(1)(i) Vinyl chloride or polyvinyl chloride is manufactured, reacted, repackaged, stored, handled or used; and

(e)(1)(ii) Vinyl chloride concentrations are in excess of the permissible exposure limit.

(e)(2) Access to regulated areas shall be limited to authorized persons.

(f) **Methods of compliance** Employee exposures to vinyl chloride shall be controlled to at or below the permissible exposure limit provided in paragraph (c) of this Section by engineering, work practice, and personal protective controls as follows:

(f)(1) Feasible engineering and work practice controls shall immediately be used to reduce exposures to at or below the permissible exposure limit.

(f)(2) Wherever feasible engineering and work practice controls, which can be instituted immediately, are not sufficient to reduce exposures to, at, or below the permissible exposure limit, they shall nonetheless be used to reduce exposures to the lowest practicable level, and shall be supplemented by respiratory protection in accordance with paragraph (g) of this Section. A program shall be established and implemented to reduce exposures to at or below the permissible exposure limit, or to the greatest extent feasible, solely by means of engineering and work practice controls, as soon as feasible.

(f)(3) Written plans for such a program shall be developed and furnished upon request for examination and copying to authorized representatives of the Assistant Secretary and the Director. Such plans must be updated at least annually.

(g) **Respiratory protection**

(g)(1) **General** For employees who use respirators required by this Section, the employer must provide each employee an appropriate respirator that complies with the requirements of this paragraph.

(g)(2) **Respirator program** The employer must implement a respiratory protection program in accordance §1910.134 (b) through (d) (except (d)(1)(iii), and (d)(3)(iii)(B)(1) and (2), and (f) through (m) which covers each employee required by this Section to use a respirator.

(g)(3) **Respirator selection**

(g)(3)(i) Employers must:

(g)(3)(i)(A) Select, and provide to employees, the appropriate respirators specified in paragraph (d)(3)(i)(A) of 29 CFR §1910.134;

(g)(3)(i)(B) Provide an organic vapor cartridge that has a service life of at least one hour when using a chemical cartridge respirator at vinyl chloride concentrations up to 10 ppm; and

(g)(3)(i)(C) Select a canister that has a service life of at least four hours when using a powered air-purifying respirator having a hood, helmet, or full or half facepiece, or a gas mask with a front-or back-mounted canister, at vinyl chloride concentrations up to 25 ppm.

(g)(3)(ii) When air-purifying respirators are used:

(g)(3)(ii)(A) Air-purifying canisters or cartridges must be replaced prior to the expiration of their service life or the end of the shift in which they are first used, whichever occurs first; and

(g)(3)(ii)(B) A continuous-monitoring and alarm system must be provided when concentrations of vinyl chloride could reasonably exceed the allowable concentrations for the devices in use. Such a system must be used to alert employees when vinyl chloride concentrations exceed the allowable concentrations for the devices in use.

(h) **Hazardous operations**

(h)(1) Employees engaged in hazardous operations, including entry of vessels to clean polyvinyl chloride residue from vessel walls, shall be provided and required to wear and use:

(h)(1)(i) Respiratory protection in accordance with paragraphs (c) and (g) of this Section; and

(h)(1)(ii) Protective garments to prevent skin contact with liquid vinyl chloride or with polyvinyl chloride residue from vessel walls. The protective garments shall be selected for the operation and its possible exposure conditions.

(h)(2) Protective garments shall be provided clean and dry for each use.

(i) **Emergency situations** A written operational plan for emergency situations shall be developed for each facility storing, handling, or otherwise using vinyl chloride as a liquid or compressed gas. Appropriate portions of the plan shall be implemented in the event of an emergency. The plan shall specifically provide that:

(i)(1) Employees engaged in hazardous operations or correcting situations of existing hazardous releases shall be equipped as required in paragraph (h) of this Section;

(i)(2) Other employees not so equipped shall evacuate the area and not return until conditions are controlled by the methods required in paragraph (f) of this Section and the emergency is abated.

(j) **Training** Each employee engaged in vinyl chloride or polyvinyl chloride operations shall be provided training in a program relating to the hazards of vinyl chloride and precautions for its safe use.

(j)(1) The program shall include:

(j)(1)(i) The nature of the health hazard from chronic exposure to vinyl chloride including specifically the carcinogenic hazard;

(j)(1)(ii) The specific nature of operations which could result in exposure to vinyl chloride in excess of the permissible limit and necessary protective steps;

(j)(1)(iii) The purpose for, proper use, and limitations of respiratory protective devices;

(j)(1)(iv) The fire hazard and acute toxicity of vinyl chloride, and the necessary protective steps;

(j)(1)(v) The purpose for and a description of the monitoring program;

(j)(1)(vi) The purpose for, and a description of, the medical surveillance program;

(j)(1)(vii) Emergency procedures;

(j)(1)(viii) Specific information to aid the employee in recognition of conditions which may result in the release of vinyl chloride; and

(j)(1)(ix) A review of this Standard at the employee's first training and indoctrination program, and annually thereafter.

(j)(2) All materials relating to the program shall be provided upon request to the Assistant Secretary and the Director.

(k) **Medical surveillance** A program of medical surveillance shall be instituted for each employee exposed, without regard to the use of respirators, to vinyl chloride in excess of the action level. The program shall provide each such employee with an opportunity for examinations and tests in accordance with this paragraph. All medical examinations and procedures shall be performed by or under the supervision of a licensed physician, and shall be provided without cost to the employee.

(k)(1) At the time of initial assignment, or upon institution of medical surveillance:

(k)(l)(i) A general physical examination shall be performed, with specific attention to detecting enlargement of liver, spleen or kidneys, or dysfunction in these organs, and for abnormalities in skin, connective tissues and the pulmonary system (See Appendix A).

(k)(1)(ii) A medical history shall be taken, including the following topics:

(k)(1)(ii)(A) Alcohol intake;

(k)(1)(ii)(B) Past history of hepatitis;

(k)(1)(ii)(C) Work history and past exposure to potential hepatotoxic agents, including drugs and chemicals;

(k)(1)(ii)(D) Past history of blood transfusions; and

(k)(1)(ii)(E) Past history of hospitalizations.

(k)(1)(iii) A serum specimen shall be obtained and determinations made of:

(k)(1)(iii)(A) Total bilirubin;

(k)(1)(iii)(B) Alkaline phosphatase;

(k)(1)(iii)(C) Serum glutamic oxalacetic transaminase (SGOT);

(k)(1)(iii)(D) Serum glutamic pyruvic transaminase (SGPT); and

(k)(1)(iii)(E) Gamma glustamyl transpeptidase.

(k)(2) Examinations must be provided in accordance with this paragraph at least annually.

(k)(3) Each employee exposed to an emergency shall be afforded appropriate medical surveillance.

(k)(4) A statement of each employee's suitability for continued exposure to vinyl chloride including use of protective equipment and respirators, shall be obtained from the examining physician promptly after any examination. A copy of the physician's statement shall be provided each employee.

(k)(5) If any employee's health would be materially impaired by continued exposure, such employee shall be withdrawn from possible contact with vinyl chloride.

(k)(6) Laboratory analyses for all biological specimens included in medical examination shall be performed by accredited laboratories.

(k)(7) If the examining physician determines that alternative medical examinations to those required by paragraph (k)(1) of this Section will provide at least equal assurance of detecting medical conditions pertinent to the exposure to vinyl chloride, the employer may accept such alternative examinations as meeting the requirements of paragraph (k)(1) of this Section, if the employer obtains a statement from the examining physician setting forth the alternative examinations and the rationale for substitution. This statement shall be available upon request for examination and copying to authorized representatives of the Assistant Secretary and the Director.

(l) **Communication of hazards**

(l)(1) **Hazard communication—general**

(l)(1)(i) Chemical manufacturers, importers, distributors and employers shall comply with all requirements of the Hazard Communication Standard (HCS) (§1910.1200) for vinyl chloride and polyvinyl chloride.

(l)(1)(ii) In classifying the hazards of vinyl chloride at least the following hazards are to be addressed: Cancer; central nervous system effects; liver effects; blood effects; and flammability.

(l)(1)(iii) Employers shall include vinyl chloride in the hazard communication program established to comply with the HCS (§1910.1200). Employers shall ensure that each employee has access to labels on containers of vinyl chloride and to safety data sheets, and is trained in accordance with the requirements of HCS and paragraph (j) of this Section.

(l)(2) **Signs**

(l)(2)(i) The employer shall post entrances to regulated areas with legible signs bearing the legend:

DANGER
VINYL CHLORIDE
MAY CAUSE CANCER
AUTHORIZED PERSONNEL ONLY

(l)(2)(ii) The employer shall post signs at areas containing hazardous operations or where emergencies currently exist. The signs shall be legible and bear the legend:

DANGER
VINYL CHLORIDE
MAY CAUSE CANCER
WEAR RESPIRATORY PROTECTION AND
PROTECTIVE CLOTHING IN THIS AREA
AUTHORIZED PERSONNEL ONLY

(l)(2)(iii) Prior to June 1, 2016, employers may use the following legend in lieu of that specified in paragraph (l)(2)(i) of this Section:

CANCER-SUSPECT AGENT AREA
AUTHORIZED PERSONNEL ONLY

(l)(2)(iv) Prior to June 1, 2016, employers may use the following legend in lieu of that specified in paragraph (l)(2)(ii) of this Section:

CANCER-SUSPECT AGENT IN THIS AREA
PROTECTIVE EQUIPMENT REQUIRED
AUTHORIZED PERSONNEL ONLY

(l)(3) **Labels**

(l)(3)(i) In addition to the other requirements in this paragraph (l), the employer shall ensure that labels for containers of polyvinyl chloride resin waste from reactors or other waste contaminated with vinyl chloride are legible and include the following information:

CONTAMINATED WITH VINYL CHLORIDE
MAY CAUSE CANCER

(l)(3)(ii) Prior to June 1, 2015, employers may include the following information on labels of containers of polyvinyl chloride resin waste from reactors or other waste contaminated with vinyl chloride in lieu of the labeling requirements in paragraphs (l)(3)(i) of this Section:

CONTAMINATED WITH VINYL CHLORIDE
CANCER-SUSPECT AGENT

(l)(4) Prior to June 1, 2015, employers may include the following information for containers of polyvinyl chloride in lieu of the labeling requirements in paragraphs (l)(1)(i) of this Section:

POLYVINYL CHLORIDE (OR TRADE NAME)
Contains
VINYL CHLORIDE
VINYL CHLORIDE IS A CANCER-SUSPECT AGENT

(l)(5)(i) Prior to June 1, 2015, employers may include either the following information in either paragraph (l)(5)(i) or (l)(5)(ii) of this Section on containers of vinyl chloride in lieu of the labeling requirements in paragraph (l)(1)(i) of this Section:

VINYL CHLORIDE
EXTREMELY FLAMMABLE GAS UNDER PRESSURE
CANCER-SUSPECT AGENT

(l)(5)(ii) In accordance with 49 CFR Parts 170–189, with the additional legend applied near the label or placard:

CANCER-SUSPECT AGENT

(l)(6) No statement shall appear on or near any required sign, label, or instruction which contradicts or detracts from the effect of any required warning, information, or instruction.

(m) **Records**

(m)(1) All records maintained in accordance with this Section shall include the name and social security number of each employee where relevant.

(m)(2) Records of required monitoring and measuring and medical records shall be provided upon request to employees, designated representatives, and the Assistant Secretary in accordance with 29 CFR §1910.1020 (a) through (e) and (g) through (i). These records shall be provided upon request to the Director. Authorized personnel rosters shall also be provided upon request to the Assistant Secretary and the Director.

(m)(2)(i) Monitoring and measuring records shall:

(m)(2)(i)(A) State the date of such monitoring and measuring and the concentrations determined and identify the instruments and methods used;

(m)(2)(i)(B) Include any additional information necessary to determine individual employee exposures where such exposures are determined by means other than individual monitoring of employees; and

(m)(2)(i)(C) Be maintained for not less than 30 years.

(m)(2)(ii) [Reserved]

(m)(2)(iii) Medical records shall be maintained for the duration of the employment of each employee plus 20 years, or 30 years, whichever is longer.

§1910.1017 Appendix A Supplementary medical information

When required tests under paragraph (k)(1) of this Section show abnormalities, the tests should be repeated as soon as practicable, preferably within 3 to 4 weeks. If tests remain abnormal, consideration should be given to withdrawal of the employee from contact with vinyl chloride, while a more comprehensive examination is made.

Additional tests which may be useful:

A. For kidney dysfunction: urine examination for albumin, red blood cells, and exfoliative abnormal cells;

B. Pulmonary system: Forced vital capacity, Forced expiratory volume at 1 second, and chest roentgenogram (posterior-anterior, 14 × 17 inches);

C. Additional serum tests: Lactic acid dehydrogenase, lactic acid dehydrogenase isoenzyme, protein determination, and protein electrophoresis;

D. For a more comprehensive examination on repeated abnormal serum tests: Hepatitis B antigen, and liver scanning.

[39 FR 35896, Oct. 4, 1974; 39 FR 41848, Dec. 3, 1974, as amended at 40 FR 13211, Mar. 25, 1975. Redesignated at 40 FR 23072, May 28, 1975 and amended at 43 FR 49751, Oct. 24, 1978; 45 FR 35282, May 23, 1980; 54 FR 24334, June 7, 1989; 58 FR 35310, June 30, 1993; 61 FR 5508, Feb. 13, 1996; 63 FR 1286, Jan. 8, 1998; 70 FR 1141, Jan. 5, 2005; 71 FR 16672, 16673, Apr. 3, 2006; 71 FR 50188, Aug. 24, 2006; 73 FR 75585, Dec. 12, 2008; 76 FR 33608, June 8, 2011]

§1910.1018 Inorganic arsenic

(a) **Scope and application** This Section applies to all occupational exposures to inorganic arsenic except that this Section does not apply to employee exposures in agriculture or resulting from pesticide application, the treatment of wood with preservatives or the utilization of arsenically preserved wood.

(b) **Definitions**

Action level means a concentration of inorganic arsenic of 5 micrograms per cubic meter of air (5 $\mu g/m^3$) averaged over any eight (8) hour period.

Assistant Secretary means the Assistant Secretary of Labor for Occupational Safety and Health, U.S. Department of Labor, or designee.

Authorized person means any person specifically authorized by the employer whose duties require the person to enter a regulated area, or any person entering such an area as a designated representative of employees for the purpose of exercising the right to observe monitoring and measuring procedures under paragraph (e) of this Section.

Director means the Director, National Institute for Occupational Safety and Health, U.S. Department of Health and Human Services, or designee.

Inorganic arsenic means copper aceto- arsenite and all inorganic compounds containing arsenic except arsine, measured as arsenic (As).

(c) **Permissible exposure limit** The employer shall assure that no employee is exposed to inorganic arsenic at concentrations greater than 10 micrograms per cubic meter of air (10 $\mu g/m^3$), averaged over any 8-hour period.

(d) [Reserved]

(e) **Exposure monitoring**

(e)(1) **General**

(e)(1)(i) Determinations of airborne exposure levels shall be made from air samples that are representative of each employee's exposure to inorganic arsenic over an eight (8) hour period.

(e)(1)(ii) For the purposes of this Section, employee exposure is that exposure which would occur if the employee were not using a respirator.

(e)(1)(iii) The employer shall collect full shift (for at least 7 continuous hours) personal samples including at least one sample for each shift for each job classification in each work area.

(e)(2) **Initial monitoring** Each employer who has a workplace or work operation covered by this Standard shall monitor each such workplace and work operation to accurately determine the airborne concentration of inorganic arsenic to which employees may be exposed.

(e)(3) **Frequency**

(e)(3)(i) If the initial monitoring reveals employee exposure to be below the action level the measurements need not be repeated except as otherwise provided in paragraph (e)(4) of this Section.

(e)(3)(ii) If the initial monitoring, required by this Section, or subsequent monitoring reveals employee exposure to be above the permissible exposure limit, the employer shall repeat monitoring at least quarterly.

(e)(3)(iii) If the initial monitoring, required by this Section, or subsequent monitoring reveals employee exposure to be above the action level and below the permissible exposure limit the employer shall repeat monitoring at least every six months.

(e)(3)(iv) The employer shall continue monitoring at the required frequency until at least two consecutive measurements, taken at least seven (7) days apart, are below the action level at which time the employer may discontinue monitoring for that employee until such time as any of the events in paragraph (e)(4) of this Section occur.

(e)(4) **Additional monitoring** Whenever there has been a production, process, control or personal change which may result in new or additional exposure to inorganic arsenic, or whenever the employer has any other reason to suspect a change which may result in new or additional exposures to inorganic arsenic, additional monitoring which complies with paragraph (e) of this Section shall be conducted.

(e)(5) **Employee notification**

(e)(5)(i) The employer must, within 15 working days after the receipt of the results of any monitoring performed under this Section, notify each affected employee of these results either individually in writing or by posting the results in an appropriate location that is accessible to affected employees.

(e)(5)(ii) Whenever the results indicate that the representative employee exposure exceeds the permissible exposure limit, the employer shall include in the written notice a statement that the permissible exposure limit was exceeded and a description of the corrective action taken to reduce exposure to or below the permissible exposure limit.

(e)(6) **Accuracy of measurement**

(e)(6)(i) The employer shall use a method of monitoring and measurement which has an accuracy (with a confidence level of 95 percent) of not less than plus or minus 25 percent for concentrations of inorganic arsenic greater than or equal to 10 $\mu g/m^3$.

(e)(6)(ii) The employer shall use a method of monitoring and measurement which has an accuracy (with confidence level of 95 percent) of not less than plus or minus 35 percent for concentrations of inorganic arsenic greater than 5 $\mu g/m^3$ but less than 10 $\mu g/m^3$.

(f) **Regulated area**

(f)(1) **Establishment** The employer shall establish regulated areas where worker exposures to inorganic arsenic, without regard to the use of respirators, are in excess of the permissible limit.

(f)(2) **Demarcation** Regulated areas shall be demarcated and segregated from the rest of the workplace in any manner that minimizes the number of persons who will be exposed to inorganic arsenic.

(f)(3) **Access** Access to regulated areas shall be limited to authorized persons or to persons otherwise authorized by the Act or regulations issued pursuant thereto to enter such areas.

(f)(4) **Provision of respirators** All persons entering a regulated area shall be supplied with a respirator, selected in accordance with paragraph (h)(2) of this Section.

(f)(5) **Prohibited activities** The employer shall assure that in regulated areas, food or beverages are not consumed, smoking products, chewing tobacco and gum are not used and cosmetics are not applied, except that these activities may be conducted in the lunchrooms, change rooms and showers required under paragraph (m) of this Section. Drinking water may be consumed in the regulated area.

(g) **Methods of compliance**

(g)(1) **Controls**

(g)(1)(i) The employer shall institute at the earliest possible time but not later than December 31, 1979, engineering and work practice controls to reduce exposures to or below the permissible exposure limit, except to the extent that the employer can establish that such controls are not feasible.

(g)(1)(ii) Where engineering and work practice controls are not sufficient to reduce exposures to or below the permissible exposure limit, they shall nonetheless be used to reduce exposures to the lowest levels achievable by these controls and shall be supplemented by the use of respirators in accordance with paragraph (h) of this Section and other necessary personal protective equipment. Employee rotation is not required as a control strategy before respiratory protection is instituted.

(g)(2) [OI] **Compliance program**

(g)(2)(i) The employer shall establish and implement a written program to reduce exposures to or below the permissible exposure limit by means of engineering and work practice controls.

(g)(2)(ii) Written plans for these compliance programs shall include at least the following:

(g)(2)(ii)(A) A description of each operation in which inorganic arsenic is emitted; e.g. machinery used, material processed, controls in place, crew size, operating procedures and maintenance practices;

(g)(2)(ii)(B) Engineering plans and studies used to determine methods selected for controlling exposure to inorganic arsenic;

(g)(2)(ii)(C) A report of the technology considered in meeting the permissible exposure limit;

(g)(2)(ii)(D) Monitoring data;

(g)(2)(ii)(E) A detailed schedule for implementation of the engineering controls and work practices that cannot be implemented immediately and for the adaption and implementation of any additional engineering and work practices necessary to meet the permissible exposure limit;

(g)(2)(ii)(F) Whenever the employer will not achieve the permissible exposure limit with engineering controls and work practices by December 31, 1979, the employer shall include in the compliance plan an analysis of the effectiveness of the various controls, shall install engineering controls and institute work practices on the quickest schedule feasible, and shall include in the compliance plan and implement a program to minimize the discomfort and maximize the effectiveness of respirator use; and

(g)(2)(ii)(G) Other relevant information.

(g)(2)(iii) Written plans for such a program shall be submitted upon request to the Assistant Secretary and the Director, and shall be available at the worksite for examination and copying by the Assistant Secretary, Director, any affected employee or authorized employee representatives.

(g)(2)(iv) The plans required by this paragraph must be revised and updated at least annually to reflect the current status of the program.

(h) **Respiratory protection**

(h)(1) **General** For employees who use respirators required by this Section, the employer must provide each employee an appropriate respirator that complies with the requirements of this paragraph. Respirators must be used during:

(h)(1)(i) Periods necessary to install or implement feasible engineering or work-practice controls;

(h)(1)(ii) Work operations, such as maintenance and repair activities, for which the employer establishes that engineering and work-practice controls are not feasible;

(h)(1)(iii) Work operations for which engineering and work-practice controls are not yet sufficient to reduce employee exposures to or below the permissible exposure limit; and

(h)(1)(iv) Emergencies.

(h)(2) **Respirator program**

(h)(2)(i) The employer must implement a respiratory protection program in accordance with §1910.134(b) through (d) (except (d)(1)(iii)), and (f) through (m), which covers each employee required by this Section to use a respirator.

(h)(2)(ii) If an employee exhibits breathing difficulty during fit testing or respirator use, they must be examined by a physician trained in pulmonary medicine to determine whether they can use a respirator while performing the required duty.

(h)(3) **Respirator selection**

(h)(3)(i) Employers must:

(h)(3)(i)(A) Select, and provide to employees, the appropriate respirators specified in paragraph (d)(3)(i)(A) of 29 CFR §1910.134;

(h)(3)(i)(B) Ensure that employees do not use half mask respirators for protection against arsenic trichloride because it is absorbed rapidly through the skin; and

(h)(3)(i)(C) Provide HEPA filters for powered and non-powered air-purifying respirators.

(h)(3)(i)(D) Select for employee use:

(h)(3)(i)(D)(1) Air-purifying respirators that have a combination HEPA filter with an appropriate gas-sorbent cartridge or canister when the employee's exposure exceeds the permissible exposure level for inorganic arsenic and the relevant limit for other gases.

(h)(3)(i)(D)(2) Front-or back-mounted gas masks equipped with HEPA filters and acid gas canisters or any full facepiece supplied-air respirators when the inorganic arsenic concentration is at or below 500 mg/m^3 ; and half mask air-purifying respirators equipped with HEPA filters and acid gas cartridges when the inorganic arsenic concentration is at or below 100 $\mu g/m^3$.

(h)(3)(ii) Employees required to use respirators may choose, and the employer must provide, a powered air-purifying respirator if it will provide proper protection. In addition, the employer must provide a combination dust and acid-gas respirator to employees who are exposed to gases over the relevant exposure limits.

(i) [Reserved]

(j) **Protective work clothing and equipment**

(j)(1) **Provision and use** Where the possibility of skin or eye irritation from inorganic arsenic exists, and for all workers working in regulated areas, the employer shall provide at no cost to the employee and assure that employees use appropriate and clean protective work clothing and equipment such as, but not limited to:

(j)(1)(i) Coveralls or similar full-body work clothing;

(j)(1)(ii) Gloves, and shoes or coverlets;

(j)(1)(iii) Face shields or vented goggles when necessary to prevent eye irritation, which comply with the requirements of §1910.133(a) (2)–(6); and

(j)(1)(iv) Impervious clothing for employees subject to exposure to arsenic trichloride.

(j)(2) **Cleaning and replacement**

(j)(2)(i) The employer shall provide the protective clothing required in paragraph (j)(1) of this Section in a freshly laundered and dry condition at least weekly, and daily if the employee works in areas where exposures are over 100 $\mu g/m^3$ of inorganic arsenic or in areas where more frequent washing is needed to prevent skin irritation.

(j)(2)(ii) The employer shall clean, launder, or dispose of protective clothing required by paragraph (j)(1) of this Section.

(j)(2)(iii) The employer shall repair or replace the protective clothing and equipment as needed to maintain their effectiveness.

(j)(2)(iv) The employer shall assure that all protective clothing is removed at the completion of a work shift only in change rooms prescribed in paragraph (m)(1) of this Section.

(j)(2)(v) The employer shall assure that contaminated protective clothing which is to be cleaned, laundered, or disposed of, is placed in a closed container in the change-room which prevents dispersion of inorganic arsenic outside the container.

(j)(2)(vi) The employer shall inform in writing any person who cleans or launders clothing required by this Section, of the potentially harmful effects including the carcinogenic effects of exposure to inorganic arsenic.

(j)(2)(vii) Labels on contaminated protective clothing and equipment.

(j)(2)(vii)(A) The employer shall ensure that the containers of contaminated protective clothing and equipment in the workplace or which are to be removed from the workplace are labeled and that the labels include the following information:

DANGER: CONTAMINATED WITH INORGANIC ARSENIC. MAY CAUSE CANCER. DO NOT REMOVE DUST BY BLOWING OR SHAKING. DISPOSE OF INORGANIC ARSENIC CONTAMINATED WASH WATER IN ACCORDANCE WITH APPLICABLE LOCAL, STATE OR FEDERAL REGULATIONS.

(j)(2)(vii)(B) Prior to June 1, 2015, employers may include the following information on containers of protective clothing and equipment in lieu of the labeling requirements in paragraphs (j)(2)(vii) of this Section:

CAUTION: Clothing contaminated with inorganic arsenic; do not remove dust by blowing or shaking. Dispose of inorganic arsenic contaminated wash water in accordance with applicable local, State or Federal regulations.

(j)(2)(viii) The employer shall prohibit the removal of inorganic arsenic from protective clothing or equipment by blowing or shaking.

(k) **Housekeeping**

(k)(1) **Surfaces** All surfaces shall be maintained as free as practicable of accumulations of inorganic arsenic.

(k)(2) **Cleaning floors** Floors and other accessible surfaces contaminated with inorganic arsenic may not be cleaned by the use of compressed air, and shoveling and brushing may be used only where vacuuming or other relevant methods have been tried and found not to be effective.

(k)(3) **Vacuuming** Where vacuuming methods are selected, the vacuums shall be used and emptied in a manner to minimize the reentry of inorganic arsenic into the workplace.

(k)(4) **Housekeeping plan** A written housekeeping and maintenance plan shall be kept which shall list appropriate frequencies for carrying out housekeeping operations, and for cleaning and maintaining dust collection equipment. The plan shall be available for inspection by the Assistant Secretary.

(k)(5) **Maintenance of equipment** Periodic cleaning of dust collection and ventilation equipment and checks of their effectiveness shall be carried out to maintain the effectiveness of the system and a notation kept of the last check of effectiveness and cleaning or maintenance.

(l) [Reserved]

(m) **Hygiene facilities and practices**

(m)(1) **Change rooms** The employer shall provide for employees working in regulated areas or subject to the possibility of skin or eye irritation from inorganic arsenic, clean change rooms equipped with storage facilities for street clothes and separate storage facilities for protective clothing and equipment in accordance with 29 CFR §1910.141(e).

(m)(2) **Showers**

(m)(2)(i) The employer shall assure that employees working in regulated areas or subject to the possibility of skin or eye irritation from inorganic arsenic shower at the end of the work shift.

(m)(2)(ii) The employer shall provide shower facilities in accordance with §1910.141(d)(3).

(m)(3) **Lunchrooms**

(m)(3)(i) The employer shall provide for employees working in regulated areas, lunchroom facilities which have a temperature controlled, positive pressure, filtered air supply, and which are readily accessible to employees working in regulated areas.

(m)(3)(ii) The employer shall assure that employees working in the regulated area or subject to the possibility of skin or eye irritation from exposure to inorganic arsenic wash their hands and face prior to eating.

(m)(4) **Lavatories** The employer shall provide lavatory facilities which comply with §1910.141(d)(1) and (2).

(m)(5) **Vacuuming clothes** The employer shall provide facilities for employees working in areas where exposure, without regard to the use of respirators, exceeds 100 $\mu g/m^3$ to vacuum their protective clothing and clean or change shoes worn in such areas before entering change rooms, lunchrooms or shower rooms required by paragraph (j) of this Section and shall assure that such employees use such facilities.

(m)(6) **Avoidance of skin irritation** The employer shall assure that no employee is exposed to skin or eye contact with arsenic trichloride, or to skin or eye contact with liquid or particulate inorganic arsenic which is likely to cause skin or eye irritation.

(n) **Medical surveillance**

(n)(1) **General**

(n)(1)(i) **Employees covered** The employer shall institute a medical surveillance program for the following employees:

(n)(1)(i)(A) All employees who are or will be exposed above the action level, without regard to the use of respirators, at least 30 days per year; and

(n)(1)(i)(B) All employees who have been exposed above the action level, without regard to respirator use, for 30 days or more per year for a total of 10 years or more of combined employment with the employer or predecessor employers prior to or after the effective date of this Standard. The determination of exposures prior to the effective date of this Standard shall be based upon prior exposure records, comparison with the first measurements taken after the effective date of this Standard, or comparison with records of exposures in areas with similar processes, extent of engineering controls utilized and materials used by that employer.

(n)(1)(ii) **Examination by physician** The employer shall assure that all medical examinations and procedures are performed by or under the supervision of a licensed physician, and shall be provided without cost to the employee, without loss of pay and at a reasonable time and place.

(n)(2) **Initial examinations** By December 1, 1978, for employees initially covered by the medical provisions of this Section, or thereafter at the time of initial assignment to an area where the employee is likely to be exposed over the action level at least 30 days per year, the employer shall provide each affected employee an opportunity for a medical examination, including at least the following elements:

(n)(2)(i) A work history and a medical history which shall include a smoking history and the presence and degree of respiratory symptoms such as breathlessness, cough, sputum production and wheezing.

(n)(2)(ii) A medical examination which shall include at least the following:

(n)(2)(ii)(A) A standard posterior-anterior chest x-ray;

(n)(2)(ii)(B) A nasal and skin examination; and

(n)(2)(ii)(C) Other examinations which the physician believes appropriate because of the employees exposure to inorganic arsenic or because of required respirator use.

(n)(3) **Periodic examinations**

(n)(3)(i) Examinations must be provided in accordance with this paragraph at least annually.

(n)(3)(ii) Whenever a covered employee has not taken the examinations specified in paragraphs (n)(2)(i) and (n)(2)(ii) of this Section within six (6) months preceding the termination of employment, the employer shall provide such examinations to the employee upon termination of employment.

(n)(4) **Additional examinations** If the employee for any reason develops signs or symptoms commonly associated with exposure to inorganic arsenic the employer shall provide an appropriate examination and emergency medical treatment.

(n)(5) **Information provided to the physician** The employer shall provide the following information to the examining physician:

(n)(5)(i) A copy of this Standard and its Appendices;

(n)(5)(ii) A description of the affected employee's duties as they relate to the employee's exposure;

(n)(5)(iii) The employee's representative exposure level or anticipated exposure level;

(n)(5)(iv) A description of any personal protective equipment used or to be used; and

(n)(5)(v) Information from previous medical examinations of the affected employee which is not readily available to the examining physician.

(n)(6) **Physician's written opinion**

(n)(6)(i) The employer shall obtain a written opinion from the examining physician which shall include:

(n)(6)(i)(A) The results of the medical examination and tests performed;

(n)(6)(i)(B) The physician's opinion as to whether the employee has any detected medical conditions which would place the employee at increased risk of material impairment of the employee's health from exposure to inorganic arsenic;

(n)(6)(i)(C) Any recommended limitations upon the employee's exposure to inorganic arsenic or upon the use of protective clothing or equipment such as respirators; and

(n)(6)(i)(D) A statement that the employee has been informed by the physician of the results of the medical examination and any medical conditions which require further explanation or treatment.

(n)(6)(ii) The employer shall instruct the physician not to reveal in the written opinion specific findings or diagnoses unrelated to occupational exposure.

(n)(6)(iii) The employer shall provide a copy of the written opinion to the affected employee.

(o) **Employee information and training**

(o)(1) **Training program**

(o)(1)(i) The employer shall train each employee who is subject to exposure to inorganic arsenic above the action level without regard to respirator use, or for whom there is the possibility of skin or eye irritation from inorganic arsenic, in accordance with the requirements of this Section. The employer shall institute a training program and ensure employee participation in the program.

(o)(1)(ii) The training program shall be provided by October 1, 1978, for employees covered by this provision, at the time of initial assignment for those subsequently covered by this provision, and at least annually for other covered employees thereafter; and the employer shall assure that each employee is informed of the following:

(o)(1)(ii)(A) The information contained in Appendix A;

(o)(1)(ii)(B) The quantity, location, manner of use, storage, sources of exposure, and the specific nature of operations which could result in exposure to inorganic arsenic as well as any necessary protective steps;

(o)(1)(ii)(C) The purpose, proper use, and limitation of respirators;

(o)(1)(ii)(D) The purpose and a description of the medical surveillance program as required by paragraph (n) of this Section;

(o)(1)(ii)(E) The engineering controls and work practices associated with the employee's job assignment; and

(o)(1)(ii)(F) A review of this Standard.

(o)(2) **Access to training materials**

(o)(2)(i) The employer shall make readily available to all affected employees a copy of this Standard and its Appendices.

(o)(2)(ii) The employer shall provide; upon request, all materials relating to the employee information and training program to the Assistant Secretary and the Director.

(p) **Communication of hazards**

(p)(1) **Hazard communication—General**

(p)(1)(i) Chemical manufacturers, importers, distributors and employers shall comply with all requirements of the Hazard Communication Standard (HCS) (§1910.1200) for inorganic arsenic.

(p)(1)(ii) In classifying the hazards of inorganic arsenic at least the following hazards are to be addressed: Cancer; liver effects; skin effects; respiratory irritation; nervous system effects; and acute toxicity effects.

(p)(1)(iii) Employers shall include inorganic arsenic in the hazard communication program established to comply with the HCS (§1910.1200). Employers shall ensure that each employee has access to labels on containers of inorganic arsenic and to safety data sheets, and is trained in accordance with the requirements of HCS and paragraph (o) of this Section.

(p)(1)(iv) The employer shall ensure that no statement appears on or near any sign or label required by this paragraph (p) which contradicts or detracts from the meaning of the required sign or label.

(p)(2) **Signs**

(p)(2)(i) The employer shall post signs demarcating regulated areas bearing the legend:

DANGER
INORGANIC ARSENIC
MAY CAUSE CANCER
DO NOT EAT, DRINK OR SMOKE
WEAR RESPIRATORY PROTECTION IN THIS AREA
AUTHORIZED PERSONNEL ONLY

(p)(2)(ii) Prior to June 1, 2016, employers may use the following legend in lieu of that specified in paragraph (p)(2)(i) of this Section:

DANGER
INORGANIC ARSENIC
CANCER HAZARD
AUTHORIZED PERSONNEL ONLY
NO SMOKING OR EATING
RESPIRATOR REQUIRED

(p)(2)(iii) The employer shall ensure that signs required by this paragraph (p) are illuminated and cleaned as necessary so that the legend is readily visible.

(p)(3)(i) Prior to June 1, 2015, in lieu of the labeling requirements in paragraphs (p)(1)(i) of this Section, employers may apply precautionary labels to all shipping and storage containers of inorganic arsenic, and to all products containing inorganic arsenic, bearing the following legend:

DANGER
CONTAINS INORGANIC ARSENIC
CANCER HAZARD
HARMFUL IF INHALED OR SWALLOWED
USE ONLY WITH ADEQUATE VENTILATION
OR RESPIRATORY PROTECTION

(p)(3)(ii) Labels are not required when the inorganic arsenic in the product is bound in such a manner so as to make unlikely the possibility of airborne exposure to inorganic arsenic. (Possible examples of products not requiring labels are semiconductors, light emitting diodes and glass.)

(q) **Recordkeeping**

(q)(1) **Exposure monitoring**

(q)(1)(i) The employer shall establish and maintain an accurate record of all monitoring required by paragraph (e) of this Section.

(q)(1)(ii) This record shall include:

(q)(1)(ii)(A) The date(s), number, duration location, and results of each of the samples taken, including a description of the sampling procedure used to determine representative employee exposure where applicable;

(q)(1)(ii)(B) A description of the sampling and analytical methods used and evidence of their accuracy;

(q)(1)(ii)(C) The type of respiratory protective devices worn, if any;

(q)(1)(ii)(D) Name, social security number, and job classification of the employees monitored and of all other employees whose exposure the measurement is intended to represent; and

(q)(1)(ii)(E) The environmental variables that could affect the measurement of the employee's exposure.

(q)(1)(iii) The employer shall maintain these monitoring records for at least 40 years or for the duration of employment plus 20 years, whichever, is longer.

(q)(2) **Medical surveillance**

(q)(2)(i) The employer shall establish and maintain an accurate record for each employee subject to medical surveillance as required by paragraph (n) of this Section.

(q)(2)(ii) This record shall include:

(q)(2)(ii)(A) The name, social security number, and description of duties of the employee;

(q)(2)(ii)(B) A copy of the physician's written opinions;

(q)(2)(ii)(C) Results of any exposure monitoring done for that employee and the representative exposure levels supplied to the physician; and

(q)(2)(ii)(D) Any employee medical complaints related to exposure to inorganic arsenic.

(q)(2)(iii) The employer shall in addition keep, or assure that the examining physician keeps, the following medical records:

(q)(2)(iii)(A) A copy of the medical examination results including medical and work history required under paragraph (n) of this Section;

(q)(2)(iii)(B) A description of the laboratory procedures and a copy of any Standards or guidelines used to interpret the test results or references to that information;

(q)(2)(iii)(C) The initial X-ray;

(q)(2)(iii)(D) The X-rays for the most recent 5 years; and

(q)(2)(iii)(E) Any X-rays with a demonstrated abnormality and all subsequent X-rays.

(q)(2)(iv) The employer shall maintain or assure that the physician maintains those medical records for at least 40 years, or for the duration of employment plus 20 years whichever is longer.

(q)(3) **Availability**

(q)(3)(i) The employer shall make available upon request all records required to be maintained by paragraph (q) of this Section to the Assistant Secretary and the Director for examination and copying.

(q)(3)(ii) Records required by this paragraph shall be provided upon request to employees, designated representatives, and the Assistant Secretary in accordance with 29 CFR §1910.1020 (a) through (e) and (g) through (i).

(q)(4) **Transfer of records**

(q)(4)(i) Whenever the employer ceases to do business, the successor employer shall receive and retain all records required to be maintained by this Section.

(q)(4)(ii) The employer shall also comply with any additional requirements involving the transfer of records set in 29 CFR §1910.1020(h).

(r) **Observation of monitoring**

(r)(1) **Employee observation** The employer shall provide affected employees or their designated representatives an opportunity to observe any monitoring of employee exposure to inorganic arsenic conducted pursuant to paragraph (e) of this Section.

(r)(2) **Observation procedures**

(r)(2)(i) Whenever observation of the monitoring of employee exposure to inorganic arsenic requires entry into an area where the use of respirators, protective clothing, or equipment is required, the employer shall provide the observer with and assure the use of such respirators, clothing, and such equipment, and shall require the observer to comply with all other applicable safety and health procedures.

(r)(2)(ii) Without interfering with the monitoring, observers shall be entitled to:

(r)(2)(ii)(A) Receive an explanation of the measurement procedures;

(r)(2)(ii)(B) Observe all steps related to the monitoring of inorganic arsenic performed at the place of exposure; and

(r)(2)(ii)(C) Record the results obtained or receive copies of the results when returned by the laboratory.

(s) **Appendices** The information contained in the Appendices to this Section is not intended by itself to create any additional obligations not otherwise imposed by this Standard nor detract from any existing obligation.

§1910.1018 Appendix A Inorganic arsenic substance information sheet

I. Substance Identification

A. Substance Inorganic Arsenic

B. Definition Copper acetoarsenite, arsenic and all inorganic compounds containing arsenic except arsine, measured as arsenic (As).

C. Permissible Exposure Limit 10 micrograms per cubic meter of air as determined as an average over an 8-hour period. No employee may be exposed to any skin or eye contact with arsenic trichloride or to skin or eye contact likely to cause skin or eye irritation.

D. Regulated Areas Only employees authorized by your employer should enter a regulated area.

II. Health Hazard Data

A. Comments The health hazard of inorganic arsenic is high.

B. Ways in which the chemical affects your body Exposure to airborne concentrations of inorganic arsenic may cause lung cancer, and can be a skin irritant. Inorganic arsenic may also affect your body if swallowed. One compound in particular, arsenic trichloride, is especially dangerous because it can be absorbed readily through the skin. Because inorganic arsenic is a poison, you should wash your hands thoroughly prior to eating or smoking.

III. Protective Clothing And Equipment

A. Respirators Respirators will be provided by your employer at no cost to you for routine use if your employer is in the process of implementing engineering and work practice controls or where engineering and work practice controls are not feasible or insufficient. You must wear respirators for non-routine activities or in emergency situations where you are likely to be exposed to levels of inorganic arsenic in excess of the permissible exposure limit. Since how well your respirator fits your face is very important, your employer is required to conduct fit tests to make sure the respirator seals properly when you wear it. These tests are simple and rapid and will be explained to you during training sessions.

B. Protective clothing If you work in a regulated area, your employer is required to provide at no cost to you, and you must wear, appropriate, clean, protective clothing and equipment. The purpose of this equipment is to prevent you from bringing to your home arsenic-contaminated dust and to protect your body from repeated skin contact with inorganic arsenic likely to cause skin irritation. This clothing should include such items as coveralls or similar full-body clothing, gloves, shoes or coverlets, and aprons. Protective equipment should include face shields or vented goggles, where eye irritation may occur.

IV. Hygiene Facilities And Practices

You must not eat, drink, smoke, chew gum or tobacco, or apply cosmetics in the regulated area, except that drinking water is permitted. If you work in a regulated area your employer is required to provide lunchrooms and other areas for these purposes.

If you work in a regulated area, your employer is required to provide showers, washing facilities, and change rooms. You must wash your face, and hands before eating and must shower at the end of the work shift. Do not take used protective clothing out of change rooms without your employer's permission. Your employer is required to provide for laundering or cleaning of your protective clothing.

V. Signs And Labels

Your employer is required to post warning signs and labels for your protection. Signs must be posted in regulated areas. The signs must warn that a cancer hazard is present, that only authorized employees may enter the area, and that no smoking or eating is allowed, and that respirators must be worn.

VI. Medical Examinations

If your exposure to arsenic is over the Action Level (5 µg/m3)—(including all persons working in regulated areas) at least 30 days per year, or you have been exposed to arsenic for more than 10 years over the Action Level, your employer is required to provide you with a medical examination. The examination shall be every 6 months for employees over 45 years old or with more than 10 years exposure over the Action Level and annually for other covered employees. The medical examination must include a medical history; a chest x-ray; a skin examination and a nasal examination. The examining physician will provide a written opinion to your employer containing the results of your medical exams. You should also receive a copy of this opinion. The physician must not tell your employer any conditions he detects unrelated to occupational exposure to arsenic but must tell you those conditions.

VII. Observation Of Monitoring

Your employer is required to monitor your exposure to arsenic and you or your representatives are entitled to observe the monitoring procedure. You are entitled to receive an explanation of the measurement procedure, and to record the results obtained. When the monitoring procedure is taking place in an area where respirators or personal protective clothing and equipment are required to be worn, you must also be provided with and must wear the protective clothing and equipment.

VIII. Access To Records

You or your representative are entitled to records of your exposure to inorganic arsenic and your medical examination records if you request your employer to provide them.

IX. Training And Notification

Additional information on all of these items plus training as to hazards of exposure to inorganic arsenic and the engineering and work practice controls associated with your job will also be provided by your employer. If you are exposed over the permissible exposure limit, your employer must inform you of that fact and the actions he is taking to reduce your exposures.

§1910.1018 Appendix B Substance technical guidelines

Arsenic, Arsenic Trioxide, Arsenic Trichloride (Three Examples)

I. Physical and chemical properties

A. Arsenic (metal)

1. Formula: As;
2. Appearance: Gray metal;
3. Melting point: Sublimes without melting at 613 °C;
4. Specific Gravity: (H_20=1):5.73;
5. Solubility in water: Insoluble;

B. Arsenic Trioxide

1. Formula: As_20_3, (As_40_6);
2. Appearance: White powder;
3. Melting point: 315 °C;
4. Specific Gravity: (H_20=1):3.74;
5. Solubility in water: 3.7 grams in 100cc of water at 20 °C;

C. Arsenic Trichloride (liquid)

1. Formula: $AsC1_3$;
2. Appearance: Colorless or pale yellow liquid;
3. Melting point: −8.5 °C;
4. Boiling point: 130.2 °C;
5. Specific Gravity (H_20=1):2.16 at 20 °C;
6. Vapor Pressure: 10mm Hg at 23.5 °C;
7. Solubility in Water: Decomposes in water.

II. Fire, explosion and reactivity data

A. Fire: Arsenic, arsenic Trioxide and Arsenic Trichloride are nonflammable.

B. Reactivity:

1. Conditions: Contributing to instability: Heat.
2. Incompatibility: Hydrogen gas can react with inorganic arsenic to form the highly toxic gas arsine.

III. Monitoring and Measurement Procedures

Samples collected should be full shift (at least 7-hour) samples. Sampling should be done using a personal sampling pump at a flow rate of 2 liters per minute. Samples should be collected on 0.8 micrometer pore size membrane filter (37mm diameter). Volatile arsenicals such as arsenic trichloride can be most easily collected in a midget bubbler filled with 15 ml. of 0.1 N NaOH.

The method of sampling and analysis should have an accuracy of not less than ± 25 percent (with a confidence limit of 95 percent) for 10 micrograms per cubic meter of air (10 $\mu g/m^3$) and ± 35 percent (with a confidence limit of 95 percent) for concentrations of inorganic arsenic between 5 and 10 $\mu g/m^3$.

§1910.1018 Appendix C
Medical surveillance guidelines

I. General

Medical examinations are to be provided for all employees exposed to levels of inorganic arsenic above the action level (5 $\mu g/m^3$) for at least 30 days per year (which would include among others, all employees, who work in regulated areas). Examinations are also to be provided to all employees who have had 10 years or more exposure above the action level for more than 30 days per year while working for the present or predecessor employer though they may no longer be exposed above the level.

An initial medical examination is to be provided to all such employees by December 1, 1978. In addition, an initial medical examination is to be provided to all employees who are first assigned to areas in which worker exposure will probably exceed 5 $\mu g/m^3$ (after the effective date of this Standard) at the time of initial assignment. In addition to its immediate diagnostic usefulness, the initial examination will provide a baseline for comparing future test results. The initial examination must include as a minimum the following elements:

(1) A work and medical history, including a smoking history, and presence and degree of respiratory symptoms such as breathlessness, cough, sputum production, and wheezing;
(2) A 14"; by 17"; posterior-anterior chest X-ray;
(3) A nasal and skin examination; and
(4) Other examinations which the physician believes appropriate because of the employee's exposure to inorganic arsenic or because of required respirator use.

Periodic examinations are also to be provided to the employees listed above. The periodic examinations shall be given annually for those covered employees 45 years of age or less with fewer than 10 years employment in areas where employee exposure exceeds the action level (5 µg/m3). Periodic examinations need not include sputum cytology and only an updated medical history is required.

Periodic examinations for other covered employees, shall be provided every six (6) months. These examinations shall include all tests required in the initial examination, except that the medical history need only be updated.

The examination contents are minimum requirements. Additional tests such as lateral and oblique X-rays or pulmonary function tests may be useful. For workers exposed to three arsenicals which are associated with lymphatic cancer, copper acetoarsenite, potassium arsenite, or sodium arsenite the examination should also include palpation of superficial lymph nodes and complete blood count.

II. Noncarcinogenic Effects

The OSHA Standard is based on minimizing risk of exposed workers dying of lung cancer from exposure to inorganic arsenic. It will also minimize skin cancer from such exposures.

The following three sections quoted from "Occupational Diseases: A Guide to Their Recognition", Revised Edition, June 1977, National Institute for Occupational Safety and Health is included to provide information on the non–neoplastic effects of exposure to inorganic arsenic. Such effects should not occur if the OSHA Standards are followed.

A. Local – Trivalent arsenic compounds are corrosive to the skin. Brief contact has no effect but prolonged contact results in a local hyperemia and later vesicular or pustular eruption. The moist mucous membranes are most sensitive to the irritant action. Conjunctiva, moist and macerated areas of skin, the eyelids, the angles of the ears, nose, mouth, and respiratory mucosa are also vulnerable to the irritant effects. The wrists are common sites of dermatitis, as are the genitalia if personal hygiene is poor. Perforations of the nasal septum may occur. Arsenic trioxide and pentoxide are capable of producing skin sensitization and contact dermatitis. Arsenic is also capable of producing keratoses, especially of the palms and soles.

B. Systemic – The acute toxic effects of arsenic are generally seen following ingestion of inorganic arsenical compounds. This rarely occurs in an industrial setting. Symptoms develop within 1/2 to 4 hours following ingestion and are usually characterized by constriction of the throat followed by dysphagia, epigastric pain, vomiting, and watery diarrhea. Blood may appear in vomitus and stools. If the amount ingested is sufficiently high, shock may develop due to severe fluid loss, and death may ensue in 24 hours. If the acute effects are survived, exfoliative dermatitis and peripheral neuritis may develop.

Cases of acute arsenical poisoning due to inhalation are exceedingly rare in industry. When it does occur, respiratory tract symptoms—cough, chest pain, dyspnea—giddiness, headache, and extreme general weakness precede gastrointestinal symptoms. The acute toxic symptoms of trivalent arsenical poisoning are due to severe inflammation of the mucous membranes and greatly increased permeability of the blood capillaries.

Chronic arsenical poisoning due to ingestion is rare and generally confined to patients taking prescribed medications. However, it can be a concomitant of inhaled inorganic arsenic from swallowed sputum and improper eating habits. Symptoms are weight loss, nausea and diarrhea alternating with constipation, pigmentation and eruption of the skin, loss of hair, and peripheral neuritis. Chronic hepatitis and cirrhosis have been described. Polyneuritis may be the salient feature, but more frequently there are numbness and parasthenias of "glove and stocking" distribution. The skin lesions are usually melanotic and keratotic and may occasionally take the form of an intradermal cancer of the squamous cell type, but without infiltrative properties. Horizontal white lines (striations) on the fingernails and toenails are commonly seen in chronic arsenical poisoning and are considered to be a diagnostic accompaniment of arsenical polyneuritis.

Inhalation of inorganic arsenic compounds is the most common cause of chronic poisoning in the industrial situation. This condition is divided into three phases based on signs and symptoms.

First Phase: The worker complains of weakness, loss of appetite, some nausea, occasional vomiting, a sense of heaviness in the stomach, and some diarrhea.

Second Phase: The worker complains of conjunctivitis, a catarrhal state of the mucous membranes of the nose, larynx, and respiratory passage. Coryza, hoarseness, and mild tracheobronchitis may occur. Perforation of the nasal septum is common, and is probably the most typical lesion of the upper respiratory tract in occupational exposure to arsenical dust. Skin lesions, eczematoid and allergic in type, are common.

Third Phase: The worker complains of symptoms of peripheral neuritis, initially of hands and feet, which is essentially sensory. In more severe cases, motor paralyses occur; the first muscles affected are usually the toe extensors and the peronei. In only the most severe cases will paralysis of flexor muscles of the feet or of the extensor muscles of hands occur.

Liver damage from chronic arsenical poisoning is still debated, and as yet the question is unanswered. In cases of chronic and acute arsenical poisoning, toxic effects to the myocardium have been reported based on EKG changes. These findings, however, are now largely discounted and the EKG changes are ascribed to electrolyte disturbances concomitant with arsenicalism. Inhalation of arsenic trioxide and other inorganic arsenical dusts does not give rise to radiological evidence or pneumoconiosis. Arsenic does have a depressant effect upon the bone marrow, with disturbances of both erythropoiesis and myelopoiesis.

Bibliography

Dinman, B. D. 1960. Arsenic; chronic human intoxication. J. Occup. Med. 2:137.

Elkins, H. B. 1959. The Chemistry of Industrial Toxicology, 2nd ed. John Wiley and Sons, New York.

Holmquist, L. 1951. Occupational arsenical dermatitis; a study among employees at a copper-ore smelting works including investigations of skin reactions to contact with arsenic compounds. Acta. Derm. Venereol. (Supp. 26) 31:1.

Pinto, S. S., and C. M. McGill. 1953. Arsenic trioxide exposure in industry. Ind. Med. Surg. 22:281.

Pinto, S. S., and K. W. Nelson. 1976. Arsenic toxicology and industrial exposure. Annu. Rev. Pharmacol. Toxicol. 16:95.

Vallee, B. L., D. D. Ulmer, and W. E. C. Wacker. 1960. Arsenic toxicology and biochemistry. AMA Arch. Indust. Health 21:132.

[39 FR 23502, June 27, 1974, as amended at 43 FR 19624, May 5, 1978; 43 FR 28472, June 30, 1978; 45 FR 35282, May 23, 1980; 54 FR 24334, June 7, 1989; 58 FR 35310, June 30, 1993; 61 FR 5508, Feb. 13, 1996; 61 FR 9245, Mar. 7, 1996; 63 FR 1286, Jan. 8, 1998; 63 FR 33468, June 18, 1998; 70 FR 1141, Jan. 5, 2005; 71 FR 16672, 16673, Apr. 3, 2006; 71 FR 50189, Aug. 24, 2006; 73 FR 75585, Dec. 12, 2008; 76 FR 33608, June 8, 2011]

§1910.1020 Access to employee exposure and medical records

(a) Purpose The purpose of this Section is to provide employees and their designated representatives a right of access to relevant exposure and medical records; and to provide representatives of the Assistant Secretary a right of access to these records in order to fulfill responsibilities under the Occupational Safety and Health Act. Access by employees, their representatives, and the Assistant Secretary is necessary to yield both direct and indirect improvements in the detection, treatment, and prevention of occupational disease. Each employer is responsible for assuring compliance with this Section, but the activities involved in complying with the access to medical records provisions can be carried out, on behalf of the employer, by the physician or other health care personnel in charge of employee medical records. Except as expressly provided, nothing in this Section is intended to affect existing legal and ethical obligations concerning the maintenance and confidentiality of employee medical information, the duty to disclose information to a patient/employee or any other aspect of the medical-care relationship, or affect existing legal obligations concerning the protection of trade secret information.

(b) **Scope and application**

(b)(1) This Section applies to each general industry, maritime, and construction employer who makes, maintains, contracts for, or has access to employee exposure or medical records, or analyses thereof, pertaining to employees exposed to toxic substances or harmful physical agents.

(b)(2) This Section applies to all employee exposure and medical records, and analyses thereof, of such employees, whether or not the records are mandated by specific Occupational Safety and Health Standards.

(b)(3) This Section applies to all employee exposure and medical records, and analyses thereof, made or maintained in any manner, including on an in-house of contractual (e.g., fee-for-service) basis. Each employer shall assure that the preservation and access requirements of this Section are complied with regardless of the manner in which the records are made or maintained.

(c) **Definitions**

(c)(1) **Access** means the right and opportunity to examine and copy.

(c)(2) **Analysis using exposure or medical records** means any compilation of data or any statistical study based at least in part on information collected from individual employee exposure or medical records or information collected from health insurance claims records, provided that either the analysis has been reported to the employer or no further work is currently being done by the person responsible for preparing the analysis.

(c)(3) **Designated representative** means any individual or organization to whom an employee gives written authorization to exercise a right of access. For the purposes of access to employee exposure records and analyses using exposure or medical records, a recognized or certified collective bargaining agent shall be treated automatically as a designated representative without regard to written employee authorization.

(c)(4) **Employee** means a current employee, a former employee, or an employee being assigned or transferred to work where there will be exposure to toxic substances or harmful physical agents. In the case of a deceased or legally incapacitated employee, the employee's legal representative may directly exercise all the employee's rights under this Section.

(c)(5) **Employee exposure record** means a record containing any of the following kinds of information:

(c)(5)(i) Environmental (workplace) monitoring or measuring of a toxic substance or harmful physical agent, including personal, area, grab, wipe, or other form of sampling, as well as related collection and analytical methodologies, calculations, and other background data relevant to interpretation of the results obtained;

(c)(5)(ii) Biological monitoring results which directly assess the absorption of a toxic substance or harmful physical agent by body systems (e.g., the level of a chemical in the blood, urine, breath, hair, fingernails, etc.), but not including results which assess the biological effect of a substance or agent or which assess an employee's use of alcohol or drugs;

(c)(5)(iii) Safety data sheets indicating that the material may pose a hazard to human health; or

(c)(5)(iv) In the absence of the above, a chemical inventory or any other record which reveals where and when used and the identity (e.g., chemical, common, or trade name) of a toxic substance or harmful physical agent.

(c)(6)

(c)(6)(i) **Employee medical record** means a record concerning the health status of an employee which is made or maintained by a physician, nurse, or other health care personnel or technician, including:

(c)(6)(i)(A) Medical and employment questionnaires or histories (including job description and occupational exposures);

(c)(6)(i)(B) The results of medical examinations (pre-employment, pre-assignment, periodic, or episodic) and laboratory tests (including chest and other X-ray examinations taken for the purposes of establishing a base-line or detecting occupational illness, and all biological monitoring not defined as an "employee exposure record");

(c)(6)(i)(C) Medical opinions, diagnoses, progress notes, and recommendations;

(c)(6)(i)(D) First aid records;

(c)(6)(i)(E) Descriptions of treatments and prescriptions; and

(c)(6)(i)(F) Employee medical complaints.

(c)(6)(ii) "Employee medical record" does not include medical information in the form of:

(c)(6)(ii)(A) Physical specimens (e.g., blood or urine samples) which are routinely discarded as a part of normal medical practice; or

(c)(6)(ii)(B) Records concerning health insurance claims if maintained separately from the employer's medical program and its records, and not accessible to the employer by employee name or other direct personal identifier (e.g., social security number, payroll number, etc.); or

(c)(6)(ii)(C) Records created solely in preparation for litigation which are privileged from discovery under the applicable rules of procedure or evidence; or

(c)(6)(ii)(D) Records concerning voluntary employee assistance programs (alcohol, drug abuse, or personal counseling programs) if maintained separately from the employer's medical program and its records.

(c)(7) **Employer** means a current employer, a former employer, or a successor employer.

(c)(8) **Exposure or exposed** means that an employee is subjected to a toxic substance or harmful physical agent in the course of employment through any route of entry (inhalation, ingestion, skin contact or absorption, etc.), and includes past exposure and potential (e.g., accidental or possible) exposure, but does not include situations where the employer can demonstrate that the toxic substance or harmful physical agent is not used, handled, stored, generated, or present in the workplace in any manner different from typical non-occupational situations.

(c)(9) **Health Professional** means a physician, occupational health nurse, industrial hygienist, toxicologist, or epidemiologist, providing medical or other occupational health services to exposed employees.

(c)(10) **Record** means any item, collection, or grouping of information regardless of the form or process by which it is maintained (e.g., paper document, microfiche, microfilm, X-ray film, or automated data processing).

(c)(11) **Specific chemical identity** means the chemical name, Chemical Abstracts Service (CAS) Registry Number, or any other information that reveals the precise chemical designation of the substance.

(c)(12)(i) **Specific written consent** means a written authorization containing the following:

(c)(12)(i)(A) The name and signature of the employee authorizing the release of medical information;

(c)(12)(i)(B) The date of the written authorization;

(c)(12)(i)(C) The name of the individual or organization that is authorized to release the medical information;

(c)(12)(i)(D) The name of the designated representative (individual or organization) that is authorized to receive the released information;

(c)(12)(i)(E) A general description of the medical information that is authorized to be released;

(c)(12)(i)(F) A general description of the purpose for the release of the medical information; and

(c)(12)(i)(G) A date or condition upon which the written authorization will expire (if less than one year).

(c)(12)(ii) A written authorization does not operate to authorize the release of medical information not in existence on the date of written authorization, unless the release of future information is expressly authorized, and does not operate for more than one year from the date of written authorization.

(c)(12)(iii) A written authorization may be revoked in writing prospectively at any time.

(c)(13) **Toxic substance or harmful physical agent** means any chemical substance, biological agent (bacteria, virus, fungus, etc.), or physical stress (noise, heat, cold, vibration, repetitive motion, ionizing and non-ionizing radiation, hypo-or hyperbaric pressure, etc.) which:

(c)(13)(i) Is listed in the latest printed edition of the National Institute for Occupational Safety and Health (NIOSH) Registry of Toxic Effects of Chemical Substances (RTECS), which is incorporated by reference as specified in §1910.6; or

(c)(13)(ii) Has yielded positive evidence of an acute or chronic health hazard in testing conducted by, or known to, the employer; or

(c)(13)(iii) Is the subject of a safety data sheet kept by or known to the employer indicating that the material may pose a hazard to human health.

(c)(14) **Trade secret** means any confidential formula, pattern, process, device, or information or compilation of information that is used in an employer's business and that gives the employer an opportunity to obtain an advantage over competitors who do not know or use it.

(d) **Preservation of records**

(d)(1) Unless a specific Occupational Safety and Health Standard provides a different period of time, each employer shall assure the preservation and retention of records as follows:

(d)(1)(i) **Employee medical records** The medical record for each employee shall be preserved and maintained for at least the duration of employment plus thirty (30) years, except that the following types of records need not be retained for any specified period:

(d)(1)(i)(A) Health insurance claims records maintained separately from the employer's medical program and its records;

(d)(1)(i)(B) First aid records (not including medical histories) of one-time treatment and subsequent observation of minor scratches, cuts, burns, splinters, and the like which do not involve medical treatment, loss of consciousness, restriction of work or motion, or transfer to another job, if made on-site by a non-physician and if maintained separately from the employer's medical program and its records; and

(d)(1)(i)(C) The medical records of employees who have worked for less than (1) year for the employer need not be retained beyond the term of employment if they are provided to the employee upon the termination of employment.

(d)(1)(ii) **Employee exposure records** Each employee exposure record shall be preserved and maintained for at least thirty (30) years, except that:

(d)(1)(ii)(A) Background data to environmental (workplace) monitoring or measuring, such as laboratory reports and worksheets, need only be retained for one (1) year as long as the sampling results, the collection methodology (sampling plan), a description of the analytical and mathematical methods used, and a summary of other background data relevant to interpretation of the results obtained, are retained for at least thirty (30) years; and

(d)(1)(ii)(B) Safety data sheets and paragraph (c)(5)(iv) records concerning the identity of a substance or agent need not be retained for any specified period as long as some record of the identity (chemical name if known) of the substance or agent, where it was used, and when it was used is retained for at least thirty (30) years;[1] and

(d)(1)(ii)(C) Biological monitoring results designated as exposure records by specific Occupational Safety and Health Standards shall be preserved and maintained as required by the specific Standard.

(d)(1)(iii) Analyses using exposure or medical records. Each analysis using exposure or medial records shall be preserved and maintained for at least thirty (30) years.

(d)(2) Nothing in this Section is intended to mandate the form, manner, or process by which an employer preserves a record as long as the information contained in the record is preserved and retrievable, except that chest X-ray films shall be preserved in their original state.

(e) **Access to records**

(e)(1) **General**

(e)(1)(i) Whenever an employee or designated representative requests access to a record, the employer shall assure that access is provided in a reasonable time, place, and manner. If the employer cannot reasonably provide access to the record within fifteen (15) working days, the employer shall within the fifteen (15) working days apprise the employee or designated representative requesting the record of the reason for the delay and the earliest date when the record can be made available.

(e)(1)(ii) The employer may require of the requester only such information as should be readily known to the requester and which may be necessary to locate or identify the records being requested (e.g. dates and locations where the employee worked during the time period in question).

(e)(1)(iii) Whenever an employee or designated representative requests a copy of a record, the employer shall assure that either:

(e)(1)(iii)(A) A copy of the record is provided without cost to the employee or representative;

(e)(1)(iii)(B) The necessary mechanical copying facilities (e.g., photocopying) are made available without cost to the employee or representative for copying the record; or

(e)(1)(iii)(C) The record is loaned to the employee or representative for a reasonable time to enable a copy to be made.

(e)(1)(iv) In the case of an original X-ray, the employer may restrict access to on-site examination or make other suitable arrangements for the temporary loan of the X-ray.

(e)(1)(v) Whenever a record has been previously provided without cost to an employee or designated representative, the employer may charge reasonable, non-discriminatory administrative costs (i.e., search and copying expenses but not including overhead expenses) for a request by the employee or designated representative for additional copies of the record, except that:

(e)(1)(v)(A) An employer shall not charge for an initial request for a copy of new information that has been added to a record which was previously provided; and

(e)(1)(v)(B) An employer shall not charge for an initial request by a recognized or certified collective bargaining agent for a copy of an employee exposure record or an analysis using exposure or medical records.

(e)(1)(vi) Nothing in this Section is intended to preclude employees and collective bargaining agents from collectively bargaining to obtain access to information in addition to that available under this Section.

(e)(2) **Employee and designated representative access**

(e)(2)(i) **Employee exposure records**

(e)(2)(i)(A) Except as limited by paragraph (f) of this Section, each employer shall, upon request, assure the access to each employee and designated representative to employee exposure records relevant to the employee. For the purpose of this Section, an exposure record relevant to the employee consists of:

(e)(2)(i)(A)(1) A record which measures or monitors the amount of a toxic substance or harmful physical agent to which the employee is or has been exposed;

(e)(2)(i)(A)(2) In the absence of such directly relevant records, such records of other employees with past or present job duties or working conditions related to or similar to those of the employee to the extent necessary to reasonably indicate the amount and nature of the toxic substances or harmful physical agents to which the employee is or has been subjected; and

(e)(2)(i)(A)(3) Exposure records to the extent necessary to reasonably indicate the amount and nature of the toxic substances or harmful physical agents at workplaces or under working conditions to which the employee is being assigned or transferred.

(e)(2)(i)(B) Requests by designated representatives for unconsented access to employee exposure records shall be in writing and shall specify with reasonable particularity:

(e)(2)(i)(B)(1) The records requested to be disclosed; and

(e)(2)(i)(B)(2) The occupational health need for gaining access to these records.

(e)(2)(ii) **Employee medical records**

(e)(2)(ii)(A) Each employer shall, upon request, assure the access of each employee to employee medical records of which the employee is the subject, except as provided in paragraph (e)(2)(ii)(D) of this Section.

(e)(2)(ii)(B) Each employer shall, upon request, assure the access of each designated representative to the employee medical records of any employee who has given the designated representative specific written consent. Appendix A to this Section contains a sample form which may be used to establish specific written consent for access to employee medical records.

(e)(2)(ii)(C) Whenever access to employee medical records is requested, a physician representing the employer may recommend that the employee or designated representative:

(e)(2)(ii)(C)(1) Consult with the physician for the purposes of reviewing and discussing the records requested;

(e)(2)(ii)(C)(2) Accept a summary of material facts and opinions in lieu of the records requested; or

(e)(2)(ii)(C)(3) Accept release of the requested records only to a physician or other designated representative.

(e)(2)(ii)(D) Whenever an employee requests access to his or her employee medical records, and a physician representing the employer believes that direct employee access to information contained in the records regarding a specific diagnosis of a terminal illness or a psychiatric condition could be detrimental to the employee's health, the employer may inform the employee that access will only be provided to a designated representative of the employee having specific written consent, and deny the employee's request for direct access to this information only. Where a designated representative with specific written consent requests access to information so withheld, the employer shall assure the access of the designated representative to this information, even when it is known that the designated representative will give the information to the employee.

(e)(2)(ii)(E) A physician, nurse, or other responsible health care personnel maintaining medical records may delete from requested medical records the identity of a family member, personal friend,

[1] Safety data sheets must be kept for those chemicals currently in use that are effected by the Hazard Communication Standard in accordance with 29 CFR §1910.1200(g).

or fellow employee who has provided confidential information concerning an employee's health status.

(e)(2)(iii) **Analyses using exposure or medical records**

(e)(2)(iii)(A) Each employee shall, upon request, assure the access of each employee and designated representative to each analysis using exposure or medical records concerning the employee's working conditions or workplace.

(e)(2)(iii)(B) Whenever access is requested to an analysis which reports the contents of employee medical records by either direct identifier (name, address, social security number, payroll number, etc.) or by information which could reasonably be used under the circumstances indirectly to identify specific employees (exact age, height, weight, race, sex, date of initial employment, job title, etc.), the employer shall assure that personal identifiers are removed before access is provided. If the employer can demonstrate that removal of personal identifiers from an analysis is not feasible, access to the personally identifiable portions of the analysis need not be provided.

(e)(3) **OSHA access**

(e)(3)(i) Each employer shall, upon request, and without derogation of any rights under the Constitution or the Occupational Safety and Health Act of 1970, 29 U.S.C. 651 et seq., that the employer chooses to exercise, assure the prompt access of representatives of the Assistant Secretary of Labor for Occupational Safety and Health to employee exposure and medical records and to analyses using exposure or medical records. Rules of agency practice and procedure governing OSHA access to employee medical records are contained in 29 CFR §1913.10.

(e)(3)(ii) Whenever OSHA seeks access to personally identifiable employee medical information by presenting to the employer a written access order pursuant to 29 CFR §1913.10(d), the employer shall prominently post a copy of the written access order and its accompanying cover letter for at least fifteen (15) working days.

(f) **Trade secrets**

(f)(1) Except as provided in paragraph (f)(2) of this Section, nothing in this Section precludes an employer from deleting from records requested by a health professional, employee, or designated representative any trade secret data which discloses manufacturing processes, or discloses the percentage of a chemical substance in mixture, as long as the health professional, employee, or designated representative is notified that information has been deleted. Whenever deletion of trade secret information substantially impairs evaluation of the place where or the time when exposure to a toxic substance or harmful physical agent occurred, the employer shall provide alternative information which is sufficient to permit the requesting party to identify where and when exposure occurred.

(f)(2) The employer may withhold the specific chemical identity, including the chemical name and other specific identification of a toxic substance from a disclosable record provided that:

(f)(2)(i) The claim that the information withheld is a trade secret can be supported;

(f)(2)(ii) All other available information on the properties and effects of the toxic substance is disclosed;

(f)(2)(iii) The employer informs the requesting party that the specific chemical identity is being withheld as a trade secret; and

(f)(2)(iv) The specific chemical identity is made available to health professionals, employees and designated representatives in accordance with the specific applicable provisions of this paragraph.

(f)(3) Where a treating physician or nurse determines that a medical emergency exists and the specific chemical identity of a toxic substance is necessary for emergency or first-aid treatment, the employer shall immediately disclose the specific chemical identity of a trade secret chemical to the treating physician or nurse, regardless of the existence of a written statement of need or a confidentiality agreement. The employer may require a written statement of need and confidentiality agreement, in accordance with the provisions of paragraphs (f)(4) and (f)(5), as soon as circumstances permit.

(f)(4) In non-emergency situations, an employer shall, upon request, disclose a specific chemical identity, otherwise permitted to be withheld under paragraph (f)(2) of this Section, to a health professional, employee, or designated representative if:

(f)(4)(i) The request is in writing;

(f)(4)(ii) The request describes with reasonable detail one or more of the following occupational health needs for the information:

(f)(4)(ii)(A) To assess the hazards of the chemicals to which employees will be exposed;

(f)(4)(ii)(B) To conduct or assess sampling of the workplace atmosphere to determine employee exposure levels;

(f)(4)(ii)(C) To conduct pre-assignment or periodic medical surveillance of exposed employees;

(f)(4)(ii)(D) To provide medical treatment to exposed employees;

(f)(4)(ii)(E) To select or assess appropriate personal protective equipment for exposed employees;

(f)(4)(ii)(F) To design or assess engineering controls or other protective measures for exposed employees; and

(f)(4)(ii)(G) To conduct studies to determine the health effects of exposure.

(f)(4)(iii) The request explains in detail why the disclosure of the specific chemical identity is essential and that, in lieu thereof, the disclosure of the following information would not enable the health professional, employee or designated representative to provide the occupational health services described in paragraph (f)(4)(ii) of this Section:

(f)(4)(iii)(A) The properties and effects of the chemical;

(f)(4)(iii)(B) Measures for controlling workers' exposure to the chemical;

(f)(4)(iii)(C) Methods of monitoring and analyzing worker exposure to the chemical; and

(f)(4)(iii)(D) Methods of diagnosing and treating harmful exposures to the chemical;

(f)(4)(iv) The request includes a description of the procedures to be used to maintain the confidentiality of the disclosed information; and,

(f)(4)(v) The health professional, employee, or designated representative and the employer or contractor of the services of the health professional or designated representative agree in a written confidentiality agreement that the health professional, employee or designated representative will not use the trade secret information for any purpose other than the health need(s) asserted and agree not to release the information under any circumstances other than to OSHA, as provided in paragraph (f)(7) of this Section, except as authorized by the terms of the agreement or by the employer.

(f)(5) The confidentiality agreement authorized by paragraph (f)(4)(iv) of this Section:

(f)(5)(i) May restrict the use of the information to the health purposes indicated in the written statement of need;

(f)(5)(ii) May provide for appropriate legal remedies in the event of a breach of the agreement, including stipulation of a reasonable pre-estimate of likely damages; and

(f)(5)(iii) May not include requirements for the posting of a penalty bond.

(f)(6) Nothing in this Section is meant to preclude the parties from pursuing non-contractual remedies to the extent permitted by law.

(f)(7) If the health professional, employee or designated representative receiving the trade secret information decides that there is a need to disclose it to OSHA, the employer who provided the information shall be informed by the health professional prior to, or at the same time as, such disclosure.

(f)(8) If the employer denies a written request for disclosure of a specific chemical identity, the denial must:

(f)(8)(i) Be provided to the health professional, employee or designated representative within thirty days of the request;

(f)(8)(ii) Be in writing;

(f)(8)(iii) Include evidence to support the claim that the specific chemical identity is a trade secret;

(f)(8)(iv) State the specific reasons why the request is being denied; and,

(f)(8)(v) Explain in detail how alternative information may satisfy the specific medical or occupational health need without revealing the specific chemical identity.

(f)(9) The health professional, employee, or designated representative whose request for information is denied under paragraph (f)(4) of this Section may refer the request and the written denial of the request to OSHA for consideration.

(f)(10) When a heath professional employee, or designated representative refers a denial to OSHA under paragraph (f)(9) of this Section, OSHA shall consider the evidence to determine if:

(f)(10)(i) The employer has supported the claim that the specific chemical identity is a trade secret;

(f)(10)(ii) The health professional employee, or designated representative has supported the claim that there is a medical or occupational health need for the information; and

(f)(10)(iii) The health professional, employee or designated representative has demonstrated adequate means to protect the confidentiality.

(f)(11)(i) If OSHA determines that the specific chemical identity requested under paragraph (f)(4) of this Section is not a bona fide trade secret, or that it is a trade secret but the requesting health professional, employee or designated representatives has a legitimate medical or occupational health need for the information, has executed a written confidentiality agreement, and has shown adequate means for complying with the terms of such agreement, the employer will be subject to citation by OSHA.

(f)(11)(ii) If an employer demonstrates to OSHA that the execution of a confidentiality agreement would not provide sufficient protection against the potential harm from the unauthorized disclosure of a trade secret specific chemical identity, the Assistant Secretary may issue such orders or impose such additional limitations or conditions upon the disclosure of the requested chemical information as may be appropriate to assure that the occupational health needs are met without an undue risk of harm to the employer.

(f)(12) Notwithstanding the existence of a trade secret claim, an employer shall, upon request, disclose to the Assistant Secretary any information which this Section requires the employer to make available. Where there is a trade secret claim, such claim shall be made no later than at the time the information is provided to the Assistant Secretary so that suitable determinations of trade secret status can be made and the necessary protections can be implemented.

(f)(13) Nothing in this paragraph shall be construed as requiring the disclosure under any circumstances of process or percentage of mixture information which is trade secret.

(g) **Employee information**

(g)(1) [OI] Upon an employee's first entering into employment, and at least annually thereafter, each employer shall inform current employees covered by this Section of the following:

(g)(1)(i) The existence, location, and availability of any records covered by this Section;

(g)(1)(ii) The person responsible for maintaining and providing access to records; and

(g)(1)(iii) Each employee's rights of access to these records.

(g)(2) Each employer shall keep a copy of this Section and its Appendices, and make copies readily available, upon request, to employees. The employer shall also distribute to current employees any informational materials concerning this Section which are made available to the employer by the Assistant Secretary of Labor for Occupational Safety and Health.

(h) [OI] **Transfer of records**

(h)(1) [OI] Whenever an employer is ceasing to do business, the employer shall transfer all records subject to this Section to the successor employer. The successor employer shall receive and maintain these records.

(h)(2) Whenever an employer is ceasing to do business and there is no successor employer to receive and maintain the records subject to this Standard, the employer shall notify affected current employees of their rights of access to records at least three (3) months prior to the cessation of the employer's business.

(i) **Appendices** The information contained in Appendices A and B to this Section is not intended, by itself, to create any additional obligations not otherwise imposed by this Section nor detract from any existing obligation.

§1910.1020 Appendix A
Sample authorization letter for the release of employee medical record information to a designated representative
(Nonmandatory)

I, ____,
(full name of worker/patient)

hereby authorize ______________________________________
(individual or organization holding the medical records)

to release to ____,
(individual or organization authorized to receive the medical information)

the following medical information from my personal medical records:
Describe generally the information desired to be released)

____

____

____

____

I give my permission for this medical information to be used for the following purpose:

____

____

____

but I do not give permission for any other use or re-disclosure of this information.

Note: Several extra lines are provided below so that you can place additional restrictions on this authorization letter if you want to. You may, however, leave these lines blank. On the other hand, you may want to (1) specify a particular expiration date for this letter (if less than one year); (2) describe medical information to be created in the future that you intend to be covered by this authorization letter; or (3) describe portions of the medical information in your records which you do not intend to be released as a result of this letter.

____

____

____

____
Full name of Employee or Legal Representative

____
Signature of Employee or Legal Representative

Date of Signature ____________________

§1910.1020 Appendix B
Availability of NIOSH Registry of Toxic Effects of Chemical Substances (RTECS)
(Nonmandatory)

The final regulation, 29 CFR §1910.1020, applies to all employee exposure and medical records, and analyses thereof, of employees exposed to toxic substances or harmful physical agents (paragraph (b)(2)). The term toxic substance or harmful physical agent is defined by paragraph (c)(13) to encompass chemical substances, biological agents, and physical stresses for which there is evidence of harmful health effects. The regulation uses the latest printed edition of the National Institute for Occupational Safety and Health (NIOSH) Registry of Toxic Effects of Chemical Substances (RTECS) as one of the chief sources of information as to whether evidence of harmful health effects exists. If a substance is listed in the latest printed RTECS, the regulation applies to exposure and medical records (and analyses of these records) relevant to employees exposed to the substance.

It is appropriate to note that the final regulation does not require that employers purchase a copy of RTECS, and many employers need not consult RTECS to ascertain whether their employee exposure or medical records are subject to the rule. Employers who do not currently have the latest printed edition of the NIOSH RTECS, however, may desire to obtain a copy. The RTECS is issued in an annual printed edition as mandated by Section 20(a)(6) of the Occupational Safety and Health Act (29 U.S.C. 669(a)(6)).

The Introduction to the 1980 printed edition describes the RTECS as follows:

"The 1980 edition of the Registry of Toxic Effects of Chemical Substances, formerly known as the Toxic Substances list, is the ninth revision prepared in compliance with the requirements of Section 20(a)(6) of the Occupational Safety and Health Act of 1970 (Public Law 91–596). The original list was completed on June 28, 1971, and has been updated annually in book format. Beginning in October 1977, quarterly revisions have been provided in microfiche. This edition of the Registry contains 168,096 listings of chemical substances: 45,156 are names of different chemicals with their associated toxicity data and 122,940 are synonyms. This edition includes approximately 5,900 new chemical compounds that did not appear in the 1979 Registry. (p. xi)

"The Registry's purposes are many, and it serves a variety of users. It is a single source document for basic toxicity information and for other data, such as chemical identifiers ad information necessary for the preparation of safety directives and hazard evaluations for chemical substances. The various types of toxic effects linked to literature citations provide researchers and occupational health scientists with an introduction to the toxicological literature, making their own review of the toxic hazards of a given substance easier. By presenting data on the lowest reported doses that produce effects by several routes of entry in various species, the Registry furnishes valuable information to those responsible for preparing safety data sheets for chemical substances in the workplace. Chemical and production engineers can use the Registry to identify the hazards which may be associated with chemical intermediates in the development of final products, and thus can more readily select substitutes or alternative processes which may be less hazardous. Some organizations, including health agencies and chemical companies, have included the NIOSH Registry accession numbers with the listing of chemicals in their files to reference toxicity information associated with those chemicals. By including foreign language chemical names, a start has been made toward providing rapid identification of substances produced in other countries. (p. xi)

"In this edition of the Registry, the editors intend to identify "all known toxic substances" which may exist in the environment and to provide pertinent data on the toxic effects from known doses entering an organism by any route described. (p xi)

"It must be reemphasized that the entry of a substance in the Registry does not automatically mean that it must be avoided. A listing does mean, however, that the substance has the documented potential of being harmful if misused, and care must be exercised to prevent tragic consequences. Thus, the Registry lists many substances that are common in everyday life and are in nearly every household in the United States. One can name a variety of such dangerous substances: prescription and non-prescription drugs; food additives; pesticide concentrates, sprays, and dusts; fungicides; herbicides; paints; glazes, dyes; bleaches and other household cleaning agents; alkalies; and various solvents and diluents. The list is extensive because chemicals have become an integral part of our existence."

The RTECS printed edition may be purchased from the Superintendent of Documents, U.S. Government Printing Office (GPO), Washington, DC 20402 (202–783–3238).

Some employers may desire to subscribe to the quarterly update to the RTECS which is published in a microfiche edition. An annual subscription to the quarterly microfiche may be purchased from the GPO (Order the "Microfiche Edition, Registry of Toxic Effects of Chemical Substances").

Both the printed edition and the microfiche edition of RTECS are available for review at many university and public libraries throughout the country. The latest RTECS editions may also be examined at the OSHA Technical Data Center, Room N2439—Rear, United States Department of Labor, 200 Constitution Avenue, NW., Washington, DC 20210 (202–523–9700), or at any OSHA Regional or Area Office (See, major city telephone directories under United States Government-Labor Department).

[53 FR 38163, Sept. 29, 1988; 53 FR 49981, Dec. 13, 1988, as amended at 54 FR 24333, June 7, 1989; 55 FR 26431, June 28, 1990; 61 FR 9235, Mar. 7, 1996. Redesignated at 61 FR 31430, June 20, 1996, as amended at 71 FR 16673, Apr. 3, 2006; 76 FR 33608, June 8, 2011]

§1910.1025 Lead

(a) Scope and application

(a)(1) This Section applies to all occupational exposure to lead, except as provided in paragraph (a)(2).

(a)(2) This Section does not apply to the construction industry or to agricultural operations covered by 29 CFR Part 1928.

(b) Definitions

Action level means employee exposure, without regard to the use of respirators, to an airborne concentration of lead of 30 micrograms per cubic meter of air (30 μg/m^3) averaged over an 8-hour period.

Assistant Secretary means the Assistant Secretary of Labor for Occupational Safety and Health, U.S. Department of Labor, or designee.

Director means the Director, National Institute for Occupational Safety and Health (NIOSH), U.S. Department of Health, Education, and Welfare, or designee.

Lead means metallic lead, all inorganic lead compounds, and organic lead soaps. Excluded from this definition are all other organic lead compounds.

(c) Permissible exposure limit (PEL)

(c)(1) The employer shall assure that no employee is exposed to lead at concentrations greater than fifty micrograms per cubic meter of air (50 μg/m^3) averaged over an 8-hour period.

(c)(2) If an employee is exposed to lead for more than 8 hours in any work day, the permissible exposure limit, as a time weighted average (TWA) for that day, shall be reduced according to the following formula:

Maximum permissible limit (in μg/m^3) = 400 ÷ hours worked in the day.

(c)(3) When respirators are used to supplement engineering and work practice controls to comply with the PEL and all the requirements of paragraph (f) have been met, employee exposure, for the purpose of determining whether the employer has complied with the PEL, may be considered to be at the level provided by the protection factor of the respirator for those periods the respirator is worn. Those periods may be averaged with exposure levels during periods when respirators are not worn to determine the employee's daily TWA exposure.

(d) Exposure monitoring

(d)(1) General

(d)(1)(i) For the purposes of paragraph (d), employee exposure is that exposure which would occur if the employee were not using a respirator.

(d)(1)(ii) With the exception of monitoring under paragraph (d)(3), the employer shall collect full shift (for at least 7 continuous hours) personal samples including at least one sample for each shift for each job classification in each work area.

(d)(1)(iii) Full shift personal samples shall be representative of the monitored employee's regular, daily exposure to lead.

(d)(2) Initial determination Each employer who has a workplace or work operation covered by this Standard shall determine if any employee may be exposed to lead at or above the action level.

(d)(3) Basis of initial determination

(d)(3)(i) The employer shall monitor employee exposures and shall base initial determinations on the employee exposure monitoring results and any of the following, relevant considerations:

(d)(3)(i)(A) Any information, observations, or calculations which would indicate employee exposure to lead;

(d)(3)(i)(B) Any previous measurements of airborne lead; and

(d)(3)(i)(C) Any employee complaints of symptoms which may be attributable to exposure to lead.

(d)(3)(ii) Monitoring for the initial determination may be limited to a representative sample of the exposed employees who the employer reasonably believes are exposed to the greatest airborne concentrations of lead in the workplace.

(d)(3)(iii) Measurements of airborne lead made in the preceding 12 months may be used to satisfy the requirement to monitor under paragraph (d)(3)(i) if the sampling and analytical methods used meet the accuracy and confidence levels of paragraph (d)(9) of this Section.

(d)(4) Positive initial determination and initial monitoring

(d)(4)(i) Where a determination conducted under paragraphs (d)(2) and (3) of this Section shows the possibility of any employee exposure at or above the action level, the employer shall conduct monitoring which is representative of the exposure for each employee in the workplace who is exposed to lead.

(d)(4)(ii) Measurements of airborne lead made in the preceding 12 months may be used to satisfy this requirement if the sampling and analytical methods used meet the accuracy and confidence levels of paragraph (d)(9) of this Section.

(d)(5) Negative initial determination Where a determination, conducted under paragraphs (d)(2) and (3) of this Section is made that no employee is exposed to airborne concentrations of lead at or above the action level, the employer shall make a written record of such determination. The record shall include at least the information specified in paragraph (d)(3) of this Section and shall also include the date of determination, location within the worksite, and the name and social security number of each employee monitored.

(d)(6) Frequency

(d)(6)(i) If the initial monitoring reveals employee exposure to be below the action level the measurements need not be repeated except as otherwise provided in paragraph (d)(7) of this Section.

(d)(6)(ii) If the initial determination or subsequent monitoring reveals employee exposure to be at or above the action level but below the permissible exposure limit the employer shall repeat monitoring in accordance with this paragraph at least every 6 months. The employer shall continue monitoring at the required frequency until at least two consecutive measurements, taken at least 7 days apart, are below the action level at which time the employer may discontinue monitoring for that employee except as otherwise provided in paragraph (d)(7) of this Section.

(d)(6)(iii) If the initial monitoring reveals that employee exposure is above the permissible exposure limit the employer shall repeat monitoring quarterly. The employer shall continue monitoring at the required frequency until at least two consecutive measurements, taken at least 7 days apart, are below the PEL but at or above the action level at which time the employer shall repeat monitoring for that employee at the frequency specified in paragraph (d)(6)(ii), except as otherwise provided in paragraph (d)(7) of this Section.

(d)(7) Additional monitoring Whenever there has been a production, process, control or personnel change which may result in new or additional exposure to lead, or whenever the employer has any other reason to suspect a change which may result in new or additional exposures to lead, additional monitoring in accordance with this paragraph shall be conducted.

(d)(8) Employee notification

(d)(8)(i) The employer must, within 15 working days after the receipt of the results of any monitoring performed under this Section, notify each affected employee of these results either individually, in writing or by posting the results in an appropriate location that is accessible to affected employees.

(d)(8)(ii) Whenever the results indicate that the representative employee exposure, without regard to respirators, exceeds the permissible exposure limit, the employer shall include in the written notice a statement that the permissible exposure limit was exceeded and a description of the corrective action taken or to be taken to reduce exposure to or below the permissible exposure limit.

(d)(9) Accuracy of measurement The employer shall use a method of monitoring and analysis which has an accuracy (to a confidence level of 95%) of not less than plus or minus 20 percent for airborne concentrations of lead equal to or greater than 30 μg/m^3.

(e) Methods of compliance

(e)(1) Engineering and work practice controls

(e)(1)(i) Where any employee is exposed to lead above the permissible exposure limit for more than 30 days per year, the employer shall implement engineering and work practice controls (including administrative controls) to reduce and maintain employee exposure to lead in accordance with the implementation schedule in Table I below, except to the extent that the employer can demonstrate that such controls are not feasible. Wherever the engineering and work practice controls which can be instituted are not sufficient to reduce employee exposure to or below the permissible exposure limit, the employer shall nonetheless use them to reduce exposures to the lowest feasible level and shall supplement them by the use of respiratory protection which complies with the requirements of paragraph (f) of this Section.

(e)(1)(ii) Where any employee is exposed to lead above the permissible exposure limit, but for 30 days or less per year, the employer shall implement engineering controls to reduce exposures to 200 μg/m^3, but thereafter may implement any combination of engineering, work practice (including administrative controls), and respiratory controls to reduce and maintain employee exposure to lead to or below 50 μg/m^3.

Table I

Industry	Compliance dates:[1] (50 $\mu g/m^3$)
Lead chemicals, secondary copper smelting	July 19, 1996
Nonferrous foundries	July 19, 1996[2]
Brass and bronze ingot manufacture	6 years[3]

[1] Calculated by counting from the date the stay on implementation of paragraph (e)(1) was lifted by the U.S. Court of Appeals for the District of Columbia, the number of years specified in the 1978 lead standard and subsequent amendments for compliance with the PEL of 50 $\mu g/m^3$ for exposure to airborne concentrations of lead levels for the particular industry.

[2] Large nonferrous foundries (20 or more employees) are required to achieve the PEL of 50 $\mu g/m^3$ by means of engineering and work practice controls. Small nonferrous foundries (fewer than 20 employees) are required to achieve an 8-hour TWA of 75 $\mu g/m^3$ by such controls.

[3] Expressed as the number of years from the date on which the Court lifts the stay on the implementation of paragraph (e)(1) for this industry for employers to achieve a lead in air concentration of 75 $\mu g/m^3$. Compliance with paragraph (e) in this industry is determined by a compliance directive that incorporates elements from the settlement agreement between OSHA and representatives of the industry.

(e)(2) Respiratory protection Where engineering and work practice controls do not reduce employee exposure to or below the 50 $\mu g/m^3$ permissible exposure limit, the employer shall supplement these controls with respirators in accordance with paragraph (f).

(e)(3) Compliance program

(e)(3)(i) Each employer shall establish and implement a written compliance program to reduce exposures to or below the permissible exposure limit, and interim levels if applicable, solely by means of engineering and work practice controls in accordance with the implementation schedule in paragraph (e)(1).

(e)(3)(ii) Written plans for these compliance programs shall include at least the following:

(e)(3)(ii)(A) A description of each operation in which lead is emitted; e.g. machinery used, material processed, controls in place, crew size, employee job responsibilities, operating procedures and maintenance practices;

(e)(3)(ii)(B) A description of the specific means that will be employed to achieve compliance, including engineering plans and studies used to determine methods selected for controlling exposure to lead;

(e)(3)(ii)(C) A report of the technology considered in meeting the permissible exposure limit;

(e)(3)(ii)(D) Air monitoring data which documents the source of lead emissions;

(e)(3)(ii)(E) A detailed schedule for implementation of the program, including documentation such as copies of purchase orders for equipment, construction contracts, etc.;

(e)(3)9ii)(F) A work practice program which includes items required under paragraphs (g), (h) and (i) of this regulation;

(e)(3)(ii)(G) An administrative control schedule required by paragraph (e)(6), if applicable; and

(e)(3)(ii)(H) Other relevant information.

(e)(3)(iii) Written programs shall be submitted upon request to the Assistant Secretary and the Director, and shall be available at the worksite for examination and copying by the Assistant Secretary, Director, any affected employee or authorized employee representatives.

(e)(3)(iv) Written programs must be revised and updated at least annually to reflect the current status of the program.

(e)(4) Mechanical ventilation

(e)(4)(i) When ventilation is used to control exposure, measurements which demonstrate the effectiveness of the system in controlling exposure, such as capture velocity, duct velocity, or static pressure shall be made at least every 3 months. Measurements of the system's effectiveness in controlling exposure shall be made within 5 days of any change in production, process, or control which might result in a change in employee exposure to lead.

(e)(4)(ii) OI **Recirculation of air** If air from exhaust ventilation is recirculated into the workplace, the employer shall assure that (A) the system has a high efficiency filter with reliable back-up filter; and (B) controls to monitor the concentration of lead in the return air and to bypass the recirculation system automatically, if it fails, are installed, operating, and maintained.

(e)(5) Administrative controls If administrative controls are used as a means of reducing employees TWA exposure to lead, the employer shall establish and implement a job rotation schedule which includes:

(e)(5)(i) Name or identification number of each affected employee;

(e)(5)(ii) Duration and exposure levels at each job or work station where each affected employee is located; and

(e)(5)(iii) Any other information which may be useful in assessing the reliability of administrative controls to reduce exposure to lead.

(f) Respiratory protection

(f)(1) General For employees who use respirators required by this Section, the employer must provide each employee an appropriate respirator that complies with the requirements of this paragraph. Respirators must be used during:

(f)(1)(i) Periods necessary to install or implement engineering or work-practice controls;

(f)(1)(ii) Work operations for which engineering and work-practice controls are not sufficient to reduce employee exposures to or below the permissible exposure limit; and

(f)(1)(iii) Periods when an employee requests a respirator.

(f)(2) Respirator program

(f)(2)(i) The employer must implement a respiratory protection program in accordance with §1910.134(b) through (d) (except (d)(1)(iii)), and (f) through (m), which covers each employee required by this Section to use a respirator.

(f)(2)(ii) OI If an employee has breathing difficulty during fit testing or respirator use, the employer must provide the employee with a medical examination in accordance with paragraph (j)(3)(i)(C) of this Section to determine whether or not the employee can use a respirator while performing the required duty.

(f)(3) Respirator selection

(f)(3)(i) Employers must:

(f)(3)(i)(A) Select, and provide to employees, the appropriate respirators specified in paragraph (d)(3)(i)(A) of 29 CFR §1910.134;

(f)(3)(i)(B) Provide employees with full facepiece respirators instead of half mask respirators for protection against lead aerosols that cause eye or skin irritation at the use concentrations;

(f)(3)(i)(C) Provide HEPA filters for powered and non-powered air-purifying respirators.

(f)(3)(ii) Employers must provide employees with a powered air-purifying respirator (PAPR) instead of a negative pressure respirator selected according to paragraph (f)(3)(i) of this Standard when an employee chooses to use a PAPR and it provides adequate protection to the employee as specified by paragraph (f)(3)(i) of this Standard.

(g) Protective work clothing and equipment

(g)(1) Provision and use If an employee is exposed to lead above the PEL, without regard to the use of respirators or where the possibility of skin or eye irritation exists, the employer shall provide at no cost to the employee and assure that the employee uses appropriate protective work clothing and equipment such as, but not limited to:

(g)(1)(i) Coveralls or similar full-body work clothing;

(g)(1)(ii) Gloves, hats, and shoes or disposable shoe coverlets; and

(g)(1)(iii) Face shields, vented goggles, or other appropriate protective equipment which complies with §1910.133 of this Part.

(g)(2) Cleaning and replacement

(g)(2)(i) The employer shall provide the protective clothing required in paragraph (g)(1) of this Section in a clean and dry condition at least weekly, and daily to employees whose exposure levels without regard to a respirator are over 200 $\mu g/m^3$ of lead as an 8-hour TWA.

(g)(2)(ii) The employer shall provide for the cleaning, laundering, or disposal of protective clothing and equipment required by paragraph (g)(1) of this Section.

(g)(2)(iii) The employer shall repair or replace required protective clothing and equipment as needed to maintain their effectiveness.

(g)(2)(iv) The employer shall assure that all protective clothing is removed at the completion of a work shift only in change rooms provided for that purpose as prescribed in paragraph (i)(2) of this Section.

(g)(2)(v) The employer shall assure that contaminated protective clothing which is to be cleaned, laundered, or disposed of, is placed in a closed container in the change-room which prevents dispersion of lead outside the container.

(g)(2)(vi) The employer shall inform in writing any person who cleans or launders protective clothing or equipment of the potentially harmful effects of exposure to lead.

(g)(2)(vii) Labeling of contaminated protective clothing and equipment.

(g)(2)(vii)(A) The employer shall ensure that labels of bags or containers of contaminated protective clothing and equipment include the following information:

DANGER: CLOTHING AND EQUIPMENT CONTAMINATED WITH LEAD. MAY DAMAGE FERTILITY OR THE UNBORN CHILD. CAUSES DAMAGE TO THE CENTRAL NERVOUS SYSTEM. DO NOT EAT, DRINK OR SMOKE WHEN HANDLING. DO NOT REMOVE DUST BY BLOWING OR SHAKING. DISPOSE OF LEAD CONTAMINATED WASH WATER IN ACCORDANCE WITH APPLICABLE LOCAL, STATE, OR FEDERAL REGULATIONS.

(g)(2)(vii)(B) Prior to June 1, 2015, employers may include the following information on bags or containers of contaminated protective clothing and equipment in lieu of the labeling requirements in paragraphs (g)(2)(vii)(A) of this Section:

CAUTION: CLOTHING CONTAMINATED WITH LEAD. DO NOT REMOVE DUST BY BLOWING OR SHAKING. DISPOSE OF LEAD CONTAMINATED WASH WATER IN ACCORDANCE WITH APPLICABLE LOCAL, STATE, OR FEDERAL REGULATIONS.

(g)(2)(viii) The employer shall prohibit the removal of lead from protective clothing or equipment by blowing, shaking, or any other means which disperses lead into the air.

(h) Housekeeping

(h)(1) **Surfaces** All surfaces shall be maintained as free as practicable of accumulations of lead.

(h)(2) Cleaning floors

(h)(2)(i) Floors and other surfaces where lead accumulates may not be cleaned by the use of compressed air.

(h)(2)(ii) Shoveling, dry or wet sweeping, and brushing may be used only where vacuuming or other equally effective methods have been tried and found not to be effective.

(h)(3) **Vacuuming** Where vacuuming methods are selected, the vacuums shall be used and emptied in a manner which minimizes the reentry of lead into the workplace.

(i) Hygiene facilities and practices

(i)(1) The employer shall assure that in areas where employees are exposed to lead above the PEL, without regard to the use of respirators, food or beverage is not present or consumed, tobacco products are not present or used, and cosmetics are not applied, except in change rooms, lunchrooms, and showers required under paragraphs (i)(2) through (i)(4) of this Section.

(i)(2) Change rooms

(i)(2)(i) The employer shall provide clean change rooms for employees who work in areas where their airborne exposure to lead is above the PEL, without regard to the use of respirators.

(i)(2)(ii) The employer shall assure that change rooms are equipped with separate storage facilities for protective work clothing and equipment and for street clothes which prevent cross-contamination.

(i)(3) Showers

(i)(3)(i) The employer shall assure that employees who work in areas where their airborne exposure to lead is above the PEL, without regard to the use of respirators, shower at the end of the work shift.

(i)(3)(ii) The employer shall provide shower facilities in accordance with §1910.141 (d)(3) of this Part.

(i)(3)(iii) The employer shall assure that employees who are required to shower pursuant to paragraph (i)(3)(i) do not leave the workplace wearing any clothing or equipment worn during the work shift.

(i)(4) Lunchrooms

(i)(4)(i) The employer shall provide lunchroom facilities for employees who work in areas where their airborne exposure to lead is above the PEL, without regard to the use of respirators.

(i)(4)(ii) The employer shall assure that lunchroom facilities have a temperature controlled, positive pressure, filtered air supply, and are readily accessible to employees.

(i)(4)(iii) The employer shall assure that employees who work in areas where their airborne exposure to lead is above the PEL without regard to the use of a respirator wash their hands and face prior to eating, drinking, smoking or applying cosmetics.

(i)(4)(iv) The employer shall assure that employees do not enter lunchroom facilities with protective work clothing or equipment unless surface lead dust has been removed by vacuuming, downdraft booth, or other cleaning method.

(i)(5) **Lavatories** The employer shall provide an adequate number of lavatory facilities which comply with §1910.141(d)(1) and (2) of this Part.

(j) Medical surveillance

(j)(1) General

(j)(1)(i) The employer shall institute a medical surveillance program for all employees who are or may be exposed at or above the action level for more than 30 days per year.

(j)(1)(ii) The employer shall assure that all medical examinations and procedures are performed by or under the supervision of a licensed physician.

(j)(1)(iii) The employer shall provide the required medical surveillance including multiple physician review under paragraph (j)(3)(iii) without cost to employees and at a reasonable time and place.

(j)(2) Biological monitoring

(j)(2)(i) Blood lead and ZPP level sampling and analysis. The employer shall make available biological monitoring in the form of blood sampling and analysis for lead and zinc protoporphyrin levels to each employee covered under paragraph (j)(1)(i) of this Section on the following schedule:

(j)(2)(i)(A) At least every 6 months to each employee covered under paragraph (j)(1)(i) of this Section;

(j)(2)(i)(B) At least every two months for each employee whose last blood sampling and analysis indicated a blood lead level at or above 40 µg/100g of whole blood. This frequency shall continue until two consecutive blood samples and analyses indicate a blood lead level below 40 µg/100g of whole blood; and

(j)(2)(i)(C) At least monthly during the removal period of each employee removed from exposure to lead due to an elevated blood lead level.

(j)(2)(ii) Follow-up blood sampling tests. Whenever the results of a blood lead level test indicate that an employee's blood lead level is at or above the numerical criterion for medical removal under paragraph (k)(1)(i)(A) of this Section, the employer shall provide a second (follow-up) blood sampling test within two weeks after the employer receives the results of the first blood sampling test.

(j)(2)(iii) Accuracy of blood lead level sampling and analysis. Blood lead level sampling and analysis provided pursuant to this Section shall have an accuracy (to a confidence level of 95 percent) within plus or minus 15 percent or 6 µg/100ml, whichever is greater, and shall be conducted by a laboratory licensed by the Center for Disease Control, United States Department of Health, Education and Welfare (CDC) or which has received a satisfactory grade in blood lead proficiency testing from CDC in the prior twelve months.

(j)(2)(iv) Employee notification. Within five working days after the receipt of biological monitoring results, the employer shall notify in writing each employee whose blood lead level is at or above 40 µg/100g:

(j)(2)(iv)(A) Of that employee's blood lead level; and

(j)(2)(iv)(B) That the Standard requires temporary medical removal with Medical Removal Protection benefits when an employee's blood lead level exceeds the numerical criterion for medical removal under paragraph (k)(1)(i) of this Section.

(j)(3) Medical examinations and consultations

(j)(3)(i) **Frequency** The employer shall make available medical examinations and consultations to each employee covered under paragraph (j)(1)(i) of this Section on the following schedule:

(j)(3)(i)(A) At least annually for each employee for whom a blood sampling test conducted at any time during the preceding 12 months indicated a blood lead level at or above 40 µg/100g;

(j)(3)(i)(B) Prior to assignment for each employee being assigned for the first time to an area in which airborne concentrations of lead are at or above the action level;

(j)(3)(i)(C) As soon as possible, upon notification by an employee either that the employee has developed signs or symptoms commonly associated with lead intoxication, that the employee desires medical advice concerning the effects of current or past exposure to lead on the employee's ability to procreate a healthy child, or that the employee has demonstrated difficulty in breathing during a respirator fitting test or during use; and

(j)(3)(i)(D) As medically appropriate for each employee either removed from exposure to lead due to a risk of sustaining material impairment to health, or otherwise limited pursuant to a final medical determination.

(j)(3)(ii) **Content** Medical examinations made available pursuant to paragraph (j)(3)(i)(A) through (B) of this Section shall include the following elements:

(j)(3)(ii)(A) A detailed work history and a medical history, with particular attention to past lead exposure (occupational and non-occupational), personal habits (smoking, hygiene), and past gastrointestinal, hematologic, renal, cardiovascular, reproductive and neurological problems;

(j)(3)(ii)(B) A thorough physical examination, with particular attention to teeth, gums, hematologic, gastrointestinal, renal, cardiovascular, and neurological systems. Pulmonary status should be evaluated if respiratory protection will be used;

(j)(3)(ii)(C) A blood pressure measurement;

(j)(3)(ii)(D) A blood sample and analysis which determines:

(j)(3)(ii)(D)(1) Blood lead level;

(j)(3)(ii)(D)(2) Hemoglobin and hematocrit determinations, red cell indices, and examination of peripheral smear morphology;

(j)(3)(ii)(D)(3) Zinc protoporphyrin;

(j)(3)(ii)(D)(4) Blood urea nitrogen; and

(j)(3)(ii)(D)(5) Serum creatinine;

(j)(3)(ii)(E) A routine urinalysis with microscopic examination; and

(j)(3)(ii)(F) Any laboratory or other test which the examining physician deems necessary by sound medical practice.

The content of medical examinations made available pursuant to paragraph (j)(3)(i)(C) through (D) of this Section shall be determined by an examining physician and, if requested by an employee, shall include pregnancy testing or laboratory evaluation of male fertility.

(j)(3)(iii) **Multiple physician review mechanism**

(j)(3)(iii)(A) If the employer selects the initial physician who conducts any medical examination or consultation provided to an employee under this Section, the employee may designate a second physician:

(j)(3)(iii)(A)(1) To review any findings, determinations or recommendations of the initial physician; and

(j)(3)(iii)(A)(2) To conduct such examinations, consultations, and laboratory tests as the second physician deems necessary to facilitate this review.

(j)(3)(iii)(B) The employer shall promptly notify an employee of the right to seek a second medical opinion after each occasion that an initial physician conducts a medical examination or consultation pursuant to this Section. The employer may condition its participation in, and payment for, the multiple physician review mechanism upon the employee doing the following within fifteen (15) days after receipt of the foregoing notification, or receipt of the initial physician's written opinion, whichever is later:

(j)(3)(iii)(B)(1) The employee informing the employer that he or she intends to seek a second medical opinion; and

(j)(3)(iii)(B)(2) The employee initiating steps to make an appointment with a second physician.

(j)(3)(iii)(C) If the findings, determinations or recommendations of the second physician differ from those of the initial physician, then the employer and the employee shall assure that efforts are made for the two physicians to resolve any disagreement.

(j)(3)(iii)(D) If the two physicians have been unable to quickly resolve their disagreement, then the employer and the employee through their respective physicians shall designate a third physician:

(j)(3)(iii)(D)(1) To review any findings, determinations or recommendations of the prior physicians; and

(j)(3)(iii)(D)(2) To conduct such examinations, consultations, laboratory tests and discussions with the prior physicians as the third physician deems necessary to resolve the disagreement of the prior physicians.

(j)(3)(iii)(E) The employer shall act consistent with the findings, determinations and recommendations of the third physician, unless the employer and the employee reach an agreement which is otherwise consistent with the recommendations of at least one of the three physicians.

(j)(3)(iv) **Information provided to examining and consulting physicians**

(j)(3)(iv)(A) The employer shall provide an initial physician conducting a medical examination or consultation under this Section with the following information:

(j)(3)(iv)(A)(1) A copy of this regulation for lead including all Appendices;

(j)(3)(iv)(A)(2) A description of the affected employee's duties as they relate to the employee's exposure;

(j)(3)(iv)(A)(3) The employee's exposure level or anticipated exposure level to lead and to any other toxic substance (if applicable);

(j)(3)(iv)(A)(4) A description of any personal protective equipment used or to be used;

(j)(3)(iv)(A)(5) Prior blood lead determinations; and

(j)(3)(iv)(A)(6) All prior written medical opinions concerning the employee in the employer's possession or control.

(j)(3)(iv)(B) The employer shall provide the foregoing information to a second or third physician conducting a medical examination or consultation under this Section upon request either by the second or third physician, or by the employee.

(j)(3)(v) **Written medical opinions**

(j)(3)(v)(A) The employer shall obtain and furnish the employee with a copy of a written medical opinion from each examining or consulting physician which contains the following information:

(j)(3)(v)(A)(1) The physician's opinion as to whether the employee has any detected medical condition which would place the employee at increased risk of material impairment of the employee's health from exposure to lead;

(j)(3)(v)(A)(2) Any recommended special protective measures to be provided to the employee, or limitations to be placed upon the employee's exposure to lead;

(j)(3)(v)(A)(3) Any recommended limitation upon the employee's use of respirators, including a determination of whether the employee can wear a powered air purifying respirator if a physician determines that the employee cannot wear a negative pressure respirator; and

(j)(3)(v)(A)(4) The results of the blood lead determinations.

(j)(3)(v)(B) The employer shall instruct each examining and consulting physician to:

(j)(3)(v)(B)(1) Not reveal either in the written opinion, or in any other means of communication with the employer, findings, including laboratory results, or diagnoses unrelated to an employee's occupational exposure to lead; and

(j)(3)(v)(B)(2) Advise the employee of any medical condition, occupational or nonoccupational, which dictates further medical examination or treatment.

(j)(3)(vi) **Alternate Physician Determination Mechanisms** The employer and an employee or authorized employee representative may agree upon the use of any expeditious alternate physician determination mechanism in lieu of the multiple physician review mechanism provided by this paragraph so long as the alternate mechanism otherwise satisfies the requirements contained in this paragraph.

(j)(4) **Chelation**

(j)(4)(i) The employer shall assure that any person whom he retains, employs, supervises or controls does not engage in prophylactic chelation of any employee at any time.

(j)(4)(ii) If therapeutic or diagnostic chelation is to be performed by any person in paragraph (j)(4)(i), the employer shall assure that it be done under the supervision of a licensed physician in a clinical setting with thorough and appropriate medical monitoring and that the employee is notified in writing prior to its occurrence.

(k) **Medical Removal Protection**

(k)(1) **Temporary medical removal and return of an employee**

(k)(1)(i) **Temporary removal due to elevated blood lead levels**

(k)(1)(i)(A) The employer shall remove an employee from work having an exposure to lead at or above the action level on each occasion that a periodic and a follow-up blood sampling test conducted pursuant to this Section indicate that the employee's blood lead level is at or above 60 μg/100g of whole blood; and

(k)(1)(i)(B) The employer shall remove an employee from work having an exposure to lead at or above the action level on each occasion that the average of the last three blood sampling tests conducted pursuant to this Section (or the average of all blood sampling tests conducted over the previous six (6) months, whichever is longer) indicates that the employee's blood lead level is at or above 50 μg/100g of whole blood; provided, however, that an employee need not be removed if the last blood sampling test indicates a blood lead level below 40 μg/100g of whole blood.

(k)(1)(ii) **Temporary removal due to a final medical determination**

(k)(1)(ii)(A) The employer shall remove an employee from work having an exposure to lead at or above the action level on each occasion that a final medical determination results in a medical finding, determination, or opinion that the employee has a detected medical condition which places the employee at increased risk of material impairment to health from exposure to lead.

(k)(1)(ii)(B) For the purposes of this Section, the phrase "final medical determination" shall mean the outcome of the multiple physician review mechanism or alternate medical determination mechanism used pursuant to the medical surveillance provisions of this Section.

(k)(1)(ii)(C) Where a final medical determination results in any recommended special protective measures for an employee, or limitations on an employee's exposure to lead, the employer shall implement and act consistent with the recommendation.

(k)(1)(iii) **Return of the employee to former job status**

(k)(1)(iii)(A) The employer shall return an employee to his or her former job status:

(k)(1)(iii)(A)(1) For an employee removed due to a blood lead level at or above 60 μg/100g, or due to an average blood lead level at or above 50 μg/100g, when two consecutive blood sampling tests indicate that the employee's blood lead level is below 40 μg/100g of whole blood;

(k)(1)(iii)(A)(2) For an employee removed due to a final medical determination, when a subsequent final medical determination results in a medical finding, determination, or opinion that the employee no longer has a detected medical condition which places the employee at increased risk of material impairment to health from exposure to lead.

(k)(1)(iii)(B) For the purposes of this Section, the requirement that an employer return an employee to his or her former job status is not intended to expand upon or restrict any rights an employee has or would have had, absent temporary medical removal, to a specific job classification or position under the terms of a collective bargaining agreement.

(k)(1)(iv) **Removal of other employee special protective measure or limitations** The employer shall remove any limitations placed on an employee or end any special protective measures provided to an employee pursuant to a final medical determination when a subsequent final medical determination indicates that the limitations or special protective measures are no longer necessary.

(k)(1)(v) **Employer options pending a final medical determination** Where the multiple physician review mechanism, or alternate medical determination mechanism used pursuant to the medical surveillance provisions of this Section, has not yet resulted in a final medical determination with respect to an employee, the employer shall act as follows:

(k(1)(v)(A) **Removal** The employer may remove the employee from exposure to lead, provide special protective measures to the employee, or place limitations upon the employee, consistent with the medical findings, determinations, or recommendations of any of the physicians who have reviewed the employee's health status.

(k)(1)(v)(B) **Return** The employer may return the employee to his or her former job status, end any special protective measures provided to the employee, and remove any limitations placed upon the employee, consistent with the medical findings, determinations, or recommendations of any of the physicians who have reviewed the employee's health status, with two exceptions. If;

(k)(1)(v)(B)(1) The initial removal, special protection, or limitation of the employee resulted from a final medical determination which differed from the findings, determinations, or recommendations of the initial physician or

(k)(1)(v)(B)(2) The employee has been on removal status for the preceding eighteen months due to an elevated blood lead level, then the employer shall await a final medical determination.

(k)(2) OI **Medical removal protection benefits**

(k)(2)(i) **Provision of medical removal protection benefits** The employer shall provide to an employee up to eighteen (18) months of medical removal protection benefits on each occasion that an employee is removed from exposure to lead or otherwise limited pursuant to this Section.

(k)(2)(ii) **Definition of medical removal protection benefits** For the purposes of this Section, the requirement that an employer provide medical removal protection benefits means that the employer shall maintain the earnings, seniority and other employment rights and benefits of an employee as though the employee had not been removed from normal exposure to lead or otherwise limited.

(k)(2)(iii) **Follow-up medical surveillance during the period of employee removal or limitation** During the period of time that an employee is removed from normal exposure to lead or otherwise limited, the employer may condition the provision of medical removal protection benefits upon the employee's participation in follow-up medical surveillance made available pursuant to this Section.

(k)(2)(iv) **Workers' compensation claims** If a removed employee files a claim for workers' compensation payments for a lead-related disability, then the employer shall continue to provide medical removal protection benefits pending disposition of the claim. To the extent that an award is made to the employee for earnings lost during the period of removal, the employer's medical removal protection obligation shall be reduced by such amount. The employer shall receive no credit for workers' compensation payments received by the employee for treatment related expenses.

(k)(2)(v) **Other credits** The employer's obligation to provide medical removal protection benefits to a removed employee shall be reduced to the extent that the employee receives compensation for earnings lost during the period of removal either from a publicly or employer-funded compensation program, or receives income from employment with another employer made possible by virtue of the employee's removal.

(k)(2)(vi) **Employees whose blood lead levels do not adequately decline within 18 months of removal** The employer shall take the following measures with respect to any employee removed from exposure to lead due to an elevated blood lead level whose blood lead level has not declined within the past eighteen (18) months of removal so that the employee has been returned to his or her former job status:

(k)(2)(vi)(A) The employer shall make available to the employee a medical examination pursuant to this Section to obtain a final medical determination with respect to the employee;

(k)(2)(vi)(B) The employer shall assure that the final medical determination obtained indicates whether or not the employee may be returned to his or her former job status, and if not, what steps should be taken to protect the employee's health;

(k)(2)(vi)(C) Where the final medical determination has not yet been obtained, or once obtained indicates that the employee may not yet be returned to his or her former job status, the employer shall continue to provide medical removal protection benefits to the employee until either the employee is returned to former job status, or a final medical determination is made that the employee is incapable of ever safely returning to his or her former job status;

(k)(2)(vi)(D) Where the employer acts pursuant to a final medical determination which permits the return of the employee to his or her former job status despite what would otherwise be an unacceptable blood lead level, later questions concerning removing the employee again shall be decided by a final medical determination. The employer need not automatically remove such an employee pursuant to the blood lead level removal criteria provided by this Section.

(k)(2)(vii) **Voluntary Removal or Restriction of An Employee** Where an employer, although not required by this Section to do so, removes an employee from exposure to lead or otherwise places limitations on an employee due to the effects of lead exposure on the employee's medical condition, the employer shall provide medical removal protection benefits to the employee equal to that required by paragraph (k)(2)(i) of this Section.

(l) Employee information and training

(l)(1) Training program

(l)(1)(i) OI Each employer who has a workplace in which there is a potential exposure to airborne lead at any level shall inform employees of the content of Appendices A and B of this regulation.

(l)(1)(ii) The employer shall train each employee who is subject to exposure to lead at or above the action level, or for whom the possibility of skin or eye irritation exists, in accordance with the requirements of this Section. The employer shall institute a training program and ensure employee participation in the program.

(l)(1)(iii) OI The employer shall provide initial training by 180 days from the effective date for those employees covered by paragraph (l)(1)(ii) on the Standard's effective date and prior to the time of initial job assignment for those employees subsequently covered by this paragraph.

(l)(1)(iv) The training program shall be repeated at least annually for each employee.

(l)(1)(v) The employer shall assure that each employee is informed of the following:

(l)(1)(v)(A) The content of this Standard and its Appendices;

(l)(1)(v)(B) The specific nature of the operations which could result in exposure to lead above the action level;

(l)(1)(v)(C) The purpose, proper selection, fitting, use, and limitations of respirators;

(l)(1)(v)(D) The purpose and a description of the medical surveillance program, and the medical removal protection program including information concerning the adverse health effects associated with excessive exposure to lead (with particular attention to the adverse reproductive effects on both males and females);

(l)(1)(v)(E) The engineering controls and work practices associated with the employee's job assignment;

(l)(1)(v)(F) The contents of any compliance plan in effect; and

(l)(1)(v)(G) Instructions to employees that chelating agents should not routinely be used to remove lead from their bodies and should not be used at all except under the direction of a licensed physician.

(l)(2) Access to information and training materials

(l)(2)(i) The employer shall make readily available to all affected employees a copy of this Standard and its Appendices.

(l)(2)(ii) The employer shall provide, upon request, all materials relating to the employee information and training program to the Assistant Secretary and the Director.

(l)(2)(iii) In addition to the information required by paragraph (l)(1)(v), the employer shall include as part of the training program, and shall distribute to employees, any materials pertaining to the Occupational Safety and Health Act, the regulations issued pursuant to that Act, and this lead standard, which are made available to the employer by the Assistant Secretary.

(m) Communication of hazards

(m)(1) Hazard communication—general

(m)(1)(i) Chemical manufacturers, importers, distributors and employers shall comply with all requirements of the Hazard Communication Standard (HCS) (§1910.1200) for lead.

(m)(1)(ii) In classifying the hazards of lead at least the following hazards are to be addressed: Reproductive/developmental toxicity; central nervous system effects; kidney effects; blood effects; and acute toxicity effects.

(m)(1)(iii) Employers shall include lead in the hazard communication program established to comply with the HCS (§1910.1200). Employers shall ensure that each employee has access to labels on containers of lead and to safety data sheets, and is trained in accordance with the requirements of HCS and paragraph (l) of this Section.

(m)(2) Signs

(m)(2)(i) The employer shall post the following warning signs in each work area where the PEL is exceeded:

DANGER
LEAD
MAY DAMAGE FERTILITY OR THE UNBORN CHILD
CAUSES DAMAGE TO THE CENTRAL NERVOUS SYSTEM
DO NOT EAT, DRINK OR SMOKE IN THIS AREA

(m)(2)(ii) The employer shall ensure that no statement appears on or near any sign required by this paragraph (m)(2) which contradicts or detracts from the meaning of the required sign.

(m)(2)(iii) The employer shall ensure that signs required by this paragraph (m)(2) are illuminated and cleaned as necessary so that the legend is readily visible.

(m)(2)(iv) The employer may use signs required by other statutes, regulations, or ordinances in addition to, or in combination with, signs required by this paragraph (m)(2).

(m)(2)(v) Prior to June 1, 2016, employers may use the following legend in lieu of that specified in paragraph (m)(2)(ii) of this Section:

WARNING
LEAD WORK AREA
POISON
NO SMOKING OR EATING

(n) **Recordkeeping**

(n)(1) **Exposure monitoring**

(n)(1)(i) The employer shall establish and maintain an accurate record of all monitoring required in paragraph (d) of this Section.

(n)(1)(ii) This record shall include:

(n)(1)(ii)(A) The date(s), number, duration, location and results of each of the samples taken, including a description of the sampling procedure used to determine representative employee exposure where applicable;

(n)(1)(ii)(B) A description of the sampling and analytical methods used and evidence of their accuracy;

(n)(1)(ii)(C) The type of respiratory protective devices worn, if any;

(n)(1)(ii)(D) Name, social security number, and job classification of the employee monitored and of all other employees whose exposure the measurement is intended to represent; and

(n)(1)(ii)(E) The environmental variables that could affect the measurement of employee exposure.

(n)(1)(iii) The employer shall maintain these monitoring records for at least 40 years or for the duration of employment plus 20 years, whichever is longer.

(n)(2) **Medical surveillance**

(n)(2)(i) The employer shall establish and maintain an accurate record for each employee subject to medical surveillance as required by paragraph (j) of this Section.

(n)(2)(ii) This record shall include:

(n)(2)(ii)(A) The name, social security number, and description of the duties of the employee;

(n)(2)(ii)(B) A copy of the physician's written opinions;

(n)(2)(ii)(C) Results of any airborne exposure monitoring done for that employee and the representative exposure levels supplied to the physician; and

(n)(2)(ii)(D) Any employee medical complaints related to exposure to lead.

(n)(2)(iii) The employer shall keep, or assure that the examining physician keeps, the following medical records:

(n)(2)(iii)(A) A copy of the medical examination results including medical and work history required under paragraph (j) of this Section;

(n)(2)(iii)(B) A description of the laboratory procedures and a copy of any standards or guidelines used to interpret the test results or references to that information;

(n)(2)(iii)(C) A copy of the results of biological monitoring.

(n)(2)(iv) The employer shall maintain or assure that the physician maintains those medical records for at least 40 years, or for the duration of employment plus 20 years, whichever is longer.

(n)(3) **Medical removals**

(n)(3)(i) The employer shall establish and maintain an accurate record for each employee removed from current exposure to lead pursuant to paragraph (k) of this Section.

(n)(3)(ii) Each record shall include:

(n)(3)(ii)(A) The name and social security number of the employee;

(n)(3)(ii)(B) The date on each occasion that the employee was removed from current exposure to lead as well as the corresponding date on which the employee was returned to his or her former job status;

(n)(3)(ii)(C) A brief explanation of how each removal was or is being accomplished; and

(n)(3)(ii)(D) A statement with respect to each removal indicating whether or not the reason for the removal was an elevated blood lead level.

(n)(3)(iii) The employer shall maintain each medical removal record for at least the duration of an employee's employment.

(n)(4) **Availability**

(n)(4)(i) The employer shall make available upon request all records required to be maintained by paragraph (n) of this Section to the Assistant Secretary and the Director for examination and copying.

(n)(4)(ii) Environmental monitoring, medical removal, and medical records required by this paragraph shall be provided upon request to employees, designated representatives, and the Assistant Secretary in accordance with 29 CFR §1910.1020 (a)–(e) and (2)–(i). Medical removal records shall be provided in the same manner as environmental monitoring records.

(n)(5) **Transfer of records**

(n)(5)(i) Whenever the employer ceases to do business, the successor employer shall receive and retain all records required to be maintained by paragraph (n) of this Section.

(n)(5)(ii) The employer shall also comply with any additional requirements involving transfer of records set forth in 29 CFR §1910.1020(h).

(o) **Observation of monitoring**

(o)(1) **Employee observation** The employer shall provide affected employees or their designated representatives an opportunity to observe any monitoring of employee exposure to lead conducted pursuant to paragraph (d) of this Section.

(o)(2) **Observation procedures**

(o)(2)(i) Whenever observation of the monitoring of employee exposure to lead requires entry into an area where the use of respirators, protective clothing or equipment is required, the employer shall provide the observer with and assure the use of such respirators, clothing and such equipment, and shall require the observer to comply with all other applicable safety and health procedures.

(o)(2)(ii) Without interfering with the monitoring, observers shall be entitled to:

(o)(2)(ii)(A) Receive an explanation of the measurement procedures;

(o)(2)(ii)(B) Observe all steps related to the monitoring of lead performed at the place of exposure; and

(o)(2)(ii)(C) Record the results obtained or receive copies of the results when returned by the laboratory.

(p) **Appendices** The information contained in the Appendices to this Section is not intended by itself, to create any additional obligations not otherwise imposed by this Standard, nor detract from any existing obligation.

§1910.1025 Appendix A
Substance data sheet for occupational exposure to lead

I. Substance Identification

A. Substance Pure lead (Pb) is a heavy metal at room temperature and pressure and is a basic chemical element. It can combine with various other substances to form numerous lead compounds.

B. Compounds Covered by the Standard The word "lead" when used in this Standard means elemental lead, all inorganic lead compounds and a class of organic lead compounds called lead soaps. This Standard does not apply to other organic lead compounds.

C. Uses Exposure to lead occurs in at least 120 different occupations, including primary and secondary lead smelting, lead storage battery manufacturing, lead pigment manufacturing and use, solder manufacturing and use, shipbuilding and ship repairing, auto manufacturing, and printing.

D. Permissible Exposure The Permissible Exposure Limit (PEL) set by the Standard is 50 micrograms of lead per cubic meter of air (50 $\mu g/m^3$), averaged over an 8-hour workday.

E. Action Level The Standard establishes an action level of 30 micrograms per cubic meter of air (30 $\mu g/m^3$), time weighted average, based on an 8-hour work-day. The action level initiates several requirements of the Standard, such as exposure monitoring, medical surveillance, and training and education.

II. Health Hazard Data

A. Ways in which lead enters your body When absorbed into your body in certain doses lead is a toxic substance. The object of the lead standard is to prevent absorption of harmful quantities of lead. The Standard is intended to protect you not only from the immediate toxic effects of lead, but also from the serious toxic effects that may not become apparent until years of exposure have passed.

Lead can be absorbed into your body by inhalation (breathing) and ingestion (eating). Lead (except for certain organic lead compounds not covered by the Standard, such as tetraethyl lead) is not absorbed through your skin. When lead is scattered in the air as a dust, fume or mist it can be inhaled and absorbed through you lungs and upper respiratory tract. Inhalation of airborne lead is generally the most important source of occupational lead absorption. You can also absorb lead through your digestive system if lead gets into your mouth and is swallowed. If you handle food, cigarettes, chewing tobacco, or make-up which have lead on them or handle them with hands contaminated with lead, this will contribute to ingestion.

A significant portion of the lead that you inhale or ingest gets into your blood stream. Once in your blood stream, lead is circulated throughout your body and stored in various organs and body tissues. Some of this lead is quickly filtered out of your body and excreted, but some remains in the blood and other tissues. As exposure to lead continues, the amount stored in your body will increase if you are absorbing more lead than your body is excreting. Even though you may not be aware of any immediate symptoms of disease, this lead stored in your tissues can be slowly causing irreversible damage, first to individual cells, then to your organs and whole body systems.

B. Effects of overexposure to lead

(1) **Short term (acute) overexposure** Lead is a potent, systemic poison that serves no known useful function once absorbed by your body. Taken in large enough doses, lead can kill you in a matter of days. A condition affecting the brain called acute encephalopathy may arise which develops quickly to seizures, coma, and death from cardiorespiratory arrest. A short term dose of lead can lead to acute encephalopathy. Short term occupational exposures of this magnitude are highly unusual, but not impossible. Similar forms of encephalopathy may, however, arise from extended, chronic exposure to lower doses of lead. There is no sharp dividing line between rapidly developing acute effects of lead, and chronic effects which take longer to acquire. Lead adversely affects numerous body systems, and causes forms of health impairment and disease which arise after periods of exposure as short as days or as long as several years.

(2) **Long-term (chronic) overexposure** Chronic overexposure to lead may result in severe damage to your blood-forming, nervous, urinary and reproductive systems. Some common symptoms of chronic overexposure include loss of appetite, metallic taste in the mouth, anxiety, constipation, nausea, pallor, excessive tiredness, weakness, insomnia, headache, nervous irritability, muscle and joint pain or soreness, fine tremors, numbness, dizziness, hyperactivity and colic. In lead colic there may be severe abdominal pain.

Damage to the central nervous system in general and the brain (encephalopathy) in particular is one of the most severe forms of lead poisoning. The most severe, often fatal, form of encephalopathy may be preceded by vomiting, a feeling of dullness progressing to drowsiness and stupor, poor memory, restlessness, irritability, tremor, and convulsions. It may arise suddenly with the onset of seizures, followed by coma, and death. There is a tendency for muscular weakness to develop at the same time. This weakness may progress to paralysis often observed as a characteristic "wrist drop" or "foot drop" and is a manifestation of a disease to the nervous system called peripheral neuropathy.

Chronic overexposure to lead also results in kidney disease with few, if any, symptoms appearing until extensive and most likely permanent kidney damage has occurred. Routine laboratory tests reveal the presence of this kidney disease only after about two-thirds of kidney function is lost. When overt symptoms of urinary dysfunction arise, it is often too late to correct or prevent worsening conditions, and progression to kidney dialysis or death is possible.

Chronic overexposure to lead impairs the reproductive systems of both men and women. Overexposure to lead may result in decreased sex drive, impotence and sterility in men. Lead can alter the structure of sperm cells raising the risk of birth defects. There is evidence of miscarriage and stillbirth in women whose husbands were exposed to lead or who were exposed to lead themselves. Lead exposure also may result in decreased fertility, and abnormal menstrual cycles in women. The course of pregnancy may be adversely affected by exposure to lead since lead crosses the placental barrier and poses risks to developing fetuses. Children born of parents either one of whom were exposed to excess lead levels are more likely to have birth defects, mental retardation, behavioral disorders or die during the first year of childhood.

Overexposure to lead also disrupts the blood-forming system resulting in decreased hemoglobin (the substance in the blood that carries oxygen to the cells) and ultimately anemia. Anemia is characterized by weakness, pallor and fatigability as a result of decreased oxygen carrying capacity in the blood.

(3) **Health protection goals of the Standard** Prevention of adverse health effects for most workers from exposure to lead throughout a working lifetime requires that worker blood lead (PbB) levels be maintained at or below forty micrograms per one hundred grams of whole blood (40 μg/100g). The blood lead levels of workers (both male and female workers) who intend to have children should be maintained below 30 μg/100g to minimize adverse reproductive health effects to the parents and to the developing fetus.

The measurement of your blood lead level is the most useful indicator of the amount of lead being absorbed by your body. Blood lead levels (PbB) are most often reported in units of milligrams (mg) or micrograms (μg) of lead (1 mg = 1000 μg) per 100grams (100g), 100 milliters (100 ml) or deciliter (dl) of blood. These three units are essentially the same. Sometime PbB's are expressed in the form of mg% or μg%. This is a shorthand notation for 100g, 100 ml, or dl.

PbB measurements show the amount of lead circulating in your blood stream, but do not give any information about the amount of lead stored in your various tissues. PbB measurements merely show current absorption of lead, not the effect that lead is having on your body or the effects that past lead exposure may have already caused. Past research into lead-related diseases, however, has focused heavily on associations between PbBs and various diseases. As a result, your PbB is an important indicator of the likelihood that you will gradually acquire a lead-related health impairment or disease.

Once your blood lead level climbs above 40 μg/100g, your risk of disease increases. There is a wide variability of individual response to lead, thus it is difficult to say that a particular PbB in a given person will cause a particular effect. Studies have associated fatal encephalopathy with PbBs as low as 150 μg/100g. Other studies have shown other forms of diseases in some workers with PbBs well below 80 μg/100g. Your PbB is a crucial indicator of the risks to your health, but one other factor is also extremely important. This factor is the length of time you have had elevated PbBs. The longer you have an elevated PbB, the greater the risk that large quantities of lead are being gradually stored in your organs and tissues (body burden). The greater your overall body burden, the greater the chances of substantial permanent damage.

The best way to prevent all forms of lead-related impairments and diseases—both short term and long term- is to maintain your PbB below 40 μg/100g. The provisions of the Standard are designed with this end in mind. Your employer has prime responsibility to assure that the provisions of the Standard are complied with both by the company and by individual workers. You as a worker, however, also have a responsibility to assist your employer in complying with the Standard. You can play a key role in protecting your own health by learning about the lead hazards and their control, learning what the Standard requires, following the Standard where it governs your own actions, and seeing that your employer complies with provisions governing his actions.

(4) **Reporting signs and symptoms of health problems** You should immediately notify your employer if you develop signs or symptoms associated with lead poisoning or if you desire medical advice concerning the effects of current or past exposure to lead on your ability to have a healthy child. You should also notify your employer if you have difficulty breathing during a respirator fit test or while wearing a respirator. In each of these cases your employer must make available to you appropriate medical examinations or consultations. These must be provided at no cost to you and at a reasonable time and place.

The Standard contains a procedure whereby you can obtain a second opinion by a physician of your choice if the employer selected the initial physician.

§1910.1025 Appendix B Employee standard summary

This Appendix summarizes key provisions of the Standard that you as a worker should become familiar with.

I. Permissible Exposure Limit (PEL)—Paragraph (c)

The Standards sets a permissible exposure limit (PEL) of fifty micrograms of lead per cubic meter of air (50 μg/m^3), averaged over an 8-hour work-day. This is the highest level of lead in air to which you may be permissibly exposed over an 8-hour workday. Since it is an 8-hour average it permits short exposures above the PEL so long as for each 8-hour work day your average exposure does not exceed the PEL.

This Standard recognizes that your daily exposure to lead can extend beyond a typical 8-hour workday as the result of overtime or other alterations in your work schedule. To deal with this, the Standard contains a formula which reduces your permissible exposure when you are exposed more than 8 hours. For example, if you are exposed to lead for 10 hours a day, the maximum permitted average exposure would be 40 μg/m^3.

II. Exposure Monitoring—Paragraph (d)

If lead is present in the workplace where you work in any quantity, your employer is required to make an initial determination of whether the action level is exceeded for any employee. This initial determination must include instrument monitoring of the air for the presence of lead and must cover the exposure of a representative number of employees who are reasonably believed to have the highest exposure levels. If your employer has conducted appropriate air sampling for lead in the past year he may use these results. If there have been any employee complaints of symptoms which may be attributable to exposure to lead or if there is any other information or observations which would indicate employee exposure to lead, this must also be considered as part of the initial determination. This initial determination must have been completed by March 31, 1979. If this initial determination shows that a reasonable possibility exists that any employee may be exposed, without regard to respirators, over the action level (30 µg/m^3) your employer must set up an air monitoring program to determine the exposure level of every employee exposed to lead at your workplace.

In carrying out this air monitoring program, your employer is not required to monitor the exposure of every employee, but he must monitor a representative number of employees and job types. Enough sampling must be done to enable each employee's exposure level to be reasonably least one full shift (at least 7 hours) air sample. In addition, these air samples must be taken under conditions which represent each employee's regular, daily exposure to lead. All initial exposure monitoring must have been completed by May 30, 1979.

If you are exposed to lead and air sampling is performed, your employer is required to quickly notify you in writing of air monitoring results which represent your exposure. If the results indicate your exposure exceeds the PEL (without regard to your use of respirators), then your employer must also notify you of this in writing, and provide you with a description of the corrective action that will be taken to reduce your exposure.

Your exposure must be rechecked by monitoring every six months if your exposure is over the action level but below the PEL. Air monitoring must be repeated every 3 months if you are exposed over the PEL. Your employer may discontinue monitoring for you if 2 consecutive measurements, taken at least two weeks apart, are below the action level. However, whenever there is a production, process, control, or personnel change at your workplace which may result in new or additional exposure to lead, or whenever there is any other reason to suspect a change which may result in new or additional exposure to lead, your employer must perform additional monitoring.

III. Methods of Compliance—Paragraph (e)

Your employer is required to assure that no employee is exposed to lead in excess of the PEL. The Standard establishes a priority of methods to be used to meet the PEL.

IV. Respiratory Protection—Paragraph (f)

Your employer is required to provide and assure your use of respirators when your exposure to lead is not controlled below the PEL by other means. The employer must pay the cost of the respirator. Whenever you request one, your employer is also required to provide you a respirator even if your air exposure level does not exceed the PEL. You might desire a respirator when, for example, you have received medical advice that your lead absorption should be decreased. Or, you may intend to have children in the near future, and want to reduce the level of lead in your body to minimize adverse reproductive effects. While respirators are the least satisfactory means of controlling your exposure, they are capable of providing significant protection if properly chosen, fitted, worn, cleaned, maintained, and replaced when they stop providing adequate protection.

Your employer is required to select respirators from the seven types listed in Table II of the Respiratory Protection section of the Standard (§1910.1025(f)). Any respirator chosen must be approved by the National Institute for Occupational Safety and Health (NIOSH) under the provisions of 42 CFR Part 84. This respirator selection table will enable your employer to choose a type of respirator that will give you a proper amount of protection based on your airborne lead exposure. Your employer may select a type of respirator that provides greater protection than that required by the Standard; that is, one recommended for a higher concentration of lead than is present in your workplace. For example, a powered air-purifying respirator (PAPR) is much more protective than a typical negative pressure respirator, and may also be more comfortable to wear. A PAPR has a filter, cartridge, or canister to clean the air, and a power source that continuously blows filtered air into your breathing zone. Your employer might make a PAPR available to you to ease the burden of having to wear a respirator for long periods of time. The Standard provides that you can obtain a PAPR upon request.

Your employer must also start a Respiratory Protection Program. This program must include written procedures for the proper selection, use, cleaning, storage, and maintenance of respirators.

Your employer must ensure that your respirator facepiece fits properly. Proper fit of a respirator facepiece is critical to your protection from airborne lead. Obtaining a proper fit on each employee may require your employer to make available several different types of respirator masks. To ensure that your respirator fits properly and that facepiece leakage is minimal, your employer must give you either a qualitative or quantitative fit test as specified in Appendix A of the Respiratory Protection Standard located at 29 CFR §1910.134.

You must also receive from your employer proper training in the use of respirators. Your employer is required to teach you how to wear a respirator, to know why it is needed, and to understand its limitations.

The Standard provides that if your respirator uses filter elements, you must be given an opportunity to change the filter elements whenever an increase in breathing resistance is detected. You also must be permitted to periodically leave your work area to wash your face and respirator facepiece whenever necessary to prevent skin irritation. If you ever have difficulty in breathing during a fit test or while using a respirator, your employer must make a medical examination available to you to determine whether you can safely wear a respirator. The result of this examination may be to give you a positive pressure respirator (which reduces breathing resistance) or to provide alternative means of protection.

V. Protective Work Clothing and Equipment—Paragraph (g)

If you are exposed to lead above the PEL, or if you are exposed to lead compounds such as lead arsenate or lead azide which can cause skin and eye irritation, your employer must provide you with protective work clothing and equipment appropriate for the hazard. If work clothing is provided, it must be provided in a clean and dry condition at least weekly, and daily if your airborne exposure to lead is greater than 200 µg/m^3. Appropriate protective work clothing and equipment can include coveralls or similar full-body work clothing, gloves, hats, shoes or disposable shoe coverlets, and face shields or vented goggles. Your employer is required to provide all such equipment at no cost to you. He is responsible for providing repairs and replacement as necessary, and also is responsible for the cleaning, laundering or disposal of protective clothing and equipment. Contaminated work clothing or equipment must be removed in change rooms and not worn home or you will extend your exposure and expose your family since lead from your clothing can accumulate in your house, car, etc. Contaminated clothing which is to be cleaned, laundered or disposed of must be placed in closed containers in the change room. At no time may lead be removed from protective clothing or equipment by any means which disperses lead into the workroom air.

VI. Housekeeping—Paragraph (h)

Your employer must establish a housekeeping program sufficient to maintain all surfaces as free as practicable of accumulations of lead dust. Vacuuming is the preferred method of meeting this requirement, and the use of compressed air to clean floors and other surfaces is absolutely prohibited. Dry or wet sweeping, shoveling, or brushing may not be used except where vaccuming or other equally effective methods have been tried and do not work. Vacuums must be used and emptied in a manner which minimizes the reentry of lead into the workplace.

VII. Hygiene Facilities and Practices—Paragraph (i)

The Standard requires that change rooms, showers, and filtered air lunchrooms be constructed and made available to workers exposed to lead above the PEL. When the PEL is exceeded the employer must assure that food and beverage is not present or consumed, tobacco products are not present or used, and cosmetics are not applied, except in these facilities. Change rooms, showers, and lunchrooms, must be used by workers exposed in excess of the PEL. After showering, no clothing or equipment worn during the shift may be worn home, and this includes shoes and underwear. Your own clothing worn during the shift should be carried home and cleaned carefully so that it does not contaminate your home. Lunchrooms may not be entered with protective clothing or equipment unless surface dust has been removed by vacuuming, downdraft booth, or other cleaning method. Finally, workers exposed above the PEL must wash both their hands and faces prior to eating, drinking, smoking or applying cosmetics.

All of the facilities and hygiene practices just discussed are essential to minimize additional sources of lead absorption from inhalation or ingestion of lead that may accumulate on you, your clothes, or your possessions. Strict compliance with these provisions can virtually eliminate several sources of lead exposure which significantly contribute to excessive lead absorption.

VIII. Medical Surveillance—Paragraph (j)

The medical surveillance program is part of the Standard's comprehensive approach to the prevention of lead-related disease. Its purpose is to supplement the main thrust of the Standard which is aimed at minimizing airborne concentrations of lead and sources of ingestion. Only medical surveillance can determine if the other provisions of the Standard have affectively protected you as an individual. Compliance with the Standard's provision will protect most workers from the adverse effects of lead exposure, but may not be satisfactory to protect individual workers (1) who have high body burdens of lead acquired over past years, (2) who have additional uncontrolled sources of non-occupational lead exposure, (3) who exhibit unusual variations in lead absorption rates, or (4) who have specific non-work related medical conditions which could be aggravated by lead exposure (e.g., renal disease, anemia). In addition, control systems may fail, or hygiene and respirator programs may be inadequate. Periodic medical surveillance of individual workers will help detect those failures. Medical surveillance will also be important to protect your reproductive ability—regardless of whether you are a man or woman.

All medical surveillance required by the Standard must be performed by or under the supervision of a licensed physician. The employer must provide required medical surveillance without cost to employees and at a reasonable time and place. The Standard's medical surveillance program has two parts-periodic biological monitoring and medical examinations.

Your employer's obligation to offer you medical surveillance is triggered by the results of the air monitoring program. Medical surveillance must be made available to all employees who are exposed in excess of the action level for more than 30 days a year. The initial phase of the medical surveillance program, which includes blood lead level tests and medical examinations, must be completed for all covered employees no later than August 28, 1979. Priority within this first round of medical surveillance must be given to employees whom the employer believes to be at greatest risk from continued exposure (for example, those with the longest prior exposure to lead, or those with the highest current exposure). Thereafter, the employer must periodically make medical surveillance—both biological monitoring and medical examinations—available to all covered employees.

Biological monitoring under the Standard consists of blood lead level (PbB) and zinc protoporphyrin tests at least every 6 months after the initial PbB test. A zinc protoporphyrin (ZPP) test is a very useful blood test which measures an effect of lead on your body. Thus biological monitoring under the Standard is currently limited to PbB testing. If a worker's PbB exceeds 40 µg/100g the monitoring frequency must be increased from every 6 months to at least every 2 months and not reduced until two consecutive PbBs indicate a blood lead level below 40 µg/100g. Each time your PbB is determined to be over 40 µg/100g, your employer must notify you of this in writing within five working days of his receipt of the test results. The employer must also inform you that the Standard requires temporary medical removal with economic protection when your PbB exceeds certain criteria. (See Discussion of Medical Removal Protection—Paragraph (k).) During the first year of the Standard, this removal criterion is 80 µg/100g. Anytime your PbB exceeds 80 µg/100g your employer must make available to you a prompt follow-up PbB test to ascertain your PbB. If the two tests both exceed 80 µg/100g and you are temporarily removed, then your employer must make successive PbB tests available to you on a monthly basis during the period of your removal.

Medical examinations beyond the initial one must be made available on an annual basis if your blood lead level exceeds 40 µg/100g at any time during the preceding year. The initial examination will provide information to establish a baseline to which subsequent data can be compared. An initial medical examination must also be made available (prior to assignment) for each employee being assigned for the first time to an area where the airborne concentration of lead equals or exceeds the action level. In addition, a medical examination or consultation must be made available as soon as possible if you notify your employer that you are experiencing signs or symptoms commonly associated with lead poisoning or that you have difficulty breathing while wearing a respirator or during a respirator fit test. You must also be provided a medical examination or consultation if you notify your employer that you desire medical advice concerning the effects of current or past exposure to lead on your ability to procreate a healthy child.

Finally, appropriate follow-up medical examinations or consultations may also be provided for employees who have been temporarily removed from exposure under the medical removal protection provisions of the Standard. (See Part IX, below.)

The Standard specifies the minimum content of pre-assignment and annual medical examinations. The content of other types of medical examinations and consultations is left up to the sound discretion of the examining physician. Pre-assignment and annual medical examinations must include: (1) a detailed work history and medical history, (2) a thorough physical examination, and (3) a series of laboratory tests designed to check your blood chemistry and your kidney function. In addition, at any time upon your request, a laboratory evaluation of male fertility will be made (microscopic examination of a sperm sample), or a pregnancy test will be given.

The Standard does not require that you participate in any of the medical procedures, tests, etc. which your employer is required to make available to you. Medical surveillance can, however, play a very important role in protecting your health. You are strongly encouraged, therefore, to participate in a meaningful fashion. The Standard contains a multiple physician review mechanism which would give you a chance to have a physician of your choice directly participate in the medical surveillance program. If you were dissatisfied with an examination by a physician chosen by your employer, you could select a second physician to conduct an independent analysis. The two doctors would attempt to resolve any differences of opinion, and select a third physician to resolve any firm dispute. Generally your employer will choose the physician who conducts medical surveillance under the lead Standard—unless you and your employer can agree on the choice of a physician or physicians. Some companies and unions have agreed in advance, for example, to use certain independent medical laboratories or panels of physicians. Any of these arrangements are acceptable so long as required medical surveillance is made available to workers.

The Standard requires your employer to provide certain information to a physician to aid in his or her examination of you. This information includes: (1) the Standard and its Appendices, (2) a description of your duties as they relate to lead exposure, (3) your exposure level, (4) a description of personal protective equipment you wear, (5) prior blood lead level results, and (6) prior written medical opinions concerning you that the employer has. After a medical examination or consultation the physician must prepare a written report which must contain: (1) the physician's opinion as to whether you have any medical condition which places you at increased risk of material impairment to health from exposure to lead, (2) any recommended special protective measures to be provided to you, (3) any blood lead level determinations, and (4) any recommended limitation on your use of respirators. This last element must include a determination of whether you can wear a powered air purifying respirator (PAPR) if you are found unable to wear a negative pressure respirator.

The medical surveillance program of the lead Standard may at some point in time serve to notify certain workers that they have acquired a disease or other adverse medical condition as a result of occupational lead exposure. If this is true, these workers might have legal rights to compensation from public agencies, their employers, firms that supply hazardous products to their employers, or other persons. Some states have laws, including worker compensation laws, that disallow a worker who learns of a job-related health impairment to sue, unless the worker sues within a short period of time after learning of the impairment. (This period of time may be a matter of months or years.) An attorney can be consulted about these possibilities. It should be stressed that OSHA is in no way trying to either encourage or discourage claims or lawsuits. However, since results of the Standard's medical surveillance program can significantly affect the legal remedies of a worker who has acquired a job-related disease or impairment, it is proper for OSHA to make you aware of this.

The medical surveillance section of the Standard also contains provisions dealing with chelation. Chelation is the use of certain drugs (administered in pill form or injected into the body) to reduce the amount of lead absorbed in body tissues. Experience accumulated by the medical and scientific communities has largely confirmed the effectiveness of this type of therapy for the treatment of very severe lead poisoning. On the other hand, it has also been established that there can be a long list of extremely harmful side effects associated with the use of chelating agents. The medical community has balanced the advantages and disadvantages resulting from the use of chelating agents in various circumstances and has established when the use of these agents is acceptable. The Standard includes these accepted limitations due to a history of abuse of chelation therapy by some lead companies. The most widely used chelating agents are calcium disodium EDTA, (Ca Na_2 EDTA), Calcium Disodium Versenate (Versenate), and d-penicillamine (pencillamine or Cupramine).

The Standard prohibits "prophylactic chelation" of any employee by any person the employer retains, supervises or controls. "Prophylactic chelation" is the routine use of chelating or similarly acting drugs to prevent elevated blood levels in workers who are occupationally exposed to lead, or the use of these drugs to routinely lower blood lead levels to predesignated concentrations believed to be 'safe'. It should be emphasized that where an employer takes a worker who has no symptoms of lead poisoning and has chelation carried out by a physician (either inside or outside of a hospital) solely to reduce the worker's blood lead level, that will generally be considered prophylactic chelation. The use of a hospital and a physician does not mean that prophylactic chelation is not being performed. Routine chelation to prevent increased or reduce current blood lead levels is unacceptable whatever the setting.

The Standard allows the use of "therapeutic" or "diagnostic" chelation if administered under the supervision of a licensed physician in a clinical setting with thorough and appropriate medical monitoring. Therapeutic chelation responds to severe lead poisoning where there are marked symptoms. Diagnostic chelation involved giving a patient a dose of the drug then collecting all urine excreted for some period of time as an aid to the diagnosis of lead poisoning.

In cases where the examining physician determines that chelation is appropriate, you must be notified in writing of this fact before such treatment. This will inform you of a potentially harmful treatment, and allow you to obtain a second opinion.

IX. Medical Removal Protection—paragraph (k)

Excessive lead absorption subjects you to increased risk of disease. Medical removal protection (MRP) is a means of protecting you when, for whatever reasons, other methods, such as engineering controls, work practices, and respirators, have failed to provide the protection you need. MRP involves the temporary removal of a worker from his or her regular job to a place of significantly lower exposure without any loss of earnings, seniority, or other employment rights or benefits. The purpose of this program is to cease further lead absorption and allow your body to naturally excrete lead which has previously been absorbed. Temporary medical removal can result from an elevated blood lead level, or a medical opinion. Up to 18 months of protection is provided as a result of either form of removal. The vast majority of removed workers, however, will return to their former jobs long before this eighteen month period expires. The Standard contains special provisions to deal with the extraordinary but possible case where a longterm worker's blood lead level does not adequately decline during eighteen months of removal.

During the first year of the Standard, if your blood lead level is 80 µg/100g or above you must be removed from any exposure where your air lead level without a respirator would be 100 µg/m^3 or above. If you are removed from your normal job you may not be returned until your blood lead level declines to at least 60 µg/100g. These criteria for removal and return will change according to the following schedule:

	Removal blood lead (µg/100g)	Air lead (µg/m^3)	Return blood lead (µg/100g)
After Mar. 1, 1980	70 and above	50 and above	At or below 50
After Mar. 1, 1981	60 and above	30 and above	At or below 40
After Mar. 1, 1983	50 and above averaged over six months	30 and above	Do

You may also be removed from exposure even if your blood lead levels are below these criteria if a final medical determination indicates that you temporarily need reduced lead exposure for medical reasons. If the physician who is implementing your employers medical program makes a final written opinion recommending your removal or other special protective measures, your employer must implement the physician's recommendation. If you are removed in this manner, you may only be returned when the doctor indicates that it is safe for you to do so.

The Standard does not give specific instructions dealing with what an employer must do with a removed worker. Your job assignment upon removal is a matter for you, your employer and your union (if any) to work out consistent with existing procedures for job assignments. Each removal must be accomplished in a manner consistent with existing collective bargaining relationships. Your employer is given broad discretion to implement temporary removals so long as no attempt is made to override existing agreements. Similarly, a removed worker is provided no right to veto an employer's choice which satisfies the Standard.

In most cases, employers will likely transfer removed employees to other jobs with sufficiently low lead exposure. Alternatively, a worker's hours may be reduced so that the time weighted average exposure is reduced, or he or she may be temporarily laid off if no other alternative is feasible.

In all of these situations, MRP benefits must be provided during the period of removal—i.e., you continue to receive the same earnings, seniority, and other rights and benefits you would have had if you had not been removed. Earnings includes more than just your base wage; it includes overtime, shift differentials, incentives, and other compensation you would have earned if you had not been removed. During the period of removal you must also be provided with appropriate follow-up medical surveillance. If you were removed because your blood lead level was too high, you must be provided with a monthly blood test. If a medical opinion caused your removal, you must be provided medical tests or examinations that the doctor believes to be appropriate. If you do not participate in this follow up medical surveillance, you may lose your eligibility for MRP benefits.

When you are medically eligible to return to your former job, your employer must return you to your "former job status." This means that you are entitled to the position, wages, benefits, etc., you would have had if you had not been removed. If you would still be in your old job if no removal had occurred that is where you go back. If not, you are returned consistent with whatever job assignment discretion your employer would have had if no removal had occurred. MRP only seeks to maintain your rights, not expand them or diminish them.

If you are removed under MRP and you are also eligible for worker compensation or other compensation for lost wages, your employer's MRP benefits obligation is reduced by the amount that you actually receive from these other sources. This is also true if you obtain other employment during the time you are laid off with MRP benefits.

The Standard also covers situations where an employer voluntarily removes a worker from exposure to lead due to the effects of lead on the employee's medical condition, even though the Standard does not require removal. In these situations MRP benefits must still be provided as though the Standard required removal. Finally, it is important to note that in all cases where removal is required, respirators cannot be used as a substitute. Respirators may be used before removal becomes necessary, but not as an alternative to a transfer to a low exposure job, or to a lay-off with MRP benefits.

X. Employee Information and Training—Paragraph (l)

Your employer is required to provide an information and training program for all employees exposed to lead above the action level or who may suffer skin or eye irritation from lead. This program must inform these employees of the specific hazards associated with their work environment, protective measures which can be taken, the danger of lead to their bodies (including their reproductive systems), and their rights under the Standard. In addition your employer must make readily available to all employees, including those exposed below the action level, a copy of the Standard and its Appendices and must distribute to all employees any materials provided to the employer by the Occupational Safety and Health Administration (OSHA).

Your employer is required to complete this training program for all employees by August 28, 1979. After this date, all new employees must be trained prior to initial assignment to areas where there is a possibility of exposure over the action level.

This training program must also be provided at least annually thereafter.

XI. Signs—Paragraph (m)

The Standard requires that the following warning sign be posted in the work areas when the exposure to lead exceeds the PEL::

DANGER
LEAD
MAY DAMAGE FERTILITY OR THE UNBORN CHILD
CAUSES DAMAGE TO THE CENTRAL NERVOUS SYSTEM
DO NOT EAT, DRINK OR SMOKE IN THIS AREA

However, prior to June 1, 2016, employers may use the following legend in lieu of that specified above:

WARNING
LEAD WORK AREA
POISON
NO SMOKING OR EATING

XII. Recordkeeping—Paragraph (n)

Your employer is required to keep all records of exposure monitoring for airborne lead. These records must include the name and job classification of employees measured, details of the sampling and analytic techniques, the results of this sampling, and the type of respiratory protection being worn by the person sampled. Your employer is also required to keep all records of biological monitoring and medical examination results. These must include the names of the employees, the physician's written opinion, and a copy of the results of the examination. All of the above kinds of records must be kept for 40 years, or for at least 20 years after your termination of employment, whichever is longer.

Recordkeeping is also required if you are temporarily removed from your job under the medical removal protection program. This record must include your name and social security number, the date of your removal and return, how the removal was or is being accomplished, and whether or not the reason for the removal was an elevated blood lead level. Your employer is required to keep each medical removal record only for as long as the duration of an employee's employment.

The Standard requires that if you request to see or copy environmental monitoring, blood lead level monitoring, or medical removal records, they must be made available to you or to a representative that you authorize. Your union also has access to these records. Medical records other than PbB's must also be provided upon request to you, to your physician or to any other person whom you may specifically designate. Your union does not have access to your personal medical records unless you authorize their access.

XIII. Observations of Monitoring—Paragraph (o)

When air monitoring for lead is performed at your workplace as required by this Standard, your employer must allow you or someone you designate to act as an observer of the monitoring. Observers are entitled to an explanation of the measurement procedure, and to record the results obtained. Since results will not normally be available at the time of the monitoring, observers are entitled to record or receive the results of the monitoring when returned by the laboratory. Your employer is required to provide the observer with any personal protective devices required to be worn by employees working in the area that is being monitored. The employer must require the observer to wear all such equipment and to comply with all other applicable safety and health procedures.

XIV. For Additional Information

A. Copies of the Standard and explanatory material may be obtained by writing or calling the OSHA Docket Office, U.S. Department of Labor, room N2634, 200 Constitution Avenue, N.W., Washington, DC 20210. Telephone: (202) 219–7894.

1. The standard and summary of the statement of reasons (preamble),Federal Register,Volume 43, pp. 52952–53014, November 14, 1978.
2. The full statement of reasons (preamble) Federal Register, vol. 43, pp. 54354–54509, November 21, 1978.
3. Partial Administrative Stay and Corrections to the standard, (44 FR 5446–5448) January 26, 1979.
4. Notice of the Partial Judicial Stay (44 FR 14554–14555) March 13, 1979.
5. Corrections to the preamble, Federal Register, vol. 44, pp. 20680–20681, April 6, 1979.
6. Additional correction to the preamble concerning the construction industry, Federal Register, vol. 44, p. 50338, August 28, 1979.
7. Appendices to the standard (Appendices A, B, C), Federal Register, Vol. 44, pp. 60980–60995, October 23, 1979.
8. Corrections to Appendices, Federal Register, Vol. 44, 68828, November 30, 1979.
9. Revision to the standard and an additional Appendix (Appendix D), Federal Register, Vol. 47, pp. 51117–51119, November 12, 1982.
10. Notice of reopening of lead rulemaking for nine remand industry sectors, Federal Register, vol. 53, pp. 11511–11513, April 7, 1988.
11. Statement of reasons, Federal Register, vol. 54, pp. 29142–29275, July 11, 1989.
12. Statement of reasons, Federal Register, vol. 55, pp. 3146–3167, January 30, 1990.
13. Correction to Appendix B, Federal Register, vol. 55, pp. 4998–4999, February 13, 1991.
14. Correction to Appendices, Federal Register, vol. 56, p. 24686, May 31, 1991.

B. Additional information about the Standard, its enforcement, and your employer's compliance can be obtained from the nearest OSHA Area Office listed in your telephone directory under United States Government/Department of Labor.

§1910.1025 Appendix C Medical surveillance guidelines

The purpose of this document is to outline the medical surveillance provisions of the Standard for inorganic lead, and to provide further information to the physician regarding the examination and evaluation of workers exposed to inorganic lead.

Section 1 provides a detailed description of the monitoring procedure including the required frequency of blood testing for exposed workers, provisions for medical removal protection (MRP), the recommended right of the employee to a second medical opinion, and notification and recordkeeping requirements of the employer. A discussion of the requirements for respirator use and respirator monitoring and OSHA's position on prophylactic chelation therapy are also included in this Section.

Section 2 discusses the toxic effects and clinical manifestations of lead poisoning and effects of lead intoxication on enzymatic pathways in heme synthesis. The adverse effects on both male and female reproductive capacity and on the fetus are also discussed.

Section 3 outlines the recommended medical evaluation of the worker exposed to inorganic lead including details of the medical history, physical examination, and recommended laboratory tests, which are based on the toxic effects of lead as discussed in Section 2.

Section 4 provides detailed information concerning the laboratory tests available for the monitoring of exposed workers. Included also is a discussion of the relative value of each test and the limitations and precautions which are necessary in the interpretation of the laboratory results.

Introduction

The primary purpose of the Occupational Safety and Health Act of 1970 is to assure, so far as possible, safe and healthful working conditions for every working man and woman. The Occupational Health Standard for inorganic lead[1] was promulgated to protect workers exposed to inorganic lead including metallic lead, all inorganic lead compounds and organic lead soaps.

Under this final Standard in effect as of March 1, 1979, occupational exposure to inorganic lead is to be limited to 50 µg/m^3 (micrograms per cubic meter) based on an 8 hour time-weighted average (TWA). This level of exposure eventually must be achieved through a combination of engineering, work practice and other administrative controls. Periods of time ranging from 1 to 10 years are provided for different industries to implement these controls. The schedule which is based on individual industry considerations is given in Table 1. Until these controls are in place, respirators must be used to meet the 50 µg/m^3 exposure limit.

The Standard also provides for a program of biological monitoring and medical surveillance for all employees exposed to levels of inorganic lead above the action level of 30 µg/m^3 (TWA) for more than 30 days per year.

Table 1

Permissible airborne lead levels by industry (µg/m^3)[1]	Effective date					
	March 1, 1979	March 1, 1980	March 1, 1981	March 1, 1982	March 1, 1984	March 1, 1989 (final)
1. Primary lead production	200	200	200	100	100	50
2. Secondary lead production	200	200	200	100	50	50
3. Lead-acid battery manufacturing	200	200	100	100	50	50
4. Nonferrous foundries	200	100	100	100	50	50
5. Lead pigment manufacturing	200	200	200	100	50	50
6. All other industries	200	50	50	50	50	50

[1] Airborne levels to be achieved without reliance on respirator protection through a combination of engineering, work practice and other administrative controls. While these controls are being implemented respirators must be used to meet the 50 µg/m^3 exposure limit.

I. Medical Surveillance and Monitoring Requirements for Workers Exposed to Inorganic Lead

Under the Occupational Health Standard for inorganic lead, a program of biological monitoring and medical surveillance is to be made available to all employees exposed to lead above the action level of 30 µg/m^3 TWA for more than 30 days each year. This program consists of periodic blood sampling and medical evaluation to be performed on a schedule which is defined by previous laboratory results, worker complaints or concerns, and the clinical assessment of the examining physician.

Under this program, the blood lead level of all employees who are exposed to lead above the action level of 30 µg/m^3 is to be determined at least every six months. The frequency is increased to every two months for employees whose last blood lead level was between 40 µg/100g whole blood and the level requiring employee medical removal to be discussed below. For employees who are removed from exposure to lead due to an elevated blood lead, a new blood lead level must be measured monthly. A zinc protoporphyrin (ZPP) is required on each occasion that a blood lead level measurement is made.

An annual medical examination and consultation performed under the guidelines discussed in Section 3 is to be made available to each employee for whom a blood test conducted at any time during the preceding 12 months indicated a blood lead level at or above 40 µg/100g. Also, an examination is to be given to all employees prior to their assignment to an area in which airborne lead concentrations reach or exceed the action level.

In addition, a medical examination must be provided as soon as possible after notification by an employee that the employee has developed signs or symptoms commonly associated with lead intoxication, that the employee desires medical advice regarding lead exposure and the ability to procreate a healthy child, or that the employee has demonstrated difficulty in breathing during a respirator fitting test or during respirator use. An examination is also to be made available to each employee removed from exposure to lead due to a risk of sustaining material impairment to health, or otherwise limited or specially protected pursuant to medical recommendations.

Results of biological monitoring or the recommendations of an examining physician may necessitate removal of an employee from further lead exposure pursuant to the Standard's medical removal protection (MRP) program. The object of the MRP program is to provide temporary medical removal to workers either with substantially elevated blood lead levels or otherwise at risk of sustaining material health impairment from continued substantial exposure to lead. The following guidelines which are summarized in Table 2 were created under the Standard for the temporary removal of an exposed employee and his or her subsequent return to work in an exposure area.

[1] The term inorganic lead used throughout the medical surveillance Appendices is meant to be synonymous with the definition of lead set forth in the Standard.

Table 2

	Effective date				
	March 1, 1979	March 1, 1980	March 1, 1981	March 1, 1982	March 1, 1983 (final)
A. Blood lead level requiring employee medical removal. (Level must be confirmed with second follow-up blood lead level within two weeks of first report.)	≥ 80 µg/100g	≥ 70 µg/100g	≥ 60 µg/100g	≥ 60 µg/100g	≥ 60µg/100g or average of last three blood samples or all blood samples over previous 6 months (whichever is over a longer time period) is 50 µg/100g or greater unless last blood sample is 40 µg/100g or less.
B. Frequency which employees exposed to action level of lead (30 µg/m³ TWA) must have blood lead level checked (ZPP is also required in each occasion that a blood lead is obtained.):					
1. Last blood lead level less than 40 µg/100g.	Every 6 months	Every 6 months	Every 6 months	Every 6 months	Every 6 months
2. Last blood lead level between 40 µg/100g and level requiring medical removal (see A above).	Every 2 months	Every 2 months	Every 2 months	Every 2 months	Every 2 months
3. Employees removed from exposure to lead because of an elevated blood lead level.	Every 1 month	Every 1 month	Every 1 month	Every 1 month	Every 1 month
C. Permissible airborne exposure limit for workers removed from work due to an elevated blood lead level (without regard to respirator protection).	100 µg/m³ 8 hr TWA	50 µg/m³ 8 hr TWA	30 µg/m³ 8 hr TWA	30 µg/m³ 8 hr TWA	30 µg/m³ 8 hr TWA
D. Blood lead level confirmed with a second blood analysis, at which employee may return to work. Permissible exposure without regard to respirator protection is listed by industry in Table I.	·60 µg/100g	·50 µg/100g	·40 µg/100g	·40 µg/100g	·40 µg/100g

Note: When medical opinion indicates that an employee is at risk of material impairment from exposure to lead, the physician can remove an employee from exposures exceeding the action level (or less) or recommend special protective measures as deemed appropriate and necessary. Medical monitoring during the medical removal period can be more stringent than noted in the table above if the physician so specifies. Return to work or removal of limitations and special protections is permitted when the physician indicates that the worker is no longer at risk of material impairment.

Under the Standard's ultimate worker removal criteria, a worker is to be removed from any work having any eight hour TWA exposure to lead of 30 µg/m³ or more whenever either of the following circumstances apply: (1) a blood lead level of 60 µg/100g or greater is obtained and confirmed by a second follow-up blood lead level performed within two weeks after the employer receives the results of the first blood sampling test, or (2) the average of the previous three blood lead determinations or the average of all blood lead determinations conducted during the previous six months, whichever encompasses the longest time period, equals or exceeds 50 µg/100g, unless the last blood sample indicates a blood lead level at or below 40 µg/100g in which case the employee need not be removed. Medical removal is to continue until two consecutive blood lead levels are 40 µg/100g or less.

During the first two years that the ultimate removal criteria are being phased in, the return criteria have been set to assure that a worker's blood lead level has substantially declined during the period of removal. From March 1, 1979 to March 1, 1980, the blood lead level requiring employee medical removal is 80 µg/100g. Workers found to have a confirmed blood lead at this level or greater need only be removed from work having a daily 8 hour TWA exposure to lead at or above 100 µg/m³. Workers so removed are to be returned to work when their blood lead levels are at or below 60 µg/100g of whole blood. From March 1, 1980 to March 1, 1981, the blood lead level requiring medical removal is 70 µg/100g. During this period workers need only be removed from jobs having a daily 8 hour TWA exposure to lead at or above 50 µg/m³ and are to be returned to work when a level of 50 µg/100g is achieved. Beginning March 1, 1981, return depends on a worker's blood lead level declining to 40 µg/100g of whole blood.

As part of the Standard, the employer is required to notify in writing each employee whose blood lead level exceeds 40 µg/100g. In addition each such employee is to be informed that the Standard requires medical removal with MRP benefits, discussed below, when an employee's blood lead level exceeds the above defined limits.

In addition to the above blood lead level criteria, temporary worker removal may also take place as a result of medical determinations and recommendations. Written medical opinions must be prepared after each examination pursuant to the Standard. If the examining physician includes a medical finding, determination or opinion that the employee has a medical condition which places the employee at increased risk of material health impairment from exposure to lead, then the employee must be removed from exposure to lead at or above the action level. Alternatively, if the examining physician recommends special protective measures for an employee (e.g., use of a powered air purifying respirator) or recommends limitations on an employee's exposure to lead, then the employer must implement these recommendations. Recommendations may be more stringent than the specific provisions of the Standard. The examining physician, therefore, is given broad flexibility to tailor special protective procedures to the needs of individual employees. This flexibility extends to the evaluation and management of pregnant workers and male and female workers who are planning to raise children. Based on the history, physical examination, and laboratory studies, the physician might recommend special protective measures or medical removal for an employee who is pregnant or who is planning to conceive a child when, in the physician's judgment, continued exposure to lead at the current job would pose a significant risk. The return of the employee to his or her former job status, or the removal of special protections or limitations, depends upon the examining physician determining that the employee is no longer at increased risk of material impairment or that special measures are no longer needed.

During the period of any form of special protection or removal, the employer must maintain the worker's earnings, seniority, and other employment rights and benefits (as though the worker had not been removed) for a period of up to 18 months. This economic protection will maximize meaningful worker participation in the medical surveillance program, and is appropriate as part of the employer's overall obligation to provide a safe and healthful workplace. The provisions of MRP benefits during the employee's removal period may, however, be conditioned upon participation in medical surveillance.

On rare occasions, an employee's blood lead level may not acceptably decline within 18 months of removal. This situation will arise only in unusual circumstances, thus the Standard relies on an individual medical examination to determine how to protect such an employee. This medical determination is to be based on both laboratory values, including lead levels, zinc protoporphyrin levels, blood counts, and other tests felt to be warranted, as well as the physician's judgment that any symptoms or findings on physical examination are a result of lead toxicity. The medical determination may be that the employee is incapable of ever safely returning to his or her former job status. The medical determination may provide additional removal time past 18 months for some employees or specify special protective measures to be implemented.

The lead Standard provides for a multiple physician review in cases where the employee wishes a second opinion concerning potential lead poisoning or toxicity. If an employee wishes a second opinion, he or she can make an appointment with a physician of his or her choice. This second physician will review the findings, recommendations or determinations of the first physician and conduct any examinations, consultations or tests deemed necessary in an attempt to make a final medical determination. If the first and second physicians do not agree in their assessment they must try to resolve their differences. If they cannot reach an agreement then they must designate a third physician to resolve the dispute.

The employer must provide examining and consulting physicians with the following specific information: a copy of the lead regulations and all appendices, a description of the employee's duties as related to exposure, the exposure level to lead and any other toxic substances (if applicable), a description of personal protective equipment used, blood lead levels, and all prior written medical opinions regarding the employee in the employer's possession or control. The employer must also obtain from the physician and provide the employee with a written medical opinion containing blood lead levels, the physicians's opinion as to whether the employee is at risk of material impairment to health, any recommended protective measures for the employee if further exposure is permitted, as well as any recommended limitations upon an employee's use of respirators.

Employers must instruct each physician not to reveal to the employer in writing or in any other way his or her findings, laboratory results, or diagnoses which are felt to be unrelated to occupational lead exposure. They must also instruct each physician to advise the employee of any occupationally or non-occupationally related medical condition requiring further treatment or evaluation.

The Standard provides for the use of respirators where engineering and other primary controls have not been fully implemented. However, the use of respirator protection shall not be used in lieu of temporary medical removal due to elevated blood lead levels or findings that an employee is at risk of material health impairment. This is based on the numerous inadequacies of respirators including skin rash where the facepiece makes contact with the skin, unacceptable stress to breathing in some workers with underlying cardiopulmonary impairment, difficulty in providing adequate fit, the tendency for respirators to create additional hazards by interfering with vision, hearing, and mobility, and the difficulties of assuring the maximum effectiveness of a complicated work practice program involving respirators. Respirators do, however, serve a useful function where engineering and work practice controls are inadequate by providing supplementary, interim, or short-term protection, provided they are properly selected for the environment in which the employee will be working, properly fitted to the employee, maintained and cleaned periodically, and worn by the employee when required.

In its final Standard on occupational exposure to inorganic lead, OSHA has prohibited prophylactic chelation. Diagnostic and therapeutic chelation are permitted only under the supervision of a licensed physician with appropriate medical monitoring in an acceptable clinical setting. The decision to initiate chelation therapy must be made on an individual basis and take into account the severity of symptoms felt to be a result of lead toxicity along with blood lead levels, ZPP levels, and other laboratory tests as appropriate. EDTA and penicillamine which are the primary chelating agents used in the therapy of occupational lead poisoning have significant potential side effects and their use must be justified on the basis of expected benefits to the worker. Unless frank and severe symptoms are present, therapeutic chelation is not recommended given the opportunity to remove a worker from exposure and allow the body to naturally excrete accumulated lead. As a diagnostic aid, the chelation mobilization test using CA-EDTA has limited applicability. According to some investigators, the test can differentiate between lead-induced and other nephropathies. The test may also provide an estimation of the mobile fraction of the total body lead burden.

Employers are required to assure that accurate records are maintained on exposure monitoring, medical surveillance, and medical removal for each employee. Exposure monitoring and medical surveillance records must be kept for 40 years or the duration of employment plus 20 years, whichever is longer, while medical removal records must be maintained for the duration of employment. All records required under the Standard must be made available upon request to the Assistant Secretary of Labor for Occupational Safety and Health and the Director of the National Institute for Occupational Safety and Health. Employers must also make environmental and biological monitoring and medical removal records available to affected employees and to former employees or their authorized employee representatives. Employees or their specifically designated representatives have access to their entire medical surveillance records.

In addition, the Standard requires that the employer inform all workers exposed to lead at or above the action level of the provisions of the Standard and all its Appendices, the purpose and description of medical surveillance and provisions for medical removal protection if temporary removal is required. An understanding of the potential health effects of lead exposure by all exposed employees along with full understanding of their rights under the lead Standard is essential for an effective monitoring program.

II. Adverse Health Effects of Inorganic Lead

Although the toxicity of lead has been known for 2,000 years, the knowledge of the complex relationship between lead exposure and human response is still being refined. Significant research into the toxic properties of lead continues throughout the world, and it should be anticipated that our understanding of thresholds of effects and margins of safety will be improved in future years. The provisions of the lead Standard are founded on two prime medical judgments: first, the prevention of adverse health effects from exposure to lead throughout a working lifetime requires that worker blood lead levels be maintained at or below 40 µg/100g and second, the blood lead levels of workers, male or female, who intend to parent in the near future should be maintained below 30 µg/100g to minimize adverse reproductive health effects to the parents and developing fetus. The adverse effects of lead on reproduction are being actively researched and OSHA encourages the physician to remain abreast of recent developments in the area to best advise pregnant workers or workers planning to conceive children.

The spectrum of health effects caused by lead exposure can be subdivided into five developmental stages: normal, physiological changes of uncertain significance, pathophysiological changes, overt symptoms (morbidity), and mortality. Within this process there are no sharp distinctions, but rather a continuum of effects. Boundaries between categories overlap due to the wide variation of individual responses and exposures in the working population. OSHA's development of the lead Standard focused on pathophysiological changes as well as later stages of disease.

1. Heme Synthesis Inhibition The earliest demonstrated effect of lead involves its ability to inhibit at least two enzymes of the heme synthesis pathway at very low blood levels. Inhibition of delta aminolevulinic acid dehydrase (ALA-D) which catalyzes the conversion of delta-aminolevulinic acid (ALA) to protoporphyrin is observed at a blood lead level below 20 µg/100g whole blood. At a blood lead level of 40 ug/100g, more than 20% of the population would have 70% inhibition of ALA-D. There is an exponential increase in ALA excretion at blood lead levels greater than 40 µg/100g.

Another enzyme, ferrochelatase, is also inhibited at low blood lead levels. Inhibition of ferrochelatase leads to increased free erythrocyte protoporphyrin (FEP) in the blood which can then bind to zinc to yield zinc protoporphyrin. At a blood lead level of 50 µg/100g or greater, nearly 100% of the population will have an increase in FEP. There is also an exponential relationship between blood lead levels greater than 40 µg/100g and the associated ZPP level, which has led to the development of the ZPP screening test for lead exposure.

While the significance of these effects is subject to debate, it is OSHA's position that these enzyme disturbances are early stages of a disease process which may eventually result in the clinical symptoms of lead poisoning. Whether or not the effects do progress to the later stages of clinical disease, disruption of these enzyme processes over a working lifetime is considered to be a material impairment of health.

One of the eventual results of lead-induced inhibition of enzymes in the heme synthesis pathway is anemia which can be asymptomatic if mild but associated with a wide array of symptoms including dizziness, fatigue, and tachycardia when more severe. Studies have indicated that lead levels as low as 50 µg/100g can be associated with a definite decreased hemoglobin, although most cases of lead-induced anemia, as well as shortened red-cell survival times, occur at lead levels exceeding 80 µg/100g. Inhibited hemoglobin synthesis is more common in chronic cases whereas shortened erythrocyte life span is more common in acute cases.

In lead-induced anemias, there is usually a reticulocytosis along with the presence of basophilic stippling, and ringed sideroblasts, although none of the above are pathognomonic for lead-induced anemia.

2. Neurological Effects Inorganic lead has been found to have toxic effects on both the central and peripheral nervous systems. The earliest stages of lead-induced central nervous system effects first manifest themselves in the form of behavioral disturbances and central nervous system symptoms including irritability, restlessness, insomnia and other sleep disturbances, fatigue, vertigo, headache, poor memory, tremor, depression, and apathy. With more severe exposure, symptoms can progress to drowsiness, stupor, hallucinations, delerium, convulsions and coma.

The most severe and acute form of lead poisoning which usually follows ingestion or inhalation of large amounts of lead is acute encephalopathy which may arise precipitously with the onset of intractable seizures, coma, cardiorespiratory arrest, and death within 48 hours.

While there is disagreement about what exposure levels are needed to produce the earliest symptoms, most experts agree that symptoms definitely can occur at blood lead levels of 60 µg/100g whole blood and therefore recommend a 40 µg/100g maximum. The central nervous system effects frequently are not reversible following discontinued exposure or chelation therapy and when improvement does occur, it is almost always only partial.

The peripheral neuropathy resulting from lead exposure characteristically involves only motor function with minimal sensory damage and has a marked predilection for the extensor muscles of the most active extremity. The peripheral neuropathy can occur with varying degrees of severity. The earliest and mildest form which can be detected in workers with blood lead levels as low as 50 µg/100g is manifested by slowing of motor nerve conduction velocity often without clinical symptoms. With progression of the neuropathy there is development of painless extensor muscle weakness usually involving the extensor muscles of the fingers and hand in the most active upper extremity, followed in severe cases by wrist drop or, much less commonly, foot drop.

In addition to slowing of nerve conduction, electromyographical studies in patients with blood lead levels greater than 50 µg/100g have demonstrated a decrease in the number of acting motor unit potentials, an increase in the duration of motor unit potentials, and spontaneous pathological activity including fibrillations and fasciculations. Whether these effects occur at levels of 40 µg/100g is undetermined.

While the peripheral neuropathies can occasionally be reversed with therapy, again such recovery is not assured particularly in the more severe neuropathies and often improvement is only partial. The lack of reversibility is felt to be due in part to segmental demyelination.

3. Gastrointestinal Lead may also affect the gastrointestinal system producing abdominal colic or diffuse abdominal pain, constipation, obstipation, diarrhea, anorexia, nausea and vomiting. Lead colic rarely develops at blood lead levels below 80 µg/100g.

4. Renal Renal toxicity represents one of the most serious health effects of lead poisoning. In the early stages of disease nuclear inclusion bodies can frequently be identified in proximal renal tubular cells. Renal function remains normal and the changes in this stage are probably reversible. With more advanced disease there is progressive interstitial fibrosis and impaired renal function. Eventually extensive interstitial fibrosis ensues with sclerotic glomeruli and dilated and atrophied proximal tubules; all represent end stage kidney disease. Azotemia can be progressive, eventually resulting in frank uremia necessitating dialysis. There is occasionally associated hypertension and hyperuricemia with or without gout.

Early kidney disease is difficult to detect. The urinalysis is normal in early lead nephropathy and the blood urea nitrogen and serum creatinine increase only when two-thirds of kidney function is lost. Measurement of creatinine clearance can often detect earlier disease as can other methods of measurement of glomerular filtration rate. An abnormal Ca-EDTA mobilization test has been used to differentiate between lead-induced and other nephropathies, but this procedure is not widely accepted. A form of Fanconi syndrome with aminoaciduria, glycosuria, and hyperphosphaturia indicating severe injury to the proximal renal tubules is occasionally seen in children.

5. Reproductive effects Exposure to lead can have serious effects on reproductive function in both males and females. In male workers exposed to lead there can be a decrease in sexual drive, impotence, decreased ability to produce healthy sperm, and sterility. Malformed sperm (teratospermia), decreased number of sperm (hypospermia), and sperm with decreased motility (asthenospermia) can all occur. Teratospermia has been noted at mean blood lead levels of 53 µg/100g and hypospermia and asthenospermia at 41 µg/100g. Furthermore, there appears to be a dose-response relationship for teratospermia in lead exposed workers.

Women exposed to lead may experience menstrual disturbances including dysmenorrhea, menorrhagia and amenorrhea. Following exposure to lead, women have a higher frequency of sterility, premature births, spontaneous miscarriages, and stillbirths.

Germ cells can be affected by lead and cause genetic damage in the egg or sperm cells before conception and result in failure to implant, miscarriage, stillbirth, or birth defects.

Infants of mothers with lead poisoning have a higher mortality during the first year and suffer from lowered birth weights, slower growth, and nervous system disorders.

Lead can pass through the placental barrier and lead levels in the mother's blood are comparable to concentrations of lead in the umbilical cord at birth. Transplacental passage becomes detectable at 12–14 weeks of gestation and increases until birth.

There is little direct data on damage to the fetus from exposure to lead but it is generally assumed that the fetus and newborn would be at least as susceptible to neurological damage as young children. Blood lead levels of 50–60 µg/100g in children can cause significant neurobehavioral impairments and there is evidence of hyperactivity at blood levels as low as 25 µg/100g. Given the overall body of literature concerning the adverse health effects of lead in children, OSHA feels that the blood lead level in children should be maintained below 30 µg/100g with a population mean of 15 µg/100g. Blood lead levels in the fetus and newborn likewise should not exceed 30 µg/100g.

Because of lead's ability to pass through the placental barrier and also because of the demonstrated adverse effects of lead on reproductive function in both the male and female as well as the risk of genetic damage of lead on both the ovum and sperm, OSHA recommends a 30 µg/100g maximum permissible blood lead level in both males and females who wish to bear children.

6. Other toxic effects Debate and research continue on the effects of lead on the human body. Hypertension has frequently been noted in occupationally exposed individuals although it is difficult to assess whether this is due to lead's adverse effects on the kidney or if some other mechanism is involved. Vascular and electrocardiographic changes have been detected but have not been well characterized. Lead is thought to impair thyroid function and interfere with the pituitary-adrenal axis, but again these effects have not been well defined.

III. Medical Evaluation

The most important principle in evaluating a worker for any occupational disease including lead poisoning is a high index of suspicion on the part of the examining physician. As discussed in Section 2, lead can affect numerous organ systems and produce a wide array of signs and symptoms, most of which are non-specific and subtle in nature at least in the early stages of disease. Unless serious concern for lead toxicity is present, many of the early clues to diagnosis may easily be overlooked.

The crucial initial step in the medical evaluation is recognizing that a worker's employment can result in exposure to lead. The worker will frequently be able to define exposures to lead and lead containing materials but often will not volunteer this information unless specifically asked. In other situations the worker may not know of any exposures to lead but the suspicion might be raised on the part of the physician because of the industry or occupation of the worker. Potential occupational exposure to lead and its compounds occur in at least 120 occupations, including lead smelting, the manufacture of lead storage batteries, the manufacture of lead pigments and products containing pigments, solder manufacture, shipbuilding and ship repair, auto manufacturing, construction, and painting.

Once the possibility for lead exposure is raised, the focus can then be directed toward eliciting information from the medical history, physical exam, and finally from laboratory data to evaluate the worker for potential lead toxicity.

A complete and detailed work history is important in the initial evaluation. A listing of all previous employment with information on work processes, exposure to fumes or dust, known exposures to lead or other toxic substances, respiratory protection used, and previous medical surveillance should all be included in the worker's record. Where exposure to lead is suspected, information concerning on-the-job personal hygiene, smoking or eating habits in work areas, laundry procedures, and use of any protective clothing or respiratory protection equipment should be noted. A complete work history is essential in the medical evaluation of a worker with suspected lead toxicity, especially when long term effects such as neurotoxicity and nephrotoxicity are considered.

The medical history is also of fundamental importance and should include a listing of all past and current medical conditions, current medications including proprietary drug intake, previous surgeries and hospitalizations, allergies, smoking history, alcohol consumption, and also non-occupational lead exposures such as hobbies (hunting, riflery). Also known childhood exposures should be elicited. Any previous history of hematological, neurological, gastrointestinal, renal, psychological, gynecological, genetic, or reproductive problems should be specifically noted.

A careful and complete review must be performed to assess both recognized complaints and subtle or slowly acquired symptoms which the worker might not appreciate as being significant. The review of symptoms should include the following:

- General—weight loss, fatigue, decreased appetite;
- Head, Eyes, Ears, Nose, Throat (HEENT)—headaches, visual disturbances or decreased visual acuity, hearing deficits or tinnitus, pigmentation of the oral mucosa, or metallic taste in mouth;
- Cardio-pulmonary—shortness of breath, cough, chest pains, palpitations, or orthopnea;
- Gastrointestinal—nausea, vomiting, heartburn, abdominal pain, constipation or diarrhea;
- Neurologic—irritability, insomnia, weakness (fatigue), dizziness, loss of memory, confusion, hallucinations, incoordination, ataxia, decreased strength in hands or feet, disturbances in gait, difficulty in climbing stairs, or seizures;
- Hematologic—pallor, easy fatigability, abnormal blood loss, melena;
- Reproductive (male and female and spouse where relevant)—history of infertility, impotence, loss of libido, abnormal menstrual periods, history of miscarriages, stillbirths, or children with birth defects; and
- Musculo-skeletal—muscle and joint pains.

The physical examination should emphasize the neurological, gastrointestinal, and cardiovascular systems. The worker's weight and blood pressure should be recorded and the oral mucosa checked for pigmentation characteristic of a possible Burtonian or lead line on the gingiva. It should be noted, however, that the lead line may not be present even in severe lead poisoning if good oral hygiene is practiced.

The presence of pallor on skin examination may indicate an anemia, which if severe might also be associated with a tachycardia. If an anemia is suspected, an active search for blood loss should be undertaken including potential blood loss through the gastrointestinal tract.

A complete neurological examination should include an adequate mental status evaluation including a search for behavioral and psychological disturbances, memory testing, evaluation for irritability, insomnia, hallucinations, and mental clouding. Gait and coordination should be examined along with close observation for tremor. A detailed evaluation of peripheral nerve function including careful sensory and motor function testing is warranted. Strength testing particularly of extensor muscle groups of all extremities is of fundamental importance.

Cranial nerve evaluation should also be included in the routine examination.

The abdominal examination should include auscultation for bowel sounds and abdominal bruits and palpation for organomegaly, masses, and diffuse abdominal tenderness.

Cardiovascular examination should evaluate possible early signs of congestive heart failure. Pulmonary status should be addressed particularly if respirator protection is contemplated.

As part of the medical evaluation, the lead Standard requires the following laboratory studies:

1. Blood lead level;
2. Hemoglobin and hematocrit determinations, red cell indices, and examination of the peripheral blood smear to evaluate red blood cell morphology;
3. Blood urea nitrogen;
4. Serum creatinine;
5. Routine urinalysis with microscopic examination; and
6. A zinc protoporphyrin level

In addition to the above, the physician is authorized to order any further laboratory or other tests which he or she deems necessary in accordance with sound medical practice. The evaluation must also include pregnancy testing or laboratory evaluation of male fertility if requested by the employee.

Additional tests which are probably not warranted on a routine basis but may be appropriate when blood lead and ZPP levels are equivocal include delta aminolevulinic acid and coproporphyrin concentrations in the urine, and dark-field illumination for detection of basophilic stippling in red blood cells.

If an anemia is detected further studies including a careful examination of the peripheral smear, reticulocyte count, stool for occult blood, serum iron, total iron binding capacity, bilirubin, and, if appropriate, vitamin B12 and folate may be of value in attempting to identify the cause of the anemia.

If a peripheral neuropathy is suspected, nerve conduction studies are warranted both for diagnosis and as a basis to monitor any therapy.

If renal disease is questioned, a 24 hour urine collection for creatinine clearance, protein, and electrolytes may be indicated. Elevated uric acid levels may result from lead-induced renal disease and a serum uric acid level might be performed.

An electrocardiogram and chest x-ray may be obtained as deemed appropriate.

Sophisticated and highly specialized testing should not be done routinely and where indicated should be under the direction of a specialist.

IV. Laboratory Evaluation

The blood lead level at present remains the single most important test to monitor lead exposure and is the test used in the medical surveillance program under the lead Standard to guide employee medical removal. The ZPP has several advantages over the blood lead level. Because of its relatively recent development and the lack of extensive data concerning its interpretation, the ZPP currently remains an ancillary test.

This section will discuss the blood lead level and ZPP in detail and will outline their relative advantages and disadvantages. Other blood tests currently available to evaluate lead exposure will also be reviewed.

The blood lead level is a good index of current or recent lead absorption when there is no anemia present and when the worker has not taken any chelating agents. However, blood lead levels along with urinary lead levels do not necessarily indicate the total body burden of lead and are not adequate measures of past exposure. One reason for this is that lead has a high affinity for bone and up to 90% of the body's total lead is deposited there. A very important component of the total lead body burden is lead in soft tissue (liver, kidney, and brain). This fraction of the lead body burden, the biologically active lead, is not entirely reflected by blood lead levels since it is a function of the dynamics of lead absorption, distribution, deposition in bone and excretion. Following discontinuation of exposure to lead, the excess body burden is only slowly mobilized from bone and other relatively stable body stores and excreted. Consequently, a high blood lead level may only represent recent heavy exposure to lead without a significant total body excess and likewise a low blood lead level does not exclude an elevated total body burden of lead.

Also due to its correlation with recent exposures, the blood lead level may vary considerably over short time intervals.

To minimize laboratory error and erroneous results due to contamination, blood specimens must be carefully collected after thorough cleaning of the skin with appropriate methods using lead-free blood containers and analyzed by a reliable laboratory. Under the Standard, samples must be analyzed in laboratories which are approved by the Center for Disease Control (CDC) or which have received satisfactory grades in proficiency testing by the CDC in the previous year. Analysis is to be made using atomic absorption spectrophotometry, anodic stripping voltammetry or any method which meets the accuracy requirements set forth by the Standard.

The determination of lead in urine is generally considered a less reliable monitoring technique than analysis of whole blood primarily due to individual variability in urinary excretion capacity as well as the technical difficulty of obtaining accurate 24 hour urine collections. In addition, workers with renal insufficiency, whether due to lead or some other cause, may have decreased lead clearance and consequently urine lead levels may underestimate the true lead burden. Therefore, urine lead levels should not be used as a routine test.

The zinc protoporphyrin test, unlike the blood lead determination, measures an adverse metabolic effect of lead and as such is a better indicator of lead toxicity than the level of blood lead itself. The level of ZPP reflects lead absorption over the preceding 3 to 4 months, and therefore is a better indicator of lead body burden. The ZPP requires more time than the blood lead to read significantly elevated levels; the return to normal after discontinuing lead exposure is also slower. Furthermore, the ZPP test is simpler, faster, and less expensive to perform and no contamination is possible. Many investigators believe it is the most reliable means of monitoring chronic lead absorption.

Zinc protoporphyrin results from the inhibition of the enzyme ferrochelatase which catalyzes the insertion of an iron molecule into the protoporphyrin molecule, which then becomes heme. If iron is not inserted into the molecule then zinc, having a greater affinity for protoporphyrin, takes the place of the iron, forming ZPP.

An elevation in the level of circulating ZPP may occur at blood lead levels as low as 20–30 μg/100g in some workers. Once the blood lead level has reached 40 μg/100g there is more marked rise in the ZPP value from its normal range of less than 100 μg/100 ml. Increases in blood lead levels beyond 40 μg/100g are associated with exponential increases in ZPP.

Whereas blood lead levels fluctuate over short time spans, ZPP levels remain relatively stable. ZPP is measured directly in red blood cells and is present for the cell's entire 120 day life-span. Therefore, the ZPP level in blood reflects the average ZPP production over the previous 3–4 months and consequently the average lead exposure during that time interval.

It is recommended that a hematocrit be determined whenever a confirmed ZPP of 50 μg/100 ml whole blood is obtained to rule out a significant underlying anemia. If the ZPP is in excess of 100 μg/100 ml and not associated with abnormal elevations in blood lead levels, the laboratory should be checked to be sure that blood leads were determined using atomic absorption spectrophotometry anodic stripping voltammetry, or any method which meets the accuracy requirements set forth by the Standard by a CDC approved laboratory which is experienced in lead level determinations. Repeat periodic blood lead studies should be obtained in all individuals with elevated ZPP levels to be certain that an associated elevated blood lead level has not been missed due to transient fluctuations in blood leads.

ZPP has a characteristic fluorescence spectrum with a peak at 594 nm which is detectable with a hematofluorimeter. The hematofluorimeter is accurate and portable and can provide on-site, instantaneous results for workers who can be frequently tested via a finger prick.

However, careful attention must be given to calibration and quality control procedures. Limited data on blood lead—ZPP correlations and the ZPP levels which are associated with the adverse health effects discussed in Section 2 are the major limitations of the test. Also it is difficult to correlate ZPP levels with environmental exposure and there is some variation of response with age and sex. Nevertheless, the ZPP promises to be an important diagnostic test for the early detection of lead toxicity and its value will increase as more data is collected regarding its relationship to other manifestations of lead poisoning.

Levels of delta-aminolevulinic acid (ALA) in the urine are also used as a measure of lead exposure. Increasing concentrations of ALA are believed to result from the inhibition of the enzyme delta-aminolevulinic acid dehydrase (ALA-D). Although the test is relatively easy to perform, inexpensive, and rapid, the disadvantages include variability in results, the necessity to collect a complete 24 hour urine sample which has a specific gravity greater than 1.010, and also the fact that ALA decomposes in the presence of light.

The pattern of porphyrin excretion in the urine can also be helpful in identifying lead intoxication. With lead poisoning, the urine concentrations of coproporphyrins I and II, porphobilinogen and uroporphyrin I rise. The most important increase, however, is that of coproporphyrin III; levels may exceed 5,000 μg/1 in the urine in lead poisoned individuals, but its correlation with blood lead levels and ZPP are not as good as those of ALA. Increases in urinary porphyrins are not diagnostic of lead toxicity and may be seen in porphyria, some liver diseases, and in patients with high reticulocyte counts.

Summary The Occupational Safety and Health Administration's Standard for inorganic lead places significant emphasis on the medical surveillance of all workers exposed to levels of inorganic lead above the action level of 30 $\mu g/m^3$ TWA. The physician has a fundamental role in this surveillance program, and in the operation of the medical removal protection program.

Even with adequate worker education on the adverse health effects of lead and appropriate training in work practices, personal hygiene and other control measures, the physician has a primary responsibility for evaluating potential lead toxicity in the worker. It is only through a careful and detailed medical and work history, a complete physical examination and appropriate laboratory testing that an accurate assessment can be made. Many of the adverse health effects of lead toxicity are either irreversible or only partially reversible and therefore early detection of disease is very important.

This document outlines the medical monitoring program as defined by the Occupational Safety and Health Standard for inorganic lead. It reviews the adverse health effects of lead poisoning and describes the important elements of the history and physical examinations as they relate to these adverse effects. Finally, the appropriate laboratory testing for evaluating lead exposure and toxicity is presented.

It is hoped that this review and discussion will give the physician a better understanding of the OSHA Standard with the ultimate goal of protecting the health and well-being of the worker exposed to lead under his or her care.

[43 FR 53007, Nov. 14, 1978]

Editorial Note: For Federal Register citations affecting §1910.1025 see the List of CFR Sections Affected, which appears in the Finding Aids section of the printed volume and at www.fdsys.gov.

§1910.1026 Chromium (VI)

(a) Scope

(a)(1) This Standard applies to occupational exposures to chromium (VI) in all forms and compounds in general industry, except:

(a)(2) Exposures that occur in the application of pesticides regulated by the Environmental Protection Agency or another Federal government agency (e.g., the treatment of wood with preservatives);

(a)(3) Exposures to portland cement; or

(a)(4) Where the employer has objective data demonstrating that a material containing chromium or a specific process, operation, or activity involving chromium cannot release dusts, fumes, or mists of chromium (VI) in concentrations at or above 0.5 μg/m^3 as an 8-hour time-weighted average (TWA) under any expected conditions of use.

(b) **Definitions** For the purposes of this Section the following definitions apply:

Action level means a concentration of airborne chromium (VI) of 2.5 micrograms per cubic meter of air (2.5 μgm/m^3) calculated as an 8-hour time-weighted average (TWA).

Assistant Secretary means the Assistant Secretary of Labor for Occupational Safety and Health, U.S. Department of Labor, or designee.

Chromium (VI) [hexavalent chromium or Cr(VI)] means chromium with a valence of positive six, in any form and in any compound.

Director means the Director of the National Institute for Occupational Safety and Health (NIOSH), U.S. Department of Health and Human Services, or designee.

Emergency means any occurrence that results, or is likely to result, in an uncontrolled release of chromium (VI). If an incidental release of chromium (VI) can be controlled at the time of release by employees in the immediate release area, or by maintenance personnel, it is not an emergency.

Employee exposure means the exposure to airborne chromium (VI) that would occur if the employee were not using a respirator.

High-efficiency particulate air [HEPA] filter means a filter that is at least 99.97 percent efficient in removing mono-dispersed particles of 0.3 micrometers in diameter or larger.

Historical monitoring data means data from chromium (VI) monitoring conducted prior to May 30, 2006, obtained during work operations conducted under workplace conditions closely resembling the processes, types of material, control methods, work practices, and environmental conditions in the employer's current operations.

Objective data means information such as air monitoring data from industry-wide surveys or calculations based on the composition or chemical and physical properties of a substance demonstrating the employee exposure to chromium (VI) associated with a particular product or material or a specific process, operation, or activity. The data must reflect workplace conditions closely resembling the processes, types of material, control methods, work practices, and environmental conditions in the employer's current operations.

Physician or other licensed health care professional [PLHCP] is an individual whose legally permitted scope of practice (i.e. , license, registration, or certification) allows him or her to independently provide or be delegated the responsibility to provide some or all of the particular health care services required by paragraph (k) of this Section.

Regulated area means an area, demarcated by the employer, where an employee's exposure to airborne concentrations of chromium (VI) exceeds, or can reasonably be expected to exceed, the PEL.

This Section means this §1910.1026 chromium (VI) Standard.

(c) **Permissible exposure limit (PEL)** The employer shall ensure that no employee is exposed to an airborne concentration of chromium (VI) in excess of 5 micrograms per cubic meter of air (5 μgm/m^3), calculated as an 8-hour time-weighted average (TWA).

(d) Exposure determination

(d)(1) **General** Each employer who has a workplace or work operation covered by this Section shall determine the 8-hour TWA exposure for each employee exposed to chromium (VI). This determination shall be made in accordance with either paragraph (d)(2) or paragraph (d)(3) of this Section.

(d)(2) **Scheduled monitoring option**

(d)(2)(i) The employer shall perform initial monitoring to determine the 8-hour TWA exposure for each employee on the basis of a sufficient number of personal breathing zone air samples to accurately characterize full shift exposure on each shift, for each job classification, in each work area. Where an employer does representative sampling instead of sampling all employees in order to meet this requirement, the employer shall sample the employee(s) expected to have the highest chromium (VI) exposures.

(d)(2)(ii) If initial monitoring indicates that employee exposures are below the action level, the employer may discontinue monitoring for those employees whose exposures are represented by such monitoring.

(d)(2)(iii) If monitoring reveals employee exposures to be at or above the action level, the employer shall perform periodic monitoring at least every six months.

(d)(2)(iv) If monitoring reveals employee exposures to be above the PEL, the employer shall perform periodic monitoring at least every three months.

(d)(2)(v) If periodic monitoring indicates that employee exposures are below the action level, and the result is confirmed by the result of another monitoring taken at least seven days later, the employer may discontinue the monitoring for those employees whose exposures are represented by such monitoring.

(d)(2)(vi) The employer shall perform additional monitoring when there has been any change in the production process, raw materials, equipment, personnel, work practices, or control methods that may result in new or additional exposures to chromium (VI), or when the employer has any reason to believe that new or additional exposures have occurred.

(d)(3) **Performance-oriented option** The employer shall determine the 8-hour TWA exposure for each employee on the basis of any combination of air monitoring data, historical monitoring data, or objective data sufficient to accurately characterize employee exposure to chromium (VI).

(d)(4) **Employee notification of determination results**

(d)(4)(i) Within 15 work days after making an exposure determination in accordance with paragraph (d)(2) or paragraph (d)(3) of this Section, the employer shall individually notify each affected employee in writing of the results of that determination or post the results in an appropriate location accessible to all affected employees.

(d)(4)(ii) Whenever the exposure determination indicates that employee exposure is above the PEL, the employer shall describe in the written notification the corrective action being taken to reduce employee exposure to or below the PEL.

(d)(5) **Accuracy of measurement** Where air monitoring is performed to comply with the requirements of this Section, the employer shall use a method of monitoring and analysis that can measure chromium (VI) to within an accuracy of plus or minus 25 percent (± 25%) and can produce accurate measurements to within a statistical confidence level of 95 percent for airborne concentrations at or above the action level.

(d)(6) **Observation of monitoring**

(d)(6)(i) Where air monitoring is performed to comply with the requirements of this Section, the employer shall provide affected employees or their designated representatives an opportunity to observe any monitoring of employee exposure to chromium (VI).

(d)(6)(ii) When observation of monitoring requires entry into an area where the use of protective clothing or equipment is required, the employer shall provide the observer with clothing and equipment and shall assure that the observer uses such clothing and equipment and complies with all other applicable safety and health procedures.

(e) Regulated areas

(e)(1) **Establishment** The employer shall establish a regulated area wherever an employee's exposure to airborne concentrations of chromium (VI) is, or can reasonably be expected to be, in excess of the PEL.

(e)(2) **Demarcation** The employer shall ensure that regulated areas are demarcated from the rest of the workplace in a manner that adequately establishes and alerts employees of the boundaries of the regulated area.

(e)(3) **Access** The employer shall limit access to regulated areas to:

(e)(3)(i) Persons authorized by the employer and required by work duties to be present in the regulated area;

(e)(3)(ii) Any person entering such an area as a designated representative of employees for the purpose of exercising the right to observe monitoring procedures under paragraph (d) of this Section; or

(e)(3)(iii) Any person authorized by the Occupational Safety and Health Act or regulations issued under it to be in a regulated area.

(f) Methods of compliance

(f)(1) [OI] Engineering and work practice controls

(f)(1)(i) Except as permitted in paragraph (f)(1)(ii) and paragraph (f)(1)(iii) of this Section, the employer shall use engineering and work practice controls to reduce and maintain employee exposure to chromium (VI) to or below the PEL unless the employer can demonstrate that such controls are not feasible. Wherever feasible engineering and work practice controls are not sufficient to reduce employee exposure to or below the PEL, the employer shall use them to reduce employee exposure to the lowest levels achievable, and shall supplement them by the use of respiratory protection that complies with the requirements of paragraph (g) of this Section.

(f)(1)(ii) Where painting of aircraft or large aircraft parts is performed in the aerospace industry, the employer shall use engineering and work practice controls to reduce and maintain employee exposure to chromium (VI) to or below 25 $\mu gm/m^3$ unless the employer can demonstrate that such controls are not feasible. The employer shall supplement such engineering and work practice controls with the use of respiratory protection that complies with the requirements of paragraph (g) of this Section to achieve the PEL.

(f)(1)(iii) Where the employer can demonstrate that a process or task does not result in any employee exposure to chromium (VI) above the PEL for 30 or more days per year (12 consecutive months), the requirement to implement engineering and work practice controls to achieve the PEL does not apply to that process or task.

(f)(2) Prohibition of rotation The employer shall not rotate employees to different jobs to achieve compliance with the PEL.

(g) Respiratory protection

(g)(1) General Where respiratory protection is required by this Section, the employer must provide each employee an appropriate respirator that complies with the requirements of this paragraph. Respiratory protection is required during:

(g)(1)(i) Periods necessary to install or implement feasible engineering and work practice controls;

(g)(1)(ii) Work operations, such as maintenance and repair activities, for which engineering and work practice controls are not feasible;

(g)(1)(iii) Work operations for which an employer has implemented all feasible engineering and work practice controls and such controls are not sufficient to reduce exposures to or below the PEL;

(g)(1)(iv) Work operations where employees are exposed above the PEL for fewer than 30 days per year, and the employer has elected not to implement engineering and work practice controls to achieve the PEL; or

(g)(1)(v) Emergencies.

(g)(2) Respiratory protection program Where respirator use is required by this Section, the employer shall institute a respiratory protection program in accordance with §1910.134, which covers each employee required to use a respirator.

(h) [OI] Protective work clothing and equipment

(h)(1) [OI] Provision and use Where a hazard is present or is likely to be present from skin or eye contact with chromium (VI), the employer shall provide appropriate personal protective clothing and equipment at no cost to employees, and shall ensure that employees use such clothing and equipment.

(h)(2) Removal and storage

(h)(2)(i) The employer shall ensure that employees remove all protective clothing and equipment contaminated with chromium (VI) at the end of the work shift or at the completion of their tasks involving chromium (VI) exposure, whichever comes first.

(h)(2)(ii) The employer shall ensure that no employee removes chromium (VI)-contaminated protective clothing or equipment from the workplace, except for those employees whose job it is to launder, clean, maintain, or dispose of such clothing or equipment.

(h)(2)(iii) When contaminated protective clothing or equipment is removed for laundering, cleaning, maintenance, or disposal, the employer shall ensure that it is stored and transported in sealed, impermeable bags or other closed, impermeable containers.

(h)(2)(iv) The employer shall ensure that bags or containers of contaminated protective clothing or equipment that are removed from change rooms for laundering, cleaning, maintenance, or disposal are labeled in accordance with the requirements of the Hazard Communication Standard, §1910.1200.

(h)(3) Cleaning and replacement

(h)(3)(i) The employer shall clean, launder, repair and replace all protective clothing and equipment required by this Section as needed to maintain its effectiveness.

(h)(3)(ii) The employer shall prohibit the removal of chromium (VI) from protective clothing and equipment by blowing, shaking, or any other means that disperses chromium (VI) into the air or onto an employee's body.

(h)(3)(iii) The employer shall inform any person who launders or cleans protective clothing or equipment contaminated with chromium (VI) of the potentially harmful effects of exposure to chromium (VI) and that the clothing and equipment should be laundered or cleaned in a manner that minimizes skin or eye contact with chromium (VI) and effectively prevents the release of airborne chromium (VI) in excess of the PEL.

(i) [OI] Hygiene areas and practices

(i)(1) [OI] General Where protective clothing and equipment is required, the employer shall provide change rooms in conformance with 29 CFR §1910.141. Where skin contact with chromium (VI) occurs, the employer shall provide washing facilities in conformance with 29 CFR §1910.141. Eating and drinking areas provided by the employer shall also be in conformance with §1910.141.

(i)(2) Change rooms The employer shall assure that change rooms are equipped with separate storage facilities for protective clothing and equipment and for street clothes, and that these facilities prevent cross-contamination.

(i)(3) Washing facilities

(i)(3)(i) The employer shall provide readily accessible washing facilities capable of removing chromium (VI) from the skin, and shall ensure that affected employees use these facilities when necessary.

(i)(3)(ii) The employer shall ensure that employees who have skin contact with chromium (VI) wash their hands and faces at the end of the work shift and prior to eating, drinking, smoking, chewing tobacco or gum, applying cosmetics, or using the toilet.

(i)(4) Eating and drinking areas

(i)(4)(i) [OI] Whenever the employer allows employees to consume food or beverages at a worksite where chromium (VI) is present, the employer shall ensure that eating and drinking areas and surfaces are maintained as free as practicable of chromium (VI);

(i)(4)(ii) The employer shall ensure that employees do not enter eating and drinking areas with protective work clothing or equipment unless surface chromium (VI) has been removed from the clothing and equipment by methods that do not disperse chromium (VI) into the air or onto an employee's body.

(i)(5) Prohibited activities The employer shall ensure that employees do not eat, drink, smoke, chew tobacco or gum, or apply cosmetics in regulated areas, or in areas where skin or eye contact with chromium (VI) occurs; or carry the products associated with these activities, or store such products in these areas.

(j) [OI] Housekeeping

(j)(1) General The employer shall ensure that:

(j)(1)(i) All surfaces are maintained as free as practicable of accumulations of chromium (VI);

(j)(1)(ii) All spills and releases of chromium (VI) containing material are cleaned up promptly.

(j)(2) Cleaning methods

(j)(2)(i) The employer shall ensure that surfaces contaminated with chromium (VI) are cleaned by HEPA-filter vacuuming or other methods that minimize the likelihood of exposure to chromium (VI).

(j)(2)(ii) Dry shoveling, dry sweeping, and dry brushing may be used only where HEPA-filtered vacuuming or other methods that minimize the likelihood of exposure to chromium (VI) have been tried and found not to be effective.

(j)(2)(iii) The employer shall not allow compressed air to be used to remove chromium (VI) from any surface unless:

(j)(2)(iii)(A) The compressed air is used in conjunction with a ventilation system designed to capture the dust cloud created by the compressed air; or

(j)(2)(iii)(B) No alternative method is feasible.

(j)(2)(iv) The employer shall ensure that cleaning equipment is handled in a manner that minimizes the reentry of chromium (VI) into the workplace.

(j)(3) Disposal The employer shall ensure that:

(j)(3)(i) [OI] Waste, scrap, debris, and any other materials contaminated with chromium (VI) and consigned for disposal are collected and disposed of in sealed, impermeable bags or other closed, impermeable containers; and

(j)(3)(ii) Bags or containers of waste, scrap, debris, and any other materials contaminated with chromium (VI) that are consigned for disposal are labeled in accordance with the requirements of the Hazard Communication Standard, 29 CFR §1910.1200.

(k) Medical surveillance

(k)(1) General

(k)(1)(i) The employer shall make medical surveillance available at no cost to the employee, and at a reasonable time and place, for all employees:

(k)(1)(i)(A) Who are or may be occupationally exposed to chromium (VI) at or above the action level for 30 or more days a year;

(k)(1)(i)(B) Experiencing signs or symptoms of the adverse health effects associated with chromium (VI) exposure; or

(k)(1)(i)(C) Exposed in an emergency.

(k)(1)(ii) The employer shall assure that all medical examinations and procedures required by this Section are performed by or under the supervision of a PLHCP.

(k)(2) Frequency The employer shall provide a medical examination:

(k)(2)(i) Within 30 days after initial assignment, unless the employee has received a chromium (VI) related medical examination that meets the requirements of this paragraph within the last twelve months;

(k)(2)(ii) Annually;

(k)(2)(iii) Within 30 days after a PLHCP's written medical opinion recommends an additional examination;

(k)(2)(iv) Whenever an employee shows signs or symptoms of the adverse health effects associated with chromium (VI) exposure;

(k)(2)(v) Within 30 days after exposure during an emergency which results in an uncontrolled release of chromium (VI); or

(k)(2)(vi) At the termination of employment, unless the last examination that satisfied the requirements of paragraph (k) of this Section was less than six months prior to the date of termination.

(k)(3) Contents of examination A medical examination consists of:

(k)(3)(i) A medical and work history, with emphasis on: Past, present, and anticipated future exposure to chromium (VI); any history of respiratory system dysfunction; any history of asthma, dermatitis, skin ulceration, or nasal septum perforation; and smoking status and history;

(k)(3)(ii) A physical examination of the skin and respiratory tract; and

(k)(3)(iii) Any additional tests deemed appropriate by the examining PLHCP.

(k)(4) Information provided to the PLHCP The employer shall ensure that the examining PLHCP has a copy of this Standard, and shall provide the following information:

(k)(4)(i) A description of the affected employee's former, current, and anticipated duties as they relate to the employee's occupational exposure to chromium (VI);

(k)(4)(ii) The employee's former, current, and anticipated levels of occupational exposure to chromium (VI);

(k)(4)(iii) A description of any personal protective equipment used or to be used by the employee, including when and for how long the employee has used that equipment; and

(k)(4)(iv) Information from records of employment-related medical examinations previously provided to the affected employee, currently within the control of the employer.

(k)(5) PLHCP's written medical opinion

(k)(5)(i) The employer shall obtain a written medical opinion from the PLHCP, within 30 days for each medical examination performed on each employee, which contains:

(k)(5)(i)(A) The PLHCP's opinion as to whether the employee has any detected medical condition(s) that would place the employee at increased risk of material impairment to health from further exposure to chromium (VI);

(k)(5)(i)(B) Any recommended limitations upon the employee's exposure to chromium (VI) or upon the use of personal protective equipment such as respirators;

(k)(5)(i)(C) A statement that the PLHCP has explained to the employee the results of the medical examination, including any medical conditions related to chromium (VI) exposure that require further evaluation or treatment, and any special provisions for use of protective clothing or equipment.

(k)(5)(ii) The PLHCP shall not reveal to the employer specific findings or diagnoses unrelated to occupational exposure to chromium (VI).

(k)(5)(iii) The employer shall provide a copy of the PLHCP's written medical opinion to the examined employee within two weeks after receiving it.

(l) Communication of chromium (VI) hazards to employees

(l)(1) Hazard communication—general

(l)(1)(i) Chemical manufacturers, importers, distributors and employers shall comply with all requirements of the Hazard Communication Standard (HCS) (§1910.1200) for chromium (VI).

(l)(1)(ii) In classifying the hazards of chromium (VI) at least the following hazards are to be addressed: Cancer, eye irritation, and skin sensitization.

(l)(1)(iii) Employers shall include chromium (VI) in the hazard communication program established to comply with the HCS (§1910.1200). Employers shall ensure that each employee has access to labels on containers of chromium (VI) and to safety data sheets, and is trained in accordance with the requirements of HCS and paragraph (l)(2) of this Section.

(l)(2) Employee information and training

(l)(2)(i) The employer shall ensure that each employee can demonstrate knowledge of at least the following:

(l)(2)(i)(A) The contents of this Section; and

(l)(2)(i)(B) The purpose and a description of the medical surveillance program required by paragraph (k) of this Section.

(l)(2)(ii) The employer shall make a copy of this Section readily available without cost to all affected employees.

(m) Recordkeeping

(m)(1) Air monitoring data

(m)(1)(i) The employer shall maintain an accurate record of all air monitoring conducted to comply with the requirements of this Section.

(m)(1)(ii) This record shall include at least the following information:

(m)(1)(ii)(A) The date of measurement for each sample taken;

(m)(1)(ii)(B) The operation involving exposure to chromium (VI) that is being monitored;

(m)(1)(ii)(C) Sampling and analytical methods used and evidence of their accuracy;

(m)(1)(ii)(D) Number, duration, and the results of samples taken;

(m)(1)(ii)(E) Type of personal protective equipment, such as respirators worn; and

(m)(1)(ii)(F) Name, social security number, and job classification of all employees represented by the monitoring, indicating which employees were actually monitored.

(m)(1)(iii) The employer shall ensure that exposure records are maintained and made available in accordance with 29 CFR §1910.1020.

(m)(2) Historical monitoring data

(m)(2)(i) Where the employer has relied on historical monitoring data to determine exposure to chromium (VI), the employer shall establish and maintain an accurate record of the historical monitoring data relied upon.

(m)(2)(ii) The record shall include information that reflects the following conditions:

(m)(2)(ii)(A) The data were collected using methods that meet the accuracy requirements of paragraph (d)(5) of this Section;

(m)(2)(ii)(B) The processes and work practices that were in use when the historical monitoring data were obtained are essentially the same as those to be used during the job for which exposure is being determined;

(m)(2)(ii)(C) The characteristics of the chromium (VI) containing material being handled when the historical monitoring data were obtained are the same as those on the job for which exposure is being determined;

(m)(2)(ii)(D) Environmental conditions prevailing when the historical monitoring data were obtained are the same as those on the job for which exposure is being determined; and

(m)(2)(ii)(E) Other data relevant to the operations, materials, processing, or employee exposures covered by the exception.

(m)(2)(iii) The employer shall ensure that historical exposure records are maintained and made available in accordance with 29 CFR §1910.1020.

(m)(3) Objective data

(m)(3)(i) The employer shall maintain an accurate record of all objective data relied upon to comply with the requirements of this Section.

(m)(3)(ii) This record shall include at least the following information:

(m)(3)(ii)(A) The chromium containing material in question;

(m)(3)(ii)(B) The source of the objective data;

(m)(3)(ii)(C) The testing protocol and results of testing, or analysis of the material for the release of chromium (VI);

(m)(3)(ii)(D) A description of the process, operation, or activity and how the data support the determination; and

(m)(3)(ii)(E) Other data relevant to the process, operation, activity, material, or employee exposures.

(m)(3)(iii) The employer shall ensure that objective data are maintained and made available in accordance with 29 CFR §1910.1020.

(m)(4) Medical surveillance

(m)(4)(i) The employer shall establish and maintain an accurate record for each employee covered by medical surveillance under paragraph (k) of this Section.

(m)(4)(ii) The record shall include the following information about the employee:

(m)(4)(ii)(A) Name and social security number;

(m)(4)(ii)(B) A copy of the PLHCP's written opinions;

(m)(4)(ii)(C) A copy of the information provided to the PLHCP as required by paragraph (k)(4) of this Section.

(m)(4)(iii) The employer shall ensure that medical records are maintained and made available in accordance with 29 CFR §1910.1020.

(n) Dates

(n)(1) For employers with 20 or more employees, all obligations of this Section, except engineering controls required by paragraph (f) of this Section, commence November 27, 2006.

(n)(2) For employers with 19 or fewer employees, all obligations of this Section, except engineering controls required by paragraph (f) of this Section, commence May 30, 2007.

(n)(3) Except as provided in (n)(4), for all employers, engineering controls required by paragraph (f) of this Section shall be implemented no later than May 31, 2010.

(n)(4) In facilities that become parties to the Settlement Agreement included in Appendix A, engineering controls required by paragraph (f) of this Section shall be implemented no later than December 31, 2008.

§1910.1026 Appendix A

In the United States Court of Appeals for the Third Circuit

Surface Finishing Industry Council et al., Petitioners, v. U.S. Occupational Safety and Health Administration, Respondent.

[Docket No. 06–2272 and consolidated cases]

Public Citizen Health Research Group et al., Petitioners, v. Occupational Safety and Health Administration, United States Department of Labor, Respondent.

[Docket No. 06–1818]

Settlement Agreement

The parties to this Settlement Agreement ("Agreement") are the Occupational Safety and Health Administration, United States Department of Labor ("OSHA"), the Surface Finishing Industry Council or its successors ("SFIC"), surface-finishing and metal-finishing facilities which have opted into this Agreement pursuant to paragraph 7 ("Company" or "Companies"), Public Citizen Health Research Group ("HRG"), and the United Steel, Paper and Forestry, Rubber, Manufacturing, Energy, Allied Industrial and Service Workers International Union ("Steelworkers").

Whereas, On February 28, 2006, OSHA promulgated a revised hexavalent chromium Standard for general industry ("the Standard") that includes a permissible exposure limit ("PEL") for hexavalent chromium of 5 micrograms per cubic meter ($\mu g/m^3$) measured as an 8-hour time-weighted average ("TWA"), and a deadline of May 31, 2010, for employers to come into compliance with this PEL through the implementation of engineering controls. The deadline for compliance with the remaining provisions of the Standard, including those requiring the use of respiratory protection to comply with the PEL, is November 27, 2006, for employers with twenty (20) or more employees, and May 30, 2007, for employers with nineteen (19) or fewer employees. 29 CFR §1910.1026, 71 FR 10100 (Feb. 28, 2006);

Whereas, SFIC filed a Petition for Review of the Standard in the Eleventh Circuit that was consolidated with other Petitions in the Third Circuit (Case No. 06–2272);

Whereas, SFIC filed a Motion for Leave to Intervene in the matter of HRG's Petition for Review in the Third Circuit (Case No. 06–1818), which has been granted;

Now, therefore, the parties to this Agreement do hereby agree to the following terms:

1. **Term of this Agreement** This Agreement will be effective upon execution and will expire on May 31, 2010.
2. **Accelerated implementation of engineering controls** The Companies agree that in accordance with 29 CFR §1910.1026(f)(1) they will implement those feasible engineering controls necessary to reduce hexavalent chromium levels at their facilities by December 31, 2008, to or below the 5 $\mu g/m^3$ PEL. In fulfilling this obligation, the Companies may select from the engineering and work practice controls listed in Exhibit A to this Agreement or adopt any other controls.
3. **Compliance plan and monitoring** In accordance with 29 CFR §1910.1026(d)(4)(ii), each Company will prepare, and update as required, a written plan setting forth the specific control steps being taken to reduce employee exposure to or below the PEL by December 31, 2008. In addition, Companies will make an initial exposure determination as required by 29 CFR §1910.1026(d)(1) using either the procedures for personal breathing zone air samples described in 29 CFR §1910.1026(d)(2) or the performance-oriented option described at 29 CFR §1910.1026(d)(3). Thereafter, Companies will conduct periodic monitoring in accordance with the "Scheduled Monitoring Option" provisions at 29 CFR §1910.1026(d)(2) and related provisions at 29 CFR §1910.1026(d)(4)–(6). The Companies agree that upon request compliance plans prepared in accordance with this paragraph, as well as all monitoring results obtained in compliance with this paragraph, will be provided to OSHA, affected employees and employee representatives.
4. **Respirator use** The respiratory protection provisions at 29 CFR §1910.1026(f) and (g) will apply to the Companies in accordance with the terms and dates set forth in the Standard, except that prior to December 31, 2008, for Companies that are in compliance with this Agreement, OSHA will enforce those respiratory protection provisions only with respect to employees who fall into one of the following six (6) categories: (1) Employees who are exposed to hexavalent chromium in excess of the PEL while performing tasks described in Exhibit B to this Agreement; (2) through November 30, 2007, employees whose exposures to hexavalent chromium exceed a "respirator threshold" of 20 $\mu g/m^3$ (measured as an 8-hour TWA); (3) beginning December 1, 2007, employees whose exposures to hexavalent chromium exceed a "respirator threshold" of 12.5 $\mu g/m^3$ (measured as an 8-hour TWA); (4) employees who are exposed to hexavalent chromium and request a respirator; (5) any other employees who are required by the Companies to wear a respirator; and (6) employees with exposures for which respirators were required under the previous hexavalent chromium Standard (1910.1000) and any other employees covered by respirator programs in effect on May 30, 2006.
5. **Employee information and training** Company employees will be trained pursuant to the provisions of 29 CFR §1910.1026(l)(2). In addition, the Companies agree to train employees in the provisions of this Agreement within sixty (60) days of the Opt-In Date (defined in paragraph 7 of this Agreement). The training regarding this Agreement shall be provided in language the employees can understand.
6. **Enforcement** Within thirty (30) days of the execution of this Agreement, OSHA will publish a notice in the Federal Register amending 29 CFR §1910.1026 as follows: (1) A copy of this Agreement will be attached to the Standard as Appendix A; (2) a new paragraph, §1910.1026(n)(4), will be added to the Standard, and will read: "In facilities that become parties to the settlement agreement included in Appendix A, engineering controls required by paragraph (f) of this Section shall be implemented no later than December 31, 2008"; and (3) existing paragraph §1910.1026(n)(3) will be amended to read: "Except as provided in (n)(4), for all employers, engineering controls required by paragraph (f) of this Section shall be implemented no later than May 31, 2010."
7. **Opt-In Date for Companies to become parties to this Agreement** The Federal Register notice described in paragraph 6 of this Agreement will provide notice of the provisions of this Agreement, and of the revisions to the Standard described in paragraph 6, and will provide until November 30, 2006, for eligible facilities to become parties to this Agreement, and be subject to all of the duties, obligations, and rights herein. The last date for signing by facilities shall be referred to as the Opt-In Date. The opt in option will be available on a facility by facility basis and only to SFIC members and other surface-finishing and metal-finishing job shop facilities within the jurisdiction of Federal OSHA. (For purposes of this Agreement, a "job shop" is defined as a facility that sells plating or anodizing services to other companies.) Moreover, the terms of this Agreement apply only with respect to the performance of surface-finishing and metal-finishing operations in those facilities. Although this Agreement applies only to facilities within the jurisdiction of Federal OSHA, OSHA will encourage States with OSHA-approved State occupational safety and health plans to either honor and implement the terms of this Agreement, including the amendments to the Standard described in paragraph 6, or to take an alternative position, which may include entering into separate arrangements with surface- and metal-finishing job shop facilities (or their representatives) in their jurisdiction.
8. **Effect on third parties** Nothing in this Agreement constitutes an admission by SFIC or the Companies that a significant risk of material health impairment exists for hexavalent chromium justifying a reduction of the PEL to 5 $\mu g/m^3$. Nor does anything in this Agreement constitute any other admission by SFIC or the Companies for purposes of this litigation or future litigation or standards-setting. This Agreement is not intended to give any rights to any third party except as expressly provided herein.
9. **OSHA inspections** OSHA may do monitoring inspections to assess compliance with and progress under this Agreement and the Standard, and nothing in this Agreement limits OSHA's right to conduct inspections at Companies" facilities in accordance with the Occupational Safety and Health Act.
10. **Scope of Agreement** The terms of this Agreement apply only in the circumstances and to the Companies specified herein. In entering into this Agreement, OSHA is not making any representations regarding its enforcement policy with respect to either: (1) The hexavalent chromium Standard as applied to employers who are not parties to this Agreement or (2) any other Occupational Safety or Health Standards.
11. **Effect of invalidation of the Standard** If the Standard is invalidated, nothing in this Agreement shall prevent the application to SFIC or the Companies of any PEL that is promulgated by OSHA on remand. This Agreement would not foreclose SFIC or the Companies from participating in rulemaking proceedings or otherwise challenging any new PEL promulgated by OSHA on remand.

12. **Withdrawal of Petitions and Interventions** SFIC agrees to move to withdraw its Petition for Review in the above-captioned case, Case No. 06–2272, within five (5) working days of the execution of this Agreement. SFIC further will move to dismiss its motion to intervene in Case No. 06–1818 and all other challenges simultaneously with its motion to withdraw in Case No. 06–2272 as Petitioner.
13. **Attorneys' fees** Each party agrees to bear its own attorneys fees, costs, and other expenses that have been incurred in connection with SFIC's Petition for Review, SFIC's intervention in HRG's Petition for Review, and the negotiation of this Agreement up to and including filing of the motions to dismiss.
14. **Support of Agreement** In the event that all or any portion of this Agreement is challenged in any forum, the signatories below agree to move to intervene in support of this Agreement.

Agreed to this 25th day of October, 2006.

Baruch A. Fellner,

Counsel for SFIC, Gibson, Dunn & Crutcher LLP, 1050 Connecticut Avenue, NW., Washington, DC 20036, (202) 955–8500.

Lauren S. Goodman,

Counsel for OSHA, United States Department of Labor, Office of the Solicitor, 200 Constitution Avenue, NW., Washington, DC 20210, (202) 693–5445.

Scott L. Nelson,

Counsel for HRG and the Steelworkers, Public Citizen Litigation Group, 1600 20th Street, NW., Washington, DC 20009, (202) 588–7724.

Exhibit A

Available Engineering and Work Practice Controls

The Companies agree that work towards the implementation of these available engineering and work practice controls should not be delayed to accommodate their completion by December 31, 2008. The Companies are encouraged to implement from among these controls as soon as practicable.

1. Parts Transfer Practices

- Minimize droplet formation. Instruments akin to garden hoses are used to rinse off parts coming out of chemical baths. This causes many small droplets to form, which are easily atomized or vaporized and contribute to airborne chromium concentration. The industry is currently developing ways to minimize the formation of small droplets, dripping, or splashing, possibly by reducing hose pressure.
- Minimize air current flow. Strong air currents across these droplets may contribute to their vaporization, and therefore minimizing air current flow across the droplets may reduce airborne hexavalent chromium levels.
- Slow part speeds as feasible. The speed at which parts are pulled out of a chemical tank causes splashing, which adds to chromium vaporization. By slowing the speed at which parts are taken out of tanks, splashing and vaporization can be minimized. The feasibility of this control must be evaluated in light of the negative effect on productivity.

2. Plating Bath Surface Tension Management and Fume Suppression

- Lower surface tension. Lower surface tension in chemical baths leads to fewer drops forming. Chromium baths currently have a surface tension of 35 dynes per centimeter. As a comparison, water has a surface tension of 72 dynes per centimeter. Lowering surface tension further would lead to reduced airborne hexavalent chromium levels.
- Fume suppressants. Fume suppressants create a physical barrier between the chemical bath and the air, which prevents vaporization. Some suppressants, however, may cause pitting or other metal damage, and therefore their use is not always possible.

3. Facility Air Disturbance Monitoring

- Improvement of local exhaust ventilation (LEV) capture efficiency. The majority of electroplating facilities are not air-conditioned. As a result, doors are kept open to let in cool air, but this causes air currents that prevent the LEVs from performing efficiently. The use of fans has a similar effect. Industry is researching how to minimize these air currents so that LEVs can perform as designed. Such methods may include the use of partitions to degrade air current flow, or checklists that may include location and positioning of cross drafts, fans, doors, windows, partitions and process equipment that Companies can use to audit their workplaces in order to improve their capture efficiency.

4. Technology Enhancements In Lieu of LEV Retrofitting

- Eductors. Many chemical baths are currently mixed via air agitation: Air pipes bubble air into the tank to keep the chemicals mixed and to prevent them from settling. An adverse effect of this agitation is that air bubbles escape at the surface of the tank, resulting in some chromium vaporization. By using eductors (horn-shaped nozzles) in tanks, the chemicals flow from a pump to create solution movement below the surface without the use of air bubbles, and the amount of chromium vaporization can be significantly reduced.

5. Different Means of Chromium Additions

- Liquid Chromium. Dry hexavalent chromium flakes are occasionally added to tanks, which can generate airborne particulates of hexavalent chromium. Adding liquid chromium at or near the surface of a tank would lower airborne chromium levels and reduce splashing from tanks.
- Hydration of flakes before addition. To add liquid chromium to tanks, the dry flakes must be hydrated. Whether this process is performed by chemical suppliers that provide plating solutions to metal finishing companies or by metal finishing companies that have the necessary experience and equipment, appropriate work practices such as mixing techniques must be implemented to minimize the potential airborne levels of hexavalent chromium.

6. Dust Control

- Better housekeeping. Chrome dust that comes off products that are polished or grinded is actually elemental chromium, not hexavalent chromium, so polishing and grinding contribute little to airborne hexavalent chromium levels. However, Companies should use good housekeeping practices, including wet mopping, and wet wipedowns, to reduce the amount of dust present.

7. Improvement and Maintenance of Existing LEVs

- Improvement and maintenance of existing LEVs. Companies may repair and maintain their current LEVs. Because the final rule indicates that at least 75 percent of the industry is in compliance with the PEL with LEVs working at 40% of capacity, increasing LEV function can materially affect compliance.

8. Other Controls

- Other methods. Companies are constantly determining best work practices and technological controls through laboratory research and practical experience. Companies will implement other engineering and work practice controls as necessary and as practicable to reduce potential hexavalent chromium workplace exposures.

Exhibit B

Workplace Tasks Requiring Respirators Where PEL Is Exceeded

Some well-known and relatively few, discrete tasks related to metal finishing activities result in potentially higher workplace exposures of hexavalent chromium. Where the applicable PEL for hexavalent chromium is exceeded, respirators shall be worn to conduct the following activities:

(1) Hexavalent chromium chemical additions In order to have the metal deposited onto the part, hexavalent chromium must be added to the plating tank periodically. This is a discrete activity that involves the addition of either a dry flake of hexavalent chromium chemicals or a liquid solution of hexavalent chromium into the plating tank. Respirators shall be worn during the period it takes to add the hexavalent chromium chemical to the tank.

(2) Hexavalent chromium preparation and mixing Different mixtures of hexavalent chromium chemicals are needed for different types of chromium plating processes. For example, hard chromium plating can require higher concentrations of hexavalent chromium because a thicker coating and longer plating process may be needed for the critical product quality and performance. Similarly, different types of decorative chromium plating processes may need different levels of hexavalent chromium and other chemicals such as catalysts. These mixtures can be in the form of dry flakes or liquid solutions. All of these different hexavalent chromium chemical mixtures are generally prepared by metal finishing suppliers and distributors. Some metal finishing companies may also prepare hexavalent chromium solutions from the dry flakes prior to addition to the plating tanks. Respirators shall be worn during the period it takes to prepare these hexavalent chromium mixtures and solutions whether the activity is conducted at a chemical supplier or a metal finishing company.

(3) Hexavalent chromium tank cleaning Occasionally, the tanks used for chromium plating may need to be emptied and cleaned. This process would involve the draining of the solution and then the removal of any residues in the tank. Workers cleaning out these tanks may have to enter the tank or reach into it to remove the residues. Respirators (as well as other appropriate PPE) shall be worn during the period it takes to clean the tanks and prepare them for use again.

(4) Hexavalent chromium painting operations Some metal finishing operations apply paints with higher concentrations of hexavalent chromium to a line of parts, particularly for aerospace applications when a high degree of corrosion protection is needed for critical product performance. Paints are generally applied in such operations with some type of spray mechanism or similar dispersion practice. In some instances, it may be difficult to keep workplace exposures below the PEL for such paint spraying activities. Respirators shall be worn during such spray painting operations.

[71 FR 10374, Feb. 28, 2006, as amended at 71 FR 63242, Oct. 30, 2006; 73 FR 75585, Dec. 12, 2008; 75 FR 12686, Mar. 17, 2010]

§1910.1027 Cadmium

(a) **Scope** This Standard applies to all occupational exposures to cadmium and cadmium compounds, in all forms, and in all industries covered by the Occupational Safety and Health Act, except the construction-related industries, which are covered under 29 CFR §1926.63.

(b) **Definitions**

Action level (AL) is defined as an airborne concentration of cadmium of 2.5 micrograms per cubic meter of air (2.5 $\mu g/m^3$), calculated as an 8-hour time-weighted average (TWA).

Assistant Secretary means the Assistant Secretary of Labor for Occupational Safety and Health, U.S. Department of Labor, or designee.

Authorized person means any person authorized by the employer and required by work duties to be present in regulated areas or any person authorized by the OSH Act or regulations issued under it to be in regulated areas.

Director means the Director of the National Institute for Occupational Safety and Health (NIOSH), U.S. Department of Health and Human Services, or designee.

Employee exposure and similar language referring to the air cadmium level to which an employee is exposed means the exposure to airborne cadmium that would occur if the employee were not using respiratory protective equipment.

Final medical determination is the written medical opinion of the employee's health status by the examining physician under paragraphs (l)(3)-(12) of this Section or, if multiple physician review under paragraph (l)(13) of this Section or the alternative physician determination under paragraph (l)(14) of this Section is invoked, it is the final, written medical finding, recommendation or determination that emerges from that process.

High-efficiency particulate air (HEPA) filter means a filter capable of trapping and retaining at least 99.97 percent of mono-dispersed particles of 0.3 micrometers in diameter.

Regulated area means an area demarcated by the employer where an employee's exposure to airborne concentrations of cadmium exceeds, or can reasonably be expected to exceed the permissible exposure limit (PEL).

This Section means this cadmium Standard.

(c) OI **Permissible Exposure Limit (PEL)** The employer shall assure that no employee is exposed to an airborne concentration of cadmium in excess of five micrograms per cubic meter of air (5 µg/m^3), calculated as an eight-hour time-weighted average exposure (TWA).

(d) OI **Exposure monitoring**

(d)(1) General

(d)(1)(i) Each employer who has a workplace or work operation covered by this Section shall determine if any employee may be exposed to cadmium at or above the action level.

(d)(1)(ii) Determinations of employee exposure shall be made from breathing zone air samples that reflect the monitored employee's regular, daily 8-hour TWA exposure to cadmium.

(d)(1)(iii) Eight-hour TWA exposures shall be determined for each employee on the basis of one or more personal breathing zone air samples reflecting full shift exposure on each shift, for each job classification, in each work area. Where several employees perform the same job tasks, in the same job classification, on the same shift, in the same work area, and the length, duration, and level of cadmium exposures are similar, an employer may sample a representative fraction of the employees instead of all employees in order to meet this requirement. In representative sampling, the employer shall sample the employee(s) expected to have the highest cadmium exposures.

(d)(2) Specific

(d)(2)(i) Initial monitoring Except as provided for in paragraphs (d)(2)(ii) and (iii) of this Section, the employer shall monitor employee exposures and shall base initial determinations on the monitoring results.

(d)(2)(ii) Where the employer has monitored after September 14, 1991, under conditions that in all important aspects closely resemble those currently prevailing and where that monitoring satisfies all other requirements of this Section, including the accuracy and confidence levels of paragraph (d)(6) of this Section, the employer may rely on such earlier monitoring results to satisfy the requirements of paragraph (d)(2)(i) of this Section.

(d)(2)(iii) Where the employer has objective data, as defined in paragraph (n)(2) of this Section, demonstrating that employee exposure to cadmium will not exceed the action level under the expected conditions of processing, use, or handling, the employer may rely upon such data instead of implementing initial monitoring.

(d)(3) Monitoring Frequency (periodic monitoring)

(d)(3)(i) If the initial monitoring or periodic monitoring reveals employee exposures to be at or above the action level, the employer shall monitor at a frequency and pattern needed to represent the levels of exposure of employees and where exposures are above the PEL to assure the adequacy of respiratory selection and the effectiveness of engineering and work practice controls. However, such exposure monitoring shall be performed at least every six months. The employer, at a minimum, shall continue these semi-annual measurements unless and until the conditions set out in paragraph (d)(3)(ii) of this Section are met.

(d)(3)(ii) If the initial monitoring or the periodic monitoring indicates that employee exposures are below the action level and that result is confirmed by the results of another monitoring taken at least seven days later, the employer may discontinue the monitoring for those employees whose exposures are represented by such monitoring.

(d)(4) Additional Monitoring The employer also shall institute the exposure monitoring required under paragraphs (d)(2)(i) and (d)(3) of this Section whenever there has been a change in the raw materials, equipment, personnel, work practices, or finished products that may result in additional employees being exposed to cadmium at or above the action level or in employees already exposed to cadmium at or above the action level being exposed above the PEL, or whenever the employer has any reason to suspect that any other change might result in such further exposure.

(d)(5) Employee Notification of Monitoring Results

(d)(5)(i) The employer must, within 15 working days after the receipt of the results of any monitoring performed under this Section, notify each affected employee of these results either individually in writing or by posting the results in an appropriate location that is accessible to employees.

(d)(5)(ii) Wherever monitoring results indicate that employee exposure exceeds the PEL, the employer shall include in the written notice a statement that the PEL has been exceeded and a description of the corrective action being taken by the employer to reduce employee exposure to or below the PEL.

(d)(6) Accuracy of measurement The employer shall use a method of monitoring and analysis that has an accuracy of not less than plus or minus 25 percent (± 25%), with a confidence level of 95 percent, for airborne concentrations of cadmium at or above the action level, the permissible exposure limit (PEL), and the separate engineering control air limit (SECAL).

(e) Regulated areas

(e)(1) Establishment The employer shall establish a regulated area wherever an employee's exposure to airborne concentrations of cadmium is, or can reasonably be expected to be in excess of the permissible exposure limit (PEL).

(e)(2) Demarcation Regulated areas shall be demarcated from the rest of the workplace in any manner that adequately establishes and alerts employees of the boundaries of the regulated area.

(e)(3) Access Access to regulated areas shall be limited to authorized persons.

(e)(4) Provision of respirators Each person entering a regulated area shall be supplied with and required to use a respirator, selected in accordance with paragraph (g)(2) of this Section.

(e)(5) Prohibited activities The employer shall assure that employees do not eat, drink, smoke, chew tobacco or gum, or apply cosmetics in regulated areas, carry the products associated with these activities into regulated areas, or store such products in those areas.

(f) Methods of compliance

(f)(1) Compliance hierarchy

(f)(1)(i) Except as specified in paragraphs (f)(1)(ii), (iii) and (iv) of this Section the employer shall implement engineering and work practice controls to reduce and maintain employee exposure to cadmium at or below the PEL, except to the extent that the employer can demonstrate that such controls are not feasible.

(f)(1)(ii) Except as specified in paragraphs (f)(1)(iii) and (iv) of this Section, in industries where a separate engineering control air limit (SECAL) has been specified for particular processes (See Table 1 in this paragraph (f)(1)(ii)), the employer shall implement engineering and work practice controls to reduce and maintain employee exposure at or below the SECAL, except to the extent that the employer can demonstrate that such controls are not feasible.

Table I
Separate Engineering Control Airborne Limits (SECALs) for Processes in Selected Industries

Industry	Process	SECAL (µg/m^3)
Nickel cadmium battery	Plate making, plate preparation	50
	All other processes	15
Zinc/Cadmium refining*	Cadmium refining, casting, melting, oxide production, sinter plant	50
Pigment manufacture	Calcine, crushing, milling, blending	50
	All other processes	15
Stabilizers*	Cadmium oxide charging, crushing, drying, blending	50
Lead smelting*	Sinter plant, blast furnace, baghouse, yard area	50
Plating*	Mechanical plating	15

* Processes in these industries that are not specified in this table must achieve the PEL using engineering controls and work practices as required in (f)(1)(i).

Cadmium

Z

Toxic and Hazardous Substances

(f)(1)(iii) The requirement to implement engineering and work practice controls to achieve the PEL or, where applicable, the SECAL does not apply where the employer demonstrates the following:

(f)(1)(iii)(A) The employee is only intermittently exposed; and

(f)(1)(iii)(B) The employee is not exposed above the PEL on 30 or more days per year (12 consecutive months).

(f)(1)(iv) Wherever engineering and work practice controls are required and are not sufficient to reduce employee exposure to or below the PEL or, where applicable, the SECAL, the employer nonetheless shall implement such controls to reduce exposures to the lowest levels achievable. The employer shall supplement such controls with respiratory protection that complies with the requirements of paragraph (g) of this Section and the PEL.

(f)(1)(v) The employer shall not use employee rotation as a method of compliance.

(f)(2) Compliance program

(f)(2)(i) Where the PEL is exceeded, the employer shall establish and implement a written compliance program to reduce employee exposure to or below the PEL by means of engineering and work practice controls, as required by paragraph (f)(1) of this Section. To the extent that engineering and work practice controls cannot reduce exposures to or below the PEL, the employer shall include in the written compliance program the use of appropriate respiratory protection to achieve compliance with the PEL.

(f)(2)(ii) Written compliance programs shall include at least the following:

(f)(2)(ii)(A) A description of each operation in which cadmium is emitted; e.g., machinery used, material processed, controls in place, crew size, employee job responsibilities, operating procedures, and maintenance practices;

(f)(2)(ii)(B) A description of the specific means that will be employed to achieve compliance, including engineering plans and studies used to determine methods selected for controlling exposure to cadmium, as well as, where necessary, the use of appropriate respiratory protection to achieve the PEL;

(f)(2)(ii)(C) A report of the technology considered in meeting the PEL;

(f)(2)(ii)(D) Air monitoring data that document the sources of cadmium emissions;

(f)(2)(ii)(E) A detailed schedule for implementation of the program, including documentation such as copies of purchase orders for equipment, construction contracts, etc.;

(f)(2)(ii)(F) A work practice program that includes items required under paragraphs (h), (i), and (j) of this Section;

(f)(2)(ii)(G) A written plan for emergency situations, as specified in paragraph (h) of this Section; and

(f)(2)(ii)(H) Other relevant information.

(f)(2)(iii) The written compliance programs shall be reviewed and updated at least annually, or more often if necessary, to reflect significant changes in the employer's compliance status.

(f)(2)(iv) Written compliance programs shall be provided upon request for examination and copying to affected employees, designated employee representatives as well as to the Assistant Secretary, and the Director.

(f)(3) Mechanical ventilation

(f)(3)(i) When ventilation is used to control exposure, measurements that demonstrate the effectiveness of the system in controlling exposure, such as capture velocity, duct velocity, or static pressure shall be made as necessary to maintain its effectiveness.

(f)(3)(ii) Measurements of the system's effectiveness in controlling exposure shall be made as necessary within five working days of any change in production, process, or control that might result in a significant increase in employee exposure to cadmium.

(f)(3)(iii) **Recirculation of air** If air from exhaust ventilation is recirculated into the workplace, the system shall have a high efficiency filter and be monitored to assure effectiveness.

(f)(3)(iv) Procedures shall be developed and implemented to minimize employee exposure to cadmium when maintenance of ventilation systems and changing of filters is being conducted.

(g) Respiratory protection

(g)(1) **General** For employees who use respirators required by this Section, the employer must provide each employee an appropriate respirator that complies with the requirements of this paragraph. Respirators must be used during:

(g)(1)(i) Periods necessary to install or implement feasible engineering and work-practice controls when employee exposure levels exceed the PEL;

(g)(1)(ii) Maintenance and repair activities, and brief or intermittent operations, for which employee exposures exceed the PEL and engineering and work-practice controls are not feasible or are not required;

(g)(1)(iii) Activities in regulated areas specified in paragraph (e) of this Section;

(g)(1)(iv) Work operations for which the employer has implemented all feasible engineering and work-practice controls and such controls are not sufficient to reduce employee exposures to or below the PEL;

(g)(1)(v) Work operations for which an employee is exposed to cadmium at or above the action level, and the employee requests a respirator;

(g)(1)(vi) Work operations for which an employee is exposed to cadmium above the PEL and engineering controls are not required by paragraph (f)(1)(ii) of this Section; and

(g)(1)(vii) Emergencies.

(g)(2) Respirator program

(g)(2)(i) The employer must implement a respiratory protection program in accordance with §1910.134(b) through (d) (except (d)(1)(iii)), and (f) through (m), which covers each employee required by this Section to use a respirator.

(g)(2)(ii) No employees must use a respirator if, based on their most recent medical examination, the examining physician determines that they will be unable to continue to function normally while using a respirator. If the physician determines that the employee must be limited in, or removed from, their current job because of their inability to use a respirator, the limitation or removal must be in accordance with paragraphs (l)(11) and (12) of this Section.

(g)(2)(iii) If an employee has breathing difficulty during fit testing or respirator use, the employer must provide the employee with a medical examination in accordance with paragraph (l)(6)(ii) of this Section to determine if the employee can use a respirator while performing the required duties.

(g)(3) Respirator selection

(g)(3)(i) Employers must:

(g)(3)(i)(A) Select, and provide to employees, the appropriate respirators specified in paragraph (d)(3)(i)(A) of 29 CFR §1910.134;

(g)(3)(i)(B) Provide employees with full facepiece respirators when they experience eye irritation; and

(g)(3)(i)(C) Provide HEPA filters for powered and non-powered air-purifying respirators.

(g)(3)(ii) The employer must provide an employee with a powered air-purifying respirator instead of a negative-pressure respirator when an employee who is entitled to a respirator chooses to use this type of respirator and such a respirator provides adequate protection to the employee.

(h) **Emergency situations** The employer shall develop and implement a written plan for dealing with emergency situations involving substantial releases of airborne cadmium. The plan shall include provisions for the use of appropriate respirators and personal protective equipment. In addition, employees not essential to correcting the emergency situation shall be restricted from the area and normal operations halted in that area until the emergency is abated.

(i) Protective work clothing and equipment

(i)(1) **Provision and use** If an employee is exposed to airborne cadmium above the PEL or where skin or eye irritation is associated with cadmium exposure at any level, the employer shall provide at no cost to the employee, and assure that the employee uses, appropriate protective work clothing and equipment that prevents contamination of the employee and the employee's garments. Protective work clothing and equipment includes, but is not limited to:

(i)(1)(i) Coveralls or similar full-body work clothing;

(i)(1)(ii) Gloves, head coverings, and boots or foot coverings; and

(i)(1)(iii) Face shields, vented goggles, or other appropriate protective equipment that complies with 29 CFR §1910.133.

(i)(2) Removal and storage

(i)(2)(i) The employer shall assure that employees remove all protective clothing and equipment contaminated with cadmium at the completion of the work shift and do so only in change rooms provided in accordance with paragraph (j)(1) of this Section.

(i)(2)(ii) The employer shall assure that no employee takes cadmium-contaminated protective clothing or equipment from the workplace, except for employees authorized to do so for purposes of laundering, cleaning, maintaining, or disposing of cadmium contaminated protective clothing and equipment at an appropriate location or facility away from the workplace.

(i)(2)(iii) The employer shall assure that contaminated protective clothing and equipment, when removed for laundering, cleaning, maintenance, or disposal, is placed and stored in sealed, impermeable bags or other closed, impermeable containers that are designed to prevent dispersion of cadmium dust.

(i)(2)(iv) The employer shall assure that bags or containers of contaminated protective clothing and equipment that are to be taken out of the change rooms or the workplace for laundering, cleaning, maintenance or disposal shall bear labels in accordance with paragraph (m)(3) of this Section.

(i)(3) **Cleaning, replacement, and disposal**

(i)(3)(i) The employer shall provide the protective clothing and equipment required by paragraph (i)(1) of this Section in a clean and dry condition as often as necessary to maintain its effectiveness, but in any event at least weekly. The employer is responsible for cleaning and laundering the protective clothing and equipment required by this paragraph to maintain its effectiveness and is also responsible for disposing of such clothing and equipment.

(i)(3)(ii) The employer also is responsible for repairing or replacing required protective clothing and equipment as needed to maintain its effectiveness. When rips or tears are detected while an employee is working they shall be immediately mended, or the worksuit shall be immediately replaced.

(i)(3)(iii) The employer shall prohibit the removal of cadmium from protective clothing and equipment by blowing, shaking, or any other means that disperses cadmium into the air.

(i)(3)(iv) The employer shall assure that any laundering of contaminated clothing or cleaning of contaminated equipment in the workplace is done in a manner that prevents the release of airborne cadmium in excess of the permissible exposure limit prescribed in paragraph (c) of this Section.

(i)(3)(v) The employer shall inform any person who launders or cleans protective clothing or equipment contaminated with cadmium of the potentially harmful effects of exposure to cadmium and that the clothing and equipment should be laundered or cleaned in a manner to effectively prevent the release of airborne cadmium in excess of the PEL.

(j) **Hygiene areas and practices**

(j)(1) **General** For employees whose airborne exposure to cadmium is above the PEL, the employer shall provide clean change rooms, handwashing facilities, showers, and lunchroom facilities that comply with 29 CFR §1910.141.

(j)(2) **Change rooms** The employer shall assure that change rooms are equipped with separate storage facilities for street clothes and for protective clothing and equipment, which are designed to prevent dispersion of cadmium and contamination of the employee's street clothes.

(j)(3) **Showers and handwashing facilities**

(j)(3)(i) The employer shall assure that employees who are exposed to cadmium above the PEL shower during the end of the work shift.

(j)(3)(ii) The employer shall assure that employees whose airborne exposure to cadmium is above the PEL wash their hands and faces prior to eating, drinking, smoking, chewing tobacco or gum, or applying cosmetics.

(j)(4) **Lunchroom facilities**

(j)(4)(i) The employer shall assure that the lunchroom facilities are readily accessible to employees, that tables for eating are maintained free of cadmium, and that no employee in a lunchroom facility is exposed at any time to cadmium at or above a concentration of 2.5 $\mu g/m^3$.

(j)(4)(ii) The employer shall assure that employees do not enter lunchroom facilities with protective work clothing or equipment unless surface cadmium has been removed from the clothing and equipment by HEPA vacuuming or some other method that removes cadmium dust without dispersing it.

(k) **Housekeeping**

(k)(1) All surfaces shall be maintained as free as practicable of accumulations of cadmium.

(k)(2) All spills and sudden releases of material containing cadmium shall be cleaned up as soon as possible.

(k)(3) Surfaces contaminated with cadmium shall, wherever possible, be cleaned by vacuuming or other methods that minimize the likelihood of cadmium becoming airborne.

(k)(4) HEPA-filtered vacuuming equipment or equally effective filtration methods shall be used for vacuuming. The equipment shall be used and emptied in a manner that minimizes the reentry of cadmium into the workplace.

(k)(5) Shoveling, dry or wet sweeping, and brushing may be used only where vacuuming or other methods that minimize the likelihood of cadmium becoming airborne have been tried and found not to be effective.

(k)(6) Compressed air shall not be used to remove cadmium from any surface unless the compressed air is used in conjunction with a ventilation system designed to capture the dust cloud created by the compressed air.

(k)(7) Waste, scrap, debris, bags, containers, personal protective equipment, and clothing contaminated with cadmium and consigned for disposal shall be collected and disposed of in sealed impermeable bags or other closed, impermeable containers. These bags and containers shall be labeled in accordance with paragraph (m) of this Section.

(l) **Medical surveillance**

(l)(1) **General**

(l)(1)(i) **Scope**

(l)(1)(i)(A) Currently exposed—The employer shall institute a medical surveillance program for all employees who are or may be exposed to cadmium at or above the action level unless the employer demonstrates that the employee is not, and will not be, exposed at or above the action level on 30 or more days per year (twelve consecutive months); and,

(l)(1)(i)(B) Previously exposed—The employer shall also institute a medical surveillance program for all employees who prior to the effective date of this Section might previously have been exposed to cadmium at or above the action level by the employer, unless the employer demonstrates that the employee did not prior to the effective date of this Section work for the employer in jobs with exposure to cadmium for an aggregated total of more than 60 months.

(l)(1)(ii) To determine an employee's fitness for using a respirator, the employer shall provide the limited medical examination specified in paragraph (l)(6) of this Section.

(l)(1)(iii) The employer shall assure that all medical examinations and procedures required by this Standard are performed by or under the supervision of a licensed physician, who has read and is familiar with the health effects Section of Appendix A to this Section, the regulatory text of this Section, the protocol for sample handling and laboratory selection in Appendix F to this Section, and the questionnaire of Appendix D to this Section. These examinations and procedures shall be provided without cost to the employee and at a time and place that is reasonable and convenient to employees.

(l)(1)(iv) The employer shall assure that the collecting and handling of biological samples of cadmium in urine (CdU), cadmium in blood (CdB), and beta-2 microglobulin in urine (β_2-M) taken from employees under this Section is done in a manner that assures their reliability and that analysis of biological samples of cadmium in urine (CdU), cadmium in blood (CdB), and beta-2 microglobulin in urine (β_2-M) taken from employees under this Section is performed in laboratories with demonstrated proficiency for that particular analyte. (See Appendix F to this Section.)

(l)(2) **Initial examination**

(l)(2)(i) The employer shall provide an initial (preplacement) examination to all employees covered by the medical surveillance program required in paragraph (l)(1)(i) of this Section. The examination shall be provided to those employees within 30 days after initial assignment to a job with exposure to cadmium or no later than 90 days after the effective date of this Section, whichever date is later.

(l)(2)(ii) The initial (preplacement) medical examination shall include:

(l)(2)(ii)(A) A detailed medical and work history, with emphasis on: Past, present, and anticipated future exposure to cadmium; any history of renal, cardiovascular, respiratory, hematopoietic, reproductive, and/or musculo-skeletal system dysfunction; current usage of medication with potential nephrotoxic side-effects; and smoking history and current status; and

(l)(2)(ii)(B) Biological monitoring that includes the following tests:

(l)(2)(ii)(B)(1) Cadmium in urine (CdU), Standardized to grams of creatinine (g/Cr);

(l)(2)(ii)(B)(2) Beta-2 microglobulin in urine (β_2-M), standardized to grams of creatinine (g/Cr), with pH specified, as described in Appendix F to this Section; and

(l)(2)(ii)(B)(3) Cadmium in blood (CdB), standardized to liters of whole blood (lwb).

(l)(2)(iii) Recent Examination: An initial examination is not required to be provided if adequate records show that the employee has been examined in accordance with the requirements of paragraph (l)(2)(ii) of this Section within the past 12 months. In that case, such records shall be maintained as part of the employee's medical record and the prior exam shall be treated as if it were an initial examination for the purposes of paragraphs (l)(3) and (4) of this Section.

(l)(3) **Actions triggered by initial biological monitoring:**

(l)(3)(i) If the results of the initial biological monitoring tests show the employee's CdU level to be at or below 3 µg/g Cr, β_2-M level to be at or below 300 µg/g Cr and CdB level to be at or below 5 µg/lwb, then:

(l)(3)(i)(A) For currently exposed employees, who are subject to medical surveillance under paragraph (l)(1)(i)(A) of this Section, the employer shall provide the minimum level of periodic medical surveillance in accordance with the requirements in paragraph (l)(4)(i) of this Section; and

(l)(3)(i)(B) For previously exposed employees, who are subject to medical surveillance under paragraph (l)(1)(i)(B) of this Section, the employer shall provide biological monitoring for CdU, β_2-M, and CdB one year after the initial biological monitoring and then the employer shall comply with the requirements of paragraph (l)(4)(v) of this Section.

(l)(3)(ii) For all employees who are subject to medical surveillance under paragraph (l)(1)(i) of this Section, if the results of the initial biological monitoring tests show the level of CdU to exceed 3 µg/g Cr, the level of β_2-M to exceed 300 µg/g Cr, or the level of CdB to exceed 5 µg/lwb, the employer shall:

(l)(3)(ii)(A) Within two weeks after receipt of biological monitoring results, reassess the employee's occupational exposure to cadmium as follows:

(l)(3)(ii)(A)(1) Reassess the employee's work practices and personal hygiene;

(l)(3)(ii)(A)(2) Reevaluate the employee's respirator use, if any, and the respirator program;

(l)(3)(ii)(A)(3) Review the hygiene facilities;

(l)(3)(ii)(A)(4) Reevaluate the maintenance and effectiveness of the relevant engineering controls; and

(l)(3)(ii)(A)(5) Assess the employee's smoking history and status.

(l)(3)(ii)(B) Within 30 days after the exposure reassessment, specified in paragraph (l)(3)(ii)(A) of this Section, take reasonable steps to correct any deficiencies found in the reassessment that may be responsible for the employee's excess exposure to cadmium; and,

(l)(3)(ii)(C) Within 90 days after receipt of biological monitoring results, provide a full medical examination to the employee in accordance with the requirements of paragraph (l)(4)(ii) of this Section. After completing the medical examination, the examining physician shall determine in a written medical opinion whether to medically remove the employee. If the physician determines that medical removal is not necessary, then until the employee's CdU level falls to or below 3 µg/g Cr, β_2-M level falls to or below 300 µg/g Cr and CdB level falls to or below 5 µg/lwb, the employer shall:

(l)(3)(ii)(C)(1) Provide biological monitoring in accordance with paragraph (l)(2)(ii)(B) of this Section on a semiannual basis; and

(l)(3)(ii)(C)(2) Provide annual medical examinations in accordance with paragraph (l)(4)(ii) of this Section.

(l)(3)(iii) For all employees who are subject to medical surveillance under paragraph (l)(1)(i) of this Section, if the results of the initial biological monitoring tests show the level of CdU to be in excess of 15 µg/g Cr, or the level of CdB to be in excess of 15 µg/lwb, or the level of β_2-M to be in excess of 1,500 µg/g Cr, the employer shall comply with the requirements of paragraphs (l)(3)(ii)(A)–(B) of this Section. Within 90 days after receipt of biological monitoring results, the employer shall provide a full medical examination to the employee in accordance with the requirements of paragraph (l)(4)(ii) of this Section. After completing the medical examination, the examining physician shall determine in a written medical opinion whether to medically remove the employee. However, if the initial biological monitoring results and the biological monitoring results obtained during the medical examination both show that: CdU exceeds 15 µg/g Cr; or CdB exceeds 15 µg/lwb; or β_2-M exceeds 1500 µg/g Cr, and in addition CdU exceeds 3 µg/g Cr or CdB exceeds 5 µg/liter of whole blood, then the physician shall medically remove the employee from exposure to cadmium at or above the action level. If the second set of biological monitoring results obtained during the medical examination does not show that a mandatory removal trigger level has been exceeded, then the employee is not required to be removed by the mandatory provisions of this paragraph. If the employee is not required to be removed by the mandatory provisions of this paragraph or by the physician's determination, then until the employee's CdU level falls to or below 3 µg/g Cr, β_2-M level falls to or below 300 µg/g Cr and CdB level falls to or below 5 µg/lwb, the employer shall:

(l)(3)(iii)(A) Periodically reassess the employee's occupational exposure to cadmium;

(l)(3)(iii)(B) Provide biological monitoring in accordance with paragraph (l)(2)(ii)(B) of this Section on a quarterly basis; and

(l)(3)(iii)(C) Provide semiannual medical examinations in accordance with paragraph (l)(4)(ii) of this Section.

(l)(3)(iv) For all employees to whom medical surveillance is provided, beginning on January 1, 1999, and in lieu of paragraphs (l)(3)(i)–(iii) of this Section:

(l)(3)(iv)(A) If the results of the initial biological monitoring tests show the employee's CdU level to be at or below 3 µg/g Cr, β_2-M level to be at or below 300 µg/g Cr and CdB level to be at or below 5 µg/lwb, then for currently exposed employees, the employer shall comply with the requirements of paragraph (l)(3)(i)(A) of this Section, and for previously exposed employees, the employer shall comply with the requirements of paragraph (l)(3)(i)(B) of this Section;

(l)(3)(iv)(B) If the results of the initial biological monitoring tests show the level of CdU to exceed 3 µg/g Cr, the level of β_2-M to exceed 300 µg/g Cr, or the level of CdB to exceed 5 µg/lwb, the employer shall comply with the requirements of paragraphs (l)(3)(ii)(A)–(C) of this Section; and,

(l)(3)(iv)(C) If the results of the initial biological monitoring tests show the level of CdU to be in excess of 7 µg/g Cr, or the level of CdB to be in excess of 10 µg/lwb, or the level of β_2-M to be in excess of 750 µg/g Cr, the employer shall: Comply with the requirements of paragraphs (l)(3)(ii)(A)–(B) of this Section; and, within 90 days after receipt of biological monitoring results, provide a full medical examination to the employee in accordance with the requirements of paragraph (l)(4)(ii) of this Section. After completing the medical examination, the examining physician shall determine in a written medical opinion whether to medically remove the employee. However, if the initial biological monitoring results and the biological monitoring results obtained during the medical examination both show that: CdU exceeds 7 µg/g Cr; or CdB exceeds 10 µg/lwb; or β_2-M exceeds 750 µg/g Cr, and in addition CdU exceeds 3 µg/g Cr or CdB exceeds 5 µg/liter of whole blood, then the physician shall medically remove the employee from exposure to cadmium at or above the action level. If the second set of biological monitoring results obtained during the medical examination does not show that a mandatory removal trigger level has been exceeded, then the employee is not required to be removed by the mandatory provisions of this paragraph. If the employee is not required to be removed by the mandatory provisions of this paragraph or by the physician's determination, then until the employee's CdU level falls to or below 3 µg/g Cr, β_2-M level falls to or below 300 µg/g Cr and CdB level falls to or below 5 µg/lwb, the employer shall: periodically reassess the employee's occupational exposure to cadmium; provide biological monitoring in accordance with paragraph (l)(2)(ii)(B) of this Section on a quarterly basis; and provide semiannual medical examinations in accordance with paragraph (l)(4)(ii) of this Section.

(l)(4) Periodic medical surveillance

(l)(4)(i) For each employee who is covered under paragraph (l)(1)(i)(A) of this Section, the employer shall provide at least the minimum level of periodic medical surveillance, which consists of periodic medical examinations and periodic biological monitoring. A periodic medical examination shall be provided within one year after the initial examination required by paragraph (l)(2) of this Section and thereafter at least biennially. Biological sampling shall be provided at least annually, either as part of a periodic medical examination or separately as periodic biological monitoring.

(l)(4)(ii) The periodic medical examination shall include:

(l)(4)(ii)(A) A detailed medical and work history, or update thereof, with emphasis on: Past, present and anticipated future exposure to cadmium; smoking history and current status; reproductive history; current use of medications with potential nephrotoxic side-effects; any history of renal, cardiovascular, respiratory, hematopoietic, and/or musculo-skeletal system dysfunction; and as part of the medical and work history, for employees who wear respirators, questions 3–11 and 25–32 in Appendix D to this Section;

(l)(4)(ii)(B) A complete physical examination with emphasis on: Blood pressure, the respiratory system, and the urinary system;

(l)(4)(ii)(C) OI A 14 inch by 17 inch, or a reasonably standard sized posterior-anterior chest X-ray (after the initial X-ray, the frequency of chest X-rays is to be determined by the examining physician);

(l)(4)(ii)(D) Pulmonary function tests, including forced vital capacity (FVC) and forced expiratory volume at 1 second (FEV1);

(l)(4)(ii)(E) Biological monitoring, as required in paragraph (l)(2)(ii)(B) of this Section;

(l)(4)(ii)(F) Blood analysis, in addition to the analysis required under paragraph (l)(2)(ii)(B) of this Section, including blood urea nitrogen, complete blood count, and serum creatinine;

(l)(4)(ii)(G) Urinalysis, in addition to the analysis required under paragraph (l)(2)(ii)(B) of this Section, including the determination of albumin, glucose, and total and low molecular weight proteins;

(l)(4)(ii)(H) For males over 40 years old, prostate palpation, or other at least as effective diagnostic test(s); and

(l)(4)(ii)(I) Any additional tests deemed appropriate by the examining physician.

(l)(4)(iii) Periodic biological monitoring shall be provided in accordance with paragraph (l)(2)(ii)(B) of this Section.

(l)(4)(iv) If the results of periodic biological monitoring or the results of biological monitoring performed as part of the periodic medical examination show the level of the employee's CdU, β_2-M, or CdB to be in excess of the levels specified in paragraphs (l)(3)(ii) or (iii); or, beginning on January 1, 1999, in excess of the levels specified in paragraphs (l)(3)(ii) or (iv) of this Section, the employer shall take the appropriate actions specified in paragraphs (l)(3)(ii)–(iv) of this Section.

(l)(4)(v) For previously exposed employees under paragraph (l)(1)(i)(B) of this Section:

(l)(4)(v)(A) If the employee's levels of CdU did not exceed 3 µg/g Cr, CdB did not exceed 5 µg/lwb, and β_2-M did not exceed 300 µg/g Cr in the initial biological monitoring tests, and if the results of the followup biological monitoring required by paragraph (l)(3)(i)(B) of this Section one year after the initial examination confirm the previous results, the employer may discontinue all periodic medical surveillance for that employee.

(l)(4)(v)(B) If the initial biological monitoring results for CdU, CdB, or β_2-M were in excess of the levels specified in paragraph (l)(3)(i) of this Section, but subsequent biological monitoring results required by paragraph (l)(3)(ii)–(iv) of this Section show that the employee's CdU levels no longer exceed 3 µg/g Cr, CdB levels no longer exceed 5 µg/lwb, and β_2-M levels no longer exceed 300 µg/g Cr, the employer shall provide biological monitoring for CdU, CdB, and β_2-M one year after these most recent biological monitoring results. If the results of the followup biological monitoring, specified in this paragraph, confirm the previous results, the employer may discontinue all periodic medical surveillance for that employee.

(l)(4)(v)(C) However, if the results of the follow-up tests specified in paragraph (l)(4)(v)(A) or (B) of this Section indicate that the level of the employee's CdU, β2–M, or CdB exceeds these same levels, the employer is required to provide annual medical examinations in accordance with the provisions of paragraph (l)(4)(ii) of this Section until the results of biological monitoring are consistently below these levels or the examining physician determines in a written medical opinion that further medical surveillance is not required to protect the employee's health.

(l)(4)(vi) A routine, biennial medical examination is not required to be provided in accordance with paragraphs (l)(3)(i) and (l)(4) of this Section if adequate medical records show that the employee has been examined in accordance with the requirements of paragraph (l)(4)(ii) of this Section within the past 12 months. In that case, such records shall be maintained by the employer as part of the employee's medical record, and the next routine, periodic medical examination shall be made available to the employee within two years of the previous examination.

(l)(5) Actions triggered by medical examinations

(l)(5)(i) If the results of a medical examination carried out in accordance with this Section indicate any laboratory or clinical finding consistent with cadmium toxicity that does not require employer action under paragraph (l)(2), (3) or (4) of this Section, the employer, within 30 days, shall reassess the employee's occupational exposure to cadmium and take the following corrective action until the physician determines they are no longer necessary:

(l)(5)(i)(A) Periodically reassess: The employee's work practices and personal hygiene; the employee's respirator use, if any; the employee's smoking history and status; the respiratory protection program; the hygiene facilities; and the maintenance and effectiveness of the relevant engineering controls;

(l)(5)(i)(B) Within 30 days after the reassessment, take all reasonable steps to correct the deficiencies found in the reassessment that may be responsible for the employee's excess exposure to cadmium;

(l)(5)(i)(C) Provide semiannual medical reexaminations to evaluate the abnormal clinical sign(s) of cadmium toxicity until the results are normal or the employee is medically removed; and

(l)(5)(i)(D) Where the results of tests for total proteins in urine are abnormal, provide a more detailed medical evaluation of the toxic effects of cadmium on the employee's renal system.

(l)(6) Examination for respirator use

(l)(6)(i) To determine an employee's fitness for respirator use, the employer shall provide a medical examination that includes the elements specified in paragraph (l)(6)(i)(A)–(D) of this Section. This examination shall be provided prior to the employee's being assigned to a job that requires the use of a respirator or no later than 90 days after this Section goes into effect, whichever date is later, to any employee without a medical examination within the preceding 12 months that satisfies the requirements of this paragraph.

(l)(6)(i)(A) A detailed medical and work history, or update thereof, with emphasis on: Past exposure to cadmium; smoking history and current status; any history of renal, cardiovascular, respiratory, hematopoietic, and/or musculoskeletal system dysfunction; a description of the job for which the respirator is required; and questions 3–11 and 25–32 in Appendix D to this Section;

(l)(6)(i)(B) A blood pressure test;

(l)(6)(i)(C) Biological monitoring of the employee's levels of CdU, CdB and β_2-M in accordance with the requirements of paragraph (l)(2)(ii)(B) of this Section, unless such results already have been obtained within the previous 12 months; and

(l)(6)(i)(D) Any other test or procedure that the examining physician deems appropriate.

(l)(6)(ii) After reviewing all the information obtained from the medical examination required in paragraph (l)(6)(i) of this Section, the physician shall determine whether the employee is fit to wear a respirator.

(l)(6)(iii) Whenever an employee has exhibited difficulty in breathing during a respirator fit test or during use of a respirator, the employer, as soon as possible, shall provide the employee with a periodic medical examination in accordance with paragraph (l)(4)(ii) of this Section to determine the employee's fitness to wear a respirator.

(l)(6)(iv) Where the results of the examination required under paragraph (l)(6)(i), (ii), or (iii) of this Section are abnormal, medical limitation or prohibition of respirator use shall be considered. If the employee is allowed to wear a respirator, the employee's ability to continue to do so shall be periodically evaluated by a physician.

(l)(7) Emergency examinations

(l)(7)(i) In addition to the medical surveillance required in paragraphs (l)(2)–(6) of this Section, the employer shall provide a medical examination as soon as possible to any employee who may have been acutely exposed to cadmium because of an emergency.

(l)(7)(ii) The examination shall include the requirements of paragraph (l)(4)(ii) of this Section, with emphasis on the respiratory system, other organ systems considered appropriate by the examining physician, and symptoms of acute overexposure, as identified in paragraphs II (B)(1)–(2) and IV of Appendix A to this Section.

(l)(8) Termination of employment examination

(l)(8)(i) At termination of employment, the employer shall provide a medical examination in accordance with paragraph (l)(4)(ii) of this Section, including a chest X-ray, to any employee to whom at any prior time the employer was required to provide medical surveillance under paragraphs (l)(1)(i) or (l)(7) of this Section. However, if the last examination satisfied the requirements of paragraph (l)(4)(ii) of this Section and was less than six months prior to the date of termination, no further examination is required unless otherwise specified in paragraphs (l)(3) or (l)(5) of this Section;

(l)(8)(ii) However, for employees covered by paragraph (l)(1)(i)(B) of this Section, if the employer has discontinued all periodic medical surveillance under paragraph (l)(4)(v) of this Section, no termination of employment medical examination is required.

(l)(9) Information provided to the physician The employer shall provide the following information to the examining physician:

(l)(9)(i) A copy of this Standard and Appendices;

(l)(9)(ii) A description of the affected employee's former, current, and anticipated duties as they relate to the employee's occupational exposure to cadmium;

(l)(9)(iii) The employee's former, current, and anticipated future levels of occupational exposure to cadmium;

(l)(9)(iv) A description of any personal protective equipment, including respirators, used or to be used by the employee, including when and for how long the employee has used that equipment; and

(l)(9)(v) relevant results of previous biological monitoring and medical examinations.

(l)(10) Physician's written medical opinion

(l)(10)(i) The employer shall promptly obtain a written, medical opinion from the examining physician for each medical examination performed on each employee. This written opinion shall contain:

(l)(10)(i)(A) The physician's diagnosis for the employee;

(l)(10)(i)(B) The physician's opinion as to whether the employee has any detected medical condition(s) that would place the employee at increased risk of material impairment to health from further exposure to cadmium, including any indications of potential cadmium toxicity;

(l)(10)(i)(C) The results of any biological or other testing or related evaluations that directly assess the employee's absorption of cadmium;

(l)(10)(i)(D) Any recommended removal from, or limitation on the activities or duties of the employee or on the employee's use of personal protective equipment, such as respirators;

(l)(10)(i)(E) A statement that the physician has clearly and carefully explained to the employee the results of the medical examination, including all biological monitoring results and any medical conditions related to cadmium exposure that require further evaluation or treatment, and any limitation on the employee's diet or use of medications.

(l)(10)(ii) The employer promptly shall obtain a copy of the results of any biological monitoring provided by an employer to an employee independently of a medical examination under paragraphs (l)(2) and (l)(4) of this Section, and, in lieu of a written medical opinion, an explanation sheet explaining those results.

(l)(10)(iii) The employer shall instruct the physician not to reveal orally or in the written medical opinion given to the employer specific findings or diagnoses unrelated to occupational exposure to cadmium.

(l)(11) Medical Removal Protection (MRP)

(l)(11)(i) General

(l)(11)(i)(A) The employer shall temporarily remove an employee from work where there is excess exposure to cadmium on each occasion that medical removal is required under paragraph (l)(3), (l)(4), or (l)(6) of this Section and on each occasion that a physician determines in a written medical opinion that the employee should be removed from such exposure. The physician's determination may be based on biological monitoring results, inability to wear a respirator, evidence of illness, other signs or symptoms of cadmium-related dysfunction or disease, or any other reason deemed medically sufficient by the physician.

(l)(11)(i)(B) The employer shall medically remove an employee in accordance with paragraph (l)(11) of this Section regardless of whether at the time of removal a job is available into which the removed employee may be transferred.

(l)(11)(i)(C) Whenever an employee is medically removed under paragraph (l)(11) of this Section, the employer shall transfer the removed employee to a job where the exposure to cadmium is within the permissible levels specified in that paragraph as soon as one becomes available.

(l)(11)(i)(D) For any employee who is medically removed under the provisions of paragraph (l)(11)(i) of this Section, the employer shall provide follow-up biological monitoring in accordance with (l)(2)(ii)(B) of this Section at least every three months and follow-up medical examinations semi-annually at least every six months until in a written medical opinion the examining physician determines that either the employee may be returned to his/her former job status as specified under paragraph (l)(11)(iv)–(v) of this Section or the employee must be permanently removed from excess cadmium exposure.

(l)(11)(i)(E) The employer may not return an employee who has been medically removed for any reason to his/her former job status until a physician determines in a written medical opinion that continued medical removal is no longer necessary to protect the employee's health.

(l)(11)(ii) Where an employee is found unfit to wear a respirator under paragraph (l)(6)(ii) of this Section, the employer shall remove the employee from work where exposure to cadmium is above the PEL.

(l)(11)(iii) Where removal is based on any reason other than the employee's inability to wear a respirator, the employer shall remove the employee from work where exposure to cadmium is at or above the action level.

(l)(11)(iv) Except as specified in paragraph (l)(11)(v) of this Section, no employee who was removed because his/her level of CdU, CdB and/or β_2-M exceeded the medical removal trigger levels in paragraph (l)(3) or (l)(4) of this Section may be returned to work with exposure to cadmium at or above the action level until the employee's levels of CdU fall to or below 3 µg/g Cr, CdB falls to or below 5 µg/lwb, and β_2-M falls to or below 300 µg/g Cr.

(l)(11)(v) However, when in the examining physician's opinion continued exposure to cadmium will not pose an increased risk to the employee's health and there are special circumstances that make continued medical removal an inappropriate remedy, the physician shall fully discuss these matters with the employee, and then in a written determination may return a worker to his/her former job status despite what would otherwise be unacceptably high biological monitoring results. Thereafter, the returned employee shall continue to be provided with medical surveillance as if he/she were still on medical removal until the employee's levels of CdU fall to or below 3 µg/g Cr, CdB falls to or below 5 µg/lwb, and β_2-M falls to or below 300 µg/g Cr.

(l)(11)(vi) Where an employer, although not required by paragraph (l)(11)(i)–(iii) of this Section to do so, removes an employee from exposure to cadmium or otherwise places limitations on an employee due to the effects of cadmium exposure on the employee's medical condition, the employer shall provide the same medical removal protection benefits to that employee under paragraph (l)(12) of this Section as would have been provided had the removal been required under paragraph (l)(11)(i)–(iii) of this Section.

(l)(12) **Medical Removal Protection Benefits (MRPB)**

(l)(12)(i) The employer shall provide MRPB for up to a maximum of 18 months to an employee each time and while the employee is temporarily medically removed under paragraph (l)(11) of this Section.

(l)(12)(ii) For purposes of this Section, the requirement that the employer provide MRPB means that the employer shall maintain the total normal earnings, seniority, and all other employee rights and benefits of the removed employee, including the employee's right to his/her former job status, as if the employee had not been removed from the employee's job or otherwise medically limited.

(l)(12)(iii) Where, after 18 months on medical removal because of elevated biological monitoring results, the employee's monitoring results have not declined to a low enough level to permit the employee to be returned to his/her former job status:

(l)(12)(iii)(A) The employer shall make available to the employee a medical examination pursuant to this Section in order to obtain a final medical determination as to whether the employee may be returned to his/her former job status or must be permanently removed from excess cadmium exposure; and

(l)(12)(iii)(B) The employer shall assure that the final medical determination indicates whether the employee may be returned to his/her former job status and what steps, if any, should be taken to protect the employee's health.

(l)(12)(iv) The employer may condition the provision of MRPB upon the employee's participation in medical surveillance provided in accordance with this Section.

(l)(13) **Multiple physician review**

(l)(13)(i) If the employer selects the initial physician to conduct any medical examination or consultation provided to an employee under this Section, the employee may designate a second physician to:

(l)(13)(i)(A) Review any findings, determinations, or recommendations of the initial physician; and

(l)(13)(i)(B) Conduct such examinations, consultations, and laboratory tests as the second physician deems necessary to facilitate this review.

(l)(13)(ii) The employer shall promptly notify an employee of the right to seek a second medical opinion after each occasion that an initial physician provided by the employer conducts a medical examination or consultation pursuant to this Section. The employer may condition its participation in, and payment for, multiple physician review upon the employee doing the following within fifteen (15) days after receipt of this notice, or receipt of the initial physician's written opinion, whichever is later:

(l)(13)(ii)(A) Informing the employer that he or she intends to seek a medical opinion; and

(l)(13)(ii)(B) Initiating steps to make an appointment with a second physician.

(l)(13)(iii) If the findings, determinations, or recommendations of the second physician differ from those of the initial physician, then the employer and the employee shall assure that efforts are made for the two physicians to resolve any disagreement.

(l)(13)(iv) If the two physicians have been unable to quickly resolve their disagreement, then the employer and the employee, through their respective physicians, shall designate a third physician to:

(l)(13)(iv)(A) Review any findings, determinations, or recommendations of the other two physicians; and

(l)(13)(iv)(B) Conduct such examinations, consultations, laboratory tests, and discussions with the other two physicians as the third physician deems necessary to resolve the disagreement among them.

(l)(13)(v) The employer shall act consistently with the findings, determinations, and recommendations of the third physician, unless the employer and the employee reach an agreement that is consistent with the recommendations of at least one of the other two physicians.

(l)(14) **Alternate physician determination** The employer and an employee or designated employee representative may agree upon the use of any alternate form of physician determination in lieu of the multiple physician review provided by paragraph (l)(13) of this Section, so long as the alternative is expeditious and at least as protective of the employee.

(l)(15) **Information the employer must provide the employee**

(l)(15)(i) The employer shall provide a copy of the physician's written medical opinion to the examined employee within two weeks after receipt thereof.

(l)(15)(ii) The employer shall provide the employee with a copy of the employee's biological monitoring results and an explanation sheet explaining the results within two weeks after receipt thereof.

(l)(15)(iii) Within 30 days after a request by an employee, the employer shall provide the employee with the information the employer is required to provide the examining physician under paragraph (l)(9) of this Section.

(l)(16) **Reporting** In addition to other medical events that are required to be reported on the OSHA Form No. 200, the employer shall report any abnormal condition or disorder caused by occupational exposure to cadmium associated with employment as specified in Chapter (V)(E) of the Reporting Guidelines for Occupational Injuries and Illnesses.

(m) **Communication of cadmium hazards to employees**

(m)(1) **Hazard communication.—general**

(m)(1)(i) Chemical manufacturers, importers, distributors and employers shall comply with all requirements of the Hazard Communication Standard (HCS) (§1910.1200) for cadmium.

(m)(1)(ii) In classifying the hazards of cadmium at least the following hazards are to be addressed: Cancer; lung effects; kidney effects; and acute toxicity effects.

(m)(1)(iii) Employers shall include cadmium in the hazard communication program established to comply with the HCS (§1910.1200). Employers shall ensure that each employee has access to labels on containers of cadmium and to safety data sheets, and is trained in accordance with the requirements of HCS and paragraph (m)(4) of this Section.

(m)(2) Warning signs

(m)(2)(i) Warning signs shall be provided and displayed in regulated areas. In addition, warning signs shall be posted at all approaches to regulated areas so that an employee may read the signs and take necessary protective steps before entering the area.

(m)(2)(ii) Warning signs required by paragraph (m)(2)(i) of this Section shall bear the following legend:

DANGER
CADMIUM
MAY CAUSE CANCER
CAUSES DAMAGE TO LUNGS AND KIDNEYS
WEAR RESPIRATORY PROTECTION IN THIS AREA
AUTHORIZED PERSONNEL ONLY

(m)(2)(iii) The employer shall ensure that signs required by this paragraph (m)(2) are illuminated, cleaned, and maintained as necessary so that the legend is readily visible.

(m)(2)(iv) Prior to June 1, 2016, employers may use the following legend in lieu of that specified in paragraph (m)(2)(ii) of this Section:

DANGER
CADMIUM
CANCER HAZARD
CAN CAUSE LUNG AND KIDNEY DISEASE
AUTHORIZED PERSONNEL ONLY
RESPIRATORS REQUIRED IN THIS AREA

(m)(3) Warning labels

(m)(3)(i) Shipping and storage containers containing cadmium or cadmium compounds shall bear appropriate warning labels, as specified in paragraph (m)(1) of this Section.

(m)(3)(ii) The warning labels for containers of contaminated protective clothing, equipment, waste, scrap, or debris shall include at least the following information:

DANGER
CONTAINS CADMIUM
MAY CAUSE CANCER
CAUSES DAMAGE TO LUNGS AND KIDNEYS
AVOID CREATING DUST

(m)(3)(iii) Prior to June 1, 2015, employers may include the following information on shipping and storage containers containing cadmium, cadmium compounds, or cadmium contaminated clothing, equipment, waste, scrap, or debris in lieu of the labeling requirements specified in paragraphs (m)(1)(i) and (m)(3)(ii) of this Section:

DANGER
CONTAINS CADMIUM
CANCER HAZARD
AVOID CREATING DUST
CAN CAUSE LUNG AND KIDNEY DISEASE

(m)(3)(iv) Where feasible, installed cadmium products shall have a visible label or other indication that cadmium is present.

(m)(4) Employee information and training

(m)(4)(i) The employer shall train each employee who is potentially exposed to cadmium in accordance with the requirements of this Section. The employer shall institute a training program, ensure employee participation in the program, and maintain a record of the contents of such program.

(m)(4)(ii) Training shall be provided prior to or at the time of initial assignment to a job involving potential exposure to cadmium and at least annually thereafter.

(m)(4)(iii) The employer shall make the training program understandable to the employee and shall assure that each employee is informed of the following:

(m)(4)(iii)(A) The health hazards associated with cadmium exposure, with special attention to the information incorporated in Appendix A to this Section;

(m)(4)(iii)(B) The quantity, location, manner of use, release, and storage of cadmium in the workplace and the specific nature of operations that could result in exposure to cadmium, especially exposures above the PEL;

(m)(4)(iii)(C) The engineering controls and work practices associated with the employee's job assignment;

(m)(4)(iii)(D) The measures employees can take to protect themselves from exposure to cadmium, including modification of such habits as smoking and personal hygiene, and specific procedures the employer has implemented to protect employees from exposure to cadmium such as appropriate work practices, emergency procedures, and the provision of personal protective equipment;

(m)(4)(iii)(E) The purpose, proper selection, fitting, proper use, and limitations of respirators and protective clothing;

(m)(4)(iii)(F) The purpose and a description of the medical surveillance program required by paragraph (l) of this Section;

(m)(4)(iii)(G) The contents of this Section and its Appendices; and

(m)(4)(iii)(H) The employee's rights of access to records under §1910.1020(e) and (g).

(m)(4)(iv) Additional access to information and training program and materials.

(m)(4)(iv)(A) The employer shall make a copy of this Section and its Appendices readily available without cost to all affected employees and shall provide a copy if requested.

(m)(4)(iv)(B) The employer shall provide to the Assistant Secretary or the Director, upon request, all materials relating to the employee information and the training program.

(n) Recordkeeping

(n)(1) Exposure monitoring

(n)(1)(i) The employer shall establish and keep an accurate record of all air monitoring for cadmium in the workplace.

(n)(1)(ii) This record shall include at least the following information:

(n)(1)(ii)(A) The monitoring date, duration, and results in terms of an 8-hour TWA of each sample taken;

(n)(1)(ii)(B) The name, social security number, and job classification of the employees monitored and of all other employees whose exposures the monitoring is intended to represent;

(n)(1)(ii)(C) A description of the sampling and analytical methods used and evidence of their accuracy;

(n)(1)(ii)(D) The type of respiratory protective device, if any, worn by the monitored employee;

(n)(1)(ii)(E) A notation of any other conditions that might have affected the monitoring results.

(n)(1)(iii) The employer shall maintain this record for at least thirty (30) years, in accordance with 29 CFR §1910.1020.

(n)(2) Objective data for exemption from requirement for initial monitoring.

(n)(2)(i) For purposes of this Section, objective data are information demonstrating that a particular product or material containing cadmium or a specific process, operation, or activity involving cadmium cannot release dust or fumes in concentrations at or above the action level even under the worst-case release conditions. Objective data can be obtained from an industry-wide study or from laboratory product test results from manufacturers of cadmium-containing products or materials. The data the employer uses from an industry-wide survey must be obtained under workplace conditions closely resembling the processes, types of material, control methods, work practices and environmental conditions in the employer's current operations.

(n)(2)(ii) The employer shall establish and maintain a record of the objective data for at least 30 years.

(n)(3) Medical surveillance

(n)(3)(i) The employer shall establish and maintain an accurate record for each employee covered by medical surveillance under paragraph (l)(1)(i) of this Section.

(n)(3)(ii) The record shall include at least the following information about the employee:

(n)(3)(ii)(A) Name, social security number, and description of the duties;

(n)(3)(ii)(B) A copy of the physician's written opinions and an explanation sheet for biological monitoring results;

(n)(3)(ii)(C) A copy of the medical history, and the results of any physical examination and all test results that are required to be provided by this Section, including biological tests, X-rays, pulmonary function tests, etc., or that have been obtained to further evaluate any condition that might be related to cadmium exposure;

(n)(3)(ii)(D) The employee's medical symptoms that might be related to exposure to cadmium; and

(n)(3)(ii)(E) A copy of the information provided to the physician as required by paragraph (l)(9)(ii)–(v) of this Section.

(n)(3)(iii) The employer shall assure that this record is maintained for the duration of employment plus thirty (30) years, in accordance with 29 CFR §1910.1020.

(n)(4) Availability

(n)(4)(i) Except as otherwise provided for in this Section, access to all records required to be maintained by paragraphs (n)(1) through (3) of this Section shall be in accordance with the provisions of 29 CFR §1910.1020.

(n)(4)(ii) Within 15 days after a request, the employer shall make an employee's medical records required to be kept by paragraph (n)(3) of this Section available for examination and copying to the subject employee, to designated representatives, to anyone having the specific written consent of the subject employee, and after the employee's death or incapacitation, to the employee's family members.

(n)(5) **Transfer of records** Whenever an employer ceases to do business and there is no successor employer to receive and retain records for the prescribed period or the employer intends to dispose of any records required to be preserved for at least 30 years, the employer shall comply with the requirements concerning transfer of records set forth in 29 CFR §1910.1020 (h).

(o) **Observation of monitoring**

(o)(1) **Employee observation** The employer shall provide affected employees or their designated representatives an opportunity to observe any monitoring of employee exposure to cadmium.

(o)(2) **Observation procedures** When observation of monitoring requires entry into an area where the use of protective clothing or equipment is required, the employer shall provide the observer with that clothing and equipment and shall assure that the observer uses such clothing and equipment and complies with all other applicable safety and health procedures.

(p) **Dates**

(p)(1) **Effective date** This Section shall become effective December 14, 1992.

(p)(2) **Start-up dates** All obligations of this Section commence on the effective date except as follows:

(p)(2)(i) **Exposure monitoring** Except for small businesses (nineteen (19) or fewer employees), initial monitoring required by paragraph (d)(2) of this Section shall be completed as soon as possible and in any event no later than 60 days after the effective date of this Standard. For small businesses, initial monitoring required by paragraph (d)(2) of this Section shall be completed as soon as possible and in any event no later than 120 days after the effective date of this Standard.

(p)(2)(ii) **Regulated areas** Except for small business, defined under paragraph (p)(2)(i) of this Section, regulated areas required to be established by paragraph (e) of this Section shall be set up as soon as possible after the results of exposure monitoring are known and in any event no later than 90 days after the effective date of this Section. For small businesses, regulated areas required to be established by paragraph (e) of this Section shall be set up as soon as possible after the results of exposure monitoring are known and in any event no later than 150 days after the effective date of this Section.

(p)(2)(iii) **Respiratory protection** Except for small businesses, defined under paragraph (p)(2)(i) of this Section, respiratory protection required by paragraph (g) of this Section shall be provided as soon as possible and in any event no later than 90 days after the effective date of this Section. For small businesses, respiratory protection required by paragraph (g) of this Section shall be provided as soon as possible and in any event no later than 150 days after the effective date of this Section.

(p)(2)(iv) **Compliance program** Written compliance programs required by paragraph (f)(2) of this Section shall be completed and available for inspection and copying as soon as possible and in any event no later than 1 year after the effective date of this Section.

(p)(2)(v) **Methods of compliance** The engineering controls required by paragraph (f)(1) of this Section shall be implemented as soon as possible and in any event no later than two (2) years after the effective date of this Section. Work practice controls shall be implemented as soon as possible. Work practice controls that are directly related to engineering controls to be implemented in accordance with the compliance plan shall be implemented as soon as possible after such engineering controls are implemented.

(p)(2)(vi) **Hygiene and lunchroom facilities**

(p)(2)(vi)(A) Handwashing facilities, permanent or temporary, shall be provided in accordance with 29 CFR §1910.141 (d)(1) and (2) as soon as possible and in any event no later than 60 days after the effective date of this Section.

(p)(2)(vi)(B) Change rooms, showers, and lunchroom facilities shall be completed as soon as possible and in any event no later than 1 year after the effective date of this Section.

(p)(2)(vii) **Employee information and training** Except for small businesses, defined under paragraph (p)(2)(i) of this Section, employee information and training required by paragraph (m)(4) of this Section shall be provided as soon as possible and in any event no later than 90 days after the effective date of this Standard. For small businesses, employee information and training required by paragraph (m)(4) of this Standard shall be provided as soon as possible and in any event no later than 180 days after the effective date of this Standard.

(p)(2)(viii) **Medical surveillance** Except for small businesses, defined under paragraph (p)(2)(i) of this Section, initial medical examinations required by paragraph (l) of this Section shall be provided as soon as possible and in any event no later than 90 days after the effective date of this Standard. For small businesses, initial medical examinations required by paragraph (l) of this Section shall be provided as soon as possible and in any event no later than 180 days after the effective date of this Standard.

(q) **Appendices** Except where portions of Appendices A, B, D, E, and F to this Section are expressly incorporated in requirements of this Section, these Appendices are purely informational and are not intended to create any additional obligations not otherwise imposed or to detract from any existing obligations.

§1910.1027 Appendix A
Substance safety data sheet

Cadmium

I. Substance Identification

A. Substance: Cadmium

B. 8-Hour, Time-weighted-average, Permissible Exposure Limit (TWA PEL):

1. TWA PEL: Five micrograms of cadmium per cubic meter of air 5 $\mu g/m^3$, time-weighted average (TWA) for an 8-hour workday.

C. Appearance: Cadmium metal—soft, blue-white, malleable, lustrous metal or grayish-white powder. Some cadmium compounds may also appear as a brown, yellow, or red powdery substance.

II. Health Hazard Data

A. Routes of Exposure Cadmium can cause local skin or eye irritation. Cadmium can affect your health if you inhale it or if you swallow it.

B. Effects of Overexposure

1 Short-term (acute) exposure: Cadmium is much more dangerous by inhalation than by ingestion. High exposures to cadmium that may be immediately dangerous to life or health occur in jobs where workers handle large quantities of cadmium dust or fume; heat cadmium-containing compounds or cadmium-coated surfaces; weld with cadmium solders or cut cadmium-containing materials such as bolts.

2. Severe exposure may occur before symptoms appear. Early symptoms may include mild irritation of the upper respiratory tract, a sensation of constriction of the throat, a metallic taste and/or a cough. A period of 1–10 hours may precede the onset of rapidly progressing shortness of breath, chest pain, and flu-like symptoms with weakness, fever, headache, chills, sweating and muscular pain. Acute pulmonary edema usually develops within 24 hours and reaches a maximum by three days. If death from asphyxia does not occur, symptoms may resolve within a week.

3. Long-term (chronic) exposure. Repeated or long-term exposure to cadmium, even at relatively low concentrations, may result in kidney damage and an increased risk of cancer of the lung and of the prostate.

C. Emergency First Aid Procedures

1. Eye exposure: Direct contact may cause redness or pain. Wash eyes immediately with large amounts of water, lifting the upper and lower eyelids. Get medical attention immediately.
2. Skin exposure: Direct contact may result in irritation. Remove contaminated clothing and shoes immediately. Wash affected area with soap or mild detergent and large amounts of water. Get medical attention immediately.
3. Ingestion: Ingestion may result in vomiting, abdominal pain, nausea, diarrhea, headache and sore throat. Treatment for symptoms must be administered by medical personnel. Under no circumstances should the employer allow any person whom he retains, employs, supervises or controls to engage in therapeutic chelation. Such treatment is likely to translocate cadmium from pulmonary or other tissue to renal tissue. Get medical attention immediately.
4. Inhalation: If large amounts of cadmium are inhaled, the exposed person must be moved to fresh air at once. If breathing has stopped, perform cardiopulmonary resuscitation. Administer oxygen if available. Keep the affected person warm and at rest. Get medical attention immediately.
5. Rescue: Move the affected person from the hazardous exposure. If the exposed person has been overcome, attempt rescue only after notifying at least one other person of the emergency and putting into effect established emergency procedures. Do not become a casualty yourself. Understand your emergency rescue procedures and know the location of the emergency equipment before the need arises.

III. Employee Information

A. Protective Clothing and Equipment

1. Respirators: You may be required to wear a respirator for non-routine activities; in emergencies; while your employer is in the process of reducing cadmium exposures through engineering controls; and where engineering controls are not feasible. If respirators are worn in the future, they must have a joint Mine Safety and Health Administration (MSHA) and National Institute for Occupational Safety and Health (NIOSH) label of approval. Cadmium does not have a detectable odor except at levels well above the permissible exposure limits. If you can smell cadmium while wearing a respirator, proceed immediately to fresh air. If you experience difficulty breathing while wearing a respirator, tell your employer.
2. Protective Clothing: You may be required to wear impermeable clothing, gloves, foot gear, a face shield, or other appropriate

protective clothing to prevent skin contact with cadmium. Where protective clothing is required, your employer must provide clean garments to you as necessary to assure that the clothing protects you adequately. The employer must replace or repair protective clothing that has become torn or otherwise damaged.

3. Eye Protection: You may be required to wear splash-proof or dust resistant goggles to prevent eye contact with cadmium.

B. Employer Requirements

1. Medical: If you are exposed to cadmium at or above the action level, your employer is required to provide a medical examination, laboratory tests and a medical history according to the medical surveillance provisions under paragraph (1) of this Standard. (See summary chart and tables in this Appendix A.) These tests shall be provided without cost to you. In addition, if you are accidentally exposed to cadmium under conditions known or suspected to constitute toxic exposure to cadmium, your employer is required to make special tests available to you.
2. Access to Records: All medical records are kept strictly confidential. You or your representative are entitled to see the records of measurements of your exposure to cadmium. Your medical examination records can be furnished to your personal physician or designated representative upon request by you to your employer.
3. Observation of Monitoring: Your employer is required to perform measurements that are representative of your exposure to cadmium and you or your designated representative are entitled to observe the monitoring procedure. You are entitled to observe the steps taken in the measurement procedure, and to record the results obtained. When the monitoring procedure is taking place in an area where respirators or personal protective clothing and equipment are required to be worn, you or your representative must also be provided with, and must wear the protective clothing and equipment.

C. Employee Requirements You will not be able to smoke, eat, drink, chew gum or tobacco, or apply cosmetics while working with cadmium in regulated areas. You will also not be able to carry or store tobacco products, gum, food, drinks or cosmetics in regulated areas because these products easily become contaminated with cadmium from the workplace and can therefore create another source of unnecessary cadmium exposure.

Some workers will have to change out of work clothes and shower at the end of the day, as part of their workday, in order to wash cadmium from skin and hair. Handwashing and cadmium-free eating facilities shall be provided by the employer and proper hygiene should always be performed before eating. It is also recommended that you do not smoke or use tobacco products, because among other things, they naturally contain cadmium. For further information, read the labeling on such products.

IV. Physician Information

A. Introduction The medical surveillance provisions of paragraph (1) generally are aimed at accomplishing three main interrelated purposes: First, identifying employees at higher risk of adverse health effects from excess, chronic exposure to cadmium; second, preventing cadmium-induced disease; and third, detecting and minimizing existing cadmium-induced disease. The core of medical surveillance in this Standard is the early and periodic monitoring of the employee's biological indicators of: (a) Recent exposure to cadmium; (b) cadmium body burden; and (c) potential and actual kidney damage associated with exposure to cadmium.

The main adverse health effects associated with cadmium overexposure are lung cancer and kidney dysfunction. It is not yet known how to adequately biologically monitor human beings to specifically prevent cadmium-induced lung cancer. By contrast, the kidney can be monitored to provide prevention and early detection of cadmium-induced kidney damage. Since, for non-carcinogenic effects, the kidney is considered the primary target organ of chronic exposure to cadmium, the medical surveillance provisions of this Standard effectively focus on cadmium-induced kidney disease. Within that focus, the aim, where possible, is to prevent the onset of such disease and, where necessary, to minimize such disease as may already exist. The by-products of successful prevention of kidney disease are anticipated to be the reduction and prevention of other cadmium-induced diseases.

B. Health Effects The major health effects associated with cadmium overexposure are described below.

1. Kidney: The most prevalent non-malignant disease observed among workers chronically exposed to cadmium is kidney dysfunction. Initially, such dysfunction is manifested as proteinuria. The proteinuria associated with cadmium exposure is most commonly characterized by excretion of low-molecular weight proteins (15,000 to 40,000 MW) accompanied by loss of electrolytes, uric acid, calcium, amino acids, and phosphate. The compounds commonly excreted include: beta-2-microglobulin (β_2-M), retinol binding protein (RBP), immunoglobulin light chains, and lysozyme. Excretion of low molecular weight proteins are characteristic of damage to the proximal tubules of the kidney (Iwao et al., 1980).

It has also been observed that exposure to cadmium may lead to urinary excretion of high-molecular weight proteins such as albumin, immunoglobulin G, and glycoproteins (Ex. 29). Excretion of high-molecular weight proteins is typically indicative of damage to the glomeruli of the kidney. Bernard et al., (1979) suggest that damage to the glomeruli and damage to the proximal tubules of the kidney may both be linked to cadmium exposure but they may occur independently of each other.

Several studies indicate that the onset of low-molecular weight proteinuria is a sign of irreversible kidney damage (Friberg et al., 1974; Roels et al., 1982; Piscator 1984; Elinder et al., 1985; Smith et al., 1986). Above specific levels of β_2-M associated with cadmium exposure it is unlikely that β_2-M levels return to normal even when cadmium exposure is eliminated by removal of the individual from the cadmium work environment (Friberg, Ex. 29, 1990).

Some studies indicate that such proteinuria may be progressive; levels of β_2-M observed in the urine increase with time even after cadmium exposure has ceased. See, for example, Elinder et al., 1985. Such observations, however, are not universal, and it has been suggested that studies in which proteinuria has not been observed to progress may not have tracked patients for a sufficiently long time interval (Jarup, Ex. 8–661).

When cadmium exposure continues after the onset of proteinuria, chronic nephrotoxicity may occur (Friberg, Ex. 29). Uremia results from the inability of the glomerulus to adequately filter blood. This leads to severe disturbance of electrolyte concentrations and may lead to various clinical complications including kidney stones (L–140–50).

After prolonged exposure to cadmium, glomerular proteinuria, glucosuria, aminoaciduria, phosphaturia, and hypercalciuria may develop (Exs. 8–86, 4–28, 14–18). Phosphate, calcium, glucose, and amino acids are essential to life, and under normal conditions, their excretion should be regulated by the kidney. Once low molecular weight proteinuria has developed, these elements dissipate from the human body. Loss of glomerular function may also occur, manifested by decreased glomerular filtration rate and increased serum creatinine. Severe cadmium-induced renal damage may eventually develop into chronic renal failure and uremia (Ex. 55).

Studies in which animals are chronically exposed to cadmium confirm the renal effects observed in humans (Friberg et al., 1986). Animal studies also confirm problems with calcium metabolism and related skeletal effects which have been observed among humans exposed to cadmium in addition to the renal effects. Other effects commonly reported in chronic animal studies include anemia, changes in liver morphology, immunosuppression and hypertension. Some of these effects may be associated with co-factors. Hypertension, for example, appears to be associated with diet as well as cadmium exposure. Animals injected with cadmium have also shown testicular necrosis (Ex. 8–86B).

2. Biological Markers

It is universally recognized that the best measures of cadmium exposures and its effects are measurements of cadmium in biological fluids, especially urine and blood. Of the two, CdU is conventionally used to determine body burden of cadmium in workers without kidney disease. CdB is conventionally used to monitor for recent exposure to cadmium. In addition, levels of CdU and CdB historically have been used to predict the percent of the population likely to develop kidney disease (Thun et al., Ex. L–140–50; WHO, Ex. 8–674; ACGIH, Exs. 8–667, 140–50).

The third biological parameter upon which OSHA relies for medical surveillance is Beta-2-microglobulin in urine (β_2-M), a low molecular weight protein. Excess β_2-M has been widely accepted by physicians and scientists as a reliable indicator of functional damage to the proximal tubule of the kidney (Exs. 8–447, 144–3–C, 4–47, L–140–45, 19–43–A).

Excess β_2-M is found when the proximal tubules can no longer reabsorb this protein in a normal manner. This failure of the proximal tubules is an early stage of a kind of kidney disease that commonly occurs among workers with excessive cadmium exposure. Used in conjunction with biological test results indicating abnormal levels of CdU and CdB, the finding of excess β_2-M can establish for an examining physician that any existing kidney disease is probably cadmium-related (Trs. 6/6/90, pp. 82–86, 122, 134). The upper limits of normal levels for cadmium in urine and cadmium in blood are 3 µg Cd/gram creatinine in urine and 5 µgCd/liter whole blood, respectively. These levels were derived from broad-based population studies.

Three issues confront the physicians in the use of β_2-M as a marker of kidney dysfunction and material impairment. First, there are a few other causes of elevated levels of β_2-M not related to cadmium exposures, some of which may be rather common diseases and some of which are serious diseases (e.g., myeloma or transient flu, Exs. 29 and 8–086). These can be medically evaluated as alternative causes (Friberg, Ex. 29). Also, there are other factors that can cause β_2-M to degrade so that low levels would result in workers with tubular dysfunction. For example, regarding the degradation of β_2-M, workers with acidic urine (pH<6) might have β_2-M levels that are within the "normal" range when in fact kidney dysfunction has occurred (Ex. L–140–1) and the low molecular weight proteins are degraded in acid urine. Thus, it is very important that the pH of urine be measured, that urine samples be buffered as necessary (See Appendix F.), and that urine samples be handled correctly, i.e., measure the pH of freshly voided urine samples, then if necessary, buffer to pH>6 (or above for shipping purposes), measure pH again and then, perhaps, freeze the sample for storage and shipping. (See also Appendix F.) Second, there is debate over the pathological significance of proteinuria, however, most world experts believe that β_2-M levels greater than 300 µg/g Cr are abnormal (Elinder, Ex. 55, Friberg, Ex. 29). Such levels signify kidney dysfunction that constitutes material impairment of health. Finally, detection of β_2-M at low levels has often been considered difficult, however, many laboratories have the capability of detecting excess β_2-M using simple kits, such as the Phadebas Delphia test, that are accurate to levels of 100 µg β_2-M/g Cr U (Ex. L–140–1).

Specific recommendations for ways to measure β_2-M and proper handling of urine samples to prevent degradation of β_2-M have been addressed by OSHA in Appendix F, in the Section on laboratory standardization. All biological samples must be analyzed in a laboratory that is proficient in the analysis of that particular analyte, under paragraph (l)(1)(iv). (See Appendix F). Specifically, under paragraph (l)(1)(iv), the employer is to assure that the collecting and handling of biological samples of cadmium in urine (CdU), cadmium in blood (CdB), and beta-2 microglobulin in urine (β_2-M) taken from employees is collected in a manner that assures reliability. The employer must also assure that analysis of biological samples of cadmium in urine (CdU), cadmium in blood (CdB), and beta-2 microglobulin in urine (β_2-M) taken from employees is performed in laboratories with demonstrated proficiency for that particular analyte. (See Appendix F.)

3. Lung and Prostate Cancer

The primary sites for cadmium-associated cancer appear to be the lung and the prostate (L–140–50). Evidence for an association between cancer and cadmium exposure derives from both epidemiological studies and animal experiments. Mortality from prostate cancer associated with cadmium is slightly elevated in several industrial cohorts, but the number of cases is small and there is not clear dose-response relationship. More substantive evidence exists for lung cancer.

The major epidemiological study of lung cancer was conducted by Thun et al., (Ex. 4–68). Adequate data on cadmium exposures were available to allow evaluation of dose-response relationships between cadmium exposure and lung cancer. A statistically significant excess of lung cancer attributed to cadmium exposure was observed in this study even when confounding variables such as co-exposure to arsenic and smoking habits were taken into consideration (Ex. L–140–50).

The primary evidence for quantifying a link between lung cancer and cadmium exposure from animal studies derives from two rat bioassay studies; one by Takenaka et al., (1983), which is a study of cadmium chloride and a second study by Oldiges and Glaser (1990) of four cadmium compounds.

Based on the above cited studies, the U.S. Environmental Protection Agency (EPA) classified cadmium as "B1", a probable human carcinogen, in 1985 (Ex. 4–4). The International Agency for Research on Cancer (IARC) in 1987 also recommended that cadmium be listed as "2A", a probable human carcinogen (Ex. 4–15). The American Conference of Governmental Industrial Hygienists (ACGIH) has recently recommended that cadmium be labeled as a carcinogen. Since 1984, NIOSH has concluded that cadmium is possibly a human carcinogen and has recommended that exposures be controlled to the lowest level feasible.

4. Non-carcinogenic Effects

Acute pneumonitis occurs 10 to 24 hours after initial acute inhalation of high levels of cadmium fumes with symptoms such as fever and chest pain (Exs. 30, 8–86B). In extreme exposure cases pulmonary edema may develop and cause death several days after exposure. Little actual exposure measurement data is available on the level of airborne cadmium exposure that causes such immediate adverse lung effects, nonetheless, it is reasonable to believe a cadmium concentration of approximately 1 mg/m^3 over an eight hour period is "immediately dangerous" (55 FR 4052, ANSI; Ex. 8–86B).

In addition to acute lung effects and chronic renal effects, long term exposure to cadmium may cause other severe effects on the respiratory system. Reduced pulmonary function and chronic lung disease indicative of emphysema have been observed in workers who have had prolonged exposure to cadmium dust or fumes (Exs. 4–29, 4–22, 4–42, 4–50, 4–63). In a study of workers conducted by Kazantzis et al., a statistically significant excess of worker deaths due to chronic bronchitis was found, which in his opinion was directly related to high cadmium exposures of 1 mg/m^3 or more (Tr. 6/8/90, pp. 156–157).

Cadmium need not be respirable to constitute a hazard. Inspirable cadmium particles that are too large to be respirable but small enough to enter the tracheobronchial region of the lung can lead to bronchoconstriction, chronic pulmonary disease, and cancer of that portion of the lung. All of these diseases have been associated with occupational exposure to cadmium (Ex. 8–86B). Particles that are constrained by their size to the extra-thoracic regions of the respiratory system such as the nose and maxillary sinuses can be swallowed through mucocillary clearance and be absorbed into the body (ACGIH, Ex. 8–692). The impaction of these particles in the upper airways can lead to anosmia, or loss of sense of smell, which is an early indication of overexposure among workers exposed to heavy metals. This condition is commonly reported among cadmium-exposed workers (Ex. 8–86–B).

C. Medical Surveillance

In general, the main provisions of the medical surveillance Section of the Standard, under paragraphs (l)(1)–(17) of the regulatory text, are as follows:

1. Workers exposed above the action level are covered;
2. Workers with intermittent exposures are not covered;
3. Past workers who are covered receive biological monitoring for at least one year;
4. Initial examinations include a medical questionnaire and biological monitoring of cadmium in blood (CdB), cadmium in urine (CdU), and Beta-2-microglobulin in urine (β_2-M);
5. Biological monitoring of these three analytes is performed at least annually; full medical examinations are performed biennially;
6. Until five years from the effective date of the standard, medical removal is required when CdU is greater than 15 µg/gram creatinine (g Cr), or CdB is greater than 15 µg/liter whole blood (lwb), or β_2-M is greater than 1500 µg/g Cr, and CdB is greater than 5 µg/lwb or CdU is greater than 3 µg/g Cr;
7. Beginning five years after the Standard is in effect, medical removal triggers will be reduced;
8. Medical removal protection benefits are to be provided for up to 18 months;
9. Limited initial medical examinations are required for respirator usage;
10. Major provisions are fully described under Section (l) of the regulatory text; they are outlined here as follows:
    - A. Eligibility;
    - B. Biological monitoring;
    - C. Actions triggered by levels of CdU, CdB, and β_2-M (See Summary Charts and Tables in Attachment-1.);
    - D. Periodic medical surveillance;
    - E. Actions triggered by periodic medical surveillance (See Appendix A Summary Chart and Tables in Attachment-1.);
    - F. Respirator usage;
    - G. Emergency medical examinations;
    - H. Termination examination;
    - I. Information to physician
    - J. Physician's medical opinion;
    - K. Medical removal protection;
    - L. Medical removal protection benefits;
    - M. Multiple physician review;
    - N. Alternate physician review;
    - O. Information employer gives to employee;
    - P. Recordkeeping; and
    - Q. Reporting on OSHA form 200.
11. The above mentioned summary of the medical surveillance provisions, the summary chart, and tables for the actions triggered at different levels of CdU, CdB and β_2-M (in Appendix A Attachment-1) are included only for the purpose of facilitating understanding of the provisions of paragraphs (l)(3) of the final cadmium Standard. The summary of the provisions, the summary chart, and the tables do not add to or reduce the requirements in paragraph (l)(3).

D. Recommendations to Physicians

1. It is strongly recommended that patients with tubular proteinuria are counseled on: The hazards of smoking; avoidance of nephrotoxins and certain prescriptions and over-the-counter medications that may exacerbate kidney symptoms; how to control diabetes and/or blood pressure; proper hydration, diet, and exercise (Ex. 19–2). A list of prominent or common nephrotoxins is attached. (See Appendix A Attachment-2.)
2. **DO NOT CHELATE; KNOW WHICH DRUGS ARE NEPHROTOXINS OR ARE ASSOCIATED WITH NEPHRITIS.**
3. The gravity of cadmium-induced renal damage is compounded by the fact there is no medical treatment to prevent or reduce the accumulation of cadmium in the kidney (Ex. 8–619). Dr. Friberg, a leading world expert on cadmium toxicity, indicated in 1992, that there is no form of chelating agent that could be used without substantial risk. He stated that tubular proteinuria has to be treated in the same way as other kidney disorders (Ex. 29).

4. After the results of a workers' biological monitoring or medical examination are received the employer is required to provide an information sheet to the patient, briefly explaining the significance of the results. (See Attachment 3 of this Appendix A.)
5. For additional information the physician is referred to the following additional resources:
   a. The physician can always obtain a copy of the preamble, with its full discussion of the health effects, from OSHA's Computerized Information System (OCIS).
   b. The Docket Officer maintains a record of the rulemaking. The Cadmium Docket (H–057A), is located at 200 Constitution Ave. NW., room N–2625, Washington, DC 20210; telephone: 202–219–7894.
   c. The following articles and exhibits in particular from that docket (H–057A):

Exhibit number	Author and paper title
8-447	Lauwerys et. al., Guide for physicians, "Health Maintenance of Workers Exposed to Cadmium," published by the Cadmium Council.
4–67	Takenaka, S., H. Oldiges, H. Konig, D. Hochrainer, G. Oberdorster. "Carcinogenicity of Cadmium Chloride Aerosols in Wistar Rats". JNCI 70:367–373, 1983. (32)
4–68	Thun, M.J., T.M. Schnoor, A.B. Smith, W.E. Halperin, R.A. Lemen. "Mortality Among a Cohort of U.S. Cadmium Production Workers—An Update." JNCI 74(2):325–33, 1985. (8)
4–25	Elinder, C.G., Kjellstrom, T., Hogstedt, C., et al ., "Cancer Mortality of Cadmium Workers." Brit. J. Ind. Med. 42:651–655, 1985. (14)
4–26	Ellis, K.J. et al., "Critical Concentrations of Cadmium in Human Renal Cortex: Dose Effect Studies to Cadmium Smelter Workers." J. Toxicol. Environ. Health 7:691–703, 1981. (76)
4–27	Ellis, K.J., S.H. Cohn and T.J. Smith. "Cadmium Inhalation Exposure Estimates: Their Significance with Respect to Kidney and Liver Cadmium Burden." J. Toxicol. Environ. Health 15:173–187, 1985.
4–28	Falck, F.Y., Jr., Fine, L.J., Smith, R.G., McClatchey, K.D., Annesley, T., England, B., and Schork, A.M. "Occupational Cadmium Exposure and Renal Status." Am. J. Ind. Med. 4:541, 1983. (64)
8–86A	Friberg, L., C.G. Elinder, et al., "Cadmium and Health a Toxicological and Epidemiological Appraisal, Volume I, Exposure, Dose, and Metabolism." CRC Press, Inc., Boca Raton, FL, 1986. (Available from the OSHA Technical Data Center)
8–86B	Friberg, L., C.G. Elinder, et a ., "Cadmium and Health: A Toxicological and Epidemiological Appraisal, Volume II, Effects and Response." CRC Press, Inc., Boca Raton, FL, 1986. (Available from the OSHA Technical Data Center)
L–140–45	Elinder, C.G., "Cancer Mortality of Cadmium Workers", Brit. J. Ind. Med., 42, 651–655, 1985.
L–140–50	Thun, M., Elinder, C.G., Friberg, L, "Scientific Basis for an Occupational Standard for Cadmium, Am. J. Ind. Med., 20; 629–642, 1991.

V. Information Sheet

The information sheet (Appendix A Attachment-3.), or an equally explanatory one, should be provided to you after any biological monitoring results are reviewed by the physician, or where applicable, after any medical examination.

Attachment 1—Appendix A Summary Chart and Tables A and B of Actions Triggered by Biological Monitoring

Appendix A Summary Chart: Section (1)(3) Medical Surveillance

Categorizing Biological Monitoring Results

(A) Biological monitoring results categories are set forth in Appendix A Table A for the periods ending December 31, 1998 and for the period beginning January 1, 1999.

(B) The results of the biological monitoring for the initial medical exam and the subsequent exams shall determine an employee's biological monitoring result category.

Actions Triggered by Biological Monitoring

(A)(i) The actions triggered by biological monitoring for an employee are set forth in Appendix A Table B.

(ii) The biological monitoring results for each employee under Section (1)(3) shall determine the actions required for that employee. That is, for any employee in biological monitoring category C, the employer will perform all of the actions for which there is an X in column C of Appendix A Table B.

(iii) An employee is assigned the alphabetical category ("A" being the lowest) depending upon the test results of the three biological markers.

(iv) An employee is assigned category A if monitoring results for all three biological markers fall at or below the levels indicated in the table listed for category A.

(v) An employee is assigned category B if any monitoring result for any of the three biological markers fall within the range of levels indicated in the table listed for category B, providing no result exceeds the levels listed for category B.

(vi) An employee is assigned category C if any monitoring result for any of the three biological markers are above the levels listed for category C.

(B) The user of Appendix A Tables A and B should know that these tables are provided only to facilitate understanding of the relevant provisions of paragraph (l)(3) of this Section. Appendix A Tables A and B are not meant to add to or subtract from the requirements of those provisions.

Appendix A Table A
Categorization of Biological Monitoring Results
Applicable Through 1998 Only

Biological marker	Monitoring result categories		
	A	B	C
Cadmium in urine (CdU) (μg/g creatinine)	≤ 3	> 3 and ≤15	>15
β_2-microglobulin (β_2–M) (μg/g creatinine)	≤ 300	> 300 and ≤1500	>1500*
Cadmium in blood (CdB) (μg/liter whole blood)	≤ 5	> 5 and ≤15	>15

* If an employee's β_2–M levels are above 1,500 μg/g creatinine, in order for mandatory medical removal to be required (See Appendix A Table B.), either the employee's CdU level must also be >3 μg/g creatinine or CdB level must also be >5 μg/liter whole blood.

Applicable Beginning January 1, 1999

Biological marker	Monitoring result categories		
	A	B	C
Cadmium in urine (CdU) (μg/g creatinine)	≤ 3	> 3 and ≤7	>7
β_2-microglobulin (β_2–M) (μg/g creatinine)	≤ 300	> 300 and ≤750	>750*
Cadmium in blood (CdB) (μg/liter whole blood)	≤ 5	> 5 and ≤10	>10

* If an employee's β_2–M levels are above 750 μg/g creatinine, in order for mandatory medical removal to be required (See Appendix A Table B.), either the employee's CdU level must also be >3 μg/g creatinine or CdB level must also be >5 μg/liter whole blood.

Appendix A Table B
Actions Determined by Biological Monitoring

This table presents the actions required based on the monitoring result in Appendix A Table A. Each item is a separate requirement in citing non-compliance. For example, a medical examination within 90 days for an employee in category B is separate from the requirement to administer a periodic medical examination for category B employees on an annual basis

Required actions	Monitoring result category		
	A[1]	B[1]	C[1]
(1) Biological monitoring:			
(a) Annual.	X		
(b) Semiannual		X	
(c) Quarterly			X
(2) Medical examination:			
(a) Biennial	X		
(b) Annual.		X	
(c) Semiannual.			X
(d) Within 90 days		X	X

Note: Table date continues on next page.

Required actions	Monitoring result category		
	A[1]	B[1]	C[1]
(3) Assess within two weeks:			
(a) Excess cadmium exposure		X	X
(b) Work practices		X	X
(c) Personal hygiene		X	X
(d) Respirator usage		X	X
e) Smoking history		X	X
(f) Hygiene facilities		X	X
(g) Engineering controls		X	X
(h) Correct within 30 days		X	X
(i) Periodically assess exposures			X
(4) Discretionary medical removal		X	X
(5) Mandatory medical removal			X[2]

[1] For all employees covered by medical surveillance exclusively because of exposures prior to the effective date of this Standard, if they are in Category A, the employer shall follow the requirements of paragraphs (l)(3)(i)(B) and (l)(4)(v)(A). If they are in Category B or C, the employer shall follow the requirements of paragraphs (l)(4)(v)(B)–(C).

[2] See footnote Appendix A Table A.

Appendix A—Attachment 2—List of Medications

A list of the more common medications that a physician, and the employee, may wish to review is likely to include some of the following: (1) Anticonvulsants: Paramethadione, phenytoin, trimethadone; (2) antihypertensive drugs: Captopril, methyldopa; (3) antimicrobials: Aminoglycosides, amphotericin B, cephalosporins, ethambutol; (4) antineoplastic agents: Cisplatin, methotrexate, mitomycin-C, nitrosoureas, radiation; (5) sulfonamide diuretics: Acetazolamide, chlorthalidone, furosemide, thiazides; (6) halogenated alkanes, hydrocarbons, and solvents that may occur in some settings: Carbon tetrachloride, ethylene glycol, toluene; iodinated radiographic contrast media; nonsteroidal anti-inflammatory drugs; and, (7) other miscellaneous compounds: Acetominophen, allopurinol, amphetamines, azathioprine, cimetidine, cyclosporine, lithium, methoxyflurane, methysergide, D-penicillamine, phenacetin, phenendione. A list of drugs associated with acute interstitial nephritis includes: (1) Antimicrobial drugs: Cephalosporins, chloramphenicol, colistin, erythromycin, ethambutol, isoniazid, para-aminosalicylic acid, penicillins, polymyxin B, rifampin, sulfonamides, tetracyclines, and vancomycin; (2) other miscellaneous drugs: Allopurinol, antipyrene, azathioprine, captopril, cimetidine, clofibrate, methyldopa, phenindione, phenylpropanolamine, phenytoin, probenecid, sulfinpyrazone, sulfonamid diuretics, triamterene; and, (3) metals: Bismuth, gold.

This list has been derived from commonly available medical textbooks (e.g., Ex. 14–18). The list has been included merely to facilitate the physician's, employer's, and employee's understanding. The list does not represent an official OSHA opinion or policy regarding the use of these medications for particular employees. The use of such medications should be under physician discretion.

Attachment 3—Biological Monitoring and Medical Examination Results

Employee____________________ Testing Date__________
Cadmium in Urine ________ µg/g Cr—Normal Levels: ≤3 µg/g Cr.
Cadmium in Blood ________ µg/lwb—Normal Levels: ≤5 µg/lwb.
Beta-2-microglobulin in Urine ________ µg/g
Cr—Normal Levels: ≤300 µg/g Cr.

Physical Examination Results:
N/A ___ Satisfactory ___ Unsatisfactory ___ (see physician again)

Physician's Review of Pulmonary Function Test:
N/A ___ Normal ___ Abnormal ___

Next biological monitoring or medical examination scheduled for

____

The biological monitoring program has been designed for three main purposes:

1) to identify employees at risk of adverse health effects from excess, chronic exposure to cadmium;
2) to prevent cadmium-induced disease(s); and
3) to detect and minimize existing cadmium-induced disease(s).

The levels of cadmium in the urine and blood provide an estimate of the total amount of cadmium in the body. The amount of a specific protein in the urine (beta-2-microglobulin) indicates changes in kidney function. All three tests must be evaluated together. A single mildly elevated result may not be important if testing at a later time indicates that the results are normal and the workplace has been evaluated to decrease possible sources of cadmium exposure. The levels of cadmium or beta-2-microglobulin may change over a period of days to months and the time needed for those changes to occur is different for each worker.

If the results for biological monitoring are above specific "high levels" [cadmium urine greater than 10 micrograms per gram of creatinine (µg/g Cr), cadmium blood greater than 10 micrograms per liter of whole blood (µg/lwb), or beta-2-microglobulin greater than 1000 micrograms per gram of creatinine (µg/g Cr)], the worker has a much greater chance of developing other kidney diseases.

One way to measure for kidney function is by measuring beta-2-microglobulin in the urine. Beta-2-microglobulin is a protein which is normally found in the blood as it is being filtered in the kidney, and the kidney reabsorbs or returns almost all of the beta-2-microglobulin to the blood. A very small amount (less than 300 µg/g Cr in the urine) of beta-2-microglobulin is not reabsorbed into the blood, but is released in the urine. If cadmium damages the kidney, the amount of beta-2-microglobulin in the urine inScreases because the kidney cells are unable to reabsorb the beta-2-microglobulin normally. An increase in the amount of beta-2-microglobulin in the urine is a very early sign of kidney dysfunction. A small increase in beta-2-microglobulin in the urine will serve as an early warning sign that the worker may be absorbing cadmium from the air, cigarettes contaminated in the workplace, or eating in areas that are cadmium contaminated.

Even if cadmium causes permanent changes in the kidney's ability to reabsorb beta-2-microglobulin, and the beta-2-microglobulin is above the "high levels", the loss of kidney function may not lead to any serious health problems. Also, renal function naturally declines as people age. The risk for changes in kidney function for workers who have biological monitoring results between the "normal values" and the "high levels" is not well known. Some people are more cadmium-tolerant, while others are more cadmium-susceptible.

For anyone with even a slight increase of beta-2-microglobulin, cadmium in the urine, or cadmium in the blood, it is very important to protect the kidney from further damage. Kidney damage can come from other sources than excess cadmium-exposure so it is also recommended that if a worker's levels are "high" he/she should receive counseling about drinking more water; avoiding cadmium-tainted tobacco and certain medications (nephrotoxins, acetaminophen); controlling diet, vitamin intake, blood pressure and diabetes; etc.

§1910.1027 Appendix B Substance Technical Guidelines for Cadmium

I. Cadmium Metal

A. Physical and Chemical Data

1. Substance Identification

Chemical name: Cadmium
Formula: Cd
Molecular Weight: 112.4
Chemical Abstracts Service (CAS) Registry No.: 7740–43–9
Other Identifiers: RETCS EU9800000; EPA D006; DOT 2570 53
Synonyms: Colloidal Cadmium: Kadmium (German): CI 77180

2. Physical data

Boiling point: (760 mm Hg): 765 °C
Melting point: 321 °C
Specific Gravity: (H_2O = @ 20 °C): 8.64
Solubility: Insoluble in water; soluble in dilute nitric acid and in sulfuric acid
Appearance: Soft, blue-white, malleable, lustrous metal or grayish-white powder

B. Fire, Explosion and Reactivity Data

1. Fire

Fire and Explosion Hazards: The finely divided metal is pyrophoric, that is the dust is a severe fire hazard and moderate explosion hazard when exposed to heat or flame. Burning material reacts violently with extinguishing agents such as water, foam, carbon dioxide, and halons.

Flash point: Flammable (dust)

Extinguishing media: Dry sand, dry dolomite, dry graphite, or sodimum chloride

2. Reactivity

Conditions contributing to instability: Stable when kept in sealed containers under normal temperatures and pressure, but dust may ignite upon contact with air. Metal tarnishes in moist air.

Incompatibilities: Ammonium nitrate, fused: Reacts violently or explosively with cadmium dust below 20 °C. Hydrozoic acid: Violent explosion occurs after 30 minutes. Acids: Reacts violently, forms hydrogen gas. Oxidizing agents or metals: Strong reaction with cadmium dust. Nitryl fluoride at slightly elevated temperature: Glowing or white incandescence occurs. Selenium: Reacts exothermically. Ammonia: Corrosive reaction. Sulfur dioxide: Corrosive reaction. Fire extinguishing agents (water, foam, carbon dioxide, and halons): Reacts violently. Tellurium: Incandescent reaction in hydrogen atmosphere

Hazardous decomposition products: The heated metal rapidly forms highly toxic, brownish fumes of oxides of cadmium.

C. Spill, Leak and Disposal Procedures

1. **Steps to be taken if the materials is released or spilled** Do not touch spilled material. Stop leak if you can do it without risk. Do not get water inside container. For large spills, dike spill for later disposal. Keep unnecessary people away. Isolate hazard area and deny entry. The Superfund Amendments and Reauthorization Act of 1986 Section 304 requires that a release equal to or greater than the reportable quantity for this substance (1 pound) must be immediately reported to the local emergency planning committee, the state emergency response commission, and the National Response Center (800) 424–8802; in Washington, DC metropolitan area (202) 426–2675.

II. Cadmium Oxide

A. Physical and Chemical Date

1. Substance identification

Chemical name: Cadmium Oxide
Formula: CdO
Molecular Weight: 128.4
CAS No.: 1306–19–0
Other Identifiers: RTECS EV1929500
Synonyms: Kadmu tlenek (Polish)

2. Physical data

Boiling point (760 mm Hg): 950 °C decomposes
Melting point: 1500 °C
Specific Gravity: (H_2O = 1@20 °C): 7.0
Solubility: Insoluble in water; soluble in acids and alkalines
Appearance: Red or brown crystals

B. Fire, Explosion and Reactivity Data

1. Fire

Fire and Explosion Hazards: Negligible fire hazard when exposed to heat or flame
Flash point: Nonflammable
Extinguishing media: Dry chemical, carbon dioxide, water spray or foam

2. Reactivity

Conditions contributing to instability: Stable under normal temperatures and pressures
Incompatibilities: Magnesium may reduce CdO_2 explosively on heating
Hazardous decomposition products: Toxic fumes of cadmium

C. Spill Leak and Disposal Procedures

1. **Steps to be taken if the material is released or spilled** Do not touch spilled material. Stop leak if you can do it without risk. For small spills, take up with sand or other absorbent material and place into containers for later disposal. For small dry spills, use a clean shovel to place material into clean, dry container and then cover. Move containers from spill area. For larger spills, dike far ahead of spill for later disposal. Keep unnecessary people away. Isolate hazard area and deny entry. The Superfund Amendments and Reauthorization Act of 1986 Section 304 requires that a release equal to or greater than the reportable quantity for this substance (1 pound) must be immediately reported to the local emergency planning committee, the state emergency response commission, and the National Response Center (800) 424–8802; in Washington, DC metropolitan area (202) 426–2675.

III. Cadmium Sulfide

A. Physical and Chemical Data

1. Substance Identification

Chemical name: Cadmium sulfide
Formula: CdS
Molecular weight: 144.5
CAS No. 1306–23–6
Other Identifiers: RTECS EV3150000
Synonyms: Aurora yellow; Cadmium Golden 366; Cadmium Lemon Yellow 527; Cadmium Orange; Cadmium Primrose 819; Cadmium Sulphide; Cadmium Yellow; Cadmium Yellow 000; Cadmium Yellow Conc. Deep; Cadmium Yellow Conc. Golden; Cadmium Yellow Conc. Lemon; Cadmium Yellow Conc. Primrose; Cadmium Yellow Oz. Dark; Cadmium Yellow Primrose 47–1400; Cadmium Yellow 10G Conc.; Cadmium Yellow 892; Cadmopur Golden Yellow N; Cadmopur Yellow: Capsebon; C.I. 77199; C.I. Pigment Orange 20; CI Pigment Yellow 37; Ferro Lemon Yellow; Ferro Orange Yellow; Ferro Yellow; Greenockite; NCI-C02711

2. Physical data

Boiling point (760 mm. Hg): sublines in N_2 at 980 °C
Melting point: 1750 degrees C (100 atm)
Specific Gravity: (H_2O = 1@ 20 °C): 4.82
Solubility: Slightly soluble in water; soluble in acid
Appearance: Light yellow or yellow-orange crystals

B. Fire, Explosion and Reactivity Data

1. Fire

Fire and Explosion Hazards: Neglible fire hazard when exposed to heat or flame
Flash point: Nonflammable
Extinguishing media: Dry chemical, carbon dioxide, water spray or foam

2. Reactivity

Conditions contributing to instability: Generally non-reactive under normal conditions. Reacts with acids to form toxic hydrogen sulfide gas
Incompatibilities: Reacts vigorously with iodinemonochloride
Hazardous decomposition products: Toxic fumes of cadmium and sulfur oxides

C. Spill Leak and Disposal Procedures

1. Steps to be taken if the material is released or spilled. Do not touch spilled material. Stop leak if you can do it without risk. For small, dry spills, with a clean shovel place material into clean, dry container and cover. Move containers from spill area. For larger spills, dike far ahead of spill for later disposal. Keep unnecessary people away. Isolate hazard and deny entry.

IV. Cadmium Chloride

A. Physical and Chemical Data

1. Substance Identification

Chemcail name: Cadmium chloride
Formula: $CdC1_2$
Molecular weight: 183.3
CAS No. 10108–64–2
Other Identifiers: RTECS EY0175000
Synonyms: Caddy; Cadmium dichloride; NA 2570 (DOT); UI-CAD; dichlorocadmium

2. Physical data

Boiling point (760 mm Hg): 960 degrees C
Melting point: 568 degrees C
Specific Gravity: (H_2O = 1 @ 20 °C): 4.05
Solubility: Soluble in water (140 g/100 cc); soluble in acetone
Appearance: Small, white crystals

B. Fire, Explosion and Reactivity Data

1. Fire

Fire and Explosion Hazards: Negligible fire and negligible explosion hazard in dust form when exposed to heat or flame
Flash point: Nonflamable
Extinguishing media: Dry chemical, carbon dioxide, water spray or foam

2. Reactivity

Conditions contributing to instability: Generally stable under normal temperatures and pressures
Incompatibilities: Bromine triflouride rapidly attacks cadmium chloride. A mixture of potassium and cadmium chloride may produce a strong explosion on impact
Hazardous decomposition products: Thermal ecompostion may release toxic fumes of hydrogen chloride, chloride, chlorine or oxides of cadmium

C. Spill Leak and Disposal Procedures

1. Steps to be taken if the materials ARE released or spilled. Do not touch spilled material. Stop leak if you can do it without risk. For small, dry spills, with a clean shovel place material into clean, dry container and cover. Move containers from spill area. For larger spills, dike far ahead of spill for later disposal. Keep unnecessary people away. Isolate hazard and deny entry. The Superfund Amendments and Reauthorization Act of 1986 Section 304 requires that a release equal to or greater than the reportable quantity for this substance (100 pounds) must be immediately reported to the local emergency planning committee, the state emergency response commission, and the National Response Center (800) 424–8802; in Washington, DC Metropolitan area (202) 426–2675

§1910.1027 Appendix C [Reserved]

§1910.1027 Appendix D Occupational health history interview with reference to Cadmium exposure

Occupational Health History Interview
With Reference to Cadmium Exposure

Directions
(To be read by employee and signed prior to the interview)

Please answer the questions you will be asked as completely and carefully as you can. These questions are asked of everyone who works with cadmium. You will also be asked to give blood and urine samples. The doctor will give your employer a written opinion on whether you are physically capable of working with cadmium. Legally, the doctor cannot share personal information you may tell him/her with your employer. The following information is considered strictly confidential. The results of the tests will go to you, your doctor and your employer. You will also receive an information sheet explaining the results of any biological monitoring or physical examinations performed.

If you are just being hired, the results of this interview and examination will be used to:

(1) Establish your health status and see if working with cadmium might be expected to cause unusual problems,
(2) Determine your health status today and see if there are changes over time,
(3) See if you can wear a respirator safely.

If you are not a new hire:

OSHA says that everyone who works with cadmium can have periodic medical examinations performed by a doctor. The reasons for this are:

(a) If there are changes in your health, either because of cadmium or some other reason, to find them early,
(b) to prevent kidney damage.

Please sign below.
I have read these directions and understand them:

______________________ ____/____/____
Employee signature Date

Thank you for answering these questions. (Suggested Format)

Name ______________________ Age ________
Social Security #______________________
Company ______________________
Job ______________________

Type of Preplacement Exam: Periodic ___ Termination ___ Initial ___ Other ___

Blood Pressure ______________ Pulse Rate ______________

1. How long have you worked at the job listed above?
Not yet hired ___ Number of months ___ Number of years ___
2. Job Duties, etc. ______________________
3. Have you ever been told by a doctor that you had bronchitis?
Yes ___ No ___
If yes, how long ago? Number of months ___ Number of years ___
4. Have you ever been told by a doctor that you had emphysema?
Yes ___ No ___
If yes, how long ago? Number of months ___ Number of years ___
5. Have you ever been told by a doctor that you had other lung problems?
Yes ___ No ___
If yes, please describe type of lungs problems and when you had these problems:
____
____
6. In the past year, have you had a cough? Yes ___ No ___
If yes, did you cough up sputum? Yes ___ No ___
If yes, how long did the cough with sputum production last?
Less than 3 months ___ 3 months or more ___
If yes, for how many years have you had episodes of cough with sputum production lasting this long?
Less than one ___ 1 year ___ 2 years ___ Longer than 2 years ___
7. Have you ever smoked cigarettes? Yes ___ No ___
8. Do you now smoke cigarettes? Yes ___ No ___
9. If you smoke or have smoked cigarettes, for how many years have you smoked, or did you smoke? Less than 1 year ___ Number of years ___
What is or was the greatest number of packs per day that you have smoked?
Number of packs ___
If you quit smoking cigarettes, how many years ago did you quit?
Less than 1 year ___ Number of years ___
How many packs a day do you now smoke? Number of packs per day ___
10. Have you ever been told by a doctor that you had a kidney or urinary tract disease or disorder? Yes ___ No ___
11. Have you ever had any of these disorders?

Kidney stones	Yes ___	No ___
Protein in urine	Yes ___	No ___
Blood in urine	Yes ___	No ___
Difficulty urinating	Yes ___	No ___
Other kidney/Urinary disorders	Yes ___	No ___

Please describe problems, age, treatment, and follow up for any kidney or urinary problems you have had:
____
____

12. Have you ever been told by a doctor or other health care provider who took your blood pressure that your blood pressure was high? Yes ___ No ___
13. Have you ever been advised to take any blood pressure medication?
Yes ___ No ___
14. Are you presently taking any blood pressure medication? Yes ___ No ___
15. Are you presently taking any other medication? Yes ___ No ___
16. Please list any blood pressure or other medications and describe how long you have been taking each one:

Medicine:	How Long Taken:
______________	______________
______________	______________
______________	______________

17. Have you ever been told by a doctor that you have diabetes? (sugar in your blood or urine) Yes ___ No ___
If yes, do you presently see a doctor about your diabetes? Yes ___ No ___
Diet alone ___ Diet plus oral medicine ___ Diet plus insulin (injection) ___
18. Have you ever been told by a doctor that you had:
Anemia Yes ___ No ___
A low blood count Yes ___ No ___
19. Do you presently feel that you tire or run out of energy sooner than normal or sooner than other people your age? Yes ___ No ___
If yes, for how long have you felt that you tire easily?
Less than 1 year ___ Number of years ___
20. Have you given blood within the last year? Yes ___ No ___
If yes, how many times? Number of times ______
How long ago was the last time you gave blood?
Less than 1 month ___ Number of months ___
21. Within the last year have you had any injuries with heavy bleeding?
Yes ___ No ___
If yes, how long ago? Less than 1 month ___ Number of months ___
Describe:
____
____
____
22. Have you recently had any surgery? Yes ___ No ___
If yes, please describe:
____
____
23. Have you seen any blood lately in your stool or after a bowel movement?
Yes ___ No ___
24. Have you ever had a test for blood in your stool? Yes ___ No ___
If yes, did the test show any blood in the stool? Yes ___ No ___
What further evaluation and treatment were done?
____
____

The following questions pertain to the ability to wear a respirator. Additional information for the physician can be found in The Respiratory Protective Devices Manual.

25. Have you ever been told by a doctor that you have asthma? Yes ___ No ___
If yes, are you presently taking any medication for asthma? Yes ___ No ___
Mark all that apply. Shots ___ Pills ___ Inhaler ___
26. Have you ever had a heart attack? Yes ___ No ___
If yes, how long ago? Number of years ___ Number of months ___
27. Have you ever had pains in your chest? Yes ___ No ___
If yes, when did it usually happen? While resting ___ While working ___
While exercising ___ Activity didn't matter ___
28. Have you ever had a thyroid problem? Yes ___ No ___
29. Have you ever had a seizure or fits? Yes ___ No ___
30. Have you ever had a stroke (cerebrovascular accident)? Yes ___ No ___
31. Have you ever had a ruptured eardrum or a serious hearing problem?
Yes ___ No ___
32. Do you now have a claustrophobia, meaning fear of crowded or closed in spaces or any psychological problems that would make it hard for you to wear a respirator? Yes ___ No ___

The following questions pertain to reproductive history.

33. Have you or your partner had a problem conceiving a child? Yes ___ No ___
If yes, specify: Self ___ Present mate ___ Previous mate ___
34. Have you or your partner consulted a physician for a fertility or other reproductive problem? Yes ___ No ___
If yes, specify who consulted the physician:
Self ___ Partner ___ Self and partner ___
If yes, specify diagnosis made:
____
____
35. Have you or your partner ever conceived a child resulting in a miscarriage, still birth or deformed offspring? Yes ___ No ___
If yes, specify: Miscarriage ___ Still birth ___ Deformed offspring ___
If outcome was a deformed offspring, please specify type:
____
____
36. Was this outcome a result of a pregnancy of:
Yours with present partner ___ Yours with a previous partner ___
37. Did the timing of any abnormal pregnancy outcome coincide with present employment?
List dates of occurrences: __________ __________ __________
38. What is the occupation of your spouse or partner?
____

For Women Only

39. Do you have menstrual periods? Yes ___ No ___
    Have you had menstrual irregularities? Yes ___ No ___
    If yes, specify type:
    ____
    ____

    If yes, what was the approximated date this problem began? ________
    Approximate date problem stopped? ________

For Men Only

40. Have you ever been diagnosed by a physician as having prostate gland problem(s)? Yes ___ No ___

If yes, please describe type of problem(s) and what was done to evaluate and treat the problem(s):
____
____

§1910.1027 Appendix E Cadmium in workplace atmospheres

Method Number: ID–189

Matrix: Air

OSHA Permissible Exposure Limits: 5 μg/m^3 (TWA), 2.5 μg/m^3 (Action Level TWA)

Collection Procedure: A known volume of air is drawn through a 37-mm diameter filter cassette containing a 0.8-μm mixed cellulose ester membrane filter (MCEF).

Recommended Air Volume: 960 L

Recommended Sampling Rate: 2.0 L/min

Analytical Procedure: Air filter samples are digested with nitric acid. After digestion, a small amount of hydrochloric acid is added. The samples are then diluted to volume with deionized water and analyzed by either flame atomic absorption spectroscopy (AAS) or flameless atomic absorption spectroscopy using a heated graphite furnace atomizer (AAS-HGA).

Detection Limits:

Qualitative: 0.2 μg/m^3 for a 200 L sample by Flame AAS, 0.007 μg/m^3 for a 60 L sample by AAS-HGA

Quantitative: 0.70 μg/m^3 for a 200 L sample by Flame AAS, 0.025 μg/m^3 for a 60 L sample by AAS-HGA

Precision and Accuracy: (Flame AAS Analysis and AAS-HGA Analysis):

Validation Level: 2.5 to 10 μg/m^3 for a 400 L air vol, 1.25 to 5.0 μg/m^3 for a 60 L air vol

CV_1(pooled): 0.010, 0.043

Analytical Bias: +4.0%, −5.8%

Overall Analytical Error: ± 6.0%, ± 14.2%

Method Classification: Validated

Date: June, 1992

Inorganic Service Branch II, OSHA Salt Lake Technical Center, Salt Lake City, Utah

Commercial manufacturers and products mentioned in this method are for descriptive use only and do not constitute endorsements by USDOL-OSHA. Similar products from other sources can be substituted.

1. Introduction

1.1. Scope

This method describes the collection of airborne elemental cadmium and cadmium compounds on 0.8-μm mixed cellulose ester membrane filters and their subsequent analysis by either flame atomic absorption spectroscopy (AAS) or flameless atomic absorption spectroscopy using a heated graphite furnace atomizer (AAS-HGA). It is applicable for both TWA and Action Level TWA Permissible Exposure Level (PEL) measurements. The two atomic absorption analytical techniques included in the method do not differentiate between cadmium fume and cadmium dust samples. They also do not differentiate between elemental cadmium and its compounds.

1.2. Principle

Airborne elemental cadmium and cadmium compounds are collected on a 0.8-μm mixed cellulose ester membrane filter (MCEF). The air filter samples are digested with concentrated nitric acid to destroy the organic matrix and dissolve the cadmium analytes. After digestion, a small amount of concentrated hydrochloric acid is added to help dissolve other metals which may be present. The samples are diluted to volume with deionized water and then aspirated into the oxidizing air/acetylene flame of an atomic absorption spectrophotometer for analysis of elemental cadmium.

If the concentration of cadmium in a sample solution is too low for quantitation by this flame AAS analytical technique, and the sample is to be averaged with other samples for TWA calculations, aliquots of the sample and a matrix modifier are later injected onto a L'vov platform in a pyrolytically-coated graphite tube of a Zeeman atomic absorption spectrophotometer/graphite furnace assembly for analysis of elemental cadmium. The matrix modifier is added to stabilize the cadmium metal and minimize sodium chloride as an interference during the high temperature charring step of the analysis (5.1., 5.2.).

1.3. History

Previously, two OSHA sampling and analytical methods for cadmium were used concurrently (5.3., 5.4.). Both of these methods also required 0.8-μm mixed cellulose ester membrane filters for the collection of air samples. These cadmium air filter samples were analyzed by either flame atomic absorption spectroscopy (5.3.) or inductively coupled plasma/atomic emission spectroscopy (ICP-AES) (5.4.). Neither of these two analytical methods have adequate sensitivity for measuring workplace exposure to airborne cadmium at the new lower TWA and Action Level TWA PEL levels when consecutive samples are taken on one employee and the sample results need to be averaged with other samples to determine a single TWA.

The inclusion of two atomic absorption analytical techniques in the new sampling and analysis method for airborne cadmium permits quantitation of sample results over a broad range of exposure levels and sampling periods. The flame AAS analytical technique included in this method is similar to the previous procedure given in the General Metals Method ID–121 (5.3.) with some modifications. The sensitivity of the AAS-HGA analytical technique included in this method is adequate to measure exposure levels at ¹⁄₁₀ the Action Level TWA, or lower, when less than full-shift samples need to be averaged together.

1.4. Properties (5.5.)

Elemental cadmium is a silver-white, blue-tinged, lustrous metal which is easily cut with a knife. It is slowly oxidized by moist air to form cadmium oxide. It is insoluble in water, but reacts readily with dilute nitric acid. Some of the physical properties and other descriptive information of elemental cadmium are given below:

CAS No.	7440–43–9
Atomic Number	48
Atomic Symbol	Cd
Atomic Weight	112.41
Melting Point	321 °C
Boiling Point	765 °C
Density	8.65 g/mL (25 °C)

The properties of specific cadmium compounds are described in reference 5.5.

1.5. Method Performance.

A synopsis of method performance is presented below. Further information can be found in Section 4.

1.5.1. The qualitative and quantitative detection limits for the flame AAS analytical technique are 0.04 μg (0.004 μg/mL) and 0.14 μg (0.014 μg/mL) cadmium, respectively, for a 10 mL solution volume. These correspond, respectively, to 0.2 μg/m^3 and 0.70 μg/m^3 for a 200 L air volume.

1.5.2. The qualitative and quantitative detection limits for the AAS-HGA analytical technique are 0.44 ng (0.044 ng/mL) and 1.5 ng (0.15 ng/mL) cadmium, respectively, for a 10 mL solution volume. These correspond, respectively, to 0.007 μg/m^3 and 0.025 μg/m^3 for a 60 L air volume.

1.5.3. The average recovery by the flame AAS analytical technique of 17 spiked MCEF samples containing cadmium in the range of 0.5 to 2.0 times the TWA target concentration of 5 μg/m^3 (assuming a 400 L air volume) was 104.0% with a pooled coefficient of variation (CV_1) of 0.010. The flame analytical technique exhibited a positive bias of +4.0% for the validated concentration range. The overall analytical error (OAE) for the flame AAS analytical technique was ± 6.0%.

1.5.4. The average recovery by the AAS-HGA analytical technique of 18 spiked MCEF samples containing cadmium in the range of 0.5 to 2.0 times the Action Level TWA target concentration of 2.5 μg/m^3 (assuming a 60 L air volume) was 94.2% with a pooled coefficient of variation (CV1) of 0.043. The AAS-HGA analytical technique exhibited a negative bias of −5.8% for the validated concentration range. The overall analytical error (OAE) for the AAS-HGA analytical technique was ± 14.2%.

1.5.5. Sensitivity in flame atomic absorption is defined as the characteristic concentration of an element required to produce a signal of 1% absorbance (0.0044 absorbance units). Sensitivity values are listed for each element by the atomic absorption spectrophotometer manufacturer and have proved to be a very valuable diagnostic tool to determine if instrumental parameters are optimized and if the instrument is performing up to specification. The sensitivity of the spectrophotometer used in the validation of the flame AAS analytical technique agreed with the manufacturer specifications (5.6.); the 2 µg/mL cadmium Standard gave an absorbance reading of 0.350 abs. units.

1.5.6. Sensitivity in graphite furnace atomic absorption is defined in terms of the characteristic mass, the number of picograms required to give an integrated absorbance value of 0.0044 absorbance-second (5.7.). Data suggests that under Stabilized Temperature Platform Furnace (STPF) conditions (see Section 1.6.2.), characteristic mass values are transferable between properly functioning instruments to an accuracy of about 20% (5.2.). The characteristic mass for STPF analysis of cadmium with Zeeman background correction listed by the manufacturer of the instrument used in the validation of the AAS-HGA analytical technique was 0.35 pg. The experimental characteristic mass value observed during the determination of the working range and detection limits of the AAS-HGA analytical technique was 0.41 pg.

1.6. Interferences

1.6.1. High concentrations of silicate interfere in determining cadmium by flame AAS (5.6.). However, silicates are not significantly soluble in the acid matrix used to prepare the samples.

1.6.2. Interferences, such as background absorption, are reduced to a minimum in the AAS-HGA analytical technique by taking full advantage of the Stabilized Temperature Platform Furnace (STPF) concept. STPF includes all of the following parameters (5.2.):

a. Integrated Absorbance,
b. Fast Instrument Electronics and Sampling Frequency,
c. Background Correction,
d. Maximum Power Heating,
e. Atomization off the L'vov platform in a pyrolytically coated graphite tube,
f. Gas Stop during Atomization,
g. Use of Matrix Modifiers.

1.7. Toxicology (5.14.)

Information listed within this section is synopsis of current knowledge of the physiological effects of cadmium and is not intended to be used as the basis for OSHA policy. IARC classifies cadmium and certain of its compounds as Group 2A carcinogens (probably carcinogenic to humans). Cadmium fume is intensely irritating to the respiratory tract. Workplace exposure to cadmium can cause both chronic and acute effects. Acute effects include tracheobronchitis, pneumonitis, and pulmonary edema. Chronic effects include anemia, rhinitis/anosmia, pulmonary emphysema, proteinuria and lung cancer. The primary target organs for chronic disease are the kidneys (non-carcinogenic) and the lungs (carcinogenic).

2. Sampling

2.1. Apparatus

2.1.1. Filter cassette unit for air sampling: A 37-mm diameter mixed cellulose ester membrane filter with a pore size of 0.8-µm contained in a 37-mm polystyrene two- or three-piece cassette filter holder (part no. MAWP 037 A0, Millipore Corp., Bedford, MA). The filter is supported with a cellulose backup pad. The cassette is sealed prior to use with a shrinkable gel band.

2.1.2. A calibrated personal sampling pump whose flow is determined to an accuracy of ± 5% at the recommended flow rate with the filter cassette unit in line.

2.2. Procedure

2.2.1. Attach the prepared cassette to the calibrated sampling pump (the backup pad should face the pump) using flexible tubing. Place the sampling device on the employee such that air is sampled from the breathing zone.

2.2.2. Collect air samples at a flow rate of 2.0 L/min. If the filter does not become overloaded, a full-shift (at least seven hours) sample is strongly recommended for TWA and Action Level TWA measurements with a maximum air volume of 960 L. If overloading occurs, collect consecutive air samples for shorter sampling periods to cover the full workshift.

2.2.3. Replace the end plugs into the filter cassettes immediately after sampling. Record the sampling conditions.

2.2.4. Securely wrap each sample filter cassette end-to-end with an OSHA Form 21 sample seal.

2.2.5. Submit at least one blank sample with each set of air samples. The blank sample should be handled the same as the other samples except that no air is drawn through it.

2.2.6. Ship the samples to the laboratory for analysis as soon as possible in a suitable container designed to prevent damage in transit.

3. Analysis

3.1. Safety Precautions

3.1.1. Wear safety glasses, protective clothing and gloves at all times.

3.1.2. Handle acid solutions with care. Handle all cadmium samples and solutions with extra care (see Sect. 1.7.). Avoid their direct contact with work area surfaces, eyes, skin and clothes. Flush acid solutions which contact the skin or eyes with copious amounts of water.

3.1.3. Perform all acid digestions and acid dilutions in an exhaust hood while wearing a face shield. To avoid exposure to acid vapors, do not remove beakers containing concentrated acid solutions from the exhaust hood until they have returned to room temperature and have been diluted or emptied.

3.1.4. Exercise care when using laboratory glassware. Do not use chipped pipets, volumetric flasks, beakers or any glassware with sharp edges exposed in order to avoid the possibility of cuts or abrasions.

3.1.5. Never pipet by mouth.

3.1.6. Refer to the instrument instruction manuals and SOPs (5.8., 5.9.) for proper and safe operation of the atomic absorption spectrophotometer, graphite furnace atomizer and associated equipment.

3.1.7. Because metallic elements and other toxic substances are vaporized during AAS flame or graphite furnace atomizer operation, it is imperative that an exhaust vent be used. Always ensure that the exhaust system is operating properly during instrument use.

3.2. Apparatus for Sample and Standard Preparation

3.2.1. Hot plate, capable of reaching 150 °C, installed in an exhaust hood

3.2.2. Phillips beakers, 125 mL

3.2.3. Bottles, narrow-mouth, polyethylene or glass with leakproof caps: used for storage of standards and matrix modifier

3.2.4. Volumetric flasks, volumetric pipets, beakers and other associated general laboratory glassware

3.2.5. Forceps and other associated general laboratory equipment

3.3. Apparatus for Flame AAS Analysis

3.3.1. Atomic absorption spectrophotometer consisting of a(an):

- Nebulizer and burner head
- Pressure regulating devices capable of maintaining constant oxidant and fuel pressures
- Optical system capable of isolating the desired wavelength of radiation (228.8 nm)
- Adjustable slit
- Light measuring and amplifying device
- Display, strip chart, or computer interface for indicating the amount of absorbed radiation
- Cadmium hollow cathode lamp or electrodeless discharge lamp (EDL) and power supply

3.3.2. Oxidant: compressed air, filtered to remove water, oil and other foreign substances.

3.3.3. Fuel: standard commercially available tanks of acetylene dissolved in acetone; tanks should be equipped with flash arresters.

Caution: Do not use grades of acetylene containing solvents other than acetone because they may damage the PVC tubing used in some instruments.

3.3.4. Pressure-reducing valves: two gauge, two-stage pressure regulators to maintain fuel and oxidant pressures somewhat higher than the controlled operating pressures of the instrument.

3.3.5. Exhaust vent installed directly above the spectrophotometer burner head.

3.4. Apparatus for AAS-HGA Analysis

3.4.1. Atomic absorption spectrophotometer consisting of a(an):

- Heated graphite furnace atomizer (HGA) with argon purge system
- Pressure-regulating devices capable of maintaining constant argon purge pressure
- Optical system capable of isolating the desired wavelength of radiation (228.8 nm)
- Adjustable slit
- Light measuring and amplifying device.
- Display, strip chart, or computer interface for indicating the amount of absorbed radiation (as integrated absorbance, peak area).

- Background corrector: Zeeman or deuterium arc. The Zeeman background corrector is recommended.
- Cadmium hollow cathode lamp or electrodeless discharge lamp (EDL) and power supply.
- Autosampler capable of accurately injecting 5 to 20 µL sample aliquots onto the L'vov Platform in a graphite tube.

3.4.2. Pyrolytically coated graphite tubes containing solid, pyrolytic L'vov platforms.

3.4.3. Polyethylene sample cups, 2.0 to 2.5 mL, for use with the autosampler.

3.4.4. Inert purge gas for graphite furnace atomizer: compressed gas cylinder of purified argon.

3.4.5. Two gauge, two-stage pressure regulator for the argon gas cylinder.

3.4.6. Cooling water supply for graphite furnace atomizer.

3.4.7. Exhaust vent installed directly above the graphite furnace atomizer.

3.5. Reagents

All reagents should be ACS analytical reagent grade or better.

3.5.1. Deionized water with a specific conductance of less than 10 µS.

3.5.2. Concentrated nitric acid, HNO_3.

3.5.3. Concentrated hydrochloric acid, HCl.

3.5.4. Ammonium phosphate, monobasic, $NH_4H_2PO_4$.

3.5.5. Magnesium nitrate, $Mg(NO_3)_2 \cdot 6H_2O$.

3.5.6. Diluting solution (4% HNO_3, 0.4% HCl): Add 40 mL HNO_3 and 4 mL HCl carefully to approximately 500 mL deionized water and dilute to 1 L with deionized water.

3.5.7. Cadmium standard stock solution, 1,000 µg/mL: Use a commercially available certified 1,000 µg/mL cadmium Standard or, alternatively, dissolve 1.0000 g of cadmium metal in a minimum volume of 1:1 HCl and dilute to 1 L with 4% HNO_3. Observe expiration dates of commercial standards. Properly dispose of commercial standards with no expiration dates or prepared standards one year after their receipt or preparation date.

3.5.8. Matrix modifier for AAS-HGA analysis: Dissolve 1.0 g $NH_4H_2PO_4$ and 0.15 g $Mg(NO_3)_2 \cdot 6H_2O$ in approximately 200 mL deionized water. Add 1 mL HNO_3 and dilute to 500 mL with deionized water.

3.5.9 Nitric Acid, 1:1 HNO_3/DI H_2O mixture: Carefully add a measured volume of concentrated HNO_3 to an equal volume of DI H_2O.

3.5.10. Nitric acid, 10% v/v: Carefully add 100 mL of concentrated HNO_3 to 500 mL of DI H_2O and dilute to 1 L.

3.6. Glassware Preparation

3.6.1. Clean Phillips beakers by refluxing with 1:1 nitric acid on a hot plate in a fume hood. Thoroughly rinse with deionized water and invert the beakers to allow them to drain dry.

3.6.2. Rinse volumetric flasks and all other glassware with 10% nitric acid and deionized water prior to use.

3.7. Standard Preparation for Flame AAS Analysis

3.7.1. Dilute stock solutions: Prepare 1, 5, 10 and 100 µg/mL cadmium standard stock solutions by making appropriate serial dilutions of 1,000 µg/mL cadmium standard stock solution with the diluting solution described in Section 3.5.6.

3.7.2. Working standards: Prepare cadmium working standards in the range of 0.02 to 2.0 µg/mL by making appropriate serial dilutions of the dilute stock solutions with the same diluting solution. A suggested method of preparation of the working standards is given below.

Working standard (µg/mL)	Std solution (µg/mL)	Aliquot (mL)	Final vol. (mL)
0.02	1	10	500
0.05	5	5	500
0.1	10	5	500
0.2	10	10	500
0.5	10	25	500
1	100	5	500
2	100	10	500

Store the working standards in 500-mL, narrow-mouth polyethylene or glass bottles with leak proof caps. Prepare every twelve months.

3.8. Standard Preparation for AAS-HGA Analysis

3.8.1. Dilute stock solutions: Prepare 10, 100 and 1,000 ng/mL cadmium standard stock solutions by making appropriate ten-fold serial dilutions of the 1,000 µg/mL cadmium standard stock solution with the diluting solution described in Section 3.5.6.

3.8.2. Working standards: Prepare cadmium working standards in the range of 0.2 to 20 ng/mL by making appropriate serial dilutions of the dilute stock solutions with the same diluting solution. A suggested method of preparation of the working standards is given below.

Working standard (ng/mL)	Std solution (ng/mL)	Aliquot (mL)	Final vol. (mL)
0.2	10	2	100
0.5	10	5	100
1	10	10	100
2	100	2	100
5	100	5	100
10	100	10	100
20	1,000	2	100

Store the working standards in narrow-mouth polyethylene or glass bottles with leakproof caps. Prepare monthly.

3.9. Sample Preparation

3.9.1. Carefully transfer each sample filter with forceps from its filter cassette unit to a clean, separate 125-mL Phillips beaker along with any loose dust found in the cassette. Label each Phillips beaker with the appropriate sample number.

3.9.2. Digest the sample by adding 5 mL of concentrated nitric acid (HNO_3) to each Phillips beaker containing an air filter sample. Place the Phillips beakers on a hot plate in an exhaust hood and heat the samples until approximately 0.5 mL remains. The sample solution in each Phillips beaker should become clear. If it is not clear, digest the sample with another portion of concentrated nitric acid.

3.9.3. After completing the HNO_3 digestion and cooling the samples, add 40 µL (2 drops) of concentrated HCl to each air sample solution and then swirl the contents. Carefully add about 5 mL of deionized water by pouring it down the inside of each beaker.

3.9.4. Quantitatively transfer each cooled air sample solution from each Phillips beaker to a clean 10-mL volumetric flask. Dilute each flask to volume with deionized water and mix well.

3.10. Flame AAS Analysis

Analyze all of the air samples for their cadmium content by flame atomic absorption spectroscopy (AAS) according to the instructions given below.

3.10.1. Set up the atomic absorption spectrophotometer for the air/acetylene flame analysis of cadmium according to the SOP (5.8.) or the manufacturer's operational instructions. For the source lamp, use the cadmium hollow cathode or electrodeless discharge lamp operated at the manufacturer's recommended rating for continuous operation. Allow the lamp to warm up 10 to 20 min or until the energy output stabilizes. Optimize conditions such as lamp position, burner head alignment, fuel and oxidant flow rates, etc. See the SOP or specific instrument manuals for details. Instrumental parameters for the Perkin-Elmer Model 603 used in the validation of this method are given in Attachment 1.

3.10.2. Aspirate and measure the absorbance of a standard solution of cadmium. The standard concentration should be within the linear range. For the instrumentation used in the validation of this method a 2 µg/mL cadmium standard gives a net absorbance reading of about 0.350 abs. units (see Section 1.5.5.) when the instrument and the source lamp are performing to manufacturer specifications.

3.10.3. To increase instrument response, scale expand the absorbance reading of the aspirated 2 µg/mL working standard approximately four times. Increase the integration time to at least 3 seconds to reduce signal noise.

3.10.4. Autozero the instrument while aspirating a deionized water blank. Monitor the variation in the baseline absorbance reading (baseline noise) for a few minutes to insure that the instrument, source lamp and associated equipment are in good operating condition.

3.10.5. Aspirate the working standards and samples directly into the flame and record their absorbance readings. Aspirate the deionized water blank immediately after every standard or sample to correct for and monitor any baseline drift and noise. Record the baseline absorbance reading of each deionized water blank. Label each standard and sample reading and its accompanying baseline reading.

3.10.6. It is recommended that the entire series of working standards be analyzed at the beginning and end of the analysis of a set of samples to establish a concentration-response curve, ensure that the standard readings agree with each other and are reproducible. Also, analyze a working standard after every five or six samples to monitor the performance of the spectrophotometer. Standard readings should agree within ± 10 to 15% of the readings obtained at the beginning of the analysis.

3.10.7. Bracket the sample readings with standards during the analysis. If the absorbance reading of a sample is above the absorbance reading of the highest working standard, dilute the sample with diluting solution and reanalyze. Use the appropriate dilution factor in the calculations.

3.10.8. Repeat the analysis of approximately 10% of the samples for a check of precision.

3.10.9. If possible, analyze quality control samples from an independent source as a check on analytical recovery and precision.

3.10.10. Record the final instrument settings at the end of the analysis. Date and label the output.

3.11. AAS-HGA Analysis

Initially analyze all of the air samples for their cadmium content by flame atomic absorption spectroscopy (AAS) according to the instructions given in Section 3.10. If the concentration of cadmium in a sample solution is less than three times the quantitative detection limit [0.04 µg/mL (40 ng/mL) for the instrumentation used in the validation] and the sample results are to be averaged with other samples for TWA calculations, proceed with the AAS-HGA analysis of the sample as described below.

3.11.1. Set up the atomic absorption spectrophotometer and HGA for flameless atomic absorption analysis of cadmium according to the SOP (5.9.) or the manufacturer's operational instructions and allow the instrument to stabilize. The graphite furnace atomizer is equipped with a pyrolytically coated graphite tube containing a pyrolytic platform. For the source lamp, use a cadmium hollow cathode or electrodeless discharge lamp operated at the manufacturer's recommended setting for graphite furnace operation. The Zeeman background corrector and EDL are recommended for use with the L'vov platform. Instrumental parameters for the Perkin-Elmer Model 5100 spectrophotometer and Zeeman HGA–600 graphite furnace used in the validation of this method are given in Attachment 2.

3.11.2. Optimize the energy reading of the spectrophotometer at 228.8 nm by adjusting the lamp position and the wavelength according to the manufacturer's instructions.

3.11.3. Set up the autosampler to inject a 5-µL aliquot of the working standard, sample or reagent blank solution onto the L'vov platform along with a 10-µL overlay of the matrix modifier.

3.11.4. Analyze the reagent blank (diluting solution, Section 3.5.6.) and then autozero the instrument before starting the analysis of a set of samples. It is recommended that the reagent blank be analyzed several times during the analysis to assure the integrated absorbance (peak area) reading remains at or near zero.

3.11.5. Analyze a working standard approximately midway in the linear portion of the working standard range two or three times to check for reproducibility and sensitivity (see Sections 1.5.5. and 1.5.6.) before starting the analysis of samples. Calculate the experimental characteristic mass value from the average integrated absorbance reading and injection volume of the analyzed working standard. Compare this value to the manufacturer's suggested value as a check of proper instrument operation.

3.11.6. Analyze the reagent blank, working standard, and sample solutions. Record and label the peak area (abs-sec) readings and the peak and background peak profiles on the printer/plotter.

3.11.7. It is recommended the entire series of working standards be analyzed at the beginning and end of the analysis of a set of samples. Establish a concentration-response curve and ensure standard readings agree with each other and are reproducible. Also, analyze a working standard after every five or six samples to monitor the performance of the system. Standard readings should agree within ± 15% of the readings obtained at the beginning of the analysis.

3.11.8. Bracket the sample readings with standards during the analysis. If the peak area reading of a sample is above the peak area reading of the highest working standard, dilute the sample with the diluting solution and reanalyze. Use the appropriate dilution factor in the calculations.

3.11.9. Repeat the analysis of approximately 10% of the samples for a check of precision.

3.11.10. If possible, analyze quality control samples from an independent source as a check of analytical recovery and precision.

3.11.11. Record the final instrument settings at the end of the analysis. Date and label the output.

3.12. Calculations

Note: Standards used for HGA analysis are in ng/mL. Total amounts of cadmium from calculations will be in ng (not µg) unless a prior conversion is made.

3.12.1. Correct for baseline drift and noise in flame AAS analysis by subtracting each baseline absorbance reading from its corresponding working standard or sample absorbance reading to obtain the net absorbance reading for each standard and sample.

3.12.2. Use a least squares regression program to plot a concentration-response curve of net absorbance reading (or peak area for HGA analysis) versus concentration (µg/mL or ng/mL) of cadmium in each working standard.

3.12.3. Determine the concentration (µg/mL or ng/mL) of cadmium in each sample from the resulting concentration-response curve. If the concentration of cadmium in a sample solution is less than three times the quantitative detection limit [0.04 µg/mL (40 ng/mL) for the instrumentation used in the validation of the method] and if consecutive samples were taken on one employee and the sample results are to be averaged with other samples to determine a single TWA, reanalyze the sample by AAS-HGA as described in Section 3.11. and report the AAS-HGA analytical results.

3.12.4. Calculate the total amount (µg or ng) of cadmium in each sample from the sample solution volume (mL):

$$\mathbf{W = (C)(sample\ vol,\ mL)(DF)}$$

Where:
W = Total cadmium in sample
C = Calculated concentration of cadmium
DF = Dilution Factor (if applicable)

3.12.5. Make a blank correction for each air sample by subtracting the total amount of cadmium in the corresponding blank sample from the total amount of cadmium in the sample.

3.12.6. Calculate the concentration of cadmium in an air sample (mg/m^3 or µg/m^3) by using one of the following equations:

$$\mathbf{mg/m^3 = W_{bc}/(Air\ vol\ sampled,\ L)}$$

or

$$\mathbf{\mu g/m^3 = (W_{bc})(1{,}000\ ng/\mu g)/(Air\ vol\ sampled,\ L)}$$

Where:
W_{bc} = blank corrected total µg cadmium in the sample.
(1 µg = 1,000 ng)

4. Backup Data

4.1. Introduction

4.1.1. The purpose of this evaluation is to determine the analytical method recovery, working standard range, and qualitative and quantitative detection limits of the two atomic absorption analytical techniques included in this method. The evaluation consisted of the following experiments:

1. An analysis of 24 samples (six samples each at 0.1, 0.5, 1 and 2 times the TWA-PEL) for the analytical method recovery study of the flame AAS analytical technique.
2. An analysis of 18 samples (six samples each at 0.5, 1 and 2 times the Action Level TWA-PEL) for the analytical method recovery study of the AAS-HGA analytical technique.
3. Multiple analyses of the reagent blank and a series of standard solutions to determine the working standard range and the qualitative and quantitative detection limits for both atomic absorption analytical techniques.

4.1.2. The analytical method recovery results at all test levels were calculated from concentration-response curves and statistically examined for outliers at the 99% confidence level. Possible outliers were determined using the Treatment of Outliers test (5.10.). In addition, the sample results of the two analytical techniques, at 0.5, 1.0 and 2.0 times their target concentrations, were tested for homogeneity of variances also at the 99% confidence level. Homogeneity of the coefficients of variation was determined using the Bartlett's test (5.11.). The overall analytical error (OAE) at the 95% confidence level was calculated using the equation (5.12.):

OAE = ± [| Bias|+(1.96)(CV_1(pooled))(100%)]

4.1.3. A derivation of the International Union of Pure and Applied Chemistry (IUPAC) detection limit equation (5.13.) was used to determine the qualitative and quantitative detection limits for both atomic absorption analytical techniques:

C_{ld}= k(sd)/m (Equation 1)

Where:

C_{ld} = the smallest reliable detectable concentration an analytical instrument can determine at a given confidence level.

k = 3 for the Qualitative Detection Limit at the 99.86% Confidence Level

= 10 for the Quantitative Detection Limit at the 99.99% Confidence Level.

sd = standard deviation of the reagent blank (Rbl) readings.

m = analytical sensitivity or slope as calculated by linear regression.

4.1.4. Collection efficiencies of metallic fume and dust atmospheres on 0.8-µm mixed cellulose ester membrane filters are well documented and have been shown to be excellent (5.11.). Since elemental cadmium and the cadmium component of cadmium compounds are nonvolatile, stability studies of cadmium spiked MCEF samples were not performed.

4.2. Equipment

4.2.1. A Perkin-Elmer (PE) Model 603 spectrophotometer equipped with a manual gas control system, a stainless steel nebulizer, a burner mixing chamber, a flow spoiler and a 10 cm. (one-slot) burner head was used in the experimental validation of the flame AAS analytical technique. A PE cadmium hollow cathode lamp, operated at the manufacturer's recommended current setting for continuous operation (4 mA), was used as the source lamp. Instrument parameters are listed in Attachment 1.

4.2.2. A PE Model 5100 spectrophotometer, Zeeman HGA–600 graphite furnace atomizer and AS–60 HGA autosampler were used in the experimental validation of the AAS-HGA analytical technique. The spectrophotometer was equipped with a PE Series 7700 professional computer and Model PR–310 printer. A PE System 2 cadmium electrodeless discharge lamp, operated at the manufacturer's recommended current setting for modulated operation (170 mA), was used as the source lamp. Instrument parameters are listed in Attachment 2.

4.3. Reagents

4.3.1. J.T. Baker Chem. Co. (Analyzed grade) concentrated nitric acid, 69.0–71.0%, and concentrated hydrochloric acid, 36.5–38.0%, were used to prepare the samples and standards.

4.3.2. Ammonium phosphate, monobasic, $NH_4H_2PO_4$ and magnesium nitrate, $Mg(NO_3)_2 6H_2O$, both manufactured by the Mallinckrodt Chem. Co., were used to prepare the matrix modifier for AAS-HGA analysis.

4.4. Standard Preparation for Flame AAS Analysis

4.4.1. Dilute stock solutions: Prepared 0.01, 0.1, 1, 10 and 100 µg/mL cadmium standard stock solutions by making appropriate serial dilutions of a commercially available 1,000 µg/mL cadmium standard stock solution (RICCA Chemical Co., Lot# A102) with the diluting solution (4% HNO_3, 0.4% HCl).

4.4.2. Analyzed standards: Prepared cadmium standards in the range of 0.001 to 2.0 µg/mL by pipetting 2 to 10 mL of the appropriate dilute cadmium stock solution into a 100-mL volumetric flask and diluting to volume with the diluting solution. (See Section 3.7.2.)

4.5. Standard Preparation for AAS-HGA Analysis

4.5.1. Dilute stock solutions: Prepared 1, 10, 100 and 1,000 ng/mL cadmium standard stock solutions by making appropriate serial dilutions of a commercially available 1,000 µg/mL cadmium standard stock solution (J.T. Baker Chemical Co., Instra-analyzed, Lot# D22642) with the diluting solution (4% HNO_3, 0.4% HCl).

4.5.2. Analyzed Standards: Prepared cadmium standards in the range of 0.1 to 40 ng/mL by pipetting 2 to 10 mL of the appropriate dilute cadmium stock solution into a 100-mL volumetric flask and diluting to volume with the diluting solution. (See Section 3.8.2.)

4.6. Detection Limits and Standard Working Range for Flame AAS Analysis

4.6.1. Analyzed the reagent blank solution and the entire series of cadmium standards in the range of 0.001 to 2.0 µg/mL three to six times according to the instructions given in Section 3.10. The diluting solution (4% HNO_3, 0.4% HCl) was used as the reagent blank. The integration time on the PE 603 spectrophotometer was set to 3.0 seconds and a four-fold expansion of the absorbance reading of the 2.0 µg/mL cadmium standard was made prior to analysis. The 2.0 µg/mL standard gave a net absorbance reading of 0.350 abs. units prior to expansion in agreement with the manufacturer's specifications (5.6.).

4.6.2. The net absorbance readings of the reagent blank and the low concentration Cd standards from 0.001 to 0.1 µg/mL and the statistical analysis of the results are shown in Table I. The standard deviation, sd, of the six net absorbance readings of the reagent blank is 1.05 abs. units. The slope, m, as calculated by a linear regression plot of the net absorbance readings (shown in Table II) of the 0.02 to 1.0 µg/mL cadmium standards versus their concentration is 772.7 abs. units/(µg/mL).

4.6.3. If these values for sd and the slope, m, are used in Eqn. 1 (Sect. 4.1.3.), the qualitative and quantitative detection limits as determined by the IUPAC Method are:

C_{ld} = (3)(1.05 abs. units)/(772.7 abs. units/(µg/mL))
= 0.0041 µg/mL for the qualitative detection limit.

C_{ld} = (10)(1.05 abs. units)/(772.7 abs. units/(µg/mL))
= 0.014 µg/mL for the quantitative detection limit

The qualitative and quantitative detection limits for the flame AAS analytical technique are 0.041 µg and 0.14 µg cadmium, respectively, for a 10 mL solution volume. These correspond, respectively, to 0.2 µg/m^3 and 0.70 µg/m^3 for a 200 L air volume.

4.6.4. The recommended Cd standard working range for flame AAS analysis is 0.02 to 2.0 µg/mL. The net absorbance readings of the reagent blank and the recommended working range standards and the statistical analysis of the results are shown in Table II. The standard of lowest concentration in the working range, 0.02 µg/mL, is slightly greater than the calculated quantitative detection limit, 0.014 µg/mL. The standard of highest concentration in the working range, 2.0 µg/mL, is at the upper end of the linear working range suggested by the manufacturer (5.6.). Although the standard net absorbance readings are not strictly linear at concentrations above 0.5 µg/mL, the deviation from linearity is only about 10% at the upper end of the recommended standard working range. The deviation from linearity is probably caused by the four-fold expansion of the signal suggested in the method. As shown in Table II, the precision of the standard net absorbance readings are excellent throughout the recommended working range; the relative standard deviations of the readings range from 0.009 to 0.064.

4.7. Detection Limits and Standard Working Range for AAS-HGA Analysis

4.7.1. Analyzed the reagent blank solution and the entire series of cadmium standards in the range of 0.1 to 40 ng/mL according to the instructions given in Section 3.11. The diluting solution (4% HNO_3, 0.4% HCl) was used as the reagent blank. A fresh aliquot of the reagent blank and of each standard was used for every analysis. The experimental characteristic mass value was 0.41 pg, calculated from the average peak area (abs-sec) reading of the 5 ng/mL standard which is approximately midway in the linear portion of the working standard range. This agreed within 20% with the characteristic mass value, 0.35 pg, listed by the manufacturer of the instrument (5.2.).

4.7.2. The peak area (abs-sec) readings of the reagent blank and the low concentration Cd standards from 0.1 to 2.0 ng/mL and statistical analysis of the results are shown in Table III. Five of the reagent blank peak area readings were zero and the sixth reading was 1 and was an outlier. The near lack of a blank signal does not satisfy a strict interpretation of the IUPAC method for determining the detection limits. Therefore, the standard deviation of the six peak area readings of the 0.2 ng/mL cadmium standard, 0.75 abs-sec, was used to calculate the detection limits by the IUPAC method. The slope, m, as calculated by a linear regression plot of the peak area (abs-sec) readings (shown in Table IV) of the 0.2 to 10 ng/mL cadmium standards versus their concentration is 51.5 abs-sec/(ng/mL).

4.7.3. If 0.75 abs-sec (sd) and 51.5 abs-sec/(ng/mL) (m) are used in Eqn. 1 (Sect. 4.1.3.), the qualitative and quantitative detection limits as determined by the IUPAC method are:

C_{ld} = (3)(0.75 abs-sec)/(51.5 abs-sec/(ng/mL) =
0.044 ng/mL for the qualitative detection limit

C_{ld} = (10)(0.75 abs-sec)/(51.5 abs-sec/(ng/mL) =
0.15 ng/mL for the quantitative detection limit

The qualitative and quantitative detection limits for the AAS-HGA analytical technique are 0.44 ng and 1.5 ng cadmium, respectively, for a 10 mL solution volume. These correspond, respectively, to 0.007 µg/m^3 and 0.025 µg/m^3 for a 60 L air volume.

4.7.4. The peak area (abs-sec) readings of the Cd standards from 0.2 to 40 ng/mL and the statistical analysis of the results are given in Table IV. The recommended standard working range for AAS-HGA analysis is 0.2 to 20 ng/mL. The standard of lowest concentration in the recommended working range is slightly greater than the calculated quantitative detection limit, 0.15 ng/

mL. The deviation from linearity of the peak area readings of the 20 ng/mL standard, the highest concentration standard in the recommended working range, is approximately 10%. The deviations from linearity of the peak area readings of the 30 and 40 ng/mL standards are significantly greater than 10%. As shown in Table IV, the precision of the peak area readings are satisfactory throughout the recommended working range; the relative standard deviations of the readings range from 0.025 to 0.083.

4.8. Analytical Method Recovery for Flame AAS Analysis

4.8.1. Four sets of spiked MCEF samples were prepared by injecting 20 µL of 10, 50, 100 and 200 µg/mL dilute cadmium stock solutions on 37 mm diameter filters (part no. AAWP 037 00, Millipore Corp., Bedford, MA) with a calibrated micropipet. The dilute stock solutions were prepared by making appropriate serial dilutions of a commercially available 1,000 µg/mL cadmium standard stock solution (RICCA Chemical Co., Lot# A102) with the diluting solution (4% HNO_3, 0.4% HCl). Each set contained six samples and a sample blank. The amount of cadmium in the prepared sets were equivalent to 0.1, 0.5, 1.0 and 2.0 times the TWA PEL target concentration of 5 µg/m^3 for a 400 L air volume.

4.8.2. The air-dried spiked filters were digested and analyzed for their cadmium content by flame atomic absorption spectroscopy (AAS) following the procedure described in Section 3. The 0.02 to 2.0 µg/mL cadmium standards (the suggested working range) were used in the analysis of the spiked filters.

4.8.3. The results of the analysis are given in Table V. One result at 0.5 times the TWA PEL target concentration was an outlier and was excluded from statistical analysis. Experimental justification for rejecting it is that the outlier value was probably due to a spiking error. The coefficients of variation for the three test levels at 0.5 to 2.0 times the TWA PEL target concentration passed the Bartlett's test and were pooled.

4.8.4. The average recovery of the six spiked filter samples at 0.1 times the TWA PEL target concentration was 118.2% with a coefficient of variation (CV_1) of 0.128. The average recovery of the spiked filter samples in the range of 0.5 to 2.0 times the TWA target concentration was 104.0% with a pooled coefficient of variation (CV_1) of 0.010. Consequently, the analytical bias found in these spiked sample results over the tested concentration range was +4.0% and the OAE was ± 6.0%.

4.9. Analytical Method Recovery for AAS-HGA Analysis

4.9.1. Three sets of spiked MCEF samples were prepared by injecting 15µL of 5, 10 and 20 µg/mL dilute cadmium stock solutions on 37 mm diameter filters (part no. AAWP 037 00, Millipore Corp., Bedford, MA) with a calibrated micropipet. The dilute stock solutions were prepared by making appropriate serial dilutions of a commercially available certified 1,000 µg/mL cadmium standard stock solution (Fisher Chemical Co., Lot# 913438–24) with the diluting solution (4% HNO_3, 0.4% HCl). Each set contained six samples and a sample blank. The amount of cadmium in the prepared sets were equivalent to 0.5, 1 and 2 times the Action Level TWA target concentration of 2.5 µg/m^3 for a 60 L air volume.

4.9.2. The air-dried spiked filters were digested and analyzed for their cadmium content by flameless atomic absorption spectroscopy using a heated graphite furnace atomizer following the procedure described in Section 3. A five-fold dilution of the spiked filter samples at 2 times the Action Level TWA was made prior to their analysis. The 0.05 to 20 ng/mL cadmium standards were used in the analysis of the spiked filters.

4.9.3. The results of the analysis are given in Table VI. There were no outliers. The coefficients of variation for the three test levels at 0.5 to 2.0 times the Action Level TWA PEL passed the Bartlett's test and were pooled. The average recovery of the spiked filter samples was 94.2% with a pooled coefficient of variation (CV1) of 0.043. Consequently, the analytical bias was −5.8% and the OAE was ± 14.2%.

4.10. Conclusions

The experiments performed in this evaluation show the two atomic absorption analytical techniques included in this method to be precise and accurate and have sufficient sensitivity to measure airborne cadmium over a broad range of exposure levels and sampling periods.

5. References

5.1. Slavin, W. Graphite Furnace AAS—A Source Book; Perkin-Elmer Corp., Spectroscopy Div.: Ridgefield, CT, 1984; p. 18 and pp. 83–90.

5.2. Grosser, Z., Ed.; Techniques in Graphite Furnace Atomic Absorption Spectrophotometry; Perkin-Elmer Corp., Spectroscopy Div.: Ridgefield, CT, 1985.

5.3. Occupational Safety and Health Administration Salt Lake Technical Center: Metal and Metalloid Particulate in Workplace Atmospheres (Atomic Absorption) (USDOL/OSHA Method No. ID–121). In OSHA Analytical Methods Manual 2nd ed. Cincinnati, OH: American Conference of Governmental Industrial Hygienists, 1991.

5.4. Occupational Safety and Health Administration Salt Lake Technical Center: Metal and Metalloid Particulate in Workplace Atmospheres (ICP) (USDOL/OSHA Method No. ID–125G). In OSHA Analytical Methods Manual 2nd ed. Cincinnati, OH: American Conference of Governmental Industrial Hygienists, 1991.

5.5. Windholz, M., Ed.; The Merck Index, 10th ed.; Merck & Co.: Rahway, NJ, 1983.

5.6. Analytical Methods for Atomic Absorption Spectrophotometry, The Perkin-Elmer Corporation: Norwalk, CT, 1982.

5.7. Slavin, W., D.C. Manning, G. Carnrick, and E. Pruszkowska: Properties of the Cadmium Determination with the Platform Furnace and Zeeman Background Correction. Spectrochim. Acta 38B:1157–1170 (1983).

5.8. Occupational Safety and Health Administration Salt Lake Technical Center: Standard Operating Procedure for Atomic Absorption. Salt Lake City, UT: USDOL/OSHA-SLTC, In progress.

5.9. Occupational Safety and Health Administration Salt Lake Technical Center: AAS-HGA Standard Operating Procedure. Salt Lake City, UT: USDOL/OSHA-SLTC, In progress.

5.10. Mandel, J.: Accuracy and Precision, Evaluation and Interpretation of Analytical Results, The Treatment of Outliers. In Treatise On Analytical Chemistry, 2nd ed., Vol.1, edited by I. M. Kolthoff and P. J. Elving. New York: John Wiley and Sons, 1978. pp. 282–285.

5.11. National Institute for Occupational Safety and Health: Documentation of the NIOSH Validation Tests by D. Taylor, R. Kupel, and J. Bryant (DHEW/NIOSH Pub. No. 77–185). Cincinnati, OH: National Institute for Occupational Safety and Health, 1977.

5.12. Occupational Safety and Health Administration Analytical Laboratory: Precision and Accuracy Data Protocol for Laboratory Validations. In OSHA Analytical Methods Manual 1st ed. Cincinnati, OH: American Conference of Governmental Industrial Hygienists (Pub. No. ISBN: 0–936712–66–X), 1985.

5.13. Long, G.L. and J.D. Winefordner: Limit of Detection—A Closer Look at the IUPAC Definition. Anal.Chem. 55:712A–724A (1983).

5.14. American Conference of Governmental Industrial Hygienists: Documentation of Threshold Limit Values and Biological Exposure Indices. 5th ed. Cincinnati, OH: American Conference of Governmental Industrial Hygienists, 1986.

Table I
Cd Detection Limit Study
[Flame AAS Analysis]

STD (µg/mL)	Absorbance reading at 228.8 nm		Statistical analysis
Reagent blank	5 4 4	2 3 3	n = 6 mean = 3.50 std dev = 1.05 CV = 0.30
0.001	6 2 6	6 4 6	n = 6 mean = 5.00 std dev = 1.67 CV = 0.335
0.002	5 7 7	7 3 4	n = 6 mean = 5.50 std dev = 1.76 CV = 0.320
0.005	7 8 8	7 8 6	n = 6 mean = 7.33 std dev = 0.817 CV = 0.111
0.010	10 10 10	9 13 10	n = 6 mean = 10.3 std dev = 1.37 CV = 0.133
0.020	20 20 20	23 22 20	n = 6 mean = 20.8 std dev = 1.33 CV = 0.064
0.050	42 42 42	42 42 45	n = 6 mean = 42.5 std dev = 1.22 CV = 0.029
0.10		84 80 83	n = 3 mean = 82.3 std dev = 2.08 CV = 0.025

Table II
Cd Standard Working Range Study
[Flame AAS Analysis]

STD (µg/mL)	Absorbance reading at 228.8 nm	Statistical analysis
Reagent blank	5 2 4 3 4 3	n = 6 mean = 3.50 std dev = 1.05 CV = 0.30
0.020	20 23 20 22 20 20	n = 6 mean = 20.8 std dev = 1.33 CV = 0.064
0.050	42 42 42 42 42 45	n = 6 mean = 42.5 std dev = 1.22 CV = 0.029
0.10	84 80 83	n = 3 mean = 82.3 std dev = 2.08 CV = 0.025
0.20	161 161 158	n = 3 mean = 160.0 std dev = 1.73 CV = 0.011
0.50	391 389 393	n = 3 mean = 391.0 std dev = 2.00 CV = 0.005
1.00	760 748 752	n = 3 mean = 753.3 std dev = 6.11 CV = 0.008
2.00	1416 1426 1401	n = 3 mean = 1414.3 std dev = 12.6 CV = 0.009

Table III
Cd Detection Limit Study
[AAS-HGA Analysis]

STD (ng/mL)	Peak area readings × 10^3 at 228.8 nm	Statistical analysis
Reagent blank	0 0 0 1 0 0	n = 6 mean = 0.167 std dev = 0.41 CV = 2.45
0.1	8 6 5 7 13 7	n = 6 mean = 7.7 std dev = 2.8 CV = 0.366
0.2	11 13 11 12 12 12	n = 6 mean = 11.8 std dev = 0.75 CV = 0.064
0.5	28 33 26 28 28 30	n = 6 mean = 28.8 std dev = 2.4 CV = 0.083
1.0	52 55 56 58 54 54	n = 6 mean = 54.8 std dev = 2.0 CV = 0.037
2.0	101 112 110 110 110 110	n = 6 mean = 108.8 std dev = 3.9 CV = 0.036

Table IV
Cd Standard Working Range Study
[AAS-HGA Analysis]

STD (ng/mL)	Peak area readings × 10^3 at 228.8 nm	Statistical analysis
0.2	11 13 11 12 12 12	n = 6 mean = 11.8 std dev = 0.75 CV = 0.064
0.5	28 33 26 28 28 30	n = 6 mean = 28.8 std dev = 2.4 CV = 0.083
1.0	52 55 56 58 54 54	n = 6 mean = 54.8 std dev = 2.0 CV = 0.037
2.0	101 112 110 110 110 110	n = 6 mean = 108.8 std dev = 3.9 CV = 0.036
5.0	247 265 268 275 259 279	n = 6 mean = 265.5 std dev = 11.5 CV = 0.044
10.0	495 520 523 513 516 533	n = 6 mean = 516.7 std dev = 12.7 CV = 0.025
20.0	950 953 951 958 949 890	n = 6 mean = 941.8 std dev = 25.6 CV = 0.027
30.0	1269 1291 1303 1307 1295 1290	n = 6 mean = 1293 std dev = 13.3 CV = 0.010
40.0	1505 1567 1535 1567 1566 1572	n = 6 mean = 1552 std dev = 26.6 CV = 0.017

Table V
Analytical Method Recovery
[Flame AAS Analysis]

Test level					
0.1x			0.5x		
µg taken	µg found	Percent rec.	µg taken	µg found	Percent rec.
2.00	0.2509	125.5	1.00	1.0715	107.2
2.00	0.2509	125.5	1.00	1.0842	108.4
2.00	0.2761	138.1	1.00	1.0842	108.4
2.00	0.2258	112.9	1.00	*1.0081	*100.8
2.00	0.2258	112.9	1.00	1.0715	107.2
2.00	0.1881	94.1	1.00	1.0842	108.4
n =		6			5
mean =		118.2			107.9
sdt dev =		15.1			0.657
CV_1 =		0.128			0.006
CV_1 (pooled) = 0.010					

Note: Table data continues on next page.

*Rejected as an outlier—this value did not pass the outlier T-test at the 99% confidence level.

Test level					
1.0x			2.0x		
µg taken	µg found	Percent rec.	µg taken	µg found	Percent rec.
2.00	2.0688	103.4	4.00	4.1504	103.8
2.00	2.0174	100.9	4.00	4.1108	102.8
2.00	2.0431	102.2	4.00	4.0581	101.5
2.00	2.0431	102.2	4.00	4.0844	102.1
2.00	2.0174	100.9	4.00	4.1504	103.8
2.00	2.0045	100.2	4.00	4.1899	104.7
n =		5			6
mean =		101.6			103.1
sdt dev =		1.174			1.199
CV_1 =		0.011			0.012

Table VI
Analytical Method Recovery
[AAS-HGA Analysis]

Test level 0.5x		
ng taken	ng found	Percent rec.
75	71.23	95.0
75	71.47	95.3
75	70.02	93.4
75	77.34	103.1
75	78.32	104.4
75	71.96	95.9
n =		6
mean =		97.9
std dev =		4.66
CV_1 =		0.048
CV1 (pooled) = 0.043		

Test level 1.0x		
ng taken	ng found	Percent rec.
150	138.00	92.0
150	138.29	92.2
150	136.30	90.9
150	146.62	97.7
150	145.17	96.8
150	144.88	96.6
n =		6
mean =		94.4
std dev =		2.98
CV_1 =		0.032
CV1 (pooled) = 0.043		

Test level 2.0x		
ng taken	ng found	Percent rec.
300	258.43	86.1
300	258.46	86.2
300	280.55	93.5
300	288.34	96.1
300	261.74	87.2
300	277.22	92.4
n =		6
mean =		90.3
std dev =		4.30
CV_1 =		0.048
CV1 (pooled) = 0.043		

Attachment 1
Instrumental Parameters for Flame AAS Analysis

Atomic Absorption Spectrophotometer (Perkin-Elmer Model 603)
Flame: Air/Acetylene—lean, blue
Oxidant Flow: 55
Fuel Flow: 32
Wavelength: 228.8 nm
Slit: 4 (0.7 nm)
Range: UV
Signal: Concentration (4 exp)
Integration Time: 3 sec

Attachment 2
Instrumental Parameters for HGA Analysis

Atomic Absorption Spectrophotometer (Perkin-Elmer Model 5100)
Signal Type: Zeeman AA
Slitwidth: 0.7 nm
Wavelength: 228.8 nm
Measurement: Peak Area
Integration Time: 6.0 sec
BOC Time: 5 sec
BOC=Background Offset Correction.

Zeeman Graphite Furnace
(Perkin-Elmer Model HGA–600)

Step	Ramp time (sec)	Hold time (sec)	Temp. (°C)	Argon flow (mL/min)	Read (sec)
1) Predry	5	10	90	300	
2) Dry	30	10	140	300	
3) Char	10	20	900	300	
4) Cool Down	1	8	30	300	
5) Atomize	0	5	1600	0	-1
6) Burnout	1	8	2500	300	

§1910.1027 Appendix F
Protocol for biological monitoring
(Nonmandatory)

1.0 Introduction

Under the final OSHA cadmium rule (29 CFR Part 1910), monitoring of biological specimens and several periodic medical examinations are required for eligible employees. These medical examinations are to be conducted regularly, and medical monitoring is to include the periodic analysis of cadmium in blood (CDB), cadmium in urine (CDU) and beta-2-microglobulin in urine (B2MU). As CDU and B2MU are to be normalized to the concentration of creatinine in urine (CRTU), then CRTU must be analyzed in conjunction with CDU and B2MU analyses.

The purpose of this protocol is to provide procedures for establishing and maintaining the quality of the results obtained from the analyses of CDB, CDU and B2MU by commercial laboratories. Laboratories conforming to the provisions of this nonmandatory protocol shall be known as "participating laboratories." The biological monitoring data from these laboratories will be evaluated by physicians responsible for biological monitoring to determine the conditions under which employees may continue to work in locations exhibiting airborne-cadmium concentrations at or above defined actions levels (see paragraphs (l)(3) and (l)(4) of the final rule). These results also may be used to support a decision to remove workers from such locations.

Under the medical monitoring program for cadmium, blood and urine samples must be collected at defined intervals from workers by physicians responsible for medical monitoring; these samples are sent to commercial laboratories that perform the required analyses and report results of these analyses to the responsible physicians. To ensure the accuracy and reliability of these laboratory analyses, the laboratories to which samples are submitted should participate in an ongoing and efficacious proficiency testing program. Availability of proficiency testing programs may vary with the analyses performed.

To test proficiency in the analysis of CDB, CDU and B2MU, a laboratory should participate either in the interlaboratory comparison program operated by the Centre de Toxicologie du Quebec (CTQ) or an equivalent program. (Currently, no laboratory in the U.S. performs proficiency testing on CDB, CDU or B2MU.) Under this program, CTQ sends participating laboratories 18 samples of each analyte (CDB, CDU and/or B2MU) annually for analysis. Participating laboratories must return the results of these analyses to CTQ within four to five weeks after receiving the samples.

The CTQ program pools analytical results from many participating laboratories to derive consensus mean values for each of the samples distributed. Results reported by each laboratory then are compared against these consensus means for the analyzed samples to determine the relative performance of each laboratory. The proficiency of a participating laboratory is a function of the extent of agreement between results submitted by the participating laboratory and the consensus values for the set of samples analyzed.

Proficiency testing for CRTU analysis (which should be performed with CDU and B2MU analyses to evaluate the results properly) also is recommended. In the U.S., only the College of American Pathologists (CAP) currently conducts CRTU proficiency testing; participating laboratories should be accredited for CRTU analysis by the CAP.

Results of the proficiency evaluations will be forwarded to the participating laboratory by the proficiency-testing laboratory, as well as to physicians designated by the participating laboratory to receive this information. In addition, the participating laboratory should, on request, submit the results of their internal Quality Assurance/Quality Control (QA/QC) program for each analytic procedure (i.e., CDB, CDU and/or B2MU) to physicians designated to receive the proficiency results. For participating laboratories offering CDU and/or B2MU analyses, QA/QC documentation also should be provided for CRTU analysis. (Laboratories should provide QA/QC information regarding CRTU analysis directly to the requesting physician if they perform the analysis in-house; if CRTU analysis is performed by another laboratory under contract, this information should be provided to the physician by the contract laboratory.)

QA/QC information, along with the actual biological specimen measurements, should be provided to the responsible physician using standard formats. These physicians then may collate the QA/QC information with proficiency test results to compare the relative performance of laboratories, as well as to facilitate evaluation of the worker monitoring data. This information supports decisions made by the physician with regard to the biological monitoring program, and for mandating medical removal.

This protocol describes procedures that may be used by the responsible physicians to identify laboratories most likely to be proficient in the analysis of samples used in the biological monitoring of cadmium; also provided are procedures for record keeping and reporting by laboratories participating in proficiency testing programs, and recommendations to assist these physicians in interpreting analytical results determined by participating laboratories. As the collection and handling of samples affects the quality of the data, recommendations are made for these tasks. Specifications for analytical methods to be used in the medical monitoring program are included in this protocol as well.

In conclusion, this document is intended as a supplement to characterize and maintain the quality of medical monitoring data collected under the final cadmium rule promulgated by OSHA (29 CFR Part 1910). OSHA has been granted authority under the Occupational Safety and Health Act of 1970 to protect workers from the effects of exposure to hazardous substances in the work place and to mandate adequate monitoring of workers to determine when adverse health effects may be occurring. This nonmandatory protocol is intended to provide guidelines and recommendations to improve the accuracy and reliability of the procedures used to analyze the biological samples collected as part of the medical monitoring program for cadmium.

2.0 Definitions

When the terms below appear in this protocol, use the following definitions.

Accuracy A measure of the bias of a data set. Bias is a systematic error that is either inherent in a method or caused by some artifact or idiosyncracy of the measurement system. Bias is characterized by a consistent deviation (positive or negative) in the results from an accepted reference value.

Arithmetic Mean The sum of measurements in a set divided by the number of measurements in a set.

Blind Samples A quality control procedure in which the concentration of analyte in the samples should be unknown to the analyst at the time that the analysis is performed.

Coefficient of Variation The ratio of the standard deviation of a set of measurements to the mean (arithmetic or geometric) of the measurements.

Compliance Samples Samples from exposed workers sent to a participating laboratory for analysis.

Control Charts Graphic representations of the results for quality control samples being analyzed by a participating laboratory.

Control Limits Statistical limits which define when an analytic procedure exceeds acceptable parameters; control limits provide a method of assessing the accuracy of analysts, laboratories, and discrete analytic runs.

Control Samples Quality control samples.

F/T The measured amount of an analyte divided by the theoretical value (defined below) for that analyte in the sample analyzed; this ratio is a measure of the recovery for a quality control sample.

Geometric Mean The natural antilog of the mean of a set of natural log-transformed data.

Geometric Standard Deviation The antilog of the standard deviation of a set of natural log-transformed data.

Limit of Detection Using a predefined level of confidence, this is the lowest measured value at which some of the measured material is likely to have come from the sample.

Mean A central tendency of a set of data; in this protocol, this mean is defined as the arithmetic mean (see definition of arithmetic mean above) unless stated otherwise.

Performance A measure of the overall quality of data reported by a laboratory.

Pools Groups of quality-control samples to be established for each target value (defined below) of an analyte. For the protocol provided in attachment 3, for example, the theoretical value of the quality control samples of the pool must be within a range defined as plus or minus (±) 50% of the target value. Within each analyte pool, there must be quality control samples of at least 4 theoretical values.

Precision The extent of agreement between repeated, independent measurements of the same quantity of an analyte.

Proficiency The ability to satisfy a specified level of analyte performance.

Proficiency Samples Specimens, the values of which are unknown to anyone at a participating laboratory, and which are submitted by a participating laboratory for proficiency testing.

Quality or Data Quality A measure of the confidence in the measurement value.

Quality Control (QC) Samples Specimens, the value of which is unknown to the analyst, but is known to the appropriate QA/QC personnel of a participating laboratory; when used as part of a laboratory QA/QC program, the theoretical values of these samples should not be known to the analyst until the analyses are complete. QC samples are to be run in sets consisting of one QC sample from each pool (see definition of "pools" above).

Sensitivity For the purposes of this protocol, the limit of detection.

Standard Deviation A measure of the distribution or spread of a data set about the mean; the standard deviation is equal to the positive square root of the variance, and is expressed in the same units as the original measurements in the data set.

Standards Samples with values known by the analyst and used to calibrate equipment and to check calibration throughout an analytic run. In a laboratory QA/QC program, the values of the standards must exceed the values obtained for compliance samples such that the lowest standard value is near the limit of detection and the highest standard is higher than the highest compliance sample or QC sample. Standards of at least three different values are to be used for calibration, and should be constructed from at least 2 different sources.

Target Value Those values of CDB, CDU or B2MU which trigger some action as prescribed in the medical surveillance section of the regulatory text of the final cadmium rule. For CDB, the target values are 5, 10 and 15 µg/l. For CDU, the target values are 3, 7, and 15 µg/g CRTU. For B2MU, the target values are 300, 750 and 1500 µg/g CRTU. (Note that target values may vary as a function of time.)

Theoretical Value (or Theoretical Amount) The reported concentration of a quality-control sample (or calibration standard) derived from prior characterizations of the sample.

Value or Measurement Value The numerical result of a measurement.

Variance A measure of the distribution or spread of a data set about the mean; the variance is the sum of the squares of the differences between the mean and each discrete measurement divided by one less than the number of measurements in the data set.

3.0 Protocol

This protocol provides procedures for characterizing and maintaining the quality of analytic results derived for the medical monitoring program mandated for workers under the final cadmium rule.

3.1 Overview

The goal of this protocol is to assure that medical monitoring data are of sufficient quality to facilitate proper interpretation. The data quality objectives (DQOs) defined for the medical monitoring program are summarized in Table 1. Based on available information, the DQOs presented in Table 1 should be achievable by the majority of laboratories offering the required analyses commercially; OSHA recommends that only laboratories meeting these DQOs be used for the analysis of biological samples collected for monitoring cadmium exposure.

Table 1
Recommended Data Quality Objectives (DQOs) for the Cadmium Medical Monitoring Program

Analyte/concentration pool	Limit of detection	Precision (CV) (%)	Accuracy
Cadmium in blood	0.5 µg/l		± 1 µg/l or 15% of the mean
≤ 2 µg/l		40	
> 2µg/l		20	
Cadmium in urine	0.5 µg/g creatinine		± 1 µg/l or 15% of the mean
≤ 2 µg/l creatinine		40	
> 2µg/l creatinine		20	
β-2-microglobulin in urine: 100 µg/g creatine	100 µg/g creatinine	5	± 15% of the mean

To satisfy the DQOs presented in Table 1, OSHA provides the following guidelines:

1. Procedures for the collection and handling of blood and urine are specified (Section 3.4.1 of this protocol);
2. Preferred analytic methods for the analysis of CDB, CDU and B2MU are defined (and a method for the determination of CRTU also is specified since CDU and B2MU results are to be normalized to the level of CRTU);
3. Procedures are described for identifying laboratories likely to provide the required analyses in an accurate and reliable manner;
4. These guidelines (Sections 3.2.1 to 3.2.3, and Section 3.3) include recommendations regarding internal QA/QC programs for participating laboratories, as well as levels of proficiency through participation in an interlaboratory proficiency program;
5. Procedures for QA/QC record keeping (Section 3.3.2), and for reporting QC/QA results are described (Section 3.3.3); and,
6. Procedures for interpreting medical monitoring results are specified (Section 3.4.3).

Methods recommended for the biological monitoring of eligible workers are:

1. The method of Stoeppler and Brandt (1980) for CDB determinations (limit of detection: 0.5 µg/l);
2. The method of Pruszkowska et al. (1983) for CDU determinations (limit of detection: 0.5 µg/l of urine); and,
3. The Pharmacia Delphia test kit (Pharmacia 1990) for the determination of B2MU (limit of detection: 100 µg/l urine).

Because both CDU and B2MU should be reported in µg/g CRTU, an independent determination of CRTU is recommended. Thus, both the OSHA Salt Lake City Technical Center (OSLTC) method (OSHA, no date) and the Jaffe method (Du Pont, no date) for the determination of CRTU are specified under this protocol (i.e., either of these 2 methods may be used). Note that although detection limits are not reported for either of these CRTU methods, the range of measurements expected for CRTU (0.9-1.7 µg/l) are well above the likely limit of detection for either of these methods (Harrison, 1987).

Laboratories using alternate methods should submit sufficient data to the responsible physicians demonstrating that the alternate method is capable of satisfying the defined data quality objectives of the program. Such laboratories also should submit a QA/QC plan that documents the performance of the alternate method in a manner entirely equivalent to the QA/QC plans proposed in Section 3.3.1.

3.2 Duties of the Responsible Physician

The responsible physician will evaluate biological monitoring results provided by participating laboratories to determine whether such laboratories are proficient and have satisfied the QA/QC recommendations. In determining which laboratories to employ for this purpose, these physicians should review proficiency and QA/QC data submitted to them by the participating laboratories.

Participating laboratories should demonstrate proficiency for each analyte (CDU, CDB and B2MU) sampled under the biological monitoring program. Participating laboratories involved in analyzing CDU and B2MU also should demonstrate proficiency for CRTU analysis, or provide evidence of a contract with a laboratory proficient in CRTU analysis.

3.2.1 Recommendations for selecting among existing laboratories

OSHA recommends that existing laboratories providing commercial analyses for CDB, CDU and/or B2MU for the medical monitoring program satisfy the following criteria:

1. Should have performed commercial analyses for the appropriate analyte (CDB, CDU and/or B2MU) on a regular basis over the last 2 years;
2. Should provide the responsible physician with an internal QA/QC plan;
3. If performing CDU or B2MU analyses, the participating laboratory should be accredited by the CAP for CRTU analysis, and should be enrolled in the corresponding CAP survey (note that alternate credentials may be acceptable, but acceptability is to be determined by the responsible physician); and,
4. Should have enrolled in the CTQ interlaboratory comparison program for the appropriate analyte (CDB, CDU and/or B2MU).

Participating laboratories should submit appropriate documentation demonstrating compliance with the above criteria to the responsible physician. To demonstrate compliance with the first of the above criteria, participating laboratories should submit the following documentation for each analyte they plan to analyze (note that each document should cover a period of at least 8 consecutive quarters, and that the period designated by the term "regular analyses" is at least once a quarter):

1. Copies of laboratory reports providing results from regular analyses of the appropriate analyte (CDB, CDU and/or B2MU);
2. Copies of 1 or more signed and executed contracts for the provision of regular analyses of the appropriate analyte (CDB, CDU and/or B2MU); or,
3. Copies of invoices sent to 1 or more clients requesting payment for the provision of regular analyses of the appropriate analyte (CDB, CDU and/or B2MU). Whatever the form of documentation submitted, the specific analytic procedures conducted should be identified directly. The forms that are copied for submission to the responsible physician also should identify the laboratory which provided these analyses.

To demonstrate compliance with the second of the above criteria, a laboratory should submit to the responsible physician an internal QA/QC plan detailing the standard operating procedures to be adopted for satisfying the recommended QA/QC procedures for the analysis of each specific analyte (CDB, CDU and/or B2MU). Procedures for internal QA/QC programs are detailed in Section 3.3.1 below.

To satisfy the third of the above criteria, laboratories analyzing for CDU or B2MU also should submit a QA/QC plan for creatinine analysis (CRTU); the QA/QC plan and characterization analyses for CRTU must come from the laboratory performing the CRTU analysis, even if the CRTU analysis is being performed by a contract laboratory.

Laboratories enrolling in the CTQ program (to satisfy the last of the above criteria) must remit, with the enrollment application, an initial fee of approximately $100 per analyte. (Note that this fee is only an estimate, and is subject to revision without notice.) Laboratories should indicate on the application that they agree to have proficiency test results sent by the CTQ directly to the physicians designated by participating laboratories.

Once a laboratory's application is processed by the CTQ, the laboratory will be assigned a code number which will be provided to the laboratory on the initial confirmation form, along with identification of the specific analytes for which the laboratory is participating. Confirmation of participation will be sent by the CTQ to physicians designated by the applicant laboratory.

3.2.2 Recommended review of laboratories selected to perform analyses

Six months after being selected initially to perform analyte determinations, the status of participating laboratories should be reviewed by the responsible physicians. Such reviews should then be repeated every 6 months or whenever additional proficiency or QA/QC documentation is received (whichever occurs first).

As soon as the responsible physician has received the CTQ results from the first 3 rounds of proficiency testing (i.e., 3 sets of 3 samples each for CDB, CDU and/or B2MU) for a participating laboratory, the status of the laboratory's continued participation should be reviewed. Over the same initial 6-month period, participating laboratories also should provide responsible physicians the results of their internal QA/QC monitoring program used to assess performance for each analyte (CDB, CDU and/or B2MU) for which the laboratory performs determinations. This information should be submitted using appropriate forms and documentation.

The status of each participating laboratory should be determined for each analyte (i.e., whether the laboratory satisfies minimum proficiency guidelines based on the proficiency samples sent by the CTQ and the results of the laboratory's internal QA/QC program). To maintain competency for analysis of CDB, CDU and/or B2MU during the first review, the laboratory should satisfy performance requirements for at least 2 of the 3 proficiency samples provided in each of the 3 rounds completed over the 6-month period. Proficiency should be maintained for the analyte(s) for which the laboratory conducts determinations.

To continue participation for CDU and/or B2MU analyse, laboratories also should either maintain accreditation for CRTU analysis in the CAP program and participate in the CAP surveys, or they should contract the CDU and B2MU analyses to a laboratory which satisfies these requirements (or which can provide documentation of accreditation/participation in an equivalent program).

The performance requirement for CDB analysis is defined as an analytical result within ±1 µg/l blood or 15% of the consensus mean (whichever is greater). For samples exhibiting a consensus mean less than 1 µg/l, the performance requirement is defined as a concentration between the detection limit of the analysis and a maximum of 2 µg/l. The purpose for redefining the acceptable interval for low CDB values is to encourage proper reporting of the actual values obtained during measurement; laboratories, therefore, will not be penalized (in terms of a narrow range of acceptability) for reporting measured concentrations smaller than 1 µg/l.

The performance requirement for CDU analysis is defined as an analytical result within ±1 µg/l urine or 15% of the consensus mean (whichever is greater). For samples exhibiting a consensus mean less than 1 µg/l urine, the performance requirement is defined as a concentration between the detection limit of the analysis and a maximum of 2 µg/l urine. Laboratories also should demonstrate proficiency in creatinine analysis as defined by the CAP. Note that reporting CDU results, other than for the CTQ proficiency samples (i.e., compliance samples), should be accompanied with results of analyses for CRTU, and these 2 sets of results should be combined to provide a measure of CDU in units of µg/g CRTU.

The performance requirement for B2MU is defined as analytical results within ± 15% of the consensus mean. Note that reporting B2MU results, other than for CTQ proficiency samples (i.e., compliance samples), should be accompanied with results of analyses for CRTU, and these 2 sets of results should be combined to provide a measure of B2MU in units of µg/g CRTU.

There are no recommended performance checks for CRTU analyses. As stated previously, laboratories performing CRTU analysis in support of CDU or B2MU analyses should be accredited by the CAP, and participating in the CAP's survey for CRTU.

Following the first review, the status of each participating laboratory should be reevaluated at regular intervals (i.e., corresponding to receipt of results from each succeeding round of proficiency testing and submission of reports from a participating laboratory's internal QA/QC program).

After a year of collecting proficiency test results, the following proficiency criterion should be added to the set of criteria used to determine the participating laboratory's status (for analyzing CDB, CDU and/or B2MU): A participating laboratory should not fail performance requirements for more than 4 samples from the 6 most recent consecutive rounds used to assess proficiency for CDB, CDU and/or B2MU separately (i.e., a total of 18 discrete proficiency samples for each analyte). Note that this requirement does not replace, but supplements, the recommendation that a laboratory should satisfy the performance criteria for at least 2 of the 3 samples tested for each round of the program.

3.2.3 Recommendations for selecting among newly-formed laboratories (or laboratories that previously failed to meet the Protocol Guidelines)

OSHA recommends that laboratories that have not previously provided commercial analyses of CDB, CDU and/or B2MU (or have done so for a period less than 2 years), or which have provided these analyses for 2 or more years but have not conformed previously with these protocol guidelines, should satisfy the following provisions for each analyte for which determinations are to be made prior to being selected to analyze biological samples under the medical monitoring program:

1. Submit to the responsible physician an internal QA/QC plan detailing the standard operating procedures to be adopted for satisfying the QA/QC guidelines (guidelines for internal QA/QC programs are detailed in Section 3.3.1);
2. Submit to the responsible physician the results of the initial characterization analyses for each analyte for which determinations are to be made;
3. Submit to the responsible physician the results, for the initial 6-month period, of the internal QA/QC program for each analyte for which determinations are to be made (if no commercial analyses have been conducted previously, a minimum of 2 mock standardization trials for each analyte should be completed per month for a 6-month period);
4. Enroll in the CTQ program for the appropriate analyte for which determinations are to be made, and arrange to have the CTQ program submit the initial confirmation of participation and proficiency test results directly to the designated physicians. Note that the designated physician should receive results from 3 completed rounds from the CTQ program before approving a laboratory for participation in the biological monitoring program;
5. Laboratories seeking participation for CDU and/or B2MU analyses should submit to the responsible physician documentation of accreditation by the CAP for CRTU analyses performed in conjunction with CDU and/or B2MU determinations (if CRTU analyses are conducted by a contract laboratory, this laboratory should submit proof of CAP accreditation to the responsible physician); and,
6. Documentation should be submitted on an appropriate form.

To participate in CDB, CDU and/or B2MU analyses, the laboratory should satisfy the above criteria for a minimum of 2 of the 3 proficiency samples provided in each of the 3 rounds of the CTQ program over a 6-month period; this procedure should be completed for each appropriate analyte. Proficiency should be maintained for each analyte to continue participation. Note that laboratories seeking participation for CDU or B2MU also should address the performance requirements for CRTU, which involves providing evidence of accreditation by the CAP and participation in the CAP surveys (or an equivalent program).

The performance requirement for CDB analysis is defined as an analytical result within ± 1 µg/l or 15% of the consensus mean (whichever is greater). For samples exhibiting a consensus mean less than 1 µg/l, the performance requirement is defined as a concentration between the detection limit of the analysis and a maximum of 2 µg/l. The purpose of redefining the acceptable interval for low CDB values is to encourage proper reporting of the actual values obtained during measurement; laboratories, therefore, will not be penalized (in terms of a narrow range of acceptability) for reporting measured concentrations less than 1 µg/l.

The performance requirement for CDU analysis is defined as an analytical result within ± 1 µg/l urine or 15% of the consensus mean (whichever is greater). For samples exhibiting a consensus mean less than 1 µg/l urine, the performance requirement is defined as a concentration that falls between the detection limit of the analysis and a maximum of 2 µg/l urine. Performance requirements for the companion CRTU analysis (defined by the CAP) also should be met. Note that reporting CDU results, other than for CTQ proficiency testing should be accompanied with results of CRTU analyses, and these 2 sets of results should be combined to provide a measure of CDU in units of µg/g CRTU.

The performance requirement for B2MU is defined as an analytical result within ±15% of the consensus mean. Note that reporting B2MU results, other than for CTQ proficiency testing should be accompanied with results of CRTU analysis, these 2 sets of results should be combined to provide a measure of B2MU in units of µg/g CRTU.

Once a new laboratory has been approved by the responsible physician for conducting analyte determinations, the status of this approval should be reviewed periodically by the responsible physician as per the criteria presented under Section 3.2.2.

Laboratories which have failed previously to gain approval of the responsible physician for conducting determinations of 1 or more analytes due to lack of compliance with the criteria defined above for existing laboratories (Section 3.2.1), may obtain approval by satisfying the criteria for newly-formed laboratories defined under this Section; for these laboratories, the second of the above criteria may be satisfied by submitting a new set of characterization analyses for each analyte for which determinations are to be made.

Reevaluation of these laboratories is discretionary on the part of the responsible physician. Reevaluation, which normally takes about 6 months, may be expedited if the laboratory can achieve 100% compliance with the proficiency test criteria using the 6 samples of each analyte submitted to the CTQ program during the first 2 rounds of proficiency testing.

For laboratories seeking reevaluation for CDU or B2MU analysis, the guidelines for CRTU analyses also should be satisfied, including accreditation for CRTU analysis by the CAP, and participation in the CAP survey program (or accreditation/participation in an equivalent program).

3.2.4 Future Modifications to the Protocol Guidelines

As participating laboratories gain experience with analyses for CDB, CDU and B2MU, it is anticipated that the performance achievable by the majority of laboratories should improve until it approaches that reported by the research groups which developed each method. OSHA, therefore, may choose to recommend stricter performance guidelines in the future as the overall performance of participating laboratories improves.

3.3 Guidelines for record keeping and reporting

To comply with these guidelines, participating laboratories should satisfy the above-stated performance and proficiency recommendations, as well as the following internal QA/QC, record keeping, and reporting provisions.

If a participating laboratory fails to meet the provisions of these guidelines, it is recommended that the responsible physician disapprove further analyses of biological samples by that laboratory until it demonstrates compliance with these guidelines. On disapproval, biological samples should be sent to a laboratory that can demonstrate compliance with these guidelines, at least until the former laboratory is reevaluated by the responsible physician and found to be in compliance.

The following record keeping and reporting procedures should be practiced by participating laboratories.

3.3.1 Internal quality assurance/quality control procedures

Laboratories participating in the cadmium monitoring program should develop and maintain an internal quality assurance/quality control (QA/QC) program that incorporates procedures for establishing and maintaining control for each of the analytic procedures (determinations of CDB, CDU and/or B2MU) for which the laboratory is seeking participation. For laboratories analyzing CDU and/or B2MU, a QA/QC program for CRTU also should be established.

Written documentation of QA/QC procedures should be described in a formal QA/QC plan; this plan should contain the following information: Sample acceptance and handling procedures (i.e., chain-of-custody); sample preparation procedures; instrument parameters; calibration procedures; and, calculations. Documentation of QA/QC procedures should be sufficient to identify analytical problems, define criteria under which analysis of compliance samples will be suspended, and describe procedures for corrective actions.

3.3.1.1 QA/QC procedures for establishing control of CDB and CDU analyses

The QA/QC program for CDB and CDU should address, at a minimum, procedures involved in calibration, establishment of control limits, internal QC analyses and maintaining control, and corrective-action protocols. Participating laboratory should develop and maintain procedures to assure that analyses of compliance samples are within control limits, and that these procedures are documented thoroughly in a QA/QC plan.

A nonmandatory QA/QC protocol is presented in Attachment 1. This attachment is illustrative of the procedures that should be addressed in a proper QA/QC program.

Calibration. Before any analytic runs are conducted, the analytic instrument should be calibrated. Calibration should be performed at the beginning of each day on which QC and/or compliance samples are run. Once calibration is established, QC or compliance samples may be run. Regardless of the type of samples run, about every fifth sample should serve as a standard to assure that calibration is being maintained.

Calibration is being maintained if the standard is within ±15% of its theoretical value. If a standard is more than ± 15% of its theoretical value, the run has exceeded control limits due to calibration error; the entire set of samples then should be reanalyzed after recalibrating or the results should be recalculated based on a statistical curve derived from that set of standards.

It is essential that the value of the highest standard analyzed be higher than the highest sample analyzed; it may be necessary, therefore, to run a high standard at the end of the run, which has been selected based on results obtained over the course of the run (i.e., higher than any standard analyzed to that point).

Standards should be kept fresh; as samples age, they should be compared with new standards and replaced if necessary.

Internal Quality Control Analyses. Internal QC samples should be determined interspersed with analyses of compliance samples. At a minimum, these samples should be run at a rate of 5% of the compliance samples or at least one set of QC samples per analysis of compliance samples, whichever is greater. If only 2 samples are run, they should contain different levels of cadmium.

Internal QC samples may be obtained as commercially-available reference materials and/or they may be internally prepared. Internally-prepared samples should be well characterized and traced, or compared to a reference material for which a consensus value is available.

Levels of cadmium contained in QC samples should not be known to the analyst prior to reporting the results of the analysis.

Internal QC results should be plotted or charted in a manner which describes sample recovery and laboratory control limits.

Internal Control Limits. The laboratory protocol for evaluating internal QC analyses per control limits should be clearly defined. Limits may be based on statistical methods (e.g., as 2σ from the laboratory mean recovery), or on proficiency testing limits (e.g.,± 1µg or 15% of the mean, whichever is greater). Statistical limits that exceed ± 40% should be reevaluated to determine the source error in the analysis.

When laboratory limits are exceeded, analytic work should terminate until the source of error is determined and corrected; compliance samples affected by the error should be reanalyzed. In addition, the laboratory protocol should address any unusual trends that develop which may be biasing the results. Numerous, consecutive results above or below laboratory mean recoveries, or outside laboratory statistical limits, indicate that problems may have developed.

Corrective Actions. The QA/QC plan should document in detail specific actions taken if control limits are exceeded or unusual trends develop. Corrective actions should be noted on an appropriate form, accompanied by supporting documentation.

In addition to these actions, laboratories should include whatever additional actions are necessary to assure that accurate data are reported to the responsible physicians.

Reference Materials. The following reference materials may be available:

Cadmium in Blood (CDB)

1. Centre de Toxicologie du Quebec, Le Centre Hospitalier de l'Universite Laval, 2705 boul. Laurier, Quebec, Que., Canada G1V 4G2. (Prepared 6 times per year at 1–15 µg Cd/l.)
2. H. Marchandise, Community Bureau of Reference-BCR, Directorate General XII, Commission of the European Communities, 200, rue de la Loi, B–1049, Brussels, Belgium. (Prepared as Bl CBM–1 at 5.37 µg Cd/l, and Bl CBM–2 at 12.38 µg Cd/l.)
3. Kaulson Laboratories Inc., 691 Bloomfield Ave., Caldwell, NJ 07006; tel: (201) 226–9494, FAX (201) 226–3244. (Prepared as #0141 [As, Cd, Hg, Pb] at 2 levels.)

Cadmium in Urine (CDU)

1. Centre de Toxicologie du Quebec, Le Centre Hospitalier de l'Universite Laval, 2705 boul. Laurier, Quebec, Que., Canada G1V 4G2. (Prepared 6 times per year.)
2. National Institute of Standards and Technology

(NIST), Dept. of Commerce, Gaithersburg, MD; tel: (301) 975–6776. (Prepared as SRM 2670 freeze-dried urine [metals]; set includes normal and elevated levels of metals; cadmium is certified for elevated level of 88.0 µg/l in reconstituted urine.)

3. Kaulson Laboratories Inc., 691 Bloomfield Ave., Caldwell, NJ 07006; tel: (201) 226–9494, FAX (201) 226–3244. (Prepared as #0140 [As, Cd, Hg, Pb] at 2 levels.)

3.3.1.2 QA/QC procedures for establishing control of B2MU

A written, detailed QA/QC plan for B2MU analysis should be developed. The QA/QC plan should contain a protocol similar to those protocols developed for the CDB/CDU analyses. Differences in analyses may warrant some differences in the QA/QC protocol, but procedures to ensure analytical integrity should be developed and followed.

Examples of performance summaries that can be provided include measurements of accuracy (i.e., the means of measured values versus target values for the control samples) and precision (i.e., based on duplicate analyses). It is recommended that the accuracy and precision measurements be compared to those reported as achievable by the Pharmacia Delphia kit (Pharmacia 1990) to determine if and when unsatisfactory analyses have arisen. If the measurement error of 1 or more of the control samples is more than 15%, the run exceeds control limits. Similarly, this decision is warranted when the average CV for duplicate samples is greater than 5%.

3.3.2 Procedures for Record Keeping

To satisfy reporting requirements for commercial analyses of CDB, CDU and/or B2MU performed for the medical monitoring program mandated under the cadmium rule, participating laboratories should maintain the following documentation for each analyte:

1. For each analytic instrument on which analyte determinations are made, records relating to the most recent calibration and QC sample analyses;
2. For these instruments, a tabulated record for each analyte of those determinations found to be within and outside of control limits over the past 2 years;
3. Results for the previous 2 years of the QC sample analyses conducted under the internal QA/QC program (this information should be: Provided for each analyte for which determinations are made and for each analytic instrument used for this purpose, sufficient to demonstrate that internal QA/QC programs are being executed properly, and consistent with data sent to responsible physicians;
4. Duplicate copies of monitoring results for each analyte sent to clients during the previous 5 years, as well as associated information; supporting material such as chain-of-custody forms also should be retained; and
5. Proficiency test results and related materials received while participating in the CTQ interlaboratory program over the past 2 years; results also should be tabulated to provide a serial record of relative error (derived per Section 3.3.3 below).

3.3.3 Reporting Procedures

Participating laboratories should maintain these documents: QA/QC program plans; QA/QC status reports; CTQ proficiency program reports; and, analytical data reports. The information that should be included in these reports is summarized in Table 2; a copy of each report should be sent to the responsible physician.

Table 2
Reporting Procedures for Laboratories Participating in the Cadmium Medical Monitoring Program

Report	Frequency (time frame)	Contents
1 QA/QC Program Plan	Once (initially)	A detailed description of the QA/QC protocol to be established by the laboratory to maintain control of analyte determinations.
2 QA/QC Status Report	Every 2 months	Results of the QC samples incorporated into regular runs for each instrument (over the period since the last report).
3 Proficiency Report	Attached to every data report	Results from the last full year of proficiency samples submitted to the CTQ program and Results of the 100 most recent QC samples incorporated into regular runs for each instrument.
4 Analytical Data Report	For all reports of data results	Date the sample was received; Date the sample was analyzed; Appropriate chain-of-custody information; Types of analyses performed; Results of the requested analyses and copy of the most current proficiency report.

As noted in Section 3.3.1, a QA/QC program plan should be developed that documents internal QA/QC procedures (defined under Section 3.3.1) to be implemented by the participating laboratory for each analyte; this plan should provide a list identifying each instrument used in making analyte determinations.

A QA/QC status report should be written bimonthly for each analyte. In this report, the results of the QC program during the reporting period should be reported for each analyte in the following manner: The number (N) of QC samples analyzed during the period; a table of the target levels defined for each sample and the corresponding measured values; the mean of F/T value (as defined below) for the set of QC samples run during the period; and, use of X ± 2$\hat{\sigma}$ (as defined below) for the set of QC samples run during the period as a measure of precision.

As noted in Section 2, an F/T value for a QC sample is the ratio of the measured concentration of analyte to the established (i.e., reference) concentration of analyte for that QC sample. The equation below describes the derivation of the mean for F/T values, X, (with N being the total number of samples analyzed):

$$\bar{X} = \frac{\Sigma(F/T)}{N}$$

The standard deviation, $\hat{\sigma}$, for these measurements is derived using the following equation (note that 2$\hat{\sigma}$ is twice this value):

$$\hat{\sigma} = \left[\frac{\Sigma(F/T - \bar{X})^2}{N - 1}\right]^{1/2}$$

The nonmandatory QA/QC protocol (see Attachment 1) indicates that QC samples should be divided into several discrete pools, and a separate estimate of precision for each pools then should be derived. Several precision estimates should be provided for concentrations which differ in average value. These precision measures may be used to document improvements in performance with regard to the combined pool.

Participating laboratories should use the CTQ proficiency program for each analyte. Results of the this program will be sent by CTQ directly to physicians designated by the participating laboratories. Proficiency results from the CTQ program are used to establish the accuracy of results from each participating laboratory, and should be provided to responsible physicians for use in trend analysis. A proficiency report consisting of these proficiency results should accompany data reports as an attachment.

For each analyte, the proficiency report should include the results from the 6 previous proficiency rounds in the following format:

1. Number (N) of samples analyzed;
2. Mean of the target levels, $(1/N)\Sigma_i$, with T_i being a consensus mean for the sample;
3. Mean of the measurements, $(1/N)\Sigma_i$, with M_i being a sample measurement;
4. A measure of error defined by:

$$(1/N)\Sigma(T_i - M_i)^2$$

Analytical data reports should be submitted to responsible physicians directly. For each sample, report the following information: The date the sample was received; the date the sample was analyzed; appropriate chain-of-custody information; the type(s) of analyses performed; and, the results of the analyses. This information should be reported on a form similar to the form provided an appropriate form. The most recent proficiency program report should accompany the analytical data reports (as an attachment).

Confidence intervals for the analytical results should be reported as X ± 2σ, with X being the measured value and 2σ the standard deviation calculated as described above.

For CDU or B2MU results, which are combined with CRTU measurements for proper reporting, the 95% confidence limits are derived from the limits for CDU or B2MU, (p), and the limits for CRTU, (q), as follows:

$$\frac{X}{Y} \pm \left(\frac{1}{Y^2}\right) (Y^2 \times p^2 + X^2 \times q^2)^{1/2}$$

For these calculations, X ± p is the measurement and confidence limit for CDU or B2MU, and Y ± q is the measurement and confidence limit for CRTU.

Participating laboratories should notify responsible physicians as soon as they receive information indicating a change in their accreditation status with the CTQ or the CAP. These physicians should not be expected to wait until formal notice of a status change has been received from the CTQ or the CAP.

3.4 Instructions to Physicians

Physicians responsible for the medical monitoring of cadmium-exposed workers must collect the biological samples from workers; they then should select laboratories to perform the required analyses, and should interpret the analytic results.

3.4.1 Sample Collection and Holding Procedures

Blood Samples. The following procedures are recommended for the collection, shipment and storage of blood samples for CDB analysis to reduce analytical variablility; these recommendations were obtained primarily through personal communications with J.P. Weber of the CTQ (1991), and from reports by the Centers for Disease Control (CDC, 1986) and Stoeppler and Brandt (1980).

To the extent possible, blood samples should be collected from workers at the same time of day. Workers should shower or thoroughly wash their hands and arms before blood samples are drawn. The following materials are needed for blood sample collection: Alcohol wipes; sterile gauze sponges; band-aids; 20-gauge, 1.5-in. stainless steel needles (sterile); preprinted labels; tourniquets; vacutainer holders; 3-ml "metal free" vacutainer tubes (i.e., dark-blue caps), with EDTA as an anti-coagulant; and, styrofoam vacutainer shipping containers.

Whole blood samples are taken by venipuncture. Each blue-capped tube should be labeled or coded for the worker and company before the sample is drawn. (Blue-capped tubes are recommended instead of red-capped tubes because the latter may consist of red coloring pigment containing cadmium, which could contaminate the samples.) Immediately after sampling, the vacutainer tubes must be thoroughly mixed by inverting the tubes at least 10 times manually or mechanically using a Vortex device (for 15 sec). Samples should be refrigerated immediately or stored on ice until they can be packed for shipment to the participating laboratory for analysis.

The CDC recommends that blood samples be shipped with a "cool pak" to keep the samples cold during shipment. However, the CTQ routinely ships and receives blood samples for cadmium analysis that have not been kept cool during shipment. The CTQ has found no deterioration of cadmium in biological fluids that were shipped via parcel post without a cooling agent, even though these deliveries often take 2 weeks to reach their destination.

Urine Samples. The following are recommended procedures for the collection, shipment and storage of urine for CDU and B2MU analyses, and were obtained primarily through personal communications with J.P. Weber of the CTQ (1991), and from reports by the CDC (1986) and Stoeppler and Brandt (1980).

Single "spot" samples are recommended. As B2M can degrade in the bladder, workers should first empty their bladder and then drink a large glass of water at the start of the visit. Urine samples then should be collected within 1 hour. Separate samples should be collected for CDU and B2MU using the following materials: Sterile urine collection cups (250 ml); small sealable plastic bags; preprinted labels; 15-ml polypropylene or polyethylene screw-cap tubes; lab gloves ("metal free"); and, preservatives (as indicated).

The sealed collection cup should be kept in the plastic bag until collection time. The workers should wash their hands with soap and water before receiving the collection cup. The collection cup should not be opened until just before voiding and the cup should be sealed immediately after filling. It is important that the inside of the container and cap are not touched by, or come into contact with, the body, clothing or other surfaces.

For CDU analyzes, the cup is swirled gently to resuspend any solids, and the 15-ml tube is filled with 10-12 ml urine. The CDC recommends the addition of 100 µl concentrated HNO_3 as a preservative before sealing the tube and then freezing the sample. The CTQ recommends minimal handling and does not acidify their interlaboratory urine reference materials prior to shipment, nor do they freeze the sample for shipment. At the CTQ, if the urine sample has much sediment, the sample is acidified in the lab to free any cadmium in the precipitate.

For B2M, the urine sample should be collected directly into a polyethylene bottle previously washed with dilute nitric acid. The pH of the urine should be measured and adjusted to 8.0 with 0.1 N NaOH immediately following collection. Samples should be frozen and stored at –20 °C until testing is performed. The B2M in the samples should be stable for 2 days when stored at 2–8 °C, and for at least 2 months at –20 °C. Repeated freezing and thawing should be avoided to prevent denaturing the B2M (Pharmacia 1990).

3.4.2 Recommendations for Evaluating Laboratories

Using standard error data and the results of proficiency testing obtained from CTQ, responsible physicians can make an informed choice of which laboratory to select to analyze biological samples. In general, laboratories with small standard errors and little disparity between target and measured values tend to make precise and accurate sample determinations. Estimates of precision provided to the physicians with each set of monitoring results can be compared to previously-reported proficiency and precision estimates. The latest precision estimates should be at least as small as the standard error reported previously by the laboratory. Moreover, there should be no indication that precision is deteriorating (i.e., increasing values for the precision estimates). If precision is deteriorating, physicians may decide to use another laboratory for these analyses. QA/QC information provided by the participating laboratories to physicians can, therefore, assist physicians in evaluating laboratory performance.

3.4.3 Use and Interpretation of Results

When the responsible physician has received the CDB, CDU and/or B2MU results, these results must be compared to the action levels discussed in the final rule for cadmium. The comparison of the sample results to action levels is straightforward. The measured value reported from the laboratory can be compared directly to the action levels; if the reported value exceeds an action level, the required actions must be initiated.

4.0 Background

Cadmium is a naturally-occurring environmental contaminant to which humans are continually exposed in food, water, and air. The average daily intake of cadmium by the U.S. population is estimated to be 10–20 µg/day. Most of this intake is via ingestion, for which absorption is estimated at 4–7% (Kowal et al. 1979). An additional nonoccupational source of cadmium is smoking tobacco; smoking a pack of cigarettes a day adds an additional 2–4 µg cadmium to the daily intake, assuming absorption via inhalation of 25–35% (Nordberg and Nordberg 1988; Friberg and Elinder 1988; Travis and Haddock 1980).

Exposure to cadmium fumes and dusts in an occupational setting where air concentrations are 20–50 µg/m^3 results in an additional daily intake of several hundred micrograms (Friberg and Elinder 1988, p. 563). In such a setting, occupational exposure to cadmium occurs primarily via inhalation, although additional exposure may occur through the ingestion of material via contaminated hands if workers eat or smoke without first washing. Some of the particles that are inhaled initially may be ingested when the material is deposited in the upper respiratory tract, where it may be cleared by mucociliary transport and subsequently swallowed.

Cadmium introduced into the body through inhalation or ingestion is transported by the albumin fraction of the blood plasma to the liver, where it accumulates and is stored principally as a bound form complexed with the protein metallothionein. Metallothionein-bound cadmium is the main form of cadmium subsequently transported to the kidney; it is these 2 organs, the liver and kidney, in which the majority of the cadmium body burden accumulates. As much as one half of the total body burden of cadmium may be found in the kidneys (Nordberg and Nordberg 1988).

Once cadmium has entered the body, elimination is slow; about 0.02% of the body burden is excreted per day via urinary/fecal elimination. The whole-body half-life of cadmium is 10–35 years, decreasing slightly with increasing age (Travis and Haddock 1980).

The continual accumulation of cadmium is the basis for its chronic noncarcinogenic toxicity. This accumulation makes the kidney the target organ in which cadmium toxicity usually is first observed (Piscator 1964). Renal damage may occur when cadmium levels in the kidney cortex approach 200 µg/g wet tissue-weight (Travis and Haddock 1980).

The kinetics and internal distribution of cadmium in the body are complex, and depend on whether occupational exposure to cadmium is ongoing or has terminated. In general, cadmium in blood is related principally to recent cadmium exposure, while cadmium in urine reflects cumulative exposure (i.e., total body burden) (Lauwerys et al. 1976; Friberg and Elinder 1988).

4.1 Health Effects

Studies of workers in a variety of industries indicate that chronic exposure to cadmium may be linked to several adverse health effects including kidney dysfunction, reduced pulmonary function, chronic lung disease and cancer (Federal Register 1990). The primary sites for cadmium-associated cancer appear to be the lung and the prostate.

Cancer. Evidence for an association between cancer and cadmium exposure comes from both epidemiological studies and animal experiments. Pott (1965) found a statistically significant elevation in the incidence of prostate cancer among a cohort of cadmium workers. Other epidemiology studies also report an elevated incidence of prostate cancer; however, the increases observed in these other studies were not statistically significant (Meridian Research, Inc. 1989).

One study (Thun et al. 1985) contains sufficiently quantitative estimates of cadmium exposure to allow evaluation of dose-response relationships between cadmium exposure and lung cancer. A statistically significant excess of lung cancer attributed to cadmium exposure was found in this study, even after accounting for confounding variables such as coexposure to arsenic and smoking habits (Meridian Research, Inc. 1989).

Evidence for quantifying a link between lung cancer and cadmium exposure comes from a single study (Takenaka et al. 1983). In this study, dose-response relationships developed from animal data were extrapolated to humans using a variety of models. OSHA chose the multistage risk model for estimating the risk of cancer for humans using these animal data. Animal injection studies also suggest an association between cadmium exposure and cancer, particularly observations of an increased incidence of tumors at sites remote from the point of injection. The International Agency for Research on Cancer (IARC) (Supplement 7, 1987) indicates that this, and related, evidence is sufficient to classify cadmium as an animal carcinogen. However, the results of these injection studies cannot be used to quantify risks attendant to human occupational exposures due to differences in routes of exposure (Meridian Research, Inc. 1989).

Based on the above-cited studies, the U.S. Environmental Protection Agency (EPA) classifies cadmium as "B1," a probable human carcinogen (USEPA 1985). IARC in 1987 recommended that cadmium be listed as a probable human carcinogen.

Kidney Dysfunction. The most prevalent nonmalignant effect observed among workers chronically exposed to cadmium is kidney dysfunction. Initially, such dysfunction is manifested by proteinuria (Meridian Research, Inc. 1989; Roth Associates, Inc. 1989). Proteinuria associated with cadmium exposure is most commonly characterized by excretion of low-molecular weight proteins (15,000–40,000 MW), accompanied by loss of electrolytes, uric acid, calcium, amino acids, and phosphate. Proteins commonly excreted include β-2-microglobulin (B2M), retinol-binding protein (RBP), immunoglobulin light chains, and lysozyme. Excretion of low molecular weight proteins is characteristic of damage to the proximal tubules of the kidney (Iwao et al. 1980).

Exposure to cadmium also may lead to urinary excretion of high-molecular weight proteins such as albumin, immunoglobulin G, and glycoproteins (Meridian Research, Inc. 1989; Roth Associates, Inc. 1989). Excretion of high-molecular weight proteins is indicative of damage to the glomeruli of the kidney. Bernard et al. (1979) suggest that cadmium-associated damage to the glomeruli and damage to the proximal tubules of the kidney develop independently of each other, but may occur in the same individual.

Several studies indicate that the onset of low-molecular weight proteinuria is a sign of irreversible kidney damage (Friberg et al. 1974; Roels et al. 1982; Piscator 1984; Elinder et al. 1985; Smith et al. 1986). For many workers, once sufficiently elevated levels of B2M are observed in association with cadmium exposure, such levels do not appear to return to normal even when cadmium exposure is eliminated by removal of the worker from the cadmium-contaminated work environment (Friberg, exhibit 29, 1990).

Some studies indicate that cadmium-induced proteinuria may be progressive; levels of B2MU increase even after cadmium exposure has ceased (Elinder et al. 1985). Other researchers have reached similar conclusions (Frieburg testimony, OSHA docket exhibit 29, Elinder testimony, OSHA docket exhibit 55, and OSHA docket exhibits 8–86B). Such observations are not universal, however (Smith et al. 1986; Tsuchiya 1976). Studies in which proteinuria has not been observed, however, may have initiated the reassessment too early (Meridian Research, Inc.1989; Roth Associates, Inc. 1989; Roels 1989).

A quantitative assessment of the risks of developing kidney dysfunction as a result of cadmium exposure was performed using the data from Ellis et al. (1984) and Falck et al. (1983). Meridian Research, Inc. (1989) and Roth Associates, Inc. (1989) employed several mathematical models to evaluate the data from the 2 studies, and the results indicate that cumulative cadmium exposure levels between 5 and 100 µg-years/m^3 correspond with a one-in-a-thousand probability of developing kidney dysfunction.

When cadmium exposure continues past the onset of early kidney damage (manifested as proteinuria), chronic nephrotoxicity may occur (Meridian Research, Inc. 1989; Roth Associates, Inc. 1989). Uremia, which is the loss of the glomerulus' ability to adequately filter blood, may result. This condition leads to severe disturbance of electrolyte concentrations, which may result in various clinical complications including atherosclerosis, hypertension, pericarditis, anemia, hemorrhagic tendencies, deficient cellular immunity, bone changes, and other problems. Progression of the disease may require dialysis or a kidney transplant.

Studies in which animals are chronically exposed to cadmium confirm the renal effects observed in humans (Friberg et al. 1986). Animal studies also confirm cadmium-related problems with calcium metabolism and associated skeletal effects, which also have been observed among humans. Other effects commonly reported in chronic animal studies include anemia, changes in liver morphology, immunosuppression and hypertension. Some of these effects may be associated with cofactors; hypertension, for example, appears to be associated with diet, as well as with cadmium exposure. Animals injected with cadmium also have shown testicular necrosis.

4.2 Objectives for Medical Monitoring

In keeping with the observation that renal disease tends to be the earliest clinical manifestation of cadmium toxicity, the final cadmium standard mandates that eligible workers must be medically monitored to prevent this condition (as well as cadmimum-induced cancer). The objectives of medical-monitoring, therefore, are to: Identify workers at significant risk of adverse health effects from excess, chronic exposure to cadmium; prevent future cases of cadmium-induced disease; detect and minimize existing cadmium-induced disease; and, identify workers most in need of medical intervention.

The overall goal of the medical monitoring program is to protect workers who may be exposed continuously to cadmium over a 45-year occupational lifespan. Consistent with this goal, the medical monitoring program should assure that:

1. Current exposure levels remain sufficiently low to prevent the accumulation of cadmium body burdens sufficient to cause disease in the future by monitoring CDB as an indicator of recent cadmium exposure;
2. Cumulative body burdens, especially among workers with undefined historical exposures, remain below levels potentially capable of leading to damage and disease by assessing CDU as an indicator of cumulative exposure to cadmium; and,
3. Health effects are not occurring among exposed workers by determining B2MU as an early indicator of the onset of cadmium-induced kidney disease.

4.3 Indicators of Cadmium Exposure and Disease

Cadmium is present in whole blood bound to albumin, in erythrocytes, and as a metallothionein-cadmium complex. The metallothionein-cadmium complex that represents the primary transport mechanism for cadmium delivery to the kidney. CDB concentrations in the general, nonexposed population average 1 µg Cd/l whole blood, with smokers exhibiting higher levels (see Section 5.1.6). Data presented in Section 5.1.6 shows that 95% of the general population not occupationally exposed to cadmium have CDB levels less than 5 µg Cd/l.

If total body burdens of cadmium remain low, CDB concentrations indicate recent exposure (i.e., daily intake). This conclusion is based on data showing that cigarette smokers exhibit CDB concentrations of 2–7 µg/l depending on the number of cigarettes smoked per day (Nordberg and Nordberg 1988), while CDB levels for those who quit smoking return to general population values (approximately 1 µg/l) within several weeks (Lauwerys et al. 1976). Based on these observations, Lauwerys et al. (1976) concluded that CDB has a biological half-life of a few weeks to less than 3 months. As indicated in Section 3.1.6, the upper 95th percentile for CDB levels observed among those who are not occupationally exposed to cadmium is 5 µg/l, which suggests that the absolute upper limit to the range reported for smokers by Nordberg and Nordberg may have been affected by an extreme value (i.e., beyond 2σ above the mean).

Among occupationally-exposed workers, the occupational history of exposure to cadmium must be evaluated to interpret CDB levels. New workers, or workers with low exposures to cadmium, exhibit CDB levels that are representative of recent exposures, similar to the general population. However, for workers with a history of chronic exposure to cadmium, who have accumulated significant stores of cadmium in the kidneys/liver, part of the CDB concentrations appear to indicate body burden. If such workers are removed from cadmium exposure, their CDB levels remain elevated, possibly for years, reflecting prior long-term accumulation of cadmium in body tissues. This condition tends to occur, however, only beyond some threshold exposure value, and possibly indicates the capacity of body tissues to accumulate cadmium which cannot be excreted readily (Friberg and Elinder 1988; Nordberg and Nordberg 1988).

CDU is widely used as an indicator of cadmium body burdens (Nordberg and Nordberg 1988). CDU is the major route of elimination and, when CDU is measured, it is commonly expressed either as µg Cd/l urine (unadjusted), µg Cd/l urine (adjusted for specific gravity), or µg Cd/g CRTU (see Section 5.2.1). The metabolic model for CDU is less complicated than CDB, since CDU is dependentin large part on the body (i.e., kidney) burden of cadmium. However, a small proportion of CDU still be attributed to recent cadmium exposure, particularly if exposure to high airborne concentrations of cadmium occurred. Note that CDU is subject to larger interindividual and day-to-day variations than CDB, so repeated measurements are recommended for CDU evaluations.

CDU is bound principally to metallothionein, regardless of whether the cadmium originates from metallothionein in plasma or from the cadmium pool accumulated in the renal tubules. Therefore, measurement of metallothionein in urine may provide information similar to CDU, while avoiding the contamination problems that may occur during collection and handling urine for cadmium analysis (Nordberg and Nordberg 1988). However, a commercial method for the determination of metallothionein at the sensitivity levels required under the final cadmium rule is not currently available; therefore, analysis of CDU is recommended.

Among the general population not occupationally exposed to cadmium, CDU levels average less than 1 µg/l (see Section 5.2.7). Normalized for creatinine (CRTU), the average CDU concentration of the general population is less than 1 µg/g CRTU. As cadmium accumulates over the lifespan, CDU increases with age. Also, cigarette smokers may eventually accumulate twice the cadmium body burden of nonsmokers, CDU is slightly higher in smokers than in nonsmokers, even several years after smoking cessation (Nordberg and Nordberg 1988). Despite variations due to age and smoking habits, 95% of those not occupationally exposed to cadmium exhibit levels of CDU less than 3 µg/g CRTU (based on the data presented in Section 5.2.7).

About 0.02% of the cadmium body burden is excreted daily in urine. When the critical cadmium concentration (about 200 ppm) in the kidney is reached, or if there is sufficient cadmium-induced kidney dysfunction, dramatic increases in CDU are observed (Nordberg and Nordberg 1988). Above 200 ppm, therefore, CDU concentrations cease to be an indicator of cadmium body burden, and are instead an index of kidney failure.

Proteinuria is an index of kidney dysfunction, and is defined by OSHA to be a material impairment. Several small proteins may be monitored as markers for proteinuria. Below levels indicative of proteinuria, these small proteins may be early indicators of increased risk of cadmium-induced renal tubular disease. Analytes useful for monitoring cadmium-induced renal tubular damage include:

1. β-2-Microglobulin (B2M), currently the most widely used assay for detecting kidney dysfunction, is the best characterized analyte available (Iwao et al. 1980; Chia et al. 1989);
2. Retinol Binding Protein (RBP) is more stable than B2M in acidic urine (i.e., B2M breakdown occurs if urinary pH is less than 5.5; such breakdown may result in false [i.e., low] B2M values [Bernard and Lauwerys, 1990]);
3. N-Acetyl-B-Glucosaminidase (NAG) is the analyte of an assay that is simple, inexpensive, reliable, and correlates with cadmium levels under 10 µg/g CRTU, but the assay is less sensitive than RBP or B2M (Kawada et al. 1989);
4. Metallothionein (MT) correlates with cadmium and B2M levels, and may be a better predictor of cadmium exposure than CDU and B2M (Kawada et al. 1989);
5. Tamm-Horsfall Glycoprotein (THG) increases slightly with elevated cadmium levels, but this elevation is small compared to increases in urinary albumin, RBP, or B2M (Bernard and Lauwerys 1990);
6. Albumin (ALB), determined by the biuret method, is not sufficiently sensitive to serve as an early indicator of the onset of renal disease (Piscator 1962);
7. Albumin (ALB), determined by the Amido Black method, is sensitive and reproducible, but involves a time-consuming procedure (Piscator 1962);
8. Glycosaminoglycan (GAG) increases among cadmium workers, but the significance of this effect is unknown because no relationship has been found between elevated GAG and other indices of tubular damage (Bernard and Lauwerys 1990);
9. Trehalase seems to increase earlier than B2M during cadmium exposure, but the procedure for analysis is complicated and unreliable (Iwata et al. 1988); and
10. Kallikrein is observed at lower concentrations among cadmium-exposed workers than among normal controls (Roels et al. 1990).

Of the above analytes, B2M appears to be the most widely used and best characterized analyte to evaluate the presence/absence, as well as the extent of, cadmium-induced renal tubular damage (Kawada, Koyama, and Suzuki 1989; Shaikh and Smith 1984; Nogawa 1984). However, it is important that samples be collected and handled so as to minimize B2M degradation under acidic urine conditions.

The threshold value of B2MU commonly used to indicate the presence of kidney damage 300 µg/g CRTU (Kjellstrom et al. 1977a; Buchet et al. 1980; and Kowal and Zirkes 1983). This value represents the upper 95th or 97.5th percentile level of urinary excretion observed among those without tubular dysfunction (Elinder, exbt L–140–45, OSHA docket H057A). In agreement with these conclusions, the data presented in Section 5.3.7 of this protocol generally indicate that the level of 300 µg/g CRTU appears to define the boundary for kidney dysfunction. It is not clear, however, that this level represents the upper 95th percentile of values observed among those who fail to demonstrate proteinuria effects.

Although elevated B2MU levels appear to be a fairly specific indicator of disease associated with cadmium exposure, other conditions that may lead to elevated B2MU levels include high fevers from influenza, extensive physical exercise, renal disease unrelated to cadmium exposure, lymphomas, and AIDS (Iwao et al. 1980; Schardun and van Epps 1987). Elevated B2M levels observed in association with high fevers from influenza or from extensive physical exercise are transient, and will return to normal levels once the fever has abated or metabolic rates return to baseline values following exercise. The other conditions linked to elevated B2M levels can be diagnosed as part of a properly-designed medical examination. Consequently, monitoring B2M, when accompanied by regular medical examinations and CDB and CDU determinations (as indicators of present and past cadmium exposure), may serve as a specific, early indicator of cadmium-induced kidney damage.

4.4 Criteria for Medical Monitoring of Cadmium Workers

Medical monitoring mandated by the final cadmium rule includes a combination of regular medical examinations and periodic monitoring of 3 analytes: CDB, CDU and B2MU. As indicated above, CDB is monitored as an indicator of current cadmium exposure, while CDU serves as an indicator of the cadmium body burden; B2MU is assessed as an early marker of irreversible kidney damage and disease.

The final cadmium rule defines a series of action levels that have been developed for each of the 3 analytes to be monitored. These action levels serve to guide the responsible physician through a decision-making process. For each action level that is exceeded, a specific response is mandated. The sequence of action levels, and the attendant actions, are described in detail in the final cadmium rule.

Other criteria used in the medical decision-making process relate to tests performed during the medical examination (including a determination of the ability of a worker to wear a respirator). These criteria, however, are not affected by the results of the analyte determinations addressed in the above paragraphs and, consequently, will not be considered further in these guidelines.

4.5 Defining to Quality and Proficiency of the Analyte Determinations

As noted above in Sections 2 and 3, the quality of a measurement should be defined along with its value to properly interpret the results. Generally, it is necessary to know the accuracy and the precision of a measurement before it can be properly evaluated. The precision of the data from a specific laboratory indicates the extent to which the repeated measurements of the same sample vary within that laboratory. The accuracy of the data provides an indication of the extent to which these results deviate from average results determined from many laboratories performing the same measurement (i.e., in the absence of an independent determination of the true value of a measurement). Note that terms are defined operationally relative to the manner in which they will be used in this protocol. Formal definitions for the terms in italics used in this Section can be found in the list of definitions (Section 2).

Another data quality criterion required to properly evaluate measurement results is the limit of detection of that measurement. For measurements to be useful, the range of the measurement which is of interest for biological monitoring purposes must lie entirely above the limit of detection defined for that measurement.

The overall quality of a laboratory's results is termed the performance of that laboratory. The degree to which a laboratory satisfies a minimum performance level is referred to as the proficiency of the laboratory. A successful medical monitoring program, therefore, should include procedures developed for monitoring and recording laboratory performance; these procedures can be used to identify the most proficient laboratories.

5.0 Overview of Medical Monitoring Tests for CDB, CDU, B2MU and CRTU

To evaluate whether available methods for assessing CDB, CDU, B2MU and CRTU are adequate for determining the parameters defined by the proposed action levels, it is necessary to review procedures available for sample collection, preparation and analysis. A variety of techniques for these purposes have been used historically for the determination of cadmium in biological matrices (including CDB and CDU), and for the determination of specific proteins in biological matrices (including B2MU). However, only the most recent techniques are capable of satisfying the required accuracy, precision and sensitivity (i.e., limit of detection) for monitoring at the levels mandated in the final cadmium rule, while still facilitating automated analysis and rapid processing.

5.1 Measuring Cadmium in Blood (CDB)

Analysis of biological samples for cadmium requires strict analytical discipline regarding collection and handling of samples. In addition to occupational settings, where cadmium contamination would be apparent, cadmium is a ubiquitous environmental contaminant, and much care should be exercised to ensure that samples are not contaminated during collection, preparation or analysis. Many common chemical reagents are contaminated with cadmium at concentrations that will interfere with cadmium analysis; because of the widespread use of cadmium compounds as colored pigments in plastics and coatings, the analyst should continually monitor each manufacturer's chemical reagents and collection containers to prevent contamination of samples.

Guarding against cadmium contamination of biological samples is particularly important when analyzing blood samples because cadmium concentrations in blood samples from nonexposed populations are generally less than 2 µg/l (2 ng/ml), while occupationally-exposed workers can be at medical risk to cadmium toxicity if blood concentrations exceed 5 µg/l (ACGIH 1991 and 1992). This narrow margin between exposed and unexposed samples requires that exceptional care be used in performing analytic determinations for biological monitoring for occupational cadmium exposure.

Methods for quantifying cadmium in blood have improved over the last 40 years primarily because of improvements in analytical instrumentation. Also, due to improvements in analytical techniques, there is less need to perform extensive multi-step sample preparations prior to analysis. Complex sample preparation was previously required to enhance method sensitivity (for cadmium), and to reduce interference by other metals or components of the sample.

5.1.1 Analytical Techniques Used To Monitor Cadmium in Biological Matrices

Table 3
Comparison of Analytical Procedures/Instrumentation for Determination of Cadmium in Biological Samples

Analytical procedure	Limit of detection [ng/(g or ml)]	Specified biological matrix	Reference	Comments
Flame Atomic Absorption Spectroscopy (FAAS)	≥ 1.0	Any matrix	Perkin-Elmer (1982)	Not sensitive enough for biomonitoring without extensive sample digestion, metal chelation and organic solvent extraction.
Graphite Furnace Atomic Absorption Spectroscopy (GFAAS)	0.04	Urine	Pruszkowska et al. (1983)	Methods of choice for routine cadmium analysis.
	≥ 0.20	Blood	Stoeppler and Brandt (1980)	
Inductively-Coupled Argon-Plasma Atomic Emission Spectroscopy (ICAP AES)	2.0	Any matrix	NIOSH (1984A)	Requires extensive sample preparation and concentration of metal with chelating resin. Advantage is simultaneous analyses for as many as 10 metals from 1 sample.
Neutron Activation Gamma Spectroscopy (NA)	1.5	In vivo (liver)	Ellis et al. (1983)	Only available in vivo method for direct determination of cadmium body tissue burdens; expensive; absolute determination of cadmium in reference materials.
Isotope Dilution Mass Spectroscopy (IDMS)	< 1.0	Any matrix	Michiels and DeBievre (1986)	Suitable for absolute determination of cadmium in reference materials; expensive.
Differential Pulse Anodic Stripping Voltammetry (DPASV)	< 1.0	Any matrix	Stoeppler and Brandt (1980)	Suitable for absolute determination of cadmium in reference materials; efficient method to check accuracy of analytical method.

A number of analytical techniques have been used for determining cadmium concentrations in biological materials. A summary of the characteristics of the most widely employed techniques is presented in Table 3. The technique most suitable for medical monitoring for cadmium is atomic absorption spectroscopy (AAS).

To obtain a measurement using AAS, a light source (i.e., hollow cathode or lectrode-free discharge lamp) containing the element of interest as the cathode, is energized and the lamp emits a spectrum that is unique for that element. This light source is focused through a sample cell, and a selected wavelength is monitored by a monochrometer and photodetector cell. Any ground state atoms in the sample that match those of the lamp element and are in the path of the emitted light may absorb some of the light and decrease the amount of light that reaches the photodetector cell. The amount of light absorbed at each characteristic wavelength is proportional to the number of ground state atoms of the corresponding element that are in the pathway of the light between the source and detector.

To determine the amount of a specific metallic element in a sample using AAS, the sample is dissolved in a solvent and aspirated into a high-temperature flame as an aerosol. At high temperatures, the solvent is rapidly evaporated or decomposed and the solute is initially solidified; the majority of the sample elements then are transformed into an atomic vapor. Next, a light beam is focused above the flame and the amount of metal in the sample can be determined by measuring the degree of absorbance of the atoms of the target element released by the flame at a characteristic wavelength.

A more refined atomic absorption technique, flameless AAS, substitutes an electrothermal, graphite furnace for the flame. An aliquot (10–100 µl) of the sample is pipetted into the cold furnace, which is then heated rapidly to generate an atomic vapor of the element.

AAS is a sensitive and specific method for the elemental analysis of metals; its main drawback is nonspecific background absorbtion and scattering of the light beam by particles of the sample as it decomposes at high temperatures; nonspecific absorbance reduces the sensitivity of the analytical method. The problem of nonspecific absorbance and scattering can be reduced by extensive sample pretreatment, such as ashing and/or acid digestion of the sample to reduce its organic content.

Current AAS instruments employ background correction devices to adjust electronically for background absorption and scattering. A common method to correct for background effects is to use a deuterium arc lamp as a second light source. A continuum light source, such as the deuterium lamp, emits a broad spectrum of wavelengths instead of specific wavelengths characteristic of a particular element, as with the hollow cathode tube. With this system, light from the primary source and the continuum source are passed alternately through the sample cell. The target element effectively absorbs light only from the primary source (which is much brighter than the continuum source at the characteristic wavelengths), while the background matrix absorbs and scatters light from both sources equally. Therefore, when the ratio of the two beams is measured electronically, the effect of nonspecific background absorption and scattering is eliminated. A less common, but more sophisticated, background correction system is based on the Zeeman effect, which uses a magnetically-activated light polarizer to compensate electronically for nonspecific absorption and scattering.

Atomic emission spectroscopy with inductively-coupled argon plasma (AES-ICAP) is widely used to analyze for metals. With this instrument, the sample is aspirated into an extremely hot argon plasma flame, which excites the metal atoms; emission spectra specific for the sample element then are generated. The quanta of emitted light passing through a monochrometer are amplified by photomultiplier tubes and measured by a photodetector to determine the amount of metal in the sample. An advantage of AES-ICAP over AAS is that multi-elemental analyses of a sample can be performed by simultaneously measuring specific elemental emission energies. However, AES-ICAP lacks the sensitivity of AAS, exhibiting a limit of detection which is higher than the limit of detection for graphite-furnace AAS (Table 3).

Neutron activation (NA) analysis and isotope dilution mass spectrometry (IDMS) are 2 additional, but highly specialized, methods that have been used for cadmium determinations. These methods are expensive because they require elaborate and sophisticated instrumentation.

NA analysis has the distinct advantage over other analytical methods of being able to determine cadmium body burdens in specific organs (e.g., liver, kidney) in vivo (Ellis et al. 1983). Neutron bombardment of the target transforms cadmium-113 to cadmium-114, which promptly decays (<10−14sec) to its ground state, emitting gamma rays that are measured using large gamma detectors; appropriate shielding and instrumentation are required when using this method.

IDMS analysis, a definitive but laborious method, is based on the change in the ratio of 2 isotopes of cadmium (cadmium 111 and 112) that occurs when a known amount of the element (with an artificially altered ratio of the same isotopes [i.e., a cadmium 111 "spike"] is added to a weighed aliquot of the sample (Michiels and De Bievre 1986).

5.1.2 Methods Developed for CDB Determinations

A variety of methods have been used for preparing and analyzing CDB samples; most of these methods rely on one of the analytical techniques described above. Among the earliest reports, Princi (1947) and Smith et al. (1955) employed a colorimetric procedure to analyze for CDB and CDU. Samples were dried and digested through several cycles with concentrated mineral acids (HNO_3 and H_2SO_4) and hydrogen peroxide (H_2O_2). The digest was neutralized, and the cadmium was complexed with diphenylthiocarbazone and extracted with chloroform. The dithizone-cadmium complex then was quantified using a spectrometer.

Colorimetric procedures for cadmium analyses were replaced by methods based on atomic absorption spectroscopy (AAS) in the early 1960s, but many of the complex sample preparation procedures were retained. Kjellstrom (1979) reports that in Japanese, American and Swedish laboratories during the early 1970s, blood samples were wet ashed with mineral acids or ashed at high temperature and wetted with nitric acid. The cadmium in the digest was complexed with metal chelators including diethyl dithiocarbamate (DDTC), ammonium pyrrolidine dithiocarbamate (APDC) or diphenylthiocarbazone (dithizone) in ammonia-citrate buffer and extracted with methyl isobutyl ketone (MIBK). The resulting solution then was analyzed by flame AAS or graphite-furnace AAS for cadmium determinations using deuterium-lamp background correction.

In the late 1970s, researchers began developing simpler preparation procedures. Roels et al. (1978) and Roberts and Clark (1986) developed simplified digestion procedures. Using the Roberts and Clark method, a 0.5 ml aliquot of blood is collected and transferred to a digestion tube containing 1 ml concentrated HNO_3. The blood is then digested at 110 °C for 4 hours. The sample is reduced in volume by continued heating, and 0.5 ml 30% H_2O_2 is added as the sample dries. The residue is dissolved in 5 ml dilute (1%) HNO_3, and 20 µl of sample is then analyzed by graphite-furnace AAS with deuterium-background correction.

The current trend in the preparation of blood samples is to dilute the sample and add matrix modifiers to reduce background interference, rather than digesting the sample to reduce organic content. The method of Stoeppler and Brandt (1980), and the abbreviated procedure published in the American Public Health Association's (APHA) Methods for Biological Monitoring (1988), are straightforward and are nearly identical. For the APHA method, a small aliquot (50–300 µl) of whole blood that has been stabilized with ethylenediaminetetraacetate (EDTA) is added to 1.0 ml 1M HNO_3, vigorously shaken and centrifuged. Aliquots (10–25 µl) of the supernatant then are then analyzed by graphite-furnace AAS with appropriate background correction.

Using the method of Stoeppler and Brandt (1980), aliquots (50–200 µl) of whole blood that have been stabilized with EDTA are pipetted into clean polystyrene tubes and mixed with 150-600 µl of 1 M HNO_3. After vigorous shaking, the solution is centrifuged and a 10–25 µl aliquot of the supernatant then is analyzed by graphite-furnace AAS with appropriate background correction.

Claeys-Thoreau (1982) and DeBenzo et al. (1990) diluted blood samples at a ratio of 1:10 with a matrix modifier (0.2% Triton X-100, a wetting agent) for direct determinations of CDB. DeBenzo et al. also demonstrated that aqueous standards of cadmium, instead of spiked, whole-blood samples, could be used to establish calibration curves if standards and samples are treated with additional small volumes of matrix modifiers (i.e., 1% HNO_3, 0.2% ammonium hydrogenphosphate and 1 mg/ml magnesium salts).

These direct dilution procedures for CDB analysis are simple and rapid. Laboratories can process more than 100 samples a day using a dedicated graphite-furnace AAS, an auto-sampler, and either a Zeeman- or a deuterium-background correction system.

Several authors emphasize using optimum settings for graphite-furnace temperatures during the drying, charring, and atomization processes associated with the flameless AAS method, and the need to run frequent QC samples when performing automated analysis.

5.1.3 Sample Collection and Handling

Sample collection procedures are addressed primarily to identify ways to minimize the degree of variability that may be introduced by sample collection during medical monitoring. It is unclear at this point the extent to which collection procedures contribute to variability among CDB samples. Sources of variation that may result from sampling procedures include time-of-day effects and introduction of external contamination during the collection process. To minimize these sources, strict adherence to a sample collection protocol is recommended. Such a protocol must include provisions for thorough cleaning of the site from which blood will be extracted; also, every effort should be made to collect samples near the same time of day. It is also important to recognize that under the recent OSHA blood-borne pathogens standard (29 CFR §1910.1030), blood samples and certain body fluids must be handled and treated as if they are infectious.

5.1.4 Best Achievable Performance

The best achievable performance using a particular method for CDB determinations is assumed to be equivalent to the performance reported by research laboratories in which the method was developed.

For their method, Roberts and Clark (1986) demonstrated a limit of detection of 0.4 µg Cd/l in whole blood, with a linear response curve from 0.4 to 16.0 µg Cd/l. They report a coefficient of variation (CV) of 6.7% at 8.0 µg/l.

The APHA (1988) reports a range of 1.0–25 µg/l, with a CV of 7.3% (concentration not stated). Insufficient documentation was available to critique this method.

Stoeppler and Brandt (1980) achieved a detection limit of 0.2 µg Cd/l whole blood, with a linear range of 0.4–12.0 µg Cd/l, and a CV of 15–30%, for samples at <1.0 µg/l. Improved precision (CV of 3.8%) was reported for CDB concentrations at 9.3 µg/l.

5.1.5 General Method Performance

For any particular method, the performance expected from commercial laboratories may be somewhat lower than that reported by the research laboratory in which the method was developed. With participation in appropriate proficiency programs and use of a proper in-house QA/QC program incorporating provisions for regular corrective actions, the performance of commercial laboratories is expected to approach that reported by research laboratories. Also, the results reported for existing proficiency programs serve as a gauge of the likely level of performance that currently can be expected from commercial laboratories offering these analyses.

Weber (1988) reports on the results of the proficiency program run by the Centre de Toxicologie du Quebec (CTQ). As indicated previously, participants in that program receive 18 blood samples per year having cadmium concentrations ranging from 0.2–20 µg/l. Currently, 76 laboratories are participating in this program. The program is established for several analytes in addition to cadmium, and not all of these laboratories participate in the cadmium proficiency-testing program.

Under the CTQ program, cadmium results from individual laboratories are compared against the consensus mean derived for each sample. Results indicate that after receiving 60 samples (i.e., after participation for approximately three years), 60% of the laboratories in the program are able to report results that fall within ±1 µg/l or 15% of the mean, whichever is greater. (For this procedure, the 15% criterion was applied to concentrations exceeding 7 µg/l.) On any single sample of the last 20 samples, the percentage of laboratories falling within the specified range is between 55 and 80%.

The CTQ also evaluates the performance of participating laboratories against a less severe standard: ±2 µg/l or 15% of the mean, whichever is greater (Weber 1988); 90% of participating laboratories are able to satisfy this Standard after approximately 3 years in the program. (The 15% criterion is used for concentrations in excess of 13 µg/l.) On any single sample of the last 15 samples, the percentage of laboratories falling within the specified range is between 80 and 95% (except for a single test for which only 60% of the laboratories achieved the desired performance).

Based on the data presented in Weber (1988), the CV for analysis of CDB is nearly constant at 20% for cadmium concentrations exceeding 5 µg/l, and increases for cadmium concentrations below 5 µg/l. At 2 µg/l, the reported CV rises to approximately 40%. At 1 µg/l, the reported CV is approximately 60%.

Participating laboratories also tend to overestimate concentrations for samples exhibiting concentrations less than 2 µg/l (see Figure 11 of Weber 1988). This problem is due in part to the proficiency evaluation criterion that allows reporting a minimum ±2.0 µg/l for evaluated CDB samples. There is currently little economic or regulatory incentive for laboratories participating in the CTQ program to achieve greater accuracy for CDB samples containing cadmium at concentrations less than 2.0 µg/l, even if the laboratory has the experience and competency to distinguish among lower concentrations in the samples obtained from the CTQ.

The collective experience of international agencies and investigators demonstrate the need for a vigorous QC program to ensure that CDB values reported by participating laboratories are indeed reasonably accurate. As Friberg (1988) stated:

"Information about the quality of published data has often been lacking. This is of concern as assessment of metals in trace concentrations in biological media are fraught with difficulties from the collection, handling, and storage of samples to the chemical analyses. This has been proven over and over again from the results of interlaboratory testing and quality control exercises. Large variations in results were reported even from 'experienced' laboratories."

The UNEP/WHO global study of cadmium biological monitoring set a limit for CDB accuracy using the maximum allowable deviation method at Y = X ± (0.1X + 1) for a targeted concentration of 10 µg Cd/l (Friberg and Vahter 1983). The performance of participating laboratories over a concentration range of 1.5–12 µg/l was reported by Lind et al. (1987). Of the 3 QC runs conducted during 1982 and 1983, 1 or 2 of the 6 laboratories failed each run. For the years 1983 and 1985, between zero and 2 laboratories failed each of the consecutive QC runs.

In another study (Vahter and Friberg 1988), QC samples consisting of both external (unknown) and internal (stated) concentrations were distributed to laboratories participating in the epidemiology research. In this study, the maximum acceptable deviation between the regression analysis of reported results and reference values was set at Y=X ± (0.05X + 0.2) for a concentration range of 0.3–5.0 µg Cd/l. It is reported that only 2 of 5 laboratories had acceptable data after the first QC set, and only 1 of 5 laboratories had acceptable data after the second QC set. By the fourth QC set, however, all 5 laboratories were judged proficient.

The need for high quality CDB monitoring is apparent when the toxicological and biological characteristics of this metal are considered; an increase in CDB from 2 to 4 µg/l could cause a doubling of the cadmium accumulation in the kidney, a critical target tissue for selective cadmium accumulation (Nordberg and Nordberg 1988).

Historically, the CDC's internal QC program for CDB cadmium monitoring program has found achievable accuracy to be ±10% of the true value at CDB concentrations ≥ 5.0 µg/l (Paschal 1990). Data on the performance of laboratories participating in this program currently are not available.

5.1.6 Observed CDB Concentrations

As stated in Section 4.3, CDB concentrations are representative of ongoing levels of exposure to cadmium. Among those who have been exposed chronically to cadmium for extended periods, however, CDB may contain a component attributable to the general cadmium body burden.

5.1.6.1 CDB Concentrations Among Unexposed Samples

Numerous studies have been conducted examining CDB concentrations in the general population, and in control groups used for comparison with cadmium-exposed workers. A number of reports have been published that present erroneously high values of CDB (Nordberg and Nordberg 1988). This problem was due to contamination of samples during sampling and analysis, and to errors in analysis. Early AAS methods were not sufficiently sensitive to accurately estimate CDB concentrations.

Table 4 presents results of recent studies reporting CDB levels for the general U.S. population not exposed occupationally to cadmium. Other surveys of tissue cadmium using U.S. samples and conducted as part of a cooperative effort among Japan, Sweden and the U.S., did not collect CDB data because standard analytical methodologies were unavailable, and because of analytic problems (Kjellstrom 1979; SWRI 1978).

Table 4
Blood Cadmium Concentrations of U.S. Population Not Occupationally Exposed to Cadmium[a]

Study No.	No. in study (n)	Sex	Age	Smoking habits[b]	Arithmetic mean (± S.D.)[c]	Absolute range or (95% CI)[d]	Geometric mean (± GSD)[e]	Lower 95th percentile of distribution[f]	Upper 95th percentile of distribution[f]	Reference
1	80	M	4 to 69	NS, S	1.13	0.35 - 3.3	0.98 ± 1.71	0.4	2.4	Kowal et al. (1979)
	88	F	4 to 69	NS, S	1.03	0.21 - 3.3	0.91 ± 1.63	0.4	2.0	
	115	M/F	4 to 69	NS	.095	0.21 - 3.3	0.85 ± 1.59	0.4	1.8	
	31	M/F	4 to 69	S	1.54	0.4 - 3.3	1.37 ± 1.65	0.6	3.2	
2	10	M	Adults	(?)	2.0 ± 2.1	(0.5 - 5.0)		[g](0)	[g](5.8)	Ellis et al. (1983)
3	24	M	Adults	NS			0.6 ± 1.87	0.2	1.8	Frieberg and Vahter (1983)
	20	M	Adults	S			1.2 ± 2.13	0.3	4.4	
	64	F	Adults	NS			0.5 ± 1.85	0.2	1.4	
	39	F	Adults	S			0.8 ± 2.22	0.2	3.1	
4	32	M	Adults	S, NS			1.2 ± 2.0	0.4	3.9	Thun et al. (1989)
5	35	M	Adults	(?)	2.1 ± 2.1	(0.5 - 7.3)		[g](0)	[g](5.6)	Mueller et al. (1989)

[a] Concentrations reported in µg Cd/l blood unless otherwise stated.
[b] NS—never smoked; S—current cigarette smoker.
[c] S.D.—Arithmetic Standard Deviation.
[d] C.I.—Confidence interval.
[e] GSD—Geometric Standard Deviation.
[f] Based on an assumed lognormal distribution.
[g] Based on an assumed normal distribution.

Arithmetic and/or geometric means and standard deviations are provided in Table 4 for measurements among the populations defined in each study listed. The range of reported measurements and/or the 95% upper and lower confidence intervals for the means are presented when this information was reported in a study. For studies reporting either an arithmetic or geometric standard deviation along with a mean, the lower and upper 95th percentile for the distribution also were derived and reported in the table.

The data provided in table 4 from Kowal et al. (1979) are from studies conducted between 1974 and 1976 evaluating CDB levels for the general population in Chicago, and are considered to be representative of the U.S. population. These studies indicate that the average CDB concentration among those not occupationally exposed to cadmium is approximately 1 µg/l.

In several other studies presented in Table 4, measurements are reported separately for males and females, and for smokers and nonsmokers. The data in this table indicate that similar CDB levels are observed among males and females in the general population, but that smokers tend to exhibit higher CDB levels than nonsmokers. Based on the Kowal et al. (1979) study, smokers not occupationally exposed to cadmium exhibit an average CDB level of 1.4 µg/l.

In general, nonsmokers tend to exhibit levels ranging to 2 µg/l, while levels observed among smokers range to 5 µg/l. Based on the data presented in Table 4, 95% of those not occupationally exposed to cadmium exhibit CDB levels less than 5 µg/l.

5.1.6.2 CDB concentrations among exposed workers

Table 5 is a summary of results from studies reporting CDB levels among workers exposed to cadmium in the work place. As in Table 4, arithmetic and/or geometric means and standard deviations are provided if reported in the listed studies. The absolute range, or the 95% confidence interval around the mean, of the data in each study are provided when reported. In addition, the lower and upper 95th percentile of the distribution are presented for each study i which a mean and corresponding standard deviation were reported. Table 5 also provides estimates of the duration, and level, of exposure to cadmium in the work place if these data were reported in the listed studies. The data presented in table 5 suggest that CDB levels are dose related. Sukuri et al. (1983) show that higher CDB levels are observed among workers experiencing higher work place exposure. This trend appears to be true of the studies listed in the table.

CDB levels reported in table 5 are higher among those showing signs of cadmium-related kidney damage than those showing no such damage. Lauwerys et al. (1976) report CDB levels among workers with kidney lesions that generally are above the levels reported for workers without kidney lesions. Ellis et al. (1983) report a similar observation comparing workers with and without renal dysfunction, although they found more overlap between the 2 groups than Lauwerys et al.

Table 5
Blood Cadmium in Workers Exposed to Cadmium in the Workplace

Study No.	Work environment (worker population monitored)	No. in study	Employment in years (mean)	Mean concentration of cadmium in air ($\mu g/m^3$)	Concentrations of Cadmium in Blood[a]					
					Arithmetic mean (± S.D.)[b]	Absolute range or (95% C.I.)[c]	Geometric mean (GSD)[d]	Lower 95th percentile of range[e] ( )[f]	Upper 95th percentile of range[e] ( )[f]	Reference
1	Ni-Cd battery plant and Cd production plant:		3-40	≤ 90						Lauwerys et al. 1976
	(Workers without kidney lesions)	96			21.4 ± 1.9			(18)	(25)	
	(Workers with kidney lesions)	25			38.8 ± 3.8			(32)	(45)	
2	Ni-Cd battery plant:									Adamsson et al. (1979)
	(Smokers)	7	(5)	10.1	22.7	7.3 – 67.2				
	(Nonsmokers)	8	(9)	7.0	7.0	4.9 – 10.5				
3	Cadmium alloy plant:									Sukuri et al. 1982
	(High exposure group)	7	(10.6)	[1,000 - 5 yrs;	20.8 ± 7.1			(7.3)	(34)	
	(Low exposure group)	9	(7.3)	40 - 5 yrs]	7.1 ± 1.1			(5.1)	(9.1)	
4	Retrospective study of workers with renal problems:	19	15-41							Roels et al. 1982
	(Before removal)		(27.2)		39.9 ± 3.7	11 – 179		(34)	(46)	
	(After removal)		[g](4.2)		14.1 ± 5.6	5.7 – 27.4		(4.4)	(24)	
5	Cadmium production plant:									Ellis et al. 1983
	(Workers without renal dysfunction)	33	1- 34		15 ± 5.7	7 – 31		(5.4)	(25)	
	(Workers with renal dysfunction)	18	10-34		24 ± 8.5	10 – 34		(9.3)	(39)	
6	Cd-Cu alloy plant	75	Up to 39				8.8 ± 1.1	7.5	10	Mason et al. 1988
7	Cadmium recovery operation—Current (19) and former (26) workers	45	(19.0)				7.9 ± 2.0	2.5	25	Thun et al. 1989
8	Cadmium recovery operation	40			10.2 ± 5.3	2.2 – 18.8		(1.3)	(19)	Mueller et al. 1989

[a] Concentrations reported in µg Cd/l blood unless otherwise stated
[b] S.D.—Standard Deviation
[c] C.I.—Confidence Interval
[d] GSD—Geometric Standard Deviation
[e] Based on an assumed lognormal distribution
[f] Based on an assumed normal distribution
[g] Years following removal

The data in table 5 also indicate that CDB levels are higher among those experiencing current occupational exposure than those who have been removed from such exposure. Roels et al. (1982) indicate that CDB levels observed among workers experiencing ongoing exposure in the work place are almost entirely above levels observed among workers removed from such exposure. This finding suggests that CDB levels decrease once cadmium exposure has ceased.

A comparison of the data presented in tables 4 and 5 indicates that CDB levels observed among cadmium-exposed workers is significantly higher than levels observed among the unexposed groups. With the exception of 2 studies presented in table 5 (1 of which includes former workers in the sample group tested), the lower 95th percentile for CDB levels among exposed workers are greater than 5 µg/l, which is the value of the upper 95th percentile for CDB levels observed among those who are not occupationally exposed. Therefore, a CDB level of 5 µg/l represents a threshold above which significant work place exposure to cadmium may be occurring.

5.1.7 Conclusions and Recommendations for CDB

Based on the above evaluation, the following recommendations are made for a CDB proficiency program.

5.1.7.1 Recommended method

The method of Stoeppler and Brandt (1980) should be adopted for analyzing CDB. This method was selected over other methods for its straightforward sample-preparation procedures, and because limitations of the method were described adequately. It also is the method used by a plurality of laboratories currently participating in the CTQ proficiency program. In a recent CTQ interlaboratory comparison report (CTQ 1991), analysis of the methods used by laboratories to measure CDB indicates that 46% (11 of 24) of the participating laboratories used the Stoeppler and Brandt methodology (HNO_3 deproteinization of blood followed by analysis of the supernatant by GF-AAS). Other CDB methods employed by participating laboratories identified in the CTQ report include dilution of blood (29%), acid digestion (12%) and miscellaneous methods (12%).

Laboratories may adopt alternate methods, but it is the responsibility of the laboratory to demonstrate that the alternate methods meet the data quality objectives defined for the Stoeppler and Brandt method (see Section 5.1.7.2 below).

5.1.7.2 Data quality objectives

Based on the above evaluation, the following data quality objectives (DQOs) should facilitate interpretation of analytical results.

Limit of Detection. 0.5 µg/l should be achievable using the Stoeppler and Brandt method. Stoeppler and Brandt (1980) report a limit of detection equivalent to ≤0.2 µg/l in whole blood using 25 µl aliquots of deproteinized, diluted blood samples.

Accuracy. Initially, some of the laboratories performing CDB measurements may be expected to satisfy criteria similar to the less severe criteria specified by the CTQ program, i.e., measurements within 2 µg/l or 15% (whichever is greater) of the target value. About 60% of the laboratories enrolled in the CTQ program could meet this criterion on the first proficiency test (Weber 1988).

Currently, approximately 12 laboratories in the CTQ program are achieving an accuracy for CDB analysis within the more severe constraints of ±1 µg/l or 15% (whichever is greater). Later, as laboratories gain experience, they should achieve the level of accuracy exhibited by these 12 laboratories. The experience in the CTQ program has shown that, even without incentives, laboratories benefit from the feedback of the program; after they have analyzed 40–50 control samples from the program, performance improves to the point where about 60% of the laboratories can meet the stricter criterion of ±1 µg/l or 15% (Weber 1988). Thus, this stricter target accuracy is a reasonable DQO.

Precision. Although Stoeppler and Brandt (1980) suggest that a coefficient of variation (CV) near 1.3% (for a 10 µg/l concentration) is achievable for within-run reproducibility, it is recognized that other factors affecting within- and between-run comparability will increase the achievable CV. Stoeppler and Brandt (1980) observed CVs that were as high as 30% for low concentrations (0.4 µg/l), and CVs of less than 5% for higher concentrations.

For internal QC samples (see Section 3.3.1), laboratories should attain an overall precision near 25%. For CDB samples with concentrations less than 2 µg/l, a target precision of 40% is reasonable, while precisions of 20% should be achievable for concentrations greater than 2 µg/l. Although these values are more strict than values observed in the CTQ interlaboratory program reported by Webber (1988), they are within the achievable limits reported by Stoeppler and Brandt (1980).

5.1.7.3 Quality assurance/quality control

Commercial laboratories providing measurement of CDB should adopt an internal QA/QC program that incorporates the following components: Strict adherence to the selected method, including all calibration requirements; regular incorporation of QC samples during actual runs; a protocol for corrective actions, and documentation of these actions; and, participation in an interlaboratory proficiency program. Note that the nonmandatory QA/QC program presented in Attachment 1 is based on the Stoeppler and Brandt method for CDB analysis. Should an alternate method be adopted, the laboratory should develop a QA/QC program satisfying the provisions of Section 3.3.1.

5.2 Measuring Cadmium in Urine (CDU)

As in the case of CDB measurement, proper determination of CDU requires strict analytical discipline regarding collection and handling of samples. Because cadmium is both ubiquitous in the environment and employed widely in coloring agents for industrial products that may be used during sample collection, preparation and analysis, care should be exercised to ensure that samples are not contaminated during the sampling procedure.

Methods for CDU determination share many of the same features as those employed for the determination of CDB. Thus, changes and improvements to methods for measuring CDU over the past 40 years parallel those used to monitor CDB. The direction of development has largely been toward the simplification of sample preparation techniques made possible because of improvements in analytic techniques.

5.2.1 Units of CDU Measurement

Procedures adopted for reporting CDU concentrations are not uniform. In fact, the situation for reporting CDU is more complicated than for CDB, where concentrations are normalized against a unit volume of whole blood.

Concentrations of solutes in urine vary with several biological factors (including the time since last voiding and the volume of liquid consumed over the last few hours); as a result, solute concentrations should be normalized against another characteristic of urine that represents changes in solute concentrations. The 2 most common techniques are either to standardize solute concentrations against the concentration of creatinine, or to standardize solute concentrations against the specific gravity of the urine. Thus, CDU concentrations have been reported in the literature as "uncorrected" concentrations of cadmium per volume of urine (i.e., µg Cd/l urine), "corrected" concentrations of cadmium per volume of urine at a standard specific gravity (i.e., µg Cd/l urine at a specific gravity of 1.020), or "corrected" mass concentration per unit mass of creatinine (i.e., µg Cd/g creatinine). (CDU concentrations [whether uncorrected or corrected for specific gravity, or normalized to creatinine] occasionally are reported in nanomoles [i.e., nmoles] of cadmium per unit mass or volume. In this protocol, these values are converted to µg of cadmium per unit mass or volume using 89 nmoles of cadmium = 10 µg.)

While it is agreed generally that urine values of analytes should be normalized for reporting purposes, some debate exists over what correction method should be used. The medical community has long favored normalization based on creatinine concentration, a common urinary constituent. Creatinine is a normal product of tissue catabolism, is excreted at a uniform rate, and the total amount excreted per day is constant on a day-to-day basis (NIOSH 1984b). While this correction method is accepted widely in Europe, and within some occupational health circles, Kowals (1983) argues that the use of specific gravity (i.e., total solids per unit volume) is more straightforward and practical (than creatinine) in adjusting CDU values for populations that vary by age or gender.

Kowals (1983) found that urinary creatinine (CRTU) is lower in females than males, and also varies with age. Creatinine excretion is highest in younger males (20–30 years old), decreases at middle age (50–60 years), and may rise slightly in later years. Thus, cadmium concentrations may be underestimated for some workers with high CRTU levels.

Within a single void urine collection, urine concentration of any analyte will be affected by recent consumption of large volumes of liquids, and by heavy physical labor in hot environments. The absolute amount of analyte excreted may be identical, but concentrations will vary widely so that urine must be corrected for specific gravity (i.e., to normalize concentrations to the quantity of total solute) using a fixed value (e.g., 1.020 or 1.024). However, since heavy-metal exposure may increase urinary protein excretion, there is a tendency to underestimate cadmium concentrations in samples with high specific gravities when specific-gravity corrections are applied.

Despite some shortcomings, reporting solute concentrations as a function of creatinine concentration is accepted generally; OSHA therefore recommends that CDU levels be reported as the mass of cadmium per unit mass of creatinine (µg/g CTRU).

Reporting CDU as µg/g CRTU requires an additional analytical process beyond the analysis of cadmium: Samples must be analyzed independently for creatinine so that results may be reported as the ratio of cadmium to creatinine concentrations found in the urine sample. Consequently, the overall quality of the analysis depends on the combined performance by a laboratory on these 2 determinations. The analysis used for CDU determinations is addressed below in terms of µg Cd/l, with analysis of creatinine addressed separately. Techniques for assessing creatinine are discussed in Section 5.4.

Techniques for deriving cadmium as a ratio of CRTU, and the confidence limits for independent measurements of cadmium and CRTU, are provided in Section 3.3.3.

5.2.2 Analytical Techniques Used To Monitor CDU

Analytical techniques used for CDU determinations are similar to those employed for CDB determinations; these techniques are summarized in Table 3. As with CDB monitoring, the technique most suitable for CDU determinations is atomic absorption spectroscopy (AAS). AAS methods used for CDU determinations typically employ a graphite furnace, with background correction made using either the deuterium-lamp or Zeeman techniques; Section 5.1.1 provides a detailed description of AAS methods.

5.2.3 Methods Developed for CDU Determinations

Princi (1947), Smith et al. (1955), Smith and Kench (1957), and Tsuchiya (1967) used colorimetric procedures similar to those described in the CDB section above to estimate CDU concentrations. In these methods, urine (50 ml) is reduced to dryness by heating in a sand bath and digested (wet ashed) with mineral acids. Cadmium then is complexed with dithiazone, extracted with chloroform and quantified by spectrophotometry. These early studies typically report reagent blank values equivalent to 0.3 µg Cd/l, and CDU concentrations among nonexposed control groups at maximum levels of 10 µg Cd/l—erroneously high values when compared to more recent surveys of cadmium concentrations in the general population.

By the mid-1970s, most analytical procedures for CDU analysis used either wet ashing (mineral acid) or high temperatures (>400 °C) to digest the organic matrix of urine, followed by cadmium chelation with APDC or DDTC solutions and extraction with MIBK. The resulting aliquots were analyzed by flame or graphite-furnace AAS (Kjellstrom 1979).

Improvements in control over temperature parameters with electrothermal heating devices used in conjunction with flameless AAS techniques, and optimization of temperature programs for controlling the drying, charring, and atomization processes in sample analyses, led to improved analytical detection of diluted urine samples without the need for sample digestion or ashing. Roels et al. (1978) successfully used a simple sample preparation, dilution of 1.0 ml aliquots of urine with 0.1 N HNO_3, to achieve accurate low-level determinations of CDU.

In the method described by Pruszkowska et al. (1983), which has become the preferred method for CDU analysis, urine samples were diluted at a ratio of 1:5 with water; diammonium hydrogenphosphate in dilute HNO_3 was used as a matrix modifier. The matrix modifier allows for a higher charring temperature without loss of cadmium through volatilization during preatomization. This procedure also employs a stabilized temperature platform in a graphite furnace, while nonspecific background absorption is corrected using the Zeeman technique. This method allows for an absolute detection limit of approximately 0.04 µg Cd/l urine.

5.2.4 Sample Collection and Handling

Sample collection procedures for CDU may contribute to variability observed among CDU measurements. Sources of variation attendant to sampling include time-of-day, the interval since ingestion of liquids, and the introduction of external contamination during the collection process. Therefore, to minimize contributions from these variables, strict adherence to a sample-collection protocol is recommended. This protocol should include provisions for normalizing the conditions under which urine is collected. Every effort also should be made to collect samples during the same time of day.

Collection of urine samples from an industrial work force for biological monitoring purposes usually is performed using "spot" (i.e., single-void) urine with the pH of the sample determined immediately. Logistic and sample-integrity problems arise when efforts are made to collect urine over long periods (e.g., 24 hrs). Unless single-void urines are used, there are numerous opportunities for measurement error because of poor control over sample collection, storage and environmental contamination.

To minimize the interval during which sample urine resides in the bladder, the following adaption to the "spot" collection procedure is recommended: The bladder should first be emptied, and then a large glass of water should be consumed; the sample may be collected within an hour after the water is consumed.

5.2.5 Best Achievable Performance

Performance using a particular method for CDU determinations is assumed to be equivalent to the performance reported by the research laboratories in which the method was developed. Pruszkowska et al. (1983) report a detection limit of 0.04 µg/l CDU, with a CV of <4% between 0–5 µg/l. The CDC reports a minimum CDU detection limit of 0.07 µg/l using a modified method based on Pruszkowska et al. (1983). No CV is stated in this protocol; the protocol contains only rejection criteria for internal QC parameters used during accuracy determinations with known standards (Attachment 8 of exhibit 106 of OSHA docket H057A). Stoeppler and Brandt (1980) report a CDU detection limit of 0.2 µ/l for their methodology.

5.2.6 General Method Performance

For any particular method, the expected initial performance from commercial laboratories may be somewhat lower than that reported by the research laboratory in which the method was developed. With participation in appropriate proficiency programs, and use of a proper in-house QA/QC program incorporating provisions for regular corrective actions, the performance of commercial laboratories may be expected to improve and approach that reported by a research laboratories. The results reported for existing proficiency programs serve to specify the initial level of performance that likely can be expected from commercial laboratories offering analysis using a particular method.

Weber (1988) reports on the results of the CTQ proficiency program, which includes CDU results for laboratories participating in the program. Results indicate that after receiving 60 samples (i.e., after participating in the program for approximately 3 years), approximately 80% of the participating laboratories report CDU results ranging between ± 2 µg/l or 15% of the consensus mean, whichever is greater. On any single sample of the last 15 samples, the proportion of laboratories falling within the specified range is between 75 and 95%, except for a single test for which only 60% of the laboratories reported acceptable results. For each of the last 15 samples, approximately 60% of the laboratories reported results within ±1 µg or 15% of the mean, whichever is greater. The range of concentrations included in this set of samples was not reported.

Another report from the CTQ (1991) summarizes preliminary CDU results from their 1991 interlaboratory program. According to the report, for 3 CDU samples with values of 9.0, 16.8, 31.5 µg/l, acceptable results (target of ± 2 µg/l or 15 % of the consensus mean, whichever is greater) were achieved by only 44–52% of the 34 laboratories participating in the CDU program. The overall CVs for these 3 CDU samples among the 34 participating laboratories were 31%, 25%, and 49%, respectively. The reason for this poor performance has not been determined.

A more recent report from the CTQ (Weber, private communication) indicates that 36% of the laboratories in the program have been able to achieve the target of ±1 µg/l or 15% for more than 75% of the samples analyzed over the last 5 years, while 45% of participating laboratories achieved a target of ±2 µg/l or 15% for more than 75% of the samples analyzed over the same period.

Note that results reported in the interlaboratory programs are in terms of µg Cd/l of urine, unadjusted for creatinine. The performance indicated, therefore, is a measure of the performance of the cadmium portion of the analyses, and does not include variation that may be introduced during the analysis of CRTU.

5.2.7 Observed CDU Concentrations

Prior to the onset of renal dysfunction, CDU concentrations provide a general indication of the exposure history (i.e., body burden) (see Section 4.3). Once renal dysfunction occurs, CDU levels appear to increase and are no longer indicative solely of cadmium body burden (Friberg and Elinder 1988).

5.2.7.1 Range of CDU concentrations observed among unexposed samples

Surveys of CDU concentrations in the general population were first reported from cooperative studies among industrial countries (i.e., Japan, U.S. and Sweden) conducted in the mid-1970s. In summarizing these data, Kjellstrom (1979) reported that CDU concentrations among Dallas, Texas men (age range: <9–59 years; smokers and nonsmokers) varied from 0.11–1.12 µg/l (uncorrected for creatinine or specific gravity). These CDU concentrations are intermediate between population values found in Sweden (range: 0.11–0.80 µg/l) and Japan (range: 0.14–2.32 µg/l).

Kowal and Zirkes (1983) reported CDU concentrations for almost 1,000 samples collected during 1978–79 from the general U.S. adult population (i.e., nine states; both genders; ages 20–74 years). They report that CDU concentrations are lognormally distributed; low levels predominated, but a small proportion of the population exhibited high levels. These investigators transformed the CDU concentrations values, and reported the same data 3 different ways: µg/l urine (unadjusted), µg/l (specific gravity adjusted to 1.020), and µg/g CRTU. These data are summarized in Tables 6 and 7.

Based on further statistical examination of these data, including the lifestyle characteristics of this group, Kowal (1988) suggested increased cadmium absorption (i.e., body burden) was correlated with low dietary intakes of calcium and iron, as well as cigarette smoking.

CDU levels presented in Table 6 are adjusted for age and gender. Results suggest that CDU levels may be slightly different among men and women (i.e., higher among men when values are unadjusted, but lower among men when the values are adjusted, for specific gravity or CRTU). Mean differences among men and women are small compared to the standard deviations, and therefore may not be significant. Levels of CDU also appear to increase with age. The data in Table 6 suggest as well that reporting CDU levels adjusted for specific gravity or as a function of CRTU results in reduced variability.

Table 6
Urine Cadmium Concentrations in the U.S. Adult Population: Normal and Concentration-Adjusted Values by Age and Sex[1]

	Geometric means (and geometric standard deviations)		
	Unadjusted ((µg/l)	SG-adjusted[2] (µg/l at 1.020)	Creatine-adjusted (µg/g)
Sex:			
Male (n = 484)	0.55 (2.9)	0.73 (2.6)	0.55 (2.7)
Female (n = 498)	0.49 (3.0)	0.86 (2.7)	0.78 (2.7)
Age:			
20–29 (n = 222)	0.32 (3.0)	0.43 (2.7)	0.32 (2.7)
30–39 (n = 141)	0.46 (3.2)	0.70 (2.8)	0.54 (2.7)
40–49 (n = 142)	0.50 (3.0)	0.81 (2.6)	0.70 (2.7)
50–59 (n = 117)	0.61 (2.9)	0.99 (2.4)	0.90 (2.3)
60–69 (n = 272)	0.76 (2.6)	1.16 (2.3)	1.03 (2.3)

[1] From Kowal and Zirkes 1983.

[2] SC-adjusted is adjusted for specific gravity.

Table 7
Urine Cadmium Concentrations in the U.S. Adult Population: Cumulative Frequency Distribution of Urinary Cadmium (N=982)[1]

Range of concentrations	Unadjusted (µg/l) percent	SG-adjusted (µg/l at 1.020) percent	Creatine-adjusted (µg/g) percent
< 0.5	43.9	28.0	35.8
0.6-1.0	71.7	56.4	65.6
1.1-1.5	84.4	74.9	81.4
1.6-2.0	91.3	84.7	88.9
2.1-3.0	97.3	94.4	95.8
3.1-4.0	98.8	97.4	97.2
4.1-5.0	99.4	98.2	97.9
5.1-10.0	99.6	99.4	99.3
10.0-20.0	99.8	99.6	99.6

[1] Source: Kowal and Zirkes (1983).

The data in the Table 6 indicate the geometric mean of CDU levels observed among the general population is 0.52 µ/g Cd/l urine (unadjusted), with a geometric standard deviation of 3.0. Normalized for creatinine, the geometric mean for the population is 0.66 µ/g CRTU, with a geometric standard deviation of 2.7. Table 7 provides the distributions of CDU concentrations for the general population studied by Kowal and Zirkes. The data in this table indicate that 95% of the CDU levels observed among those not occupationally exposed to cadmium are below 3 µ/g CRTU.

5.2.7.2 Range of CDU concentrations observed among exposed workers

Table 8 is a summary of results from available studies of CDU concentrations observed among cadmium-exposed workers. In this table, arithmetic and/or geometric means and standard deviations are provided if reported in these studies. The absolute range for the data in each study, or the 95% confidence interval around the mean of each study, also are provided when reported. The lower and upper 95th percentile of the distribution are presented for each study in which a mean and corresponding standard deviation were reported. Table 8 also provides estimates of the years of exposure, and the levels of exposure, to cadmium in the work place if reported in these studies. Concentrations reported in this table are in µ/g CRTU, unless otherwise stated.

Table 8
Urine Cadmium Concentrations in Workers Exposed to Cadmium in the Workplace

Study No.	Work environment (worker population monitored)	No. in Study (n)	Employment in years (mean)	Mean concentration of cadmium in air (µg/m³)	Concentration of Cadmium in Urine[a]					
					Arithmetic mean (± S.D.)[b]	Absolute range or (95% C.I.)[c]	Geometric mean (GSD)[d]	Lower 95th percentile of range ( )[f]	Upper 95th percentile of range[e] ( )[f]	Reference
1	Ni-Cd battery plant and Cd production plant		3-40	± 9.0						Lauwerys et al. 1976.
	(Workers without kidney lesions)	96			16.3 ± 16.7			(0)	(44)	
	(Workers with kidney lesions)	25			48.2 ± 42.6			(0)	(120)	
2	Ni-Cd battery plant									Adamsson et al. (1979)
	(Smokers)	7	(5)	10.1	5.5	1.0–14.7				
	(Nonsmokers)	8	(9)	7.0	3.6	0.5–9.3				
3	Cadmium salts production facility	148	(15-4)		15.8	2–150				Butchet et al. 1980
4	Retrospective study of workers with renal problems	19	15-41							Roels et al.1982
	(Before removal)		(27.2)		39.4 ± 28.1	10.8–117		(0)	(88)	
	(After removal)		(4.2)[g]		16.4 ± 9.0	80–42.3		(1.0)	(32)	
5	Cadmium production plant									Ellis et al. 1983
	(Workers without renal dysfunction)	33	1-34		9.4 ± 6.9	2-27		(0)	(21)	
	(Workers with renal dysfunction)	18	10-34		22.8 ± 12.7	8–55		(1)	(45)	
6	Cd-Cu alloy plant	75	Up to 39	Note [h]	6.9 ± 9.4			(0)	(23)	Mason et al. 1988
7	Cadmium recovery operation	45	(19)	87	9.3 ± 6.9			(0)	(21)	Thun et al. 1989
8	Pigment manufacturing plant	29	(12.8)	0.18-3.0		0.2–9.5	1.1			Mueller et al. 1989
9	Pigment manufacturing plant	26	(12.1)	≤ 3.0			1.25 ± 2.45	0.3	6	Kawada et al. 1990

[a] Concentrations reported in µg/g Cr
[b] S.D.—Standard Deviation
[c] C.I.—Confidence Interval
[d] GSD—Geometric Standard Deviation
[e] Based on an assumed lognormal distribution
[f] Based on an assumed normal distribution
[g] Years following removal
[h] Equivalent to 50 for 20–22 yrs

Data in Table 8 from Lauwerys et al. (1976) and Ellis et al. (1983) indicate that CDU concentrations are higher among those exhibiting kidney lesions or dysfunction than among those lacking these symptoms. Data from the study by Roels et al. (1982) indicate that CDU levels decrease among workers removed from occupational exposure to cadmium in comparison to workers experiencing ongoing exposure. In both cases, however, the distinction between the 2 groups is not as clear as with CDB; there is more overlap in CDU levels observed among each of the paired populations than is true for corresponding CDB levels. As with CDB levels, the data in Table 8 suggest increased CDU concentrations among workers who experienced increased overall exposure.

Although a few occupationally-exposed workers in the studies presented in Table 8 exhibit CDU levels below 3 µg/g CRTU, most of those workers exposed to cadmium levels in excess of the PEL defined in the final cadmium rule exhibit CDU levels above 3 µg/g CRTU; this level represents the upper 95th percentile of the CDU distribution observed among those who are not occupationally exposed to cadmium (Table 7).

The mean CDU levels reported in Table 8 among occupationally-exposed groups studied (except 2) exceed 3 µg/g CRTU. Correspondingly, the level of exposure reported in these studies (with 1 exception) are significantly higher than what workers will experience under the final cadmium rule. The 2 exceptions are from the studies by Mueller et al. (1989) and Kawada et al. (1990); these studies indicate that workers exposed to cadmium during pigment manufacture do not exhibit CDU levels as high as those levels observed among workers exposed to cadmium in other occupations. Exposure levels, however, were lower in the pigment manufacturing plants studied. Significantly, workers removed from occupational cadmium exposure for an average of 4 years still exhibited CDU levels in excess of 3 µg/g CRTU (Roels et al. 1982). In the single-exception study with a reported level of cadmium exposure lower than levels proposed in the final rule (i.e., the study of a pigment manufacturing plant by Kawada et al. 1990), most of the workers exhibited CDU levels less than 3 µg/g CRTU (i.e., the mean value was only 1.3 µg/g CRTU). CDU levels among workers with such limited cadmium exposure are expected to be significantly lower than levels of other studies reported in Table 8.

Based on the above data, a CDU level of 3 µg/g CRTU appear to represent a threshold above which significant work place exposure to cadmium occurs over the work span of those being monitored. Note that this threshold is not as distinct as the corresponding threshold described for CDB. In general, the variability associated with CDU measurements among exposed workers appears to be higher than the variability associated with CDB measurements among similar workers.

5.2.8 Conclusions and Recommendations for CDU

The above evaluation supports the following recommendations for a CDU proficiency program. These recommendations address only sampling and analysis procedures for CDU determinations specifically, which are to be reported as an unadjusted µg Cd/l urine. Normalizing this result to creatinine requires a second analysis for CRTU so that the ratio of the 2 measurements can be obtained. Creatinine analysis is addressed in Section 5.4. Formal procedures for combining the 2 measurements to derive a value and a confidence limit for CDU in µg/g CRTU are provided in Section 3.3.3.

5.2.8.1 Recommended method

The method of Pruszkowska et al. (1983) should be adopted for CDU analysis. This method is recommended because it is simple, straightforward and reliable (i.e., small variations in experimental conditions do not affect the analytical results).

A synopsis of the methods used by laboratories to determine CDU under the interlaboratory program administered by the CTQ (1991) indicates that more than 78% (24 of 31) of the participating laboratories use a dilution method to prepare urine samples for CDU analysis. Laboratories may adopt alternate methods, but it is the responsibility of the laboratory to demonstrate that the alternate methods provide results of comparable quality to the Pruszkowska method.

5.2.8.2 Data quality objectives

The following data quality objectives should facilitate interpretation of analytical results, and are achievable based on the above evaluation.

Limit of Detection. A level of 0.5 µg/l (i.e., corresponding to a detection limit of 0.5 µg/g CRTU, assuming 1g CRT/l urine) should be achievable. Pruszkowska et al. (1983) achieved a limit of detection of 0.04 µg/l for CDU based on the slope of the curve for their working standards (0.35 pg Cd/0.0044, A signal = 1% absorbance using GF-AAS).

The CDC reports a minimum detection limit for CDU of 0.07 µg/l using a modified Pruszkowska method. This limit of detection was defined as 3 times the standard deviation calculated from 10 repeated measurements of a "low level" CDU test sample (Attachment 8 of exhibit 106 of OSHA docket H057A).

Stoeppler and Brandt (1980) report a limit of detection for CDU of 0.2 µg/l using an aqueous dilution (1:2) of the urine samples.

Accuracy. A recent report from the CTQ (Weber, private communication) indicates that 36% of the laboratories in the program achieve the target of ± 1 µg/l or 15% for more than 75% of the samples analyzed over the last 5 years, while 45% of participating laboratories achieve a target of ± 2 µg/l or 15% for more than 75% of the samples analyzed over the same period. With time and a strong incentive for improvement, it is expected that the proportion of laboratories successfully achieving the stricter level of accuracy should increase. It should be noted, however, these indices of performance do not include variations resulting from the ancillary measurement of CRTU (which is recommended for the proper recording of results). The low cadmium levels expected to be measured indicate that the analysis of creatinine will contribute relatively little to the overall variability observed among creatinine-normalized CDU levels (see Section 5.4). The initial target value for reporting CDU under this program, therefore, is set at ± 1 µg/g CRTU or 15% (whichever is greater).

Precision. For internal QC samples (which are recommended as part of an internal QA/QC program, Section 3.3.1), laboratories should attain an overall precision of 25%. For CDB samples with concentrations less than 2 µg/l, a target precision of 40% is acceptable, while precisions of 20% should be achievable for CDU concentrations greater than 2 µg/l. Although these values are more stringent than those observed in the CTQ interlaboratory program reported by Webber (1988), they are well within limits expected to be achievable for the method as reported by Stoeppler and Brandt (1980).

5.2.8.3 Quality assurance/quality control

Commercial laboratories providing CDU determinations should adopt an internal QA/QC program that incorporates the following components: Strict adherence to the selected method, including calibration requirements; regular incorporation of QC samples during actual runs; a protocol for corrective actions, and documentation of such actions; and, participation in an interlaboratory proficiency program. Note that the nonmandatory program presented in Attachment 1 as an example of an acceptable QA/QC program, is based on using the Pruszkowska method for CDU analysis. Should an alternate method be adopted by a laboratory, the laboratory should develop a QA/QC program equivalent to the nonmandatory program, and which satisfies the provisions of Section 3.3.1.

5.3 Monitoring β-2–Microglobulin in Urine (B2MU)

As indicated in Section 4.3, B2MU appears to be the best of several small proteins that may be monitored as early indicators of cadmium-induced renal damage. Several analytic techniques are available for measuring B2M.

5.3.1 Units of B2MU Measurement

Procedures adopted for reporting B2MU levels are not uniform. In these guidelines, OSHA recommends that B2MU levels be reported as µg/g CRTU, similar to reporting CDU concentrations. Reporting B2MU normalized to the concentration of CRTU requires an additional analytical process beyond the analysis of B2M: Independent analysis for creatinine so that results may be reported as a ratio of the B2M and creatinine concentrations found in the urine sample. Consequently, the overall quality of the analysis depends on the combined performance on these 2 analyses. The analysis used for B2MU determinations is described in terms of µg B2M/l urine, with analysis of creatinine addressed separately. Techniques used to measure creatinine are provided in Section 5.4. Note that Section 3.3.3 provides techniques for deriving the value of B2M as function of CRTU, and the confidence limits for independent measurements of B2M and CRTU.

5.3.2 Analytical Techniques Used To Monitor B2MU

One of the earliest tests used to measure B2MU was the radial immunodiffusion technique. This technique is a simple and specific method for identification and quantitation of a number of proteins found in human serum and other body fluids when the protein is not readily differentiated by standard electrophoretic procedures. A quantitative relationship exists between the concentration of a protein deposited in a well that is cut into a thin agarose layer containing the corresponding monospecific antiserum, and the distance that the resultant complex diffuses. The wells are filled with an unknown serum and the standard (or control), and incubated in a moist environment at room temperature. After the optimal point of diffusion has been reached, the diameters of the resulting precipion rings are measured. The diameter of a ring is related to the concentration of the constituent substance. For B2MU determinations required in the medical monitoring program, this method requires a process that may be insufficient to concentrate the protein to levels that are required for detection.

Radioimmunoassay (RIA) techniques are used widely in immunologic assays to measure the concentration of antigen or antibody in body-fluid samples. RIA procedures are based on competitive-binding techniques. If antigen concentration is being measured, the principle underlying the procedure is that radioactive-labeled antigen competes with the sample's unlabeled antigen for binding sites on a known amount of immobile antibody. When these 3 components are present in the system, an equilibrium exists. This equilibrium is followed by a separation of the free and bound forms of the antigen. Either free or bound radioactive-labeled antigen can be assessed to determine the amount of antigen in the sample. The analysis is performed by measuring the level of radiation emitted either by the bound complex following removal of the solution containing the free antigen, or by the isolated solution containing the residual-free antigen. The main advantage of the RIA method is the extreme sensitivity of detection for emitted radiation and the corresponding ability to detect trace amounts of antigen. Additionally, large numbers of tests can be performed rapidly.

The enzyme-linked immunosorbent assay (ELISA) techniques are similar to RIA techniques except that nonradioactive labels are employed. This technique is safe, specific and rapid, and is nearly as sensitive as RIA techniques. An enzyme-labeled antigen is used in the immunologic assay; the labeled antigen detects the presence and quantity of unlabeled antigen in the sample. In a representative ELISA test, a plastic plate is coated with antibody (e.g., antibody to B2M). The antibody reacts with antigen (B2M) in the urine and forms an antigen-antibody complex on the plate. A second anti-B2M antibody (i.e., labeled with an enzyme) is added to the mixture and forms an antibody-antigen-antibody complex. Enzyme activity is measured spectrophotometrically after the addition of a specific chromogenic substrate which is activated by the bound enzyme. The results of a typical test are calculated by comparing the spectrophotometric reading of a serum sample to that of a control or reference serum. In general, these procedures are faster and require less laboratory work than other methods.

In a fluorescent ELISA technique (such as the one employed in the Pharmacia Delphia test for B2M), the labeled enzyme is bound to a strong fluorescent dye. In the Pharmacia Delphia test, an antigen bound to a fluorescent dye competes with unlabeled antigen in the sample for a predetermined amount of specific, immobile antibody. Once equilibrium is reached, the immobile phase is removed from the labeled antigen in the sample solution and washed; an enhancement solution then is added that liberates the fluorescent dye from the bound antigen-antibody complex. The enhancement solution also contains a chelate that complexes with the fluorescent dye in solution; this complex increases the fluorescent properties of the dye so that it is easier to detect.

To determine the quantity of B2M in a sample using the Pharmacia Delphia test, the intensity of the fluorescence of the enhancement solution is measured. This intensity is proportional to the concentration of labeled antigen that bound to the immobile antibody phase during the initial competition with unlabeled antigen from the sample. Consequently, the intensity of the fluorescence is an inverse function of the concentration of antigen (B2M) in the original sample. The relationship between the fluorescence level and the B2M concentration in the sample is determined using a series of graded standards, and extrapolating these standards to find the concentration of the unknown sample.

5.3.3 Methods Developed for B2MU Determinations

B2MU usually is measured by radioimmunoassay (RIA) or enzyme-linked immunosorbent assay (ELISA); however, other methods (including gel electrophoresis, radial immunodiffusion, and nephelometric assays) also have been described (Schardun and van Epps 1987). RIA and ELISA methods are preferred because they are sensitive at concentrations as low as micrograms per liter, require no concentration processes, are highly reliable and use only a small sample volume.

Based on a survey of the literature, the ELISA technique is recommended for monitoring B2MU. While RIAs provide greater sensitivity (typically about 1 µg/l, Evrin et al. 1971), they depend on the use of radioisotopes; use of radioisotopes requires adherence to rules and regulations established by the Atomic Energy Commission, and necessitates an expensive radioactivity counter for testing. Radioisotopes also have a relatively short half-life, which corresponds to a reduced shelf life, thereby increasing the cost and complexity of testing. In contrast, ELISA testing can be performed on routine laboratory spectrophotometers, do not necessitate adherence to additional rules and regulations governing the handling of radioactive substances, and the test kits have long shelf lives. Further, the range of sensitivity commonly achieved by the recommended ELISA test (i.e., the Pharmacia Delphia test) is approximately 100 µg/l (Pharmacia 1990), which is sufficient for monitoring B2MU levels resulting from cadmium exposure. Based on the studies listed in Table 9 (Section 5.3.7), the average range of B2M concentrations among the general, nonexposed population falls between 60 and 300 µg/g CRTU. The upper 95th percentile of distributions, derived from studies in Table 9 which reported standard deviations, range between 180 and 1,140 µg/g CRTU. Also, the Pharmacia Delphia test currently is the most widely used test for assessing B2MU.

5.3.4 Sample Collection and Handling

As with CDB or CDU, sample collection procedures are addressed primarily to identify ways to minimize the degree of variability introduced by sample collection during medical monitoring. It is unclear the extent to which sample collection contributes to B2MU variability. Sources of variation include time-of-day effects, the interval since consuming liquids and the quantity of liquids consumed, and the introduction of external contamination during the collection process. A special problem unique to B2M sampling is the sensitivity of this protein to degradation under acid conditions commonly found in the bladder. To minimize this problem, strict adherence to a sampling protocol is recommended. The protocol should include provisions for normalizing the conditions under which the urine is collected. Clearly, it is important to minimize the interval urine spends in the bladder. It also is recommended that every effort be made to collect samples during the same time of day.

Collection of urine samples for biological monitoring usually is performed using "spot" (i.e., single-void) urine. Logistics and sample integrity become problems when efforts are made to collect urine over extended periods (e.g., 24 hrs). Unless single-void urines are used, numerous opportunities exist for measurement error because of poor control over sample collection, storage and environmental contamination.

To minimize the interval that sample urine resides in the bladder, the following adaption to the "spot" collection procedure is recommended: The bladder should be emptied and then a large glass of water should be consumed; the sample then should be collected within an hour after the water is consumed.

5.3.5 Best Achievable Performance

The best achievable performance is assumed to be equivalent to the performance reported by the manufacturers of the Pharmacia Delphia test kits (Pharmacia 1990). According to the insert that comes with these kits, QC results should be within ±2 SDs of the mean for each control sample tested; a CV of less than or equal to 5.2% should be maintained. The total CV reported for test kits is less than or equal to 7.2%.

5.3.6 General Method Performance

Unlike analyses for CDB and CDU, the Pharmacia Delphia test is standardized in a commercial kit that controls for many sources of variation. In the absence of data to the contrary, it is assumed that the achievable performance reported by the manufacturer of this test kit will serve as an achievable performance objective. The CTQ proficiency testing program for B2MU analysis is expected to use the performance parameters defined by the test kit manufacturer as the basis of the B2MU proficiency testing program.

Note that results reported for the test kit are expressed in terms of µg B2M/l of urine, and have not been adjusted for creatinine. The indicated performance, therefore, is a measure of the performance of the B2M portion of the analyses only, and does not include variation that may have been introduced during the analysis of creatinine.

5.3.7 Observed B2MU Concentrations

As indicated in Section 4.3, the concentration of B2MU may serve as an early indicator of the onset of kidney damage associated with cadmium exposure.

5.3.7.1 Range of B2MU concentrations among unexposed samples

Most of the studies listed in Table 9 report B2MU levels for those who were not occupationally exposed to cadmium. Studies noted in the second column of this table (which contain the footnote "d") reported B2MU concentrations among cadmium-exposed workers who, nonetheless, showed no signs of proteinuria. These latter studies are included in this table because, as indicated in Section 4.3, monitoring B2MU is intended to provide advanced warning of the onset of kidney dysfunction associated with cadmium exposure, rather than to distinguish relative exposure. This table, therefore, indicates the range of B2MU levels observed among those who had no symptoms of renal dysfunction (including cadmium-exposed workers with none of these symptoms).

Table 9
B-2–Microglobulin Concentrations Observed in Urine Among Those Not Occupationally Exposed to Cadmium

Study No.	No. in study	Geometric mean	Geometric standard deviation	Lower 95th percentile of distribution[a]	Upper 95th percentile of distribution[a]	Reference
1	133 m[b]	115 µg/g[c]	4.03	12	1,140 µg/g[c]	Ishizaki et al. 1989
2	161 f[b]	146 µg/g[c]	3.11	23	940 µg/g[c]	Ishizaki et al. 1989
3	10	84 µg/g				Ellis et al. 1983
4	203	76 µg/l				Stewart and Hughes 1981

Study No.	No. in study	Geometric mean	Geometric standard deviation	Lower 95th percentile of distribution[a]	Upper 95th percentile of distribution[a]	Reference
5	9	103 µg/g				Chia et al. 1989
6	47[d]	86 µg/L	1.9	30 µg/1	250 µg/L	Kjellstrom et al. 1977
7	1,000[e]	68.1 µg/gr Cr[f]	3.1 m & f	< 10 µg/gr Cr[h]	320 µg/gr Cr[h]	Kowal 1983
8	87	71 µg/g[i]		7[h]	200[h]	Buchet et al. 1980
9	10	0.073 mg/24h				Evrin et al. 1971
10	59	156 µg/g	1.1[j]	130	180	Mason et al. 1988
11	8	118 µg/g				Iwao et al. 1980
12	34	79 µg/g				Wibowo et al. 1982
13	41 m				400 µg/gr Cr[k]	Falck et al. 1983
14	35[n]	67				Roels et al. 1991
15	31[d]	63				Roels et al. 1991
16	36[d]	77[i]				Miksche et al. 1981
17	18[n]	130				Kawada et al. 1989
18	32[p]	122				Kawada et al. 1989
19	18[d]	295	1.4	170	510	Thun et al. 1989

[a] Based on an assumed lognormal distribution
[b] m = males, f = females
[c] Aged general population from non-polluted area; 47.9% population aged 50–69; 52.1% ≥ 70 years of age; values reported in study
[d] Exposed workers without proteinuria
[e] 492 females, 484 male
[f] Creatinine adjusted; males = 68.1 µg/g Cr, females = 64.3 µg/g Cr
[h] Reported in the study
[i] Arithmetic mean
[j] Geometric standard error
[k] Upper 95% tolerance limits: for Falck this is based on the 24 hour urine sample
[n] Controls
[p] Exposed synthetic resin and pigment workers without proteinuria; Cadmium in urine levels up to 10 µg/g Cr

To the extent possible, the studies listed in Table 9 provide geometric means and geometric standard deviations for measurements among the groups defined in each study. For studies reporting a geometric standard deviation along with a mean, the lower and upper 95th percentile for these distributions were derived and reported in the table.

The data provided from 15 of the 19 studies listed in Table 9 indicate that the geometric mean concentration of B2M observed among those who were not occupationally exposed to cadmium is 70–170 µg/g CRTU. Data from the 4 remaining studies indicate that exposed workers who exhibit no signs of proteinuria show mean B2MU levels of 60–300 µg/g CRTU. B2MU values in the study by Thun et al. (1989), however, appear high in comparison to the other 3 studies. If this study is removed, B2MU levels for those who are not occupationally exposed to cadmium are similar to B2MU levels found among cadmium-exposed workers who exhibit no signs of kidney dysfunction. Although the mean is high in the study by Thun et al., the range of measurements reported in this study is within the ranges reported for the other studies.

Determining a reasonable upper limit from the range of B2M concentrations observed among those who do not exhibit signs of proteinuria is problematic. Elevated B2MU levels are among the signs used to define the onset of kidney dysfunction. Without access to the raw data from the studies listed in Table 9, it is necessary to rely on reported standard deviations to estimate an upper limit for normal B2MU concentrations (i.e., the upper 95th percentile for the distributions measured). For the 8 studies reporting a geometric standard deviation, the upper 95th percentiles for the distributions are 180–1140 µg/g CRTU. These values are in general agreement with the upper 95th percentile for the distribution (i.e., 631 µg/g CRTU) reported by Buchet et al. (1980). These upper limits also appear to be in general agreement with B2MU values (i.e., 100–690 µg/g CRTU) reported as the normal upper limit by Iwao et al. (1980), Kawada et al. (1989), Wibowo et al. (1982), and Schardun and van Epps (1987). These values must be compared to levels reported among those exhibiting kidney dysfunction to define a threshold level for kidney dysfunction related to cadmium exposure.

5.3.7.2 Range of B2MU concentrations among exposed workers

Table 10 presents results from studies reporting B2MU determinations among those occupationally exposed to cadmium in the work place; in some of these studies, kidney dysfunction was observed among exposed workers, while other studies did not make an effort to distinguish among exposed workers based on kidney dysfunction. As with Table 9, this table provides geometric means and geometric standard deviations for the groups defined in each study if available. For studies reporting a geometric standard deviation along with a mean, the lower and upper 95th percentiles for the distributions are derived and reported in the table.

Table 10
B-2-Microglobulin Concentrations Observed in Urine Among Occupationally-Exposed workers

Study No.	N	Concentration of B-2-Microglobulin in urine				Reference
		Geometric mean (µg/g)[a]	Geom std dev	L 95% of range[b]	U 95% of range[b]	
1	1,424	160	6.19	8.1	3,300	Ishizaki et al., 1989
2	1,754	260	6.50	12	5,600	Ishizaki et al., 1989
3	33	210				Ellis et al., 1983
4	65	210				Chia et al., 1989
5	[c]44	5,700	6.49	[d]300	[d]98,000	Kjellstrom et al., 1977
6	148	[e]180		[f]110	[f]280	Buchet et al., 1980
7	37	160	3.90	17	1,500	Kenzaburo et al., 1979
8	[c]45	3,300	8.7	[d]310	[d]89,000	Mason et al., 1988
9	[c]10	6,100	5.99	[f]650	[f]57,000	Falck et al., 1983
10	[c]11	3,900	2.96	[d]710	[d]15,000	Elinder et al., 1985
11	[c]12	300				Roels et al., 1991
12	[g]8	7,400				Roels et al., 1991
13	[c]23	[h]1,800				Roels et al., 1989
14	10	690				Iwao et al., 1980
15	34	71				Wibowo et al., 1982
16	[c]15	4,700	6.49	[d]590	[d]93,000	Thun et al., 1989

[a] Unless otherwise stated
[b] Based on an assumed lognormal distribution
[c] Among workers diagnosed as having renal dysfunction; for Elinder this means β 2 levels greater than 300 micrograms per gram creatinine (µg/gr Cr); for Roels, 1991, range = 31 – 35, 170 µgβ_2/gr Cr and geometric mean = 63 among healthy workers; for Mason β_2 > 300 µg/gr Cr
[d] Based on a detailed review of the data by OSHA
[e] Arthmetic mean
[f] Reported in the study
[g] Retired workers
[h] 1,800 µgβ_2/gr Cr for first survey; second survey = 1,600; third survey = 2,600; fourth survey = 2,600; fifth survey = 2,600

The data provided in Table 10 indicate that the mean B2MU concentration observed among workers experiencing occupational exposure to cadmium (but with undefined levels of proteinuria) is 160–7400 µg/g CRTU. One of these studies reports geometric means lower than this range (i.e., as low as 71 µg/g CRTU); an explanation for this wide spread in average concentrations is not available.

Seven of the studies listed in Table 10 report a range of B2MU levels among those diagnosed as having renal dysfunction. As indicated in this table, renal dysfunction (proteinuria) is defined in several of these studies by B2MU levels in excess of 300 µg/g CRTU (see footnote "c" of Table 10); therefore, the range of B2MU levels observed in these studies is a function of the operational definition used to identify those with renal dysfunction. Nevertheless, a B2MU level of 300 µg/g CRTU appears to be a meaningful threshold for identifying those having early signs of kidney damage. While levels much higher than 300 µg/g CRTU have been observed among those with renal dysfunction, the vast majority of those not occupationally exposed to cadmium exhibit much lower B2MU concentrations (see Table 9). Similarly, the vast majority of workers not exhibiting renal dysfunction are found to have levels below 300 µg/g CRTU (Table 9).

The 300 µg/g CRTU level for B2MU proposed in the above paragraph has support among researchers as the threshold level that distinguishes between cadmium-exposed workers with and without kidney dysfunction. For example, in the guide for physicians who must evaluate cadmium-exposed workers written for the Cadmium Council by Dr. Lauwerys, levels of B2M greater than 200–300 µg/g CRTU are considered to require additional medical evaluation for kidney dysfunction (exhibit 8–447, OSHA docket H057A). The most widely used test for measuring B2M (i.e., the Pharmacia Delphia test) defines B2MU levels above 300 µg/l as abnormal (exhibit L–140–1, OSHA docket H057A).

Dr. Elinder, chairman of the Department of Nephrology at the Karolinska Institute, testified at the hearings on the proposed cadmium rule. According to Dr. Elinder (exhibit L–140–45, OSHA docket H057A), the normal concentration of B2MU has been well documented (Evrin and Wibell 1972; Kjellstrom et al. 1977a; Elinder et al. 1978, 1983; Buchet et al. 1980; Jawaid et al. 1983; Kowal and Zirkes, 1983). Elinder stated that the upper 95 or 97.5 percentiles for B2MU among those without tubular dysfunction is below 300 µg/g CRTU (Kjellstrom et al. 1977a; Buchet et al. 1980; Kowal and Zirkes, 1983). Elinder defined levels of B2M above 300 µg/g CRTU as "slight" proteinuria.

5.3.8 Conclusions and Recommendations for B2MU

Based on the above evaluation, the following recommendations are made for a B2MU proficiency testing program. Note that the following discussion addresses only sampling and analysis for B2MU determinations (i.e., to be reported as an unadjusted µg B2M/l urine). Normalizing this result to creatinine requires a second analysis for CRTU (see Section 5.4) so that the ratio of the 2 measurements can be obtained.

5.3.8.1 Recommended method

The Pharmacia Delphia method (Pharmacia 1990) should be adopted as the standard method for B2MU determinations. Laboratories may adopt alternate methods, but it is the responsibility of the laboratory to demonstrate that alternate methods provide results of comparable quality to the Pharmacia Delphia method.

5.3.8.2 Data quality objectives

The following data quality objectives should facilitate interpretation of analytical results, and should be achievable based on the above evaluation.

Limit of Detection. A limit of 100 µg/l urine should be achievable, although the insert to the test kit (Pharmacia 1990) cites a detection limit of 150 µg/l; private conversations with representatives of Pharmacia, however, indicate that the lower limit of 100 µg/l should be achievable provided an additional standard of 100 µg/l B2M is run with the other standards to derive the calibration curve (Section 3.3.1.1). The lower detection limit is desirable due to the proximity of this detection limit to B2MU values defined for the cadmium medical monitoring program.

Accuracy. Because results from an interlaboratory proficiency testing program are not available currently, it is difficult to define an achievable level of accuracy. Given the general performance parameters defined by the insert to the test kits, however, an accuracy of ± 15% of the target value appears achievable.

Due to the low levels of B2MU to be measured generally, it is anticipated that the analysis of creatinine will contribute relatively little to the overall variability observed among creatinine-normalized B2MU levels (see Section 5.4). The initial level of accuracy for reporting B2MU levels under this program should be set at ± 15%.

Precision. Based on precision data reported by Pharmacia (1990), a precision value (i.e., CV) of 5% should be achievable over the defined range of the analyte. For internal QC samples (i.e., recommended as part of an internal QA/QC program, Section 3.3.1), laboratories should attain precision near 5% over the range of concentrations measured.

5.3.8.3 Quality assurance/quality control

Commercial laboratories providing measurement of B2MU should adopt an internal QA/QC program that incorporates the following components: Strict adherence to the Pharmacia Delphia method, including calibration requirements; regular use of QC samples during routine runs; a protocol for corrective actions, and documentation of these actions; and, participation in an interlaboratory proficiency program. Procedures that may be used to address internal QC requirements are presented in Attachment 1. Due to differences between analyses for B2MU and CDB/CDU, specific values presented in Attachment 1 may have to be modified. Other components of the program (including characterization runs), however, can be adapted to a program for B2MU.

5.4 Monitoring Creatinine in Urine (CRTU)

Because CDU and B2MU should be reported relative to concentrations of CRTU, these concentrations should be determined in addition CDU and B2MU determinations.

5.4.1 Units of CRTU Measurement

CDU should be reported as µg Cd/g CRTU, while B2MU should be reported as µg B2M/g CRTU. To derive the ratio of cadmium or B2M to creatinine, CRTU should be reported in units of g crtn/l of urine. Depending on the analytical method, it may be necessary to convert results of creatinine determinations accordingly.

5.4.2 Analytical Techniques Used To Monitor CRTU

Of the techniques available for CRTU determinations, an absorbance spectrophotometric technique and a high-performance liquid chromatography (HPLC) technique are identified as acceptable in this protocol.

5.4.3 Methods Developed for CRTU Determinations

CRTU analysise performed in support of either CDU or B2MU determinations should be performed using either of the following 2 methods:

1. The Du Pont method (i.e., Jaffe method), in which creatinine in a sample reacts with picrate under alkaline conditions, and the resulting red chromophore is monitored (at 510 nm) for a fixed interval to determine the rate of the reaction; this reaction rate is proportional to the concentration of creatinine present in the sample (a copy of this method is provided in Attachment 2 of this protocol); or,
2. The OSHA SLC Technical Center (OSLTC) method, in which creatinine in an aliquot of sample is separated using an HPLC column equipped with a UV detector; the resulting peak is quantified using an electrical integrator (a copy of this method is provided in Attachment 3 of this protocol).

5.4.4 Sample Collection and Handling

CRTU samples should be segregated from samples collected for CDU or B2MU analysis. Sample-collection techniques have been described under Section 5.2.4. Samples should be preserved either to stabilize CDU (with HNO_3) or B2MU (with NaOH). Neither of these procedures should adversely affect CRTU analysis (see Attachment 3).

5.4.5 General Method Performance

Data from the OSLTC indicate that a CV of 5% should be achievable using the OSLTC method (Septon, L private communication). The achievable accuracy of this method has not been determined.

Results reported in surveys conducted by the CAP (CAP 1991a, 1991b and 1992) indicate that a CV of 5% is achievable. The accuracy achievable for CRTU determinations has not been reported.

Laboratories performing creatinine analysis under this protocol should be CAP accredited and should be active participants in the CAP surveys.

5.4.6 Observed CRTU Concentrations

Published data suggest the range of CRTU concentrations is 1.0–1.6 g in 24-hour urine samples (Harrison 1987). These values are equivalent to about 1 g/l urine.

5.4.7 Conclusions and Recommendations for CRTU

5.4.7.1 Recommended method

Use either the Jaffe method (Attachment 2) or the OSLTC method (Attachment 3). Alternate methods may be acceptable provided adequate performance is demonstrated in the CAP program.

5.4.7.2 Data quality objectives

Limit of Detection. This value has not been formally defined; however, a value of 0.1 g/l urine should be readily achievable.

Accuracy. This value has not been defined formally; accuracy should be sufficient to retain accreditation from the CAP.

Precision. A CV of 5% should be achievable using the recommended methods.

6.0 References

Adamsson E, Piscator M, and Nogawa K. (1979). Pulmonary and gastrointestinal exposure to cadmium oxide dust in a battery factory. Environmental Health Perspectives, 28, 219–222.

American Conference of Governmental Industrial Hygienists (ACGIH). (1986). Documentation of the Threshold Limit Values and Biological Exposure Indices. 5th edition. p. BEI–55.

Bernard A, Buchet J, Roels H, Masson P, and Lauwerys R. (1979). Renal excretion of proteins and enzymes in workers exposed to cadmium. European Journal of Clinical Investigation, 9, 11–22.

Bernard A and Lauwerys R. (1990). Early markers of cadmium nephrotoxicity: Biological significance and predictive value. Toxocological and Environmental Chemistry, 27, 65–72.

Braunwald E, Isselbacher K, Petersdorf R, Wilson J, Martin J, and Fauci A (Eds.). (1987). Harrison's Principles of Internal Medicine. New York: McGraw-Hill Book Company.

Buchet J, Roels H, Bernard I, and Lauwerys R. (1980). Assessment of renal funcion of workers exposed to inorganic lead, cadmium, or mercury vapor. Journal of Occupational Medicine, 22, 741–750.

CAP. (1991). Urine Chemistry, Series 1: Survey (Set U-B).

College of American Pathologists.

CAP. (1991). Urine Chemistry, Series 1: Survey (Set U-C). College of American

Pathologists.

CAP. (1992). Urine Chemistry, Series 1: Survey (Set U-A). College of American Pathologists.

CDC. (1986). Centers for Disease Control, Division of Environmental Health Laboratory Sciences, Center for Environmental Health, Atlanta, Georgia. Docket No. 106A. Lake Couer d'Alene, Idaho cadmium and lead study: 86–0030, Specimen collection and shipping protocol.

CDC. (1990). Centers for Disease Control, Nutritional Biochemistry Branch. 4/27/90 Draft SOP for Method 0360A "Determination of cadmium in urine by graphite furnace atomic absorption spectrometry with Zeeman background correction.

Centre de Toxicologie du Quebec. (1991). Interlaboratory comparison program report for run #2. Shipping date 3/11/91. Addition BLR 9/19.

Chia K, Ong C, Ong H, and Endo G. (1989). Renal tubular function of workers exposed to low levels of cadmium. British Journal of Industrial Medicine, 46, 165–170.

Claeys-Thoreau F. (1982). Determination of low levels of cadmium and lead in biological fluids with simple dilution by atomic absorption spectrophotometry using Zeeman effect background absorption and the L'Vov platform. Atomic Spectroscopy, 3, 188–191.

DeBenzo Z, Fraile R, and Carrion N. (1990). Electrothermal atomization atomic absorption spectrometry with stabilized aqueous standards for the determination of cadmium in whole blood. Analytica Chimica Acta, 231, 283–288.

Elinder C, Edling C, Lindberg E, Kagedal B, and Vesterberg O. (1985). Assessment of renal function in workers previously exposed to cadmium. British Journal of Internal Medicine, 42, 754.

Ellis K, Cohn S, and Smith T. (1985). Cadmium inhalation exposure estimates: Their significance with respect to kidney and liver cadmium burden. Journal of Toxicology and Environmental Health, 15, 173–187.

Ellis K, Yasumura S, Vartsky D, and Cohn S. (1983). Evaluation of biological indicators of body burden of cadmium in humans. Fundamentals and Applied Toxicology, 3, 169–174.

Ellis K, Yeun K, Yasumura S, and Cohn S. (1984). Dose-response analysis of cadmium in man: Body burden vs kidney function. Environmental Research, 33, 216–226.

Evrin P, Peterson A, Wide I, and Berggard I. (1971). Radioimmunoassay of B–2-microglobulin in human biological fluids. Scandanavian Journal of Clinical Laboratory Investigation, 28, 439–443.

Falck F, Fine L, Smith R, Garvey J, Schork A, England B, McClatchey K, and Linton J. (1983). Metallothionein and occupational exposure to cadmium. British Journal of Industrial Medicine, 40, 305–313.

Federal Register.(1990). Occupational exposure to cadmium: Proposed rule. 55/22/4052–4147, February 6.

Friberg, Exhibit 29, (1990). Exhibit No. 29 of the OSHA Federal Docket H057A. Washington, DC.

Friberg L. (1988). Quality assurance. In T. Clarkson (Ed.), Biological Monitoring of Toxic Metals (pp. 103–105). New York: Plenum Press.

Friberg L, and Elinder C. (1988). Cadmium toxicity in humans. In Essential and Trace Elements in Human Health and Disease (pp. 559–587). Docket Number 8–660.

Friberg L, Elinder F, et al. (1986). Cadmium and Health: A Toxicological and Epidemiological Appraisal. Volume II, Effects and Response. Boca Raton, FL: CRC Press.

Friberg L, Piscator M, Nordberg G, and Kjellstrom T. (1974). Cadmium in the Environment (2nd ed.). Cleveland:CRC.

Friberg L and Vahter M. (1983). Assessment of exposure to lead and cadmium through biological monitoring: Results of a UNEP/WHO global study. Environmental Research, 30, 95–128.

Gunter E, and Miller D. (1986). Laboratory procedures used by the division of environmental health laboratory sciences center for environmental health, Centers for Disease Control for the hispanic health and nutrition examination survey (HHANES). Atlanta, GA: Centers for Disease Control.

Harrison. (1987). Harrison's Principles of Internal Medicine. Braunwald, E; Isselbacher, KJ; Petersdorf, RG; Wilson, JD; Martin, JB; and Fauci, AS Eds. Eleventh Ed. McGraw Hill Book Company. San Francisco.

Henry J. (1991). Clinical Diagnosis and Management by Laboratory Methods (18th edition). Philadelphia: WB Saunders Company.

IARC (1987). IRAC Monographs on the Evaluation of Carcinogenic Risks to Humans. Overall Evaluation of Carcinogenicity: Update of Volume 1–42. Supplemental 7, 1987.

Ishizaki M, Kido T, Honda R, Tsuritani I, Yamada Y, Nakagawa H, and Nogawa K. (1989). Dose-response relationship between urinary cadmium and B-2-microglobulin in a Japanese environmentally cadmium exposed population. Toxicology, 58, 121–131.

Iwao S, Tsuchiya K, and Sakurai H. (1980). Serum and urinary B-2-microglobulin among cadmium-exposed workers. Journal of Occupational Medicine, 22, 399–402.

Iwata K, Katoh T, Morikawa Y, Aoshima K, Nishijo M, Teranishi H, and Kasuya M. (1988). Urinary trehalase activity as an indicator of kidney injury due to environmental cadmium exposure. Archives of Toxicology, 62, 435–439.

Kawada T, Koyama H, and Suzuki S. (1989). Cadmium, NAG activity, and B-2-microglobulin in the urine of cadmium pigment workers. British Journal of Industrial Medicine, 46, 52–55.

Kawada T, Tohyama C, and Suzuki S. (1990). Significance of the excretion of urinary indicator proteins for a low level of occupational exposure to cadmium. International Archives of Occupational Environmental Health, 62, 95–100.

Kjellstrom T. (1979). Exposure and accumulation of cadmium in populations from Japan, the United States, and Sweden. Environmental Health Perspectives, 28, 169–197.

Kjellstrom T, Evrin P, and Rahnster B. (1977). Dose-response analysis of cadmium-induced tubular proteinuria. Environmental Research, 13, 303–317.

Kjellstrom T, Shiroishi K, and Evrin P. (1977). Urinary B-2-microglobulin excretion among people exposed to cadmium in the general environment. Environmental Research, 13, 318–344.

Kneip T, & Crable J (Eds.). (1988). Method 107. Cadmium in blood. Methods for biological monitoring (pp.161–164). Washington, DC: American Public Health Association.

Kowal N. (1988). Urinary cadmium and B-2-microglobulin: Correlation with nutrition and smoking history. Journal of Toxicology and Environmental Health, 25, 179–183.

Kowal N, Johnson D, Kraemer D, and Pahren H. (1979). Normal levels of cadmium in diet, urine, blood, and tissues of inhabitants of the United States. Journal of Toxicology and Environmental Health, 5, 995–1014.

Kowal N and Zirkes M. (1983). Urinary cadmium and B-2-microglobulin: Normal values and concentration adjustment. Journal of Toxicology and Environmental Health, 11, 607–624.

Lauwerys R, Buchet J, and Roels H. (1976). The relationship between cadmium exposure or body burden and the concentration of cadmium in blood and urine in man. International Archives of Occupational and Environmental Health, 36, 275–285

Lauwerys R, Roels H, Regniers, Buchet J, and Bernard A. (1979). Significance of cadmium concentration in blood and in urine in workers exposed to cadmium. Environmental Research, 20, 375–391.

Lind B, Elinder C, Friberg L, Nilsson B, Svartengren M, and Vahter M. (1987). Quality control in the analysis of lead and cadmium in blood. Fresenius' Zeitschrift fur Analytical Chemistry, 326, 647–655.

Mason H, Davison A, Wright A, Guthrie C, Fayers P, Venables K, Smith N, Chettle D, Franklin D, Scott M, Holden H, Gompertz D, and Newman-Taylor A. (1988). Relations between liver cadmium, cumulative exposure, and renal function in cadmium alloy workers. British Journal of Industrial Medicine, 45, 793–802.

Meridian Research, Inc. (1989). Quantitative Assessment of Cancer Risks Associated with Occupational Exposure to Cd. Prepared by Meridian Research, Inc. and Roth Associates, Inc. for the Occupational Safety & Health Administration. June 12, 1989.

Meridian Research, Inc and Roth Associates, Inc. (1989). Quantitative Assessment of the Risk of Kidney Dysfunction Associated with Occupational Exposure to Cd. Prepared by Meridian Research, Inc. and Roth Associates, Inc. for the Occupational Safety & Health Administration. July 31 1989.

Micheils E and DeBievre P. (1986). Method 25–Determination of cadmium in whole blood by isotope dilution mass spectrometry. O'Neill I, Schuller P, and Fishbein L (Eds.), Environmental Carcinogens Selected Methods of Analysis (Vol. 8). Lyon, France: International Agency for Research on Cancer.

Mueller P, Smith S, Steinberg K, and Thun M. (1989). Chronic renal tubular effects in relation to urine cadmium levels. Nephron, 52, 45–54.

NIOSH. (1984a). Elements in blood or tissues. Method 8005 issued 5/15/85 and Metals in urine. Method 8310 issued 2/15/84 In P. Eller (Ed.), NIOSH Manual of Analytical Methods (Vol. 1, Ed. 3). Cincinnati, Ohio: US-DHHS.

NIOSH. (1984b). Lowry L. Section F: Special considerations for biological samples in NIOSH Manual of Analytical Methods (Vol. 1, 3rd ed). P. Eller (Ed.). Cincinnati, Ohio: US-DHHS.

Nordberg G and Nordberg M. (1988). Biological monitoring of cadmium. In T. Clarkson, L. Friberg, G. Nordberg, and P. Sager (Eds.), Biological Monitoring of Toxic Metals, New York: Plenum Press.

Nogawa K. (1984). Biologic indicators of cadmium nephrotoxicity in persons with low-level cadmium exposure. Environmental Health Perspectives, 54, 163–169.

OSLTC (no date). Analysis of Creatinine for the Normalization of Cadmium and Beta-2-Microglobulin Concentrations in Urine. OSHA Salt Lake Technical Center. Salt Lake City, UT. Paschal. (1990). Attachment 8 of exhibit 106 of the OSHA docket H057A.

Perkin-Elmer Corporation. (1982). Analytical Methods for Atomic Absorption Spectroscopy.

Perkin-Elmer Corporation. (1977). Analytical Methods Using the HGA Graphite Furnace.

Pharmacia Diagnostics. (1990). Pharmacia DELFIA system B-2-microglobulin kit insert. Uppsala, Sweden: Pharmacia Diagnostics.

Piscator M. (1962). Proteinuria in chronic cadmium poisoning. Archives of Environmental Health,5, 55–62.

Potts, C.L. (1965). Cadmium Proteinuria—The Health Battery Workers Exposed to Cadmium Oxide dust. Ann Occup Hyg, 3:55–61, 1965.

Princi F. (1947). A study of industrial exposures to cadmium. Journal of Industrial Hygiene and Toxicology, 29, 315–320.

Pruszkowska E, Carnick G, and Slavin W. (1983). Direct determination of cadmium in urine with use of a stabilized temperature platform furnace and Zeeman background correction. Clinical Chemistry, 29, 477–480.

Roberts C and Clark J. (1986). Improved determination of cadmium in blood and plasma by flameless atomic absorption spectroscopy. Bulletin of Environmental Contamination and Toxicology, 36, 496–499.

Roelandts I. (1989). Biological reference materials. Soectrochimica Acta, 44B, 281–290.

Roels H, Buchet R, Lauwerys R, Bruaux P, Clays-Thoreau F, Laafontaine A, Overschelde J, and Verduyn J. (1978). Lead and cadmium absorption among children near a nonferrous metal plant. Environmental Research, 15, 290–308.

Roels H, Djubgang J, Buchet J, Bernard A, and Lauwerys R. (1982). Evolution of cadmium-induced renal dysfunction in workers removed from exposure. Scandanavian Journal of Work and Environmental Health, 8, 191–200.

Roels H, Lauwerys R, and Buchet J. (1989). Health significance of cadmium induced renal dysfunction: A five year follow-up. British Journal of Industrial Medicine, 46, 755–764.

Roels J, Lauwerys R, Buchet J, Bernard A, Chettle D, Harvey T, and Al-Haddad I. (1981). In vivo measurements of liver and kidney cadmium in workers exposed to this metal: Its significance with respect to cadmium in blood and urine. Environmental Research, 26, 217–240.

Roels H, Lauwerys R, Buchet J, Bernard A, Lijnen P, and Houte G. (1990). Urinary kallikrein activity in workers exposed to cadmium, lead, or mercury vapor. British Journal of Industrial Medicine, 47, 331–337.

Sakurai H, Omae K, Toyama T, Higashi T, and Nakadate T. (1982). Cross-sectional study of pulmonary function in cadmium alloy workers. Scandanavian Journal of Work and Environmental Health, 8, 122–130.

Schardun G and van Epps L. (1987). B-2-microglobulin: Its significance in the evaluation of renal function. Kidney International, 32, 635–641.

Shaikh Z, and Smith L. (1984). Biological indicators of cadmium exposure and toxicity. Experentia, 40, 36–43.

Smith J and Kench J. (1957). Observations on urinary cadmium and protein excretion in men exposed to cadmium oxide dust and fume. British Journal of Industrial Medicine, 14, 240–245.

Smith J, Kench J, and Lane R. (1955). Determination of Cadmium in urine and observations on urinary cadmium and protein excretion in men exposed to cadmium oxide dust. British Journal of Industrial Medicine, 12, 698–701.

SWRI (Southwest Research Institute). (1978). The distribution of cadmium and other metals in human tissues. Health Effects Research Lab, Research Triangle Park, NC, Population Studies Division. NTIS No. PB–285–200.

Stewart M and Hughes E. (1981). Urinary B–2-microglobulin in the biological monitoring of cadmium workers. British Journal of Industrial Medicine, 38, 170–174.

Stoeppler K and Brandt M. (1980). Contributions to automated trace analysis. part V. Determination of cadmium in whole blood and urine by electrothermal atomic absorption spectrophotometry. Fresenius' Zeitschrift fur Analytical Chemistry, 300, 372–380.

Takenaka et al. (1983). Carcinogencity of Cd Chloride Aerosols in White Rates. INCI 70: 367–373, 1983.

Thun M, Osorio A, Schober S, Hannon W, Lewis B, and Halperin W. (1989). Nephropathy in cadmium workers: Assessment of risk from airborne occupational exposure to cadmium. British Journal of Industrial Medicine, 46, 689–697.

Thun M, Schnorr T, Smith A, Halperin W, and Lemen R. (1985). Mortality among a cohort of US cadmium production workers—an update. Journal of the National Cancer Institute, 74, 325–333.

Travis D and Haddock A. (1980). Interpretation of the observed age-dependency of cadmium body burdens in man. Environmental Research, 22, 46–60.

Tsuchiya K. (1967). Proteinuria of workers exposed to cadmium fume. Archives of Environmental Health, 14, 875–880.

Tsuchiya K. (1976). Proteinuria of cadmium workers. Journal of Occupational Medicine, 18, 463–470.

Tsuchiya K, Iwao S, Sugita M, Sakurai H. (1979). Increased urinary B-2-microglobulin in cadmium exposure: Dose-effect relationship and biological significance of B-2-microglobulin. Environmental Health Perspectives, 28, 147–153.

USEPA. (1985). Updated Mutagenicity and Carcinogenicity Assessments of Cd: Addendum to the Health Assessment Document for Cd (May 1981). Final Report. June 1985.

Vahter M and Friberg L. (1988). Quality control in integrated human exposure monitoring of lead and cadmium. Fresenius' Zeitschrift fur Analytical Chemistry, 332, 726–731.

Weber J. (1988). An interlaboratory comparison programme for several toxic substances in blood and urine. The Science of the Total Environment, 71, 111–123.

Weber J. (1991a). Accuracy and precision of trace metal determinations in biological fluids. In K. Subramanian, G. Iyengar, and K. Okamot (Eds.), Biological Trace Element Research -Multidisciplinary Perspectives, ACS Symposium Series 445. Washington, DC: American Chemical Society.

Weber J. (1991b). Personal communication about interlaboratory program and shipping biological media samples for cadmium analyses.

Wibowo A, Herber R, van Deyck W, and Zielhuis R. (1982). Biological assessment of exposure in factories with second degree usage of cadmium compounds. International Archives of Occupational Environmental Health, 49, 265–273.

Attachment 1—Nonmandatory Protocol for an Internal Quality Assurance/Quality Control Program

The following is an example of the type of internal quality assurance/quality control program that assures adequate control to satisfy OSHA requirements under this protocol. However, other approaches may also be acceptable.

As indicated in Section 3.3.1 of the protocol, the QA/QC program for CDB and CDU should address, at a minimum, the following:

- calibration;
- establishment of control limits;
- internal QC analyses and maintaining control; and
- corrective action protocols.

This illustrative program includes both initial characterization runs to establish the performance of the method and ongoing analysis of quality control samples intermixed with compliance samples to maintain control.

Calibration

Before any analytical runs are conducted, the analytic instrument must be calibrated. This is to be done at the beginning of each day on which quality control samples and/or compliance samples are run. Once calibration is established, quality control samples or compliance samples may be run. Regardless of the type of samples run, every fifth sample must be a standard to assure that the calibration is holding.

Calibration is defined as holding if every standard is within plus or minus (±) 15% of its theoretical value. If a standard is more than plus or minus 15% of its theoretical value, then the run is out of control due to calibration error and the entire set of samples must either be reanalyzed after recalibrating or results should be recalculated based on a statistical curve derived from the measurement of all standards.

It is essential that the highest standard run is higher than the highest sample run. To assure that this is the case, it may be necessary to run a high standard at the end of the run, which is selected based on the results obtained over the course of the run.

All standards should be kept fresh, and as they get old, they should be compared with new standards and replaced if they exceed the new standards by ± 5%.

Initial Characterization Runs and Establishing Control

A participating laboratory should establish four pools of quality control samples for each of the analytes for which determinations will be made. The concentrations of quality control samples within each pool are to be centered around each of the four target levels for the particular analyte identified in Section 4.4 of the protocol.

Within each pool, at least 4 quality control samples need to be established with varying concentrations ranging between plus or minus 50% of the target value of that pool. Thus for the medium-high cadmium in blood pool, the theoretical values of the quality control samples may range from 5 to 15 µg/l, (the target value is 10 µg/l). At least 4 unique theoretical values must be represented in this pool.

The range of theoretical values of plus or minus 50% of the target value of a pool means that there will be overlap of the pools. For example, the range of values for the medium-low pool for cadmium in blood is 3.5 to 10.5 µg/l while the range of values for the medium-high pool is 5 to 15 µg/l. Therefore, it is possible for a quality control sample from the medium-low pool to have a higher concentration of cadmium than a quality control sample from the medium-high pool.

Quality control samples may be obtained as commercially available reference materials, internally prepared, or both. Internally prepared samples should be well characterized and traced or compared to a reference material for which a consensus value for concentration is available. Levels of analyte in the quality control samples must be concealed from the analyst prior to the reporting of analytical results. Potential sources of materials that may be used to construct quality control samples are listed in Section 3.3.1 of the protocol.

Before any compliance samples are analyzed, control limits must be established. Control limits should be calculated for every pool of each analyte for which determinations will be made and control charts should be kept for each pool of each analyte. A separate set of control charts and control limits should be established for each analytical instrument in a laboratory that will be used for analysis of compliance samples.

At the beginning of this QA/QC program, control limits should be based on the results of the analysis of 20 quality control samples from each pool of each analyte. For any given pool, the 20 quality control samples should be run on 20 different days. Although no more than one sample should be run from any single pool on a particular day, a laboratory may run quality control samples from different pools on the same day. This constitutes a set of initial characterization runs.

For each quality control sample analyzed, the value F/T (defined in the glossary) should be calculated. To calculate the control limits for a pool of an analyte, it is first necessary to calculate the mean, X, of the F/T values for each quality control sample in a pool and then to calculate its standard deviation σ. Thus, for the control limit for a pool, X is calculated as:

$$X = \frac{\Sigma\ (F/T)}{N}$$

and σ is calculated as:

$$\sigma = \left[\frac{\Sigma\ (F/T - x)^2}{N - 1}\right]^{1/2}$$

Where N is the number of quality control samples run for a pool.

The control limit for a particular pool is then given by the mean plus or minus 2 standard deviations (X ± 3σ).

The control limits may be no greater than 40% of the mean F/T value. If three standard deviations are greater than 40% of the mean F/T value, then analysis of compliance samples may not begin.[1] Instead, an investigation into the causes of the large standard deviation should begin, and the inadequacies must be remedied. Then, control limits must be reestablished which will mean repeating the running 20 quality control samples from each pool over 20 days.

Internal Quality Control Analyses and Maintaining Control

Once control limits have been established for each pool of an analyte, analysis of compliance samples may begin. During any run of compliance samples, quality control samples are to be interspersed at a rate of no less than 5% of the compliance sample workload. When quality control samples are run, however, they should be run in sets consisting of one quality control sample from each pool. Therefore, it may be necessary, at times, to intersperse quality control samples at a rate greater than 5%.

There should be at least one set of quality control samples run with any analysis of compliance samples. At a minimum, for example, 4 quality control samples should be run even if only 1 compliance sample is run. Generally, the number of quality control samples that should be run are a multiple of four with the minimum equal to the smallest multiple of four that is greater than 5% of the total number of samples to be run. For example, if 300 compliance samples of an analyte are run, then at least 16 quality control samples should be run (16 is the smallest multiple of four that is greater than 15, which is 5% of 300).

Control charts for each pool of an analyte (and for each instrument in the laboratory to be used for analysis of compliance samples) should be established by plotting F/T versus date as the quality control sample results are reported. On the graph there should be lines representing the control limits for the pool, the mean F/T limits for the pool, and the theoretical F/T of 1.000. Lines representing plus or minus (±) σ should also be represented on the charts. A theoretical example of a control chart is presented in Figure 1.

Figure 1
Theoretical Example of a Control Chart for a Pool of an Analyte

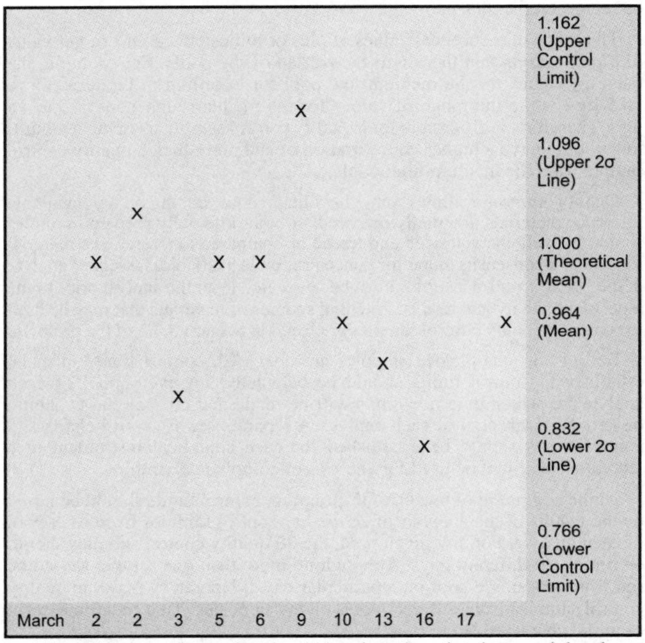

All quality control samples should be plotted on the chart, and the charts should be checked for visual trends. If a quality control sample falls above or below the control limits for its pool, then corrective steps must be taken (see the section on corrective actions below). Once a laboratory's program has been established, control limits should be updated every 2 months.

The updated control limits should be calculated from the results of the last 100 quality control samples run for each pool. If 100 quality control samples from a pool have not been run at the time of the update, then the limits should be based on as many as have been run provided at least 20 quality control samples from each pool have been run over 20 different days.

The trends that should be looked for on the control charts are:

1. 10 consecutive quality control samples falling above or below the mean;
2. 3 consecutive quality control samples falling more than 2σ from the mean (above or below the 2σ lines of the chart); or
3. the mean calculated to update the control limits falls more than 10% above or below the theoretical mean of 1.000.

[1] Note that the value, "40%", may change over time as experience is gained with the program.

If any of these trends is observed, then all analysis must be stopped, and an investigation into the causes of the errors must begin. Before the analysis of compliance samples may resume, the inadequacies must be remedied and the control limits must be reestablished for that pool of an analyte. Reestablishment of control limits will entail running 20 sets of quality control samples over 20 days.

Note that alternative procedures for defining internal quality control limits may also be acceptable. Limits may be based, for example, on proficiency testing, such as ± 1 μg or 15% of the mean (whichever is greater). These should be clearly defined.

Corrective actions

Corrective action is the term used to describe the identification and remediation of errors occurring within an analysis. Corrective action is necessary whenever the result of the analysis of any quality control sample falls outside of the established control limits. The steps involved may include simple things like checking calculations of basic instrument maintenance, or it may involve more complicated actions like major instrument repair. Whatever the source of error, it must be identified and corrected (and a Corrective Action Report (CAR) must be completed. CARs should be kept on file by the laboratory.

Attachment 2—Creatinine in Urine (Jaffe Procedure)

Intended use: The CREA pack is used in the Du Pont ACA®discrete clinical analyzer to quantitatively measure creatinine in serum and urine.

Summary: The CREA method employs a modification of the kinetic Jaffe reaction reported by Larsen. This method has been reported to be less susceptible than conventional methods to interference from non-creatinine, Jaffe-positive compounds.[1]

A split sample comparison between the CREA method and a conventional Jaffe procedure on Autoanalyzer® showed a good correlation. (See Specific Performance Characteristics).

Note: Numbered subscripts refer to the bibliography and lettered subscripts refer to footnotes.

Autoanalyzer®, is a registered trademark of Technicon Corp., Tarrytown, NY.

Principles of Procedure: In the presence of a strong base such as NaOH, picrate reacts with creatinine to form a red chromophore. The rate of increasing absorbance at 510 nm due to the formation of this chromophore during a 17.07-second measurement period is directly proportional to the creatinine concentration in the sample.

$$\text{Creatinine} + \text{Picrate} \xrightarrow{\text{NaOH}} \text{Red chromophore (absorbs at 510 nm)}$$

Reagents:

Compartment[a]	Form	Ingredient	Quantity[b]
No. 2, 3, & 4	Liquid	Picrate	0.11 mmol.
6	Liquid	NaOH (for pH adjustment)[c]	

[a] Compartments are numbered 1–7, with compartment #7 located closest to pack fill position #2
[b] Nominal value at manufacture
[c] See Precautions

Precautions: Compartment #6 contains 75μL of 10 N NaOH; avoid contact; skin irritant; rinse contacted area with water. Comply with OSHA'S Bloodborne Pathogens Standard while handling biological samples (29 CFR §1910.1039).

Used packs contain human body fluids; handle with appropriate care.

For *IN VITRO DIAGNOSTIC* use

Mixing and Diluting:

Mixing and diluting are automatically performed by the ACA® discrete clinical analyzer. The sample cup must contain sufficient quantity to accommodate the sample volume plus the "dead volume"; precise cup filling is not required.

Sample Cup Volumes (μL)

Analyzer	Standard		Microsystem	
	Dead	Total	Dead	Total
II, III	120	3000	10	500
IV, SX	120	3000	30	500
V	90	3000	10	500

Storage of Unprocessed Packs: Store at 2–8 °C. Do not freeze. Do not expose to temperatures above 35 °C or to direct sunlight.

Expiration: Refer to EXPIRATION DATE on the tray label.

Specimen Collection: Serum or urine can be collected and stored by normal procedures.[2]

Known Interfering Substances[3]

- Serum Protein Influence—Serum protein levels exert a direct influence on the CREA assay. The following should be taken into account when this method is used for urine samples and when it is calibrated:

  Aqueous creatinine standards or urine specimens will give CREA results depressed by approximately 0.7 mg/dL [62 µmol/L][d] and will be less precise than samples containing more than 3 g/dL [30 g/L] protein.

  All urine specimens should be diluted with an albumin solution to give a final protein concentration of at least 3 g/dL [30 g/L]. Du Pont Enzyme Diluent (Cat. #790035–901) may be used for this purpose.
- High concentration of endrogenous bilirubin (>20 mg/dL [>342 µmol/L]) will give depressed CREA results (average depression 0.8 mg/dL [71 µmol/L]).[4]
- Grossly hemolyzed (hemoglobin >100 mg/dL [>62 µmol/L]) or visibly lipemic specimens may cause falsely elevated CREA results.[5,6]
- The following cephalosporin antibiotics do not interfere with the CREA method when present at the concentrations indicated. Systematic inaccuracies (bias) due to these substances are less than or equal to 0.1 mg/dL [8.84 µmol/L] at CREA concentrations of approximately 1 mg/dL [88 µmol/L].

Antibiotic	Peak serum level[7,8,9]		Drug concentration	
	mg/dL	[mmol/L]	mg/dL	[mmol/L]
Cephaloridine	1.4	0.3	25	6.0
Cephalexin	0.6–2.0	0.2–0.6	25	7.2
Cephamandole	1.3–2.5	0.3–0.5	25	4.9
Cephapirin	2.0	D0.4	25	5.6
Cephradine	1.5–2.0	0.4–0.6	25	7.1
Cefazolin	2.5–5.0	0.55–1.1	50	11.0

- The following cephalosporin antibiotics have been shown to affect CREA results when present at the indicated concentrations. System inaccuracies (bias) due to these substances are greater that 0.1 mg/dL [8.84 µmol/L] at CREA concentrations of:

Antibiotic	Peak serum level[8,10]		Drug concentration		
	mg/dL	[mmol/L]	mg/dL	[mmol/L]	Effect
Cephalothin	1–6	0.2–1.5	100	25.2	↓20–25%
Cephoxitin	2.0	0.5	5.0	1.2	↑35–40%

- The single wavelength measurement used in this method eliminates interference from chromophores whose 510 nm absorbance is constant throughout the measurement period.
- Each laboratory should determine the acceptability of its own blood collection tubes and serum separation products. Variations in these products may exist between manufacturers and, at times, from lot to lot.

Procedure:

Test Materials

Item	II, III Du Pont Cat. No.	IV, SX Du Pont Cat. No.	V Du Pont Cat. No.
ACA® CREA Analytical Test Pack	701976901	701976901	701976901
Sample System Kit or	710642901	710642901	713697901
Micro Sample System Kit and	702694901	710356901	NA
Micro Sample System Holders	702785000	NA	NA
DYLUX® Photosensitive			
Printer Paper	700036000	NA	NA
Thermal Printer Paper	NA	710639901	713645901
Du Pont Purified Water	704209901	710615901	710815901
Cell Wash Solution	701864901	710664901	710864901

[d] Systeme international d'unites (S.I.Units) are in brackets.

Test Steps: The operator need only load the sample kit and appropriate test pack(s) into a properly prepared ACA®discrete clinical analyzer. It automatically advances the pack(s) through the test steps and prints a result(s). See the Instrument Manual of the ACA®analyzer for details of mechanical travel of the test pack(s).

Preset Creatinine (CREA)—Test Conditions

- Sample Volume: 200 µL
- Diluent: Purified Water
- Temperature: 37.0 ± 0.1 °C
- Reaction Period: 29 seconds
- Type of Measurement: Rate
- Measurement Period: 17.07 seconds
- Wavelength: 510 nm
- Units: mg/dL [µmol/L]

CALIBRATION: The general calibration procedure is described in the Calibration/Verification chapter of the Manuals.

The following information should be considered when calibrating the CREA method.

- Assay Range: 0–20 mg/mL [0–1768 µmol/L][e].
- Reference Material: Protein containing primary standards[f] or secondary calibrators such as Du Pont Elevated Chemistry Control (Cat. #790035903) and Normal Chemistry Control (Cat.•#790035905)[g].
- Suggested Calibration Levels: 1,5,20, mg/mL [88, 442, 1768 µmol/L].
- Calibration Scheme: 3 levels, 3 packs per level.
- Frequency: Each new pack lot. Every 3 months for any one pack lot.

Preset Creatinine (CREA) Test Conditions

Item	ACA®II analyzer	ACA®III, IV, SX, V analyzer
Count by	One (1) [Five (5)]	NA
Decimal Point	0.0 mg/dL	000.0 mg/dL
Location	[000.0 µmol/L]	[000 µmol/L]
Assigned Starting	999.8	−1.000 E1
Point or Offset C_0	[9823.]	[−8.840 E2]
Scale Factor or Assigned	0.2000 mg/dL/count[h]	2.004 E-1[h]
Linear Term C_1[h]	[0.3536 µmol/L/count]	[1.772E1]

[h] The preset scale factor (linear term) was derived from the molar absorptivity of the indicator and is based on an absorbance to activity relationship (sensitivity) of 0.596 (mA/min)/(U/L). Due to small differences in filters and electronic components between instruments, the actual scale factor (linear term) may differ slightly from that given above.

Quality Control: Two types of quality control procedures are recommended:

- General Instrument Check. Refer to the Filter Balance Procedure and the Absorbance Test Method described in the ACA Analyzer Instrument Manual. Refer also to the ABS Test Methodology literature.
- Creatinine Method Check. At least once daily run a CREA test on a solution of known creatinine activity such as an assayed control or calibration standard other than that used to calibrate the CREA method. For further details review the Quality Assurance Section of the Chemistry Manual. The result obtained should fall within acceptable limits defined by the day-to-day variability of the system as measured in the user's laboratory. (See SPECIFIC PERFORMANCE CHARACTERISTICS for guidance.) If the result falls outside the laboratory's acceptable limits, follow the procedure outlined in the Chemistry Troubleshooting Section of the Chemistry Manual.

A possible system malfunction is indicated when analysis of a sample with five consecutive test packs gives the following results:

Level	SD
1 mg/dL	>0.15 mg/dL
[88 µmol/L]	[>13 µmol/L]
20 mg/dL	>0.68 mg/dL
[1768 µmol/L]	[>60 µmol/L]

Refer to the procedure outlined in the Trouble Shooting Section of the Manual.

Results: The ACA® analyzer automatically calculates and prints the CREA result in mg/dL [µmol/L].

[e] For the results in S.I. units [µmol/L] the conversion factory is 88.4.

[f] Refer to the Creatinine Standard Preparation and Calibration Procedure available on request from a Du Pont Representative

[g] If the Du Pont Chemistry Controls are being used, prepare them according to the instructions on the product insert sheets

Limitation of Procedure: Results >20 mg/dL [1768 µmol/L]:

- Dilute with suitable protein base diluent. Reassay. Correct for diluting before reporting.

The reporting system contains error messages to warn the operator of specific malfunctions. Any report slip containing a letter code or word immediately following the numerical value should not be reported. Refer to the Manual for the definition of error codes.

Reference Interval

Serum:[11,i]	
Males	0.8–1.3 md/dL [71–115 µmol/L]
Females	0.6–1.0 md/dL [53–88 µmol/L]
Urine:[12]	
Males	0.6–2.5 g/24 hr [53–221 mmol/24 hr]
Females	0.6–1.5 g/24 hr [53–133 mmol/24 hr]

[i] Reference interval data obtained from 200 apparently healthy individuals (71 males, 129 females) between the ages of 19 and 72.

Each laboratory should establish its own reference intervals for CREA as performed on the analyzer.

Specific Performance Characteristics[j]

Reproducibility[k]

Material	Mean	Standard deviation (% CV)	
		Within-run	Between-day
Lyophilized	1.3	0.05 (3.7)	0.05 (3.7)
Control	[115]	[4.4]	[4.4]
Lyophilized	20.6	0.12 (0.6)	0.37 (1.8)
Control	[1821]	[10.6]	[32.7]

[j] All specific performance characteristics tests were run after normal recommended equipment quality control checks were performed (see Instrument Manual).

[k] Specimens at each level were analyzed in duplicate for twenty days. The within-run and between-day standard deviations were calculated by the analysis of variance method.

Correlation—Regression Statistics[l]

Comparative method	Slope	Intercept	Correlation coefficient	n
Autoanalyzer®	1.03	0.03[2.7]	0.997	260

[l] Model equation for regression statistics is:
Result of ACA® Analyzer = Slope (Comparative method result) + intercept

Assay Range[m]

0.0–20.0 mg/dl

[0–1768 µmol]

Analytical Specificity

See KNOWN INTERFERING SUBSTANCES Section for details.

Bibliography

1 Larsen, K, Clin Chem Acta 41, 209 (1972).
2 Tietz, NW, Fundamentals of Clinical Chemistry, W. B. Saunders Co., Philadelphia, PA, 1976, pp 47–52, 1211.
3 Supplementary information pertaining to the effects of various drugs and patient conditions on in vivo or in vitro diagnostic levels can be found in "Drug Interferences with Clinical Laboratory Tests," Clin. Chem 21 (5) (1975), and "Effects of Disease on Clinical Laboratory Tests," Clin Chem, 26 (4) 1D–476D (1980).
4 Watkins, R. Fieldkamp, SC, Thibert, RJ, and Zak, B, Clin Chem, 21, 1002 (1975).
5 Kawas, EE, Richards, AH, and Bigger, R, An Evaluation of a Kinetic Creatinine Test for the Du Pont ACA, Du Pont Company, Wilmington, DE (February 1973). (Reprints available from DuPont Company, Diagnostic Systems).
6 Westgard, JO, Effects of Hemolysis and Lipemia on ACA Creatinine Method, 0.200 µL, Sample Size, Du Pont Company, Wilmington, DE (October 1972).
7 Physicians' Desk Reference, Medical Economics Company, 33 Edition, 1979.
8 Henry, JB, Clinical Diagnosis and Management by Laboratory Methods, W.B. Saunders Co., Philadelphia, PA 1979, Vol. III.
9 Krupp, MA, Tierney, LM Jr., Jawetz, E, Roe, RI, Camargo, CA, Physicians Handbook, Lange Medical Publications, Los Altos, CA, 1982 pp 635–636.
10 Sarah, AJ, Koch, TR, Drusano, GL, Celoxitin Falsely Elevates Creatinine Levels, JAMA 247, 205–206 (1982).
11 Gadsden, RH, and Phelps, CA, A Normal Range Study of Amylase in Urine and Serum on the Du Pont ACA, Du Pont Company, Wilmington, DE (March 1978). (Reprints available from DuPont Company, Diagnostic Systems)
12 Dicht, JJ, Reference Intervals for Serum Amylase and Urinary Creatinine on the Du Pont ACA® Discrete Clinical Analyzer, Du Pont Company, Wilmington, DE (November 1984).

Attachment 3—Analysis of Creatinine for the Normalization of Cadmium and Beta–2–Microglobulin Concentrations in Urine (OSLTC Procedure).

Matrix: Urine.

Target concentration: 1.1 g/L (this amount is representative of creatinine concentrations found in urine).

Procedure: A 1.0 mL aliquot of urine is passed through a C18 SEP-PAK® (Waters Associates). Approximately 30 mL of HPLC (high performance liquid chromatography) grade water is then run through the SEP-PAK. The resulting solution is diluted to volume in a 100-mL volumetric flask and analyzed by HPLC using an ultraviolet (UV) detector.

Special requirements: After collection, samples should be appropriately stabilized for cadmium (Cd) analysis by using 10% high purity (with low Cd background levels) nitric acid (exactly 1.0 mL of 10% nitric acid per 10 mL of urine) or stabilized for Beta-2–Microglobulin (B2M) by taking to pH 7 with dilute NaOH (exactly 1.0 mL of 0.11 N NaOH per 10 mL of urine). If not immediately analyzed, the samples should be frozen and shipped by overnight mail in an insulated container.

Dated: January 1992

David B. Armitage
Duane Lee
Chemists
Organic Service Branch II, OSHA Technical Center, Salt Lake City, Utah

1. General Discussion

1.1 Background

1.1.1. History of procedure

Creatinine has been analyzed by several methods in the past. The earliest methods were of the wet chemical type. As an example, creatinine reacts with sodium picrate in basic solution to form a red complex, which is then analyzed colorimetrically (Refs. 5.1. and 5.2.).

Since industrial hygiene laboratories will be analyzing for Cd and B2M in urine, they will be normalizing those concentrations to the concentration of creatinine in urine. A literature search revealed several HPLC methods (Refs. 5.3., 5.4., 5.5. and 5.6.) for creatinine in urine and because many industrial hygiene laboratories have HPLC equipment, it was desirable to develop an industrial hygiene HPLC method for creatinine in urine. The method of Hausen, Fuchs, and Wachter was chosen as the starting point for method development. SEP-PAKs were used for sample clarification and cleanup in this method to protect the analytical column. The urine aliquot which has been passed through the SEP-PAK is then analyzed by reverse-phase HPLC using ion-pair techniques.

This method is very similar to that of Ogata and Taguchi (Ref. 5.6.), except they used centrifugation for sample clean-up. It is also of note that they did a comparison of their HPLC results to those of the Jaffe method (a picric acid method commonly used in the health care industry) and found a linear relationship of close to 1:1. This indicates that either HPLC or colorimetric methods may be used to measure creatinine concentrations in urine.

1.1.2. Physical properties (Ref. 5.7.)

Molecular weight: 113.12

Molecular formula: C_4–H_7–N_3–0

Chemical name: 2-amino-1,5-dihydro-1-methyl-4H-imidazol-4-one

CAS No.: 60–27–5

Melting point: 300 °C (decomposes)

Appearance: white powder

Solubility: soluble in water; slightly soluble in alcohol; practically insoluble in acetone, ether, and chloroform

Synonyms: 1-methylglycocyamidine, 1-methylhydantoin-2-imide

Structure: see Figure #1

Figure 1 – Structure

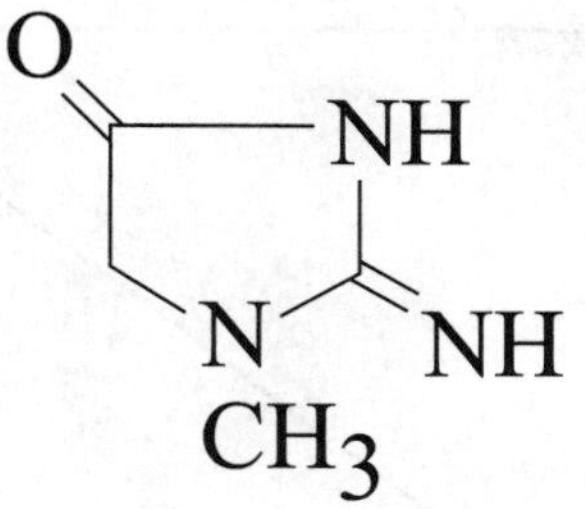

1.2. Advantages

1.2.1. This method offers a simple, straightforward, and specific alternative method to the Jaffe method.

1.2.2. HPLC instrumentation is commonly found in many industrial hygiene laboratories.

2. Sample stabilization procedure

2.1. Apparatus

Metal-free plastic container for urine sample

2.2. Reagents

2.2.1. Stabilizing Solution—

(1) Nitric acid (10%, high purity with low Cd background levels) for stabilizing urine for Cd analysis or

(2) NaOH, 0.11 N, for stabilizing urine for B2M analysis

2.2.2. HPLC grade water

2.3. Technique

2.3.1. Stabilizing solution is added to the urine sample (see Section 2.2.1.). The stabilizing solution should be such that for each 10 mL of urine, add exactly 1.0 mL of stabilizer solution. (Never add water or urine to acid or base. Always add acid or base to water or urine.) Exactly 1.0 mL of 0.11 N NaOH added to 10 mL of urine should result in a pH of 7. Or add 1.0 mL of 10% nitric acid to 10 mL of urine.

2.3.2. After sample collection seal the plastic bottle securely and wrap it with an appropriate seal. Urine samples should be frozen and then shipped by overnight mail (if shipping is necessary) in an insulated container. (Do not fill plastic bottle too full. This will allow for expansion of contents during the freezing process.)

2.4. The Effect of Preparation and Stabilization Techniques on Creatinine Concentrations

Three urine samples were prepared by making one sample acidic, not treating a second sample, and adjusting a third sample to pH 7. The samples were analyzed in duplicate by two different procedures. For the first procedure a 1.0 mL aliquot of urine was put in a 100-mL volumetric flask, diluted to volume with HPLC grade water, and then analyzed directly on an HPLC. The other procedure used SEP-PAKs. The SEP-PAK was rinsed with approximately 5 mL of methanol followed by approximately 10 mL of HPLC grade water and both rinses were discarded. Then, 1.0 mL of the urine sample was put through the SEP-PAK, followed by 30 mL of HPLC grade water. The urine and water were transferred to a 100-mL volumetric flask, diluted to volume with HPLC grade water, and analyzed by HPLC. These three urine samples were analyzed on the day they were obtained and then frozen. The results show that whether the urine is acidic, untreated or adjusted to pH 7, the resulting answer for creatinine is essentially unchanged. The purpose of stabilizing the urine by making it acidic or neutral is for the analysis of Cd or B2M respectively.

Comparison of Preparation & Stabilization Techniques

Sample	w/o SEP-PAK g/L creatinine	with SEP-PAK g/L creatinine
Acid	1.10	1.10
Acid	1.11	1.10
Untreated	1.12	1.11
Untreated	1.11	1.12
pH 7	1.08	1.02
pH 7	1.11	1.08

2.5. Storage

After 4 days and 54 days of storage in a freezer, the samples were thawed, brought to room temperature and analyzed using the same procedures as in Section 2.4. The results of several days of storage show that the resulting answer of creatinine is essentially unchanged.

Storage Data

Sample	4 days		54 days	
	w/o SEP-PAK g/L creatinine	with SEP-PAK g/L creatinine	w/o SEP-PAK g/L creatinine	with SEP-PAK g/L creatinine
Acid	1.09	1.09	1.08	1.09
Acid	1.10	1.10	1.09	1.10
Acid			1.09	1.09
Untreated	1.13	1.14	1.09	1.11
Untreated	1.15	1.14	1.10	1.10
Untreated			1.09	1.10
pH 7	1.14	1.13	1.12	1.12
pH 7	1.14	1.13	1.12	1.12
pH 7			1.12	1.12

2.6. Interferences

None.

2.7. Safety precautions

2.7.1. Make sure samples are properly sealed and frozen before shipment to avoid leakage.

2.7.2. Follow the appropriate shipping procedures.

The following modified special safety precautions are based on those recommended by the Centers for Disease Control (CDC) (Ref. 5.8.). and OSHA's Bloodborne Pathogens standard (29 CFR §1910.1039).

2.7.3. Wear gloves, lab coat, and safety glasses while handling all human urine products. Disposable plastic, glass, and paper (pipet tips, gloves, etc.) that contact urine should be placed in a biohazard autoclave bag. These bags should be kept in appropriate containers until sealed and autoclaved. Wipe down all work surfaces with 10% sodium hypochlorite solution when work is finished.

2.7.4. Dispose of all biological samples and diluted specimens in a biohazard autoclave bag at the end of the analytical run.

2.7.5. Special care should be taken when handling and dispensing nitric acid. Always remember to add acid to water (or urine). Nitric acid is a corrosive chemical capable of severe eye and skin damage. Wear metal-free gloves, a lab coat, and safety glasses. If the nitric acid comes in contact with any part of the body, quickly wash with copious quantities of water for at least 15 minutes.

2.7.6. Special care should be taken when handling and dispensing NaOH. Always remember to add base to water (or urine). NaOH can cause severe eye and skin damage. Always wear the appropriate gloves, a lab coat, and safety glasses. If the NaOH comes in contact with any part of the body, quickly wash with copious quantities of water for at least 15 minutes.

3. Analytical procedure

3.1. Apparatus

3.1.1. A high performance liquid chromatograph equipped with pump, sample injector and UV detector

3.1.2. A C18 HPLC column; 25 cm × 4.6 mm I.D

3.1.3. An electronic integrator, or some other suitable means of determining analyte response

3.1.4. Stripchart recorder

3.1.5. C18 SEP-PAKs (Waters Associates) or equivalent

3.1.6. Luer-lock syringe for sample preparation (5 mL or 10 mL)

3.1.7. Volumetric pipettes and flasks for standard and sample preparation

3.1.8. Vacuum system to aid sample preparation (optional)

3.2. Reagents

3.2.1. Water, HPLC grade

3.2.2. Methanol, HPLC grade

3.2.3. PIC B–7® (Waters Associates) in small vials

3.2.4. Creatinine, anhydrous, Sigma Chemical Corp., purity not listed

3.2.5. 1–Heptanesulfonic acid, sodium salt monohydrate

3.2.6. Phosphoric acid

3.2.7. Mobile phase. It can be prepared by mixing one vial of PIC B–7 into a 1 L solution of 50% methanol and 50% water. The mobile phase can also be made by preparing a solution that is 50% methanol and 50% water with 0.005M heptanesulfonic acid and adjusting the pH of the solution to 3.5 with phosphoric acid.

3.3. Standard preparation

3.3.1. Stock standards are prepared by weighing 10 to 15 mg of creatinine. This is transferred to a 25-mL volumetric flask and diluted to volume with HPLC grade water.

3.3.2. Dilutions to a working range of 3 to 35 µg/mL are made in either HPLC grade water or HPLC mobile phase (standards give the same detector response in either solution).

3.4. Sample preparation

3.4.1. The C18 SEP-PAK is connected to a Luer-lock syringe. It is rinsed with 5 mL HPLC grade methanol and then 10 mL of HPLC grade water. These rinses are discarded.

3.4.2. Exactly 1.0 mL of urine is pipetted into the syringe. The urine is put through the SEP-PAK into a suitable container using a vacuum system.

3.4.3. The walls of the syringe are rinsed in several stages with a total of approximately 30 mL of HPLC grade water. These rinses are put through the SEP-PAK into the same container. The resulting solution is transferred to a 100-mL volumetric flask and then brought to volume with HPLC grade water.

3.5. Analysis (conditions and hardware are those used in this evaluation.)

3.5.1. Instrument conditions

Column: Zorbax® ODS, 5–6 µm particle size; 25 cm × 4.6 mm I.D.

Mobile phase: See Section 3.2.7.

Detector: Dual wavelength UV; 229 nm (primary) 254 nm (secondary)

Flow rate: 0.7 mL/minute

Retention time: 7.2 minutes

Sensitivity: 0.05 AUFS

Injection volume: 20µl

3.5.2. Chromatogram (see Figure #2)

Figure 2 – Chromatogram of a Creatinine Standard

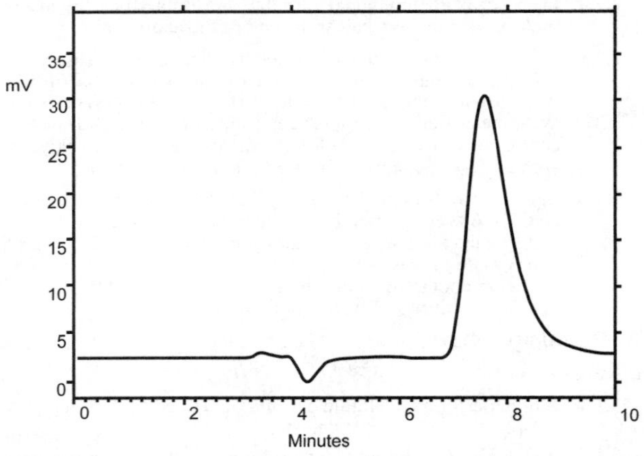

3.6. Interferences

3.6.1. Any compound that has the same retention time as creatinine and absorbs at 229 nm is an interference.

3.6.2. HPLC conditions may be varied to circumvent interferences. In addition, analysis at another UV wavelength (i.e. 254 nm) would allow a comparison of the ratio of response of a standard to that of a sample. Any deviations would indicate an interference.

3.7. Calculations

3.7.1. A calibration curve is constructed by plotting detector response versus standard concentration (See Figure #3).

3.7.2. The concentration of creatinine in a sample is determined by finding the concentration corresponding to its detector response. (See Figure #3).

Figure 3 – Calibration Curve For Creatinine

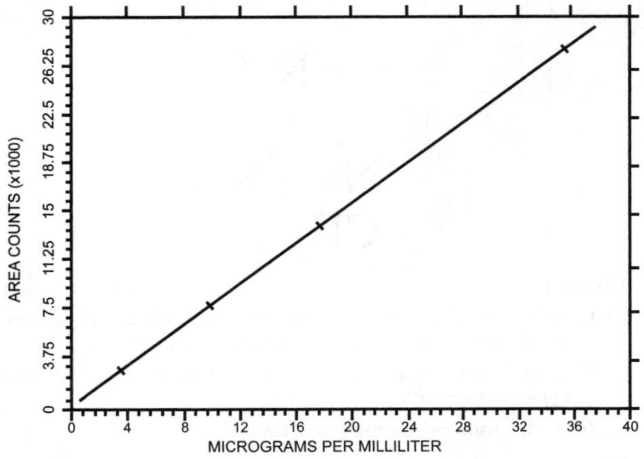

3.7.3. The µg/mL creatinine from Section 3.7.2. is then multiplied by 100 (the dilution factor). This value is equivalent to the micrograms of creatinine in the 1.0 mL stabilized urine aliquot or the milligrams of creatinine per liter of urine. The desired units, g/L, is determined by the following relationship:

$$g/L = \frac{\mu g/ml}{1000} = \frac{mg/L}{1000}$$

3.7.4. The resulting value for creatinine is used to normalize the urinary concentration of the desired analyte (A) (Cd or B2M) by using the following formula.

$$\mu g\ A/g\ creatinine = \frac{\mu g\ A/L\ (experimental)}{g/L\ creatinine}$$

Where A is the desired analyte. The protocol of reporting such normalized results is µg A/g creatinine.

3.8. Safety precautions See Section 2.7.

4. Conclusions

The determination of creatinine in urine by HPLC is a good alternative to the Jaffe method for industrial hygiene laboratories. Sample clarification with SEP-PAKs did not change the amount of creatinine found in urine samples. However, it does protect the analytical column. The results of this creatinine in urine procedure are unaffected by the pH of the urine sample under the conditions tested by this procedure. Therefore, no special measures are required for creatinine analysis whether the urine sample has been stabilized with 10% nitric acid for the Cd analysis or brought to a pH of 7 with 0.11 N NaOH for the B2M analysis.

5. References

5.1. Clark, L.C.; Thompson, H.L.; Anal. Chem. 1949, 21, 1218.

5.2. Peters, J.H.; J. Biol. Chem. 1942, 146, 176.

5.3. Hausen, V.A.; Fuchs, D.; Wachter, H.; J. Clin. Chem. Clin. Biochem. 1981, 19, 373–378.

5.4. Clark, P.M.S.; Kricka L.J.; Patel, A.; J. Liq. Chrom. 1980, 3(7), 1031–1046.

5.5. Ballerini, R.; Chinol, M.; Cambi, A.; J. Chrom. 1979, 179, 365–369.

5.6. Ogata, M.; Taguchi, T.; Industrial Health 1987, 25, 225–228.

5.7. "Merck Index", 11th ed.; Windholz, Martha Ed.; Merck: Rahway, N.J., 1989; p 403.

5.8. Kimberly, M.; "Determination of Cadmium in Urine by Graphite Furnace Atomic Absorption Spectrometry with Zeeman Background Correction.", Centers for Disease Control, Atlanta, Georgia, unpublished, update 1990.

[57 FR 42389, Sept. 14, 1992, as amended at 57 FR 49272, Oct. 30, 1992;

58 FR 21781, Apr. 23, 1993; 61 FR 5508, Feb. 13, 1996; 63 FR 1288, Jan. 8, 1998; 70 FR 1142, Jan. 5, 2005; 71 FR 16672, 16673, Apr. 3, 2006; 71 FR 50189, Aug. 24, 2006; 73 FR 75585, Dec. 12, 2008; 76 FR 33608, June 8, 2011]

§1910.1028 Benzene

(a) Scope and application

(a)(1) This Section applies to all occupational exposures to benzene. Chemical Abstracts Service Registry No. 71–43–2, except as provided in paragraphs (a)(2) and (a)(3) of this Section.

(a)(2) This Section does not apply to:

(a)(2)(i) The storage, transportation, distribution, dispensing, sale or use of gasoline, motor fuels, or other fuels containing benzene subsequent to its final discharge from bulk wholesale storage facilities, except that operations where gasoline or motor fuels are dispensed for more than 4 hours per day in an indoor location are covered by this Section;

(a)(2)(ii) Loading and unloading operations at bulk wholesale storage facilities which use vapor control systems for all loading and unloading operations, except for the provisions of 29 CFR §1910.1200 as incorporated into this Section and the emergency provisions of paragraphs (g) and (i)(4) of this Section;

(a)(2)(iii) The storage, transportation, distribution or sale of benzene or liquid mixtures containing more than 0.1 percent benzene in intact containers or in transportation pipelines while sealed in such a manner as to contain benzene vapors or liquid, except for the provisions of 29 CFR §1910.1200 as incorporated into this Section and the emergency provisions of paragraphs (g) and (i)(4) of this Section;

(a)(2)(iv) Containers and pipelines carrying mixtures with less than 0.1 percent benzene and natural gas processing plants processing gas with less than 0.1 percent benzene;

(a)(2)(v) Work operations where the only exposure to benzene is from liquid mixtures containing 0.5 percent or less of benzene by volume, or the vapors released from such liquids until September 12, 1988; work operations where the only exposure to benzene is from liquid mixtures containing 0.3 percent or less of benzene by volume or the vapors released from such liquids from September 12, 1988, to September 12, 1989; and work operations where the only exposure to benzene is from liquid mixtures containing 0.1 percent or less of benzene by volume or the vapors released from such liquids after September 12, 1989; except that tire building machine operators using solvents with more than 0.1 percent benzene are covered by paragraph (i) of this Section;

(a)(2)(vi) Oil and gas drilling, production and servicing operations;

(a)(2)(vii) Coke oven batteries;

(a)(3) The cleaning and repair of barges and tankers which have contained benzene are excluded from paragraph (f) methods of compliance, paragraph (e)(1) exposure monitoring-general, and paragraph (e)(6) accuracy of monitoring. Engineering and work practice controls shall be used to keep exposures below 10 ppm unless it is proven to be not feasible.

(b) Definitions

Action level means an airborne concentration of benzene of 0.5 ppm calculated as an 8-hour time-weighted average.

Assistant Secretary means the Assistant Secretary of Labor for Occupational Safety and Health, U.S. Department of Labor, or designee.

Authorized person means any person specifically authorized by the employer whose duties require the person to enter a regulated area, or any person entering such an area as a designated representative of employees for the purpose of exercising the right to observe monitoring and measuring procedures under paragraph (l) of this Section, or any other person authorized by the Act or regulations issued under the Act.

Benzene (C6H6) (CAS Registry No. 71–43–2) means liquefied or gaseous benzene. It includes benzene contained in liquid mixtures and the benzene vapors released by these liquids. It does not include trace amounts of unreacted benzene contained in solid materials.

Bulk wholesale storage facility means a bulk terminal or bulk plant where fuel is stored prior to its delivery to wholesale customers.

Container means any barrel, bottle, can, cylinder, drum, reaction vessel, storage tank, or the like, but does not include piping systems.

Day means any part of a calendar day.

Director means the Director of the National Institute for Occupational Safety and Health, U.S. Department of Health and Human Services, or designee.

Emergency means any occurrence such as, but not limited to, equipment failure, rupture of containers, or failure of control equipment which may or does result in an unexpected significant release of benzene.

Employee exposure means exposure to airborne benzene which would occur if the employee were not using respiratory protective equipment.

Regulated area means any area where airborne concentrations of benzene exceed or can reasonably be expected to exceed, the permissible exposure limits, either the 8-hour time weighted average exposure of 1 ppm or the short-term exposure limit of 5 ppm for 15 minutes.

Vapor control system means any equipment used for containing the total vapors displaced during the loading of gasoline, motor fuel or other fuel tank trucks and the displacing of these vapors through a vapor processing system or balancing the vapor with the storage tank. This equipment also includes systems containing the vapors displaced from the storage tank during the unloading of the tank truck which balance the vapors back to the tank truck.

(c) Permissible exposure limits (PELs)

(c)(1) Time-weighted average limit (TWA). The employer shall assure that no employee is exposed to an airborne concentration of benzene in excess of one part of benzene per million parts of air (1 ppm) as an 8-hour time-weighted average.

(c)(2) Short-term exposure limit (STEL). The employer shall assure that no employee is exposed to an airborne concentration of benzene in excess of five (5) ppm as averaged over any 15 minute period.

(d) Regulated areas

(d)(1) The employer shall establish a regulated area wherever the airborne concentration of benzene exceeds or can reasonably be expected to exceed the permissible exposure limits, either the 8-hour time weighted average exposure of 1 ppm or the short-term exposure limit of 5 ppm for 15 minutes.

(d)(2) Access to regulated areas shall be limited to authorized persons.

(d)(3) Regulated areas shall be determined from the rest of the workplace in any manner that minimizes the number of employees exposed to benzene within the regulated area.

(e) Exposure monitoring

(e)(1) General

(e)(1)(i) Determinations of employee exposure shall be made from breathing zone air samples that are representative of each employee's average exposure to airborne benzene.

(e)(1)(ii) Representative 8-hour TWA employee exposures shall be determined on the basis of one sample or samples representing the full shift exposure for each job classification in each work area.

(e)(1)(iii) Determinations of compliance with the STEL shall be made from 15 minute employee breathing zone samples measured at operations where there is reason to believe exposures are high, such as where tanks are opened, filled, unloaded or gauged; where containers or process equipment are opened and where benzene is used for cleaning or as a solvent in an uncontrolled situation. The employer may use objective data, such as measurements from brief period measuring devices, to determine where STEL monitoring is needed.

(e)(1)(iv) Except for initial monitoring as required under paragraph (e)(2) of this Section, where the employer can document that one shift will consistently have higher employee exposures for an operation, the employer shall only be required to determine representative employee exposure for that operation during the shift on which the highest exposure is expected.

(e)(2) Initial monitoring

(e)(2)(i) Each employer who has a place of employment covered under paragraph (a)(1) of this Section shall monitor each of these workplaces and work operations to determine accurately the airborne concentrations of benzene to which employees may be exposed.

(e)(2)(ii) The initial monitoring required under paragraph (e)(2)(i) of this Section shall be completed by 60 days after the effective date of this Standard or within 30 days of the introduction of benzene into the workplace. Where the employer has monitored within one year prior to the effective date of this Standard and the monitoring satisfies all other requirements of this Section, the employer may rely on such earlier monitoring results to satisfy the requirements of paragraph (e)(2)(i) of this Section.

(e)(3) Periodic monitoring and monitoring frequency

(e)(3)(i) If the monitoring required by paragraph (e)(2)(i) of this Section reveals employee exposure at or above the action level, but at or below the TWA, the employer shall repeat such monitoring for each such employee at least every year.

(e)(3)(ii) If the monitoring required by paragraph (e)(2)(i) of this Section reveals employee exposure above the TWA, the employer shall repeat such monitoring for each such employee at least every six (6) months.

(e)(3)(iii) The employer may alter the monitoring schedule from every six months to annually for any employee for whom two consecutive measurements taken at least 7 days apart indicate that the employee exposure has decreased to the TWA or below, but is at or above the action level.

(e)(3)(iv) Monitoring for the STEL shall be repeated as necessary to evaluate exposures of employees subject to short term exposures.

(e)(4) **Termination of monitoring**

(e)(4)(i) If the initial monitoring required by paragraph (e)(2)(i) of this Section reveals employee exposure to be below the action level the employer may discontinue the monitoring for that employee, except as otherwise required by paragraph (e)(5) of this Section.

(e)(4)(ii) If the periodic monitoring required by paragraph (e)(3) of this Section reveals that employee exposures, as indicated by at least two consecutive measurements taken at least 7 days apart, are below the action level the employer may discontinue the monitoring for that employee, except as otherwise required by paragraph (e)(5).

(e)(5) **Additional monitoring**

(e)(5)(i) The employer shall institute the exposure monitoring required under paragraphs (e)(2) and (e)(3) of this Section when there has been a change in the production, process, control equipment, personnel or work practices which may result in new or additional exposures to benzene, or when the employer has any reason to suspect a change which may result in new or additional exposures.

(e)(5)(ii) Whenever spills, leaks, ruptures or other breakdowns occur that may lead to employee exposure, the employer shall monitor (using area or personal sampling) after the cleanup of the spill or repair of the leak, rupture or other breakdown to ensure that exposures have returned to the level that existed prior to the incident.

(e)(6) **Accuracy of monitoring** Monitoring shall be accurate, to a confidence level of 95 percent, to within plus or minus 25 percent for airborne concentrations of benzene.

(e)(7) **Employee notification of monitoring results**

(e)(7)(i) The employer must, within 15 working days after the receipt of the results of any monitoring performed under this section, notify each affected employee of these results either individually in writing or by posting the results in an appropriate location that is accessible to employees.

(e)(7)(ii) Whenever the PELs are exceeded, the written notification required by paragraph (e)(7)(i) of this Section shall contain the corrective action being taken by the employer to reduce the employee exposure to or below the PEL, or shall refer to a document available to the employee which states the corrective actions to be taken.

(f) **Methods of compliance**

(f)(1) **Engineering controls and work practices**

(f)(1)(i) The employer shall institute engineering controls and work practices to reduce and maintain employee exposure to benzene at or below the permissible exposure limits, except to the extent that the employer can establish that these controls are not feasible or where the provisions of paragraph (f)(1)(iii) or (g)(1) of this Section apply.

(f)(1)(ii) Wherever the feasible engineering controls and work practices which can be instituted are not sufficient to reduce employee exposure to or below the PELs, the employer shall use them to reduce employee exposure to the lowest levels achievable by these controls and shall supplement them by the use of respiratory protection which complies with the requirements of paragraph (g) of this Section.

(f)(1)(iii) Where the employer can document that benzene is used in a workplace less than a total of 30 days per year, the employer shall use engineering controls, work practice controls or respiratory protection or any combination of these controls to reduce employee exposure to benzene to or below the PELs, except that employers shall use engineering and work practice controls, if feasible, to reduce exposure to or below 10 ppm as an 8-hour TWA.

(f)(2) **Compliance program**

(f)(2)(i) When any exposures are over the PEL, the employer shall establish and implement a written program to reduce employee exposure to or below the PEL primarily by means of engineering and work practice controls, as required by paragraph (f)(1) of this Section.

(f)(2)(ii) The written program shall include a schedule for development and implementation of the engineering and work practice controls. These plans shall be reviewed and revised as appropriate based on the most recent exposure monitoring data, to reflect the current status of the program.

(f)(2)(iii) Written compliance programs shall be furnished upon request for examination and copying to the Assistant Secretary, the Director, affected employees and designated employee representatives.

(g) **Respiratory protection**

(g)(1) **General** For employees who use respirators required by this Section, the employer must provide each employee an appropriate respirator that complies with the requirements of this paragraph. Respirators must be used during:

(g)(1)(i) Periods necessary to install or implement feasible engineering and work-practice controls.

(g)(1)(ii) Work operations for which the employer establishes that compliance with either the TWA or STEL through the use of engineering and work-practice controls is not feasible; for example, some maintenance and repair activities, vessel cleaning, or other operations for which engineering and work-practice controls are infeasible because exposures are intermittent and limited in duration.

(g)(1)(iii) Work operations for which feasible engineering and work-practice controls are not yet sufficient, or are not required under paragraph (f)(1)(iii) of this Section, to reduce employee exposure to or below the PELs.

(g)(1)(iv) Emergencies.

(g)(2) **Respirator program**

(g)(2)(i) The employer must implement a respiratory protection program in accordance with §1910.134(b) through (d) (except (d)(1)(iii), (d)(3)(iii)(B)(1) and (2)), and (f) through (m), which covers each employee required by this Section to use a respirator.

(g)(2)(ii) For air-purifying respirators, the employer must replace the air-purifying element at the expiration of its service life or at the beginning of each shift in which such elements are used, whichever comes first.

(g)(2)(iii) If NIOSH approves an air-purifying element with an end-of-service-life indicator for benzene, such an element may be used until the indicator shows no further useful life.

(g)(3) **Respirator selection**

(g)(3)(i) Employers must:

(g)(3)(i)(A) Select, and provide to employees, the appropriate respirators specified in paragraph (d)(3)(i)(A) of 29 CFR §1910.134.

(g)(3)(i)(B) Provide employees with any organic vapor gas mask or any self-contained breathing apparatus with a full facepiece to use for escape.

(g)(3)(i)(C) Use an organic vapor cartridge or canister with powered and non-powered air-purifying respirators, and a chin-style canister with full facepiece gas masks.

(g)(3)(i)(D) Ensure that canisters used with non-powered air-purifying respirators have a minimum service life of four hours when tested at 150 ppm benzene at a flow rate of 64 liters per minute (LPM), a temperature of 25 °C, and a relative humidity of 85%; for canisters used with tight-fitting or loose-fitting powered air-purifying respirators, the flow rates for testing must be 115 LPM and 170 LPM, respectively.

(g)(3)(ii) Any employee who cannot use a negative-pressure respirator must be allowed to use a respirator with less breathing resistance, such as a powered air-purifying respirator or supplied-air respirator.

(h) **Protective clothing and equipment** Personal protective clothing and equipment shall be worn where appropriate to prevent eye contact and limit dermal exposure to liquid benzene. Protective clothing and equipment shall be provided by the employer at no cost to the employee and the employer shall assure its use where appropriate. Eye and face protection shall meet the requirements of 29 CFR §1910.133.

(i) [OI] **Medical surveillance**

(i)(1) **General**

(i)(1)(i) The employer shall make available a medical surveillance program for employees who are or may be exposed to benzene at or above the action level 30 or more days per year; for employees who are or may be exposed to benzene at or above the PELs 10 or more days per year; for employees who have been exposed to more than 10 ppm of benzene for 30 or more days in a year prior to the effective date of the standard when employed by their current employer; and for employees involved in the tire building operations called tire building machine operators, who use solvents containing greater than 0.1 percent benzene.

(i)(1)(ii) The employer shall assure that all medical examinations and procedures are performed by or under the supervision of a licensed physician and that all laboratory tests are conducted by an accredited laboratory.

(i)(1)(iii) The employer shall assure that persons other than licensed physicians who administer the pulmonary function testing required by this section shall complete a training course in spirometry sponsored by an appropriate governmental, academic or professional institution.

(i)(1)(iv) The employer shall assure that all examinations and procedures are provided without cost to the employee and at a reasonable time and place.

(i)(2) **Initial examination**

(i)(2)(i) Within 60 days of the effective date of this Standard, or before the time of initial assignment, the employer shall provide each employee covered by paragraph (i)(1)(i) of this Section with a medical examination including the following elements:

(i)(2)(i)(A) A detailed occupational history which includes:

(i)(2)(i)(A)(1) Past work exposure to benzene or any other hematological toxins,

(i)(2)(i)(A)(2) A family history of blood dyscrasias including hematological neoplasms;

(i)(2)(i)(A)(3) A history of blood dyscrasias including genetic hemoglobin abnormalities, bleeding abnormalities, abnormal function of formed blood elements;

(i)(2)(i)(A)(4) A history of renal or liver dysfunction;

(i)(2)(i)(A)(5) A history of medicinal drugs routinely taken;

(i)(2)(i)(A)(6) A history of previous exposure to ionizing radiation and

(i)(2)(i)(A)(7) Exposure to marrow toxins outside of the current work situation.

(i)(2)(i)(B) A complete physical examination.

(i)(2)(i)(C) Laboratory tests. A complete blood count including a leukocyte count with differential, a quantitative thrombocyte count, hematocrit, hemoglobin, erythrocyte count and erythrocyte indices (MCV, MCH, MCHC). The results of these tests shall be reviewed by the examining physician.

(i)(2)(i)(D) Additional tests as necessary in the opinion of the examining physician, based on alterations to the components of the blood or other signs which may be related to benzene exposure; and

(i)(2)(i)(E) For all workers required to wear respirators for at least 30 days a year, the physical examination shall pay special attention to the cardiopulmonary system and shall include a pulmonary function test.

(i)(2)(ii) No initial medical examination is required to satisfy the requirements of paragraph (i)(2)(i) of this Section if adequate records show that the employee has been examined in accordance with the procedures of paragraph (i)(2)(i) of this Section within the twelve months prior to the effective date of this Standard.

(i)(3) Periodic examinations

(i)(3)(i) The employer shall provide each employee covered under paragraph (i)(1)(i) of this Section with a medical examination annually following the previous examination. These periodic examinations shall incude at least the following elements:

(i)(3)(i)(A) A brief history regarding any new exposure to potential marrow toxins, changes in medicinal drug use, and the appearance of physical signs relating to blood disorders:

(i)(3)(i)(B) A complete blood count including a leukocyte count with differential, quantitative thrombocyte count, hemoglobin, hematocrit, erythrocyte count and erythrocyte indices (MCV, MCH, MCHC); and

(i)(3)(i)(C) Appropriate additional tests as necessary, in the opinion of the examining physician, in consequence of alterations in the components of the blood or other signs which may be related to benzene exposure.

(i)(3)(ii) Where the employee develops signs and symptoms commonly associated with toxic exposure to benzene, the employer shall provide the employee with an additional medical examination which shall include those elements considered appropriate by the examining physician.

(i)(3)(iii) For persons required to use respirators for at least 30 days a year, a pulmonary function test shall be performed every three (3) years. A specific evaluation of the cardiopulmonary system shall be made at the time of the pulmonary function test.

(i)(4) Emergency examinations

(i)(4)(i) In addition to the surveillance required by (i)(1)(i), if an employee is exposed to benzene in an emergency situation, the employer shall have the employee provide a urine sample at the end of the employee's shift and have a urinary phenol test performed on the sample within 72 hours. The urine specific gravity shall be corrected to 1.024.

(i)(4)(ii) If the result of the urinary phenol test is below 75 mg phenol/L of urine, no further testing is required.

(i)(4)(iii) If the result of the urinary phenol test is equal to or greater than 75 mg phenol/L of urine, the employer shall provide the employee with a complete blood count including an erythrocyte count, leukocyte count with differential and thrombocyte count at monthly intervals for a duration of three (3) months following the emergency exposure.

(i)(4)(iv) If any of the conditions specified in paragraph (i)(5)(i) of this Section exists, then the further requirements of paragraph (i)(5) of this Section shall be met and the employer shall, in addition, provide the employees with periodic examinations if directed by the physician.

(i)(5) Additional examinations and referrals

(i)(5)(i) Where the results of the complete blood count required for the initial and periodic examinations indicate any of the following abnormal conditions exist, then the blood count shall be repeated within 2 weeks.

(i)(5)(i)(A) The hemoglobin level or the hematocrit falls below the normal limit [outside the 95% confidence interval (C.I.)] as determined by the laboratory for the particular geographic area and/or these indices show a persistent downward trend from the individual's pre-exposure norms; provided these findings cannot be explained by other medical reasons.

(i)(5)(i)(B) The thrombocyte (platelet) count varies more than 20 percent below the employee's most recent values or falls outside the normal limit (95% C.I.) as determined by the laboratory.

(i)(5)(i)(C) The leukocyte count is below 4,000 per mm^3 or there is an abnormal differential count.

(i)(5)(ii) If the abnormality persists, the examining physician shall refer the employee to a hematologist or an internist for further evaluation unless the physician has good reason to believe such referral is unnecessary. (See Appendix C for examples of conditions where a referral may be unnecessary.)

(i)(5)(iii) The employer shall provide the hematologist or internist with the information required to be provided to the physician under paragraph (i)(6) of this Section and the medical record required to be maintained by paragraph (k)(2)(ii) of this Section.

(i)(5)(iv) The hematologist's or internist's evaluation shall include a determination as to the need for additional tests, and the employer shall assure that these tests are provided.

(i)(6) Information provided to the physician The employer shall provide the following information to the examining physician:

(i)(6)(i) A copy of this Regulation and its Appendices;

(i)(6)(ii) A description of the affected employee's duties as they relate to the employee's exposure;

(i)(6)(iii) The employee's actual or representative exposure level:

(i)(6)(iv) A description of any personal protective equipment used or to be used; and

(i)(6)(v) Information from previous employment-related medical examinations of the affected employee which is not otherwise available to the examining physician.

(i)(7) Physician's written opinions

(i)(7)(i) For each examination under this section, the employer shall obtain and provide the employee with a copy of the examining physician's written opinion within 15 days of the examination. The written opinion shall be limited to the following information:

(i)(7)(i)(A) The occupationally pertinent results of the medical examination and tests;

(i)(7)(i)(B) The physician's opinion concerning whether the employee has any detected medical conditions which would place the employee's health at greater than normal risk of material impairment from exposure to benzene;

(i)(7)(i)(C) The physician's recommended limitations upon the employee's exposure to benzene or upon the employee's use of protective clothing or equipment and respirators;

(i)(7)(i)(D) A statement that the employee has been informed by the physician of the results of the medical examination and any medical conditions resulting from benzene exposure which require further explanation or treatment.

(i)(7)(ii) The written opinion obtained by the employer shall not reveal specific records, findings and diagnoses that have no bearing on the employee's ability to work in a benzene-exposed workplace.

(i)(8) Medical removal plan

(i)(8)(i) When a physician makes a referral to a hematologist/internist as required under paragraph (i)(5)(ii) of this Section, the employee shall be removed from areas where exposures may exceed the action level until such time as the physician makes a determination under paragraph (i)(8)(ii) of this Section.

(i)(8)(ii) Following the examination and evaluation by the hematologist/internist, a decision to remove an employee from areas where benzene exposure is above the action level or to allow the employee to return to areas where benzene exposure is above the action level shall be made by the physician in consultation with the hematologist/internist. This decision shall be communicated in writing to the employer and employee. In the case of removal, the physician shall state the required probable duration of removal from occupational exposure to benzene above the action level and the requirements for future medical examinations to review the decision.

(i)(8)(iii) For any employee who is removed pursuant to paragraph (i)(8)(ii) of this Section, the employer shall provide a follow-up examination. The physician, in consultation with the hematologist/internist, shall make a decision within 6 months of the date the employee was removed as to whether the employee shall be returned to the usual job or whether the employee should be removed permanently.

(i)(8)(iv) Whenever an employee is temporarily removed from benzene exposure pursuant to paragraph (i)(8)(i) or (i)(8)(ii) of this Section, the employer shall transfer the employee to a comparable job for which the employee is qualified (or can be trained for in a short period) and where benzene exposures are as low as possible, but in no event higher than the action level. The employer shall maintain the employee's current wage rate, seniority and other benefits. If there is no such job available, the employer shall provide medical removal protection benefits until such a job becomes available or for 6 months, whichever comes first.

(i)(8)(v) Whenever an employee is removed permanently from benzene exposure based on a physician's recommendation pursuant to paragraph (i)(8)(iii) of this Section, the employee shall be given the opportunity to transfer to another position which is available or later becomes available for which the employee is qualified (or can be trained for in a short period) and where benzene exposures are as low as possible but in no event higher than the action level. The employer shall assure that such employee suffers no reduction in current wage rate, seniority or other benefits as a result of the transfer.

(i)(9) **Medical removal protection benefits**

(i)(9)(i) The employer shall provide to an employee 6 months of medical removal protection benefits immediately following each occasion an employee is removed from exposure to benzene because of hematological findings pursuant to paragraphs (i)(8)(i) and (ii) of this Section, unless the employee has been transferred to a comparable job where benzene exposures are below the action level.

(i)(9)(ii) For the purposes of this section, the requirement that an employer provide medical removal protection benefits means that the employer shall maintain the current wage rate, seniority and other benefits of an employee as though the employee had not been removed.

(i)(9)(iii) The employer's obligation to provide medical removal protection benefits to a removed employee shall be reduced to the extent that the employee receives compensation for earnings lost during the period of removal either from a publicly or employer-funded compensation program, or from employment with another employer made possible by virtue of the employee's removal.

(j) **Communication of hazards**

(j)(1) **Hazard communication–general**

(j)(1)(i) Chemical manufacturers, importers, distributors and employers shall comply with all requirements of the Hazard Communication Standard (HCS) (§1910.1200) for benzene.

(j)(1)(ii) In classifying the hazards of benzene at least the following hazards are to be addressed: Cancer; central nervous system effects; blood effects; aspiration; skin, eye, and respiratory tract irritation; and flammability.

(j)(1)(iii) Employers shall include benzene in the hazard communication program established to comply with the HCS (§1910.1200). Employers shall ensure that each employee has access to labels on containers of benzene and to safety data sheets, and is trained in accordance with the requirements of HCS and paragraph (j)(3) of this Section.

(j)(2) **Warning signs and labels.**

(j)(2)(i) The employer shall post signs at entrances to regulated areas.l The signs shall bear the following legend:

DANGER
BENZENE
MAY CAUSE CANCER
HIGHLY FLAMMABLE LIQUIDS AND VAPOR
DO NOT SMOKE
WEAR RESPIRATORY PROTECTION IN THIS AREA
AUTHORIZED PERSONNEL ONLY

(j)(2)(ii) Prior to June 1, 2016, employers may use the following legend in lieu of that specified in paragraph (j)(2)(i) of this Section:

DANGER
CONTAINS BENZENE
CANCER HAZARD
FLAMMABLE–NO SMOKING
AUTHORIZED PERSONNEL ONLY
RESPIRATOR REQUIRED

(j)(2)(iii) The employer shall ensure that labels or other appropriate forms of warning are provided for containers of benzene within the workplace. There is no requirement to label pipes. The labels shall comply with the requirements of paragraph (j)(1) of this Section and §1910.1200(f).

(j)(3)(iv) Prior to June 1, 2015, employers shall include the following legend or similar language on the labels or other appropriate forms of warning:

DANGER
CONTAINS BENZENE
CANCER HAZARD

(j)(2) **Safety data sheets**

(j)(2)(i) Employers shall obtain or develop, and shall provide access to their employees, to a safety data sheet (SDS) which addresses benzene and complies with 29 CFR §1910.1200.

(j)(2)(ii) Employers who are manufacturers or importers shall:

(j)(2)(ii)(A) Comply with paragraph (a) of this Section, and

(j)(2)(ii)(B) Comply with the requirement in OSHA's Hazard Communication Standard, 29 CFR §1910.1200, that they deliver to downstream employers an SDS which addresses benzene.

(j)(3) **Information and training**

(j)(3)(i) The employer shall provide employees with information and training at the time of their initial assignment to a work area where benzene is present. If exposures are above the action level, employees shall be provided with information and training at least annually thereafter.

(j)(3)(ii) The training program shall be in accordance with the requirements of 29 CFR §1910.1200(h)(1) and (2), and shall include specific information on benzene for each category of information included in that Section.

(j)(3)(iii) In addition to the information required under 29 CFR §1910.1200, the employer shall:

(j)(3)(iii)(A) Provide employees with an explanation of the contents of this Section, including Appendices A and B, and indicate to them where the standard is available; and

(j)(3)(iii)(B) Describe the medical surveillance program required under paragraph (i) of this Section, and explain the information contained in Appendix C.

(k) **Recordkeeping**

(k)(1) **Exposure measurements**

(k)(1)(i) The employer shall establish and maintain an accurate record of all measurements required by paragraph (e) of this Section, in accordance with 29 CFR §1910.1020.

(k)(1)(ii) This record shall include:

(k)(1)(ii)(A) The dates, number, duration, and results of each of the samples taken, including a description of the procedure used to determine representative employee exposures;

(k)(1)(ii)(B) A description of the sampling and analytical methods used;

(k)(1)(ii)(C) A description of the type of respiratory protective devices worn, if any; and

(k)(1)(ii)(D) The name, social security number, job classification and exposure levels of the employee monitored and all other employees whose exposure the measurement is intended to represent.

(k)(1)(iii) The employer shall maintain this record for at least 30 years, in accordance with 29 CFR §1910.1020.

(k)(2) **Medical surveillance**

(k)(2)(i) The employer shall establish and maintain an accurate record for each employee subject to medical surveillance required by paragraph (i) of this Section, in accordance with 29 CFR §1910.1020.

(k)(2)(ii) This record shall include:

(k)(2)(ii)(A) The name and social security number of the employee;

(k)(2)(ii)(B) The employer's copy of the physician's written opinion on the initial, periodic and special examinations, including results of medical examinations and all tests, opinions and recommendations;

(k)(2)(ii)(C) Any employee medical complaints related to exposure to benzene;

(k)(2)(ii)(D) A copy of the information provided to the physician as required by paragraphs (i)(6)(ii) through (v) of this Section; and

(k)(2)(ii)(E) A copy of the employee's medical and work history related to exposure to benzene or any other hematologic toxins.

(k)(2)(iii) The employer shall maintain this record for at least the duration of employment plus 30 years, in accordance with 29 CFR §1910.1020.

(k)(3) **Availability**

(k)(3)(i) The employer shall assure that all records required to be maintained by this section shall be made available upon request to the Assistant Secretary and the Director for examination and copying.

(k)(3)(ii) Employee exposure monitoring records required by this paragraph shall be provided upon request for examination and copying to employees, employee representatives, and the Assistant Secretary in accordance with 29 CFR §1910.20 (a) through (e) and (g) through (i).

(k)(3)(iii) Employee medical records required by this paragraph shall be provided upon request for examination and copying, to the subject employee, to anyone having the specific written consent of the subject employee, and to the Assistant Secretary in accordance with 29 CFR §1910.1020.

(k)(4) **Transfer of records** The employer shall comply with the requirements involving transfer of records as set forth in 29 CFR §1910.1020(h).

(l) **Observation of monitoring**

(l)(1) **Employee observation** The employer shall provide affected employees, or their designated representatives, an opportunity to observe the measuring or monitoring of employee exposure to benzene conducted pursuant to paragraph (e) of this Section.

(l)(2) **Observation procedures** When observation of the measuring or monitoring of employee exposure to benzene requires entry into areas where the use of protective clothing and equipment or respirators is required, the employer shall provide the observer with personal protective clothing and equipment or respirators required to be worn by employees working in the area, assure the use of such clothing and equipment or respirators, and require the observer to comply with all other applicable safety and health procedures.

(m) [Reserved]

(n) **Appendices** The information contained in Appendices A, B, C, and D is not intended, by itself, to create any additional obligations not otherwise imposed or to detract from any existing obligations.

§1910.1028 Appendix A Substance safety data sheets, Benzene

I. Substance Identification

A. Substance: Benzene.

B. Permissible Exposure: Except as to the use of gasoline, motor fuels and other fuels subsequent to discharge from bulk terminals and other exemptions specified in §1910.1028(a)(2):

1. Airborne: The maximum time-weighted average (TWA) exposure limit is 1 part of benzene vapor per million parts of air (1 ppm) for an 8-hour workday and the maximum short-term exposure limit (STEL) is 5 ppm for any 15-minute period.
2. Dermal: Eye contact shall be prevented and skin contact with liquid benzene shall be limited.

C. Appearance and odor: Benzene is a clear, colorless liquid with a pleasant, sweet odor. The odor of benzene does not provide adequate warning of its hazard.

II. Health Hazard Data

A. Ways in which benzene affects your health Benzene can affect your health if you inhale it, or if it comes in contact with your skin or eyes. Benzene is also harmful if you happen to swallow it.

B. Effects of overexposure

1. Short-term (acute) overexposure: If you are overexposed to high concentrations of benzene, well above the levels where its odor is first recognizable, you may feel breathless, irritable, euphoric, or giddy; you may experience irritation in eyes, nose, and respiratory tract. You may develop a headache, feel dizzy, nauseated, or intoxicated. Severe exposures may lead to convulsions and loss of consciousness.
2. Long-term (chronic) exposure: Repeated or prolonged exposure to benzene, even at relatively low concentrations, may result in various blood disorders, ranging from anemia to leukemia, an irreversible, fatal disease. Many blood disorders associated with benzene exposure may occur without symptoms.

III. Protective Clothing and Equipment

A. Respirators Respirators are required for those operations in which engineering controls or work practice controls are not feasible to reduce exposure to the permissible level. However, where employers can document that benzene is present in the workplace less than 30 days a year, respirators may be used in lieu of engineering controls. If respirators are worn, they must have joint Mine Safety and Health Administration and the National Institute for Occupational Safety and Health (NIOSH) seal of approval, and cartridge or canisters must be replaced before the end of their service life, or the end of the shift, whichever occurs first. If you experience difficulty breathing while wearing a respirator, you may request a positive pressure respirator from your employer. You must be thoroughly trained to use the assigned respirator, and the training will be provided by your employer.

B. Protective Clothing You must wear appropriate protective clothing (such as boots, gloves, sleeves, aprons, etc.) over any parts of your body that could be exposed to liquid benzene.

C. Eye and Face Protection You must wear splash-proof safety goggles if it is possible that benzene may get into your eyes. In addition, you must wear a face shield if your face could be splashed with benzene liquid.

IV. Emergency and First Aid Procedures

A. Eye and face exposure If benzene is splashed in your eyes, wash it out immediately with large amounts of water. If irritation persists or vision appears to be affected see a doctor as soon as possible.

B. Skin exposure If benzene is spilled on your clothing or skin, remove the contaminated clothing and wash the exposed skin with large amounts of water and soap immediately. Wash contaminated clothing before you wear it again.

C. Breathing If you or any other person breathes in large amounts of benzene, get the exposed person to fresh air at once. Apply artificial respiration if breathing has stopped. Call for medical assistance or a doctor as soon as possible. Never enter any vessel or confined space where the benzene concentration might be high without proper safety equipment and at least one other person present who will stay outside. A life line should be used.

D. Swallowing If benzene has been swallowed and the patient is conscious, do not induce vomiting. Call for medical assistance or a doctor immediately.

V. Medical Requirements

If you are exposed to benzene at a concentration at or above 0.5 ppm as an 8-hour time-weighted average, or have been exposed at or above 10 ppm in the past while employed by your current employer, your employer is required to provide a medical examination and history and laboratory tests within 60 days of the effective date of this Standard and annually thereafter. These tests shall be provided without cost to you. In addition, if you are accidentally exposed to benzene (either by ingestion, inhalation, or skin/eye contact) under emergency conditions known or suspected to constitute toxic exposure to benzene, your employer is required to make special laboratory tests available to you.

VI. Observation of Monitoring

Your employer is required to perform measurements that are representative of your exposure to benzene and you or your designated representative are entitled to observe the monitoring procedure. You are entitled to observe the steps taken in the measurement procedure, and to record the results obtained. When the monitoring procedure is taking place in an area where respirators or personal protective clothing and equipment are required to be worn, you or your representative must also be provided with, and must wear the protective clothing and equipment.

VII. Access to Records

You or your representative are entitled to see the records of measurements of your exposure to benzene upon written request to your employer. Your medical examination records can be furnished to yourself, your physician or designated representative upon request by you to your employer.

VIII. Precautions for Safe Use, Handling and Storage

Benzene liquid is highly flammable. It should be stored in tightly closed containers in a cool, well ventilated area. Benzene vapor may form explosive mixtures in air. All sources of ignition must be controlled. Use nonsparking tools when opening or closing benzene containers. Fire extinguishers, where provided, must be readily available. Know where they are located and how to operate them. Smoking is prohibited in areas where benzene is used or stored. Ask your supervisor where benzene is used in your area and for additional plant safety rules.

§1910.1028 Appendix B Substance technical guidelines, Benzene

I. Physical and Chemical Data

A. Substance identification

1. Synonyms: Benzol, benzole, coal naphtha, cyclohexatriene, phene, phenyl hydride, pyrobenzol. (Benzin, petroleum benzin and Benzine do not contain benzene).
2. Formula: C_6H_6(CAS Registry Number: 71–43–2)

B. Physical data

1. Boiling Point (760 mm Hg); 80.1 °C (176 °F)
2. Specific Gravity (water = 1): 0.879
3. Vapor Density (air = 1): 2.7
4. Melting Point: 5.5 °C (42 °F)
5. Vapor Pressure at 20 °C (68 °F): 75 mm Hg
6. Solubility in Water: .06%
7. Evaporation Rate (ether = 1): 2.8
8. Appearance and Odor: Clear, colorless liquid with a distinctive sweet odor

II. Fire, Explosion, and Reactivity Hazard Data

A. Fire

1. Flash Point (closed cup): −11 °C (12 °F)
2. Autoignition Temperature: 580 °C (1076 °F)
3. Flammable limits in Air. % by Volume: Lower: 1.3%, Upper: 7.5%
4. Extinguishing Media: Carbon dioxide, dry chemical, or foam
5. Special Fire-Fighting procedures: Do not use solid stream of water, since stream will scatter and spread fire. Fine water spray can be used to keep fire-exposed containers cool.
6. Unusual fire and explosion hazards: Benzene is a flammable liquid. Its vapors can form explosive mixtures. All ignition sources must be controlled when benzene is used, handled, or stored. Where liquid or vapor may be released, such areas shall be considered as hazardous locations. Benzene vapors are heavier than air; thus the vapors may travel along the ground and be ignited by open flames or sparks at locations remote from the site at which benzene is handled.
7. Benzene is classified as a 1 B flammable liquid for the purpose of conforming to the requirements of 29 CFR §1910.106. A concentration exceeding 3,250 ppm is considered a potential fire explosion hazard.

Locations where benzene may be present in quantities sufficient to produce explosive or ignitable mixtures are considered Class I Group D for the purposes of conforming to the requirements of 29 CFR §1910.309.

B. Reactivity

1. Conditions contributing to instability: Heat
2. Incompatibility: Heat and oxidizing materials
3. Hazardous decomposition products: Toxic gases and vapors (such as carbon monoxide)

III. Spill and Leak Procedures

A. Steps to be taken if the material is released or spilled As much benzene as possible should be absorbed with suitable materials, such as dry sand or earth. That remaining must be flushed with large amounts of water. Do not flush benzene into a confined space, such as a sewer, because of explosion danger. Remove all ignition sources. Ventilate enclosed places.

B. Waste disposal method Disposal methods must conform to other jurisdictional regulations. If allowed, benzene may be disposed of: (a) By absorbing it in dry sand or earth and disposing in a sanitary landfill; (b) if small quantities, by removing it to a safe location from buildings or other combustible sources, pouring it in dry sand or earth and cautiously igniting it; and (c) if large quantities, by atomizing it in a suitable combustion chamber.

IV. Miscellaneous Precautions

A. High exposure to benzene can occur when transferring the liquid from one container to another. Such operations should be well ventilated and good work practices must be established to avoid spills.

B. Use non-sparking tools to open benzene containers which are effectively grounded and bonded prior to opening and pouring.

C. Employers must advise employees of all plant areas and operations where exposure to benzene could occur. Common operations in which high exposures to benzene may be encountered are: the primary production and utilization of benzene, and transfer of benzene.

§1910.1028 Appendix C Medical surveillance guidelines for Benzene

I. Route of Entry

Inhalation; skin absorption.

II. Toxicology

Benzene is primarily an inhalation hazard. Systemic absorption may cause depression of the hematopoietic system, pancytopenia, aplastic anemia, and leukemia. Inhalation of high concentrations can affect central nervous system function. Aspiration of small amounts of liquid benzene immediately causes pulmonary edema and hemorrhage of pulmonary tissue. There is some absorption through the skin. Absorption may be more rapid in the case of abraded skin, and benzene may be more readily absorbed if it is present in a mixture or as a contaminant in solvents which are readily absorbed. The defatting action of benzene may produce primary irritation due to repeated or prolonged contact with the skin. High concentration are irritating to the eyes and the mucuous membranes of the nose, and respiratory tract.

III. Signs and Symptoms

Direct skin contact with benzene may cause erythema. Repeated or prolonged contact may result in drying, scaling dermatitis, or development of secondary skin infections. In addition, there is benzene absorption through the skin. Local effects of benzene vapor or liquid on the eye are slight. Only at very high concentrations is there any smarting sensation in the eye. Inhalation of high concentrations of benzene may have an initial stimulatory effect on the central nervous system characterized by exhilaration, nervous excitation, and/or giddiness, followed by a period of depression, drowsiness, or fatigue. A sensation of tightness in the chest accompanied by breathlessness may occur and ultimately the victim may lose consciousness. Tremors, convulsions and death may follow from respiratory paralysis or circulatory collapse in a few minutes to several hours following severe exposures.

The detrimental effect on the blood-forming system of prolonged exposure to small quantities of benzene vapor is of extreme importance. The hematopoietic system is the chief target for benzene's toxic effects which are manifested by alterations in the levels of formed elements in the peripheral blood. These effects have occurred at concentrations of benzene which may not cause irritation of mucous membranes, or any unpleasant sensory effects. Early signs and symptoms of benzene morbidity are varied, often not readily noticed and non-specific. Subjective complaints of headache, dizziness, and loss of appetite may precede or follow clinical signs. Rapid pulse and low blood pressure, in addition to a physical appearance of anemia, may accompany a subjective complaint of shortness of breath and excessive tiredness. Bleeding from the nose, gums, or mucous membranes, and the development of purpuric spots (small bruises) may occur as the condition progresses. Clinical evidence of leukopenia, anemia, and thrombocytopenia, singly or in combination, has been frequently reported among the first signs.

Bone marrow may appear normal, aplastic, or hyperplastic, and may not, in all situations, correlate with peripheral blood forming tissues. Because of variations in the susceptibility to benzene morbidity, there is no "typical" blood picture. The onset of effects of prolonged benzene exposure may be delayed for many months or years after the actual exposure has ceased and identification or correlation with benzene exposure must be sought out in the occupational history.

IV. Treatment of Acute Toxic Effects

Remove from exposure immediately. Make sure you are adequately protected and do not risk being overcome by fumes. Give oxygen or artificial resuscitation if indicated. Flush eyes, wash skin if contaminated and remove all contaminated clothing. Symptoms of intoxication may persist following severe exposures. Recovery from mild exposures is usually rapid and complete.

V. Surveillance and Preventive Considerations

A. General

The principal effects of benzene exposure which form the basis for this regulation are pathological changes in the hematopoietic system, reflected by changes in the peripheral blood and manifesting clinically as pancytopenia, aplastic anemia, and leukemia. Consequently, the medical surveillance program is designed to observe, on a regular basis, blood indices for early signs of these effects, and although early signs of leukemia are not usually available, emerging diagnostic technology and innovative regimes make consistent surveillance for leukemia, as well as other hematopoietic effects, essential.

Initial examinations are to be provided within 60 days of the effective date of this Standard, or at the time of initial assignment, and periodic examinations annually thereafter. There are special provisions for medical tests in the event of hematologic abnormalities or for emergency situations.

The blood values which require referral to a hematologist or internist are noted in the standard in paragraph (i)(5). The standard specifies that blood abnormalities that persist must be referred "unless the physician has good reason to believe such referral is unnecessary" (paragraph (i)(5)). Examples of conditions that could make a referral unnecessary despite abnormal blood limits are iron or folate deficiency, menorrhagia, or blood loss due to some unrelated medical abnormality.

Symptoms and signs of benzene toxicity can be non-specific. Only a detailed history and appropriate investigative procedures will enable a physician to rule out or confirm conditions that place the employee at increased risk. To assist the examining physician with regard to which laboratory tests are necessary and when to refer an employee to the specialist, OSHA has established the following guidelines.

B. Hematology Guidelines

A minimum battery of tests is to be performed by strictly standardized methods.

1. Red cell, white cell, platelet counts, white blood cell differential, hematacrit and red cell indices must be performed by an accredited laboratory. The normal ranges for the red cell and white cell counts are influenced by altitude, race, and sex, and therefore should be determined by the accredited laboratory in the specific area where the tests are performed.

   Either a decline from an absolute normal or an individual's base line to a subnormal value or a rise to a supra-normal value, are indicative of potential toxicity, particularly if all blood parameters decline. The normal total white blood count is approximately 7,200/mm^3 plus or minus 3,000. For cigarette smokers the white count may be higher and the upper range may be 2,000 cells higher than normal for the laboratory. In addition, infection, allergies and some drugs may raise the white cell count. The normal platelet count is approximately 250,000 with a range of 140,000 to 400,000. Counts outside this range should be regarded as possible evidence of benzene toxicity.

   Certain abnormalities found through routine screening are of greater significance in the benzene-exposed worker and require prompt consultation with a specialist, namely:

   a. Thrombocytopenia.

   b. A trend of decreasing white cell, red cell, or platelet indices in an individual over time is more worrisome than an isolated abnormal finding at one test time. The importance of trend highlights the need to compare an individual's test results to baseline and/or previous periodic tests.

   c. A constellation or pattern of abnormalities in the different blood indices is of more significance than a single abnormality. A low white count not associated with any abnormalities in other cell indices may be a normal statistical variation, whereas if the low white count is accompanied by decreases in the platelet and/or red cell indices, such a pattern is more likely to be associated with benzene toxicity and merits thorough investigation.

Anemia, leukopenia, macrocytosis or an abnormal differential white blood cell count should alert the physician to further investigate and/or refer the patient if repeat tests confirm the abnormalities. If routine screening detects an abnormality, follow-up tests which may be helpful in establishing the etiology of the abnormality are the peripheral blood smear and the reticulocyte count.

The extreme range of normal for reticulocytes is 0.4 to 2.5 percent of the red cells, the usual range being 0.5 to 1.2 percent of the red cells, but the typical value is in the range of 0.8 to 1.0 percent. A decline in reticulocytes to levels of less than 0.4 percent is to be regarded as possible evidence (unless another specific cause is found) of benzene toxicity requiring accelerated surveillance. An increase in reticulocyte levels to about 2.5 percent may also be consistent with (but is not as characteristic of) benzene toxicity.

2. An important diagnostic test is a careful examination of the peripheral blood smear. As with reticulocyte count the smear should be with fresh uncoagulated blood obtained from a needle tip following venipuncture or from a drop of earlobe blood (capillary blood). If necessary, the smear may, under certain limited conditions, be made from a blood sample anticoagulated with EDTA (but never with oxalate or heparin). When the smear is to be prepared from a specimen of venous blood which has been collected by a commercial Vacutainer® type tube containing neutral EDTA, the smear should be made as soon as possible after the venesection. A delay of up to 12 hours is permissible between the drawing of the blood specimen into EDTA and the preparation of the smear if the blood is stored at refrigerator (not freezing) temperature.
3. The minimum mandatory observations to be made from the smear are:
   a. The differential white blood cell count;
   b. Description of abnormalities in the appearance of red cells;
   c. Description of any abnormalities in the platelets; and
   d. A careful search must be made throughout of every blood smear for immature white cells such as band forms (in more than normal proportion, i.e., over 10 percent of the total differential count), any number of metamyelocytes, myelocytes or myeloblasts. Any nucleate or multinucleated red blood cells should be reported. Large "giant" platelets or fragments of megakaryocytes must be recognized.

   An increase in the proportion of band forms among the neutrophilic granulocytes is an abnormality deserving special mention, for it may represent a change which should be considered as an early warning of benzene toxicity in the absence of other causative factors (most commonly infection). Likewise, the appearance of metamyelocytes, in the absence of another probable cause, is to be considered a possible indication of benzene-induced toxicity.

   An upward trend in the number of basophils, which normally do not exceed about 2.0 percent of the total white cells, is to be regarded as possible evidence of benzene toxicity. A rise in the eosinophil count is less specific but also may be suspicious of toxicity if the rises above 6.0 percent of the total white count.

   The normal range of monocytes is from 2.0 to 8.0 percent of the total white count with an average of about 5.0 percent. About 20 percent of individuals reported to have mild but persisting abnormalities caused by exposure to benzene show a persistent monocytosis. The findings of a monocyte count which persists at more than 10 to 12 percent of the normal white cell count (when the total count is normal) or persistence of an absolute monocyte count in excess of 800/mm^3 should be regarded as a possible sign of benzene-induced toxicity.

   A less frequent but more serious indication of benzene toxicity is the finding in the peripheral blood of the so-called "pseudo" (or acquired) Pelger-Huet anomaly. In this anomaly many, or sometimes the majority, of the neutrophilic granulocytes possess two round nuclear segements–less often one or three round segments–rather than three normally elongated segments. When this anomaly is not hereditary, it is often but not invariably predictive of subsequent leukemia. However, only about two percent of patients who ultimately develop acute myelogenous leukemia show the acquired Pelger-Huet anomaly. Other tests that can be administered to investigate blood abnormalities are discussed below; however, such procedures should be undertaken by the hematologist.

   An uncommon sign, which cannot be detected from the smear, but can be elicited by a "sucrose water test" of peripheral blood, is transient paroxysmal nocturnal hemoglobinuria (PNH), which may first occur insidiously during a period of established aplastic anemia, and may be followed within one to a few years by the appearance of rapidly fatal acute myelogenous leukemia. Clinical detection of PNH, which occurs in only one or two percent of those destined to have acute myelogenous leukemia, may be difficult; if the "sucrose water test" is positive, the somewhat more definitive Ham test, also known as the acid-serum hemolysis test, may provide confirmation.
   e. Individuals documented to have developed acute myelogenous leukemia years after initial exposure to benzene may have progressed through a preliminary phase of hematologic abnormality. In some instances pancytopenia (i.e., a lowering in the counts of all circulating blood cells of bone marrow origin, but not to the extent implied by the term "aplastic anemia") preceded leukemia for many years. Depression of a single blood cell type or platelets may represent a harbinger of aplasia or leukemia. The finding of two or more cytopenias, or pancytopenia in a benzene-exposed individual, must be regarded as highly suspicious of more advanced although still reversible, toxicity. "Pancytopenia" coupled with the appearance of immature cells (myelocytes, myeloblasts, erythroblasts, etc.), with abnormal cells (pseudo Pelger-Huet anomaly, atypical nuclear heterochromatin, etc.), or unexplained elevations of white blood cells must be regarded as evidence of benzene overexposure unless proved otherwise. Many severely aplastic patients manifested the ominous finding of 5–10 percent myeloblasts in the marrow, occasional myeloblasts and myelocytes in the blood and 20–30% monocytes. It is evident that isolated cytopenias, pancytopenias, and even aplastic anemias induced by benzene may be reversible and complete recovery has been reported on cessation of exposure. However, since any of these abnormalities is serious, the employee must immediately be removed from any possible exposure to benzene vapor. Certain tests may substantiate the employee's prospects for progression or regression. One such test would be an examination of the bone marrow, but the decision to perform a bone marrow aspiration or needle biopsy is made by the hematologist.

   The findings of basophilic stippling in circulating red blood cells (usually found in 1 to 5% of red cells following marrow injury), and detection in the bone marrow of what are termed "ringed sideroblasts" must be taken seriously, as they have been noted in recent years to be premonitory signs of subsequent leukemia.

   Recently peroxidase-staining of circulating or marrow neutrophil granulocytes, employing benzidine dihydrochloride, have revealed the disappearance of, or diminution in, peroxidase in a sizable proportion of the granulocytes, and this has been reported as an early sign of leukemia. However, relatively few patients have been studied to date. Granulocyte granules are normally strongly peroxidase positive. A steady decline in leukocyte alkaline phosphatase has also been reported as suggestive of early acute leukemia. Exposure to benzene may cause an early rise in serum iron, often but not always associated with a fall in the reticulocyte count. Thus, serial measurements of serum iron levels may provide a means of determining whether or not there is a trend representing sustained suppression of erythropoiesis.

   Measurement of serum iron, determination of peroxidase and of alkaline phosphatase activity in peripheral granulocytes can be performed in most pathology laboratories. Peroxidase and alkaline phosphatase staining are usually undertaken when the index of suspecion for leukemia is high.

§1910.1028 Appendix D Sampling and analytical methods for Benzene monitoring and measurement procedures

Measurements taken for the purpose of determining employee exposure to benzene are best taken so that the representative average 8-hour exposure may be determined from a single 8-hour sample or two (2) 4-hour samples. Short-time interval samples (or grab samples) may also be used to determine average exposure level if a minimum of five measurements are taken in a random manner over the 8-hour work shift. Random sampling means that any portion of the work shift has the same change of being sampled as any other. The arithmetic average of all such random samples taken on one work shift is an estimate of an employee's average level of exposure for that work shift. Air samples should be taken in the employee's breathing zone (air that would most nearly represent that inhaled by the employee). Sampling and analysis must be performed with procedures meeting the requirements of the standard.

There are a number of methods available for monitoring employee exposures to benzene. The sampling and analysis may be performed by collection of the benzene vaptor or charcoal absorption tubes, with subsequent chemical analysis by gas chromatography. Sampling and analysis may also be performed by portable direct reading instruments, real-time continuous monitoring systems, passive dosimeters or other suitable methods. The employer has the obligation of selecting a monitoring method which meets the accuracy and precision requirements of the standard under his unique field conditions. The standard requires that the method of monitoring must have an accuracy, to a 95 percent confidence level, of not less than plus or minus 25 percent for concentrations of benzene greater than or equal to 0.5 ppm.

The OSHA Laboratory modified NIOSH Method S311 and evaluated it at a benzene air concentration of 1 ppm. A procedure for determining the benzene concentration in bulk material samples was also evalauted. This work, reported in OSHA Laboratory Method No. 12, includes the following two analytical procedures:

I. OSHA Method 12 for Air Samples

Analyte: Benzene

Matrix: Air

Procedure: Adsorption on charcoal, desorption with carbon disulfide, analysis by GC

Detection limit: 0.04 ppm

Recommended air volume and sampling rate: 10L to 0.2 L/min.

1. Principle of the Method

1.1. A known volume of air is drawn through a charcoal tube to trap the organic vapors present.

1.2. The charcoal in the tube is transferred to a small, stoppered vial, and the anlyte is desorbed with carbon disulfide.

1.3. An aliquot of the desorbed sample is injected into a gas chromatograph.

1.4. The area of the resulting peak is determined and compared with areas obtained from standards.

2. Advantages and disadvantages of the method

2.1. The sampling device is small, portable, and involved no liquids. Interferences are minimal, and most of those which do occur can be eliminated by altering chromatographic conditions. The samples are analyzed by means of a quick, instrumental method.

2.2. The amount of sample which can be taken is limited by the number of milligrams that the tube will hold before overloading. When the sample value obtained for the backup section of the charcoal tube exceeds 25 percent of that found on the front section, the possibility of sample loss exists.

3. Apparatus

3.1. A calibrated personal sampling pump whose flow can be determined within ± 5 percent at the recommended flow rate.

3.2. Charcoal tubes: Glass with both ends flame sealed, 7 cm long with a 6-mm O.D. and a 4-mm I.D., containing 2 sections of 20/40 mesh activated charcoal separated by a 2-mm portion of urethane foam. The activated charcoal is prepared from coconut shells and is fired at 600 °C prior to packing. The adsorbing section contains 100 mg of charcoal, the back-up section 50 mg. A 3-mm portion of urethane foam is placed between the outlet end of the tube and the back-up section. A plug of silanized glass wool is placed in front of the adsorbing section. The pressure drop across the tube must be less than one inch of mercury at a flow rate of 1 liter per minute.

3.3. Gas chromatograph equipped with a flame ionization detector

3.4. Column (10-ft × 1/8-in stainless steel) packed with 80/100 Supelcoport coated with 20 percent SP 2100, 0.1 percent CW 1500

3.5. An electronic integrator or some other suitable method for measuring peak area

3.6. Two-milliliter sample vials with Teflon-lined caps

3.7. Microliter syringes: 10-microliter (10-µL) syringe, and other convenient sizes for making standards, 1-µL syringe for sample injections

3.8. Pipets: 1.0 mL delivery pipet

3.9. Volumetric flasks: convenient sizes for making standard solutions

4. Reagents

4.1. Chromatographic quality carbon disulfide (CS_2). Most commercially available carbon disulfide contains a trace of benzene which must be removed. It can be removed with the following procedure:

Heat under reflux for 2 to 3 hours, 500 mL of carbon disulfide, 10 mL concentrated sulfuric acid, and 5 drops of concentrated nitric acid. The benzene is converted to nitrobenzene. The carbon disulfide layer is removed, dried with anhydrous sodium sulfate, and distilled. The recovered carbon disulfide should be benzene free. (It has recently been determined that benzene can also be removed by passing the carbon disulfide through 13x molecular sieve).

4.2. Benzene, reagent grade

4.3. p-Cymene, reagent grade, (internal standard)

4.4. Desorbing reagent. The desorbing reagent is prepared by adding 0.05 mL of p-cymene per milliliter of carbon disulfide. (The internal standard offers a convenient means correcting analytical response for slight inconsistencies in the size of sample injections. If the external standard technique is preferred, the internal standard can be eliminated).

4.5. Purified GC grade helium, hydrogen and air

5. Procedure

5.1. Cleaning of equipment. All glassware used for the laboratory analysis should be properly cleaned and free of organics which could interfere in the analysis.

5.2. Calibration of personal pumps. Each pump must be calibrated with a representative charcoal tube in the line.

5.3. Collection and shipping of samples.

5.3.1. Immediately before sampling, break the ends of the tube to provide an opening at least one-half the internal diameter of the tube (2 mm).

5.3.2. The smaller section of the charcoal is used as the backup and should be placed nearest the sampling pump.

5.3.3. The charcoal tube should be placed in a vertical position during sampling to minimize channeling through the charcoal.

5.3.4. Air being sampled should not be passed through any hose or tubing before entering the charcoal tube.

5.3.5. A sample size of 10 liters is recommended. Sample at a flow rate of approximately 0.2 liters per minute. The flow rate should be known with an accuracy of at least ± 5 percent.

5.3.6. The charcoal tubes should be capped with the supplied plastic caps immediately after sampling.

5.3.7. Submit at least one blank tube (a charcoal tube subjected to the same handling procedures, without having any air drawn through it) with each set of samples.

5.3.8. Take necessary shipping and packing precautions to minimize breakage of samples.

5.4. Analysis of samples

5.4.1. Preparation of samples. In preparation for analysis, each charcoal tube is scored with a file in front of the first section of charcoal and broken open. The glass wool is removed and discarded. The charcoal in the first (larger) section is transferred to a 2-ml vial. The separating section of foam is removed and discarded; the second section is transferred to another capped vial. These two sections are analyzed separately.

5.4.2. Desorption of samples. Prior to analysis, 1.0 mL of desorbing solution is pipetted into each sample container. The desorbing solution consists of 0.05 µL internal standard per mL of carbon disulfide. The sample vials are capped as soon as the solvent is added. Desorption should be done for 30 minutes with occasional shaking.

5.4.3. GC conditions. Typical operating conditions for the gas chromatograph are:

1. 30 mL/min (60 psig) helium carrier gas flow;
2. 30 mL/min (40 psig) hydrogen gas flow to detector;
3. 240 mL/min (40 psig) air flow to detector;
4. 150 °C injector temperature;
5. 250 °C detector temperature; and
6. 100 °C column temperature.

5. 4.4. Injection size. 1 µL.

5. 4.5. Measurement of area. The peak areas are measured by an electronic integrator or some other suitable form of area measurement.

5.4.6. An internal standard procedure is used. The integrator is calibrated to report results in ppm for a 10 liter air sample after correction for desorption efficiency.

5.5. Determination of desorption efficiency

5.5.1. Importance of determination. The desorption efficiency of a particular compound can vary from one laboratory to another and from one lot of chemical to another. Thus, it is necessary to determine, at least once, the percentage of the specific compound that is removed in the desorption process, provided the same batch of charcoal is used.

5.5.2. Procedure for determining desorption efficiency. The reference portion of the charcoal tube is removed. To the remaining portion, amounts representing 0.5X, 1X, and 2X and (X represents target concentration) based on a 10 L air sample are injected into several tubes at each level. Dilutions of benzene with carbon disulfide are made to allow injection of measurable quantities. These tubes are then allowed to equilibrate at least overnight. Following equilibration they are analyzed following the same procedure as the samples. Desorption efficiency is determined by dividing the amount of benzene found by amount spiked on the tube.

6. Calibration and standards A series of standards varying in concentration over the range of interest is prepared and analyzed under the same GC conditions that will be used on the samples. A calibration curve is prepared by plotting concentration (μg/mL) versus peak area.

7. Calculations Benzene air concentration can be calculated from the following equation:

$$mg/m^3 = (A)(B) / (C)(D)$$

Where:
A = μg/mL benzene, obtained from the calibration curve
B = desorption volume (1 mL)
C = Liters of air sampled
D = desorption efficiency

The concentration in mg/m^3 can be converted to ppm (at 25°C and 760 mm) with following equation:

$$ppm = (mg/m^3)(24.46) / (78.11)$$

Where:
24.46 = molar volume of an ideal gas
25 °C and 760 mm
78.11 = molecular weight of benzene

8. Backup Data

8.1. Detection limit—Air Samples

The detection limit for the analytical procedure is 1.28 ng with a coefficient of variation of 0.023 at this level. This would be equivalent to an air concentration of 0.04 ppm for a 10 L air sample. This amount provided a chromatographic peak that could be identifiable in the presence of possible interferences. The detection limit data were obtained by making 1 μL injections of a 1.283 μg/mL standard.

Injection	Area Count	
1	655.4	
2	617.5	
3	662.0	X = 640.2
4	641.1	SD =14.9
5	636.4	CV = 0.023
6	629.2	

8.2. Pooled coefficient of variation—Air Samples The pooled coefficient of variation for the analytical procedure was determined by 1 μL replicate injections of analytical standards. The standards were 16.04, 32.08, and 64.16 μg/mL, which are equivalent to 0.5, 1.0, and 2.0 ppm for a 10 L air sample respectively.

Injection	Area Counts		
	0.5 ppm	1.0 ppm	2.0 ppm
1	3996.5	8130.2	16481
2	4059.4	8235.6	16493
3	4052.0	8307.9	16535
4	4027.2	8263.2	16609
5	4046.8	8291.1	16552
6	4137.9	8288.8	16618
X =	4053.3	8254.0	16548.3
SD=	47.2	62.5	57.1
CV=	0.0116	0.0076	0.0034
CV = 0.008			

8.3. Storage data—Air Samples

Samples were generated at 1.03 ppm benzene at 80% relative humidity, 22 °C, and 643 mm. All samples were taken for 50 minutes at 0.2 L/min. Six samples were analyzed immediately and the rest of the samples were divided into two groups by fifteen samples each. One group was stored at refrigerated temperature of −25 °C, and the other group was stored at ambient temperature (approximately 23 °C). These samples were analyzed over a period of fifteen days. The results are tabulated below.

Percent Recovery

Day analyzed	Refrigerated			Ambient		
0	97.4	98.7	98.9	97.4	98.7	98.9
0	97.1	100.6	100.9	97.1	100.6	100.9
2	95.8	96.4	95.4	95.4	96.6	96.9
5	93.9	93.7	92.4	92.4	94.3	94.1
9	93.6	95.5	94.6	95.2	95.6	96.6
13	94.3	95.3	93.7	91.0	95.0	94.6
15	96.8	95.8	94.2	92.9	96.3	95.9

8.4. Desorption data

Samples were prepared by injecting liquid benzene onto the A section of charcoal tubes. Samples were prepared that would be equivalent to 0.5, 1.0, and 2.0 ppm for a 10 L air sample.

Percent Recovery

Sample	0.5 ppm	1.0 ppm	2.0 ppm
1	99.4	98.8	99.5
2	99.5	98.7	99.7
3	99.2	98.6	99.8
4	99.4	99.1	100.0
5	99.2	99.0	99.7
6	99.8	99.1	99.9
X =	99.4	98.9	99.8
SD=	0.22	0.21	0.18
CV=	0.0022	0.0021	0.0018
X = 99.4			

8.5. Carbon disulfide

Carbon disulfide from a number of sources was analyzed for benzene contamination. The results are given in the following table. The benzene contamiant can be removed with the procedures given in Section 4.1.

Sample	μg Benzene/mL	ppm equivalent (for 10 L air sample)
Aldrich Lot 83017	4.20	0.13
Baker Lot 720364	1.01	0.03
Baker Lot 822351	1.01	0.03
Malinkrodt Lot WEMP	1.74	0.05
Malinkrodt Lot WDSJ	5.65	0.18
Malinkrodt Lot WHGA	2.90	0.09
Treated CS_2		

II. OSHA Laboratory Method No. 12 for Bulk Samples

Analyte: Benzene

Matrix: Bulk Samples

Procedure: Bulk Samples are analyzed directly by high performance liquid chromatography (HPLC)

Detection limits: 0.01% by volume

1. Principle of the method

1.1. An aliquot of the bulk sample to be analyzed is injected into a liquid chromatograph.

1.2. The peak area for benzene is determined and compared to areas obtained from standards.

2. Advantages and disadvantages of the method

2.1. The analytical procedure is quick, sensitive, and reproducible.

2.2. Reanalysis of samples is possible.

2.3. Interferences can be circumvented by proper selection of HPLC parameters.

2.4. Samples must be free of any particulates that may clog the capillary tubing in the liquid chromatograph. This may require distilling the sample or clarifying with a clarification kit.

3. Apparatus

3.1. Liquid chromatograph equipped with a UV detector

3.2. HPLC Column that will separate benzene from other components in the bulk sample being analyzed. The column used for validation studies was a Waters uBondapack C18, 30 cm × 3.9 mm

3.3. A clarification kit to remove any particulates in the bulk, if necessary

3.4. A micro-distillation apparatus to distill any samples, if necessary

3.5. An electronic integrator or some other suitable method of measuring peak areas

3.6. Microliter syringes—10 µL syringe and other convenient sizes for making standards. 10 µL syringe for sample injections

3.7. Volumetric flasks, 5 mL and other convenient sizes for preparing standards and making dilutions

4. Reagents

4.1. Benzene, reagent grade

4.2. HPLC grade water, methyl alcohol, and isopropyl alcohol

5. Collection and shipment of samples

5.1. Samples should be transported in glass containers with Teflon-lined caps.

5.2. Samples should not be put in the same container used for air samples.

6. Analysis of samples

6.1. Sample preparation

If necessary, the samples are distilled or clarified. Samples are analyzed undiluted. If the benzene concentration is out of the working range, suitable dilutions are made with isopropyl alcohol.

6.2. HPLC conditions

The typical operating conditions for the high performance liquid chromatograph are:

1. Mobile phase—Methyl alcohol/water, 50/50
2. Analytical wavelength—254 nm
3. Injection size—10 µL

6.3. Measurement of peak area and calibration

Peak areas are measured by an integrator or other suitable means. The integrator is calibrated to report results % in benzene by volume.

7. Calculations

Since the integrator is programmed to report results in % benzene by volume in an undiluted sample, the following equation is used:

% Benzene by Volume = A × B

Where:
A=% by volume on report
B=Dilution Factor
(B=1 for undiluted sample)

8. Backup Data

8.1. Detection limit—Bulk Samples

The detection limit for the analytical procedure for bulk samples is 0.88 µg, with a coefficient of variation of 0.019 at this level. This amount provided a chromatographic peak that could be identifiable in the presence of possible interferences. The detection limit date were obtained by making 10 µL injections of a 0.10% by volume standard.

Injection	Area Count	
1	45386	
2	44214	
3	43822	X = 44040.1
4	44062	SD = 852.5
6	42724	CV = 0.019

8.2. Pooled coefficient of variation—Bulk Samples

The pooled coefficient of variation for analytical procedure was determined by 50 µL replicate injections of analytical standards. The standards were 0.01, 0.02, 0.04, 0.10, 1.0, and 2.0% benzene by volume.

Area count (Percent)

Injection No.	0.01	0.02	0.04	0.10	1.0	2.0
1	45386	84737	166097	448497	4395380	9339150
2	44241	84300	170832	441299	4590800	9484900
3	43822	83835	164160	443719	4593200	9557580
4	44062	84381	164445	444842	4642350	9677060
5	44006	83012	168398	442564	4646430	9766240
6	42724	81957	173002	443975	4646260	
X =	44040.1	83703.6	167872	444149	4585767	9564986
SD =	852.5	1042.2	3589.8	2459.1	96839.3	166233
CV =	0.0194	0.0125	0.0213	0.0055	0.0211	0.0174
CV =	0.017					

[52 FR 34562, Sept. 11, 1987, as amended at 54 FR 24334, June 7, 1989; 61 FR 5508, Feb. 13, 1996; 63 FR 1289, Jan. 8, 1998; 63 FR 20099, Apr. 23, 1998; 70 FR 1142, Jan. 5, 2005; 71 FR 16673, Apr. 3, 2006; 71 FR 50189, Aug. 24, 2006; 73 FR 75585, Dec. 12, 2008; 76 FR 33608, June 8, 2011]

§1910.1029 OI
Coke oven emissions

(a) **Scope and application** This Section applies to the control of employee exposure to coke oven emissions, except that this section shall not apply to working conditions with regard to which other Federal agencies exercise statutory authority to prescribe or enforce standards affecting occupational safety and health.

(b) **Definitions** For the purpose of this section:

Authorized person means any person specifically authorized by the employer whose duties require the person to enter a regulated area, or any person entering such an area as a designated representative of employees for the purpose of exercising the opportunity to observe monitoring and measuring procedures under paragraph (n) of this Section.

Beehive oven means a coke oven in which the products of carbonization other than coke are not recovered, but are released into the ambient air.

Coke oven means a retort in which coke is produced by the destructive distillation or carbonization of coal.

Coke oven battery means a structure containing a number of slot-type coke ovens.

Coke oven emissions means the benzene-soluble fraction of total particulate matter present during the destructive distillation or carbonization of coal for the production of coke.

Director means the Director, National Institute for Occupational Safety and Health, U.S. Department of Health, Education, and Welfare, or his or her designee.

Emergency means any occurrence such as, but not limited to, equipment failure which is likely to, or does, result in any massive release of coke oven emissions.

Existing coke oven battery means a battery in operation or under construction on January 20, 1977, and which is not a rehabilitated coke oven battery.

Rehabilitated coke oven battery means a battery which is rebuilt, overhauled, renovated, or restored such as from the pad up, after January 20, 1977.

Secretary means the Secretary of Labor, U.S. Department of Labor, or his or her designee.

Stage charging means a procedure by which a predetermined volume of coal in each larry car hopper is introduced into an oven such that no more than two hoppers are discharging simultaneously.

Sequential charging means a procedure, usually automatically timed, by which a predetermined volume of coal in each larry car hopper is introduced into an oven such that no more than two hoppers commence or finish discharging simultaneously although, at some point, all hoppers are discharging simultaneously.

Pipeline charging means any apparatus used to introduce coal into an oven which uses a pipe or duct permanently mounted onto an oven and through which coal is charged.

Green plush means coke which when removed from the oven results in emissions due to the presence of unvolatilized coal.

(c) **Permissible exposure limit** The employer shall assure that no employee in the regulated area is exposed to coke oven emissions at concentrations greater than 150 micrograms per cubic meter of air (150 µg/m^3), averaged over any 8-hour period.

(d) Regulated areas

(d)(1) The employer shall establish regulated areas and shall limit access to them to authorized persons.

(d)(2) The employer shall establish the following as regulated areas:

(d)(2)(i) [O1] The coke oven battery including topside and its machinery, pushside and its machinery, coke side and its machinery, and the battery ends; the wharf; and the screening station;

(d)(2)(ii) The beehive oven and its machinery.

(e) [O1] **Exposure monitoring and measurement**

(e)(1) Monitoring program

(e)(1)(i) Each employer who has a place of employment where coke oven emissions are present shall monitor employees employed in the regulated area to measure their exposure to coke oven emissions.

(e)(1)(ii) The employer shall obtain measurements which are representative of each employee's exposure to coke oven emissions over an eight-hour period. All measurements shall determine exposure without regard to the use of respiratory protection.

(e)(1)(iii) [O1] The employer shall collect fullshift (for at least seven continuous hours) personal samples, including at least one sample during each shift for each battery and each job classification within the regulated areas including at least the following job classifications:

(e)(1)(iii)(A) Lidman;

(e)(1)(iii)(B) Tar chaser;

(e)(1)(iii)(C) Larry car operator;

(e)(1)(iii)(D) Luterman;

(e)(1)(iii)(E) Machine operator, coke side;

(e)(1)(iii)(F) Benchman, coke side;

(e)(1)(iii)(G) Benchman, pusher side;

(e)(1)(iii)(H) Heater;

(e)(1)(iii)(I) Quenching car operator;

(e)(1)(iii)(J) Pusher machine operator;

(e)(1)(iii)(K) Screening station operator;

(e)(1)(iii)(L) Wharfman;

(e)(1)(iii)(M) Oven patcher;

(e)(1)(iii)(N) Oven repairman;

(e)(1)(iii)(O) Spellman; and

(e)(1)(iii)(P) Maintenance personnel.

(e)(1)(iv) The employer shall repeat the monitoring and measurements required by this paragraph (e)(1) at least every three months.

(e)(2) Redetermination Whenever there has been a production, process, or control change which may result in new or additional exposure to coke oven emissions, or whenever the employer has any other reason to suspect an increase in employee exposure, the employer shall repeat the monitoring and measurements required by paragraph (e)(1) of this Section for those employees affected by such change or increase.

(e)(3) Employee notification

(e)(3)(i) The employer must, within 15 working days after the receipt of the results of any monitoring performed under this Section, notify each affected employee of these results either individually in writing or by posting the results in an appropriate location that is accessible to employees.

(e)(3)(ii) Whenever such results indicate that the representative employee exposure exceeds the permissible exposure limit, the employer shall, in such notification, inform each employee of that fact and of the corrective action being taken to reduce exposure to or below the permissible exposure limit.

(e)(4) Accuracy of measurement The employer shall use a method of monitoring and measurement which has an accuracy (with a confidence level of 95%) of not less than plus or minus 35% for concentrations of coke oven emissions greater than or equal to 150 $\mu g/m^3$.

(f) Methods of compliance The employer shall control employee exposure to coke oven emissions by the use of engineering controls, work practices and respiratory protection as follows:

(f)(1) Priority of compliance methods

(f)(1)(i) Existing coke oven batteries

(f)(1)(i)(A) The employer shall institute the engineering and work practice controls listed in paragraphs (f)(2), (f)(3) and (f)(4) of this Section in existing coke oven batteries at the earliest possible time, but not later than January 20, 1980, except to the extent that the employer can establish that such controls are not feasible. In determining the earliest possible time for institution of engineering and work practice controls, the requirement, effective August 27, 1971, to implement feasible administrative or engineering controls to reduce exposures to coal tar pitch volatiles, shall be considered. Wherever the engineering and work practice controls which can be instituted are not sufficient to reduce employee exposures to or below the permissible exposure limit, the employer shall nonetheless use them to reduce exposures to the lowest level achievable by these controls and shall supplement them by the use of respiratory protection which complies with the requirements of paragraph (g) of this Section.

(f)(1)(i)(B) The engineering and work practice controls required under paragraphs (f)(2), (f)(3) and (f)(4) of this Section are minimum requirements generally applicable to all existing coke oven batteries. If, after implementing all controls required by paragraphs (f)(2), (f)(3) and (f)(4) of this Section, or after January 20, 1980, whichever is sooner, employee exposures still exceed the permissible exposure limit, employers shall implement any other engineering and work practice controls necessary to reduce exposure to or below the permissible exposure limit except to the extent that the employer can establish that such controls are not feasible. Whenever the engineering and work practice controls which can be instituted are not sufficient to reduce employee exposures to or below the permissible exposure limit, the employer shall nonetheless use them to reduce exposures to the lowest level achievable by these controls and shall supplement them by the use of respiratory protection which complies with the requirements of paragraph (g) of this Section.

(f)(1)(ii) New or rehabilitated coke oven batteries

(f)(1)(ii)(A) The employer shall institute the best available engineering and work practice controls on all new or rehabilitated coke oven batteries to reduce and maintain employee exposures at or below the permissible exposure limit, except to the extent that the employer can establish that such controls are not feasible. Wherever the engineering and work practice controls which can be instituted are not sufficient to reduce employee exposures to or below the permissible exposure limit, the employer shall nonetheless use them to reduce exposures to the lowest level achievable by these controls and shall supplement them by the use of respiratory protection which complies with the requirements of paragraph (g) of this Section.

(f)(1)(ii)(B) If, after implementing all the engineering and work practice controls required by paragraph (f)(1)(ii)(A) of this Section, employee exposures still exceed the permissible exposure limit, the employer shall implement any other engineering and work practice controls necessary to reduce exposure to or below the permissible exposure limit except to the extent that the employer can establish that such controls are not feasible. Wherever the engineering and work practice controls which can be instituted are not sufficient to reduce employee exposures to or below the permissible exposure limit, the employer shall nonetheless use them to reduce exposures to the lowest level achievable by these controls and shall supplement them by the use of respiratory protection which complies with the requirements of paragraph (g) of this Section.

(f)(1)(iii) Beehive ovens

(f)(1)(iii)(A) The employer shall institute engineering and work practice controls on all beehive ovens at the earliest possible time to reduce and maintain employee exposures at or below the permissible exposure limit, except to the extent that the employer can establish that such controls are not feasible. In determining the earliest possible time for institution of engineering and work practice controls, the requirement, effective August 27, 1971, to implement feasible administrative or engineering controls to reduce exposures to coal tar pitch volatiles, shall be considered. Wherever the engineering and work practice controls which can be instituted are not sufficient to reduce employee exposures to or below the permissible exposure limit, the employer shall nonetheless use them to reduce exposures to the lowest level achievable by these controls and shall supplement them by the use of respiratory protection which complies with the requirements of paragraph (g) of this Section.

(f)(1)(iii)(B) If, after implementing all engineering and work practice controls required by paragraph (f)(1)(iii)(A) of this Section, employee exposures still exceed the permissible exposure limit, the employer shall implement any other engineering and work practice controls necessary to reduce exposures to or below the permissible exposure limit except to the extent that the employer can establish that such controls are not feasible. Whenever the engineering and work practice controls which can be instituted are not sufficient to reduce employee exposures to or below the permissible exposure limit, the employer shall nonetheless use them to reduce exposures to the lowest level achievable by these controls and shall supplement them by the use of respiratory protection which complies with the requirements of paragraph (g) of this Section.

(f)(2) Engineering controls

(f)(2)(i) Charging The employer shall equip and operate existing coke oven batteries with all of the following engineering controls to control coke oven emissions during charging operations:

(f)(2)(i)(A) One of the following methods of charging:

(f)(2)(i)(A)(1) Stage charging as described in paragraph (f)(3)(i)(B) of this Section; or (f)(2)(i)(A)(2) Sequential charging as described in paragraph (f)(3)(i)(B) of this Section except that paragraph (f)(3)(i)(B)(3)(iv) of this Section does not apply to sequential charging; or

(f)(2)(i)(A)(3) Pipeline charging or other forms of enclosed charging in accordance with paragraph (f)(2)(i) of this Section, except that paragraphs (f)(2)(i)(B), (D), (E), (F) and (H) of this Section do not apply;

(f)(2)(i)(B) Drafting from two or more points in the oven being charged, through the use of double collector mains, or a fixed or moveable jumper pipe system to another oven, to effectively remove the gases from the oven to the collector mains;

(f)(2)(i)(C) Aspiration systems designed and operated to provide sufficient negative pressure and flow volume to effectively move the gases evolved during charging into the collector mains, including sufficient steam pressure, and steam jets of sufficient diameter;

(f)(2)(i)(D) Mechanical volumetric controls on each larry car hopper to provide the proper amount of coal to be charged through each charging hole so that the tunnel head will be sufficient to permit the gases to move from the oven into the collector mains;

(f)(2)(i)(E) Devices to facilitate the rapid and continuous flow of coal into the oven being charged, such as stainless steel liners, coal vibrators or pneumatic shells;

(f)(2)(i)(F) Individually operated larry car drop sleeves and slide gates designed and maintained so that the gases are effectively removed from the oven into the collector mains;

(f)(2)(i)(G) OI Mechanized gooseneck and standpipe cleaners;

(f)(2)(i)(H) Air seals on the pusher machine leveler bars to control air infiltration during charging; and

(f)(2)(i)(I) Roof carbon cutters or a compressed air system or both on the pusher machine rams to remove roof carbon.

(f)(2)(ii) **Coking** The employer shall equip and operate existing coke oven batteries with all of the following engineering controls to control coke oven emissions during coking operations;

(f)(2)(ii)(A) A pressure control system on each battery to obtain uniform collector main pressure;

(f)(2)(ii)(B) Ready access to door repair facilities capable of prompt and efficient repair of doors, door sealing edges and all door parts;

(f)(2)(ii)(C) An adequate number of spare doors available for replacement purposes;

(f)(2)(ii)(D) Chuck door gaskets to control chuck door emissions until such door is repaired, or replaced; and

(f)(2)(ii)(E) Heat shields on door machines.

(f)(3) **Work practice controls**

(f)(3)(i) **Charging** The employer shall operate existing coke oven batteries with all of the following work practices to control coke oven emissions during the charging operation:

(f)(3)(i)(A) Establishment and implementation of a detailed, written inspection and cleaning procedure for each battery consisting of at least the following elements:

(f)(3)(i)(A)(1) Prompt and effective repair or replacement of all engineering controls;

(f)(3)(i)(A)(2) OI Inspection and cleaning of goosenecks and standpipes prior to each charge to a specified minimum diameter sufficient to effectively move the evolved gases from the oven to the collector mains;

(f)(3)(i)(A)(3) Inspection for roof carbon build-up prior to each charge and removal of roof carbon as necessary to provide an adequate gas channel so that the gases are effectively moved from the oven into the collector mains;

(f)(3)(i)(A)(4) Inspection of the steam aspiration system prior to each charge so that sufficient pressure and volume is maintained to effectively move the gases from the oven to the collector mains;

(f)(3)(i)(A)(5) Inspection of steam nozzles and liquor sprays prior to each charge and cleaning as necessary so that the steam nozzles and liquor sprays are clean;

(f)(3)(i)(A)(6) Inspection of standpipe caps prior to each charge and cleaning and luting or both as necessary so that the gases are effectively moved from the oven to the collector mains; and

(f)(3)(i)(A)(7) Inspection of charging holes and lids for cracks, warpage and other defects prior to each charge and removal of carbon to prevent emissions, and application of luting material to standpipe and charging hole lids where necessary to obtain a proper seal.

(f)(3)(i)(B) Establishment and implementation of a detailed written charging procedure, designed and operated to eliminate emissions during charging for each battery, consisting of at least the following elements:

(f)(3)(i)(B)(1) Larry car hoppers filled with coal to a predetermined level in accordance with the mechanical volumetric controls required under paragraph (f)(2)(i)(D) of this Section so as to maintain a sufficient gas passage in the oven to be charged;

(f)(3)(i)(B)(2) The larry car aligned over the oven to be charged, so that the drop sleeves fit tightly over the charging holes; and

(f)(3)(i)(B)(3) The oven charged in accordance with the following sequence of requirements:

(f)(3)(i)(B)(3)(i) The aspiration system turned on;

(f)(3)(i)(B)(3)(ii) Coal charged through the outermost hoppers, either individually or together depending on the capacity of the aspiration system to collect the gases involved;

(f)(3)(i)(B)(3)(iii) The charging holes used under paragraph (f)(3)(i)(B)(3)(ii) of this Section relidded or otherwise sealed off to prevent leakage of coke oven emissions;

(f)(3)(i)(B)(3)(iv) If four hoppers are used, the third hopper discharged and relidded or otherwise sealed off to prevent leakage of coke oven emissions;

(f)(3)(i)(B)(3)(v) The final hopper discharged until the gas channel at the top of the oven is blocked and then the chuck door opened and the coal leveled;

(f)(3)(i)(B)(3)(vi) When the coal from the final hopper is discharged and the leveling operation complete, the charging hole relidded or otherwise sealed off to prevent leakage of coke oven emissions; and

(f)(3)(i)(B)(3)(vii) The aspiration system turned off only after the charging holes have been closed.

(f)(3)(i)(C) Establishment and implementation of a detailed written charging procedure, designed and operated to eliminate emissions during charging of each pipeline or enclosed charged battery.

(f)(3)(ii) **Coking** The employer shall operate existing coke oven batteries pursuant to a detailed written procedure established and implemented for the control of coke oven emissions during coking, consisting of at least the following elements:

(f)(3)(ii)(A) Checking oven back pressure controls to maintain uniform pressure conditions in the collecting main;

(f)(3)(ii)(B) Repair, replacement and adjustment of oven doors and chuck doors and replacement of door jambs so as to provide a continuous metal-to-metal fit;

(f)(3)(ii)(C) Cleaning of oven doors, chuck doors and door jambs each coking cycle so as to provide an effective seal;

(f)(3)(ii)(D) An inspection system and corrective action program to control door emissions to the maximum extent possible; and

(f)(3)(ii)(E) Luting of doors that are sealed by luting each coking cycle and reluting, replacing or adjusting as necessary to control leakage.

(f)(3)(iii) **Pushing** The employer shall operate existing coke oven batteries with the following work practices to control coke oven emissions during pushing operations:

(f)(3)(iii)(A) Coke and coal spillage quenched as soon as practicable and not shoveled into a heated oven; and

(f)(3)(iii)(B) A detailed written procedure for each battery established and implemented for the control of emissions during pushing consisting of the following elements:

(f)(3)(iii)(B)(1) Dampering off the ovens and removal of charging hole lids to effectively control coke oven emissions during the push;

(f)(3)(iii)(B)(2) Heating of the coal charge uniformly for a sufficient period so as to obtain proper coking including preventing green pushes;

(f)(3)(iii)(B)(3) Prevention of green pushes to the maximum extent possible;

(f)(3)(iii)(B)(4) Inspection, adjustment and correction of heating flue temperatures and defective flues at least weekly and after any green push, so as to prevent green pushes;

(f)(3)(iii)(B)(5) Cleaning of heating flues and related equipment to prevent green pushes, at least weekly and after any green push.

(f)(3)(iv) **Maintenance and repair** The employer shall operate existing coke oven batteries pursuant to a detailed written procedure of maintenance and repair established and implemented for the effective control of coke oven emissions consisting of the following elements:

(f)(3)(iv)(A) Regular inspection of all controls, including goosenecks, standpipes, standpipe caps, charging hold lids and castings, jumper pipes and air seals for cracks, misalignment or other defects and prompt implementation of the necessary repairs as soon as possible;

(f)(3)(iv)(B) Maintaining the regulated area in a neat, orderly condition free of coal and coke spillage and debris;

(f)(3)(iv)(C) Regular inspection of the damper system, aspiration system and collector main for cracks or leakage, and prompt implementation of the necessary repairs;

(f)(3)(iv)(D) Regular inspection of the heating system and prompt implementation of the necessary repairs;

(f)(3)(iv)(E) Prevention of miscellaneous fugitive topside emissions;

(f)(3)(iv)(F) Regular inspection and patching of oven brickwork;

(f)(3)(iv)(G) Maintenance of battery equipment and controls in good working order;

(f)(3)(iv)(H) Maintenance and repair of coke oven doors, chuck doors, door jambs and seals; and

(f)(3)(iv)(I) Repairs instituted and completed as soon as possible, including temporary repair measures instituted and completed where necessary, including but not limited to:

(f)(3)(iv)(I)(*1*) Prevention of miscellaneous fugitive topside emissions; and

(f)(3)(iv)(I)(*2*) Chuck door gaskets, which shall be installed prior to the start of the next coking cycle.

(f)(4) **Filtered air**

(f)(4)(i) OI The employer shall provide positive-pressure, temperature controlled filtered air for larry car, pusher machine, door machine, and quench car cabs.

(f)(4)(ii) OI The employer shall provide standby pulpits on the battery topside, at the wharf, and at the screening station, equipped with positive-pressure, temperature controlled filtered air.

(f)(5) **Emergencies** Whenever an emergency occurs, the next coking cycle may not begin until the cause of the emergency is determined and corrected, unless the employer can establish that it is necessary to initiate the next coking cycle in order to determine the cause of the emergency.

(f)(6) **Compliance program**

(f)(6)(i) Each employer shall establish and implement a written program to reduce exposures solely by means of the engineering and work practice controls required in paragraph (f) of this Section.

(f)(6)(ii) The written program shall include at least the following:

(f)(6)(ii)(A) A description of each coke oven operation by battery, including work force and operating crew, coking time, operating procedures and maintenance practices;

(f)(6)(ii)(B) Engineering plans and other studies used to determine the controls for the coke battery;

(f)(6)(ii)(C) A report of the technology considered in meeting the permissible exposure limit;

(f)(6)(ii)(D) Monitoring data obtained in accordance with paragraph (e) of this Section;

(f)(6)(ii)(E) A detailed schedule for the implementation of the engineering and work practice controls required in paragraph (f) of this Section; and

(f)(6)(ii)(F) Other relevant information.

(f)(6)(iii) If, after implementing all controls required by paragraph (f)(2)–(f)(4) of this Section, or after January 20, 1980, whichever is sooner, or after completion of a new or rehabilitated battery the permissible exposure limit is still exceeded, the employer shall develop a detailed written program and schedule for the implementation of any additional engineering controls and work practices necessary to reduce exposure to or below the permissible exposure limit.

(f)(6)(iv) Written plans for such programs shall be submitted, upon request, to the Secretary and the Director, and shall be available at the worksite for examination and copying by the Secretary, the Director, and the authorized employee representative. The plans required under paragraph (f)(6) of this Section shall be revised and updated at least annually to reflect the current status of the program.

(f)(7) **Training in compliance procedures** The employer shall incorporate all written procedures and schedules required under this paragraph (f) in the information and training program required under paragraph (k) of this Section and, where appropriate, post in the regulated area.

(g) **Respiratory protection**

(g)(1) **General** For employees who use respirators required by this Section, the employer must provide each employee an appropriate respirator that complies with the requirements of this paragraph. Respirators must be used during:

(g)(1)(i) Periods necessary to install or implement feasible engineering and work-practice controls.

(g)(1)(ii) Work operations, such as maintenance and repair activity, for which engineering and work-practice controls are technologically not feasible.

(g)(1)(iii) Work operations for which feasible engineering and work-practice controls are not yet sufficient to reduce employee exposure to or below the permissible exposure limit.

(g)(1)(iv) Emergencies

(g)(2) **Respirator program** The employer must implement a respiratory protection program in accordance with §1910.134(b) through (d) (except (d)(1)(iii)), and (f) through (m), which covers each employee required by this Section to use a respirator.

(g)(3) **Respirator selection** Employers must select, and provide to employees, the appropriate respirators specified in paragraph (d)(3)(i)(A) of 29 CFR §1910.134; however, employers may use a filtering facepiece respirator only when it functions as a filter respirator for coke oven emissions particulates.

(h) **Protective clothing and equipment**

(h)(1) OI **Provision and use** The employer shall provide and assure the use of appropriate protective clothing and equipment, such as but not limited to:

(h)(1)(i) Flame resistant jacket and pants;

(h)(1)(ii) Flame resistant gloves;

(h)(1)(iii) Face shields or vented goggles which comply with §1910.133(a)(2) of this part;

(h)(1)(iv) Footwear providing insulation from hot surfaces for footwear;

(h)(1)(v) Safety shoes which comply with §1910.136 of this part; and

(h)(1)(vi) Protective helmets which comply with §1910.135 of this part.

(h)(2) **Cleaning and replacement**

(h)(2)(i) The employer shall provide the protective clothing required by paragraphs (h)(1)(i) and (ii) of this Section in a clean and dry condition at least weekly.

(h)(2)(ii) The employer shall clean, launder, or dispose of protective clothing required by paragraphs (h)(1)(i) and (ii) of this Section.

(h)(2)(iii) The employer shall repair or replace the protective clothing and equipment as needed to maintain their effectiveness.

(h)(2)(iv) The employer shall assure that all protective clothing is removed at the completion of a work shift only in change rooms prescribed in paragraph (i)(1) of this Section.

(h)(2)(v) The employer shall assure that contaminated protective clothing which is to be cleaned, laundered, or disposed of, is placed in a closable container in the change room.

(h)(2)(vi) The employer shall inform any person who cleans or launders protective clothing required by this Section, of the potentially harmful effects of exposure to coke oven emissions.

(i) **Hygiene facilities and practices**

(i)(1) OI **Change rooms** The employer shall provide clean change rooms equipped with storage facilities for street clothes and separate storage facilities for protective clothing and equipment whenever employees are required to wear protective clothing and equipment in accordance with paragraph (h)(1) of this Section.

(i)(2) **Showers**

(i)(2)(i) The employer shall assure that employees working in the regulated area shower at the end of the work shift.

(i)(2)(ii) The employer shall provide shower facilities in accordance with §1910.141(d)(3) of this part.

(i)(3) **Lunchrooms** The employer shall provide lunchroom facilities which have a temperature controlled, positive pressure, filtered air supply, and which are readily accessible to employees working in the regulated area.

(i)(4) **Lavatories**

(i)(4)(i) The employer shall assure that employees working in the regulated area wash their hands and face prior to eating.

(i)(4)(ii) The employer shall provide lavatory facilities in accordance with §1910.141(d)(1) and (2) of this part.

(i)(5) **Prohibition of activities in the regulated area**

(i)(5)(i) The employer shall assure that in the regulated area, food or beverages are not present or consumed, smoking products are not present or used, and cosmetics are not applied, except that these activities may be conducted in the lunchrooms, change rooms and showers required under paragraphs (i)(1)–(i)(3) of this Section.

(i)(5)(ii) Drinking water may be consumed in the regulated area.

(j) OI **Medical surveillance**

(j)(1) **General requirements**

(j)(1)(i) Each employer shall institute a medical surveillance program for all employees who are employed in a regulated area at least 30 days per year.

(j)(1)(ii) This program shall provide each employee covered under paragraph (j)(1)(i) of this Section with an opportunity for medical examinations in accordance with this paragraph (j).

(j)(1)(iii) The employer shall inform any employee who refuses any required medical examination of the possible health consequences of such refusal and shall obtain a signed statement from the employee indicating that the employee understands the risk involved in the refusal to be examined.

(j)(1)(iv) The employer shall assure that all medical examinations and procedures are performed by or under the supervision of a licensed physician, and are provided without cost to the employee.

(j)(2) **Initial examinations** At the time of initial assignment to a regulated area or upon the institution of the medical surveillance program, the employer shall provide a medical examination for employees covered under paragraph (j)(1)(i) of this Section including at least the following elements:

(j)(2)(i) A work history and medical history which shall include smoking history and the presence and degree of respiratory symptoms, such as breathlessness, cough, sputum production, and wheezing;

(j)(2)(ii) [OI] A standard posterior-anterior chest x-ray;

(j)(2)(iii) Pulmonary function tests including forced vital capacity (FVC) and forced expiratory volume at one second (FEV 1.0) with recording of type of equipment used;

(j)(2)(iv) Weight;

(j)(2)(v) A skin examination;

(j)(2)(vi) Urinalysis for sugar, albumin, and hematuria; and

(j)(2)(vii) A urinary cytology examination.

(j)(3) **Periodic examinations**

(j)(3)(i) The employer shall provide the examinations specified in paragraphs (j)(2)(i)–(vi) of this Section at least annually for employees covered under paragraph (j)(1)(i) of this Section.

(j)(3)(ii) The employer must provide the examinations specified in paragraphs (j)(2)(i) through (j)(2)(vii) of this Section at least annually for employees 45 years of age or older or with five (5) or more years employment in the regulated area.

(j)(3)(iii) Whenever an employee who is 45 years of age or older or with five (5) or more years employment in a regulated area transfers or is transferred from employment in a regulated area, the employer must continue to provide the examinations specified in paragraphs (j)(2)(i) through (j)(2)(vii) of this Section at least annually as long as that employee is employed by the same employer or a successor employer.

(j)(3)(iv) Whenever an employee has not taken the examinations specified in paragraphs (j)(3)(i)–(iii) of this Section with the six (6) months preceding the termination of employment the employer shall provide such examinations to the employee upon termination of employment.

(j)(4) **Information provided to the physician** The employer shall provide the following information to the examining physician:

(j)(4)(i) A copy of this regulation and its Appendices;

(j)(4)(ii) A description of the affected employee's duties as they relate to the employee's exposure;

(j)(4)(iii) The employee's exposure level or estimated exposure level;

(j)(4)(iv) A description of any personal protective equipment used or to be used; and

(j)(4)(v) Information from previous medical examinations of the affected employee which is not readily available to the examining physician.

(j)(5) **Physician's written opinion**

(j)(5)(i) The employer shall obtain a written opinion from the examining physician which shall include:

(j)(5)(i)(A) The results of the medical examinations;

(j)(5)(i)(B) The physician's opinion as to whether the employee has any detected medical conditions which would place the employee at increased risk of material impairment of the employee's health from exposure to coke oven emissions;

(j)(5)(i)(C) Any recommended limitations upon the employee's exposure to coke oven emissions or upon the use of protective clothing or equipment such as respirators; and

(j)(5)(i)(D) A statement that the employee has been informed by the physician of the results of the medical examination and any medical conditions which require further explanation or treatment.

(j)(5)(ii) The employer shall instruct the physician not to reveal in the written opinion specific findings or diagnoses unrelated to occupational exposure.

(j)(5)(iii) The employer shall provide a copy of the written opinion to the affected employee.

(k) **Employee information and training**

(k)(1) **Training program**

(k)(1)(i) The employer shall train each employee who is employed in a regulated area in accordance with the requirements of this Section. The employer shall institute a training program and ensure employee participation in the program.

(k)(1)(ii) The training program shall be provided as of January 27, 1977 for employees who are employed in the regulated area at that time or at the time of initial assignment to a regulated area.

(k)(1)(iii) The training program shall be provided at least annually for all employees who are employed in the regulated area, except that training regarding the occupational safety and health hazards associated with exposure to coke oven emissions and the purpose, proper use, and limitations of respiratory protective devices shall be provided at least quarterly until January 20, 1978.

(k)(1)(iv) The training program shall include informing each employee of:

(k)(1)(iv)(A) The information contained in the substance information sheet for coke oven emissions (Appendix A);

(k)(1)(iv)(B) The purpose, proper use, and limitations of respiratory protective devices required in accordance with paragraph (g) of this Section;

(k)(1)(iv)(C) The purpose for and a description of the medical surveillance program required by paragraph (j) of this Section including information on the occupational safety and health hazards associated with exposure to coke oven emissions;

(k)(1)(iv)(D) A review of all written procedures and schedules required under paragraph (f) of this Section; and

(k)(1)(iv)(E) A review of this Standard.

(k)(2) **Access to training materials**

(k)(2)(i) The employer shall make a copy of this Standard and its Appendices readily available to all employees who are employed in the regulated area.

(k)(2)(ii) The employer shall provide upon request all materials relating to the employee information and training program to the Secretary and the Director.

(l) **Communication of hazards**

(l)(1) **Hazard communication—general** The employer shall include coke oven emissions in the program established to comply with the Hazard Communication Standard (HCS) (§1910.1200). The employer shall ensure that each employee has access to labels on containers of chemicals and substances associated with coke oven processes and to safety data sheets, and is trained in accordance with the provisions of HCS and paragraph (k) of this Section. The employer shall ensure that at least the following hazard is addressed: Cancer.

(l)(2) **Signs**

(l)(2)(i) The employer shall post signs in the regulated area bearing the legend:

DANGER
COKE OVEN EMISSIONS
MAY CAUSE CANCER
DO NOT EAT, DRINK OR SMOKE
WEAR RESPIRATORY PROTECTION IN THIS AREA
AUTHORIZED PERSONNEL ONLY

(l)(2)(ii) In addition, the employer shall post signs in the areas where the permissible exposure limit is exceeded bearing the legend:

WEAR RESPIRATORY PROTECTION IN THIS AREA

(l)(2)(iii) The employer shall ensure that no statement appears on or near any sign required by this paragraph (l) which contradicts or detracts from the effects of the required sign.

(l)(2)(iv) The employer shall ensure that signs required by this paragraph (l)(2) are illuminated and cleaned as necessary so that the legend is readily visible.

(l)(2)(v) Prior to June 1, 2016, employers may use the following legend in lieu of that specified in paragraph (l)(2)(i) of this Section:

DANGER
CANCER HAZARD
AUTHORIZED PERSONNEL ONLY
NO SMOKING OR EATING

(l)(2)(vi) Prior to June 1, 2016, employers may use the following legend in lieu of that specified in paragraph (l)(2)(ii) of this Section:

DANGER
RESPIRATOR REQUIRED

(l)(3) **Labels**

(l)(3)(i) The employer shall ensure that labels of containers of contaminated protective clothing and equipment include the following information:

CONTAMINATED WITH COKE EMISSIONS
MAY CAUSE CANCER
DO NOT REMOVE DUST BY BLOWING OR SHAKING

(l)(3)(ii) Prior to June 1, 2015, employers may include the following information on contaminated protective clothing and equipment in lieu of the labeling requirements in paragraph (l)(3)(i) of this Section:

CAUTION
CLOTHING CONTAMINATED WITH COKE EMISSIONS
DO NOT REMOVE DUST BY BLOWING OR SHAKING

Coke oven emissions

Z

Toxic and Hazardous Substances

(m) **Recordkeeping**

(m)(1) **Exposure measurements** The employer shall establish and maintain an accurate record of all measurements taken to monitor employee exposure to coke oven emissions required in paragraph (e) of this Section.

(m)(1)(i) This record shall include:

(m)(1)(i)(A) Name, social security number, and job classification of the employees monitored;

(m)(1)(i)(B) The date(s), number, duration and results of each of the samples taken, including a description of the sampling procedure used to determine representative employee exposure where applicable;

(m)(1)(i)(C) The type of respiratory protective devices worn, if any;

(m)(1)(i)(D) A description of the sampling and analytical methods used and evidence of their accuracy; and

(m)(1)(i)(E) The environmental variables that could affect the measurement of employee exposure.

(m)(1)(ii) The employer shall maintain this record for at lest 40 years or for the duration of employment plus 20 years, whichever is longer.

(m)(2) **Medical surveillance** The employer shall establish and maintain an accurate record for each employee subject to medical surveillance as required by paragraph (j) of this Section.

(m)(2)(i) The record shall include:

(m)(2)(i)(A) The name, social security number, and description of duties of the employee;

(m)(2)(i)(B) A copy of the physician's written opinion;

(m)(2)(i)(C) The signed statement of any refusal to take a medical examination under paragraph (j)(1)(ii) of this Section; and

(m)(2)(i)(D) Any employee medical complaints related to exposure to coke oven emissions.

(m)(2)(ii) The employer shall keep, or assure that the examining physician keeps, the following medical records:

(m)(2)(ii)(A) A copy of the medical examination results including medical and work history required under paragraph (j)(2) of this Section;

(m)(2)(ii)(B) A description of the laboratory procedures used and a copy of any standards or guidelines used to interpret the test results;

(m)(2)(ii)(C) The initial x-ray;

(m)(2)(ii)(D) The x-rays for the most recent five (5) years;

(m)(2)(ii)(E) Any x-ray with a demonstrated abnormality and all subsequent x-rays;

(m)(2)(ii)(F) The initial cytologic examination slide and written description;

(m)(2)(ii)(G) The cytologic examination slide and written description for the most recent 10 years; and

(m)(2)(ii)(H) Any cytologic examination slides with demonstrated atypia, if such atypia persists for 3 years, and all subsequent slides and written descriptions.

(m)(2)(iii) The employer shall maintain medical records required under paragraph (m)(2) of this Section for at least 40 years, or for the duration of employment plus 20 years, whichever is longer.

(m)(3) [OI] **Availability**

(m)(3)(i) The employer shall make available upon request all records required to be maintained by paragraph (m) of this section to the Secretary and the Director for examination and copying.

(m)(3)(ii) Employee exposure measurement records and employee medical records required by this paragraph shall be provided upon request to employees, designated representatives, and the Assistant Secretary in accordance with 29 CFR §1910.1020(a)–(e) and (g)–(i).

(m)(4) [OI] **Transfer of records**

(m)(4)(i) Whenever the employer ceases to do business, the successor employer shall receive and retain all records required to be maintained by paragraph (m) of this Section.

(m)(4)(ii) The employer shall also comply with any additional requirements involving transfer of records set forth in 29 CFR §1910.1020(h).

(n) **Observation of monitoring**

(n)(1) **Employee observation** The employer shall provide affected employees or their representatives an opportunity to observe any measuring or monitoring of employee exposure to coke oven emissions conducted pursuant to paragraph (e) of this Section.

(n)(2) **Observation procedures**

(n)(2)(i) Whenever observation of the measuring or monitoring of employee exposure to coke oven emissions requires entry into an area where the use of protective clothing or equipment is required, the employer shall provide the observer with and assure the use of such equipment and shall require the observer to comply with all other applicable safety and health procedures.

(n)(2)(ii) Without interfering with the measurement, observers shall be entitled to:

(n)(2)(ii)(A) An Explanation of the measurement procedures;

(n)(2)(ii)(B) Observe all steps related to the measurement of coke oven emissions performed at the place of exposure; and

(n)(2)(ii)(C) Record the results obtained.

(o) [Reserved]

(p) **Appendices** The information contained in the Appendices to this Section is not intended, by itself, to create any additional obligations not otherwise imposed or to detract from any existing obligation.

§1910.1029 Appendix A Coke oven emissions substance information sheet

I. Substance Identification

A. Substance: Coke Oven Emissions

B. Definition: The benzene-soluble fraction of total particulate matter present during the destructive distillation or carbonization of coal for the production of coke.

C. Permissible Exposure Limit: 150 micrograms per cubic meter of air determined as an average over an 8-hour period.

D. Regulated areas: Only employees authorized by your employer should enter a regulated area. The employer is required to designate the following areas as regulated areas: the coke oven battery, including topside and its machinery, pushside and its machinery, cokeside and its machinery, and the battery ends; the screening station; and the wharf; and the beehive ovens and their machinery.

II. Health Hazard Data

Exposure to coke oven emissions is a cause of lung cancer, and kidney cancer, in humans. Although there have not been an excess number of skin cancer cases in humans, repeated skin contact with coke oven emissions should be avoided.

III. Protective Clothing and Equipment

A. Respirators: Respirators will be provided by your employer for routine use if your employer is in the process of implementing engineering and work practice controls or where engineering and work practice controls are not feasible or insufficient to reduce exposure to or below the PEL. You must wear respirators for non-routine activities or in emergency situations where you are likely to be exposed to levels of coke oven emissions in excess of the permissible exposure limit. Until January 20, 1978, the routine wearing of respirators is voluntary. Until that date, if you choose not to wear a respirator you do not have to do so. You must still have your respirator with you and you must still wear it if you are near visible emissions. Since how well your respirator fits your face is very important, your employer is required to conduct fit tests to make sure the respirator seals properly when you wear it. These tests are simple and rapid and will be explained to you during your training sessions.

B. Protective clothing: Your employer is required to provide, and you must wear, appropriate, clean, protective clothing and equipment to protect your body from repeated skin contact with coke oven emissions and from the heat generated during the coking process. This clothing should include such items as jacket and pants and flame resistant gloves. Protective equipment should include face shield or vented goggles, protective helmets and safety shoes, insulated from hot surfaces where appropriate.

IV. Hygiene Facilities and Practices

You must not eat, drink, smoke, chew gum or tobacco, or apply cosmetics in the regulated area, except that drinking water is permitted. Your employer is required to provide lunchrooms and other areas for these purposes.

Your employer is required to provide showers, washing facilities, and change rooms. If you work in a regulated area, you must wash your face, and hands before eating. You must shower at the end of the work shift. Do not take used protective clothing out of the change rooms without your employer's permission. Your employer is required to provide for laundering or cleaning of your protective clothing.

V. Signs and Labels

Your employer is required to post warning signs and labels for your protection. Signs must be posted in regulated areas. The signs must warn that a cancer hazard is present, that only authorized employees may enter the area, and that no smoking or eating is allowed. In regulated areas where coke oven emissions are above the permissible exposure limit, the signs should also warn that respirators must be worn.

VI. Medical Examinations

If you work in a regulated area at least 30 days per year, your employer is required to provide you with a medical examination every year. The medical examination must include a medical history, a chest x-ray, pulmonary function test, weight comparison, skin examination, a urinalysis, and a urine cytology exam for early detection of urinary cancer. The urine cytology exam is only included in the initial exam until you are either 45 years or older, or have 5 or more years employment in the regulated areas when the medical exams including this test, but excepting the x-ray exam, are to be given every six months; under these conditions, you are to be given an x-ray exam at least once a year. The examining physician will provide a written opinion to your employer containing the results of the medical exams. You should also receive a copy of this opinion.

VII. Observation of Monitoring

Your employer is required to monitor your exposure to coke oven emissions and you are entitled to observe the monitoring procedure. You are entitled to receive an explanation of the measurement procedure, observe the steps taken in the measurement procedure, and to record the results obtained. When the monitoring procedure is taking place in an area where respirators or personal protective clothing and equipment are required to be worn, you must also be provided with and must wear the protective clothing and equipment.

VIII. Access to Records

You or your representative are entitled to records of your exposure to coke oven emissions upon request to your employer. Your medical examination records can be furnished to your physician upon request to your employer.

IX. Training and Education

Additional information on all of these items plus training as to hazards of coke oven emissions and the engineering and work practice controls associated with your job will also be provided by your employer.

§1910.1029 Appendix B Industrial hygiene and medical surveillance guidelines

I. Industrial Hygiene Guidelines

A. Sampling (Benzene-Soluble Fraction Total Particulate Matter)

Samples collected should be full shift (at least 7-hour) samples. Sampling should be done using a personal sampling pump with pulsation damper at a flow rate of 2 liters per minute. Samples should be collected on 0.8 micrometer pore size silver membrane filters (37 mm diameter) preceded by Gelman glass fiber type A-E filters encased in three-piece plastic (polystyrene) field monitor cassettes. The cassette face cap should be on and the plug removed. The rotameter should be checked every hour to ensure that proper flow rates are maintained.

A minimum of three full-shift samples should be collected for each job classification on each battery, at least one from each shift. If disparate results are obtained for particular job classification, sampling should be repeated. It is advisable to sample each shift on more than one day to account for environmental variables (wind, precipitation, etc.) which may affect sampling. Differences in exposures among different work shifts may indicate a need to improve work practices on a particular shift. Sampling results from different shifts for each job classification should not be averaged. Multiple samples from same shift on each battery may be used to calculate an average exposure for a particular job classification.

B. Analysis

1. All extraction glassware is cleaned with dichromic acid cleaning solution, rinsed with tap water, then dionized water, acetone, and allowed to dry completely. The glassware is rinsed with nanograde benzene before use. The Teflon cups are cleaned with benzene then with acetone.
2. Pre-weigh the 2 ml Teflon cups to one hundredth of a milligram (0.01 mg) on an autobalance AD 2 Tare weight of the cups is about 50 mg.
3. Place the silver membrane filter and glass fiber filter into a 15 ml test tube.
4. Extract with 5 ml of benzene for five minutes in an ultrasonic cleaner.
5. Filter the extract in 15 ml medium glass fritted funnels.
6. Rinse test tube and filters with two 1.5 ml aliquots of benzene and filter through the fritted glass funnel.
7. Collect the extract and two rinses in a 10 ml Kontes graduated evaporative concentrator.
8. Evaporate down to 1 ml while rinsing the sides with benzene.
9. Pipet 0.5 ml into the Teflon cup and evaporate to dryness in a vacuum oven at 40 °C for 3 hours.
10 Weigh the Teflon cup and the weight gain is due to the benzene soluble residue in half the Sample.

II. Medical Surveillance Guidelines

A. General The minimum requirements for the medical examination for coke oven workers are given in paragraph (j) of the standard. The initial examination is to be provided to all coke oven workers who work at least 30 days in the regulated area. The examination includes a 14" x 17"; posterior-anterior chest x-ray reading, pulmonary function tests (FVC and FEV 1.0), weight, urinalysis, skin examination, and a urinary cytologic examination. These tests are needed to serve as the baseline for comparing the employee's future test results. Periodic exams include all the elements of the initial exam, except that the urine cytologic test is to be performed only on those employees who are 45 years or older or who have worked for 5 or more years in the regulated area; periodic exams, with the exception of x-rays, are to be performed semiannually for this group instead of annually; for this group, x-rays will continue to be given at least annually. The examination contents are minimum requirements; additional tests such as lateral and oblique x-rays or additional pulmonary function tests may be performed if deemed necessary.

B. Pulmonary function tests

Pulmonary function tests should be performed in a manner which minimizes subject and operator bias. There has been shown to be learning effects with regard to the results obtained from certain tests, such as FEV 1.0. Best results can be obtained by multiple trials for each subject. The best of three trials or the average of the last three of five trials may be used in obtaining reliable results. The type of equipment used (manufacturer, model, etc.) should be recorded with the results as reliability and accuracy varies and such information may be important in the evaluation of test results. Care should be exercised to obtain the best possible testing equipment.

[39 FR 23502, June 27, 1974, 41 FR 46784, Oct. 22, 1976, as amended at 42 FR 3304, Jan. 18, 1977; 45 FR 35283, May 23, 1980; 50 FR 37353, 37354, Sept. 13, 1985; 54 FR 24334, June 7, 1989; 61 FR 5508, Feb. 13, 1996; 63 FR 1290, Jan. 8, 1998; 63 FR 33468, June 18, 1998; 70 FR 1142, Jan. 5, 2005; 71 FR 16672, 16673, Apr. 3, 2006; 71 FR 50189, Aug. 24, 2006; 73 FR 75585, Dec. 12, 2008; 76 FR 33608, June 8, 2011]

§1910.1030 Bloodborne pathogens

(a) **Scope and Application** This Section applies to all occupational exposure to blood or other potentially infectious materials as defined by paragraph (b) of this Section.

(b) **Definitions** For purposes of this Section, the following shall apply:

Assistant Secretary means the Assistant Secretary of Labor for Occupational Safety and Health, or designated representative.

Blood means human blood, human blood components, and products made from human blood.

Bloodborne Pathogens means pathogenic microorganisms that are present in human blood and can cause disease in humans. These pathogens include, but are not limited to, hepatitis B virus (HBV) and human immunodeficiency virus (HIV).

Clinical Laboratory means a workplace where diagnostic or other screening procedures are performed on blood or other potentially infectious materials.

Contaminated means the presence or the reasonably anticipated presence of blood or other potentially infectious materials on an item or surface.

Contaminated Laundry means laundry which has been soiled with blood or other potentially infectious materials or may contain sharps.

Contaminated Sharps means any contaminated object that can penetrate the skin including, but not limited to, needles, scalpels, broken glass, broken capillary tubes, and exposed ends of dental wires.

Decontamination means the use of physical or chemical means to remove, inactivate, or destroy bloodborne pathogens on a surface or item to the point where they are no longer capable of transmitting infectious particles and the surface or item is rendered safe for handling, use, or disposal.

Director means the Director of the National Institute for Occupational Safety and Health, U.S. Department of Health and Human Services, or designated representative.

Engineering controls means controls (e.g., sharps disposal containers, self-sheathing needles, safer medical devices, such as sharps with engineered sharps injury protections and needleless systems) that isolate or remove the bloodborne pathogens hazard from the workplace.

Exposure Incident means a specific eye, mouth, other mucous membrane, non-intact skin, or parenteral contact with blood or other potentially infectious materials that results from the performance of an employee's duties.

Handwashing facilities means a facility providing an adequate supply of running potable water, soap, and single-use towels or air-drying machines.

Licensed Healthcare Professional is a person whose legally permitted scope of practice aAllows him or her to independently perform the activities required by paragraph (f) Hepatitis B Vaccination and Post-exposure Evaluation and Follow-up.

HBV means hepatitis B virus.

HIV means human immunodeficiency virus.

Needleless systems means a device that does not use needles for:

(1) The collection of bodily fluids or withdrawal of body fluids after initial venous or arterial access is established;
(2) The administration of medication or fluids; or
(3) Any other procedure involving the potential for occupational exposure to bloodborne pathogens due to percutaneous injuries from contaminated sharps.

Occupational Exposure means reasonably anticipated skin, eye, mucous membrane, or parenteral contact with blood or other potentially infectious materials that may result from the performance of an employee's duties.

Other Potentially Infectious Materials means

(1) The following human body fluids: semen, vaginal secretions, cerebrospinal fluid, synovial fluid, pleural fluid, pericardial fluid, peritoneal fluid, amniotic fluid, saliva in dental procedures, any body fluid that is visibly contaminated with blood, and all body fluids in situations where it is difficult or impossible to differentiate between body fluids;

(2) Any unfixed tissue or organ (other than intact skin) from a human (living or dead); and

(3) HIV-containing cell or tissue cultures, organ cultures, and HIV- or HBV-containing culture medium or other solutions; and blood, organs, or other tissues from experimental animals infected with HIV or HBV.

Parenteral means piercing mucous membranes or the skin barrier through such events as needlesticks, human bites, cuts, and abrasions.

Personal Protective Equipment is specialized clothing or equipment worn by an employee for protection against a hazard. General work clothes (e.g., uniforms, pants, shirts or blouses) not intended to function as protection against a hazard are not considered to be personal protective equipment.

Production Facility means a facility engaged in industrial-scale, large-volume or high concentration production of HIV or HBV.

Regulated Waste means liquid or semi-liquid blood or other potentially infectious materials; contaminated items that would release blood or other potentially infectious materials in a liquid or semi-liquid state if compressed; items that are caked with dried blood or other potentially infectious materials and are capable of releasing these materials during handling; contaminated sharps; and pathological and microbiological wastes containing blood or other potentially infectious materials.

Research Laboratory means a laboratory producing or using research-laboratory-scale amounts of HIV or HBV. Research laboratories may produce high concentrations of HIV or HBV but not in the volume found in production facilities.

Sharps with engineered sharps injury protections means a nonneedle sharp or a needle device used for withdrawing body fluids, accessing a vein or artery, or administering medications or other fluids, with a built-in safety feature or mechanism that effectively reduces the risk of an exposure incident.

Source Individual means any individual, living or dead, whose blood or other potentially infectious materials may be a source of occupational exposure to the employee. Examples include, but are not limited to, hospital and clinic patients; clients in institutions for the developmentally disabled; trauma victims; clients of drug and alcohol treatment facilities; residents of hospices and nursing homes; human remains; and individuals who donate or sell blood or blood components.

Sterilize means the use of a physical or chemical procedure to destroy all microbial life including highly resistant bacterial endospores.

Universal Precautions is an approach to infection control. According to the concept of Universal Precautions, all human blood and certain human body fluids are treated as if known to be infectious for HIV, HBV, and other bloodborne pathogens.

Work Practice Controls means controls that reduce the likelihood of exposure by altering the manner in which a task is performed (e.g., prohibiting recapping of needles by a two-handed technique).

(c) Exposure control

(c)(1) Exposure Control Plan

(c)(1)(i) Each employer having an employee(s) with occupational exposure as defined by paragraph (b) of this Section shall establish a written Exposure Control Plan designed to eliminate or minimize employee exposure.

(c)(1)(ii) The Exposure Control Plan shall contain at least the following elements:

(c)(1)(ii)(A) The exposure determination required by paragraph (c)(2);

(c)(1)(ii)(B) The schedule and method of implementation for paragraphs (d) Methods of Compliance, (e) HIV and HBV Research Laboratories and Production Facilities, (f) Hepatitis B Vaccination and Post-Exposure Evaluation and Follow-up, (g) Communication of Hazards to Employees, and (h) Recordkeeping, of this Standard; and

(c)(1)(ii)(C) The procedure for the evaluation of circumstances surrounding exposure incidents as required by paragraph (f)(3)(i) of this Standard.

(c)(1)(iii) Each employer shall ensure that a copy of the Exposure Control Plan is accessible to employees in accordance with 29 CFR §1910.1020(e).

(c)(1)(iv) The Exposure Control Plan shall be reviewed and updated at least annually and whenever necessary to reflect new or modified tasks and procedures which affect occupational exposure and to reflect new or revised employee positions with occupational exposure. The review and update of such plans shall also:

(c)(1)(iv)(A) Reflect changes in technology that eliminate or reduce exposure to bloodborne pathogens; and

(c)(1)(iv)(B) Document annually consideration and implementation of appropriate commercially available and effective safer medical devices designed to eliminate or minimize occupational exposure.

(c)(1)(v) An employer, who is required to establish an Exposure Control Plan shall solicit input from non-managerial employees responsible for direct patient care who are potentially exposed to injuries from contaminated sharps in the identification, evaluation, and selection of effective engineering and work practice controls and shall document the solicitation in the Exposure Control Plan.

(c)(1)(vi) The Exposure Control Plan shall be made available to the Assistant Secretary and the Director upon request for examination and copying.

(c)(2) Exposure determination

(c)(2)(i) Each employer who has an employee(s) with occupational exposure as defined by paragraph (b) of this Section shall prepare an exposure determination. This exposure determination shall contain the following:

(c)(2)(i)(A) A list of all job classifications in which all employees in those job classifications have occupational exposure;

(c)(2)(i)(B) A list of job classifications in which some employees have occupational exposure, and

(c)(2)(i)(C) A list of all tasks and procedures or groups of closely related task and procedures in which occupational exposure occurs and that are performed by employees in job classifications listed in accordance with the provisions of paragraph (c)(2)(i)(B) of this Standard.

(c)(2)(ii) This exposure determination shall be made without regard to the use of personal protective equipment.

(d) Methods of compliance

(d)(1) **General** Universal precautions shall be observed to prevent contact with blood or other potentially infectious materials. Under circumstances in which differentiation between body fluid types is difficult or impossible, all body fluids shall be considered potentially infectious materials.

(d)(2) Engineering and work practice controls

(d)(2)(i) Engineering and work practice controls shall be used to eliminate or minimize employee exposure. Where occupational exposure remains after institution of these controls, personal protective equipment shall also be used.

(d)(2)(ii) Engineering controls shall be examined and maintained or replaced on a regular schedule to ensure their effectiveness.

(d)(2)(iii) Employers shall provide handwashing facilities which are readily accessible to employees.

(d)(2)(iv) When provision of handwashing facilities is not feasible, the employer shall provide either an appropriate antiseptic hand cleanser in conjunction with clean cloth/paper towels or antiseptic towelettes. When antiseptic hand cleansers or towelettes are used, hands shall be washed with soap and running water as soon as feasible.

(d)(2)(v) Employers shall ensure that employees wash their hands immediately or as soon as feasible after removal of gloves or other personal protective equipment.

(d)(2)(vi) Employers shall ensure that employees wash hands and any other skin with soap and water, or flush mucous membranes with water immediately or as soon as feasible following contact of such body areas with blood or other potentially infectious materials.

(d)(2)(vii) Contaminated needles and other contaminated sharps shall not be bent, recapped, or removed except as noted in paragraphs (d)(2)(vii)(A) and (d)(2)(vii)(B) below. Shearing or breaking of contaminated needles is prohibited.

(d)(2)(vii)(A) Contaminated needles and other contaminated sharps shall not be bent, recapped or removed unless the employer can demonstrate that no alternative is feasible or that such action is required by a specific medical or dental procedure.

(d)(2)(vii)(B) Such bending, recapping or needle removal must be accomplished through the use of a mechanical device or a one-handed technique.

(d)(2)(viii) Immediately or as soon as possible after use, contaminated reusable sharps shall be placed in appropriate containers until properly reprocessed. These containers shall be:

(d)(2)(viii)(A) Puncture resistant;

(d)(2)(viii)(B) Labeled or color-coded in accordance with this Standard;

(d)(2)(viii)(C) Leakproof on the sides and bottom; and

(d)(2)(viii)(D) In accordance with the requirements set forth in paragraph (d)(4)(ii)(E) for reusable sharps.

(d)(2)(ix) Eating, drinking, smoking, applying cosmetics or lip balm, and handling contact lenses are prohibited in work areas where there is a reasonable likelihood of occupational exposure.

(d)(2)(x) Food and drink shall not be kept in refrigerators, freezers, shelves, cabinets or on countertops or benchtops where blood or other potentially infectious materials are present.

(d)(2)(xi) All procedures involving blood or other potentially infectious materials shall be performed in such a manner as to minimize splashing, spraying, spattering, and generation of droplets of these substances.

(d)(2)(xii) Mouth pipetting/suctioning of blood or other potentially infectious materials is prohibited.

(d)(2)(xiii) Specimens of blood or other potentially infectious materials shall be placed in a container which prevents leakage during collection, handling, processing, storage, transport, or shipping.

(d)(2)(xiii)(A) The container for storage, transport, or shipping shall be labeled or color-coded according to paragraph (g)(1)(i) and closed prior to being stored, transported, or shipped. When a facility utilizes Universal Precautions in the handling of all specimens, the labeling/color-coding of specimens is not necessary provided containers are recognizable as containing specimens. This exemption only applies while such specimens/containers remain within the facility. Labeling or color-coding in accordance with paragraph (g)(1)(i) is required when such specimens/containers leave the facility.

(d)(2)(xiii)(B) If outside contamination of the primary container occurs, the primary container shall be placed within a second container which prevents leakage during handling, processing, storage, transport, or shipping and is labeled or color-coded according to the requirements of this Standard.

(d)(2)(xiii)(C) If the specimen could puncture the primary container, the primary container shall be placed within a secondary container which is puncture-resistant in addition to the above characteristics.

(d)(2)(xiv) Equipment which may become contaminated with blood or other potentially infectious materials shall be examined prior to servicing or shipping and shall be decontaminated as necessary, unless the employer can demonstrate that decontamination of such equipment or portions of such equipment is not feasible.

(d)(2)(xiv)(A) A readily observable label in accordance with paragraph (g)(1)(i)(H) shall be attached to the equipment stating which portions remain contaminated.

(d)(2)(xiv)(B) The employer shall ensure that this information is conveyed to all affected employees, the servicing representative, and/or the manufacturer, as appropriate, prior to handling, servicing, or shipping so that appropriate precautions will be taken.

(d)(3) Personal protective equipment

(d)(3)(i) Provision When there is occupational exposure, the employer shall provide, at no cost to the employee, appropriate personal protective equipment such as, but not limited to, gloves, gowns, laboratory coats, face shields or masks and eye protection, and mouthpieces, resuscitation bags, pocket masks, or other ventilation devices. Personal protective equipment will be considered "appropriate" only if it does not permit blood or other potentially infectious materials to pass through to or reach the employee's work clothes, street clothes, undergarments, skin, eyes, mouth, or other mucous membranes under normal conditions of use and for the duration of time which the protective equipment will be used.

(d)(3)(ii) Use The employer shall ensure that the employee uses appropriate personal protective equipment unless the employer shows that the employee temporarily and briefly declined to use personal protective equipment when, under rare and extraordinary circumstances, it was the employee's professional judgment that in the specific instance its use would have prevented the delivery of health care or public safety services or would have posed an increased hazard to the safety of the worker or co-worker. When the employee makes this judgement, the circumstances shall be investigated and documented in order to determine whether changes can be instituted to prevent such occurrences in the future.

(d)(3)(iii) Accessibility The employer shall ensure that appropriate personal protective equipment in the appropriate sizes is readily accessible at the worksite or is issued to employees. Hypoallergenic gloves, glove liners, powderless gloves, or other similar alternatives shall be readily accessible to those employees who are allergic to the gloves normally provided.

(d)(3)(iv) Cleaning, Laundering, and Disposal The employer shall clean, launder, and dispose of personal protective equipment required by paragraphs (d) and (e) of this Standard, at no cost to the employee.

(d)(3)(v) Repair and Replacement The employer shall repair or replace personal protective equipment as needed to maintain its effectiveness, at no cost to the employee.

(d)(3)(vi) If a garment(s) is penetrated by blood or other potentially infectious materials, the garment(s) shall be removed immediately or as soon as feasible.

(d)(3)(vii) All personal protective equipment shall be removed prior to leaving the work area.

(d)(3)(viii) When personal protective equipment is removed it shall be placed in an appropriately designated area or container for storage, washing, decontamination or disposal.

(d)(3)(ix) Gloves Gloves shall be worn when it can be reasonably anticipated that the employee may have hand contact with blood, other potentially infectious materials, mucous membranes, and non-intact skin; when performing vascular access procedures except as specified in paragraph (d)(3)(ix)(D); and when handling or touching contaminated items or surfaces.

(d)(3)(ix)(A) Disposable (single use) gloves such as surgical or examination gloves, shall be replaced as soon as practical when contaminated or as soon as feasible if they are torn, punctured, or when their ability to function as a barrier is compromised.

(d)(3)(ix)(B) Disposable (single use) gloves shall not be washed or decontaminated for re-use.

(d)(3)(ix)(C) Utility gloves may be decontaminated for re-use if the integrity of the glove is not compromised. However, they must be discarded if they are cracked, peeling, torn, punctured, or exhibit other signs of deterioration or when their ability to function as a barrier is compromised.

(d)(3)(ix)(D) If an employer in a volunteer blood donation center judges that routine gloving for all phlebotomies is not necessary then the employer shall:

(d)(3)(ix)(D)(1) Periodically reevaluate this policy;

(d)(3)(ix)(D)(2) Make gloves available to all employees who wish to use them for phlebotomy;

(d)(3)(ix)(D)(3) Not discourage the use of gloves for phlebotomy; and

(d)(3)(ix)(D)(4) Require that gloves be used for phlebotomy in the following circumstances:

(d)(3)(ix)(D)(4)(i) When the employee has cuts, scratches, or other breaks in his or her skin;

(d)(3)(ix)(D)(4)(ii) When the employee judges that hand contamination with blood may occur, for example, when performing phlebotomy on an uncooperative source individual; and

(d)(3)(ix)(D)(4)(iii) When the employee is receiving training in phlebotomy.

(d)(3)(x) Masks, Eye Protection, and Face Shields Masks in combination with eye protection devices, such as goggles or glasses with solid side shields, or chin-length face shields, shall be worn whenever splashes, spray, spatter, or droplets of blood or other potentially infectious materials may be generated and eye, nose, or mouth contamination can be reasonably anticipated.

(d)(3)(xi) Gowns, Aprons, and Other Protective Body Clothing Appropriate protective clothing such as, but not limited to, gowns, aprons, lab coats, clinic jackets, or similar outer garments shall be worn in occupational exposure situations. The type and characteristics will depend upon the task and degree of exposure anticipated.

(d)(3)(xii) Surgical caps or hoods and/or shoe covers or boots shall be worn in instances when gross contamination can reasonably be anticipated (e.g., autopsies, orthopaedic surgery).

(d)(4) Housekeeping

(d)(4)(i) General Employers shall ensure that the worksite is maintained in a clean and sanitary condition. The employer shall determine and implement an appropriate written schedule for cleaning and method of decontamination based upon the location within the facility, type of surface to be cleaned, type of soil present, and tasks or procedures being performed in the area.

(d)(4)(ii) All equipment and environmental and working surfaces shall be cleaned and decontaminated after contact with blood or other potentially infectious materials.

(d)(4)(ii)(A) Contaminated work surfaces shall be decontaminated with an appropriate disinfectant after completion of procedures; immediately or as soon as feasible when surfaces are overtly contaminated or after any spill of blood or other potentially infectious materials; and at the end of the work shift if the surface may have become contaminated since the last cleaning.

(d)(4)(ii)(B) Protective coverings, such as plastic wrap, aluminum foil, or imperviously-backed absorbent paper used to cover equipment and environmental surfaces, shall be removed and replaced as soon as feasible when they become overtly contaminated or at the end of the workshift if they may have become contaminated during the shift.

(d)(4)(ii)(C) All bins, pails, cans, and similar receptacles intended for reuse which have a reasonable likelihood for becoming contaminated with blood or other potentially infectious materials shall be inspected and decontaminated on a regularly scheduled basis and cleaned and decontaminated immediately or as soon as feasible upon visible contamination.

(d)(4)(ii)(D) Broken glassware which may be contaminated shall not be picked up directly with the hands. It shall be cleaned up using mechanical means, such as a brush and dust pan, tongs, or forceps.

(d)(4)(ii)(E) Reusable sharps that are contaminated with blood or other potentially infectious materials shall not be stored or processed in a manner that requires employees to reach by hand into the containers where these sharps have been placed.

(d)(4)(iii) Regulated Waste

(d)(4)(iii)(A) Contaminated Sharps Discarding and Containment

(d)(4)(iii)(A)(1) Contaminated sharps shall be discarded immediately or as soon as feasible in containers that are:

(d)(4)(iii)(A)(1)(i) Closable;

(d)(4)(iii)(A)(1)(ii) Puncture resistant;

(d)(4)(iii)(A)(1)(iii) Leakproof on sides and bottom; and

(d)(4)(iii)(A)(1)(iv) Labeled or color-coded in accordance with paragraph (g)(1)(i) of this Standard.

(d)(4)(iii)(A)(2) During use, containers for contaminated sharps shall be:

(d)(4)(iii)(A)(2)(i) Easily accessible to personnel and located as close as is feasible to the immediate area where sharps are used or can be reasonably anticipated to be found (e.g., laundries);

(d)(4)(iii)(A)(2)(ii) Maintained upright throughout use; and

(d)(4)(iii)(A)(2)(iii) Replaced routinely and not be allowed to overfill.

(d)(4)(iii)(A)(3) When moving containers of contaminated sharps from the area of use, the containers shall be:

(d)(4)(iii)(A)(3)(i) Closed immediately prior to removal or replacement to prevent spillage or protrusion of contents during handling, storage, transport, or shipping;

(d)(4)(iii)(A)(3)(ii) Placed in a secondary container if leakage is possible. The second container shall be:

(d)(4)(iii)(A)(3)(ii)(A) Closable;

(d)(4)(iii)(A)(3)(ii)(B) Constructed to contain all contents and prevent leakage during handling, storage, transport, or shipping; and

(d)(4)(iii)(A)(3)(ii)(C) Labeled or color-coded according to paragraph (g)(1)(i) of this Standard.

(d)(4)(iii)(A)(4) Reusable containers shall not be opened, emptied, or cleaned manually or in any other manner which would expose employees to the risk of percutaneous injury.

(d)(4)(iii)(B) Other Regulated Waste Containment

(d)(4)(iii)(B)(1) Regulated waste shall be placed in containers which are:

(d)(4)(iii)(B)(1)(i) Closable;

(d)(4)(iii)(B)(1)(ii) Constructed to contain all contents and prevent leakage of fluids during handling, storage, transport or shipping;

(d)(4)(iii)(B)(1)(iii) Labeled or color-coded in accordance with paragraph (g)(1)(i) this Standard; and

(d)(4)(iii)(B)(1)(iv) Closed prior to removal to prevent spillage or protrusion of contents during handling, storage, transport, or shipping.

(d)(4)(iii)(B)(2) If outside contamination of the regulated waste container occurs, it shall be placed in a second container. The second container shall be:

(d)(4)(iii)(B)(2)(i) Closable;

(d)(4)(iii)(B)(2)(ii) Constructed to contain all contents and prevent leakage of fluids during handling, storage, transport or shipping;

(d)(4)(iii)(B)(2)(iii) Labeled or color-coded in accordance with paragraph (g)(1)(i) of this Standard; and

(d)(4)(iii)(B)(2)(iv) Closed prior to removal to prevent spillage or protrusion of contents during handling, storage, transport, or shipping.

(d)(4)(iii)(C) Disposal of all regulated waste shall be in accordance with applicable regulations of the United States, States and Territories, and political subdivisions of States and Territories.

(d)(4)(iv) Laundry

(d)(4)(iv)(A) Contaminated laundry shall be handled as little as possible with a minimum of agitation.

(d)(4)(iv)(A)(1) Contaminated laundry shall be bagged or containerized at the location where it was used and shall not be sorted or rinsed in the location of use.

(d)(4)(iv)(A)(2) Contaminated laundry shall be placed and transported in bags or containers labeled or color-coded in accordance with paragraph (g)(1)(i) of this Standard. When a facility utilizes Universal Precautions in the handling of all soiled laundry, alternative labeling or color-coding is sufficient if it permits all employees to recognize the containers as requiring compliance with Universal Precautions.

(d)(4)(iv)(A)(3) Whenever contaminated laundry is wet and presents a reasonable likelihood of soak-through of or leakage from the bag or container, the laundry shall be placed and transported in bags or containers which prevent soak-through and/or leakage of fluids to the exterior.

(d)(4)(iv)(B) The employer shall ensure that employees who have contact with contaminated laundry wear protective gloves and other appropriate personal protective equipment.

(d)(4)(iv)(C) When a facility ships contaminated laundry off-site to a second facility which does not utilize Universal Precautions in the handling of all laundry, the facility generating the contaminated laundry must place such laundry in bags or containers which are labeled or color-coded in accordance with paragraph (g)(1)(i).

(e) HIV and HBV Research Laboratories and Production Facilities

(e)(1) This paragraph applies to research laboratories and production facilities engaged in the culture, production, concentration, experimentation, and manipulation of HIV and HBV. It does not apply to clinical or diagnostic laboratories engaged solely in the analysis of blood, tissues, or organs. These requirements apply in addition to the other requirements of the standard.

(e)(2) Research laboratories and production facilities shall meet the following criteria:

(e)(2)(i) **Standard microbiological practices** All regulated waste shall either be incinerated or decontaminated by a method such as autoclaving known to effectively destroy bloodborne pathogens.

(e)(2)(ii) **Special practices**

(e)(2)(ii)(A) Laboratory doors shall be kept closed when work involving HIV or HBV is in progress.

(e)(2)(ii)(B) Contaminated materials that are to be decontaminated at a site away from the work area shall be placed in a durable, leakproof, labeled or color-coded container that is closed before being removed from the work area.

(e)(2)(ii)(C) Access to the work area shall be limited to authorized persons. Written policies and procedures shall be established whereby only persons who have been advised of the potential biohazard, who meet any specific entry requirements, and who comply with all entry and exit procedures shall be allowed to enter the work areas and animal rooms.

(e)(2)(ii)(D) When other potentially infectious materials or infected animals are present in the work area or containment module, a hazard warning sign incorporating the universal biohazard symbol shall be posted on all access doors. The hazard warning sign shall comply with paragraph (g)(1)(ii) of this Standard.

(e)(2)(ii)(E) All activities involving other potentially infectious materials shall be conducted in biological safety cabinets or other physical-containment devices within the containment module. No work with these other potentially infectious materials shall be conducted on the open bench.

(e)(2)(ii)(F) Laboratory coats, gowns, smocks, uniforms, or other appropriate protective clothing shall be used in the work area and animal rooms. Protective clothing shall not be worn outside of the work area and shall be decontaminated before being laundered.

(e)(2)(ii)(G) Special care shall be taken to avoid skin contact with other potentially infectious materials. Gloves shall be worn when handling infected animals and when making hand contact with other potentially infectious materials is unavoidable.

(e)(2)(ii)(H) Before disposal all waste from work areas and from animal rooms shall either be incinerated or decontaminated by a method such as autoclaving known to effectively destroy bloodborne pathogens.

(e)(2)(ii)(I) Vacuum lines shall be protected with liquid disinfectant traps and high-efficiency particulate air (HEPA) filters or filters of equivalent or superior efficiency and which are checked routinely and maintained or replaced as necessary.

(e)(2)(ii)(J) Hypodermic needles and syringes shall be used only for parenteral injection and aspiration of fluids from laboratory animals and diaphragm bottles. Only needle-locking syringes or disposable syringe-needle units (i.e., the needle is integral to the syringe) shall be used for the injection or aspiration of other potentially infectious materials. Extreme caution shall be used when handling needles and syringes. A needle shall not be bent, sheared, replaced in the sheath or guard, or removed from the syringe following use. The needle and syringe shall be promptly placed in a puncture-resistant container and autoclaved or decontaminated before reuse or disposal.

(e)(2)(ii)(K) All spills shall be immediately contained and cleaned up by appropriate professional staff or others properly trained and equipped to work with potentially concentrated infectious materials.

(e)(2)(ii)(L) A spill or accident that results in an exposure incident shall be immediately reported to the laboratory director or other responsible person.

(e)(2)(ii)(M) A biosafety manual shall be prepared or adopted and periodically reviewed and updated at least annually or more often if necessary. Personnel shall be advised of potential hazards, shall be required to read instructions on practices and procedures, and shall be required to follow them.

(e)(2)(iii) **Containment equipment**

(e)(2)(iii)(A) Certified biological safety cabinets (Class I, II, or III) or other appropriate combinations of personal protection or physical containment devices, such as special protective clothing, respirators, centrifuge safety cups, sealed centrifuge rotors, and containment caging for animals, shall be used for all activities with other potentially infectious materials that pose a threat of exposure to droplets, splashes, spills, or aerosols.

(e)(2)(iii)(B) Biological safety cabinets shall be certified when installed, whenever they are moved and at least annually.

(e)(3) **HIV and HBV research laboratories shall meet the following criteria**

(e)(3)(i) Each laboratory shall contain a facility for hand washing and an eye wash facility which is readily available within the work area.

(e)(3)(ii) An autoclave for decontamination of regulated waste shall be available.

(e)(4) **HIV and HBV production facilities shall meet the following criteria**

(e)(4)(i) The work areas shall be separated from areas that are open to unrestricted traffic flow within the building. Passage through two sets of doors shall be the basic requirement for entry into the work area from access corridors or other contiguous areas. Physical separation of the high-containment work area from access corridors or other areas or activities may also be provided by a double-doored clothes-change room (showers may be included), airlock, or other access facility that requires passing through two sets of doors before entering the work area.

(e)(4)(ii) The surfaces of doors, walls, floors and ceilings in the work area shall be water resistant so that they can be easily cleaned. Penetrations in these surfaces shall be sealed or capable of being sealed to facilitate decontamination.

(e)(4)(iii) Each work area shall contain a sink for washing hands and a readily available eye wash facility. The sink shall be foot, elbow, or automatically operated and shall be located near the exit door of the work area.

(e)(4)(iv) Access doors to the work area or containment module shall be self-closing.

(e)(4)(v) An autoclave for decontamination of regulated waste shall be available within or as near as possible to the work area.

(e)(4)(vi) A ducted exhaust-air ventilation system shall be provided. This system shall create directional airflow that draws air into the work area through the entry area. The exhaust air shall not be recirculated to any other area of the building, shall be discharged to the outside, and shall be dispersed away from occupied areas and air intakes. The proper direction of the airflow shall be verified (i.e., into the work area).

(e)(5) **Training Requirements** Additional training requirements for employees in HIV and HBV research laboratories and HIV and HBV production facilities are specified in paragraph (g)(2)(ix).

(f) **Hepatitis B vaccination and post-exposure evaluation and follow-up**

(f)(1) **General**

(f)(1)(i) The employer shall make available the hepatitis B vaccine and vaccination series to all employees who have occupational exposure, and post-exposure evaluation and follow-up to all employees who have had an exposure incident.

(f)(1)(ii) The employer shall ensure that all medical evaluations and procedures including the hepatitis B vaccine and vaccination series and post-exposure evaluation and follow-up, including prophylaxis, are:

(f)(1)(ii)(A) Made available at no cost to the employee;

(f)(1)(ii)(B) Made available to the employee at a reasonable time and place;

(f)(1)(ii)(C) Performed by or under the supervision of a licensed physician or by or under the supervision of another licensed healthcare professional; and

(f)(1)(ii)(D) Provided according to recommendations of the U.S. Public Health Service current at the time these evaluations and procedures take place, except as specified by this paragraph (f).

(f)(1)(iii) The employer shall ensure that all laboratory tests are conducted by an accredited laboratory at no cost to the employee.

(f)(2) **Hepatitis B Vaccination**

(f)(2)(i) Hepatitis B vaccination shall be made available after the employee has received the training required in paragraph (g)(2)(vii)(I) and within 10 working days of initial assignment to all employees who have occupational exposure unless the employee has previously received the complete hepatitis B vaccination series, antibody testing has revealed that the employee is immune, or the vaccine is contraindicated for medical reasons.

(f)(2)(ii) The employer shall not make participation in a prescreening program a prerequisite for receiving hepatitis B vaccination.

(f)(2)(iii) If the employee initially declines hepatitis B vaccination but at a later date while still covered under the standard decides to accept the vaccination, the employer shall make available hepatitis B vaccination at that time.

(f)(2)(iv) The employer shall assure that employees who decline to accept hepatitis B vaccination offered by the employer sign the statement in Appendix A.

(f)(2)(v) If a routine booster dose(s) of hepatitis B vaccine is recommended by the U.S. Public Health Service at a future date, such booster dose(s) shall be made available in accordance with Section (f)(1)(ii).

(f)(3) **Post-exposure Evaluation and Follow-up** Following a report of an exposure incident, the employer shall make immediately available to the exposed employee a confidential medical evaluation and follow-up, including at least the following elements:

(f)(3)(i) Documentation of the route(s) of exposure, and the circumstances under which the exposure incident occurred;

(f)(3)(ii) Identification and documentation of the source individual, unless the employer can establish that identification is infeasible or prohibited by state or local law;

(f)(3)(ii)(A) The source individual's blood shall be tested as soon as feasible and after consent is obtained in order to determine HBV and HIV infectivity. If consent is not obtained, the employer shall establish that legally required consent cannot be obtained. When the source individual's consent is not required by law, the source individual's blood, if available, shall be tested and the results documented.

(f)(3)(ii)(B) When the source individual is already known to be infected with HBV or HIV, testing for the source individual's known HBV or HIV status need not be repeated.

(f)(3)(ii)(C) Results of the source individual's testing shall be made available to the exposed employee, and the employee shall be informed of applicable laws and regulations concerning disclosure of the identity and infectious status of the source individual.

(f)(3)(iii) Collection and testing of blood for HBV and HIV serological status;

(f)(3)(iii)(A) The exposed employee's blood shall be collected as soon as feasible and tested after consent is obtained.

(f)(3)(iii)(B) If the employee consents to baseline blood collection, but does not give consent at that time for HIV serologic testing, the sample shall be preserved for at least 90 days. If, within 90 days of the exposure incident, the employee elects to have the baseline sample tested, such testing shall be done as soon as feasible.

(f)(3)(iv) Post-exposure prophylaxis, when medically indicated, as recommended by the U.S. Public Health Service;

(f)(3)(v) Counseling; and

(f)(3)(vi) Evaluation of reported illnesses.

(f)(4) **Information Provided to the Healthcare Professional**

(f)(4)(i) The employer shall ensure that the healthcare professional responsible for the employee's hepatitis B vaccination is provided a copy of this regulation.

(f)(4)(ii) The employer shall ensure that the healthcare professional evaluating an employee after an exposure incident is provided the following information:

(f)(4)(ii)(A) A copy of this regulation;

(f)(4)(ii)(B) A description of the exposed employee's duties as they relate to the exposure incident;

(f)(4)(ii)(C) Documentation of the route(s) of exposure and circumstances under which exposure occurred;

(f)(4)(ii)(D) Results of the source individual's blood testing, if available; and

(f)(4)(ii)(E) All medical records relevant to the appropriate treatment of the employee including vaccination status which are the employer's responsibility to maintain.

(f)(5) **Healthcare Professional's Written Opinion** The employer shall obtain and provide the employee with a copy of the evaluating healthcare professional's written opinion within 15 days of the completion of the evaluation.

(f)(5)(i) The healthcare professional's written opinion for Hepatitis B vaccination shall be limited to whether Hepatitis B vaccination is indicated for an employee, and if the employee has received such vaccination.

(f)(5)(ii) The healthcare professional's written opinion for post-exposure evaluation and follow-up shall be limited to the following information:

(f)(5)(ii)(A) That the employee has been informed of the results of the evaluation; and

(f)(5)(ii)(B) That the employee has been told about any medical conditions resulting from exposure to blood or other potentially infectious materials which require further evaluation or treatment.

(f)(5)(iii) All other findings or diagnoses shall remain confidential and shall not be included in the written report.

(f)(6) **Medical recordkeeping** Medical records required by this Standard shall be maintained in accordance with paragraph (h)(1) of this Section.

(g) **Communication of hazards to employees**

(g)(1) **Labels and signs**

(g)(1)(i) Labels

(g)(1)(i)(A) Warning labels shall be affixed to containers of regulated waste, refrigerators and freezers containing blood or other potentially infectious material; and other containers used to store, transport or ship blood or other potentially infectious materials, except as provided in paragraph (g)(1)(i)(E), (F) and (G).

(g)(1)(i)(B) Labels required by this Section shall include the following legend:

BIOHAZARD

(g)(1)(i)(C) These labels shall be fluorescent orange or orange-red or predominantly so, with lettering and symbols in a contrasting color.

(g)(1)(i)(D) Labels shall be affixed as close as feasible to the container by string, wire, adhesive, or other method that prevents their loss or unintentional removal.

(g)(1)(i)(E) Red bags or red containers may be substituted for labels.

(g)(1)(i)(F) Containers of blood, blood components, or blood products that are labeled as to their contents and have been released for transfusion or other clinical use are exempted from the labeling requirements of paragraph (g).

(g)(1)(i)(G) Individual containers of blood or other potentially infectious materials that are placed in a labeled container during storage, transport, shipment or disposal are exempted from the labeling requirement.

(g)(1)(i)(H) Labels required for contaminated equipment shall be in accordance with this paragraph and shall also state which portions of the equipment remain contaminated.

(g)(1)(i)(I) Regulated waste that has been decontaminated need not be labeled or color-coded.

(g)(1)(ii) **Signs**

(g)(1)(ii)(A) The employer shall post signs at the entrance to work areas specified in paragraph (e), HIV and HBV Research Laboratory and Production Facilities, which shall bear the following legend:

BIOHAZARD

(Name of the Infectious Agent)
(Special requirements for entering the area)
(Name, telephone number of the laboratory director
or other responsible person)

(g)(1)(ii)(B) These signs shall be fluorescent orange-red or predominantly so, with lettering and symbols in a contrasting color.

(g)(2) **Information and Training**

(g)(2)(i) The employer shall train each employee with occupational exposure in accordance with the requirements of this Section. Such training must be provided at no cost to the employee and during working hours. The employer shall institute a training program and ensure employee participation in the program.

(g)(2)(ii) Training shall be provided as follows:

(g)(2)(ii)(A) At the time of initial assignment to tasks where occupational exposure may take place;

(g)(2)(ii)(B) At least annually thereafter.

(g)(2)(iii) [Reserved]

(g)(2)(iv) Annual training for all employees shall be provided within one year of their previous training.

(g)(2)(v) Employers shall provide additional training when changes such as modification of tasks or procedures or institution of new tasks or procedures affect the employee's occupational exposure. The additional training may be limited to addressing the new exposures created.

(g)(2)(vi) Material appropriate in content and vocabulary to educational level, literacy, and language of employees shall be used.

(g)(2)(vii) The training program shall contain at a minimum the following elements:

(g)(2)(vii)(A) An accessible copy of the regulatory text of this Standard and an explanation of its contents;

(g)(2)(vii)(B) A general explanation of the epidemiology and symptoms of bloodborne diseases;

(g)(2)(vii)(C) An explanation of the modes of transmission of bloodborne pathogens;

(g)(2)(vii)(D) An explanation of the employer's exposure control plan and the means by which the employee can obtain a copy of the written plan;

(g)(2)(vii)(E) An explanation of the appropriate methods for recognizing tasks and other activities that may involve exposure to blood and other potentially infectious materials;

(g)(2)(vii)(F) An explanation of the use and limitations of methods that will prevent or reduce exposure including appropriate engineering controls, work practices, and personal protective equipment;

(g)(2)(vii)(G) Information on the types, proper use, location, removal, handling, decontamination and disposal of personal protective equipment;

(g)(2)(vii)(H) An explanation of the basis for selection of personal protective equipment;

(g)(2)(vii)(I) Information on the hepatitis B vaccine, including information on its efficacy, safety, method of administration, the benefits of being vaccinated, and that the vaccine and vaccination will be offered free of charge;

(g)(2)(vii)(J) Information on the appropriate actions to take and persons to contact in an emergency involving blood or other potentially infectious materials;

(g)(2)(vii)(K) An explanation of the procedure to follow if an exposure incident occurs, including the method of reporting the incident and the medical follow-up that will be made available;

(g)(2)(vii)(L) Information on the post-exposure evaluation and follow-up that the employer is required to provide for the employee following an exposure incident;

(g)(2)(vii)(M) An explanation of the signs and labels and/or color coding required by paragraph (g)(1); and

(g)(2)(vii)(N) An opportunity for interactive questions and answers with the person conducting the training session.

(g)(2)(viii) The person conducting the training shall be knowledgeable in the subject matter covered by the elements contained in the training program as it relates to the workplace that the training will address.

(g)(2)(ix) Additional Initial Training for Employees in HIV and HBV Laboratories and Production Facilities. Employees in HIV or HBV research laboratories and HIV or HBV production facilities shall receive the following initial training in addition to the above training requirements.

(g)(2)(ix)(A) The employer shall assure that employees demonstrate proficiency in standard microbiological practices and techniques and in the practices and operations specific to the facility before being allowed to work with HIV or HBV.

(g)(2)(ix)(B) The employer shall assure that employees have prior experience in the handling of human pathogens or tissue cultures before working with HIV or HBV.

(g)(2)(ix)(C) The employer shall provide a training program to employees who have no prior experience in handling human pathogens. Initial work activities shall not include the handling of infectious agents. A progression of work activities shall be assigned as techniques are learned and proficiency is developed. The employer shall assure that employees participate in work activities involving infectious agents only after proficiency has been demonstrated.

(h) Recordkeeping

(h)(1) Medical Records

(h)(1)(i) The employer shall establish and maintain an accurate record for each employee with occupational exposure, in accordance with 29 CFR §1910.1020.

(h)(1)(ii) This record shall include:

(h)(1)(ii)(A) The name and social security number of the employee;

(h)(1)(ii)(B) A copy of the employee's hepatitis B vaccination status including the dates of all the hepatitis B vaccinations and any medical records relative to the employee's ability to receive vaccination as required by paragraph (f)(2);

(h)(1)(ii)(C) A copy of all results of examinations, medical testing, and follow-up procedures as required by paragraph (f)(3);

(h)(1)(ii)(D) The employer's copy of the healthcare professional's written opinion as required by paragraph (f)(5); and

(h)(1)(ii)(E) A copy of the information provided to the healthcare professional as required by paragraphs (f)(4)(ii)(B)(C) and (D).

(h)(1)(iii) **Confidentiality** The employer shall ensure that employee medical records required by paragraph (h)(1) are:

(h)(1)(iii)(A) Kept confidential; and

(h)(1)(iii)(B) Not disclosed or reported without the employee's express written consent to any person within or outside the workplace except as required by this Section or as may be required by law.

(h)(1)(iv) The employer shall maintain the records required by paragraph (h) for at least the duration of employment plus 30 years in accordance with 29 CFR §1910.1020.

(h)(2) Training Records

(h)(2)(i) Training records shall include the following information:

(h)(2)(i)(A) The dates of the training sessions;

(h)(2)(i)(B) The contents or a summary of the training sessions;

(h)(2)(i)(C) The names and qualifications of persons conducting the training; and

(h)(2)(i)(D) The names and job titles of all persons attending the training sessions.

(h)(2)(ii) Training records shall be maintained for 3 years from the date on which the training occurred.

(h)(3) Availability

(h)(3)(i) The employer shall ensure that all records required to be maintained by this Section shall be made available upon request to the Assistant Secretary and the Director for examination and copying.

(h)(3)(ii) Employee training records required by this paragraph shall be provided upon request for examination and copying to employees, to employee representatives, to the Director, and to the Assistant Secretary.

(h)(3)(iii) Employee medical records required by this paragraph shall be provided upon request for examination and copying to the subject employee, to anyone having written consent of the subject employee, to the Director, and to the Assistant Secretary in accordance with 29 CFR §1910.1020.

(h)(4) **Transfer of Records** The employer shall comply with the requirements involving transfer of records set forth in 29 CFR §1910.1020(h).

(h)(5) Sharps injury log

(h)(5)(i) The employer shall establish and maintain a sharps injury log for the recording of percutaneous injuries from contaminated sharps. The information in the sharps injury log shall be recorded and maintained in such manner as to protect the confidentiality of the injured employee. The sharps injury log shall contain, at a minimum:

(h)(5)(i)(A) The type and brand of device involved in the incident,

(h)(5)(i)(B) The department or work area where the exposure incident occurred, and

(h)(5)(i)(C) An explanation of how the incident occurred.

(h)(5)(ii) The requirement to establish and maintain a sharps injury log shall apply to any employer who is required to maintain a log of occupational injuries and illnesses under 29 CFR Part §1904.

(h)(5)(iii) The sharps injury log shall be maintained for the period required by 29 CFR §1904.33.

(i) Dates

(i)(1) **Effective Date** The standard shall become effective on March 6, 1992.

(i)(2) The Exposure Control Plan required by paragraph (c) of this Section shall be completed on or before May 5, 1992.

(i)(3) Paragraph (g)(2) Information and Training and (h) Recordkeeping of this Section shall take effect on or before June 4, 1992.

(i)(4) Paragraphs (d)(2) Engineering and Work Practice Controls, (d)(3) Personal Protective Equipment, (d)(4) Housekeeping, (e) HIV and HBV Research Laboratories and Production Facilities, (f) Hepatitis B Vaccination and Post-Exposure Evaluation and Follow-up, and (g)(1) Labels and Signs of this Section, shall take effect July 6, 1992.

§1910.1030 Appendix A
Hepatitis B Vaccine Declination
(Mandatory)

I understand that due to my occupational exposure to blood or other potentially infectious materials I may be at risk of acquiring hepatitis B virus (HBV) infection. I have been given the opportunity to be vaccinated with hepatitis B vaccine, at no charge to myself. However, I decline hepatitis B vaccination at this time. I understand that by declining this vaccine, I continue to be at risk of acquiring hepatitis B, a serious disease. If in the future I continue to have occupational exposure to blood or other potentially infectious materials and I want to be vaccinated with hepatitis B vaccine, I can receive the vaccination series at no charge to me.

[56 FR 64175, Dec. 6, 1991, as amended at 57 FR 12717, Apr. 13, 1992; 57 FR 29206, July 1, 1992; 61 FR 5508, Feb. 13, 1996; 66 FR 5325, Jan. 18, 2001; 71 FR 16672, 16673, Apr. 3, 2006; 73 FR 75586, Dec. 12, 2008; 76 FR 33608, June 8, 2011]

§1910.1043
Cotton dust

(a) Scope and application

(a)(1) This Section, in its entirety, applies to the control of employee exposure to cotton dust in all workplaces where employees engage in yarn manufacturing, engage in slashing and weaving operations, or work in waste houses for textile operations.

(a)(2) This Section does not apply to the handling or processing of woven or knitted materials; to maritime operations covered by 29 CFR Parts 1915 and 1918; to harvesting or ginning of cotton; or to the construction industry.

(a)(3) Only paragraphs (h) Medical surveillance, (k)(2) through (4) Recordkeeping—Medical Records, and Appendices B, C and D of this Section apply in all work places where employees exposed to cotton dust engage in cottonseed processing or waste processing operations.

(a)(4) This Section applies to yarn manufacturing and slashing and weaving operations exclusively using washed cotton (as defined by paragraph (n) of this Section) only to the extent specified by paragraph (n) of this Section.

(a)(5) This Section, in its entirety, applies to the control of all employees exposure to the cotton dust generated in the preparation of washed cotton from opening until the cotton is thoroughly wetted.

(a)(6) This Section does not apply to knitting, classing or warehousing operations except that employers with these operations, if requested by NIOSH, shall grant NIOSH access to their employees and workplaces for exposure monitoring and medical examinations for purposes of a health study to be performed by NIOSH on a sampling basis.

(b) **Definitions** For the purpose of this Section:

Assistant Secretary means the Assistant Secretary of Labor for Occupational Safety and Health, U.S. Department of Labor, or designee;

Blow down means the general cleaning of a room or a part of a room by the use of compressed air.

Blow off means the use of compressed air for cleaning of short duration and usually for a specific machine or any portion of a machine.

Cotton dust means dust present in the air during the handling or processing of cotton, which may contain a mixture of many substances including ground up plant matter, fiber, bacteria, fungi, soil, pesticides, non-cotton plant matter and other contaminants which may have accumulated with the cotton during the growing, harvesting and subsequent processing or storage periods. Any dust present during the handling and processing of cotton through the weaving or knitting of fabrics, and dust present in other operations or manufacturing processes using raw or waste cotton fibers or cotton fiber byproducts from textile mills are considered cotton dust within this definition. Lubricating oil mist associated with weaving operations is not considered cotton dust.

Director means the Director of the National Institute for Occupational Safety and Health (NIOSH), U.S. Department of Health and Human Services, or designee.

Equivalent Instrument means a cotton dust sampling device that meets the vertical elutriator equivalency requirements as described in paragraph (d)(1)(iii) of this Section.

Lint-free respirable cotton dust means particles of cotton dust of approximately 15 micrometers or less aerodynamic equivalent diameter;

Vertical elutriator cotton dust sampler or vertical elutriator means a dust sampler which has a particle size cut-off at approximately 15 micrometers aerodynamic equivalent diameter when operating at the flow rate of 7.4 ±0.2 liters of air per minute;

Waste processing means waste recycling (sorting, blending, cleaning and willowing) and garnetting.

Yarn manufacturing means all textile mill operations from opening to, but not including, slashing and weaving.

(c) Permissible exposure limits and action levels

(c)(1) Permissible exposure limits (PEL)

(c)(1)(i) The employer shall assure that no employee who is exposed to cotton dust in yarn manufacturing and cotton washing operations is exposed to airborne concentrations of lint-free respirable cotton dust greater than 200 μg/m^3 mean concentration, averaged over an eight-hour period, as measured be a vertical elutriator or an equivalent instrument.

(c)(1)(ii) The employer shall assure that no employee who is exposed to cotton dust in textile mill waste house operations or is exposed in yarn manufacturing to dust from "lower grade washed cotton" as defined in paragraph (n)(5) of this Section is exposed to airborne concentrations of lint-free respirable cotton dust greater than 500 μg/m^3 mean concentration, averaged over an eight-hour period, as measured by a vertical elutriator or an equivalent instrument.

(c)(1)(iii) The employer shall assure that no employee who is exposed to cotton dust in the textile processes known as slashing and weaving is exposed to airborne concentrations of lint-free respirable cotton dust greater than 750 μg/m^3 mean concentration, averaged over an eight hour period, as measured by a vertical elutriator or an equivalent instrument.

(c)(2) Action levels

(c)(2)(i) The action level for yarn manufacturing and cotton washing operations is an airborne concentration of lint-free respirable cotton dust of 100 μg/m^3 mean concentration, averaged over an eight-hour period, as measured by a vertical elutriator or an equivalent instrument.

(c)(2)(ii) The action level for waste houses for textile operations is an airborne concentration of lint-free respirable cotton dust of 250 μg/m^3 mean concentration, averaged over an eight-hour period, as measured by a vertical elutriator or an equivalent instrument.

(c)(2)(iii) The action level for the textile processes known as slashing and weaving is an airborne concentration of lint-free respirable cotton dust of 375 μg/m^3 mean concentration, averaged over an eight-hour period, as measured by a vertical elutriator or an equivalent instrument.

(d) Exposure monitoring and measurement

(d)(1) General

(d)(1)(i) For the purposes of this Section, employee exposure is that exposure which would occur if the employee were not using a respirator.

(d)(1)(ii) The sampling device to be used shall be either the vertical elutriator cotton dust sampler or an equivalent instrument.

(d)(1)(iii) If an alternative to the vertical elutriator cotton dust sampler is used, the employer shall establish equivalency by reference to an OSHA opinion or by documenting, based on data developed by the employer or supplied by the manufacturer, that the alternative sampling devices meets the following criteria:

(d)(1)(iii)(A) It collects respirable particulates in the same range as the vertical elutriator (approximately 15 microns);

(d)(1)(iii)(B) Replicate exposure data used to establish equivalency are collected in side-by-side field and laboratory comparisons; and

(d)(1)(iii)(C) A minimum of 100 samples over the range of 0.5 to 2 times the permissible exposure limit are collected, and 90% of these samples have an accuracy range of plus or minus 25 per cent of the vertical elutriator reading with a 95% confidence level as demonstrated by a statistically valid protocol. (An acceptable protocol for demonstrating equivalency is described in Appendix E of this Section.)

(d)(1)(iv) OSHA will issue a written opinion stating that an instrument is equivalent to a vertical elutriator cotton dust sampler if

(d)(1)(iv)(A) A manufacturer or employer requests an opinion in writing and supplies the following information:

(d)(1)(iv)(A)(1) Sufficient test data to demonstrate that the instrument meets the requirements specified in this paragraph and the protocol specified in Appendix E of this Section;

(d)(1)(iv)(A)(2) Any other relevant information about the instrument and its testing requested by OSHA; and

(d)(1)(iv)(A)(3) A certification by the manufacturer or employer that the information supplied is accurate, and

(d)(1)(iv)(B) If OSHA finds, based on information submitted about the instrument, that the instrument meets the requirements for equivalency specified by paragraph (d) of this Section.

(d)(2) Initial monitoring Each employer who has a place of employment within the scope of paragraph (a)(1), (a)(4), or (a)(5) of this Section shall conduct monitoring by obtaining measurements which are representative of the exposure of all employees to airborne concentrations of lint-free respirable cotton dust over an eight-hour period. The sampling program shall include at least one determination during each shift for each work area.

(d)(3) Periodic monitoring

(d)(3)(i) If the initial monitoring required by paragraph (d)(2) of this Section or any subsequent monitoring reveals employee exposure to be at or below the permissible exposure limit, the employer shall repeat the monitoring for those employees at least annually.

(d)(3)(ii) If the initial monitoring required by paragraph (d)(2) of this Section or any subsequent monitoring reveals employee exposure to be above the PEL, the employer shall repeat the monitoring for those employees at least every six months.

(d)(3)(iii) Whenever there has been a production, process, or control change which may result in new or additional exposure to cotton dust, or whenever the employer has any other reason to suspect an increase in employee exposure, the employer shall repeat the monitoring and measurements for those employees affected by the change or increase.

(d)(4) Employee notification

(d)(4)(i) The employer must, within 15 working days after the receipt of the results of any monitoring performed under this Section, notify each affected employee of these results either individually in writing or by posting the results in an appropriate location that is accessible to employees.

(d)(4)(ii) Whenever the results indicate that the employee's exposure exceeds the applicable permissible exposure limit specified in paragraph (c) of this Section, the employer shall include in the written notice a statement that the permissible exposure limit was exceeded and a description of the corrective action taken to reduce exposure below the permissible exposure limit.

(e) Methods of compliance

(e)(1) Engineering and work practice controls The employer shall institute engineering and work practice controls to reduce and maintain employee exposure to cotton dust at or below the permissible exposure limit specified in paragraph (c) of this Section, except to the extent that the employer can establish that such controls are not feasible.

(e)(2) Whenever feasible engineering and work practice controls are not sufficient to reduce employee exposure to or below the permissible exposure limit, the employer shall nonetheless institute these controls to reduce exposure to the lowest feasible level, and shall supplement these controls with the use of respirators which shall comply with the provisions of paragraph (f) of this Section.

(e)(3) Compliance program

(e)(3)(i) Where the most recent exposure monitoring data indicates that any employee is exposed to cotton dust levels greater than the permissible exposure limit, the employer shall establish and implement a written program sufficient to reduce exposures to or below the permissible exposure limit solely by means of engineering controls and work practices as required by paragraph (e)(1) of this Section.

(e)(3)(ii) The written program shall include at least the following:

(e)(3)(ii)(A) A description of each operation or process resulting in employee exposure to cotton dust at levels greater than the PEL;

(e)(3)(ii)(B) Engineering plans and other studies used to determine the controls for each process;

(e)(3)(ii)(C) A report of the technology considered in meeting the permissible exposure limit;

(e)(3)(ii)(D) Monitoring data obtained in accordance with paragraph (d) of this Section;

(e)(3)(ii)(E) A detailed schedule for development and implementation of engineering and work practice controls, including exposure levels projected to be achieved by such controls;

(e)(3)(ii)(F) Work practice program; and

(e)(3)(ii)(G) Other relevant information.

(e)(3)(iii) The employer's schedule as set forth in the compliance program, shall project completion of the implementation of the compliance program no later than March 27, 1984 or as soon as possible if monitoring after March 27, 1984 reveals exposures over the PEL, except as provided in paragraph (m)(2)(ii)(B) of this Section.

(e)(3)(iv) The employer shall complete the steps set forth in his program by the dates in the schedule.

(e)(3)(v) Written programs shall be submitted, upon request, to the Assistant Secretary and the Director, and shall be available at the worksite for examination and copying by the Assistant Secretary, the Director, and any affected employee or their designated representatives.

(e)(3)(vi) The written program required under paragraph (e)(3) of this Section shall be revised and updated when necessary to reflect the current status of the program and current exposure levels.

(e)(4) **Mechanical ventilation** When mechanical ventilation is used to control exposure, measurements which demonstrate the effectiveness of the system to control exposure, such as capture velocity, duct velocity, or static pressure shall be made at reasonable intervals.

(f) **Respiratory protection**

(f)(1) **General** For employees who are required to use respirators by this Section, the employer must provide each employee an appropriate respirator that complies with the requirements of this paragraph. Respirators must be used during:

(f)(1)(i) Periods necessary to install or implement feasible engineering and work-practice controls;

(f)(1)(ii) Maintenance and repair activities for which engineering and work-practice controls are not feasible;

(f)(1)(iii) Work operations for which feasible engineering and work-practice controls are not yet sufficient to reduce employee exposure to or below the permissible exposure limits;

(f)(1)(iv) Work operations specified under paragraph (g)(1) of this Section;

(f)(1)(v) Periods for which an employee requests a respirator.

(f)(2) **Respirator program**

(f)(2)(i) The employer must implement a respiratory protection program in accordance with §1910.134(b) through (d) (except (d)(1)(iii)), and (f) through (m), which covers each employee required by this Section to use a respirator.

(f)(2)(ii) Whenever a physician determines that an employee who works in an area in which the cotton-dust concentration exceeds the PEL is unable to use a respirator, including a powered air-purifying respirator, the employee must be given the opportunity to transfer to an available position, or to a position that becomes available later, that has a cotton-dust concentration at or below the PEL. The employer must ensure that such employees retain their current wage rate or other benefits as a result of the transfer.

(f)(3) **Respirator selection**

(f)(3)(i) Employers must:

(f)(3)(i)(A) Select, and provide to employees, the appropriate respirators specified in paragraph (d)(3)(i)(A) of 29 CFR §1910.134; however, employers must not select or use filtering facepieces for protection against cotton dust concentrations greater than five times (5×) the PEL.

(f)(3)(i)(B) Provide HEPA filters for powered and non-powered air-purifying respirators used at cotton dust concentrations greater than ten times (10×) the PEL.

(f)(3)(ii) Employers must provide an employee with a powered air-purifying respirator (PAPR) instead of a non-powered air-purifying respirator selected according to paragraph (f)(3)(i) of this Standard when the employee chooses to use a PAPR and it provides adequate protection to the employee as specified by paragraph (f)(3)(i) of this Standard.

(g) **Work practices** Each employer shall, regardless of the level of employee exposure, immediately establish and implement a written program of work practices which shall minimize cotton dust exposure. The following shall be included were applicable:

(g)(1) Compressed air "blow down" cleaning shall be prohibited where alternative means are feasible. Where compressed air is used for cleaning, the employees performing the "blow down" or "blow off" shall wear suitable respirators. Employees whose presence is not required to perform "blow down" or "blow off" shall be required to leave the area affected by the "blow down" or "blow off" during this cleaning operation.

(g)(2) Cleaning of clothing or floors with compressed air shall be prohibited.

(g)(3) Floor sweeping shall be performed with a vacuum or with methods designed to minimize dispersal of dust.

(g)(4) In areas where employees are exposed to concentrations of cotton dust greater than the permissible exposure limit, cotton and cotton waste shall be stacked, sorted, baled, dumped, removed or otherwise handled by mechanical means, except where the employer can show that it is infeasible to do so. Where infeasible, the method used for handling cotton and cotton waste shall be the method which reduces exposure to the lowest level feasible.

(h) **Medical surveillance**

(h)(1) **General**

(h)(1)(i) Each employer covered by the standard shall institute a program of medical surveillance for all employees exposed to cotton dust.

(h)(1)(ii) The employer shall assure that all medical examinations and procedures are performed by or under the supervision of a licensed physician and are provided without cost to the employee.

(h)(1)(iii) Persons other than licensed physicians, who administer the pulmonary function testing required by this Section shall have completed a NIOSH-approved training course in spirometry.

(h)(2) **Initial examinations** The employer shall provide medical surveillance to each employee who is or may be exposed to cotton dust. For new employees, this examination shall be provided prior to initial assignment. The medical surveillance shall include at least the following:

(h)(2)(i) A medical history;

(h)(2)(ii) The standardized questionnaire contained in Appendix B; and

(h)(2)(iii) A pulmonary function measurement, including a determination of forced vital capacity (FVC) and forced expiratory volume in one second (FEV_1), the FEV_1/FVC ratio, and the percentage that the measured values of FEV_1 and FVC differ from the predicted values, using the standard tables in Appendix C. These determinations shall be made for each employee before the employee enters the workplace on the first day of the work week, preceded by at least 35 hours of no exposure to cotton dust. The tests shall be repeated during the shift, no less than 4 and no more than 10 hours after the beginning of the work shift; and, in any event, no more than one hour after cessation of exposure. Such exposure shall be typical of the employee's usual workplace exposure. The predicted FEV_1 and FVC for blacks shall be multiplied by 0.85 to adjust for ethnic differences.

(h)(2)(iv) Based upon the questionnaire results, each employee shall be graded according to Schilling's byssinosis classification system.

(h)(3) **Periodic examinations**

(h)(3)(i) The employer shall provide at least annual medical surveillance for all employees exposed to cotton dust above the action level in yarn manufacturing, slashing and weaving, cotton washing and waste house operations. The employer shall provide medical surveillance at least every two years for all employees exposed to cotton dust at or below the action level, for all employees exposed to cotton dust from washed cotton (except from washed cotton defined in paragraph (n)(3) of this Section), and for all employees exposed to cotton dust in cottonseed processing and waste processing operations. Periodic medical surveillance shall include at least an update of the medical history, standardized questionnaire (App. B–111), Schilling byssinosis grade, and the pulmonary function measurements in paragraph (h)(2)(iii) of this Section.

(h)(3)(ii) Medical surveillance as required in paragraph (h)(3)(i) of this Section shall be provided every six months for all employees in the following categories:

(h)(3)(ii)(A) An FEV_1 of greater than 80 percent of the predicted value, but with an FEV_1 decrement of 5 percent or 200 ml. on a first working day;

(h)(3)(ii)(B) An FEV_1 of less than 80 percent of the predicted value; or

(h)(3)(ii)(C) Where, in the opinion of the physician, any significant change in questionnaire findings, pulmonary function results, or other diagnostic tests have occurred.

(h)(3)(iii) An employee whose FEV_1 is less than 60 percent of the predicted value shall be referred to a physician for a detailed pulmonary examination.

(h)(3)(iv) A comparison shall be made between the current examination results and those of previous examinations and a determination made by the physician as to whether there has been a significant change.

(h)(4) **Information provided to the physician** The employer shall provide the following information to the examination physician:

(h)(4)(i) A copy of this regulation and its Appendices:

(h)(4)(ii) A description of the affected employee's duties as they relate to the employee's exposure;

(h)(4)(iii) The employee's exposure level or anticipated exposure level;

(h)(4)(iv) A description of any personal protective equipment used or to be used; and

(h)(4)(v) Information from previous medical examinations of the affected employee which is not readily available to the examining physician.

(h)(5) **Physician's written opinion**

(h)(5)(i) The employer shall obtain and furnish the employee with a copy of a written opinion from the examining physician containing the following:

(h)(5)(i)(A) The results of the medical examination and tests including the FEV_1, FVC, AND FEV_1/FVC ratio;

(h)(5)(i)(B) The physician's opinion as to whether the employee has any detected medical conditions which would place the employee at increased risk of material impairment of the employee's health from exposure to cotton dust;

(h)(5)(i)(C) The physician's recommended limitations upon the employee's exposure to cotton dust or upon the employee's use of respirators including a determination of whether an employee can wear a negative pressure respirator, and where the employee cannot, a determination of the employee's ability to wear a powered air purifying respirator; and

(h)(5)(i)(D) A statement that the employee has been informed by the physician of the results of the medical examination and any medical conditions which require further examination or treatment.

(h)(5)(ii) The written opinion obtained by the employer shall not reveal specific findings or diagnoses unrelated to occupational exposure.

(i) **Employee education and training**

(i)(1) **Training program**

(i)(1)(i) The employer shall train each employee exposed to cotton dust in accordance with the requirements of this Section. The employer shall institute a training program and ensure employee participation in the program.

(i)(1)(i)(A) The acute and long term health hazards associated with exposure to cotton dust;

(i)(1)(i)(B) The names and descriptions of jobs and processes which could result in exposure to cotton dust at or above the PEL.

(i)(1)(i)(C) The measures, including work practices required by paragraph (g) of this Section, necessary to protect the employee from exposures in excess of the permissible exposure limit;

(i)(1)(i)(D) The purpose, proper use and limitations of respirators required by paragraph (f) of this Section;

(i)(1)(i)(E) The purpose for and a description of the medical surveillance program required by paragraph (h) of this Section and other information which will aid exposed employees in understanding the hazards of cotton dust exposure; and

(i)(1)(i)(F) The contents of this Standard and its Appendices.

(i)(1)(ii) The training program shall be provided prior to initial assignment and shall be repeated annually for each employee exposed to cotton dust, when job assignments or work processes change and when employee performance indicates a need for retraining.

(i)(2) **Access to training materials**

(i)(2)(i) Each employer shall post a copy of this Section with its Appendices in a public location at the workplace, and shall, upon request, make copies available to employees.

(i)(2)(ii) The employer shall provide all materials relating to the employee training and information program to the Assistant Secretary and the Director upon request.

(j) **Signs**

(j)(1) The employer shall post the following warning sign in each work area where the permissible exposure limit for cotton dust is exceeded:

DANGER
COTTON DUST
CAUSES DAMAGE TO LUNGS (BYSSINOSIS)
WEAR RESPIRATORY PROTECTION IN THIS AREA

(j)(2) Prior to June 1, 2016, employers may use the following legend in lieu of that specified in paragraph (j)(1) of this Section:

WARNING
COTTON DUST WORK AREA
MAY CAUSE ACUTE OR DELAYED
LUNG INJURY (BYSSINOSIS)
RESPIRATORS REQUIRED IN THIS AREA

(k) **Recordkeeping**

(k)(1) **Exposure measurements**

(k)(1)(i) The employer shall establish and maintain an accurate record of all measurements required by paragraph (d) of this Section.

(k)(1)(ii) The record shall include:

(k)(1)(ii)(A) A log containing the items listed in paragraph IV (a) of Appendix A, and the dates, number, duration, and results of each of the samples taken, including a description of the procedure used to determine representative employee exposure;

(k)(1)(ii)(B) The type of protective devices worn, if any, and length of time worn; and

(k)(1)(ii)(C) The names, social security numbers, job classifications, and exposure levels of employees whose exposure the measurement is intended to represent.

(k)(1)(iii) The employer shall maintain this record for at least 20 years.

(k)(2) **Medical surveillance**

(k)(2)(i) The employer shall establish and maintain an accurate medical record for each employee subject to medical surveillance required by paragraph (h) of this Section.

(k)(2)(ii) The record shall include:

(k)(2)(ii)(A) The name and social security number and description of the duties of the employee;

(k)(2)(ii)(B) A copy of the medical examination results including the medical history, questionnaire response, results of all tests, and the physician's recommendation;

(k)(2)(ii)(C) A copy of the physician's written opinion;

(k)(2)(ii)(D) Any employee medical complaints related to exposure to cotton dust;

(k)(2)(ii)(E) A copy of this Standard and its Appendices, except that the employer may keep one copy of the standard and the Appendices for all employees, provided that he references the standard and Appendices in the medical surveillance record of each employee; and

(k)(2)(ii)(F) A copy of the information provided to the physician as required by paragraph (h)(4) of this Section.

(k)(2)(iii) The employer shall maintain this record for at least 20 years.

(k)(3) **Availability**

(k)(3)(i) The employer shall make all records required to be maintained by paragraph (k) of this Section available to the Assistant Secretary and the Director for examination and copying.

(k)(3)(ii) Employee exposure measurement records and employee medical records required by this paragraph shall be provided upon request to employees, designated representatives, and the Assistant Secretary in accordance with 29 CFR §1910.1020 (a) through (e) and (g) through (i).

(k)(4) **Transfer of records**

(k)(4)(i) Whenever the employer ceases to do business, the successor employer shall receive and retain all records required to be maintained by paragraph (k) of this Section.

(k)(4)(ii) The employer shall also comply with any additional requirements involving transfer of records set forth in 29 CFR §1910.1020(h).

(l) **Observation of monitoring**

(l)(1) The employer shall provide affected employees or their designated representatives an opportunity to observe any measuring or monitoring of employee exposure to cotton dust conducted pursuant to paragraph (d) of this Section.

(l)(2) Whenever observation of the measuring or monitoring of employee exposure to cotton dust requires entry into an area where the use of personal protective equipment is required, the employer shall provide the observer with and assure the use of such equipment and shall require the observer to comply with all other applicable safety and health procedures.

(l)(3) Without interfering with the measurement, observers shall be entitled to:

(l)(3)(i) An explanation of the measurement procedures;

(l)(3)(ii) An opportunity to observe all steps related to the measurement of airborne concentrations of cotton dust performed at the place of exposure; and

(l)(3)(iii) An opportunity to record the results obtained.

(m) **Washed Cotton**

(m)(1) **Exemptions** Cotton, after it has been washed by the processes described in this paragraph, is exempt from all or parts of this Section as specified if the requirements of this paragraph are met.

(m)(2) **Initial requirements**

(m)(2)(i) In order for an employer to qualify as exempt or partially exempt from this Standard for operations using washed cotton, the employer must demonstrate that the cotton was washed in a facility which is open to inspection by the Assistant Secretary and the employer must provide sufficient accurate documentary evidence to demonstrate that the washing methods utilized meet the requirements of this paragraph.

(m)(2)(ii) An employer who handles or processes cotton which has been washed in a facility not under the employer's control and claims an exemption or partial exemption under this paragraph, must obtain from the cotton washer and make available at the worksite, to the Assistant Secretary, to any affected employee, or to their designated representative the following:

(m)(2)(ii)(A) A certification by the washer of the cotton of the grade of cotton, the type of washing process, and that the batch meets the requirements of this paragraph;

(m)(2)(ii)(B) Sufficient accurate documentation by the washer of the cotton grades and washing process; and

(m)(2)(ii)(C) An authorization by the washer that the Assistant Secretary or the Director may inspect the washer's washing facilities and documentation of the process.

(m)(3) **Medical and dyed cotton** Medical grade (USP) cotton, cotton that has been scoured, bleached and dyed, and mercerized yarn shall be exempt from all provisions of this Standard.

(m)(4) **Higher grade washed cotton** The handling or processing of cotton classed as "low middling light spotted or better" (color grade 52 or better and leaf grade code 5 or better according to the 1993 USDA classification system) shall be exempt from all provisions of the standard except the requirements of paragraphs (h) medical surveillance, (k)(2) through (4) recordkeeping—medical records, and Appendices B, C, and D of this Section, if they have been washed on one of the following systems:

(m)(4)(i) On a continuous batt system or a rayon rinse system including the following conditions:

(m)(4)(i)(A) With water;

(m)(4)(i)(B) At a temperature of no less than 60 °C;

(m)(4)(i)(C) With a water-to-fiber ratio of no less than 40:1; and

(m)(4)(i)(D) With the bacterial levels in the wash water controlled to limit bacterial contamination of the cotton.

(m)(4)(ii) On a batch kier washing system including the following conditions:

(m)(4)(ii)(A) With water;

(m)(4)(ii)(B) With cotton fiber mechanically opened and thoroughly prewetted before forming the cake;

(m)(4)(ii)(C) For low-temperature processing, at a temperature of no less than 60 °C with a water-to-fiber ratio of no less than 40:1; or, for high-temperature processing, at a temperature of no less than 93 °C with a water-to-fiber ratio of no less than 15:1;

(m)(4)(ii)(D) With a minimum of one wash cycle followed by two rinse cycles for each batch, using fresh water in each cycle; and

(m)(4)(ii)(E) With bacterial levels in the wash water controlled to limit bacterial contamination of the cotton.

(m)(5) **Lower grade washed cotton** The handling and processing of cotton of grades lower than "low middling light spotted," that has been washed as specified in paragraph (n)(4) of this Section and has also been bleached, shall be exempt from all provisions of the standard except the requirements of paragraphs (c)(1)(ii) Permissible Exposure Limit, (d) Exposure Monitoring, (h) Medical Surveillance, (k) Recordkeeping, and Appendices B, C and D of this Section.

(m)(6) Mixed grades of washed cotton. If more than one grade of washed cotton is being handled or processed together, the requirements of the grade with the most stringent exposure limit, medical and monitoring requirements shall be followed.

(n) **Appendices**

(n)(1) Appendices B, C, and D of this Section are incorporated as part of this Section and the contents of these Appendices are mandatory.

(n)(2) Appendix A of this Section contains information which is not intended to create any additional obligations not otherwise imposed or to detract from any existing obligations.

(n)(3) Appendix E of this Section is a protocol which may be followed in the validation of alternative measuring devices as equivalent to the vertical elutriator cotton dust sampler. Other protocols may be used if it is demonstrated that they are statistically valid, meet the requirements in paragraph (d)(l)(iii) of this Section, and are appropriate for demonstrating equivalency.

§1910.1043 Appendix A
Air sampling and analytical procedures for determining concentrations of cotton dust

I. Sampling Locations

The sampling procedures must be designed so that samples of the actual dust concentrations are collected accurately and consistently and reflect the concentrations of dust at the place and time of sampling. Sufficient number of 6-hour area samples in each distinct work area of the plant should be collected at locations which provide representative samples of air to which the worker is exposed. In order to avoid filter overloading, sampling time may be shortened when sampling in dusty areas. Samples in each work area should be gathered simultaneously or sequentially during a normal operating period. The daily time-weighted average (TWA) exposure of each worker can then be determined by using the following formula:

- Summation of hours spent in each location and the dust concentration in that location.
- Total hours exposed
- A time-weighted average concentration should be computed for each worker and properly logged and maintained on file for review.

II. Sampling Equipment

(A) Sampler The instrument selected for monitoring is the Lumsden-Lynch vertical elutriator. It should operate at a flow rate of 7.4 ± 0.2 liters/minute.

The samplers should be cleaned prior to sampling. The pumps should be monitored during sampling.

(B) Filter Holder A three-piece cassette constructed of polystyrene designed to hold a 37-mm diameter filter should be used. Care must be exercised to insure that an adequate seal exists between elements of the cassette.

(C) Filers and Support Pads The membrane filters used should be polyvinyl chloride with a 5-um pore size and 37-mm diameter. A support pad, commonly called a backup pad, should be used under the filter membrane in the field monitor cassette.

(D) Balance A balance sensitive to 10 micrograms should be used.

(E) Monitoring equipment for use in Class III hazardous locations must be approved for use in such locations, in accordance with the requirements of the OSHA electrical standards in Subpart S of Part §1910.

III. Instrument Calibration Procedure

Samplers shall be calibrated when first received from the factory, after repair, and after receiving any abuse. The samplers should be calibrated in the laboratory both before they are used in the field and after they have been used to collect a large number of field samples. The primary standard, such as a spirometer or other standard calibrating instruments such as a wet test meter or a large bubble meter or dry gas meter, should be used. Instructions for calibration with the wet test meter follow. If another calibration device is selected, equivalent procedures should be used:

(A) Level wet test meter. Check the water level which should just touch the calibration point at the left side of the meter. If water level is low, add water 1–2 °F. warmer than room temperature of till point. Run the meter for 30 minutes before calibration;

(B) Place the polyvinyl chloride membrane filter in the filter cassette;

(C) Assemble the calibration sampling train;

(D) Connect the wet test meter to the train.

The pointer on the meter should run clockwise and a pressure drop of not more than 1.0 inch of water indicated. If the pressure drop is greater than 1.0, disconnect and check the system;

(E) Operate the system for ten minutes before starting the calibration;

(F) Check the vacuum gauge on the pump to insure that the pressure drop across the orifice exceeds 17 inches of mercury;

(G) Record the following on calibration data sheets:

(1) Wet test meter reading, start and finish;
(2) Elapsed time, start and finish (at least two minutes);
(3) Pressure drop at manometer;
(4) Air temperature;
(5) Barometric pressure; and
(6) Limiting orifice number.

(H) Calculate the flow rate and compare against the flow of 7.4 ± 0.2 liters/minute. If flow is between these limits, perform calibration again, average results, and record orifice number and flow rate. If flow is not within these limits, discard or modify orifice and repeat procedure.

(i) Record the name of the person performing the calibration, the date, serial number of the wet test meter, and the number of the critical orifices being calibrated.

IV. Sampling Procedure

(A) Sampling data sheets should include a log of:

(1) The date of the sample collection;
(2) The time of sampling;
(3) The location of the sampler;
(4) The sampler serial number;
(5) The cassette number;
(6) The time of starting and stopping the sampling and the duration of sampling;
(7) The weight of the filter before and after sampling;
(8) The weight of dust collected (corrected for controls);
(9) The dust concentration measured;
(10) Other pertinent information; and
(11) Name of person taking sample.

(B) Assembly of filter cassette should be as follows:

(1) Loosely assemble 3-piece cassette;
(2) Number cassette;
(3) Place absorbant pad in cassette;
(4) Weigh filter to an accuracy of 10 μg;
(5) Place filter in cassette;

(6) Record weight of filter in log, using cassette number for identification;
(7) Fully assemble cassette, using pressure to force parts tightly together;
(8) Install plugs top and bottom;
(9) Put shrink band on cassette, covering joint between center and bottom parts of cassette; and
(10) Set cassette aside until shrink band dries thoroughly.

(C) Sampling collection should be performed as follows:
(1) Clean lint out of the motor and elutriator;
(2) Install vertical elutriator in sampling locations specified above with inlet 4½ to 5½ feet from floor (breathing zone height);
(3) Remove top section of cassette;
(4) Install cassette in ferrule of elutriator;
(5) Tape cassette to ferrule with masking tape or similar material for air-tight seal;
(6) Remove bottom plug of cassette and attach hose containing critical orifice;
(7) Start elutriator pump and check to see if gauge reads above 17 in. of Hg vacuum;
(8) Record starting time, cassette number, and sampler number;
(9) At end of sampling period stop pump and record time; and
(10) Controls with each batch of samples collected, two additional filter cassettes should be subjected to exactly the same handling as the samples, except that they are not opened. These control filters should be weighed in the same manner as the sample filters.

Any difference in weight in the control filters would indicate that the procedure for handling sample filters may not be adequate and should be evaluated to ascertain the cause of the difference, whether and what necessary corrections must be made, and whether additional samples must be collected.

(D) Shipping. The cassette with samples should be collected, along with the appropriate number of blanks, and shipped to the analytical laboratory in a suitable container to prevent damage in transit.

(E) Weighing of the sample should be achieved as follows:
(1) Remove shrink band;
(2) Remove top and middle sections of cassette and botton plug;
(3) Remove filter from cassette and weigh to an accuracy of 10 μg; and
(4) Record weight in log against original weight.

(F) Calculation of volume of air sampled should be determined as follows:
(1) From starting and stopping times of sampling period, determine length of time in minutes of sampling period; and
(2) Multiply sampling time in minutes by flow rate of critical orifice in liters per minute and divide by 1000 to find air quantity in cubic meters.

(G) Calculation of Dust Concentrations should be made as follows:
(1) Subtract weight of clean filter from dirty filter and apply control correction to find actual weight of sample. Record this weight (in μg) in log; and
(2) Divide mass of sample in μg by air volume in cubic meters to find dust concentration in μg/m. Record in log.

§1910.1043 Appendices B–1 – B–III
Respiratory Questionnaires

Appendix B-I
Respiratory Questionnaire

A. IDENTIFICATION DATA

PLANT ______________________

NAME ______________________
(Surname)
____
(First Names)

ADDRESS ______________________
____

SOCIAL SECURITY NO ______________________

DATE OF INTERVIEW ______________________
Day Month (figures) Year (last 2 digits)

DATE OF BIRTH ______________________

AGE _____ (8, 9) SEX [M] ___ [F] ___ (10)
RACE [W] ___ [N] ___ [IND] ___ [OTHER] ___ (11)

INTERVIEWER 1 2 3 4 5 6 7 8 (12)

WORK SHIFT 1ST ___ 2ND ___ 3RD ___ (13) STANDING HEIGHT __________ (14, 15) WEIGHT __________ (16, 18)

PRESENT WORK AREA ______________________

If working in more than one specified work area, X area where most of the work shift is spent. If "other," but spending 25% of the work shift in one of the specified work areas, classify in that work area. If carding department employee, check area within that department where most of the work shift is spent (if in doubt, check "throughout"). For work areas such as spinning and weaving where many work rooms may b e involved, be sure to check the specific work room to which the employee is assigned - if he works in more than one room within a department classify as 7 (all) for that department.

	Workroom Number	Open (19)	Pick (20)	Area	Card# 1 (21)	#2 (22)	Spin (23)	Wind (24)	Twist (25)	Spool (26)	Warp (27)	Slash (28)	Weave (29)	Other (30)
AT RISK (cotton & cotton blend)	1			Cards										
	2			Draw										
	3			Comb										
	4			Rove										
	5			Thru Out										
	6													
	7 (all)													
Control (synthetic & wool)	8													
Ex-Worker (cotton)	9													

Use actual wording of each question. Put X in appropriate space after each question. When in doubt record 'No'. When no square, circle appropriate answer..

B. COUGH

Do you usually cough first thing in the morning? (on getting up)* Yes ___ No ___ (31)
(Count a cough with first smoke or on "first going out of doors." Exclude clearing throat or a single cough.)

Do you usually cough during the day or at night? Yes ___ No ___ (32)
(Ignore an occasional cough.)

If "Yes" to either question (31-32):
Do you cough like this on most days for a as much as three months a year? Yes ___ No ___ (33)

Do you cough on any particular day of the week: Yes ___ No ___ (34)

If "Yes": which day: (1) Mon. (2) Tues. (3) Wed. (4) Thur. (5) Fri. (6) Sat. (7) Sun. (35)

C. PHLEGM or alternative word to suit local custom.

Do you usually bring up any phlegm from your chest first thing in the morning? (on getting up)* Yes ___ No ___ (36)
(Count phlegm with the first smoke or on "first going out of doors." Exclude phlegm from the nose. Count swallowed phlegm.)

Do you usually bring up any phlegm from your chest during the day or at night? (Accept twice or more.)

If "Yes" to either question (36) or (37):
Do you bring up phlegm like this on most days for as much as three months each year?

If "Yes" to question (33) or (38):

How long have you had this phlegm? (cough) (1) ☐ 2 yeas or less (2) ☐ More than 2 years–9 years (3) ☐ 10-19 years
(4) ☐ 20+ years (39) Write in number of years _____

*These words are for subjects who work at night.

Note: Questionnaire continues on next page.

D. CHEST ILLNESSES

In the past three years, have you had a period of (increased) **cough and phlegm lasting for 3 weeks or more? (1) ☐ No (2) ☐ Yes, only one period (3) ☐ Yes, two or more periods (40)

During the past 3 years have you had any chest illness which has kept you off work, indoors at home or in bed? (For as long as one week, flu?) Yes ___ No ___ (41)

If "Yes" to (41):

Did you bring up (more) phlegm than usual in any of these illnesses? Yes ___ No ___ (42)

If "Yes" to (42):

During the past three years have you had: Only one such illness with increased phlegm? (1) ☐ More than one such illness: (2) ☐ Br. Grade ________

E. TIGHTNESS

Does your chest ever feel tight or your breathing become difficult? Yes ___ No ___ (45)

Is your chest tight or your breathing difficult on any particular day of the week? (after a week or 10 days away from the mill) Yes ___ No ___ (46)

If "Yes", Which day? Mon. [(1) Sometimes / (2) Always] (3) Tues. (4) Wed. (5) Thur. (6) Fri. (7) Sat. (8) Sun. (47)

If "Yes" Monday: At what time on Monday does your chest feel tight or your breathing difficult? 1 ☐ Before entering the mill (48) 2 ☐ After entering the mill

(Ask only if NO to Question (45)

In the past, has your chest ever been tight or your breathing difficult on any particular day of the week? Yes ___ No ___ (49)

If "Yes" Which day? Mon. [(1) Sometimes / (2) Always] (3) Tues. (4) Wed. (5) Thur. (6) Fri. (7) Sat. (8) Sun. (50)

F. BREATHLESSNESS

If disabled from walking by any condition other than heart or lung disease put "X" here ☐ (51) and leave questions (52-60) unasked

Are you ever troubled by shortness of breath, when hurrying on the level or walking up a slight hill? Yes ___ No ___ (52)

If "No", grade is 1. If "Yes", proceed to next question.

Do you get short of breath walking with other people at an ordinary pace on the level? Yes ___ No ___ (53)

If "No", grade is 2. If "Yes", proceed to next question.

Do you have to stop for breath when walking at your own pace on the level? Yes ___ No ___ (54)

If "No", grade is 3. If "Yes", proceed to next question.

Are you short of breath on washing or dressing? Yes ___ No ___ (55)

If "No", grade is 4. If "Yes", grade is 5. Dyspnea Grd. ______(56)

ON MONDAYS

Are you ever troubled by shortness of breath, when hurrying on the level or walking up a slight hill? Yes ___ No ___ (57)

If "No", grade is 1. If "Yes", proceed to next question.

Do you get short of breath walking with other people at an ordinary pace on the level? Yes ___ No ___ (58)

If "No", grade is 2. If "Yes", proceed to next question.

Do you have to stop for breath when walking at your own pace on the level? Yes ___ No ___ (59)

If "No", grade is 3. If "Yes", proceed to next question.

Are you short of breath on washing or dressing? Yes ___ No ___ (60)

If "No", grade is 4. If "Yes", grade is 5. Br. Grd. __________ (61)

G. OTHER ILLNESSES AND ALLERGY HISTORY

Do you have a heart condition for which you are under a doctor's care? Yes ___ No ___ (62)

Have you ever had asthma? Yes ___ No ___ (63)

If "Yes", did it begin: [1] ☐ Before age 30 [2] ☐ After age 30

If "Yes" before 30, did you have asthma before ever going to work in a textile mill? Yes ___ No ___ (64)

Have you ever had hay fever or other allergies (other than above)? Yes ___ No ___ (65)

H. TOBACCO SMOKING*

Do you smoke? Record 'Yes' if regular smoker up to one month ago (Cigarettes, cigar or pipe) Yes ___ No ___ (65)

If "No" to (63)

Have you ever smoked? (Cigarettes, cigars, pipe. Record "No" if subject has never smoked as much as one cigarette a day, or 1 oz. of tobacco a month, for as long as one year) Yes ___ No ___ (65)

If "Yes" to (63), what have you smoked and for how many years? (Write in specific numbers of years in the appropriate square

	(1)	(2)	(3)	(4)	(5)	(6)	(7)	(8)	(9)	
Years	(<5)	(5-9)	(10-14)	(15-19)	(20-24)	(25-29)	(30-34)	(35-39)	(>40_	
Cigarettes										(68)
Pipe										(69)
Cigars										(70)

If cigarettes, how many packs per day? (1) ☐ less than 1/2 pack (2) ☐ 1/2 pack, but less than 1 pack (71)

Write in number of cigarettes) ___________ (3) ☐ 1 pack, but less than 1 1/2 packs (4) ☐ 1 1/2 packs or more

Number of pack years ____________ (72, 73)

If an ex smoker (cigarettes, cigar or pipe), how long since you stopped? (Write in number of years) __________ (1) ☐ 0-1 year (2) ☐ 1-4 years (74) (3) ☐ 5-9 years (4) ☐ 10+ years

* Have you changed your smoking habits since last interview? If "Yes", specify what changes.

____

I. OCCUPATIONAL HISTORY

Have you ever worked in:

A foundry? (As long as one year) Yes ___ No ___ (75)

Stone or mineral mining, quarry or processing? (As long as one year) Yes ___ No ___ (75)

Asbestos milling or processing? (Ever) Yes ___ No ___ (75)

Other dust,s fumes or smoke? If yes, specify ______________________ Yes ___ No ___ (75)

Type of exposure ______________________ Length of exposure __________

** Ask only on first interview.

At what age did you firs go to work in a textile mill? (Write in specific age in appropriate square)

(1)	(2)	(3)	(4)	(5)	(6)
<20	20-24	25-29	30-34	35-39	40+

Appendix B-II
Respiratory Questionnaire for Non-Textile Workers for the Cotton Industry

A. IDENTIFICATION

Identification No. ____________________ Interviewer Code ____________________

Location ____________________ Date of Interview ____________________

A. IDENTIFICATION

1. NAME ____________________ (Last) (First) (Middle Initial

5. BIRTHDAY __________ (Mo.) (Day) (Year) 6. AGE LAST BIRTHDAY ______

2. CURRENT ADDRESS ____________________ (Number, Street, or Rural Route) ____________________ (City or Town, County, State, Zip Code)

7. SEX 1 ☐ Male 2 ☐ Female

8. ETHNIC GROUP OR ANCESTRY
1. ☐ White, not of Hispanic Origin
2. ☐ Black, not of Hispanic Origin
3. ☐ Hispanic
4. ☐ American Indian or Alaskan Native
5. ☐ Asian or Pacific Islander
6. ☐ Other: __________

3. PHONE NUMBER __________ (Area Code)

9. Standing Height ______(cm.)

11. Work Shift 1st ☐ 2nd ☐ 3rd ☐

4. SOCIAL SECURITY NO __________ (optional; see below)

10. WEIGHT __________

12. PRESENT WORK AREA
Please indicate primary assigned work area and percent of time spent at that site. It at other location, please indicate and note percent of time for each
PRIMARY WORK AREA ____________________
SPECIFIC JOB ____________________

13. APPROPRIATE INDUSTRY
1 ☐ Garnetting 2 ☐ Cottonseed Oil Mill 3 ☐ Cotton Warehouse 4 ☐ Utilization 5 ☐ Cotton Classification 6 ☐ Cotton ginning

(Furnishing your Social Security number is voluntary. Your refusal to provide this number will not affect any right, benefit, or privilege to which you would be entitled if you did provide your Social Security number. Your Social Security number is being requested since it will permit use in future determinations in statistical research studies.)

B. OCCUPATIONAL HISTORY TABLE

Complete the following table showing the entire work history of the individual from present to initial employment. Sporadic, part-time periods of employment, each of no significant duration, should be grouped if possible.

INDUSTRY AND LOCATION	TENURE OF EMPLOYMENT		SPECIFIC OCCUPATION	AVERAGE NO. DAYS WORKED PER WEEK	HAZARDOUS HEALTH EXPOSURE ASSOCIATED WITH WORK		
	FROM 19___	TO 19___			YES	NO	IF YES, DESCRIBE

C. SYMPTOMS

Use actual wording of each question. Put X in appropriate space after each question. When in doubt record "No".

COUGH

1. Do you usually cough first thing in the morning? (on getting up)* (Count a cough with first smoke or on "first going out of doors". Exclude clearing throat or a single cough.) 1 ☐ Yes 2 ☐ No
2. Do you usually cough during the day or at night? (Ignore an occasional cough.) 1 ☐ Yes 2 ☐ No

If YES to either question 1 or 2:
3. Do you cough like this on most days for as much as three months a year? 1 ☐ Yes 2 ☐ No
4. Do you cough on any particular day of the week? 1 ☐ Yes 2 ☐ No

If YES:
5. Which day? Mon. Tue. Wed. Thur. Fri. Sat. Sun. ____________

PHLEGM

6. Do you usually bring up any phlegm from your chest first thing in the morning? (on getting up)* (Count phlegm with the first smoke or on "first going out of doors.". Exclude phlegm from the nose. Count swallowed phlegm.) 1 ☐ Yes 2 ☐ No
7. Do you usually bring up any phlegm form your chest during he day or at night? (Accept twice or more.) 1 ☐ Yes 2 ☐ No

If YES to question 6 or 7:
8. Do you bring up phlegm like this on most days for as much as three months each year? 1 ☐ Yes 2 ☐ No

If YES to question 3 or 8:
9. How long have you had this phlegm? (cough) (1) ☐ 2 years or less 2) ☐ More than 2 years - 9 years (3) ☐ 10-19 years (4) ☐ 20+ years
(Write in number of years) ______

CHEST ILLNESS

10. In the past three years, have you had a period of (increased) cough and phlegm lasting for 3 weeks or more? 1 ☐ Yes 2 ☐ No

For subjects who usually have phlegm:
11. During the past 3 years have you had any chest illness which has kept you off work, indoors at home or in bed? (For as long as one week, flu?) 1 ☐ Yes 2 ☐ No

If YES to 11:
12. Did you bring up (more)phlegm than usual in any of these illnesses? 1 ☐ Yes 2 ☐ No

IF YES to 12: During the past three years have you had:
13. Only one such illness with increased phlegm? 1 ☐ Yes 2 ☐ No
14. More than one such illness: 1 ☐ Yes 2 ☐ No

Br. Grade ______

Note: Questionnaire continues on next page.

TIGHTNESS

15. Does you chest ever feel tight or your breathing become difficult? — 1 ☐ Yes 2 ☐ No

16. Is your chest tight or your breathing difficult on any particular day of the week? (after a week or 10 days away from the mill) — 1 ☐ Yes 2 ☐ No

17. If YES, which day? Mon. (1) Sometimes / (2) Always; (3) Tues. (4) Wed. (5) Thur. (6) Fri. (7) Sat. (8) Sun.

18. If YES Monday: At what time on Monday does your chest feel tight or your breathing difficult? ☐ Before entering mll ☐ After entering mill

(ASK ONLY IF NO TO QUESTION 15)

19. In the past, has your chest ever been tight or your breathing difficult on any particular day of the week? — 1 ☐ Yes 2 ☐ No

20. If YES, which day? Mon. (1) Sometimes / (2) Always; (3) Tues. (4) Wed. (5) Thur. (6) Fri. (7) Sat. (8) Sun.

* These words are for subjects who work at night

BREATHLESSNESS

21. If disabled from walking by any condition other than heart or lung disease put "X" in the space and leave questions (22-30) unasked. ☐

22. Are you ever troubled by shortness of breath, when hurrying on the level or walking up a slight hill? — 1 ☐ Yes 2 ☐ No

If NO, grade is 1. If YES, proceed to next question.

23. Do you get short of breath walking with other people at an ordinary pace on the level? — 1 ☐ Yes 2 ☐ No

If NO, grade is 2. If YES, proceed to next question.

24. Do you have to stop for breath when walking at your own pace on the level? — 1 ☐ Yes 2 ☐ No

If NO, grade is 3. If YES, proceed to next question.

25. Are you short of breath on washing or dressing? — 1 ☐ Yes 2 ☐ No

26. — Dyspnea Grd. ________

ON MONDAYS:

27 Are you ever troubled by shortness of breath, when hurrying on the level or walking up a slight hill? — 1 ☐ Yes 2 ☐ No

If NO, grade is 1. If YES, proceed t next question.

28. Do you get short of breath walking with other people at an ordinary pace on the level? — 1 ☐ Yes 2 ☐ No

If NO, grade is 2. If YES, proceed to next question.

29. Do you have to stop for breath when walking a your won pace on the level? — 1 ☐ Yes 2 ☐ No

If NO, grade is 3. If YES proceed to next question.

30. Are you short of breath on washing or dressing? — 1 ☐ Yes 2 ☐ No

If NO, grade is 4. If YES, grade is 5.

31. — Br. Grd. _______

OTHER ILLNESSES AND ALLERGY HISTORY — 1 ☐ Yes 2 ☐ No

32. Do you have a heart condition for which you are under a doctor's care? — 1 ☐ Yes 2 ☐ No

33. Have you ever had asthma — 1 ☐ Yes 2 ☐ No

If YES, did it begin: (1) Before age 30 ☐ (2) After age 30 ☐

34. If YES before 30: did you have asthma before ever going to work in a textile mill? — 1 ☐ Yes 2 ☐ No

35. Have you ever had hay fever or other allergies (other than above)? — 1 ☐ Yes 2 ☐ No

TOBACCO SMOKING

36. Do you smoke? Record YES if regular smoker up to one month ago. (Cigarettes, cigar or pipe) — 1 ☐ Yes 2 ☐ No

If NO to (33)

37. Have you ever smoked? (Cigarettes, cigars, pipe. Record NO if subject has never smoked as much as one cigarette a day, or 1 oz. of tobacco a month, for as long as one year.) — 1 ☐ Yes 2 ☐ No

If YES to (33) or (34), what have you smoked for how many years? (Write in specific number of years in the appropriate square.)

		(1)	(2)	(3)	(4)	(5)	(6)	(7)	(8)	(9)
	Years	(<5)	(5-9)	(10-14)	(15-19)	(20-24)	(25-29)	(30-34)	(35-30)	(>40)
38.	Cigarettes									
39.	Pipe									
40.	Cigars									

41. If cigarettes, how many packs per day? ☐ Less than 1/2 pack ☐ 1/2 pack, but less than 1 pack ☐ 1 pack, but less than 1 1/2 packs ☐ 1 1/2 packs or more

Write in number of cigarettes _________

42. Number of pack years: _________

43. If an ex-smoker (cigarettes, cigar or pipe), how long since you stopped? ☐ 0-1 year ☐ 1-4 years ☐ 5-9 years ☐ 10+ years

(Write in number of years.) _________

D. OCCUPATIONAL HISTORY

Have you ever worked in — 1 ☐ Yes 2 ☐ No

44. A foundry? (As long as one year) — 1 ☐ Yes 2 ☐ No

45. Stone or mineral mining, quarring or processing? (As long as one year) — 1 ☐ Yes 2 ☐ No

46. Asbestos milling or processing? (Ever) — 1 ☐ Yes 2 ☐ No

47. Cotton or cotton blend mill? (For controls only) — 1 ☐ Yes 2 ☐ No

48. Other dusts, fumes or smoke? If yes, specify.

Type of exposure ________________

Length of exposure ____________

Appendix B-III
Abbreviated Respiratory Questionnaire

A. IDENTIFICATION DATA

PLANT ______________________ SOCIAL SECURITY NO ______________________

NAME ______________________ DATE OF INTERVIEW ______________________
(Surname) DAY MONTH (figures) YEAR (last 2 digits)

______________________ DATE OF BIRTH ______________________
(First Names)

ADDRESS ______________________ AGE _____ (8, 9) SEX [M] ___ [F] ___ (10)

______________________ RACE [W] ___ [N] ___ [IND] ___ [OTHER] ___ (11)

INTERVIEWER 1 2 3 4 5 6 7 8 (12)

WORK SHIFT 1ST ___ 2ND ___ 3RD ___ (13) STANDING HEIGHT _________ (14, 15) WEIGHT _________ (16, 18)

PRESENT WORK AREA ______________________

If working in more than one specified work area, X area where most of the work shift is spent. If "other," but spending 25% of the work shift in one of the specified work areas, classify in that work area. If carding department employee, check area within that department where most of the work shift is spent (if in doubt, check "throughout"). For work areas such as spinning and weaving where many work rooms may b e involved, be sure to check the specific work room to which the employee is assigned - if he works in more than one room within a department classify as 7 (all) for that department.

	Workroom Number	Open (19)	Pick (20)	Area	Card #1 (21)	#2 (22)	Spin (23)	Wind (24)	Twist (25)	Spool (26)	Warp (27)	Slash (28)	Weave (29)	Other (30)
AT RISK (cotton & cotton blend)	1			Cards										
	2			Draw										
	3			Comb										
	4			Rove										
	5			Thru Out										
	6													
	7 (all)													
Control (synthetic & wool)	8													
Ex-Worker cotton)	9													

Use actual wording of each question. Put X in appropriate space after each question. When in doubt record "No".

B. COUGH

Do you usually cough first thing in the morning? (on getting up)* Yes ___ No ___ (31)
(Count a cough with first smoke or on "first going out of doors." Exclude clearing throat or a single cough.)

Do you usually cough during the day or at night? (Ignore an occasional cough.) Yes ___ No ___ (32)

If "Yes" to either question (31-32):
Do you cough like this on most days for a as much as three months a year? Yes ___ No ___ (33)

Do you cough on any particular day of the week: Yes ___ No ___ (34)

If "Yes": which day: (1) Mon. (2) Tues. (3) Wed. (4) Thur. (5) Fri. (6) Sat. (7) Sun. (35)

C. PHLEGM or alternative word to suit local custom.

Do you usually bring up any phlegm from your chest first thing in the morning? (on getting up)* Yes ___ No ___ (36)
(Count phlegm with the first smoke or on "first going out of doors." Exclude phlegm from the nose. Count swallowed phlegm.)

Do you usually bring up any phlegm from your chest during the day or at night? (Accept twice or more.) Yes ___ No ___ (37)

If "Yes" to question (36) or (37):
Do you bring up phlegm like this on most days for as much as three months each year? Yes ___ No ___ (38)

If "Yes" to question (33) or (38):

How long have you had this phlegm? (cough) (1) ☐ 2 years or less (2) ☐ More than 2 years–9 years (3) ☐ 10-19 years (4) ☐ 20+ years (39)
Write in number of years _____

D. TIGHTNESS

Does your chest ever feel tight or your breathing become difficult? Yes ___ No ___ (45)

Is your chest tight or your breathing difficult on any particular day of the week? Yes ___ No ___ (46)
(after a week or 10 days away from the mill)

If "Yes", Which day? Mon. [(1) Sometimes / (2) Always] (3) Tues. (4) Wed. (5) Thur. (6) Fri. (7) Sat. (8) Sun. (47)

If "Yes" Monday: At what time on Monday does your chest feel tight or your breathing difficult?
1 ☐ Before entering the mill (48)
2 ☐ After entering the mill

(Ask only if NO to Question (45)

In the past, has your chest ever been tight or your breathing difficult on any particular day of the week? Yes ___ No ___ (49)

If "Yes" Which day? Mon. [(1) Sometimes / (2) Always] (3) Tues. (4) Wed. (5) Thur. (6) Fri. (7) Sat. (8) Sun. (50)

E. TOBACCO SMOKING

Have you changed your smoking habits since last interview? If "Yes". specify what changes.

____

*These words are for subjects who work at night

§1910.1043 Appendix C
Spirometry prediction tables for normal males and females

Table 1.
PREDICTED FVC FOR MALES (KNUDSON, ET AL.: AM. REV. RESPIR. DIS. 1976, 113, 587.)

	AGE																								
HT	17	19	21	23	25	27	29	31	33	35	37	39	41	43	45	47	49	51	53	55	57	59	61	63	65
60.0	3.44	3.59	3.75	3.91	3.72	3.66	3.61	3.55	3.49	3.43	3.37	3.32	3.26	3.20	3.14	3.08	3.03	2.97	2.91	2.85	2.79	2.74	2.68	2.62	2.56
60.5	3.50	3.66	3.81	3.97	3.80	3.75	3.69	3.63	3.57	3.51	3.46	3.40	3.34	3.28	3.22	3.17	3.11	3.05	2.99	2.93	2.88	2.82	2.76	2.70	2.64
61.0	3.56	3.72	3.88	4.03	3.89	3.83	3.77	3.71	3.66	3.60	3.54	3.48	3.42	3.37	3.31	3.25	3.19	3.13	3.08	3.02	2.96	2.90	2.84	2.79	2.73
61.5	3.63	3.78	3.94	4.10	3.97	3.91	3.85	3.80	3.74	3.68	3.62	3.56	3.51	3.45	3.39	3.33	3.27	3.22	3.16	3.10	3.04	2.98	2.93	2.87	2.81
62.0	3.69	3.85	4.00	4.16	4.05	3.99	3.94	3.88	3.82	3.76	3.70	3.65	3.59	3.53	3.47	3.41	3.36	3.30	3.24	3.18	3.12	3.07	3.01	2.95	2.89
62.5	3.76	3.91	4.07	4.22	4.13	4.08	4.02	3.96	3.90	3.84	3.79	3.73	3.67	3.61	3.55	3.50	3.44	3.38	3.32	3.26	3.21	3.15	3.09	3.03	2.97
63.0	3.82	3.97	4.13	4.26	4.22	4.16	4.10	4.04	3.99	3.93	3.87	3.81	3.75	3.70	3.64	3.58	3.52	3.46	3.41	3.35	3.29	3.23	3.17	3.12	3.06
63.5	3.88	4.04	4.19	4.35	4.30	4.24	4.18	4.13	4.07	4.01	3.95	3.89	3.84	3.78	3.72	3.66	3.60	3.55	3.49	3.43	3.37	3.31	3.26	3.20	3.14
64.0	3.95	4.10	4.26	4.41	4.38	4.32	4.27	4.21	4.15	4.09	4.03	3.98	3.92	3.86	3.80	3.74	3.69	3.63	3.57	3.51	3.45	3.40	3.34	3.28	3.22
64.5	4.01	4.17	4.32	4.48	4.46	4.41	4.35	4.29	4.23	4.17	4.12	4.06	4.00	3.94	3.88	3.83	3.77	3.71	3.65	3.59	3.54	3.48	3.42	3.36	3.30
65.0	4.07	4.23	4.39	4.54	4.55	4.49	4.43	4.37	43.2	4.26	4.20	4.14	4.08	4.03	3.97	3.91	3.85	3.79	3.74	3.68	3.62	3.56	3.50	3.45	3.39
65.5	4.14	4.29	4.45	4.60	4.63	4.57	4.51	4.46	4.40	4.34	4.28	4.22	4.17	4.11	4.05	3.99	3.93	3.88	3.82	3.76	3.70	3.64	3.59	3.53	3.47
66.0	4.20	4.36	4.51	4.67	4.71	4.65	4.60	4.54	4.48	4.42	4.36	4.31	4.25	4.19	4.13	4.07	4.02	3.96	3.90	3.84	3.78	3.73	3.67	3.61	3.55
66.5	4.26	4.42	4.58	4.73	4.80	4.74	4.68	4.62	4.56	4.51	4.45	4.39	4.33	4.27	4.22	4.16	4.10	4.04	3.98	3.93	3.87	3.81	3.75	3.69	3.64
67.0	4.33	4.48	4.64	4.80	4.88	4.82	4.76	4.70	4.65	4.59	4.53	4.47	4.41	4.36	4.30	4.24	4.18	4.12	4.07	4.01	3.95	3.89	3.83	3.78	3.72
67.5	4.39	4.55	4.70	4.86	4.96	4.90	4.84	4.79	4.73	4.67	4.61	4.65	4.50	4.44	4.38	4.32	4.26	4.21	4.15	4.09	4.03	3.97	3.92	3.86	3.80
68.0	4.45	4.61	4.77	4.92	5.04	4.98	4.93	4.87	4.81	4.75	4.69	4.64	4.58	4.52	4.46	4.40	4.35	4.29	4.23	4.17	4.11	4.06	4.00	3.94	3.88
68.5	4.52	4.67	4.83	4.99	5.13	5.07	5.01	4.95	4.89	4.84	4.78	4.72	4.66	4.60	4.55	4.49	4.43	4.37	4.31	4.26	4.20	4.14	4.04	4.02	3.97
69.0	4.58	4.74	4.89	5.05	5.21	5.12	5.06	5.03	4.98	4.92	4.86	4.80	4.74	4.69	4.63	4.57	4.51	4.45	4.40	4.34	4.28	4.22	4.16	4.11	4.05
69.5	4.64	4.80	4.96	5.11	5.29	5.23	5.17	5.12	5.06	5.00	4.94	4.88	4.83	4.77	4.71	4.65	4.59	4.54	4.48	4.42	4.36	4.30	4.25	4.19	4.13
70.0	4.71	4.86	5.02	5.18	5.37	5.32	5.26	5.20	5.14	5.08	5.02	4.97	4.91	4.85	4.79	4.74	4.68	4.62	4.56	4.50	4.44	4.39	4.33	4.27	4.21
70.5	4.77	4.93	5.08	5.24	5.46	5.40	5.34	5.28	5.22	5.17	5.11	5.05	4.99	4.93	4.88	4.82	4.76	4.70	4.64	4.59	4.53	4.47	4.41	4.35	4.30
71.0	4.83	4.99	5.15	5.30	5.54	5.48	5.42	5.36	5.31	5.25	5.19	5.13	5.07	5.02	4.96	4.90	4.84	4.78	4.73	4.67	4.61	4.55	4.49	4.44	4.38
71.5	4.90	5.05	5.21	5.37	5.62	5.56	5.50	5.45	5.39	5.33	5.27	5.21	5.16	5.10	5.04	4.98	4.92	4.87	4.81	4.75	4.69	4.63	4.58	4.52	4.46
72.0	4.96	5.12	5.27	5.43	5.70	5.65	5.59	5.53	5.47	5.41	5.36	5.30	5.24	5.18	5.12	5.07	5.01	4.95	4.89	4.83	4.78	4.72	4.66	4.60	4.54
72.5	5.03	5.18	5.34	5.49	5.79	5.73	5.67	5.61	5.55	5.50	5.44	5.38	5.32	5.26	5.21	5.15	5.09	5.03	4.97	4.92	4.86	4.80	4.72	4.68	4.63
73.0	5.09	5.24	5.40	5.56	5.87	5.81	5.75	5.69	5.64	5.58	5.52	5.46	5.40	5.35	5.29	5.23	5.17	5.11	5.06	5.00	4.94	4.88	4.82	4.77	4.71
73.5	5.15	5.31	5.46	5.62	5.95	5.89	5.83	5.78	5.72	5.66	5.60	5.54	5.49	5.43	5.67	5.31	5.26	5.20	6.14	5.08	5.02	4.96	4.91	4.85	4.79
74.0	5.22	5.37	5.53	5.68	6.03	5.98	5.92	5.86	5.80	5.74	5.69	5.63	5.57	5.51	5.45	5.40	5.34	5.28	5.22	5.16	5.11	5.05	4.99	4.93	4.87
74.5	5.28	5.44	5.59	5.75	6.12	6.06	6.00	5.94	5.88	5.83	5.77	5.71	5.65	5.59	5.54	5.48	5.42	5.36	5.30	5.25	5.19	5.13	5.07	5.01	4.96
75.0	5.34	5.50	5.65	5.81	6.20	6.14	6.08	6.02	5.97	5.91	5.85	5.79	5.73	5.68	5.62	5.56	5.50	5.44	5.39	5.33	5.27	5.21	5.15	5.10	5.04
75.5	5.41	5.56	5.72	5.87	6.28	6.22	6.17	6.11	6.05	5.99	5.93	5.88	5.82	5.76	5.70	5.64	5.59	5.53	5.47	5.41	5.35	5.30	5.24	5.18	5.12
76.0	5.47	5.63	5.78	5.94	6.36	6.31	6.25	6.19	6.13	6.07	6.02	5.96	5.90	5.84	5.78	5.73	5.67	5.61	5.55	5.49	5.44	5.38	5.32	5.26	5.20
76.5	5.53	5.69	5.85	6.00	6.45	6.39	6.33	6.27	6.21	6.16	6.10	6.04	5.98	5.92	5.87	5.81	5.75	5.69	5.63	5.58	5.52	5.46	5.46	5.34	5.29
77.0	5.60	5.75	5.91	6.06	6.53	6.47	6.41	6.35	6.30	6.24	6.18	6.12	6.06	6.01	5.95	5.89	5.83	5.77	5.72	5.66	5.60	5.54	5.48	5.43	5.37
77.5	5.66	5.82	5.97	6.13	6.61	6.55	6.50	6.44	6.38	6.32	6.26	6.21	6.15	6.09	6.03	5.97	5.92	5.86	5.80	5.74	5.68	5.63	5.57	5.51	5.45
78.0	5.72	5.88	6.04	6.19	6.69	6.64	6.58	6.52	6.46	6.40	6.35	6.29	6.23	6.17	6.11	6.06	6.00	5.94	5.88	5.82	5.77	5.71	5.65	5.59	5.53
78.5	5.79	5.94	6.10	6.26	6.78	6.72	6.66	6.60	6.54	6.49	6.43	6.37	6.31	6.25	6.20	6.14	6.08	6.02	5.96	5.91	5.85	5.79	5.73	5.67	5.62
79.0	5.85	6.01	6.16	6.32	6.86	6.80	6.74	6.68	6.63	6.57	6.51	6.45	6.39	6.34	6.28	6.22	6.16	6.10	6.05	5.99	5.93	5.87	5.81	5.76	5.70
79.5	5.91	6.07	6.23	6.38	6.94	6.88	6.83	6.77	6.71	6.65	6.59	6.54	6.48	6.42	6.36	6.30	6.25	6.19	6.13	6.07	6.01	5.96	5.90	5.84	5.78
80.0	5.98	6.13	6.29	6.45	7.02	6.97	6.91	6.85	6.79	6.73	6.68	6.62	6.56	6.50	6.44	6.39	6.33	6.27	6.21	6.15	6.10	6.04	5.98	5.92	5.86
80.5	6.04	6.20	6.35	6.51	7.11	7.05	6.99	6.93	6.87	6.82	6.76	6.70	6.64	6.58	6.53	6.47	6.41	6.35	6.29	6.24	6.18	6.12	6.06	6.00	5.93
81.0	6.10	6.26	6.42	6.57	7.19	7.13	7.07	7.02	6.96	6.90	6.84	6.78	6.73	6.67	6.61	6.55	6.49	6.44	6.38	6.32	6.26	6.20	6.15	6.09	6.03
81.5	6.17	6.32	6.48	6.64	7.27	7.21	7.16	7.10	7.04	6.98	6.92	6.87	6.81	6.75	6.69	6.63	6.58	6.52	6.46	6.40	6.34	6.29	6.23	6.17	6.11
82.0	6.23	6.39	6.54	6.70	7.35	7.30	7.24	7.18	7.12	7.06	7.01	6.95	6.89	6.83	6.77	6.72	6.66	6.60	6.54	6.48	6.43	6.37	6.31	6.25	6.19
82.5	6.30	6.45	6.61	6.76	7.44	7.38	7.32	7.26	7.20	7.15	7.09	7.03	6.97	6.91	6.86	6.80	6.74	6.68	6.62	6.57	6.51	6.45	6.39	6.33	6.28
83.0	6.36	6.51	6.67	6.83	7.52	7.46	7.40	7.35	7.29	7.23	7.17	7.11	7.06	7.00	6.94	6.88	6.82	6.77	6.71	6.65	6.59	6.53	6.48	6.42	6.36
83.5	6.42	6.58	6.73	6.89	7.60	7.54	7.49	7.43	7.37	7.31	7.25	7.20	7.14	7.08	7.02	6.96	6.91	6.85	6.79	6.73	6.67	6.62	6.56	6.50	6.44
84.0	6.49	6.64	6.80	6.95	7.68	7.63	7.57	7.51	7.45	7.39	7.34	7.28	7.22	7.16	7.10	7.05	6.99	6.93	6.87	6.81	6.76	6.70	6.64	6.58	6.52
84.5	6.55	6.71	6.86	7.20	7.77	7.71	7.65	7.59	7.53	7.48	7.42	7.36	7.30	7.24	7.19	7.13	7.07	7.01	6.95	6.90	6.84	6.78	6.72	6.66	6.61
85.0	6.61	6.77	6.92	7.08	7.85	7.79	7.73	7.68	7.62	7.56	7.50	7.44	7.39	7.33	7.27	7.21	7.15	7.10	7.04	6.98	6.92	6.86	6.81	6.75	6.69

Table 2.
PREDICTED FVC_1 FOR MALES (KNUDSON, ET AL.: AM. REV. RESPIR. DIS. 1976, 113, 587.)

	AGE																							
HT	17	19	21	23	25	27	29	31	33	35	37	39	41	43	45	47	49	51	53	55	57	59	61	53	65
60.0	2.97	3.06	3.15	3.24	3.05	2.99	2.94	2.88	2.83	2.78	2.72	2.67	2.61	2.56	2.51	2.45	2.40	2.34	2.29	2.24	2.18	2.13	2.07	2.02	1.97
60.5	3.03	3.12	3.21	3.30	3.11	3.06	3.00	2.95	2.50	2.84	2.79	2.73	2.68	2.63	2.57	2.52	2.46	2.41	2.36	2.30	2.25	2.19	2.14	2.09	2.03
61.0	3.08	3.17	3.26	3.35	3.18	3.12	3.07	3.02	2.96	2.91	2.85	2.80	2.75	2.69	2.64	2.58	2.53	2.48	2.42	2.37	2.31	2.26	2.21	2.15	2.10
61.5	3.14	3.23	3.32	3.41	3.24	3.19	3.14	3.08	3.03	2.97	2.92	2.87	2.81	2.76	2.70	2.65	2.60	2.54	2.49	2.43	2.38	2.33	2.27	2.22	2.16
62.0	3.20	3.29	3.38	3.47	3.31	3.26	3.20	3.15	3.09	3.04	2.99	2.93	2.88	2.82	2.77	2.72	2.66	2.61	2.55	2.50	2.45	2.39	2.34	2.28	2.23
62.5	3.26	3.35	3.44	3.53	3.38	3.32	3.27	3.22	3.16	3.11	3.05	3.00	2.95	2.89	2.84	2.78	2.73	2.68	2.62	2.57	2.51	2.46	2.41	2.35	2.30
63.0	3.32	3.41	3.50	3.59	3.44	3.39	3.34	3.28	3.23	3.17	3.12	3.07	3.01	2.96	2.90	2.85	2.80	2.74	2.69	2.63	2.58	2.53	2.47	2.42	2.36
63.5	3.38	3.47	3.56	3.65	3.51	3.46	3.40	3.35	3.29	3.24	3.19	3.13	3.08	3.02	2.97	2.92	2.86	2.81	2.75	2.70	2.65	2.59	2.54	2.48	2.43
64.0	3.43	3.52	3.61	3.70	3.58	3.52	3.47	3.41	3.36	3.31	3.25	3.20	3.14	3.09	3.04	2.98	2.93	2.87	2.82	2.77	2.71	2.66	2.60	2.55	2.50
64.5	3.49	3.58	3.67	3.76	3.64	3.59	3.53	3.48	3.43	3.37	3.32	3.26	3.21	3.16	3.10	3.05	2.99	2.94	2.86	2.83	2.78	2.72	2.67	2.62	2.56
65.0	3.55	3.64	3.73	3.82	3.71	3.65	3.60	3.55	3.49	3.44	3.38	3.33	3.28	3.22	3.17	3.11	3.06	3.01	2.95	2.90	2.84	2.79	2.74	2.68	2.63
65.5	3.61	3.70	3.79	3.88	3.77	3.72	3.67	3.61	3.56	3.50	3.45	3.40	3.34	3.29	3.23	3.18	3.13	3.07	3.02	2.96	2.91	2.86	2.80	2.75	2.69
66.0	3.67	3.76	3.85	3.94	3.84	3.79	3.73	3.68	3.62	3.57	3.52	3.46	3.41	3.35	3.30	3.25	3.19	3.14	3.08	3.03	2.98	2.82	2.87	2.81	2.76
66.5	3.73	3.82	3.91	4.00	3.91	3.85	3.80	3.74	3.69	3.64	3.58	3.53	3.47	3.42	3.37	3.31	3.26	3.20	3.15	3.10	3.04	2.99	2.93	2.88	2.83
67.0	3.79	3.88	3.97	4.06	3.97	3.92	3.88	3.81	3.76	3.70	3.65	3.59	3.54	3.49	3.43	3.38	3.32	3.27	3.22	3.16	3.11	3.05	3.00	2.95	2.89
67.5	3.84	3.93	4.02	4.11	4.04	3.98	3.93	3.88	3.82	3.77	3.71	3.66	3.61	3.55	3.50	3.44	3.39	3.34	3.28	3.23	3.17	3.12	3.07	3.01	2.96
68.0	3.90	3.99	4.08	4.17	4.10	4.05	4.00	3.94	3.89	3.83	3.78	3.73	3.67	3.62	3.56	3.51	3.46	3.40	3.35	3.29	3.24	3.19	3.13	3.08	3.02
68.5	3.96	4.05	4.14	4.23	4.17	4.12	4.06	4.01	3.95	3.90	3.85	3.79	3.74	3.68	3.63	3.58	3.52	3.47	3.41	3.36	3.31	3.25	3.20	3.14	3.09
69.0	4.02	4.11	4.20	4.29	4.24	4.18	4.13	4.07	4.02	3.97	3.91	3.86	3.80	3.75	3.70	3.64	3.59	3.53	3.48	3.43	3.37	3.32	3.26	3.21	3.16
69.5	4.08	4.17	4.26	4.35	4.30	4.25	4.19	4.14	4.09	4.03	3.98	3.92	3.87	3.82	3.76	3.71	3.65	3.60	3.55	3.49	3.44	3.38	3.33	3.28	3.22
70.0	4.14	4.23	4.32	4.41	4.37	4.31	4.26	4.21	4.15	4.10	4.04	3.99	3.94	3.88	3.83	3.77	3.72	3.67	3.61	3.56	3.50	3.45	3.40	3.34	3.29
70.5	4.19	4.28	4.37	4.46	4.43	4.38	4.33	4.27	4.22	4.16	4.11	4.06	4.00	3.95	3.89	3.84	3.79	3.73	3.68	3.62	3.57	3.52	3.46	3.41	3.35
71.0	4.25	4.34	4.43	4.52	4.50	4.45	4.39	4.34	4.28	4.23	4.18	4.12	4.07	4.01	3.96	3.91	3.85	3.80	3.74	3.69	3.64	3.58	3.53	3.47	3.42
71.5	4.31	4.40	4.49	4.58	4.57	4.51	4.46	4.40	4.35	4.30	4.24	4.19	4.13	4.08	4.03	3.97	3.92	3.86	.3.81	3.76	3.70	3.65	3.59	3.54	3.49
72.0	4.37	4.46	4.55	4.64	4.63	4.58	4.52	4.47	4.42	4.36	4.31	4.25	4.20	4.15	4.09	4.04	3.98	3.93	3.88	3.82	3.77	3.71	3.66	3.61	3.55
72.5	4.43	4.52	4.61	4.70	4.70	4.64	4.59	4.54	4.48	4.43	4.37	4.32	4.27	4.21	4.16	4.10	4.05	4.00	3.94	3.86	3.83	3.78	3.73	3.67	3.62
73.0	4.49	4.58	4.67	4.76	4.76	4.71	4.66	4.60	4.55	4.49	4.44	4.39	4.33	4.28	4.22	4.17	4.12	4.06	4.01	3.95	3.90	3.85	3.79	3.74	3.68
73.5	4.54	4.63	4.72	4.81	4.83	4.78	4.72	4.67	4.61	4.56	4.51	4.45	4.40	4.34	4.29	4.24	4.18	4.13	4.07	4.02	3.97	3.91	3.86	3.80	3.75
74.0	4.60	4.69	4.78	4.87	4.90	4.84	4.79	4.73	4.68	4.63	4.57	4.52	4.46	4.41	4.36	4.30	4.25	4.19	4.14	4.09	4.03	3.98	3.92	3.87	3.82
74.5	4.66	4.75	4.84	4.93	4.96	4.91	4.85	4.80	4.75	4.69	4.64	4.58	4.53	4.48	4.42	4.37	4.31	4.26	4.21	4.15	4.10	4.04	3.99	3.94	3.88
75.0	4.72	4.81	4.90	4.99	5.03	4.97	4.92	4.87	4.81	4.76	4.70	4.65	4.60	4.54	4.49	4.43	4.38	4.33	4.27	4.22	4.16	4.11	4.06	4.00	3.95
75.5	4.78	4.87	4.96	5.05	5.09	5.04	4.99	4.93	4.88	4.82	4.77	4.72	4.66	4.61	4.55	4.50	4.45	4.39	4.34	4.28	4.23	4.18	4.12	4.07	4.01
76.0	4.84	4.93	5.02	5.11	5.16	5.11	5.05	5.00	4.94	4.89	4.84	4.78	4.73	4.67	4.62	4.57	4.51	4.46	4.40	4.35	4.30	4.24	4.19	4.13	4.08
76.5	4.90	4.99	5.08	5.17	5.23	5.17	5.12	5.06	5.01	4.96	4.90	4.85	4.79	4.74	4.69	4.63	4.58	4.52	4.47	4.42	4.36	4.31	4.25	4.20	4.15
77.0	4.95	5.04	5.13	5.22	5.29	5.24	5.18	5.13	5.08	5.02	4.97	4.91	4.86	4.81	4.75	4.70	4.64	4.59	4.54	4.48	4.43	4.37	4.32	4.27	4.21
77.5	5.10	5.10	5.19	5.28	5.36	5.30	5.25	5.20	5.14	5.09	5.03	4.98	4.93	4.87	4.82	4.76	4.71	4.66	4.60	4.55	4.49	4.44	4.39	4.33	4.28
78.0	5.07	5.16	5.25	5.34	5.42	5.37	5.32	5.26	5.21	5.15	5.10	5.05	4.99	4.94	4.88	4.83	4.78	4.72	4.67	4.61	4.56	4.51	4.45	4.40	4.34
78.5	5.13	5.22	5.31	5.40	5.49	5.44	5.38	5.33	5.27	5.22	5.17	5.11	5.06	5.00	4.95	4.90	4.84	4.79	4.73	4.68	4.63	4.57	4.52	4.46	4.41
79.0	5.19	5.28	5.37	5.46	5.56	5.50	5.45	5.39	5.34	5.29	5.23	5.18	5.12	5.07	5.02	4.96	4.91	4.85	4.80	4.75	4.69	4.64	4.58	4.53	4.48
79.5	5.25	5.34	5.43	5.52	5.62	5.57	5.51	5.46	5.41	5.35	5.30	5.21	5.19	5.14	5.08	5.03	4.97	4.92	4.87	4.81	4.76	4.70	4.65	4.60	4.54
80.0	5.30	5.39	5.48	5.57	5.69	5.63	5.58	5.53	5.47	5.42	5.36	5.31	5.26	5.20	5.15	5.09	5.04	4.99	4.93	4.88	4.82	4.77	4.72	4.66	4.61
80.5	5.36	5.45	5.54	5.63	5.75	5.70	5.65	5.59	5.54	5.48	5.43	5.38	5.32	5.27	5.21	5.16	5.11	5.05	5.00	4.94	4.89	4.84	4.78	4.73	4.67
81.0	5.42	5.51	5.60	5.69	5.82	5.77	5.71	5.66	5.60	5.55	5.50	5.44	5.39	5.33	5.28	5.23	5.17	5.12	5.06	5.01	4.96	4.90	4.85	4.79	4.74
81.5	5.48	5.57	5.66	5.75	5.89	5.83	5.78	5.72	5.67	5.62	5.56	5.51	5.45	5.40	5.35	5.29	5.24	5.18	5.13	5.08	5.02	4.97	4.91	4.86	4.81
82.0	5.54	5.63	5.72	5.81	5.95	5.90	5.84	5.79	5.74	5.68	5.63	5.57	5.52	5.47	5.41	5.36	5.30	5.25	5.20	5.14	5.09	5.03	4.98	4.93	4.87
82.5	5.30	5.69	5.78	5.87	6.02	5.96	5.91	5.86	5.80	5.75	5.69	6.64	5.59	5.53	5.48	5.42	5.37	5.32	5.26	5.21	5.15	5.10	5.05	4.99	4.95
83.0	5.65	5.74	5.83	5.92	6.08	6.03	5.98	5.92	5.87	5.81	5.76	5.71	5.65	5.60	5.54	5.49	5.44	5.38	5.33	5.27	5.22	5.17	5.11	5.06	5.00
83.5	5.71	5.80	5.90	5.98	6.15	6.10	6.04	5.99	5.93	5.88	5.83	5.77	5.72	5.66	5.61	5.56	5.50	5.45	5.39	5.34	5.29	5.23	5.18	5.12	5.07
84.0	5.77	5.86	5.95	6.04	6.22	6.16	6.11	6.05	6.00	5.98	5.89	5.84	5.78	5.73	5.68	5.62	5.57	5.51	5.46	5.41	5.35	5.30	5.24	5.19	5.14
84.5	5.83	5.92	6.01	6.10	6.28	6.23	6.12	6.17	6.07	6.01	5.96	5.90	5.85	5.80	5.74	5.69	5.63	5.58	5.53	5.47	5.42	5.36	5.31	5.26	5.20
85.0	5.89	5.98	6.07	6.16	6.36	6.29	6.24	6.19	6.13	6.06	6.02	5.97	5.92	5.86	5.81	5.75	5.70	5.65	5.59	5.54	5.58	5.43	5.38	5.32	5.27

Table 3.

PREDICTED FVC FOR FEMALES (KNUDSON, ET AL.: AM. REV. RESPIR. DIS. 1976, 113, 587.)

	AGE																								
HT	17	19	21	23	25	27	29	31	33	35	37	39	41	43	45	47	49	51	53	55	57	59	61	63	65
52.0	2.45	2.64	2.65	2.61	2.56	2.52	2.47	2.43	2.39	2.34	2.30	2.25	2.21	2.17	2.12	2.08	2.03	1.99	1.95	1.90	1.86	1.81	1.77	1.73	1.68
52.5	2.50	2.68	2.70	2.65	2.61	2.57	2.52	2.48	2.43	2.39	2.35	2.30	2.26	2.21	2.17	2.13	2.08	2.04	1.99	1.95	1.91	1.86	1.82	1.77	1.73
53.0	2.54	2.72	2.74	2.70	2.66	2.61	2.57	2.52	2.48	2.44	2.39	2.35	2.30	2.26	2.22	2.17	2.13	2.08	2.04	2.00	1.95	1.91	1.86	1.82	1.78
53.5	2.58	2.76	2.79	2.75	2.70	2.66	2.62	2.57	2.53	2.48	2.44	2.40	2.35	2.31	2.26	2.22	2.18	2.13	2.09	2.04	2.00	1.96	1.91	1.87	1.82
54.0	2.62	2.81	2.84	2.79	2.75	2.71	2.66	2.62	2.57	2.53	2.49	2.44	2.40	2.35	2.31	2.27	2.22	2.18	2.13	2.09	2.05	2.00	1.96	1.91	1.87
54.5	2.66	2.85	2.89	2.84	2.80	2.75	2.71	2.67	2.62	2.58	2.53	2.49	2.45	2.40	2.36	2.31	2.27	2.23	2.18	2.14	2.09	2.05	2.01	1.96	1.92
55.0	2.71	2.89	2.93	2.89	2.84	2.80	2.76	2.71	2.67	2.62	2.58	2.54	2.49	2.45	2.40	2.36	2.32	2.27	2.23	2.19	2.14	2.10	2.05	2.01	1.96
55.5	2.75	2.93	2.98	2.94	2.89	2.85	2.80	2.76	2.72	2.67	2.63	2.58	2.54	2.50	2.45	2.41	2.36	2.32	2.28	2.23	2.19	2.14	2.10	2.06	2.01
56.0	2.79	2.97	3.03	2.98	2.94	2.89	2.85	2.81	2.76	2.72	2.67	2.63	2.59	2.54	2.50	2.45	2.41	2.37	2.32	2.28	2.23	2.19	2.15	2.10	2.06
56.5	2.83	3.01	3.07	3.03	2.99	2.94	2.90	2.85	2.81	2.77	2.72	2.68	2.63	2.59	2.55	2.60	2.46	2.41	2.37	2.33	2.28	2.24	2.19	2.15	2.11
57.0	2.87	3.06	3.12	3.08	3.03	2.99	2.94	2.90	2.86	2.81	2.77	2.72	2.68	2.64	2.59	2.55	2.50	2.46	2.42	2.37	2.33	2.28	2.24	2.20	2.15
57.5	2.91	3.10	3.17	3.12	3.08	3.04	2.99	2.95	2.90	2.86	2.82	2.77	2.73	2.66	2.64	2.60	2.55	2.51	2.46	2.42	2.38	2.33	2.29	2.24	2.20
58.0	2.96	3.14	3.21	3.17	3.13	3.08	3.04	2.99	2.95	2.91	2.86	2.82	2.77	2.73	2.69	2.64	2.60	2.55	2.51	2.47	2.42	2.38	2.33	2.29	2.25
58.5	3.00	3.18	3.26	3.22	3.17	3.13	3.09	3.04	3.00	2.95	2.91	2.87	2.82	2.78	2.73	269	2.65	2.60	2.56	2.51	2.47	2.43	2.38	2.34	2.29
59.0	3.04	3.22	3.31	3.26	3.22	3.18	3.13	3.09	3.04	3.00	2.96	2.91	2.87	2.82	2.78	2.74	2.69	2.65	2.60	2.56	2.52	2.47	2.43	2.38	2.34
59.5	3.08	3.27	3.36	3.31	3.27	3.22	3.18	3.14	3.09	3.05	3.00	2.96	2.92	2.87	2.83	2.78	2.74	2.70	2.65	2.61	2.56	2.52	2.48	2.43	2.39
60.0	3.12	3.31	3.40	3.36	3.31	3.27	3.23	3.18	3.14	3.09	3.05	3.01	2.97	2.92	2.88	2.83	2.79	2.74	2.70	2.65	2.61	2.57	2.52	2.48	2.43
60.5	3.17	3.35	3.45	3.41	3.36	3.32	3.27	3.23	3.19	3.14	3.10	3.05	3.01	2.97	2.92	2.88	2.83	2.79	2.75	2.70	2.66	2.61	2.57	2.53	2.48
61.0	3.21	3.39	3.50	3.45	3.41	3.36	3.32	3.28	3.23	3.19	3.14	3.10	3.06	3.01	2.97	2.92	2.88	2.84	2.79	2.75	2.70	2.66	2.62	2.57	2.53
61.5	3.25	3.43	3.54	3.50	3.46	3.41	3.37	3.32	3.28	3.24	3.19	3.15	3.10	3.06	3.02	2.97	2.93	2.88	2.84	2.80	2.75	2.71	2.66	2.62	2.58
62.0	3.29	3.48	3.59	3.55	3.50	3.46	3.41	3.37	3.33	3.26	3.24	3.19	3.15	3.11	3.06	3.02	2.97	2.93	2.89	2.84	2.80	2.75	2.71	2.67	2.62
62.5	3.33	3.52	3.64	3.59	3.55	3.51	3.46	3.42	3.37	3.33	3.29	3.27	3.20	3.15	3.11	3.07	3.02	2.98	2.93	2.89	2.85	2.80	2.76	2.71	2.67
63.0	3.38	3.56	3.68	3.64	3.60	3.55	3.51	3.46	3.42	3.38	3.33	3.29	3.24	3.20	3.16	3.11	3.07	3.02	2.98	2.94	2.89	2.85	2.80	2.76	2.72
63.5	3.42	3.60	3.73	3.69	3.64	3.60	3.56	3.51	3.47	3.42	3.38	3.34	3.29	3.25	3.20	3.16	3.12	3.07	3.03	2.98	2.94	2.90	2.85	2.81	2.76
64.0	3.46	3.64	3.78	3.73	3.69	3.65	3.60	3.56	3.61	3.47	3.43	3.38	3.34	3.29	3.25	3.21	3.16	3.12	3.07	3.03	2.99	2.94	2.90	2.85	2.81
64.5	3.50	3.69	3.83	3.78	3.74	3.69	3.65	3.61	3.56	3.52	3.47	3.43	3.39	3.34	3.30	3.25	3.21	3.17	3.12	3.08	3.03	2.99	2.95	2.90	2.86
65.0	3.54	3.73	3.87	3.83	3.78	3.74	3.70	3.65	3.61	3.56	3.52	3.48	3.43	3.39	3.34	3.30	3.26	3.21	3.17	3.12	.3.08	3.04	2.99	2.95	2.90
65.5	3.59	3.77	3.92	3.88	3.83	3.79	3.74	3.70	3.66	3.61	3.57	3.52	3.48	3.44	3.39	3.35	3.30	3.26	3.22	3.17	3.13	3.08	3.04	3.00	2.95
66.0	3.63	3.81	3.97	3.92	3.88	3.83	3.79	3.75	3.70	3.66	3.61	3.57	3.53	3.46	3.44	3.39	3.35	3.31	3.26	3.22	3.17	3.13	3.09	3.04	3.00
66.5	3.67	3.85	4.01	3.97	3.93	3.88	3.84	3.79	3.75	3.71	3.66	3.62	3.57	3.53	3.49	3.44	3.40	3.35	3.31	3.27	3.22	3.18	3.13	3.09	3.05
67.0	3.71	3.89	4.06	4.02	3.97	3.93	3.88	3.84	3.80	3.75	3.71	3.66	3.62	3.58	3.53	3.49	3.44	3.40	3.36	3.31	3.27	3.22	3.18	3.14	3.09
67.5	3.75	3.94	4.11	4.06	4.02	3.98	3.93	3.89	3.84	3.80	3.76	3.71	3.67	3.62	3.58	3.54	3.49	3.45	3.40	3.36	3.32	3.27	3.23	3.18	3.14
68.0	3.79	3.98	4.15	4.11	4.07	4.02	3.98	3.93	3.89	3.85	3.80	3.76	3.71	3.67	3.63	3.58	3.54	3.49	3.45	3.41	3.36	3.32	3.27	3.23	3.19
68.5	3.84	4.02	4.20	4.16	4.11	4.07	4.03	3.98	3.94	3.89	3.85	3.81	3.76	3.72	3.67	3.63	3.59	3.54	3.50	3.45	3.41	3.37	3.32	3.28	3.23
69.0	3.88	4.06	4.25	4.20	4.16	4.12	4.07	4.03	3.98	3.94	3.90	3.85	3.61	3.76	3.72	3.68	3.63	3.59	3.54	3.50	3.46	3.41	3.37	3.32	3.28
69.5	3.92	4.10	4.30	4.29	4.21	4.16	4.12	4.08	4.03	3.99	3.94	3.90	3.86	3.81	3.77	3.72	3.68	3.64	3.59	3.55	3.50	3.46	3.42	3.37	3.33
70.0	3.96	4.15	4.34	4.30	4.25	4.21	4.17	4.12	4.08	4.03	3.99	3.95	3.90	3.86	3.81	3.77	3.73	3.68	3.64	3.59	3.55	3.51	3.46	3.42	3.37
70.5	4.00	4.19	4.39	4.35	4.30	4.26	4.21	4.17	4.13	4.08	4.04	3.99	3.95	3.91	3.86	3.82	3.77	3.73	3.69	3.64	3.60	3.55	3.51	3.47	3.42
71.0	4.05	4.23	4.44	4.39	4.35	4.30	4.26	4.22	4.17	4.13	4.08	4.04	4.00	3.95	3.91	3.86	3.82	3.78	3.73	3.69	3.64	3.60	3.56	3.51	3.47
71.5	4.09	4.27	4.48	4.44	4.40	4.35	4.31	4.26	4.22	4.18	4.13	4.09	4.04	4.00	3.96	3.91	3.87	3.82	3.78	3.74	3.69	3.65	3.60	3.56	3.52
72.0	4.13	4.31	4.53	4.49	4.44	4.40	4.35	4.31	4.27	4.22	4.18	4.13	4.09	4.05	4.00	3.96	3.91	3.87	3.83	3.78	3.74	3.69	3.65	3.61	3.56
72.5	4.17	4.36	4.58	4.53	4.49	4.45	4.40	4.36	4.31	4.27	4.23	4.18	4.14	4.09	4.05	4.01	3.96	3.92	3.87	3.83	3.75	3.74	3.70	3.65	3.61
73.0	4.21	4.40	4.62	4.58	4.54	4.49	4.45	4.40	4.36	4.32	4.27	4.23	4.18	4.14	4.10	4.05	4.01	3.96	3.92	3.88	3.83	3.79	3.74	3.70	3.66
73.5	4.26	4.44	4.67	4.63	4.50	4.54	4.50	4.45	4.41	4.36	4.32	4.28	4.23	4.19	4.14	4.10	4.06	4.01	3.97	3.92	3.88	3.84	3.79	3.75	3.70
74.0	4.30	4.48	4.72	4.67	4.63	4.59	4.54	4.50	4.45	4.41	4.37	4.32	4.28	4.23	4.19	4.15	4.10	4.06	4.01	3.97	3.93	3.88	3.84	3.79	3.75
74.5	4.34	4.52	4.77	4.72	4.68	4.63	4.59	4.55	4.50	4.46	4.41	4.37	4.33	4.28	4.24	4.19	4.15	4.11	4.04	4.20	3.97	3.93	3.89	3.84	3.80
75.0	4.38	4.57	4.81	4.77	4.72	4.68	4.64	4.59	4.55	4.50	4.46	4.42	4.37	4.33	4.28	4.24	4.20	4.15	4.11	4.06	4.02	3.98	3.93	3.89	3.84
75.5	4.42	4.61	4.86	4.82	4.77	4.73	4.68	4.64	4.60	4.55	4.51	4.46	4.42	4.38	4.33	4.29	4.24	4.20	4.16	4.11	4.07	4.02	3.98	3.94	3.89
76.0	4.47	4.65	4.91	4.86	4.82	4.77	4.73	4.69	4.64	4.60	4.55	4.51	4.47	4.42	4.38	4.33	4.29	4.25	4.20	4.16	4.11	4.07	4.03	3.98	3.94
76.5	4.51	4.69	4.95	4.91	4.87	4.82	4.78	4.73	4.69	4.65	4.60	4.56	4.51	4.47	4.43	4.38	4.34	4.29	4.25	4.21	4.16	4.12	4.07	4.03	3.99
77.0	4.55	4.73	5.00	4.96	4.91	4.87	4.82	4.78	4.74	4.69	4.65	4.60	4.56	4.52	4.47	4.43	4.38	4.34	4.30	4.25	4.21	4.16	4.12	4.08	4.03

Table 4.

PREDICTED FVC_1 FOR FEMALES (KNUDSON, ET AL.: AM. REV. RESPIR. DIS. 1976, 113, 587.)

	AGE																								
HT	17	19	21	23	25	27	29	31	33	35	37	39	41	43	45	47	49	51	53	55	57	59	61	63	65
52.0	2.31	2.48	2.33	2.29	2.25	2.21	2.16	2.12	2.08	2.04	2.00	1.95	1.91	1.87	1.83	1.79	1.74	1.70	1.66	1.62	1.58	1.53	1.49	1.45	1.41
52.5	2.34	2.51	2.37	2.32	2.28	2.24	2.20	2.16	2.11	2.07	2.03	1.99	1.95	1.90	1.86	1.82	1.78	1.74	1.69	1.65	1.61	1.57	1.53	1.48	1.44
53.0	2.38	2.55	2.40	2.36	2.32	2.27	2.23	2.19	2.15	2.11	2.06	2.02	1.98	1.94	1.90	1.85	1.81	1.77	1.73	1.69	1.64	1.60	1.56	1.52	1.48
53.5	2.41	2.58	2.43	2.39	2.35	2.31	2.27	2.22	2.18	2.14	2.10	2.06	2.01	1.97	1.93	1.89	1.85	1.80	1.76	1.72	1.68	1.64	1.59	1.55	1.51
54.0	2.45	2.62	2.47	2.43	2.38	2.34	2.30	2.26	2.22	2.17	2.13	2.09	2.05	2.01	1.96	1.92	1.88	1.84	1.80	1.75	1.71	1.67	1.63	1.59	1.54
54.5	2.48	2.65	2.50	2.46	2.42	2.38	2.33	2.29	2.25	2.21	2.17	2.12	2.08	2.04	2.00	1.96	1.91	1.87	1.83	1.79	1.75	1.70	1.66	1.62	1.58
55.0	2.51	2.68	2.54	2.49	2.45	2.41	2.37	2.33	2.28	2.24	2.20	2.16	2.12	2.07	2.03	1.99	1.95	1.91	1.86	1.82	1.78	1.74	1.70	1.65	1.61
55.5	2.55	2.72	2.57	2.53	2.49	2.45	2.40	2.36	2.32	2.28	2.24	2.19	2.15	2.11	2.07	2.03	1.98	1.94	1.90	1.86	1.82	1.77	1.73	1.69	1.65
56.0	2.58	2.75	2.61	2.56	2.52	2.48	2.44	2.40	2.35	2.31	2.27	2.23	2.19	2.14	2.10	2.06	2.02	1.98	1.93	1.89	1.85	1.81	1.77	1.72	1.68
56.5	2.62	2.79	2.64	2.60	2.56	2.51	2.47	2.43	2.39	2.35	2.30	2.26	2.22	2.18	2.14	2.09	2.06	2.01	1.97	1.93	1.88	1.84	1.80	1.76	1.72
57.0	2.65	2.82	2.67	2.63	2.59	2.55	2.51	2.46	2.42	2.38	2.34	2.30	2.25	2.21	2.17	2.13	2.09	2.04	2.00	1.96	1.92	1.88	1.83	1.79	1.75
57.5	2.69	2.86	2.71	2.67	2.62	2.58	2.54	2.50	2.46	2.41	2.37	2.33	2.29	2.25	2.20	2.16	2.12	2.08	2.04	1.99	1.95	1.91	1.87	1.83	1.78
58.0	2.72	2.89	2.74	2.70	2.66	2.62	2.57	2.53	2.49	2.45	2.41	2.36	2.32	2.28	2.24	2.20	2.15	2.11	2.07	2.03	1.99	1.94	1.90	1.86	1.82
58.5	2.75	2.92	2.78	2.75	2.69	2.65	2.61	2.57	2.52	2.48	2.44	2.40	2.36	2.31	2.27	2.23	2.19	2.15	2.10	2.06	2.02	1.98	1.94	1.89	1.85
59.0	2.79	2.96	2.81	2.77	2.73	2.69	2.64	2.60	2.56	2.52	2.48	2.43	2.39	2.35	2.31	2.27	2.22	2.18	2.14	2.10	2.06	2.01	1.97	1.93	1.89
59.5	2.82	2.99	2.85	2.80	2.76	2.72	2.68	2.64	2.59	2.55	2.51	2.47	2.43	2.38	2.34	2.30	2.26	2.22	2.17	2.13	2.09	2.05	2.01	1.96	1.92
60.0	2.86	3.03	2.88	2.84	2.80	2.75	2.71	2.67	2.63	2.59	2.54	2.50	2.46	2.42	2.38	2.33	2.29	2.25	2.21	2.17	2.12	2.08	2.04	2.00	1.96
60.5	2.89	3.06	2.91	2.87	2.83	2.79	2.75	2.70	2.66	2.62	2.58	2.54	2.49	2.45	2.41	2.37	2.33	2.25	2.24	2.20	2.16	2.12	2.07	2.03	1.99
61.0	2.93	3.10	2.95	2.91	2.86	2.82	2.78	2.74	2.70	2.65	2.61	2.57	2.53	2.49	2.44	2.40	2.36	2.32	2.28	2.23	2.19	2.15	2.11	2.07	2.02
61.5	2.96	3.13	2.98	2.94	2.90	2.86	2.81	2.77	2.73	2.69	2.65	2.60	2.56	2.52	2.48	2.44	2.39	2.35	2.31	2.27	2.23	2.18	2.14	2.10	2.06
62.0	2.99	3.16	3.02	2.97	2.93	2.89	2.85	2.81	2.76	2.72	2.68	2.64	2.60	2.55	2.51	2.47	2.43	2.39	2.34	2.30	2.26	2.22	2.18	2.13	2.09
62.5	3.03	3.20	3.05	3.01	2.97	2.93	2.88	2.84	2.80	2.76	2.72	2.57	2.63	2.59	2.55	2.51	2.46	2.42	2.38	2.34	2.30	2.25	2.21	2.17	2.13
63.0	3.06	3.23	3.09	3.04	3.00	2.96	2.92	2.86	2.83	2.79	2.75	2.71	2.67	2.62	2.58	2.54	2.50	2.46	2.41	2.37	2.33	2.29	2.28	2.20	2.16
63.5	3.10	3.27	3.12	3.08	3.04	2.99	2.95	2.91	2.87	2.83	2.78	2.74	2.70	2.66	2.62	2.57	2.53	2.49	2.45	2.41	2.36	2.32	2.28	2.24	2.20
64.0	3.13	3.30	3.15	3.11	3.07	3.03	2.99	2.94	2.90	2.86	2.82	2.78	2.73	2.69	2.65	2.61	2.57	2.52	2.48	2.44	2.40	2.36	2.31	2.27	2.23
64.5	3.17	3.34	3.19	3.15	3.10	3.06	3.02	2.98	2.94	2.89	2.85	2.81	2.77	2.73	2.68	2.64	2.60	2.56	2.52	2.47	2.43	2.39	2.35	2.31	2.26
65.0	3.20	3.37	3.22	3.18	3.14	3.10	3.05	3.01	2.97	2.93	2.89	2.84	2.80	2.76	2.72	2.68	2.63	2.59	2.55	2.51	2.47	2.42	2.38	2.34	2.30
65.5	3.23	3.40	3.26	3.21	3.17	3.13	3.09	3.05	3.00	2.96	2.92	2.88	2.84	2.79	2.75	2.71	2.67	2.63	2.58	2.54	2.50	2.46	2.42	2.37	2.33
66.0	3.27	3.44	3.29	3.25	3.21	3.17	3.12	3.08	3.04	3.00	2.96	2.91	2.87	2.83	2.79	2.75	2.70	2.66	2.62	2.58	2.54	2.49	2.45	2.41	2.37
66.5	3.30	3.47	3.33	3.28	3.24	3.20	3.16	.3.12	3.07	3.03	2.99	2.95	2.91	2.86	2.82	2.78	2.74	2.70	2.65	2.61	2.57	2.53	2.49	2.44	2.40
67.0	3.34	3.51	3.36	3.32	3.28	3.23	3.19	3.15	3.11	3.07	3.02	2.98	2.94	2.90	2.86	2.81	2.77	2.73	2.69	2.65	2.60	2.56	2.52	2.48	2.44
67.5	3.34	3.54	3.36	3.35	3.31	3.27	3.23	3.18	3.14	3.10	3.06	3.02	2.97	2.94	2.89	2.85	2.81	2.76	2.72	2.68	2.64	2.60	2.55	2.51	2.47
68.0	3.41	3.58	3.43	3.39	3.34	3.30	3.26	3.22	3.18	3.13	3.09	3.05	3.01	2.97	2.92	2.88	2.84	2.80	2.76	2.71	2.67	2.63	2.59	2.55	2.50
68.5	3.44	3.61	3.46	3.42	3.38	3.34	3.29	3.25	3.21	3.17	3.13	3.08	3.04	3.00	2.96	2.92	2.87	2.83	2.79	2.75	2.71	2.66	2.62	2.58	2.54
69.0	3.47	3.64	3.50	3.46	3.41	3.37	3.33	3.29	3.25	3.20	3.16	3.12	3.08	3.04	2.99	2.95	2.91	2.87	2.83	2.78	2.74	2.70	2.66	2.62	2.57
69.5	3.51	3.68	3.53	3.49	3.45	3.41	3.36	3.32	3.28	3.24	3.20	3.15	3.11	3.07	3.03	2.99	2.94	2.90	2.86	2.82	2.78	2.73	2.69	2.65	2.61
70.0	3.54	3.71	3.57	3.52	3.48	3.44	3.40	3.36	3.31	3.27	3.23	3.19	3.15	3.10	3.06	3.02	2.98	2.94	2.89	2.85	2.81	2.77	2.73	2.68	2.64
70.5	3.58	3.75	3.60	3.56	3.52	3.47	3.43	3.39	3.35	3.31	3.26	3.22	3.18	3.14	3.10	3.05	3.01	2.97	2.93	2.89	2.84	2.80	2.76	2.72	2.68
71.0	3.61	3.78	3.63	3.59	3.55	3.51	3.47	3.42	3.38	3.34	3.30	3.26	3.21	3.17	3.13	3.09	3.05	3.00	2.96	2.92	2.88	2.84	2.79	2.75	2.71
71.5	3.65	3.82	3.67	3.63	3.58	3.54	3.50	3.46	3.42	3.37	3.33	3.29	3.25	3.21	3.16	3.12	3.08	3.04	3.00	2.95	2.91	2.87	2.83	2.79	2.74
72.0	3.68	3.85	3.70	3.66	3.62	3.58	3.52	3.49	3.45	3.41	3.37	3.32	3.28	3.24	3.20	3.16	3.11	3.07	3.03	2.99	2.95	2.90	2.86	2.82	2.78
72.5	3.71	3.88	3.74	3.70	3.65	3.61	3.57	3.53	3.49	3.44	3.40	3.36	3.32	3.28	3.23	3.19	3.15	3.11	3.07	3.02	2.98	2.94	2.90	2.86	2.81
73.0	3.75	3.92	3.77	3.73	3.69	3.65	3.60	3.56	3.52	3.47	3.44	3.39	3.35	3.31	3.27	3.23	3.18	3.14	3.10	3.06	3.02	2.97	2.93	2.89	2.85
73.5	3.78	3.95	3.81	3.76	3.72	3.68	3.64	3.60	3.55	3.51	3.47	3.43	3.39	3.34	3.30	3.26	3.22	3.18	3.13	3.09	3.05	3.01	2.97	2.92	2.88
74.0	3.82	3.99	3.84	3.80	3.76	3.71	3.67	3.63	3.59	3.55	3.50	3.46	3.42	3.38	3.34	3.29	3.25	3.21	3.17	3.13	3.08	3.04	3.00	2.96	2.92
74.5	3.85	4.02	3.87	3.83	3.79	3.75	3.71	3.66	3.62	3.58	3.54	3.50	3.45	3.41	3.37	3.33	3.29	3.24	3.20	3.16	3.12	3.08	3.03	2.99	2.95
75.0	3.89	4.06	3.91	3.87	3.82	3.78	3.74	3.70	3.66	3.61	3.57	3.53	3.49	3.45	3.40	3.36	3.32	3.28	3.24	3.19	3.15	3.11	3.07	3.03	2.98
75.5	3.92	4.09	3.94	3.90	3.86	3.82	3.77	3.73	3.69	3.65	3.61	3.56	3.52	3.48	3.44	3.40	3.35	3.31	3.27	3.23	3.19	3.14	3.10	3.06	3.02
76.0	3.95	4.12	3.98	3.94	3.89	3.85	3.81	3.77	3.73	3.68	3.64	3.60	3.56	3.52	3.47	3.43	3.39	3.35	3.31	3.56	3.22	3.18	3.14	3.10	3.05
76.5	3.99	4.16	4.01	3.97	3.93	3.89	3.84	3.80	3.76	3.72	3.68	3.63	3.59	3.55	3.51	3.47	3.42	3.38	3.34	3.30	3.26	3.21	3.17	3.13	3.09
77.0	4.02	4.19	4.05	4.00	3.96	3.92	3.86	3.84	3.79	3.75	3.71	3.67	3.63	3.58	3.54	3.50	3.46	3.42	3.37	3.33	3.29	3.25	3.21	3.16	3.12

§1910.1043 Appendix D Pulmonary function standards for cotton dust standard

The spirometric measurements of pulmonary function shall conform to the following minimum standards, and these standards are not intended to preclude additional testing or alternate methods which can be determined to be superior.

I. Apparatus

A. The instrument shall be accurate to within ±50 milliliters or within ± 3 percent of reading, whichever is greater.

B. The instrument should be capable of measuring vital capacity from 0 to 7 liters BTPS.

C. The instrument shall have a low inertia and offer low resistance to airflow such that the resistance to airflow at 12 liters per second must be less than 1.5 cm H_2O/(liter/sec).

D. The zero time point for the purpose of timing the FEV_1 shall be determined by extrapolating the steepest portion of the volume time curve back to the maximal inspiration volume (1, 2, 3, 4) or by an equivalent method.

E. Instruments incorporating measurements of airflow to determine volume shall conform to the same volume accuracy stated in (a) of this Section when presented with flow rates from at least 0 to 12 liters per second.

F. The instrument or user of the instrument must have a means of correcting volumes to body temperature saturated with water vapor (BTPS) under conditions of varying ambient spirometer temperatures and barometric pressures.

G. The instrument used shall provide a tracing or display of either flow versus volume or volume versus time during the entire forced expiration. A tracing or display is necessary to determine whether the patient has performed the test properly. The tracing must be stored and available for recall and must be of sufficient size that hand measurements may be made within requirement of paragraph (a) of this Section. If a paper record is made it must have a paper speed of at least 2 cm/sec and a volume sensitivity of at least 10.0 mm of chart per liter of volume.

H. The instrument shall be capable of accumulating volume for a minimum of 10 seconds and shall not stop accumulating volume before (1) the volume change for a 0.5 second interval is less than 25 milliliters, or (2) the flow is less than 50 milliliters per second for a 0.5 second interval.

I. The forced vital capacity (FVC) and forced expiratory volume in 1 second ($FEV_{1.0}$) measurements shall comply with the accuracy requirements stated in paragraph (a) of this Section. That is, they should be accurately measured to within ± 50 ml or within ± 3 percent of reading, whichever is greater.

J. The instrument must be capable of being calibrated in the field with respect to the FEV_1 and FVC. This calibration of the FEV_1 and FVC may be either directly or indirectly through volume and time base measurements. The volume calibration source should provide a volume displacement of at least 2 liters and should be accurate to within ± 30 milliliters.

II. Technique for Measurement of Forced Vital Capacity Maneuver

A. Use of a nose clip is recommended but not required. The procedures shall be explained in simple terms to the patient who shall be instructed to loosen any tight clothing and stand in front of the apparatus. The subject may sit, but care should be taken on repeat testing that the same position be used and, if possible, the same spirometer. Particular attention shall be given to insure that the chin is slightly elevated with the neck slightly extended. The patient shall be instructed to make a full inspiration from a normal breathing pattern and then blow into the apparatus, without interruption, as hard, fast, and completely as possible. At least three forced expirations shall be carried out. During the maneuvers, the patient shall be observed for compliance with instruction. The expirations shall be checked visually for reproducibility from flow-volume or volume-time tracings or displays. The following efforts shall be judged unacceptable when the patient:

1. Has not reached full inspiration preceding the forced expiration;
2. Has not used maximal effort during the entire forced expiration;
3. Has not continued the expiration for at least 5 seconds or until an obvious plateau in the volume time curve has occurred;
4. Has coughed or closed his glottis;
5. Has an obstructed mouthpiece or a leak around the mouthpiece (obstruction due to tongue being placed in front of mouthpiece, false teeth falling in front of mouthpiece, etc.;
6. Has an unsatisfactory start of expiration, one characterized by excessive hesitation (or false starts), and therefore not allowing back extrapolation of time 0 (extrapolated volume on the volume time tracing must be less than 10 percent of the FVC);
7. Has an excessive variability between the three acceptable curves. The variation between the two largest FVC's and FEV_1's of the three satisfactory tracings should not exceed 10 percent or ± 100 milliliters, whichever is greater.

B. Periodic and routine recalibration of the instrument or method for recording FVC and $FEV_{1.0}$ should be performed using a syringe or other volume source of at least 2 liters.

III. Interpretation of Spirogram

A. The first step in evaluating a spirogram should be to determine whether or not the patient has performed the test properly or as described in II above. From the three satisfactory tracings, the forced vital capacity (FVC) and forced expiratory volume in 1 second ($FEV_{1.0}$) shall be measured and recorded. The largest observed FVC and largest observed FEV_1 shall be used in the analysis regardless of the curve(s) on which they occur.

B. The following guidelines are recommended by NIOSH for the evaluation and management of workers exposed to cotton dust. It is important to note that employees who show reductions in FEV_1/FVC ratio below .75 or drops in Monday FEV_1 of 5 percent or greater on their initial screening exam, should be re-evaluated within a month of the first exam. Those who show consistent decrease in lung function, as shown on the following table, should be managed as recommended.

IV. Qualifications of Personnel Administering the Test

Technicians who perform pulmonary function testing should have the basic knowledge required to produce meaningful results. Training consisting of approximately 16 hours of formal instruction should cover the following areas.

A. Basic physiology of the forced vital capacity maneuver and the determinants of airflow limitation with emphasis on the relation to reproducibility of results;

B. Instrumentation requirements including calibration procedures, sources of error and their correction;

C. Performance of the testing including subject coaching, recognition of improperly performed maneuvers and corrective actions;

D. Data quality with emphasis on reproducibility;

E. Actual use of the equipment under supervised conditions;

F. Measurement of tracings and calculations of results.

§1910.1043 Appendix E Vertical elutriator equivalency protocol

A. Samples to be taken — In order to ascertain equivalency, it is necessary to collect a total of 100 samples from at least 10 sites in a mill. That is, there should be 10 replicate readings at each of 10 sites. The sites should represent dust levels which vary over the allowable range of 0.5 to 2 times the permissible exposure limit. Each sample requires the use of two vertical elutriators (VE's) and at least one but not more than two alternative devices (AD's). Thus, the end result is 200 VE readings and either 100 or 200 AD readings. The 2 VE readings and the 1 or 2 AD readings at each time and site must be made simultaneously. That is, the two VE's and one or two AD's must be arranged together in such a way that they are measuring essentially the same dust levels.

B. Data averaging —The two VE readings taken at each site are then averaged. These averages are to be used as the 100 VE readings. If two alternate devices were used, their test results are also averaged. Thus, after this step is accomplished, there will be 100 VE readings and 100 AD readings.

C. Differences —For each of the 100 sets of measurements (VE and AD) the difference is obtained as the average VE reading minus the AD reading. Call these differences D_i. Thus, we have.

$$D_i = VE_i - AD_i,\ i = 1,2,\ldots,100 \quad (1)$$

Next we compute the arithmetic mean and standard deviations of the differences, using equations (2) and (3), respectively.

$$\overline{X_D} = \frac{1}{N}\sum_{i=1}^{N} D_i \quad (2)$$

$$S_D = \sqrt{\frac{\sum D_i^2 - \frac{\sum D_1^{\,2}}{N}}{N-1}} \quad (3)$$

Where N equals the number of differences (100 in this case), X_D is the arithmetic mean and S_D is the standard deviation.

We next calculate the critical value as $T = KS_D + |X_D|$ where K=1.87, based on 100 samples.

D. Equivalency test The next step is to obtain the average of the 100 VE readings. This is obtained by equation (4)

$$\overline{X}_{VE} = \frac{1}{N}\left(\sum_{i=1}^{N} VE_i\right) \quad (4)$$

We next multiply 0.25 by X_{VE}. If $T \leq 0.25\ X_{VE}$, we can say that the alternate device has passed the equivalency test.

[43 FR 27394, June 23, 1978; 43 FR 35035, Aug. 8, 1978, as amended at 45 FR 67340, Oct. 10, 1980; 50 FR 51173, Dec. 13, 1985; 51 FR 24325, July 3, 1986; 54 FR 24334, June 7, 1989; 61 FR 5508, Feb. 13, 1996; 63 FR 1290, Jan. 8, 1998; 65 FR 76567, Dec. 7, 2000; 70 FR 1142, Jan. 5, 2005; 71 FR 16672, 16673, Apr. 3, 2006; 71 FR 50189, Aug. 24, 2006; 73 FR 75586, Dec. 12, 2008; 76 FR 33609, June 8, 2011]

§1910.1044 1,2–dibromo–3–chloropropane

(a) Scope and application

(a)(1) This Section applies to occupational exposure to 1,2-dibromo-3-chloropropane (DBCP).

(a)(2) This Section does not apply to:

(a)(2)(i) Exposure to DBCP which results solely from the application and use of DBCP as a pesticide; or

(a)(2)(ii) The storage, transportation, distribution or sale of DBCP in intact containers sealed in such a manner as to prevent exposure to DBCP vapors or liquid, except for the requirements of paragraphs (i), (n) and (o) of this Section.

(b) Definitions

Authorized person means any person required by his duties to be present in regulated areas and authorized to do so by his employer, by this Section, or by the Act. Authorized person also includes any person entering such areas as a designated representative of employees exercising an opportunity to observe employee exposure monitoring.

DBCP means 1,2-dibromo-3-chloropropane, Chemical Abstracts Service Registry Number 96–12–8, and includes all forms of DBCP.

Director means the Director, National Institute for Occupational Safety and Health, U.S. Department of Health and Human Services, or designee.

Emergency means any occurrence such as, but not limited to equipment failure, rupture of containers, or failure of control equipment which may, or does, result in an unexpected release of DBCP.

OSHA Area Office means the Area Office of the Occupational Safety and Health Administration having jurisdiction over the geographic area where the affected workplace is located.

Assistant Secretary means the Assistant Secretary of Labor for Occupational Safety and Health, U.S. Department of Labor, or designee.

(c) Permissible exposure limit

(c)(1) **Inhalation** The employer shall assure that no employee is exposed to an airborne concentration of DBCP in excess of 1 part DBCP per billion parts of air (ppb) as an 8-hour time-weighted average.

(c)(2) **Dermal and eye exposure** The employer shall assure that no employee is exposed to eye or skin contact with DBCP.

(d) [Reserved]

(e) Regulated areas

(e)(1) The employer shall establish, within each place of employment, regulated areas wherever DBCP concentrations are in excess of the permissible exposure limit.

(e)(2) The employer shall limit access to regulated areas to authorized persons.

(f) Exposure monitoring

(f)(1) **General**

(f)(1)(i) Determinations of airborne exposure levels shall be made from air samples that are representative of each employee's exposure to DBCP over an 8-hour period.

(f)(1)(ii) For the purposes of this paragraph, employee exposure is that exposure which would occur if the employee were not using a respirator.

(f)(2) **Initial** Each employer who has a place of employment in which DBCP is present, shall monitor each workplace and work operation to accurately determine the airborne concentrations of DBCP to which employees may be exposed.

(f)(3) **Frequency**

(f)(3)(i) If the monitoring required by this Section reveals employee exposures to be at or below the permissible exposure limit, the employer must repeat these measurements at least every 6 months.

(f)(3)(ii) If the monitoring required by this Section reveals employee exposures to be in excess of the permissible exposure limit, the employer must repeat these measurements for each such employee at least quarterly. The employer must continue quarterly monitoring until at least two consecutive measurements, taken at least seven (7) days apart, are at or below the permissible exposure limit. Thereafter the employer must monitor at least every 6 months.

(f)(4) **Additional** Whenever there has been a production, process, control, or personnel change which may result in any new or additional exposure to DBCP, or whenever the employer has any reason to suspect new or additional exposures to DBCP, the employer shall monitor the employees potentially affected by such change for the purpose of redetermining their exposure.

(f)(5) **Employee notification**

(f)(5)(i) The employer must, within 15 working days after the receipt of the results of any monitoring performed under this Section, notify each employee of these results either individually in writing or by posting the results in an appropriate location that is accessible to employees.

(f)(5)(ii) Whenever the results indicate that employee exposure exceeds the permissible exposure limit, the employer shall include in the written notice a statement that the permissible exposure limit was exceeded and a description of the corrective action being taken to reduce exposure to or below the permissible exposure limit.

(f)(6) **Accuracy of measurement** The employer shall use a method of measurement which has an accuracy, to a confidence level of 95 percent, of not less than plus or minus 25 percent for concentrations of DBCP at or above the permissible exposure limit.

(g) Methods of compliance

(g)(1) **Priority of compliance methods** The employer shall institute engineering and work practice controls to reduce and maintain employee exposures to DBCP at or below the permissible exposure limit, except to the extent that the employer establishes that such controls are not feasible. Where feasible engineering and work practice controls are not sufficient to reduce employee exposures to within the permissible exposure limit, the employer shall nonetheless use them to reduce exposures to the lowest level achievable by these controls, and shall supplement them by use of respiratory protection.

(g)(2) **Compliance program**

(g)(2)(i) The employer shall establish and implement a written program to reduce employee exposures to DBCP to or below the permissible exposure limit solely by means of engineering and work practice controls as required by paragraph (g)(1) of this Section.

(g)(2)(ii) The written program shall include a detailed schedule for development and implementation of the engineering and work practice controls. These plans must be revised at least annually to reflect the current status of the program.

(g)(2)(iii) Written plans for these compliance programs shall be submitted upon request to the Assistant Secretary and the Director, and shall be available at the worksite for examination and copying by the Assistant Secretary, the Director, and any affected employee or designated representative of employees.

(g)(2)(iv) The employer shall institute and maintain at least the controls described in his most recent written compliance program.

(h) Respiratory protection

(h)(1) **General** For employees who are required to use respirators by this Section, the employer must provide each employee an appropriate respirator that complies with the requirements of this paragraph. Respirators must be used during:

(h)(1)(i) Periods necessary to install or implement feasible engineering and work-practice controls.

(h)(1)(ii) Maintenance and repair activities for which engineering and work-practice controls are not feasible.

(h)(1)(iii) Work operations for which feasible engineering and work-practice controls are not yet sufficient to reduce employee exposure to or below the permissible exposure limit.

(h)(1)(iv) Emergencies.

(h)(2) **Respirator program** The employer must implement a respiratory protection program in accordance with §1910.134(b) through (d) (except (d)(1)(iii)), and (f) through (m), which covers each employee required by this Section to use a respirator.

(h)(3) **Respirator selection** Employers must:

(h)(3)(i) Select, and provide to employees, the appropriate atmosphere-supplying respirator specified in paragraph (d)(3)(i)(A) of 29 CFR §1910.134.

(h)(3)(ii) Provide employees with one of the following respirator options to use for entry into, or escape from, unknown DBCP concentrations:

(h)(3)(ii)(A) A combination respirator that includes a supplied-air respirator with a full facepiece operated in a pressure-demand or other positive-pressure or continuous-flow mode, as well as an auxiliary self-contained breathing apparatus (SCBA) operated in a pressure-demand or positive-pressure mode.

(h)(3)(ii)(B) An SCBA with a full facepiece operated in a pressure-demand or other positive-pressure mode.

(i) **Emergency situations**

(i)(1) **Written plans**

(i)(1)(i) A written plan for emergency situations shall be developed for each workplace in which DBCP is present.

(i)(1)(ii) Appropriate portions of the plan shall be implemented in the event of an emergency.

(i)(2) Employees engaged in correcting emergency conditions shall be equipped as required in paragraphs (h) and (j) of this Section until the emergency is abated.

(i)(3) **Evacuation** Employees not engaged in correcting the emergency shall be removed and restricted from the area and normal operations in the affected area shall not be resumed until the emergency is abated.

(i)(4) **Alerting employees** Where there is a possibility of employee exposure to DBCP due to the occurrence of an emergency, a general alarm shall be installed and maintained to promptly alert employees of such occurrences.

(i)(5) **Medical surveillance** For any employee exposed to DBCP in an emergency situation, the employer shall provide medical surveillance in accordance with paragraph (m)(6) of this Section.

(i)(6) **Exposure monitoring**

(i)(6)(i) Following an emergency, the employer shall conduct monitoring which complies with paragraph (f) of this Section.

(i)(6)(ii) In workplaces not normally subject to periodic monitoring, the employer may terminate monitoring when two consecutive measurements indicate exposures below the permissible exposure limit.

(j) **Protective clothing and equipments**

(j)(1) **Provision and use** Where there is any possibility of eye or dermal contact with liquid or solid DBCP, the employer shall provide, at no cost to the employee, and assure that the employee wears impermeable protective clothing and equipment to protect the area of the body which may come in contact with DBCP. Eye and face protection shall meet the requirements of §1910.133 of this Part.

(j)(2) **Removal and storage**

(j)(2)(i) The employer shall assure that employees remove DBCP contaminated work clothing only in change rooms provided in accordance with paragraph (l) (1) of this Section.

(j)(2)(ii) The employer shall assure that employees promptly remove any protective clothing and equipment which becomes contaminated with DBCP-containing liquids and solids. This clothing shall not be reworn until the DBCP has been removed from the clothing or equipment.

(j)(2)(iii) The employer shall assure that no employee takes DBCP contaminated protective devices and work clothing out of the change room, except those employees authorized to do so for the purpose of laundering, maintenance, of disposal.

(j)(2)(iv) DBCP-contaminated protective devices and work clothing shall be placed and stored in closed containers which prevent dispersion of the DBCP outside the container.

(j)(2)(v) Containers of DBCP-contaminated protective devices or work clothing which are to be taken out of change rooms or the workplace for cleaning, maintenance or disposal shall bear labels with the following information: CONTAMINATED WITH 1,2–Dibromo-3-chloropropane (DBCP), MAY CAUSE CANCER.

(j)(3) **Cleaning and replacement**

(j)(3)(i) The employer shall clean, launder, repair, or replace protective clothing and equipment required by this paragraph to maintain their effectiveness. The employer shall provide clean protective clothing and equipment at least daily to each affected employee.

(j)(3)(ii) The employer shall inform any person who launders or clean DBCP-contaminated protective clothing or equipment of the potentially harmful effects of exposure to DBCP.

(j)(3)(iii) The employer shall prohibit the removal of DBCP from protective clothing and equipment by blowing or shaking.

(k) **Housekeeping**

(k)(1) **Surfaces**

(k)(1)(i) All workplace surfaces shall be maintained free of visible accumulations of DBCP.

(k)(1)(ii) Dry sweeping and the use of compressed air for the cleaning of floors and other surfaces is prohibited where DBCP dusts or liquids are present.

(k)(1)(iii) Where vacuuming methods are selected to clean floors and other surfaces, either portable units or a permanent system may be used.

(k)(1)(iii)(A) If a portable unit is selected, the exhaust shall be attached to the general workplace exhaust ventilation system or collected within the vacuum unit, equipped with high efficiency filters or other appropriate means of contaminant removal, so that DBCP is not reintroduced into the workplace air; and

(k)(1)(iii)(B) Portable vacuum units used to collect DBCP may not be used for other cleaning purposes and shall be labeled as prescribed by paragraph (j)(2)(v) of this Section.

(k)(1)(iv) Cleaning of floors and other surfaces contaminated with DBCP-containing dusts shall not be performed by washing down with a hose, unless a fine spray has first been laid down.

(k)(2) **Liquids** Where DBCP is present in a liquid form, or as a resultant vapor, all containers or vessels containing DBCP shall be enclosed to the maximum extent feasible and tightly covered when not in use.

(k)(3) **Waste disposal** DBCP waste scrap, debris, containers or equipment, shall be disposed of in sealed bags or other closed containers which prevent dispersion of DBCP outside the container.

(l) **Hygiene facilities and practices**

(l)(1) **Change rooms** The employer shall provide clean change rooms equipped with storage facilities for street clothes and separate storage facilities for protective clothing and equipment whenever employees are required to wear protective clothing and equipment in accordance with paragraphs (h) and (j) of this Section.

(l)(2) **Showers**

(l)(2)(i) The employer shall assure that employees working in the regulated area shower at the end of the work shift.

(l)(2)(ii) The employer shall assure that employees whose skin becomes contaminated with DBCP-containing liquids or solids immediately wash or shower to remove any DBCP from the skin.

(l)(2)(iii) The employer shall provide shower facilities in accordance with 29 CFR §1910.141(d)(3).

(l)(3) **Lunchrooms** The employer shall provide lunchroom facilities which have a temperature controlled, positive pressure, filtered air supply, and which are readily accessible to employees working in regulated areas.

(l)(4) **Lavatories**

(l)(4)(i) The employer shall assure that employees working in the regulated area remove protective clothing and wash their hands and face prior to eating.

(l)(4)(ii) The employer shall provide a sufficient number of lavatory facilities which comply with 29 CFR §1910.141(d)(1) and (2).

(l)(5) **Prohibition of activities in regulated areas** The employer shall assure that, in regulated areas, food or beverages are not present or consumed, smoking products and implements are not present or used, and cosmetics are not present or applied.

(m) **Medical surveillance**

(m)(1) **General**

(m)(1)(i) The employer shall make available a medical surveillance program for employees who work in regulated areas and employees who are subjected to DBCP exposures in an emergency situation.

(m)(1)(ii) All medical examinations and procedures shall be performed by or under the supervision of a licensed physician, and shall be provided without cost to the employee.

(m)(2) **Frequency and content** At the time of initial assignment, and annually thereafter, the employer shall provide a medical examination for employees who work in regulated areas, which includes at least the following:

(m)(2)(i) A medical and occupational history including reproductive history.

(m)(2)(ii) A physical examination, including examination of the genito-urinary tract, testicle size and body habitus, including a determination of sperm count.

(m)(2)(iii) A serum specimen shall be obtained and the following determinations made by radioimmunoassay techniques utilizing National Institutes of Health (NIH) specific antigen or one of equivalent sensitivity:

(m)(2)(iii)(A) Serum follicle stimulating hormone (FSH);

(m)(2)(iii)(B) Serum luteinizing hormone (LH); and

(m)(2)(iii)(C) Serum total estrogen (females).

(m)(2)(iv) Any other tests deemed appropriate by the examining physician.

(m)(3) **Additional examinations** If the employee for any reason develops signs or symptoms commonly associated with exposure to DBCP, the employer shall provide the employee with a medical examination which shall include those elements considered appropriate by the examining physician.

(m)(4) **Information provided to the physician** The employer shall provide the following information to the examining physician:

(m)(4)(i) A copy of this regulation and its Appendices;

(m)(4)(ii) A description of the affected employee's duties as they relate to the employee's exposure;

(m)(4)(iii) The level of DBCP to which the employee is exposed; and (m)(4)(iv) A description of any personal protective equipment used or to be used.

(m)(5) Physician's written opinion

(m)(5)(i) For each examination under this Section, the employer shall obtain and provide the employee with a written opinion from the examining physician which shall include:

(m)(5)(i)(A) The results of the medical tests performed;

(m)(5)(i)(B) The physician's opinion as to whether the employee has any detected medical condition which would place the employee at an increased risk of material impairment of health from exposure to DBCP; and

(m)(5)(i)(C) Any recommended limitations upon the employee's exposure to DBCP or upon the use of protective clothing and equipment such as respirators.

(m)(5)(ii) The employer shall instruct the physician not to reveal in the written opinion specific findings or diagnoses unrelated to occupational exposure.

(m)(6) **Emergency situations** If the employee is exposed to DBCP in an emergency situation, the employer shall provide the employee with a sperm count test as soon as practicable, or, if the employee has been vasectionized or is unable to produce a semen specimen, the hormone tests contained in paragraph (m)(2)(iii) of this Section. The employer shall provide these same tests three months later.

(n) Employee information and training

(n)(1) Training program

(n)(1)(i) The employer shall train each employee who may be exposed to DBCP in accordance with the requirements of this Section. The employer shall institute a training program and ensure employee participation in the program.

(n)(1)(ii) The employer shall assure that each employee is informed of the following:

(n)(1)(ii)(A) The information contained in Appendix A;

(n)(1)(ii)(B) The quantity, location, manner of use, release or storage of DBCP and the specific nature of operations which could result in exposure to DBCP as well as any necessary protective steps;

(n)(1)(ii)(C) The purpose, proper use, and limitations of respirators;

(n)(1)(ii)(D) The purpose and description of the medical surveillance program required by paragraph (m) of this Section; and

(n)(1)(ii)(E) A review of this Standard, including Appendices.

(n)(2) Access to training materials

(n)(2)(i) The employer shall make a copy of this Standard and its Appendices readily available to all affected employees.

(n)(2)(ii) The employer shall provide, upon request, all materials relating to the employee information and training program to the Assistant Secretary and the Director.

(o) Communication of hazards

(o)(1) Hazard communication—general

(o)(1)(i) Chemical manufacturers, importers, distributors and employers shall comply with all requirements of the Hazard Communication Standard (HCS) (§1910.1200) for DBCP.

(o)(1)(ii) In classifying the hazards of DBCP at least the following hazards are to be addressed: Cancer; reproductive effects; liver effects; kidney effects; central nervous system effects; skin, eye and respiratory tract irritation; and acute toxicity effects.

(o)(1)(iii) Employers shall include DBCP in the hazard communication program established to comply with the HCS (§1910.1200). Employers shall ensure that each employee has access to labels on containers of DBCP and to safety data sheets, and is trained in accordance with the requirements of HCS and paragraph (n) of this Section.

(o)(1)(iv) The employer shall ensure that no statement appears on or near any sign or label required by this paragraph (o) which contradicts or detracts from the meaning of the required sign or label.

(o)(2) Signs

(o)(2)(i) The employer shall post signs to clearly indicate all regulated areas. These signs shall bear the legend:

DANGER
1,2-Dibromo-3-chloropropane
MAY CAUSE CANCER
WEAR RESPIRATORY PROTECTION IN THIS AREA
AUTHORIZED PERSONNEL ONLY

(o)(2)(ii) Prior to June 1, 2016, employers may use the following legend in lieu of that specified in paragraph (o)(2) of this Section:

DANGER
1,2-Dibromo-3-chloropropane
(Insert appropriate trade or common names)
CANCER HAZARD
AUTHORIZED PERSONNEL ONLY
RESPIRATOR REQUIRED

(o)(3) Labels

(o)(3)(i) Where DBCP or products containing DBCP are sold, distributed or otherwise leave the employer's workplace bearing appropriate labels required by EPA under the regulations in 40 CFR Part §162, the labels required by this paragraph (o)(3) need not be affixed.

(o)(3)(ii) The employer shall ensure that the precautionary labels required by this paragraph (o)(3) are readily visible and legible.

(o)(3)(iii) Prior to June 1, 2015, employers may include the following information on containers of DBCP or products containing DBCP, DBCP-contaminated protective devices or work clothing or DBCP-contaminated portable vacuums in lieu of the labeling requirements in paragraphs (j)(2)(v), (k)(l)(iii)(b) and (o)(1)(i) of this Section:

DANGER
1,2-Dibromo-3-chloropropane
CANCER HAZARD

(p) Recordkeeping

(p)(1) Exposure monitoring

(p)(1)(i) The employer shall establish and maintain an accurate record of all monitoring required by paragraph (f) of this Section.

(p)(1)(ii) This record shall include:

(p)(1)(ii)(A) The dates, number, duration and results of each of the samples taken, including a description of the sampling procedure used to determine representative employee exposure;

(p)(1)(ii)(B) A description of the sampling and analytical methods used;

(p)(1)(ii)(C) Type of respiratory protective devices worn, if any; and

(p)(1)(ii)(D) Name, social security number, and job classification of the employee monitored and of all other employees whose exposure the measurement is intended to represent.

(p)(1)(iii) The employer shall maintain this record for at least 40 years or the duration of employment plus 20 years, whichever is longer.

(p)(2) Medical surveillance

(p)(2)(i) The employer shall establish and maintain an accurate record for each employee subject to medical surveillance required by paragraph (m) of this Section.

(p)(2)(ii) This record shall include:

(p)(2)(ii)(A) The name and social security number of the employee;

(p)(2)(ii)(B) A copy of the physician's written opinion;

(p)(2)(ii)(C) Any employee medical complaints related to exposure to DBCP;

(p)(2)(ii)(D) A copy of the information provided the physician as required by paragraphs (m)(4)(ii) through (m)(4)(iv) of this Section; and

(p)(2)(ii)(E) A copy of the employee's medical and work history.

(p)(2)(iii) The employer shall maintain this record for at least 40 years or the duration of employment plus 20 years, whichever is longer.

(p)(3) Availability

(p)(3)(i) The employer shall assure that all records required to be maintained by this Section be made available upon request to the Assistant Secretary and the Director for examination and copying.

(p)(3)(ii) Employee exposure monitoring records and employee medical records required by this paragraph shall be provided upon request to employees, designated representatives, and the Assistant Secretary in accordance with 29 CFR §1910.1020 (a) through (e) and (g) through (i).

(p)(4) Transfer of records

(p)(4)(i) If the employer ceases to do business, the successor employer shall receive and retain all records required to be maintained by paragraph (p) of this Section for the prescribed period.

(p)(4)(ii) The employer shall also comply with any additional requirements involving transfer of records set forth in 29 CFR §1910.1020(h).

(q) Observation of monitoring

(q)(1) **Employee observation** The employer shall provide affected employees, or their designated representatives, with an opportunity to observe any monitoring of employee exposure to DBCP required by this Section.

(q)(2) Observation procedures

(q)(2)(i) Whenever observation of the measuring or monitoring of employee exposure to DBCP requires entry into an area where the use of protective clothing or equipment is required, the employer shall provide the observer with personal protective clothing or equipment required to be worn by employees working in the area, assure the use of such clothing and equipment, and require the observer to comply with all other applicable safety and health procedures.

(q)(2)(ii) Without interfering with the monitoring or measurement, observers shall be entitled to:

(q)(2)(ii)(A) Receive an explanation of the measurement procedures;

(q)(2)(ii)(B) Observe all steps related to the measurement of airborne concentrations of DBCP performed at the place of exposure; and

(q)(2)(ii)(C) Record the results obtained.

(r) **Appendices** The information contained in the Appendices is not intended, by itself, to create any additional obligations not otherwise imposed or to detract from any existing obligation.

§1910.1044 Appendix A Substance safety data sheet for DBCP

I. Substance Identification

A. Synonyms and trades names: DBCP; Dibromochloropropane; Fumazone (Dow Chemical Company TM); Nemafume; Nemagon (Shell Chemical Co. TM); Nemaset; BBC 12; and OS 1879.

B. Permissible exposure:

1. Airborne. 1 part DBCP vapor per billion parts of air (1 ppb); time-weighted average (TWA) for an 8-hour workday.
2. Dermal. Eye contact and skin contact with DBCP are prohibited.

C. Appearance and odor: Technical grade DBCP is a dense yellow or amber liquid with a pungent odor. It may also appear in granular form, or blended in varying concentrations with other liquids.

D. Uses: DBCP is used to control nematodes, very small worm-like plant parasites, on crops including cotton, soybeans, fruits, nuts, vegetables and ornamentals.

II. Health Hazard Data

A. Routes of entry: Employees may be exposed:

1. Through inhalation (breathing);
2. Through ingestion (swallowing);
3. Skin contact; and
4. Eye contact.

B. Effects of exposure:

1. Acute exposure DBCP may cause drowsiness, irritation of the eyes, nose, throat and skin, nausea and vomiting. In addition, overexposure may cause damage to the lungs, liver or kidneys.
2. Chronic exposure Prolonged or repeated exposure to DBCP has been shown to cause sterility in humans. It also has been shown to produce cancer and sterility in laboratory animals and has been determined to constitute an increased risk of cancer in man.
3. Reporting Signs and Symptoms If you develop any of the above signs or symptoms that you think are caused by exposure to DBCP, you should inform your employer.

III. Emergency First Aid Procedures

A. Eye exposure If DBCP liquid or dust containing DBCP gets into your eyes, wash your eyes immediately with large amounts of water, lifting the lower and upper lids occasionally. Get medical attention immediately. Contact lenses should not be worn when working with DBCP.

B. Skin exposure If DBCP liquids or dusts containing DBCP get on your skin, immediately wash using soap or mild detergent and water. If DBCP liquids or dusts containing DBCP penetrate through your clothing, remove the clothing immediately and wash. If irritation is present after washing get medical attention.

C. Breathing If you or any person breathe in large amounts of DBCP, move the exposed person to fresh air at once. If breathing has stopped, perform artificial respiration. Do not use mouth-to-mouth. Keep the affected person warm and at rest. Get medical attention as soon as possible.

D. Swallowing When DBCP has been swallowed and the person is conscious, give the person large amounts of water immediately. After the water has been swallowed, try to get the person to vomit by having him touch the back of his throat with his finger. Do not make an unconscious person vomit. Get medical attention immediately.

E. Rescue Notify someone. Put into effect the established emergency rescue procedures. Know the locations of the emergency rescue equipment before the need arises.

IV. Respirators and Protective Clothing

A. Respirators You may be required to wear a respirator in emergencies and while your employer is in the process of reducing DBCP exposures through engineering controls. If respirators are worn, they must have a National Institute for Occupational Safety and Health (NIOSH) approval label (Older respirators may have a Bureau of Mines Approval label). For effective protection, a respirator must fit your face and head snugly. The respirator should not be loosened or removed in work situations where its use is required. DBCP does not have a detectable odor except at 1,000 times or more above the permissible exposure limit. If you can smell DBCP while wearing a respirator, the respirator is not working correctly; go immediately to fresh air. If you experience difficulty breathing while wearing a respirator, tell your employer.

B. Protective clothing When working with DBCP you must wear for your protection impermeable work clothing provided by your employer. (Standard rubber and neoprene protective clothing do not offer adequate protection).

DBCP must never be allowed to remain on the skin. Clothing and shoes must not be allowed to become contaminated with DBCP, and if they do, they must be promptly removed and not worn again until completely free of DBCP. Turn in impermeable clothing that has developed leaks for repair or replacement.

C. Eye protection You must wear splash-proof safety goggles where there is any possibility of DBCP liquid or dust contacting your eyes.

V. Precautions for Safe Use, Handling, and Storage

A. DBCP must be stored in tightly closed containers in a cool, well-ventilated area.

B. If your work clothing may have become contaminated with DBCP, or liquids or dusts containing DBCP, you must change into uncontaminated clothing before leaving the work premises.

C. You must promptly remove any protective clothing that becomes contaminated with DBCP. This clothing must not be reworn until the DBCP is removed from the clothing.

D. If your skin becomes contaminated with DBCP, you must immediately and thoroughly wash or shower with soap or mild detergent and water to remove any DBCP from your skin.

E. You must not keep food, beverages, cosmetics, or smoking materials, nor eat or smoke, in regulated areas.

F. If you work in a regulated area, you must wash your hands thoroughly with soap or mild detergent and water, before eating, smoking or using toilet facilities.

G. If you work in a regulated area, you must remove any protective equipment or clothing before leaving the regulated area.

H. Ask your supervisor where DBCP is used in your work area and for any additional safety and health rules.

VI. Access to Information

A. Each year, your employer is required to inform you of the information contained in this Substance Safety Data Sheet for DBCP. In addition, your employer must instruct you in the safe use of DBCP, emergency procedures, and the correct use of protective equipment.

B. Your employer is required to determine whether you are being exposed to DBCP. You or your representative have the right to observe employee exposure measurements and to record the result obtained. Your employer is required to inform you of your exposure. If your employer determines that you are being overexposed, he is required to inform you of the actions which are being taken to reduce your exposure.

C. Your employer is required to keep records of your exposure and medical examinations. Your employer is required to keep exposure and medical data for at least 40 years or the duration of your employment plus 20 years, whichever is longer.

D. Your employer is required to release exposure and medical records to you, your physician, or other individual designated by you upon your written request.

§1910.1044 Appendix B Substance technical guidelines for DBCP

I. Physical and Chemical Data

A. Substance Identification

1. Synonyms: 1,2-dibromo-3-chloropropane; DBCP, Fumazone; Nemafume; Nemagon; Nemaset; BBC 12; OS 1879. DBCP is also included in agricultural pesticides and fumigants which include the phrase "Nema—" in their name.
2. Formula: $C_3H_5Br_2\ C_1$.
3. Molecular Weight: 236.

B. Physical Data:

1. Boiling point (760 mm HG): 195 ° C (383 °F)
2. Specific gravity (water=1): 2.093.
3. Vapor density (air = 1 at boiling point of DBCP): Data not available.
4. Melting point: 6 °C (43 °F).
5. Vapor pressure at 20 °C (68F): 0.8 mm Hg
6. Solubility in water: 1000 ppm.
7. Evaporation rate (Butyl Acetate = 1): very much less than 1.
8. Appearance and odor: Dense yellow or amber liquid with a pungent odor at high concentrations. Any detectable odor of DBCP indicates overexposure.

II. Fire Explosion and Reactivity Hazard Data

A. Fire

1. Flash point: 170 °F (77 °C)
2. Autoignition temperature: Data not available.
3. Flammable limits in air, percent by volume: Data not available.
4. Extinguishing media: Carbon dioxide, dry chemical.
5. Special fire-fighting procedures: Do not use a solid stream of water since a stream will scatter and spread the fire. Use water spray to cool containers exposed to a fire.
6. Unusual fire and explosion hazards: None known.
7. For purposes of complying with the requirements of §1910.106, liquid DBCP is classified as a Class III A combustible liquid.
8. For the purpose of complying with §1910.309, the classification of hazardous locations as described in article 500 of the National Electrical Code for DBCP shall be Class I, Group D.
9. For the purpose of compliance with §1910.157, DBCP is classified as a Class B fire hazard.
10. For the purpose of compliance with §1910.178, locations classified as hazardous locations due to the presence of DBCP shall be Class I, Group D.
11. Sources of ignition are prohibited where DBCP presents a fire or explosion hazard.

B. Reactivity

1. Conditions contributing to instability: None known.
2. Incompatibilities: Reacts with chemically active metals, such as aluminum, magnesium and tin alloys.
3. Hazardous decomposition products: Toxic gases and vapors (such as HBr, HCl and carbon monoxide) may be released in a fire involving DBCP.
4. Special precautions: DBCP will attack some rubber materials and coatings.

III. Spill, Leak and Disposal Procedures

A. If DBCP is spilled or leaked, the following steps should be taken:

1. The area should be evacuated at once and re-entered only after thorough ventilation;
2. Ventilate area of spill or leak;
3. If in liquid form, collect for reclamation or absorb in paper, vermiculite, dry sand, earth or similar material;
4. If in solid form, collect spilled material in the most convenient and safe manner for reclamation or for disposal.

B. Persons not wearing protective equipment must be restricted from areas of spills or leaks until cleanup has been completed.

C. Waste Disposal Methods:

1. For small quantities of liquid DBCP, absorb on paper towels, remove to a safe place (such as a fume hood) and burn the paper. Large quantities can be reclaimed or collected and atomized in a suitable combustion chamber equipped with an appropriate effluent gas cleaning device. If liquid DBCP is absorbed in vermiculite, dry sand, earth or similar material and placed in sealed containers it may be disposed of in a State-approved sanitary landfill.
2. If in solid form, for small quantities, place on paper towels, remove to a safe place (such as a fume hood) and burn. Large quantities may be reclaimed. However, if this is not practical, dissolve in a flammable solvent (such as alcohol) and atomize in a suitable combustion chamber equipped with an appropriate effluent gas cleaning device. DBCP in solid form may also be disposed in a State-approved sanitary landfill.

IV. Monitoring and Measurement Procedures

A. Exposure above the permissible exposure limit

1. Eight Hour Exposure Evaluation: Measurements taken for the purpose of determining employee exposure under this Section are best taken so that the average 8-hour exposure may be determined from a single 8-hour sample or two (2) 4-hour samples. Air samples should be taken in the employee's breathing zone (air that would most nearly represent that inhaled by the employee).
2. Monitoring Techniques: The sampling and analysis under this Section may be performed by collecting the DBCP vapor on petroleum based charcoal absorption tubes with subsequent chemical analyses. The method of measurement chosen should determine the concentration of airborne DBCP at the permissible exposure limit to an accuracy of plus or minus 25 percent. If charcoal tubes are used, a total volume of 10 liters should be collected at a flow rate of 50 cc. per minute for each tube. Analyze the resultant samples as you would samples of halogenated solvent.

B. Since many of the duties relating to employee protection are dependent on the results of monitoring and measuring procedures, employers should assure that the evaluation of employee exposures is performed by a competent industrial hygienist or other technically qualified person.

V. Protective Clothing

Employees should be required to wear appropriate protective clothing to prevent any possibility of skin contact with DBCP. Because DBCP is absorbed through the skin, it is important to prevent skin contact with both liquid and solid forms of DBCP. Protective clothing should include impermeable coveralls or similar fullbody work clothing, gloves, headcoverings, and workshoes or shoe coverings. Standard rubber and neoprene gloves do not offer adequate protection and should not be relied upon to keep DBCP off the skin. DBCP should never be allowed to remain on the skin. Clothing and shoes should not be allowed to become contaminated with the material, and if they do, they should be promptly removed and not worn again until completely free of the material. Any protective clothing which has developed leaks or is otherwise found to be defective should be repaired or replaced. Employees should also be required to wear splash-proof safety goggles where there is any possibility of DBCP contacting the eyes.

VI. Housekeeping and Hygiene Facilities

1. The workplace must be kept clean, orderly and in a sanitary condition;
2. Dry sweeping and the use of compressed air is unsafe for the cleaning of floors and other surfaces where DBCP dust or liquids are found. To minimize the contamination of air with dust, vacuuming with either portable or permanent systems must be used. If a portable unit is selected, the exhaust must be attached to the general workplace exhaust ventilation system, or collected within the vacuum unit equipped with high efficiency filters or other appropriate means of contamination removal and not used for other purposes. Units used to collect DBCP must be labeled.
3. Adequate washing facilities with hot and cold water must be provided, and maintained in a sanitary condition. Suitable cleansing agents should also be provided to assure the effective removal of DBCP from the skin.
4. Change or dressing rooms with individual clothes storage facilities must be provided to prevent the contamination of street clothes with DBCP. Because of the hazardous nature of DBCP, contaminated protective clothing must be stored in closed containers for cleaning or disposal.

VII. Miscellaneous Precautions

A. Store DBCP in tightly closed containers in a cool, well ventilated area.

B. Use of supplied-air suits or other impervious clothing (such as acid suits) may be necessary to prevent skin contact with DBCP. Supplied-air suits should be selected, used, and maintained under the supervision of persons knowledgeable in the limitations and potential life-endangering characteristics of supplied-air suits.

C. The use of air-conditioned suits may be necessary in warmer climates.

D. Advise employees of all areas and operations where exposure to DBCP could occur.

VIII. Common Operations

Common operations in which exposure to DBCP is likely to occur are: during its production; and during its formulation into pesticides and fumigants.

§1910.1044 Appendix C
Medical surveillance guidelines for DBCP

I. Route of Entry

Inhalation; skin absorption

II. Toxicology

Recent data collected on workers involved in the manufacture and formulation of DBCP has shown that DBCP can cause sterility at very low levels of exposure. This finding is supported by studies showing that DBCP causes sterility in animals. Chronic exposure to DBCP resulted in pronounced necrotic action on the parenchymatous organs (i.e., liver, kidney, spleen) and on the testicles of rats at concentrations as low as 5 ppm. Rats that were chronically exposed to DBCP also showed changes in the composition of the blood, showing low RBC, hemoglobin, and WBC, and high reticulocyte levels as well as functional hepatic disturbance, manifesting itself in a long prothrombin time. Reznik et al. noted a single dose of 100 mg produced profound depression of the nervous system of rats. Their condition gradually improved. Acute exposure also resulted in the destruction of the sex gland activity of male rats as well as causing changes in the estrous cycle in female rats. Animal studies have also associated DBCP with an increased incidence of carcinoma. Olson, et al. orally administered DBCP to rats and mice 5 times per week at experimentally predetermined maximally tolerated doses and at half those doses. As early as ten weeks after initiation of treatment, DBCP induced a high incidence of squamous cell carcinomas of the stomach with metastases in both species. DBCP also induced mammary adenocarcinomas in the female rats at both dose levels.

III. Signs and Symptoms

A. Inhalation: Nausea, eye irritation, conjunctivitis, respiratory irritation, pulmonary congestion or edema, CNS depression with apathy, sluggishness, and ataxia.

B. Dermal: Erythema or inflammation and dermatitis on repeated exposure.

IV. Special Tests

A. Semen analysis: The following information excerpted from the document "Evaluation of Testicular Function", submitted by the Corporate Medical Department of the Shell Oil Company (exhibit 39–3), may be useful to physicians conducting the medical surveillance program;

In performing semen analyses certain minimal but specific criteria should be met:

1. It is recommended that a minimum of three valid semen analyses be obtained in order to make a determination of an individual's average sperm count.
2. A period of sexual abstinence is necessary prior to the collection of each masturbatory sample. It is recommended that intercourse or masturbation be performed 48 hours before the actual specimen collection. A period of 48 hours of abstinence would follow; then the masturbatory sample would be collected.
3. Each semen specimen should be collected in a clean, widemouthed, glass jar (not necessarily pre-sterilized) in a manner designated by the examining physician. Any part of the seminal fluid exam should be initialed only after liquifaction is complete, i.e., 30 to 45 minutes after collection.
4. Semen volume should be measured to the nearest 1/10 of a cubic centimeter.
5. Sperm density should be determined using routine techniques involving the use of a white cell pipette and a hemocytometer chamber. The immobilizing fluid most effective and most easily obtained for this process is distilled water.
6. Thin, dry smears of the semen should be made for a morphologic classification of the sperm forms and should be stained with either hematoxalin or the more difficult, yet more precise, Papanicolaou technique. Also of importance to record is obvious sperm agglutination, pyospermia, delayed liquifaction (greater than 30 minutes), and hyperviscosity. In addition, pH, using nitrazine paper, should be determined.
7. A total morphology evaluation should include percentages of the following:
   a. Normal (oval) forms;
   b. Tapered forms;
   c. Amorphous forms (include large and small sperm shapes);
   d. Duplicated (either heads or tails) forms; and
   e. Immature forms.
8. Each sample should be evaluated for sperm viability (percent viable sperm moving at the time of examination) as well as sperm motility (subjective characterization of "purposeful forward sperm progression" of the majority of those viable sperm analyzed) within two hours after collection, ideally by the same or equally qualified examiner.

B. Serum determinations: The following serum determinations should be performed by radioimmuno-assay techniques using National Institutes of Health (NIH) specific antigen or antigen preparations of equivalent sensitivity:

1. Serum follicle stimulating hormone (FSH);
2. Serum luteinizing hormone (LH); and
3. Serum total estrogen (females only).

V. Treatment

Remove from exposure immediately, give oxygen or artificial resuscitation if indicated. Contaminated clothing and shoes should be removed immediately. Flush eyes and wash contaminated skin. If swallowed and the person is conscious, induce vomiting. Recovery from mild exposures is usually rapid and complete.

VI. Surveillance and Preventive Considerations

A. Other considerations DBCP can cause both acute and chronic effects. It is important that the physician become familiar with the operating conditions in which exposure to DBCP occurs. Those with respiratory disorders may not tolerate the wearing of negative pressure respirators.

B. Surveillance and screening Medical histories and laboratory examinations are required for each employee subject to exposure to DBCP. The employer should screen employees for history of certain medical conditions (listed below) which might place the employee at increased risk from exposure.

1. Liver disease. The primary site of biotransformation and detoxification of DBCP is the liver. Liver dysfunctions likely to inhibit the conjugation reactions will tend to promote the toxic actions of DBCP. These precautions should be considered before exposing persons with impaired liver function to DBCP.
2. Renal disease. Because DBCP has been associated with injury to the kidney it is important that special consideration be given to those with possible impairment of renal function.
3. Skin desease. DBCP can penetrate the skin and can cause erythema on prolonged exposure. Persons with pre-existing skin disorders may be more susceptible to the effects of DBCP.
4. Blood dyscrasias. DBCP has been shown to decrease the content of erythrocytes, hemoglobin, and leukocytes in the blood, as well as increase the prothrombin time. Persons with existing blood disorders may be more susceptible to the effects of DBCP.
5. Reproductive disorders. Animal studies have associated DBCP with various effects on the reproductive organs. Among these effects are atrophy of the testicles and changes in the estrous cycle. Persons with pre-existing reproductive disorders may be at increased risk to these effects of DBCP.

References

1. Reznik, Ya. B. and Sprinchan, G. K.: Experimental Data on the Gonadotoxic effect of Nemagon, Gig. Sanit., (6), 1975, pp. 101–102, (translated from Russian).
2. Faydysh, E. V., Rakhmatullaev, N. N. and Varshavskii, V. A.: The Cytotoxic Action of Nemagon in a Subacute Experiment, Med. Zh. Uzbekistana, (No. 1), 1970, pp. 64–65, (translated from Russian).
3. Rakhmatullaev, N. N.: Hygienic Characteristics of the Nematocide Nemagon in Relation to Water Pollution Control, Hyg. Sanit., 36(3), 1971, pp. 344–348, (translated from Russian).
4. Olson, W. A. et al.: Induction of Stomach Cancer in Rats and Mice by Halogenated Aliphatic Fumigants, Journal of the National Cancer Institute, (51), 1973, pp. 1993–1995.
5. Torkelson, T. R. et al.: Toxicologic Investigations of 1,2-Dibromo-3-chloropropane, Toxicology and Applied Pharmacology, 3, 1961 pp. 545–559.

[43 FR 11527, Mar. 17, 1978, as amended at 45 FR 35283, May 23, 1980; 49 FR 18295, Apr. 30, 1984; 54 FR 24334, June 7, 1989; 58 FR 35310, June 30, 1993; 61 FR 5508, Feb. 13, 1996; 63 FR 1291, Jan. 8, 1998; 70 FR 1142, Jan. 5, 2005; 71 FR 16772, Apr. 3, 2006; 71 FR 50189, Aug. 24, 2006; 73 FR 75586, Dec. 12, 2008; 76 FR 33609, June 8, 2011]

§1910.1045 Acrylonitrile

(a) Scope and application

(a)(1) This Section applies to all occupational exposures to acrylonitrile (AN), Chemical Abstracts Service Registry No. 000107131, except as provided in paragraphs (a)(2) and (a)(3) of this Section.

(a)(2) This Section does not apply to exposures which result solely from the processing, use, and handling of the following materials:

(a)(2)(i) ABS resins, SAN resins, nitrile barrier resins, solid nitrile elastomers, and acrylic and modacrylic fibers, when these listed materials are in the form of finished polymers, and products fabricated from such finished polymers;

(a)(2)(ii) Materials made from and/or containing AN for which objective data is reasonably relied upon to demonstrate that the material is not capable of releasing AN in airborne concentrations in excess of 1 ppm as an eight (8)-hour time-weighted average, under the expected conditions of processing, use, and handling which will cause the greatest possible release; and

(a)(2)(iii) Solid materials made from and/or containing AN which will not be heated above 170 °F during handling, use, or processing.

(a)(3) An employer relying upon exemption under paragraph (a)(2)(ii) shall maintain records of the objective data supporting that exemption, and of the basis of the employer's reliance on the data, as provided in paragraph (q) of this Section.

(b) Definitions

Acrylonitrile or AN means acrylonitrile monomer, chemical formula CH2 = CHCN.

Action level means a concentration of AN of 1 ppm as an eight (8)-hour time-weighted average.

Assistant Secretary means the Assistant Secretary of Labor for Occupational Safety and Health, U.S. Department of Labor, or designee.

Authorized person means any person specifically authorized by the employer whose duties require the person to enter a regulated area, or any person entering such an area as a designated representative of employees for the purpose of exercising the opportunity to observe monitoring procedures under paragraph (r) of this Section.

Decontamination means treatment of materials and surfaces by water washdown, ventilation, or other means, to assure that the materials will not expose employees to airborne concentrations of AN above 1 means the Director, National Institute for Occupational Safety and Health, U.S. Department of Health and Human Services, or designee.

Emergency means any occurrence such as, but not limited to, equipment failure, rupture of containers, or failure of control equipment, which results in an unexpected massive release of AN.

Liquid AN means AN monomer in liquid form, and liquid or semiliquid polymer intermediates, including slurries, suspensions, emulsions, and solutions, produced during the polymerization of AN.

OSHA Area Office means the Area Office of the Occupational Safety and Health Administration having jurisdiction over the geographic area where the affected workplace is located.

(c) **Permissible exposure limits**

(c)(1) **Inhalation**

(c)(1)(i) **Time weighted average limit (TWA)** The employer shall assure that no employee is exposed to an airborne concentration of acrylonitrile in excess of two (2) parts acrylonitrile per million parts of air (2 ppm) as an eight (8)-hour time-weighted average.

(c)(1)(ii) **Ceiling limit** The employer shall assure that no employee is exposed to an airborne concentration of acrylonitrile in excess of ten (10) ppm as averaged over any fifteen (15)-minute period during the work day.

(c)(2) **Dermal and eye exposure** The employer shall assure that no employee is exposed to skin contact or eye contact with liquid AN.

(d) [Reserved]

(e) **Exposure monitoring**

(e)(1) **General**

(e)(1)(i) Determinations of airborne exposure levels shall be made from air samples that are representative of each employee's exposure to AN over an eight (8)-hour period.

(e)(1(ii) For the purposes of this Section, employee exposure is that exposure which would occur if the employee were not using a respirator.

(e)(2) **Initial monitoring** Each employer who has a place of employment in which AN is present shall monitor each such workplace and work operation to accurately determine the airborne concentrations of AN to which employees may be exposed.

(e)(3) **Frequency**

(e)(3)(i) If the monitoring required by this Section reveals employee exposure to be below the action level, the employer may discontinue monitoring for that employee.

(e)(3)(ii) If the monitoring required by this Section reveals employee exposure to be at or above the action level but at or below the permissible exposure limits, the employer must repeat such monitoring for each such employee at least every 6 months. The employer must continue these measurements every 6 months until at least two consecutive measurements taken at least seven (7) days a part, are below the action level, and thereafter the employer may discontinue monitoring for that employee.

(e)(3)(iii) If the monitoring required by this Section reveals employee exposure to be in excess of the permissible exposure limits, the employer must repeat these determinations for each such employee at least quarterly. The employer must continue these quarterly measurements until at least two consecutive measurements, taken at least seven (7) days apart, are at or below the permissible exposure limits, and thereafter the employer must monitor at least every 6 months.

(e)(4) **Additional monitoring** Whenever there has been a production, process, control, or personnel change which may result in new or additional exposures to AN, or whenever the employer has any other reason to suspect a change which may result in new or additional exposures to AN, additional monitoring which complies with this paragraph shall be conducted.

(e)(5) **Employee notification**

(e)(5)(i) The employer must, within 15 working days after the receipt of the results of any monitoring performed under this Section, notify each affected employee of these results either individually in writing or by posting the results in an appropriate location that is accessible to employees.

(e)(5)(ii) Whenever the results indicate that the representative employee exposure exceeds the permissible exposure limits, the employer shall include in the written notice a statement that the permissible exposure limits were exceeded and a description of the corrective action being taken to reduce exposure to or below the permissible exposure limits.

(e)(6) **Accuracy of measurement** The method of measurement of employee exposures shall be accurate to a confidence level of 95 percent, to within plus or minus 35 percent for concentrations of AN at or above the permissible exposure limits, and plus or minus 50 percent for concentrations of AN below the permissible exposure limits.

(f) **Regulated areas**

(f)(1) The employer shall establish regulated areas where AN concentrations are in excess of the permissible exposure limits.

(f)(2) Regulated areas shall be demarcated and segregated from the rest of the workplace, in any manner that minimizes the number of persons who will be exposed to AN.

(f)(3) Access to regulated areas shall be limited to authorized persons or to persons otherwise authorized by the act or regulations issued pursuant thereto.

(f)(4) The employer shall assure that food or beverages are not present or consumed, tobacco products are not present or used, and cosmetics are not applied in the regulated area.

(g) **Methods of compliance**

(g)(1) **Engineering and work practice controls**

(g)(1)(i) By November 2, 1980, the employer shall institute engineering and work practice controls to reduce and maintain employee exposures to AN, to or below the permissible exposure limits, except to the extent that the employer establishes that such controls are not feasible.

(g)(1)(ii) Wherever the engineering and work practice controls which can be instituted are not sufficient to reduce employee exposures to or below the permissible exposure limits, the employer shall nonetheless use them to reduce exposures to the lowest levels achievable by these controls, and shall supplement them by the use of respiratory protection which complies with the requirements of paragraph (h) of this Section.

(g)(2) **Compliance program**

(g)(2)(i) The employer shall establish and implement a written program to reduce employee exposures to or below the permissible exposure limits solely by means of engineering and work practice controls, as required by paragraph (g)(1) of this Section.

(g)(2)(ii) Written plans for these compliance programs shall include at least the following:

(g)(2)(ii)(A) A description of each operation or process resulting in employee exposure to AN above the permissible exposure limits;

(g)(2)(ii)(B) An outline of the nature of the engineering controls and work practices to be applied to the operation or process in question;

(g)(2)(ii)(C) A report of the technology considered in meeting the permissible exposure limits;

(g)(2)(ii)(D) A schedule for implementation of engineering and work practice controls for the operation or process, which shall project completion no later than November 2, 1980; and

(g)(2)(ii)(E) Other relevant information.

(g)(2)(iii) The employer shall complete the steps set forth in the compliance program by the dates in the schedule.

(g)(2)(iv) Written plans shall be submitted upon request to the Assistant Secretary and the Director, and shall be available at the worksite for examination and copying by the Assistant Secretary, the Director, or any affected employee or representative.

(g)(2)(v) The plans required by this paragraph must be revised and updated at least annually to reflect the current status of the program.

(h) **Respiratory protection**

(h)(1) **General** For employees who use respirators required by this Section, the employer must provide each employee an appropriate respirator that complies with the requirements of this paragraph. Respirators must be used during:

(h)(1)(i) Periods necessary to install or implement feasible engineering and work-practice controls;

(h)(1)(ii) Work operations, such as maintenance and repair activities or reactor cleaning, for which the employer establishes that engineering and work-practice controls are not feasible;

(h)(1)(iii) Work operations for which feasible engineering and work-practice controls are not yet sufficient to reduce employee exposure to or below the permissible exposure limits; and

(h)(1)(iv) Emergencies.

(h)(2) **Respirator program**

(h)(2)(i) The employer must implement a respiratory protection program in accordance with §1910.134(b) through (d) (except (d)(1)(iii), (d)(3)(iii)(B)(1), and (2)), and (f) through (m), which covers each employee required by this Section to use a respirator.

(h)(2)(ii) If air-purifying respirators (chemical-cartridge or chemical-canister types) are used:

(h)(2)(ii)(A) The air-purifying canister or cartridge must be replaced prior to the expiration of its service life or at the completion of each shift, whichever occurs first.

(h)(2)(ii)(B) A label must be attached to the cartridge or canister to indicate the date and time at which it is first installed on the respirator.

(h)(3) Respirator selection. Employers must:

(h)(3)(i) Select, and provide to employees, the appropriate respirators specified in paragraph (d)(3)(i)(A) of 29 CFR §1910.134.

(h)(3)(ii) For escape, provide employees with any organic vapor respirator or any self-contained breathing apparatus permitted for use under paragraph (h)(3)(i) of this Standard.

(i) **Emergency situations**

(i)(1) **Written plans**

(i)(1)(i) A written plan for emergency situations shall be developed for each workplace where liquid AN is present. Appropriate portions of the plan shall be implemented in the event of an emergency.

(i)(1)(ii) The plan shall specifically provide that employees engaged in correcting emergency conditions shall be equipped as required in paragraph (h) of this Section until the emergency is abated.

(i)(1)(iii) Employees not engaged in correcting the emergency shall be evacuated from the area and shall not be permitted to return until the emergency is abated.

(i)(2) **Alerting employees** Where there is the possibility of employee exposure to AN in excess of the ceiling limit, a general alarm shall be installed and used to promptly alert employees of such occurrences.

(j) Protective clothing and equipment

(j)(1) **Provision and use** Where eye or skin contact with liquid AN may occur, the employer shall provide at no cost to the employee, and assure that employees wear, impermeable protective clothing or other equipment to protect any area of the body which may come in contact with liquid AN. The provision of §1910.132 and §1910.133 shall be complied with.

(j)(2) Cleaning and replacement

(j)(2)(i) The employer shall clean, launder, maintain, or replace protective clothing and equipment required by this Section as needed to maintain their effectiveness.

(j)(2)(ii) The employer shall assure that impermeable protective clothing which contacts or is likely to have contacted liquid AN shall be decontaminated before being removed by the employee.

(j)(2)(iii) The employer shall assure that an employee whose nonimpermeable clothing becomes wetted with liquid AN shall immediately remove that clothing and proceed to shower. The clothing shall be decontaminated before it is removed from the regulated area.

(j)(2)(iv) The employer shall assure that no employee removes protective clothing or equipment from the change room, except for those employees authorized to do so for the purpose of laundering, maintenance, or disposal.

(j)(2)(v) The employer shall inform any person who launders or cleans protective clothing or equipment of the potentially harmful effects of exposure to AN.

(k) Housekeeping

(k)(1) All surfaces shall be maintained free of visible accumulations of liquid AN.

(k)(2) For operations involving liquid AN, the employer shall institute a program for detecting leaks and spills of liquid AN, including regular visual inspections.

(k)(3) Where spills of liquid AN are detected, the employer shall assure that surfaces contacted by the liquid AN are decontaminated. Employees not engaged in decontamination activities shall leave the area of the spill, and shall not be permitted in the area until decontamination is completed.

(l) **Waste disposal** AN waste, scrap, debris, bags, containers, or equipment shall be decontaminated before being incorporated in the general waste disposal system.

(m) Hygiene facilities and practices

(m)(1) Where employees are exposed to airborne concentrations of AN above the permissible exposure limits, or where employees are required to wear protective clothing or equipment pursuant to paragraph (j) of this Section, the facilities required by 29 CFR §1910.141, including clean change rooms and shower facilities, shall be provided by the employer for the use of those employees, and the employer shall assure that the employees use the facilities provided.

(m)(2) [OI] The employer shall assure that employees wearing protective clothing or equipment for protection from skin contact with liquid AN shall shower at the end of the work shift.

(m)(3) The employer shall assure that, in the event of skin or eye exposure to liquid AN, the affected employee shall shower immediately to minimize the danger of skin absorption.

(m)(4) The employer shall assure that employees working in the regulated area wash their hands and faces prior to eating.

(n) Medical surveillance

(n)(1) General

(n)(1)(i) The employer shall institute a program of medical surveillance for each employee who is or will be exposed to AN at or above the action level, without regard to the use of respirators. The employer shall provide each such employee with an opportunity for medical examinations and tests in accordance with this paragraph.

(n)(1)(ii) The employer shall assure that all medical examinations and procedures are performed by or under the supervision of a licensed physician, and that they shall be provided without cost to the employee.

(n)(2) **Initial examinations** At the time of initial assignment, or upon institution of the medical surveillance program, the employer shall provide each affected employee an opportunity for a medical examination, including at least the following elements:

(n)(2)(i) A work history and medical history with special attention to skin, respiratory, and gastrointestinal systems, and those nonspecific symptoms, such as headache, nausea, vomiting, dizziness, weakness, or other central nervous system dysfunctions that may be associated with acute or with chronic exposure to AN;

(n)(2)(ii) A complete physical examination giving particular attention to the peripheral and central nervous system, gastrointestinal system, respiratory system, skin, and thyroid;

(n)(2)(iii) [OI] A 14- by 17-inch posteroanterior chest X-ray; and

(n)(2)(iv) Further tests of the intestinal tract, including fecal occult blood screening, for all workers 40 years of age or older, and for any other affected employees for whom, in the opinion of the physician, such testing is appropriate.

(n)(3) Periodic examinations

(n)(3)(i) The employer shall provide the examinations specified in paragraph (n)(2) of this Section at least annually for all employees specified in paragraph (n)(1) of this Section.

(n)(3)(ii) If an employee has not had the examination specified in paragraph (n)(2) of this Section within 6 months preceding termination of employment, the employer shall make such examination available to the employee prior to such termination.

(n)(4) **Additional examinations** If the employee for any reason develops signs or symptoms which may be associated with exposure to AN, the employer shall provide an appropriate examination and emergency medical treatment.

(n)(5) **Information provided to the physician** The employer shall provide the following information to the examining physician:

(n)(5)(i) A copy of this Standard and its Appendices;

(n)(5)(ii) A description of the affected employee's duties as they relate to the employee's exposure;

(n)(5)(iii) The employee's representative exposure level;

(n)(5)(iv) The employee's anticipated or estimated exposure level (for preplacement examinations or in cases of exposure due to an emergency);

(n)(5)(v) A description of any personal protective equipment used or to be used; and

(n)(5)(vi) Information from previous medical examinations of the affected employee, which is not otherwise available to the examining physician.

(n)(6) Physician's written opinion

(n)(6)(i) The employer shall obtain a written opinion from the examining physician which shall include:

(n)(6)(i)(A) The results of the medical examination and test performed;

(n)(6)(i)(B) The physician's opinion as to whether the employee has any detected medical condition(s) which would place the employee at an increased risk of material impairment of the employee's health from exposure to AN;

(n)(6)(i)(C) Any recommended limitations upon the employee's exposure to AN or upon the use of protective clothing and equipment such as respirators; and

(n)(6)(i)(D) A statement that the employee has been informed by the physician of the results of the medical examination and any medical conditions which require further examination or treatment.

(n)(6)(ii) The employer shall instruct the physician not to reveal in the written opinion specific findings or diagnoses unrelated to occupational exposure to AN.

(n)(6)(iii) The employer shall provide a copy of the written opinion to the affected employee.

(o) Employee information and training

(o)(1) Training program

(o)(1)(i) The employer shall train each employee exposed to AN above the action level, each employee whose exposures are maintained below the action level by engineering and work practice controls, and each employee subject to potential skin or eye contact with liquid AN in accordance with the requirements of this Section. The employer shall institute a training program and ensure employee participation in the program.

(o)(1)(ii) Training shall be provided at the time of initial assignment, or upon institution of the training program, and at least annually thereafter, and the employer shall assure that each employee is informed of the following:

(o)(1)(ii)(A) The information contained in Appendices A and B;

(o)(1)(ii)(B) The quantity, location, manner of use, release, or storage of AN, and the specific nature of operations which could result in exposure to AN, as well as any necessary protective steps;

(o)(1)(ii)(C) The purpose, proper use, and limitations of respirators and protective clothing;

(o)(1)(ii)(D) The purpose and a description of the medical surveillance program required by paragraph (n) of this Section;

(o)(1)(ii)(E) The emergency procedures developed, as required by paragraph (i) of this Section;

(o)(1)(ii)(F) Engineering and work practice controls, their function, and the employee's relationship to these controls; and

(o)(1)(ii)(G) A review of this Standard.

(o)(2) **Access to training materials**

(o)(2)(i) The employer shall make a copy of this Standard and its Appendices readily available to all affected employees.

(o)(2)(ii) The employer shall provide, upon request, all materials relating to the employee information and training program to the Assistant Secretary and the Director.

(p) **Communication of hazards**

(p)(1) **Hazard communication—general**

(p)(1)(i) Chemical manufacturers, importers, distributors and employers shall comply with all requirements of the Hazard Communication Standard (HCS) (§1910.1200) for AN and AN-based materials not exempted under paragraph (a)(2) of this Section.

(p)(1)(ii) In classifying the hazards of AN and AN-based materials at least the following hazards are to be addressed: Cancer; central nervous system effects; liver effects; skin sensitization; skin, respiratory, and eye irritation; acute toxicity effects; and flammability.

(p)(1)(iii) Employers shall include AN and AN-based materials in the hazard communication program established to comply with the HCS (§1910.1200). Employers shall ensure that each employee has access to labels on containers of AN and AN-based materials and to safety data sheets, and is trained in accordance with the requirements of HCS and paragraph (o) of this Section.

(p)(1)(iv) The employer shall ensure that no statement appears on or near any sign or label required by this paragraph (p) that contradicts or detracts from the required sign or label.

(p)(2) **Signs**

(p)(2)(i) The employer shall post signs to clearly indicate all workplaces where AN concentrations exceed the permissible exposure limits. The signs shall bear the following legend:

DANGER
ACRYLONITRILE (AN)
MAY CAUSE CANCER
RESPIRATORY PROTECTION MAY BE REQUIRED IN THIS AREA
AUTHORIZED PERSONNEL ONLY

(p)(2)(ii) The employer shall ensure that signs required by this paragraph (p)(2) are illuminated and cleaned as necessary so that the legend is readily visible.

(p)(2)(iii) Prior to June 1, 2016, employers may use the following legend in lieu of that specified in paragraph (p)(2)(i) of this Section:

DANGER
ACRYLONITRILE (AN)
CANCER HAZARD
AUTHORIZED PERSONNEL ONLY
RESPIRATORS MAY BE REQUIRED

(p)(3) **Labels**

(p)(3)(i) The employer shall ensure that precautionary labels are in compliance with paragraph (p)(1)(i) of this Section and are affixed to all containers of liquid AN and AN-based materials not exempted under paragraph (a)(2) of this Section. The employer shall ensure that the labels remain affixed when the materials are sold, distributed, or otherwise leave the employer's workplace.

(p)(3)(ii) Prior to June 1, 2015, employers may include the following information on precautionary labels required by this paragraph (p)(3) in lieu of the labeling requirements in paragraph (p)(1) of this Section:

DANGER
CONTAINS ACRYLONITRILE (AN)
CANCER HAZARD

(p)(3)(iii) The employer shall ensure that the precautionary labels required by this paragraph (p)(3) are readily visible and legible.

(q) **Recordkeeping**

(q)(1) **Objective data for exempted operations**

(q)(1)(i) Where the processing, use, and handling of materials made from or containing AN are exempted pursuant to paragraph (a)(2)(ii) of this Section, the employer shall establish and maintain an accurate record of objective data reasonably relied upon in support of the exemption.

(q)(1)(ii) This record shall include at least the following information:

(q)(1)(ii)(A) The material qualifying for exemption;

(q)(1)(ii)(B) The source of the objective data;

(q)(1)(ii)(C) The testing protocol, results of testing, and/or analysis of the material for the release of AN;

(q)(1)(ii)(D) A description of the operation exempted and how the data supports the exemption; and

(q)(1)(ii)(E) Other data relevant to the operations, materials, and processing covered by the exemption.

(q)(1)(iii) The employer shall maintain this record for the duration of the employer's reliance upon such objective data.

(q)(2) **Exposure monitoring**

(q)(2)(i) The employer shall establish and maintain an accurate record of all monitoring required by paragraph (e) of this Section.

(q)(2)(ii) This record shall include:

(q)(2)(ii)(A) The dates, number, duration, and results of each of the samples taken, including a description of the sampling procedure used to determine representative employee exposure;

(q)(2)(ii)(B) A description of the sampling and analytical methods used and the data relied upon to establish that the methods used meet the accuracy and precision requirements of paragraph (e)(6) of this Section;

(q)(2)(ii)(C) Type of respiratory protective devices worn, if any; and

(q)(2)(ii)(D) Name, social security number, and job classification of the employee monitored and of all other employees whose exposure the measurement is intended to represent.

(q)(2)(iii) The employer shall maintain this record for at least forty (40) years, or for the duration of employment plus twenty (20) years, whichever is longer.

(q)(3) **Medical surveillance**

(q)(3)(i) The employer shall establish and maintain an accurate record for each employee subject to medical surveillance as required by paragraph (n) of this Section.

(q)(3)(ii) This record shall include:

(q)(3)(ii)(A) A copy of the physician's written opinions;

(q)(3)(ii)(B) Any employee medical complaints related to exposure to AN;

(q)(3)(ii)(C) A copy of the information provided to the physician as required by paragraph (n)(5) of this Section; and

(q)(3)(ii)(D) A copy of the employee's medical and work history.

(q)(3)(iii) The employer shall assure that this record be maintained for at least forty (40) years, or for the duration of employment plus twenty (20) years, whichever is longer.

(q)(4) **Availability**

(q)(4)(i) The employer shall make all records required to be maintained by this Section available, upon request, to the Assistant Secretary and the Director for examination and copying.

(q)(4)(ii) Records required by paragraphs (q)(1) through (q)(3) of this Section shall be provided upon request to employees, designated representatives, and the Assistant Secretary in accordance with 29 CFR §1910.1020 (a) through (e) and (g) through (i). Records required by paragraph (g)(1) shall be provided in the same manner as exposure monitoring records.

(q)(5) **Transfer of records**

(q)(5)(i) Whenever the employer ceases to do business, the successor employer shall receive and retain all records required to be maintained by this Section for the prescribed period.

(q)(5)(ii) The employer shall also comply with any additional requirements involving transfer of records set forth in 29 CFR §1910.1020(h).

(r) **Observation of monitoring**

(r)(1) **Employee observation** The employer shall provide affected employees, or their designated representatives, an opportunity to observe any monitoring of employee exposure to AN conducted pursuant to paragraph (e) of this Section.

(r)(2) **Observation procedures**

(r)(2)(i) Whenever observation of the monitoring of employee exposure to AN requires entry into an area where the use of protective clothing or equipment is required, the employer shall provide the observer with personal protective clothing and equipment required to be worn by employees working in the area, assure the use of such clothing and equipment, and require the observer to comply with all other applicable safety and health procedures.

(r)(2)(ii) Without interfering with the monitoring, observers shall be entitled:

(r)(2)(ii)(A) To receive an explanation of the measurement procedures;

(r)(2)(ii)(B) To observe all steps related to the measurement of airborne concentrations of AN performed at the place of exposure; and

(r)(2)(ii)(C) To record the results obtained.

(s) [Reserved]

(t) **Appendices** The information contained in the Appendices is not intended, by itself, to create any additional obligation not otherwise imposed, or to detract from any obligation.

§1910.1045 Appendix A Substance safety data sheet for Acrylonitrile

I. Substance Identification

A. Substance: Acrylonitrile (CH_2CHCN).

B. Synonyms: Propenenitrile; vinyl cyanide; cyanoethylene; AN; VCN; acylon; carbacryl; fumigrian; ventox.

C. Acrylonitrile can be found as a liquid or vapor, and can also be found in polymer resins, rubbers, plastics, polyols, and other polymers having acrylonitrile as a raw or intermediate material.

D. AN is used in the manufacture of acrylic and modiacrylic fibers, acrylic plastics and resins, speciality polymers, nitrile rubbers, and other organic chemicals. It has also been used as a fumigant.

E. Appearance and odor: Colorless to pale yellow liquid with a pungent odor which can only be detected at concentrations above the permissible exposure level, in a range of 13–19 parts AN per million parts of air (13–19 ppm).

F. Permissible exposure: Exposure may not exceed either:

1. Two parts AN per million parts of air (2 ppm) averaged over the 8-hour workday; or
2. Ten parts AN per million parts of air (10 ppm) averaged over any 15-minute period in the workday.
3. In addition, skin and eye contact with liquid AN is prohibited.

II. Health Hazard Data

A. Acrylonitrile can affect your body if you inhale the vapor (breathing), if it comes in contact with your eyes or skin, or if you swallow it. It may enter your body through your skin.

B. Effects of overexposure:

1. Short-term exposure: Acrylonitrile can cause eye irritation, nausea, vomiting, headache, sneezing, weakness, and light-headedness. At high concentrations, the effects of exposure may go on to loss of consciousness and death. When acrylonitrile is held in contact with the skin after being absorbed into shoe leather or clothing, it may produce blisters following several hours of no apparent effect. Unless the shoes or clothing are removed immediately and the area washed, blistering will occur. Usually there is no pain or inflammation associated with blister formation.
2. Long-term exposure: Acrylonitrile has been shown to cause cancer in laboratory animals and has been associated with higher incidences of cancer in humans. Repeated or prolonged exposure of the skin to acrylonitrile may produce irritation and dermatitis.
3. Reporting signs and symptoms: You should inform your employer if you develop any signs or symptoms and suspect they are caused by exposure to acrylonitrile.

III. Emergency First Aid Procedures

A. Eye exposure: If acrylonitrile gets into your eyes, wash your eyes immediately with large amounts of water, lifting the lower and upper lids occasionally. Get medical attention immediately. Contact lenses should not be worn when working with this chemical.

B. Skin exposure: If acrylonitrile gets on your skin, immediately wash the contaminated skin with water. If acrylonitrile soaks through your clothing, especially your shoes, remove the clothing immediately and wash the skin with water. If symptoms occur after washing, get medical attention immediately. Thoroughly wash the clothing before reusing. Contaminated leather shoes or other leather articles should be discarded.

C. Inhalation: If you or any other person breathes in large amounts of acrylonitrile, move the exposed person to fresh air at once. If breathing has stopped, perform artificial respiration. Keep the affected person warm and at rest. Get medical attention as soon as possible.

D. Swallowing: When acrylonitrile has been swallowed, give the person large quantities of water immediately. After the water has been swallowed, try to get the person to vomit by having him touch the back of his throat with his finger. Do not make an unconscious person vomit. Get medical attention immediately.

E. Rescue: Move the affected person from the hazardous exposure. If the exposed person has been overcome, notify someone else and put into effect the established emergency procedures. Do not become a casualty yourself. Understand your emergency rescue procedures and know the location of the emergency equipment before the need arises.

F. Special first aid procedures: First aid kits containing an adequate supply (at least two dozen) of amyl nitrite pearls, each containing 0.3 ml, should be maintained at each site where acrylonitrile is used. When a person is suspected of receiving an overexposure to acrylonitrile, immediately remove that person from the contaminated area using established rescue procedures. Contaminated clothing must be removed and the acrylonitrile washed from the skin immediately. Artificial respiration should be started at once if breathing has stopped. If the person is unconscious, amyl nitrite may be used as an antidote by a properly trained individual in accordance with established emergency procedures. Medical aid should be obtained immediately.

IV. Respirators and Protective Clothing

A. Respirators You may be required to wear a respirator for nonroutine activities, in emergencies, while your employer is in the process of reducing acrylonitrile exposures through engineering controls, and in areas where engineering controls are not feasible. If respirators are worn, they must have a label issued by the National Institute for Occupational Safety and Health under the provisions of 42 CFR Part §84 stating that the respirators have been approved for use with organic vapors. For effective protection, respirators must fit your face and head snugly. Respirators must not be loosened or removed in work situations where their use is required.

Acrylonitrile does not have a detectable odor except at levels above the permissible exposure limits. Do not depend on odor to warn you when a respirator cartridge or canister is exhausted. Cartridges or canisters must be changed daily or before the end-of-service-life, whichever comes first. Reuse of these may allow acrylonitrille to gradually filter through the cartridge and cause exposures which you cannot detect by odor. If you can smell acrylonitrile while wearing a respirator, proceed immediately to fresh air. If you experience difficulty breathing while wearing a respirator, tell your employer.

B. Supplied-air suits In some work situations, the wearing of supplied-air suits may be necessary. Your employer must instruct you in their proper use and operation.

C. Protective clothing: You must wear impervious clothing, gloves, face shield, or other appropriate protective clothing to prevent skin contact with liquid acrylonitrile. Where protective clothing is required, your employer is required to provide clean garments to you as necessary to assume that the clothing protects you adequately.

Replace or repair impervious clothing that has developed leaks.

Acrylonitrile should never be allowed to remain on the skin. Clothing and shoes which are not impervious to acrylonitrile should not be allowed to become contaminated with acrylonitrile, and if they do the clothing and shoes should be promptly removed and decontaminated. The clothing should be laundered or discarded after the AN is removed. Once acrylonitrile penetrates shoes or other leather articles, they should not be worn again.

D. Eye protection: You must wear splashproof safety goggles in areas where liquid acrylonitrile may contact your eyes. In addition, contact lenses should not be worn in areas where eye contact with acrylonitrile can occur.

V. Precautions for Safe Use, Handling, and Storage

A. Acrylonitrile is a flammable liquid, and its vapors can easily form explosive mixtures in air.

B. Acrylonitrile must be stored in tightly closed containers in a cool, well-ventilated area, away from heat, sparks, flames, strong oxidizers (especially bromine), strong bases, copper, copper alloys, ammonia, and amines.

C. Sources of ignition such as smoking and open flames are prohibited wherever acrylonitrile is handled, used, or stored in a manner that could create a potential fire or explosion hazard.

D. You should use non-sparking tools when opening or closing metal containers of acrylonitrile, and containers must be bonded and grounded when pouring or transferring liquid acrylonitrile.

E. You must immediately remove any non-impervious clothing that becomes wetted with acrylonitrile, and this clothing must not be reworn until the acrylonitrile is removed from the clothing.

F. Impervious clothing wet with liquid acrylonitrile can be easily ignited. This clothing must be washed down with water before you remove it.

G. If your skin becomes wet with liquid acrylonitrile, you must promptly and thoroughly wash or shower with soap or mild detergent to remove any acrylonitrile from your skin.

H. You must not keep food, beverages, or smoking materials, nor are you permitted to eat or smoke in regulated areas where acrylonitrile concentrations are above the permissible exposure limits.

I. If you contact liquid acrylonitrile, you must wash your hands thoroughly with soap or mild detergent and water before eating, smoking, or using toilet facilities.

J. Fire extinguishers and quick drenching facilities must be readily available, and you should know where they are and how to operate them.

K. Ask your supervisor where acrylonitrile is used in your work area and for any additional plant safety and health rules.

VI. Access to Information

A. Each year, your employer is required to inform you of the information contained in this Substance Safety Data Sheet for acrylonitrile. In addition, you employer must instruct you in the proper work practices for using acrylonitrile, emergency procedures, and the correct use of protective equipment.

B. Your employer is required to determine whether you are being exposed to acrylonitrile. You or your representative has the right to observe employee measurements and to record the results obtained. Your employer is required to inform you of your exposure. If your employer determines that you are being overexposed, he or she is required to inform you of the actions which are being taken to reduce your exposure to within permissible exposure limits.

C. Your employer is required to keep records of your exposures and medical examinations. These records must be kept by the employer for at least forty (40) years or for the period of your employment plus twenty (20) years, whichever is longer.

D. Your employer is required to release your exposure and medical records to you or your representative upon your request.

§1910.1045 Appendix B Substance technical guidelines for Acrylonitrile

I. Physical and Chemical Data

A. Substance identification:

1. Synonyms: AN; VCN; vinyl cyanide; propenenitrile; cyanoethylene; Acrylon; Carbacryl; Fumigrain; Ventox.
2. Formula: $CH_2 = CHCN$.
3. Molecular weight: 53.1.

B. Physical data:

1. Boiling point (760 mm Hg): 77.3 °C (171 °F);
2. Specific gravity (water = 1): 0.81 (at 20 °C or 68 °F);
3. Vapor density (ai r =1 at boiling point of acrylonitrile): 1.83;
4. Melting point: −83 °C (−117 °F);
5. Vapor pressure (@20 °F): 83 mm Hg;
6. Solubility in water, percent by weight @20 °C (68 °F): 7.35;
7. Evaporation rate (Butyl Acetate = 1): 4.54; and
8. Appearance and odor: Colorless to pale yellow liquid with a pungent odor at concentrations above the permissible exposure level. Any detectable odor of acrylonitrile may indicate overexposure.

II. Fire, Explosion, and Reactivity Hazard Data

A. Fire:

1. Flash point: −1 °C (30 °F) (closed cup).
2. Autoignition temperature: 481 °C (898 °F).
3. Flammable limits air, percent by volume: Lower: 3, Upper: 17.
4. Extinguishing media: Alcohol foam, carbon dioxide, and dry chemical.
5. Special fire-fighting procedures: Do not use a solid stream of water, since the stream will scatter and spread the fire. Use water to cool containers exposed to a fire.
6. Unusual fire and explosion hazards: Acrylonitrile is a flammable liquid. Its vapors can easily form explosive mixtures with air. All ignition sources must be controlled where acrylonitrile is handled, used, or stored in a manner that could create a potential fire or explosion hazard. Acrylonitrile vapors are heavier than air and may travel along the ground and be ignited by open flames or sparks at locations remote from the site at which acrylonitrile is being handled.
7. For purposes of compliance with the requirements of 29 CFR §1910.106, acrylonitrile is classified as a class IB flammable liquid. For example, 7,500 ppm, approximately one-fourth of the lower flammable limit, would be considered to pose a potential fire and explosion hazard.
8. For purposes of compliance with 29 CFR §1910.157, acrylonitrile is classified as a Class B fire hazard.
9. For purpose of compliance with 29 CFR §1919.309, locations classified as hazardous due to the presence of acrylonitrile shall be Class I, Group D.

B. Reactivity:

1. Conditions contributing to instability: Acrylonitrile will polymerize when hot, and the additional heat liberated by the polymerization may cause containers to explode. Pure AN may self-polymerize, with a rapid build-up of pressure, resulting in an explosion hazard. Inhibitors are added to the commercial product to prevent self-polymerization.
2. Incompatibilities: Contact with strong oxidizers (especially bromine) and strong bases may cause fires and explosions. Contact with copper, copper alloys, ammonia, and amines may start serious decomposition.
3. Hazardous decompostion products: Toxic gases and vapors (such as hydrogen cyanide, oxides of nitrogen, and carbon monoxide) may be released in a fire involving acrylonitrile and certain polymers made from acrylonitrile.
4. Special precautions: Liquid acrylonitrile will attack some forms of plastics, rubbers, and coatings.

III. Spill, Leak, and Disposal Procedures

A. If acrylonitrile is spilled or leaked, the following steps should be taken:

1. Remove all ignition sources.
2. The area should be evacuated at once and re-entered only after the area has been thoroughly ventilated and washed down with water.
3. If liquid acrylonitrile or polymer intermediate, collect for reclamation or absorb in paper, vermiculite, dry sand, earth, or similar material, or wash down with water into process sewer system.

B. Persons not wearing protective equipment should be restricted from areas of spills or leaks until clean-up has been completed.

C. Waste disposal methods: Waste material shall be disposed of in a manner that is not hazardous to employees or to the general population. Spills of acrylonitrile and flushing of such spills shall be channeled for appropriate treatment or collection for disposal. They shall not be channeled directly into the sanitary sewer system. In selecting the method of waste disposal, applicable local, State, and Federal regulations should be consulted.

IV. Monitoring and Measurement Procedures

A. Exposure above the Permissible Exposure Limit:

1. Eight-hour exposure evaluation: Measurements taken for the purpose of determining employee exposure under this Section are best taken so that the average 8-hour exposure may be determined from a single 8-hour sample or two (2) 4-hour samples. Air samples should be taken in the employee's breathing zone (air that would most nearly represent that inhaled by the employee.)
2. Ceiling evaluation: Measurements taken for the purpose of determining employee exposure under this Section must be taken during periods of maximum expected airborne concentrations of acrylonitrile in the employee's breathing zone. A minimum of three (3) measurements should be taken on one work shift. The average of all measurements taken is an estimate of the employee's ceiling exposure.
3. Monitoring techniques: The sampling and analysis under this Section may be performed by collecting the acrylonitrile vapor on charcoal adsorption tubes or other composition adsorption tubes, with subsequent chemical analysis. Sampling and analysis may also be performed by instruments such as real-time continuous monitoring systems, portable direct-reading instruments, or passive dosimeters. Analysis of resultant samples should be by gas chromatograph.

Appendix D lists methods of sampling and analysis which have been tested by NIOSH and OSHA for use with acrylonitrile. NIOSH and OSHA have validated modifications of NIOSH Method S–156 (See Appendix D) under laboratory conditions for concentrations below 1 ppm. The employer has the obligation of selecting a monitoring method which meets the accuracy and precision requirements of the standard under his unique field conditions. The standard requires that methods of monitoring must be accurate, to a 95-percent confidence level, to ±35-percent for concentrations of AN at or above 2 ppm, and to ±50-percent for concentrations below 2 ppm. In addition to the methods described in Appendix D, there are numerous other methods available for monitoring for AN in the workplace. Details on these other methods have been submitted by various companies to the rulemaking record, and are available at the OSHA Docket Office.

B. Since many of the duties relating to employee exposure are dependent on the results of monitoring and measuring procedures, employers shall assure that the evaluation of employee exposures is performed by a competent industrial hygienist or other technically qualified person.

V. Protective Clothing

Employees shall be provided with and required to wear appropriate protective clothing to prevent any possibility of skin contact with liquid AN. Because acrylonitrile is absorbed through the skin, it is important to prevent skin contact with liquid AN. Protective clothing shall include impermeable coveralls or similar full-body work clothing, gloves, head-coverings, as appropriate to protect areas of the body which may come in contact with liquid AN.

Employers should ascertain that the protective garmets are impermeable to acrylonitrile. Non-impermeable clothing and shoes should not be allowed to become contaminated with liquid AN. If permeable clothing does become contaminated, it should be promptly removed, placed in a regulated area for removal of the AN, and not worn again until the AN is removed. If leather footwear or other leather garments become wet from acrylonitrile, they should be replaced and not worn again, due to the ability of leather to absorb acrylonitrile and hold it against the skin. Since there is no pain associated with the blistering which may result from skin contact with liquid AN, it is essential that the employee be informed of this hazard so that he or she can be protected.

Any protective clothing which has developed leaks or is otherwise found to be defective shall be repaired or replaced. Clean protective clothing shall be provided to the employee as necessary to assure its protectiveness. Whenever impervious clothing becomes wet with liquid AN, it shall be washed down with water before being removed by the employee. Employees are also required to wear splash-proof safety goggles where there is any possibility of acrylonitrile contacting the eyes.

VI. Housekeeping and Hygiene Facilities

For purposes of complying with 29 CFR §1910.141, the following items should be emphasized:

A. The workplace should be kept clean, orderly, and in a sanitary condition. The employer is required to institute a leak and spill detection program for operations involving liquid AN in order to detect sources of fugitive AN emissions.

B. Dry sweeping and the use of compressed air is unsafe for the cleaning of floors and other surfaces where liquid AN may be found.

C. Adequate washing facilities with hot and cold water are to be provided, and maintained in a sanitary condition. Suitable cleansing agents are also to be provided to assure the effective removal of acrylonitrile from the skin.

D. Change or dressing rooms with individual clothes storage facilities must be provided to prevent the contamination of street clothes with acrylonitrile. Because of the hazardous nature of acrylonitrile, contaminated protective clothing should be placed in a regulated area designated by the employer for removal of the AN before the clothing is laundered or disposed of.

VII. Miscellaneous Precautions

A. Store acrylonitrile in tightly-closed containers in a cool, well-ventilated area and take necessary precautions to avoid any explosion hazard.

B. High exposures to acrylonitrile can occur when transferring the liquid from one container to another.

C. Non-sparking tools must be used to open and close metal acrylonitrile containers. These containers must be effectively grounded and bonded prior to pouring.

D. Never store uninhibited acrylonitrile.

E. Acrylonitrile vapors are not inhibited. They may form polymers and clog vents of storage tanks.

F. Use of supplied-air suits or other impervious coverings may be necessary to prevent skin contact with and provide respiratory protection from acrylonitrile where the concentration of acrylonitrile is unknown or is above the ceiling limit. Supplied-air suits should be selected, used, and maintained under the immediate supervision of persons knowledgeable in the limitations and potential life-endangering characteristics of supplied-air suits.

G. Employers shall advise employees of all areas and operations where exposure to acrylonitrile could occur.

VIII. Common Operations

Common operations in which exposure to acrylonitrile is likely to occur include the following: Manufacture of the acrylonitrile monomer; synthesis of acrylic fibers, ABS, SAN, and nitrile barrier plastics and resins, nitrile rubber, surface coatings, specialty chemicals, use as a chemical intermediate, use as a fumigant and in the cyanoethylation of cotton.

§1910.1045 Appendix C Medical surveillance guidelines for Acrylonitrile

I. Route of Entry

Inhalation; skin absorption; ingestion.

II. Toxicology

Acrylonitrile vapor is an asphyxiant due to inhibitory action on metabolic enzyme systems. Animals exposed to 75 or 100 ppm for 7 hours have shown signs of anoxia; in some animals which died at the higher level, cyanomethemoglobin was found in the blood. Two human fatalities from accidental poisoning have been reported; one was caused by inhalation of an unknown concentration of the vapor, and the other was thought to be caused by skin absorption or inhalation. Most cases of intoxication from industrial exposure have been mild, with rapid onset of eye irritation, headache, sneezing, and nausea. Weakness, lightheadedness, and vomiting may also occur. Exposure to high concentrations may produce profound weakness, asphyxia, and death. The vapor is a severe eye irritant. Prolonged skin contract with the liquid may result in absorption with systemic effects, and in the formation of large blisters after a latent period of several hours. Although there is usually little or no pain or inflammation, the affected skin resembles a second-degree thermal burn. Solutions spilled on exposed skin, or on areas covered only by a light layer of clothing, evaporate rapidly, leaving no irritation, or, at the most, mild transient redness. Repeated spills on exposed skin may result in dermatitis due to solvent effects.

Results after 1 year of a planned 2-year animal study on the effects of exposure to acrylonitrile have indicated that rats ingesting as little as 35 ppm in their drinking water develop tumors of the central nervous system. The interim results of this study have been supported by a similar study being conducted by the same laboratory, involving exposure of rats by inhalation of acrylonitrile vapor, which has shown similar types of tumors in animals exposed to 80 ppm.

In addition, the preliminary results of an epidemiological study being performed by duPont on a cohort of workers in their Camden, S.C. acrylic fiber plant indicate a statistically significant increase in the incidence of colon and lung cancers among employees exposed to acrylonitrile.

III. Signs and Symptoms of Acute Overexposure

Asphyxia and death can occur from exposure to high concentrations of acrylonitrile. Symptoms of overexposure include eye irritation, headache, sneezing, nausea and vomiting, weakness, and light-headedness. Prolonged skin contact can cause blisters on the skin with appearance of a second-degree burn, but with little or no pain. Repeated skin contact may produce scaling dermatitis.

IV. Treatment of Acute Overexposure

Remove employee from exposure. Immediately flush eyes with water and wash skin with soap or mild detergent and water. If AN has been swallowed, and person is conscious, induce vomiting. Give artificial resuscitation if indicated. More severe cases, such as those associated with loss of consciousness, may be treated by the intravenous administration of sodium nitrite, followed by sodium thiosulfate, although this is not as effective for acrylonitrile poisoning as for inorganic cyanide poisoning.

V. Surveillance and Preventive Considerations

A. As noted above, exposure to acrylonitrile has been linked to increased incidence of cancers of the colon and lung in employees of the duPont acrylic fiber plant in Camden, S.C. In addition, the animal testing of acrylonitrile has resulted in the development of cancers of the central nervous system in rats exposed by either inhalation or ingestion. The physician should be aware of the findings of these studies in evaluating the health of employees exposed to acrylonitrile.

Most reported acute effects of occupational exposure to acrylonitrile are due to its ability to cause tissue anoxia and asphyxia. The effects are similar to those caused by hydrogen cyanide. Liquid acrylonitrile can be absorbed through the skin upon prolonged contact. The liquid readily penetrates leather, and will produce burns of the feet if footwear contaminated with acrylonitrile is not removed.

It is important for the physician to become familiar with the operating conditions in which exposure to acrylonitrile may occur. Those employees with skin diseases may not tolerate the wearing of whatever protective clothing may be necessary to protect them from exposure. In addition, those with chronic respiratory disease may not tolerate the wearing of negative-pressure respirators.

B. Surveillance and screening Medical histories and laboratory examinations are required for each employee subject to exposure to acrylonitrile above the action level. The employer must screen employees for history of certain medical conditions which might place the employee at increased risk from exposure.

1. **Central nervous system dysfunction** Acute effects of exposure to acrylonitrile generally involve the central nervous system. Symptoms of acrylonitrile exposure include headache, nausea, dizziness, and general weakness. The animal studies cited above suggest possible carcinogenic effects of acrylonitrile on the central nervous system, since rats exposed by either inhalation or ingestion have developed similar CNS tumors.
2. **Respiratory disease** The du Pont data indicate an increased risk of lung cancer among employees exposed to acrylonitrile.
3. **Gastrointestinal disease** The du Pont data indicate an increased risk of cancer of the colon among employees exposed to acrylonitrile. In addition, the animal studies show possible tumor production in the stomachs of the rats in the ingestion study.
4. **Skin disease** Acrylonitrile can cause skin burns when prolonged skin contact with the liquid occurs. In addition, repeated skin contact with the liquid can cause dermatitis.
5. **General** The purpose of the medical procedures outlined in the standard is to establish a baseline for future health monitoring. Persons unusually susceptible to the effects of anoxia or those with anemia would be expected to be at increased risk. In addition to emphasis on the CNS, respiratory and gastro-intestinal systems, the cardiovascular system, liver, and kidney function should also be stressed.

§1910.1045 Appendix D Sampling and analytical methods for Acrylonitrile

There are many methods available for monitoring employee exposures to acrylonitrile. Most of these involve the use of charcoal tubes and sampling pumps, with analysis by gas chromatograph. The essential differences between the charcoal tube methods include, among others, the use of different desorbing solvents, the use of different lots of charcoal, and the use of different equipment for analysis of the samples.

Besides charcoal, considerable work has been performed on methods using porous polymer sampling tubes and passive dosimeters. In addition, there are several portable gas analyzers and monitoring units available on the open market.

This Appendix contains details for the methods which have been tested at OSHA Analytical Laboratory in Salt Lake City, and NIOSH in Cincinnati. Each is a variation on NIOSH Method S–156, which is also included for reference. This does not indicate that these methods are the only ones which will be satisfactory. There also may be workplace situations in which these methods are not adequate, due to such factors as high humidity. Copies of the other methods available to OSHA are available in the rulemaking record, and may be obtained from the OSHA Docket Office. These include, the Union Carbide, Monsanto, Dow Chemical and Dow Badische methods, as well as NISOH Method P & CAM 127.

Employers who note problems with sample breakthrough should try larger charcoal tubes. Tubes of larger capacity are available, and are often used for sampling vinyl chloride. In addition, lower flow rates and shorter sampling times should be beneficial in minimizing breakthrough problems.

Whatever method the employer chooses, he must assure himself of the method's accuracy and precision under the unique conditions present in his workplace.

NIOSH Method S–156 (Unmodified)

Analyte: Acrylonitrile.

Matrix: Air.

Procedure: Absorption on charcoal, desorption with methanol, GC.

1. Principle of the method (Reference 11.1)

1.1 A known volume of air is drawn through a charcoal tube to trap the organic vapors present.

1.2 The charcoal in the tube is transferred to a small, stoppered sample container, and the analyte is desorbed with methanol.

1.3 An aliquot of the desorbed sample is injected into a gas chromatograph.

1.4 The area of the resulting peak is determined and compared with areas obtained for standards.

2. Range and sensitivity

2.1 This method was validated over the range of 17.5–70.0 mg/cu m at an atmospheric temperature and pressure of 22 °C and 760 MM Hg, using a 20-liter sample. Under the conditions of sample size (20–liters) the probable useful range of this method is 4.5–135 mg-cu m. The method is capable of measuring much smaller amounts if the desorption efficiency is adequate. Desorption efficiency must be determined over the range used.

2.2 The upper limit of the range of the method is dependent on the adsorptive capacity of the charcoal tube. This capacity varies with the concentrations of acrylonitrile and other substances in the air. The first section of the charcoal tube was found to hold at least 3.97 mg of acrylonitrile when a test atmosphere containing 92.0 mg/cu m of acrylonitrile in air was sampled 0.18 liter per minute for 240 minutes; at that time the concentration of acrylonitrile in the effluent was less than 5 percent of that in the influent. (The charcoal tube consists of two sections of activated charcoal separated by a section of urethane foam. See Section 6.2.) If a particular atmosphere is suspected of containing a large amount of contaminant, a smaller sampling volume should be taken.

3. Interference

3.1 When the amount of water in the air is so great that condensation actually occurs in the tube, organic vapors will not be trapped efficiently. Preliminary experiments using toluene indicate that high humidity severely decreases the breakthrough volume.

3.2 When interfering compounds are known or suspected to be present in the air, such information, including their suspected identities, should be transmitted with the sample.

3.3 It must be emphasized that any compound which has the same retention time as the analyte at the operating conditions described in this method is an interference. Retention time data on a single column cannot be considered proof of chemical identity.

3.4 If the possibility of interference exists, separation conditions (column packing, temperature, etc.) must be changed to circumvent the problem.

4. Precision and accuracy

4.1 The Coefficient of Variation (CVT) for the total analytical and sampling method in the range of 17.5–70.0 mg/cu m was 0.073. This value corresponds to a 3.3 mg/cu m standard deviation at the (previous) OSHA standard level (20 ppm). Statistical information and details of the validation and experimental test procedures can be found in Reference 11.2.

4.2 On the average the concentrations obtained at the 20 ppm level using the overall sampling and analytical method were 6.0 percent lower than the "true" concentrations for a limited number of laboratory experiments. Any difference between the "found" and "true" concentrations may not represent a bias in the sampling and analytical method, but rather a random variation from the experimentally determined "true" concentration. Therefore, no recovery correction should be applied to the final result in Section 10.5.

5. Advantages and disadvantages of the method

5.1 The sampling device is small, portable, and involves no liquids. Interferences are minimal, and most of those which do occur can be eliminated by altering chromatographic conditions. The tubes are analyzed by means of a quick, instrumental method.

The method can also be used for the simultaneous analysis of two or more substances suspected to be present in the same sample by simply changing gas chromatographic conditions.

5.2 One disadvantage of the method is that the amount of sample which can be taken is limited by the number of milligrams that the tube will hold before overloading. When the sample value obtained for the backup section of the charcoal tube exceeds 25 percent of that found on the front section, the possibility of sample loss exists.

5.3 Furthermore, the precision of the method is limited by the reproducibility of the pressure drop across the tubes. This drop will affect the flow rate and cause the volume to be imprecise, because the pump is usually calibrated for one tube only.

6. Apparatus

6.1 A calibrated personal sampling pump whose flow can be determined within ± 5 percent at the recommended flow rate. (Reference 11.3).

6.2 Charcoal tubes: Glass tubes with both ends flame sealed, 7 cm long with a 6-mm O.D. and a 4-mm I.D., containing 2 sections of 20/40 mesh activated charcoal separated by a 2-mm portion of urethane foam. The activated charcoals prepared from coconut shells and is fired at 600 °C prior to packing. The adsorbing section contains 100 mg of charcoal, the backup section 50 mg. A 3-mm portion of urethane foam is placed between the outlet end of the tube and the backup section. A plug of silicated glass wool is placed in front of the adsorbing section. The pressure drop across the tube must be less than 1 inch of mercury at a flow rate of 1 liter per minute.

6.3 Gas chromatograph equipped with a flame ionization detector.

6.4 Column (4–ft×1/4-in stainless steel) packed with 50/80 mesh Poropak, type Q.

6.5 An electronic integrator or some other suitable method for measuring peak areas.

6.6 Two-milliliter sample containers with glass stoppers or Teflon-lined caps. If an automatic sample injector is used, the associated vials may be used.

6.7 Microliter syringes: 10-microliter and other convenient sizes for making standards.

6.8 Pipets: 1.0-ml delivery pipets.

6.9 Volumetric flask: 10-ml or convenient sizes for making standard solutions.

7. Reagents

7.1 Chromatographic quality methanol.

7.2 Acrylonitrile, reagent grade.

7.3 Hexane, reagent grade.

7.4 Purified nitrogen.

7.5 Prepurified hydrogen.

7.6 Filtered compressed air.

8. Procedure

8.1 Cleaning of equipment All glassware used for the laboratory analysis should be detergent washed and thoroughly rinsed with tap water and distilled water.

8.2 Calibration of personal pumps. Each personal pump must be calibrated with a representative charcoal tube in the line. This will minimize errors associated with uncertainties in the sample volume collected.

8.3 Collection and shipping of samples

8.3.1 Immediately before sampling, break the ends of the tube to provide an opening at least one-half the internal diameter of the tube (2 mm).

8.3.2 The smaller section of charcoal is used as a backup and should be positioned nearest the sampling pump.

8.3.3 The charcoal tube should be placed in a vertical direction during sampling to minimize channeling through the charcoal.

8.3.4 Air being sampled should not be passed through any hose or tubing before entering the charcoal tube.

8.3.5 A maximum sample size of 20 liters is recommended. Sample at a flow of 0.20 liter per minute or less. The flow rate should be known with an accuracy of at least ± 5 percent.

8.3.6 The temperature and pressure of the atmosphere being sampled should be recorded. If pressure reading is not available, record the elevation.

8.3.7 The charcoal tubes should be capped with the supplied plastic caps immediately after sampling. Under no circumstances should rubber caps be used.

8.3.8 With each batch of 10 samples submit one tube from the same lot of tubes which was used for sample collection and which is subjected to exactly the same handling as the samples except that no air is drawn through it. Label this as a blank.

8.3.9 Capped tubes should be packed tightly and padded before they are shipped to minimize tube breakage during shipping.

8.3.10 A sample of the bulk material should be submitted to the laboratory in a glass container with a Teflon-lined cap. This sample should not be transported in the same container as the charcoal tubes.

8.4 Analysis of samples

8.4.1 Preparation of samples In preparation for analysis, each charcoal tube is scored with a file in front of the first section of charcoal and broken open. The glass wool is removed and discarded. The charcoal in the first (larger) section is transferred to a 2-ml stoppered sample container. The separating section of foam is removed and discarded; the second section is transferred to another stoppered container. These two sections are analyzed separately.

8.4.2 Desorption of samples Prior to analysis, 1.0 ml of methanol is pipetted into each sample container. Desorption should be done for 30 minutes. Tests indicate that this is adequate if the sample is agitated occasionally during this period. If an automatic sample injector is used, the sample vials should be capped as soon as the solvent is added to minimize volatilization.

8.4.3 GC conditions The typical operating conditions for the gas chromatograph are:

1. 50 ml/min (60 psig) nitrogen carrier gas flow.
2. 65 ml/min (24 psig) hydrogen gas flow to detector.
3. 500 ml/min (50 psig) air flow to detector.
4. 235 °C injector temperature.
5. 255 °C manifold temperature (detector).
6. 155 °C column temperature.

8.4.4 Injection The first step in the analysis is the injection of the sample into the gas chromatograph. To eliminate difficulties arising from blowback or distillation within the syringe needle, one should employ the solvent flush injection technique. The 10-microliter syringe is first flushed with solvent several times to wet the barrel and plunger. Three microliters of solvent are drawn into the syringe to increase the accuracy and reproducibility of the injected sample volume. The needle is removed from the solvent, and the plunger is pulled back about 0.2 microliter to separate the solvent flush from the sample with a pocket of air to be used as a marker. The needle is then immersed in the sample, and a 5-microliter aliquot is withdrawn, taking into consideration the volume of the needle, since the sample in the needle will be completely injected. After the needle is removed from the sample and prior to injection, the plunger is pulled back 1.2 microliters to minimize evaporation of the sample from the tip of the needle. Observe that the sample occupies 4.9–5.0 microliters in the barrel of the syringe. Duplicate injections of each sample and standard should be made. No more than a 3 percent difference in area is to be expected. An automatic sample injector can be used if it is shown to give reproducibility at least as good as the solvent flush method.

8.4.5 Measurement of area The area of the sample peak is measured by an electronic integrator or some other suitable form of area measurement, and preliminary results are read from a standard curve prepared as discussed below.

8.5 Determination of desorption efficiency

8.5.1 Importance of determination The desorption efficiency of a particular compound can vary from one laboratory to another and also from one batch of charcoal to another. Thus, it is necessary to determine at least once the percentage of the specific compound that is removed in the desorption process, provided the same batch of charcoal is used.

8.5.2 Procedure for determining desorption efficiency Activated charcoal equivalent to the amount in the first section of the sampling tube (100 mg) is measured into a 2.5 in, 4-mm I.D. glass tube, flame sealed at one end. This charcoal must be from the same batch as that used in obtaining the samples and can be obtained from unused charcoal tubes. The open end is capped with Parafilm. A known amount of hexane solution of acrylonitrile containing 0.239 g/ml is injected directly into the activated charcoal with a microliter syringe, and tube is capped with more Parafilm. When using an automatic sample injector, the sample injector vials, capped with Teflon-faced septa, may be used in place of the glass tube.

The amount injected is equivalent to that present in a 20-liter air sample at the selected level.

Six tubes at each of three levels (0.5X, 1X, and 2X of the standard) are prepared in this manner and allowed to stand for at least overnight to assure complete adsorption of the analyte onto the charcoal. These tubes are referred to as the sample. A parallel blank tube should be treated in the same manner except that no sample is added to it. The sample and blank tubes are desorbed and analyzed in exactly the same manner as the sampling tube described in section 8.4.

Two or three standards are prepared by injecting the same volume of compound into 1.0 ml of methanol with the same syringe used in the preparation of the samples. These are analyzed with the samples.

The desorption efficiency (D.E.) equals the average weight in mg recovered from the tube divided by the weight in mg added to the tube, or

$$\text{D.E.} = \frac{\text{Average weight recovered (mg)}}{\text{weight added (mg)}}$$

The desorption efficiency is dependent on the amount of analyte collected on the charcoal. Plot the desorption efficiency versus weight of analyte found. This curve is used in section 10.4 to correct for adsorption losses.

9. Calibration and standards

It is convenient to express concentration of standards in terms of mg/1.0 ml methanol, because samples are desorbed in this amount of methanol. The density of the analyte is used to convert mg into microliters for easy measurement with a microliter syringe. A series of standards, varying in concentration over the range of interest, is prepared and analyzed under the same GC conditions and during the same time period as the unknown samples. Curves are established by plotting concentration in mg/1.0 ml versus peak area.

Note: Since no internal standard is used in the method, standard solutions must be analyzed at the same time that the sample analysis is done. This will minimize the effect of known day-to-day variations and variations during the same day of the FID response.

10. Calculations

10.1 Read the weight, in mg, corresponding to each peak area from the standard curve. No volume corrections are needed, because the standard curve is based on mg/1.0 ml methanol and the volume of sample injected is identical to the volume of the standards injected.

10.2 Corrections for the bank must be made for each sample.

$$\text{mg} = \text{mg sample} - \text{mg blank}$$

Where:
mg sample = mg found in front section of sample tube.
mg sample = mg found in front section of blank tube.
A similar procedure is followed for the backup sections.

10.3 Add the weights found in the front and backup sections to get the total weight in the sample.

10.4 Read the desorption efficiency from the curve (see sec. 8.5.2) for the amount found in the front section. Divide the total weight by this desorption efficiency to obtain the corrected mg/sample.

$$\text{Corrected mg/sample} = \frac{\text{Total weight}}{\text{D.E.}}$$

10.5 The concentration of the analyte in the air sampled can be expressed in mg/cu m.

$$\text{mg/cu m} = \text{Corrected mg (section 10.4)} \times \frac{\text{1,000 (liter/cu m)}}{\text{air volume sampled (liter)}}$$

10.6 Another method of expressing concentration is ppm.

$$\text{ppm} = \text{m mg/cu} \times 24.45 / \text{M.W.} \times 760/\text{P} \times \text{T.} + 273/298$$

Where:

P = Pressure (mm Hg) of air sampled.
T = Temperature (°C) of air sampled.
24.45 = Molar volume (liter/mole) at 25 °C and 760 mm Hg.
M.W. = Molecular weight (g/mole) of analyte.
760 = Standard pressure (mm Hg).
298 = Standard temperature (°K).

11. References

11.1 White, L. D. et al., "A Convenient Optimized Method for the Analysis of Selected Solvent Vapors in the Industrial Atmosphere," Amer. Ind. Hyg. Assoc. J., 31: 225 (1970).

11.2 Documentation of NIOSH Validation Tests, NIOSH Contract No. CDC–99–74–45.

11.3 Final Report, NIOSH Contract HSM–99–71–31, "Personal Sampler Pump for Charcoal Tubes," September 15, 1972.

NIOSH Modification of NIOSH Method S–156

The NIOSH recommended method for low levels for acrylonitrile is a modification of method S–156. It differs in the following respects:

(1) Samples are desorbed using 1 ml of 1 percent acetone in CS2rather than methanol.

(2) The analytical column and conditions are:

Column: 20 percent SP–1000 on 80/100 Supelcoport 10 feet × 1/8inch S.S.
Conditions:
Injector temperature: 200 °C.
Detector temperature: 100 °C.
Column temperature: 85 °C.
Helium flow: 25 ml/min.
Air flow: 450 ml/min.
Hydrogen flow: 55 ml/min.

(3) A 2 μl injection of the desorbed analyte is used.

(4) A sampling rate of 100 ml/min is recommended.

OSHA Laboratory Modification of NIOSH Method S–156

Analyte: Acrylonitrile.

Matrix: Air.

Procedure: Adsorption on charcoal, desorption with methanol, GC.

1. Principle of the Method (Reference 1)

1.1 A known volume of air is drawn through a charcoal tube to trap the organic vapors present.

1.2 The charcoal in the tube is transferred to a small, stoppered sample vial, and the analyte is desorbed with methanol.

1.3 An aliquot of the desorbed sample is injected into a gas chromatograph.

1.4 The area of the resulting peak is determined and compared with areas obtained for standards.

2. Advantages and disadvantages of the method

2.1 The sampling device is small, portable, and involves no liquids. Interferences are minimal, and most of those which do occur can be eliminated by altering chromatographic conditions. The tubes are analyzed by means of a quick, instrumental method.

2.2 This method may not be adequate for the simultaneous analysis of two or more substances.

2.3 The amount of sample which can be taken is limited by the number of milligrams that the tube will hold before overloading. When the sample value obtained for the backup section of the charcoal tube exceeds 25 percent of that found on the front section, the possibility of sample loss exists.

2.4 The precision of the method is limited by the reproducibility of the pressure drop across the tubes. This drop will affect the flow rate and cause the volume to be imprecise, because the pump is usually calibrated for one tube only.

3. Apparatus

3.1 A calibrated personal sampling pump whose flow can be determined within ± 5 percent at the recommended flow rate.

3.2 Charcoal tubes: Glass tube with both ends flame sealed, 7 cm long with a 6-mm O.D. and a 4-mm I.D., containing 2 sections of 20/40 mesh activated charcoal separated by a 2-mm portion of urethane foam. The activated charcoal is prepared from coconut shells and is fired at 600 °C prior to packing. The adsorbing section contains 100 mg of charcoal, the back-up section 50 mg. A 3-mm portion of urethane foam is placed between the outlet end of the tube and the back-up section. A plug of sililated glass wool is placed in front of the adsorbing section. The pressure drop across the tube must be less than one inch of mercury at a flow rate of 1 liter per minute.

3.3 Gas chromatograph equipped with a nitrogen phosphorus detector.

3.4 Column (10-ft. × 1/8-in. stainless steel) packed with 100/120 Supelcoport coated with 10 percent SP 1000.

3.5 n electronic integrator or some other suitable method for measuring peak area.

3.6 Two-milliliter sample vials with Teflon-lined caps

3.7 Microliter syringes: 10-microliter, and other convenient sizes for making standards.

3.8 Pipets: 1.0-ml delivery pipets.

3.9 Volumetric flasks: convenient sizes for making standard solutions.

4. Reagents

4.1 Chromatographic quality methanol.

4.2 Acrylonitrile, reagent grade.

4.3 Filtered compressed air.

4.4 Purified hydrogen.

4.5 Purified helium.

5. Procedure

5.1 Cleaning of equipment. All glassware used for the laboratory analysis should be properly cleaned and free of organics which could interfere in the analysis.

5.2 Calibration of personal pumps. Each pump must be calibrated with a representative charcoal tube in the line.

5.3 Collection and shipping of samples.

5.3.1 Immediately before sampling, break the ends of the tube to provide an opening at least one-half the internal diameter of the tube (2 mm).

5.3.2 The smaller section of the charcoal is used as the backup and should be placed nearest the sampling pump.

5.3.3 The charcoal should be placed in a vertical position during sampling to minimize channeling through the charcoal.

5.3.4 Air being sampled should not be passed through any hose or tubing before entering the charcoal tube.

5.3.5 A sample size of 20 liters is recommended. Sample at a flow rate of approximately 0.2 liters per minute. The flow rate should be known with an accuracy of at least ± 5 percent.

5.3.6 The temperature and pressure of the atmosphere being sampled should be recorded.

5.3.7 The charcoal tubes should be capped with the supplied plastic caps immediately after sampling. Rubber caps should not be used.

5.3.8 Submit at least one blank tube (a charcoal tube subjected to the same handling procedures, without having any air drawn through it) with each set of samples.

5.3.9 Take necessary shipping and packing precautions to minimize breakage of samples.

5.4 Analysis of samples

5.4.1 Preparation of samples In preparation for analysis, each charcoal tube is scored with a file in front of the first section of charcoal and broken open. The glass wool is removed and discarded. The charcoal in the first (larger) section is transferred to a 2-ml vial. The separating section of foam is removed and discarded; the section is transferred to another capped vial. These two sections are analyzed separately.

5.4.2 Desorption of samples Prior to analysis, 1.0 ml of methanol is pipetted into each sample container. Desorption should be done for 30 minutes in an ultrasonic bath. The sample vials are recapped as soon as the solvent is added.

5.4.3 GC conditions. The typical operating conditions for the gas chromatograph are:

1. 30 ml/min (60 psig) helium carrier gas flow.
2. 3.0 ml/min (30 psig) hydrogen gas flow to detector.
3. 50 ml/min (60 psig) air flow to detector.
4. 200 °C injector temperature.
5. 200 °C dejector temperature.
6. 100 °C column temperature.

5.4.4 Injection. Solvent flush technique or equivalent.

5.4.5 Measurement of area. The area of the sample peak is measured by an electronic integrator or some other suitable form of area measurement, and preliminary results are read from a standard curve prepared as discussed below.

5.5 Determination of desorption efficiency

5.5.1 Importance of determination. The desorption efficiency of a particular compound can vary from one laboratory to another and also from one batch of charcoal to another. Thus, it is necessary to determine, at least once, the percentage of the specific compound that is removed in the desorption process, provided the same batch of charcoal is used.

5.5.2 Procedure for determining desorption efficiency. The reference portion of the charcoal tube is removed. To the remaining portion, amounts representing 0.5X, 1X, and 2X (X represents TLV) based on a 20 l air sample are injected onto several tubes at each level. Dilutions of acrylonitrile with methanol are made to allow injection of measurable quantities. These tubes are then allowed to equilibrate at least overnight. Following equilibration they are analyzed following the same procedure as the samples A curve of the desorption efficiency amt recovered/amt added is plotted versus amount of analyte found. This curve is used to correct for adsorption losses.

6. Calibration and standards

A series of standards, varying in concentration over the range of interest, is prepared and analyzed under the same GC conditions and during the same time period as the unknown samples. Curves are prepared by plotting concentration versus peak area.

Note: Since no internal standard is used in the method, standard solutions must be analyzed at the same time that the sample analysis is done. This will minimize the effect of known day-to-day variations and variations during the same day of the NPD response. Multiple injections are necessary.

7. Calculations

Read the weight, corresponding to each peak area from the standard curve, correct for the blank, correct for the desorption efficiency, and make necessary air volume corrections.

8. Reference. NIOSH Method S–156

[43 FR 45809, Oct. 3, 1978, as amended at 45 FR 35283, May 23, 1980; 54 FR 24334, June 7, 1989; 58 FR 35310, June 30, 1993; 61 FR 5508, Feb. 13, 1996; 63 FR 1291, Jan. 8, 1998; 63 FR 20099, Apr. 23, 1998; 70 FR 1142, Jan. 5, 2005; 71 FR 16672, 16673, Apr. 3, 2006; 71 FR 50190, Aug. 24, 2006; 73 FR 75586, Dec. 12, 2008; 76 FR 33609, June 8, 2011]

§1910.1047 [OI] Ethylene Oxide

(a) Scope and application

(a)(1) This Section applies to all occupational exposures to ethylene oxide (EtO), Chemical Abstracts Service Registry No. 75–21–8, except as provided in paragraph (a)(2) of this Section.

(a)(2) [OI] This Section does not apply to the processing, use, or handling of products containing EtO where objective data are reasonably relied upon that demonstrate that the product is not capable of releasing EtO in airborne concentrations at or above the action level, and may not reasonably be foreseen to release EtO in excess of the excursion limit, under the expected conditions of processing, use, or handling that will cause the greatest possible release.

(a)(3) Where products containing EtO are exempted under paragraph (a)(2) of this Section, the employer shall maintain records of the objective data supporting that exemption and the basis for the employer's reliance on the data, as provided in paragraph (k)(1) of this Section.

(b) **Definitions:** For the purpose of this Section, the following definitions shall apply:

Action level means a concentration of airborne EtO of 0.5 ppm calculated as an eight (8)-hour time-weighted average.

Assistant Secretary means the Assistant Secretary of Labor for Occupational Safety and Health, U.S. Department of Labor, or designee.

Authorized person means any person specifically authorized by the employer whose duties require the person to enter a regulated area, or any person entering such an area as a designated representative of employees for the purpose of exercising the right to observe monitoring and measuring procedures under paragraph (l) of this Section, or any other person authorized by the Act or regulations issued under the Act.

Director means the Director of the National Institute for Occupational Safety and Health, U.S. Department of Health and Human Services, or designee.

Emergency means any occurrence such as, but not limited to, equipment failure, rupture of containers, or failure of control equipment that is likely to or does result in an unexpected significant release of EtO.

Employee exposure means exposure to airborne EtO which would occur if the employee were not using respiratory protective equipment.

Ethylene oxide or **EtO** means the three-membered ring organic compound with chemical formula C_2H_4O.

(c) Permissible exposure limits

(c)(1) **8-hour time weighted average (TWA)** The employer shall ensure that no employee is exposed to an airborne concentration of EtO in excess of one (1) part EtO per million parts of air (1 ppm) as an 8-hour time-weighted average (8-hour TWA).

(c)(2) **Excursion limit** The employer shall ensure that no employee is exposed to an airborne concentration of EtO in excess of 5 parts of EtO per million parts of air (5 ppm) as averaged over a sampling period of fifteen (15) minutes.

(d) Exposure monitoring

(d)(1) General

(d)(1)(i) Determinations of employee exposure shall be made from breathing zone air samples that are representative of the 8-hour TWA and 15-minute short-term exposures of each employee.

(d)(1)(ii) Representative 8-hour TWA employee exposure shall be determined on the basis of one or more samples representing full-shift exposure for each shift for each job classification in each work area. Representative 15-minute short-term employee exposures shall be determined on the basis of one or more samples representing 15-minute exposures associated with operations that are most likely to produce exposures above the excursion limit for each shift for each job classification in each work area.

(d)(1)(iii) Where the employer can document that exposure levels are equivalent for similar operations in different work shifts, the employer need only determine representative employee exposure for that operation during one shift.

(d)(2) Initial monitoring

(d)(2)(i) Each employer who has a workplace or work operation covered by this Standard, except as provided for in paragraph (a)(2) or (d)(2)(ii) of this Section, shall perform initial monitoring to determine accurately the airborne concentrations of EtO to which employees may be exposed.

(d)(2)(ii) Where the employer has monitored after June 15, 1983 and the monitoring satisfies all other requirements of this Section, the employer may rely on such earlier monitoring results to satisfy the requirements of paragraph (d)(2)(i) of this Section.

(d)(2)(iii) Where the employer has previously monitored for the excursion limit and the monitoring satisfies all other requirements of this Sections, the employer may rely on such earlier monitoring results to satisfy the requirements of paragraph (d)(2)(i) of this Section.

(d)(3) Monitoring frequency (periodic monitoring)

(d)(3)(i) If the monitoring required by paragraph (d)(2) of this Section reveals employee exposure at or above the action level but at or below the 8-hour TWA, the employer shall repeat such monitoring for each such employee at least every 6 months.

(d)(3)(ii) If the monitoring required by paragraph (d)(2)(i) of this Section reveals employee exposure above the 8-hour TWA, the employer shall repeat such monitoring for each such employee at least every 3 months.

(d)(3)(iii) The employer may alter the monitoring schedule from quarterly to semiannually for any employee for whom two consecutive measurements taken at least 7 days apart indicate that the employee's exposure has decreased to or below the 8-hour TWA.

(d)(3)(iv) If the monitoring required by paragraph (d)(2)(i) of this Section reveals employee exposure above the 15 minute excursion limit, the employer shall repeat such monitoring for each such employee at least every 3 months, and more often as necessary to evaluate exposure the employee's short-term exposures.

(d)(4) Termination of monitoring

(d)(4)(i) If the initial monitoring required by paragraph (d)(2)(i) of this Section reveals employee exposure to be below the action level, the employer may discontinue TWA monitoring for those employees whose exposures are represented by the initial monitoring.

(d)(4)(ii) If the periodic monitoring required by paragraph (d)(3) of this Section reveals that employee exposures, as indicated by at least two consecutive measurements taken at least 7 days apart, are below the action level, the employer may discontinue TWA monitoring for those employees whose exposures are represented by such monitoring.

(d)(4)(iii) If the initial monitoring required by paragraph (d)(2)(1) of this Section reveals employee exposure to be at or below the excursion limit, the employer may discontinue excursion limit monitoring for those employees whose exposures are represented by the initial monitoring.

(d)(4)(iv) If the periodic monitoring required by paragraph (d)(3) of this Section reveals that employee exposures, as indicated by at least two consecutive measurements taken at least 7 days apart, are at or below the excursion limit, the employer may discontinue excursion limit monitoring for those employees whose exposures are represented by such monitoring.

(d)(5) **Additional monitoring** Notwithstanding the provisions of paragraph (d)(4) of this Section, the employer shall institute the exposure monitoring required under paragraphs (d)(2)(i) and (d)(3) of this Section whenever there has been a change in the production, process, control equipment, personnel or work practices that may result in new or additional exposures to EtO or when the employer has any reason to suspect that a change may result in new or additional exposures.

(d)(6) **Accuracy of monitoring**

(d)(6)(i) Monitoring shall be accurate, to a confidence level of 95 percent, to within plus or minus 25 percent for airborne concentrations of EtO at the 1 ppm TWA and to within plus or minus 35 percent for airborne concentrations of EtO at the action level of 0.5 ppm.

(d)(6)(ii) Monitoring shall be accurate, to a confidence level of 95 percent, to within plus or minus 35 percent for airborne concentrations of EtO at the excursion limit.

(d)(7) **Employee notification of monitoring results**

(d)(7)(i) The employer must, within 15 working days after the receipt of the results of any monitoring performed under this Section, notify each affected employee of these results either individually in writing or by posting the results in an appropriate location that is accessible to employees.

(d)(7)(ii) The written notification required by paragraph (d)(7)(i) of this Section shall contain the corrective action being taken by the employer to reduce employee exposure to or below the TWA and/or excursion limit, wherever monitoring results indicated that the TWA and/or excursion limit has been exceeded.

(e) **Regulated areas**

(e)(1) The employer shall establish a regulated area wherever occupational exposure to airborne concentrations of EtO may exceed the TWA or wherever the EtO concentration exceeds or can reasonably be expected to exceed the excursion limit.

(e)(2) Access to regulated areas shall be limited to authorized persons.

(d)(3) Regulated areas shall be demarcated in any manner that minimizes the number of employees within the regulated area.

(f) **Methods of compliance**

(f)(1) **Engineering controls and work practices**

(f)(1)(i) The employer shall institute engineering controls and work practices to reduce and maintain employee exposure to or below the TWA and to or below the excursion limit, except to the extent that such controls are not feasible.

(f)(1)(ii) Wherever the feasible engineering controls and work practices that can be instituted are not sufficient to reduce employee exposure to or below the TWA and to or below the excursion limit, the employer shall use them to reduce employee exposure to the lowest levels achievable by these controls and shall supplement them by the use of respiratory protection that complies with the requirements of paragraph (g) of this Section.

(f)(1)(iii) Engineering controls are generally infeasible for the following operations: collection of quality assurance sampling from sterilized materials removal of biological indicators from sterilized materials: loading and unloading of tank cars; changing of ethylene oxide tanks on sterilizers; and vessel cleaning. For these operations, engineering controls are required only where the Assistant Secretary demonstrates that such controls are feasible.

(f)(2) **Compliance program**

(f)(2)(i) Where the TWA or excursion limit is exceeded, the employer shall establish and implement a written program to reduce exposure to or below the TWA and to or below the excursion limit by means of engineering and work practice controls, as required by paragraph (f)(1) of this Section, and by the use of respiratory protection where required or permitted under this Section.

(f)(2)(ii) The compliance program shall include a schedule for periodic leak detection surveys and a written plan for emergency situations, as specified in paragraph (h)(i) of this Section.

(f)(2)(iii) Written plans for a program required in paragraph (f)(2) shall be developed and furnished upon request for examination and copying to the Assistant Secretary, the Director, affected employees and designated employee representatives. Such plans shall be reviewed at least every 12 months, and shall be updated as necessary to reflect significant changes in the status of the employer's compliance program.

(f)(2)(iv) The employer shall not implement a schedule of employee rotation as a means of compliance with the TWA or excursion limit.

(g) **Respiratory protection and personal protective equipment**

(g)(1) **General** For employees who use respirators required by this Section, the employer must provide each employee an appropriate respirator that complies with the requirements of this paragraph. Respirators must be used during:

(g)(1)(i) Periods necessary to install or implement feasible engineering and work-practice controls;

(g)(1)(ii) Work operations, such as maintenance and repair activities and vessel cleaning, for which engineering and work-practice controls are not feasible;

(g)(1)(iii) Work operations for which feasible engineering and work-practice controls are not yet sufficient to reduce employee exposure to or below the TWA;

(g)(1)(iv) Emergencies.

(g)(2) **Respirator program** The employer must implement a respiratory protection program in accordance with §1910.134(b) through (d) (except (d)(i)(iii)), and (f) through (m), which covers each employee required by this Section to use a respirator.

(g)(3) **Respirator selection** Employers must:

(g)(3)(i) Select, and provide to employees, the appropriate respirators specified in paragraph (d)(3)(i)(A) of 29 CFR §1910.134; however, employers must not select or use half masks of any type because EtO may cause eye irritation or injury;

(g)(3)(ii) Equip each air-purifying, full facepiece respirator with a front- or back-mounted canister approved for protection against ethylene oxide;

(g)(3)(iii) For escape, provide employees with any respirator permitted for use under paragraphs (g)(3)(i) and (ii) of this Standard.

(g)(4) **Protective clothing and equipment** When employees could have eye or skin contact with EtO or EtO solutions, the employer must select and provide, at no cost to the employee, appropriate protective clothing or other equipment in accordance with 29 CFR §1910.132 and §1910.133 to protect any area of the employee's body that may come in contact with the EtO or EtO solution, and must ensure that the employee wears the protective clothing and equipment provided.

(h) **Emergency situations**

(h)(1) **Written plan**

(h)(1)(i) A written plan for emergency situations shall be developed for each workplace where there is a possibility of an emergency. Appropriate portions of the plan shall be implemented in the event of an emergency.

(h)(1)(ii) The plan shall specifically provide that employees engaged in correcting emergency conditions shall be equipped with respiratory protection as required by paragraph (g) of this Section until the emergency is abated.

(h)(1)(iii) The plan shall include the elements prescribed in 29 CFR §1910.38 and 29 CFR §1910.39, "Emergency action plans" and "Fire prevention plans," respectively.

(h)(2) **Alerting employees** Where there is the possibility of employee exposure to EtO due to an emergency, means shall be developed to alert potentially affected employees of such occurrences promptly. Affected employees shall be immediately evacuated from the area in the event that an emergency occurs.

(i) **Medical Surveillance**

(i)(1) **General**

(i)(1)(i) **Employees covered**

(i)(1)(i)(A) The employer shall institute a medical surveillance program for all employees who are or may be exposed to EtO at or above the action level, without regard to the use of respirators, for at least 30 days a year.

(i)(1)(i)(B) The employer shall make available medical examinations and consultations to all employees who have been exposed to EtO in an emergency situation.

(i)(1)(ii) **Examination by a physician** The employer shall ensure that all medical examinations and procedures are performed by or under the supervision of a licensed physician, and are provided without cost to the employee, without loss of pay, and at a reasonable time and place.

(i)(2) **Medical examinations and consultations**

(i)(2)(i) **Frequency** The employer shall make available medical examinations and consultations to each employee covered under paragraph (i)(1)(i) of this Section on the following schedules:

(i)(2)(i)(A) Prior to assignment of the employee to an area where exposure may be at or above the action level for at least 30 days a year;

(i)(2)(i)(B) At least annually each employee exposed at or above the action level for at least 30 days in the past year;

(i)(2)(i)(C) At termination of employment or reassignment to an area where exposure to EtO is not at or above the action level for at least 30 days a year;

(i)(2)(i)(D) As medically appropriate for any employee exposed during an emergency;

(i)(2)(i)(E) As soon as possible, upon notification by an employee either (1) that the employee has developed signs or symptoms indicating possible overexposure to EtO, or (2) that the employee desires medical advice concerning the effects of current or past exposure to EtO on the employee's ability to produce a healthy child;

(i)(2)(i)(F) If the examining physician determines that any of the examinations should be provided more frequently than specified, the employer shall provide such examinations to affected employees at the frequencies recommended by the physician.

(i)(2)(ii) Content

(i)(2)(ii)(A) Medical examinations made available pursuant to paragraphs (i)(2)(i)(A)–(D) of this Section shall include:

(i)(2)(ii)(A)(1) A medical and work history with special emphasis directed to symptoms related to the pulmonary, hematologic, neurologic, and reproductive systems and to the eyes and skin;

(i)(2)(ii)(A)(2) A physical examination with particular emphasis given to the pulmonary, hematologic, neurologic, and reproductive systems and to the eyes and skin;

(i)(2)(ii)(A)(3) A complete blood count to include at least a white cell count (including differential cell count), red cell count, hematocrit, and hemoglobin;

(i)(2)(ii)(A)(4) Any laboratory or other test which the examining physician deems necessary by sound medical practice.

(i)(2)(ii)(B) The content of medical examinations or consultation made available pursuant to paragraph (i)(2)(i)(E) of this Section shall be determined by the examining physician, and shall include pregnancy testing or laboratory evaluation of fertility, if requested by the employee and deemed appropriate by the physician.

(i)(3) Information provided to the physician The employer shall provide the following information to the examining physician:

(i)(3)(i) A copy of this Standard and Appendices A, B, and C;

(i)(3)(ii) A description of the affected employee's duties as they relate to the employee's exposure;

(i)(3)(iii) The employee's representative exposure level or anticipated exposure level;

(i)(3)(iv) A description of any personal protective and respiratory equipment used or to be used;

(i)(3)(v) Information from previous medical examinations of the affected employee that is not otherwise available to the examining physician.

(i)(4) Physician's written opinion

(i)(4)(i) The employer shall obtain a written opinion from the examining physician. This written opinion shall contain the results of the medical examination and shall include:

(i)(4)(i)(A) The physician's opinion as to whether the employee has any detected medical conditions that would place the employee at an increased risk of material health impairment from exposure to EtO;

(i)(4)(i)(B) Any recommended limitations on the employee or upon the use of personal protective equipment such as clothing or respirators; and

(i)(4)(i)(C) A statement that the employee has been informed by the physician of the results of the medical examination and of any medical conditions resulting from EtO exposure that require further explanation or treatment.

(i)(4)(ii) The employer shall instruct the physician not to reveal in the written opinion given to the employer specific findings or diagnoses unrelated to occupational exposure to EtO.

(i)(4)(iii) The employer shall provide a copy of the physician's written opinion to the affected employee within 15 days from its receipt.

(j) Communication of hazards

(j)(1) Hazard communication—general

(j)(1)(i) Chemical manufacturers, importers, distributors and employers shall comply with all requirements of the Hazard Communication Standard (HCS) (§1910.1200) for EtO.

(j)(1)(ii) In classifying the hazards of EtO at least the following hazards are to be addressed: Cancer; reproductive effects; mutagenicity; central nervous system; skin sensitization; skin, eye and respiratory tract irritation; acute toxicity effects; and flammability.

(j)(1)(iii) Employers shall include EtO in the hazard communication program established to comply with the HCS (§1910.1200). Employers shall ensure that each employee has access to labels on containers of EtO and to safety data sheets, and is trained in accordance with the requirements of HCS and paragraph (j)(3) of this Section.

(j)(2) Signs and labels

(j)(2)(i) Signs

(j)(2)(i)(A) The employer shall post and maintain legible signs demarcating regulated areas and entrances or access ways to regulated areas that bear the following legend:

DANGER
ETHYLENE OXIDE
MAY CAUSE CANCER
MAY DAMAGE FERTILITY OR THE UNBORN CHILD
RESPIRATORY PROTECTION AND PROTECTIVE CLOTHING MAY BE REQUIRED IN THIS AREA
AUTHORIZED PERSONNEL ONLY

(j)(2)(i)(B) Prior to June 1, 2016, employers may use the following legend in lieu of that specified in paragraph (j)(2)(i)(A) of this Section:

DANGER
ETHYLENE OXIDE
CANCER HAZARD AND REPRODUCTIVE HAZARD
AUTHORIZED PERSONNEL ONLY
RESPIRATORS AND PROTECTIVE CLOTHING MAY BE REQUIRED TO BE WORN IN THIS AREA

(j)(2)(ii) Labels

(j)(2)(ii)(A) The employer shall ensure that labels are affixed to all containers of EtO whose contents are capable of causing employee exposure at or above the action level or whose contents may reasonably be foreseen to cause employee exposure above the excursion limit, and that the labels remain affixed when the containers of EtO leave the workplace. For the purposes of this paragraph (j)(2)(ii), reaction vessels, storage tanks, and pipes or piping systems are not considered to be containers.

(j)(2)(ii)(B) Prior to June 1, 2015, employers may include the following information on containers of EtO in lieu of the labeling requirements in paragraph (j)(1)(i) of this Section:

(j)(2)(ii)(B)(1)

DANGER
CONTAINS ETHYLENE OXIDE
CANCER HAZARD AND REPRODUCTIVE HAZARD;

(j)(2)(ii)(B)(2) A warning statement against breathing airborne concentrations of EtO.

(j)(2)(ii)(C) The labeling requirements under this Section do not apply where EtO is used as a pesticide, as such term is defined in the Federal Insecticide, Fungicide, and Rodenticide Act (7 U.S.C. 136 et seq.), when it is labeled pursuant to that Act and regulations issued under that Act by the Environmental Protection Agency.

(j)(3) Information and training

(j)(3)(i) The employer shall provide employees who are potentially exposed to EtO at or above the action level or above the excursion limit with information and training on EtO at the time of initial assignment and at least annually thereafter.

(j)(3)(ii) Employees shall be informed of the following:

(j)(3)(ii)(A) The requirements of this Section with an explanation of its contents, including Appendices A and B;

(j)(3)(ii)(B) Any operations in their work area where EtO is present;

(j)(3)(ii)(C) The location and availability of the written EtO final rule; and

(j)(3)(ii)(D) The medical surveillance program required by paragraph (i) of this Section with an explanation of the information in Appendix C.

(j)(3)(iii) Employee training shall include at least:

(j)(3)(iii)(A) Methods and observations that may be used to detect the presence or release of EtO in the work area (such as monitoring conducted by the employer, continuous monitoring devices, etc.);

(j)(3)(iii)(B) The physical and health hazards of EtO;

(j)(3)(iii)(C) The measures employees can take to protect themselves from hazards associated with EtO exposure, including specific procedures the employer has implemented to protect employees from exposure to EtO, such as work practices, emergency procedures, and personal protective equipment to be used; and

(j)(3)(iii)(D) The details of the hazard communication program developed by the employer, including an explanation of the labeling system and how employees can obtain and use the appropriate hazard information.

(k) Recordkeeping

(k)(1) Objective data for exempted operations

(k)(1)(i) Where the processing, use, or handling of products made from or containing EtO are exempted from other requirements of this Section under paragraph (a)(2) of this Section, or where objective data have been relied on in lieu of initial monitoring under paragraph (d)(2)(ii) of this Section, the employer shall establish and maintain an accurate record of objective data reasonably relied upon in support of the exemption.

(k)(1)(ii) This record shall include at least the following information:

(k)(1)(ii)(A) The product qualifying for exemption;

(k)(1)(ii)(B) The source of the objective data;

(k)(1)(ii)(C) The testing protocol, results of testing, and/or analysis of the material for the release of EtO;

(k)(1)(ii)(D) A description of the operation exempted and how the data support the exemption; and (k)(1)(ii)(E) Other data relevant to the operations, materials, processing, or employee exposures covered by the exemption.

(k)(1)(iii) The employer shall maintain this record for the duration of the employer's reliance upon such objective data.

(k)(2) Exposure measurements

(k)(2)(i) The employer shall keep an accurate record of all measurements taken to monitor employee exposure to EtO as prescribed in paragraph (d) of this Section.

(k)(2)(ii) This record shall include at least the following information:

(k)(2)(ii)(A) The date of measurement;

(k)(2)(ii)(B) The operation involving exposure to EtO which is being monitored;

(k)(2)(ii)(C) Sampling and analytical methods used and evidence of their accuracy;

(k)(2)(ii)(D) Number, duration, and results of samples taken;

(k)(2)(ii)(E) Type of protective devices worn, if any; and

(k)(2)(ii)(F) Name, social security number and exposure of the employees whose exposures are represented.

(k)(2)(iii) The employer shall maintain this record for at least thirty (30) years, in accordance with 29 CFR §1910.1020.

(k)(3) Medical surveillance

(k)(3)(i) The employer shall establish and maintain an accurate record for each employee subject to medical surveillance by paragraph (i)(1)(i) of this Section, in accordance with 29 CFR §1910.1020.

(k)(3)(ii) The record shall include at least the following information:

(k)(3)(ii)(A) The name and social security number of the employee;

(k)(3)(ii)(B) Physicians' written opinions;

(k)(3)(ii)(C) Any employee medical complaints related to exposure to EtO; and

(k)(3)(ii)(D) A copy of the information provided to the physician as required by paragraph (i)(3) of this Section.

(k)(3)(iii) The employer shall ensure that this record is maintained for the duration of employment plus thirty (30) years, in accordance with 29 CFR §1910.1020.

(k)(4) Availability

(k)(4)(i) The employer, upon written request, shall make all records required to be maintained by this Section available to the Assistant Secretary and the Director for examination and copying.

(k)(4)(ii) The employer, upon request, shall make any exemption and exposure records required by paragraphs (k)(1) and (2) of this Section available for examination and copying to affected employees, former employees, designated representatives and the Assistant Secretary, in accordance with 29 CFR §1910.1020 (a) through (e) and (g) through (i).

(k)(4)(iii) The employer, upon request, shall make employee medical records required by paragraph (k)(3) of this Section available for examination and copying to the subject employee, anyone having the specific written consent of the subject employee, and the Assistant Secretary, in accordance with 29 CFR §1910.1020.

(k)(5) Transfer of records The employer shall comply with the requirements concerning transfer of records set forth in 29 CFR §1910.1020(h).

(l) Observation of monitoring

(l)(1) Employee observation The employer shall provide affected employees or their designated representatives an opportunity to observe any monitoring of employee exposure to EtO conducted in accordance with paragraph (d) of this Section.

(l)(2) Observation procedures When observation of the monitoring of employee exposure to EtO requires entry into an area where the use of protective clothing or equipment is required, the observer shall be provided with and be required to use such clothing and equipment and shall comply with all other applicable safety and health procedures.

(m) [Reserved]

(n) Appendices The information contained in the Appendices is not intended by itself to create any additional obligations not otherwise imposed or to detract from any existing obligation.

§1910.1047 Appendix A Substance safety data sheet for Ethylene Oxide (Nonmandatory)

I. Substance Identification

A. Substance: Ethylene oxide (C_2H_4O).

B. Synonyms: dihydrooxirene, dimethylene oxide, EO, 1,2-epoxyethane, EtO, ETO, oxacyclopropane, oxane, oxidoethane, alpha/beta-oxidoethane, oxiran, oxirane.

C. Ethylene oxide can be found as a liquid or vapor.

D. EtO is used in the manufacture of ethylene glycol, surfactants, ethanolamines, glycol ethers, and other organic chemicals. EtO is also used as a sterilant and fumigant.

E. Appearance and odor: Colorless liquid below 10.7 °C (51.3 °F) or colorless gas with ether-like odor detected at approximately 700 parts EtO per million parts of air (700 ppm).

F. Permissible Exposure: Exposure may not exceed 1 part EtO per million parts of air averaged over the 8-hour workday.

II. Health Hazard Data

A. Ethylene oxide can cause bodily harm if you inhale the vapor, if it comes into contact with your eyes or skin, or if you swallow it.

B. Effects of overexposure:

1. Ethylene oxide in liquid form can cause eye irritation and injury to the cornea, frostbite, and severe irritation and blistering of the skin upon prolonged or confined contact. Ingestion of EtO can cause gastric irritation and liver injury. Acute effects from inhalation of EtO vapors include respiratory irritation and lung injury, headache, nausea, vomiting, diarrhea, shortness of breath, and cyaonosis (blue or purple coloring of skin). Exposure has also been associated with the occurrence of cancer, reproductive effects, mutagenic changes, neurotoxicity, and sensitization.
2. EtO has been shown to cause cancer in laboratory animals and has been associated with higher incidences of cancer in humans. Adverse reproductive effects and chromosome damage may also occur from EtO exposure.
   a. Reporting signs and symptoms: You should inform your employer if you develop any signs or symptoms and suspect that they are caused by exposure to EtO.

III Emergency First Aid Procedures

A, Eye exposure: If EtO gets into your eyes, wash your eyes immediately with large amounts of water, lifting the lower and upper eyelids. Get medical attention immediately. Contact lenses should not be worn when working with this chemical.

B. Skin exposure: If EtO gets on your skin, immediately wash the contaminated skin with water. If EtO soaks through your clothing, especially your shoes, remove the clothing immediately and wash the skin with water using an emergency deluge shower. Get medical attention immediately. Thoroughly wash contaminated clothing before reusing. Contaminated leather shoes or other leather articles should not be reused and should be discarded.

C. Inhalation: If large amounts of EtO are inhaled, the exposed person must be moved to fresh air at once. If breathing has stopped, perform cardiopulmonary resuscitation. Keep the affected person warm and at rest. Get medical attention immediately.

D. Swallowing: When EtO has been swallowed, give the person large quantities of water immediately. After the water has been swallowed, try to get the person to vomit by having him or her touch the back of the throat with his or her finger. Do not make an unconscious person vomit. Get medical attention immediately.

E. Rescue: Move the affected person from the hazardous exposure. If the exposed person has been overcome, attempt rescue only after notifying at least one other person of the emergency and putting into effect established emergency procedures. Do not become a casualty yourself. Understand your emergency rescue procedures and know the location of the emergency equipment before the need arises.

IV. Respirators and Protective Clothing

A. Respirators You may be required to wear a respirator for nonroutine activities, in emergencies, while your employer is in the process of reducing EtO exposures through engineering controls, and in areas where engineering controls are not feasible. As of the effective date of this Standard, only air-supplied, positive-pressure, full-facepiece respirators are approved for protection against EtO. If air-purifying respirators are worn in the future, they must have a label issued by the National Institute for Occupational Safety and Health under the provisions of 42 CFR Part §84 stating that the respirators have been approved for use with ethylene oxide. For effective protection, respirators must fit your face and head snugly. Respirators must not be loosened or removed in work situations where their use is required.

EtO does not have a detectable odor except at levels well above the permissible exposure limits. If you can smell EtO while wearing a respirator, proceed immediately to fresh air. If you experience difficulty breathing while wearing a respirator, tell your employer.

B. Protective clothing: You may be required to wear impermeable clothing, gloves, a face shield, or other appropriate protective clothing to prevent skin contact with liquid EtO or EtO-containing solutions. Where protective clothing is required, your employer must provide clean garments to you as necessary to assure that the clothing protects you adequately.

Replace or repair protective clothing that has become torn or otherwise damaged.

EtO must never be allowed to remain on the skin. Clothing and shoes which are not impermeable to EtO should not be allowed to become contaminated with EtO, and if they do, the clothing should be promptly removed and decontaminated. Contaminated leather shoes should be discarded. Once EtO penetrates shoes or other leather articles, they should not be worn again.

C. Eye protection: You must wear splashproof safety goggles in areas where liquid EtO or EtO-containing solutions may contact your eyes. In addition, contact lenses should not be worn in areas where eye contact with EtO can occur.

V. Precautions for Safe Use, Handling, and Storage

A. EtO is a flammable liquid, and its vapors can easily form explosive mixtures in air.

B. EtO must be stored in tightly closed containers in a cool, well-ventilated area, away from heat, sparks, flames, strong oxidizers, alkalines, and acids, strong bases, acetylide-forming metals such as cooper, silver, mercury and their alloys.

C. Sources of ignition such as smoking material, open flames and some electrical devices are prohibited wherever EtO is handled, used, or stored in a manner that could create a potential fire or explosion hazard.

D. You should use non-sparking tools when opening or closing metal containers of EtO, and containers must be bonded and grounded in the rare instances in which liquid EtO is poured or transferred.

E. Impermeable clothing wet with liquid EtO or EtO-containing solutions may be easily ignited. If your are wearing impermeable clothing and are splashed with liquid EtO or EtO-containing solution, you should immediately remove the clothing while under an emergency deluge shower.

F. If your skin comes into contact with liquid EtO or EtO-containing solutions, you should immediately remove the EtO using an emergency deluge shower.

G. You should not keep food, beverages, or smoking materials in regulated areas where employee exposures are above the permissible exposure limits.

H. Fire extinguishers and emergency deluge showers for quick drenching should be readily available, and you should know where they are and how to operate them.

I. Ask your supervisor where EtO is used in your work area and for any additional plant safety and health rules.

VI. Access to Information

A. Each year, your employer is required to inform you of the information contained in this Standard and Appendices for EtO. In addition, your employer must instruct you in the proper work practices for using EtO emergency procedures, and the correct use of protective equipment.

B. Your employer is required to determine whether you are being exposed to EtO. You or your representative has the right to observe employee measurements and to record the results obtained. Your employer is required to inform you of your exposure. If your employer determine that you are being overexposed, he or she is required to inform you of the actions which are being taken to reduce your exposure to within permissible exposure limits.

C. Your employer is required to keep records of your exposures and medical examinations. These exposure records must be kept by the employer for at least thirty (30) years. Medical records must be kept for the period of your employment plus thirty (30) years.

D. Your employer is required to release your exposure and medical records to your physician or designated representative upon your written request.

VII. Sterilant Use of Eto in Hospitals and Health Care Facilities

This Section of Appendix A, for informational purposes, sets forth EPA's recommendations for modifications in workplace design and practice in hospitals and health care facilities for which the Environmental Protection Agency has registered EtO for uses as a sterilant or fumigant under the Federal Insecticide, Funigicide, and Rodenticide Act, 7 U.S.C. 136 et seq. These new recommendations, published in the Federal Register by EPA at 49 FR 15268, as modified in today's Register, are intended to help reduce the exposure of hospital and health care workers to EtO to 1 ppm. EPA's recommended workplace design and workplace practice are as follows:

1. Workplace Design

a. Installation of gas line hand valves. Hand valves must be installed on the gas supply line at the connection to the supply cylinders to minimize leakage during cylinder change.

b. Installation of capture boxes. Sterilizer operations result in a gas/water discharge at the completion of the process. This discharge is routinely piped to a floor drain which is generally located in an equipment or an adjacent room. When the floor drain is not in the same room as the sterilizer and workers are not normally present, all that is necessary is that the room be well ventilated.

The installation of a "capture box" will be required for those work place layouts where the floor drain is located in the same room as the sterilizer or in a room where workers are normally present. A "capture box" is a piece of equipment that totally encloses the floor drain where the discharge from the sterilizer is pumped. The "capture box" is to be vented directly to a non-recirculating or dedicated ventilation system. Sufficient air intake should be allowed at the bottom of the box to handle the volume of air that is ventilated from the top of the box. The "capture box" can be made of metal, plastic, wood or other equivalent material. The box is intended to reduce levels of EtO discharged into the work room atmosphere. The use of a "capture box" is not required if: (1) The vacuum pump discharge floor drain is located in a well ventilated equipment or other room where workers are not normally present or (2) the water sealed vacuum pump discharges directly to a closed sealed sewer line (check local plumbing codes).

If it is impractical to install a vented "capture box" and a well ventilated equipment or other room is not feasible, a box that can be sealed over the floor drain may be used if: (1) The floor drain is located in a room where workers are not normally present and EtO cannot leak into an occupied area, and (2) the sterilizer in use is less than 12 cubic feet in capacity (check local plumbing codes).

c. Ventilation of aeration units

i. Existing aeration units. Existing units must be vented to a non-recirculating or dedicated system or vented to an equipment or other room where workers are not normally present and which is well ventilated. Aerator units must be positioned as close as possible to the sterilizer to minimize the exposure from the off-gassing of sterilized items.

ii. Installation of new aerator units (where none exist). New aerator units must be vented as described above for existing aerators. Aerators must be in place by July 1, 1986.

d. Ventilation during cylinder change. Workers may be exposed to short but relatively high levels of EtO during the change of gas cylinders. To reduce exposure from this route, users must select one of three alternatives designed to draw off gas that may be released when the line from the sterilizer to the cylinder is disconnected:

i. Location of cylinders in a well ventilated equipment room or other room where workers are not normally present.

ii. Installation of a flexible hose (at least 4&inch; in diameter) to a non-recirculating or dedicated ventilation system and located in the area of cylinder change in such a way that the hose can be positioned at the point where the sterilizer gas line is disconnected from the cylinder.

iii. Installation of a hood that is part of a non-recirculating or dedicated system and positioned no more than one foot above the point where the change of cylinders takes place.

e. Ventilation of sterilizer door area. One of the major sources of exposure to EtO occurs when the sterilizer door is opened following the completion of the sterilization process. In order to reduce this avenue of exposure, a hood or metal canopy closed on each end must be installed over the sterilizer door. The hood or metal canopy must be connected to a non-recirculating or dedicated ventilation system or one that exhausts gases to a well ventilated equipment or other room where workers are not normally present. A hood or canopy over the sterilizer door is required for use even with those sterilizers that have a purge cycle and must be in place by July 1, 1986.

f. Ventilation of sterilizer relief valve. Sterilizers are typically equipped with a safety relief device to release gas in case of increased pressure in the sterilizer. Generally, such relief devices are used on pressure vessels. Although these pressure relief devices are rarely opened for hospital and health care sterilizers, it is suggested that they be designed to exhaust vapor from the sterilizer by one of the following methods:

i. Through a pipe connected to the outlet of the relief valve ventilated directly outdoors at a point high enough to be away from passers by, and not near any windows that open, or near any air conditioning or ventilation air intakes;

ii. Through a connection to an existing or new non-recirculating or dedicated ventilation system;

iii. Through a connection to a well ventilated equipment or other room where workers are not normally present.

g. Ventilation systems Each hospital and health care facility affected by this notice that uses EtO for the sterilization of equipment and supplies must have a ventilation system which enables compliance with the requirements of Section (b) through (f) in the manner described in these Sections and within the timeframes allowed. Thus, each affected hospital and health care facility must have or install a non-recirculating or dedicated ventilation equipment or other room where workers are not normally present in which to vent EtO.

h. Installation of alarm systems An audible and visual indicator alarm system must be installed to alert personnel of ventilation system failures, i.e., when the ventilation fan motor is not working.

2. Workplace Practices

All the workplace practices discussed in this unit must be permanently posted near the door of each sterilizer prior to use by any operator.

a. Changing of supply line filters. Filters in the sterilizer liquid line must be changed when necessary, by the following procedure:
   i. Close the cylinder valve and the hose valve;
   ii. Disconnect the cylinder hose (piping) from the cylinder;
   iii. Open the hose valve and bleed slowly into a proper ventilating system at or near the in-use supply cylinders;
   iv. Vacate the area until the line is empty;
   v. Change the filter;
   vi. Reconnect the lines and reverse the value position;
   vii. Check hoses, filters, and valves for leaks with a fluorocarbon leak detector (for those sterilizers using the 88 percent chlorofluorocarbon, 12 percent ethylene oxide mixture (12/88)).

b. Restricted access area
   i. Areas involving use of EtO must be designated as restricted access areas. They must be identified with signs or floor marks near the sterilizer door, aerator, vacuum pump floor drain discharge, and in-use cylinder storage.
   ii. All personnel must be excluded from the restricted area when certain operations are in progress, such as discharging a vacuum pump, emptying a sterilizer liquid line, or venting a non-purge sterilizer with the door ajar or other operations where EtO might be released directly into the face of workers.

c. Door opening procedures
   i. Sterilizers with purge cycles. A load treated in a sterilizer equipped with a purge cycle should be removed immediately upon completion of the cycle (provided no time is lost opening the door after cycle is completed). If this is not done, the purge cycle should be repeated before opening door.
   ii. Sterilizers without purge cycles. For a load treated in a sterilizer not equipped with a purge cycle, the sterilizer door must be ajar 6&inch; for 15 minutes, and then fully opened for at least another 15 minutes before removing the treated load. The length of time of the second period should be established by peak monitoring for one hour after the two 15-minute periods suggested. If the level is above 10 ppm time-weighted average for 8 hours, more time should be added to the second waiting period (door wide open). However, in no case may the second period be shortened to less than 15 minutes.

d. Chamber unloading procedures.
   i. Procedures for unloading the chamber must include the use of baskets or rolling carts, or baskets and rolling tables to transfer treated loads quickly, thus avoiding excessive contact with treated articles, and reducing the duration of exposures.
   ii. If rolling carts are used, they should be pulled not pushed by the sterilizer operators to avoid offgassing exposure.

e. Maintenance. A written log should be instituted and maintained documenting the date of each leak detection and any maintenance procedures undertaken. This is a suggested use practice and is not required.
   i. Leak detection. Sterilizer door gaskets, cylinder and vacuum piping, hoses, filters, and valves must be checked for leaks under full pressure with a Fluorocarbon leak detector (for 12/88 systems only) every two weeks by maintenance personnel. Also, the cylinder piping connections must be checked after changing cylinders. Particular attention in leak detection should be given to the automatic solenoid valves that control the flow of EtO to the sterilizer. Specifically, a check should be made at the EtO gasline entrance port to the sterilizer, while the sterilizer door is open and the solenoid valves are in a closed position.
   ii. Maintenance procedures. Sterilizer/areator door gaskets, valves, and fittings must be replaced when necessary as determined by maintenance personnel in their bi-weekly checks; in addition, visual inspection of the door gaskets for cracks, debris, and other foreign substances should be conducted daily by the operator.

§1910.1047 Appendix B Substance technical guidelines for Ethylene Oxide

(Nonmandatory)

I. Physical and Chemical Data

A. Substance identification:

1. Synonyms: dihydrooxirene, dimethylene oxide, EO, 1,2-epoxyethane, EtO ETO oxacyclopropane, oxane, oxidoethane, alpha/beta-oxidoethane, oxiran, oxirane.
2. Formula: (C_2H_4O).
3. Molecular weight: 44.06

B. Physical data:

1. Boiling point (760 mm Hg): 10.70 °C (51.3 °F);
2. Specific gravity (water = 1): 0.87 (at 20 °C or 68 °F)
3. Vapor density (air = 1): 1.49;
4. Vapor pressure (at 20 °C); 1,095 mm Hg;
5. Solubility in water: complete;
6. Appearance and odor: colorless liquid; gas at temperature above 10.7 °F or 51.3 °C with ether-like odor above 700 ppm.

II. Fire, Explosion, and Reactivity Hazard Data

A. Fire:

1. Flash point: less than O °F (open cup);
2. Stability: decomposes violently at temperatures above 800 °F;
3. Flammable limits in air, percent by volume: Lower: 3, Upper: 100;
4. Extinguishing media: Carbon dioxide for small fires, polymer or alcohol foams for large fires;
5. Special fire fighting procedures: Dilution of ethylene oxide with 23 volumes of water renders it non-flammable;
6. Unusual fire and explosion hazards: Vapors of EtO will burn without the presence of air or other oxidizers. EtO vapors are heavier than air and may travel along the ground and be ignited by open flames or sparks at locations remote from the site at which EtO is being used
7. For purposes of compliance with the requirements of 29 CFR §1910.106, EtO is classified as a flammable gas. For example, 7,500 ppm, approximately one-fourth of the lower flammable limit, would be considered to pose a potential fire and explosion hazard.
8. For purposes of compliance with 29 CFR §1910.155, EtO is classified as a Class B fire hazard.
9. For purpose of compliance with 29 CFR §1919.307, locations classified as hazardous due to the presence of EtO shall be Class I.

B. Reactivity:

1. Conditions contributing to instability: EtO will polymerize violently if contaminated with aqueous alkalies, amines, mineral acids, metal chlorides, or metal oxides. Violent decomposition will also occur at temperatures above 800 °F;
2. Incompatibilities: Alkalines and acids;
3. Hazardous decomposition products: Carbon monoxide and carbon dioxide.

III. Spill, Leak, and Disposal Procedures

A. If EtO is spilled or leaked, the following steps should be taken:

1. Remove all ignition sources;
2. The area should be evacuated at once and re-entered only after the area has been thoroughly ventilated and washed down with water.

B. Persons not wearing appropriate protective equipment should be restricted from areas of spills or leaks until cleanup has been completed.

C. Waste disposal methods: Waste material should be disposed of in a manner that is not hazardous to employees or to the general population. In selecting the method of waste disposal, applicable local, State, and Federal regulations should be consulted.

IV. Monitoring and Measurement Procedures

A. Exposure above the Permissible Exposure Limit:

1. Eight-hour exposure evaluation: Measurements taken for the purpose of determining employee exposure under this Section are best taken with consecutive samples covering the full shift. Air samples should be taken in the employee's breathing zone (air that would most nearly represent that inhaled by the employee.)
2. Monitoring techniques: The sampling and analysis under this Section may be performed by collection of the EtO vapor on charcoal adsorption tubes or other composition adsorption tubes, with subsequent chemical analysis. Sampling and analysis may also be performed by instruments such as real-time continuous monitoring systems, portable direct reading instruments, or passive dosimeters as long as measurements taken using these methods accurately evaluate the concentration of EtO in employees' breathing zones.

   Appendix D describes the validated method of sampling and analysis which has been tested by OSHA for use with EtO. Other available methods are also described in Appendix D. The employer has the obligation of selecting a monitoring method which meets the accuracy and precision requirements of the standard under his unique field conditions. The standard requires that the method of monitoring should be accurate, to a 95 percent confidence level, to plus or minus 25 percent for concentrations of EtO at 1 ppm, and to plus or minus 35 percent for concentrations at 0.5 ppm. In addition to the method described in Appendix D, there are numerous other methods available for monitoring for EtO in the workplace. Details on these other methods have been submitted by various companies to the rulemaking record, and are available at the OSHA Docket Office.

B. Since many of the duties relating to employee exposure are dependent on the results of measurement procedures, employers should assure that the evaluation of employee exposures is performed by a technically qualified person.

V. Protective Clothing and Equipment

Employees should be provided with and be required to wear appropriate protective clothing wherever there is significant potential for skin contact with liquid EtO or EtO-containing solutions. Protective clothing shall include impermeable coveralls or similar full-body work clothing, gloves, and head coverings, as appropriate to protect areas of the body which may come in contact with liquid EtO or EtO-containing solutions.

Employers should ascertain that the protective garments are impermeable to EtO. Permeable clothing, including items made of rubber, and leather shoes should not be allowed to become contaminated with liquid EtO. If permeable clothing does become contaminated, it should be immediately removed, while the employer is under an emergency deluge shower. If leather footwear or other leather garments become wet from EtO they should be discarded and not be worn again, because leather absorbs EtO and holds it against the skin.

Any protective clothing that has been damaged or is otherwise found to be defective should be repaired or replaced. Clean protective clothing should be provided to the employee as necessary to assure employee protection. Whenever impermeable clothing becomes wet with liquid EtO, it should be washed down with water before being removed by the employee. Employees are also required to wear splash-proof safety goggles where there is any possibility of EtO contacting the eyes.

VI. Miscellaneous Precautions

A. Store EtO in tightly closed containers in a cool, well-ventilated area and take all necessary precautions to avoid any explosion hazard.

B. Non-sparking tools must be used to open and close metal containers. These containers must be effectively grounded and bonded.

C. Do not incinerate EtO cartridges, tanks or other containers.

D. Employers should advise employees of all areas and operations where exposure to EtO occur.

VII. Common Operations

Common operations in which exposure to EtO is likely to occur include the following: Manufacture of EtO, surfactants, ethanolamines, glycol ethers, and specialty chemicals, and use as a sterilant in the hospital, health product and spice industries.

§1910.1047 Appendix C Medical surveillance guidelines for Ethylene Oxide (Nonmandatory)

I. Route of Entry

Inhalation.

II. Toxicology

Clinical evidence of adverse effects associated with the exposure to EtO is present in the form of increased incidence of cancer in laboratory animals (leukemia, stomach, brain), mutation in offspring in animals, and resorptions and spontaneous abortions in animals and human populations respectively. Findings in humans and experimental animals exposed to airborne concentrations of EtO also indicate damage to the genetic material (DNA). These include hemoglobin alkylation, unsecheduled DNA synthesis, sister chromatid exchange chromosomal aberration, and functional sperm abnormalities.

Ethylene oxide in liquid form can cause eye irritation and injury to the cornea, frostbite, severe irritation, and blistering of the skin upon prolonged or confined contact. Ingestion of EtO can cause gastric irritation and liver injury. Other effects from inhalation of EtO vapors include respiratory irritation and lung injury, headache, nausea, vomiting, diarrhea, dyspnea and cyanosis.

III. Signs and Symptoms of Acute Overexposure

The early effects of acute overexposure to EtO are nausea and vomiting, headache, and irritation of the eyes and respiratory passages. The patient may notice a "peculiar taste" in the mouth. Delayed effects can include pulmonary edema, drowsiness, weakness, and incoordination. Studies suggest that blood cell changes, an increase in chromosomal aberrations, and spontaneous abortion may also be causally related to acute overexposure to EtO.

Skin contact with liquid or gaseous EtO causes characteristic burns and possibly even an allergic-type sensitization. The edema and erythema occurring from skin contact with EtO progress to vesiculation with a tendency to coalesce into blebs with desquamation. Healing occurs within three weeks, but there may be a residual brown pigmentation. A 40–80% solution is extremely dangerous, causing extensive blistering after only brief contact. Pure liquid EtO causes frostbite because of rapid evaporation. In contrast, the eye is relatively insensitive to EtO, but there may be some irritation of the cornea.

Most reported acute effects of occupational exposure to EtO are due to contact with EtO in liquid phase. The liquid readily penetrates rubber and leather, and will produce blistering if clothing or footwear contaminated with EtO are not removed.

IV. Surveillance and Preventive Considerations

As noted above, exposure to EtO has been linked to an increased risk of cancer and reproductive effects including decreased male fertility, fetotoxicity, and spontaneous abortion. EtO workers are more likely to have chromosomal damage than similar groups not exposed to EtO. At the present, limited studies of chronic effects in humans resulting from exposure to EtO suggest a causal association with leukemia. Animal studies indicate leukemia and cancers at other sites (brain, stomach) as well. The physician should be aware of the findings of these studies in evaluating the health of employees exposed to EtO.

Adequate screening tests to determine an employee's potential for developing serious chronic diseases, such as cancer, from exposure to EtO do not presently exist. Laboratory tests may, however, give evidence to suggest that an employee is potentially overexposed to EtO. It is important for the physician to become familiar with the operating conditions in which exposure to EtO is likely to occur. The physician also must become familiar with the signs and symptoms that indicate a worker is receiving otherwise unrecognized and unacceptable exposure to EtO. These elements are especially important in evaluating the medical and work histories and in conducting the physical exam. When an unacceptable exposure in an active employee is identified by the physician, measures taken by the employer to lower exposure should also lower the risk of serious long-term consequences.

The employer is required to institute a medical surveillance program for all employees who are or will be exposed to EtO at or above the action level (0.5 ppm) for at least 30 days per year, without regard to respirator use. All examinations and procedures must be performed by or under the supervision of a licensed physician at a reasonable time and place for the employee and at no cost to the employee.

Although broad latitude in prescribing specific tests to be included in the medical surveillance program is extended to the examining physician, OSHA requires inclusion of the following elements in the routine examination:

(i) Medical and work histories with special emphasis directed to symptoms related to the pulmonary, hematologic, neurologic, and reproductive systems and to the eyes and skin;

(ii) Physical examination with particular emphasis given to the pulmonary, hematologic, neurologic, and reproductive systems and to the eyes and skin;

(iii) Complete blood count to include at least a white cell count (including differential cell count), red cell count, hematocrit, and hemoglobin;

(iv) Any laboratory or other test which the examining physician deems necessary by sound medical practice.

If requested by the employee, the medical examinations shall include pregnancy testing or laboratory evaluation of fertility as deemed appropriate by the physician.

In certain cases, to provide sound medical advice to the employer and the employee, the physician must evaluate situations not directly related to EtO. For example, employees with skin diseases may be unable to tolerate wearing protective clothing. In addition those with chronic respiratory diseases may not tolerate the wearing of negative pressure (air purifying) respirators. Additional tests and procedures that will help the physician determine which employees are medically unable to wear such respirators should include: An evaluation of cardiovascular function, a baseline chest x-ray to be repeated at five year intervals, and a pulmonary function test to be repeated every three years. The pulmonary function test should include measurement of the employee's forced vital capacity (FVC), forced expiratory volume at one second (FEV1), as well as calculation of the ratios of FEV1 to FVC, and measured FVC and measured FEV1 to expected values corrected for variation due to age, sex, race, and height.

The employer is required to make the prescribed tests available at least annually to employees who are or will be exposed at or above the action level, for 30 or more days per year; more often than specified if recommended by the examining physician; and upon the employee's termination of employment or reassignment to another work area. While little is known about the long term consequences of high short-term exposures, it appears prudent to monitor such affected employees closely in light of existing health data. The employer shall provide physician recommended examinations to any employee exposed to EtO in emergency conditions. Likewise, the employer shall make available medical consultations including physician recommended exams to employees who believe they are suffering signs or symptoms of exposure to EtO.

The employer is required to provide the physician with the following information: a copy of this Standard and its Appendices; a description of the affected employee's duties as they relate to the employee exposure level; and information from the employee's previous medical examinations which is not readily available to the examining physician. Making this information available to the physician will aid in the evaluation of the employee's health in relation to assigned duties and fitness to wear personal protective equipment, when required.

The employer is required to obtain a written opinion from the examining physician containing the results of the medical examinations; the physician's opinion as to whether the employee has any detected medical conditions which would place the employee at increased risk of material impairment of his or her health from exposure to EtO; any recommended restrictions upon the employee's exposure to EtO, or upon the use of protective clothing or equipment such as respirators; and a statement that the employee has been informed by the physician of the results of the medical examination and of any medical conditions which require further explanation or treatment. This written opinion must not reveal specific findings or diagnoses unrelated to occupational exposure to EtO, and a copy of the opinion must be provided to the affected employee.

The purpose in requiring the examining physician to supply the employer with a written opinion is to provide the employer with a medical basis to aid in the determination of initial placement of employees and to assess the employee's ability to use protective clothing and equipment.

§1910.1047 Appendix D Sampling and analytical methods for Ethylene Oxide (Nonmandatory)

A number of methods are available for monitoring employee exposures to EtO. Most of these involve the use of charcoal tubes and sampling pumps, followed by analysis of the samples by gas chromatograph. The essential differences between the charcoal tube methods include, among others, the use of different desorbing solvents, the use of different lots of charcoal, and the use of different equipment for analysis of the samples.

Besides charcoal, methods using passive dosimeters, gas sampling bags, impingers, and detector tubes have been utilized for determination of EtO exposure. In addition, there are several commercially available portable gas analyzers and monitoring units.

This Appendix contains details for the method which has been tested at the OSHA Analytical Laboratory in Salt Lake City. Inclusion of this method in the Appendix does not mean that this method is the only one which will be satisfactory. Copies of descriptions of other methods available are available in the rulemaking record, and may be obtained from the OSHA Docket Office. These include the Union Carbide, Dow Chemical, 3M, and DuPont methods, as well as NIOSH Method S–286. These methods are briefly described at the end of this Appendix.

Employers who note problems with sample breakthrough using the OSHA or other charcoal methods should try larger charcoal tubes. Tubes of larger capacity are available. In addition, lower flow rates and shorter sampling times should be beneficial in minimizing breakthrough problems. Whatever method the employer chooses, he must assure himself of the method's accuracy and precision under the unique conditions present in his workplace.

Ethylene Oxide

Method No.: 30.

Matrix: Air.

Target Concentration: 1.0 ppm (1.8 mg/m^3).

Procedure: Samples are collected on two charcoal tubes in series and desorbed with 1% CS_2 in benzene. The samples are derivatized with HBr and treated with sodium carbonate. Analysis is done by gas chromatography with an electron capture detector.

Recommended Air Volume and Sampling Rate: 1 liter and 0.05 Lpm.

Detection Limit of the Overall Procedure: 13.3 ppb (0.024 mg/m^3) (Based on 1.0 liter air sample).

Reliable Quantitation Limit: 52.2 ppb (0.094 mg/m^3) (Based on 1.0 liter air sample).

Standard Error of Estimate: 6.59% (See Backup Section 4.6).

Special Requirements: Samples must be analyzed within 15 days of sampling date.

Status of Method: The sampling and analytical method has been subjected to the established evaluation procedures of the Organic Method Evaluations Branch.

Date: August 1981.

Chemist: Wayne D. Potter.
Organic Solvents Branch, OSHA Analytical Laboratory,
Salt Lake City, Utah

1. General Discussion

1.1 Background.

1.1.1 History of Procedure

Ethylene oxide samples analyzed at the OSHA Laboratory have normally been collected on activated charcoal and desorbed with carbon disulfide. The analysis is performed with a gas chromatograph equipped with a FID (Flame ionization detector) as described in NIOSH Method S286 (Ref. 5.1). This method is based on a PEL of 50 ppm and has a detection limit of about 1 ppm.

Recent studies have prompted the need for a method to analyze and detect ethylene oxide at very low concentrations.

Several attempts were made to form an ultraviolet (UV) sensitive derivative with ethylene oxide for analysis with HPLC. Among those tested that gave no detectable product were: p-anisidine, methylimidazole, aniline, and 2,3,6-trichlorobenzoic acid. Each was tested with catalysts such as triethylamine, aluminum chloride, methylene chloride and sulfuric acid but no detectable derivative was produced.

The next derivatization attempt was to react ethylene oxide with HBr to form 2-bromoethanol. This reaction was successful. An ECD (electron capture detector) gave a very good response for 2-bromoethanol due to the presence of bromine. The use of carbon disulfide as the desorbing solvent gave too large a response and masked the 2-bromoethanol. Several other solvents were tested for both their response on the ECD and their ability to desorb ethylene oxide from the charcoal. Among those tested were toluene, xylene, ethyl benzene, hexane, cyclohexane and benzene. Benzene was the only solvent tested that gave a suitable response on the ECD and a high desorption. It was found that the desorption efficiency was improved by using 1% CS2with the benzene. The carbon disulfide did not significantly improve the recovery with the other solvents. SKC Lot 120 was used in all tests done with activated charcoal.

1.1.2 Physical Properties (Ref. 5.2–5.4)

Synonyms: Oxirane; dimethylene oxide, 1,2-epoxy-ethane; oxane; C_2H_4O; ETO;
Molecular Weight: 44.06
Boiling Point: 10.7 °C (51.3°)
Melting Point: −111 °C
Description: Colorless, flammable gas
Vapor Pressure: 1095 mm. at 20 °C
Odor: Ether-like odor
Lower Explosive Limits: 3.0% (by volume)
Flash Point (TOC): Below 0 °F
Molecular Structure: CH_2—CH_2

1.2 Limit Defining Parameters

1.2.1 Detection Limit of the Analytical Procedure

The detection limit of the analytical procedure is 12.0 picograms of ethylene oxide per injection. This is the amount of analyte which will give a peak whose height is five times the height of the baseline noise. (See Backup Data Section 4.1).

1.2.2 Detection Limit of the Overall Procedure

The detection limit of the overall procedure is 24.0 ng of ethylene oxide per sample.

This is the amount of analyte spiked on the sampling device which allows recovery of an amount of analyte equivalent to the detection limit of the analytical procedure. (See Backup Data Section 4.2).

1.2.3 Reliable Quantitation Limit

The reliable quantitation limit is 94.0 nanograms of ethylene oxide per sample. This is the smallest amount of analyte which can be quantitated within the requirements of 75% recovery and 95% confidence limits. (See Backup Data Section 4.2).

It must be recognized that the reliable quantitation limit and detection limits reported in the method are based upon optimization of the instrument for the smallest possible amount of analyte. When the target concentration of an analyte is exceptionally higher than these limits, they may not be attainable at the routine operating parameters. In this case, the limits reported on analysis reports will be based on the operating parameters used during the analysis of the samples.

1.2.4 Sensitivity

The sensitivity of the analytical procedure over a concentration range representing 0.5 to 2 times the target concentration based on the recommended air volume is 34105 area units per µg/mL. The sensitivity is determined by the slope of the calibration curve (See Backup Data Section 4.3).

The sensitivity will vary somewhat with the particular instrument used in the analysis.

1.2.5 Recovery

The recovery of analyte from the collection medium must be 75% or greater. The average recovery from spiked samples over the range of 0.5 to 2 times the target concentration is 88.0% (See Backup Section 4.4). At lower concentrations the recovery appears to be non-linear.

1.2.6 **Precision (Analytical Method Only)**

The pooled coefficient of variation obtained from replicate determination of analytical standards at 0.5X, 1X and 2X the target concentration is 0.036 (See Backup Data Section 4.5).

1.2.7 **Precision (Overall Procedure)**

The overall procedure must provide results at the target concentration that are 25% of better at the 95% confidence level. The precision at the 95% confidence level for the 15 day storage test is plus or minus 12.9% (See Backup Data Section 4.6).

This includes an additional plus or minus 5% for sampling error.

1.3 Advantages

1.3.1 The sampling procedure is convenient.

1.3.2 The analytical procedure is very sensitive and reproducible.

1.3.3 Reanalysis of samples is possible.

1.3.4 Samples are stable for at least 15 days at room temperature.

1.3.5 Interferences are reduced by the longer GC retention time of the new derivative.

1.4 Disadvantages

1.4.1 Two tubes in series must be used because of possible breakthrough and migration.

1.4.2 The precision of the sampling rate may be limited by the reproducibility of the pressure drop across the tubes. The pumps are usually calibrated for one tube only.

1.4.3 The use of benzene as the desorption solvent increases the hazards of analysis because of the potential carcinogenic effects of benzene.

1.4.4 After repeated injections there can be a buildup of residue formed on the electron capture detector which decreases sensitivity.

1.4.5 Recovery from the charcoal tubes appears to be nonlinear at low concentrations.

2. Sampling Procedure

2.1 Apparatus

2.1.1 A calibrated personal sampling pump whose flow can be determined within plus or minus 5% of the recommended flow.

2.1.2 SKC Lot 120 Charcoal tubes: glass tube with both ends flame sealed, 7 cm long with a 6 mm O.D. and a 4-mm I.D., containing 2 sections of coconut shell charcoal separated by a 2-mm portion of urethane foam. The adsorbing section contains 100 mg of charcoal, the backup section 50 mg. A 3-mm portion of urethane foam is placed between the outlet end of the tube and the backup section. A plug of silylated glass wool is placed in front of the adsorbing section.

2.2 Reagents

2.2.1 None required.

2.3 Sampling Technique

2.3.1 Immediately before sampling, break the ends of the charcoal tubes. All tubes must be from the same lot.

2.3.2 Connect two tubes in series to the sampling pump with a short section of flexible tubing. A minimum amount of tubing is used to connect the two sampling tubes together. The tube closer to the pump is used as a backup. This tube should be identified as the backup tube.

2.3.3 The tubes should be placed in a vertical position during sampling to minimize channeling.

2.3.4 Air being sampled should not pass through any hose or tubing before entering the charcoal tubes.

2.3.5 Seal the charcoal tubes with plastic caps immediately after sampling. Also, seal each sample with OSHA seals lengthwise.

2.3.6 With each batch of samples, submit at least one blank tube from the same lot used for samples. This tube should be subjected to exactly the same handling as the samples (break, seal, transport) except that no air is drawn through it.

2.3.7 Transport the samples (and corresponding paperwork) to the lab for analysis.

2.3.8 If bulk samples are submitted for analysis, they should be transported in glass containers with Teflon-lined caps. These samples must be mailed separately from the container used for the charcoal tubes.

2.4 Breakthrough

2.4.1 The breakthrough (5% breakthrough) volume for a 3.0 mg/m ethylene oxide sample stream at approximately 85% relative humidity, 22 °C and 633 mm is 2.6 liters sampled at 0.05 liters per minute. This is equivalent to 7.8 μg of ethylene oxide. Upon saturation of the tube it appeared that the water may be displacing ethylene oxide during sampling.

2.5 Desorption Efficiency

2.5.1 The desorption efficiency, from liquid injection onto charcoal tubes, averaged 88.0% from 0.5 to 2.0 × the target concentration for a 1.0 liter air sample. At lower ranges it appears that the desorption efficiency is non-linear (See Backup Data Section 4.2).

2.5.2 The desorption efficiency may vary from one laboratory to another and also from one lot of charcoal to another. Thus, it is necessary to determine the desorption efficiency for a particular lot of charcoal.

2.6 Recommended Air Volume and Sampling Rate

2.6.1 The recommended air volume is 1.0 liter.

2.6.2 The recommended maximum sampling rate is 0.05 Lpm.

2.7 Interferences

2.7.1 Ethylene glycol and Freon 12 at target concentration levels did not interfere with the collection of ethylene oxide.

2.7.2 Suspected interferences should be listed on the sample data sheets.

2.7.3 The relative humidity may affect the sampling procedure.

2.8 Safety Precautions

2.8.1 Attach the sampling equipment to the employee so that it does not interfere with work performance.

2.8.2 Wear safety glasses when breaking the ends of the sampling tubes.

2.8.3 If possible, place the sampling tubes in a holder so the sharp end is not exposed while sampling.

3. Analytical Method

3.1 Apparatus

3.1.1 Gas chromatograph equipped with a linearized electron capture detector.

3.1.2 GC column capable of separating the derivative of ethylene oxide (2-bromoethanol) from any interferences and the 1% CS_2 in benzene solvent. The column used for validation studies was: 10 ft × 1/8 inch stainless steel 20% SP–2100, .1% Carbowax 1500 on 100/120 Supelcoport.

3.1.3 An electronic integrator or some other suitable method of measuring peak areas.

3.1.4 Two milliliter vials with Teflon-lined caps.

3.1.5 Gas tight syringe—500 μL or other convenient sizes for preparing standards.

3.1.6 Microliter syringes—10 μL or other convenient sizes for diluting standards and 1 μL for sample injections.

3.1.7 Pipets for dispensing the 1% CS_2 in benzene solvent. The Glenco 1 mL dispenser is adequate and convenient.

3.1.8 Volumetric flasks—5 mL and other convenient sizes for preparing standards.

3.1.9 Disposable Pasteur pipets.

3.2 Reagents

3.2.1 Benzene, reagent grade.

3.2.2 Carbon Disulfide, reagent grade.

3.2.3 Ethylene oxide, 99.7% pure.

3.2.4 Hydrobromic Acid, 48% reagent grade.

3.2.5 Sodium Carbonate, anhydrous, reagent grade.

3.2.6 Desorbing reagent, 99% Benzene/1% CS_2.

3.3 Sample Preparation

3.3.1 The front and back sections of each sample are transferred to separate 2-mL vials.

3.3.2 Each sample is desorbed with 1.0 mL of desorbing reagent.

3.3.3 The vials are sealed immediately and allowed to desorb for one hour with occasional shaking.

3.3.4 Desorbing reagent is drawn off the charcoal with a disposable pipet and put into clean 2-mL vials.

3.3.5 One drop of HBr is added to each vial. Vials are resealed and HBr is mixed well with the desorbing reagent.

3.3.6 About 0.15 gram of sodium carbonate is carefully added to each vial. Vials are again resealed and mixed well.

3.4 Standard Preparation

3.4.1 Standards are prepared by injecting the pure ethylene oxide gas into the desorbing reagent.

3.4.2 A range of standards are prepared to make a calibration curve. A concentration of 1.0 µL of ethylene oxide gas per 1 mL desorbing reagent is equivalent to 1.0 ppm air concentration (all gas volumes at 25 °C and 760 mm) for the recommended 1 liter air sample. This amount is uncorrected for desorption efficiency (See Backup Data Section 4.2. for desorption efficiency corrections).

3.4.3 One drop of HBr per mL of standard is added and mixed well.

3.4.4 About 0.15 grams of sodium carbonate is carefully added for each drop of HBr (A small reaction will occur).

3.5 Analysis

3.5.1 GC Conditions.
Nitrogen flow rate—10mL/min.
Injector Temperature—250 °C
Detector Temperature—300 °C
Column Temperature—100 °C
Injection size—0.8 µL
Elution time—3.9 minutes

3.5.2 Peak areas are measured by an integrator or other suitable means.

3.5.3 The integrator results are in area units and a calibration curve is set up with concentration vs. area units.

3.6 Interferences

3.6.1 Any compound having the same retention time of 2-bromoethanol is a potential interference. Possible interferences should be listed on the sample data sheets.

3.6.2 GC parameters may be changed to circumvent interferences.

3.6.3 There are usually trace contaminants in benzene. These contaminants, however, posed no problem of interference.

3.6.4 Retention time data on a single column is not considered proof of chemical identity. Samples over the 1.0 ppm target level should be confirmed by GC/Mass Spec or other suitable means.

3.7 Calculations

3.7.1 The concentration in µg/mL for a sample is determined by comparing the area of a particular sample to the calibration curve, which has been prepared from analytical standards.

3.7.2 The amount of analyte in each sample is corrected for desorption efficiency by use of a desorption curve.

3.7.3 Analytical results (A) from the two tubes that compose a particular air sample are added together.

3.7.4 The concentration for a sample is calculated by the following equation:

$$\text{ETO, mg / m}^3 = \frac{AXB}{C}$$

where:

A=µg/mL
B=desorption volume in milliliters
C=air volume in liters.

3.7.5 To convert mg/m^3 to parts per million (ppm) the following relationship is used:

$$\text{ETO, ppm} = \frac{\text{mg/m}^3 \text{ x } 24.45}{44.05}$$

where:
mg/m^3 = results from 3.7.4
24.45 = molar volume at 25 °C and 760mm Hg
44.05 = molecular weight of ETO.

3.8 Safety Precautions

3.8.1 Ethylene oxide and benzene are potential carcinogens and care must be exercised when working with these compounds.

3.8.2 All work done with the solvents (preparation of standards, desorption of samples, etc.) should be done in a hood.

3.8.3 Avoid any skin contact with all of the solvents.

3.8.4 Wear safety glasses at all times.

3.8.5 Avoid skin contact with HBr because it is highly toxic and a strong irritant to eyes and skin.

4. Backup Data

4.1 Detection Limit Data

The detection limit was determined by injecting 0.8 µL of a 0.015 µg/mL standard of ethylene oxide into 1% CS_2 in benzene. The detection limit of the analytical procedure is taken to be 1.20×10^{-5}µg per injection. This is equivalent to 8.3 ppb (0.015 mg/m^3) for the recommended air volume.

4.2 Desorption Efficiency

Ethylene oxide was spiked onto charcoal tubes and the following recovery data was obtained.

Amount spiked (µg)	Amount recovered (µg)	Percent recovery
4.5	4.32	96.0
3.0	2.61	87.0
2.25	2.025	90.0
1.5	1.365	91.0
1.5	1.38	92.0
.75	.6525	87.0
.375	.315	84.0
.375	.312	83.2
.1875	.151	80.5
.094	.070	74.5

At lower amounts the recovery appears to be non-linear.

4.3 Sensitivity Data

The following data was used to determine the calibration curve.

Injection	0.5×.75 µg/mL	1×1.5 µg/mL	2×3.0 µg/mL
1	30904	59567	111778
2	30987	62914	106016
3	32555	58578	106122
4	32242	57173	109716
X	31672	59558	108408

Slope = 34.105.

4.4 Recovery

The recovery was determined by spiking ethylene oxide onto lot 120 charcoal tubes and desorbing with 1% CS^2 in Benzene. Recoveries were done at 0.5, 1.0, and 2.0 x the target concentration (1 ppm) for the recommended air volume.

Percent Recovery

Sample	0.5x	1.0x	2.0x
1	88.7	95.0	91.7
2	83.8	95.0	87.3
3	84.2	91.0	86.0
4	88.0	91.0	83.0
5	88.0	86.0	85.0
X	86.5	90.5	87.0

Weighted Average = 88.2.

4.5 Precision of the Analytical Procedure

The following data was used to determine the precision of the analytical method:

Concentration	0.5×.75 µg/mL	1×1.5 µg/mL	2×3.0 µg/mL
Injection	.7421	1.4899	3.1184
	.7441	1.5826	3.0447
	.7831	1.4628	2.9149
	.7753	1.4244	2.9185
Average	.7612	1.4899	2.9991
Standard Deviation	.0211	.0674	.0998
CV	.0277	.0452	.0333

$$CV = \frac{3(.0277)^2 + 3(.0452)^2 + 3(.0333)^2}{3 + 3 + 3}$$

CV + 0.036

4.6 Storage Data

Samples were generated at 1.5 mg/m^3 ethylene oxide at 85% relative humidity, 22 °C and 633 mm. All samples were taken for 20 minutes at 0.05 Lpm. Six samples were analyzed as soon as possible and fifteen samples were stored at refrigerated temperature (5 °C) and fifteen samples were stored at ambient temperature (23 °C). These stored samples were analyzed over a period of nineteen days.

Percent Recovery

Day analyzed	Refrigerated	Ambient
1	87.0	87.0
1	93.0	93.0
1	94.0	94.0
1	92.0	92.0
4	92.0	91.0
4	93.0	88.0
4	91.0	89.0
6	92.0	
6	92.0	
8		92.0
8		86.0
10	91.7	
10	95.5	
10	95.7	
11		90.0
11		82.0
13	78.0	
13	81.4	
13	82.4	
14		78.5
14		72.1
18	66.0	
18	68.0	
19		64.0
19		77.0

4.7 Breakthrough Data

Breakthrough studies were done at 2 ppm (3.6 mg/m^3) at approximately 85% relative humidity at 22 °C (ambient temperature). Two charcoal tubes were used in series. The backup tube was changed every 10 minutes and analyzed for breakthrough. The flow rate was 0.050 Lpm.

Tube No.	Time (minutes)	Percent breakthrough
1	10	(1)
2	20	(1)
3	30	(1)
4	40	1.23
5	50	3.46
6	60	18.71
7	70	39.2
8	80	53.3
9	90	72.0
10	100	96.0
11	110	113.0
12	120	133.9

[1] None.

The 5% breakthrough volume was reached when 2.6 liters of test atmosphere were drawn through the charcoal tubes.

5. References

5.1 "NIOSH Manual of Analytical Methods," 2nd ed. NIOSH: Cincinnati, 1977; Method S286.

5.2 "IARC Monographs on the Evaluation of Carcinogenic Risk of Chemicals to Man," International Agency for Research on Cancer: Lyon, 1976; Vol. II, p. 157.

5.3 Sax., N.I. "Dangerous Properties of Industrial Materials," 4th ed.; Van Nostrand Reinhold Company. New York, 1975; p. 741.

5.4 "The Condensed Chemical Dictionary", 9th ed.; Hawley, G.G., ed.; Van Nostrand Reinhold Company, New York, 1977; p. 361.

Summary of Other Sampling Procedures

OSHA believes that served other types of monitoring equipment and techniques exist for monitoring time-weighted averages. Considerable research and method development is currently being performed, which will lead to improvements and a wider variety of monitoring techniques. A combination of monitoring procedures can be used. There probably is no one best method for monitoring personal exposure to ethylene oxide in all cases. There are advantages, disadvantages, and limitations to each method. The method of choice will depend on the need and requirements. Some commonly used methods include the use of charcoal tubes, passive dosimeters, Tedler gas sampling bags, detector tubes, photoionization detection units, infrared detection units and gas chromatographs. A number of these methods are described below.

A. Charcoal Tube Sampling Procedures

Qazi-Ketcham method (Ex. 11–133) — This method consists of collecting EtO on Columbia JXC activated carbon, desorbing the EtO with carbon disulfide and analyzing by gas chromatography with flame ionization detection. Union Carbide has recently updated and revalidated this monitoring procedures. This method is capable of determining both eight-hour time-weighted average exposures and short-term exposures. The method was validated to 0.5 ppm. Like other charcoal collecting procedures, the method requires considerable analytical expertise.

ASTM-proposed method —The Ethylene Oxide Industry Council (EOIC) has contracted with Clayton Environmental Consultants, Inc. to conduct a collaborative study for the proposed method. The ASTM-Proposed method is similar to the method published by Qazi and Ketcham is the November 1977 American Industrial Hygiene Association Journal, and to the method of Pilney and Coyne, presented at the 1979 American Industrial Hygiene Conference. After the air to be sampled is drawn through an activated charcoal tube, the ethylene oxide is desorbed from the tube using carbon disulfide and is quantitated by gas chromatography utilizing a flame ionization detector. The ASTM-proposed method specifies a large two-section charcoal tube, shipment in dry ice, storage at less than −5 °C, and analysis within three weeks to prevent migration and sample loss. Two types of charcoal tubes are being tested—Pittsburgh Coconut-Based (PCB) and Columbia JXC charcoal. This collaborative study will give an indication of the inter- and intralaboratory precision and accuracy of the ASTM-proposed method. Several laboratories have considerable expertise using the Qazi-Ketcham and Dow methods.

B. Passive Monitors—Ethylene oxide diffuses into the monitor and is collected in the sampling media. The DuPont Pro-Tek badge collects EtO in an absorbing solution, which is analyzed colorimetrically to determine the amount of EtO present. The 3M 350 badge collects the EtO on chemically treated charcoal. Other passive monitors are currently being developed and tested. Both 3M and DuPont have submitted data indicating their dosimeters meet the precision and accuracy requirements of the proposed ethylene oxide standard. Both presented laboratory validation data to 0.2 ppm (Exs. 11–65, 4–20, 108, 109, 130).

C. Tedlar Gas Sampling Bags–Samples are collected by drawing a known volume of air into a Tedlar gas sampling bag. The ethylene oxide concentration is often determined on-site using a portable gas chromatograph or portable infrared spectometer.

D. Detector tubes—A known volume of air is drawn through a detector tube using a small hand pump. The concentration of EtO is related to the length of stain developed in the tube. Detector tubes are economical, easy to use, and give an immediate readout. Unfortunately, partly because they are nonspecific, their accuracy is often questionable. Since the sample is taken over a short period of time, they may be useful for determining the source of leaks.

E. Direct Reading Instruments—There are numerous types of direct reading instruments, each having its own strengths and weaknesses (Exs. 135B, 135C, 107, 11–78, 11–153). Many are relatively new, offering greater sensitivity and specificity. Popular ethylene oxide direct reading instruments include infrared detection units, photoionization detection units, and gas chromatographs.

Portable infrared analyzers provide an immediate, continuous indication of a concentration value; making them particularly useful for locating high concentration pockets, in leak detection and in ambient air monitoring. In infrared detection units, the amount of infrared light absorbed by the gas being analyzed at selected infrared wavelengths is related to the concentration of a particular component. Various models have either fixed or variable infrared filters, differing cell pathlengths, and microcomputer controls for greater sensitivity, automation, and interference elimination.

A fairly recent detection system is photoionization detection. The molecules are ionized by high energy ultraviolet light. The resulting current is measured. Since different substances have different ionization potentials, other organic compounds may be ionized. The lower the lamp energy, the better the selectivity. As a continuous monitor, photoionization detection can be useful for locating high concentration pockets, in leak detection, and continuous ambient air monitoring. Both portable and stationary gas chromatographs are available with various types of detectors, including photoionization detectors. A gas chromatograph with a photoionization detector retains the photionization sensitivity, but minimizes or eliminates interferences. For several GC/PID units, the sensitivity is in the 0.1–0.2 ppm EtO range. The GC/PID with microprocessors can sample up to 20 sample points sequentially, calculate and record data, and activate alarms or ventilation systems. Many are quite flexible and can be configured to meet the specific analysis needs for the workplace.

DuPont presented their laboratory validation data of the accuracy of the Qazi-Ketcham charcoal tube, the PCB charcoal tube, Miran 103 IR analyzer, 3M #3550 monitor and the Du Pont C–70 badge. Quoting Elbert V. Kring:

We also believe that OSHA's proposed accuracy in this Standard is appropriate. At plus or minus 25 percent at one part per million, and plus or minus 35 percent below that. And, our data indicates there's only one monitoring method, right now, that we've tested thoroughly, that meets that accuracy requirements. That is the Du Pont Pro-Tek badge* * *. We also believe that this kind of data should be confirmed by another independent laboratory, using the same type dynamic chamber testing (Tr. 1470).

Additional data by an independent laboratory following their exact protocol was not submitted. However, information was submitted on comparisons and precision and accuracy of those monitoring procedures which indicate far better precision and accuracy of those monitoring procedures than that obtained by Du Pont (Ex. 4–20, 130, 11–68, 11–133, 130, 135A).

The accuracy of any method depends to a large degree upon the skills and experience of those who not only collect the samples but also those who analyze the samples. Even for methods that are collaboratively tested, some laboratories are closer to the true values than others. Some laboratories may meet the precision and accuracy requirements of the method; others may consistently far exceed them for the same method.

[49 FR 25796, June 22, 1984, as amended at 50 FR 9801, Mar. 12, 1985; 50 FR 41494, Oct. 11, 1985; 51 FR 25053, July 10, 1986; 53 FR 11436, 11437, Apr. 6, 1988; 53 FR 27960, July 26, 1988; 54 FR 24334, June 7, 1989; 61 FR 5508, Feb. 13, 1996; 63 FR 1292, Jan. 8, 1998; 67 FR 67965, Nov. 7, 2002; 70 FR 1143, Jan. 5, 2005; 71 FR 16672, 16673, Apr. 3, 2006; 71 FR 50190, Aug. 24, 2006; 73 FR 75586, Dec. 12, 2008; 76 FR 33609, June 8, 2011]

§1910.1048 Formaldehyde

(a) Scope and application This Standard applies to all occupational exposures to formaldehyde, i.e. from formaldehyde gas, its solutions, and materials that release formaldehyde.

(b) Definitions For purposes of this Standard, the following definitions shall apply:

Action level means a concentration of 0.5 part formaldehyde per million parts of air (0.5 ppm) calculated as an eight (8)-hour time-weighted average (TWA) concentration.

Assistant Secretary means the Assistant Secretary of Labor for the Occupational Safety and Health Administration, U.S. Department of Labor, or designee.

Authorized person means any person required by work duties to be present in regulated areas, or authorized to do so by the employer, by this Section, or by the OSH Act of 1970.

Director means the Director of the National Institute for Occupational Safety and Health, U.S. Department of Health and Human Services, or designee.

Emergency is any occurrence, such as but not limited to equipment failure, rupture of containers, or failure of control equipment that results in an uncontrolled release of a significant amount of formaldehyde.

Employee exposure means the exposure to airborne formaldehyde which would occur without corrections for protection provided by any respirator that is in use.

Formaldehyde means the chemical substance, HCHO, Chemical Abstracts Service Registry No. 50–00–0.

(c) Permissible Exposure Limit (PEL)

(c)(1) TWA: The employer shall assure that no employee is exposed to an airborne concentration of formaldehyde which exceeds 0.75 parts formaldehyde per million parts of air (0.75 ppm) as an 8-hour TWA.

(c)(2) Short Term Exposure Limit (STEL): The employer shall assure that no employee is exposed to an airborne concentration of formaldehyde which exceeds two parts formaldehyde per million parts of air (2 ppm) as a 15-minute STEL.

(d) Exposure monitoring

(d)(1) General

(d)(1)(i) Each employer who has a workplace covered by this Standard shall monitor employees to determine their exposure to formaldehyde.

(d)(1)(ii) Exception. Where the employer documents, using objective data, that the presence of formaldehyde or formaldehyde-releasing products in the workplace cannot result in airborne concentrations of formaldehyde that would cause any employee to be exposed at or above the action level or the STEL under foreseeable conditions of use, the employer will not be required to measure employee exposure to formaldehyde.

(d)(1)(iii) When an employee's exposure is determined from representative sampling, the measurements used shall be representative of the employee's full shift or short-term exposure to formaldehyde, as appropriate.

(d)(1)(iv) Representative samples for each job classification in each work area shall be taken for each shift unless the employer can document with objective data that exposure levels for a given job classification are equivalent for different work shifts.

(d)(2) Initial monitoring The employer shall identify all employees who may be exposed at or above the action level or at or above the STEL and accurately determine the exposure of each employee so identified.

(d)(2)(i) Unless the employer chooses to measure the exposure of each employee potentially exposed to formaldehyde, the employer shall develop a representative sampling strategy and measure sufficient exposures within each job classification for each workshift to correctly characterize and not underestimate the exposure of any employee within each exposure group.

(d)(2)(ii) The initial monitoring process shall be repeated each time there is a change in production, equipment, process, personnel, or control measures which may result in new or additional exposure to formaldehyde.

(d)(2)(iii) If the employer receives reports of signs or symptoms of respiratory or dermal conditions associated with formaldehyde exposure, the employer shall promptly monitor the affected employee's exposure.

(d)(3) Periodic monitoring

(d)(3)(i) The employer shall periodically measure and accurately determine exposure to formaldehyde for employees shown by the initial monitoring to be exposed at or above the action level or at or above the STEL.

(d)(3)(ii) If the last monitoring results reveal employee exposure at or above the action level, the employer shall repeat monitoring of the employees at least every 6 months.

(d)(3)(iii) If the last monitoring results reveal employee exposure at or above the STEL, the employer shall repeat monitoring of the employees at least once a year under worst conditions.

(d)(4) Termination of monitoring The employer may discontinue periodic monitoring for employees if results from two consecutive sampling periods taken at least 7 days apart show that employee exposure is below the action level and the STEL. The results must be statistically representative and consistent with the employer's knowledge of the job and work operation.

(d)(5) Accuracy of monitoring Monitoring shall be accurate, at the 95 percent confidence level, to within plus or minus 25 percent for airborne concentrations of formaldehyde at the TWA and the STEL and to within plus or minus 35 percent for airborne concentrations of formaldehyde at the action level.

(d)(6) Employee notification of monitoring results The employer must, within 15 working days after the receipt of the results of any monitoring performed under this Section, notify each affected employee of these results either individually in writing or by posting the results in an appropriate location that is accessible to employees. If employee exposure is above the PEL, affected employees shall be provided with a description of the corrective actions being taken by the employer to decrease exposure.

(d)(7) Observation of monitoring

(d)(7)(i) The employer shall provide affected employees or their designated representatives an opportunity to observe any monitoring of employee exposure to formaldehyde required by this Standard.

(d)(7)(ii) When observation of the monitoring of employee exposure to formaldehyde requires entry into an area where the use of protective clothing or equipment is required, the employer shall provide the clothing and equipment to the observer, require the observer to use such clothing and equipment, and assure that the observer complies with all other applicable safety and health procedures.

(e) **Regulated areas**

(e)(1) **Signs**

(e)(1)(i) The employer shall establish regulated areas where the concentration of airborne formaldehyde exceeds either the TWA or the STEL and post all entrances and access ways with signs bearing the following legend:

DANGER
FORMALDEHYDE
MAY CAUSE CANCER
CAUSES SKIN, EYE, AND RESPIRATORY IRRITATION
AUTHORIZED PERSONNEL ONLY

(e)(1)(ii) Prior to June 1, 2016, employers may use the following legend in lieu of that specified in paragraph (e)(1)(i) of this Section:

DANGER
FORMALDEHYDE
IRRITANT AND POTENTIAL CANCER HAZARD
AUTHORIZED PERSONNEL ONLY

(e)(2) The employer shall limit access to regulated areas to authorized persons who have been trained to recognize the hazards of formaldehyde.

(e)(3) An employer at a multiemployer worksite who establishes a regulated area shall communicate the access restrictions and locations of these areas to other employers with work operations at that worksite.

(f) **Methods of compliance**

(f)(1) Engineering controls and work practices. The employer shall institute engineering and work practice controls to reduce and maintain employee exposures to formaldehyde at or below the TWA and the STEL.

(f)(2) Exception. Whenever the employer has established that feasible engineering and work practice controls cannot reduce employee exposure to or below either of the PELs, the employer shall apply these controls to reduce employee exposures to the extent feasible and shall supplement them with respirators which satisfy this Standard.

(g) **Respiratory protection**

(g)(1) **General** For employees who use respirators required by this Section, the employer must provide each employee an appropriate respirator that complies with the requirements of this paragraph. Respirators must be used during:

(g)(1)(i) Periods necessary to install or implement feasible engineering and work-practice controls;

(g)(1)(ii) Work operations, such as maintenance and repair activities or vessel cleaning, for which the employer establishes that engineering and work-practice controls are not feasible;

(g)(1)(iii) Work operations for which feasible engineering and work-practice controls are not yet sufficient to reduce employee exposure to or below the PELs.

(g)(1)(iv) Emergencies.

(g)(2) **Respirator program**

(g)(2)(i) The employer must implement a respiratory protection program in accordance with §1910.134(b) through (d) (except (d)(1)(iii), (d)(3)(iii)(B)(1), and (2)), and (f) through (m), which covers each employee required by this Section to use a respirator.

(g)(2)(ii) When employees use air-purifying respirators with chemical cartridges or canisters that do not contain end-of-service-life indicators approved by the National Institute for Occupational Safety and Health, employers must replace these cartridges or canisters as specified by paragraphs (d)(3)(iii)(B)(1) and (B)(2) of 29 CFR §1910.134, or at the end of the workshift, whichever condition occurs first.

(g)(3) **Respirator selection**

(g)(3)(i) Employers must:

(g)(3)(i)(A) Select, and provide to employees, the appropriate respirators specified in paragraph (d)(3)(i)(A) of 29 CFR §1910.134;

(g)(3)(i)(B) Equip each air-purifying, full facepiece respirator with a canister or cartridge approved for protection against formaldehyde;

(g)(3)(i)(C) For escape, provide employees with one of the following respirator options: A self-contained breathing apparatus operated in the demand or pressure-demand mode; or a full facepiece respirator having a chin-style, or a front-or back-mounted industrial-size, canister or cartridge approved for protection against formaldehyde.

(g)(3)(ii) Employers may substitute an air-purifying, half mask respirator for an air-purifying, full facepiece respirator when they equip the half mask respirator with a cartridge approved for protection against formaldehyde and provide the affected employee with effective gas-proof goggles.

(g)(3)(iii) Employers must provide employees who have difficulty using negative pressure respirators with powered air-purifying respirators permitted for use under paragraph (g)(3)(i)(A) of this Standard and that affords adequate protection against formaldehyde exposures.

(h) **Protective equipment and clothing** Employers shall comply with the provisions of 29 CFR §1910.132 and 29 CFR §1910.133. When protective equipment or clothing is provided under these provisions, the employer shall provide these protective devices at no cost to the employee and assure that the employee wears them.

(h)(1) **Selection** The employer shall select protective clothing and equipment based upon the form of formaldehyde to be encountered, the conditions of use, and the hazard to be prevented.

(h)(1)(i) All contact of the eyes and skin with liquids containing 1 percent or more formaldehyde shall be prevented by the use of chemical protective clothing made of material impervious to formaldehyde and the use of other personal protective equipment, such as goggles and face shields, as appropriate to the operation.

(h)(1)(ii) [OI] Contact with irritating or sensitizing materials shall be prevented to the extent necessary to eliminate the hazard.

(h)(1)(iii) Where a face shield is worn, chemical safety goggles are also required if there is a danger of formaldehyde reaching the area of the eye.

(h)(1)(iv) Full body protection shall be worn for entry into areas where concentrations exceed 100 ppm and for emergency reentry into areas of unknown concentration.

(h)(2) **Maintenance of protective equipment and clothing**

(h)(2)(i) The employer shall assure that protective equipment and clothing that has become contaminated with formaldehyde is cleaned or laundered before its reuse.

(h)(2)(ii) When formaldehyde-contaminated clothing and equipment is ventilated, the employer shall establish storage areas so that employee exposure is minimized.

(h)(2)(ii)(A) **Signs** Storage areas for contaminated clothing and equipment shall have signs bearing the following legend:

DANGER
FORMALDEHYDE-CONTAMINATED [CLOTHING] EQUIPMENT
MAY CAUSE CANCER
CAUSES SKIN, EYE AND RESPIRATORY IRRITATION
DO NOT BREATHE VAPOR
DO NOT GET ON SKIN

(h)(2)(ii)(B) Labels The employer shall ensure containers for contaminated clothing and equipment are labeled consistent with the Hazard Communication Standard, §1910.1200, and shall, as a minimum, include the following:

DANGER
FORMALDEHYDE-CONTAMINATED [CLOTHING] EQUIPMENT
MAY CAUSE CANCER
CAUSES SKIN, EYE, AND RESPIRATORY IRRITATION
DO NOT BREATHE VAPOR
DO NOT GET ON SKIN

(C) Prior to June 1, 2016, employers may use the following legend in lieu of that specified in paragraph (h)(2)(ii)(A) of this Section:

DANGER
FORMALDEHYDE-CONTAMINATED [CLOTHING] EQUIPMENT
AVOID INHALATION AND SKIN CONTACT

(h)(2)(ii)(D) Prior to June 1, 2015, employers may include the following information on containers of protective clothing and equipment in lieu of the labeling requirements in paragraphs (h)(2)(ii)(B) of this Section:

DANGER
FORMALDEHYDE-CONTAMINATED [CLOTHING] EQUIPMENT
AVOID INHALATION AND SKIN CONTACT

(h)(2)(iii) The employer shall assure that only persons trained to recognize the hazards of formaldehyde remove the contaminated material from the storage area for purposes of cleaning, laundering, or disposal.

(h)(2)(iv) The employer shall assure that no employee takes home equipment or clothing that is contaminated with formaldehyde.

(h)(2)(v) The employer shall repair or replace all required protective clothing and equipment for each affected employee as necessary to assure its effectiveness.

(h)(2)(vi) The employer shall inform any person who launders, cleans, or repairs such clothing or equipment of formaldehyde's potentially harmful effects and of procedures to safely handle the clothing and equipment.

(i) **Hygiene protection**

(i)(1) The employer shall provide change rooms, as described in 29 CFR §1910.141 for employees who are required to change from work clothing into protective clothing to prevent skin contact with formaldehyde.

(i)(2) If employees' skin may become spashed with solutions containing 1 percent or greater formaldehyde, for example, because of equipment failure or improper work practices, the employer shall provide conveniently located quick drench showers and assure that affected employees use these facilities immediately.

(i)(3) If there is any possibility that an employee's eyes may be splashed with solutions containing 0.1 percent or greater formaldehyde, the employer shall provide acceptable eyewash facilities within the immediate work area for emergency use.

(j) **Housekeeping** For operations involving formaldehyde liquids or gas, the employer shall conduct a program to detect leaks and spills, including regular visual inspections.

(j)(1) Preventative maintenance of equipment, including surveys for leaks, shall be undertaken at regular intervals.

(j)(2) In work areas where spillage may occur, the employer shall make provisions to contain the spill, to decontaminate the work area, and to dispose of the waste.

(j)(3) The employer shall assure that all leaks are repaired and spills are cleaned promptly by employees wearing suitable protective equipment and trained in proper methods for cleanup and decontamination.

(j)(4) Formaldehyde-contaminated waste and debris resulting from leaks or spills shall be placed for disposal in sealed containers bearing a label warning of formaldehyde's presence and of the hazards associated with formaldehyde. The employer shall ensure that the labels are in accordance with paragraph (m) of this Section.

(k) **Emergencies** For each workplace where there is the possibility of an emergency involving formaldehyde, the employer shall assure appropriate procedures are adopted to minimize injury and loss of life. Appropriate procedures shall be implemented in the event of an emergency.

(l) OI **Medical surveillance**

(l)(1) **Employees covered**

(l)(1)(i) The employer shall institute medical surveillance programs for all employees exposed to formaldehyde at concentrations at or exceeding the action level or exceeding the STEL.

(l)(1)(ii) The employer shall make medical surveillance available for employees who develop signs and symptoms of overexposure to formaldehyde and for all employees exposed to formaldehyde in emergencies. When determining whether an employee may be experiencing signs and symptoms of possible overexposure to formaldehyde, the employer may rely on the evidence that signs and symptoms associated with formaldehyde exposure will occur only in exceptional circumstances when airborne exposure is less than 0.1 ppm and when formaldehyde is present in material in concentrations less than 0.1 percent.

(l)(2) **Examination by a physician** All medical procedures, including administration of medical disease questionnaires, shall be performed by or under the supervision of a licensed physician and shall be provided without cost to the employee, without loss of pay, and at a reasonable time and place.

(l)(3) **Medical disease questionnaire** The employer shall make the following medical surveillance available to employees prior to assignment to a job where formaldehyde exposure is at or above the action level or above the STEL and annually thereafter. The employer shall also make the following medical surveillance available promptly upon determining that an employee is experiencing signs and symptoms indicative of possible overexposure to formaldehyde.

(l)(3)(i) Administration of a medical disease questionnaire, such as in Appendix D, which is designed to elicit information on work history, smoking history, any evidence of eye, nose, or throat irritation; chronic airway problems or hyperreactive airway disease: allergic skin conditions or dermatitis; and upper or lower respiratory problems.

(l)(3)(ii) A determination by the physician, based on evaluation of the medical disease questionnaire, of whether a medical examination is necessary for employees not required to wear respirators to reduce exposure to formaldehyde.

(l)(4) **Medical examinations** Medical examinations shall be given to any employee who the physician feels, based on information in the medical disease questionnaire, may be at increased risk from exposure to formaldehyde and at the time of initial assignment and at least annually thereafter to all employees required to wear a respirator to reduce exposure to formaldehyde. The medical examination shall include:

(l)(4)(i) A physical examination with emphasis on evidence of irritation or sensitization of the skin and respiratory system, shortness of breath, or irritation of the eyes;

(l)(4)(ii) Laboratory examinations for respirator wearers consisting of baseline and annual pulmonary function tests. As a minimum, these tests shall consist of forced vital capacity (FVC), forced expiratory volume in one second (FEV_1), and forced expiratory flow (FEF);

(l)(4)(iii) Any other test which the examining physician deems necessary to complete the written opinion;

(l)(4)(iv) Counseling of employees having medical conditions that would be directly or indirectly aggravated by exposure to formaldehyde on the increased risk of impairment of their health.

(l)(5) **Examinations for employees exposed in an emergency** The employer shall make medical examinations available as soon as possible to all employees who have been exposed to formaldehyde in an emergency.

(l)(5)(i) The examination shall include a medical and work history with emphasis on any evidence of upper or lower respiratory problems, allergic conditions, skin reaction or hypersensitivity, and any evidence of eye, nose, or throat irritation.

(l)(5)(ii) Other examinations shall consist of those elements considered appropriate by the examining physician.

(l)(6) **Information provided to the physician** The employer shall provide the following information to the examining physician:

(l)(6)(i) A copy of this Standard and Appendix A, C, D, and E;

(l)(6)(ii) A description of the affected employee's job duties as they relate to the employee's exposure to formaldehyde;

(l)(6)(iii) The representative exposure level for the employee's job assignment;

(l)(6)(iv) Information concerning any personal protective equipment and respiratory protection used or to be used by the employee; and

(l)(6)(v) Information from previous medical examinations of the affected employee within the control of the employer.

(l)(6)(vi) In the event of a nonroutine examination because of an emergency, the employer shall provide to the physician as soon as possible: A description of how the emergency occurred and the exposure the victim may have received.

(l)(7) **Physician's written opinion**

(l)(7)(i) For each examination required under this Standard, the employer shall obtain a written opinion from the examining physician. This written opinion shall contain the results of the medical examination except that it shall not reveal specific findings or diagnoses unrelated to occupational exposure to formaldehyde. The written opinion shall include:

(l)(7)(i)(A) The physician's opinion as to whether the employee has any medical condition that would place the employee at an increased risk of material impairment of health from exposure to formaldehyde;

(l)(7)(i)(B) Any recommended limitations on the employee's exposure or changes in the use of personal protective equipment, including respirators;

(l)(7)(i)(C) A statement that the employee has been informed by the physician of any medical conditions which would be aggravated by exposure to formaldehyde, whether these conditions may have resulted from past formaldehyde exposure or from exposure in an emergency, and whether there is a need for further examination or treatment.

(l)(7)(ii) The employer shall provide for retention of the results of the medical examination and tests conducted by the physician.

(l)(7)(iii) The employer shall provide a copy of the physician's written opinion to the affected employee within 15 days of its receipt.

(l)(8) **Medical removal**

(l)(8)(i) The provisions of paragraph (l)(8) apply when an employee reports significant irritation of the mucosa of the eyes or the upper airways, respiratory sensitization, dermal irritation, or dermal sensitization attributed to workplace formaldehyde exposure. Medical removal provisions do not apply in the case of dermal irritation or dermal sensitization when the product suspected of causing the dermal condition contains less than 0.05% formaldehyde.

(l)(8)(ii) An employee's report of signs or symptoms of possible overexposure to formaldehyde shall be evaluated by a physician selected by the employer pursuant to paragraph (l)(3). If the physician determines that a medical examination is not necessary under paragraph (l)(3)(ii), there shall be a two-week evaluation and remediation period to permit the employer to ascertain whether the signs or symptoms subside untreated or with the use of creams, gloves, first aid treatment or personal protective equipment. Industrial hygiene measures that limit the employee's exposure to formaldehyde may also be implemented during this period. The employee shall be referred immediately to a physician prior to expiration of the two-week period if the signs or symptoms worsen. Earnings, seniority and benefits may not be altered during the two-week period by virtue of the report.

(l)(8)(iii) If the signs or symptoms have not subsided or been remedied by the end of the two-week period, or earlier if signs or symptoms warrant, the employee shall be examined by a physician selected by the employer. The physician shall presume, absent contrary evidence, that observed dermal irritation or dermal sensitization are not attributable to formaldehyde when products to which the affected employee is exposed contain less than 0.1% formaldehyde.

(l)(8)(iv) Medical examinations shall be conducted in compliance with the requirements of paragraph (l)(5)(i) and (ii). Additional guidelines for conducting medical exams are contained in Appendix C.

(l)(8)(v) If the physician finds that significant irritation of the mucosa of the eyes or of the upper airways, respiratory sensitization, dermal irritation, or dermal sensitization result from workplace formaldehyde exposure and recommends restrictions or removal, the employer shall promptly comply with the restrictions or recommendation of removal. In the event of a recommendation of removal, the employer shall remove the effected employee from the current formaldehyde exposure and if possible, transfer the employee to work having no or significantly less exposure to formaldehyde.

(l)(8)(vi) When an employee is removed pursuant to paragraph (l)(8)(v), the employer shall transfer the employee to comparable work for which the employee is qualified or can be trained in a short period (up to 6 months), where the formaldehyde exposures are as low as possible, but not higher than the action level. The employer shall maintain the employee's current earnings, seniority, and other benefits. If there is no such work available, the employer shall maintain the employee's current earnings, seniority and other benefits until such work becomes available, until the employee is determined to be unable to return to workplace formaldehyde exposure, until the employee is determined to be able to return to the original job status, or for six months, whichever comes first.

(l)(8)(vii) The employer shall arrange for a follow-up medical examination to take place within six months after the employee is removed pursuant to this paragraph. This examination shall determine if the employee can return to the original job status, or if the removal is to be permanent. The physician shall make a decision within six months of the date the employee was removed as to whether the employee can be returned to the original job status, or if the removal is to be permanent.

(l)(8)(viii) An employer's obligation to provide earnings, seniority and other benefits to a removed employee may be reduced to the extent that the employee receives compensation for earnings lost during the period of removal either from a publicly or employer-funded compensation program or from employment with another employer made possible by virtue of the employee's removal.

(l)(8)(ix) In making determinations of the formaldehyde content of materials under this paragraph the employer may rely on objective data.

(l)(9) Multiple physician review

(l)(9)(i) After the employer selects the initial physician who conducts any medical examination or consultation to determine whether medical removal or restriction is appropriate, the employee may designate a second physician to review any findings, determinations or recommendations of the initial physician and to conduct such examinations, consultations, and laboratory tests as the second physician deems necessary and appropriate to evaluate the effects of formaldehyde exposure and to facilitate this review.

(l)(9)(ii) The employer shall promptly notify an employee of the right to seek a second medical opinion after each occasion that an initial physician conducts a medical examination or consultation for the purpose of medical removal or restriction.

(l)(9)(iii) The employer may condition its participation in, and payment for, the multiple physician review mechanism upon the employee doing the following within fifteen (15) days after receipt of the notification of the right to seek a second medical opinion, or receipt of the initial physician's written opinion, whichever is later;

(l)(9)(iii)(A) The employee informs the employer of the intention to seek a second medical opinion, and

(l)(9)(iii)(B) The employee initiates steps to make an appointment with a second physician.

(l)(9)(iv) If the findings, determinations or recommendations of the second physician differ from those of the initial physician, then the employer and the employee shall assure that efforts are made for the two physicians to resolve the disagreement. If the two physicians are unable to quickly resolve their disagreement, then the employer and the employee through their respective physicians shall designate a third physician who shall be a specialist in the field at issue:

(l)(9)(iv)(A) To review the findings, determinations or recommendations of the prior physicians; and

(l)(9)(iv)(B) To conduct such examinations, consultations, laboratory tests and discussions with the prior physicians as the third physician deems necessary to resolve the disagreement of the prior physicians.

(l)(9)(v) In the alternative, the employer and the employee or authorized employee representative may jointly designate such third physician.

(l)(9)(vi) The employer shall act consistent with the findings, determinations and recommendations of the third physician, unless the employer and the employee reach an agreement which is otherwise consistent with the recommendations of at least one of the three physicians.

(m) Communication of hazards

(m)(1) Hazard communication—General

(m)(1)(i) Chemical manufacturers, importers, distributors and employers shall comply with all requirements of the Hazard Communication Standard (HCS) (§1910.1200) for formaldehyde.

(m)(1)(ii) In classifying the hazards of formaldehyde at least the following hazards are to be addressed: Cancer; skin and respiratory sensitization; eye, skin and respiratory tract irritation; acute toxicity effects; and flammability.

(m)(1)(iii) Employers shall include formaldehyde in the hazard communication program established to comply with the HCS (§1910.1200). Employers shall ensure that each employee has access to labels on containers of formaldehyde and to safety data sheets, and is trained in accordance with the requirements of HCS and paragraph (n) of this Section.

(m)(1)(iv) Paragraphs (m)(1)(i), (m)(1)(ii), and (m)(1)(iii) of this Section apply to chemicals associated with formaldehyde gas, all mixtures or solutions composed of greater than 0.1 percent formaldehyde, and materials capable of releasing formaldehyde into the air at concentrations reaching or exceeding 0.1 ppm.

(m)(1)(v) In making the determinations of anticipated levels of formaldehyde release, the employer may rely on objective data indicating the extent of potential formaldehyde release under reasonably foreseeable conditions of use.

(m)(2) Manufacturers and importers who produce or import formaldehyde or formaldehyde-containing products shall provide downstream employers using or handling these products with an objective determination through the required labels and MDSs if these items may constitute a health hazard within the meaning of 29 CFR §1910.1200(d) under normal conditions of use.

(m)(2)(i) In addition to the requirements in paragraphs (m)(1) through (m)(1)(iv) of this Section, for materials listed in paragraph (m)(1)(iv) capable of releasing formaldehyde at levels above 0.5 ppm, labels shall appropriately address all hazards as defined in paragraph (d) of §1910.1200 and Appendices A and B to §1910.1200, including cancer and respiratory sensitization, and shall contain the hazard statement "May Cause Cancer."

(m)(2)(ii) As a minimum, for all materials listed in paragraph (m)(1)(i) and (iv) of this Section capable of releasing formaldehyde at levels of 0.1 ppm to 0.5 ppm, labels shall identify that the product contains formaldehyde; list the name and address of the responsible party; and state that physical and health hazard information is readily available from the employer and from safety data sheets.

(m)(2)(iii) Prior to June 1, 2015, employers may include the phrase "Potential Cancer Hazard" in lieu of "May Cause Cancer" as specified in paragraph (m)(2)(i) of this Section.

(m)(3) Labels

(m)(3)(i) The employer shall assure that hazard warning labels complying with the requirements of 29 CFR §1910.1200(f) are affixed to all containers of materials listed in paragraph (m)(1)(i), except to the extent that 29 CFR §1910.1200(f) is inconsistent with this paragraph.

(m)(3)(ii) Information on labels. As a minimum, for all materials listed in paragraph (m)(1)(i) capable of releasing formaldehyde at levels of 0.1 ppm to 0.5 ppm, labels shall identify that the product contains formaldehyde; list the name and address of the responsible party; and state that physical and health hazard information is readily available from the employer and from safety data sheets.

(m)(3)(iii) For materials listed in paragraph (m)(1)(i) capable of releasing formaldehyde at levels above 0.5 ppm, labels shall appropriately address all hazards as defined in 29 CFR §1910.1200(d) and 29 CFR §1910.1200 Appendices A and B, including respiratory sensitization, and shall contain the words "Potential Cancer Hazard."

(m)(3)(iv) In making the determinations of anticipated levels of formaldehyde release, the employer may rely on objective data indicating the extent of potential formaldehyde release under reasonably foreseeable conditions of use.

(m)(3)(v) Substitute warning labels. The employer may use warning labels required by other statutes, regulations, or ordinances which impart the same information as the warning statements required by this paragraph.

(m)(4) Safety data sheets

(m)(4)(i) Any employer who uses formaldehyde-containing materials listed in paragraph (m)(1)(i) shall comply with the requirements of 29 CFR §1910.1200(g) with regard to the development and updating of safety data sheets.

(m)(4)(ii) Manufacturers, importers, and distributors of formaldehyde-containing materials listed in paragraph (m)(1)(i) shall assure that safety data sheets and updated information are provided to all employers purchasing such materials at the time of the initial shipment and at the time of the first shipment after a safety data sheet is updated.

(m)(5) Written hazard communication program The employer shall develop, implement, and maintain at the workplace, a written hazard communication program for formaldehyde exposures in the workplace, which at a minimum describes how the requirements specified in this paragraph for labels and other forms of warning and safety data sheets, and paragraph (n) for employee information and training, will be met. Employers in multi-employer workplaces shall comply with the requirements of 29 CFR §1910.1200(e)(2).

(n) [OI] **Employee information and training**

(n)(1) **Participation** The employer shall assure that all employees who are assigned to workplaces where there is exposure to formaldehyde participate in a training program, except that where the employer can show, using objective data, that employees are not exposed to formaldehyde at or above 0.1 ppm, the employer is not required to provide training.

(n)(2) **Frequency** Employers shall provide such information and training to employees at the time of initial assignment, and whenever a new exposure to formaldehyde is introduced into the work area. The training shall be repeated at least annually.

(n)(3) **Training program** The training program shall be conducted in a manner which the employee is able to understand and shall include:

(n)(3)(i) A discussion of the contents of this regulation and the contents of the Safety Data Sheet.

(n)(3)(ii) The purpose for and a description of the medical surveillance program required by this Standard, including:

(n)(3)(ii)(A) A description of the potential health hazards associated with exposure to formaldehyde and a description of the signs and symptoms of exposure to formaldehyde;

(n)(3)(ii)(B) Instructions to immediately report to the employer the development of any adverse signs or symptoms that the employee suspects is attributable to formaldehyde exposure.

(n)(3)(iii) Description of operations in the work area where formaldehyde is present and an explanation of the safe work practices appropriate for limiting exposure to formaldehyde in each job;

(n)(3)(iv) The purpose for, proper use of, and limitations of personal protective clothing and equipment;

(n)(3)(v) Instructions for the handling of spills, emergencies, and clean-up procedures;

(n)(3)(vi) An explanation of the importance of engineering and work practice controls for employee protection and any necessary instruction in the use of these controls; and

(n)(3)(vii) A review of emergency procedures including the specific duties or assignments of each employee in the event of an emergency.

(n)(4) **Access to training materials**

(n)(4)(i) The employer shall inform all affected employees of the location of written training materials and shall make these materials readily available, without cost, to the affected employees.

(n)(4)(ii) The employer shall provide, upon request, all training materials relating to the employee training program to the Assistant Secretary and the Director.

(o) **Recordkeeping**

(o)(1) **Exposure measurements** The employer shall establish and maintain an accurate record of all measurements taken to monitor employee exposure to formaldehyde. This record shall include:

(o)(1)(i) The date of measurement;

(o)(1)(ii) The operation being monitored;

(o)(1)(iii) The methods of sampling and analysis and evidence of their accuracy and precision;

(o)(1)(iv) The number, durations, time, and results of samples taken;

(o)(1)(v) The types of protective devices worn; and

(o)(1)(vi) The names, job classifications, social security numbers, and exposure estimates of the employees whose exposures are represented by the actual monitoring results.

(o)(2) **Exposure determinations** Where the employer has determined that no monitoring is required under this Standard, the employer shall maintain a record of the objective data relied upon to support the determination that no employee is exposed to formaldehyde at or above the action level.

(o)(3) **Medical surveillance** The employer shall establish and maintain an accurate record for each employee subject to medical surveillance under this Standard. This record shall include:

(o)(3)(i) The name and social security number of the employee;

(o)(3)(ii) The physician's written opinion;

(o)(3)(iii) A list of any employee health complaints that may be related to exposure to formaldehyde; and

(o)(3)(iv) A copy of the medical examination results, including medical disease questionnaires and results of any medical tests required by the standard or mandated by the examining physician.

(o)(4) **Respirator fit testing**

(o)(4)(i) The employer shall establish and maintain accurate records for employees subject to negative pressure respirator fit testing required by this Standard.

(o)(4)(ii) This record shall include:

(o)(4)(ii)(A) A copy of the protocol selected for respirator fit testing;

(o)(4)(ii)(B) A copy of the results of any fit testing performed;

(o)(4)(ii)(C) The size and manufacturer of the types of respirators available for selection;

(o)(4)(ii)(D) The date of the most recent fit testing, the name and social security number of each tested employee, and the respirator type and facepiece selected.

(o)(5) **Record retention** The employer shall retain records required by this Standard for at least the following periods:

(o)(5)(i) Exposure records and determinations shall be kept for at least 30 years.

(o)(5)(ii) Medical records shall be kept for the duration of employment plus 30 years.

(o)(5)(iii) Respirator fit testing records shall be kept until replaced by a more recent record.

(o)(6) **Availability of records**

(o)(6)(i) Upon request, the employer shall make all records maintained as a requirement of this Standard available for examination and copying to the Assistant Secretary and the Director.

(o)(6)(ii) The employer shall make employee exposure records, including estimates made from representative monitoring and available upon request for examination, and copying to the subject employee, or former employee, and employee representatives in accordance with 29 CFR §1910.1020 (a)–(e) and (g)–(i).

(o)(6)(iii) Employee medical records required by this Standard shall be provided upon request for examination and coying, to the subject employee or former employee or to anyone having the specific written consent of the subject employee or former employee in accordance with 29 CFR §1910.1020 (a)–(e) and (g)–(i).

§1910.1048 Appendix A Substance technical guidelines for Formalin

The following Substance Technical Guideline for Formalin provides information on uninhibited formalin solution (37% formaldehyde, no methanol stabilizer). It is designed to inform employees at the production level of their rights and duties under the formaldehyde standard whether their job title defines them as workers or supervisors. Much of the information provided is general; however, some information is specific for formalin. When employee exposure to formaldehyde is from resins capable of releasing formaldehyde, the resin itself and other impurities or decomposition products may also be toxic, and employers should include this information as well when informing employees of the hazards associated with the materials they handle. The precise hazards associated with exposure to formaldehyde depend both on the form (solid, liquid, or gas) of the material and the concentration of formaldehyde present. For example, 37–50 percent solutions of formaldehyde present a much greater hazard to the skin and eyes from spills or splashes than solutions containing less than 1 percent formaldehyde. Individual Substance Technical Guidelines used by the employer for training employees should be modified to properly give information on the material actually being used.

Substance Identification

Chemical Name: Formaldehyde
Chemical Family: Aldehyde
Chemical Formula: HCHO
Molecular Weight: 30.03
Chemical Abstracts Service Number (CAS Number): 50–00–0
Synonyms: Formalin; Formic Aldehyde; Paraform; Formol; Formalin (Methanol-free); Fyde; Formalith; Methanal; Methyl Aldehyde; Methylene Glycol; Methylene Oxide; Tetraoxymethalene; Oxomethane; Oxymethylene

Components and Contaminants

Percent: 37.0 Formaldehyde
Percent: 63.0 Water
(**Note**—Inhibited solutions contain methanol.)
Other Contaminants: Formic acid (alcohol free)
Exposure Limits:
OSHA TWA—0.75 ppm
OSHA STEL—2 ppm

Physical Data

Description: Colorless liquid, pungent odor
Boiling point: 214 °F (101 °C)
Specific Gravity: 1.08 (H_2O = 1 @ 20 °C)
pH: 2.8–4.0
Solubility in Water: Miscible
Solvent Solubility: Soluble in alcohol and acetone
Vapor Density: 1.04 (Air = 1 @ 20 °C)
Odor Threshold: 0.8 – 1 ppm

Fire and Explosion Hazard

Moderate fire and explosion hazard when exposed to heat or flame.

The flash point of 37% formaldehyde solutions is above normal room temperature, but the explosion range is very wide, from 7 to 73% by volume in air.

Reaction of formaldehyde with nitrogen dioxide, nitromethane, perchloric acid and aniline, or peroxyformic acid yields explosive compounds.

Flash Point: 185 °F (85 °C) closed cup
Lower Explosion Limit: 7%
Upper Explosion Limit: 73%
Autoignition Temperature: 806 °F (430 °C)
Flammability (OSHA): Category 4 flammable liquid

Extinguishing Media: Use dry chemical, "alcohol foam", carbon dioxide, or water in flooding amounts as fog. Solid streams may not be effective. Cool fire-exposed containers with water from side until well after fire is out.

Use of water spray to flush spills can also dilute the spill to produce nonflammable mixtures. Water runoff, however, should be contained for treatment.

National Fire Protection Association Section 325M Designation:

Health: 2—Materials hazardous to health, but areas may be entered with full-faced mask self-contained breathing apparatus which provides eye protection.

Flammability: 2—Materials which must be moderately heated before ignition will occur. Water spray may be used to extinguish the fire because the material can be cooled below its flash point.

Reactivity: D—Materials which (in themselves) are normally stable even under fire exposure conditions and which are not reactive with water. Normal fire fighting procedures may be used.

Reactivity

Stability: Formaldehyde solutions may self-polymerize to form paraformaldehyde which precipitates.

Incompatibility (Materials to Avoid): Strong oxidizing agents, caustics, strong alkalies, isocyanates, anhydrides, oxides, and inorganic acids. Formaldehyde reacts with hydrochloric acid to form the potent carcinogen, bis-chloromethyl ether. Formaldehyde reacts with nitrogen dioxide, nitromethane, perchloric acid and aniline, or peroxyformic acid to yield explosive compounds. A violent reaction occurs when formaldehyde is mixed with strong oxidizers.

Hazardous Combustion or Decomposition Products: Oxygen from the air can oxidize formaldehyde to formic acid, especially when heated. Formic acid is corrosive.

Health Hazard Data

Acute Effects of Exposure

Ingestion (Swallowing): Liquids containing 10 to 40% formaldehyde cause severe irritation and inflammation of the mouth, throat, and stomach. Severe stomach pains will follow ingestion with possible loss of consciousness and death. Ingestion of dilute formaldehyde solutions (0.03–0.04%) may cause discomfort in the stomach and pharynx.

Inhalation (Breathing): Formaldehyde is highly irritating to the upper respiratory tract and eyes. Concentrations of 0.5 to 2.0 ppm may irritate the eyes, nose, and throat of some individuals. Concentrations of 3 to 5 ppm also cause tearing of the eyes and are intolerable to some persons. Concentrations of 10 to 20 ppm cause difficulty in breathing, burning of the nose and throat, cough, and heavy tearing of the eyes, and 25 to 30 ppm causes severe respiratory tract injury leading to pulmonary edema and pneumonitis. A concentration of 100 ppm is immediately dangerous to life and health. Deaths from accidental exposure to high concentrations of formaldehyde have been reported.

Skin (Dermal): Formalin is a severe skin irritant and a sensitizer. Contact with formalin causes white discoloration, smarting, drying, cracking, and scaling. Prolonged and repeated contact can cause numbness and a hardening or tanning of the skin. Previously exposed persons may react to future exposure with an allergic eczematous dermatitis or hives.

Eye Contact: Formaldehyde solutions splashed in the eye can cause injuries ranging from transient discomfort to severe, permanent corneal clouding and loss of vision. The severity of the effect depends on the concentration of formaldehyde in the solution and whether or not the eyes are flushed with water immediately after the accident.

Note. The perception of formaldehyde by odor and eye irritation becomes less sensitive with time as one adapts to formaldehyde. This can lead to overexposure if a worker is relying on formaldehyde's warning properties to alert him or her to the potential for exposure.

Acute Animal Toxicity:
Oral, rats: LD_{50} = 800 mg/kg
Oral, mouse: LD_{50} = 42 mg/kg
Inhalation, rats: LCLo = 250 mg/kg
Inhalation, mouse: LCLo = 900 mg/kg
Inhalation, rats: LC_{50} = 590 mg/kg

Chronic Effects of Exposure

Carcinogenicity: Formaldehyde has the potential to cause cancer in humans. Repeated and prolonged exposure increases the risk. Various animal experiments have conclusively shown formaldehyde to be a carcinogen in rats. In humans, formaldehyde exposure has been associated with cancers of the lung, nasopharynx and oropharynx, and nasal passages.

Mutagenicity: Formaldehyde is genotoxic in several in vitro test systems showing properties of both an initiator and a promoter.

Toxicity: Prolonged or repeated exposure to formaldehyde may result in respiratory impairment. Rats exposed to formaldehyde at 2 ppm developed benign nasal tumors and changes of the cell structure in the nose as well as inflamed mucous membranes of the nose. Structural changes in the epithelial cells in the human nose have also been observed. Some persons have developed asthma or bronchitis following exposure to formaldehyde, most often as the result of an accidental spill involving a single exposure to a high concentration of formaldehyde.

Emergency and First Aid Procedures

Ingestion (Swallowing): If the victim is conscious, dilute, inactivate, or absorb the ingested formaldehyde by giving milk, activated charcoal, or water. Any organic material will inactivate formaldehyde. Keep affected person warm and at rest. Get medical attention immediately. If vomiting occurs, keep head lower than hips.

Inhalation (Breathing): Remove the victim from the exposure area to fresh air immediately. Where the formaldehyde concentration may be very high, each rescuer must put on a self-contained breathing apparatus before attempting to remove the victim, and medical personnel should be informed of the formaldehyde exposure immediately. If breathing has stopped, give artificial respiration. Keep the affected person warm and at rest. Qualified first-aid or medical personnel should administer oxygen, if available, and maintain the patient's airways and blood pressure until the victim can be transported to a medical facility. If exposure results in a highly irritated upper respiratory tract and coughing continues for more than 10 minutes, the worker should be hospitalized for observation and treatment.

Skin Contact: Remove contaminated clothing (including shoes) immediately. Wash the affected area of your body with soap or mild detergent and large amounts of water until no evidence of the chemical remains (at least 15 to 20 minutes). If there are chemical burns, get first aid to cover the area with sterile, dry dressing, and bandages. Get medical attention if you experience appreciable eye or respiratory irritation.

Eye Contact: Wash the eyes immediately with large amounts of water occasionally lifting lower and upper lids, until no evidence of chemical remains (at least 15 to 20 minutes). In case of burns, apply sterile bandages loosely without medication. Get medical attention immediately. If you have experienced appreciable eye irritation from a splash or excessive exposure, you should be referred promptly to an opthamologist for evaluation.

Emergency Procedures

Emergencies: If you work in an area where a large amount of formaldehyde could be released in an accident or from equipment failure, your employer must develop procedures to be followed in event of an emergency. You should be trained in your specific duties in the event of an emergency, and it is important that you clearly understand these duties. Emergency equipment must be accessible and you should be trained to use any equipment that you might need. Formaldehyde contaminated equipment must be cleaned before reuse.

If a spill of appreciable quantity occurs, leave the area quickly unless you have specific emergency duties. Do not touch spilled material. Designated persons may stop the leak and shut off ignition sources if these procedures can be done without risk. Designated persons should isolate the hazard area and deny entry except for necessary people protected by suitable protective clothing and respirators adequate for the exposure. Use water spray to reduce vapors. Do not smoke, and prohibit all flames or flares in the hazard area.

Special Firefighting Procedures: Learn procedures and responsibilities in the event of a fire in your workplace. Become familiar with the appropriate equipment and supplies and their location. In firefighting, withdraw immediately in case of rising sound from venting safety device or any discoloration of storage tank due to fire.

Spill, Leak, and Disposal Procedures

Occupational Spill: For small containers, place the leaking container in a well ventilated area. Take up small spills with absorbent material and place the waste into properly labeled containers for later disposal. For larger spills, dike the spill to minimize contamination and facilitate salvage or disposal. You may be able to neutralize the spill with sodium hydroxide or sodium sulfite. Your employer must comply with EPA rules regarding the clean-up of toxic waste and notify state and local authorities, if required. If the spill is greater than 1,000 lb/day, it is reportable under EPA's Superfund legislation.

Waste Disposal: Your employer must dispose of waste containing formaldehyde in accordance with applicable local, state, and Federal law and in a manner that minimizes exposure of employees at the site and of the clean-up crew.

Monitoring and Measurement Procedures

Monitoring Requirements: If your exposure to formaldehyde exceeds the 0.5 ppm action level or the 2 ppm STEL, your employer must monitor your exposure. Your employer need not measure every exposure if a "high exposure" employee can be identified. This person usually spends the greatest amount of time nearest the process equipment. If you are a "representative employee", you will be asked to wear a sampling device to collect formaldehyde. This device may be a passive badge, a sorbent tube attached to a pump, or an impinger containing liquid. You should perform your work as usual, but inform the person who is conducting the monitoring of any difficulties you are having wearing the device.

Evaluation of 8-hour Exposure: Measurements taken for the purpose of determining time-weighted average (TWA) exposures are best taken with samples covering the full shift. Samples collected must be taken from the employee's breathing zone air.

Short-term Exposure Evaluation: If there are tasks that involve brief but intense exposure to formaldehyde, employee exposure must be measured to assure compliance with the STEL. Sample collections are for brief periods, only 15 minutes, but several samples may be needed to identify the peak exposure.

Monitoring Techniques: OSHA's only requirement for selecting a method for sampling and analysis is that the methods used accurately evaluate the concentration of formaldehyde in employees' breathing zones. Sampling and analysis may be performed by collection of formaldehyde on liquid or solid sorbents with subsequent chemical analysis. Sampling and analysis may also be performed by passive diffusion monitors and short-term exposure may be measured by instruments such as real-time continuous monitoring systems and portable direct reading instruments.

Notification of Results: Your employer must inform you of the results of exposure monitoring representative of your job. You may be informed in writing, but posting the results where you have ready access to them constitutes compliance with the standard.

Protective Equipment and Clothing

[Material impervious to formaldehyde is needed if the employee handles formaldehyde solutions of 1% or more. Other employees may also require protective clothing or equipment to prevent dermatitis.]

Respiratory Protection: Use NIOSH-approved full facepiece negative pressure respirators equipped with approved cartridges or canisters within the use limitations of these devices. (Present restrictions on cartridges and canisters do not permit them to be used for a full workshift.) In all other situations, use positive pressure respirators such as the positive-pressure air purifying respirator or the self-contained breathing apparatus (SCBA). If you use a negative pressure respirator, your employer must provide you with fit testing of the respirator at least once a year.

Protective Gloves: Wear protective (impervious) gloves provided by your employer, at no cost, to prevent contact with formalin. Your employer should select these gloves based on the results of permeation testing and in accordance with the ACGIH Guidelines for Selection of Chemical Protective Clothing.

Eye Protection: If you might be splashed in the eyes with formalin, it is essential that you wear goggles or some other type of complete protection for the eye. You may also need a face shield if your face is likely to be splashed with formalin, but you must not substitute face shields for eye protection. (This section pertains to formaldehyde solutions of 1% or more.)

Other Protective Equipment: You must wear protective (impervious) clothing and equipment provided by your employer at no cost to prevent repeated or prolonged contact with formaldehyde liquids. If you are required to change into whole-body chemical protective clothing, your employer must provide a change room for your privacy and for storage of your normal clothing.

If you are splashed with formaldehyde, use the emergency showers and eyewash fountains provided by your employer immediately to prevent serious injury. Report the incident to your supervisor and obtain necessary medical support.

Entry Into an IDLH Atmosphere

Enter areas where the formaldehyde concentration might be 100 ppm or more only with complete body protection including a self-contained breathing apparatus with a full facepiece operated in a positive pressure mode or a supplied air respirator with full facepiece and operated in a positive pressure mode. This equipment is essential to protect your life and health under such extreme conditions.

Engineering Controls

Ventilation is the most widely applied engineering control method for reducing the concentration of airborne substances in the breathing zones of workers. There are two distinct types of ventilation.

Local Exhaust: Local exhaust ventilation is designed to capture airborne contaminants as near to the point of generation as possible. To protect you, the direction of contaminant flow must always be toward the local exhaust system inlet and away from you.

General (Mechanical): General dilution ventilation involves continuous introduction of fresh air into the workroom to mix with the contaminated air and lower your breathing zone concentration of formaldehyde. Effectiveness depends on the number of air changes per hour. Where devices emitting formaldehyde are spread out over a large area, general dilution ventilation may be the only practical method of control.

Work Practices: Work practices and administrative procedures are an important part of a control system. If you are asked to perform a task in a certain manner to limit your exposure to formaldehyde, it is extremely important that you follow these procedures.

Medical Surveillance

Medical surveillance helps to protect employees' health. You are encouraged strongly to participate in the medical surveillance program.

Your employer must make a medical surveillance program available at no expense to you and at a reasonable time and place if you are exposed to formaldehyde at concentrations above 0.5 ppm as an 8-hour average or 2 ppm over any 15-minute period. You will be offered medical surveillance at the time of your initial assignment and once a year afterward as long as your exposure is at least 0.5 ppm (TWA) or 2 ppm (STEL). Even if your exposure is below these levels, you should inform your employer if you have signs and symptoms that you suspect, through your training, are related to your formaldehyde exposure because you may need medical surveillance to determine if your health is being impaired by your exposure.

The surveillance plan includes:

(a) A medical disease questionnaire;

(b) A physical examination if the physician determines this is necessary.

If you are required to wear a respirator, your employer must offer you a physical examination and a pulmonary function test every year.

The physician must collect all information needed to determine if you are at increased risk from your exposure to formaldehyde. At the physician's discretion, the medical examination may include other tests, such as a chest x-ray, to make this determination.

After a medical examination the physician will provide your employer with a written opinion which includes any special protective measures recommended and any restrictions on your exposure. The physician must inform you of any medical conditions you have which would be aggravated by exposure to formaldehyde.

All records from your medical examinations, including disease surveys, must be retained at your employer's expense.

Emergencies

If you are exposed to formaldehyde in an emergency and develop signs or symptoms associated with acute toxicity from formaldehyde exposure, your employer must provide you with a medical examination as soon as possible. This medical examination will include all steps necessary to stabilize your health. You may be kept in the hospital for observation if your symptoms are severe to ensure that any delayed effects are recognized and treated.

§1910.1048 Appendix B Sampling strategy and analytical methods for Formaldehyde

To protect the health of employees, exposure measurements must be unbiased and representative of employee exposure. The proper measurement of employee exposure requires more than a token commitment on the part of the employer. OSHA's mandatory requirements establish a baseline; under the best of circumstances all questions regarding employee exposure will be answered. Many employers, however, will wish to conduct more extensive monitoring before undertaking expensive commitments, such as engineering controls, to assure that the modifications are truly necessary. The following sampling strategy, which was developed at NIOSH by Nelson A. Leidel, Kenneth A. Busch, and Jeremiah R. Lynch and described in NIOSH publication No. 77–173 (Occupational Exposure Sampling Strategy Manual) will assist the employer in developing a strategy for determining the exposure of his or her employees.

There is no one correct way to determine employee exposure. Obviously, measuring the exposure of every employee exposed to formaldehyde will provide the most information on any given day. Where few employees are exposed, this may be a practical solution. For most employers, however, use of the following strategy will give just as much information at less cost.

Exposure data collected on a single day will not automatically guarantee the employer that his or her workplace is always in compliance with the formaldehyde standard. This does not imply, however, that it is impossible for an employer to be sure that his or her worksite is in compliance with the standard. Indeed, a properly designed sampling strategy showing that all employees are exposed below the PELs, at least with a 95 percent certainty, is compelling evidence that the exposure limits are being achieved provided that measurements are conducted using valid sampling strategy and approved analytical methods.

There are two PELs, the TWA concentration and the STEL. Most employers will find that one of these two limits is more critical in the control of their operations, and OSHA expects that the employer will concentrate monitoring efforts on the critical component. If the more difficult exposure is controlled, this information, along with calculations to support the assumptions, should be adequate to show that the other exposure limit is also being achieved.

Sampling Strategy

Determination of the Need for Exposure Measurements

The employer must determine whether employees may be exposed to concentrations in excess of the action level. This determination becomes the first step in an employee exposure monitoring program that minimizes employer sampling burdens while providing adequate employee protection. If employees may be exposed above the action level, the employer must measure exposure. Otherwise, an objective determination that employee exposure is low provides adequate evidence that exposure potential has been examined.

The employer should examine all available relevant information, eg. insurance company and trade association data and information from suppliers or exposure data collected from similar operations. The employer may also use previously-conducted sampling including area monitoring. The employer must make a determination relevant to each operation although this need not be on a separate piece of paper. If the employer can demonstrate conclusively that no employee is exposed above the action level or the STEL through the use of objective data, the employer need proceed no further on employee exposure monitoring until such time that conditions have changed and the determination is no longer valid.

If the employer cannot determine that employee exposure is less than the action level and the STEL, employee exposure monitoring will have to be conducted.

Workplace Material Survey

The primary purpose of a survey of raw material is to determine if formaldehyde is being used in the work environment and if so, the conditions under which formaldehyde is being used.

The first step is to tabulate all situations where formaldehyde is used in a manner such that it may be released into the workplace atmosphere or contaminate the skin. This information should be available through analysis of company records and information on the SDSs available through provisions of this Standard and the Hazard Communication standard.

If there is an indication from materials handling records and accompanying SDSs that formaldehyde is being used in the following types of processes or work operations, there may be a potential for releasing formaldehyde into the workplace atmosphere:

(1) Any operation that involves grinding, sanding, sawing, cutting, crushing, screening, sieving, or any other manipulation of material that generates formaldehyde-bearing dust;
(2) Any processes where there have been employee complaints or symptoms indicative of exposure to formaldehyde;
(3) Any liquid or spray process involving formaldehyde;
(4) Any process that uses formaldehyde in preserved tissue;
(5) Any process that involves the heating of a formaldehyde-bearing resin.

Processes and work operations that use formaldehyde in these manners will probably require further investigation at the worksite to determine the extent of employee monitoring that should be conducted.

Workplace Observations

To this point, the only intention has been to provide an indication as to the existence of potentially exposed employees. With this information, a visit to the workplace is needed to observe work operations, to identify potential health hazards, and to determine whether any employees may be exposed to hazardous concentrations of formaldehyde.

In many circumstances, sources of formaldehyde can be identified through the sense of smell. However, this method of detection should be used with caution because of olfactory fatigue.

Employee location in relation to source of formaldehyde is important in determining if an employee may be significantly exposed to formaldehyde. In most instances, the closer a worker is to the source, the higher the probability that a significant exposure will occur.

Other characteristics should be considered. Certain high temperature operations give rise to higher evaporation rates. Locations of open doors and windows provide natural ventilation that tend to dilute formaldehyde emissions. General room ventilation also provides a measure of control.

Calculation of Potential Exposure Concentrations

By knowing the ventilation rate in a workplace and the quantity of formaldehyde generated, the employer may be able to determine by calculation if the PELs might be exceeded. To account for poor mixing of formaldehyde into the entire room, locations of fans and proximity of employees to the work operation, the employer must include a safety factor. If an employee is relatively close to a source, particularly if he or she is located downwind, a safety factor of 100 may be necessary. For other situations, a factor of 10 may be acceptable. If the employer can demonstrate through such calculations that employee exposure does not exceed the action level or the STEL, the employer may use this information as objective data to demonstrate compliance with the standard.

Sampling Strategy

Once the employer determines that there is a possibility of substantial employee exposure to formaldehyde, the employer is obligated to measure employee exposure.

The next step is selection of a maximum risk employee. When there are different processes where employees may be exposed to formaldehyde, a maximum risk employee should be selected for each work operation.

Selection of the maximum risk employee requires professional judgment. The best procedure for selecting the maximum risk employee is to observe employees and select the person closest to the source of formaldehyde. Employee mobility may affect this selection; eg. if the closest employee is mobile in his tasks, he may not be the maximum risk employee. Air movement patterns and differences in work habits will also affect selection of the maximum risk employee.

When many employees perform essentially the same task, a maximum risk employee cannot be selected. In this circumstance, it is necessary to resort to random sampling of the group of workers. The objective is to select a subgroup of adequate size so that there is a high probability that the random sample will contain at least one worker with high exposure if one exists. The number of persons in the group influences the number that need to be sampled to ensure that at least one individual from the highest 10 percent exposure group is contained in the sample. For example, to have 90 percent confidence in the results, if the group size is 10, nine should be sampled; for 50, only 18 need to be sampled.

If measurement shows exposure to formaldehyde at or above the action level or the STEL, the employer needs to identify all other employees who may be exposed at or above the action level or STEL and measure or otherwise accurately characterize the exposure of these employees.

Whether representative monitoring or random sampling are conducted, the purpose remains the same—to determine if the exposure of any employee is above the action level. If the exposure of the most exposed employee is less than the action level and the STEL, regardless of how the employee is identified, then it is reasonable to assume that measurements of exposure of the other employees in that operation would be below the action level and the STEL.

Exposure Measurements

There is no "best" measurement strategy for all situations. Some elements to consider in developing a strategy are:

(1) Availability and cost of sampling equipment;
(2) Availability and cost of analytic facilities;
(3) Availability and cost of personnel to take samples;
(4) Location of employees and work operations;
(5) Intraday and interday variations in the process;
(6) Precision and accuracy of sampling and analytic methods; and
(7) Number of samples needed.

Samples taken for determining compliance with the STEL differ from those that measure the TWA concentration in important ways. STEL samples are best taken in a nonrandom fashion using all available knowledge relating to the area, the individual, and the process to obtain samples during periods of maximum expected concentrations. At least three measurements on a shift are generally needed to spot gross errors or mistakes; however, only the highest value represents the STEL.

If an operation remains constant throughout the workshift, a much greater number of samples would need to be taken over the 32 discrete nonoverlapping periods in an 8-hour workshift to verify compliance with a STEL. If employee exposure is truly uniform throughout the workshift, however, an employer in compliance with the 1 ppm TWA would be in compliance with the 2 ppm STEL, and this determination can probably be made using objective data.

Need To Repeat the Monitoring Strategy

Interday and intraday fluctuations in employee exposure are mostly influenced by the physical processes that generate formaldehyde and the work habits of the employee. Hence, in-plant process variations influence the employer's determination of whether or not additional controls need to be imposed. Measurements that employee exposure is low on a day that is not representative of worst conditions may not provide sufficient information to determine whether or not additional engineering controls should be installed to achieve the PELs.

The person responsible for conducting sampling must be aware of systematic changes which will negate the validity of the sampling results. Systematic changes in formaldehyde exposure concentration for an employee can occur due to:

(1) The employee changing patterns of movement in the workplace;
(2) Closing of plant doors and windows;
(3) Changes in ventilation from season to season;
(4) Decreases in ventilation efficiency or abrupt failure of engineering control equipment;
(5) Changes in the production process or work habits of the employee.

Any of these changes, if they may result in additional exposure that reaches the next level of action (i.e. 0.5 or 1.0 ppm as an 8-hr average or 2 ppm over 15 minutes) require the employer to perform additional monitoring to reassess employee exposure.

A number of methods are suitable for measuring employee exposure to formaldehyde or for characterizing emissions within the worksite. The preamble to this Standard describes some methods that have been widely used or subjected to validation testing. A detailed analytical procedure derived from the OSHA Method 52 for acrolein and formaldehyde is presented below for informational purposes.

Inclusion of OSHA's method in this Appendix in no way implies that it is the only acceptable way to measure employee exposure to formaldehyde. Other methods that are free from significant interferences and that can determine formaldehyde at the permissible exposure limits within ± 25 percent of the "true" value at the 95 percent confidence level are also acceptable. Where applicable, the method should also be capable of measuring formaldehyde at the action level to ±35 percent of the "true" value with a 95 percent confidence level. OSHA encourages employers to choose methods that will be best for their individual needs. The employer must exercise caution, however, in choosing an appropriate method since some techniques suffer from interferences that are likely to be present in workplaces of certain industry sectors where formaldehyde is used.

OSHA's Analytical Laboratory Method

Method No: 52

Matrix: Air

Target Concentration: 1 ppm (1.2 mg/m^3)

Procedures: Air samples are collected by drawing known volumes of air through sampling tubes containing XAD–2 adsorbent which have been coated with 2-(hydroxymethyl) piperidine. The samples are desorbed with toluene and then analyzed by gas chromatography using a nitrogen selective detector.

Recommended Sampling Rate and Air Volumes: 0.1 L/min and 24 L

Reliable Quantitation Limit: 16 ppb (20 μg/m^3)

Standard Error of Estimate at the Target Concentration: 7.3%

Status of the Method: A sampling and analytical method that has been subjected to the established evaluation procedures of the Organic Methods Evaluation Branch.

Date: March 1985

1. General Discussion

1.1 Background: The current OSHA method for collecting acrolein vapor recommends the use of activated 13X molecular sieves. The samples must be stored in an ice bath during and after sampling and also they must be analyzed within 48 hours of collection. The current OSHA method for collecting formaldehyde vapor recommends the use of bubblers containing 10% methanol in water as the trapping solution.

This work was undertaken to resolve the sample stability problems associated with acrolein and also to eliminate the need to use bubblers to sample formaldehyde. A goal of this work was to develop and/or to evaluate a common sampling and analytical procedure for acrolein and formaldehyde.

NIOSH has developed independent methodologies for acrolein and formaldehyde which recommend the use of reagent-coated adsorbent tubes to collect the aldehydes as stable derivatives. The formaldehyde sampling tubes contain Chromosorb 102 adsorbent coated with N-benzylethanolamine (BEA) which reacts with formaldehyde vapor to form a stable oxazolidine compound. The acrolein sampling tubes contain XAD–2 adsorbent coated with 2-(hydroxymethyl)piperidine (2–HMP) which reacts with acrolein vapor to form a different, stable oxazolidine derivative. Acrolein does not appear to react with BEA to give a suitable reaction product. Therefore, the formaldehyde procedure cannot provide a common method for both aldehydes. However, formaldehyde does react with 2–HMP to form a very suitable reaction product. It is the quantitative reaction of acrolein and formaldehyde with 2–HMP that provides the basis for this evaluation.

This sampling and analytical procedure is very similar to the method recommended by NIOSH for acrolein. Some changes in the NIOSH methodology were necessary to permit the simultaneous determination of both aldehydes and also to accommodate OSHA laboratory equipment and analytical techniques.

1.2 Limit-defining parameters: The analyte air concentrations reported in this method are based on the recommended air volume for each analyte collected separately and a desorption volume of 1 mL. The amounts are presented as acrolein and/or formaldehyde, even though the derivatives are the actual species analyzed.

1.2.1 Detection limits of the analytical procedure: The detection limit of the analytical procedure was 386 pg per injection for formaldehyde. This was the amount of analyte which gave a peak whose height was about five times the height of the peak given by the residual formaldehyde derivative in a typical blank front section of the recommended sampling tube.

1.2.2 Detection limits of the overall procedure: The detection limits of the overall procedure were 482 ng per sample (16 ppb or 20 μg/m^3 for formaldehyde). This was the amount of analyte spiked on the sampling device which allowed recoveries approximately equal to the detection limit of the analytical procedure.

1.2.3 Reliable quantitation limits: The reliable quantitation limit was 482 ng per sample (16 ppb or 20 μg/m^3) for formaldehyde. These were the smallest amounts of analyte which could be quantitated within the limits of a recovery of at least 75% and a precision (± 1.96 SD) of ±25% or better.

The reliable quantitation limit and detection limits reported in the method are based upon optimization of the instrument for the smallest possible amount of analyte. When the target concentration of an analyte is exceptionally higher than these limits, they may not be attainable at the routine operating parameters.

1.2.4 Sensitivity: The sensitivity of the analytical procedure over concentration ranges representing 0.4 to 2 times the target concentration, based on the recommended air volumes, was 7,589 area units per μg/mL for formaldehyde. This value was determined from the slope of the calibration curve. The sensitivity may vary with the particular instrument used in the analysis.

1.2.5 Recovery: The recovery of formaldehyde from samples used in an 18-day storage test remained above 92% when the samples were stored at ambient temperature. These values were determined from regression lines which were calculated from the storage data. The recovery of the analyte from the collection device must be at least 75% following storage.

1.2.6 Precision (analytical method only): The pooled coefficient of variation obtained from replicate determinations of analytical standards over the range of 0.4 to 2 times the target concentration was 0.0052 for formaldehyde (Section 4.3).

1.2.7 Precision (overall procedure): The precision at the 95% confidence level for the ambient temperature storage tests was ± 14.3% for formaldehyde. These values each include an additional ± 5% for sampling error. The overall procedure must provide results at the target concentrations that are ± 25% at the 95% confidence level.

1.2.8 Reproducibility: Samples collected from controlled test atmospheres and a draft copy of this procedure were given to a chemist unassociated with this evaluation. The formaldehyde samples were analyzed following 15 days storage. The average recovery was 96.3% and the standard deviation was 1.7%.

1.3 Advantages:

1.3.1 The sampling and analytical procedures permit the simultaneous determination of acrolein and formaldehyde.

1.3.2 Samples are stable following storage at ambient temperature for at least 18 days.

1.4 Disadvantages: None

2. Sampling Procedure

2.1 Apparatus:

2.1.1 Samples are collected by use of a personal sampling pump that can be calibrated to within ± 5% of the recommended 0.1 L/min sampling rate with the sampling tube in line.

2.1.2 Samples are collected with laboratory prepared sampling tubes. The sampling tube is constructed of silane treated glass and is about 8-cm long. The ID is 4 mm and the OD is 6 mm. One end of the tube is tapered so that a glass wool end plug will hold the contents of the tube in place during sampling. The other end of the sampling tube is open to its full 4-mm ID to facilitate packing of the tube. Both ends of the tube are fire-polished for safety. The tube is packed with a 75-mg backup section, located nearest the tapered end and a 150-mg sampling section of pretreated XAD–2 adsorbent which has been coated with 2–HMP. The two sections of coated adsorbent are separated and retained with small plugs of silanized glass wool. Following packing, the sampling tubes are sealed with two 7/32 inch OD plastic end caps. Instructions for the pretreatment and the coating of XAD–2 adsorbent are presented in Section 4 of this method.

2.1.3 Sampling tubes, similar to those recommended in this method, are marketed by Supelco, Inc. These tubes were not available when this work was initiated; therefore, they were not evaluated.

2.2 Reagents: None required

2.3 Technique:

2.3.1 Properly label the sampling tube before sampling and then remove the plastic end caps.

2.3.2 Attach the sampling tube to the pump using a section of flexible plastic tubing such that the large, front section of the sampling tube is exposed directly to the atmosphere. Do not place any tubing ahead of the sampling tube. The sampling tube should be attached in the worker's breathing zone in a vertical manner such that it does not impede work performance.

2.3.3 After sampling for the appropriate time, remove the sampling tube from the pump and then seal the tube with plastic end caps.

2.3.4 Include at least one blank for each sampling set. The blank should be handled in the same manner as the samples with the exception that air is not drawn through it.

2.3.5 List any potential interferences on the sample data sheet.

2.4 Breakthrough:

2.4.1 Breakthrough was defined as the relative amount of analyte found on a backup sample in relation to the total amount of analyte collected on the sampling train.

2.4.2 For formaldehyde collected from test atmospheres containing 6 times the PEL, the average 5% breakthrough air volume was 41 L. The sampling rate was 0.1 L/min and the average mass of formaldehyde collected was 250 μg.

2.5 Desorption Efficiency: No desorption efficiency corrections are necessary to compute air sample results because analytical standards are prepared using coated adsorbent. Desorption efficiencies were determined, however, to investigate the recoveries of the analytes from the sampling device. The average recovery over the range of 0.4 to 2 times the target concentration, based on the recommended air volumes, was 96.2% for formaldehyde. Desorption efficiencies were essentially constant over the ranges studied.

2.6 Recommended Air Volume and Sampling Rate:

2.6.1 The recommended air volume for formaldehyde is 24 L.

2.6.2 The recommended sampling rate is 0.1 L/min.

2.7 Interferences:

2.7.1 Any collected substance that is capable of reacting 2-HMP and thereby depleting the derivatizing agent is a potential interference. Chemicals which contain a carbonyl group, such as acetone, may be capable or reacting with 2-HMP.

2.7.2 There are no other known interferences to the sampling method.

2.8 Safety Precautions:

2.8.1 Attach the sampling equipment to the worker in such a manner that it well not interfere with work performance or safety.

2.8.2 Follow all safety practices that apply to the work area being sampled.

3. Analytical Procedure

3.1 Apparatus:

3.1.1 A gas chromatograph (GC), equipped with a nitrogen selective detector. A Hewlett-Packard Model 5840A GC fitted with a nitrogen-phosphorus flame ionization detector (NPD) was used for this evaluation. Injections were performed using a Hewlett-Packard Model 7671A automatic sampler.

3.1.2 A GC column capable of resolving the analytes from any interference. A 6 ft × ¼ in OD (2mm ID) glass GC column containing 10% UCON 50–HB–5100 + 2% KOH on 80/100 mesh Chromosorb W-AW was used for the evaluation. Injections were performed on-column.

3.1.3 Vials, glass 2-mL with Teflon-lined caps.

3.1.4 Volumetric flasks, pipets, and syringes for preparing standards, making dilutions, and performing injections.

3.2 Reagents:

3.2.1 Toluene and dimethylformamide. Burdick and Jackson solvents were used in this evaluation.

3.2.2 Helium, hydrogen, and air, GC grade.

3.2.3 Formaldehyde, 37%, by weight, in water. Aldrich Chemical, ACS Reagent Grade formaldehyde was used in this evaluation.

3.2.4 Amberlite XAD–2 adsorbent coated with 2-(hydroxymethyl— piperidine (2-HMP), 10% by weight (Section 4).

3.2.5 Desorbing solution with internal standard. This solution was prepared by adding 20 μL of dimethylformamide to 100 mL of toluene.

3.3 Standard preparation:

3.3.1 Formaldehyde: Prepare stock standards by diluting known volumes of 37% formaldehyde solution with methanol. A procedure to determine the formaldehyde content of these standards is presented in Section 4. A standard containing 7.7 mg/mL formaldehyde was prepared by diluting 1 mL of the 37% reagent to 50 mL with methanol.

3.3.2 It is recommended that analytical standards be prepared about 16 hours before the air samples are to be analyzed in order to ensure the complete reaction of the analytes with 2–HMP. However, rate studies have shown the reaction to be greater than 95% complete after 4 hours. Therefore, one or two standards can be analyzed after this reduced time if sample results are outside the concentration range of the prepared standards.

3.3.3 Place 150-mg portions of coated XAD–2 adsorbent, from the same lot number as used to collect the air samples, into each of several glass 2-mL vials. Seal each vial with a Teflon-lined cap.

3.3.4 Prepare fresh analytical standards each day by injecting appropriate amounts of the diluted analyte directly onto 150-mg portions of coated adsorbent. It is permissible to inject both acrolein and formaldehyde on the same adsorbent portion. Allow the standards to stand at room temperature. A standard, approximately the target levels, was prepared by injecting 11 μL of the acrolein and 12 μL of the formaldehyde stock standards onto a single coated XAD–2 adsorbent portion.

3.3.5 Prepare a sufficient number of standards to generate the calibration curves. Analytical standard concentrations should bracket sample concentrations. Thus, if samples are not in the concentration range of the prepared standards, additional standards must be prepared to determine detector response.

3.3.7 Desorb the standards in the same manner as the samples following the 16-hour reaction time.

3.4 Sample preparation:

3.4.1 Transfer the 150-mg section of the sampling tube to a 2-mL vial. Place the 75-mg section in a separate vial. If the glass wool plugs contain a significant number of adsorbent beads, place them with the appropriate sampling tube section. Discard the glass wool plugs if they do not contain a significant number of adsorbent beads.

3.4.2 Add 1 mL of desorbing solution to each vial.

3.4.3 Seal the vials with Teflon-lined caps and then allow them to desorb for one hour. Shake the vials by hand with vigorous force several times during the desorption time.

3.4.4 Save the used sampling tubes to be cleaned and recycled.

3.5 Analysis:

3.5.1 GC Conditions

Column Temperature:

Bi-level temperature program—First level: 100 to 140 °C at 4 °C/min following completion of the first level;

Second level: 140 to 180 °C at 20 °C/min following completion of the first level.

Isothermal period: Hold column at 180 °C until the recorder pen returns to baseline (usually about 25 min after injection).

Injector temperature: 180 °C

Helium flow rate: 30 mL/min (detector response will be reduced if nitrogen is substituted for helium carrier gas.)

Injection volume: 0.8 μL

GC column: Six-ft ×1/4-in OD (2 mm ID) glass GC column containing 10% UCON 50–HB–5100+2% KOH on 80/100 Chromosorb W-AW.

NPD conditions:

Hydrogen flow rate: 3 mL/min

Air flow rate: 50 mL/min

Detector temperature: 275 °C

3.5.2 Chromatogram: For an example of a typical chromatogram, see Figure 4.11 in OSHA Method 52.

3.5.3 Use a suitable method, such as electronic integration, to measure detector response.

3.5.4 Use an internal standard method to prepare the calibration curve with several standard solutions of different concentrations. Prepare the calibration curve daily. Program the integrator to report results in µg/mL.

3.5.5 Bracket sample concentrations with standards.

3.6 Interferences (Analytical)

3.6.1 Any compound with the same general retention time as the analytes and which also gives a detector response is a potential interference. Possible interferences should be reported to the laboratory with submitted samples by the industrial hygienist.

3.6.2 GC parameters (temperature, column, etc.) may be changed to circumvent interferences.

3.6.3 A useful means of structure designation is GC/MS. It is recommended this procedure be used to confirm samples whenever possible.

3.6.4 The coated adsorbent usually contains a very small amount of residual formaldehyde derivative (Section 4.8).

3.7 Calculations:

3.7.1 Results are obtained by use of calibration curves. Calibration curves are prepared by plotting detector response against concentration for each standard. The best line through the data points is determined by curve fitting.

3.7.2 The concentration, in µg/mL, for a particular sample is determined by comparing its detector response to the calibration curve. If either of the analytes is found on the backup section, it is added to the amount found on the front section. Blank corrections should be performed before adding the results together.

3.7.3 The acrolein and/or formaldehyde air concentration can be expressed using the following equation:

$$\text{mg/m}^3 = (A)(B) / C$$

where A = µg/mL from 3.7.2, B = desorption volume, and C = L of air sampled.

No desorption efficiency corrections are required.

3.7.4 The following equation can be used to convert results in mg/m^3 to ppm.

$$\text{ppm} = (\text{mg/m}^3)(24.45) / \text{MW}$$

where mg/m^3 = result from 3.7.3, 24.45 = molar volume of an ideal gas at 760 mm Hg and 25 °C, MW = molecular weight (30.0).

4. Backup Data

4.1 Backup data on detection limits, reliable quantitation limits, sensitivity and precision of the analytical method, breakthrough, desorption efficiency, storage, reproducibility, and generation of test atmospheres are available in OSHA Method 52, developed by the Organics Methods Evaluation Branch, OSHA Analytical Laboratory, Salt Lake City, Utah.

4.2 Procedure to Coat XAD–2 Adsorbent with 2–HMP:

4.2.1 Apparatus: Soxhlet extraction apparatus, rotary evaporation apparatus, vacuum dessicator, 1–L vacuum flask, 1–L round-bottomed evaporative flask, 1–L Erlenmeyer flask, 250-mL Buchner funnel with a coarse fritted disc, etc.

4.2.2 Reagents:

4.2.2.1 Methanol, isooctane, and toluene.

4.2.2.2 2-(Hydroxymethyl)piperidine.

4.2.2.3 Amberlite XAD–2 non-ionic polymeric adsorbent, 20 to 60 mesh, Aldrich Chemical XAD–2 was used in this evaluation.

4.2.3 Procedure: Weigh 125 g of crude XAD–2 adsorbent into a 1–L Erlenmeyer flask. Add about 200 mL of water to the flask and then swirl the mixture to wash the adsorbent. Discard any adsorbent that floats to the top of the water and then filter the mixture using a fritted Buchner funnel. Air dry the adsorbent for 2 minutes. Transfer the adsorbent back to the Erlenmeyer flask and then add about 200 mL of methanol to the flask. Swirl and then filter the mixture as before. Transfer the washed adsorbent back to the Erlenmeyer flask and then add about 200 mL of methanol to the flask. Swirl and then filter the mixture as before. Transfer the washed adsorbent to a 1–L round-bottomed evaporative flask, add 13 g of 2–HMP and then 200 mL of methanol, swirl the mixture and then allow it to stand for one hour. Remove the methanol at about 40 °C and reduced pressure using a rotary evaporation apparatus. Transfer the coated adsorbent to a suitable container and store it in a vacuum desiccator at room temperature overnight. Transfer the coated adsorbent to a Soxhlet extractor and then extract the material with toluene for about 24 hours. Discard the contaminated toluene, add methanol in its place and then continue the Soxhlet extraction for an additional 4 hours. Transfer the adsorbent to a weighted 1–L round-bottom evaporative flask and remove the methanol using the rotary evaporation apparatus. Determine the weight of the adsorbent and then add an amount of 2-HMP, which is 10% by weight of the adsorbent. Add 200 mL of methanol and then swirl the mixture. Allow the mixture to stand for one hour. Remove the methanol by rotary evaporation. Transfer the coated adsorbent to a suitable container and store it in a vacuum desiccator until all traces of solvents are gone. Typically, this will take 2–3 days. The coated adsorbent should be protected from contamination. XAD–2 adsorbent treated in this manner will probably not contain residual acrolein derivative. However, this adsorbent will often contain residual formaldehyde derivative levels of about 0.1 µg per 150 mg of adsorbent. If the blank values for a batch of coated adsorbent are too high, then the batch should be returned to the Soxhlet extractor, extracted with toluene again and then recoated. This process can be repeated until the desired blank levels are attained.

The coated adsorbent is now ready to be packed into sampling tubes. The sampling tubes should be stored in a sealed container to prevent contamination. Sampling tubes should be stored in the dark at room temperature. The sampling tubes should be segregated by coated adsorbent lot number. A sufficient amount of each lot number of coated adsorbent should be retained to prepare analytical standards for use with air samples from that lot number.

4.3 A Procedure to Determine Formaldehyde by Acid Titration: Standardize the 0.1 N HCl solution using sodium carbonate and methyl orange indicator.

Place 50 mL of 0.1 M sodium sulfite and three drops of thymophthalein indicator into a 250-mL Erlenmeyer flask. Titrate the contents of the flask to a colorless endpoint with 0.1 N HCl (usually one or two drops is sufficient). Transfer 10 mL of the formaldehyde/methanol solution (prepared in 3.3.1) into the same flask and titrate the mixture with 0.1 N HCl, again, to a colorless endpoint. The formaldehyde concentration of the standard may be calculated by the following equation:

$$\text{Formaldehyde, mg/mL} = \frac{\text{acid titer x acid normality x 30.0}}{\text{mL of sample}}$$

This method is based on the quantitative liberation of sodium hydroxide when formaldehyde reacts with sodium sulfite to form the formaldehyde-bisulfite addition product. The volume of sample may be varied depending on the formaldehyde content but the solution to be titrated must contain excess sodium sulfite. Formaldehyde solutions containing substantial amounts of acid or base must be neutralized before analysis.

§1910.1048 Appendix C Medical surveillance–Formaldehyde

I. Health Hazards

The occupational health hazards of formaldehyde are primarily due to its toxic effects after inhalation, after direct contact with the skin or eyes by formaldehyde in liquid or vapor form, and after ingestion.

II. Toxicology

A. Acute Effects of Exposure

1. Inhalation (breathing): Formaldehyde is highly irritating to the upper airways. The concentration of formaldehyde that is immediately dangerous to life and health is 100 ppm. Concentrations above 50 ppm can cause severe pulmonary reactions within minutes. These include pulmonary edema, pneumonia, and bronchial irritation which can result in death. Concentrations above 5 ppm readily cause lower airway irritation characterized by cough, chest tightness and wheezing. There is some controversy regarding whether formaldehyde gas is a pulmonary sensitizer which can cause occupational asthma in a previously normal individual. Formaldehyde can produce symptoms of bronchial asthma in humans. The mechanism may be either sensitization of the individual by exposure to formaldehyde or direct irritation by formaldehyde in persons with pre-existing asthma. Upper airway irritation is the most common respiratory effect reported by workers and can occur over a wide range of concentrations, most frequently above 1 ppm. However, airway irritation has occurred in some workers with exposures to formaldehyde as low as 0.1 ppm. Symptoms of upper airway irritation include dry or sore throat, itching and burning sensations of the nose, and nasal congestion. Tolerance to this level of exposure may develop within 1–2 hours. This tolerance can permit workers remaining in an environment of gradually increasing formaldehyde concentrations to be unaware of their increasingly hazardous exposure.
2. Eye contact: Concentrations of formaldehyde between 0.05 ppm and 0.5 ppm produce a sensation of irritation in the eyes with burning, itching, redness, and tearing. Increased rate of blinking and eye closure generally protects the eye from damage at these low levels, but these

protective mechanisms may interfere with some workers' work abilities. Tolerance can occur in workers continuously exposed to concentrations of formaldehyde in this range. Accidental splash injuries of human eyes to aqueous solutions of formaldehyde (formalin) have resulted in a wide range of ocular injuries including corneal opacities and blindness. The severity of the reactions have been directly dependent on the concentration of formaldehyde in solution and the amount of time lapsed before emergency and medical intervention.

3. Skin contact: Exposure to formaldehyde solutions can cause irritation of the skin and allergic contact dermatitis. These skin diseases and disorders can occur at levels well below those encountered by many formaldehyde workers. Symptoms include erythema, edema, and vesiculation or hives. Exposure to liquid formalin or formaldehyde vapor can provoke skin reactions in sensitized individuals even when airborne concentrations of formaldehyde are well below 1 ppm.

4. Ingestion: Ingestion of as little as 30 ml of a 37 percent solution of formaldehyde (formalin) can result in death. Gastrointestinal toxicity after ingestion is most severe in the stomach and results in symptoms which can include nausea, vomiting, and servere abdominal pain. Diverse damage to other organ systems including the liver, kidney, spleen, pancreas, brain, and central nervous systems can occur from the acute response to ingestion of formaldehyde.

B. Chronic Effects of Exposure

Long term exposure to formaldehyde has been shown to be associated with an increased risk of cancer of the nose and accessory sinuses, nasopharyngeal and oropharyngeal cancer, and lung cancer in humans. Animal experiments provide conclusive evidence of a causal relationship between nasal cancer in rats and formaldehyde exposure. Concordant evidence of carcinogenicity includes DNA binding, genotoxicity in short-term tests, and cytotoxic changes in the cells of the target organ suggesting both preneoplastic changes and a dose-rate effect. Formaldehyde is a complete carcinogen and appears to exert an effect on at least two stages of the carcinogenic process.

III. Surveillance considerations

A. History

1. Medical and occupational history: Along with its acute irritative effects, formaldehyde can cause allergic sensitization and cancer. One of the goals of the work history should be to elicit information on any prior or additional exposure to formaldehyde in either the occupational or the non-occupational setting.

2. Respiratory history: As noted above, formaldehyde has recognized properties as an airway irritant and has been reported by some authors as a cause of occupational asthma. In addition, formaldehyde has been associated with cancer of the entire respiratory system of humans. For these reasons, it is appropriate to include a comprehensive review of the respiratory system in the medical history. Components of this history might include questions regarding dyspnea on exertion, shortness of breath, chronic airway complaints, hyperreactive airway disease, rhinitis, bronchitis, bronchiolitis, asthma, emphysema, respiratory allergic reaction, or other preexisting pulmonary disease.

   In addition, generalized airway hypersensitivity can result from exposures to a single sensitizing agent. The examiner should, therefore, elicit any prior history of exposure to pulmonary irritants, and any short- or long-term effects of that exposure.

   Smoking is known to decrease mucociliary clearance of materials deposited during respiration in the nose and upper airways. This may increase a worker's exposure to inhaled materials such as formaldehyde vapor. In addition, smoking is a potential confounding factor in the investigation of any chronic respiratory disease, including cancer. For these reasons, a complete smoking history should be obtained.

3. Skin Disorders: Because of the dermal irritant and sensitizing effects of formaldehyde, a history of skin disorders should be obtained. Such a history might include the existence of skin irritation, previously documented skin sensitivity, and other dermatologic disorders. Previous exposure to formaldehyde and other dermal sensitizers should be recorded.

4. History of atopic or allergic diseases: Since formaldehyde can cause allergic sensitization of the skin and airways, it might be useful to identify individuals with prior allergen sensitization. A history of atopic disease and allergies to formaldehyde or any other substances should also be obtained. It is not definitely known at this time whether atopic diseases and allergies to formaldehyde or any other substances should also be obtained. Also it is not definitely known at this time whether atopic individuals have a greater propensity to develop formaldehyde sensitivity than the general population, but identification of these individuals may be useful for ongoing surveillance.

5. Use of disease questionnaires: Comparison of the results from previous years with present results provides the best method for detecting a general deterioration in health when toxic signs and symptoms are measured subjectively. In this way recall bias does not affect the results of the analysis. Consequently, OSHA has determined that the findings of the medical and work histories should be kept in a standardized form for comparison of the year-to-year results.

B. Physical Examination

1. Mucosa of eyes and airways: Because of the irritant effects of formaldehyde, the examining physician should be alert to evidence of this irritation. A speculum examination of the nasal mucosa may be helpful in assessing possible irritation and cytotoxic changes, as may be indirect inspection of the posterior pharynx by mirror.

2. Pulmonary system: A conventional respiratory examination, including inspection of the thorax and auscultation and percussion of the lung fields should be performed as part of the periodic medical examination. Although routine pulmonary function testing is only required by the standard once every year for persons who are exposed over the TWA concentration limit, these tests have an obvious value in investigating possible respiratory dysfunction and should be used wherever deemed appropriate by the physician. In cases of alleged formaldehyde-induced airway disease, other possible causes of pulmonary disfunction (including exposures to other substances) should be ruled out. A chest radiograph may be useful in these circumstances. In cases of suspected airway hypersensitivity or allergy, it may be appropriate to use bronchial challenge testing with formaldehyde or methacholine to determine the nature of the disorder. Such testing should be performed by or under the supervision of a physician experienced in the procedures involved.

3. Skin: The physician should be alert to evidence of dermal irritation of sensitization, including reddening and inflammation, urticaria, blistering, scaling, formation of skin fissures, or other symptoms. Since the integrity of the skin barrier is compromised by other dermal diseases, the presence of such disease should be noted. Skin sensitivity testing carries with it some risk of inducing sensitivity, and therefore, skin testing for formaldehyde sensitivity should not be used as a routine screening test. Sensitivity testing may be indicated in the investigation of a suspected existing sensitivity. Guidelines for such testing have been prepared by the North American Contact Dermatitis Group.

C. Additional Examinations or Tests

The physician may deem it necessary to perform other medical examinations or tests as indicated. The standard provides a mechanism whereby these additional investigations are covered under the standard for occupational exposure to formaldehyde.

D. Emergencies

The examination of workers exposed in an emergency should be directed at the organ systems most likely to be affected. Much of the content of the examination will be similar to the periodic examination unless the patient has received a severe acute exposure requiring immediate attention to prevent serious consequences. If a severe overexposure requiring medical intervention or hospitalization has occurred, the physician must be alert to the possibility of delayed symptoms. Followup nonroutine examinations may be necessary to assure the patient's well-being.

E. Employer Obligations

The employer is required to provide the physician with the following information: A copy of this Standard and Appendices A, C, D, and E; a description of the affected employee's duties as they relate to his or her exposure concentration; an estimate of the employee's exposure including duration (e.g. 15 hr/wk, three 8-hour shifts, full-time); a description of any personal protective equipment, including respirators, used by the employee; and the results of any previous medical determinations for the affected employee related to formaldehyde exposure to the extent that this information is within the employer's control.

F. Physician's Obligations

The standard requires the employer to obtain a written statement from the physician. This statement must contain the physician's opinion as to whether the employee has any medical condition which would place him or her at increased risk of impaired health from exposure to formaldehyde or use of respirators, as appropriate. The physician must also state his opinion regarding any restrictions that should be placed on the employee's exposure to formaldehyde or upon the use of protective clothing or equipment such as respirators. If the employee wears a respirator as a result of his or her exposure to formaldehyde, the physician's opinion must also contain a statement regarding the suitability of the employee to wear the type of respirator assigned. Finally, the physician must inform the employer that the employee has been told the results of the medical examination and of any medical conditions which require further explanation or treatment. This written opinion is not to contain any information on specific findings or diagnoses unrelated to occupational exposure to formaldehyde.

The purpose in requiring the examining physician to supply the employer with a written opinion is to provide the employer with a medical basis to assist the employer in placing employees initially, in assuring that their health is not being impaired by formaldehyde, and to assess the employee's ability to use any required protective equipment.

§1910.1048 Appendix D
Medical disease questionnaire
(NonMandatory)

NONMANDATORY MEDICAL DISEASE QUESTIONNAIRE

A. Identification

Plant Name________________ Date ________

Employee Name________________

S.S. # ________________

Job Title________________ Height: ________

Birthdate: ________ Age: ______ Sex ____ Weight: ________

Height:________ Weight:________

B. Medical History

1. Have you ever been in the hospital as a patient? Yes ☐ No ☐
   If yes, what kind of problem were you having?
2. Have you ever had any kind of operation? Yes ☐ No ☐
   If yes, what kind?________
3. Do you take any kind of medicine regularly? Yes ☐ No ☐
   If yes, what kind?________
4. Are you allergic to any drugs, foods, or chemicals? Yes ☐ No ☐
   If yes, what kind of allergy is it?________
   What causes the allergy?________
5. Have you ever been told that you have asthma, hayfever, or sinusitis? Yes ☐ No ☐
6. Have you ever been told that you have emphysema, bronchitis, or any other respiratory problems? Yes ☐ No ☐
7. Have you ever been told you had hepatitis? Yes ☐ No ☐
8. Have you ever been told that you had cirrhosis? Yes ☐ No ☐
9. Have you ever been told that you had cancer? Yes ☐ No ☐
10. Have you ever had arthritis or joint pain? Yes ☐ No ☐
11. Have you ever been told that you had high blood pressure? Yes ☐ No ☐
12. Have you ever had a heart attack or heart trouble? Yes ☐ No ☐

B–1. Medical History Update

1. Have you been in the hospital as a patient any time within the past year? Yes ☐ No ☐
   If so, for what condition?________
2. Have you been under the care of a physician during the past year? Yes ☐ No ☐
   If so, for what condition?________
3. Is there any change in your breathing since last year? Yes ☐ No ☐
   Better? ☐ Worse? ☐ No change? ☐
   If change, do you know why? ________
4. Is your general health different this year from last year? Yes ☐ No ☐
   If different, in what way?
5. Have you in the past year or are you now taking any medication on a regular basis? Yes ☐ No ☐
   Name Rx ________
   Condition being treated________

C. Occupational History

1. How long have you worked for your present employer? ______
2. What jobs have you held with this employer? Include job title and length of time in each job. ________
3. In each of these jobs, how many hours a day were you exposed to chemicals?
4. What chemicals have you worked with most of the time?
5. Have you ever noticed any type of skin rash you feel was related to your work? Yes ☐ No ☐
   Wheeze? Yes ☐ No ☐
   Become short of breath or cause your chest to become tight? Yes ☐ No ☐
7. Are you exposed to any dust or chemicals at home? Yes ☐ No ☐
   If yes, explain: ________
8. In other jobs, have you ever had exposure to:
   Wood dust? Yes ☐ No ☐ Nickel or chromium? Yes ☐ No ☐
   Silica (foundry, sand blasting)? Yes ☐ No ☐
   Arsenic or asbestos? Yes ☐ No ☐
   Organic solvents? Yes ☐ No ☐ Urethane foams? Yes ☐ No ☐

C–1. Occupational History Update

1. Are you working on the same job this year as you were last year? Yes ☐ No ☐
   If not, how has your job changed?________
2. What chemicals are you exposed to on your job?
3. How many hours a day are you exposed to chemicals? ________

4. Have you noticed any skin rash within the past year you feel was related to your work? Yes ☐ No ☐
   If so, explain circumstances: ________
5. Have you noticed that any chemical makes you cough, be short of breath, or wheeze? Yes ☐ No ☐
   If so, can you identify it? ________

D. Miscellaneous

1. Do you smoke? Yes ☐ No ☐
   If so, how much and for how long?
   Pipe ________ Cigars ________ Cigarettes ________
2. Do you drink alcohol in any form? Yes ☐ No ☐
   If so, how much, how long, and how often?
3. Do you wear glasses or contact lenses? Yes ☐ No ☐
4. Do you get any physical exercise other than that required to do your job? Yes ☐ No ☐
   If so, explain: ________
5. Do you have any hobbies or "side jobs" that require you to use chemicals, such as furniture stripping, sand blasting, insulation or manufacture of urethane foam, furniture, etc? Yes ☐ No ☐
   If so, please describe, giving type of business or hobby, chemicals used and length of exposures. ________

E. Symptoms Questionnaire

1. Do you ever have any shortness of breath? Yes ☐ No ☐
   If yes, do you have to rest after climbing several flights of stairs? Yes ☐ No ☐
   If yes, if you walk on the level with people your own age, do you walk slower than they do? Yes ☐ No ☐
   If yes, if you walk slower than a normal pace, do you have to limit the distance that you walk? Yes ☐ No ☐
   If yes, do you have to stop and rest while bathing or dressing? Yes ☐ No ☐
2. Do you cough as much as three months out of the year? Yes ☐ No ☐
   If yes, have you had this cough for more than two years? Yes ☐ No ☐
   If yes, do you ever cough anything up from chest? Yes ☐ No ☐
3. Do you ever have a feeling of smothering, unable to take a deep breath, or tightness in your chest? Yes ☐ No ☐
   If yes, do you notice that this on any particular day of the week? Yes ☐ No ☐
   If yes, what day of the week?________
   If yes, do you notice that this occurs at any particular place? Yes ☐ No ☐
   If yes, do you notice that this is worse after you have returned to work after being off for several days? Yes ☐ No ☐
4. Have you ever noticed any wheezing in your chest? Yes ☐ No ☐
   If yes, is this only with colds or other infections? Yes ☐ No ☐
   Is this caused by exposure to any kind of dust or other material? Yes ☐ No ☐
   If yes, what kind? ________
5. Have you noticed any burning, tearing, or redness of your eyes when you are at work? Yes ☐ No ☐
   If so, explain circumstances: ________
6. Have you noticed any sore or burning throat or itchy or burning nose when you are at work? Yes ☐ No ☐
   If so, explain circumstances: ________
7. Have you noticed any stuffiness or dryness of your nose? Yes ☐ No ☐
8. Do you ever have swelling of the eyelids or face? Yes ☐ No ☐
9. Have you ever been jaundiced? Yes ☐ No ☐
   If yes, was this accompanied by any pain? Yes ☐ No ☐
10. Have you ever had a tendency to bruise easily or bleed excessively? Yes ☐ No ☐
11. Do you have frequent headaches that are not relieved by aspirin or tylenol? Yes ☐ No ☐
    If yes, do they occur at any particular time of the day or week? Yes ☐ No ☐
    If yes, when do they occur? ________
12. Do you have frequent episodes of nervousness or irritability? Yes ☐ No ☐
13. Do you tend to have trouble concentrating or remembering? Yes ☐ No ☐
14. Do you ever feel dizzy, light-headed, excessively drowsy or like you have been drugged? Yes ☐ No ☐
15. Does your vision ever become blurred? Yes ☐ No ☐
16. Do you have numbness or tingling of the hands or feet or other parts of your body? Yes ☐ No ☐
17. Have you ever had chronic weakness or fatigue? Yes ☐ No ☐
18. Have you ever had any swelling of your feet or ankles to the point where you could not wear your shoes? Yes ☐ No ☐
19. Are you bothered by heartburn or indigestion? Yes ☐ No ☐
20. Do you ever have itching, dryness, or peeling and scaling of the hands? Yes ☐ No ☐
21. Do you ever have a burning sensation in the hands, or reddening of the skin? Yes ☐ No ☐
22. Do you ever have cracking or bleeding of the skin on your hands? Yes ☐ No ☐
23. Are you under a physician's care? Yes ☐ No ☐
    If yes, for what are you being treated? ________
24. Do you have any physical complaints today? Yes ☐ No ☐
    If yes, explain: ________
25. Do you have other health conditions not covered by these questions? Yes ☐ No ☐
    If yes, explain: ________

[57 FR 22310, May 27, 1992; 57 FR 27161, June 18, 1992; 61 FR 5508, Feb. 13, 1996; 63 FR 1292, Jan. 8, 1998; 63 FR 20099, Apr. 23, 1998; 70 FR 1143, Jan. 5, 2005; 71 FR 16672, 16673, Apr. 3, 2006; 71 FR 50190, Aug. 24, 2006; 73 FR 75586, Dec. 12, 2008]

§1910.1050 Methylenedianiline

(a) Scope and application

(a)(1) This Section applies to all occupational exposures to MDA, Chemical Abstracts Service Registry No. 101–77–9, except as provided in paragraphs (a)(2) through (a)(7) of this Section.

(a)(2) Except as provided in paragraphs (a)(8) and (e)(5) of this Section, this Section does not apply to the processing, use, and handling of products containing MDA where initial monitoring indicates that the product is not capable of releasing MDA in excess of the action level under the expected conditions of processing, use, and handling which will cause the greatest possible release; and where no "dermal exposure to MDA" can occur.

(a)(3) Except as provided in paragraph (a)(8) of this Section, this Section does not apply to the processing, use, and handling of products containing MDA where objective data are reasonably relied upon which demonstrate the product is not capable of releasing MDA under the expected conditions of processing, use, and handling which will cause the greatest possible release; and where no "dermal exposure to MDA" can occur.

(a)(4) This Section does not apply to the storage, transportation, distribution or sale of MDA in intact containers sealed in such a manner as to contain the MDA dusts, vapors, or liquids, except for the provisions of 29 CFR §1910.1200 and paragraph (d) of this Section.

(a)(5) This Section does not apply to the construction industry as defined in 29 CFR §1910.12(b). (Exposure to MDA in the construction industry is covered by 29 CFR §1926.60.)

(a)(6) Except as provided in paragraph (a)(8) of this Section, this Section does not apply to materials in any form which contain less than 0.1% MDA by weight or volume.

(a)(7) Except as provided in paragraph (a)(8) of this Section, this Section does not apply to "finished articles containing MDA."

(a)(8) Where products containing MDA are exempted under paragraphs (a)(2) through (a)(7) of this Section, the employer shall maintain records of the initial monitoring results or objective data supporting that exemption and the basis for the employer's reliance on the data, as provided in the recordkeeping provision of paragraph (n) of this Section.

(b) **Definition** For the purpose of this Section, the following definitions shall apply:

Action level means a concentration of airborne MDA of 5 ppb as an eight (8)-hour time-weighted average.

Assistant Secretary means the Assistant Secretary of Labor for Occupational Safety and Health, U.S. Department of Labor, or designee.

Authorized person means any person specifically authorized by the employer whose duties require the person to enter a regulated area, or any person entering such an area as a designated representative of employees, for the purpose of exercising the right to observe monitoring and measuring procedures under paragraph (o) of this Section, or any other person authorized by the Act or regulations issued under the Act.

Container means any barrel, bottle, can, cylinder, drum, reaction vessel, storage tank, commercial packaging or the like, but does not include piping systems.

Dermal exposure to MDA occurs where employees are engaged in the handling, application or use of mixtures or materials containing MDA, with any of the following non-airborne forms of MDA:

(i) Liquid, powdered, granular, or flaked mixtures containing MDA in concentrations greater than 0.1% by weight or volume; and

(ii) Materials other than "finished articles" containing MDA in concentrations greater than 0.1% by weight or volume.

Director means the Director of the National Institute for Occupational Safety and Health, U.S. Department of Health and Human Services, or designee.

Emergency means any occurrence such as, but not limited to, equipment failure, rupture of containers, or failure of control equipment which results in an unexpected and potentially hazardous release of MDA.

Employee exposure means exposure to MDA which would occur if the employee were not using respirators or protective work clothing and equipment.

Finished article containing MDA is defined as a manufactured item:

(i) Which is formed to a specific shape or design during manufacture;

(ii) Which has end use function(s) dependent in whole or part upon its shape or design during end use; and

(iii) Where applicable, is an item which is fully cured by virtue of having been subjected to the conditions (temperature, time) necessary to complete the desired chemical reaction.

4,4′ Methylenedianiline or **MDA** means the chemical 4,4′-diaminodiphenyl-diphenylmethane, Chemical Abstract Service Registry number 101–77–9, in the form of a vapor, liquid, or solid. The definition also includes the salts of MDA.

Regulated areas means areas where airborne concentrations of MDA exceed or can reasonably be expected to exceed, the permissible exposure limits, or where dermal exposure to MDA can occur.

STEL means short term exposure limit as determined by any 15 minute sample period.

(c) **Permissible exposure limits (PEL)** The employer shall assure that no employee is exposed to an airborne concentration of MDA in excess of ten parts per billion (10 ppb) as an 8-hour time-weighted average or a STEL of 100 ppb.

(d) **Emergency situations**

(d)(1) **Written plan**

(d)(1)(i) A written plan for emergency situations shall be developed for each workplace where there is a possibility of an emergency. Appropriate portions of the plan shall be implemented in the event of an emergency.

(d)(1)(ii) The plan shall specifically provide that employees engaged in correcting emergency conditions shall be equipped with the appropriate personal protective equipment and clothing as required in paragraphs (h) and (i) of this Section until the emergency is abated.

(d)(1)(iii) The plan shall specifically include provisions for alerting and evacuating affected employees as well as the elements prescribed in 29 CFR §1910.38 and 29 CFR §1910.39, "Emergency action plans" and "Fire prevention plans," respectively.

(d)(2) **Alerting employees** Where there is the possibility of employee exposure to MDA due to an emergency, means shall be developed to alert promptly those employees who have the potential to be directly exposed. Affected employees not engaged in correcting emergency conditions shall be evacuated immediately in the event that an emergency occurs. Means shall also be developed and implemented for alerting other employees who may be exposed as a result of the emergency.

(e) **Exposure monitoring**

(e)(1) **General**

(e)(1)(i) Determinations of employee exposure shall be made from breathing zone air samples that are representative of each employee's exposure to airborne MDA over an eight (8) hour period. Determination of employee exposure to the STEL shall be made from breathing zone air samples collected over a 15 minute sampling period.

(e)(1)(ii) Representative employee exposure shall be determined on the basis of one or more samples representing full shift exposure for each shift for each job classification in each work area where exposure to MDA may occur.

(e)(1)(iii) Where the employer can document that exposure levels are equivalent for similar operations in different work shifts, the employer shall only be required to determine representative employee exposure for that operation during one shift.

(e)(2) **Initial monitoring** Each employer who has a workplace or work operation covered by this Standard shall perform initial monitoring to determine accurately the airborne concentrations of MDA to which employees may be exposed.

(e)(3) **Periodic monitoring and monitoring frequency**

(e)(3)(i) If the monitoring required by paragraph (e)(2) of this Section reveals employee exposure at or above the action level, but at or below the PELs, the employer shall repeat such representative monitoring for each such employee at least every six (6) months.

(e)(3)(ii) If the monitoring required by paragraph (e)(2) of this Section reveals employee exposure above the PELs, the employer shall repeat such monitoring for each such employee at least every three (3) months.

(e)(3)(iii) The employer may alter the monitoring schedule from every three months to every six months for any employee for whom two consecutive measurements taken at least 7 days apart indicate that the employee exposure has decreased to below the TWA but above the action level.

(e)(4) **Termination of monitoring**

(e)(4)(i) If the initial monitoring required by paragraph (e)(2) of this Section reveals employee exposure to be below the action level, the employer may discontinue the monitoring for that employee, except as otherwise required by paragraph (e)(5) of this Section.

(e)(4)(ii) If the periodic monitoring required by paragraph (e)(3) of this Section reveals that employee exposures, as indicated by at least two consecutive measurements taken at least 7 days apart, are below the action level the employer may discontinue the monitoring for that employee, except as otherwise required by paragraph (e)(5) of this Section.

(e)(5) **Additional monitoring** The employer shall institute the exposure monitoring required under paragraphs (e)(2) and (e)(3) of this Section when there has been a change in production process, chemicals present, control equipment, personnel, or work practices which may result in new or additional exposures to MDA, or when the employer has any reason to suspect a change which may result in new or additional exposures.

(e)(6) **Accuracy of monitoring** Monitoring shall be accurate, to a confidence level of 95 percent, to within plus or minus 25 percent for airborne concentrations of MDA.

(e)(7) **Employee notification of monitoring results**

(e)(7)(i) The employer shall, within 15 working days after the receipt of the results of any monitoring performed under this Standard, notify each employee of these results, in writing, either individually or by posting of results in an appropriate location that is accessible to affected employees.

(e)(7)(ii) The written notification required by paragraph (e)(7)(i) of this Section shall contain the corrective action being taken by the employer to reduce the employee exposure to or below the PELs, wherever the PELs are exceeded.

(e)(8) **Visual monitoring** The employer shall make routine inspections of employee hands, face and forearms potentially exposed to MDA. Other potential dermal exposures reported by the employee must be referred to the appropriate medical personnel for observation. If the employer determines that the employee has been exposed to MDA the employer shall:

(e)(8)(i) Determine the source of exposure;

(e)(8)(ii) Implement protective measures to correct the hazard; and

(e)(8)(iii) Maintain records of the corrective actions in accordance with paragraph (n) of this Section.

(f) **Regulated areas**

(f)(1) **Establishment**

(f)(1)(i) **Airborne exposures** The employer shall establish regulated areas where airborne concentrations of MDA exceed or can reasonably be expected to exceed, the permissible exposure limits.

(f)(1)(ii) [OI] **Dermal exposures** Where employees are subject to dermal exposure to MDA the employer shall establish those work areas as regulated areas.

(f)(2) **Demarcation** Regulated areas shall be demarcated from the rest of the workplace in a manner that minimizes the number of persons potentially exposed.

(f)(3) **Access** Access to regulated areas shall be limited to authorized persons.

(f)(4) **Personal protective equipment and clothing** Each person entering a regulated area shall be supplied with, and required to use, the appropriate personal protective clothing and equipment in accordance with paragraphs (h) and (i) of this Section.

(f)(5) **Prohibited activities** The employer shall ensure that employees do not eat, drink, smoke, chew tobacco or gum, or apply cosmetics in regulated areas.

(g) **Methods of compliance**

(g)(1) **Engineering controls and work practices**

(g)(1)(i) The employer shall institute engineering controls and work practices to reduce and maintain employee exposure to MDA at or below the PELs except to the extent that the employer can establish that these controls are not feasible or where the provisions of paragraph (g)(1)(ii) or (h)(1) (i) through (iv) of this Section apply.

(g)(1)(ii) Wherever the feasible engineering controls and work practices which can be instituted are not sufficient to reduce employee exposure to or below the PELs, the employer shall use them to reduce employee exposure to the lowest levels achievable by these controls and shall supplement them by the use of respiratory protective devices which comply with the requirements of paragraph (h) of this Section.

(g)(2) **Compliance program**

(g)(2)(i) The employer shall establish and implement a written program to reduce employee exposure to or below the PELs by means of engineering and work practice controls, as required by paragraph (g)(1) of this Section, and by use of respiratory protection where permitted under this Section. The program shall include a schedule for periodic maintenance (e.g., leak detection) and shall include the written plan for emergency situations as specified in paragraph (d) of this Section.

(g)(2)(ii) Upon request this written program shall be furnished for examination and copying to the Assistant Secretary, the Director, affected employees, and designated employee representatives. The employer shall review and, as necessary, update such plans at least once every 12 months to make certain they reflect the current status of the program.

(g)(3) **Employee rotation** Employee rotation shall not be permitted as a means of reducing exposure.

(h) **Respiratory protection**

(h)(1) **General** For employees who use respirators required by this Section, the employer must provide each employee an appropriate respirator that complies with the requirements of this paragraph. Respirators must be used during:

(h)(1)(i) Periods necessary to install or implement feasible engineering and work-practice controls;

(h)(1)(ii) Work operations for which the employer establishes that engineering and work-practice controls are not feasible;

(h)(1)(iii) Work operations for which feasible engineering and work-practice controls are not yet sufficient to reduce employee exposure to or below the PEL;

(h)(1)(iv) Emergencies.

(h)(2) **Respirator program** The employer must implement a respiratory protection program in accordance with §1910.134 (b) through (d) (except (d)(1)(iii)), and (f) through (m), which covers each employee required by this Section to use a respirator.

(h)(3) **Respirator selection**

(h)(3)(i) Employers must:

(h)(3)(i)(A) Select, and provide to employees, the appropriate respirators specified in paragraph (d)(3)(i)(A) of 29 CFR §1910.134

(h)(3)(i)(B) Provide HEPA filters for powered and non-powered air-purifying respirators;

(h)(3)(i)(C) For escape, provide employees with one of the following respirator options: Any self-contained breathing apparatus with a full facepiece or hood operated in the positive-pressure or continuous-flow mode; or a full facepiece air-purifying respirator;

(h)(3)(i)(D) Provide a combination HEPA filter and organic vapor canister or cartridge with powered or non-powered air-purifying respirators when MDA is in liquid form or used as part of a process requiring heat.

(h)(3)(ii) Any employee who cannot use a negative-pressure respirator must be given the option of using a positive-pressure respirator, or a supplied-air respirator operated in the continuous-flow or pressure-demand mode.

(i) **Protective work clothing and equipment**

(i)(1) **Provision and use** Where employees are subject to dermal exposure to MDA, where liquids containing MDA can be splashed into the eyes, or where airborne concentrations of MDA are in excess of the PEL, the employer shall provide, at no cost to the employee, and ensure that the employee uses, appropriate protective work clothing and equipment which prevent contact with MDA such as, but not limited to:

(i)(1)(i) Aprons, coveralls or other full-body work clothing;

(i)(1)(ii) Gloves, head coverings, and foot coverings; and

(i)(1)(iii) Face shields, chemical goggles; or

(i)(1)(iv) Other appropriate protective equipment which comply with §1910.133.

(i)(2) **Removal and storage**

(i)(2)(i) The employer shall ensure that, at the end of their work shift, employees remove MDA-contaminated protective work clothing and equipment that is not routinely removed throughout the day in change rooms provided in accordance with the provisions established for change rooms.

(i)(2)(ii) The employer shall ensure that, during their work shift, employees remove all other MDA-contaminated protective work clothing or equipment before leaving a regulated area.

(i)(2)(iii) The employer shall ensure that no employee takes MDA-contaminated work clothing or equipment out of the change room, except those employees authorized to do so for the purpose of laundering, maintenance, or disposal.

(i)(2)(iv) MDA-contaminated work clothing or equipment shall be placed and stored in closed containers which prevent dispersion of the MDA outside the container.

(i)(2)(v) Containers of MDA-contaminated protective work clothing or equipment which are to be taken out of change rooms or the workplace for cleaning, maintenance, or disposal, shall bear labels warning of the hazards of MDA.

(i)(3) **Cleaning and replacement**

(i)(3)(i) The employer shall provide the employee with clean protective clothing and equipment. The employer shall ensure that protective work clothing or equipment required by this paragraph is cleaned, laundered, repaired, or replaced at intervals appropriate to maintain its effectiveness.

(i)(3)(ii) The employer shall prohibit the removal of MDA from protective work clothing or equipment by blowing, shaking, or any methods which allow MDA to re-enter the workplace.

(i)(3)(iii) The employer shall ensure that laundering of MDA-contaminated clothing shall be done so as to prevent the release of MDA in the workplace.

(i)(3)(iv) Any employer who gives MDA-contaminated clothing to another person for laundering shall inform such person of the requirement to prevent the release of MDA.

(i)(3)(v) The employer shall inform any person who launders or cleans protective clothing or equipment contaminated with MDA of the potentially harmful effects of exposure.

(i)(3)(vi) MDA-contaminated clothing shall be transported in properly labeled, sealed, impermeable bags or containers.

(j) **Hygiene facilities and practices**

(j)(1) **Change rooms**

(j)(1)(i) The employer shall provide clean change rooms for employees, who must wear protective clothing, or who must use protective equipment because of their exposure to MDA.

(j)(1)(ii) Change rooms must be equipped with separate storage for protective clothing and equipment and for street clothes which prevents MDA contamination of street clothes.

(j)(2) **Showers**

(j)(2)(i) The employer shall ensure that employees, who work in areas where there is the potential for exposure resulting from airborne MDA (e.g., particulates or vapors) above the action level, shower at the end of the work shift.

(j)(2)(i)(A) Shower facilities required by this paragraph shall comply with §1910.141(d)(3).

(j)(2)(i)(B) The employer shall ensure that employees who are required to shower pursuant to the provisions contained herein do not leave the workplace wearing any protective clothing or equipment worn during the work shift.

(j)(2)(ii) Where dermal exposure to MDA occurs, the employer shall ensure that materials spilled or deposited on the skin are removed as soon as possible by methods which do not facilitate the dermal absorption of MDA.

(j)(3) **Lunch facilities**

(j)(3)(i) **Availability and construction**

(j)(3)(i)(A) Whenever food or beverages are consumed at the worksite and employees are exposed to MDA at or above the PEL or are subject to dermal exposure to MDA the employer shall provide readily accessible lunch areas.

(j)(3)(i)(B) Lunch areas located within the workplace and in areas where there is the potential for airborne exposure to MDA at or above the PEL shall have a positive pressure, temperature controlled, filtered air supply.

(j)(3)(i)(C) Lunch areas may not be located in areas within the workplace where the potential for dermal exposure to MDA exists.

(j)(3)(ii) The employer shall ensure that employees who have been subjected to dermal exposure to MDA or who have been exposed to MDA above the PEL wash their hands and faces with soap and water prior to eating, drinking, smoking, or applying cosmetics.

(j)(3)(iii) The employer shall ensure that employees exposed to MDA do not enter lunch facilities with MDA-contaminated protective work clothing or equipment.

(k) **Communication of hazards**

(k)(1) **Hazard communication—general**

(k)(1)(i) Chemical manufacturers, importers, distributors and employers shall comply with all requirements of the Hazard Communication Standard (HCS) (§1910.1200) for MDA.

(k)(1)(ii) In classifying the hazards of MDA at least the following hazards are to be addressed: Cancer; liver effects; and skin sensitization.

(k)(1)(iii) Employers shall include MDA in the hazard communication program established to comply with the HCS (§1910.1200). Employers shall ensure that each employee has access to labels on containers of MDA and to safety data sheets, and is trained in accordance with the requirements of HCS and paragraph (k)(4) of this Section.

(k)(2) **Signs and labels**

(k)(2)(i) **Signs**

(k)(2)(i)(A) The employer shall post and maintain legible signs demarcating regulated areas and entrances or access ways to regulated areas that bear the following legend:

DANGER
MDA
MAY CAUSE CANCER
CAUSES DAMAGE TO THE LIVER
RESPIRATORY PROTECTION AND PROTECTIVE CLOTHING MAY BE REQUIRED IN THIS AREA
AUTHORIZED PERSONNEL ONLY

(k)(2)(1)(B) Prior to June 1, 2016, employers may use the following legend in lieu of that specified in paragraph (k)(2)(i)(A) of this Section:

DANGER
MDA
MAY CAUSE CANCER
LIVER TOXIN
AUTHORIZED PERSONNEL ONLY
RESPIRATORS AND PROTECTIVE CLOTHING MAY BE REQUIRED TO BE WORN IN THIS AREA

(k)(2)(ii) **Labels** Prior to June 1, 2015, employers may include the following information workplace labels in lieu of the labeling requirements in paragraph (k)(1) of this Section:

(k)(2)(ii)(A) For pure MDA:

DANGER
CONTAINS MDA
MAY CAUSE CANCER
LIVER TOXIN

(k)(2)(ii)(B) For mixtures containing MDA:

DANGER
CONTAINS MDA
CONTAINS MATERIALS WHICH MAY CAUSE CANCER
LIVER TOXIN

(k)(3) **Safety data sheets (SDS)** In meeting the obligation to provide safety data sheets, employers shall make appropriate use of the information found in Appendices A and B to §1910.1050.

(k)(4) **Information and training**

(k)(4)(i) The employer shall provide employees with information and training on MDA, in accordance with 29 CFR §1910.1200(h), at the time of initial assignment and at least annually thereafter.

(k)(4)(ii) In addition to the information required under 29 CFR §1910.1200, the employer shall:

(k)(4)(ii)(A) Provide an explanation of the contents of this Section, including Appendices A and B, and indicate to employees where a copy of the standard is available;

(k)(4)(ii)(B) Describe the medical surveillance program required under paragraph (m) of this Section, and explain the information contained in Appendix C; and

(k)(4)(ii)(C) Describe the medical removal provision required under paragraph (m) of this Section.

(k)(5) **Access to training materials**

(k)(5)(i) The employer shall make readily available to all affected employees, without cost, all written materials relating to the employee training program, including a copy of this regulation.

(k)(5)(ii) The employer shall provide to the Assistant Secretary and the Director, upon request, all information and training materials relating to the employee information and training program.

(l) **Housekeeping**

(l)(1) All surfaces shall be maintained as free as practicable of visible accumulations of MDA.

(l)(2) The employer shall institute a program for detecting MDA leaks, spills, and discharges, including regular visual inspections of operations involving liquid or solid MDA.

(l)(3) All leaks shall be repaired and liquid or dust spills cleaned up promptly.

(l)(4) Surfaces contaminated with MDA may not be cleaned by the use of compressed air.

(l)(5) Shoveling, dry sweeping, and other methods of dry clean-up of MDA may be used where HEPA-filtered vacuuming and/or wet cleaning are not feasible or practical.

(l)(6) Waste, scrap, debris, bags, containers, equipment, and clothing contaminated with MDA shall be collected and disposed of in a manner to prevent the re-entry of MDA into the workplace.

(m) **Medical surveillance**

(m)(1) **General**

(m)(1)(i) The employer shall make available a medical surveillance program for employees exposed to MDA:

(m)(1)(i)(A) Employees exposed at or above the action level for 30 or more days per year;

(m)(1)(i)(B) Employees who are subject to dermal exposure to MDA for 15 or more days per year;

(m)(1)(i)(C) Employees who have been exposed in an emergency situation;

(m)(1)(i)(D) Employees whom the employer, based on results from compliance with paragraph (e)(8) of this Section, has reason to believe are being dermally exposed; and

(m)(1)(i)(E) Employees who show signs or symptoms of MDA exposure.

(m)(1)(ii) The employer shall ensure that all medical examinations and procedures are performed by, or under the supervision of, a licensed physician, at a reasonable time and place, and provided without cost to the employee.

(m)(2) **Initial examinations**

(m)(2)(i) Within 150 days of the effective date of this Standard, or before the time of initial assignment, the employer shall provide each employee covered by paragraph (m)(1)(i) of this Section with a medical examination including the following elements:

(m)(2)(i)(A) A detailed history which includes:

(m)(2)(i)(A)(1) Past work exposure to MDA or any other toxic substances;

(m)(2)(i)(A)(2) A history of drugs, alcohol, tobacco, and medication routinely taken (duration and quantity); and

(m)(2)(i)(A)(3) A history of dermatitis, chemical skin sensitization, or previous hepatic disease.

(m)(2)(i)(B) A physical examination which includes all routine physical examination parameters, skin examination, and signs of liver disease.

(m)(2)(i)(C) Laboratory tests including:

(m)(2)(i)(C)(1) Liver function tests and

(m)(2)(i)(C)(2) Urinalysis.

(m)(2)(i)(D) Additional tests as necessary in the opinion of the physician.

(m)(2)(ii) No initial medical examination is required if adequate records show that the employee has been examined in accordance with the requirements of this Section within the previous six months prior to the effective date of this Standard or prior to the date of initial assignment.

(m)(3) **Periodic examinations**

(m)(3)(i) The employer shall provide each employee covered by this Section with a medical examination at least annually following the initial examination. These periodic examinations shall include at least the following elements:

(m)(3)(i)(A) A brief history regarding any new exposure to potential liver toxins, changes in drug, tobacco, and alcohol intake, and the appearance of physical signs relating to the liver, and the skin;

(m)(3)(i)(B) The appropriate tests and examinations including liver function tests and skin examinations; and

(m)(3)(i)(C) Appropriate additional tests or examinations as deemed necessary by the physician.

(m)(3)(ii) If in the physicians' opinion the results of liver function tests indicate an abnormality, the employee shall be removed from further MDA exposure in accordance with paragraph (m)(9) of this Section. Repeat liver function tests shall be conducted on advice of the physician.

(m)(4) **Emergency examinations** If the employer determines that the employee has been exposed to a potentially hazardous amount of MDA in an emergency situation as addressed in paragraph (d) of this Section, the employer shall provide medical examinations in accordance with paragraphs (m)(3)(i) and (ii) of this Section. If the results of liver function testing indicate an abnormality, the employee shall be removed in accordance with paragraph (m)(9) of this Section. Repeat liver function tests shall be conducted on the advice of the physician. If the results of the tests are normal, tests must be repeated two to three weeks from the initial testing. If the results of the second set of tests are normal and, on the advice of the physician, no additional testing is required.

(m)(5) **Additional examinations** Where the employee develops signs and symptoms associated with exposure to MDA, the employer shall provide the employee with an additional medical examination including a liver function test. Repeat liver function tests shall be conducted on the advice of the physician. If the results of the tests are normal, tests must be repeated two to three weeks from the initial testing. If the results of the second set of tests are normal and, on the advice of the physician, no additional testing is required.

(m)(6) **Multiple physician review mechanism**

(m)(6)(i) If the employer selects the initial physician who conducts any medical examination or consultation provided to an employee under this Section, and the employee has signs or symptoms of occupational exposure to MDA (which could include an abnormal liver function test), and the employee disagrees with the opinion of the examining physician, and this opinion could affect the employee's job status, the employee may designate an appropriate, mutually acceptable second physician:

(m)(6)(i)(A) To review any findings, determinations, or recommendations of the initial physician; and

(m)(6)(i)(B) To conduct such examinations, consultations, and laboratory tests as the second physician deems necessary to facilitate this review.

(m)(6)(ii) The employer shall promptly notify an employee of the right to seek a second medical opinion after each occasion that an initial physician conducts a medical examination or consultation pursuant to this Section. The employer may condition its participation in, and payment for, the multiple physician review mechanism upon the employee doing the following within fifteen (15) days after receipt of the foregoing notification, or receipt of the initial physician's written opinion, whichever is later:

(m)(6)(ii)(A) The employee informing the employer that he or she intends to seek a second medical opinion, and

(m)(6)(ii)(B) The employee initiating steps to make an appointment with a second physician.

(m)(6)(iii) If the findings, determinations, or recommendations of the second physician differ from those of the initial physician, then the employer and the employee shall assure that efforts are made for the two physicians to resolve any disagreement.

(m)(6)(iv) If the two physicians have been unable to resolve quickly their disagreement, then the employer and the employee through their respective physicians shall designate a third physician;

(m)(6)(iv)(A) To review any findings, determinations, or recommendations of the prior physicians; and

(m)(6)(iv)(B) To conduct such examinations, consultations, laboratory tests, and discussions with the prior physicians as the third physician deems necessary to resolve the disagreement of the prior physicians.

(m)(6)(v) The employer shall act consistent with the findings, determinations, and recommendations of the third physician, unless the employer and the employee reach an agreement which is otherwise consistent with the recommendations of at least one of the three physicians.

(m)(7) **Information provided to the examining and consulting physicians**

(m)(7)(i) The employer shall provide the following information to the examining physician:

(m)(7)(i)(A) A copy of this regulation and its Appendices;

(m)(7)(i)(B) A description of the affected employee's duties as they relate to the employee's potential exposure to MDA;

(m)(7)(i)(C) The employee's current actual or representative MDA exposure level;

(m)(7)(i)(D) A description of any personal protective equipment used or to be used; and

(m)(7)(i)(E) Information from previous employment-related medical examinations of the affected employee.

(m)(7)(ii) The employer shall provide the foregoing information to a second physician under this Section upon request either by the second physician, or by the employee.

(m)(8) **Physician's written opinion**

(m)(8)(i) For each examination under this Section, the employer shall obtain, and provide the employee with a copy of, the examining physician's written opinion within 15 days of its receipt. The written opinion shall include the following:

(m)(8)(i)(A) The occupationally-pertinent results of the medical examination and tests;

(m)(8)(i)(B) The physician's opinion concerning whether the employee has any detected medical conditions which would place the employee at increased risk of material impairment of health from exposure to MDA;

(m)(8)(i)(C) The physician's recommended limitations upon the employee's exposure to MDA or upon the employee's use of protective clothing or equipment and respirators; and

(m)(8)(i)(D) A statement that the employee has been informed by the physician of the results of the medical examination and any medical conditions resulting from MDA exposure which require further explanation or treatment.

(m)(8)(ii) The written opinion obtained by the employer shall not reveal specific findings or diagnoses unrelated to occupational exposures.

(m)(9) **Medical removal**

(m)(9)(i) Temporary medical removal of an employee

(m)(9)(i)(A) Temporary removal resulting from occupational exposure. The employee shall be removed from work environments in which exposure to MDA is at or above the action level or where dermal exposure to MDA may occur, following an initial examination (paragraph (m)(2) of this Section), periodic examinations (paragraph (m)(3) of this Section), an emergency situation paragraph (m)(4) of this Section, or an additional examination (paragraph (m)(5) of this Section) in the following circumstances:

(m)(9)(i)(A)(1) When the employee exhibits signs and/or symptoms indicative of acute exposure to MDA; or

(m)(9)(i)(A)(2) When the examining physician determines that an employee's abnormal liver function tests are not associated with MDA exposure but that the abnormalities may be exacerbated as a result of occupational exposure to MDA.

(m)(9)(i)(B) Temporary removal due to a final medical determination.

(m)(9)(i)(B)(1) The employer shall remove an employee from work environments in which exposure to MDA is at or above the action level or where dermal exposure to MDA may occur, on each occasion that there is a final medical determination or opinion that the employee has a detected medical condition which places the employee at increased risk of material impairment to health from exposure to MDA.

(m)(9)(i)(B)(2) For the purposes of this Section, the phrase "final medical determination" shall mean the outcome of the physician review mechanism used pursuant to the medical surveillance provisions of this Section.

(m)(9)(i)(B)(3) Where a final medical determination results in any recommended special protective measures for an employee, or limitations on an employee's exposure to MDA, the employer shall implement and act consistent with the recommendation.

(m)(9)(ii) Return of the employee to former job status.

(m)(9)(ii)(A) The employer shall return an employee to his or her former job status:

(m)(9)(ii)(A)(1) When the employee no longer shows signs or symptoms of exposure to MDA, or upon the advice of the physician.

(m)(9)(ii)(A)(2) When a subsequent final medical determination results in a medical finding, determination, or opinion that the employee no longer has a detected medical condition which places the employee at increased risk of material impairment to health from exposure to MDA.

(m)(9)(ii)(B) For the purposes of this Section, the requirement that an employer return an employee to his or her former job status is not intended to expand upon or restrict any rights an employee has or would have had, absent temporary medical removal, to a specific job classification or position under the terms of a collective bargaining agreement.

(m)(9)(iii) Removal of other employee special protective measure or limitations. The employer shall remove any limitations placed on an employee, or end any special protective measures provided to an employee, pursuant to a final medical determination, when a subsequent final medical determination indicates that the limitations or special protective measures are no longer necessary.

(m)(9)(iv) Employer options pending a final medical determination. Where the physician review mechanism used pursuant to the medical surveillance provisions of this Section, has not yet resulted in a final medical determination with respect to an employee, the employer shall act as follows:

(m)(9)(iv)(A) Removal. The employer may remove the employee from exposure to MDA, provide special protective measures to the employee, or place limitations upon the employee, consistent with the medical findings, determinations, or recommendations of any of the physicians who have reviewed the employee's health status;

(m)(9)(iv)(B) Return. The employer may return the employee to his or her former job status, and end any special protective measures provided to the employee, consistent with the medical findings, determinations, or recommendations of any of the physicians who have reviewed the employee's health status, with two exceptions.

(m)(9)(iv)(B)(1) If the initial removal, special protection, or limitation of the employee resulted from a final medical determination which differed from the findings, determinations, or recommendations of the initial physician; or

(m)(9)(iv)(B)(2) If the employee has been on removal status for the preceding six months as a result of exposure to MDA, then the employer shall await a final medical determination.

(m)(9)(v) Medical removal protection benefits

(m)(9)(v)(A) Provisions of medical removal protection benefits. The employer shall provide to an employee up to six (6) months of medical removal protection benefits on each occasion that an employee is removed from exposure to MDA or otherwise limited pursuant to this Section.

(m)(9)(v)(B) Definition of medical removal protection benefits. For the purposes of this Section, the requirement that an employer provide medical removal protection benefits means that the employer shall maintain the earnings, seniority, and other employment rights and benefits of an employee as though the employee had not been removed from normal exposure to MDA or otherwise limited.

(m)(9)(v)(C) Follow-up medical surveillance during the period of employee removal or limitations. During the period of time that an employee is removed from normal exposure to MDA or otherwise limited, the employer may condition the provision of medical removal protection benefits upon the employee's participation in follow-up medical surveillance made available pursuant to this Section.

(m)(9)(v)(D) Workers' compensation claims. If a removed employee files a claim for workers' compensation payments for a MDA-related disability, then the employer shall continue to provide medical removal protection benefits pending disposition of the claim. To the extent that an award is made to the employee for earnings lost during the period of removal, the employer's medical removal protection obligation shall be reduced by such amount. The employer shall receive no credit for workers' compensation payments received by the employee for treatment-related expenses.

(m)(9)(v)(E) Other credits. The employer's obligation to provide medical removal protection benefits to a removed employee shall be reduced to the extent that the employee receives compensation for earnings lost during the period of removal either from a publicly or employer-funded compensation program, or receives income from non-MDA-related employment with any employer made possible by virtue of the employee's removal.

(m)(9)(v)(F) Employees who do not recover within the 6 months of removal. The employer shall take the following measures with respect to any employee removed from exposure to MDA:

(m)(9)(v)(F)(1) The employer shall make available to the employee a medical examination pursuant to this Section to obtain a final medical determination with respect to the employee;

(m)(9)(v)(F)(2) The employer shall assure that the final medical determination obtained indicates whether or not the employee may be returned to his or her former job status, and, if not, what steps should be taken to protect the employee's health;

(m)(9)(v)(F)(3) Where the final medical determination has not yet been obtained, or, once obtained indicates that the employee may not yet be returned to his or her former job status, the employer shall continue to provide medical removal protection benefits to the employee until either the employee is returned to former job status, or a final medical determination is made that the employee is incapable of ever safely returning to his or her former job status; and

(m)(9)(v)(F)(4) Where the employer acts pursuant to a final medical determination which permits the return of the employee to his or her former job status, despite what would otherwise be an abnormal liver function test, later questions concerning removing the employee again shall be decided by a final medical determination. The employer need not automatically remove such an employee pursuant to the MDA removal criteria provided by this Section.

(m)(9)(vi) Voluntary removal or restriction of an employee. Where an employer, although not required by this Section to do so, removes an employee from exposure to MDA or otherwise places limitations on an employee due to the effects of MDA exposure on the employee's medical condition, the employer shall provide medical removal protection benefits to the employee equal to that required by paragraph (m)(9)(v) of this Section.

(n) **Recordkeeping**

(n)(1) **Monitoring data for exempted employers**

(n)(1)(i) Where as a result of the initial monitoring the processing, use, or handling of products made from or containing MDA are exempted from other requirements of this Section under paragraph (a)(2) of this Section, the employer shall establish and maintain an accurate record of monitoring relied on in support of the exemption.

(n)(1)(ii) This record shall include at least the following information:

(n)(1)(ii)(A) The product qualifying for exemption;

(n)(1)(ii)(B) The source of the monitoring data (e.g., was monitoring performed by the employer or a private contractor);

(n)(1)(ii)(C) The testing protocol, results of testing, and/or analysis of the material for the release of MDA;

(n)(1)(ii)(D) A description of the operation exempted and how the data support the exemption (e.g., are the monitoring data representative of the conditions at the affected facility); and

(n)(1)(ii)(E) Other data relevant to the operations, materials, processing, or employee exposures covered by the exemption.

(n)(1)(iii) The employer shall maintain this record for the duration of the employer's reliance upon such objective data.

(n)(2) **Objective data for exempted employers**

(n)(2)(i) Where the processing, use, or handling of products made from or containing MDA are exempted from other requirements of this Section under paragraph (a) of this Section, the employer shall establish and maintain an accurate record of objective data relied upon in support of the exemption.

(n)(2)(ii) This record shall include at least the following information:

(n)(2)(ii)(A) The product qualifying for exemption;

(n)(2)(ii)(B) The source of the objective data;

(n)(2)(ii)(C) The testing protocol, results of testing, and/or analysis of the material for the release of MDA;

(n)(2)(ii)(D) A description of the operation exempted and how the data support the exemption; and

(n)(2)(ii)(E) Other data relevant to the operations, materials, processing, or employee exposures covered by the exemption.

(n)(2)(iii) The employer shall maintain this record for the duration of the employer's reliance upon such objective data.

(n)(3) **Exposure measurements**

(n)(3)(i) The employer shall establish and maintain an accurate record of all measurements required by paragraph (e) of this Section, in accordance with 29 CFR §1910.1020.

(n)(3)(ii) This record shall include:

(n)(3)(ii)(A) The dates, number, duration, and results of each of the samples taken, including a description of the procedure used to determine representative employee exposures;

(n)(3)(ii)(B) Identification of the sampling and analytical methods used;

(n)(3)(ii)(C) A description of the type of respiratory protective devices worn, if any; and

(n)(3)(ii)(D) The name, social security number, job classification and exposure levels of the employee monitored and all other employees whose exposure the measurement is intended to represent.

(n)(3)(iii) The employer shall maintain this record for at least 30 years, in accordance with 29 CFR §1910.1020.

(n)(4) **Medical surveillance**

(n)(4)(i) The employer shall establish and maintain an accurate record for each employee subject to medical surveillance required by paragraph (m) of this Section, in accordance with 29 CFR §1910.1020.

(n)(4)(ii) This record shall include:

(n)(4)(ii)(A) The name, social security number and description of the duties of the employee;

(n)(4)(ii)(B) The employer's copy of the physician's written opinion on the initial, periodic, and any special examinations, including results of medical examination and all tests, opinions, and recommendations;

(n)(4)(ii)(C) Results of any airborne exposure monitoring done for that employee and the representative exposure levels supplied to the physician; and

(n)(4)(ii)(D) Any employee medical complaints related to exposure to MDA;

(n)(4)(iii) The employer shall keep, or assure that the examining physician keeps, the following medical records:

(n)(4)(iii)(A) A copy of this Standard and its Appendices, except that the employer may keep one copy of the standard and its Appendices for all employees provided the employer references the standard and its Appendices in the medical surveillance record of each employee;

(n)(4)(iii)(B) A copy of the information provided to the physician as required by any paragraphs in the regulatory text;

(n)(4)(iii)(C) A description of the laboratory procedures and a copy of any standards or guidelines used to interpret the test results or references to the information;

(n)(4)(iii)(D) A copy of the employee's medical and work history related to exposure to MDA; and

(n)(4)(iv) The employer shall maintain this record for at least the duration of employment plus 30 years, in accordance with 29 CFR §1910.1020.

(n)(5) **Medical removals**

(n)(5)(i) The employer shall establish and maintain an accurate record for each employee removed from current exposure to MDA pursuant to paragraph (m) of this Section.

(n)(5)(ii) Each record shall include:

(n)(5)(ii)(A) The name and social security number of the employee;

(n)(5)(ii)(B) The date of each occasion that the employee was removed from current exposure to MDA as well as the corresponding date on which the employee was returned to his or her former job status;

(n)(5)(ii)(C) A brief explanation of how each removal was or is being accomplished; and

(n)(5)(ii)(D) A statement with respect to each removal indicating the reason for the removal.

(n)(5)(iii) The employer shall maintain each medical removal record for at least the duration of an employee's employment plus 30 years.

(n)(6) **Availability**

(n)(6)(i) The employer shall assure that records required to be maintained by this Section shall be made available, upon request, to the Assistant Secretary and the Director for examination and copying.

(n)(6)(ii) Employee exposure monitoring records required by this Section shall be provided upon request for examination and copying to employees, employee representatives, and the Assistant Secretary in accordance with 29 CFR §1910.1020 (a)–(e) and (g)–(i).

(n)(6)(iii) Employee medical records required by this Section shall be provided upon request for examination and copying, to the subject employee, to anyone having the specific written consent of the subject employee, and to the Assistant Secretary in accordance with 29 CFR §1910.1020.

(n)(7) **Transfer of records** The employer shall comply with the requirements involving transfer of records set forth in 29 CFR §1910.1020(h).

(o) **Observation of monitoring**

(o)(1) **Employee observation** The employer shall provide affected employees, or their designated representatives, an opportunity to observe the measuring or monitoring of employee exposure to MDA conducted pursuant to paragraph (e) of this Section.

(o)(2) **Observation procedures** When observation of the measuring or monitoring of employee exposure to MDA requires entry into areas where the use of protective clothing and equipment or respirators is required, the employer shall provide the observer with personal protective clothing and equipment or respirators required to be worn by employees working in the area, assure the use of such clothing and equipment or respirators, and require the observer to comply with all other applicable safety and health procedures.

(p) [Reserved]

(q) **Appendices** The information contained in Appendices A, B, C, and D of this Section is not intended, by itself, to create any additional obligations not otherwise imposed by this Standard nor detract from any existing obligation.

§1910.1050 Appendix A Substance data sheet for 4,4'Methylenedianiline

I. Substance Identification

A. Substance: Methylenedianiline (MDA)

B. Permissible Exposure:

1. Airborne: Ten parts per billion parts of air (10 ppb), time-weighted average (TWA) for an 8-hour workday and an action level of five parts per billion parts of air (5 ppb).
2. Dermal: Eye contact and skin contact with MDA are not permitted.

C. Appearance and odor: White to tan solid; amine odor

II. Health Hazard Data

A. Ways in which MDA affects your health. MDA can affect your health if you inhale it, or if it comes in contact with your skin or eyes. MDA is also harmful if you happen to swallow it. Do not get MDA in eyes, on skin, or on clothing.

B. Effects of overexposure.

1. Short-term (acute) overexposure: Overexposure to MDA may produce fever, chills, loss of appetite, vomiting, jaundice. Contact may irritate skin, eyes and mucous membranes. Sensitization may occur.
2. Long-term (chronic) exposure. Repeated or prolonged exposure to MDA, even at relatively low concentrations, may cause cancer. In addition, damage to the liver, kidneys, blood, and spleen may occur with long term exposure.
3. Reporting signs and symptoms. You should inform your employer if you develop any signs or symptoms which you suspect are caused by exposure to MDA including yellow staining of the skin.

III. Protective Clothing and Equipment

A. Respirators. Respirators are required for those operations in which engineering controls or work-practice controls are not adequate or feasible to reduce exposure to the permissible limit. If respirators are worn, they must have a label issued by the National Institute for Occupational Safety and Health under the provisions of 42 CFR Part §84 stating that the respirators have been approved for this purpose, and cartridges and canisters must be replaced in accordance with the requirements of 29 CFR §1910.134. If you experience difficulty breathing while wearing a respirator, you can request a positive-pressure respirator from your employer. You must be thoroughly trained to use the assigned respirator, and the training must be provided by your employer.

MDA does not have a detectable odor except at levels well above the permissible exposure limits. Do not depend on odor to warn you when a respirator canister is exhausted. If you can smell MDA while wearing a respirator, proceed immediately to fresh air. If you experience difficulty breathing while wearing a respirator, tell your employer.

B. Protective Clothing. You may be required to wear coveralls, aprons, gloves, face shields, or other appropriate protective clothing to prevent skin contact with MDA. Where protective clothing is required, your employer is required to provide clean garments to you, as necessary, to assure that the clothing protects you adequately. Replace or repair impervious clothing that has developed leaks.

MDA should never be allowed to remain on the skin. Clothing and shoes which are not impervious to MDA should not be allowed to become contaminated with MDA, and if they do, the clothing and shoes should be promptly removed and decontaminated. The clothing should be laundered to remove MDA or discarded. Once MDA penetrates shoes or other leather articles, they should not be worn again.

C. Eye protection. You must wear splashproof safety goggles in areas where liquid MDA may contact your eyes. Contact lenses should not be worn in areas where eye contact with MDA can occur. In addition, you must wear a face shield if your face could be splashed with MDA liquid.

IV. Emergency and First Aid Procedures

A. Eye and face exposure. If MDA is splashed into the eyes, wash the eyes for at least 15 minutes. See a doctor as soon as possible.

B. Skin exposure. If MDA is spilled on your clothing or skin, remove the contaminated clothing and wash the exposed skin with large amounts of soap and water immediately. Wash contaminated clothing before you wear it again.

C. Breathing. If you or any other person breathes in large amounts of MDA, get the exposed person to fresh air at once. Apply artificial respiration if breathing has stopped. Call for medical assistance or a doctor as soon as possible. Never enter any vessel or confined space where the MDA concentration might be high without proper safety equipment and at least one other person present who will stay outside. A life line should be used.

D. Swallowing. If MDA has been swallowed and the patient is conscious, do not induce vomiting. Call for medical assistance or a doctor immediately.

V. Medical Requirements

If you are exposed to MDA at a concentration at or above the action level for more than 30 days per year, or exposed to liquid mixtures more than 15 days per year, your employer is required to provide a medical examination, including a medical history and laboratory tests, within 60 days of the effective date of this Standard and annually thereafter. These tests shall be provided without cost to you. In addition, if you are accidentally exposed to MDA (either by ingestion, inhalation, or skin/eye contact) under conditions known or suspected to constitute toxic exposure to MDA, your employer is required to make special examinations and tests available to you.

VI. Observation of Monitoring

Your employer is required to perform measurements that are representative of your exposure to MDA and you or your designated representative are entitled to observe the monitoring procedure. You are entitled to observe the steps taken in the measurement procedure and to record the results obtained. When the monitoring procedure is taking place in an area where respirators or personal protective clothing and equipment are required to be worn, you and your representative must also be provided with, and must wear, the protective clothing and equipment.

VII. Access to Records

You or your representative are entitled to see the records of measurements of your exposure to MDA upon written request to your employer. Your medical examination records can be furnished to your physician or designated representative upon request by you to your employer.

VIII. Precautions for Safe Use, Handling and Storage

A. Material is combustible. Avoid strong acids and their anhydrides. Avoid strong oxidants. Consult supervisor for disposal requirements.

B. Emergency clean-up. Wear self-contained breathing apparatus and fully clothe the body in the appropriate personal protective clothing and equipment.

§1910.1050 Appendix B
Substance technical guidelines, MDA

I. Identification

A. Substance identification.

1. Synonyms: CAS No. 101–77–9. 4,4′-methylenedianiline; 4,4′-methylenebisaniline; methylenedianiline; dianilinomethane.
2. Formula: $C_{13}H_{14}N_2$

II. Physical Data

1. Appearance and Odor: White to tan solid; amine odor
2. Molecular Weight: 198.26
3. Boiling Point: 398–399 °C at 760 mm Hg
4. Melting Point: 88–93 °C (190–100 °F)
5. Vapor Pressure: 9 mmHg at 232 °C
6. Evaporation Rate (n-butyl acetate = 1): Negligible
7. Vapor Density (Air = 1): Not Applicable
8. Volatile Fraction by Weight: Negligible
9. Specific Gravity (Water = 1): Slight
10. Heat of Combustion: −8.40 kcal/g
11. Solubility in Water: Slightly soluble in cold water, very soluble in alcohol, benzene, ether, and many organic solvents.

III. Fire, Explosion, and Reactivity Hazard Data

1. Flash Point: 190 °C (374 °F) Setaflash closed cup
2. Flash Point: 226 °C (439 °F) Cleveland open cup
3. Extinguishing Media: Water spray; Dry Chemical; Carbon dioxide.
4. Special Fire Fighting Procedures: Wear self-contained breathing apparatus and protective clothing to prevent contact with skin and eyes.
5. Unusual Fire and Explosion Hazards: Fire or excessive heat may cause production of hazardous decomposition products.

IV. Reactivity Data

1. Stability: Stable
2. Incompatibility: Strong oxidizers
3. Hazardous Decomposition Products: As with any other organic material, combustion may produce carbon monoxide. Oxides of nitrogen may also be present.
4. Hazardous Polymerization: Will not occur.

V. Spill and Leak Procedures

1. Sweep material onto paper and place in fiber carton.
2. Package appropriately for safe feed to an incinerator or dissolve in compatible waste solvents prior to incineration.
3. Dispose of in an approved incinerator equipped with afterburner and scrubber or contract with licensed chemical waste disposal service.
4. Discharge treatment or disposal may be subject to federal, state, or local laws.
5. Wear appropriate personal protective equipment.

VI. Special Storage and Handling Precautions

A. High exposure to MDA can occur when transferring the substance from one container to another. Such operations should be well ventilated and good work practices must be established to avoid spills.

B. Pure MDA is a solid with a low vapor pressure. Grinding or heating operations increase the potential for exposure.

C. Store away from oxidizing materials.

D. Employers shall advise employees of all areas and operations where exposure to MDA could occur.

VII. Housekeeping and Hygiene Facilities

A. The workplace should be kept clean, orderly, and in a sanitary condition.

The employer should institute a leak and spill detection program for operations involving MDA in order to detect sources of fugitive MDA emissions.

B. Adequate washing facilities with hot and cold water are to be provided and maintained in a sanitary condition. Suitable cleansing agents should also be provided to assure the effective removal of MDA from the skin.

VIII. Common Operations

Common operations in which exposure to MDA is likely to occur include the following: Manufacture of MDA; Manufacture of Methylene diisocyanate; Curing agent for epoxy resin structures; Wire coating operations; and filament winding.

§1910.1050 Appendix C
Medical surveillance guidelines for MDA

I. Route of Entry

Inhalation; skin absorption; ingestion. MDA can be inhaled, absorbed through the skin, or ingested.

II. Toxicology

MDA is a suspect carcinogen in humans. There are several reports of liver disease in humans and animals resulting from acute exposure to MDA. A well documented case of an acute cardiomyopathy secondary to exposure to MDA is on record. Numerous human cases of hepatitis secondary to MDA are known. Upon direct contact MDA may also cause damage to the eyes. Dermatitis and skin sensitization have been observed. Almost all forms of acute environmental hepatic injury in humans involve the hepatic parenchyma and produce hepatocellular jaundice. This agent produces intrahepatic cholestasis. The clinical picture consists of cholestatic jaundice, preceded or accompanied by abdominal pain, fever, and chills. Onset in about 60% of all observed cases is abrupt with severe abdominal pain. In about 30% of observed cases, the illness presented and evolved more slowly and less dramatically, with only slight abdominal pain. In about 10% of the cases only jaundice was evident. The cholestatic nature of the jaundice is evident in the prominence of itching, the histologic predominance of bile stasis, and portal inflammatory infiltration, accompanied by only slight parenchymal injury in most cases, and by the moderately elevated transaminase values. Acute, high doses, however, have been known to cause hepatocellular damage resulting in elevated SGPT, SGOT, alkaline phosphatase and bilirubin.

Absorption through the skin is rapid. MDA is metabolized and excreted over a 48-hour period. Direct contact may be irritating to the skin, causing dermatitis. Also MDA which is deposited on the skin is not thoroughly removed through washing.

MDA may cause bladder cancer in humans. Animal data supporting this assumption is not available nor is conclusive human data. However, human data collected on workers at a helicopter manufacturing facility where MDA is used suggests a higher incidence of bladder cancer among exposed workers.

III. Signs and Symptoms

Skin may become yellow from contact with MDA.

Repeated or prolonged contact with MDA may result in recurring dermatitis (red-itchy, cracked skin) and eye irritation. Inhalation, ingestion or absorption through the skin at high concentrations may result in hepatitis, causing symptoms such as fever and chills, nausea and vomiting, dark urine, anorexia, rash, right upper quadrant pain and jaundice. Corneal burns may occur when MDA is splashed in the eyes.

IV. Treatment of Acute Toxic Effects/Emergency Situation

If MDA gets into the eyes, immediately wash eyes with large amounts of water. If MDA is splashed on the skin, immediately wash contaminated skin with mild soap or detergent. Employee should be removed from exposure and given proper medical treatment. Medical tests required under the emergency section of the medical surveillance section (M)(4) must be conducted.

If the chemical is swallowed do not induce vomiting but remove by gastric lavage.

§1910.1050 Appendix D Sampling and analytical methods for MDA monitoring and measurement procedures

Measurements taken for the purpose of determining employee exposure to MDA are best taken so that the representative average 8-hour exposure may be determined from a single 8-hour sample or two (2) 4-hour samples. Short-time interval samples (or grab samples) may also be used to determine average exposure level if a minimum of five measurements are taken in a random manner over the 8-hour work shift. Random sampling means that any portion of the work shift has the same chance of being sampled as any other. The arithmetic average of all such random samples taken on one work shift is an estimate of an employee's average level of exposure for that work shift. Air samples should be taken in the employee's breathing zone (air that would most nearly represent that inhaled by the employee).

There are a number of methods available for monitoring employee exposures to MDA. The method OSHA currently uses is included below.

The employer, however, has the obligation of selecting any monitoring method which meets the accuracy and precision requirements of the standard under his unique field conditions. The standard requires that the method of monitoring must have an accuracy, to a 95 percent confidence level, of not less than plus or minus 25 percent for the select PEL.

OSHA Methodology Sampling Procedure Apparatus

Samples are collected by use of a personal sampling pump that can be calibrated within ± 5% of the recommended flow rate with the sampling filter in line.

Samples are collected on 37 mm Gelman type A/E glass fiber filters treated with sulfuric acid. The filters are prepared by soaking each filter with 0.5 mL of 0.26N H_2SO_4. (0.26 N H_2SO_4 can be prepared by diluting 1.5 mL of 36N H_2SO_4 to 200 mL with deionized water.) The filters are dried in an oven at 100 degrees C for one hour and then assembled into two-piece 37 mm polystyrene cassettes with backup pads. The cassettes are sealed with shrink bands and the ends are plugged with plastic plugs.

After sampling, the filters are carefully removed from the cassettes and individually transferred to small vials containing approximately 2 mL deionized water. The vials must be tightly sealed. The water can be added before or after the filters are transferred. The vials must be sealable and capable of holding at least 7 mL of liquid. Small glass scintillation vials with caps containing Teflon liners are recommended.

Reagents

Deionized water is needed for addition to the vials.

Sampling Technique

Immediately before sampling, remove the plastic plugs from the filter cassettes.

Attach the cassette to the sampling pump with flexible tubing and place the cassette in the employee's breathing zone.

After sampling, seal the cassettes with plastic plugs until the filters are transferred to the vials containing deionized water.

At some convenient time within 10 hours of sampling, transfer the sample filters to vials.

Seal the small vials lengthwise.

Submit at least one blank filter with each sample set. Blanks should be handled in the same manner as samples, but no air is drawn through them.

Record sample volumes (in L of air) for each sample, along with any potential interferences.

Retention Efficiency

A retention efficiency study was performed by drawing 100 L of air (80% relative humidity) at 1 L/min through sample filters that had been spiked with 0.814 µg MDA. Instead of using backup pads, blank acid-treated filters were used as backups in each cassette. Upon analysis, the top filters were found to have an average of 91.8% of the spiked amount. There was no MDA found on the bottom filters, so the amount lost was probably due to the slight instability of the MDA salt.

Extraction Efficiency

The average extraction efficiency for six filters spiked at the target concentration is 99.6%.

The stability of extracted and derivatized samples was verified by reanalyzing the above six samples the next day using fresh standards. The average extraction efficiency for the reanalyzed samples is 98.7%.

Recommended Air Volume and Sampling Rate

The recommended air volume is 100 L.

The recommended sampling rate is 1 L/min.

Interferences (Sampling)

MDI appears to be a positive interference. It was found that when MDI was spiked onto an acid-treated filter, the MDI converted to MDA after air was drawn through it.

Suspected interferences should be reported to the laboratory with submitted samples.

Safety Precautions (Sampling)

Attach the sampling equipment to the employees so that it will not interfere with work performance or safety.

Follow all safety procedures that apply to the work area being sampled.

Analytical Procedure

Apparatus: The following are required for analysis.

- A GC equipped with an electron capture detector. For this evaluation a Tracor 222 Gas Chromatograph equipped with a Nickel 63 High Temperature Electron Capture Detector and a Linearizer was used.
- A GC column capable of separating the MDA derivative from the solvent and interferences. A 6 ft × 2 mm ID glass column packed with 3% OV–101 coated on 100/120 Gas Chrom Q was used in this evaluation.
- A electronic integrator or some other suitable means of measuring peak areas or heights.
- Small resealable vials with Teflon-lined caps capable of holding 4 mL.
- A dispenser or pipet for toluene capable of delivering 2.0 mL.
- Pipets (or repipets with plastic or Teflon tips) capable of delivering 1 mL for the sodium hydroxide and buffer solutions.
- A repipet capable of delivering 25 µL HFAA.
- Syringes for preparation of standards and injection of standards and samples into a GC.
- Volumetric flasks and pipets to dilute the pure MDA in preparation of standards.
- Disposable pipets to transfer the toluene layers after the samples are extracted.

Reagents

0.5 NaOH prepared from reagent grade NaOH.

Toluene, pesticide grade. Burdick and Jackson distilled in glass toluene was used.

Heptafluorobutyric acid anhydride (HFAA). HFAA from Pierce Chemical Company was used.

pH 7.0 phosphate buffer, prepared from 136 g potassium dihydrogen phosphate and 1 L deionized water. The pH is adjusted to 7.0 with saturated sodium hydroxide solution.

4,4′ -Methylenedianiline (MDA), reagent grade.

Standard Preparation

Concentrated stock standards are prepared by diluting pure MDA with toluene. Analytical standards are prepared by injecting uL amounts of diluted stock standards into vials that contain 2.0 mL toluene.

25 uL HFAA are added to each vial and the vials are capped and shaken for 10 seconds.

After 10 min, 1 mL of buffer is added to each vial.

The vials are recapped and shaken for 10 seconds.

After allowing the layers to separate, aliquots of the toluene (upper) layers are removed with a syringe and analyzed by GC.

Analytical standard concentrations should bracket sample concentrations. Thus, if samples fall out of the range of prepared standards, additional standards must be prepared to ascertain detector response.

Sample Preparation

The sample filters are received in vials containing deionized water.

1 mL of 0.5N NaOH and 2.0 mL toluene are added to each vial.

The vials are recapped and shaken for 10 min.

After allowing the layers to separate, approximately 1 mL aliquots of the toluene (upper) layers are transferred to separate vials with clean disposable pipets.

The toluene layers are treated and analyzed.

Analysis

GC conditions
Zone temperatures:
Column—220 °C
Injector—235 °C
Detector—335 °C
Gas flows, Ar/CH4 Column—28 mL/min(95/5) Purge—40 mL/min
Injection volume: 5.0 uL Column: 6 ft × 1/8 in ID glass, 3% OV–101 on 100/120 Gas Chrom Q
Retention time of MDA derivative: 3.5 min

Chromatogram

Peak areas or heights are measured by an integrator or other suitable means.

A calibration curve is constructed by plotting response (peak areas or heights) of standard injections versus ug of MDA per sample. Sample concentrations must be bracketed by standards.

Interferences (Analytical)

Any compound that gives an electron capture detector response and has the same general retention time as the HFAA derivative of MDA is a potential interference. Suspected interferences reported to the laboratory with submitted samples by the industrial hygienist must be considered before samples are derivatized.

GC parameters may be changed to possibly circumvent interferences.

Retention time on a single column is not considered proof of chemical identity. Analyte identity should be confirmed by GC/MS if possible.

Calculations

The analyte concentration for samples is obtained from the calibration curve in terms of ug MDA per sample. The extraction efficiency is 100%. If any MDA is found on the blank, that amount is subtracted from the sample amounts. The air concentrations are calculated using the following formulae.

$$\mu g/m^3 = (\mu g \text{ MDA per sample})\,(1000)/(\text{L of air sampled})$$

$$ppb = (\mu g/m^3)\,(24.46)/(198.3) = (\mu g/m^3)\,(0.1233)$$

where 24.46 is the molar volume at 25 degrees C and 760 mm Hg

Safety Precautions (Analytical)

Avoid skin contact and inhalation of all chemicals.

Restrict the use of all chemicals to a fume hood if possible.

Wear safety glasses and a lab coat at all times while in the lab area.

[57 FR 35666, Aug. 10, 1992, as amended at 57 FR 49649, Nov. 3, 1992; 61 FR 5508, Feb. 13, 1996; 63 FR 1293, Jan. 8, 1998; 67 FR 67965, Nov. 7, 2002; 71 FR 16672, 16673, Apr. 3, 2006; 71 FR 50190, Aug. 24, 2006; 73 FR 75586, Dec. 12, 2008; 76 FR 33609, June 8, 2011]

§1910.1051 1,3–Butadiene

(a) Scope and application

(a)(1) This Section applies to all occupational exposures to 1,3-Butadiene (BD), Chemical Abstracts Service Registry No. 106–99–0, except as provided in paragraph (a)(2) of this Section.

(a)(2)(i) Except for the recordkeeping provisions in paragraph (m)(1) of this Section, this Section does not apply to the processing, use, or handling of products containing BD or to other work operations and streams in which BD is present where objective data are reasonably relied upon that demonstrate the work operation or the product or the group of products or operations to which it belongs may not reasonably be foreseen to release BD in airborne concentrations at or above the action level or in excess of the STEL under the expected conditions of processing, use, or handling that will cause the greatest possible release or in any plausible accident.

(a)(2)(ii) This Section also does not apply to work operations, products or streams where the only exposure to BD is from liquid mixtures containing 0.1% or less of BD by volume or the vapors released from such liquids, unless objective data become available that show that airborne concentrations generated by such mixtures can exceed the action level or STEL under reasonably predictable conditions of processing, use or handling that will cause the greatest possible release.

(a)(2)(iii) Except for labeling requirements and requirements for emergency response, this Section does not apply to the storage, transportation, distribution or sale of BD or liquid mixtures in intact containers or in transportation pipelines sealed in such a manner as to fully contain BD vapors or liquid.

(a)(3) Where products or processes containing BD are exempted under paragraph (a)(2) of this Section, the employer shall maintain records of the objective data supporting that exemption and the basis for the employer's reliance on the data, as provided in paragraph (m)(1) of this Section.

(b) Definitions: For the purpose of this Section, the following definitions shall apply:

Action level means a concentration of airborne BD of 0.5 ppm calculated as an eight (8)-hour time-weighted average.

Assistant Secretary means the Assistant Secretary of Labor for Occupational Safety and Health, U.S. Department of Labor, or designee.

Authorized person means any person specifically designated by the employer, whose duties require entrance into a regulated area, or a person entering such an area as a designated representative of employees to exercise the right to observe monitoring and measuring procedures under paragraph (d)(8) of this Section, or a person designated under the Act or regulations issued under the Act to enter a regulated area.

1,3–Butadiene means an organic compound with chemical formula $CH_2 = CH - CH = CH_2$ that has a molecular weight of approximately 54.15 gm/mole.

Business day means any Monday through Friday, except those days designated as federal, state, local or company specific holidays.

Complete Blood Count (CBC) means laboratory tests performed on whole blood specimens and includes the following: White blood cell count (WBC), hematocrit (Hct), red blood cell count (RBC), hemoglobin (Hgb), differential count of white blood cells, red blood cell morphology, red blood cell indices, and platelet count.

Day means any part of a calendar day.

Director means the Director of the National Institute for Occupational Safety and Health (NIOSH), U.S. Department of Health and Human Services, or designee.

Emergency situation means any occurrence such as, but not limited to, equipment failure, rupture of containers, or failure of control equipment that may or does result in an uncontrolled significant release of BD.

Employee exposure means exposure of a worker to airborne concentrations of BD which would occur if the employee were not using respiratory protective equipment.

Objective data means monitoring data, or mathematical modelling or calculations based on composition, chemical and physical properties of a material, stream or product.

Permissible Exposure Limits, PELs means either the 8 hour Time Weighted Average (8-hr TWA) exposure or the Short-Term Exposure Limit (STEL).

Physician or other licensed health care professional is an individual whose legally permitted scope of practice (i.e., license, registration, or certification) allows him or her to independently provide or be delegated the responsibility to provide one or more of the specific health care services required by paragraph (k) of this Section.

Regulated area means any area where airborne concentrations of BD exceed or can reasonably be expected to exceed the 8-hour time weighted average (8-hr TWA) exposure of 1 ppm or the short-term exposure limit (STEL) of 5 ppm for 15 minutes.

This Section means this 1,3-butadiene standard.

(c) Permissible exposure limits (PELs)

(c)(1) **Time-weighted average (TWA) limit** The employer shall ensure that no employee is exposed to an airborne concentration of BD in excess of one (1) part BD per million parts of air (ppm) measured as an eight (8)-hour time-weighted average.

(c)(2) **Short-term exposure limit (STEL)** The employer shall ensure that no employee is exposed to an airborne concentration of BD in excess of five parts of BD per million parts of air (5 ppm) as determined over a sampling period of fifteen (15) minutes.

(d) Exposure monitoring

(d)(1) General

(d)(1)(i) Determinations of employee exposure shall be made from breathing zone air samples that are representative of the 8-hour TWA and 15-minute short-term exposures of each employee.

(d)(1)(ii) Representative 8-hour TWA employee exposure shall be determined on the basis of one or more samples representing full-shift exposure for each shift and for each job classification in each work area.

(d)(1)(iii) Representative 15-minute short-term employee exposures shall be determined on the basis of one or more samples representing 15-minute exposures associated with operations that are most likely to produce exposures above the STEL for each shift and for each job classification in each work area.

(d)(1)(iv) [OI] Except for the initial monitoring required under paragraph (d)(2) of this Section, where the employer can document that exposure levels are equivalent for similar operations on different work shifts, the employer need only determine representative employee exposure for that operation from the shift during which the highest exposure is expected.

(d)(2) **Initial monitoring**

(d)(2)(i) Each employer who has a workplace or work operation covered by this Section, shall perform initial monitoring to determine accurately the airborne concentrations of BD to which employees may be exposed, or shall rely on objective data pursuant to paragraph (a)(2)(i) of this Section to fulfill this requirement. The initial monitoring required under this paragraph shall be completed within 60 days of the introduction of BD into the workplace.

(d)(2)(ii) Where the employer has monitored within two years prior to the effective date of this Section and the monitoring satisfies all other requirements of this Section, the employer may rely on such earlier monitoring results to satisfy the requirements of paragraph (d)(2)(i) of this Section, provided that the conditions under which the initial monitoring was conducted have not changed in a manner that may result in new or additional exposures.

(d)(3) **Periodic monitoring and its frequency**

(d)(3)(i) If the initial monitoring required by paragraph (d)(2) of this Section reveals employee exposure to be at or above the action level but at or below both the 8-hour TWA limit and the STEL, the employer shall repeat the representative monitoring required by paragraph (d)(1) of this Section every twelve months.

(d)(3)(ii) If the initial monitoring required by paragraph (d)(2) of this Section reveals employee exposure to be above the 8-hour TWA limit, the employer shall repeat the representative monitoring required by paragraph (d)(1)(ii) of this Section at least every three months until the employer has collected two samples per quarter (each at least 7 days apart) within a two-year period, after which such monitoring must occur at least every six months.

(d)(3)(iii) If the initial monitoring required by paragraph (d)(2) of this Section reveals employee exposure to be above the STEL, the employer shall repeat the representative monitoring required by paragraph (d)(1)(iii) of this Section at least every three months until the employer has collected two samples per quarter (each at least 7 days apart) within a two-year period, after which such monitoring must occur at least every six months.

(d)(3)(iv) The employer may alter the monitoring schedule from every six months to annually for any required representative monitoring for which two consecutive measurements taken at least 7 days apart indicate that employee exposure has decreased to or below the 8-hour TWA, but is at or above the action level.

(d)(4) **Termination of monitoring**

(d)(4)(i) If the initial monitoring required by paragraph (d)(2) of this Section reveals employee exposure to be below the action level and at or below the STEL, the employer may discontinue the monitoring for employees whose exposures are represented by the initial monitoring.

(d)(4)(ii) If the periodic monitoring required by paragraph (d)(3) of this Section reveals that employee exposures, as indicated by at least two consecutive measurements taken at least 7 days apart, are below the action level and at or below the STEL, the employer may discontinue the monitoring for those employees who are represented by such monitoring.

(d)(5) **Additional monitoring**

(d)(5)(i) The employer shall institute the exposure monitoring required under paragraph (d) of this Section whenever there has been a change in the production, process, control equipment, personnel or work practices that may result in new or additional exposures to BD or when the employer has any reason to suspect that a change may result in new or additional exposures.

(d)(5)(ii) Whenever spills, leaks, ruptures or other breakdowns occur that may lead to employee exposure above the 8-hr TWA limit or above the STEL, the employer shall monitor [using leak source, such as direct reading instruments, area or personal monitoring], after the cleanup of the spill or repair of the leak, rupture or other breakdown, to ensure that exposures have returned to the level that existed prior to the incident.

(d)(6) **Accuracy of monitoring** Monitoring shall be accurate, at a confidence level of 95 percent, to within plus or minus 25 percent for airborne concentrations of BD at or above the 1 ppm TWA limit and to within plus or minus 35 percent for airborne concentrations of BD at or above the action level of 0.5 ppm and below the 1 ppm TWA limit.

(d)(7) **Employee notification of monitoring results**

(d)(7)(i) The employer must, within 15 working days after the receipt of the results of any monitoring performed under this Section, notify each affected employee of these results either individually in writing or by posting the results in an appropriate location that is accessible to employees.

(d)(7)(ii) The employer shall, within 15 business days after receipt of any monitoring performed under this Section indicating the 8-hour TWA or STEL has been exceeded, provide the affected employees, in writing, with information on the corrective action being taken by the employer to reduce employee exposure to or below the 8-hour TWA or STEL and the schedule for completion of this action.

(d)(8) **Observation of monitoring**

(d)(8)(i) **Employee observation** The employer shall provide affected employees or their designated representatives an opportunity to observe any monitoring of employee exposure to BD conducted in accordance with paragraph (d) of this Section.

(d)(8)(ii) **Observation procedures** When observation of the monitoring of employee exposure to BD requires entry into an area where the use of protective clothing or equipment is required, the employer shall provide the observer at no cost with protective clothing and equipment, and shall ensure that the observer uses this equipment and complies with all other applicable safety and health procedures.

(e) **Regulated areas**

(e)(1) The employer shall establish a regulated area wherever occupational exposures to airborne concentrations of BD exceed or can reasonably be expected to exceed the permissible exposure limits, either the 8-hr TWA or the STEL.

(e)(2) Access to regulated areas shall be limited to authorized persons.

(e)(3) Regulated areas shall be demarcated from the rest of the workplace in any manner that minimizes the number of employees exposed to BD within the regulated area.

(e)(4) An employer at a multi-employer worksite who establishes a regulated area shall communicate the access restrictions and locations of these areas to other employers with work operations at that worksite whose employees may have access to these areas.

(f) **Methods of compliance**

(f)(1) **Engineering controls and work practices**

(f)(1)(i) The employer shall institute engineering controls and work practices to reduce and maintain employee exposure to or below the PELs, except to the extent that the employer can establish that these controls are not feasible or where paragraph (h)(1)(i) of this Section applies.

(f)(1)(ii) Wherever the feasible engineering controls and work practices which can be instituted are not sufficient to reduce employee exposure to or below the 8-hour TWA or STEL, the employer shall use them to reduce employee exposure to the lowest levels achievable by these controls and shall supplement them by the use of respiratory protection that complies with the requirements of paragraph (h) of this Section.

(f)(2) **Compliance plan**

(f)(2)(i) Where any exposures are over the PELs, the employer shall establish and implement a written plan to reduce employee exposure to or below the PELs primarily by means of engineering and work practice controls, as required by paragraph (f)(1) of this Section, and by the use of respiratory protection where required or permitted under this Section. No compliance plan is required if all exposures are under the PELs.

(f)(2)(ii) The written compliance plan shall include a schedule for the development and implementation of the engineering controls and work practice controls including periodic leak detection surveys.

(f)(2)(iii) Copies of the compliance plan required in paragraph (f)(2) of this Section shall be furnished upon request for examination and copying to the Assistant Secretary, the Director, affected employees and designated employee representatives. Such plans shall be reviewed at least every 12 months, and shall be updated as necessary to reflect significant changes in the status of the employer's compliance program.

(f)(2)(iv) The employer shall not implement a schedule of employee rotation as a means of compliance with the PELs.

(g) **Exposure Goal Program**

(g)(1) For those operations and job classifications where employee exposures are greater than the action level, in addition to compliance with the PELs, the employer shall have an exposure goal program that is intended to limit employee exposures to below the action level during normal operations.

(g)(2) Written plans for the exposure goal program shall be furnished upon request for examination and copying to the Assistant Secretary, the Director, affected employees and designated employee representatives.

(g)(3) Such plans shall be updated as necessary to reflect significant changes in the status of the exposure goal program.

(g)(4) Respirator use is not required in the exposure goal program.

(g)(5) The exposure goal program shall include the following items unless the employer can demonstrate that the item is not feasible, will have no significant effect in reducing employee exposures, or is not necessary to achieve exposures below the action level:

(g)(5)(i) A leak prevention, detection, and repair program;

(g)(5)(ii) A program for maintaining the effectiveness of local exhaust ventilation systems;

(g)(5)(iii) The use of pump exposure control technology such as, but not limited to, mechanical double-sealed or seal-less pumps;

(g)(5)(iv) Gauging devices designed to limit employee exposure, such as magnetic gauges on rail cars;

(g)(5)(v) Unloading devices designed to limit employee exposure, such as a vapor return system;

(g)(5)(vi) A program to maintain BD concentration below the action level in control rooms by use of engineering controls.

(h) Respiratory protection

(h)(1) General For employees who use respirators required by this Section, the employer must provide each employee an appropriate respirator that complies with the requirements of this paragraph. Respirators must be used during:

(h)(1)(i) Periods necessary to install or implement feasible engineering and work-practice controls;

(h)(1)(ii) Non-routine work operations that are performed infrequently and for which employee exposures are limited in duration;

(h)(1)(iii) Work operations for which feasible engineering and work-practice controls are not yet sufficient to reduce employee exposures to or below the PELs.

(h)(1)(iv) Emergencies.

(h)(2) Respirator program

(h)(2)(i) The employer must implement a respiratory protection program in accordance with §1910.134(b) through (d) (except (d)(1)(iii), (d)(3)(iii)(B)(1), and (2)), and (f) through (m), which covers each employee required by this Section to use a respirator.

(h)(2)(ii) If air-purifying respirators are used, the employer must replace the air-purifying filter elements according to the replacement schedule set for the class of respirators listed in Table 1 of this Section, and at the beginning of each work shift.

(h)(2)(iii) Instead of using the replacement schedule listed in Table 1 of this Section, the employer may replace cartridges or canisters at 90% of their expiration service life, provided the employer:

(h)(2)(iii)(A) Demonstrates that employees will be adequately protected by this procedure.

(h)(2)(iii)(B) Uses BD breakthrough data for this purpose that have been derived from tests conducted under worst-case conditions of humidity, temperature, and air-flow rate through the filter element, and the employer also describes the data supporting the cartridge-or canister-change schedule, as well as the basis for using the data in the employer's respirator program.

(h)(2)(iv) A label must be attached to each filter element to indicate the date and time it is first installed on the respirator.

(h)(2)(v) If NIOSH approves an end-of-service-life indicator (ESLI) for an air-purifying filter element, the element may be used until the ESLI shows no further useful service life or until the element is replaced at the beginning of the next work shift, whichever occurs first.

(h)(2)(vi) Regardless of the air-purifying element used, if an employee detects the odor of BD, the employer must replace the air-purifying element immediately.

(h)(3) Respirator selection

(h)(3)(i) The employer must select appropriate respirators from Table 1 of this Section.

Concentration of airborne BD (ppm) or condition of use	Minimum required respirator
Less than or equal to 5 ppm (5 times PEL)	(a) Air-purifying half mask or full facepiece respirator equipped with approved BD or organic vapor cartridges or canisters. Cartridges or canisters shall be replaced every 4 hours.
Less than or equal to 10 ppm (10 times PEL)	(a) Air-purifying half mask or full facepiece respirator equipped with approved BD or organic vapor cartridges or canisters. Cartridges or canisters shall be replaced every 3 hours.
Less than or equal to 25 ppm (25 times PEL)	(a) Air-purifying full facepiece respirator equipped with approved BD or organic vapor cartridges or canisters. Cartridges or canisters shall be replaced every 2 hours.
	(b) Any powered air-purifying respirator equipped with approved BD or organic vapor cartridges. PAPR cartridges shall be replaced every 2 hours.
	(c) Continuous flow supplied air respirator equipped with a hood or helmet.
Less than or equal to 50 ppm (50 times PEL)	(a) Air-purifying full facepiece respirator equipped with approved BD or organic vapor cartridges or canisters. Cartridges or canisters shall be replaced every (1) hour.
	(b) Powered air-purifying respirator equipped with a tight-fitting facepiece and an approved BD or organic vapor cartridges. PAPR cartridges shall be replaced every (1) hour.
Less than or equal to 1,000 ppm (1,000 times PEL)	(a) Supplied air respirator equipped with a half mask of full facepiece and operated in a pressure demand or other positive pressure mode.
Greater than 1000 ppm unknown concentration, or firefighting	(a) Self-contained breathing apparatus equipped with a full facepiece and operated in a pressure demand or other positive pressure mode.
	(b) Any supplied air respirator equipped with a full facepiece and operated in a pressure demand or other positive pressure mode in combination with an auxiliary self-contained breathing apparatus operated in a pressure demand or other positive pressure mode.
Escape from IDLH conditions	(a) Any positive pressure self-contained breathing apparatus with an appropriate service life.
	(b) A air-purifying full facepiece respirator equipped with a front or back mounted BD or organic vapor canister.

Note: Respirators approved for use in higher concentrations are permitted to be used in lower concentrations. Full facepiece is required when eye irritation is anticipated.

(h)(3)(ii) Air-purifying respirators must have filter elements approved by NIOSH for organic vapors or BD.

(h)(3)(iii) When an employee whose job requires the use of a respirator cannot use a negative-pressure respirator, the employer must provide the employee with a respirator that has less breathing resistance than the negative-pressure respirator, such as a powered air-purifying respirator or supplied-air respirator, when the employee is able to use it and if it provides the employee adequate protection.

(i) Protective clothing and equipment Where appropriate to prevent eye contact and limit dermal exposure to BD, the employer shall provide protective clothing and equipment at no cost to the employee and shall ensure its use. Eye and face protection shall meet the requirements of 29 CFR §1910.133.

(j) Emergency situations Written plan. A written plan for emergency situations shall be developed, or an existing plan shall be modified, to contain the applicable elements specified in 29 CFR §1910.38 and 29 CFR §1910.39, "Emergency action plans" and "Fire prevention plans," respectively, and in 29 CFR §1910.120, "Hazardous Waste Operations and Emergency Response," for each workplace where there is the possibility of an emergency.

(k) Medical screening and surveillance

(k)(1) Employees covered The employer shall institute a medical screening and surveillance program as specified in this paragraph for:

(k)(1)(i) Each employee with exposure to BD at concentrations at or above the action level on 30 or more days or for employees who have or may have exposure to BD at or above the PELs on 10 or more days a year;

(k)(1)(ii) Employers (including successor owners) shall continue to provide medical screening and surveillance for employees, even after transfer to a non-BD exposed job and regardless of when the employee is transferred, whose work histories suggest exposure to BD:

(k)(1)(ii)(A) At or above the PELs on 30 or more days a year for 10 or more years;

(k)(1)(ii)(B) At or above the action level on 60 or more days a year for 10 or more years; or

(k)(1)(ii)(C) Above 10 ppm on 30 or more days in any past year; and

(k)(1)(iii) Each employee exposed to BD following an emergency situation.

(k)(2) **Program administration**

(k)(2)(i) The employer shall ensure that the health questionnaire, physical examination and medical procedures are provided without cost to the employee, without loss of pay, and at a reasonable time and place.

(k)(2)(ii) Physical examinations, health questionnaires, and medical procedures shall be performed or administered by a physician or other licensed health care professional.

(k)(2)(iii) Laboratory tests shall be conducted by an accredited laboratory.

(k)(3) **Frequency of medical screening activities** The employer shall make medical screening available on the following schedule:

(k)(3)(i) For each employee covered under paragraphs (j)(1)(i)–(ii) of this Section, a health questionnaire and complete blood count with differential and platelet count (CBC) every year, and a physical examination as specified below:

(k)(3)(i)(A) An initial physical examination that meets the requirements of this rule, if twelve months or more have elapsed since the last physical examination conducted as part of a medical screening program for BD exposure;

(k)(3)(i)(B) Before assumption of duties by the employee in a job with BD exposure;

(k)(3)(i)(C) Every 3 years after the initial physical examination;

(k)(3)(i)(D) At the discretion of the physician or other licensed health care professional reviewing the annual health questionnaire and CBC;

(k)(3)(i)(E) At the time of employee reassignment to an area where exposure to BD is below the action level, if the employee's past exposure history does not meet the criteria of paragraph (j)(1)(ii) of this Section for continued coverage in the screening and surveillance program, and if twelve months or more have elapsed since the last physical examination; and

(k)(3)(i)(F) At termination of employment if twelve months or more have elapsed since the last physical examination.

(k)(3)(ii) Following an emergency situation, medical screening shall be conducted as quickly as possible, but not later than 48 hours after the exposure.

(k)(3)(iii) For each employee who must wear a respirator, physical ability to perform the work and use the respirator must be determined as required by 29 CFR §1910.134.

(k)(4) **Content of medical screening**

(k)(4)(i) Medical screening for employees covered by paragraphs (j)(1)(i)–(ii) of this Section shall include:

(k)(4)(i)(A) A baseline health questionnaire that includes a comprehensive occupational and health history and is updated annually. Particular emphasis shall be placed on the hematopoietic and reticuloendothelial systems, including exposure to chemicals, in addition to BD, that may have an adverse effect on these systems, the presence of signs and symptoms that might be related to disorders of these systems, and any other information determined by the examining physician or other licensed health care professional to be necessary to evaluate whether the employee is at increased risk of material impairment of health from BD exposure. Health questionnaires shall consist of the sample forms in Appendix C to this Section, or be equivalent to those samples;

(k)(4)(i)(B) A complete physical examination, with special emphasis on the liver, spleen, lymph nodes, and skin;

(k)(4)(i)(C) A CBC; and

(k)(4)(i)(D) Any other test which the examining physician or other licensed health care professional deems necessary to evaluate whether the employee may be at increased risk from exposure to BD.

(k)(4)(ii) Medical screening for employees exposed to BD in an emergency situation shall focus on the acute effects of BD exposure and at a minimum include: A CBC within 48 hours of the exposure and then monthly for three months; and a physical examination if the employee reports irritation of the eyes, nose throat, lungs, or skin, blurred vision, coughing, drowsiness, nausea, or headache. Continued employee participation in the medical screening and surveillance program, beyond these minimum requirements, shall be at the discretion of the physician or other licensed health care professional.

(k)(5) **Additional medical evaluations and referrals**

(k)(5)(i) Where the results of medical screening indicate abnormalities of the hematopoietic or reticuloendothelial systems, for which a non-occupational cause is not readily apparent, the examining physician or other licensed health care professional shall refer the employee to an appropriate specialist for further evaluation and shall make available to the specialist the results of the medical screening.

(k)(5)(ii) The specialist to whom the employee is referred under this paragraph shall determine the appropriate content for the medical evaluation, e.g., examinations, diagnostic tests and procedures, etc.

(k)(6) **Information provided to the physician or other licensed health care professional** The employer shall provide the following information to the examining physician or other licensed health care professional involved in the evaluation:

(k)(6)(i) A copy of this Section including its Appendices;

(k)(6)(ii) A description of the affected employee's duties as they relate to the employee's BD exposure;

(k)(6)(iii) The employee's actual or representative BD exposure level during employment tenure, including exposure incurred in an emergency situation;

(j)(6)(iv) A description of pertinent personal protective equipment used or to be used; and

(k)(6)(v) Information, when available, from previous employment-related medical evaluations of the affected employee which is not otherwise available to the physician or other licensed health care professional or the specialist.

(k)(7) **The written medical opinion**

(k)(7)(i) For each medical evaluation required by this Section, the employer shall ensure that the physician or other licensed health care professional produces a written opinion and provides a copy to the employer and the employee within 15 business days of the evaluation. The written opinion shall be limited to the following information:

(k)(7)(i)(A) The occupationally pertinent results of the medical evaluation;

(k)(7)(i)(B) A medical opinion concerning whether the employee has any detected medical conditions which would place the employee's health at increased risk of material impairment from exposure to BD;

(k)(7)(i)(C) Any recommended limitations upon the employee's exposure to BD; and

(k)(7)(i)(D) A statement that the employee has been informed of the results of the medical evaluation and any medical conditions resulting from BD exposure that require further explanation or treatment.

(k)(7)(ii) The written medical opinion provided to the employer shall not reveal specific records, findings, and diagnoses that have no bearing on the employee's ability to work with BD.

Note: However, this provision does not negate the ethical obligation of the physician or other licensed health care professional to transmit any other adverse findings directly to the employee.

(k)(8) **Medical surveillance**

(k)(8)(i) The employer shall ensure that information obtained from the medical screening program activities is aggregated (with all personal identifiers removed) and periodically reviewed, to ascertain whether the health of the employee population of that employer is adversely affected by exposure to BD.

(k)(8)(ii) Information learned from medical surveillance activities must be disseminated to covered employees, as defined in paragraph (k)(1) of this Section, in a manner that ensures the confidentiality of individual medical information.

(l) **Communication of BD hazards to employees**

(l)(1) **Hazard communication—general**

(l)(1)(i) Chemical manufacturers, importers, distributors and employers shall comply with all requirements of the Hazard Communication Standard (HCS) (§1910.1200) for BD.

(l)(1)(ii) In classifying the hazards of BD at least the following hazards are to be addressed: Cancer; eye and respiratory tract irritation; central nervous system effects; and flammability.

(l)(1)(iii) Employers shall include BD in the hazard communication program established to comply with the HCS (§1910.1200). Employers shall ensure that each employee has access to labels on containers of BD and to safety data sheets, and is trained in accordance with the requirements of HCS and paragraph (l)(2) of this Section.

(l)(2) **Employee information and training**

(l)(2)(i) The employer shall provide all employees exposed to BD with information and training in accordance with the requirements of the Hazard Communication Standard, 29 CFR §1910.1200, 29 CFR §1915.1200, and 29 CFR §1926.59.

(l)(2)(ii) The employer shall train each employee who is potentially exposed to BD at or above the action level or the STEL in accordance with the requirements of this Section. The employer shall institute a training program, ensure employee participation in the program, and maintain a record of the contents of such program.

(l)(2)(iii) Training shall be provided prior to or at the time of initial assignment to a job potentially involving exposure to BD at or above the action level or STEL and at least annually thereafter.

(l)(2)(iv) The training program shall be conducted in a manner that the employee is able to understand. The employee shall ensure that each employee exposed to BD over the action level or STEL is informed of the following:

(l)(2)(iv)(A) The health hazards associated with BD exposure, and the purpose and a description of the medical screening and surveillance program required by this Section;

(l)(2)(iv)(B) The quantity, location, manner of use, release, and storage of BD and the specific operations that could result in exposure to BD, especially exposures above the PEL or STEL;

(l)(2)(iv)(C) The engineering controls and work practices associated with the employee's job assignment, and emergency procedures and personal protective equipment;

(l)(2)(iv)(D) The measures employees can take to protect themselves from exposure to BD.

(l)(2)(iv)(E) The contents of this Standard and its Appendices, and

(l)(2)(iv)(F) The right of each employee exposed to BD at or above the action level or STEL to obtain:

(l)(2)(iv)(F)(1) medical examinations as required by paragraph (j) of this Section at no cost to the employee;

(l)(2)(iv)(F)(2) the employee's medical records required to be maintained by paragraph (m)(4) of this Section; and

(l)(2)(iv)(F)(3) all air monitoring results representing the employee's exposure to BD and required to be kept by paragraph (m)(2) of this Section.

(l)(3) Access to information and training materials

(l)(3)(i) The employer shall make a copy of this Standard and its Appendices readily available without cost to all affected employees and their designated representatives and shall provide a copy if requested.

(l)(3)(ii) The employer shall provide to the Assistant Secretary or the Director, or the designated employee representatives, upon request, all materials relating to the employee information and the training program.

(m) Recordkeeping

(m)(1) Objective data for exemption from initial monitoring

(m)(1)(i) Where the processing, use, or handling of products or streams made from or containing BD are exempted from other requirements of this Section under paragraph (a)(2) of this Section, or where objective data have been relied on in lieu of initial monitoring under paragraph (d)(2)(ii) of this Section, the employer shall establish and maintain a record of the objective data reasonably relied upon in support of the exemption.

(m)(1)(ii) This record shall include at least the following information:

(m)(1)(ii)(A) The product or activity qualifying for exemption;

(m)(1)(ii)(B) The source of the objective data;

(m)(1)(ii)(C) The testing protocol, results of testing, and analysis of the material for the release of BD;

(m)(1)(ii)(D) A description of the operation exempted and how the data support the exemption; and

(m)(1)(ii)(E) Other data relevant to the operations, materials, processing, or employee exposures covered by the exemption.

(m)(1)(iii) The employer shall maintain this record for the duration of the employer's reliance upon such objective data.

(m)(2) Exposure measurements

(m)(2)(i) The employer shall establish and maintain an accurate record of all measurements taken to monitor employee exposure to BD as prescribed in paragraph (d) of this Section.

(m)(2)(ii) The record shall include at least the following information:

(m)(2)(ii)(A) The date of measurement;

(m)(2)(ii)(B) The operation involving exposure to BD which is being monitored;

(m)(2)(ii)(C) Sampling and analytical methods used and evidence of their accuracy;

(m)(2)(ii)(D) Number, duration, and results of samples taken;

(m)(2)(ii)(E) Type of protective devices worn, if any;

(m)(2)(ii)(F) Name, social security number and exposure of the employees whose exposures are represented;

(m)(2)(ii)(G) The written corrective action and the schedule for completion of this action required by paragraph (d)(7)(ii) of this Section.

(m)(2)(iii) The employer shall maintain this record for at least 30 years in accordance with 29 CFR §1910.1020.

(m)(3) [Reserved]

(m)(4) Medical screening and surveillance

(m)(4)(i) The employer shall establish and maintain an accurate record for each employee subject to medical screening and surveillance under this Section.

(m)(4)(ii) The record shall include at least the following information:

(m)(4)(ii)(A) The name and social security number of the employee;

(m)(4)(ii)(B) Physician's or other licensed health care professional's written opinions as described in paragraph (k)(7) of this Section;

(m)(4)(ii)(C) A copy of the information provided to the physician or other licensed health care professional as required by paragraphs (k)(7)(ii)–(iv) of this Section.

(m)(4)(iii) Medical screening and surveillance records shall be maintained for each employee for the duration of employment plus 30 years, in accordance with 29 CFR §1910.1020.

(m)(5) Availability

(m)(5)(i) The employer, upon written request, shall make all records required to be maintained by this Section available for examination and copying to the Assistant Secretary and the Director.

(m)(5)(ii) Access to records required to be maintained by paragraphs (l)(1)–(3) of this Section shall be granted in accordance with 29 CFR §1910.1020(e).

(m)(6) **Transfer of records** The employer shall transfer medical and exposure records as set forth in 29 CFR §1910.1020(h).

(m)(6)(ii) The employer shall transfer medical and exposure records as set forth in 29 CFR §1910.1020(h).

(n) [Reserved]

(o) Appendices

(o)(1) Appendix E to this Section is mandatory.

(o)(2) Appendices A, B, C, D, and F to this Section are informational and are not intended to create any additional obligations not otherwise imposed or to detract from any existing obligations.

§1910.1051 Appendix A Substance safety data sheet for 1,3–Butadiene

I. Substance Identification

A. Substance: 1,3-Butadiene ($CH_2 = CH - CH = CH_2$).

B. Synonyms: 1,3-Butadiene (BD); butadiene; biethylene; bi-vinyl; divinyl; butadiene-1,3; buta-1,3-diene; erythrene; NCI-C50602; CAS–106–99–0.

C. BD can be found as a gas or liquid.

D. BD is used in production of styrene-butadiene rubber and polybutadiene rubber for the tire industry. Other uses include copolymer latexes for carpet backing and paper coating, as well as resins and polymers for pipes and automobile and appliance parts. It is also used as an intermediate in the production of such chemicals as fungicides.

E. Appearance and odor: BD is a colorless, non-corrosive, flammable gas with a mild aromatic odor at standard ambient temperature and pressure.

F. Permissible exposure: Exposure may not exceed 1 part BD per million parts of air averaged over the 8-hour workday, nor may short-term exposure exceed 5 parts of BD per million parts of air averaged over any 15-minute period in the 8-hour workday.

II. Health Hazard Data

A. BD can affect the body if the gas is inhaled or if the liquid form, which is very cold (cryogenic), comes in contact with the eyes or skin.

B. Effects of overexposure: Breathing very high levels of BD for a short time can cause central nervous system effects, blurred vision, nausea, fatigue, headache, decreased blood pressure and pulse rate, and unconsciousness. There are no recorded cases of accidental exposures at high levels that have caused death in humans, but this could occur. Breathing lower levels of BD may cause irritation of the eyes, nose, and throat. Skin contact with liquefied BD can cause irritation and frostbite.

C. Long-term (chronic) exposure: BD has been found to be a potent carcinogen in rodents, inducing neoplastic lesions at multiple target sites in mice and rats. A recent study of BD-exposed workers showed that exposed workers have an increased risk of developing leukemia. The risk of leukemia increases with increased exposure to BD. OSHA has concluded that there is strong evidence that workplace exposure to BD poses an increased risk of death from cancers of the lymphohematopoietic system.

D. Reporting signs and symptoms: You should inform your supervisor if you develop any of these signs or symptoms and suspect that they are caused by exposure to BD.

III. Emergency First Aid Procedures

In the event of an emergency, follow the emergency plan and procedures designated for your work area. If you have been trained in first aid procedures, provide the necessary first aid measures. If necessary, call for additional assistance from co-workers and emergency medical personnel.

A. Eye and Skin Exposures: If there is a potential that liquefied BD can come in contact with eye or skin, face shields and skin protective equipment must be provided and used. If liquefied BD comes in contact with the eye, immediately flush the eyes with large amounts of water, occasionally lifting the lower and the upper lids. Flush repeatedly. Get medical attention immediately. Contact lenses should not be worn when working with this chemical. In the event of skin contact, which can cause frostbite, remove any contaminated clothing and flush the affected area repeatedly with large amounts of tepid water.

B. Breathing: If a person breathes in large amounts of BD, move the exposed person to fresh air at once. If breathing has stopped, begin cardiopulmonary resuscitation (CPR) if you have been trained in this procedure. Keep the affected person warm and at rest. Get medical attention immediately.

C. Rescue: Move the affected person from the hazardous exposure. If the exposed person has been overcome, call for help and begin emergency rescue procedures. Use extreme caution so that you do not become a casualty. Understand the plant's emergency rescue procedures and know the locations of rescue equipment before the need arises.

IV. Respirators and Protective Clothing

A. Respirators: Good industrial hygiene practices recommend that engineering and work practice controls be used to reduce environmental concentrations to the permissible exposure level. However, there are some exceptions where respirators may be used to control exposure. Respirators may be used when engineering and work practice controls are not technically feasible, when such controls are in the process of being installed, or when these controls fail and need to be supplemented or during brief, non-routine, intermittent exposure. Respirators may also be used in situations involving non-routine work operations which are performed infrequently and in which exposures are limited in duration, and in emergency situations. In some instances cartridge respirator use is allowed, but only with strict time constraints. For example, at exposure below 5 ppm BD, a cartridge (or canister) respirator, either full or half face, may be used, but the cartridge must be replaced at least every 4 hours, and it must be replaced every 3 hours when the exposure is between 5 and 10 ppm. If the use of respirators is necessary, the only respirators permitted are those that have been approved by the National Institute for Occupational Safety and Health (NIOSH). In addition to respirator selection, a complete respiratory protection program must be instituted which includes regular training, maintenance, fit testing, inspection, cleaning, and evaluation of respirators. If you can smell BD while wearing a respirator, proceed immediately to fresh air, and change cartridge (or canister) before re-entering an area where there is BD exposure. If you experience difficulty in breathing while wearing a respirator, tell your supervisor.

B. Protective Clothing: Employees should be provided with and required to use impervious clothing, gloves, face shields (eight-inch minimum), and other appropriate protective clothing necessary to prevent the skin from becoming frozen by contact with liquefied BD (or a vessel containing liquid BD).

Employees should be provided with and required to use splash-proof safety goggles where liquefied BD may contact the eyes.

V. Precautions for Safe Use, Handling, and Storage

A. Fire and Explosion Hazards: BD is a flammable gas and can easily form explosive mixtures in air. It has a lower explosive limit of 2%, and an upper explosive limit of 11.5%. It has an autoignition temperature of 420 °C (788 °F). Its vapor is heavier than air (vapor density, 1.9) and may travel a considerable distance to a source of ignition and flash back. Usually it contains inhibitors to prevent self-polymerization (which is accompanied by evolution of heat) and to prevent formation of explosive peroxides. At elevated temperatures, such as in fire conditions, polymerization may take place. If the polymerization takes place in a container, there is a possibility of violent rupture of the container.

B. Hazard: Slightly toxic. Slight respiratory irritant. Direct contact of liquefied BD on skin may cause freeze burns and frostbite.

C. Storage: Protect against physical damage to BD containers. Outside or detached storage of BD containers is preferred. Inside storage should be in a cool, dry, well-ventilated, noncombustible location, away from all possible sources of ignition. Store cylinders vertically and do not stack. Do not store with oxidizing material.

D. Usual Shipping Containers: Liquefied BD is contained in steel pressure apparatus.

E. Electrical Equipment: Electrical installations in Class I hazardous locations, as defined in Article 500 of the National Electrical Code, should be in accordance with Article 501 of the Code. If explosion-proof electrical equipment is necessary, it shall be suitable for use in Group B. Group D equipment may be used if such equipment is isolated in accordance with Section 501–5(a) by sealing all conduit 1/2- inch size or larger. See Venting of Deflagrations (NFPA No. 68, 1994), National Electrical Code (NFPA No. 70, 1996), Static Electricity (NFPA No. 77, 1993), Lightning Protection Systems (NFPA No. 780, 1995), and Fire Hazard Properties of Flammable Liquids, Gases and Volatile Solids (NFPA No. 325, 1994).

F. Fire Fighting: Stop flow of gas. Use water to keep fire-exposed containers cool. Fire extinguishers and quick drenching facilities must be readily available, and you should know where they are and how to operate them.

G. Spill and Leak: Persons not wearing protective equipment and clothing should be restricted from areas of spills or leaks until clean-up has been completed. If BD is spilled or leaked, the following steps should be taken:

1. Eliminate all ignition sources.
2. Ventilate area of spill or leak.
3. If in liquid form, for small quantities, allow to evaporate in a safe manner.
4. Stop or control the leak if this can be done without risk. If source of leak is a cylinder and the leak cannot be stopped in place, remove the leaking cylinder to a safe place and repair the leak or allow the cylinder to empty.

H. Disposal: This substance, when discarded or disposed of, is a hazardous waste according to Federal regulations (40 CFR Part §261). It is listed as hazardous waste number D001 due to its ignitability. The transportation, storage, treatment, and disposal of this waste material must be conducted in compliance with 40 CFR Parts 262, 263, 264, 268 and 270. Disposal can occur only in properly permitted facilities. Check state and local regulation of any additional requirements as these may be more restrictive than federal laws and regulation.

I. You should not keep food, beverages, or smoking materials in areas where there is BD exposure, nor should you eat or drink in such areas.

J. Ask your supervisor where BD is used in your work area and ask for any additional plant safety and health rules.

VI. Medical Requirements

Your employer is required to offer you the opportunity to participate in a medical screening and surveillance program if you are exposed to BD at concentrations exceeding the action level (0.5 ppm BD as an 8-hour TWA) on 30 days or more a year, or at or above the 8 hr TWA (1 ppm) or STEL (5 ppm for 15 minutes) on 10 days or more a year. Exposure for any part of a day counts. If you have had exposure to BD in the past, but have been transferred to another job, you may still be eligible to participate in the medical screening and surveillance program. The OSHA rule specifies the past exposures that would qualify you for participation in the program. These past exposure are work histories that suggest the following: (1) That you have been exposed at or above the PELs on 30 days a year for 10 or more years; (2) that you have been exposed at or above the action level on 60 days a year for 10 or more years; or (3) that you have been exposed above 10 ppm on 30 days in any past year. Additionally, if you are exposed to BD in an emergency situation, you are eligible for a medical examination within 48 hours. The basic medical screening program includes a health questionnaire, physical examination, and blood test. These medical evaluations must be offered to you at a reasonable time and place, and without cost or loss of pay.

VII. Observation of Monitoring

Your employer is required to perform measurements that are representative of your exposure to BD and you or your designated representative are entitled to observe the monitoring procedure. You are entitled to observe the steps taken in the measurement procedure, and to record the results obtained. When the monitoring procedure is taking place in an area where respirators or personal protective clothing and equipment are required to be worn, you or your representative must also be provided with, and must wear, the protective clothing and equipment.

VIII. Access to Information

A. Each year, your employer is required to inform you of the information contained in this Appendix. In addition, your employer must instruct you in the proper work practices for using BD, emergency procedures, and the correct use of protective equipment.

B. Your employer is required to determine whether you are being exposed to BD. You or your representative has the right to observe employee measurements and to record the results obtained. Your employer is required to inform you of your exposure. If your employer determines that you are being overexposed, he or she is required to inform you of the actions which are being taken to reduce your exposure to within permissible exposure limits and of the schedule to implement these actions.

C. Your employer is required to keep records of your exposures and medical examinations. These records must be kept by the employer for at least thirty (30) years.

D. Your employer is required to release your exposure and medical records to you or your representative upon your request.

§1910.1051 Appendix B Substance technical guidelines for 1,3–Butadiene (Nonmandatory)

I. Physical and Chemical Data

A. Substance identification:

1. Synonyms: 1,3-Butadiene (BD); butadiene; biethylene; bivinyl; divinyl; butadiene-1,3; buta-1,3-diene; erythrene; NCI-C50620; CAS–106–99–0.
2. Formula: $CH_2 = CH - CH = CH_2$.
3. Molecular weight: 54.1.

B. Physical data:

1. Boiling point (760 mm Hg): −4.7 °C (23.5 °F).
2. Specific gravity (water=1): 0.62 at 20 °C (68 °F).
3. Vapor density (air=1 at boiling point of BD): 1.87.
4. Vapor pressure at 20 °C (68 °F): 910 mm Hg.
5. Solubility in water, g/100 g water at 20 °C (68 °F): 0.05.
6. Appearance and odor: Colorless, flammable gas with a mildly aromatic odor. Liquefied BD is a colorless liquid with a mildly aromatic odor.

II. Fire, Explosion, and Reactivity Hazard Data

A. Fire:

1. Flash point: −76 °C (−105 °F) for take out; liquefied BD; Not applicable to BD gas.
2. Stability: A stabilizer is added to the monomer to inhibit formation of polymer during storage. Forms explosive peroxides in air in absence of inhibitor.
3. Flammable limits in air, percent by volume: Lower: 2.0; Upper: 11.5.
4. Extinguishing media: Carbon dioxide for small fires, polymer or alcohol foams for large fires.
5. Special fire fighting procedures: Fight fire from protected location or maximum possible distance. Stop flow of gas before extinguishing fire. Use water spray to keep fire-exposed cylinders cool.
6. Unusual fire and explosion hazards: BD vapors are heavier than air and may travel to a source of ignition and flash back. Closed containers may rupture violently when heated.
7. For purposes of compliance with the requirements of 29 CFR §1910.106, BD is classified as a flammable gas. For example, 7,500 ppm, approximately one-fourth of the lower flammable limit, would be considered to pose a potential fire and explosion hazard.
8. For purposes of compliance with 29 CFR §1910.155, BD is classified as a Class B fire hazard.
9. For purposes of compliance with 29 CFR §1910.307, locations classified as hazardous due to the presence of BD shall be Class I.

B. Reactivity:

1. Conditions contributing to instability: Heat. Peroxides are formed when inhibitor concentration is not maintained at proper level. At elevated temperatures, such as in fire conditions, polymerization may take place.
2. Incompatibilities: Contact with strong oxidizing agents may cause fires and explosions. The contacting of crude BD (not BD monomer) with copper and copper alloys may cause formations of explosive copper compounds.
3. Hazardous decomposition products: Toxic gases (such as carbon monoxide) may be released in a fire involving BD.
4. Special precautions: BD will attack some forms of plastics, rubber, and coatings. BD in storage should be checked for proper inhibitor content, for self-polymerization, and for formation of peroxides when in contact with air and iron. Piping carrying BD may become plugged by formation of rubbery polymer.

C. Warning Properties:

1. Odor Threshold: An odor threshold of 0.45 ppm has been reported in The American Industrial Hygiene Association (AIHA) Report, Odor Thresholds for Chemicals with Established Occupational Health Standards. (Ex. 32–28C)
2. Eye Irritation Level: Workers exposed to vapors of BD (concentration or purity unspecified) have complained of irritation of eyes, nasal passages, throat, and lungs. Dogs and rabbits exposed experimentally to as much as 6700 ppm for 7 ½ hours a day for 8 months have developed no histologically demonstrable abnormality of the eyes.
3. Evaluation of Warning Properties: Since the mean odor threshold is about half of the 1 ppm PEL, and more than 10-fold below the 5 ppm STEL, most wearers of air purifying respirators should still be able to detect breakthrough before a significant overexposure to BD occurs.

III. Spill, Leak, and Disposal Procedures

A. Persons not wearing protective equipment and clothing should be restricted from areas of spills or leaks until cleanup has been completed. If BD is spilled or leaked, the following steps should be taken:

1. Eliminate all ignition sources.
2. Ventilate areas of spill or leak.
3. If in liquid form, for small quantities, allow to evaporate in a safe manner.
4. Stop or control the leak if this can be done without risk. If source of leak is a cylinder and the leak cannot be stopped in place, remove the leaking cylinder to a safe place and repair the leak or allow the cylinder to empty.

B. Disposal: This substance, when discarded or disposed of, is a hazardous waste according to Federal regulations (40 CFR Part §261). It is listed by the EPA as hazardous waste number D001 due to its ignitability. The transportation, storage, treatment, and disposal of this waste material must be conducted in compliance with 40 CFR Parts 262, 263, 264, 268 and 270. Disposal can occur only in properly permitted facilities. Check state and local regulations for any additional requirements because these may be more restrictive than federal laws and regulations.

IV. Monitoring and Measurement Procedures

A. Exposure above the Permissible Exposure Limit (8-hr TWA) or Short-Term Exposure Limit (STEL):

1. 8-hr TWA exposure evaluation: Measurements taken for the purpose of determining employee exposure under this Standard are best taken with consecutive samples covering the full shift. Air samples must be taken in the employee's breathing zone (air that would most nearly represent that inhaled by the employee).
2. STEL exposure evaluation: Measurements must represent 15 minute exposures associated with operations most likely to exceed the STEL in each job and on each shift.
3. Monitoring frequencies: Table 1 gives various exposure scenarios and their required monitoring frequencies, as required by the final standard for occupational exposure to butadiene.

Table 1
Five Exposure Scenarios and Their Associated Monitoring Frequencies

Action level	8-hr TWA	STEL	Required monitoring activity
–*	-	-	No 8-hr TWA or STEL monitoring required.
+*	-	-	No STEL monitoring required. Monitor 8-hr TWA annually.
+	+	-	No STEL monitoring required. Periodic monitoring 8-hr TWA, in accordance with (d)(3)(ii).**
+	+	+	Periodic monitoring 8-hr TWA, in accordance with (d)(3)(ii)**. Periodic monitoring STEL, in accordance with (d)(3)(iii).
+	-	+	Periodic monitoring STEL, in accordance with (d)(3)(iii). Monitor 8-hr TWA, annually.

* Exposure Scenario, Limit Exceeded: + = Yes, −= No.
** The employer may decrease the frequency of exposure monitoring to annually when at least 2 consecutive measurements taken at least 7 days apart show exposures to be below the 8 hr TWA, but at or above the action level.

4. Monitoring techniques: Appendix D describes the validated method of sampling and analysis which has been tested by OSHA for use with BD. The employer has the obligation of selecting a monitoring method which meets the accuracy and precision requirements of the standard under his or her unique field conditions. The standard requires that the method of monitoring must be accurate, to a 95 percent confidence level, to plus or minus 25 percent for concentrations of BD at or above 1 ppm, and to plus or minus 35 percent for concentrations below 1 ppm.

V. Personal Protective Equipment

A. Employees should be provided with and required to use impervious clothing, gloves, face shields (eight-inch minimum), and other appropriate protective clothing necessary to prevent the skin from becoming frozen from contact with liquid BD.

B. Any clothing which becomes wet with liquid BD should be removed immediately and not re-worn until the butadiene has evaporated.

C. Employees should be provided with and required to use splash proof safety goggles where liquid BD may contact the eyes.

VI. Housekeeping and Hygiene Facilities

For purposes of complying with 29 CFR §1910.141, the following items should be emphasized:

A. The workplace should be kept clean, orderly, and in a sanitary condition.

B. Adequate washing facilities with hot and cold water are to be provided and maintained in a sanitary condition.

VII. Additional Precautions

A. Store BD in tightly closed containers in a cool, well-ventilated area and take all necessary precautions to avoid any explosion hazard.

B. Non-sparking tools must be used to open and close metal containers. These containers must be effectively grounded.

C. Do not incinerate BD cartridges, tanks or other containers.

D. Employers must advise employees of all areas and operations where exposure to BD might occur.

§1910.1051 Appendix C Medical screening and surveillance for 1,3–Butadiene

(Nonmandatory)

I. Basis for Medical Screening and Surveillance Requirements

A. Route of Entry Inhalation

B. Toxicology

Inhalation of BD has been linked to an increased risk of cancer, damage to the reproductive organs, and fetotoxicity. Butadiene can be converted via oxidation to epoxybutene and diepoxybutane, two genotoxic metabolites that may play a role in the expression of BD's toxic effects.

BD has been tested for carcinogenicity in mice and rats. Both species responded to BD exposure by developing cancer at multiple primary organ sites. Early deaths in mice were caused by malignant lymphomas, primarily lymphocytic type, originating in the thymus.

Mice exposed to BD have developed ovarian or testicular atrophy. Sperm head morphology tests also revealed abnormal sperm in mice exposed to BD; lethal mutations were found in a dominant lethal test. In light of these results in animals, the possibility that BD may adversely affect the reproductive systems of male and female workers must be considered.

Additionally, anemia has been observed in animals exposed to butadiene. In some cases, this anemia appeared to be a primary response to exposure; in other cases, it may have been secondary to a neoplastic response.

C. Epidemiology

Epidemiologic evidence demonstrates that BD exposure poses an increased risk of leukemia. Mild alterations of hematologic parameters have also been observed in synthetic rubber workers exposed to BD.

II. Potential Adverse Health Effects

A. Acute

Skin contact with liquid BD causes characteristic burns or frostbite. BD is gaseous form can irritate the eyes, nasal passages, throat, and lungs. Blurred vision, coughing, and drowsiness may also occur. Effects are mild at 2,000 ppm and pronounced at 8,000 ppm for exposures occurring over the full workshift.

At very high concentrations in air, BD is an anesthetic, causing narcosis, respiratory paralysis, unconsciousness, and death. Such concentrations are unlikely, however, except in an extreme emergency because BD poses an explosion hazard at these levels.

B. Chronic

The principal adverse health effects of concern are BD-induced lymphoma, leukemia and potential reproductive toxicity. Anemia and other changes in the peripheral blood cells may be indicators of excessive exposure to BD.

C. Reproductive

Workers may be concerned about the possibility that their BD exposure may be affecting their ability to procreate a healthy child. For workers with high exposures to BD, especially those who have experienced difficulties in conceiving, miscarriages, or stillbirths, appropriate medical and laboratory evaluation of fertility may be necessary to determine if BD is having any adverse effect on the reproductive system or on the health of the fetus.

III. Medical Screening Components At-A-Glance

A. Health Questionnaire

The most important goal of the health questionnaire is to elicit information from the worker regarding potential signs or symptoms generally related to leukemia or other blood abnormalities. Therefore, physicians or other licensed health care professionals should be aware of the presenting symptoms and signs of lymphohematopoietic disorders and cancers, as well as the procedures necessary to confirm or exclude such diagnoses. Additionally, the health questionnaire will assist with the identification of workers at greatest risk of developing leukemia or adverse reproductive effects from their exposures to BD.

Workers with a history of reproductive difficulties or a personal or family history of immune deficiency syndromes, blood dyscrasias, lymphoma, or leukemia, and those who are or have been exposed to medicinal drugs or chemicals known to affect the hematopoietic or lymphatic systems may be at higher risk from their exposure to BD. After the initial administration, the health questionnaire must be updated annually.

B. Complete Blood Count (CBC)

The medical screening and surveillance program requires an annual CBC, with differential and platelet count, to be provided for each employee with BD exposure. This test is to be performed on a blood sample obtained by phlebotomy of the venous system or, if technically feasible, from a fingerstick sample of capillary blood. The sample is to be analyzed by an accredited laboratory.

Abnormalities in a CBC may be due to a number of different etiologies. The concern for workers exposed to BD includes, but is not limited to, timely identification of lymphohematopoietic cancers, such as leukemia and non-Hodgkin's lymphoma. Abnormalities of portions of the CBC are identified by comparing an individual's results to those of an established range of normal values for males and females. A substantial change in any individual employee's CBC may also be viewed as "abnormal" for that individual even if all measurements fall within the population-based range of normal values. It is suggested that a flowsheet for laboratory values be included in each employee's medical record so that comparisons and trends in annual CBCs can be easily made.

A determination of the clinical significance of an abnormal CBC shall be the responsibility of the examining physician, other licensed health care professional, or medical specialist to whom the employee is referred. Ideally, an abnormal CBC should be compared to previous CBC measurements for the same employee, when available. Clinical common sense may dictate that a CBC value that is very slightly outside the normal range does not warrant medical concern. A CBC abnormality may also be the result of a temporary physical stressor, such as a transient viral illness, blood donation, or menorrhagia, or laboratory error. In these cases, the CBC should be repeated in a timely fashion, i.e., within 6 weeks, to verify that return to the normal range has occurred. A clinically significant abnormal CBC should result in removal of the employee from further exposure to BD. Transfer of the employee to other work duties in a BD-free environment would be the preferred recommendation.

C. Physical Examination

The medical screening and surveillance program requires an initial physical examination for workers exposed to BD; this examination is repeated once every three years. The initial physical examination should assess each worker's baseline general health and rule out clinical signs of medical conditions that may be caused by or aggravated by occupational BD exposure. The physical examination should be directed at identification of signs of lymphohematopoietic disorders, including lymph node enlargement, splenomegaly, and hepatomegaly.

Repeated physical examinations should update objective clinical findings that could be indicative of interim development of a lymphohematopoietic disorder, such as lymphoma, leukemia, or other blood abnormality. Physical examinations may also be provided on an as needed basis in order to follow up on a positive answer on the health questionnaire, or in response to an abnormal CBC. Physical examination of workers who will no longer be working in jobs with BD exposure are intended to rule out lymphohematopoietic disorders.

The need for physical examinations for workers concerned about adverse reproductive effects from their exposure to BD should be identified by the physician or other licensed health care professional and provided accordingly. For these workers, such consultations and examinations may relate to developmental toxicity and reproductive capacity.

Physical examination of workers acutely exposed to significant levels of BD should be especially directed at the respiratory system, eyes, sinuses, skin, nervous system, and any region associated with particular complaints. If the worker has received a severe acute exposure, hospitalization may be required to assure proper medical management. Since this type of exposure may place workers at greater risk of blood abnormalities, a CBC must be obtained within 48 hours and repeated at one, two, and three months.

§1910.1051 Appendix D Sampling and analytical method for 1,3–Butadiene (Nonmandatory)

OSHA Method No.: 56.

Matrix: Air.

Target concentration: 1 ppm (2.21 mg/m^3)

Procedure: Air samples are collected by drawing known volumes of air through sampling tubes containing charcoal adsorbent which has been coated with 4-tert-butylcatechol. The samples are desorbed with carbon disulfide and then analyzed by gas chromatography using a flame ionization detector.

Recommended sampling rate and air volume: 0.05 L/min and 3 L.

Detection limit of the overall procedure: 90 ppb (200 ug/m^3) (based on 3 L air volume).

Reliable quantitation limit: 155 ppb (343 ug/m^3) (based on 3 L air volume).

Standard error of estimate at the target concentration: 6.5%.

Special requirements: The sampling tubes must be coated with 4-tert-butylcatechol. Collected samples should be stored in a freezer.

Status of method: A sampling and analytical method has been subjected to the established evaluation procedures of the Organic Methods Evaluation Branch, OSHA Analytical Laboratory, Salt Lake City, Utah 84165.

1. Background

This work was undertaken to develop a sampling and analytical procedure for BD at 1 ppm. The current method recommended by OSHA for collecting BD uses activated coconut shell charcoal as the sampling medium (Ref. 5.2). This method was found to be inadequate for use at low BD levels because of sample instability.

The stability of samples has been significantly improved through the use of a specially cleaned charcoal which is coated with 4-tert-butylcatechol (TBC). TBC is a polymerization inhibitor for BD (Ref. 5.3).

1.1.1 Toxic effects

Symptoms of human exposure to BD include irritation of the eyes, nose and throat. It can also cause coughing, drowsiness and fatigue. Dermatitis and frostbite can result from skin exposure to liquid BD. (Ref. 5.1)

NIOSH recommends that BD be handled in the workplace as a potential occupational carcinogen. This recommendation is based on two inhalation studies that resulted in cancers at multiple sites in rats and in mice. BD has also demonstrated mutagenic activity in the presence of a liver microsomal activating system. It has also been reported to have adverse reproductive effects. (Ref. 5.1)

1.1.2. Potential workplace exposure

About 90% of the annual production of BD is used to manufacture styrene-butadiene rubber and Polybutadiene rubber. Other uses include: Polychloroprene rubber, acrylonitrile butadiene-stryene resins, nylon intermediates, styrene-butadiene latexes, butadiene polymers, thermoplastic elastomers, nitrile resins, methyl methacrylate-butadiene styrene resins and chemical intermediates. (Ref. 5.1)

1.1.3. Physical properties (Ref. 5.1)

CAS No.: 106–99–0
Molecular weight: 54.1
Appearance: Colorless gas
Boiling point: −4.41 °C (760 mm Hg)
Freezing point: −108.9 °C
Vapor pressure: 2 atm @ 15.3 °C; 5 atm @ 47 °C
Explosive limits: 2 to 11.5% (by volume in air)
Odor threshold: 0.45 ppm
Structural formula: $H_2C:CHCH:CH_2$
Synonyms: BD; biethylene; bivinyl; butadiene; divinyl; buta-1,3-diene; alpha-gamma-butadiene; erythrene; NCI-C50602; pyrrolylene; vinylethylene.

1.2. Limit defining parameters

The analyte air concentrations listed throughout this method are based on an air volume of 3 L and a desorption volume of 1 mL. Air concentrations listed in ppm are referenced to 25 °C and 760 mm Hg.

1.2.1. Detection limit of the analytical procedure

The detection limit of the analytical procedure was 304 pg per injection. This was the amount of BD which gave a response relative to the interferences present in a standard.

1.2.2. Detection limit of the overall procedure

The detection limit of the overall procedure was 0.60 µg per sample (90 ppb or 200 µg/m^3). This amount was determined graphically. It was the amount of analyte which, when spiked on the sampling device, would allow recovery approximately equal to the detection limit of the analytical procedure.

1.2.3. Reliable quantitation limit

The reliable quantitation limit was 1.03 µg per sample (155 ppb or 343 µg/m^3). This was the smallest amount of analyte which could be quantitated within the limits of a recovery of at least 75% and a precision (± 1.96 SD) of ± 25% or better.

1.2.4. Sensitivity[1]

The sensitivity of the analytical procedure over a concentration range representing 0.6 to 2 times the target concentration, based on the recommended air volume, was 387 area units per µg/mL. This value was determined from the slope of the calibration curve. The sensitivity may vary with the particular instrument used in the analysis.

1.2.5. Recovery

The recovery of BD from samples used in storage tests remained above 77% when the samples were stored at ambient temperature and above 94% when the samples were stored at refrigerated temperature. These values were determined from regression lines which were calculated from the storage data. The recovery of the analyte from the collection device must be at least 75% following storage.

1.2.6. Precision (analytical method only)

The pooled coefficient of variation obtained from replicate determinations of analytical standards over the range of 0.6 to 2 times the target concentration was 0.011.

1.2.7. Precision (overall procedure)

The precision at the 95% confidence level for the refrigerated temperature storage test was ± 12.7%. This value includes an additional ±5% for sampling error. The overall procedure must provide results at the target concentrations that are ± 25% at the 95% confidence level.

1.2.8. Reproducibility

Samples collected from a controlled test atmosphere and a draft copy of this procedure were given to a chemist unassociated with this evaluation. The average recovery was 97.2% and the standard deviation was 6.2%.

2. Sampling procedure

2.1. Apparatus

2.1.1. Samples are collected by use of a personal sampling pump that can be calibrated to within ± 5% of the recommended 0.05 L/min sampling rate with the sampling tube in line.

2.1.2. Samples are collected with laboratory prepared sampling tubes. The sampling tube is constructed of silane-treated glass and is about 5-cm long. The ID is 4 mm and the OD is 6 mm. One end of the tube is tapered so that a glass wool end plug will hold the contents of the tube in place during sampling. The opening in the tapered end of the sampling tube is at least one-half the ID of the tube (2 mm). The other end of the sampling tube is open to its full 4-mm ID to facilitate packing of the tube. Both ends of the tube are fire-polished for safety. The tube is packed with 2 sections of pretreated charcoal which has been coated with TBC. The tube is packed with a 50-mg backup section, located nearest the tapered end, and with a 100-mg sampling section of charcoal. The two sections of coated adsorbent are separated and retained with small plugs of silanized glass wool. Following packing, the sampling tubes are sealed with two 7⁄32 inch OD plastic end caps. Instructions for the pretreatment and coating of the charcoal are presented in Section 4.1 of this method.

2.2. Reagents

None required.

2.3. Technique

2.3.1. Properly label the sampling tube before sampling and then remove the plastic end caps.

2.3.2. Attach the sampling tube to the pump using a section of flexible plastic tubing such that the larger front section of the sampling tube is exposed directly to the atmosphere. Do not place any

[1] The reliable quantitation limit and detection limits reported in the method are based upon optimization of the instrument for the smallest possible amount of analyte. When the target concentration of an analyte is exceptionally higher than these limits, they may not be attainable at the routine operation parameters.

tubing ahead of the sampling tube. The sampling tube should be attached in the worker's breathing zone in a vertical manner such that it does not impede work performance.

2.3.3. After sampling for the appropriate time, remove the sampling tube from the pump and then seal the tube with plastic end caps. Wrap the tube lengthwise.

2.3.4. Include at least one blank for each sampling set. The blank should be handled in the same manner as the samples with the exception that air is not drawn through it.

2.3.5. List any potential interferences on the sample data sheet.

2.3.6. The samples require no special shipping precautions under normal conditions. The samples should be refrigerated if they are to be exposed to higher than normal ambient temperatures. If the samples are to be stored before they are shipped to the laboratory, they should be kept in a freezer. The samples should be placed in a freezer upon receipt at the laboratory.

2.4. Breakthrough

(Breakthrough was defined as the relative amount of analyte found on the backup section of the tube in relation to the total amount of analyte collected on the sampling tube. Five-percent breakthrough occurred after sampling a test atmosphere containing 2.0 ppm BD for 90 min at 0.05 L/min. At the end of this time 4.5 L of air had been sampled and 20.1 µg of the analyte was collected. The relative humidity of the sampled air was 80% at 23 °C.)

Breakthrough studies have shown that the recommended sampling procedure can be used at air concentrations higher than the target concentration. The sampling time, however, should be reduced to 45 min if both the expected BD level and the relative humidity of the sampled air are high.

2.5. Desorption efficiency

The average desorption efficiency for BD from TBC coated charcoal over the range from 0.6 to 2 times the target concentration was 96.4%. The efficiency was essentially constant over the range studied.

2.6. Recommended air volume and sampling rate

2.6.1. The recommended air volume is 3L.

2.6.2. The recommended sampling rate is 0.05 L/min for 1 hour.

2.7. Interferences

There are no known interferences to the sampling method.

2.8. Safety precautions

2.8.1. Attach the sampling equipment to the worker in such a manner that it will not interfere with work performance or safety.

2.8.2. Follow all safety practices that apply to the work area being sampled.

3. Analytical procedure

3.1. Apparatus

3.1.1. A gas chromatograph (GC), equipped with a flame ionization detector (FID).[2]

3.1.2. A GC column capable of resolving the analytes from any interference.[3]

3.1.3. Vials, glass 2-mL with Teflon-lined caps.

3.1.4. Disposable Pasteur-type pipets, volumetric flasks, pipets and syringes for preparing samples and standards, making dilutions and performing injections.

3.2. Reagents

3.2.1. Carbon disulfide.[4]

The benzene contaminant that was present in the carbon disulfide was used as an internal standard (ISTD) in this evaluation.

3.2.2. Nitrogen, hydrogen and air, GC grade.

3.2.3. BD of known high purity.[5]

3.3. Standard preparation

3.3.1. Prepare standards by diluting known volumes of BD gas with carbon disulfide. This can be accomplished by injecting the appropriate volume of BD into the headspace above the 1-mL of carbon disulfide contained in sealed 2-mL vial. Shake the vial after the needle is removed from the septum.[6]

3.3.2. The mass of BD gas used to prepare standards can be determined by use of the following equations:

$$MV = (760/BP)(273 + T) / (273)(22.41)$$

Where:
MV = ambient molar volume
BP = ambient barometric pressure
T = ambient temperature

$$\mu g/\mu L = 54.09/MV$$

µg/standard = (µg/µL)(µL) BD used to prepare the standard

3.4. Sample preparation

3.4.1. Transfer the 100-mg section of the sampling tube to a 2-mL vial. Place the 50-mg section in a separate vial. If the glass wool plugs contain a significant amount of charcoal, place them with the appropriate sampling tube section.

3.4.2. Add 1-mL of carbon disulfide to each vial.

3.4.3. Seal the vials with Teflon-lined caps and then allow them to desorb for one hour. Shake the vials by hand vigorously several times during the desorption period.

3.4.4. If it is not possible to analyze the samples within 4 hours, separate the carbon disulfide from the charcoal, using a disposable Pasteur-type pipet, following the one hour. This separation will improve the stability of desorbed samples.

3.4.5. Save the used sampling tubes to be cleaned and repacked with fresh adsorbent.

3.5. Analysis

3.5.1. GC Conditions

Column temperature: 95 °C
Injector temperature: 180 °C
Detector temperature: 275 °C
Carrier gas flow rate: 30 mL/min
Injection volume: 0.80 µL
GC column: 20-ft ×⅛" OD stainless steel GC column containing 20%

FFAP on 80/100 Chromabsorb W-AW-DMCS.

3.5.2. Chromatogram. See Section 4.2.

3.5.3. Use a suitable method, such as electronic or peak heights, to measure detector response.

3.5.4. Prepare a calibration curve using several standard solutions of different concentrations. Prepare the calibration curve daily. Program the integrator to report the results in µg/mL.

3.5.5. Bracket sample concentrations with standards.

3.6. Interferences (analytical)

3.6.1. Any compound with the same general retention time as the analyte and which also gives a detector response is a potential interference. Possible interferences should be reported by the industrial hygienist to the laboratory with submitted samples.

3.6.2. GC parameters (temperature, column, etc.) may be changed to circumvent interferences.

3.6.3. A useful means of structure designation is GC/MS. It is recommended that this procedure be used to confirm samples whenever possible.

3.7. Calculations

3.7.1. Results are obtained by use of calibration curves. Calibration curves are prepared by plotting detector response against concentration for each standard. The best line through the data points is determined by curve fitting.

3.7.2. The concentration, in ug/mL, for a particular sample is determined by comparing its detector response to the calibration curve. If any analyte is found on the backup section, this amount is added to the amount found on the front section. Blank corrections should be performed before adding the results together.

3.7.3. The BD air concentration can be expressed using the following equation:

$$mg/m^3 = (A)(B)/(C)(D)$$

Where:
A = µg/mL from Section 3.7.2
B = volume
C = L of air sampled
D = efficiency

---

[2] A Hewlett-Packard Model 5840A GC was used for this evaluation. Injections were performed using a Hewlett-Packard Model 7671A automatic sampler.

[3] A 20-ft ×⅛-inch OD stainless steel GC column containing 20% FFAP on 80/100 mesh Chromabsorb W-AW-DMCS was used for this evaluation.

[4] Fisher Scientific Company A.C.S. Reagent Grade solvent was used in this evaluation.

[5] Matheson Gas Products, CP Grade 1,3-butadiene was used in this study.

[6] A standard containing 7.71 µg/mL (at ambient temperature and pressure) was prepared by diluting 4 µL of the gas with 1-mL of carbon disulfide.

3.7.4. The following equation can be used to convert results in mg/m3 to ppm:

$$ppm = (mg/m^3)(24.46) / 54.09$$

Where:
mg/m^3 = result from Section 3.7.3.
24.46 = molar volume of an ideal gas at 760 mm Hg and 25 °C.

3.8. Safety precautions (analytical)

3.8.1. Avoid skin contact and inhalation of all chemicals.

3.8.2. Restrict the use of all chemicals to a fume hood whenever possible.

3.8.3. Wear safety glasses and a lab coat in all laboratory areas.

4. Additional Information

4.1. A procedure to prepare specially cleaned charcoal coated with TBC

4.1.1. Apparatus

4.1.1.1. Magnetic stirrer and stir bar.

4.1.1.2. Tube furnace capable of maintaining a temperature of 700 °C and equipped with a quartz tube that can hold 30 g of charcoal.[8]

4.1.1.3. A means to purge nitrogen gas through the charcoal inside the quartz tube.

4.1.1.4. Water bath capable of maintaining a temperature of 60 °C.

4.1.1.5. Miscellaneous laboratory equipment: One-liter vacuum flask, 1–L Erlenmeyer flask, 350–M1 Buchner funnel with a coarse fitted disc, 4-oz brown bottle, rubber stopper, Teflon tape etc.

4.1.2. Reagents

4.1.2.1. Phosphoric acid, 10% by weight, in water.[9]

4.1.2.2. 4-tert-Butylcatechol (TBC).[10]

4.1.2.3. Specially cleaned coconut shell charcoal, 20/40 mesh.[11]

4.1.2.4. Nitrogen gas, GC grade.

4.1.3. Procedure

Weigh 30g of charcoal into a 500-mL Erlenmeyer flask. Add about 250 mL of 10% phosphoric acid to the flask and then swirl the mixture. Stir the mixture for 1 hour using a magnetic stirrer. Filter the mixture using a fitted Buchner funnel. Wash the charcoal several times with 250-mL portions of deionized water to remove all traces of the acid. Transfer the washed charcoal to the tube furnace quartz tube. Place the quartz tube in the furnace and then connect the nitrogen gas purge to the tube. Fire the charcoal to 700 °C. Maintain that temperature for at least 1 hour. After the charcoal has cooled to room temperature, transfer it to a tared beaker. Determine the weight of the charcoal and then add an amount of TBC which is 10% of the charcoal, by weight.

CAUTION TBC is toxic and should only be handled in a fume hood while wearing gloves.

Carefully mix the contents of the beaker and then transfer the mixture to a 4-oz bottle. Stopper the bottle with a clean rubber stopper which has been wrapped with Teflon tape. Clamp the bottle in a water bath so that the water level is above the charcoal level. Gently heat the bath to 60 °C and then maintain that temperature for 1 hour. Cool the charcoal to room temperature and then transfer the coated charcoal to a suitable container.

The coated charcoal is now ready to be packed into sampling tubes. The sampling tubes should be stored in a sealed container to prevent contamination. Sampling tubes should be stored in the dark at room temperature. The sampling tubes should be segregated by coated adsorbent lot number.

4.2 Chromatograms

The chromatograms were obtained using the recommended analytical method. The chart speed was set at 1 cm/min for the first three min and then at 0.2 cm/min for the time remaining in the analysis.

The peak which elutes just before BD is a reaction product between an impurity on the charcoal and TBC. This peak is always present, but it is easily resolved from the analyte. The peak which elutes immediately before benzene is an oxidation product of TBC.

[8] A Lindberg Type 55035 Tube furnace was used in this evaluation.
[9] Baker Analyzed" Reagent grade was diluted with water for use in this evaluation.
[10] The Aldrich Chemical Company 99% grade was used in this evaluation.
[11] Specially cleaned charcoal was obtained from Supelco, Inc. for use in this evaluation. The cleaning process used by Supelco is propriatory.

5. References

5.1. "Current Intelligence Bulletin 41, 1,3-Butadiene", U.S. Dept. of Health and Human Services, Public Health Service, Center for Disease Control, NIOSH.

5.2. "NIOSH Manual of Analytical Methods", 2nd ed; U.S. Dept. of Health Education and Welfare, National Institute for Occupational Safety and Health: Cincinnati, OH. 1977, Vol. 2, Method No. S91 DHEW (NIOSH) Publ. (US), No. 77–157–B.

5.3. Hawley, G.C., Ed. "The Condensed Chemical Dictionary", 8th ed.; Van Nostrand Rienhold Company: New York, 1971; 139.5.4. Chem. Eng. News (June 10, 1985), (63), 22–66.

§1910.1051 Appendix E [Reserved]

§1910.1051 Appendix F Medical Questionnaires

(Nonmandatory)

1,3-Butadiene (BD) Initial Health Questionnaire.

DIRECTIONS:
You have been asked to answer the questions on this form because you work with DB (butadiene). These questions are about your work, medical history, and health concerns. Please do your best to answer all of the questions. If you need help, please tell the doctor or health care professional who reviews this form.
This form is a confidential medical record. Only information directly related to your health and safety on the job may be given to your employer. Personal health information will not be given to anyone without your consent.

Date: ____________ SSN: _______/____/__________

Name: ______________________________________
(Last) (First) (MI)

Job Title: ______________________________

Company's Name: ________)________________________

Supervisor's Name: _______________________________

Supervisor's Phone No.: (____) _____ - _____________

Work History

1. Please list all jobs you have had in the past, starting with the job you have now and moving back in time to your first job. (For more space, write on the back of this page.)

	Main Job Duty	Years	Company Name City, State	Chemicals
1				
2				
3				
4				
5				
6				
7				
8				

2. Please describe what you do during a typical work day. Be sure to tell about your work with DB.
____
____

3. Please check any of these chemicals that you work with now or have worked with in the past:

___ benzene
___ glue
___ toluene
___ inks, dyes
___ other solvents, grease cutters
___ insecticides (like DDT, lindane, etc.)
___ paints, varnishes, thinners, strippers
___ dust
___ carbon tetrachloride ("carbon tet")
___ arsine
___ carbon disulfide
___ lead
___ cement
___ petroleum products
___ nitrites

4. Please check the protective clothing or equipment you use at the job you have now:

___ gloves
___ coveralls
___ respirator
___ dust mask
___ safety glasses, goggles

Please circle your answer:

5. Does your protective clothing or equipment fit you properly? Yes No
6. Have you ever made changes in your protective clothing or equipment to make it fit better? Yes No
7. Have you been exposed to BD when you were not wearing protective clothing or equipment? Yes No
8. Where do you eat, drink, and/or smoke when you are at work? (Please check all that apply.)

___ Cafeteria/restaurant/snack bar ___ Smoking lounge
___ Break room/employee lounge ___ At my work station

9. Have you been exposed to radiation (like X-rays or nuclear material) at the job you have now or at past jobs? Yes No
10. Do you have any hobbies that expose you to dusts or chemicals (including paints, glues, etc.)? Yes No
11. Do you have any second or side jobs? Yes No

If Yes, what are your duties their? ______

12. Were you in the military? Yes No

If Yes, what did you do in the military? ______

Family Health History

1. In the FAMILY MEMBER column, across from the disease name, write which family member, if any, had the disease.

DISEASE	FAMILY MEMBER
Cancer	
Lymphoma	
Sickle Cell Disease or Trait	
Immune Disease	
Leukemia	
Anemia	

2. Please fill in the following information about family health:

Relative	Alive?	Age at death?	Cause of death?
Father			
Mother			
Brother/Sister			
Brother/Sister			
Brother/Sister			

Personal Health History

Birth Date ___/___/___ Age ___ Sex ___ Height ______ Weight ______

Please circle your answer:

1. Do you smoke any tobacco products? Yes No
2. Have you ever had any kind of surgery or operation? Yes No

If Yes, what type of surgery? ______

3. Have you ever been in the hospital for any other reasons? Yes No

If Yes, please describe the reason: ______

4. Do you have any on-going or current medical problems or conditions? Yes No

If Yes, please describe: ______

5. Do you now have, or have you ever had, any of the following? Please check all that apply to you.

___ unexplained fever
___ anemia ("low blood")
___ HIV/AIDS
___ weakness
___ sickle cell
___ yellowing of skin
___ bruising easily
___ lupus
___ weight loss
___ kidney problems
___ still birth
___ eye redness
___ lumps you can feel
___ child with birth defect
___ miscarriage
___ skin rash
___ bloody stools
___ leukemia/ lymphoma
___ neck mass/ swelling
___ wheezing
___ enlarged lymph nodes
___ liver disease
___ cancer
___ infertility
___ drinking problems
___ thyroid problems
___ night sweats
___ chest pain
___ autoimmune disease
___ overly tired
___ lung problems
___ rheumatoid arthritis
___ mononucleosis ("mono")
___ nagging cough

Please circle your answer:

6. Do you have any symptoms or health problems that you think may be related to your work with BD? Yes No

If Yes, please describe: ______

7. Have any of your co-workers had similar symptoms or problems? Yes No Don't know

If Yes, please describe: ______

8. Do you notice any irritation of your eyes, nose, throat, lungs, or skin when working with DB? Yes No
9. Do you notice any blurred vision, coughing, drowsiness, nausea or headache when working with DB? Yes No
10. Do you take any medications (including birth control or over-the-counter)? Yes No

If Yes, please list: ______

11. Are you allergic to any medication, food, or chemicals? Yes No

If Yes, please list: ______

12. Do you have any health conditions not covered by this questionnaire that you think are affected by your work with DB? Yes No

If Yes, please explain: ______

13. Did you understand all the questions? Yes No

______
Signature

1,3-Butadiene (BD) Update Health Questionnaire.

DIRECTIONS:

You have been asked to answer the questions on this form because you work with DB (butadiene). These questions are about your work, medical history, and health concerns. Please do your best to answer all of the questions. If you need help, please tell the doctor or health care professional who reviews this form.

This form is a confidential medical record. Only information directly related to your health and safety on the job may be given to your employer. Personal health information will not be given to anyone without your consent.

Date: ______ SSN: ___/___/___

Name: ______
(Last) (First) (MI)

Job Title: ______

Company's Name: ______

Supervisor's Name: ______

Supervisor's Phone No.: (___) ___ - ______

Present Work History

1. Please describe any NEW duties that you have at your job: ______
2. Please list any additional job titles you have: ______

Please circle your answer:

3. Are you exposed to any other chemicals in your work since the last time you were evaluated for exposure to DB? Yes No

If Yes, please list what they are: ______

4. Does your personal protective equipment and clothing fit you properly? Yes No
5. Have you made changes in this equipment or clothing to make it fit better? Yes No

Note: Form continues on next page.

6. Have you been exposed to DB when you were not wearing protective equipment or clothing? Yes No

7. Are you exposed to any NEW chemicals at home or while working on hobbies? Yes No

If Yes, please list what they are: ____________________

8. Since your last BD health evaluation, have you started working any NEW second or side jobs? Yes No

If Yes, what are your duties there: ____________________

Personal Health History

1. What is your current weight? ________ pounds

2. Have you been diagnosed with any NEW medical conditions or illness since your last evaluation? Yes No

If Yes, please tell what they are: ____________________

3. Since your last evaluation, have you been in the hospital for any illness, injuries, or surgery? Yes No

If Yes, please describe: ____________________

4. Do you have any of the following? Please place a check for all that apply to you.

___ unexplained fever	___ bruising easily	___ still birth
___ anemia ("low blood")	___ lupus	___ eye redness
___ HIV/AIDS	___ weight loss	___ lumps you can feel
___ weakness	___ kidney problems	___ child with birth defect
___ sickle cell	___ enlarged lymph nodes	___ autoimmune disease
___ miscarriage	___ liver disease	___ overly tired
___ skin rash	___ cancer	___ lung problems
___ bloody rash	___ infertility	___ rheumatoid arthritis
___ leukemia/lymphoma	___ drinking problems	___ mononucleosis ("mono")
___ neck mass/swelling	___ thyroid problems	___ nagging cough
___ wheezing	___ night sweats	
___ yellowing of skin	___ chest pain	

Please circle your answer:

5. Do you have any symptoms or health problems that you think may be related to your work with BD? Yes No

If Yes, please describe: ____________________

6. Have any of your co-workers had similar symptoms or problems? Yes No Don't know

If Yes, please describe: ____________________

7. Do you notice any irritation of your eyes, nose, throat, lungs, or skin when working with BD Yes No

8. Do you have any blurred vision, coughing, drowsiness, nausea, or headache when working with BD? Yes No

9. Have you been taking any NEW medication (including birth controll or over-the-counter)? Yes No

If Yes, please list: ____________________

10. Have you developed any NEW allergies to medications, foods, or chemicals? Yes No

If Yes, please list: ____________________

11. Do you have any health conditions not covered by this questionnaire that you think are affected by your work with BD Yes No

If Yes, please explain: ____________________

12. Did you understand all the questions? Yes No

____
Signature

[61 FR 56831, Nov. 4, 1996, as amended at 63 FR 1294, Jan. 8, 1998; 67 FR 67965, Nov. 7, 2002; 70 FR 1143, Jan. 5, 2005; 71 FR 16672, 16674, Apr. 3, 2006; 73 FR 75587, Dec. 12, 2008; 76 FR 33609, June 8, 2011]

§1910.1052 Methylene Chloride

This occupational health standard establishes requirements for employers to control occupational exposure to methylene chloride (MC). Employees exposed to MC are at increased risk of developing cancer, adverse effects on the heart, central nervous system and liver, and skin or eye irritation. Exposure may occur through inhalation, by absorption through the skin, or through contact with the skin. MC is a solvent which is used in many different types of work activities, such as paint stripping, polyurethane foam manufacturing, and cleaning and degreasing. Under the requirements of paragraph (d) of this Section, each covered employer must make an initial determination of each employee's exposure to MC. If the employer determines that employees are exposed below the action level, the only other provisions of this Section that apply are that a record must be made of the determination, the employees must receive information and training under paragraph (l) of this Section and, where appropriate, employees must be protected from contact with liquid MC under paragraph (h) of this Section. The provisions of the MC standard are as follows:

(a) **Scope and application** This Section applies to all occupational exposures to methylene chloride (MC), Chemical Abstracts Service Registry Number 75–09–2, in general industry, construction and shipyard employment.

(b) **Definitions** For the purposes of this Section, the following definitions shall apply:

Action level means a concentration of airborne MC of 12.5 parts per million (ppm) calculated as an eight (8)-hour time-weighted average (TWA).

Assistant Secretary means the Assistant Secretary of Labor for Occupational Safety and Health, U.S. Department of Labor, or designee.

Authorized person means any person specifically authorized by the employer and required by work duties to be present in regulated areas, or any person entering such an area as a designated representative of employees for the purpose of exercising the right to observe monitoring and measuring procedures under paragraph (d) of this Section, or any other person authorized by the OSH Act or regulations issued under the Act.

Director means the Director of the National Institute for Occupational Safety and Health, U.S. Department of Health and Human Services, or designee.

Emergency means any occurrence, such as, but not limited to, equipment failure, rupture of containers, or failure of control equipment, which results, or is likely to result in an uncontrolled release of MC. If an incidental release of MC can be controlled by employees such as maintenance personnel at the time of release and in accordance with the leak/spill provisions required by paragraph (f) of this Section, it is not considered an emergency as defined by this Standard.

Employee exposure means exposure to airborne MC which occurs or would occur if the employee were not using respiratory protection.

Methylene chloride (MC) means an organic compound with chemical formula, CH2Cl2. Its Chemical Abstracts Service Registry Number is 75–09–2. Its molecular weight is 84.9 g/mole.

Physician or other licensed health care professional is an individual whose legally permitted scope of practice (i.e., license, registration, or certification) allows him or her to independently provide or be delegated the responsibility to provide some or all of the health care services required by paragraph (j) of this Section.

Regulated area means an area, demarcated by the employer, where an employee's exposure to airborne concentrations of MC exceeds or can reasonably be expected to exceed either the 8-hour TWA PEL or the STEL.

Symptom means central nervous system effects such as headaches, disorientation, dizziness, fatigue, and decreased attention span; skin effects such as chapping, erythema, cracked skin, or skin burns; and cardiac effects such as chest pain or shortness of breath.

This Section means this methylene chloride standard.

(c) **Permissible exposure limits (PELs)**

(c)(1) Eight-hour time-weighted average (TWA) PEL. The employer shall ensure that no employee is exposed to an airborne concentration of MC in excess of twenty-five parts of MC per million parts of air (25 ppm) as an 8-hour TWA.

(c)(2) Short-term exposure limit (STEL). The employer shall ensure that no employee is exposed to an airborne concentration of MC in excess of one hundred and twenty-five parts of MC per million parts of air (125 ppm) as determined over a sampling period of fifteen minutes.

(d) **Exposure monitoring**

(d)(1) **Characterization of employee exposure**

(d)(1)(i) Where MC is present in the workplace, the employer shall determine each employee's exposure by either:

(d)(1)(i)(A) Taking a personal breathing zone air sample of each employee's exposure; or

(d)(1)(i)(B) Taking personal breathing zone air samples that are representative of each employee's exposure.

(d)(1)(ii) **Representative samples** The employer may consider personal breathing zone air samples to be representative of employee exposures when they are taken as follows:

(d)(1)(ii)(A) 8-hour TWA PEL. The employer has taken one or more personal breathing zone air samples for at least one employee in each job classification in a work area during every work shift, and the employee sampled is expected to have the highest MC exposure;

(d)(1)(ii)(B) Short-term exposure limits. The employer has taken one or more personal breathing zone air samples which indicate the highest likely 15-minute exposures during such operations for at least one employee in each job classification in the work area during every work shift, and the employee sampled is expected to have the highest MC exposure;

(d)(1)(ii)(C) Exception. Personal breathing zone air samples taken during one work shift may be used to represent employee exposures on other work shifts where the employer can document that the tasks performed and conditions in the workplace are similar across shifts.

(d)(1)(iii) Accuracy of monitoring. The employer shall ensure that the methods used to perform exposure monitoring produce results that are accurate to a confidence level of 95 percent, and are:

(d)(1)(iii)(A) Within plus or minus 25 percent for airborne concentrations of MC above the 8-hour TWA PEL or the STEL; or

(d)(1)(iii)(B) Within plus or minus 35 percent for airborne concentrations of MC at or above the action level but at or below the 8-hour TWA PEL.

(d)(2) **Initial determination** Each employer whose employees are exposed to MC shall perform initial exposure monitoring to determine each affected employee's exposure, except under the following conditions:

(d)(2)(i) Where objective data demonstrate that MC cannot be released in the workplace in airborne concentrations at or above the action level or above the STEL. The objective data shall represent the highest MC exposures likely to occur under reasonably foreseeable conditions of processing, use, or handling. The employer shall document the objective data exemption as specified in paragraph (m) of this Section;

(d)(2)(ii) Where the employer has performed exposure monitoring within 12 months prior to April 10, 1997 and that exposure monitoring meets all other requirements of this Section, and was conducted under conditions substantially equivalent to existing conditions; or

(d)(2)(iii) Where employees are exposed to MC on fewer than 30 days per year (e.g., on a construction site), and the employer has measurements by direct-reading instruments which give immediate results (such as a detector tube) and which provide sufficient information regarding employee exposures to determine what control measures are necessary to reduce exposures to acceptable levels.

(d)(3) **Periodic monitoring** Where the initial determination shows employee exposures at or above the action level or above the STEL, the employer shall establish an exposure monitoring program for periodic monitoring of employee exposure to MC in accordance with Table 1.

Table 1
Initial Determination Exposure Scenarios and Their Associated Monitoring Frequencies

Exposure scenario	Required monitoring activity
Below the action level and at or below the STEL	No 8-hour TWA or STEL monitoring required.
Below the action level and above the STEL	No 8-hour TWA monitoring required; monitor STEL exposures every three months.
At or above the action level, at or below the TWA, and at or below the STEL	Monitor 8-hour TWA exposures every six months.
At or above the action level, at or below the TWA, and above the STEL	Monitor 8-hour TWA exposures every six months and monitor STEL exposures every three months.
Above the TWA and at or below the STEL	Monitor 8-hour TWA exposures every three months. In addition, without regard to the last sentence of the note to paragraph (d)(3), the following employers must monitor STEL exposures every three months until either the date by which they must achieve the 8-hour TWA PEL under paragraph (n) of this Section or the date by which they in fact achieve the 8-hour TWA PEL, whichever comes first: employers engaged in polyurethane foam manufacturing; foam fabrication; furniture refinishing; general aviation aircraft stripping; product formulation; use of MC-based adhesives for boat building and repair, recreational vehicle manufacture, van conversion, or upholstery; and use of MC in construction work for restoration and preservation of buildings, painting and paint removal, cabinet making, or floor refinishing and resurfacing.
Above the TWA and above the STEL	Monitor 8-hour TWA exposures and STEL exposures every three months.

[**Note to paragraph (d)(3):** The employer may decrease the frequency of 8-hour TWA exposure monitoring to every six months when at least two consecutive measurements taken at least seven days apart show exposures to be at or below the 8-hour TWA PEL. The employer may discontinue the periodic 8-hour TWA monitoring for employees where at least two consecutive measurements taken at least seven days apart are below the action level. The employer may discontinue the periodic STEL monitoring for employees where at least two consecutive measurements taken at least 7 days apart are at or below the STEL.]

(d)(4) **Additional monitoring**

(d)(4)(i) The employer shall perform exposure monitoring when a change in workplace conditions indicates that employee exposure may have increased. Examples of situations that may require additional monitoring include changes in production, process, control equipment, or work practices, or a leak, rupture, or other breakdown.

(d)(4)(ii) Where exposure monitoring is performed due to a spill, leak, rupture or equipment breakdown, the employer shall clean-up the MC and perform the appropriate repairs before monitoring.

(d)(5) **Employee notification of monitoring results**

(d)(5)(i) The employer shall, within 15 working days after the receipt of the results of any monitoring performed under this Section, notify each affected employee of these results in writing, either individually or by posting of results in an appropriate location that is accessible to affected employees.

(d)(5)(ii) Whenever monitoring results indicate that employee exposure is above the 8-hour TWA PEL or the STEL, the employer shall describe in the written notification the corrective action being taken to reduce employee exposure to or below the 8-hour TWA PEL or STEL and the schedule for completion of this action.

(d)(6) **Observation of monitoring**

(d)(6)(i) **Employee observation** The employer shall provide affected employees or their designated representatives an opportunity to observe any monitoring of employee exposure to MC conducted in accordance with this Section.

(d)(6)(ii) **Observation procedures** When observation of the monitoring of employee exposure to MC requires entry into an area where the use of protective clothing or equipment is required, the employer shall provide, at no cost to the observer(s), and the observer(s) shall be required to use such clothing and equipment and shall comply with all other applicable safety and health procedures.

(e) **Regulated areas**

(e)(1) The employer shall establish a regulated area wherever an employee's exposure to airborne concentrations of MC exceeds or can reasonably be expected to exceed either the 8-hour TWA PEL or the STEL.

(e)(2) The employer shall limit access to regulated areas to authorized persons.

(e)(3) The employer shall supply a respirator, selected in accordance with paragraph (h)(3) of this Section, to each person who enters a regulated area and shall require each affected employee to use that respirator whenever MC exposures are likely to exceed the 8-hour TWA PEL or STEL.

[**Note to paragraph (e)(3):** An employer who has implemented all feasible engineering, work practice and administrative controls (as required in paragraph (f) of this Section), and who has established a regulated area (as required by paragraph (e)(1) of this Section) where MC exposure can be reliably predicted to exceed the 8-hour TWA PEL or the STEL only on certain days (for example, because of work or process schedule) would need to have affected employees use respirators in that regulated area only on those days.]

(e)(4) The employer shall ensure that, within a regulated area, employees do not engage in non-work activities which may increase dermal or oral MC exposure.

(e)(5) The employer shall ensure that while employees are wearing respirators, they do not engage in activities (such as taking medication or chewing gum or tobacco) which interfere with respirator seal or performance.

(e)(6) The employer shall demarcate regulated areas from the rest of the workplace in any manner that adequately establishes and alerts employees to the boundaries of the area and minimizes the number of authorized employees exposed to MC within the regulated area.

(e)(7) An employer at a multi-employer worksite who establishes a regulated area shall communicate the access restrictions and locations of these areas to all other employers with work operations at that worksite.

(f) **Methods of compliance**

(f)(1) **Engineering and work practice controls** The employer shall institute and maintain the effectiveness of engineering controls and work practices to reduce employee exposure to or below the PELs except to the extent that the employer can demonstrate that such controls are not feasible. Wherever the feasible engineering controls and work practices which can be instituted are not sufficient to reduce employee exposure to or below the 8–TWA PEL or STEL, the employer shall use them to reduce employee exposure to the lowest levels achievable by these controls and shall supplement them by the use of respiratory protection that complies with the requirements of paragraph (g) of this Section.

(f)(2) **Prohibition of rotation** The employer shall not implement a schedule of employee rotation as a means of compliance with the PELs.

(f)(3) **Leak and spill detection**

(f)(3)(i) The employer shall implement procedures to detect leaks of MC in the workplace. In work areas where spills may occur, the employer shall make provisions to contain any spills and to safely dispose of any MC-contaminated waste materials.

(f)(3)(ii) The employer shall ensure that all incidental leaks are repaired and that incidental spills are cleaned promptly by employees who use the appropriate personal protective equipment and are trained in proper methods of cleanup.

[**Note to paragraph (f)(3)(ii):** See Appendix A of this Section for examples of procedures that satisfy this requirement. Employers covered by this Standard may also be subject to the hazardous waste and emergency response provisions contained in 29 CFR §1910.120 (q).]

(g) OI **Respiratory protection**

(g)(1) **General** For employees who use respirators required by this Section, the employer must provide each employee an appropriate respirator that complies with the requirements of this paragraph. Respirators must be used during:

(g)(1)(i) Periods when an employee's exposure to MC exceeds the 8-hour TWA PEL, or STEL (for example, when an employee is using MC in a regulated area);

(g)(1)(ii) Periods necessary to install or implement feasible engineering and work-practice controls;

(g)(1)(iii) A few work operations, such as some maintenance operations and repair activities, for which the employer demonstrates that engineering and work-practice controls are infeasible;

(g)(1)(iv) Work operations for which feasible engineering and work-practice controls are not sufficient to reduce employee exposures to or below the PELs;

(g)(1)(v) Emergencies.

(g)(2) **Respirator program**

(g)(2)(i) The employer must implement a respiratory protection program in accordance with §1910.13(b) through (m) (except (d)(1)(iii)), which covers each employee required by this Section to use a respirator.

(g)(2)(ii) Employers who provide employees with gas masks with organic-vapor canisters for the purpose of emergency escape must replace the canisters after any emergency use and before the gas masks are returned to service.

(g)(3) **Respirator selection** Employers must:

(g)(3)(i) Select, and provide to employees, the appropriate atmosphere-supplying respirator specified in paragraph (d)(3)(i)(A) of 29 CFR §1910.134; however, employers must not select or use half masks of any type because MC may cause eye irritation or damage.

(g)(3)(ii) For emergency escape, provide employees with one of the following respirator options: A self-contained breathing apparatus operated in the continuous-flow or pressure-demand mode; or a gas mask with an organic vapor canister.

(g)(4) **Medical evaluation** Before having an employee use a supplied-air respirator in the negative-pressure mode, or a gas mask with an organic-vapor canister for emergency escape, the employer must:

(g)(4)(i) Have a physician or other licensed health-care professional (PLHCP) evaluate the employee's ability to use such respiratory protection.

(g)(4)(ii) Ensure that the PLHCP provides their findings in a written opinion to the employee and the employer.

(h) **Protective Work Clothing and Equipment**

(h)(1) Where needed to prevent MC-induced skin or eye irritation, the employer shall provide clean protective clothing and equipment which is resistant to MC, at no cost to the employee, and shall ensure that each affected employee uses it. Eye and face protection shall meet the requirements of 29 CFR §1910.133 or 29 CFR §1915.153, as applicable.

(h)(2) The employer shall clean, launder, repair and replace all protective clothing and equipment required by this paragraph as needed to maintain their effectiveness.

(h)(3) The employer shall be responsible for the safe disposal of such clothing and equipment.

[**Note to paragraph (h)(3):** See Appendix A for examples of disposal procedures that will satisfy this requirement.]

(i) **Hygiene facilities**

(i)(1) If it is reasonably foreseeable that employees' skin may contact solutions containing 0.1 percent or greater MC (for example, through splashes, spills or improper work practices), the employer shall provide conveniently located washing facilities capable of removing the MC, and shall ensure that affected employees use these facilities as needed.

(i)(2) If it is reasonably foreseeable that an employee's eyes may contact solutions containing 0.1 percent or greater MC (for example through splashes, spills or improper work practices), the employer shall provide appropriate eyewash facilities within the immediate work area for emergency use, and shall ensure that affected employees use those facilities when necessary.

(j) **Medical surveillance**

(j)(1) **Affected employees** The employer shall make medical surveillance available for employees who are or may be exposed to MC as follows:

(j)(1)(i) At or above the action level on 30 or more days per year, or above the 8- hour TWA PEL or the STEL on 10 or more days per year;

(j)(1)(ii) Above the 8–TWA PEL or STEL for any time period where an employee has been identified by a physician or other licensed health care professional as being at risk from cardiac disease or from some other serious MC-related health condition and such employee requests inclusion in the medical surveillance program;

(j)(1)(iii) During an emergency.

(j)(2) **Costs** The employer shall provide all required medical surveillance at no cost to affected employees, without loss of pay and at a reasonable time and place.

(j)(3) **Medical personnel** The employer shall ensure that all medical surveillance procedures are performed by a physician or other licensed health care professional, as defined in paragraph (b) of this Section.

(j)(4) **Frequency of medical surveillance** The employer shall make medical surveillance available to each affected employee as follows:

(j)(4)(i) **Initial surveillance** The employer shall provide initial medical surveillance under the schedule provided by paragraph (n)(2)(iii) of this Section, or before the time of initial assignment of the employee, whichever is later. The employer need not provide the initial surveillance if medical records show that an affected employee has been provided with medical surveillance that complies with this Section within 12 months before April 10, 1997.

(j)(4)(ii) **Periodic medical surveillance** The employer shall update the medical and work history for each affected employee annually. The employer shall provide periodic physical examinations, including appropriate laboratory surveillance, as follows:

(j)(4)(ii)(A) For employees 45 years of age or older, within 12 months of the initial surveillance or any subsequent medical surveillance; and

(j)(4)(ii)(B) For employees younger than 45 years of age, within 36 months of the initial surveillance or any subsequent medical surveillance.

(j)(4)(iii) **Termination of employment or reassignment** When an employee leaves the employer's workplace, or is reassigned to an area where exposure to MC is consistently at or below the action level and STEL, medical surveillance shall be made available if six months or more have elapsed since the last medical surveillance.

(j)(4)(iv) **Additional surveillance** The employer shall provide additional medical surveillance at frequencies other than those listed above when recommended in the written medical opinion. (For example, the physician or other licensed health care professional may determine an examination is warranted in less than 36 months for employees younger than 45 years of age based upon evaluation of the results of the annual medical and work history.)

(j)(5) **Content of medical surveillance**

(j)(5)(i) **Medical and work history** The comprehensive medical and work history shall emphasize neurological symptoms, skin conditions, history of hematologic or liver disease, signs or symptoms suggestive of heart disease (angina, coronary artery disease), risk factors for cardiac disease, MC exposures, and work practices and personal protective equipment used during such exposures.

[**Note to paragraph (j)(5)(i):** See Appendix B of this Section for an example of a medical and work history format that would satisfy this requirement.]

(j)(5)(ii) **Physical examination** Where physical examinations are provided as required above, the physician or other licensed health care professional shall accord particular attention to the lungs, cardiovascular system (including blood pressure and pulse), liver, nervous system, and skin. The physician or other licensed health care professional shall determine the extent and nature of the physical examination based on the health status of the employee and analysis of the medical and work history.

(j)(5)(iii) **Laboratory surveillance** The physician or other licensed health care professional shall determine the extent of any required laboratory surveillance based on the employee's observed health status and the medical and work history.

[**Note to paragraph (j)(5)(iii):** See Appendix B of this Section for information regarding medical tests. Laboratory surveillance may include before- and after-shift carboxyhemoglobin determinations, resting ECG, hematocrit, liver function tests and cholesterol levels.]

(j)(5)(iv) **Other information or reports** The medical surveillance shall also include any other information or reports the physician or other licensed health care professional determines are necessary to assess the employee's health in relation to MC exposure.

(j)(6) **Content of emergency medical surveillance** The employer shall ensure that medical surveillance made available when an employee has been exposed to MC in emergency situations includes, at a minimum:

(j)(6)(i) Appropriate emergency treatment and decontamination of the exposed employee;

(j)(6)(ii) Comprehensive physical examination with special emphasis on the nervous system, cardiovascular system, lungs, liver and skin, including blood pressure and pulse;

(j)(6)(iii) Updated medical and work history, as appropriate for the medical condition of the employee; and

(j)(6)(iv) Laboratory surveillance, as indicated by the employee's health status.

[**Note to paragraph (j)(6)(iv):** See Appendix B for examples of tests which may be appropriate.]

(j)(7) **Additional examinations and referrals** Where the physician or other licensed health care professional determines it is necessary, the scope of the medical examination shall be expanded and the appropriate additional medical surveillance, such as referrals for consultation or examination, shall be provided.

(j)(8) **Information provided to the physician or other licensed health care professional** The employer shall provide the following information to a physician or other licensed health care professional who is involved in the diagnosis of MC-induced health effects:

(j)(8)(i) A copy of this Section including its applicable Appendices;

(j)(8)(ii) A description of the affected employee's past, current and anticipated future duties as they relate to the employee's MC exposure;

(j)(8)(iii) The employee's former or current exposure levels or, for employees not yet occupationally exposed to MC, the employee's anticipated exposure levels and the frequency and exposure levels anticipated to be associated with emergencies;

(j)(8)(iv) A description of any personal protective equipment, such as respirators, used or to be used; and

(j)(8)(v) Information from previous employment-related medical surveillance of the affected employee which is not otherwise available to the physician or other licensed health care professional.

(j)(9) **Written medical opinions**

(j)(9)(i) For each physical examination required by this Section, the employer shall ensure that the physician or other licensed health care professional provides to the employer and to the affected employee a written opinion regarding the results of that examination within 15 days of completion of the evaluation of medical and laboratory findings, but not more than 30 days after the examination. The written medical opinion shall be limited to the following information:

(j)(9)(i)(A) The physician or other licensed health care professional's opinion concerning whether exposure to MC may contribute to or aggravate the employee's existing cardiac, hepatic, neurological (including stroke) or dermal disease or whether the employee has any other medical condition(s) that would place the employee's health at increased risk of material impairment from exposure to MC.

(j)(9)(i)(B) Any recommended limitations upon the employee's exposure to MC, including removal from MC exposure, or upon the employee's use of respirators, protective clothing, or other protective equipment.

(j)(9)(i)(C) A statement that the employee has been informed by the physician or other licensed health care professional that MC is a potential occupational carcinogen, of risk factors for heart disease, and the potential for exacerbation of underlying heart disease by exposure to MC through its metabolism to carbon monoxide; and

(j)(9)(i)(D) A statement that the employee has been informed by the physician or other licensed health care professional of the results of the medical examination and any medical conditions resulting from MC exposure which require further explanation or treatment.

(j)(9)(ii) The employer shall instruct the physician or other licensed health care professional not to reveal to the employer, orally or in the written opinion, any specific records, findings, and diagnoses that have no bearing on occupational exposure to MC.

[**Note to paragraph (j)(9)(ii):** The written medical opinion may also include information and opinions generated to comply with other OSHA health standards.]

(j)(10) **Medical presumption** For purposes of this paragraph (j) of this Section, the physician or other licensed health care professional shall presume, unless medical evidence indicates to the contrary, that a medical condition is unlikely to require medical removal from MC exposure if the employee is not exposed to MC above the 8-hour TWA PEL. If the physician or other licensed health care professional recommends removal for an employee exposed below the 8-hour TWA PEL, the physician or other licensed health care professional shall cite specific medical evidence, sufficient to rebut the presumption that exposure below the 8-hour TWA PEL is unlikely to require removal, to support the recommendation. If such evidence is cited by the physician or other licensed health care professional, the employer must remove the employee. If such evidence is not cited by the physician or other licensed health care professional, the employer is not required to remove the employee.

(j)(11) **Medical Removal Protection (MRP)**

(j)(11)(i) Temporary medical removal and return of an employee.

(j)(11)(i)(A) Except as provided in paragraph (j)(10) of this Section, when a medical determination recommends removal because the employee's exposure to MC may contribute to or aggravate the employee's existing cardiac, hepatic, neurological (including stroke), or skin disease, the employer must provide medical removal protection benefits to the employee and either:

(j)(11)(i)(A)(1) Transfer the employee to comparable work where methylene chloride exposure is below the action level; or

(j)(11)(i)(A)(2) Remove the employee from MC exposure.

(j)(11)(i)(B) If comparable work is not available and the employer is able to demonstrate that removal and the costs of extending MRP benefits to an additional employee, considering feasibility in relation to the size of the employer's business and the other requirements of this Standard, make further reliance on MRP an inappropriate remedy, the employer may retain the additional employee in the existing job until transfer or removal becomes appropriate, provided:

(j)(11)(i)(B)(1) The employer ensures that the employee receives additional medical surveillance, including a physical examination at least every 60 days until transfer or removal occurs; and

(j)(11)(i)(B)(2) The employer or PLHCP informs the employee of the risk to the employee's health from continued MC exposure.

(j)(11)(i)(C) The employer shall maintain in effect any job-related protective measures or limitations, other than removal, for as long as a medical determination recommends them to be necessary.

(j)(11)(ii) End of MRP benefits and return of the employee to former job status.

(j)(11)(ii)(A) The employer may cease providing MRP benefits at the earliest of the following:

(j)(11)(ii)(A)(1) Six months;

(j)(11)(ii)(A)(2) Return of the employee to the employee's former job status following receipt of a medical determination concluding that the employee's exposure to MC no longer will aggravate any cardiac, hepatic, neurological (including stroke), or dermal disease;

(j)(11)(ii)(A)(3) Receipt of a medical determination concluding that the employee can never return to MC exposure.

(j)(11)(ii)(B) For the purposes of this paragraph (j), the requirement that an employer return an employee to the employee's former job status is not intended to expand upon or restrict any rights an employee has or would have had, absent temporary medical removal, to a specific job classification or position under the terms of a collective bargaining agreement.

(j)(12) **Medical removal protection benefits**

(j)(12)(i) For purposes of this paragraph (j), the term medical removal protection benefits means that, for each removal, an employer must maintain for up to six months the earnings, seniority, and other employment rights and benefits of the employee as though the employee had not been removed from MC exposure or transferred to a comparable job.

(j)(12)(ii) During the period of time that an employee is removed from exposure to MC, the employer may condition the provision of medical removal protection benefits upon the employee's participation in follow-up medical surveillance made available pursuant to this Section.

(j)(12)(iii) If a removed employee files a workers' compensation claim for a MC-related disability, the employer shall continue the MRP benefits required by this paragraph until either the claim is resolved or the 6-month period for payment f MRP benefits has passed, whichever occurs first. To the extent the employee is entitled to indemnity payments for earnings lost during the period of removal, the employer's obligation to provide medical removal protection benefits to the employee shall be reduced by the amount of such indemnity payments.

(j)(12)(iv) The employer's obligation to provide medical removal protection benefits to a removed employee shall be reduced to the extent that the employee receives compensation for earnings lost during the period of removal from either a publicly or an employer-funded compensation program, or receives income from employment with another employer made possible by virtue of the employee's removal.

(j)(13) **Voluntary removal or restriction of an employee** Where an employer, although not required by this Section to do so, removes an employee from exposure to MC or otherwise places any limitation on an employee due to the effects of MC exposure on the employee's medical condition, the employer shall provide medical removal protection benefits to the employee equal to those required by paragraph (j)(12) of this Section.

(j)(14) **Multiple health care professional review mechanism**

(j)(14)(i) If the employer selects the initial physician or licensed health care professional (PLHCP) to conduct any medical examination or consultation provided to an employee under this paragraph (j)(11), the employer shall notify the employee of the right to seek a second medical opinion each time the employer provides the employee with a copy of the written opinion of that PLHCP.

(j)(14)(ii) If the employee does not agree with the opinion of the employer-selected PLHCP, notifies the employer of that fact, and takes steps to make an appointment with a second PLHCP within 15 days of receiving a copy of the written opinion of the initial PLHCP, the employer shall pay for the PLHCP chosen by the employee to perform at least the following:

(j)(14)(ii)(A) Review any findings, determinations or recommendations of the initial PLHCP; and

(j)(14)(ii)(B) Conduct such examinations, consultations, and laboratory tests as the PLHCP deems necessary to facilitate this review.

(j)(14)(iii) If the findings, determinations or recommendations of the second PLHCP differ from those of the initial PLHCP, then the employer and the employee shall instruct the two health care professionals to resolve the disagreement.

(j)(14)(iv) If the two health care professionals are unable to resolve their disagreement within 15 days, then those two health care professionals shall jointly designate a PLHCP who is a specialist in the field at issue. The employer shall pay for the specialist to perform at least the following:

(j)(14)(iv)(A) Review the findings, determinations, and recommendations of the first two PLHCPs; and

(j)(14)(iv)(B) Conduct such examinations, consultations, laboratory tests and discussions with the prior PLHCPs as the specialist deems necessary to resolve the disagreements of the prior health care professionals.

(j)(14)(v) The written opinion of the specialist shall be the definitive medical determination. The employer shall act consistent with the definitive medical determination, unless the employer and employee agree that the written opinion of one of the other two PLHCPs shall be the definitive medical determination.

(j)(14)(vi) The employer and the employee or authorized employee representative may agree upon the use of any expeditious alternate health care professional determination mechanism in lieu of the multiple health care professional review mechanism provided by this paragraph so long as the alternate mechanism otherwise satisfies the requirements contained in this paragraph.

(k) [OI] **Hazard communication**

(k)(1) **Hazard communication—general**

(k)(1)(i) Chemical manufacturers, importers, distributors and employers shall comply with all requirements of the Hazard Communication Standard (HCS) (§1910.1200) for MC.

(k)(1)(ii) In classifying the hazards of MC at least the following hazards are to be addressed: Cancer, cardiac effects (including elevation of carboxyhemoglobin), central nervous system effects, liver effects, and skin and eye irritation.

(k)(1)(iii) Employers shall include MC in the hazard communication program established to comply with the HCS (§1910.1200). Employers shall ensure that each employee has access to labels on containers of MC and to safety data sheets, and is trained in accordance with the requirements of HCS and paragraph (l) of this Section.

(k)(2) [Reserved].

(l) **Employee information and training**

(l)(1) The employer shall provide information and training for each affected employee prior to or at the time of initial assignment to a job involving potential exposure to MC.

(l)(2) The employer shall ensure that information and training is presented in a manner that is understandable to the employees.

(l)(3) In addition to the information required under the Hazard Communication Standard at 29 CFR §1910.1200, 29 CFR §1915.1200, or 29 CFR §1926.59, as appropriate:

(l)(3)(i) The employer shall inform each affected employee of the requirements of this Section and information available in its Appendices, as well as how to access or obtain a copy of it in the workplace;

(l)(3)(ii) Wherever an employee's exposure to airborne concentrations of MC exceeds or can reasonably be expected to exceed the action level, the employer shall inform each affected employee of the quantity, location, manner of use, release, and storage of MC and the specific operations in the workplace that could result in exposure to MC, particularly noting where exposures may be above the 8-hour TWA PEL or STEL;

(l)(4) The employer shall train each affected employee as required under the Hazard Communication standard at 29 CFR §1910.1200, 29 CFR §1915.1200, or 29 CFR §1926.59, as appropriate.

(l)(5) The employer shall re-train each affected employee as necessary to ensure that each employee exposed above the action level or the STEL maintains the requisite understanding of the principles of safe use and handling of MC in the workplace.

(l)(6) Whenever there are workplace changes, such as modifications of tasks or procedures or the institution of new tasks or procedures, which increase employee exposure, and where those exposures exceed or can reasonably be expected to exceed the action level, the employer shall update the training as necessary to ensure that each affected employee has the requisite proficiency.

(l)(7) An employer whose employees are exposed to MC at a multi-employer worksite shall notify the other employers with work operations at that site in accordance with the requirements of the Hazard Communication Standard, 29 CFR §1910.1200, 29 CFR §1915.1200, or 29 CFR §1926.59, as appropriate.

(l)(8) The employer shall provide to the Assistant Secretary or the Director, upon request, all available materials relating to employee information and training.

(m) **Recordkeeping**

(m)(1) **Objective data**

(m)(1)(i) Where an employer seeks to demonstrate that initial monitoring is unnecessary through reasonable reliance on objective data showing that any materials in the workplace containing MC will not release MC at levels which exceed the action level or the STEL under foreseeable conditions of exposure, the employer shall establish and maintain an accurate record of the objective data relied upon in support of the exemption.

(m)(1)(ii) This record shall include at least the following information:

(m)(1)(ii)(A) The MC-containing material in question;

(m)(1)(ii)(B) The source of the objective data;

(m)(1)(ii)(C) The testing protocol, results of testing, and/or analysis of the material for the release of MC;

(m)(1)(ii)(D) A description of the operation exempted under paragraph (d)(2)(i) of this Section and how the data support the exemption; and

(m)(1)(ii)(E) Other data relevant to the operations, materials, processing, or employee exposures covered by the exemption.

(m)(1)(iii) The employer shall maintain this record for the duration of the employer's reliance upon such objective data.

(m)(2) **Exposure measurements**

(m)(2)(i) The employer shall establish and keep an accurate record of all measurements taken to monitor employee exposure to MC as prescribed in paragraph (d) of this Section.

(m)(2)(ii) Where the employer has 20 or more employees, this record shall include at least the following information:

(m)(2)(ii)(A) The date of measurement for each sample taken;

(m)(2)(ii)(B) The operation involving exposure to MC which is being monitored;

(m)(2)(ii)(C) Sampling and analytical methods used and evidence of their accuracy;

(m)(2)(ii)(D) Number, duration, and results of samples taken;

(m)(2)(ii)(E) Type of personal protective equipment, such as respiratory protective devices, worn, if any; and

(m)(2)(ii)(F) Name, social security number, job classification and exposure of all of the employees represented by monitoring, indicating which employees were actually monitored.

(m)(2)(iii) Where the employer has fewer than 20 employees, the record shall include at least the following information:

(m)(2)(iii)(A) The date of measurement for each sample taken;

(m)(2)(iii)(B) Number, duration, and results of samples taken; and

(m)(2)(iii)(C) Name, social security number, job classification and exposure of all of the employees represented by monitoring, indicating which employees were actually monitored.

(m)(2)(iv) The employer shall maintain this record for at least thirty (30) years, in accordance with 29 CFR §1910.1020.

(m)(3) **Medical surveillance**

(m)(3)(i) The employer shall establish and maintain an accurate record for each employee subject to medical surveillance under paragraph (j) of this Section.

(m)(3)(ii) The record shall include at least the following information:

(m)(3)(ii)(A) The name, social security number and description of the duties of the employee;

(m)(3)(ii)(B) Written medical opinions; and

(m)(3)(ii)(C) Any employee medical conditions related to exposure to MC.

(m)(3)(iii) The employer shall ensure that this record is maintained for the duration of employment plus thirty (30) years, in accordance with 29 CFR §1910.1020.

[OI] indicates an OSHA Letter of Interpretation exists for this specific reference. Please see www.oshainterpretation.us for details.

(m)(4) **Availability**

(m)(4)(i) The employer, upon written request, shall make all records required to be maintained by this Section available to the Assistant Secretary and the Director for examination and copying in accordance with 29 CFR §1910.1020.

[**Note to paragraph (m)(4)(i):** All records required to be maintained by this Section may be kept in the most administratively convenient form (for example, electronic or computer records would satisfy this requirement).]

(m)(4)(ii) The employer, upon request, shall make any employee exposure and objective data records required by this Section available for examination and copying by affected employees, former employees, and designated representatives in accordance with 29 CFR §1910.1020.

(m)(4)(iii) The employer, upon request, shall make employee medical records required to be kept by this Section available for examination and copying by the subject employee and by anyone having the specific written consent of the subject employee in accordance with 29 CFR §1910.1020.

(m)(5) **Transfer of records** The employer shall comply with the requirements concerning transfer of records set forth in 29 CFR §1910.1020(h).

(n) [Reserved]

(o) **Appendices** The information contained in the Appendices does not, by itself, create any additional obligations not otherwise imposed or detract from any existing obligation.

[**Note to paragraph (o):** The requirement of 29 CFR §1910.1052(g)(1) to use respiratory protection whenever an employee's exposure to methylene chloride exceeds or can reasonably be expected to exceed the 8-hour TWA PEL is hereby stayed until August 31, 1998 for employers engaged in polyurethane foam manufacturing; foam fabrication; furniture refinishing; general aviation aircraft stripping; formulation of products containing methylene chloride; boat building and repair; recreational vehicle manufacture; van conversion; upholstery; and use of methylene chloride in construction work for restoration and preservation of buildings, painting and paint removal, cabinet making and/or floor refinishing and resurfacing.

The requirement of 29 CFR §1910.1052(f)(1) to implement engineering controls to achieve the 8-hour TWA PEL and STEL is hereby stayed until December 10, 1998 for employers with more than 100 employees engaged in polyurethane foam manufacturing and for employers with more than 20 employees engaged in foam fabrication; furniture refinishing; general aviation aircraft stripping; formulation of products containing methylene chloride; boat building and repair; recreational vehicle manufacture; van conversion; upholstery; and use of methylene chloride in construction work for restoration and preservation of buildings, painting and paint removal, cabinet making and/or floor refinishing and resurfacing.]

§1910.1052 Appendix A Substance safety data sheet and technical guideline for Methylene Chloride

I. Substance Identification.

A. Substance: Methylene chloride (CH_2C_{12}).

B. Synonyms: MC, Dichloromethane (DCM); Methylene dichloride; Methylene bichloride; Methane dichloride; CAS: 75–09–2; NCI-C50102.

C. Physical data:

1. Molecular weight: 84.9.
2. Boiling point (760 mm Hg): 39.8 °C (104 °F).
3. Specific gravity (water=1): 1.3.
4. Vapor density (air=1 at boiling point): 2.9.
5. Vapor pressure at 20 °C (68 °F): 350 mm Hg.
6. Solubility in water, g/100 g water at 20 °C (68 °F)=1.32.
7. Appearance and odor: colorless liquid with a chloroform-like odor.

D. Uses

MC is used as a solvent, especially where high volatility is required. It is a good solvent for oils, fats, waxes, resins, bitumen, rubber and cellulose acetate and is a useful paint stripper and degreaser. It is used in paint removers, in propellant mixtures for aerosol containers, as a solvent for plastics, as a degreasing agent, as an extracting agent in the pharmaceutical industry and as a blowing agent in polyurethane foams. Its solvent property is sometimes increased by mixing with methanol, petroleum naphtha or tetrachloroethylene.

E. Appearance and odor

MC is a clear colorless liquid with a chloroform-like odor. It is slightly soluble in water and completely miscible with most organic solvents.

F. Permissible exposure:

Exposure may not exceed 25 parts MC per million parts of air (25 ppm) as an eight-hour time-weighted average (8-hour TWA PEL) or 125 parts of MC per million parts of air (125 ppm) averaged over a 15-minute period (STEL).

II. Health Hazard Data

A. MC can affect the body if it is inhaled or if the liquid comes in contact with the eyes or skin. It can also affect the body if it is swallowed.

B. Effects of overexposure:

1. Short-term Exposure:

MC is an anesthetic. Inhaling the vapor may cause mental confusion, light-headedness, nausea, vomiting, and headache. Continued exposure may cause increased light-headedness, staggering, unconsciousness, and even death. High vapor concentrations may also cause irritation of the eyes and respiratory tract. Exposure to MC may make the symptoms of angina (chest pains) worse. Skin exposure to liquid MC may cause irritation. If liquid MC remains on the skin, it may cause skin burns. Splashes of the liquid into the eyes may cause irritation.

2. Long-term (chronic) exposure:

The best evidence that MC causes cancer is from laboratory studies in which rats, mice and hamsters inhaled MC 6 hours per day, 5 days per week for 2 years. MC exposure produced lung and liver tumors in mice and mammary tumors in rats. No carcinogenic effects of MC were found in hamsters.

There are also some human epidemiological studies which show an association between occupational exposure to MC and increases in biliary (bile duct) cancer and a type of brain cancer. Other epidemiological studies have not observed a relationship between MC exposure and cancer. OSHA interprets these results to mean that there is suggestive (but not absolute) evidence that MC is a human carcinogen.

C. Reporting signs and symptoms:

You should inform your employer if you develop any signs or symptoms and suspect that they are caused by exposure to MC.

D. Warning Properties:

1. Odor Threshold:

Different authors have reported varying odor thresholds for MC. Kirk-Othmer and Sax both reported 25 to 50 ppm; Summer and May both reported 150 ppm; Spector reports 320 ppm. Patty, however, states that since one can become adapted to the odor, MC should not be considered to have adequate warning properties.

2. Eye Irritation Level:

Kirk-Othmer reports that "MC vapor is seriously damaging to the eyes." Sax agrees with Kirk-Othmer's statement. The ACGIH Documentation of TLVs states that irritation of the eyes has been observed in workers exposed to concentrations up to 5000 ppm.

3. Evaluation of Warning Properties:

Since a wide range of MC odor thresholds are reported (25–320 ppm), and human adaptation to the odor occurs, MC is considered to be a material with poor warning properties.

III. Emergency First Aid Procedures

In the event of emergency, institute first aid procedures and send for first aid or medical assistance.

A. Eye and Skin Exposures:

If there is a potential for liquid MC to come in contact with eye or skin, face shields and skin protective equipment must be provided and used. If liquid MC comes in contact with the eye, get medical attention. Contact lenses should not be worn when working with this chemical.

B. Breathing:

If a person breathes in large amounts of MC, move the exposed person to fresh air at once. If breathing has stopped, perform cardiopulmonary resuscitation. Keep the affected person warm and at rest. Get medical attention as soon as possible.

C. Rescue:

Move the affected person from the hazardous exposure immediately. If the exposed person has been overcome, notify someone else and put into effect the established emergency rescue procedures. Understand the facility's emergency rescue procedures and know the locations of rescue equipment before the need arises. Do not become a casualty yourself.

IV. Respirators, Protective Clothing, and Eye Protection

A. Respirators

Good industrial hygiene practices recommend that engineering controls be used to reduce environmental concentrations to the permissible exposure level. However, there are some exceptions where respirators may be used to control exposure. Respirators may be used when engineering and work practice controls are not feasible, when such controls are in the process of being installed, or when these controls fail and need to be supplemented. Respirators may also be used for operations which require entry into tanks or closed vessels, and in emergency situations.

If the use of respirators is necessary, the only respirators permitted are those that have been approved by the Mine Safety and Health Administration

(MSHA) or the National Institute for Occupational Safety and Health (NIOSH). Supplied-air respirators are required because air-purifying respirators do not provide adequate respiratory protection against MC.

In addition to respirator selection, a complete written respiratory protection program should be instituted which includes regular training, maintenance, inspection, cleaning, and evaluation. If you can smell MC while wearing a respirator, proceed immediately to fresh air. If you experience difficulty in breathing while wearing a respirator, tell your employer.

B. Protective Clothing:

Employees must be provided with and required to use impervious clothing, gloves, face shields (eight-inch minimum), and other appropriate protective clothing necessary to prevent repeated or prolonged skin contact with liquid MC or contact with vessels containing liquid MC. Any clothing which becomes wet with liquid MC should be removed immediately and not reworn until the employer has ensured that the protective clothing is fit for reuse. Contaminated protective clothing should be placed in a regulated area designated by the employer for removal of MC before the clothing is laundered or disposed of. Clothing and equipment should remain in the regulated area until all of the MC contamination has evaporated; clothing and equipment should then be laundered or disposed of as appropriate.

C. Eye Protection:

Employees should be provided with and required to use splash-proof safety goggles where liquid MC may contact the eyes.

V. Housekeeping and Hygiene Facilities

For purposes of complying with 29 CFR §1910.141, the following items should be emphasized:

A. The workplace should be kept clean, orderly, and in a sanitary condition. The employer should institute a leak and spill detection program for operations involving liquid MC in order to detect sources of fugitive MC emissions.

B. Emergency drench showers and eyewash facilities are recommended. These should be maintained in a sanitary condition. Suitable cleansing agents should also be provided to assure the effective removal of MC from the skin.

C. Because of the hazardous nature of MC, contaminated protective clothing should be placed in a regulated area designated by the employer for removal of MC before the clothing is laundered or disposed of.

VI. Precautions for Safe Use, Handling, and Storage

A. Fire and Explosion Hazards:

MC has no flash point in a conventional closed tester, but it forms flammable vapor-air mixtures at approximately 100 °C (212 °F), or higher. It has a lower explosion limit of 12%, and an upper explosion limit of 19% in air. It has an autoignition temperature of 556.1 °C (1033 °F), and a boiling point of 39.8 °C (104 °F). It is heavier than water with a specific gravity of 1.3. It is slightly soluble in water.

B. Reactivity Hazards:

Conditions contributing to the instability of MC are heat and moisture. Contact with strong oxidizers, caustics, and chemically active metals such as aluminum or magnesium powder, sodium and potassium may cause fires and explosions.

Special precautions: Liquid MC will attack some forms of plastics, rubber, and coatings.

C. Toxicity:

Liquid MC is painful and irritating if splashed in the eyes or if confined on the skin by gloves, clothing, or shoes. Vapors in high concentrations may cause narcosis and death. Prolonged exposure to vapors may cause cancer or exacerbate cardiac disease.

D. Storage:

Protect against physical damage. Because of its corrosive properties, and its high vapor pressure, MC should be stored in plain, galvanized or lead lined, mild steel containers in a cool, dry, well ventilated area away from direct sunlight, heat source and acute fire hazards.

E. Piping Material:

All piping and valves at the loading or unloading station should be of material that is resistant to MC and should be carefully inspected prior to connection to the transport vehicle and periodically during the operation.

F. Usual Shipping Containers:

Glass bottles, 5- and 55-gallon steel drums, tank cars, and tank trucks.

Note: This Section addresses MC exposure in marine terminal and longshore employment only where leaking or broken packages allow MC exposure that is not addressed through compliance with 29 CFR Parts 1917 and 1918, respectively.

G. Electrical Equipment:

Electrical installations in Class I hazardous locations as defined in Article 500 of the National Electrical Code, should be installed according to Article 501 of the code; and electrical equipment should be suitable for use in atmospheres containing MC vapors. See Flammable and Combustible Liquids Code (NFPA No. 325M), Chemical Safety Data Sheet SD–86 (Manufacturing Chemists' Association, Inc.).

H. Fire Fighting:

When involved in fire, MC emits highly toxic and irritating fumes such as phosgene, hydrogen chloride and carbon monoxide. Wear breathing apparatus and use water spray to keep fire-exposed containers cool. Water spray may be used to flush spills away from exposures. Extinguishing media are dry chemical, carbon dioxide, foam. For purposes of compliance with 29 CFR §1910.307, locations classified as hazardous due to the presence of MC shall be Class I.

I. Spills and Leaks:

Persons not wearing protective equipment and clothing should be restricted from areas of spills or leaks until cleanup has been completed. If MC has spilled or leaked, the following steps should be taken:

1. Remove all ignition sources.
2. Ventilate area of spill or leak.
3. Collect for reclamation or absorb in vermiculite, dry sand, earth, or a similar material.

J. Methods of Waste Disposal:

Small spills should be absorbed onto sand and taken to a safe area for atmospheric evaporation. Incineration is the preferred method for disposal of large quantities by mixing with a combustible solvent and spraying into an incinerator equipped with acid scrubbers to remove hydrogen chloride gases formed. Complete combustion will convert carbon monoxide to carbon dioxide. Care should be taken for the presence of phosgene.

K. You should not keep food, beverage, or smoking materials, or eat or smoke in regulated areas where MC concentrations are above the permissible exposure limits.

L. Portable heating units should not be used in confined areas where MC is used.

M. Ask your supervisor where MC is used in your work area and for any additional plant safety and health rules.

VII. Medical Requirements

Your employer is required to offer you the opportunity to participate in a medical surveillance program if you are exposed to MC at concentrations at or above the action level (12.5 ppm 8-hour TWA) for more than 30 days a year or at concentrations exceeding the PELs (25 ppm 8-hour TWA or 125 ppm 15-minute STEL) for more than 10 days a year. If you are exposed to MC at concentrations over either of the PELs, your employer will also be required to have a physician or other licensed health care professional ensure that you are able to wear the respirator that you are assigned. Your employer must provide all medical examinations relating to your MC exposure at a reasonable time and place and at no cost to you.

VIII. Monitoring and Measurement Procedures

A. Exposure above the Permissible Exposure Limit:

1. Eight-hour exposure evaluation: Measurements taken for the purpose of determining employee exposure under this Section are best taken with consecutive samples covering the full shift. Air samples must be taken in the employee's breathing zone.
2. Monitoring techniques: The sampling and analysis under this Section may be performed by collection of the MC vapor on two charcoal adsorption tubes in series or other composition adsorption tubes, with subsequent chemical analysis. Sampling and analysis may also be performed by instruments such as real-time continuous monitoring systems, portable direct reading instruments, or passive dosimeters as long as measurements taken using these methods accurately evaluate the concentration of MC in employees" breathing zones.

OSHA method 80 is an example of a validated method of sampling and analysis of MC. Copies of this method are available from OSHA or can be downloaded from the Internet at http://www.osha.gov. The employer has the obligation of selecting a monitoring method which meets the accuracy and precision requirements of the standard under his or her unique field conditions. The standard requires that the method of monitoring must be accurate, to a 95 percent confidence level, to plus or minus 25 percent for concentrations of MC at or above 25 ppm, and to plus or minus 35 percent for concentrations at or below 25 ppm. In addition to OSHA method 80, there are numerous other methods available for monitoring for MC in the workplace.

B. Since many of the duties relating to employee exposure are dependent on the results of measurement procedures, employers must assure that the evaluation of employee exposure is performed by a technically qualified person.

IX. Observation of Monitoring

Your employer is required to perform measurements that are representative of your exposure to MC and you or your designated representative are entitled to observe the monitoring procedure. You are entitled to observe the steps taken in the measurement procedure, and to record the results obtained. When the monitoring procedure is taking place in an area where respirators or personal protective clothing and equipment are required to be worn, you or your representative must also be provided with, and must wear, protective clothing and equipment.

X. Access to Information

A. Your employer is required to inform you of the information contained in this Appendix. In addition, your employer must instruct you in the proper work practices for using MC, emergency procedures, and the correct use of protective equipment.

B. Your employer is required to determine whether you are being exposed to MC. You or your representative has the right to observe employee measurements and to record the results obtained. Your employer is required to inform you of your exposure. If your employer determines that you are being over exposed, he or she is required to inform you of the actions which are being taken to reduce your exposure to within permissible exposure limits.

C. Your employer is required to keep records of your exposures and medical examinations. These records must be kept by the employer for at least thirty (30) years.

D. Your employer is required to release your exposure and medical records to you or your representative upon your request.

E. Your employee is required to provide labels and safety data sheets (SDSs) for all materials, mixtures or solutions composed of greater than 0.1 percent MC. These materials, mixtures or solutions would be classified and labeled in accordance with §1910.1200.

Danger
Contains Methylene Chloride
Potential Cancer Hazard

May worsen heart disease because methylene chloride is converted to carbon monoxide in the body.

May cause dizziness, headache, irritation of the throat and lungs, loss of consciousness and death at high concentrations (for example, if used in a poorly ventilated room).

Avoid Skin Contact. Contact with liquid causes skin and eye irritation.

XI. Common Operations and Controls

The following list includes some common operations in which exposure to MC may occur and control methods which may be effective in each case:

Operations	Controls
Use as solvent in paint and varnish removers; manufacture of aerosols; cold cleaning and ultrasonic cleaning; and as a solvent in furniture stripping.	General dilution ventilation; local exhaust ventilation; personal protective equipment; substitution.
Use as solvent in vapor degreasing.	Process enclosure; local exhaust ventilation; chilling coils; substitution.
Use as a secondary refrigerant in air conditioning and scientific testing.	General dilution ventilation; local exhaust ventilation; personal protective equipment.

§1910.1052 Appendix B Medical surveillance for Methylene Chloride

I. Primary Route of Entry

Inhalation.

II. Toxicology

Methylene Chloride (MC) is primarily an inhalation hazard. The principal acute hazardous effects are the depressant action on the central nervous system, possible cardiac toxicity and possible liver toxicity. The range of CNS effects are from decreased eye/hand coordination and decreased performance in vigilance tasks to narcosis and even death of individuals exposed at very high doses. Cardiac toxicity is due to the metabolism of MC to carbon monoxide, and the effects of carbon monoxide on heart tissue. Carbon monoxide displaces oxygen in the blood, decreases the oxygen available to heart tissue, increasing the risk of damage to the heart, which may result in heart attacks in susceptible individuals. Susceptible individuals include persons with heart disease and those with risk factors for heart disease.

Elevated liver enzymes and irritation to the respiratory passages and eyes have also been reported for both humans and experimental animals exposed to MC vapors.

MC is metabolized to carbon monoxide and carbon dioxide via two separate pathways. Through the first pathway, MC is metabolized to carbon monoxide as an end-product via the P–450 mixed function oxidase pathway located in the microsomal fraction of the cell. This biotransformation of MC to carbon monoxide occurs through the process of microsomal oxidative dechlorination which takes place primarily in the liver. The amount of conversion to carbon monoxide is significant as measured by the concentration of carboxyhemoglobin, up to 12% measured in the blood following occupational exposure of up to 610 ppm. Through the second pathway, MC is metabolized to carbon dioxide as an end product (with formaldehyde and formic acid as metabolic intermediates) via the glutathione dependent enzyme found in the cytosolic fraction of the liver cell. Metabolites along this pathway are believed to be associated with the carcinogenic activity of MC.

MC has been tested for carcinogenicity in several laboratory rodents. These rodent studies indicate that there is clear evidence that MC is carcinogenic to male and female mice and female rats. Based on epidemiologic studies, OSHA has concluded that there is suggestive evidence of increased cancer risk in MC-related worker populations. The epidemiological evidence is consistent with the finding of excess cancer in the experimental animal studies. NIOSH regards MC as a potential occupational carcinogen and the International Agency for Research Cancer (IARC) classifies MC as an animal carcinogen. OSHA considers MC as a suspected human carcinogen.

III. Medical Signs and Symptoms of Acute Exposure

Skin exposure to liquid MC may cause irritation or skin burns. Liquid MC can also be irritating to the eyes. MC is also absorbed through the skin and may contribute to the MC exposure by inhalation.

At high concentrations in air, MC may cause nausea, vomiting, light-headedness, numbness of the extremities, changes in blood enzyme levels, and breathing problems, leading to bronchitis and pulmonary edema, unconsciousness and even death.

At lower concentrations in air, MC may cause irritation to the skin, eye, and respiratory tract and occasionally headache and nausea. Perhaps the greatest problem from exposure to low concentrations of MC is the CNS effects on coordination and alertness that may cause unsafe operations of machinery and equipment, leading to self-injury or accidents.

Low levels and short duration exposures do not seem to produce permanent disability, but chronic exposures to MC have been demonstrated to produce liver toxicity in animals, and therefore, the evidence is suggestive for liver toxicity in humans after chronic exposure.

Chronic exposure to MC may also cause cancer.

IV. Surveillance and Preventive Considerations

As discussed above, MC is classified as a suspect or potential human carcinogen. It is a central nervous system (CNS) depressant and a skin, eye and respiratory tract irritant. At extremely high concentrations, MC has caused liver damage in animals.

MC principally affects the CNS, where it acts as a narcotic. The observation of the symptoms characteristic of CNS depression, along with a physical examination, provides the best detection of early neurological disorders. Since exposure to MC also increases the carboxyhemoglobin level in the blood, ambient carbon monoxide levels would have an additive effect on that carboxyhemoglobin level. Based on such information, a periodic post-shift carboxyhemoglobin test as an index of the presence of carbon monoxide in the blood is recommended, but not required, for medical surveillance.

Based on the animal evidence and three epidemiologic studies previously mentioned, OSHA concludes that MC is a suspect human carcinogen. The medical surveillance program is designed to observe exposed workers on a regular basis. While the medical surveillance program cannot detect MC-induced cancer at a preneoplastic stage, OSHA anticipates that, as in the past, early detection and treatments of cancers leading to enhanced survival rates will continue to evolve.

A. Medical and Occupational History:

The medical and occupational work history plays an important role in the initial evaluation of workers exposed to MC. It is therefore extremely important for the examining physician or other licensed health care professional to evaluate the MC-exposed worker carefully and completely and to focus the examination on MC's potentially associated health hazards. The medical evaluation must include an annual detailed work and medical history with special emphasis on cardiac history and neurological symptoms.

An important goal of the medical history is to elicit information from the worker regarding potential signs or symptoms associated with increased levels of carboxyhemoglobin due to the presence of carbon monoxide in the blood. Physicians or other licensed health care professionals should ensure that the smoking history of all MC exposed employees is known. Exposure to MC may cause a significant increase in carboxyhemoglobin level in all exposed persons. However, smokers as well as workers with anemia or heart disease and those concurrently exposed to carbon monoxide are at especially high risk of toxic effects because of an already reduced oxygen carrying capacity of the blood.

A comprehensive or interim medical and work history should also include occurrence of headache, dizziness, fatigue, chest pain, shortness of breath, pain in the limbs, and irritation of the skin and eyes.

In addition, it is important for the physician or other licensed health care professional to become familiar with the operating conditions in which exposure to MC is likely to occur. The physician or other licensed health care professional also must become familiar with the signs and symptoms that may indicate that a worker is receiving otherwise unrecognized and exceptionally high exposure levels of MC.

An example of a medical and work history that would satisfy the requirement for a comprehensive or interim work history is represented by the following:

The following is a list of recommended questions and issues for the self-administered questionnaire for methylene chloride exposure.

Questionnaire For Methylene Chloride Exposure

I. Demographic Information

1. Name
2. Social Security Number
3. Date
4. Date of Birth
5. Age
6. Present occupation
7. Sex
8. Race

II. Occupational History

1. Have you ever worked with methylene chloride, dichloromethane, methylene dichloride, or CH_2Cl_2 (all are different names for the same chemical)? Please list which on the occupational history form if you have not already.
2. If you have worked in any of the following industries and have not listed them on the occupational history form, please do so.
   Furniture stripping
   Polyurethane foam manufacturing
   Chemical manufacturing or formulation
   Pharmaceutical manufacturing
   Any industry in which you used solvents to clean and degrease equipment or parts
   Construction, especially painting and refinishing
   Aerosol manufacturing
   Any industry in which you used aerosol adhesives
3. If you have not listed hobbies or household projects on the occupational history form, especially furniture refinishing, spray painting, or paint stripping, please do so.

III. Medical History

A. General

1. Do you consider yourself to be in good health? If no, state reason(s).
2. Do you or have you ever had:
   a. Persistent thirst
   b. Frequent urination (three times or more at night)
   c. Dermatitis or irritated skin
   d. Non-healing wounds
3. What prescription or non-prescription medications do you take, and for what reasons?
4. Are you allergic to any medications, and what type of reaction do you have?

B. Respiratory

1. Do you have or have you ever had any chest illnesses or diseases? Explain.
2. Do you have or have you ever had any of the following:
   a. Asthma
   b. Wheezing
   c. Shortness of breath
3. Have you ever had an abnormal chest X-ray? If so, when, where, and what were the findings?
4. Have you ever had difficulty using a respirator or breathing apparatus? Explain.
5. Do any chest or lung diseases run in your family? Explain.
6. Have you ever smoked cigarettes, cigars, or a pipe? Age started:
7. Do you now smoke?
8. If you have stopped smoking completely, how old were you when you stopped?
9. On the average of the entire time you smoked, how many packs of cigarettes, cigars, or bowls of tobacco did you smoke per day?

C. Cardiovascular

1. Have you ever been diagnosed with any of the following: Which of the following apply to you now or did apply to you at some time in the past, even if the problem is controlled by medication? Please explain any yes answers (i.e., when problem was diagnosed, length of time on medication).
   a. High cholesterol or triglyceride level
   b. Hypertension (high blood pressure)
   c. Diabetes
   d. Family history of heart attack, stroke, or blocked arteries
2. Have you ever had chest pain? If so, answer the next five questions.
   a. What was the quality of the pain (i.e., crushing, stabbing, squeezing)?
   b. Did the pain go anywhere (i.e., into jaw, left arm)?
   c. What brought the pain out?
   d. How long did it last?
   e. What made the pain go away?
3. Have you ever had heart disease, a heart attack, stroke, aneurysm, or blocked arteries anywhere in you body? Explain (when, treatment).
4. Have you ever had bypass surgery for blocked arteries in your heart or anywhere else? Explain.
5. Have you ever had any other procedures done to open up a blocked artery (balloon angioplasty, carotid endarterectomy, clot-dissolving drug)?
6. Do you have or have you ever had (explain each):
   a. Heart murmur
   b. Irregular heartbeat
   c. Shortness of breath while lying flat
   d. Congestive heart failure
   e. Ankle swelling
   f. Recurrent pain anywhere below the waist while walking
7. Have you ever had an electrocardiogram (EKG)? When?
8. Have you ever had an abnormal EKG? If so, when, where, and what were the findings?
9. Do any heart diseases, high blood pressure, diabetes, high cholesterol, or high triglycerides run in your family? Explain.

D. Hepatobiliary and Pancreas

1. Do you now or have you ever drunk alcoholic beverages?
   Age started: ____ Age stopped: ____.
2. Average numbers per week:
   a. Beers: ____, ounces in usual container:
   b. Glasses of wine: ____, ounces per glass:
   c. Drinks: ____, ounces in usual container:
3. Do you have or have you ever had (explain each):
   a. Hepatitis (infectious, autoimmune, drug-induced, or chemical)
   b. Jaundice
   c. Elevated liver enzymes or elevated bilirubin
   d. Liver disease or cancer

E. Central Nervous System

1. Do you or have you ever had (explain each):
   a. Headache
   b. Dizziness
   c. Fainting
   d. Loss of consciousness
   e. Garbled speech
   f. Lack of balance
   g. Mental/psychiatric illness
   h. Forgetfulness

F. Hematologic

1. Do you have, or have you ever had (explain each):
   a. Anemia
   b. Sickle cell disease or trait
   c. Glucose-6-phosphate dehydrogenase deficiency
   d. Bleeding tendency disorder
2. If not already mentioned previously, have you ever had a reaction to sulfa drugs or to drugs used to prevent or treat malaria? What was the drug? Describe the reaction.

B. Physical Examination

The complete physical examination, when coupled with the medical and occupational history, assists the physician or other licensed health care professional in detecting pre-existing conditions that might place the employee at increased risk, and establishes a baseline for future health monitoring. These examinations should include:

1. Clinical impressions of the nervous system, cardiovascular function and pulmonary function, with additional tests conducted where indicated or determined by the examining physician or other licensed health care professional to be necessary.
2. An evaluation of the advisability of the worker using a respirator, because the use of certain respirators places an additional burden on the cardiopulmonary system. It is necessary for the attending physician or other licensed health care professional to evaluate the cardiopulmonary function of these workers, in order to inform the employer in a written medical opinion of the worker's ability or fitness to work in an area requiring the use of certain types of respiratory protective equipment. The presence of facial hair or scars that might interfere with the worker's ability to wear certain types of respirators should also be noted during the examination and in the written medical opinion.

   Because of the importance of lung function to workers required to wear certain types of respirators to protect themselves from MC exposure, these workers must receive an assessment of pulmonary function before they begin to wear a negative pressure respirator and at least annually thereafter. The recommended pulmonary function tests include measurement of the employee's forced vital capacity (FVC), forced expiratory volume at one second (FEV1), as well as calculation of the ratios of FEV1 to FVC, and the ratios of measured FVC and measured FEV1 to expected respective values corrected for variation due to age, sex, race, and height. Pulmonary function evaluation must be conducted by a physician or other licensed health care professional experienced in pulmonary function tests.

The following is a summary of the elements of a physical exam which would fulfill the requirements under the MC standard:

Physical Exam

I. Skin and appendages
   1. Irritated or broken skin
   2. Jaundice
   3. Clubbing cyanosis, edema
   4. Capillary refill time
   5. Pallor

II. Head
   1. Facial deformities
   2. Scars
   3. Hair growth

III. Eyes
   1. Scleral icterus
   2. Corneal arcus
   3. Pupillary size and response
   4. Fundoscopic exam

IV. Chest
   1. Standard exam

V. Heart
   1. Standard exam
   2. Jugular vein distension
   3. Peripheral pulses

VI. Abdomen
   1. Liver span

VII. Nervous System
   1. Complete standard neurologic exam

VIII. Laboratory
   1. Hemoglobin and hematocrit
   2. Alanine aminotransferase (ALT, SGPT)
   3. Post-shift carboxyhemoglobin

IX. Studies
   1. Pulmonary function testing
   2. Electrocardiogram

An evaluation of the oxygen carrying capacity of the blood of employees (for example by measured red blood cell volume) is considered useful, especially for workers acutely exposed to MC.

It is also recommended, but not required, that end of shift carboxyhemoglobin levels be determined periodically, and any level above 3% for non-smokers and above 10% for smokers should prompt an investigation of the worker and his workplace. This test is recommended because MC is metabolized to CO, which combines strongly with hemoglobin, resulting in a reduced capacity of the blood to transport oxygen in the body. This is of particular concern for cigarette smokers because they already have a diminished hemoglobin capacity due to the presence of CO in cigarette smoke.

C. Additional Examinations and Referrals

1. Examination by a Specialist

   When a worker examination reveals unexplained symptoms or signs (i.e. in the physical examination or in the laboratory tests), follow-up medical examinations are necessary to assure that MC exposure is not adversely affecting the worker's health. When the examining physician or other licensed health care professional finds it necessary, additional tests should be included to determine the nature of the medical problem and the underlying cause. Where relevant, the worker should be sent to a specialist for further testing and treatment as deemed necessary.

   The final rule requires additional investigations to be covered and it also permits physicians or other licensed health care professionals to add appropriate or necessary tests to improve the diagnosis of disease should such tests become available in the future.

2. Emergencies

   The examination of workers exposed to MC in an emergency should be directed at the organ systems most likely to be affected. If the worker has received a severe acute exposure, hospitalization may be required to assure proper medical intervention. It is not possible to precisely define "severe," but the physician or other licensed health care professional's judgement should not merely rest on hospitalization. If the worker has suffered significant conjunctival, oral, or nasal irritation, respiratory distress, or discomfort, the physician or other licensed health care professional should instigate appropriate follow-up procedures. These include attention to the eyes, lungs and the neurological system. The frequency of follow-up examinations should be determined by the attending physician or other licensed health care professional. This testing permits the early identification essential to proper medical management of such workers.

D. Employer Obligations

The employer is required to provide the responsible physician or other licensed health care professional and any specialists involved in a diagnosis with the following information: a copy of the MC Standard including relevant Appendices, a description of the affected employee's duties as they relate to his or her exposure to MC; an estimate of the employee's exposure including duration (e.g., 15hr/wk, three 8-hour shifts/wk, full time); a description of any personal protective equipment used by the employee, including respirators; and the results of any previous medical determinations for the affected employee related to MC exposure to the extent that this information is within the employer's control.

E. Physicians' or Other Licensed Health Care Professionals' Obligations

The standard requires the employer to ensure that the physician or other licensed health care professional provides a written statement to the employee and the employer. This statement should contain the physician's or licensed health care professional's opinion as to whether the employee has any medical condition placing him or her at increased risk of impaired health from exposure to MC or use of respirators, as appropriate. The physician or other licensed health care professional should also state his or her opinion regarding any restrictions that should be placed on the employee's exposure to MC or upon the use of protective clothing or equipment such as respirators. If the employee wears a respirator as a result of his or her exposure to MC, the physician or other licensed health care professional's opinion should also contain a statement regarding the suitability of the employee to wear the type of respirator assigned. Furthermore, the employee should be informed by the physician or other licensed health care professional about the cancer risk of MC and about risk factors for heart disease, and the potential for exacerbation of underlying heart disease by exposure to MC through its metabolism to carbon monoxide. Finally, the physician or other licensed health care professional should inform the employer that the employee has been told the results of the medical examination and of any medical conditions which require further explanation or treatment. This written opinion must not contain any information on specific findings or diagnosis unrelated to employee's occupational exposures.

The purpose in requiring the examining physician or other licensed health care professional to supply the employer with a written opinion is to provide the employer with a medical basis to assist the employer in placing employees initially, in assuring that their health is not being impaired by exposure to MC, and to assess the employee's ability to use any required protective equipment.

§1910.1052 Appendix C Questions and Answers Methylene Chloride Control in Furniture Stripping

CDC
CENTERS FOR DISEASE CONTROL AND PREVENTION

NIOSH

—Questions and Answers— Methylene Chloride Control in Furniture Stripping

U.S. DEPARTMENT OF HEALTH AND HUMAN SERVICES
Public Health Service
Centers for Disease Control and Prevention
National Institute for Occupational Safety and Health
September 1993

Q's & A's

DISCLAIMER

Copies of this and other NIOSH documents are available from

Publications Dissemination, DSDTT

National Institute for Occupational Safety and Health
4676 Columbia Parkway
Cincinnati, OH 45226
FAX (513) 533-8573

For information about other occupational safety and health problems, call
1-800-35-NIOSH
DHHS (NIOSH) Publication No. 93-133

Q's & A's

Introduction

This Pamphlet answers commonly asked questions about the hazards from exposure to methylene chloride. It also describes approaches to controlling methylene chloride exposure during the most common furniture stripping processes. Although these approaches were developed and field tested by NIOSH, each setting requires custom installation because of the different air flow interferences at each site.

What is the Stripping Solution Base?

The most common active ingredient in paint removers is a chemical called methylene chloride. Methylene chloride is present in the paint remover to penetrate, blister, and finally lift the old finish. Other chemicals in paint removers work to accelerate the stripping process, to retard evaporation, and to act as thickening agents. These other ingredients may include: methanol, toluene, acetone, or paraffin.[1]

Is Methylene Chloride Bad for Me?

Exposure to methylene chloride may cause short-term health effects or long-term health effects.

Short-Term (Acute) Health Effects

Exposure to high levels of paint removers over short periods of time can cause irritation to the skin, eyes, mucous membranes, and respiratory tract. Other symptoms of high exposure are dizziness headache, and lack of coordination. The occurrence of any of these symptoms indicates that you are being exposed to high levels of the methylene chloride. At the onset of any of these symptoms, you should leave the work area, get some fresh air, and determine why the levels were high.

A portion of inhaled methylene chloride is converted by the body to carbon monoxide, which can lower the blood's ability to carry oxygen. When the solvent is used properly, however, the levels of carbon monoxide should not be hazardous. Individuals with cardiovascular or pulmonary health problems should check with their physician before using the paint stripper. Individuals experiencing severe symptoms such as shortness of breath or chest pains should obtain proper medical care immediately.[2]

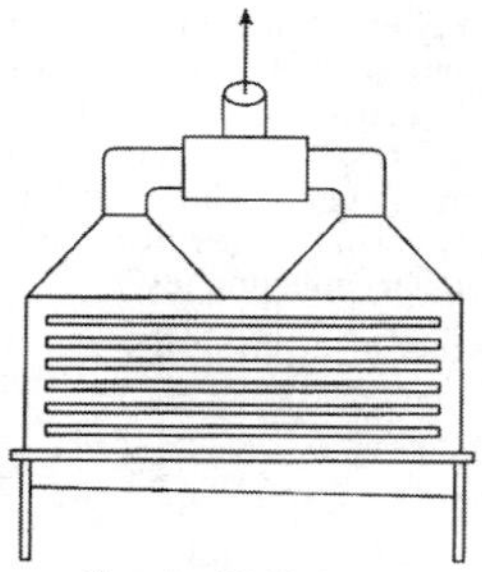

Figure 1 — Slot Hood

Long-term (Chronic) Health Effects

Methylene chloride has been shown to cause cancer in certain laboratory animal tests. The available human studies do not provide the necessary information to determine whether methylene chloride causes cancer in humans. However, as a result of the animal studies, methylene chloride is considered a potential occupational carcinogin. There is also considerable indirect evidence to suggest that workers exposed to methylene chloride may be at increased risk of developing ischemic heart disease. Therefore it is prudent to minimize exposures to solvent vapors.[3]

Q's & A's

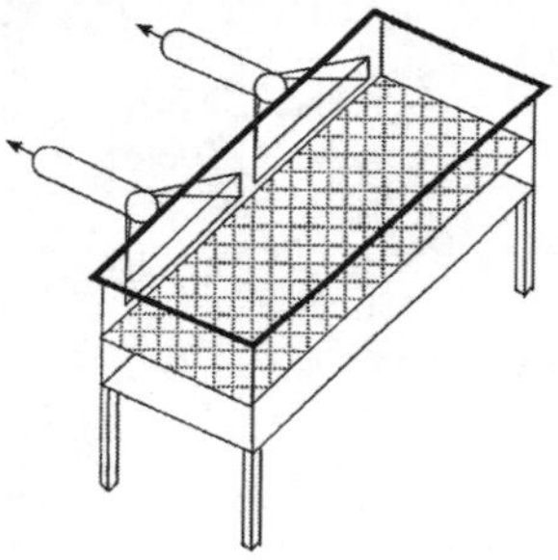

Figure 2 — Downdraft Hood

What Do Federal Agencies Say About Methylene Chloride?

In 1991, the Occupational Safety and Health Administration published a Notice of Proposed Rulemaking for methylene chloride. The proposed standard would establish an eight-hour time-weighted average exposure limit of 25 parts per million (ppm), as well as a short-term exposure limit of 125 ppm determined from a 15 minute sampling period. That is a sharp reduction from the current limit of 500 ppm. The proposed standard would also set a 12.5 ppm action level (a level that would trigger periodic exposure monitoring and medical surveillance provisions.[4]

The National Institute for Occupational Safety and Health recommends that methylene chloride be regarded as a "potential occupational carcinogen." NIOSH further recommends that occupational exposure to methylene chloride be controlled to the lowest feasible limit. This recommendation was based on the observation of cancers and tumors in both rats and mice exposed to methylene chloride in air.[5]

How Can I Be Exposed to Methylene Chloride while Stripping Furniture?

Methylene chloride can be inhaled when vapors are in the air. Inhalation of the methylene chloride vapors is generally the most important source of exposure. Methylene chloride evaporates quicker than most chemicals. The odor threshold of methylene chloride is 300 ppm.[6] Therefore, once you smell methylene chloride, you are being over-exposed. Pouring, moving, or stirring the chemical will increase the rate of evaporation.

Methylene chloride can be absorbed through the skin either by directly touching the chemical or through your gloves. Methylene chloride can be swallowed if it gets on your hands, clothes, or beard, or if food or drinks become contaminated.

How Can Breathing Exposures be Reduced?

Install a Local Exhaust Ventilation System

Local exhaust ventilation can be used to control exposures. Local exhaust ventilation systems capture contaminated air from the source before it spreads into the workers' breathing zone.[7] If engineering controls are not effective, only a self-contained breathing apparatus equipped with a full facepiece and operated in a positive-pressure mode or a supplied-air respirator affords the necessary level of protection. Air-purifying respirators such as organic vapor cartridges can only be used for escape situations.[8]

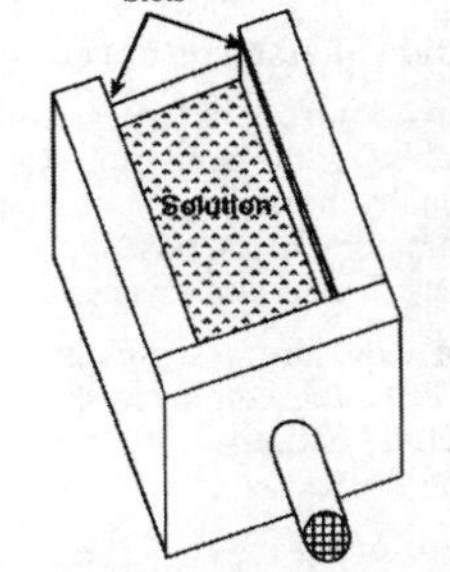

Figure 3 — Slot Hood for Dip Tank

A local exhaust system consists of the following: a hood, a fan, ductwork, and a replacement air system.[9,10,11] Two processes are commonly used in furniture stripping: flow-over and dip tanks. For flow-over systems there are two common local exhaust controls for methylene chloride — a slot hood and a downdraft hood. A slot hood of different design is most often used for dip tanks. (See Figures 1, 2, and 3)

The hood is made of sheet metal and connected to the tank. All designs require a centrifugal fan to exhaust the fumes, ductwork connecting the hood and the fan, and a replacement air system to bring conditioned air into the building to replace the air exhausted.

In constructing or designing a slot or downdraft hood, use the following data:

Slot hood (Figure 1)

- At least 2200 cfm per 8' X 4' tank
- 1 - 2 inch slots
- Slot velocity - 1000 fpm
- 3 - 5 slots
- Plenum at least 1 foot deep

Downdraft hood (Figure 2)

- At least 1600 cfm per 8' X 4' tank
- Plenum at least 9" deep

Slot hood for Dip Tank (Figure 3)

- At least 2900 cfm per 8' X 4' tank
- ¼" slot that runs the length of the front and back of the tank
- Slot velocity — 3200 fpm
- Plenum on the sides of the tank should be 6" deep by 36" long
- 12" duct leads from the center of the front
- plenum to the fan

Safe work practices

Workers can lower exposure by decreasing their access to the methylene chloride.[12]

1) Turn on dip tank control system several minutes before entering the stripping area.

2) Avoid unnecessary transferring or moving of stripping solution.

3) Keep face out of the air stream between the solution-covered furniture and the exhaust system.

4) Keep face out of vapor zone above the stripping solution and dip tank.

5) Retrieve dropped items with a long handled tool.

6) Keep the solution-recycling system off when not in use. Cover reservoir for recycling system.

7) Cover dip tank when not in use.

8) Provide adequate ventilation for rinse area.

Q's & A's

REFERENCES

[1] Halogenated Solvents Industry Alliance and Consumer Product Safety Commission [1990]. Stripping Paint from Wood (Pamphlet for consumers on how to strip furniture and precautions to take). Washington DC: Consumer Product Safety Commission.

[2] Ibid.

[3] NIOSH [1992]. NIOSH Testimony on Occupational Safety and Health Administration's proposed rule on occupational exposure to methylene chloride, September 21, 1991, OSHA Docket No. H-71. NIOSH policy statements. Cincinnati, OH: U.S. Department of Health and Human Services, Public Health Service, Centers for Disease Control, National Institute for Occupational Safety and Health.

[4] 56 Fed. Reg. 57036 [1991]. Occupational Safety and Health Administration: Proposed rule on occupational exposure to methylene chloride.

[5] NIOSH [1992].

[6] Kirk, R.E. and P.F. Othmer, Eds. [1978]. Encyclopedia of Chemical Technology, 3rd Ed., Vol. 5:690. New York: John Wiley & Sons, Inc.

[7] ACGIH [1988]. Industrial Ventilation: A Manual of Recommended Practice. 20th Ed. Cincinnati, OH: American Conference of Governmental Industrial Hygienists.

[8] NIOSH [1992].

[9] Fairfield, C.L. and A.A Beasley [1991]. In-depth Survey Report at the Association for Retarded Citizens, Meadowlands, PA. The Control of Methylene Chloride During Furniture Stripping. Cincinnati, OH: U.S. Department of Health and Human Services, Public Health Service, Centers for Disease Control, National Institute for Occupational Safety and Health.

[10] Fairfiled, C.L. [1991]. In-depth Survey Report at the J.M. Murray Center, Cortland, NY. The Control of Methylene Chloride During Furniture Stripping. Cincinnati, OH: U.S. Department of Health and Human Services, Public Health Service, Centers for Disease Control, National Institute for Occupational Safety and Health.

[11] Hall, R.M., K.F. Martinez, and P.A. Jensen [1992]. In-depth Survey Report at Tri-County Furniture Stripping and Refinishing, Cincinnati, OH. The Control of Methylene Chloride During Furniture Stripping. Cincinnati, OH: U.S. Department of Health and Human Services, Centers for Disease Control, National Institute for Occupational Safety and Health.

[12] Fairfield, C.L., and A.A Beasley [1991]. In depth Survey Report at the Association for Retarded Citizens, Meadowlands, PA. The Control of Methylene Chloride During Furniture Stripping. Cincinnati, OH: U.S. Department of Health and Human Services, Public Health Service, Centers for Disease Control, National Institute for Occupational Safety and Health.

[13] Roder, M [1991]. Memorandum of March 11, 1991 from Michael Roder of the Divison of Safety Research to Cheryl L. Fairfield of the Division of Physical Sciences and Engineering, National Institute for Occupational Safety and Health, Centers for Disease Control, Public health Service, U.S. Department of Health and Human Services.

[14] Kwick Kleen Industrial Solvents, Inc. [1981]. Operations Manual, Kwick Kleen Industrial Solvents, Inc., Vincennes, IN.

[15] ACGIH [1900].

[16] *Ibid.*

[17] Gerritsen,W.B. and C.H. Buschmann [1960]. Phosgene Poisoning Caused by the Use of Chemical Paint Removers containing Methylene Chloride in Ill-Ventilated Rooms Heated by Kerosene Stoves. British Journal of Industrial Medicine *17* :187

Q's & A's

Where Should I go for More Information?

The NIOSH 800- number is a toll-free technical information service that provides convenient public access to NIOSH and its information resources. Callers may request information about any aspect of occupational safety and health

1-800-35-NIOSH

(1-800-356-4674)

★ U. S. GOVERNMENT PRINTING OFFICE: 1993: 550-147/80026

Q's & A's

How Can Skin Exposures be Reduced?

Skin exposures can be reduced by wearing gloves whenever you are in contact with the stripping solution. [13]

1) Two gloves should be worn. The inner glove should be made from polyethylene/ethylene vinyl alcohol (e.g. Silver Shield® or 4H®). This material, however, does not provide good physical resistance against tears, so an outer glove made from nitrile or neoprene should be worn

2) Shoulder-length gloves will be more protective.

3) Change gloves before the break-through time occurs. Rotate several pairs of gloves throughout the day. let the gloves dry in a warm well ventilated area at least over night before reuse.

4) Keep gloves clean by rinsing often. Keep gloves in good condition. Inspect the gloves before use for pin-holes, cracks, thin spots, and stiffer than normal or sticky surfaces.

5) Wear a face shield or goggles to protect face and eyes.

What Other Problems Occur

Stripping Solution Temperature

Most manufacturers of stripping solution recommend controlling the solution to a temperature of 70°F. This temperature is required for the wax in the solution to form a vapor barrier on top of the solution to keep the solution from evaporating too quickly. If the temperature is too high, the wax will not form the vapor barrier. If it is too cold, the wax will solidify and separate from the solvent causing increased evaporation. Use a belt heater to heat the solution to the correct temperature. Call your solution manufacturer for the correct temperature for your solution.[14]

Make-Up Air

Air will enter a building in an amount equal to the amount of air exhausted whether or not provision is made for this replacement. If a local exhaust system is added a make-up or replacement air system must be added to replace the air removed. Without a replacement air system, air will enter the building through cracks causing uncontrollable eddy currents. If the building perimeter is tightly sealed, it will prevent the air from entering and severely decrease the amount exhausted from the ventilation system. This will cause the building to be under negative pressure and decrease the performance of the exhaust system.[15]

Dilution Ventilation

With general or dilution ventilation, uncontaminated air is moved through the workroom by means of fans or open windows, which dilutes the pollutants in the air. Dilution ventilation does not provide effective protection to other workers and does not confine the methylene chloride vapors to one area.[16]

Phosgene Poisoning from Use of Kerosene Heaters

Do not use kerosene heaters or other open flame heaters while stripping furniture. Use of kerosene heaters in connection with methylene chloride can create lethal or dangerous concentrations of phosgene. Methylene chloride vapor is mixed with the air used for the combustion of kerosene in kerosene stoves. The vapor thus passes through the flames, coming into close contact with carbon monoxide at high temperatures. Any chlorine formed by decomposition may, under these conditions, react with carbon monoxide and form phosgene.[17]

[62 FR 1601, Jan. 10, 1997, as amended at 62 FR 42667, Aug. 8, 1997; 62 FR 54383, Oct. 20, 1997; 62 FR 66277, Dec. 18, 1997; 63 FR 1295, Jan. 8, 1998; 63 FR 20099, Apr. 23, 1998; 63 FR 50729, Sept. 22, 1998; 71 FR 16674, Apr. 3, 2006; 71 FR 50190, Aug. 24, 2006; 73 FR 75587, Dec. 12, 2008]

§1910.1053 Respirable crystalline silica

(a) Scope and application

(a)(1) This Section applies to all occupational exposures to respirable crystalline silica, except:

(a)(1)(i) Construction work as defined in 29 CFR 1910.12(b) (occupational exposures to respirable crystalline silica in construction work are covered under 29 CFR 1926.1153);

(a)(1)(ii) Agricultural operations covered under 29 CFR part 1928; and

(a)(1)(iii) Exposures that result from the processing of sorptive clays.

(a)(2) This Section does not apply where the employer has objective data demonstrating that employee exposure to respirable crystalline silica will remain below 25 micrograms per cubic meter of air (25 μg/m^3) as an 8-hour time-weighted average (TWA) under any foreseeable conditions.

(a)(3) This Section does not apply if the employer complies with 29 CFR 1926.1153 and:

(a)(3)(i) The task performed is indistinguishable from a construction task listed on Table 1 in paragraph (c) of 29 CFR 1926.1153; and

(a)(3)(ii) The task will not be performed regularly in the same environment and conditions.

(b) Definitions For the purposes of this Section the following definitions apply:

Action level means a concentration of airborne respirable crystalline silica of 25 μg/m^3, calculated as an 8-hour TWA.

Assistant Secretary means the Assistant Secretary of Labor for Occupational Safety and Health, U.S. Department of Labor, or designee.

Director means the Director of the National Institute for Occupational Safety and Health (NIOSH), U.S. Department of Health and Human Services, or designee.

Employee exposure means the exposure to airborne respirable crystalline silica that would occur if the employee were not using a respirator.

High-efficiency particulate air [HEPA] filter means a filter that is at least 99.97 percent efficient in removing mono-dispersed particles of 0.3 micrometers in diameter.

Objective data means information, such as air monitoring data from industry-wide surveys or calculations based on the composition of a substance, demonstrating employee exposure to respirable crystalline silica associated with a particular product or material or a specific process, task, or activity. The data must reflect workplace conditions closely resembling or with a higher exposure potential than the processes, types of material, control methods, work practices, and environmental conditions in the employer's current operations.

Physician or other licensed health care professional [PLHCP] means an individual whose legally permitted scope of practice (i.e., license, registration, or certification) allows him or her to independently provide or be delegated the responsibility to provide some or all of the particular health care services required by paragraph (i) of this Section.

Regulated area means an area, demarcated by the employer, where an employee's exposure to airborne concentrations of respirable crystalline silica exceeds, or can reasonably be expected to exceed, the PEL.

Respirable crystalline silica means quartz, cristobalite, and/or tridymite contained in airborne particles that are determined to be respirable by a sampling device designed to meet the characteristics for respirable-particle-size-selective samplers specified in the International Organization for Standardization (ISO) 7708:1995: Air Quality—Particle Size Fraction Definitions for Health-Related Sampling.

Specialist means an American Board Certified Specialist in Pulmonary Disease or an American Board Certified Specialist in Occupational Medicine.

This Section means this respirable crystalline silica standard, 29 CFR §1910.1053.

(c) **Permissible exposure limit (PEL)** The employer shall ensure that no employee is exposed to an airborne concentration of respirable crystalline silica in excess of 50 $\mu g/m^3$, calculated as an 8-hour TWA.

(d) **Exposure assessment**

(d)(1) **General** The employer shall assess the exposure of each employee who is or may reasonably be expected to be exposed to respirable crystalline silica at or above the action level in accordance with either the performance option in paragraph (d)(2) or the scheduled monitoring option in paragraph (d)(3) of this Section.

(d)(2) **Performance option** The employer shall assess the 8-hour TWA exposure for each employee on the basis of any combination of air monitoring data or objective data sufficient to accurately characterize employee exposures to respirable crystalline silica.

(d)(3) **Scheduled monitoring option**

(d)(3)(i) The employer shall perform initial monitoring to assess the 8-hour TWA exposure for each employee on the basis of one or more personal breathing zone air samples that reflect the exposures of employees on each shift, for each job classification, in each work area. Where several employees perform the same tasks on the same shift and in the same work area, the employer may sample a representative fraction of these employees in order to meet this requirement. In representative sampling, the employer shall sample the employee(s) who are expected to have the highest exposure to respirable crystalline silica.

(d)(3)(ii) If initial monitoring indicates that employee exposures are below the action level, the employer may discontinue monitoring for those employees whose exposures are represented by such monitoring.

(d)(3)(iii) Where the most recent exposure monitoring indicates that employee exposures are at or above the action level but at or below the PEL, the employer shall repeat such monitoring within six months of the most recent monitoring.

(d)(3)(iv) Where the most recent exposure monitoring indicates that employee exposures are above the PEL, the employer shall repeat such monitoring within three months of the most recent monitoring.

(d)(3)(v) Where the most recent (non-initial) exposure monitoring indicates that employee exposures are below the action level, the employer shall repeat such monitoring within six months of the most recent monitoring until two consecutive measurements, taken 7 or more days apart, are below the action level, at which time the employer may discontinue monitoring for those employees whose exposures are represented by such monitoring, except as otherwise provided in paragraph (d)(4) of this Section.

(d)(4) **Reassessment of exposures** The employer shall reassess exposures whenever a change in the production, process, control equipment, personnel, or work practices may reasonably be expected to result in new or additional exposures at or above the action level, or when the employer has any reason to believe that new or additional exposures at or above the action level have occurred.

(d)(5) **Methods of sample analysis** The employer shall ensure that all samples taken to satisfy the monitoring requirements of paragraph (d) of this Section are evaluated by a laboratory that analyzes air samples for respirable crystalline silica in accordance with the procedures in Appendix A to this Section.

(d)(6) **Employee notification of assessment results**

(d)(6)(i) Within 15 working days after completing an exposure assessment in accordance with paragraph (d) of this Section, the employer shall individually notify each affected employee in writing of the results of that assessment or post the results in an appropriate location accessible to all affected employees.

(d)(6)(ii) Whenever an exposure assessment indicates that employee exposure is above the PEL, the employer shall describe in the written notification the corrective action being taken to reduce employee exposure to or below the PEL.

(d)(7) **Observation of monitoring**

(d)(7)(i) Where air monitoring is performed to comply with the requirements of this Section, the employer shall provide affected employees or their designated representatives an opportunity to observe any monitoring of employee exposure to respirable crystalline silica.

(d)(7)(ii) When observation of monitoring requires entry into an area where the use of protective clothing or equipment is required for any workplace hazard, the employer shall provide the observer with protective clothing and equipment at no cost and shall ensure that the observer uses such clothing and equipment.

(e) **Regulated areas**

(e)(1) **Establishment** The employer shall establish a regulated area wherever an employee's exposure to airborne concentrations of respirable crystalline silica is, or can reasonably be expected to be, in excess of the PEL.

(e)(2) **Demarcation**

(e)(2)(i) The employer shall demarcate regulated areas from the rest of the workplace in a manner that minimizes the number of employees exposed to respirable crystalline silica within the regulated area.

(e)(2)(ii) The employer shall post signs at all entrances to regulated areas that bear the legend specified in paragraph (j)(2) of this Section.

(e)(3) **Access** The employer shall limit access to regulated areas to:

(e)(3)(A) Persons authorized by the employer and required by work duties to be present in the regulated area;

(e)(3)(B) Any person entering such an area as a designated representative of employees for the purpose of exercising the right to observe monitoring procedures under paragraph (d) of this Section; and

(e)(3)(C) Any person authorized by the Occupational Safety and Health Act or regulations issued under it to be in a regulated area.

(e)(4) **Provision of respirators** The employer shall provide each employee and the employee's designated representative entering a regulated area with an appropriate respirator in accordance with paragraph (g) of this Section and shall require each employee and the employee's designated representative to use the respirator while in a regulated area.

(f) **Methods of compliance**

(f)(1) **Engineering and work practice controls** The employer shall use engineering and work practice controls to reduce and maintain employee exposure to respirable crystalline silica to or below the PEL, unless the employer can demonstrate that such controls are not feasible. Wherever such feasible engineering and work practice controls are not sufficient to reduce employee exposure to or below the PEL, the employer shall nonetheless use them to reduce employee exposure to the lowest feasible level and shall supplement them with the use of respiratory protection that complies with the requirements of paragraph (g) of this Section.

(f)(2) **Written exposure control plan**

(f)(2)(i) The employer shall establish and implement a written exposure control plan that contains at least the following elements:

(f)(2)(i)(A) A description of the tasks in the workplace that involve exposure to respirable crystalline silica;

(f)(2)(i)(B) A description of the engineering controls, work practices, and respiratory protection used to limit employee exposure to respirable crystalline silica for each task; and

(f)(2)(i)(C) A description of the housekeeping measures used to limit employee exposure to respirable crystalline silica.

(f)(2)(ii) The employer shall review and evaluate the effectiveness of the written exposure control plan at least annually and update it as necessary.

(f)(2)(iii) The employer shall make the written exposure control plan readily available for examination and copying, upon request, to each employee covered by this Section, their designated representatives, the Assistant Secretary and the Director.

(f)(3) **Abrasive blasting** In addition to the requirements of paragraph (f)(1) of this Section, the employer shall comply with other OSHA standards, when applicable, such as 29 CFR 1910.94 (Ventilation), 29 CFR 1915.34 (Mechanical paint removers), and 29 CFR 1915 Subpart I (Personal Protective Equipment), where abrasive blasting is conducted using crystalline silica-containing blasting agents, or where abrasive blasting is conducted on substrates that contain crystalline silica.

(g) **Respiratory protection**

(g)(1) **General** Where respiratory protection is required by this Section, the employer must provide each employee an appropriate respirator that complies with the requirements of this paragraph and 29 CFR 1910.134. Respiratory protection is required:

(g)(1)(i) Where exposures exceed the PEL during periods necessary to install or implement feasible engineering and work practice controls;

(g)(1)(ii) Where exposures exceed the PEL during tasks, such as certain maintenance and repair tasks, for which engineering and work practice controls are not feasible;

(g)(1)(iii) During tasks for which an employer has implemented all feasible engineering and work practice controls and such controls are not sufficient to reduce exposures to or below the PEL; and

(g)(1)(iv) During periods when the employee is in a regulated area.

(g)(2) **Respiratory protection program** Where respirator use is required by this Section, the employer shall institute a respiratory protection program in accordance with 29 CFR 1910.134.

(h) **Housekeeping**

(h)(1) The employer shall not allow dry sweeping or dry brushing where such activity could contribute to employee exposure to respirable crystalline silica unless wet sweeping, HEPA-filtered vacuuming or other methods that minimize the likelihood of exposure are not feasible.

(h)(2) The employer shall not allow compressed air to be used to clean clothing or surfaces where such activity could contribute to employee exposure to respirable crystalline silica unless:

(h)(2)(i) The compressed air is used in conjunction with a ventilation system that effectively captures the dust cloud created by the compressed air; or

(h)(2)(ii) No alternative method is feasible.

(i) **Medical surveillance**

(i)(1) **General**

(i)(1)(i) The employer shall make medical surveillance available at no cost to the employee, and at a reasonable time and place, for each employee who will be occupationally exposed to respirable crystalline silica at or above the action level for 30 or more days per year.

(i)(1)(ii) The employer shall ensure that all medical examinations and procedures required by this Section are performed by a PLHCP as defined in paragraph (b) of this Section.

(i)(2) **Initial examination** The employer shall make available an initial (baseline) medical examination within 30 days after initial assignment, unless the employee has received a medical examination that meets the requirements of this Section within the last three years. The examination shall consist of:

(i)(2)(i) A medical and work history, with emphasis on: Past, present, and anticipated exposure to respirable crystalline silica, dust, and other agents affecting the respiratory system; any history of respiratory system dysfunction, including signs and symptoms of respiratory disease (e.g., shortness of breath, cough, wheezing); history of tuberculosis; and smoking status and history;

(i)(2)(ii) A physical examination with special emphasis on the respiratory system;

(i)(2)(iii) A chest X-ray (a single posteroanterior radiographic projection or radiograph of the chest at full inspiration recorded on either film (no less than 14 x 17 inches and no more than 16 x 17 inches) or digital radiography systems), interpreted and classified according to the International Labour Office (ILO) International Classification of Radiographs of Pneumoconioses by a NIOSH-certified B Reader;

(i)(2)(iv) A pulmonary function test to include forced vital capacity (FVC) and forced expiratory volume in one second (FEV1) and FEV1/FVC ratio, administered by a spirometry technician with a current certificate from a NIOSH-approved spirometry course;

(i)(2)(v) Testing for latent tuberculosis infection; and

(i)(2)(vi) Any other tests deemed appropriate by the PLHCP.

(i)(3) **Periodic examinations** The employer shall make available medical examinations that include the procedures described in paragraph (i)(2) of this Section (except paragraph (i)(2)(v)) at least every three years, or more frequently if recommended by the PLHCP.

(i)(4) **Information provided to the PLHCP** The employer shall ensure that the examining PLHCP has a copy of this standard, and shall provide the PLHCP with the following information:

(i)(4)(i) A description of the employee's former, current, and anticipated duties as they relate to the employee's occupational exposure to respirable crystalline silica;

(i)(4)(ii) The employee's former, current, and anticipated levels of occupational exposure to respirable crystalline silica;

(i)(4)(iii) A description of any personal protective equipment used or to be used by the employee, including when and for how long the employee has used or will use that equipment; and

(i)(4)(iv) Information from records of employment-related medical examinations previously provided to the employee and currently within the control of the employer.

(i)(5) **PLHCP's written medical report for the employee** The employer shall ensure that the PLHCP explains to the employee the results of the medical examination and provides each employee with a written medical report within 30 days of each medical examination performed. The written report shall contain:

(i)(5)(i) A statement indicating the results of the medical examination, including any medical condition(s) that would place the employee at increased risk of material impairment to health from exposure to respirable crystalline silica and any medical conditions that require further evaluation or treatment;

(i)(5)(ii) Any recommended limitations on the employee's use of respirators;

(i)(5)(iii) Any recommended limitations on the employee's exposure to respirable crystalline silica; and

(i)(5)(iv) A statement that the employee should be examined by a specialist (pursuant to paragraph (i)(7) of this Section) if the chest X-ray provided in accordance with this Section is classified as 1/0 or higher by the B Reader, or if referral to a specialist is otherwise deemed appropriate by the PLHCP.

(i)(6) **PLHCP's written medical opinion for the employer**

(i)(6)(i) The employer shall obtain a written medical opinion from the PLHCP within 30 days of the medical examination. The written opinion shall contain only the following:

(i)(6)(i)(A) The date of the examination;

(i)(6)(i)(B) A statement that the examination has met the requirements of this Section; and

(i)(6)(i)(C) Any recommended limitations on the employee's use of respirators.

(i)(6)(ii) If the employee provides written authorization, the written opinion shall also contain either or both of the following:

(i)(6)(ii)(A) Any recommended limitations on the employee's exposure to respirable crystalline silica;

(i)(6)(ii)(B) A statement that the employee should be examined by a specialist (pursuant to paragraph (i)(7) of this Section) if the chest X-ray provided in accordance with this Section is classified as 1/0 or higher by the B Reader, or if referral to a specialist is otherwise deemed appropriate by the PLHCP.

(i)(6)(iii) The employer shall ensure that each employee receives a copy of the written medical opinion described in paragraph (i)(6)(i) and (ii) of this Section within 30 days of each medical examination performed.

(i)(7) **Additional examinations**

(i)(7)(i) If the PLHCP's written medical opinion indicates that an employee should be examined by a specialist, the employer shall make available a medical examination by a specialist within 30 days after receiving the PLHCP's written opinion.

(i)(7)(ii) The employer shall ensure that the examining specialist is provided with all of the information that the employer is obligated to provide to the PLHCP in accordance with paragraph (i)(4) of this Section.

(i)(7)(iii) The employer shall ensure that the specialist explains to the employee the results of the medical examination and provides each employee with a written medical report within 30 days of the examination. The written report shall meet the requirements of paragraph (i)(5) (except paragraph (i)(5)(iv)) of this Section.

(i)(7)(iv) The employer shall obtain a written opinion from the specialist within 30 days of the medical examination. The written opinion shall meet the requirements of paragraph (i)(6) (except paragraph (i)(6)(i)(B) and (i)(6)(ii)(B)) of this Section.

(j) **Communication of respirable crystalline silica hazards to employees**

(j)(1) **Hazard communication** The employer shall include respirable crystalline silica in the program established to comply with the hazard communication standard (HCS) (29 CFR 1910.1200). The employer shall ensure that each employee has access to labels on containers of crystalline silica and safety data sheets, and is trained in accordance with the provisions of HCS and paragraph (j)(3) of this Section. The employer shall ensure that at least the following hazards are addressed: Cancer, lung effects, immune system effects, and kidney effects.

(j)(2) **Signs** The employer shall post signs at all entrances to regulated areas that bear the following legend:

DANGER
RESPIRABLE CRYSTALLINE SILICA
MAY CAUSE CANCER
CAUSES DAMAGE TO LUNGS
WEAR RESPIRATORY PROTECTION IN THIS AREA
AUTHORIZED PERSONNEL ONLY

(j)(3) **Employee information and training**

(j)(3)(i) The employer shall ensure that each employee covered by this Section can demonstrate knowledge and understanding of at least the following:

(j)(3)(i)(A) The health hazards associated with exposure to respirable crystalline silica;

(j)(3)(i)(B) Specific tasks in the workplace that could result in exposure to respirable crystalline silica;

(j)(3)(i)(C) Specific measures the employer has implemented to protect employees from exposure to respirable crystalline silica, including engineering controls, work practices, and respirators to be used;

(j)(3)(i)(D) The contents of this Section; and

(j)(3)(i)(E) The purpose and a description of the medical surveillance program required by paragraph (i) of this Section.

(j)(3)(ii) The employer shall make a copy of this Section readily available without cost to each employee covered by this Section.

(k) **Recordkeeping**

(k)(1) **Air monitoring data**

(k)(1)(i) The employer shall make and maintain an accurate record of all exposure measurements taken to assess employee exposure to respirable crystalline silica, as prescribed in paragraph (d) of this Section.

(k)(1)(ii) This record shall include at least the following information:

(k)(1)(ii)(A) The date of measurement for each sample taken;

(k)(1)(ii)(B) The task monitored;

(k)(1)(ii)(C) Sampling and analytical methods used;

(k)(1)(ii)(D) Number, duration, and results of samples taken;

(k)(1)(ii)(E) Identity of the laboratory that performed the analysis;

(k)(1)(ii)(F) Type of personal protective equipment, such as respirators, worn by the employees monitored; and

(k)(1)(ii)(G) Name, social security number, and job classification of all employees represented by the monitoring, indicating which employees were actually monitored.

(k)(1)(iii) The employer shall ensure that exposure records are maintained and made available in accordance with 29 CFR 1910.1020.

(k)(2) **Objective data**

(k)(2)(i) The employer shall make and maintain an accurate record of all objective data relied upon to comply with the requirements of this Section.

(k)(2)(ii) This record shall include at least the following information:

(k)(2)(ii)(A) The crystalline silica-containing material in question;

(k)(2)(ii)(B) The source of the objective data;

(k)(2)(ii)(C) The testing protocol and results of testing;

(k)(2)(ii)(D) A description of the process, task, or activity on which the objective data were based; and

(k)(2)(ii)(E) Other data relevant to the process, task, activity, material, or exposures on which the objective data were based.

(k)(2)(iii) The employer shall ensure that objective data are maintained and made available in accordance with 29 CFR 1910.1020.

(k)(3) **Medical surveillance**

(k)(3)(i) The employer shall make and maintain an accurate record for each employee covered by medical surveillance under paragraph (i) of this Section.

(k)(3)(ii) The record shall include the following information about the employee:

(k)(3)(ii)(A) Name and social security number;

(k)(3)(ii)(B) A copy of the PLHCPs' and specialists' written medical opinions; and

(k)(3)(ii)(C) A copy of the information provided to the PLHCPs and specialists.

(k)(3)(iii) The employer shall ensure that medical records are maintained and made available in accordance with 29 CFR 1910.1020.

(l) **Dates**

(l)(1) This Section is effective June 23, 2016.

(l)(2) Except as provided for in paragraphs (l)(3) and (4) of this Section, all obligations of this Section commence June 23, 2018.

(l)(3) For hydraulic fracturing operations in the oil and gas industry:

(l)(3)(i) All obligations of this Section, except obligations for medical surveillance in paragraph (i)(1)(i) and engineering controls in paragraph (f)(1) of this Section, commence June 23, 2018;

(l)(3)(ii) Obligations for engineering controls in paragraph (f)(1) of this Section commence June 23, 2021; and

(l)(3)(iii) Obligations for medical surveillance in paragraph (i)(1)(i) commence in accordance with paragraph (l)(4) of this Section.

(l)(4) The medical surveillance obligations in paragraph (i)(1)(i) commence on June 23, 2018, for employees who will be occupationally exposed to respirable crystalline silica above the PEL for 30 or more days per year. Those obligations commence June 23, 2020, for employees who will be occupationally exposed to respirable crystalline silica at or above the action level for 30 or more days per year.

§1910.1053 Appendix A
Methods of sampling analysis

This Appendix specifies the procedures for analyzing air samples for respirable crystalline silica, as well as the quality control procedures that employers must ensure that laboratories use when performing an analysis required under 29 CFR 1910.1053 (d)(5). Employers must ensure that such a laboratory:

1. Evaluates all samples using the procedures specified in one of the following analytical methods: OSHA ID-142; NMAM 7500; NMAM 7602; NMAM 7603; MSHA P-2; or MSHA P-7;
2. Is accredited to ANS/ISO/IEC Standard 17025:2005 with respect to crystalline silica analyses by a body that is compliant with ISO/IEC Standard 17011:2004 for implementation of quality assessment programs;
3. Uses the most current National Institute of Standards and Technology (NIST) or NIST traceable standards for instrument calibration or instrument calibration verification;
4. Implements an internal quality control (QC) program that evaluates analytical uncertainty and provides employers with estimates of sampling and analytical error;
5. Characterizes the sample material by identifying polymorphs of respirable crystalline silica present, identifies the presence of any interfering compounds that might affect the analysis, and makes any corrections necessary in order to obtain accurate sample analysis; and
6. Analyzes quantitatively for crystalline silica only after confirming that the sample matrix is free of uncorrectable analytical interferences, corrects for analytical interferences, and uses a method that meets the following performance specifications:
   - 6.1 Each day that samples are analyzed, performs instrument calibration checks with standards that bracket the sample concentrations;
   - 6.2 Uses five or more calibration standard levels to prepare calibration curves and ensures that standards are distributed through the calibration range in a manner that accurately reflects the underlying calibration curve; and
   - 6.3 Optimizes methods and instruments to obtain a quantitative limit of detection that represents a value no higher than 25 percent of the PEL based on sample air volume.

§1910.1053 Appendix B
Medical surveillance guidelines

Introduction

The purpose of this Appendix is to provide medical information and recommendations to aid physicians and other licensed health care professionals (PLHCPs) regarding compliance with the medical surveillance provisions of the respirable crystalline silica standard (29 CFR 1910.1053). Appendix B is for informational and guidance purposes only and none of the statements in Appendix B should be construed as imposing a mandatory requirement on employers that is not otherwise imposed by the standard.

Medical screening and surveillance allow for early identification of exposure-related health effects in individual employee and groups of employees, so that actions can be taken to both avoid further exposure and prevent or address adverse health outcomes. Silica-related diseases can be fatal, encompass a variety of target organs, and may have public health consequences when considering the increased risk of a latent tuberculosis (TB) infection becoming active. Thus, medical surveillance of silica-exposed employees requires that PLHCPs have a thorough knowledge of silica-related health effects.

This Appendix is divided into seven sections. Section 1 reviews silica-related diseases, medical responses, and public health responses. Section 2 outlines the components of the medical surveillance program for employees exposed to silica. Section 3 describes the roles and responsibilities of the PLHCP implementing the program and of other medical specialists and public health professionals. Section 4 provides a discussion of considerations, including confidentiality. Section 5 provides a list of additional resources and Section 6 lists references. Section 7 provides sample forms for the written medical report for the employee, the written medical opinion for the employer and the written authorization.

1. Recognition of Silica-Related Diseases

1.1. Overview The term "silica" refers specifically to the compound silicon dioxide (SiO_2). Silica is a major component of sand, rock, and mineral ores. Exposure to fine (respirable size) particles of crystalline forms of silica is associated with adverse health effects, such as silicosis, lung cancer, chronic obstructive pulmonary disease (COPD), and activation of latent TB infections. Exposure to respirable crystalline silica can occur in industry settings such as foundries, abrasive blasting operations, paint manufacturing, glass and concrete product manufacturing, brick making, china and pottery manufacturing, manufacturing of plumbing fixtures, and many construction activities including highway repair, masonry, concrete work, rock drilling, and tuck-pointing. New uses of silica continue to emerge. These include countertop manufacturing, finishing, and installation (Kramer et al. 2012; OSHA 2015) and hydraulic fracturing in the oil and gas industry (OSHA 2012).

Silicosis is an irreversible, often disabling, and sometimes fatal fibrotic lung disease. Progression of silicosis can occur despite removal from further exposure. Diagnosis of silicosis requires a history of exposure to silica and radiologic findings characteristic of silica exposure. Three different presentations of silicosis (chronic, accelerated, and acute) have been defined. Accelerated and acute silicosis are much less common than chronic silicosis. However, it is critical to recognize all cases of accelerated and acute silicosis because these are life-threatening illnesses and because they are caused by substantial overexposures to respirable crystalline silica. Although any case of silicosis indicates a breakdown in prevention, a case of acute or accelerated silicosis implies current high exposure and a very marked breakdown in prevention.

In addition to silicosis, employees exposed to respirable crystalline silica, especially those with accelerated or acute silicosis, are at increased risks of contracting active TB and other infections (ATS 1997; Rees and Murray 2007). Exposure to respirable crystalline silica also increases an employee's risk of developing lung cancer, and the higher the cumulative exposure, the higher the risk (Steenland et al. 2001; Steenland and Ward 2014). Symptoms for these diseases and other respirable crystalline silica-related diseases are discussed below.

1.2. Chronic Silicosis Chronic silicosis is the most common presentation of silicosis and usually occurs after at least 10 years of exposure to respirable crystalline silica. The clinical presentation of chronic silicosis is:

1.2.1. Symptoms—shortness of breath and cough, although employees may not notice any symptoms early in the disease. Constitutional symptoms, such as fever, loss of appetite and fatigue, may indicate other diseases associated with silica exposure, such as TB infection or lung cancer. Employees with these symptoms should immediately receive further evaluation and treatment.

1.2.2. Physical Examination—may be normal or disclose dry rales or rhonchi on lung auscultation.

1.2.3. Spirometry—may be normal or may show only a mild restrictive or obstructive pattern.

1.2.4. Chest X-ray—classic findings are small, rounded opacities in the upper lung fields bilaterally. However, small irregular opacities and opacities in other lung areas can also occur. Rarely, "eggshell calcifications" in the hilar and mediastinal lymph nodes are seen.

1.2.5. Clinical Course—chronic silicosis in most cases is a slowly progressive disease. Under the respirable crystalline silica standard, the PLHCP is to recommend that employees with a 1/0 category X-ray be referred to an American Board Certified Specialist in Pulmonary Disease or Occupational Medicine. The PLHCP and/or Specialist should counsel employees regarding work practices and personal habits that could affect employees' respiratory health.

1.3. Accelerated Silicosis Accelerated silicosis generally occurs within 5-10 years of exposure and results from high levels of exposure to respirable crystalline silica. The clinical presentation of accelerated silicosis is:

1.3.1. Symptoms—shortness of breath, cough, and sometimes sputum production. Employees with exposure to respirable crystalline silica, and especially those with accelerated silicosis, are at high risk for activation of TB infections, atypical mycobacterial infections, and fungal superinfections. Constitutional symptoms, such as fever, weight loss, hemoptysis (coughing up blood), and fatigue may herald one of these infections or the onset of lung cancer.

1.3.2. Physical Examination—rales, rhonchi, or other abnormal lung findings in relation to illnesses present. Clubbing of the digits, signs of heart failure, and cor pulmonale may be present in severe lung disease.

1.3.3. Spirometry—restrictive or mixed restrictive/obstructive pattern.

1.3.4. Chest X-ray—small rounded and/or irregular opacities bilaterally. Large opacities and lung abscesses may indicate infections, lung cancer, or progression to complicated silicosis, also termed progressive massive fibrosis.

1.3.5. Clinical Course—accelerated silicosis has a rapid, severe course. Under the respirable crystalline silica standard, the PLHCP can recommend referral to a Board Certified Specialist in either Pulmonary Disease or Occupational Medicine, as deemed appropriate, and referral to a Specialist is recommended whenever the diagnosis of accelerated silicosis is being considered.

1.4. Acute Silicosis Acute silicosis is a rare disease caused by inhalation of extremely high levels of respirable crystalline silica particles. The pathology is similar to alveolar proteinosis with lipoproteinaceous material accumulating in the alveoli. Acute silicosis develops rapidly, often, within a few months to less than 2 years of exposure, and is almost always fatal. The clinical presentation of acute silicosis is as follows:

1.4.1. Symptoms—sudden, progressive, and severe shortness of breath. Constitutional symptoms are frequently present and include fever, weight loss, fatigue, productive cough, hemoptysis (coughing up blood), and pleuritic chest pain.

1.4.2. Physical Examination—dyspnea at rest, cyanosis, decreased breath sounds, inspiratory rales, clubbing of the digits, and fever.

1.4.3. Spirometry—restrictive or mixed restrictive/obstructive pattern.

1.4.4. Chest X-ray—diffuse haziness of the lungs bilaterally early in the disease. As the disease progresses, the "ground glass" appearance of interstitial fibrosis will appear.

1.4.5. Clinical Course—employees with acute silicosis are at especially high risk of TB activation, nontuberculous mycobacterial infections, and fungal superinfections. Acute silicosis is immediately life-threatening. The employee should be urgently referred to a Board Certified Specialist in Pulmonary Disease or Occupational Medicine for evaluation and treatment. Although any case of silicosis indicates a breakdown in prevention, a case of acute or accelerated silicosis implies a profoundly high level of silica exposure and may mean that other employees are currently exposed to dangerous levels of silica.

1.5. COPD COPD, including chronic bronchitis and emphysema, has been documented in silica-exposed employees, including those who do not develop silicosis. Periodic spirometry tests are performed to evaluate each employee for progressive changes consistent with the development of COPD. In addition to evaluating spirometry results of individual employees over time, PLHCPs may want to be aware of general trends in spirometry results for groups of employees from the same workplace to identify possible problems that might exist at that workplace. (See Section 2 of this Appendix on Medical Surveillance for further discussion.) Heart disease may develop secondary to lung diseases such as COPD. A recent study by Liu et al. 2014 noted a significant exposure-response trend between cumulative silica exposure and heart disease deaths, primarily due to pulmonary heart disease, such as cor pulmonale.

1.6. Renal and Immune System Silica exposure has been associated with several types of kidney disease, including glomerulonephritis, nephrotic syndrome, and end stage renal disease requiring dialysis. Silica exposure has also been associated with other autoimmune conditions, including progressive systemic sclerosis, systemic lupus erythematosus, and rheumatoid arthritis. Studies note an association between employees with silicosis and serologic markers for autoimmune diseases, including antinuclear antibodies, rheumatoid factor, and immune complexes (Jalloul and Banks 2007; Shtraichman et al. 2015).

1.7. TB and Other Infections Silica-exposed employees with latent TB are 3 to 30 times more likely to develop active pulmonary TB infection (ATS 1997; Rees and Murray 2007). Although respirable crystalline silica exposure does not cause TB infection, individuals with latent TB infection are at increased risk for activation of disease if they have higher levels of respirable crystalline silica exposure, greater profusion of radiographic abnormalities, or a diagnosis of silicosis. Demographic characteristics, such as immigration from some countries, are associated with increased rates of latent TB infection. PLHCPs can review the latest Centers for Disease Control and Prevention (CDC) information on TB incidence rates and high risk populations online (See Section 5 of this Appendix). Additionally, silica-exposed employees are at increased risk for contracting nontuberculous mycobacterial infections, including Mycobacterium avium-intracellulare and Mycobacterium kansaii.

1.8. Lung Cancer The National Toxicology Program has listed respirable crystalline silica as a known human carcinogen since 2000 (NTP 2014). The International Agency for Research on Cancer (2012) has also classified silica as Group 1 (carcinogenic to humans). Several studies have indicated that the risk of lung cancer from exposure to respirable crystalline silica and smoking is greater than additive (Brown 2009; Liu et al. 2013). Employees should be counseled on smoking cessation.

2. Medical Surveillance

PLHCPs who manage silica medical surveillance programs should have a thorough understanding of the many silica-related diseases and health effects outlined in Section 1 of this Appendix. At each clinical encounter, the PLHCP should consider silica-related health outcomes, with particular vigilance for acute and accelerated silicosis. In this Section, the required components of medical surveillance under the respirable crystalline silica standard are reviewed, along with additional guidance and recommendations for PLHCPs performing medical surveillance examinations for silica-exposed employees.

2.1. History

2.1.1. The respirable crystalline silica standard requires the following: A medical and work history, with emphasis on: Past, present, and anticipated exposure to respirable crystalline silica, dust, and other agents affecting the respiratory system; any history of respiratory system dysfunction, including signs and symptoms of respiratory disease (e.g., shortness of breath, cough, wheezing); history of TB; and smoking status and history.

2.1.2. Further, the employer must provide the PLHCP with the following information:

2.1.2.1. A description of the employee's former, current, and anticipated duties as they relate to the employee's occupational exposure to respirable crystalline silica;

2.1.2.2. The employee's former, current, and anticipated levels of occupational exposure to respirable crystalline silica;

2.1.2.3. A description of any personal protective equipment used or to be used by the employee, including when and for how long the employee has used or will use that equipment; and

2.1.2.4. Information from records of employment-related medical examinations previously provided to the employee and currently within the control of the employer.

2.1.3. Additional guidance and recommendations: A history is particularly important both in the initial evaluation and in periodic examinations. Information on past and current medical conditions (particularly a history of kidney disease, cardiac disease, connective tissue disease, and other immune diseases), medications, hospitalizations and surgeries may uncover health risks, such as immune suppression, that could put an employee at increased health risk from exposure to silica. This information is important when counseling the employee on risks and safe work practices related to silica exposure.

2.2. Physical Examination

2.2.1. The respirable crystalline silica standard requires the following: A physical examination, with special emphasis on the respiratory system. The physical examination must be performed at the initial examination and every three years thereafter.

2.2.2. Additional guidance and recommendations: Elements of the physical examination that can assist the PHLCP include: An examination of the cardiac system, an extremity examination (for clubbing, cyanosis, edema, or joint abnormalities), and an examination of other pertinent organ systems identified during the history.

2.3. TB Testing

2.3.1. The respirable crystalline silica standard requires the following: Baseline testing for TB on initial examination.

2.3.2. Additional guidance and recommendations:

2.3.2.1. Current CDC guidelines (See Section 5 of this Appendix) should be followed for the application and interpretation of Tuberculin skin tests (TST). The interpretation and documentation of TST reactions should be performed within 48 to 72 hours of administration by trained PLHCPs.

2.3.2.2. PLHCPs may use alternative TB tests, such as interferon-γ release assays (IGRAs), if sensitivity and specificity are comparable to TST (Mazurek et al. 2010; Slater et al. 2013). PLHCPs can consult the current CDC guidelines for acceptable tests for latent TB infection.

2.3.2.3. The silica standard allows the PLHCP to order additional tests or test at a greater frequency than required by the standard, if deemed appropriate. Therefore, PLHCPs might perform periodic (e.g., annual) TB testing as appropriate, based on employees' risk factors. For example, according to the American Thoracic Society (ATS), the diagnosis of silicosis or exposure to silica for 25 years or more are indications for annual TB testing (ATS 1997). PLHCPs should consult the current CDC guidance on risk factors for TB (See Section 5 of this Appendix).

2.3.2.4. Employees with positive TB tests and those with indeterminate test results should be referred to the appropriate agency or specialist, depending on the test results and clinical picture. Agencies, such as local public health departments, or specialists, such as a pulmonary or infectious disease specialist, may be the appropriate referral. Active TB is a nationally notifiable disease. PLHCPs should be aware of the reporting requirements for their region. All States have TB Control Offices that can be contacted for further information. (See Section 5 of this Appendix for links to CDC's TB resources and State TB Control Offices.)

2.3.2.5. The following public health principles are key to TB control in the U.S. (ATS-CDC-IDSA 2005):

(1) Prompt detection and reporting of persons who have contracted active TB;

(2) Prevention of TB spread to close contacts of active TB cases;

(3) Prevention of active TB in people with latent TB through targeted testing and treatment; and

(4) Identification of settings at high risk for TB transmission so that appropriate infection-control measures can be implemented.

2.4. Pulmonary Function Testing

2.4.1. The respirable crystalline silica standard requires the following: Pulmonary function testing must be performed on the initial examination and every three years thereafter. The required pulmonary function test is spirometry and must include forced vital capacity (FVC), forced expiratory volume in one second (FEV1), and FEV1/FVC ratio. Testing must be administered by a spirometry technician with a current certificate from a National Institute for Occupational Health and Safety (NIOSH)-approved spirometry course.

2.4.2. Additional guidance and recommendations: Spirometry provides information about individual respiratory status and can be used to track an employee's respiratory status over time or as a surveillance tool to follow individual and group respiratory function. For quality results, the ATS and the American College of Occupational and Environmental Medicine (ACOEM) recommend use of the third National Health and Nutrition Examination Survey (NHANES III) values, and ATS publishes recommendations for spirometry equipment (Miller et al. 2005; Townsend 2011; Redlich et al. 2014). OSHA's publication, Spirometry Testing in Occupational Health Programs: Best Practices for Healthcare Professionals, provides helpful guidance (See Section 5 of this Appendix). Abnormal spirometry results may warrant further clinical evaluation and possible recommendations for limitations on the employee's exposure to respirable crystalline silica.

2.5. Chest X-ray

2.5.1. The respirable crystalline silica standard requires the following: A single posteroanterior (PA) radiographic projection or radiograph of the chest at full inspiration recorded on either film (no less than 14 x 17 inches and no more than 16 x 17 inches) or digital radiography systems. A chest X-ray must be performed on the initial examination and every three years thereafter. The chest X-ray must be interpreted and classified according to the International Labour Office (ILO) International Classification of Radiographs of Pneumoconioses by a NIOSH-certified B Reader.

Chest radiography is necessary to diagnose silicosis, monitor the progression of silicosis, and identify associated conditions such as TB. If the B reading indicates small opacities in a profusion of 1/0 or higher, the employee is to receive a recommendation for referral to a Board Certified Specialist in Pulmonary Disease or Occupational Medicine.

2.5.2. Additional guidance and recommendations: Medical imaging has largely transitioned from conventional film-based radiography to digital radiography systems. The ILO Guidelines for the Classification of Pneumoconioses has historically provided film-based chest radiography as a referent standard for comparison to individual exams. However, in 2011, the ILO revised the guidelines to include a digital set of referent standards that were derived from the prior film-based standards. To assist in assuring that digitally-acquired radiographs are at least as safe and effective as film radiographs, NIOSH has prepared guidelines, based upon accepted contemporary professional recommendations (See Section 5 of this Appendix). Current research from Laney et al. 2011 and Halldin et al.

2014 validate the use of the ILO digital referent images. Both studies conclude that the results of pneumoconiosis classification using digital references are comparable to film-based ILO classifications. Current ILO guidance on radiography for pneumoconioses and B-reading should be reviewed by the PLHCP periodically, as needed, on the ILO or NIOSH Web sites (See Section 5 of this Appendix).

2.6. Other Testing Under the respirable crystalline silica standards, the PLHCP has the option of ordering additional testing he or she deems appropriate. Additional tests can be ordered on a case-by-case basis depending on individual signs or symptoms and clinical judgment. For example, if an employee reports a history of abnormal kidney function tests, the PLHCP may want to order a baseline renal function tests (e.g., serum creatinine and urinalysis). As indicated above, the PLHCP may order annual TB testing for silica-exposed employees who are at high risk of developing active TB infections. Additional tests that PLHCPs may order based on findings of medical examinations include, but is not limited to, chest computerized tomography (CT) scan for lung cancer or COPD, testing for immunologic diseases, and cardiac testing for pulmonary-related heart disease, such as cor pulmonale.

3. Roles and Responsibilities

3.1. PLHCP The PLHCP designation refers to "an individual whose legally permitted scope of practice (i.e., license, registration, or certification) allows him or her to independently provide or be delegated the responsibility to provide some or all of the particular health care services required" by the respirable crystalline silica standard. The legally permitted scope of practice for the PLHCP is determined by each State. PLHCPs who perform clinical services for a silica medical surveillance program should have a thorough knowledge of respirable crystalline silica-related diseases and symptoms. Suspected cases of silicosis, advanced COPD, or other respiratory conditions causing impairment should be promptly referred to a Board Certified Specialist in Pulmonary Disease or Occupational Medicine.

Once the medical surveillance examination is completed, the employer must ensure that the PLHCP explains to the employee the results of the medical examination and provides the employee with a written medical report within 30 days of the examination. The written medical report must contain a statement indicating the results of the medical examination, including any medical condition(s) that would place the employee at increased risk of material impairment to health from exposure to respirable crystalline silica and any medical conditions that require further evaluation or treatment. In addition, the PLHCP's written medical report must include any recommended limitations on the employee's use of respirators, any recommended limitations on the employee's exposure to respirable crystalline silica, and a statement that the employee should be examined by a Board Certified Specialist in Pulmonary Disease or Occupational medicine if the chest X-ray is classified as 1/0 or higher by the B Reader, or if referral to a Specialist is otherwise deemed appropriate by the PLHCP.

The PLHCP should discuss all findings and test results and any recommendations regarding the employee's health, worksite safety and health practices, and medical referrals for further evaluation, if indicated. In addition, it is suggested that the PLHCP offer to provide the employee with a complete copy of their examination and test results, as some employees may want this information for their own records or to provide to their personal physician or a future PLHCP. Employees are entitled to access their medical records.

Under the respirable crystalline silica standard, the employer must ensure that the PLHCP provides the employer with a written medical opinion within 30 days of the employee examination, and that the employee also gets a copy of the written medical opinion for the employer within 30 days. The PLHCP may choose to directly provide the employee a copy of the written medical opinion. This can be particularly helpful to employees, such as construction employees, who may change employers frequently. The written medical opinion can be used by the employee as proof of up-to-date medical surveillance. The following lists the elements of the written medical report for the employee and written medical opinion for the employer. (Sample forms for the written medical report for the employee, the written medical opinion for the employer, and the written authorization are provided in Section 7 of this Appendix.)

3.1.1. The written medical report for the employee must include the following information:

3.1.1.1. A statement indicating the results of the medical examination, including any medical condition(s) that would place the employee at increased risk of material impairment to health from exposure to respirable crystalline silica and any medical conditions that require further evaluation or treatment;

3.1.1.2. Any recommended limitations upon the employee's use of a respirator;

3.1.1.3. Any recommended limitations on the employee's exposure to respirable crystalline silica; and

3.1.1.4. A statement that the employee should be examined by a Board Certified Specialist in Pulmonary Disease or Occupational Medicine, where the standard requires or where the PLHCP has determined such a referral is necessary. The standard requires referral to a Board Certified Specialist in Pulmonary Disease or Occupational Medicine for a chest X-ray B reading indicating small opacities in a profusion of 1/0 or higher, or if the PHLCP determines that referral to a Specialist is necessary for other silica-related findings.

3.1.2. The PLHCP's written medical opinion for the employer must include only the following information:

3.1.2.1. The date of the examination;

3.1.2.2. A statement that the examination has met the requirements of this Section; and

3.1.2.3. Any recommended limitations on the employee's use of respirators.

3.1.2.4. If the employee provides the PLHCP with written authorization, the written opinion for the employer shall also contain either or both of the following:

(1) Any recommended limitations on the employee's exposure to respirable crystalline silica; and

(2) A statement that the employee should be examined by a Board Certified Specialist in Pulmonary Disease or Occupational Medicine if the chest X-ray provided in accordance with this Section is classified as 1/0 or higher by the B Reader, or if referral to a Specialist is otherwise deemed appropriate.

3.1.2.5. In addition to the above referral for abnormal chest X-ray, the PLHCP may refer an employee to a Board Certified Specialist in Pulmonary Disease or Occupational Medicine for other findings of concern during the medical surveillance examination if these findings are potentially related to silica exposure.

3.1.2.6. Although the respirable crystalline silica standard requires the employer to ensure that the PLHCP explains the results of the medical examination to the employee, the standard does not mandate how this should be done. The written medical opinion for the employer could contain a statement that the PLHCP has explained the results of the medical examination to the employee.

3.2. Medical Specialists The silica standard requires that all employees with chest X-ray B readings of 1/0 or higher be referred to a Board Certified Specialist in Pulmonary Disease or Occupational Medicine. If the employee has given written authorization for the employer to be informed, then the employer shall make available a medical examination by a Specialist within 30 days after receiving the PLHCP's written medical opinion.

3.2.1. The employer must provide the following information to the Board Certified Specialist in Pulmonary Disease or Occupational Medicine:

3.2.1.1. A description of the employee's former, current, and anticipated duties as they relate to the employee's occupational exposure to respirable crystalline silica;

3.2.1.2. The employee's former, current, and anticipated levels of occupational exposure to respirable crystalline silica;

3.2.1.3. A description of any personal protective equipment used or to be used by the employee, including when and for how long the employee has used or will use that equipment; and

3.2.1.4. Information from records of employment-related medical examinations previously provided to the employee and currently within the control of the employer.

3.2.2. The PLHCP should make certain that, with written authorization from the employee, the Board Certified Specialist in Pulmonary Disease or Occupational Medicine has any other pertinent medical and occupational information necessary for the specialist's evaluation of the employee's condition.

3.2.3. Once the Board Certified Specialist in Pulmonary Disease or Occupational Medicine has evaluated the employee, the employer must ensure that the Specialist explains to the employee the results of the medical examination and provides the employee with a written medical report within 30 days of the examination. The employer must also ensure that the Specialist provides the employer with a written medical opinion within 30 days of the employee examination. (Sample forms for the written medical report for the employee, the written medical opinion for the employer and the written authorization are provided in Section 7 of this Appendix.)

3.2.4. The Specialist's written medical report for the employee must include the following information:

3.2.4.1. A statement indicating the results of the medical examination, including any medical condition(s) that would place the employee at increased risk of material impairment to health from exposure to respirable crystalline silica and any medical conditions that require further evaluation or treatment;

3.2.4.2. Any recommended limitations upon the employee's use of a respirator; and

3.2.4.3. Any recommended limitations on the employee's exposure to respirable crystalline silica.

3.2.5. The Specialist's written medical opinion for the employer must include the following information:

3.2.5.1. The date of the examination; and

3.2.5.2. Any recommended limitations on the employee's use of respirators.

3.2.5.3. If the employee provides the Board Certified Specialist in Pulmonary Disease or Occupational Medicine with written authorization, the written medical opinion for the employer shall also contain any recommended limitations on the employee's exposure to respirable crystalline silica.

3.2.5.4. Although the respirable crystalline silica standard requires the employer to ensure that the Board Certified Specialist in Pulmonary Disease or Occupational Medicine explains the results of the medical examination to the employee, the standard does not mandate how this should be done. The written medical opinion for the employer could contain a statement that the Specialist has explained the results of the medical examination to the employee.

3.2.6. After evaluating the employee, the Board Certified Specialist in Pulmonary Disease or Occupational Medicine should provide feedback to the PLHCP as appropriate, depending on the reason for the referral. OSHA believes that because the PLHCP has the primary relationship with the employer and employee, the Specialist may want to communicate his or her findings to the PLHCP and have the PLHCP simply update the original medical report for the employee and medical opinion for the employer. This is permitted under the standard, so long as all requirements and time deadlines are met.

3.3. Public Health Professionals PLHCPs might refer employees or consult with public health professionals as a result of silica medical surveillance. For instance, if individual cases of active TB are identified, public health professionals from state or local health departments may assist in diagnosis and treatment of individual cases and may evaluate other potentially affected persons, including coworkers. Because silica-exposed employees are at increased risk of progression from latent to active TB, treatment of latent infection is recommended. The diagnosis of active TB, acute or accelerated silicosis, or other silica-related diseases and infections should serve as sentinel events suggesting high levels of exposure to silica and may require consultation with the appropriate public health agencies to investigate potentially similarly exposed coworkers to assess for disease clusters. These agencies include local or state health departments or OSHA. In addition, NIOSH can provide assistance upon request through their Health Hazard Evaluation program. (See Section 5 of this Appendix)

4. Confidentiality and Other Considerations

The information that is provided from the PLHCP to the employee and employer under the medical surveillance Section of OSHA's respirable crystalline silica standard differs from that of medical surveillance requirements in previous OSHA standards. The standard requires two separate written communications, a written medical report for the employee and a written medical opinion for the employer. The confidentiality requirements for the written medical opinion are more stringent than in past standards. For example, the information the PLHCP can (and must) include in his or her written medical opinion for the employer is limited to: The date of the examination, a statement that the examination has met the requirements of this Section, and any recommended limitations on the employee's use of respirators. If the employee provides written authorization for the disclosure of any limitations on the employee's exposure to respirable crystalline silica, then the PLHCP can (and must) include that information in the written medical opinion for the employer as well. Likewise, with the employee's written authorization, the PLHCP can (and must) disclose the PLHCP's referral recommendation (if any) as part of the written medical opinion for the employer. However, the opinion to the employer must not include information regarding recommended limitations on the employee's exposure to respirable crystalline silica or any referral recommendations without the employee's written authorization.

The standard also places limitations on the information that the Board Certified Specialist in Pulmonary Disease or Occupational Medicine can provide to the employer without the employee's written authorization. The Specialist's written medical opinion for the employer, like the PLHCP's opinion, is limited to (and must contain): The date of the examination and any recommended limitations on the employee's use of respirators. If the employee provides written authorization, the written medical opinion can (and must) also contain any limitations on the employee's exposure to respirable crystalline silica.

The PLHCP should discuss the implication of signing or not signing the authorization with the employee (in a manner and language that he or she understands) so that the employee can make an informed decision regarding the written authorization and its consequences. The discussion should include the risk of ongoing silica exposure, personal risk factors, risk of disease progression, and possible health and economic consequences. For instance, written authorization is required for a PLHCP to advise an employer that an employee should be referred to a Board Certified Specialist in Pulmonary Disease or Occupational Medicine for evaluation of an abnormal chest X-ray (B-reading 1/0 or greater). If an employee does not sign an authorization, then the employer will not know and cannot facilitate the referral to a Specialist and is not required to pay for the Specialist's examination. In the rare case where an employee is diagnosed with acute or accelerated silicosis, co-workers are likely to be at significant risk of developing those diseases as a result of inadequate controls in the workplace. In this case, the PLHCP and/or Specialist should explain this concern to the affected employee and make a determined effort to obtain written authorization from the employee so that the PLHCP and/or Specialist can contact the employer.

Finally, without written authorization from the employee, the PLHCP and/or Board Certified Specialist in Pulmonary Disease or Occupational Medicine cannot provide feedback to an employer regarding control of workplace silica exposure, at least in relation to an individual employee. However, the regulation does not prohibit a PLHCP and/or Specialist from providing an employer with general recommendations regarding exposure controls and prevention programs in relation to silica exposure and silica-related illnesses, based on the information that the PLHCP receives from the employer such as employees' duties and exposure levels. Recommendations may include increased frequency of medical surveillance examinations, additional medical surveillance components, engineering and work practice controls, exposure monitoring and personal protective equipment. For instance, more frequent medical surveillance examinations may be a recommendation to employers for employees who do abrasive blasting with silica because of the high exposures associated with that operation.

ACOEM's Code of Ethics and discussion is a good resource to guide PLHCPs regarding the issues discussed in this Section (See Section 5 of this Appendix).

5. Resources

5.1. American College of Occupational and Environmental Medicine (ACOEM):

ACOEM Code of Ethics. Accessed at:http://www.acoem.org/codeofconduct.aspx

Raymond, L.W. and Wintermeyer, S. (2006) ACOEM evidenced-based statement on medical surveillance of silica-exposed workers: Medical surveillance of workers exposed to crystalline silica. J Occup Environ Med, 48, 95-101.

5.2. Center for Disease Control and Prevention (CDC)

Tuberculosis Web page: http://www.cdc.gov/tb/default.htm

State TB Control Offices Web page: http://www.cdc.gov/tb/links/tboffices.htm

Tuberculosis Laws and Policies Web page: http://www.cdc.gov/tb/programs/laws/default.htm

CDC. (2013). Latent Tuberculosis Infection: A Guide for Primary Health Care Providers. Accessed at: http://www.cdc.gov/tb/publications/ltbi/pdf/targetedltbi.pdf

5.3. International Labour Organization

International Labour Office (ILO). (2011) Guidelines for the use of the ILO International Classification of Radiographs of Pneumoconioses, Revised edition 2011. Occupational Safety and Health Series No. 22: http://www.ilo.org/safework/info/publications/WCMS_168260/lang-en/index.htm

5.4. National Institute of Occupational Safety and Health (NIOSH)

NIOSH B Reader Program Web page. (Information on interpretation of X-rays for silicosis and a list of certified B-readers). Accessed at: http://www.cdc.gov/niosh/topics/chestradiography/breader-info.html

NIOSH Guideline (2011). Application of Digital Radiography for the Detection and Classification of Pneumoconiosis. NIOSH publication number 2011-198. Accessed at: http://www.cdc.gov/niosh/docs/2011-198/

NIOSH Hazard Review (2002), Health Effects of Occupational Exposure to Respirable Crystalline Silica. NIOSH publication number 2002-129: Accessed at http://www.cdc.gov/niosh/docs/2002-129/

NIOSH Health Hazard Evaluations Programs. (Information on the NIOSH Health Hazard Evaluation (HHE) program, how to request an HHE and how to look up an HHE report). Accessed at: http://www.cdc.gov/niosh/hhe/

5.5. National Industrial Sand Association:

Occupational Health Program for Exposure to Crystalline Silica in the Industrial Sand Industry. National Industrial Sand Association, 2nd ed. 2010. Can be ordered at: http://www.sand.org/silica-occupational-health-program

5.6. Occupational Safety and Health Administration (OSHA)

Contacting OSHA: http://www.osha.gov/html/Feed_Back.html

OSHA's Clinicians Web page. (OSHA resources, regulations and links to help clinicians navigate OSHA's Web site and aid clinicians in caring for workers.) Accessed at: http://www.osha.gov/dts/oom/clinicians/index.html

OSHA's Safety and Health Topics Web page on Silica. Accessed at: http://www.osha.gov/dsg/topics/silicacrystalline/index.html

OSHA (2013). Spirometry Testing in Occupational Health Programs: Best Practices for Healthcare Professionals. (OSHA 3637-03 2013). Accessed at: http://www.osha.gov/Publications/OSHA3637.pdf

OSHA/NIOSH (2011). Spirometry: OSHA/NIOSH Spirometry InfoSheet (OSHA 3415-1-11). (Provides guidance to employers). Accessed at http://www.osha.gov/Publications/osha3415.pdf

OSHA/NIOSH (2011) Spirometry: OSHA/NIOSH Spirometry Worker Info. (OSHA 3418-3-11). Accessed at http://www.osha.gov/Publications/osha3418.pdf

5.7. Other

Steenland, K. and Ward E. (2014). Silica: A lung carcinogen. CA Cancer J Clin, 64, 63-69. (This article reviews not only silica and lung cancer but also all the known silica-related health effects. Further, the authors provide guidance to clinicians on medical surveillance of silica-exposed workers and worker counselling on safety practices to minimize silica exposure.)

6. References

American Thoracic Society (ATS). Medical Section of the American Lung Association (1997). Adverse effects of crystalline silica exposure. Am J Respir Crit Care Med, 155, 761-765.

American Thoracic Society (ATS), Centers for Disease Control (CDC), Infectious Diseases Society of America (IDSA) (2005). Controlling Tuberculosis in the United States. Morbidity and Mortality Weekly Report (MMWR), 54(RR12), 1-81. Accessed at: http://www.cdc.gov/mmwr/preview/mmwrhtml/rr5412a1.htm

Brown, T. (2009). Silica exposure, smoking, silicosis and lung cancer—complex interactions. Occupational Medicine, 59, 89-95.

Halldin, C.N., Petsonk, E.L., and Laney, A.S. (2014). Validation of the International Labour Office digitized standard images for recognition and classification of radiographs of pneumoconiosis. Acad Radiol, 21, 305-311.

International Agency for Research on Cancer. (2012). Monographs on the evaluation of carcinogenic risks to humans: Arsenic, Metals, Fibers, and Dusts Silica Dust, Crystalline, in the Form of Quartz or Cristobalite. A Review of Human Carcinogens. Volume 100 C. Geneva, Switzerland: World Health Organization.

Jalloul, A.S. and Banks D.E. (2007). Chapter 23. The health effects of silica exposure. In: Rom, W.N. and Markowitz, S.B. (Eds). Environmental and Occupational Medicine, 4th edition. Lippincott, Williams and Wilkins, Philadelphia, 365-387.

Kramer, M.R., Blanc, P.D., Fireman, E., Amital, A., Guber, A., Rahman, N.A., and Shitrit, D. (2012). Artifical stone silicosis: Disease resurgence among artificial stone workers. Chest, 142, 419-424.

Laney, A.S., Petsonk, E.L., and Attfield, M.D. (2011). Intramodality and intermodality comparisons of storage phosphor computed radiography and conventional film-screen radiography in the recognition of small pneumonconiotic opacities. Chest, 140, 1574-1580.

Liu, Y., Steenland, K., Rong, Y., Hnizdo, E., Huang, X., Zhang, H., Shi, T., Sun, Y., Wu, T., and Chen, W. (2013). Exposure-response analysis and risk assessment for lung cancer in relationship to silica exposure: A 44-year cohort study of 34,018 workers. Am J Epi, 178, 1424-1433.

Liu, Y., Rong, Y., Steenland, K., Christiani, D.C., Huang, X., Wu, T., and Chen, W. (2014). Long-term exposure to crystalline silica and risk of heart disease mortality. Epidemiology, 25, 689-696.

Mazurek, G.H., Jereb, J., Vernon, A., LoBue, P., Goldberg, S., Castro, K. (2010). Updated guidelines for using interferon gamma release assays to detect Mycobacterium tuberculosis infection—United States. Morbidity and Mortality Weekly Report (MMWR), 59(RR05), 1-25.

Miller, M.R., Hankinson, J., Brusasco, V., Burgos, F., Casaburi, R., Coates, A., Crapo, R., Enright, P., van der Grinten, C.P., Gustafsson, P., Jensen, R., Johnson, D.C., MacIntyre, N., McKay, R., Navajas, D., Pedersen, O.F., Pellegrino, R., Viegi, G., and Wanger, J. (2005). American Thoracic Society/European Respiratory Society (ATS/ERS) Task Force: Standardisation of Spirometry. Eur Respir J, 26, 319-338.

National Toxicology Program (NTP) (2014). Report on Carcinogens, Thirteenth Edition. Silica, Crystalline (respirable Size). Research Triangle Park, NC: U.S. Department of Health and Human Services, Public Health Service. http://ntp.niehs.nih.gov/ntp/roc/content/profiles/silica.pdf

Occupational Safety and Health Administration/National Institute for Occupational Safety and Health (OSHA/NIOSH) (2012). Hazard Alert. Worker exposure to silica during hydraulic fracturing.

Occupational Safety and Health Administration/National Institute for Occupational Safety and Health (OSHA/NIOSH) (2015). Hazard alert. Worker exposure to silica during countertop manufacturing, finishing, and installation. (OSHA-HA-3768-2015).

Redlich, C.A., Tarlo, S.M., Hankinson, J.L., Townsend, M.C, Eschenbacher, W.L., Von Essen, S.G., Sigsgaard, T., Weissman, D.N. (2014). Official American Thoracic Society technical standards: Spirometry in the occupational setting. Am J Respir Crit Care Med; 189, 984-994.

Rees, D. and Murray, J. (2007). Silica, silicosis and tuberculosis. Int J Tuberc Lung Dis, 11(5), 474-484.

Shtraichman, O., Blanc, P.D., Ollech, J.E., Fridel, L., Fuks, L., Fireman, E., and Kramer, M.R. (2015). Outbreak of autoimmune disease in silicosis linked to artificial stone. Occup Med, 65, 444-450.

Slater, M.L., Welland, G., Pai, M., Parsonnet, J., and Banaei, N. (2013). Challenges with QuantiFERON-TB gold assay for large-scale, routine screening of U.S. healthcare workers. Am J Respir Crit Care Med, 188,1005-1010.

Steenland, K., Mannetje, A., Boffetta, P., Stayner, L., Attfield, M., Chen, J., Dosemeci, M., DeKlerk, N., Hnizdo, E., Koskela, R., and Checkoway, H. (2001). International Agency for Research on Cancer. Pooled exposure-response analyses and risk assessment for lung cancer in 10 cohorts of silica-exposed workers: An IARC multicentre study. Cancer Causes Control, 12(9): 773-84.

Steenland, K. and Ward E. (2014). Silica: A lung carcinogen. CA Cancer J Clin, 64, 63-69.

Townsend, M.C. ACOEM Guidance Statement. (2011). Spirometry in the occupational health setting—2011 Update. J Occup Environ Med, 53, 569-584.

7. Sample Forms

Three sample forms are provided. The first is a sample written medical report for the employee. The second is a sample written medical opinion for the employer. And the third is a sample written authorization form that employees sign to clarify what information the employee is authorizing to be released to the employer.

WRITTEN MEDICAL REPORT FOR EMPLOYEE

EMPLOYEE NAME: ______________________ **DATE OF EXAMINATION:** ___________

TYPE OF EXAMINATION
[ ] Initial examination [ ] Periodic examination [ ] Special examination
[ ] Other: ____

RESULTS OF MEDICAL EXAMINATION:

Physical Examination —	[ ] Normal	[ ] Abnormal (see below)	[ ] Not performed
Chest X-Ray —	[ ] Normal	[ ] Abnormal (see below)	[ ] Not performed
Breathing Test (Spirometry) —	[ ] Normal	[ ] Abnormal (see below)	[ ] Not performed
Test for Tuberculosis —	[ ] Normal	[ ] Abnormal (see below)	[ ] Not performed
Other: ____________	[ ] Normal	[ ] Abnormal (see below)	[ ] Not performed

Results reported as abnormal: ____
____

[ ] **Your health may be at increased reisk from exposure to respirable crystalline silica due to the following:**
____

RECOMMENDATIONS:
[ ] No limitations on respirator use
[ ] Recommended limitations on use of respirator: ______________________________
[ ] Recommended limitation on exposure to respirable crystalline silica: ______________________________
____

Dates for recommended limitation, if applicable: ____________ to ____________
MM/DD/YYYY MM/DD/YYYY

[ ] **I recommend that you be examined by a Board Certified Specialist in Pulmonary Disease or Occupational Medicine**

[ ] Other recommendations*:
____
____

Your next periodic examination for silica exposure should be in: [ ] 3 years [ ] Other: ____________
MM/DD/YYYY

Examining Provider: ______________________________ Date: ______________
(signature)

Provider Name: ______________________________
Office Address: ______________________________ Office phone: ______________

*These findings may not be related to respirable crystalline silica exposure or may not be work-related, and therefore may not be covered by the employer. These findings may necessitate follow-up and treatment by you personal physician.

Respirable Crystalline Silica standard (§1910.1053 or §1926.1153)

WRITTEN MEDICAL OPINION FOR EMPLOYER

EMPLOYER: ______________________________

EMPLOYEE NAME: ______________________________ **DATE OF EXAMINATION:** __________

TYPE OF EXAMINATION:

[ ] Initial examination [ ] Periodic examination [ ] Specialist examination
[ ] Other: ______________________________

USE OF RESPIRATOR:
[ ] No limitation on respirator use
[ ] Recommended limitations on use of respirator: ______________________________

Dates for recommended limitations, if applicable: __________ to __________
MM/DD/YYYY MM/DD/YYYY

The employee has provided written authorization for disclosure of the following to the employer (if applicable):

[ ] This employee should be examined by an American Board Certified Specialist in Pulmonary Disease or Occupational Medicine
[ ] Recommended limitations on exposure to respirable crystalline silica: ______________________________

Dates for exposure limitations noted above: __________ to __________
MM/DD/YYYY MM/DD/YYYY

NEXT PERIODIC EVALUATION: [ ] 3 Years [ ] Other: __________
MM/DD/YYYY

Examining Provider: ______________________________ Date: __________
(signature)
Provider Name: ______________________________ Provider's specialty: __________
Office Address: ______________________________ Office Phone: __________

[ ] I attest that the results have been explained to the employee.

The following is required to be checked by the Physician or other Licensed Health Care Professional (PLHCP):

[ ] I attest that this medical examination has met the requirements of the medical surveillance section of the OSHA Respirable Crystalline Silica standard (§1910.1053(h) or §1926.1153(h)).

— —

AUTHORIZATION FOR CRYSTALLINE SILICA OPINION TO EMPLOYER

This medical examination for exposure to crystalline silica could reveal a medical condition that results in recommendations for (1) limitations on respirator use, (2) limitations on exposure to crystalline silica, or (3) examination by a specialist in pulmonary disease or occupational medicine. Recommended limitations on respirator use will be included in the written opinion to the employer. If you want your employer to know about limitations on crystalline silica exposure or recommendations for a specialist examination, you will need to give authorization for the written opinion to the employer to include one or both of those recommendations.

I hereby authorize the opinion to the employer to contain the following information, if relevant (please check all that apply):

□ Recommendations for limitations on crystalline silica exposure

□ Recommendations for a specialist examination

OR

□ I do not authorize the opinion to the employer to contain anything other than recommended limitations on respirator use.

Please read and initial:

___ I understand that if I do not authorize my employer to receive the recommendation for specialist examination, the employer will not be responsible for arranging and covering costs of a specialist examination.

____
Name (printed)

______________________________ __________
Signature Date

§1910.1096 Ionizing radiation

(a) **Definitions applicable to this Section**

(a)(1) **Radiation** includes alpha rays, beta rays, gamma rays, X-rays, neutrons, high-speed electrons, high-speed protons, and other atomic particles; but such term does not include sound or radio waves, or visible light, or infrared or ultraviolet light.

(a)(2) **Radioactive material** means any material which emits, by spontaneous nuclear disintegration, corpuscular or electromagnetic emanations.

(a)(3) **Restricted area** means any area access to which is controlled by the employer for purposes of protection of individuals from exposure to radiation or radioactive materials.

(a)(4) **Unrestricted area** means any area access to which is not controlled by the employer for purposes of protection of individuals from exposure to radiation or radioactive materials.

(a)(5) **Dose** means the quantity of ionizing radiation absorbed, per unit of mass, by the body or by any portion of the body. When the provisions in this Section specify a dose during a period of time, the dose is the total quantity of radiation absorbed, per unit of mass, by the body or by any portion of the body during such period of time. Several different units of dose are in current use. Definitions of units used in this Section are set forth in paragraphs (a)(6) and (7) of this Section.

(a)(6) **Rad** means a measure of the dose of any ionizing radiation to body tissues in terms of the energy absorbed per unit of mass of the tissue. One rad is the dose corresponding to the absorption of 100 ergs per gram of tissue (1 millirad (mrad) = 0.001 rad).

(a)(7) **Rem** means a measure of the dose of any ionizing radiation to body tissue in terms of its estimated biological effect relative to a dose of 1 roentgen (r) of X-rays (1 millirem (mrem) = 0.001 rem). The relation of the rem to other dose units depends upon the biological effect under consideration and upon the conditions for irradiation. Each of the following is considered to be equivalent to a dose of 1 rem:

(a)(7)(i) A dose of 1 roentgen due to X- or gamma radiation;

(a)(7)(ii) A dose of 1 rad due to X-, gamma, or beta radiation;

(a)(7)(iii) A dose of 0.1 rad due to neutrons or high energy protons;

(a)(7)(iv) A dose of 0.05 rad due to particles heavier than protons and with sufficient energy to reach the lens of the eye;

(a)(7)(v) If it is more convenient to measure the neutron flux, or equivalent, than to determine the neutron dose in rads, as provided in paragraph (a)(7)(iii) of this Section, 1 rem of neutron radiation may, for purposes of the provisions in this Section be assumed to be equivalent to 14 million neutrons per square centimeter incident upon the body; or, if there is sufficient information to estimate with reasonable accuracy the approximate distribution in energy of the neutrons, the incident number of neutrons per square centimeter equivalent to 1 rem may be estimated from Table G–17:

Table G–17
Neutron Flux Dose Equivalents

Neutron energy (million electron volts (Mev))	Number of neutrons per square centimeter equivalent to a dose of 1 rem (neutrons/cm²)	Average flux to deliver 100 millirem in 40 hours (neutrons/cm² per sec.)
Thermal	970×10^6	670
0.0001	720×10^6	500
0.005	820×10^6	570
0.02	400×10^6	280
0.1	120×10^6	80
0.5	43×10^6	30
1.0	26×10^6	18
2.5	29×10^6	20
5.0	26×10^6	18
7.5	24×10^6	17
10	24×10^6	17
10 to 30	14×10^6	10

(a)(8) For determining exposures to X- or gamma rays up to 3 Mev., the dose limits specified in this Section may be assumed to be equivalent to the "air dose". For the purpose of this Section air dose means that the dose is measured by a properly calibrated appropriate instrument in air at or near the body surface in the region of the highest dosage rate.

(b) **Exposure of individuals to radiation in restricted areas**

(b)(1) Except as provided in paragraph (b)(2) of this Section, no employer shall possess, use, or transfer sources of ionizing radiation in such a manner as to cause any individual in a restricted area to receive in any period of one calendar quarter from sources in the employer's possession or control a dose in excess of the limits specified in Table G–18:

Table G–18

	Rems per calendar quarter
Whole body: Head and trunk; active blood-forming organs; lens of eyes; or gonads	1 ¼
Hands and forearms; feet and ankles	18 ¾
Skin of whole body	7 ½

(b)(2) An employer may permit an individual in a restricted area to receive doses to the whole body greater than those permitted under subparagraph (1) of this paragraph, so long as:

(b)(2)(i) During any calendar quarter the dose to the whole body shall not exceed 3 rems; and

(b)(2)(ii) The dose to the whole body, when added to the accumulated occupational dose to the whole body, shall not exceed 5 (N–18) rems, where "N" equals the individual's age in years at his last birthday; and

(b)(2)(iii) The employer maintains adequate past and current exposure records which show that the addition of such a dose will not cause the individual to exceed the amount authorized in this subparagraph. As used in this subparagraph Dose to the whole body shall be deemed to include any dose to the whole body, gonad, active bloodforming organs, head and trunk, or lens of the eye.

(b)(3) No employer shall permit any employee who is under 18 years of age to receive in any period of one calendar quarter a dose in excess of 10 percent of the limits specified in Table G–18.

(b)(4) Calendar quarter means any 3-month period determined as follows:

(b)(4)(i) The first period of any year may begin on any date in January: Provided, That the second, third, and fourth periods accordingly begin on the same date in April, July, and October, respectively, and that the fourth period extends into January of the succeeding year, if necessary to complete a 3-month quarter. During the first year of use of this method of determination, the first period for that year shall also include any additional days in January preceding the starting date for the first period; or

(b)(4)(ii) The first period in a calendar year of 13 complete, consecutive calendar weeks; the second period in a calendar year of 13 complete, consecutive weeks; the third period in a calendar year of 13 complete, consecutive calendar weeks; the fourth period in a calendar year of 13 complete, consecutive calendar weeks. If at the end of a calendar year there are any days not falling within a complete calendar week of that year, such days shall be included within the last complete calendar week of that year. If at the beginning of any calendar year there are days not falling within a complete calendar week of that year, such days shall be included within the last complete calendar week of the previous year; or

(b)(4)(iii) The four periods in a calendar year may consist of the first 14 complete, consecutive calendar weeks; the next 12 complete, consecutive calendar weeks, the next 14 complete, consecutive calendar weeks, and the last 12 complete, consecutive calendar weeks. If at the end of a calendar year there are any days not falling within a complete calendar week of that year, such days shall be included (for purposes of this Section) within the last complete calendar week of the year. If at the beginning of any calendar year there are days not falling within a complete calendar week of that year, such days shall be included (for purposes of this Section) within the last complete week of the previous year.

(c) **Exposure to airborne radioactive material**

(c)(1) No employer shall possess, use or transport radioactive material in such a manner as to cause any employee, within a restricted area, to be exposed to airborne radioactive material in an average concentration in excess of the limits specified in Table 1 of Appendix B to 10 CFR Part §20. The limits given in Table 1 are for exposure to the concentrations specified for 40 hours in any workweek of 7 consecutive days. In any such period where the number of hours of exposure is less than 40, the limits specified in the table may be increased proportionately. In any such period where the number of hours of exposure is greater than 40, the limits specified in the table shall be decreased proportionately.

(c)(2) No employer shall possess, use, or transfer radioactive material in such a manner as to cause any individual within a restricted area, who is under 18 years of age, to be exposed to airborne radioactive material in an average concentration in excess of the limits specified in Table II of Appendix B to 10 CFR Part §20. For purposes of this paragraph, concentrations may be averaged over periods not greater than 1 week.

(c)(3) Exposed as used in this paragraph means that the individual is present in an airborne concentration. No allowance shall be made for the use of protective clothing or equipment, or particle size.

(d) Precautionary procedures and personal monitoring

(d)(1) Every employer shall make such surveys as may be necessary for him to comply with the provisions in this Section. Survey means an evaluation of the radiation hazards incident to the production, use, release, disposal, or presence of radioactive materials or other sources of radiation under a specific set of conditions. When appropriate, such evaluation includes a physical survey of the location of materials and equipment, and measurements of levels of radiation or concentrations of radioactive material present.

(d)(2) Every employer shall supply appropriate personnel monitoring equipment, such as film badges, pocket chambers, pocket dosimeters, or film rings, and shall require the use of such equipment by:

(d)(2)(i) Each employee who enters a restricted area under such circumstances that he receives, or is likely to receive, a dose in any calendar quarter in excess of 25 percent of the applicable value specified in paragraph (b)(1) of this Section; and

(d)(2)(ii) Each employee under 18 years of age who enters a restricted area under such circumstances that he receives, or is likely to receive, a dose in any calendar quarter in excess of 5 percent of the applicable value specified in paragraph (b)(1) of this Section; and

(d)(2)(iii) Each employee who enters a high radiation area.

(d)(3) As used in this Section

(d)(3)(i) **Personnel monitoring equipment** means devices designed to be worn or carried by an individual for the purpose of measuring the dose received (e.g., film badges, pocket chambers, pocket dosimeters, film rings, etc.);

(d)(3)(ii) **Radiation area** means any area, accessible to personnel, in which there exists radiation at such levels that a major portion of the body could receive in any 1 hour a dose in excess of 5 millirem, or in any 5 consecutive days a dose in excess of 100 millirem; and

(d)(3)(iii) **High radiation area** means any area, accessible to personnel, in which there exists radiation at such levels that a major portion of the body could receive in any one hour a dose in excess of 100 millirem.

(e) Caution signs, labels, and signals

(e)(1) General

(e)(1)(i) Symbols prescribed by this paragraph shall use the conventional radiation caution colors (magenta or purple on yellow background). The symbol prescribed by this paragraph is the conventional three-bladed design:

Figure G–10
RADIATION SYMBOL

1. Cross–hatched area is to be magenta or purple.
2. Background is to be yellow.

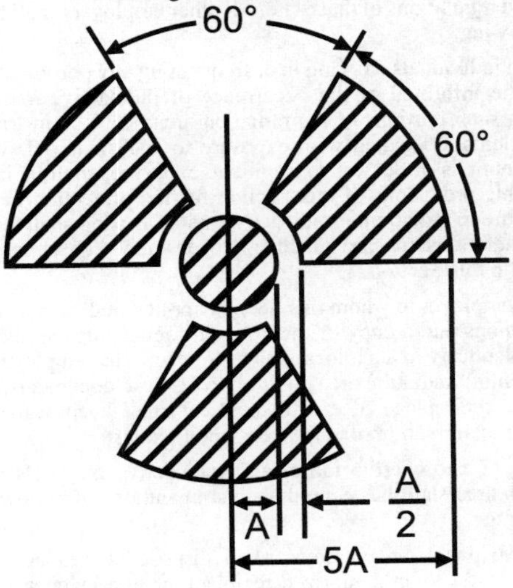

(e)(1)(ii) [Reserved]

(e)(2) **Radiation area** Each radiation area shall be conspicuously posted with a sign or signs bearing the radiation caution symbol described in subparagraph (1) of this paragraph and the words:

CAUTION
RADIATION AREA

(e)(3) High radiation area

(e)(3)(i) Each high radiation area shall be conspicuously posted with a sign or signs bearing the radiation caution symbol and the words:

CAUTION
HIGH RADIATION AREA

(e)(3)(ii) Each high radiation area shall be equipped with a control device which shall either cause the level of radiation to be reduced below that at which an individual might receive a dose of 100 millirems in 1 hour upon entry into the area or shall energize a conspicuous visible or audible alarm signal in such a manner that the individual entering and the employer or a supervisor of the activity are made aware of the entry. In the case of a high radiation area established for a period of 30 days or less, such control device is not required.

(e)(4) Airborne radioactivity area

(e)(4)(i) As used in the provisions of this Section, airborne radioactivity area means:

(e)(4)(i)(A) Any room, enclosure, or operating area in which airborne radioactive materials, composed wholly or partly of radioactive material, exist in concentrations in excess of the amounts specified in column 1 of Table 1 of Appendix B to 10 CFR Part §20 or

(e)(4)(i)(B) Any room, enclosure, or operating area in which airborne radioactive materials exist in concentrations which, averaged over the number of hours in any week during which individuals are in the area, exceed 25 percent of the amounts specified in column 1 of Table 1 of Appendix B to 10 CFR Part §20.

(e)(4)(ii) Each airborne radioactivity area shall be conspicuously posted with a sign or signs bearing the radiation caution symbol described in paragraph (e)(1) of this Section and the words:

CAUTION
AIRBORNE RADIOACTIVITY AREA

(e)(5) Additional requirements

(e)(5)(i) Each area or room in which radioactive material is used or stored and which contains any radioactive material (other than natural uranium or thorium) in any amount exceeding 10 times the quantity of such material specified in Appendix C to 10 CFR Part §20 shall be conspicuously posted with a sign or signs bearing the radiation caution symbol described in paragraph (e)(1) of this Section and the words:

CAUTION
RADIOACTIVE MATERIALS

(e)(5)(ii) Each area or room in which natural uranium or thorium is used or stored in an amount exceeding 100 times the quantity of such material specified in 10 CFR Part §20 shall be conspicuously posted with a sign or signs bearing the radiation caution symbol described in paragraph (e)(1) of this Section and the words:

CAUTION
RADIOACTIVE MATERIALS

(e)(6) Containers

(e)(6)(i) Each container in which is transported, stored, or used a quantity of any radioactive material (other than natural uranium or thorium) greater than the quantity of such material specified in Appendix C to 10 CFR Part §20 shall bear a durable, clearly visible label bearing the radiation caution symbol described in paragraph (e)(1) of this Section and the words:

CAUTION
RADIOACTIVE MATERIALS

(e)(6)(ii) Each container in which natural uranium or thorium is transported, stored, or used in a quantity greater than 10 times the quantity specified in Appendix C to 10 CFR Part §20 shall bear a durable, clearly visible label bearing the radiation caution symbol described in paragraph (e)(1) of this Section and the words:

CAUTION
RADIOACTIVE MATERIALS

(e)(6)(iii) Notwithstanding the provisions of paragraphs (e)(6)(i) and (ii) of this Section a label shall not be required:

(e)(6)(iii)(A) If the concentration of the material in the container does not exceed that specified in column 2 of Table 1 of Appendix B to 10 CFR Part §20, or

(e)(6)(iii)(B) For laboratory containers, such as beakers, flasks, and test tubes, used transiently in laboratory procedures, when the user is present.

(e)(6)(iv) Where containers are used for storage, the labels required in this subparagraph shall state also the quantities and kinds of radioactive materials in the containers and the date of measurement of the quantities.

(f) Immediate evacuation warning signal

(f)(1) Signal characteristics

(f)(1)(i) The signal shall be a midfrequency complex sound wave amplitude modulated at a subsonic frequency. The complex sound wave in free space shall have a fundamental frequency (f1) between 450 and 500 hertz (Hz) modulated at a subsonic rate between 4 and 5 hertz.

(f)(1)(ii) The signal generator shall not be less than 75 decibels at every location where an individual may be present whose immediate, rapid, and complete evacuation is essential.

(f)(1)(iii) A sufficient number of signal units shall be installed such that the requirements of paragraph (f)(1)(ii) of this Section are met at every location where an individual may be present whose immediate, rapid, and complete evacuation is essential.

(f)(1)(iv) The signal shall be unique in the plant or facility in which it is installed.

(f)(1)(v) The minimum duration of the signal shall be sufficient to insure that all affected persons hear the signal.

(f)(1)(vi) The signal-generating system shall respond automatically to an initiating event without requiring any human action to sound the signal.

(f)(2) Design objectives

(f)(2)(i) The signal-generating system shall be designed to incorporate components which enable the system to produce the desired signal each time it is activated within one-half second of activation.

(f)(2)(ii) The signal-generating system shall be provided with an automatically activated secondary power supply which is adequate to simultaneously power all emergency equipment to which it is connected, if operation during power failure is necessary, except in those systems using batteries as the primary source of power.

(f)(2)(iii) All components of the signal-generating system shall be located to provide maximum practicable protection against damage in case of fire, explosion, corrosive atmosphere, or other environmental extremes consistent with adequate system performance.

(f)(2)(iv) The signal-generating system shall be designed with the minimum number of components necessary to make it function as intended, and should utilize components which do not require frequent servicing such as lubrication or cleaning.

(f)(2)(v) Where several activating devices feed activating information to a central signal generator, failure of any activating device shall not render the signal-generator system inoperable to activating information from the remaining devices.

(f)(2)(vi) The signal-generating system shall be designed to enhance the probability that alarm occurs only when immediate evacuation is warranted. The number of false alarms shall not be so great that the signal will come to be disregarded and shall be low enough to minimize personal injuries or excessive property damage that might result from such evacuation.

(f)(3) Testing

(f)(3)(i) Initial tests, inspections, and checks of the signal-generating system shall be made to verify that the fabrication and installation were made in accordance with design plans and specifications and to develop a thorough knowledge of the performance of the system and all components under normal and hostile conditions.

(f)(3)(ii) Once the system has been placed in service, periodic tests, inspections, and checks shall be made to minimize the possibility of malfunction.

(f)(3)(iii) Following significant alterations or revisions to the system, tests and checks similar to the initial installation tests shall be made.

(f)(3)(iv) Tests shall be designed to minimize hazards while conducting the tests.

(f)(3)(v) Prior to normal operation the signal-generating system shall be checked physically and functionally to assure reliability and to demonstrate accuracy and performance. Specific tests shall include:

(f)(3)(v)(A) All power sources;

(f)(3)(v)(B) Calibration and calibration stability;

(f)(3)(v)(C) Trip levels and stability;

(f)(3)(v)(D) Continuity of function with loss and return of required services such as AC or DC power, air pressure, etc;

(f)(3)(v)(E) All indicators;

(f)(3)(v)(F) Trouble indicator circuits and signals, where used;

(f)(3)(v)(G) Air pressure (if used;

(f)(3)(v)(H) Determine that sound level of the signal is within the limit of paragraph (f)(1)(ii) of this Section at all points that require immediate evacuation.

(f)(3)(vi) In addition to the initial startup and operating tests, periodic scheduled performance tests and status checks must be made to insure that the system is at all times operating within design limits and capable of the required response. Specific periodic tests or checks or both shall include:

(f)(3)(vi)(A) Adequacy of signal activation device;

(f)(3)(vi)(B) All power sources;

(f)(3)(vi)(C) Function of all alarm circuits and trouble indicator circuits including trip levels;

(f)(3)(vi)(D) Air pressure (if used);

(f)(3)(vi)(E) Function of entire system including operation without power where required;

(f)(3)(vi)(F) Complete operational tests including sounding of the signal and determination that sound levels are adequate.

(f)(3)(vii) Periodic tests shall be scheduled on the basis of need, experience, difficulty, and disruption of operations. The entire system should be operationally tested at least quarterly.

(f)(3)(viii) All employees whose work may necessitate their presence in an area covered by the signal shall be made familiar with the actual sound of the signal—preferably as it sounds at their work location. Before placing the system into operation, all employees normally working in the area shall be made acquainted with the signal by actual demonstration at their work locations.

(g) Exceptions from posting requirements Notwithstanding the provisions of paragraph (e) of this Section:

(g)(1) A room or area is not required to be posted with a caution sign because of the presence of a sealed source, provided the radiation level 12 inches from the surface of the source container or housing does not exceed 5 millirem per hour.

(g)(2) Rooms or other areas in onsite medical facilities are not required to be posted with caution signs because of the presence of patients containing radioactive material, provided that there are personnel in attendance who shall take the precautions necessary to prevent the exposure of any individual to radiation or radioactive material in excess of the limits established in the provisions of this Section.

(g)(3) Caution signs are not required to be posted at areas or rooms containing radioactive materials for periods of less than 8 hours: Provided, that:

(g)(3)(i) The materials are constantly attended during such periods by an individual who shall take the precautions necessary to prevent the exposure of any individual to radiation or radioactive materials in excess of the limits established in the provisions of this Section; and

(g)(3)(ii) Such area or room is subject to the employer's control.

(h) Exemptions for radioactive materials packaged for shipment. Radioactive materials packaged and labeled in accordance with regulations of the Department of Transportation published in 49 CFR Chapter I, are exempt from the labeling and posting requirements of this Subpart during shipment, provided that the inside containers are labeled in accordance with the provisions of paragraph (e) of this Section.

(i) Instruction of personnel, posting

(i)(1) Employers regulated by the Nuclear Regulatory Commission shall be governed by 10 CFR Part §20 standards. Employers in a State named in paragraph (p)(3) of this Section shall be governed by the requirements of the laws and regulations of that State. All other employers shall be regulated by the following:

(i)(2) ⁰₁ All individuals working in or frequenting any portion of a radiation area shall be informed of the occurrence of radioactive materials or of radiation in such portions of the radiation area; shall be instructed in the safety problems associated with exposure to such materials or radiation and in precautions or devices to minimize exposure; shall be instructed in the applicable provisions of this Section for the protection of employees from exposure to radiation or radioactive materials; and shall be advised of reports of radiation exposure which employees may request pursuant to the regulations in this Section.

(i)(3) Each employer to whom this Section applies shall post a current copy of its provisions and a copy of the operating procedures applicable to the work conspicuously in such locations as to insure that employees working in or frequenting radiation areas will observe these documents on the way to and from their place of employment, or shall keep such documents available for examination of employees upon request.

(j) Storage of radioactive materials Radioactive materials stored in a nonradiation area shall be secured against unauthorized removal from the place of storage.

(k) Waste disposal No employer shall dispose of radioactive material except by transfer to an authorized recipient, or in a manner approved by the Nuclear Regulatory Commission or a State named in paragraph (p)(3) of this Section.

(l) Notification of incidents

(l)(1) Immediate notification Each employer shall immediately notify the Assistant Secretary of Labor or his duly authorized representative, for employees not protected by the Nuclear Regulatory Commission by means of 10 CFR Part §20; paragraph (p)(2) of this Section, or the requirements of the laws and regulations of States named in paragraph (p)(3) of this Section, by telephone or telegraph of any incident involving radiation which may have caused or threatens to cause:

(l)(1)(i) Exposure of the whole body of any individual to 25 rems or more of radiation; exposure of the skin of the whole body of any individual to

150 rems or more of radiation; or exposure of the feet, ankles, hands, or forearms of any individual to 375 rems or more of radiation; or

(l)(1)(ii) The release of radioactive material in concentrations which, if averaged over a period of 24 hours, would exceed 5,000 times the limit specified for such materials in Table II of Appendix B to 10 CFR Part §20.

(l)(2) **Twenty-four hour notification** Each employer shall within 24 hours following its occurrence notify the Assistant Secretary of Labor or his duly authorized representative for employees not protected by the Nuclear Regulatory Commission by means of 10 CFR Part §20; paragraph (p)(2) of this Section, or the requirements of the laws and applicable regulations of States named in paragraph (p)(3) of this Section, by telephone or telegraph of any incident involving radiation which may have caused or threatens to cause:

(l)(2)(i) Exposure of the whole body of any individual to 5 rems or more of radiation; exposure of the skin of the whole body of any individual to 30 rems or more of radiation; or exposure of the feet, ankles, hands, or forearms to 75 rems or more of radiation; or

(l)(2)(ii) [Reserved]

(m) **Reports of overexposure and excessive levels and concentrations**

(m)(1) In addition to any notification required by paragraph (1) of this Section each employer shall make a report in writing within 30 days to the Assistant Secretary of Labor or his duly authorized representative, for employees not protected by the Nuclear Regulatory Commission by means of 10 CFR Part §20; or under paragraph (p)(2) of this Section, or the requirements of the laws and regulations of States named in paragraph (p)(3) of this Section, of each exposure of an individual to radiation or concentrations of radioactive material in excess of any applicable limit in this Section. Each report required under this paragraph shall describe the extent of exposure of persons to radiation or to radioactive material; levels of radiation and concentration of radioactive material involved, the cause of the exposure, levels of concentrations; and corrective steps taken or planned to assure against a recurrence.

(m)(2) In any case where an employer is required pursuant to the provisions of this paragraph to report to the U.S. Department of Labor any exposure of an individual to radiation or to concentrations of radioactive material, the employer shall also notify such individual of the nature and extent of exposure. Such notice shall be in writing and shall contain the following statement: "You should preserve this report for future reference."

(n) **Records**

(n)(1) Every employer shall maintain records of the radiation exposure of all employees for whom personnel monitoring is required under paragraph (d) of this Section and advise each of his employees of his individual exposure on at least an annual basis.

(n)(2) Every employer shall maintain records in the same units used in tables in paragraph (b) of this Section and Appendix B to 10 CFR Part §20.

(o) **Disclosure to former employee of individual employee's record**

(o)(1) At the request of a former employee an employer shall furnish to the employee a report of the employee's exposure to radiation as shown in records maintained by the employer pursuant to paragraph (n)(1) of this Section. Such report shall be furnished within 30 days from the time the request is made, and shall cover each calendar quarter of the individual's employment involving exposure to radiation or such lesser period as may be requested by the employee. The report shall also include the results of any calculations and analysis of radioactive material deposited in the body of the employee. The report shall be in writing and contain the following statement: "You should preserve this report for future reference."

(o)(2) [Reserved]

(p) **Nuclear Regulatory Commission licensees—NRC contractors operating NRC plants and facilities—NRC Agreement State licensees or registrants**

(p)(1) Any employer who possesses or uses source material, byproduct material, or special nuclear material, as defined in the Atomic Energy Act of 1954, as amended, under a license issued by the Nuclear Regulatory Commission and in accordance with the requirements of 10 CFR Part §20 shall be deemed to be in compliance with the requirements of this Section with respect to such possession and use.

(p)(2) NRC contractors operating NRC plants and facilities: Any employer who possesses or uses source material, byproduct material, special nuclear material, or other radiation sources under a contract with the Nuclear Regulatory Commission for the operation of NRC plants and facilities and in accordance with the standards, procedures, and other requirements for radiation protection established by the Commission for such contract pursuant to the Atomic Energy Act of 1954 as amended (42 U.S.C. 2011 et seq.), shall be deemed to be in compliance with the requirements of this Section with respect to such possession and use.

(p)(3) **NRC-agreement State licensees or registrants:**

(p)(3)(i) **Atomic Energy Act sources** Any employer who possesses or uses source material, byproduct material, or special nuclear material, as defined in the Atomic Energy Act of 1954, as amended (42 U.S.C. 2011 et seq.), and has either registered such sources with, or is operating under a license issued by, a State which has an agreement in effect with the Nuclear Regulatory Commission pursuant to Section 274(b) (42 U.S.C. 2021(b)) of the Atomic Energy Act of 1954, as amended, and in accordance with the requirements of that State's laws and regulations shall be deemed to be in compliance with the radiation requirements of this Section, insofar as his possession and use of such material is concerned, unless the Secretary of Labor, after conference with the Nuclear Regulatory Commission, shall determine that the State's program for control of these radiation sources is incompatible with the requirements of this Section. Such agreements currently are in effect only in the States of Alabama, Arkansas, California, Kansas, Kentucky, Florida, Mississippi, New Hampshire, New York, North Carolina, Texas, Tennessee, Oregon, Idaho, Arizona, Colorado, Louisiana, Nebraska, Washington, Maryland, North Dakota, South Carolina, and Georgia.

(p)(3)(ii) **Other sources** Any employer who possesses or uses radiation sources other than source material, byproduct material, or special nuclear material, as defined in the Atomic Energy Act of 1954, as amended (42 U.S.C. 2011 et seq.), and has either registered such sources with, or is operating under a license issued by a State which has an agreement in effect with the Nuclear Regulatory Commission pursuant to Section 274(b) (42 U.S.C. 2021(b)) of the Atomic Energy Act of 1954, as amended, and in accordance with the requirements of that State's laws and regulations shall be deemed to be in compliance with the radiation requirements of this Section, insofar as his possession and use of such material is concerned, provided the State's program for control of these radiation sources is the subject of a currently effective determination by the Assistant Secretary of Labor that such program is compatible with the requirements of this Section. Such determinations currently are in effect only in the States of Alabama, Arkansas, California, Kansas, Kentucky, Florida, Mississippi, New Hampshire, New York, North Carolina, Texas, Tennessee, Oregon, Idaho, Arizona, Colorado, Louisiana, Nebraska, Washington, Maryland, North Dakota, South Carolina, and Georgia.

[39 FR 23502, June 27, 1974, as amended at 43 FR 49746, Oct. 24, 1978; 43 FR 51759, Nov. 7, 1978; 49 FR 18295, Apr. 30, 1984; 58 FR 35309, June 30, 1993. Redesignated at 61 FR 31430, June 20, 1996]

§1910.1200 Hazard communication

(a) **Purpose**

(a)(1) The purpose of this Section is to ensure that the hazards of all chemicals produced or imported are classified, and that information concerning the classified hazards is transmitted to employers and employees. The requirements of this Section are intended to be consistent with the provisions of the United Nations Globally Harmonized System of Classification and Labeling of Chemicals (GHS), Revision 3. The transmittal of information is to be accomplished by means of comprehensive hazard communication programs, which are to include container labeling and other forms of warning, safety data sheets and employee training.

(a)(2) This occupational safety and health standard is intended to address comprehensively the issue of classifying the potential hazards of chemicals, and communicating information concerning hazards and appropriate protective measures to employees, and to preempt any legislative or regulatory enactments of a state, or political subdivision of a state, pertaining to this subject. Classifying the potential hazards of chemicals and communicating information concerning hazards and appropriate protective measures to employees, may include, for example, but is not limited to, provisions for: developing and maintaining a written hazard communication program for the workplace, including lists of hazardous chemicals present; labeling of containers of chemicals in the workplace, as well as of containers of chemicals being shipped to other workplaces; preparation and distribution of safety data sheets to employees and downstream employers; and development and implementation of employee training programs regarding hazards of chemicals and protective measures. Under Section 18 of the Act, no state or political subdivision of a state may adopt or enforce any requirement relating to the issue addressed by this Federal Standard, except pursuant to a Federally-approved state plan.

(b) **Scope and application**

(b)(1) This Section requires chemical manufacturers or importers to classify the hazards of chemicals which they produce or import, and all employers to provide information to their employees about the hazardous chemicals to which they are exposed, by means of a hazard communication program, labels and other forms of warning, safety data sheets, and information and training. In addition, this Section requires distributors to transmit the required information to employers. (Employers who do not produce or import chemicals need only focus on those parts of this rule that deal with establishing a workplace program and communicating information to their workers.)

(b)(2) This Section applies to any chemical which is known to be present in the workplace in such a manner that employees may be exposed under normal conditions of use or in a foreseeable emergency.

(b)(3) This Section applies to laboratories only as follows:

(b)(3)(i) Employers shall ensure that labels on incoming containers of hazardous chemicals are not removed or defaced;

(b)(3)(ii) Employers shall maintain any safety data sheets that are received with incoming shipments of hazardous chemicals, and ensure that they are readily accessible during each workshift to laboratory employees when they are in their work areas;

(b)(3)(iii) Employers shall ensure that laboratory employees are provided information and training in accordance with paragraph (h) of this Section, except for the location and availability of the written hazard communication program under paragraph (h)(2)(iii) of this Section; and,

(b)(3)(iv) Laboratory employers that ship hazardous chemicals are considered to be either a chemical manufacturer or a distributor under this rule, and thus must ensure that any containers of hazardous chemicals leaving the laboratory are labeled in accordance with paragraph (f) of this Section, and that a safety data sheet is provided to distributors and other employers in accordance with paragraphs (g)(6) and (g)(7) of this Section.

(b)(4) In work operations where employees only handle chemicals in sealed containers which are not opened under normal conditions of use (such as are found in marine cargo handling, warehousing, or retail sales), this Section applies to these operations only as follows:

(b)(4)(i) Employers shall ensure that labels on incoming containers of hazardous chemicals are not removed or defaced;

(b)(4)(ii) Employers shall maintain copies of any safety data sheets that are received with incoming shipments of the sealed containers of hazardous chemicals, shall obtain a safety data sheet as soon as possible for sealed containers of hazardous chemicals received without a safety data sheet if an employee requests the safety data sheet, and shall ensure that the safety data sheets are readily accessible during each work shift to employees when they are in their work area(s); and

(b)(4)(iii) Employers shall ensure that employees are provided with information and training in accordance with paragraph (h) of this Section (except for the location and availability of the written hazard communication program under paragraph (h)(2)(iii) of this Section), to the extent necessary to protect them in the event of a spill or leak of a hazardous chemical from a sealed container.

(b)(5) This Section does not require labeling of the following chemicals:

(b)(5)(i) Any pesticide as such term is defined in the Federal Insecticide, Fungicide, and Rodenticide Act (7 U.S.C. 136 et seq.), when subject to the labeling requirements of that Act and labeling regulations issued under that Act by the Environmental Protection Agency;

(b)(5)(ii) Any chemical substance or mixture as such terms are defined in the Toxic Substances Control Act (15 U.S.C. 2601 et seq.), when subject to the labeling requirements of that Act and labeling regulations issued under that Act by the Environmental Protection Agency;

(b)(5)(iii) Any food, food additive, color additive, drug, cosmetic, or medical or veterinary device or product, including materials intended for use as ingredients in such products (e.g. flavors and fragrances), as such terms are defined in the Federal Food, Drug, and Cosmetic Act (21 U.S.C. 301 et seq.) or the Virus-Serum-Toxin Act of 1913 (21 U.S.C. 151 et seq.), and regulations issued under those Acts, when they are subject to the labeling requirements under those Acts by either the Food and Drug Administration or the Department of Agriculture;

(b)(5)(iv) Any distilled spirits (beverage alcohols), wine, or malt beverage intended for nonindustrial use, as such terms are defined in the Federal Alcohol Administration Act (27 U.S.C. 201 et seq.) and regulations issued under that Act, when subject to the labeling requirements of that Act and labeling regulations issued under that Act by the Bureau of Alcohol, Tobacco, Firearms and Explosives;

(b)(5)(v) Any consumer product or hazardous substance as those terms are defined in the Consumer Product Safety Act (15 U.S.C. 2051 et seq.) and Federal Hazardous Substances Act (15 U.S.C. 1261 et seq.) respectively, when subject to a consumer product safety standard or labeling requirement of those Acts, or regulations issued under those Acts by the Consumer Product Safety Commission; and

(b)(5)(vi) Agricultural or vegetable seed treated with pesticides and labeled in accordance with the Federal Seed Act (7 U.S.C. 1551 et seq.) and the labeling regulations issued under that Act by the Department of Agriculture.

(b)(6) This Section does not apply to:

(b)(6)(i) Any hazardous waste as such term is defined by the Solid Waste Disposal Act, as amended by the Resource Conservation and Recovery Act of 1976, as amended (42 U.S.C. 6901 et seq.), when subject to regulations issued under that Act by the Environmental Protection Agency;

(b)(6)(ii) Any hazardous substance as such term is defined by the Comprehensive Environmental Response, Compensation and Liability Act (CERCLA) (42 U.S.C. 9601 et seq.) when the hazardous substance is the focus of remedial or removal action being conducted under CERCLA in accordance with Environmental Protection Agency regulations;

(b)(6)(iii) Tobacco or tobacco products;

(b)(6)(iv) Wood or wood products, including lumber which will not be processed, where the chemical manufacturer or importer can establish that the only hazard they pose to employees is the potential for flammability or combustibility (wood or wood products which have been treated with a hazardous chemical covered by this Standard, and wood which may be subsequently sawed or cut, generating dust, are not exempted);

(b)(6)(v) Articles (as that term is defined in paragraph (c) of this Section);

(b)(6)(vi) Food or alcoholic beverages which are sold, used, or prepared in a retail establishment (such as a grocery store, restaurant, or drinking place), and foods intended for personal consumption by employees while in the workplace;

(b)(6)(vii) Any drug, as that term is defined in the Federal Food, Drug, and Cosmetic Act (21 U.S.C. 301 et seq.), when it is in solid, final form for direct administration to the patient (e.g., tablets or pills); drugs which are packaged by the chemical manufacturer for sale to consumers in a retail establishment (e.g., over-the-counter drugs); and drugs intended for personal consumption by employees while in the workplace (e.g., first aid supplies);

(b)(6)(viii) Cosmetics which are packaged for sale to consumers in a retail establishment, and cosmetics intended for personal consumption by employees while in the workplace;

(b)(6)(ix) Any consumer product or hazardous substance, as those terms are defined in the Consumer Product Safety Act (15 U.S.C. 2051 et seq.) and Federal Hazardous Substances Act (15 U.S.C. 1261 et seq.) respectively, where the employer can show that it is used in the workplace for the purpose intended by the chemical manufacturer or importer of the product, and the use results in a duration and frequency of exposure which is not greater than the range of exposures that could reasonably be experienced by consumers when used for the purpose intended;

(b)(6)(x) Nuisance particulates where the chemical manufacturer or importer can establish that they do not pose any physical or health hazard covered under this Section;

(b)(6)(xi) Ionizing and nonionizing radiation; and,

(b)(6)(xii) Biological hazards.

(c) Definitions

Article means a manufactured item other than a fluid or particle: (i) which is formed to a specific shape or design during manufacture; (ii) which has end use function(s) dependent in whole or in part upon its shape or design during end use; and (iii) which under normal conditions of use does not release more than very small quantities, e.g., minute or trace amounts of a hazardous chemical (as determined under paragraph (d) of this Section), and does not pose a physical hazard or health risk to employees.

Assistant Secretary means the Assistant Secretary of Labor for Occupational Safety and Health, U.S. Department of Labor, or designee.

Chemical means any substance, or mixture of substances.

Chemical manufacturer means an employer with a workplace where chemical(s) are produced for use or distribution.

Chemical name means the scientific designation of a chemical in accordance with the nomenclature system developed by the International Union of Pure and Applied Chemistry (IUPAC) or the Chemical Abstracts Service (CAS) rules of nomenclature, or a name that will clearly identify the chemical for the purpose of conducting a hazard classification.

Classification means to identify the relevant data regarding the hazards of a chemical; review those data to ascertain the hazards associated with the chemical; and decide whether the chemical will be classified as hazardous according to the definition of hazardous chemical in this Section. In addition, classification for health and physical hazards includes the determination of the degree of hazard, where appropriate, by comparing the data with the criteria for health and physical hazards.

Commercial account means an arrangement whereby a retail distributor sells hazardous chemicals to an employer, generally in large quantities over time and/or at costs that are below the regular retail price.

Common name means any designation or identification such as code name, code number, trade name, brand name or generic name used to identify a chemical other than by its chemical name.

Container means any bag, barrel, bottle, box, can, cylinder, drum, reaction vessel, storage tank, or the like that contains a hazardous chemical. For purposes of this Section, pipes or piping systems, and engines, fuel tanks, or other operating systems in a vehicle, are not considered to be containers.

Designated representative means any individual or organization to whom an employee gives written authorization to exercise such employee's rights under this Section. A recognized or certified collective bargaining agent shall be treated automatically as a designated representative without regard to written employee authorization.

Director means the Director, National Institute for Occupational Safety and Health, U.S. Department of Health and Human Services, or designee.

Distributor means a business, other than a chemical manufacturer or importer, which supplies hazardous chemicals to other distributors or to employers.

Employee means a worker who may be exposed to hazardous chemicals under normal operating conditions or in foreseeable emergencies. Workers such as office workers or bank tellers who encounter hazardous chemicals only in non-routine, isolated instances are not covered.

Employer means a person engaged in a business where chemicals are either used, distributed, or are produced for use or distribution, including a contractor or subcontractor.

Exposure or exposed means that an employee is subjected in the course of employment to a chemical that is a physical or health hazard, and includes potential (e.g. accidental or possible) exposure. "Subjected" in terms of health hazards includes any route of entry (e.g. inhalation, ingestion, skin contact or absorption.)

Foreseeable emergency means any potential occurrence such as, but not limited to, equipment failure, rupture of containers, or failure of control equipment which could result in an uncontrolled release of a hazardous chemical into the workplace.

Hazard category means the division of criteria within each hazard class, e.g., oral acute toxicity and flammable liquids include four hazard categories. These categories compare hazard severity within a hazard class and should not be taken as a comparison of hazard categories more generally.

Hazard class means the nature of the physical or health hazards, e.g., flammable solid, carcinogen, oral acute toxicity.

Hazard not otherwise classified (HNOC) means an adverse physical or health effect identified through evaluation of scientific evidence during the classification process that does not meet the specified criteria for the physical and health hazard classes addressed in this Section. This does not extend coverage to adverse physical and health effects for which there is a hazard class addressed in this Section, but the effect either falls below the cut-off value/concentration limit of the hazard class or is under a GHS hazard category that has not been adopted by OSHA (e.g., acute toxicity Category 5).

Hazard statement means a statement assigned to a hazard class and category that describes the nature of the hazard(s) of a chemical, including, where appropriate, the degree of hazard.

Hazardous chemical means any chemical which is classified as a physical hazard or a health hazard, a simple asphyxiant, combustible dust, pyrophoric gas, or hazard not otherwise classified.

Health hazard means a chemical which is classified as posing one of the following hazardous effects: acute toxicity (any route of exposure); skin corrosion or irritation; serious eye damage or eye irritation; respiratory or skin sensitization; germ cell mutagenicity; carcinogenicity; reproductive toxicity; specific target organ toxicity (single or repeated exposure); or aspiration hazard. The criteria for determining whether a chemical is classified as a health hazard are detailed in Appendix A to §1910.1200 -- Health Hazard Criteria.

Immediate use means that the hazardous chemical will be under the control of and used only by the person who transfers it from a labeled container and only within the work shift in which it is transferred.

Importer means the first business with employees within the Customs Territory of the United States which receives hazardous chemicals produced in other countries for the purpose of supplying them to distributors or employers within the United States.

Label means an appropriate group of written, printed or graphic information elements concerning a hazardous chemical that is affixed to, printed on, or attached to the immediate container of a hazardous chemical, or to the outside packaging.

Label elements means the specified pictogram, hazard statement, signal word and precautionary statement for each hazard class and category.

Mixture means a combination or a solution composed of two or more substances in which they do not react.

Physical hazard means a chemical that is classified as posing one of the following hazardous effects: explosive; flammable (gases, aerosols, liquids, or solids); oxidizer (liquid, solid or gas); self-reactive; pyrophoric (liquid or solid); self-heating; organic peroxide; corrosive to metal; gas under pressure; or in contact with water emits flammable gas. See Appendix B to §1910.1200—Physical Hazard Criteria.

Pictogram means a composition that may include a symbol plus other graphic elements, such as a border, background pattern, or color, that is intended to convey specific information about the hazards of a chemical. Eight pictograms are designated under this Standard for application to a hazard category.

Precautionary statement means a phrase that describes recommended measures that should be taken to minimize or prevent adverse effects resulting from exposure to a hazardous chemical, or improper storage or handling.

Product identifier means the name or number used for a hazardous chemical on a label or in the SDS. It provides a unique means by which the user can identify the chemical. The product identifier used shall permit cross-references to be made among the list of hazardous chemicals required in the written hazard communication program, the label and the SDS.

Produce means to manufacture, process, formulate, blend, extract, generate, emit, or repackage.

Pyrophoric gas means a chemical in a gaseous state that will ignite spontaneously in air at a temperature of 130 degrees F (54.4 degrees C) or below.

Responsible party means someone who can provide additional information on the hazardous chemical and appropriate emergency procedures, if necessary.

Safety data sheet (SDS) means written or printed material concerning a hazardous chemical that is prepared in accordance with paragraph (g) of this Section.

Signal word means a word used to indicate the relative level of severity of hazard and alert the reader to a potential hazard on the label. The signal words used in this Section are "danger" and "warning." "Danger" is used for the more severe hazards, while "warning" is used for the less severe.

Simple asphyxiant means a substance or mixture that displaces oxygen in the ambient atmosphere, and can thus cause oxygen deprivation in those who are exposed, leading to unconsciousness and death.

Specific chemical identity means the chemical name, Chemical Abstracts Service (CAS) Registry Number, or any other information that reveals the precise chemical designation of the substance.

Substance means chemical elements and their compounds in the natural state or obtained by any production process, including any additive necessary to preserve the stability of the product and any impurities deriving from the process used, but excluding any solvent which may be separated without affecting the stability of the substance or changing its composition.

Trade secret means any confidential formula, pattern, process, device, information or compilation of information that is used in an employer's business, and that gives the employer an opportunity to obtain an advantage over competitors who do not know or use it. Appendix E to §1910.1200—Definition of Trade Secret, sets out the criteria to be used in evaluating trade secrets.

Use means to package, handle, react, emit, extract, generate as a byproduct, or transfer.

Work area means a room or defined space in a workplace where hazardous chemicals are produced or used, and where employees are present.

Workplace means an establishment, job site, or project, at one geographical location containing one or more work areas.

(d) Hazard classification

(d)(1) Chemical manufacturers and importers shall evaluate chemicals produced in their workplaces or imported by them to classify the chemicals in accordance with this Section. For each chemical, the chemical manufacturer or importer shall determine the hazard classes, and where appropriate, the category of each class that apply to the chemical being classified. Employers are not required to classify chemicals unless they choose not to rely on the classification performed by the chemical manufacturer or importer for the chemical to satisfy this requirement.

(d)(2) Chemical manufacturers, importers or employers classifying chemicals shall identify and consider the full range of available scientific literature and other evidence concerning the potential hazards. There is no requirement to test the chemical to determine how to classify its hazards. Appendix A to §1910.1200 shall be consulted for classification of health hazards, and Appendix B to §1910.1200 shall be consulted for the classification of physical hazards.

(d)(3) Mixtures

(d)(3)(i) Chemical manufacturers, importers, or employers evaluating chemicals shall follow the procedures described in Appendices A and B to §1910.1200 to classify the hazards of the chemicals, including determinations regarding when mixtures of the classified chemicals are covered by this Section.

(d)(3)(ii) When classifying mixtures they produce or import, chemical manufacturers and importers of mixtures may rely on the information provided on the current safety data sheets of the individual ingredients, except where the chemical manufacturer or importer knows, or in the exercise of reasonable diligence should know, that the safety data sheet misstates or omits information required by this Section.

(e) Written hazard communication program

(e)(1) Employers shall develop, implement, and maintain at each workplace, a written hazard communication program which at least describes how the criteria specified in paragraphs (f), (g), and (h) of this Section for labels and other forms of warning, safety data sheets, and employee information and training will be met, and which also includes the following:

(e)(1)(i) A list of the hazardous chemicals known to be present using a product identifier that is referenced on the appropriate safety data sheet (the list may be compiled for the workplace as a whole or for individual work areas); and,

(e)(1)(ii) The methods the employer will use to inform employees of the hazards of non-routine tasks (for example, the cleaning of reactor vessels), and the hazards associated with chemicals contained in unlabeled pipes in their work areas.

(e)(2) **"Multi-employer workplaces."** Employers who produce, use, or store hazardous chemicals at a workplace in such a way that the employees of other employer(s) may be exposed (for example, employees of a construction contractor working on-site) shall additionally ensure that the hazard communication programs developed and implemented under this paragraph (e) include the following:

(e)(2)(i) The methods the employer will use to provide the other employer(s) on-site access to safety data sheets for each hazardous chemical the other employer(s)' employees may be exposed to while working;

(e)(2)(ii) The methods the employer will use to inform the other employer(s) of any precautionary measures that need to be taken to protect employees during the workplace's normal operating conditions and in foreseeable emergencies; and,

(e)(2)(iii) The methods the employer will use to inform the other employer(s) of the labeling system used in the workplace.

(e)(3) The employer may rely on an existing hazard communication program to comply with these requirements, provided that it meets the criteria established in this paragraph (e).

(e)(4) The employer shall make the written hazard communication program available, upon request, to employees, their designated representatives, the Assistant Secretary and the Director, in accordance with the requirements of 29 CFR §1910.1020 (e).

(e)(5) Where employees must travel between workplaces during a workshift, i.e., their work is carried out at more than one geographical location, the written hazard communication program may be kept at the primary workplace facility.

(f) **Labels and other forms of warning**

(f)(1) **Labels on shipped containers** The chemical manufacturer, importer, or distributor shall ensure that each container of hazardous chemicals leaving the workplace is labeled, tagged or marked. Hazards not otherwise classified do not have to be addressed on the container. Where the chemical manufacturer or importer is required to label, tag or mark the following shall be provided:

(f)(1)(i) Product identifier;
(f)(1)(ii) Signal word;
(f)(1)(iii) Hazard statement(s);
(f)(1)(iv) Pictogram(s);
(f)(1)(v) Precautionary statement(s); and,
(f)(1)(vi) Name, address, and telephone number of the chemical manufacturer, importer, or other responsible party.

(f)(2) The chemical manufacturer, importer, or distributor shall ensure that the information provided under (f)(1)(i) through (v) is in accordance with Appendix C, Allocation of Label Elements, for each hazard class and associated hazard category for the hazardous chemical, prominently displayed, and in English (other languages may also be included if appropriate).

(f)(3) The chemical manufacturer, importer, or distributor shall ensure that the information provided under paragraphs (f)(1)(ii) through (iv) is located together on the label, tag, or mark.

(f)(4) **Solid materials**

(f)(4)(i) For solid metal (such as a steel beam or a metal casting), solid wood, or plastic items that are not exempted as articles due to their downstream use, or shipments of whole grain, the required label may be transmitted to the customer at the time of the initial shipment, and need not be included with subsequent shipments to the same employer unless the information on the label changes;

(f)(4)(ii) The label may be transmitted with the initial shipment itself, or with the safety data sheet that is to be provided prior to or at the time of the first shipment; and,

(f)(4)(iii) This exception to requiring labels on every container of hazardous chemicals is only for the solid material itself, and does not apply to hazardous chemicals used in conjunction with, or known to be present with, the material and to which employees handling the items in transit may be exposed (for example, cutting fluids or pesticides in grains).

(f)(5) Chemical manufacturers, importers, or distributors shall ensure that each container of hazardous chemicals leaving the workplace is labeled, tagged, or marked in accordance with this Section in a manner which does not conflict with the requirements of the Hazardous Materials Transportation Act (49 U.S.C. 1801 et seq.) and regulations issued under that Act by the Department of Transportation.

(f)(6) **Workplace labeling** Except as provided in paragraphs (f)(7) and (f)(8) of this Section, the employer shall ensure that each container of hazardous chemicals in the workplace is labeled, tagged or marked with either:

(f)(6)(i) The information specified under paragraphs (f)(1)(i) through (v) of this Section for labels on shipped containers; or,

(f)(6)(ii) Product identifier and words, pictures, symbols, or combination thereof, which provide at least general information regarding the hazards of the chemicals, and which, in conjunction with the other information immediately available to employees under the hazard communication program, will provide employees with the specific information regarding the physical and health hazards of the hazardous chemical.

(f)(7) The employer may use signs, placards, process sheets, batch tickets, operating procedures, or other such written materials in lieu of affixing labels to individual stationary process containers, as long as the alternative method identifies the containers to which it is applicable and conveys the information required by paragraph (f)(6) of this Section to be on a label. The employer shall ensure the written materials are readily accessible to the employees in their work area throughout each work shift.

(f)(8) The employer is not required to label portable containers into which hazardous chemicals are transferred from labeled containers, and which are intended only for the immediate use of the employee who performs the transfer. For purposes of this Section, drugs which are dispensed by a pharmacy to a health care provider for direct administration to a patient are exempted from labeling.

(f)(9) The employer shall not remove or deface existing labels on incoming containers of hazardous chemicals, unless the container is immediately marked with the required information.

(f)(10) The employer shall ensure that workplace labels or other forms of warning are legible, in English, and prominently displayed on the container, or readily available in the work area throughout each work shift. Employers having employees who speak other languages may add the information in their language to the material presented, as long as the information is presented in English as well.

(f)(11) Chemical manufacturers, importers, distributors, or employers who become newly aware of any significant information regarding the hazards of a chemical shall revise the labels for the chemical within six months of becoming aware of the new information, and shall ensure that labels on containers of hazardous chemicals shipped after that time contain the new information. If the chemical is not currently produced or imported, the chemical manufacturer, importer, distributor, or employer shall add the information to the label before the chemical is shipped or introduced into the workplace again.

(g) **Safety data sheets**

(g)(1) Chemical manufacturers and importers shall obtain or develop a safety data sheet for each hazardous chemical they produce or import. Employers shall have a safety data sheet in the workplace for each hazardous chemical which they use.

(g)(2) The chemical manufacturer or importer preparing the safety data sheet shall ensure that it is in English (although the employer may maintain copies in other languages as well), and includes at least the following Section numbers and headings, and associated information under each heading, in the order listed (See Appendix D to §1910.1200--Safety Data Sheets, for the specific content of each Section of the safety data sheet):

(g)(2)(i) Section 1, Identification;
(g)(2)(ii) Section 2, Hazard(s) identification;
(g)(2)(iii) Section 3, Composition/information on ingredients;
(g)(2)(iv) Section 4, First-aid measures;
(g)(2)(v) Section 5, Fire-fighting measures;
(g)(2)(vi) Section 6, Accidental release measures;
(g)(2)(vii) Section 7, Handling and storage;
(g)(2)(viii) Section 8, Exposure controls/personal protection;
(g)(2)(ix) Section 9, Physical and chemical properties;
(g)(2)(x) Section 10, Stability and reactivity;
(g)(2)(xi) Section 11, Toxicological information.

Note 1 to paragraph (g)(2): To be consistent with the GHS, an SDS must also include the following headings in this order:

(g)(2)(xii) Section 12, Ecological information;
(g)(2)(xiii) Section 13, Disposal considerations;
(g)(2)(xiv) Section 14, Transport information; and
(g)(2)(xv) Section 15, Regulatory information.

Note 2 to paragraph (g)(2): OSHA will not be enforcing information requirements in Sections 12 through 15, as these areas are not under its jurisdiction.

(g)(2)(xvi) Section 16, Other information, including date of preparation or last revision.

(g)(3) If no relevant information is found for any sub-heading within a Section on the safety data sheet, the chemical manufacturer, importer or employer preparing the safety data sheet shall mark it to indicate that no applicable information was found.

(g)(4) Where complex mixtures have similar hazards and contents (i.e. the chemical ingredients are essentially the same, but the specific composition varies from mixture to mixture), the chemical manufacturer, importer or employer may prepare one safety data sheet to apply to all of these similar mixtures.

(g)(5) The chemical manufacturer, importer or employer preparing the safety data sheet shall ensure that the information provided accurately reflects the scientific evidence used in making the hazard classification. If the chemical manufacturer, importer or employer preparing the safety data sheet becomes newly aware of any significant information regarding the hazards of a chemical, or ways to protect against the hazards, this new information shall be added to the safety data sheet within three months. If the chemical is not currently being produced or imported the chemical manufacturer or importer shall add the information to the safety data sheet before the chemical is introduced into the workplace again.

(g)(6)(i) Chemical manufacturers or importers shall ensure that distributors and employers are provided an appropriate safety data sheet with their initial shipment, and with the first shipment after a safety data sheet is updated;

(g)(6)(ii) The chemical manufacturer or importer shall either provide safety data sheets with the shipped containers or send them to the distributor or employer prior to or at the time of the shipment;

(g)(6)(iii) If the safety data sheet is not provided with a shipment that has been labeled as a hazardous chemical, the distributor or employer shall obtain one from the chemical manufacturer or importer as soon as possible; and,

(g)(6)(iv) The chemical manufacturer or importer shall also provide distributors or employers with a safety data sheet upon request.

(g)(7)(i) Distributors shall ensure that safety data sheets, and updated information, are provided to other distributors and employers with their initial shipment and with the first shipment after a safety data sheet is updated;

(g)(7)(ii) The distributor shall either provide safety data sheets with the shipped containers, or send them to the other distributor or employer prior to or at the time of the shipment;

(g)(7)(iii) Retail distributors selling hazardous chemicals to employers having a commercial account shall provide a safety data sheet to such employers upon request, and shall post a sign or otherwise inform them that a safety data sheet is available;

(g)(7)(iv) Wholesale distributors selling hazardous chemicals to employers over-the-counter may also provide safety data sheets upon the request of the employer at the time of the over-the-counter purchase, and shall post a sign or otherwise inform such employers that a safety data sheet is available;

(g)(7)(v) If an employer without a commercial account purchases a hazardous chemical from a retail distributor not required to have safety data sheets on file (i.e., the retail distributor does not have commercial accounts and does not use the materials), the retail distributor shall provide the employer, upon request, with the name, address, and telephone number of the chemical manufacturer, importer, or distributor from which a safety data sheet can be obtained;

(g)(7)(vi) Wholesale distributors shall also provide safety data sheets to employers or other distributors upon request; and,

(g)(7)(vii) Chemical manufacturers, importers, and distributors need not provide safety data sheets to retail distributors that have informed them that the retail distributor does not sell the product to commercial accounts or open the sealed container to use it in their own workplaces.

(g)(8) The employer shall maintain in the workplace copies of the required safety data sheets for each hazardous chemical, and shall ensure that they are readily accessible during each work shift to employees when they are in their work area(s). (Electronic access and other alternatives to maintaining paper copies of the safety data sheets are permitted as long as no barriers to immediate employee access in each workplace are created by such options.)

(g)(9) Where employees must travel between workplaces during a workshift, i.e., their work is carried out at more than one geographical location, the safety data sheets may be kept at the primary workplace facility. In this situation, the employer shall ensure that employees can immediately obtain the required information in an emergency.

(g)(10) Safety data sheets may be kept in any form, including operating procedures, and may be designed to cover groups of hazardous chemicals in a work area where it may be more appropriate to address the hazards of a process rather than individual hazardous chemicals. However, the employer shall ensure that in all cases the required information is provided for each hazardous chemical, and is readily accessible during each work shift to employees when they are in their work area(s).

(g)(11) Safety data sheets shall also be made readily available, upon request, to designated representatives, the Assistant Secretary, and the Director, in accordance with the requirements of 29 CFR §1910.1020(e).

(h) Employee information and training

(h)(1) Employers shall provide employees with effective information and training on hazardous chemicals in their work area at the time of their initial assignment, and whenever a new chemical hazard the employees have not previously been trained about is introduced into their work area. Information and training may be designed to cover categories of hazards (e.g., flammability, carcinogenicity) or specific chemicals. Chemical-specific information must always be available through labels and safety data sheets.

(h)(2) Information. Employees shall be informed of:

(h)(2)(i) The requirements of this Section;

(h)(2)(ii) Any operations in their work area where hazardous chemicals are present; and,

(h)(2)(iii) The location and availability of the written hazard communication program, including the required list(s) of hazardous chemicals, and safety data sheets required by this Section.

(h)(3) **Training** Employee training shall include at least:

(h)(3)(i) Methods and observations that may be used to detect the presence or release of a hazardous chemical in the work area (such as monitoring conducted by the employer, continuous monitoring devices, visual appearance or odor of hazardous chemicals when being released, etc.);

(h)(3)(ii) The physical, health, simple asphyxiation, combustible dust, and pyrophoric gas hazards, as well as hazards not otherwise classified, of the chemicals in the work area;

(h)(3)(iii) The measures employees can take to protect themselves from these hazards, including specific procedures the employer has implemented to protect employees from exposure to hazardous chemicals, such as appropriate work practices, emergency procedures, and personal protective equipment to be used; and,

(h)(3)(iv) The details of the hazard communication program developed by the employer, including an explanation of the labels received on shipped containers and the workplace labeling system used by their employer; the safety data sheet, including the order of information and how employees can obtain and use the appropriate hazard information.

(i) Trade secrets

(i)(1) The chemical manufacturer, importer, or employer may withhold the specific chemical identity, including the chemical name, other specific identification of a hazardous chemical, or the exact percentage (concentration) of the substance in a mixture, from the safety data sheet, provided that:

(i)(1)(i) The claim that the information withheld is a trade secret can be supported;

(i)(1)(ii) Information contained in the safety data sheet concerning the properties and effects of the hazardous chemical is disclosed;

(i)(1)(iii) The safety data sheet indicates that the specific chemical identity and/or percentage of composition is being withheld as a trade secret; and,

(i)(1)(iv) The specific chemical identity and percentage is made available to health professionals, employees, and designated representatives in accordance with the applicable provisions of this paragraph.

(i)(2) Where a treating physician or nurse determines that a medical emergency exists and the specific chemical identity and/or specific percentage of composition of a hazardous chemical is necessary for emergency or first-aid treatment, the chemical manufacturer, importer, or employer shall immediately disclose the specific chemical identity or percentage composition of a trade secret chemical to that treating physician or nurse, regardless of the existence of a written statement of need or a confidentiality agreement. The chemical manufacturer, importer, or employer may require a written statement of need and confidentiality agreement, in accordance with the provisions of paragraphs (i)(3) and (4) of this Section, as soon as circumstances permit.

(i)(3) In non-emergency situations, a chemical manufacturer, importer, or employer shall, upon request, disclose a specific chemical identity or percentage composition, otherwise permitted to be withheld under paragraph (i)(1) of this Section, to a health professional (i.e. physician, industrial hygienist, toxicologist, epidemiologist, or occupational health nurse) providing medical or other occupational health services to exposed employee(s), and to employees or designated representatives, if:

(i)(3)(i) The request is in writing;

(i)(3)(ii) The request describes with reasonable detail one or more of the following occupational health needs for the information:

(i)(3)(ii)(A) To assess the hazards of the chemicals to which employees will be exposed;

(i)(3)(ii)(B) To conduct or assess sampling of the workplace atmosphere to determine employee exposure levels;

(i)(3)(ii)(C) To conduct pre-assignment or periodic medical surveillance of exposed employees;

(i)(3)(ii)(D) To provide medical treatment to exposed employees;

(i)(3)(ii)(E) To select or assess appropriate personal protective equipment for exposed employees;

(i)(3)(ii)(F) To design or assess engineering controls or other protective measures for exposed employees; and

(i)(3)(ii)(G) To conduct studies to determine the health effects of exposure.

(i)(3)(iii) The request explains in detail why the disclosure of the specific chemical identity or percentage composition is essential and that, in lieu thereof, the disclosure of the following information to the health professional, employee, or designated representative, would not satisfy the purposes described in paragraph (i)(3)(ii) of this Section:

(i)(3)(iii)(A) The properties and effects of the chemical;

(i)(3)(iii)(B) Measures for controlling workers' exposure to the chemical;

(i)(3)(iii)(C) Methods of monitoring and analyzing worker exposure to the chemical; and

(i)(3)(iii)(D) Methods of diagnosing and treating harmful exposures to the chemical;

(i)(3)(iv) The request includes a description of the procedures to be used to maintain the confidentiality of the disclosed information; and,

(i)(3)(v) The health professional, and the employer or contractor of the services of the health professional (i.e. downstream employer, labor organization, or individual employee), employee, or designated representative, agree in a written confidentiality agreement that the health professional, employee, or designated representative, will not use the trade secret information for any purpose other than the health need(s) asserted and agree not to release the information under any circumstances other than to OSHA, as provided in paragraph (i)(6) of this Section, except as authorized by the terms of the agreement or by the chemical manufacturer, importer, or employer.

(i)(4) The confidentiality agreement authorized by paragraph (i)(3)(iv) of this Section:

(i)(4)(i) May restrict the use of the information to the health purposes indicated in the written statement of need;

(i)(4)(ii) May provide for appropriate legal remedies in the event of a breach of the agreement, including stipulation of a reasonable pre-estimate of likely damages; and

(i)(4)(iii) May not include requirements for the posting of a penalty bond.

(i)(5) Nothing in this Standard is meant to preclude the parties from pursuing non-contractual remedies to the extent permitted by law.

(i)(6) If the health professional, employee, or designated representative receiving the trade secret information decides that there is a need to disclose it to OSHA, the chemical manufacturer, importer, or employer who provided the information shall be informed by the health professional, employee, or designated representative prior to, or at the same time as, such disclosure.

(i)(7) If the chemical manufacturer, importer, or employer denies a written request for disclosure of a specific chemical identity or percentage composition, the denial must:

(i)(7)(i) Be provided to the health professional, employee, or designated representative, within thirty days of the request;

(i)(7)(ii) Be in writing;

(i)(7)(iii) Include evidence to support the claim that the specific chemical identity or percent of composition is a trade secret;

(i)(7)(iv) State the specific reasons why the request is being denied; and,

(i)(7)(v) Explain in detail how alternative information may satisfy the specific medical or occupational health need without revealing the trade secret.

(i)(8) The health professional, employee, or designated representative whose request for information is denied under paragraph (i)(3) of this Section may refer the request and the written denial of the request to OSHA for consideration.

(i)(9) When a health professional, employee, or designated representative refers the denial to OSHA under paragraph (i)(8) of this Section, OSHA shall consider the evidence to determine if:

(i)(9)(i) The chemical manufacturer, importer, or employer has supported the claim that the specific chemical identity or percentage composition is a trade secret;

(i)(9)(ii) The health professional, employee, or designated representative has supported the claim that there is a medical or occupational health need for the information; and

(i)(9)(iii) The health professional, employee or designated representative has demonstrated adequate means to protect the confidentiality.

(i)(10)(i) If OSHA determines that the specific chemical identity or percentage composition requested under paragraph (i)(3) of this Section is not a "bona fide" trade secret, or that it is a trade secret, but the requesting health professional, employee, or designated representative has a legitimate medical or occupational health need for the information, has executed a written confidentiality agreement, and has shown adequate means to protect the confidentiality of the information, the chemical manufacturer, importer, or employer will be subject to citation by OSHA.

(i)(10)(ii) If a chemical manufacturer, importer, or employer demonstrates to OSHA that the execution of a confidentiality agreement would not provide sufficient protection against the potential harm from the unauthorized disclosure of a trade secret, the Assistant Secretary may issue such orders or impose such additional limitations or conditions upon the disclosure of the requested chemical information as may be appropriate to assure that the occupational health services are provided without an undue risk of harm to the chemical manufacturer, importer, or employer.

(i)(11) If a citation for a failure to release trade secret information is contested by the chemical manufacturer, importer, or employer, the matter will be adjudicated before the Occupational Safety and Health Review Commission in accordance with the Act's enforcement scheme and the applicable Commission rules of procedure. In accordance with the Commission rules, when a chemical manufacturer, importer, or employer continues to withhold the information during the contest, the Administrative Law Judge may review the citation and supporting documentation "in camera" or issue appropriate orders to protect the confidentiality of such matters.

(i)(12) Notwithstanding the existence of a trade secret claim, a chemical manufacturer, importer, or employer shall, upon request, disclose to the Assistant Secretary any information which this Section requires the chemical manufacturer, importer, or employer to make available. Where there is a trade secret claim, such claim shall be made no later than at the time the information is provided to the Assistant Secretary so that suitable determinations of trade secret status can be made and the necessary protections can be implemented.

(i)(13) Nothing in this paragraph shall be construed as requiring the disclosure under any circumstances of process information which is a trade secret.

(j) Effective dates

(j)(1) Employers shall train employees regarding the new label elements and safety data sheets format by December 1, 2013.

(j)(2) Chemical manufacturers, importers, distributors, and employers shall be in compliance with all modified provisions of this Section no later than June 1, 2015, except:

(j)(2)(i) After December 1, 2015, the distributor shall not ship containers labeled by the chemical manufacturer or importer unless the label has been modified to comply with paragraph (f)(1) of this Section

(j)(2)(ii) All employers shall, as necessary, update any alternative workplace labeling used under paragraph (f)(6), update the hazard communication program required by paragraph (h)(1), and provide any additional employee training in accordance with paragraph (h)(3) for newly identified physical or health hazards no later than June 1, 2016.

(j)(3) Chemical manufacturers, importers, distributors, and employers may comply with either §1910.1200 revised as of October 1, 2011, or the current version of this Standard, or both during the transition period.

§1910.1200 Appendix A
Health hazard criteria
(Mandatory)

A.0 GENERAL CLASSIFICATION CONSIDERATIONS

A.0.1 Classification

A.0.1.1 The term "hazard classification" is used to indicate that only the intrinsic hazardous properties of chemicals are considered. Hazard classification incorporates three steps:

(a) identification of relevant data regarding the hazards of a chemical;

(b) subsequent review of those data to ascertain the hazards associated with the chemical;

(c) determination of whether the chemical will be classified as hazardous and the degree of hazard.

A.0.1.2 For many hazard classes, the criteria are semi quantitative or qualitative and expert judgment is required to interpret the data for classification purposes.

A.0.2 Available data, test methods and test data quality

A.0.2.1 There is no requirement for testing chemicals.

A.0.2.2 The criteria for determining health hazards are test method neutral, i.e., they do not specify particular test methods, as long as the methods are scientifically validated.

A.0.2.3 The term "scientifically validated" refers to the process by which the reliability and the relevance of a procedure are established for a particular purpose. Any test that determines hazardous properties, which is conducted according to recognized scientific principles, can be used for purposes of a hazard determination for health hazards. Test conditions need to be standardized so that the results are reproducible with a given substance, and the standardized test yields "valid" data for defining the hazard class of concern.

A.0.2.4 Existing test data are acceptable for classifying chemicals, although expert judgment also may be needed for classification purposes.

A.0.2.5 The effect of a chemical on biological systems is influenced, by the physico-chemical properties of the substance and/or ingredients of the mixture and the way in which ingredient substances are biologically available. A chemical need not be classified when it can be shown by conclusive experimental data from scientifically validated test methods that the chemical is not biologically available.

A.0.2.6 For classification purposes, epidemiological data and experience on the effects of chemicals on humans (e.g., occupational data, data from accident databases) shall be taken into account in the evaluation of human health hazards of a chemical.

A.0.3 Classification based on weight of evidence

A.0.3.1 For some hazard classes, classification results directly when the data satisfy the criteria. For others, classification of a chemical shall be determined on the basis of the total weight of evidence using expert judgment. This means that all available information bearing on the classification of hazard shall be considered together, including the results of valid in vitro tests, relevant animal data, and human experience such as epidemiological and clinical studies and well-documented case reports and observations.

A.0.3.2 The quality and consistency of the data shall be considered. Information on chemicals related to the material being classified shall be considered as appropriate, as well as site of action and mechanism or mode of action study results. Both positive and negative results shall be considered together in a single weight-of-evidence determination.

A.0.3.3 Positive effects which are consistent with the criteria for classification, whether seen in humans or animals, shall normally justify classification. Where evidence is available from both humans and animals and there is a conflict between the findings, the quality and reliability of the evidence from both sources shall be evaluated in order to resolve the question of classification. Reliable, good quality human data shall generally have precedence over other data. However, even well-designed and conducted epidemiological studies may lack a sufficient number of subjects to detect relatively rare but still significant effects, or to assess potentially confounding factors. Therefore, positive results from well-conducted animal studies are not necessarily negated by the lack of positive human experience but require an assessment of the robustness, quality and statistical power of both the human and animal data.

A.0.3.4 Route of exposure, mechanistic information, and metabolism studies are pertinent to determining the relevance of an effect in humans. When such information raises doubt about relevance in humans, a lower classification may be warranted. When there is scientific evidence demonstrating that the mechanism or mode of action is not relevant to humans, the chemical should not be classified.

A.0.3.5 Both positive and negative results are considered together in the weight of evidence determination. However, a single positive study performed according to good scientific principles and with statistically and biologically significant positive results may justify classification.

A.0.4 Considerations for the classification of mixtures

A.0.4.1 For most hazard classes, the recommended process of classification of mixtures is based on the following sequence:

(a) Where test data are available for the complete mixture, the classification of the mixture will always be based on those data;

(b) Where test data are not available for the mixture itself, the bridging principles designated in each health hazard chapter of this Appendix shall be considered for classification of the mixture;

(c) If test data are not available for the mixture itself, and the available information is not sufficient to allow application of the above-mentioned bridging principles, then the method(s) described in each chapter for estimating the hazards based on the information known will be applied to classify the mixture (e.g., application of cut-off values/concentration limits).

A.0.4.2 An exception to the above order or precedence is made for Carcinogenicity, Germ Cell Mutagenicity, and Reproductive Toxicity. For these three hazard classes, mixtures shall be classified based upon information on the ingredient substances, unless on a case-by-case basis, justification can be provided for classifying based upon the mixture as a whole. See chapters A.5, A.6, and A.7 for further information on case-by-case bases.

A.0.4.3 Use of cut-off values/concentration limits

A.0.4.3.1 When classifying an untested mixture based on the hazards of its ingredients, cut-off values/concentration limits for the classified ingredients of the mixture are used for several hazard classes. While the adopted cut-off values/concentration limits adequately identify the hazard for most mixtures, there may be some that contain hazardous ingredients at lower concentrations than the specified cut-off values/concentration limits that still pose an identifiable hazard. There may also be cases where the cut-off value/concentration limit is considerably lower than the established non-hazardous level for an ingredient.

A.0.4.3.2 If the classifier has information that the hazard of an ingredient will be evident (i.e., it presents a health risk) below the specified cut-off value/concentration limit, the mixture containing that ingredient shall be classified accordingly.

A.0.4.3.3 In exceptional cases, conclusive data may demonstrate that the hazard of an ingredient will not be evident (i.e., it does not present a health risk) when present at a level above the specified cut-off value/concentration limit(s). In these cases the mixture may be classified according to those data. The data must exclude the possibility that the ingredient will behave in the mixture in a manner that would increase the hazard over that of the pure substance. Furthermore, the mixture must not contain ingredients that would affect that determination.

A.0.4.4 Synergistic or antagonistic effects

When performing an assessment in accordance with these requirements, the evaluator must take into account all available information about the potential occurrence of synergistic effects among the ingredients of the mixture. Lowering classification of a mixture to a less hazardous category on the basis of antagonistic effects may be done only if the determination is supported by sufficient data.

A.0.5 Bridging principles for the classification of mixtures where test data are not available for the complete mixture

A.0.5.1 Where the mixture itself has not been tested to determine its toxicity, but there are sufficient data on both the individual ingredients and similar tested mixtures to adequately characterize the hazards of the mixture, these data shall be used in accordance with the following bridging principles, subject to any specific provisions for mixtures for each hazard class. These principles ensure that the classification process uses the available data to the greatest extent possible in characterizing the hazards of the mixture.

A.0.5.1.1 Dilution

For mixtures classified in accordance with A.1 through A.10 of this Appendix, if a tested mixture is diluted with a diluent that has an equivalent or lower toxicity classification than the least toxic original ingredient, and which is not expected to affect the toxicity of other ingredients, then:

(a) the new diluted mixture shall be classified as equivalent to the original tested mixture; or

(b) for classification of acute toxicity in accordance with A.1 of this Appendix, paragraph A.1.3.6 (the additivity formula) shall be applied.

A.0.5.1.2 Batching

For mixtures classified in accordance with A.1 through A.10 of this Appendix, the toxicity of a tested production batch of a mixture can be assumed to be substantially equivalent to that of another untested production batch of the same mixture, when produced by or under the control of the same chemical manufacturer, unless there is reason to believe there is significant variation such that the toxicity of the untested batch has changed. If the latter occurs, a new classification is necessary.

A.0.5.1.3 Concentration of mixtures

For mixtures classified in accordance with A.1, A.2, A.3, A.8, A.9, or A.10 of this Appendix, if a tested mixture is classified in Category 1, and the concentration of the ingredients of the tested mixture that are in Category 1 is increased, the resulting untested mixture shall be classified in Category 1.

A.0.5.1.4 Interpolation within one toxicity category

For mixtures classified in accordance with A.1, A.2, A.3, A.8, A.9, or A.10 of this Appendix, for three mixtures (A, B and C) with identical ingredients, where mixtures A and B have been tested and are in the same toxicity category, and where untested mixture C has the same toxicologically active ingredients as mixtures A and B but has concentrations of toxicologically active ingredients intermediate to the concentrations in mixtures A and B, then mixture C is assumed to be in the same toxicity category as A and B.

A.0.5.1.5 Substantially similar mixtures

For mixtures classified in accordance with A.1 through A.10 of this Appendix, given the following set of conditions:

(a) Where there are two mixtures:

(i) A + B;

(ii) C + B;

(b) the concentration of ingredient B is essentially the same in both mixtures;

(c) the concentration of ingredient A in mixture (i) equals that of ingredient C in mixture (ii);

(d) and data on toxicity for A and C are available and substantially equivalent; i.e., they are in the same hazard category and are not expected to affect the toxicity of B; then

If mixture (i) or (ii) is already classified based on test data, the other mixture can be assigned the same hazard category.

A.0.5.1.6 Aerosols

For mixtures classified in accordance with A.1, A.2, A.3, A.4, A.8, or A.9 of this Appendix, an aerosol form of a mixture shall be classified in the same hazard category as the tested, non-aerosolized form of the mixture, provided the added propellant does not affect the toxicity of the mixture when spraying.

A.1 ACUTE TOXICITY

A.1.1 Definition

Acute toxicity refers to those adverse effects occurring following oral or dermal administration of a single dose of a substance, or multiple doses given within 24 hours, or an inhalation exposure of 4 hours.

A.1.2 Classification criteria for substances

A.1.2.1 Substances can be allocated to one of four toxicity categories based on acute toxicity by the oral, dermal or inhalation route according to the numeric cut-off criteria as shown in Table A.1.1. Acute toxicity values are expressed as (approximate) LD50 (oral, dermal) or LC50 (inhalation) values or as acute toxicity estimates (ATE). See the footnotes following Table A.1.1 for further explanation on the application of these values.

Table A.1.1
Acute Toxicity Hazard Categories and Acute Toxicity Estimate (ATE) Values Defining the Respective Categories

Exposure route	Category 1	Category 2	Category 3	Category 4
Oral (mg/kg bodyweight) see: Notes (a)(b)	≤5	>5 and ≤50	>50 and ≤300	>300 and ≤2000
Dermal (mg/kg bodyweight) see: Notes (a)(b)	≤50	>50 and ≤200	>200 and ≤1000	>1000 and ≤2000
Inhalation - Gases (ppmV) see: Notes (a)(b)(c)	≤100	>100 and ≤500	>500 and ≤2500	>2500 and ≤20000
Inhalation - Vapors (mg/l) see: Notes (a)(b)(c)(d)	≤0.5	>0.5 and ≤2.0	>2.0 and ≤10.0	>10.0 and ≤20.0
Inhalation – Dusts and Mists (mg/l) see: Notes (a)(b)(c)	≤0.05	>0.05 and ≤0.5	>0.5 and ≤1.0	>1.0 and ≤5.0

Notes to Table A.1.1:
Gas concentrations are expressed in parts per million per volume (ppmV).
(a) The acute toxicity estimate (ATE) for the classification of a substance is derived using the LD_{50}/LC_{50} where available;
(b) The acute toxicity estimate (ATE) for the classification of a substance or ingredient in a mixture is derived using:
(i) the LD_{50}/LC_{50} where available. Otherwise,
(ii) the appropriate conversion value from Table 1.2 that relates to the results of a range test, or
(iii) the appropriate conversion value from Table 1.2 that relates to a classification category;
(c) Inhalation cut-off values in the table are based on 4 hour testing exposures. Conversion of existing inhalation toxicity data which has been generated according to 1 hour exposure is achieved by dividing by a factor of 2 for gases and vapors and 4 for dusts and mists;
(d) For some substances the test atmosphere will be a vapor which consists of a combination of liquid and gaseous phases. For other substances the test atmosphere may consist of a vapor which is nearly all the gaseous phase. In these latter cases, classification is based on ppmV as follows: Category 1 (100 ppmV), Category 2 (500 ppmV), Category 3 (2500 ppmV), Category 4 (20000 ppmV).
The terms "dust", "mist" and "vapor" are defined as follows:
(i) Dust: solid particles of a substance or mixture suspended in a gas (usually air);
(ii) Mist: liquid droplets of a substance or mixture suspended in a gas (usually air);
(iii) Vapor: the gaseous form of a substance or mixture released from its liquid or solid state.

A.1.2.3 The preferred test species for evaluation of acute toxicity by the oral and inhalation routes is the rat, while the rat or rabbit are preferred for evaluation of acute dermal toxicity. Test data already generated for the classification of chemicals under existing systems should be accepted when reclassifying these chemicals under the harmonized system. When experimental data for acute toxicity are available in several animal species, scientific judgment should be used in selecting the most appropriate LD_{50} value from among scientifically validated tests.

A.1.3 Classification criteria for mixtures

A.1.3.1 The approach to classification of mixtures for acute toxicity is tiered, and is dependent upon the amount of information available for the mixture itself and for its ingredients. The flow chart of Figure A.1.1 indicates the process that must be followed:

Figure A.1.1
Tiered approach to classification of mixtures for acute toxicity

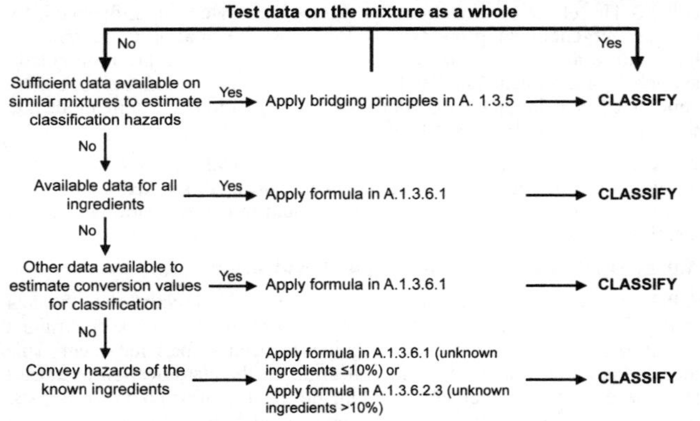

A.1.3.2 Classification of mixtures for acute toxicity may be carried out for each route of exposure, but is only required for one route of exposure as long as this route is followed (estimated or tested) for all ingredients and there is no relevant evidence to suggest acute toxicity by multiple routes. When there is relevant evidence of acute toxicity by multiple routes of exposure, classification is to be conducted for all appropriate routes of exposure. All available information shall be considered. The pictogram and signal word used shall reflect the most severe hazard category; and all relevant hazard statements shall be used.

A.1.3.3 For purposes of classifying the hazards of mixtures in the tiered approach:

(a) The "relevant ingredients" of a mixture are those which are present in concentrations ≥1% (weight/weight for solids, liquids, dusts, mists and vapors and volume/volume for gases). If there is reason to suspect that an ingredient present at a concentration < 1% will affect classification of the mixture for acute toxicity, that ingredient shall also be considered relevant. Consideration of ingredients present at a concentration <1% is particularly important when classifying untested mixtures which contain ingredients that are classified in Category 1 and Category 2;

(b) Where a classified mixture is used as an ingredient of another mixture, the actual or derived acute toxicity estimate (ATE) for that mixture is used when calculating the classification of the new mixture using the formulas in A.1.3.6.1 and A.1.3.6.2.4.

(c) If the converted acute toxicity point estimates for all ingredients of a mixture are within the same category, then the mixture should be classified in that category.

(d) When only range data (or acute toxicity hazard category information) are available for ingredients in a mixture, they may be converted to point estimates in accordance with Table A.1.2 when calculating the classification of the new mixture using the formulas in A.1.3.6.1 and A.1.3.6.2.4.

A.1.3.4 Classification of mixtures where acute toxicity test data are available for the complete mixture

Where the mixture itself has been tested to determine its acute toxicity, it is classified according to the same criteria as those used for substances, presented in Table A.1.1. If test data for the mixture are not available, the procedures presented below must be followed.

A.1.3.5 Classification of mixtures where acute toxicity test data are not available for the complete mixture: bridging principles

A.1.3.5.1 Where the mixture itself has not been tested to determine its acute toxicity, but there are sufficient data on both the individual ingredients and similar tested mixtures to adequately characterize the hazards of the mixture, these data will be used in accordance with the following bridging principles as found in paragraph A.0.5 of this Appendix: Dilution, Batching, Concentration of mixtures, Interpolation within one toxicity category, Substantially similar mixtures, and Aerosols.

A.1.3.6 Classification of mixtures based on ingredients of the mixture (additivity formula)

A.1.3.6.1 Data available for all ingredients

The acute toxicity estimate (ATE) of ingredients is considered as follows:

(a) Include ingredients with a known acute toxicity, which fall into any of the acute toxicity categories, or have an oral or dermal LD_{50} greater than 2000 but less than or equal to 5000 mg/kg body weight (or the equivalent dose for inhalation);

(b) Ignore ingredients that are presumed not acutely toxic (e.g., water, sugar);

(c) Ignore ingredients if the data available are from a limit dose test (at the upper threshold for Category 4 for the appropriate route of exposure as provided in Table A.1.1) and do not show acute toxicity.

Ingredients that fall within the scope of this paragraph are considered to be ingredients with a known acute toxicity estimate (ATE). See note (b) to Table A.1.1 and paragraph A.1.3.3 for appropriate application of available data to the equation below, and paragraph A.1.3.6.2.4.

The ATE of the mixture is determined by calculation from the ATE values for all relevant ingredients according to the following formula below for oral, dermal or inhalation toxicity:

$$\frac{100}{ATE_{mix}} = \sum_{n} \frac{Ci}{ATE_i}$$

Where:
Ci = concentration of ingredient i
n ingredients and i is running from 1 to n
ATEi = acute toxicity estimate of ingredient i.

A.1.3.6.2 Data are not available for one or more ingredients of the mixture

A.1.3.6.2.1 Where an ATE is not available for an individual ingredient of the mixture, but available information provides a derived conversion value, the formula in A.1.3.6.1 may be applied. This information may include evaluation of:

(a) Extrapolation between oral, dermal and inhalation acute toxicity estimates. Such an evaluation requires appropriate pharmacodynamic and pharmacokinetic data;

(b) Evidence from human exposure that indicates toxic effects but does not provide lethal dose data;

(c) Evidence from any other toxicity tests/assays available on the substance that indicates toxic acute effects but does not necessarily provide lethal dose data; or

(d) Data from closely analogous substances using structure/activity relationships.

A.1.3.6.2.2 This approach requires substantial supplemental technical information, and a highly trained and experienced expert, to reliably estimate acute toxicity. If sufficient information is not available to reliably estimate acute toxicity, proceed to the provisions of A.1.3.6.2.3.

A.1.3.6.2.3 In the event that an ingredient with unknown acute toxicity is used in a mixture at a concentration ≥1%, and the mixture has not been classified based on testing of the mixture as a whole, the mixture cannot be attributed a definitive acute toxicity estimate. In this situation the mixture is classified based on the known ingredients only. (Note: A statement that x percent of the mixture consists of ingredient(s) of unknown toxicity is required on the label and safety data sheet in such cases; see Appendix C to this Section, Allocation of Label Elements and Appendix D to this Section, Safety Data Sheets.)

Where an ingredient with unknown acute toxicity is used in a mixture at a concentration ≥ 1%, and the mixture is not classified based on testing of the mixture as a whole, a statement that X% of the mixture consists of ingredient(s) of unknown acute toxicity is required on the label and safety data sheet in such cases; see Appendix C to this Section, Allocation of Label Elements and Appendix D to this Section, Safety Data Sheets.)

A.1.3.6.2.4 If the total concentration of the relevant ingredient(s) with unknown acute toxicity is ≤ 10% then the formula presented in A.1.3.6.1 must be used. If the total concentration of the relevant ingredient(s) with unknown acute toxicity is < 10%, the formula presented in A.1.3.6.1 is corrected to adjust for the percentage of the unknown ingredient(s) as follows:

$$\frac{100 - (\Sigma C_{unknown} \text{ if} > 10\%)}{ATE_{mix}} = \sum_{n} \frac{Ci}{ATE_i}$$

Table A.1.2
Conversion From Experimentally Obtained Acute Toxicity Range Values (or Acute Toxicity Hazard Categories) to Acute Toxicity Point Estimates for Use in the Formulas for the Classification of Mixtures

Exposure routes	Classification category or experimentally obtained acute toxicity range estimate	Converted acute toxicity point estimate
Oral (mg/kg bodyweight)	0 <Category 1 ≤5	0.5
	5 <Category 2 ≤50	5
	50 <Category 3 ≤300	100
	300 <Category 4 ≤2000	500
Dermal (mg/kg bodyweight)	0 <Category 1 ≤50	5
	50 <Category 2 ≤200	50
	200 <Category 3 ≤1000	300
	1000 <Category 4 ≤2000	1100
Gases (ppmV)	0 <Category 1 ≤100	10
	100 <Category 2 ≤500	100
	500 <Category 3 ≤2500	700
	2500 <Category 4 ≤20000	4500
Vapors (mg/l)	0 <Category 1 ≤0.5	0.05
	0. 5 <Category 2 ≤2.0	0.5
	2.0 <Category 3 ≤10.0	3
	10.0 <Category 4 ≤20.0	11
Dust/mist (mg/l)	0 <Category 1 ≤0.05	0.005
	0.05 <Category 2 ≤0.5	0.05
	0.5 <Category 3 ≤1.0	0.5
	1.0 <Category 4 ≤5.0	1.5

Note: Gas concentrations are expressed in parts per million per volume (ppmV).

A.2 SKIN CORROSION/IRRITATION

A.2.1 Definitions and general considerations

A.2.1.1 Skin corrosion is the production of irreversible damage to the skin; namely, visible necrosis through the epidermis and into the dermis, following the application of a test substance for up to 4 hours. Corrosive reactions are typified by ulcers, bleeding, bloody scabs, and, by the end of observation at 14 days, by discoloration due to blanching of the skin, complete areas of alopecia, and scars. Histopathology should be considered to evaluate questionable lesions.

Skin irritation is the production of reversible damage to the skin following the application of a test substance for up to 4 hours.

A.2.1.2 Skin corrosion/irritation shall be classified using a tiered approach as detailed in figure A.2.1. Emphasis shall be placed upon existing human data (See A.0.2.6), followed by other sources of information. Classification results directly when the data satisfy the criteria in this Section. In case the criteria cannot be directly applied, classification of a substance or a mixture is made on the basis of the total weight of evidence (See A.0.3.1). This means that all available information bearing on the determination of skin corrosion/irritation is considered together, including the results of appropriate scientifically validated in-vitro tests, relevant animal data, and human data such as epidemiological and clinical studies and well-documented case reports and observations.

A.2.2 Classification criteria for substances using animal test data

A.2.2.1 Corrosion

A.2.2.1.1 A corrosive substance is a chemical that produces destruction of skin tissue, namely, visible necrosis through the epidermis and into the dermis, in at least 1 of 3 tested animals after exposure up to a 4-hour duration. Corrosive reactions are typified by ulcers, bleeding, bloody scabs and, by the end of observation at 14 days, by discoloration due to blanching of the skin, complete areas of alopecia and scars. Histopathology should be considered to discern questionable lesions.

A.2.2.1.2 Three sub-categories of Category 1 are provided in Table A.2.1, all of which shall be regulated as Category 1.

Table A.2.1
Skin Corrosion Category and Sub-Categories

Category 1: corrosive	Corrosive sub-categories	Corrosive in ≥1 of 3 animals	
		Exposure	Observation
	1A	≤3 min	≤1 h
	1B	>3 min ≤1 h	≤14 days
	1C	>1 h ≤4 h	≤14 days

A.2.2.2 Irritation

A.2.2.2.1 A single irritant category (Category 2) is presented in the Table A.2.2. The major criterion for the irritant category is that at least 2 tested animals have a mean score of ≥ 2.3 ≥ 4.0.

Table A.2.2
Skin Irritation Category

	Criteria
Irritant (Category 2)	(1) Mean value of ≥2.3 ≤4.0 for erythema/eschar or for edema in at least 2 of 3 tested animals from gradings at 24, 48 and 72 hours after patch removal or, if reactions are delayed, from grades on 3 consecutive days after the onset of skin reactions; or (2) Inflammation that persists to the end of the observation period normally 14 days in at least 2 animals, particularly taking into account alopecia (limited area), hyperkeratosis, hyperplasia, and scaling; or (3) In some cases where there is pronounced variability of response among animals, with very definite positive effects related to chemical exposure in a single animal but less than the criteria above

A.2.2.2.2 Animal irritant responses within a test can be quite variable, as they are with corrosion. A separate irritant criterion accommodates cases when there is a significant irritant response but less than the mean score criterion for a positive test. For example, a substance might be designated as an irritant if at least 1 of 3 tested animals shows a very elevated mean score throughout the study, including lesions persisting at the end of an observation period of normally 14 days. Other responses could also fulfil this criterion. However, it should be ascertained that the responses are the result of chemical exposure. Addition of this criterion increases the sensitivity of the classification system.

A.2.2.2.3 Reversibility of skin lesions is another consideration in evaluating irritant responses. When inflammation persists to the end of the observation period in 2 or more test animals, taking into consideration alopecia (limited area), hyperkeratosis, hyperplasia and scaling, then a chemical should be considered to be an irritant.

A.2.3 Classification Criteria for Substances Using Other Data Elements

A.2.3.1 Existing human and animal data including information from single or repeated exposure should be the first line of analysis, as they give information directly relevant to effects on the skin. If a substance is highly toxic by the dermal route, a skin corrosion/irritation study may not be practicable since the amount of test substance to be applied would considerably exceed the toxic dose and, consequently, would result in the death of the animals. When observations are made of skin corrosion/irritation in acute toxicity studies and are observed up through the limit dose, these data may be used for classification provided that the dilutions used and species tested are equivalent. In vitro alternatives that have been scientifically validated shall be used to make classification decisions. Solid substances (powders) may become corrosive or irritant when moistened or in contact with moist skin or mucous membranes. Likewise, pH extremes like ≤ 2 and ≥ 11.5 may indicate skin effects, especially when associated with significant buffering capacity. Generally, such substances are expected to produce significant effects on the skin. In the absence of any other information, a substance is considered corrosive (Skin Category 1) if it has a pH ≤ 2 or a pH ≥ 11.5. However, if consideration of alkali/acid reserve suggests the substance or mixture may not be corrosive despite the low or high pH value, then further evaluation may be necessary. In some cases enough information may be available from structurally related compounds to make classification decisions.

A.2.3.2 A tiered approach to the evaluation of initial information shall be used (Figure A.2.1) recognizing that all elements may not be relevant in certain cases.

A.2.3.3 The tiered approach explains how to organize information on a substance and to make a weight-of-evidence decision about hazard assessment and hazard classification.

A.2.3.4 All the above information that is available on a substance shall be evaluated. Although information might be gained from the evaluation of single parameters within a tier, there is merit in considering the totality of existing information and making an overall weight of evidence determination. This is especially true when there is information available on some but not all parameters. Emphasis shall be placed upon existing human experience and data, followed by animal experience and testing data, followed by other sources of information, but case-by-case determinations are necessary.

Figure A.2.1
Tiered evaluation of skin corrosion and irritation potential

Step	Parameter	Finding	Conclusion
1a:	Existing human or animal data[1]	→ Skin corrosive	→ Category 1[2]
	↓ Not corrosive or no data		
1b:	Existing human or animal data[1]	→ Skin irritant	→ Category 2[2]
	↓ Not an irritant or no data		
1c:	Existing human or animal data[1]	→ Not a skin corrosive or skin irritant	→ Not Classified
	↓ No/Insufficient data		
2:	Other, existing skin data in animals[3]	→ Skin corrosive → Skin irritant	→ Category 1[2] → Category 2[2]
	↓ No/Insufficient data		
3:	Existing skin corrosive *ex vivo / in vitro* data[4]	→ Positive: Skin corrosive	→ Category 1[2]
	↓ Not corrosive or no data		
	Existing skin irritation *ex vivo / in vitro* data[4]	→ Positive: Skin irritant → Negative: Not a skin irritant[5]	→ Category 2[2] → Not Classified
	↓ No/Insufficient data		
4:	pH-Based assessment (with consideration of buffering capacity of the chemical, or no buffering capacity data)[5]	→ pH≤ 2 or ≥ 11.5	→ Category 1[2]
	↓ Not a pH extreme, No pH data or extreme pH with low/no buffering capacity		
5:	Validated Structure/Activity Relationship (SAR) models	→ Skin corrosive → Skin irritant	→ Category 1[2] → Category 2[2]
	↓ No/Insufficient data		
6:	Consideration of the total Weight of Evidence[6]	→ Skin corrosive → Skin irritant	→ Category 1[2] → Category 2[2]
	↓ No concern based on consideration of the sum of available data		
7:	Not Classified	→	Not Classified

Notes to Figure A.2.1

1 Evidence of existing human or animal data may be derived from single or repeated exposure(s) in occupational, consumer, transportation, or emergency response scenarios; from ethically-conducted human clinical studies; or from purposely-generated data from animal studies conducted according to scientifically validated test methods (at present, there is no internationally accepted test method for human skin irritation testing).

2 Classify in the appropriate harmonized category, as shown in Tables A.2.1 and A.2.2.

3 Pre-existing animal data (e.g. from an acute dermal toxicity test or a sensitisation test) should be carefully reviewed to determine if sufficient skin corrosion/irritation evidence is available through other, similar information. For example, classification/categorization may be done on the basis of whether a chemical has or has not produced any skin irritation in an acute dermal toxicity test in animals at the limit dose, or produces very toxic effects in an acute dermal toxicity test in animals. In the latter case, the chemical would be classified as being very hazardous by the dermal route for acute toxicity, and it would be moot whether the chemical is also irritating or corrosive on the skin. It should be kept in mind in evaluating acute dermal toxicity information that the reporting of dermal lesions may be incomplete, testing and observations may be made on a species other than the rabbit, and species may differ in sensitivity in their responses.

4 Evidence from studies using scientifically validated protocols with isolated human/animal tissues or other, non-tissue-based, though scientifically validated, protocols should be assessed. Examples of scientifically validated test methods for skin corrosion include OECD TG 430 (Transcutaneous Electrical Resistance Test (TER)), 431 (Human Skin Model Test), and 435 (Membrane Barrier Test Method). OECD TG 439 (Reconstructed Human Epidermis Test Method) is a scientifically validated in vitro test method for skin irritation.

5 Measurement of pH alone may be adequate, but assessment of acid or alkali reserve (buffering capacity) would be preferable. Presently, there is no scientifically validated and internationally accepted method for assessing this parameter.

6 All information that is available on a chemical should be considered and an overall determination made on the total weight of evidence. This is especially true when there is conflict in information available on some parameters. Professional judgment should be exercised in making such a determination.

A.2.4 Classification Criteria for Mixtures

A.2.4.1 Classification of mixtures when data are available for the complete mixture

A.2.4.1.1 The mixture shall be classified using the criteria for substances (See A.2.3).

A.2.4.2 Classification of mixtures when data are not available for the complete mixture: bridging principles

A.2.4.2.1 Where the mixture itself has not been tested to determine its skin corrosion/irritation, but there are sufficient data on both the individual ingredients and similar tested mixtures to adequately characterize the hazards of the mixture, these data will be used in accordance with the following bridging principles, as found in paragraph A.0.5 of this Appendix: Dilution, Batching, Concentration of mixtures, Interpolation within one toxicity category, Substantially similar mixtures, and Aerosols.

A.2.4.3 Classification of mixtures when data are available for all ingredients or only for some ingredients of the mixture

A.2.4.3.1 For purposes of classifying the skin corrosion/irritation hazards of mixtures in the tiered approach:

The "relevant ingredients" of a mixture are those which are present in concentrations ≥1% (weight/weight for solids, liquids, dusts, mists and vapors and volume/volume for gases.) If the classifier has reason to suspect that an ingredient present at a concentration <1% will affect classification of the mixture for skin corrosion/irritation, that ingredient shall also be considered relevant.

A.2.4.3.2 In general, the approach to classification of mixtures as irritant or corrosive to skin when data are available on the ingredients, but not on the mixture as a whole, is based on the theory of additivity, such that each corrosive or irritant ingredient contributes to the overall irritant or corrosive properties of the mixture in proportion to its potency and concentration. A weighting factor of 10 is used for corrosive ingredients when they are present at a concentration below the concentration limit for classification with Category 1, but are at a concentration that will contribute to the classification of the mixture as an irritant. The mixture is classified as corrosive or irritant when the sum of the concentrations of such ingredients exceeds a cut-off value/concentration limit.

A.2.4.3.3 Table A.2.3 below provides the cut-off value/concentration limits to be used to determine if the mixture is considered to be an irritant or a corrosive to the skin.

A.2.4.3.4 Particular care shall be taken when classifying certain types of chemicals such as acids and bases, inorganic salts, aldehydes, phenols, and surfactants. The approach explained in A.2.4.3.1 and A.2.4.3.2 might not work given that many of such substances are corrosive or irritant at concentrations < 1%. For mixtures containing strong acids or bases the pH should be used as classification criteria since pH will be a better indicator of corrosion than the concentration limits of Table A.2.3. A mixture containing corrosive or irritant ingredients that cannot be classified based on the additivity approach shown in Table A.2.3, due to chemical characteristics that make this approach unworkable, should be classified as Skin Category 1 if it contains ≥ 1% of a corrosive ingredient and as Skin Category 2 when it contains ≥ 3% of an irritant ingredient. Classification of mixtures with ingredients for which the approach in Table A.2.3 does not apply is summarized in Table A.2.4 below.

A.2.4.3.5 On occasion, reliable data may show that the skin corrosion/irritation of an ingredient will not be evident when present at a level above the generic concentration cut-off values mentioned in Tables A.2.3 and A.2.4. In these cases the mixture could be classified according to those data (See Use of cut-off values/concentration limits, paragraph A.0.4.3 of this Appendix).

A.2.4.3.6 If there are data showing that (an) ingredient(s) may be corrosive or irritant at a concentration of < 1% (corrosive) or < 3% (irritant), the mixture shall be classified accordingly (See Use of cut-off values / concentration limits, paragraph A.0.4.3 of this Appendix).

Table A.2.3
Concentration of Ingredients of a Mixture Classified as Skin Category 1 or 2 That Would Trigger Classification of the Mixture as Hazardous to Skin
[Category 1 or 2]

Sum of ingredients classified as:	Concentration triggering classification of a mixture as:	
	Skin corrosive	Skin irritant
	Category 1	Category 2
Skin Category 1	≥5%	≥1% but <5%
Skin Category 2		≥10%
(10 × Skin Category 1) + Skin Category 2		≥10%

Table A.2.4
Concentration of Ingredients of a Mixture for Which the Additivity Approach Does Not Apply, That Would Trigger Classification of the Mixture as Hazardous to Skin

Ingredient:	Concentration:	Mixture classified as: Skin
Acid with pH ≤2	≥1%	Category 1.
Base with pH ≥11.5	≥1%	Category 1.
Other corrosive (Category 1) ingredients for which additivity does not apply	≥1%	Category 1.
Other irritant (Category 2) ingredients for which additivity does not apply, including acids and bases	≥3%	Category 2.

A.3 SERIOUS EYE DAMAGE/EYE IRRITATION

A.3.1 Definitions and general considerations

A.3.1.1 Serious eye damage is the production of tissue damage in the eye, or serious physical decay of vision, following application of a test substance to the anterior surface of the eye, which is not fully reversible within 21 days of application.

Eye irritation is the production of changes in the eye following the application of test substance to the anterior surface of the eye, which are fully reversible within 21 days of application.

A.3.1.2 Serious eye damage/eye irritation shall be classified using a tiered approach as detailed in figure A.3.1. Emphasis shall be placed upon existing human data (See A.0.2.6), followed by animal data, followed by other sources of information. Classification results directly when the data satisfy the criteria in this Section. In case the criteria cannot be directly applied, classification of a substance or a mixture is made on the basis of the total weight of evidence (See A.0.3.1). This means that all available information bearing on the determination of serious eye damage/eye irritation is considered together, including the results of appropriate scientifically validated in vitro tests, relevant animal data, and human data such as epidemiological and clinical studies and well-documented case reports and observations.

A.3.2 Classification criteria for substances using animal test data

A.3.2.1 Irreversible effects on the eye/serious damage to eyes (Category 1)

A single hazard category is provided in Table A.3.1, for substances that have the potential to seriously damage the eyes. Category 1, irreversible effects on the eye, includes the criteria listed below. These observations include animals with grade 4 cornea lesions and other severe reactions (e.g. destruction of cornea) observed at any time during the test, as well as persistent corneal opacity, discoloration of the cornea by a dye substance, adhesion, pannus, and interference with the function of the iris or other effects that impair sight. In this context, persistent lesions are considered those which are not fully reversible within an observation period of normally 21 days. Category 1 also contains substances fulfilling the criteria of corneal opacity ≥ 3 and/or iritis > 1.5 detected in a Draize eye test with rabbits, because severe lesions like these usually do not reverse within a 21-day observation period.

Table A.3.1
Irreversible Eye Effects

A substance is classified as Serious Eye Damage Category 1 (irreversible effects on the eye) when it produces:
(a) at least in one tested animal, effects on the cornea, iris or conjunctiva that are not expected to reverse or have not fully reversed within an observation period of normally 21 days; and/or
(b) at least in 2 of 3 tested animals, a positive response of: (i) corneal opacity ≥3; and/or (ii) iritis >1.5; calculated as the mean scores following grading at 24, 48 and 72 hours after instillation of the substance.

A.3.2.2 Reversible effects on the eye (Category 2)

A single category is provided in Table A.3.2 for substances that have the potential to induce reversible eye irritation

Table A.3.2
Reversible Eye Effects

A substance is classified as **Eye irritant Category 2A (irritating to eyes)** when it produces in at least in 2 of 3 tested animals a positive response of:
(i) corneal opacity ≥1; and/or (ii) iritis ≥1; and/or (iii) conjunctival redness ≥2; and/or (iv) conjunctival edema (chemosis) ≥2 calculated as the mean scores following grading at 24, 48 and 72 hours after instillation of the substance, and which fully reverses within an observation period of normally 21 days.
An eye irritant is considered mildly irritating to eyes (Category 2B) when the effects listed above are fully reversible within 7 days of observation.

A.3.2.3 For those chemicals where there is pronounced variability among animal responses, this information may be taken into account in determining the classification.

A.3.3 Classification Criteria for Substances Using Other Data Elements

A.3.3.1 Existing human and animal data should be the first line of analysis, as they give information directly relevant to effects on the eye. Possible skin corrosion shall be evaluated prior to consideration of serious eye damage/eye irritation in order to avoid testing for local effects on eyes with skin corrosive substances. In vitro alternatives that have been scientifically validated and accepted shall be used to make classification decisions. Likewise, pH extremes like ≤ 2 and ≥ 11.5, may indicate serious eye damage, especially when associated with significant buffering capacity. Generally, such substances are expected to produce significant effects on the eyes. In the absence of any other information, a mixture/substance is considered to cause serious eye damage (Eye Category 1) if it has a pH ≤ 2 or ≥ 11.5. However, if consideration of acid/alkaline reserve suggests the substance may not have the potential to cause serious eye damage despite the low or high pH value, then further evaluation may be necessary. In some cases enough information may be available from structurally related compounds to make classification decisions.

A.3.3.2 A tiered approach to the evaluation of initial information shall be used where applicable, recognizing that all elements may not be relevant in certain cases (Figure A.3.1).

A.3.3.3 The tiered approach explains how to organize existing information on a substance and to make a weight-of-evidence decision, where appropriate, about hazard assessment and hazard classification.

A.3.3.4 All the above information that is available on a substance shall be evaluated. Although information might be gained from the evaluation of single parameters within a tier, consideration should be given to the totality of existing information and making an overall weight of evidence determination. This is especially true when there is conflict in information available on some parameters.

Figure A.3.1
Evaluation strategy for serious eye damage and eye irritation (See also Figure A.2.1)

Step	Parameter	Finding	Conclusion
1a:	Existing human or animal data, eye[1]	Serious Eye Damage	Category 1[2]
		Eye Irritant	Category 2[2]
	↓ No/Insufficient data or unknown ↓		
1b:	Existing human or animal data, skin corrosion[1]	Skin corrosive	Category 1[2]
	↓ No/Insufficient data or unknown ↓		
1c:	Existing human or animal data, eye[1]	Existing data that show that substance does not cause serious eye damage or eye irritation	Not Classified
	↓ No/Insufficient data ↓		
2:	Other, existing skin/eye data in animals[3]	Yes; existing data that show that substance does not cause serious eye damage or eye irritation	Category 1 or Category 2[2]
	↓ No/Insufficient data ↓		
3:	Existing ex vivo / in vitro data[4]	Positive: serious eye damage	Category 1[2]
		Positive: eye irritant	Category 2[2]
	↓ No/Insufficient data / negative responce ↓		
4:	pH-Based assessment (with consideration of buffering capacity of the chemical, or no buffering capacity data)[5]	pH≤ 2 or ≥ 11.5	Category 1[2]
	↓ Not a pH extreme, No pH data or extreme pH with low/no buffering capacity ↓		
5:	Validated Structure/Activity Relationship (SAR) models	Severe damge to eyes	Category 1[2]
		Eye irritant	Category 2[2]
		Skin corrosive	Category 1[2]
	↓ No/Insufficient data ↓		
6:	Consideration of the total Weight of Evidence[6]	Serious eye damage	Category 1[2]
		Eye irritant	Category 2[2]
	↓ No concern based on consideration of the sum of available data ↓		
7:	Not Classified		

Notes to Figure A.3.1:

[1] Evidence of existing human or animal data may be derived from single or repeated exposure(s) in occupational, consumer, transportation, or emergency response scenarios; from ethically-conducted human clinical studies; or from purposely-generated data from animal studies conducted according to scientifically validated test methods. At present, there are no internationally accepted test methods for human skin or eye irritation testing.

[2] Classify in the appropriate harmonized category, as shown in Tables A.3.1 and A.3.2.

[3] Pre-existing animal data should be carefully reviewed to determine if sufficient skin or eye corrosion/irritation evidence is available through other, similar information.

[4] Evidence from studies using scientifically validated protocols with isolated human/animal tissues or other, non-tissue-based, though scientifically validated, protocols should be assessed. Examples of, scientifically validated test methods for identifying eye corrosives and severe irritants (i.e., Serious Eye Damage) include OECD TG 437 (Bovine Corneal Opacity and Permeability (BCOP)) and TG 438 (Isolated Chicken Eye). Positive test results from a scientifically validated in vitro test for skin corrosion would likely also lead to a conclusion to classify as causing Serious Eye Damage.

[5] Measurement of pH alone may be adequate, but assessment of acid or alkali reserve (buffering capacity) would be preferable.

[6] All information that is available on a chemical should be considered and an overall determination made on the total weight of evidence. This is especially true when there is conflict in information available on some parameters. The weight of evidence including information on skin irritation could lead to classification of eye irritation. It is recognized that not all skin irritants are eye irritants as well. Professional judgment should be exercised in making such a determination.

A.3.4 Classification Criteria for Mixtures

A.3.4.1 Classification of mixtures when data are available for the complete mixture

A.3.4.1.1 The mixture will be classified using the criteria for substances

A.3.4.1.2 Unlike other hazard classes, there are alternative tests available for skin corrosivity of certain types of chemicals that can give an accurate result for classification purposes, as well as being simple and relatively inexpensive to perform. When considering testing of the mixture, chemical manufacturers are encouraged to use a tiered weight of evidence strategy as included in the criteria for classification of substances for skin corrosion and serious eye damage and eye irritation to help ensure an accurate classification, as well as avoid unnecessary animal testing. In the absence of any other information, a mixture is considered to cause serious eye damage (Eye Category 1) if it has a pH ≤ 2 or ≥ 11.5. However, if consideration of acid/alkaline reserve suggests the substance or mixture may not have the potential to cause serious eye damage despite the low or high pH value, then further evaluation may be necessary.

A.3.4.2 Classification of mixtures when data are not available for the complete mixture: bridging principles

A.3.4.2.1 Where the mixture itself has not been tested to determine its skin corrosivity or potential to cause serious eye damage or eye irritation, but there are sufficient data on both the individual ingredients and similar tested mixtures to adequately characterize the hazards of the mixture, these data will be used in accordance with the following bridging principles, as found in paragraph A.0.5 of this Appendix: Dilution, Batching, Concentration of mixtures, Interpolation within one toxicity category, Substantially similar mixtures, and Aerosols.

A.3.4.3 Classification of mixtures when data are available for all ingredients or only for some ingredients of the mixture

A.3.4.3.1 For purposes of classifying the eye corrosion/irritation hazards of mixtures in the tiered approach:

The "relevant ingredients" of a mixture are those which are present in concentrations ≥1% (weight/weight for solids, liquids, dusts, mists and vapors and volume/volume for gases.) If the classifier has reason to suspect that an ingredient present at a concentration <1% will affect classification of the mixture for eye corrosion/irritation, that ingredient shall also be considered relevant.

A.3.4.3.2 In general, the approach to classification of mixtures as seriously damaging to the eye or eye irritant when data are available on the ingredients, but not on the mixture as a whole, is based on the theory of additivity, such that each corrosive or irritant ingredient contributes to the overall irritant or corrosive properties of the mixture in proportion to its potency and concentration. A weighting factor of 10 is used for corrosive ingredients when they are present at a concentration below the concentration limit for classification with Category 1, but are at a concentration that will contribute to the classification of the mixture as an irritant. The mixture is classified as seriously damaging to the eye or eye irritant when the sum of the concentrations of such ingredients exceeds a threshold cut-off value/concentration limit.

A.3.4.3.3 Table A.3.3 provides the cut-off value/concentration limits to be used to determine if the mixture should be classified as seriously damaging to the eye or an eye irritant.

A.3.4.3.4 Particular care must be taken when classifying certain types of chemicals such as acids and bases, inorganic salts, aldehydes, phenols, and surfactants. The approach explained in A.3.4.3.1 and A.3.4.3.2 might not work given that many of such substances are corrosive or irritant at concentrations < 1%. For mixtures containing strong acids or bases, the pH should be used as classification criteria (See A.3.4.1) since pH will be a better indicator of serious eye damage than the concentration limits of Table A.3.3. A mixture containing corrosive or irritant ingredients that cannot be classified based on the additivity approach applied in Table A.3.3 due to chemical characteristics that make this approach unworkable, should be classified as Eye Category 1 if it contains ≥ 1% of a corrosive ingredient and as Eye Category 2 when it contains ≥ 3% of an irritant ingredient. Classification of mixtures with ingredients for which the approach in Table A.3.3 does not apply is summarized in Table A.3.4.

A.3.4.3.5 On occasion, reliable data may show that the reversible/irreversible eye effects of an ingredient will not be evident when present at a level above the generic cut-off values/concentration limits mentioned in Tables A.3.3 and A.3.4. In these cases the mixture could be classified according to those data (See also A.0.4.3 Use of cut-off values/concentration limits"). On occasion, when it is expected that the skin corrosion/irritation or the reversible/irreversible eye effects of an ingredient will not be evident when present at a level above the generic concentration/cut-off levels mentioned in Tables A.3.3 and A.3.4, testing of the mixture may be considered. In those cases, the tiered weight of evidence strategy should be applied as referred to in Section A.3.3, Figure A.3.1 and explained in detail in this chapter.

A.3.4.3.6 If there are data showing that (an) ingredient(s) may be corrosive or irritant at a concentration of < 1% (corrosive) or < 3% (irritant), the mixture should be classified accordingly (See also paragraph A.0.4.3, Use of cut-off values/concentration limits).

Table A.3.3
Concentration of Ingredients of a Mixture Classified as Skin Category 1 and/or Eye Category 1 or 2 That Would Trigger Classification of the Mixtures as Hazardous to the Eye

Sum of ingredients classified as:	Concentration triggering classification of a mixture as:	
	Irreversible eye effects	Reversible eye effects
	Category 1	Category 2
Eye or Skin Category 1	≥3%	≥1% but <3%.
Eye Category 2		≥10%.
(10 × Eye Category 1) + Eye Category 2		≥10%.
Skin Category 1 + Eye Category 1	≥3%	≥1% but <3%.
10 × (Skin Category 1 + Eye Category 1) + Eye Category 2		≥10%.

Note: A mixture may be classified as Eye Category 2B in cases when all relevant ingredients are classified as Eye Category 2B.

Table A.3.4
Concentration of Ingredients of a Mixture for Which the Additivity Approach Does Not Apply, That Would Trigger Classification of the Mixture as Hazardous to the Eye

Ingredient	Concentration	Mixture classified as: Eye
Acid with pH ≤2	≥1%	Category 1.
Base with pH ≥11.5	≥1%	Category 1.
Other corrosive (Category 1) ingredients for which additivity does not apply	≥1%	Category 1.
Other irritant (Category 2) ingredients for which additivity does not apply, including acids and bases	≥3%	Category 2.

A.4 RESPIRATORY OR SKIN SENSITIZATION

A.4.1 Definitions and General Considerations

A.4.1.1 Respiratory sensitizer means a chemical that will lead to hypersensitivity of the airways following inhalation of the chemical.

Skin sensitizer means a chemical that will lead to an allergic response following skin contact.

A.4.1.2 For the purpose of this chapter, sensitization includes two phases: the first phase is induction of specialized immunological memory in an individual by exposure to an allergen. The second phase is elicitation, i.e., production of a cell-mediated or antibody-mediated allergic response by exposure of a sensitized individual to an allergen.

A.4.1.3 For respiratory sensitization, the pattern of induction followed by elicitation phases is shared in common with skin sensitization. For skin sensitization, an induction phase is required in which the immune system learns to react; clinical symptoms can then arise when subsequent exposure is sufficient to elicit a visible skin reaction (elicitation phase). As a consequence, predictive tests usually follow this pattern in which there is an induction phase, the response to which is measured by a standardized elicitation phase, typically involving a patch test. The local lymph node assay is the exception, directly measuring the induction response. Evidence of skin sensitization in humans normally is assessed by a diagnostic patch test.

A.4.1.4 Usually, for both skin and respiratory sensitization, lower levels are necessary for elicitation than are required for induction.

A.4.1.5 The hazard class "respiratory or skin sensitization" is differentiated into:

(a) Respiratory sensitization; and
(b) Skin sensitization.

A.4.2 Classification Criteria for Substances

A.4.2.1 Respiratory Sensitizers

A.4.2.1.1 Hazard Categories.

A.4.2.1.1.1 Effects seen in either humans or animals will normally justify classification in a weight of evidence approach for respiratory sensitizers. Substances may be allocated to one of the two sub-categories 1A or 1B using a weight of evidence approach in accordance with the criteria given in Table A.4.1 and on the basis of reliable and good quality evidence from human cases or epidemiological studies and/or observations from appropriate studies in experimental animals.

A.4.2.1.1.2 Where data are not sufficient for sub-categorization, respiratory sensitizers shall be classified in Category 1.

Table A.4.1
Hazard Category and Sub-Categories for Respiratory Sensitizers

Category 1	Respiratory sensitizer
	A substance is classified as a respiratory sensitizer. (a) if there is evidence in humans that the substance can lead to specific respiratory hypersensitivity and/or (b) if there are positive results from an appropriate animal test.[1]
Sub-category 1A	Substances showing a high frequency of occurrence in humans; or a probability of occurrence of a high sensitization rate in humans based on animal or other tests.[1] Severity of reaction may also be considered.
Sub-category 1B	Substances showing a low to moderate frequency of occurrence in humans; or a probability of occurrence of a low to moderate sensitization rate in humans based on animal or other tests.[1] Severity of reaction may also be considered.

[1] At this writing, recognized and validated animal models for the testing of respiratory hypersensitivity are not available. Under certain circumstances, data from animal studies may provide valuable information in a weight of evidence assessment.

A.4.2.1.2 Human evidence.

A.4.2.1.2.1 Evidence that a substance can lead to specific respiratory hypersensitivity will normally be based on human experience. In this context, hypersensitivity is normally seen as asthma, but other hypersensitivity reactions such as rhinitis/conjunctivitis and alveolitis are also considered. The condition will have the clinical character of an allergic reaction. However, immunological mechanisms do not have to be demonstrated.

A.4.2.1.2.2 When considering the human evidence, it is necessary that in addition to the evidence from the cases, the following be taken into account:

(a) The size of the population exposed;
(b) The extent of exposure.

A.4.2.1.2.3 The evidence referred to above could be:

(a) Clinical history and data from appropriate lung function tests related to exposure to the substance, confirmed by other supportive evidence which may include:
  (i) In vivo immunological test (e.g., skin prick test);
  (ii) In vitro immunological test (e.g., serological analysis);
  (iii) Studies that may indicate other specific hypersensitivity reactions where immunological mechanisms of action have not been proven, e.g., repeated low-level irritation, pharmacologically mediated effects;
  (iv) A chemical structure related to substances known to cause respiratory hypersensitivity;

(b) Data from positive bronchial challenge tests with the substance conducted according to accepted guidelines for the determination of a specific hypersensitivity reaction.

A.4.2.1.2.4 Clinical history should include both medical and occupational history to determine a relationship between exposure to a specific substance and development of respiratory hypersensitivity. Relevant information includes aggravating factors both in the home and workplace, the onset and progress of the disease, family history and medical history of the patient in question. The medical history should also include a note of other allergic or airway disorders from childhood and smoking history.

A.4.2.1.2.5 The results of positive bronchial challenge tests are considered to provide sufficient evidence for classification on their own. It is, however, recognized that in practice many of the examinations listed above will already have been carried out.

A.4.2.1.3 Animal studies.

A.4.2.1.3.1 Data from appropriate animal studies[2] which may be indicative of the potential of a substance to cause sensitization by inhalation in humans[3] may include:

(a) Measurements of Immunoglobulin E (IgE) and other specific immunological parameters, for example in mice
(b) Specific pulmonary responses in guinea pigs.

[2] At this writing, recognized and validated animal models for the testing of respiratory hypersensitivity are not available. Under certain circumstances, data from animal studies may provide valuable information in a weight of evidence assessment.

[3] The mechanisms by which substances induce symptoms of asthma are not yet fully known. For preventive measures, these substances are considered respiratory sensitizers. However, if on the basis of the evidence, it can be demonstrated that these substances induce symptoms of asthma by irritation only in people with bronchial hyperactivity, they should not be considered as respiratory sensitizers.

A.4.2.2 Skin Sensitizers

A.4.2.2.1 Hazard categories.

A.4.2.2.1.1 Effects seen in either humans or animals will normally justify classification in a weight of evidence approach for skin sensitizers. Substances may be allocated to one of the two sub-categories 1A or 1B using a weight of evidence approach in accordance with the criteria given in Table A.4.2 and on the basis of reliable and good quality evidence from human cases or epidemiological studies and/or observations from appropriate studies in experimental animals according to the guidance values provided in A.4.2.2.2.1 and A.4.2.2.3.2 for sub-category 1A and in A.4.2.2.2.2 and A.4.2.2.3.3 for sub-category 1B.

A.4.2.2.1.2 Where data are not sufficient for sub-categorization, skin sensitizers shall be classified in Category 1.

Table A.4.2
Hazard Category and Sub-Categories for Skin Sensitizers

Category 1	Skin sensitizer
	A substance is classified as a skin sensitizer. (a) if there is evidence in humans that the substance can lead to sensitization by skin contact in a substantial number of persons, or (b) if there are positive results from an appropriate animal test.
Sub-category 1A	Substances showing a high frequency of occurrence in humans and/or a high potency in animals can be presumed to have the potential to produce significant sensitization in humans. Severity of reaction may also be considered.
Sub-category 1B	Substances showing a low to moderate frequency of occurrence in humans and/or a low to moderate potency in animals can be presumed to have the potential to produce sensitization in humans. Severity of reaction may also be considered.

A.4.2.2.2 Human evidence.

A.4.2.2.2.1 Human evidence for sub-category 1A may include:

(a) Positive responses at ≤500 μg/cm^2 (Human Repeat Insult Patch Test (HRIPT), Human Maximization Test (HMT)—induction threshold);

(b) Diagnostic patch test data where there is a relatively high and substantial incidence of reactions in a defined population in relation to relatively low exposure;

(c) Other epidemiological evidence where there is a relatively high and substantial incidence of allergic contact dermatitis in relation to relatively low exposure.

A.4.2.2.2.2 Human evidence for sub-category 1B may include:

(a) Positive responses at >500 μg/cm^2 (HRIPT, HMT—induction threshold);

(b) Diagnostic patch test data where there is a relatively low but substantial incidence of reactions in a defined population in relation to relatively high exposure;

(c) Other epidemiological evidence where there is a relatively low but substantial incidence of allergic contact dermatitis in relation to relatively high exposure.

A.4.2.2.3 Animal studies

A.4.2.2.3.1 For Category 1, when an adjuvant type test method for skin sensitization is used, a response of at least 30% of the animals is considered as positive. For a non-adjuvant Guinea pig test method a response of at least 15% of the animals is considered positive. For Category 1, a stimulation index of three or more is considered a positive response in the local lymph node assay.[4]

A.4.2.2.3.2 Animal test results for sub-category 1A can include data with values indicated in Table A.4.3 below:

Table A.4.3
Animal Test Results for Sub-Category 1A

Assay	Criteria
Local lymph node assay	EC3 value ≤2%.
Guinea pig maximization test	≥30% responding at ≤0.1% intradermal induction dose or
	≥60% responding at >0.1% to ≤1% intradermal induction dose.
Buehler assay	≥15% responding at ≤0.2% topical induction dose or
	≥60% responding at >0.2% to ≤20% topical induction dose.

Note: EC3 refers to the estimated concentration of test chemical required to induce a stimulation index of 3 in the local lymph node assay.

A.4.2.2.3.3 Animal test results for sub-category 1B can include data with values indicated in Table A.4.4 below:

Table A.4.4
Animal Test Results for Sub-Category 1B

Assay	Criteria
Local lymph node assay	EC3 value >2%.
Guinea pig maximization test	≥30% to <60% responding at >0.1% to ≤1% intradermal induction dose or
	≥30% responding at >1% intradermal induction dose.
Buehler assay	≥15% to <60% responding at >0.2% to ≤20% topical induction dose or
	≥15% responding at >20% topical induction dose.

Note: EC3 refers to the estimated concentration of test chemical required to induce a stimulation index of 3 in the local lymph node assay.

A.4.2.2.4 Specific considerations.

A.4.2.2.4.1 For classification of a substance, evidence shall include one or more of the following using a weight of evidence approach:

(a) Positive data from patch testing, normally obtained in more than one dermatology clinic;

(b) Epidemiological studies showing allergic contact dermatitis caused by the substance. Situations in which a high proportion of those exposed exhibit characteristic symptoms are to be looked at with special concern, even if the number of cases is small;

(c) Positive data from appropriate animal studies;

(d) Positive data from experimental studies in man (See paragraph A.0.2.6 of this Appendix);

(e) Well documented episodes of allergic contact dermatitis, normally obtained in more than one dermatology clinic;

(f) Severity of reaction.

A.4.2.2.4.2 Evidence from animal studies is usually much more reliable than evidence from human exposure. However, in cases where evidence is available from both sources, and there is conflict between the results, the quality and reliability of the evidence from both sources must be assessed in order to resolve the question of classification on a case-by-case basis. Normally, human data are not generated in controlled experiments with volunteers for the purpose of hazard classification but rather as part of risk assessment to confirm lack of effects seen in animal tests. Consequently, positive human data on skin sensitization are usually derived from case-control or other, less defined studies. Evaluation of human data must, therefore, be carried out with caution as the frequency of cases reflect, in addition to the inherent properties of the substances, factors such as the exposure situation, bioavailability, individual predisposition and preventive measures taken. Negative human data should not normally be used to negate positive results from animal studies. For both animal and human data, consideration should be given to the impact of vehicle.

A.4.2.2.4.3 If none of the above-mentioned conditions are met, the substance need not be classified as a skin sensitizer. However, a combination of two or more indicators of skin sensitization, as listed below, may alter the decision. This shall be considered on a case-by-case basis.

(a) Isolated episodes of allergic contact dermatitis;

(b) Epidemiological studies of limited power, e.g., where chance, bias or confounders have not been ruled out fully with reasonable confidence;

(c) Data from animal tests, performed according to existing guidelines, which do not meet the criteria for a positive result described in A.4.2.2.3, but which are sufficiently close to the limit to be considered significant;

(d) Positive data from non-standard methods;

(e) Positive results from close structural analogues.

[4] Test methods for skin sensitization are described in OECD Guideline 406 (the Guinea Pig Maximization test and the Buehler guinea pig test) and Guideline 429 (Local Lymph Node Assay). Other methods may be used provided that they are scientifically validated. The Mouse Ear Swelling Test (MEST), appears to be a reliable screening test to detect moderate to strong sensitizers, and can be used, in accordance with professional judgment, as a first stage in the assessment of skin sensitization potential.

A.4.2.2.4.4 Immunological contact urticaria.

A.4.2.2.4.4.1 Substances meeting the criteria for classification as respiratory sensitizers may, in addition, cause immunological contact urticaria. Consideration shall be given to classifying these substances as skin sensitizers.

A.4.2.2.4.4.2 Substances which cause immunological contact urticaria without meeting the criteria for respiratory sensitizers shall be considered for classification as skin sensitizers.

A.4.2.2.4.4.3 There is no recognized animal model available to identify substances which cause immunological contact urticaria. Therefore, classification will normally be based on human evidence, similar to that for skin sensitization.

A.4.3 Classification Criteria for Mixtures

A.4.3.1 Classification of Mixtures When Data Are Available for the Complete Mixture

When reliable and good quality evidence, as described in the criteria for substances, from human experience or appropriate studies in experimental animals, is available for the mixture, then the mixture shall be classified by weight of evidence evaluation of these data. Care must be exercised in evaluating data on mixtures that the dose used does not render the results inconclusive.

A.4.3.2 Classification of Mixtures When Data Are Not Available for the Complete Mixture: Bridging Principles

A.4.3.2.1 Where the mixture itself has not been tested to determine its sensitizing properties, but there are sufficient data on both the individual ingredients and similar tested mixtures to adequately characterize the hazards of the mixture, these data will be used in accordance with the following agreed bridging principles as found in paragraph A.0.5 of this Appendix: Dilution, Batching, Concentration of mixtures, Interpolation, Substantially similar mixtures, and Aerosols.

A.4.3.3 Classification of Mixtures When Data Are Available for All Ingredients or Only for Some Ingredients of the Mixture

The mixture shall be classified as a respiratory or skin sensitizer when at least one ingredient has been classified as a respiratory or skin sensitizer and is present at or above the appropriate cut-off value/concentration limit for the specific endpoint as shown in Table A.4.5.

Table A.4.5
Cut-Off Values/Concentration Limits of Ingredients of a Mixture Classified as Either Respiratory Sensitizers or Skin Sensitizers That Would Trigger Classification of the Mixture

Ingredient classified as:	Cut-off values/concentration limits triggering classification of a mixture as:		
	Respiratory Sensitizer Category 1		Skin Sensitizer Category 1
	Solid/liquid	Gas	All physical states
Respiratory Sensitizer, Category 1	≥0.1%	≥0.1%	
Respiratory Sensitizer, Sub-category 1A	≥0.1%	≥0.1%	
Respiratory Sensitizer, Sub-category 1B	≥1.0%	≥0.2%	
Skin Sensitizer, Category 1			≥0.1%
Skin Sensitizer, Sub-category 1A			≥0.1%
Skin Sensitizer, Sub-category 1B			≥1.0%

A.5 GERM CELL MUTAGENICITY

A.5.1 Definitions and General Considerations

A.5.1.1 A **mutation** is defined as a permanent change in the amount or structure of the genetic material in a cell. The term mutation applies both to heritable genetic changes that may be manifested at the phenotypic level and to the underlying DNA modifications when known (including, for example, specific base pair changes and chromosomal translocations). The term mutagenic and mutagen will be used for agents giving rise to an increased occurrence of mutations in populations of cells and/or organisms.

A.5.1.2 The more general terms genotoxic and genotoxicity apply to agents or processes which alter the structure, information content, or segregation of DNA, including those which cause DNA damage by interfering with normal replication processes, or which in a non-physiological manner (temporarily) alter its replication. Genotoxicity test results are usually taken as indicators for mutagenic effects.

A.5.1.3 This hazard class is primarily concerned with chemicals that may cause mutations in the germ cells of humans that can be transmitted to the progeny. However, mutagenicity/genotoxicity tests in vitro and in mammalian somatic cells in vivo are also considered in classifying substances and mixtures within this hazard class.

A.5.2 Classification Criteria for Substances

A.5.2.1 The classification system provides for two different categories of germ cell mutagens to accommodate the weight of evidence available. The two-category system is described in the Figure A.5.1.

Figure A.5.1
Hazard Categories for Germ Cell Mutagens

CATEGORY 1: Substances known to induce heritable mutations or to be regarded as if they induce heritable mutations in the germ cells of humans.
Category 1A: Substances known to induce heritable mutations in germ cells of humans. Positive evidence from human epidemiological studies.
Category 1B: Substances which should be regarded as if they induce heritable mutations in the germ cells of humans. (a) Positive result(s) from in vivo heritable germ cell mutagenicity tests in mammals; or (b) Positive result(s) from in vivo somatic cell mutagenicity tests in mammals, in combination with some evidence that the substance has potential to cause mutations to germ cells. This supporting evidence may, for example, be derived from mutagenicity/genotoxicity tests in germ cells in vivo, or by demonstrating the ability of the substance or its metabolite(s) to interact with the genetic material of germ cells; or (c) Positive results from tests showing mutagenic effects in the germ cells of humans, without demonstration of transmission to progeny; for example, an increase in the frequency of aneuploidy in sperm cells of exposed people.
CATEGORY 2: Substances which cause concern for humans owing to the possibility that they may induce heritable mutations in the germ cells of humans.
Positive evidence obtained from experiments in mammals and/or in some cases from in vitro experiments, obtained from: (a) Somatic cell mutagenicity tests in vivo, in mammals; or (b) Other in vivo somatic cell genotoxicity tests which are supported by positive results from in vitro mutagenicity assays.

Note: Substances which are positive in in vitro mammalian mutagenicity assays, and which also show chemical structure activity relationship to known germ cell mutagens, should be considered for classification as Category 2 mutagens.

A.5.2.2 Specific considerations for classification of substances as germ cell mutagens:

A.5.2.2.1 To arrive at a classification, test results are considered from experiments determining mutagenic and/or genotoxic effects in germ and/or somatic cells of exposed animals. Mutagenic and/or genotoxic effects determined in in vitro tests shall also be considered.

A.5.2.2.2 The system is hazard based, classifying chemicals on the basis of their intrinsic ability to induce mutations in germ cells. The scheme is, therefore, not meant for the (quantitative) risk assessment of chemical substances.

A.5.2.2.3 Classification for heritable effects in human germ cells is made on the basis of scientifically validated tests. Evaluation of the test results shall be done using expert judgment and all the available evidence shall be weighed for classification.

A.5.2.2.4 The classification of substances shall be based on the total weight of evidence available, using expert judgment. In those instances where a single well-conducted test is used for classification, it shall provide clear and unambiguous positive results. The relevance of the route of exposure used in the study of the substance compared to the route of human exposure should also be taken into account.

A.5.3 Classification Criteria for Mixtures[5]

A.5.3.1 Classification of Mixtures When Data Are Available for All Ingredients or Only for Some Ingredients of the Mixture

A.5.3.1.1 Classification of mixtures shall be based on the available test data for the individual ingredients of the mixture using cut-off values/concentration limits for the ingredients classified as germ cell mutagens.

A.5.3.1.2 The mixture will be classified as a mutagen when at least one ingredient has been classified as a Category 1A, Category 1B or Category 2 mutagen and is present at or above the appropriate cut-off value/concentration limit as shown in Table A.5.1 below for Category 1 and 2 respectively.

[5] It should be noted that the classification criteria for health hazards usually include a tiered scheme in which test data available on the complete mixture are considered as the first tier in the evaluation, followed by the applicable bridging principles, and lastly, cut-off values/concentration limits or additivity. However, this approach is not used for Germ Cell Mutagenicity. These criteria for Germ Cell Mutagenicity consider the cut-off values/concentration limits as the primary tier and allow the classification to be modified only on a case-by-case evaluation based on available test data for the mixture as a whole.

Table A.5.1
Cut-Off Values/Concentration Limits of Ingredients of a Mixture Classified as Germ Cell Mutagens That Would Trigger Classification of the Mixture

Ingredient classified as:	Cut-off/concentration limits triggering classification of a mixture as:	
	Category 1 mutagen	Category 2 mutagen
Category 1A/B mutagen	≥0.1%	
Category 2 mutagen		≥1.0%

Note: The cut-off values/concentration limits in the table above apply to solids and liquids (w/w units) as well as gases (v/v units).

A.5.3.2 Classification of Mixtures When Data Are Available for the Mixture Itself

The classification may be modified on a case-by-case basis based on the available test data for the mixture as a whole. In such cases, the test results for the mixture as a whole must be shown to be conclusive taking into account dose and other factors such as duration, observations and analysis (e.g. statistical analysis, test sensitivity) of germ cell mutagenicity test systems.

A.5.3.3 Classification of Mixtures When Data Are Not Available for the Complete Mixture: Bridging Principles

A.5.3.3.1 Where the mixture itself has not been tested to determine its germ cell mutagenicity hazard, but there are sufficient data on both the individual ingredients and similar tested mixtures to adequately characterize the hazards of the mixture, these data will be used in accordance with the following bridging principles as found in paragraph A.0.5 of this Appendix: Dilution, Batching, and Substantially similar mixtures.

A.5.4 Examples of Scientifically Validated Test Methods

A.5.4.1 Examples of in vivo heritable germ cell mutagenicity tests are:
(a) Rodent dominant lethal mutation test (OECD 478)
(b) Mouse heritable translocation assay (OECD 485)
(c) Mouse specific locus test

A.5.4.2 Examples of in vivo somatic cell mutagenicity tests are:
(a) Mammalian bone marrow chromosome aberration test (OECD 475)
(b) Mouse spot test (OECD 484)
(c) Mammalian erythrocyte micronucleus test (OECD 474)

A.5.4.3 Examples of mutagenicity/genotoxicity tests in germ cells are:
(a) Mutagenicity tests:
  (i) Mammalian spermatogonial chromosome aberration test (OECD 483)
  (ii) Spermatid micronucleus assay
(b) Genotoxicity tests:
  (i) Sister chromatid exchange analysis in spermatogonia
  (ii) Unscheduled DNA synthesis test (UDS) in testicular cells

A.5.4.4 Examples of genotoxicity tests in somatic cells are:
(a) Liver Unscheduled DNA Synthesis (UDS) in vivo (OECD 486)
(b) Mammalian bone marrow Sister Chromatid Exchanges (SCE)

A.5.4.5 Examples of in vitro mutagenicity tests are:
(a) In vitro mammalian chromosome aberration test (OECD 473)
(b) In vitro mammalian cell gene mutation test (OECD 476)
(c) Bacterial reverse mutation tests (OECD 471)

A.5.4.6 As new, scientifically validated tests arise, these may also be used in the total weight of evidence to be considered.

A.6 CARCINOGENICITY

A.6.1 Definitions

Carcinogen means a substance or a mixture of substances which induce cancer or increase its incidence. Substances and mixtures which have induced benign and malignant tumors in well-performed experimental studies on animals are considered also to be presumed or suspected human carcinogens unless there is strong evidence that the mechanism of tumor formation is not relevant for humans.

Classification of a substance or mixture as posing a carcinogenic hazard is based on its inherent properties and does not provide information on the level of the human cancer risk which the use of the substance or mixture may represent.

A.6.2 Classification Criteria for Substances[6]

A.6.2.1 For the purpose of classification for carcinogenicity, substances are allocated to one of two categories based on strength of evidence and additional weight of evidence considerations. In certain instances, route-specific classification may be warranted.

[6] See Nonmandatory Appendix F Part A for further guidance regarding hazard classification for carcinogenicity. This Appendix is consistent with the GHS and is provided as guidance excerpted from the International Agency for Research on Cancer (IARC) "Monographs on the Evaluation of Carcinogenic Risks to Humans" (2006).

Figure A.6.1
Hazard Categories for Carcinogens

CATEGORY 1: Known or presumed human carcinogens .
The classification of a substance as a Category 1 carcinogen is done on the basis of epidemiological and/or animal data. This classification is further distinguished on the basis of whether the evidence for classification is largely from human data (Category 1A) or from animal data (Category 1B):
Category 1A: Known to have carcinogenic potential for humans. Classification in this category is largely based on human evidence.
Category 1B: Presumed to have carcinogenic potential for humans. Classification in this category is largely based on animal evidence.
The classification of a substance in Category 1A and 1B is based on strength of evidence together with weight of evidence considerations (See paragraph A.6.2.5). Such evidence may be derived from: —human studies that establish a causal relationship between human exposure to a substance and the development of cancer (known human carcinogen); or —animal experiments for which there is sufficient evidence to demonstrate animal carcinogenicity (presumed human carcinogen). In addition, on a case by case basis, scientific judgment may warrant a decision of presumed human carcinogenicity derived from studies showing limited evidence of carcinogenicity in humans together with limited evidence of carcinogenicity in experimental animals.
CATEGORY 2: Suspected human carcinogens.
The classification of a substance in Category 2 is done on the basis of evidence obtained from human and/or animal studies, but which is not sufficiently convincing to place the substance in Category 1A or B. This classification is based on strength of evidence together with weight of evidence considerations (See paragraph A.6.2.5). Such evidence may be from either limited evidence of carcinogenicity in human studies or from limited evidence of carcinogenicity in animal studies.
Other considerations: Where the weight of evidence for the carcinogenicity of a substance does not meet the above criteria, any positive study conducted in accordance with established scientific principles, and which reports statistically significant findings regarding the carcinogenic potential of the substance, must be noted on the safety data sheet.

A.6.2.2 Classification as a carcinogen is made on the basis of evidence from reliable and acceptable methods, and is intended to be used for substances which have an intrinsic property to produce such toxic effects. The evaluations are to be based on all existing data, peer-reviewed published studies and additional data accepted by regulatory agencies.

A.6.2.3 Carcinogen classification is a one-step, criterion-based process that involves two interrelated determinations: evaluations of strength of evidence and consideration of all other relevant information to place substances with human cancer potential into hazard categories.

A.6.2.4 Strength of evidence involves the enumeration of tumors in human and animal studies and determination of their level of statistical significance. Sufficient human evidence demonstrates causality between human exposure and the development of cancer, whereas sufficient evidence in animals shows a causal relationship between the agent and an increased incidence of tumors. Limited evidence in humans is demonstrated by a positive association between exposure and cancer, but a causal relationship cannot be stated. Limited evidence in animals is provided when data suggest a carcinogenic effect, but are less than sufficient. (Guidance on consideration of important factors in the classification of carcinogenicity and a more detailed description of the terms "limited" and "sufficient" have been developed by the International Agency for Research on Cancer (IARC) and are provided in nonmandatory Appendix F).

A.6.2.5 Weight of evidence: Beyond the determination of the strength of evidence for carcinogenicity, a number of other factors should be considered that influence the overall likelihood that an agent may pose a carcinogenic hazard in humans. The full list of factors that influence this determination is very lengthy, but some of the important ones are considered here.

A.6.2.5.1 These factors can be viewed as either increasing or decreasing the level of concern for human carcinogenicity. The relative emphasis accorded to each factor depends upon the amount and coherence of evidence bearing on each. Generally there is a requirement for more complete information to decrease than to increase the level of concern. Additional considerations should be used in evaluating the tumor findings and the other factors in a case-by-case manner.

A.6.2.5.2 Some important factors which may be taken into consideration, when assessing the overall level of concern are:
(a) Tumor type and background incidence;
(b) Multisite responses;
(c) Progression of lesions to malignancy;
(d) Reduced tumor latency;

Additional factors which may increase or decrease the level of concern include:

(e) Whether responses are in single or both sexes;
(f) Whether responses are in a single species or several species;
(g) Structural similarity or not to a substance(s) for which there is good evidence of carcinogenicity;
(h) Routes of exposure;
(i) Comparison of absorption, distribution, metabolism and excretion between test animals and humans;
(j) The possibility of a confounding effect of excessive toxicity at test doses; and,
(k) Mode of action and its relevance for humans, such as mutagenicity, cytotoxicity with growth stimulation, mitogenesis, immunosuppression.

Mutagenicity: It is recognized that genetic events are central in the overall process of cancer development. Therefore evidence of mutagenic activity in vivo may indicate that a substance has a potential for carcinogenic effects.

A.6.2.5.3 A substance that has not been tested for carcinogenicity may in certain instances be classified in Category 1A, Category 1B, or Category 2 based on tumor data from a structural analogue together with substantial support from consideration of other important factors such as formation of common significant metabolites, e.g., for benzidine congener dyes.

A.6.2.5.4 The classification should also take into consideration whether or not the substance is absorbed by a given route(s); or whether there are only local tumors at the site of administration for the tested route(s), and adequate testing by other major route(s) show lack of carcinogenicity.

A.6.2.5.5 It is important that whatever is known of the physico-chemical, toxicokinetic and toxicodynamic properties of the substances, as well as any available relevant information on chemical analogues, i.e., structure activity relationship, is taken into consideration when undertaking classification.

A.6.3 Classification Criteria for Mixtures[7]

A.6.3.1 The mixture shall be classified as a carcinogen when at least one ingredient has been classified as a Category 1 or Category 2 carcinogen and is present at or above the appropriate cut-off value/concentration limit as shown in Table A.6.1.

Table A.6.1

Cut-Off Values/Concentration Limits of Ingredients of a Mixture Classified as Carcinogen That Would Trigger Classification of the Mixture

Ingredient classified as:	Category 1 carcinogen	Category 2 carcinogen
Category 1 carcinogen	≥0.1%	
Category 2 carcinogen		≥0.1% (note 1).

Note: If a Category 2 carcinogen ingredient is present in the mixture at a concentration between 0.1% and 1%, information is required on the SDS for a product. However, a label warning is optional. If a Category 2 carcinogen ingredient is present in the mixture at a concentration of ≥1%, both an SDS and a label is required and the information must be included on each.

A.6.3.2 Classification of Mixtures When Data Are Available for the Complete Mixture

A mixture may be classified based on the available test data for the mixture as a whole. In such cases, the test results for the mixture as a whole must be shown to be conclusive taking into account dose and other factors such as duration, observations and analysis (e.g., statistical analysis, test sensitivity) of carcinogenicity test systems.

A.6.3.3 Classification of Mixtures When Data Are Not Available for the Complete Mixture: Bridging Principles

Where the mixture itself has not been tested to determine its carcinogenic hazard, but there are sufficient data on both the individual ingredients and similar tested mixtures to adequately characterize the hazards of the mixture, these data will be used in accordance with the following bridging principles as found in paragraph A.0.5 of this Appendix: Dilution; Batching; and Substantially similar mixtures.

A.6.4 Classification of Carcinogenicity[8]

A.6.4.1 Chemical manufacturers, importers and employers evaluating chemicals may treat the following sources as establishing that a substance is a carcinogen or potential carcinogen for hazard communication purposes in lieu of applying the criteria described herein:

A.6.4.1.1 National Toxicology Program (NTP), "Report on Carcinogens" (latest edition);

A.6.4.1.2 International Agency for Research on Cancer (IARC) "Monographs on the Evaluation of Carcinogenic Risks to Humans" (latest editions)

A.6.4.2 Where OSHA has included cancer as a health hazard to be considered by classifiers for a chemical covered by 29 CFR Part §1910, Subpart Z, Toxic and Hazardous Substances, chemical manufacturers, importers, and employers shall classify the chemical as a carcinogen.

A.7 REPRODUCTIVE TOXICITY

A.7.1 Definitions and General Considerations

A.7.1.1 Reproductive toxicity includes adverse effects on sexual function and fertility in adult males and females, as well as adverse effects on development of the offspring. Some reproductive toxic effects cannot be clearly assigned to either impairment of sexual function and fertility or to developmental toxicity. Nonetheless, chemicals with these effects shall be classified as reproductive toxicants.

For classification purposes, the known induction of genetically based inheritable effects in the offspring is addressed in Germ cell mutagenicity (See A.5).

A.7.1.2 Adverse effects on sexual function and fertility means any effect of chemicals that interferes with reproductive ability or sexual capacity. This includes, but is not limited to, alterations to the female and male reproductive system, adverse effects on onset of puberty, gamete production and transport, reproductive cycle normality, sexual behavior, fertility, parturition, pregnancy outcomes, premature reproductive senescence, or modifications in other functions that are dependent on the integrity of the reproductive systems.

A.7.1.3 Adverse effects on development of the offspring means any effect of chemicals which interferes with normal development of the conceptus either before or after birth, which is induced during pregnancy or results from parental exposure. These effects can be manifested at any point in the life span of the organism. The major manifestations of developmental toxicity include death of the developing organism, structural abnormality, altered growth and functional deficiency.

A.7.1.4 Adverse effects on or via lactation are also included in reproductive toxicity, but for classification purposes, such effects are treated separately (See A.7.2.1).

A.7.2 Classification Criteria for Substances

A.7.2.1 For the purpose of classification for reproductive toxicity, substances shall be classified in one of two categories in accordance with Figure A.7.1(a). Effects on sexual function and fertility, and on development, shall be considered. In addition, effects on or via lactation shall be classified in a separate hazard category in accordance with Figure A.7.1(b).

Figure A.7.1(a)

Hazard Categories for Reproductive Toxicants

CATEGORY 1: Known or presumed human reproductive toxicant.
Substance shall be classified in Category 1 for reproductive toxicity when they are known to have produced an adverse effect on sexual function and fertility or on development in humans or when there is evidence from animal studies, possibly supplemented with other information, to provide a strong presumption that the substance has the capacity to interfere with reproduction in humans. The classification of a substance is further distinguished on the basis of whether the evidence for classification is primarily from human data (Category 1A) or from animal data (Category 1B).
Category 1A: Known human reproductive toxicant.
The classification of a substance in this category is largely based on evidence from humans.
Category 1B: Presumed human reproductive toxicant.
The classification of a substance in this category is largely based on evidence from experimental animals. Data from animal studies shall provide sufficient evidence of an adverse effect on sexual function and fertility or on development in the absence of other toxic effects, or if occurring together with other toxic effects the adverse effect on reproduction is considered not to be a secondary non-specific consequence of other toxic effects. However, when there is mechanistic information that raises doubt about the relevance of the effect for humans, classification in Category 2 may be more appropriate.
CATEGORY 2: Suspected human reproductive toxicant.
Substances shall be classified in Category 2 for reproductive toxicity when there is some evidence from humans or experimental animals, possibly supplemented with other information, of an adverse effect on sexual function and fertility, or on development, in the absence of other toxic effects, or if occurring together with other toxic effects the adverse effect on reproduction is considered not to be a secondary non-specific consequence of the other toxic effects, and where the evidence is not sufficiently convincing to place the substance in Category 1. For instance, deficiencies in the study may make the quality of evidence less convincing, and in view of this, Category 2 would be the more appropriate classification.

[7] It should be noted that the classification criteria for health hazards usually include a tiered scheme in which test data available on the complete mixture are considered as the first tier in the evaluation, followed by the applicable bridging principles, and lastly, cut-off values/concentration limit or additivity. However, this approach is not used for Carcinogenicity. These criteria for Carcinogenicity consider the cut-off values/concentration limits as the primary tier and allow the classification to be modified only on a case-by-case evaluation based on available test data for the mixture as a whole.

[8] See Nonmandatory Appendix F for further guidance regarding hazard classification for carcinogenicity and how to relate carcinogenicity classification information from IARC and NTP to GHS.

Figure A.7.1(b)
Hazard Category for Effects on or Via Lactation

EFFECTS ON OR VIA LACTATION
Effects on or via lactation shall be classified in a separate single category. Chemicals that are absorbed by women and have been shown to interfere with lactation or that may be present (including metabolites) in breast milk in amounts sufficient to cause concern for the health of a breastfed child, shall be classified to indicate this property hazardous to breastfed babies. This classification shall be assigned on the basis of:
(a) absorption, metabolism, distribution and excretion studies that indicate the likelihood the substance would be present in potentially toxic levels in breast milk; and/or (b) results of one or two generation studies in animals which provide clear evidence of adverse effect in the offspring due to transfer in the milk or adverse effect on the quality of the milk; and/or (c) human evidence indicating a hazard to babies during the lactation period.

A.7.2.2 Basis of Classification

A.7.2.2.1 Classification is made on the basis of the criteria, outlined above, an assessment of the total weight of evidence, and the use of expert judgment. Classification as a reproductive toxicant is intended to be used for substances which have an intrinsic, specific property to produce an adverse effect on reproduction and substances should not be so classified if such an effect is produced solely as a non-specific secondary consequence of other toxic effects.

A.7.2.2.2 In the evaluation of toxic effects on the developing offspring, it is important to consider the possible influence of maternal toxicity.

A.7.2.2.3 For human evidence to provide the primary basis for a Category 1A classification there must be reliable evidence of an adverse effect on reproduction in humans. Evidence used for classification shall be from well conducted epidemiological studies, if available, which include the use of appropriate controls, balanced assessment, and due consideration of bias or confounding factors. Less rigorous data from studies in humans may be sufficient for a Category 1A classification if supplemented with adequate data from studies in experimental animals, but classification in Category 1B may also be considered.

A.7.2.3 Weight of Evidence

A.7.2.3.1 Classification as a reproductive toxicant is made on the basis of an assessment of the total weight of evidence using expert judgment. This means that all available information that bears on the determination of reproductive toxicity is considered together. Included is information such as epidemiological studies and case reports in humans and specific reproduction studies along with sub-chronic, chronic and special study results in animals that provide relevant information regarding toxicity to reproductive and related endocrine organs. Evaluation of substances chemically related to the material under study may also be included, particularly when information on the material is scarce. The weight given to the available evidence will be influenced by factors such as the quality of the studies, consistency of results, nature and severity of effects, level of statistical significance for intergroup differences, number of endpoints affected, relevance of route of administration to humans and freedom from bias. Both positive and negative results are considered together in a weight of evidence determination. However, a single, positive study performed according to good scientific principles and with statistically or biologically significant positive results may justify classification (See also A.7.2.2.3).

A.7.2.3.2 Toxicokinetic studies in animals and humans, site of action and mechanism or mode of action study results may provide relevant information, which could reduce or increase concerns about the hazard to human health. If it is conclusively demonstrated that the clearly identified mechanism or mode of action has no relevance for humans or when the toxicokinetic differences are so marked that it is certain that the hazardous property will not be expressed in humans then a chemical which produces an adverse effect on reproduction in experimental animals should not be classified.

A.7.2.3.3 In some reproductive toxicity studies in experimental animals the only effects recorded may be considered of low or minimal toxicological significance and classification may not necessarily be the outcome. These effects include, for example, small changes in semen parameters or in the incidence of spontaneous defects in the fetus, small changes in the proportions of common fetal variants such as are observed in skeletal examinations, or in fetal weights, or small differences in postnatal developmental assessments.

A.7.2.3.4 Data from animal studies shall provide sufficient evidence of specific reproductive toxicity in the absence of other systemic toxic effects. However, if developmental toxicity occurs together with other toxic effects in the dam (mother), the potential influence of the generalized adverse effects should be assessed to the extent possible. The preferred approach is to consider adverse effects in the embryo/fetus first, and then evaluate maternal toxicity, along with any other factors which are likely to have influenced these effects, as part of the weight of evidence. In general, developmental effects that are observed at maternally toxic doses should not be automatically discounted. Discounting developmental effects that are observed at maternally toxic doses can only be done on a case-by-case basis when a causal relationship is established or refuted.

A.7.2.3.5 If appropriate information is available it is important to try to determine whether developmental toxicity is due to a specific maternally mediated mechanism or to a non-specific secondary mechanism, like maternal stress and the disruption of homeostasis. Generally, the presence of maternal toxicity should not be used to negate findings of embryo/fetal effects, unless it can be clearly demonstrated that the effects are secondary non-specific effects. This is especially the case when the effects in the offspring are significant, e.g., irreversible effects such as structural malformations. In some situations it is reasonable to assume that reproductive toxicity is due to a secondary consequence of maternal toxicity and discount the effects, for example if the chemical is so toxic that dams fail to thrive and there is severe inanition; they are incapable of nursing pups; or they are prostrate or dying.

A.7.2.4 Maternal Toxicity

A.7.2.4.1 Development of the offspring throughout gestation and during the early postnatal stages can be influenced by toxic effects in the mother either through non-specific mechanisms related to stress and the disruption of maternal homeostasis, or by specific maternally-mediated mechanisms. So, in the interpretation of the developmental outcome to decide classification for developmental effects it is important to consider the possible influence of maternal toxicity. This is a complex issue because of uncertainties surrounding the relationship between maternal toxicity and developmental outcome. Expert judgment and a weight of evidence approach, using all available studies, shall be used to determine the degree of influence to be attributed to maternal toxicity when interpreting the criteria for classification for developmental effects. The adverse effects in the embryo/fetus shall be first considered, and then maternal toxicity, along with any other factors which are likely to have influenced these effects, as weight of evidence, to help reach a conclusion about classification.

A.7.2.4.2 Based on pragmatic observation, it is believed that maternal toxicity may, depending on severity, influence development via non-specific secondary mechanisms, producing effects such as depressed fetal weight, retarded ossification, and possibly resorptions and certain malformations in some strains of certain species. However, the limited numbers of studies which have investigated the relationship between developmental effects and general maternal toxicity have failed to demonstrate a consistent, reproducible relationship across species. Developmental effects which occur even in the presence of maternal toxicity are considered to be evidence of developmental toxicity, unless it can be unequivocally demonstrated on a case by case basis that the developmental effects are secondary to maternal toxicity. Moreover, classification shall be considered where there is a significant toxic effect in the offspring, e.g., irreversible effects such as structural malformations, embryo/fetal lethality, or significant post-natal functional deficiencies.

A.7.2.4.3 Classification shall not automatically be discounted for chemicals that produce developmental toxicity only in association with maternal toxicity, even if a specific maternally-mediated mechanism has been demonstrated. In such a case, classification in Category 2 may be considered more appropriate than Category 1. However, when a chemical is so toxic that maternal death or severe inanition results, or the dams (mothers) are prostrate and incapable of nursing the pups, it is reasonable to assume that developmental toxicity is produced solely as a secondary consequence of maternal toxicity and discount the developmental effects. Classification is not necessarily the outcome in the case of minor developmental changes, e.g., a small reduction in fetal/pup body weight or retardation of ossification when seen in association with maternal toxicity.

A.7.2.4.4 Some of the endpoints used to assess maternal toxicity are provided below. Data on these endpoints, if available, shall be evaluated in light of their statistical or biological significance and dose-response relationship.

(a) Maternal mortality: An increased incidence of mortality among the treated dams over the controls shall be considered evidence of maternal toxicity if the increase occurs in a dose-related manner and can be attributed to the systemic toxicity of the test material. Maternal mortality greater than 10% is considered excessive and the data for that dose level shall not normally be considered to need further evaluation.

(b) Mating index (Number of animals with seminal plugs or sperm/Number of mated × 100)

(c) Fertility index (Number of animals with implants/Number of matings × 100)

(d) Gestation length (If allowed to deliver)

(e) Body weight and body weight change: Consideration of the maternal body weight change and/or adjusted (corrected) maternal body weight shall be included in the evaluation of maternal toxicity whenever such data are available. The calculation of an adjusted (corrected) mean maternal body weight change, which is the difference between the initial and terminal body weight minus the gravid uterine weight (or alternatively, the sum of the weights of the fetuses), may indicate whether the effect is maternal or intrauterine. In rabbits, the body weight gain may not be a useful indicator of maternal toxicity because of normal fluctuations in body weight during pregnancy.

(f) Food and water consumption (if relevant): The observation of a significant decrease in the average food or water consumption in treated dams (mothers) compared to the control group may be useful in evaluating maternal toxicity, particularly when the test material is administered in the diet or drinking water. Changes in food or water consumption must be evaluated in conjunction with maternal body weights when determining if the effects noted are reflective of maternal toxicity or more simply, unpalatability of the test material in feed or water.

(g) Clinical evaluations (including clinical signs, markers, and hematology and clinical chemistry studies): The observation of increased incidence of significant clinical signs of toxicity in treated dams (mothers) relative to the control group is useful in evaluating maternal toxicity. If this is to be used as the basis for the assessment of maternal toxicity, the types, incidence, degree and duration of clinical signs shall be reported in the study. Clinical signs of maternal intoxication include, but are not limited to: coma, prostration, hyperactivity, loss of righting reflex, ataxia, or labored breathing.

(h) Post-mortem data: Increased incidence and/or severity of post-mortem findings may be indicative of maternal toxicity. This can include gross or microscopic pathological findings or organ weight data, including absolute organ weight, organ-to-body weight ratio, or organ-to-brain weight ratio. When supported by findings of adverse histopathological effects in the affected organ(s), the observation of a significant change in the average weight of suspected target organ(s) of treated dams (mothers), compared to those in the control group, may be considered evidence of maternal toxicity.

A.7.2.5 Animal and Experimental Data

A.7.2.5.1 A number of scientifically validated test methods are available, including methods for developmental toxicity testing (e.g., OECD Test Guideline 414, ICH Guideline S5A, 1993), methods for peri- and post-natal toxicity testing (e.g., ICH S5B, 1995), and methods for one or two-generation toxicity testing (e.g., OECD Test Guidelines 415, 416)

A.7.2.5.2 Results obtained from screening tests (e.g., OECD Guidelines 421—Reproduction/Developmental Toxicity Screening Test, and 422—Combined Repeated Dose Toxicity Study with Reproduction/Development Toxicity Screening Test) can also be used to justify classification, although the quality of this evidence is less reliable than that obtained through full studies.

A.7.2.5.3 Adverse effects or changes, seen in short- or long-term repeated dose toxicity studies, which are judged likely to impair reproductive function and which occur in the absence of significant generalized toxicity, may be used as a basis for classification, e.g., histopathological changes in the gonads.

A.7.2.5.4 Evidence from in vitro assays, or non-mammalian tests, and from analogous substances using structure-activity relationship (SAR), can contribute to the procedure for classification. In all cases of this nature, expert judgment must be used to assess the adequacy of the data. Inadequate data shall not be used as a primary support for classification.

A.7.2.5.5 It is preferable that animal studies are conducted using appropriate routes of administration which relate to the potential route of human exposure. However, in practice, reproductive toxicity studies are commonly conducted using the oral route, and such studies will normally be suitable for evaluating the hazardous properties of the substance with respect to reproductive toxicity. However, if it can be conclusively demonstrated that the clearly identified mechanism or mode of action has no relevance for humans or when the toxicokinetic differences are so marked that it is certain that the hazardous property will not be expressed in humans then a substance which produces an adverse effect on reproduction in experimental animals should not be classified.

A.7.2.5.6 Studies involving routes of administration such as intravenous or intraperitoneal injection, which may result in exposure of the reproductive organs to unrealistically high levels of the test substance, or elicit local damage to the reproductive organs, e.g., by irritation, must be interpreted with extreme caution and on their own are not normally the basis for classification.

A.7.2.5.7 There is general agreement about the concept of a limit dose, above which the production of an adverse effect may be considered to be outside the criteria which lead to classification. Some test guidelines specify a limit dose, other test guidelines qualify the limit dose with a statement that higher doses may be necessary if anticipated human exposure is sufficiently high that an adequate margin of exposure would not be achieved. Also, due to species differences in toxicokinetics, establishing a specific limit dose may not be adequate for situations where humans are more sensitive than the animal model.

A.7.2.5.8 In principle, adverse effects on reproduction seen only at very high dose levels in animal studies (for example doses that induce prostration, severe inappetence, excessive mortality) do not normally lead to classification, unless other information is available, for example, toxicokinetics information indicating that humans may be more susceptible than animals, to suggest that classification is appropriate.

A.7.2.5.9 However, specification of the actual "limit dose" will depend upon the test method that has been employed to provide the test results.

A.7.3 Classification Criteria for Mixtures[9]

A.7.3.1 Classification of Mixtures When Data Are Available for All Ingredients or Only for Some Ingredients of the Mixture

A.7.3.1.1 The mixture shall be classified as a reproductive toxicant when at least one ingredient has been classified as a Category 1 or Category 2 reproductive toxicant and is present at or above the appropriate cut-off value/concentration limit specified in Table A.7.1 for Category 1 and 2, respectively.

A.7.3.1.2 The mixture shall be classified for effects on or via lactation when at least one ingredient has been classified for effects on or via lactation and is present at or above the appropriate cut-off value/concentration limit specified in Table A.7.1 for the additional category for effects on or via lactation.

Table A.7.1
Cut-Off Values/Concentration Limits of Ingredients of a Mixture Classified as Reproductive Toxicants or for Effects on or via Lactation That Trigger Classification of the Mixture

Ingredients classified as:	Cut-off values/concentration limits triggering classification of a mixture as:		
	Category 1 reproductive toxicant	Category 2 reproductive toxicant	Additional category for effects on or via lactation
Category 1 reproductive toxicant	≥0.1%		
Category 2 reproductive toxicant		≥0.1%	
Additional category for effects on or via lactation			≥0.1%

A.7.3.2 Classification of Mixtures When Data Are Available for the Complete Mixture

Available test data for the mixture as a whole may be used for classification on a case-by-case basis. In such cases, the test results for the mixture as a whole must be shown to be conclusive taking into account dose and other factors such as duration, observations and analysis (e.g., statistical analysis, test sensitivity) of reproduction test systems.

A.7.3.3 Classification of Mixtures When Data Are Not Available for the Complete Mixture: Bridging Principles

A.7.3.3.1 Where the mixture itself has not been tested to determine its reproductive toxicity, but there are sufficient data on both the individual ingredients and similar tested mixtures to adequately characterize the hazards of the mixture, these data shall be used in accordance with the following bridging principles as found in paragraph A.0.5 of this Appendix: Dilution, Batching, and Substantially similar mixtures.

A.8 SPECIFIC TARGET ORGAN TOXICITY SINGLE EXPOSURE

A.8.1 Definitions and General Considerations

A.8.1.1 Specific target organ toxicity—single exposure, (STOT–SE) means specific, non-lethal target organ toxicity arising from a single exposure to a chemical. All significant health effects that can impair function, both reversible and irreversible, immediate and/or delayed and not specifically addressed in A.1 to A.7 and A.10 of this Appendix are included. Specific target organ toxicity following repeated exposure is classified in accordance with SPECIFIC TARGET ORGAN TOXICITY—REPEATED EXPOSURE (A.9 of this Appendix) and is therefore not included here.

A.8.1.2 Classification identifies the chemical as being a specific target organ toxicant and, as such, it presents a potential for adverse health effects in people who are exposed to it.

A.8.1.3 The adverse health effects produced by a single exposure include consistent and identifiable toxic effects in humans; or, in experimental animals, toxicologically significant changes which have affected the function or morphology of a tissue/organ, or have produced serious changes to the biochemistry or hematology of the organism, and these changes are relevant for human health. Human data is the primary source of evidence for this hazard class.

A.8.1.4 Assessment shall take into consideration not only significant changes in a single organ or biological system but also generalized changes of a less severe nature involving several organs.

[9] It should be noted that the classification criteria for health hazards usually include a tiered scheme in which test data available on the complete mixture are considered as the first tier in the evaluation, followed by the applicable bridging principles, and lastly, cut-off values/concentration limits or additivity. However, this approach is not used for Reproductive Toxicity. These criteria for Reproductive Toxicity consider the cut-off values/concentration limits as the primary tier and allow the classification to be modified only on a case-by-case evaluation based on available test data for the mixture as a whole.

A.8.1.4 Assessment shall take into consideration not only significant changes in a single organ or biological system but also generalized changes of a less severe nature involving several organs.

A.8.1.5 Specific target organ toxicity can occur by any route that is relevant for humans, i.e., principally oral, dermal or inhalation.

A.8.1.6 The classification criteria for specific organ systemic toxicity single exposure are organized as criteria for substances Categories 1 and 2 (See A.8.2.1), criteria for substances Category 3 (See A.8.2.2) and criteria for mixtures (See A.8.3). See also Figure A.8.1.

A.8.2 Classification Criteria for Substances

A.8.2.1 Substances of Category 1 and Category 2

A.8.2.1.1 Substances shall be classified for immediate or delayed effects separately, by the use of expert judgment on the basis of the weight of all evidence available, including the use of recommended guidance values (See A.8.2.1.9). Substances shall then be classified in Category 1 or 2, depending upon the nature and severity of the effect(s) observed, in accordance with Figure A.8.1.

Figure A.8.1
Hazard Categories for Specific Target Organ Toxicity Following Single Exposure

CATEGORY 1:
Substances that have produced significant toxicity in humans, or that, on the basis of evidence from studies in experimental animals can be presumed to have the potential to produce significant toxicity in humans following single exposure Substances are classified in Category 1 for STOT-SE on the basis of: (a) reliable and good quality evidence from human cases or epidemiological studies; or (b) observations from appropriate studies in experimental animals in which significant and/or severe toxic effects of relevance to human health were produced at generally low exposure concentrations. Guidance dose/concentration values are provided below (See A.8.2.1.9) to be used as part of weight-of-evidence evaluation.
CATEGORY 2:
Substances that, on the basis of evidence from studies in experimental animals, can be presumed to have the potential to be harmful to human health following single exposure Substances are classified in Category 2 for STOT-SE on the basis of observations from appropriate studies in experimental animals in which significant toxic effects, of relevance to human health, were produced at generally moderate exposure concentrations. Guidance dose/concentration values are provided below (See A.8.2.1.9) in order to help in classification. In exceptional cases, human evidence can also be used to place a substance in Category 2 (See A.8.2.1.6).
CATEGORY 3:
Transient target organ effects There are target organ effects for which a substance does not meet the criteria to be classified in Categories 1 or 2 indicated above. These are effects which adversely alter human function for a short duration after exposure and from which humans may recover in a reasonable period without leaving significant alteration of structure or function. This category only includes narcotic effects and respiratory tract irritation. Substances are classified specifically for these effects as discussed in A.8.2.2.

Note: The primary target organ/system shall be identified where possible, and where this is not possible, the substance shall be identified as a general toxicant. The data shall be evaluated and, where possible, shall not include secondary effects (e.g., a hepatotoxicant can produce secondary effects in the nervous or gastro-intestinal systems).

A.8.2.1.2 The relevant route(s) of exposure by which the classified substance produces damage shall be identified.

A.8.2.1.3 Classification is determined by expert judgment, on the basis of the weight of all evidence available including the guidance presented below.

A.8.2.1.4 Weight of evidence of all available data, including human incidents, epidemiology, and studies conducted in experimental animals is used to substantiate specific target organ toxic effects that merit classification.

A.8.2.1.5 The information required to evaluate specific target organ toxicity comes either from single exposure in humans (e.g., exposure at home, in the workplace or environmentally), or from studies conducted in experimental animals. The standard animal studies in rats or mice that provide this information are acute toxicity studies which can include clinical observations and detailed macroscopic and microscopic examination to enable the toxic effects on target tissues/organs to be identified. Results of acute toxicity studies conducted in other species may also provide relevant information.

A.8.2.1.6 In exceptional cases, based on expert judgment, it may be appropriate to place certain substances with human evidence of target organ toxicity in Category 2: (a) when the weight of human evidence is not sufficiently convincing to warrant Category 1 classification, and/or (b) based on the nature and severity of effects. Dose/concentration levels in humans shall not be considered in the classification and any available evidence from animal studies shall be consistent with the Category 2 classification. In other words, if there are also animal data available on the substance that warrant Category 1 classification, the chemical shall be classified as Category 1.

A.8.2.1.7 Effects considered to support classification for Category 1 and 2

A.8.2.1.7.1 Classification is supported by evidence associating single exposure to the substance with a consistent and identifiable toxic effect.

A.8.2.1.7.2 Evidence from human experience/incidents is usually restricted to reports of adverse health consequences, often with uncertainty about exposure conditions, and may not provide the scientific detail that can be obtained from well-conducted studies in experimental animals.

A.8.2.1.7.3 Evidence from appropriate studies in experimental animals can furnish much more detail, in the form of clinical observations, and macroscopic and microscopic pathological examination and this can often reveal hazards that may not be life-threatening but could indicate functional impairment. Consequently all available evidence, and evidence relevance to human health, must be taken into consideration in the classification process. Relevant toxic effects in humans and/or animals include, but are not limited to:

(a) Morbidity resulting from single exposure;

(b) Significant functional changes, more than transient in nature, in the respiratory system, central or peripheral nervous systems, other organs or other organ systems, including signs of central nervous system depression and effects on special senses (e.g., sight, hearing and sense of smell);

(c) Any consistent and significant adverse change in clinical biochemistry, hematology, or urinalysis parameters;

(d) Significant organ damage that may be noted at necropsy and/or subsequently seen or confirmed at microscopic examination;

(e) Multi-focal or diffuse necrosis, fibrosis or granuloma formation in vital organs with regenerative capacity;

(f) Morphological changes that are potentially reversible but provide clear evidence of marked organ dysfunction; and,

(g) Evidence of appreciable cell death (including cell degeneration and reduced cell number) in vital organs incapable of regeneration.

A.8.2.1.8 Effects considered not to support classification for Category 1 and 2

Effects may be seen in humans and/or animals that do not justify classification. Such effects include, but are not limited to:

(a) Clinical observations or small changes in bodyweight gain, food consumption or water intake that may have some toxicological importance but that do not, by themselves, indicate "significant" toxicity;

(b) Small changes in clinical biochemistry, hematology or urinalysis parameters and/or transient effects, when such changes or effects are of doubtful or of minimal toxicological importance;

(c) Changes in organ weights with no evidence of organ dysfunction;

(d) Adaptive responses that are not considered toxicologically relevant; and,

(e) Substance-induced species-specific mechanisms of toxicity, i.e., demonstrated with reasonable certainty to be not relevant for human health, shall not justify classification.

A.8.2.1.9 Guidance values to assist with classification based on the results obtained from studies conducted in experimental animals for Category 1 and 2

A.8.2.1.9.1 In order to help reach a decision about whether a substance shall be classified or not, and to what degree it shall be classified (Category 1 vs. Category 2), dose/concentration "guidance values" are provided for consideration of the dose/concentration which has been shown to produce significant health effects. The principal argument for proposing such guidance values is that all chemicals are potentially toxic and there has to be a reasonable dose/concentration above which a degree of toxic effect is acknowledged.

A.8.2.1.9.2 Thus, in animal studies, when significant toxic effects are observed that indicate classification, consideration of the dose/concentration at which these effects were seen, in relation to the suggested guidance values, provides useful information to help assess the need to classify (since the toxic effects are a consequence of the hazardous property(ies) and also the dose/concentration).

A.8.2.1.9.3 The guidance value (C) ranges for single-dose exposure which has produced a significant non-lethal toxic effect are those applicable to acute toxicity testing, as indicated in Table A.8.1.

Table A.8.1
Guidance Value Ranges for Single-Dose Exposures

Route of exposure	Units	Guidance value ranges for:		
		Category 1	Category 2	Category 3
Oral (rat)	mg/kg body weight	C ≤300	2000 ≥C >300	Guidance values do not apply.
Dermal (rat or rabbit)	mg/kg body weight	C ≤1,000	2000 ≥C >1,000	
Inhalation (rat) gas	ppmV/4h	C ≤2,500	20,000 ≥C >2,500	
Inhalation (rat) vapor	mg/1/4h	C ≤10	20 ≥C >10	
Inhalation (rat) dust/ mist/fume	mg/l/4h	C ≤1.0	5.0 ≥C >1.0	

A.8.2.1.9.4 The guidance values and ranges mentioned in Table A.8.1 are intended only for guidance purposes, i.e., to be used as part of the weight of evidence approach, and to assist with decisions about classification. They are not intended as strict demarcation values. Guidance values are not provided for Category 3 since this classification is primarily based on human data; animal data may be included in the weight of evidence evaluation.

A.8.2.1.9.5 Thus, it is feasible that a specific profile of toxicity occurs at a dose/concentration below the guidance value, e.g., <2000 mg/kg body weight by the oral route, however the nature of the effect may result in the decision not to classify. Conversely, a specific profile of toxicity may be seen in animal studies occurring at above a guidance value, e.g., ≥2000 mg/kg body weight by the oral route, and in addition there is supplementary information from other sources, e.g., other single dose studies, or human case experience, which supports a conclusion that, in view of the weight of evidence, classification is the prudent action to take.

A.8.2.1.10 Other considerations

A.8.2.1.10.1 When a substance is characterized only by use of animal data the classification process includes reference to dose/concentration guidance values as one of the elements that contribute to the weight of evidence approach.

A.8.2.1.10.2 When well-substantiated human data are available showing a specific target organ toxic effect that can be reliably attributed to single exposure to a substance, the substance shall be classified. Positive human data, regardless of probable dose, predominates over animal data. Thus, if a substance is unclassified because specific target organ toxicity observed was considered not relevant or significant to humans, if subsequent human incident data become available showing a specific target organ toxic effect, the substance shall be classified.

A.8.2.1.10.3 A substance that has not been tested for specific target organ toxicity shall, where appropriate, be classified on the basis of data from a scientifically validated structure activity relationship and expert judgment-based extrapolation from a structural analogue that has previously been classified together with substantial support from consideration of other important factors such as formation of common significant metabolites.

A.8.2.2 Substances of Category 3

A.8.2.2.1 Criteria for respiratory tract irritation

The criteria for classifying substances as Category 3 for respiratory tract irritation are:

(a) Respiratory irritant effects (characterized by localized redness, edema, pruritis and/or pain) that impair function with symptoms such as cough, pain, choking, and breathing difficulties are included. It is recognized that this evaluation is based primarily on human data;

(b) Subjective human observations supported by objective measurements of clear respiratory tract irritation (RTI) (e.g., electrophysiological responses, biomarkers of inflammation in nasal or bronchoalveolar lavage fluids);

(c) The symptoms observed in humans shall also be typical of those that would be produced in the exposed population rather than being an isolated idiosyncratic reaction or response triggered only in individuals with hypersensitive airways. Ambiguous reports simply of "irritation" should be excluded as this term is commonly used to describe a wide range of sensations including those such as smell, unpleasant taste, a tickling sensation, and dryness, which are outside the scope of classification for respiratory tract irritation;

(d) There are currently no scientifically validated animal tests that deal specifically with RTI; however, useful information may be obtained from the single and repeated inhalation toxicity tests. For example, animal studies may provide useful information in terms of clinical signs of toxicity (dyspnoea, rhinitis etc) and histopathology (e.g., hyperemia, edema, minimal inflammation, thickened mucous layer) which are reversible and may be reflective of the characteristic clinical symptoms described above. Such animal studies can be used as part of weight of evidence evaluation; and,

(e) This special classification will occur only when more severe organ effects including the respiratory system are not observed as those effects would require a higher classification.

A.8.2.2.2 Criteria for narcotic effects

The criteria for classifying substances in Category 3 for narcotic effects are:

(a) Central nervous system depression including narcotic effects in humans such as drowsiness, narcosis, reduced alertness, loss of reflexes, lack of coordination, and vertigo are included. These effects can also be manifested as severe headache or nausea, and can lead to reduced judgment, dizziness, irritability, fatigue, impaired memory function, deficits in perception and coordination, reaction time, or sleepiness; and,

(b) Narcotic effects observed in animal studies may include lethargy, lack of coordination righting reflex, narcosis, and ataxia. If these effects are not transient in nature, then they shall be considered for classification as Category 1 or 2.

A.8.3 Classification Criteria for Mixtures

A.8.3.1 Mixtures are classified using the same criteria as for substances, or alternatively as described below. As with substances, mixtures may be classified for specific target organ toxicity following single exposure, repeated exposure, or both.

A.8.3.2 Classification of Mixtures When Data Are Available for the Complete Mixture

When reliable and good quality evidence from human experience or appropriate studies in experimental animals, as described in the criteria for substances, is available for the mixture, then the mixture shall be classified by weight of evidence evaluation of this data. Care shall be exercised in evaluating data on mixtures, that the dose, duration, observation or analysis, do not render the results inconclusive.

A.8.3.3 Classification of Mixtures When Data Are Not Available for the Complete Mixture: Bridging Principles

A.8.3.3.1 Where the mixture itself has not been tested to determine its specific target organ toxicity, but there are sufficient data on both the individual ingredients and similar tested mixtures to adequately characterize the hazards of the mixture, these data shall be used in accordance with the following bridging principles as found in paragraph A.0.5 of this Appendix: Dilution, Batching, Concentration of mixtures, Interpolation within one toxicity category, Substantially similar mixtures, or Aerosols.

A.8.3.4 Classification of Mixtures When Data Are Available for All Ingredients or Only for Some Ingredients of the Mixture

A.8.3.4.1 Where there is no reliable evidence or test data for the specific mixture itself, and the bridging principles cannot be used to enable classification, then classification of the mixture is based on the classification of the ingredient substances. In this case, the mixture shall be classified as a specific target organ toxicant (specific organ specified), following single exposure, repeated exposure, or both when at least one ingredient has been classified as a Category 1 or Category 2 specific target organ toxicant and is present at or above the appropriate cut-off value/concentration limit specified in Table A.8.2 for Categories 1 and 2, respectively.

Table A.8.2
Cut-Off Values/Concentration Limits of Ingredients of a Mixture Classified as a Specific Target Organ Toxicant That Would Trigger Classification of the Mixture as Category 1 or 2

Ingredient classified as:	Cut-off values/concentration limits triggering classification of a mixture as:	
	Category 1	Category 2
Category 1 Target organ toxicant	≥1.0%	
Category 2 Target organ toxicant		≥1.0%

A.8.3.4.2 These cut-off values and consequent classifications shall be applied equally and appropriately to both single- and repeated-dose target organ toxicants.

A.8.3.4.3 Mixtures shall be classified for either or both single and repeated dose toxicity independently.

A.8.3.4.4 Care shall be exercised when toxicants affecting more than one organ system are combined that the potentiation or synergistic interactions are considered, because certain substances can cause target organ toxicity at <1% concentration when other ingredients in the mixture are known to potentiate its toxic effect.

A.8.3.4.5 Care shall be exercised when extrapolating the toxicity of a mixture that contains Category 3 ingredient(s). A cut-off value/concentration limit of 20%, considered as an additive of all Category 3 ingredients for each hazard endpoint, is appropriate; however, this cut-off value/concentration limit may be higher or lower depending on the Category 3 ingredient(s) involved and the fact that some effects such as respiratory tract irritation may not occur below a certain concentration while other effects such as narcotic effects may occur below this 20% value. Expert judgment shall be exercised. Respiratory tract irritation and narcotic effects are to be evaluated separately in accordance with the criteria given in A.8.2.2. When conducting classifications for these hazards, the contribution of each ingredient should be considered additive, unless there is evidence that the effects are not additive.

A.9 SPECIFIC TARGET ORGAN TOXICITY REPEATED OR PROLONGED EXPOSURE

A.9.1 Definitions and general considerations

A.9.1.1 Specific target organ toxicity—repeated exposure (STOT–RE) means specific target organ toxicity arising from repeated exposure to a substance or mixture. All significant health effects that can impair function, both reversible and irreversible, immediate and/or delayed and not specifically addressed in A.1 to A.7 and A.10 of this Appendix are included. Specific target organ toxicity following a single-event exposure is classified in accordance with SPECIFIC TARGET ORGAN TOXICITY—SINGLE EXPOSURE (A.8 of this Appendix) and is therefore not included here.

A.9.1.2 Classification identifies the substance or mixture as being a specific target organ toxicant and, as such, it may present a potential for adverse health effects in people who are exposed to it.

A.9.1.3 These adverse health effects produced by repeated exposure include consistent and identifiable toxic effects in humans, or, in experimental animals, toxicologically significant changes which have affected the function or morphology of a tissue/organ, or have produced serious changes to the biochemistry or hematology of the organism and these changes are relevant for human health. Human data will be the primary source of evidence for this hazard class.

A.9.1.4 Assessment shall take into consideration not only significant changes in a single organ or biological system but also generalized changes of a less severe nature involving several organs.

A.9.1.5 Specific target organ toxicity can occur by any route that is relevant for humans, e.g., principally oral, dermal or inhalation.

A.9.2 Classification Criteria for Substances

A.9.2.1 Substances shall be classified as STOT–RE by expert judgment on the basis of the weight of all evidence available, including the use of recommended guidance values which take into account the duration of exposure and the dose/concentration which produced the effect(s), (See A.9.2.9). Substances shall be placed in one of two categories, depending upon the nature and severity of the effect(s) observed, in accordance with Figure A.9.1.

Figure A.9.1
Hazard Categories for Specific Target Organ Toxicity Following Repeated Exposure

CATEGORY 1:
Substances that have produced significant toxicity in humans, or that, on the basis of evidence from studies in experimental animals can be presumed to have the potential to produce significant toxicity in humans following repeated or prolonged exposure Substances are classified in Category 1 for specific target organ toxicity (repeated exposure) on the basis of: (a) reliable and good quality evidence from human cases or epidemiological studies; or, (b) observations from appropriate studies in experimental animals in which significant and/or severe toxic effects, of relevance to human health, were produced at generally low exposure concentrations. Guidance dose/concentration values are provided below (See A.9.2.9) to be used as part of weight-of-evidence evaluation.
CATEGORY 2:
Substances that, on the basis of evidence from studies in experimental animals can be presumed to have the potential to be harmful to human health following repeated or prolonged exposure Substances are classified in Category 2 for specific target organ toxicity (repeated exposure) on the basis of observations from appropriate studies in experimental animals in which significant toxic effects, of relevance to human health, were produced at generally moderate exposure concentrations. Guidance dose/concentration values are provided below (See A.9.2.9) in order to help in classification. In exceptional cases human evidence can also be used to place a substance in Category 2 (See A.9.2.6).

Note: The primary target organ/system shall be identified where possible, or the substance shall be identified as a general toxicant. The data shall be carefully evaluated and, where possible, shall not include secondary effects (e.g., a hepatotoxicant can produce secondary effects in the nervous or gastro-intestinal systems).

A.9.2.2 The relevant route of exposure by which the classified substance produces damage shall be identified.

A.9.2.3 Classification is determined by expert judgment, on the basis of the weight of all evidence available including the guidance presented below.

A.9.2.4 Weight of evidence of all data, including human incidents, epidemiology, and studies conducted in experimental animals, is used to substantiate specific target organ toxic effects that merit classification.

A.9.2.5 The information required to evaluate specific target organ toxicity comes either from repeated exposure in humans, e.g., exposure at home, in the workplace or environmentally, or from studies conducted in experimental animals. The standard animal studies in rats or mice that provide this information are 28 day, 90 day or lifetime studies (up to 2 years) that include hematological, clinico-chemical and detailed macroscopic and microscopic examination to enable the toxic effects on target tissues/organs to be identified. Data from repeat dose studies performed in other species may also be used. Other long-term exposure studies, e.g., for carcinogenicity, neurotoxicity or reproductive toxicity, may also provide evidence of specific target organ toxicity that could be used in the assessment of classification.

A.9.2.6 In exceptional cases, based on expert judgment, it may be appropriate to place certain substances with human evidence of specific target organ toxicity in Category 2: (a) when the weight of human evidence is not sufficiently convincing to warrant Category 1 classification, and/or (b) based on the nature and severity of effects. Dose/concentration levels in humans shall not be considered in the classification and any available evidence from animal studies shall be consistent with the Category 2 classification. In other words, if there are also animal data available on the substance that warrant Category 1 classification, the substance shall be classified as Category 1.

A.9.2.7 Effects Considered To Support Classification

A.9.2.7.1 Classification is supported by reliable evidence associating repeated exposure to the substance with a consistent and identifiable toxic effect.

A.9.2.7.2 Evidence from human experience/incidents is usually restricted to reports of adverse health consequences, often with uncertainty about exposure conditions, and may not provide the scientific detail that can be obtained from well-conducted studies in experimental animals.

A.9.2.7.3 Evidence from appropriate studies in experimental animals can furnish much more detail, in the form of clinical observations, hematology, clinical chemistry, macroscopic and microscopic pathological examination and this can often reveal hazards that may not be life-threatening but could indicate functional impairment. Consequently all available evidence, and relevance to human health, must be taken into consideration in the classification process. Relevant toxic effects in humans and/or animals include, but are not limited to:

(a) Morbidity or death resulting from repeated or long-term exposure. Morbidity or death may result from repeated exposure, even to relatively low doses/concentrations, due to bioaccumulation of the substance or its metabolites, or due to the overwhelming of the de-toxification process by repeated exposure;
(b) Significant functional changes in the central or peripheral nervous systems or other organ systems, including signs of central nervous system depression and effects on special senses (e.g., sight, hearing and sense of smell);
(c) Any consistent and significant adverse change in clinical biochemistry, hematology, or urinalysis parameters;
(d) Significant organ damage that may be noted at necropsy and/or subsequently seen or confirmed at microscopic examination;
(e) Multi-focal or diffuse necrosis, fibrosis or granuloma formation in vital organs with regenerative capacity;
(f) Morphological changes that are potentially reversible but provide clear evidence of marked organ dysfunction (e.g., severe fatty change in the liver); and,
(g) Evidence of appreciable cell death (including cell degeneration and reduced cell number) in vital organs incapable of regeneration.

A.9.2.8 Effects Considered Not To Support Classification

Effects may be seen in humans and/or animals that do not justify classification. Such effects include, but are not limited to:

(a) Clinical observations or small changes in bodyweight gain, food consumption or water intake that may have some toxicological importance but that do not, by themselves, indicate "significant" toxicity;
(b) Small changes in clinical biochemistry, hematology or urinalysis parameters and/or transient effects, when such changes or effects are of doubtful or of minimal toxicological importance;
(c) Changes in organ weights with no evidence of organ dysfunction;
(d) Adaptive responses that are not considered toxicologically relevant;
(e) Substance-induced species-specific mechanisms of toxicity, i.e., demonstrated with reasonable certainty to be not relevant for human health, shall not justify classification.

A.9.2.9 Guidance Values To Assist With Classification Based on the Results Obtained From Studies Conducted in Experimental Animals

A.9.2.9.1 In studies conducted in experimental animals, reliance on observation of effects alone, without reference to the duration of experimental exposure and dose/concentration, omits a fundamental concept of toxicology, i.e., all substances are potentially toxic, and what determines the toxicity is a function of the dose/concentration and the duration of exposure. In most studies conducted in experimental animals the test guidelines use an upper limit dose value.

A.9.2.9.2 In order to help reach a decision about whether a substance shall be classified or not, and to what degree it shall be classified (Category 1 vs. Category 2), dose/concentration "guidance values" are provided in Table A.9.1 for consideration of the dose/concentration which has been shown to produce significant health effects. The principal argument for proposing such guidance values is that all chemicals are potentially toxic and there has to be a reasonable dose/concentration above which a degree of toxic effect is acknowledged. Also, repeated-dose studies conducted in experimental animals are designed to produce toxicity at the highest dose used in order to optimize the test objective and so most studies will reveal some toxic effect at least at this highest dose. What is therefore to be decided is not only what effects have been produced, but also at what dose/concentration they were produced and how relevant is that for humans.

A.9.2.9.3 Thus, in animal studies, when significant toxic effects are observed that indicate classification, consideration of the duration of experimental exposure and the dose/concentration at which these effects were seen, in relation to the suggested guidance values, provides useful information to help assess the need to classify (since the toxic effects are a consequence of the hazardous property(ies) and also the duration of exposure and the dose/concentration).

A.9.2.9.4 The decision to classify at all can be influenced by reference to the dose/concentration guidance values at or below which a significant toxic effect has been observed.

A.9.2.9.5 The guidance values refer to effects seen in a standard 90-day toxicity study conducted in rats. They can be used as a basis to extrapolate equivalent guidance values for toxicity studies of greater or lesser duration, using dose/exposure time extrapolation similar to Haber's rule for inhalation, which states essentially that the effective dose is directly proportional to the exposure concentration and the duration of exposure. The assessment should be done on a case-by-case basis; for example, for a 28-day study the guidance values below would be increased by a factor of three.

A.9.2.9.6 Thus for Category 1 classification, significant toxic effects observed in a 90-day repeated-dose study conducted in experimental animals and seen to occur at or below the (suggested) guidance values (C) as indicated in Table A.9.1 would justify classification:

Table A.9.1
Guidance Values To Assist in Category 1 Classification
[Applicable to a 90-day study]

Route of exposure	Units	Guidance values (dose/concentration)
Oral (rat)	mg/kg body weight/day	C ≤10
Dermal (rat or rabbit)	mg/kg body weight/day	C ≤20
Inhalation (rat) gas	ppmV/6h/day	C ≤50
Inhalation (rat) vapor	mg/liter/6h/day	C ≤0.2
Inhalation (rat) dust/ mist/fume	mg/liter/6h/day	C ≤0.02

A.9.2.9.7 For Category 2 classification, significant toxic effects observed in a 90-day repeated-dose study conducted in experimental animals and seen to occur within the (suggested) guidance value ranges as indicated in Table A.9.2 would justify classification:

Table A.9.2
Guidance Values To Assist in Category 2 Classification
[Applicable to a 90-day study]

Route of exposure	Units	Guidance values (dose/concentration)
Oral (rat)	mg/kg body weight/day	10 <C ≤100
Dermal (rat or rabbit)	mg/kg body weight/day	20 <C ≤200
Inhalation (rat) gas	ppmV/6h/day	50 <C ≤250
Inhalation (rat) vapor	mg/liter/6h/day	0.2 <C ≤1.0
Inhalation (rat) dust/ mist/fume	mg/liter/6h/day	0.02 <C ≤0.2

A.9.2.9.8 The guidance values and ranges mentioned in A.2.9.9.6 and A.2.9.9.7 are intended only for guidance purposes, i.e., to be used as part of the weight of evidence approach, and to assist with decisions about classification. They are not intended as strict demarcation values.

A.9.2.9.9 Thus, it is possible that a specific profile of toxicity occurs in repeat-dose animal studies at a dose/concentration below the guidance value, e.g., <100 mg/kg body weight/day by the oral route, however the nature of the effect, e.g., nephrotoxicity seen only in male rats of a particular strain known to be susceptible to this effect, may result in the decision not to classify. Conversely, a specific profile of toxicity may be seen in animal studies occurring at above a guidance value, e.g., ≥100 mg/kg body weight/day by the oral route, and in addition there is supplementary information from other sources, e.g., other long-term administration studies, or human case experience, which supports a conclusion that, in view of the weight of evidence, classification is prudent.

A.9.2.10 Other Considerations

A.9.2.10.1 When a substance is characterized only by use of animal data the classification process includes reference to dose/concentration guidance values as one of the elements that contribute to the weight of evidence approach.

A.9.2.10.2 When well-substantiated human data are available showing a specific target organ toxic effect that can be reliably attributed to repeated or prolonged exposure to a substance, the substance shall be classified. Positive human data, regardless of probable dose, predominates over animal data. Thus, if a substance is unclassified because no specific target organ toxicity was seen at or below the dose/concentration guidance value for animal testing, if subsequent human incident data become available showing a specific target organ toxic effect, the substance shall be classified.

A.9.2.10.3 A substance that has not been tested for specific target organ toxicity may in certain instances, where appropriate, be classified on the basis of data from a scientifically validated structure activity relationship and expert judgment-based extrapolation from a structural analogue that has previously been classified together with substantial support from consideration of other important factors such as formation of common significant metabolites.

A.9.3 Classification Criteria for Mixtures

A.9.3.1 Mixtures are classified using the same criteria as for substances, or alternatively as described below. As with substances, mixtures may be classified for specific target organ toxicity following single exposure, repeated exposure, or both.

A.9.3.2 Classification of Mixtures When Data Are Available for the Complete Mixture

When reliable and good quality evidence from human experience or appropriate studies in experimental animals, as described in the criteria for substances, is available for the mixture, then the mixture shall be classified by weight of evidence evaluation of these data. Care shall be exercised in evaluating data on mixtures, that the dose, duration, observation or analysis, do not render the results inconclusive.

A.9.3.3 Classification of Mixtures When Data Are Not Available for the Complete Mixture: Bridging Principles

A.9.3.3.1 Where the mixture itself has not been tested to determine its specific target organ toxicity, but there are sufficient data on both the individual ingredients and similar tested mixtures to adequately characterize the hazards of the mixture, these data shall be used in accordance with the following bridging principles as found in paragraph A.0.5 of this Appendix: Dilution; Batching; Concentration of mixtures; Interpolation within one toxicity category; Substantially similar mixtures; and Aerosols.

A.9.3.4 Classification of Mixtures When Data Are Available for All Ingredients or Only for Some Ingredients of the Mixture

A.9.3.4.1 Where there is no reliable evidence or test data for the specific mixture itself, and the bridging principles cannot be used to enable classification, then classification of the mixture is based on the classification of the ingredient substances. In this case, the mixture shall be classified as a specific target organ toxicant (specific organ specified), following single exposure, repeated exposure, or both when at least one ingredient has been classified as a Category 1 or Category 2 specific target organ toxicant and is present at or above the appropriate cut-off value/concentration limit specified in Table A.9.3 for Category 1 and 2 respectively.

Table A.9.3
Cut-Off Value/Concentration Limits of Ingredients of a Mixture Classified as a Specific Target Organ Toxicant That Would Trigger Classification of the Mixture as Category 1 or 2

Ingredient classified as:	Cut-off values/concentration limits triggering classification of a mixture as:	
	Category 1	Category 2
Category 1 Target organ toxicant	≥1.0%	
Category 2 Target organ toxicant		≥1.0%

A.9.3.4.2 These cut-off values and consequent classifications shall be applied equally and appropriately to both single- and repeated-dose target organ toxicants.

A.9.3.4.3 Mixtures shall be classified for either or both single- and repeated-dose toxicity independently.

A.9.3.4.4 Care shall be exercised when toxicants affecting more than one organ system are combined that the potentiation or synergistic interactions are considered, because certain substances can cause specific target organ toxicity at <1% concentration when other ingredients in the mixture are known to potentiate its toxic effect.

A.10 ASPIRATION HAZARD

A.10.1 Definitions and General and Specific Considerations

A.10.1.1 **Aspiration** means the entry of a liquid or solid chemical directly through the oral or nasal cavity, or indirectly from vomiting, into the trachea and lower respiratory system.

A.10.1.2 Aspiration toxicity includes severe acute effects such as chemical pneumonia, varying degrees of pulmonary injury or death following aspiration.

A.10.1.3 Aspiration is initiated at the moment of inspiration, in the time required to take one breath, as the causative material lodges at the crossroad of the upper respiratory and digestive tracts in the laryngopharyngeal region.

A.10.1.4 Aspiration of a substance or mixture can occur as it is vomited following ingestion. This may have consequences for labeling, particularly where, due to acute toxicity, a recommendation may be considered to induce vomiting after ingestion. However, if the substance/mixture also presents an aspiration toxicity hazard, the recommendation to induce vomiting may need to be modified.

A.10.1.5 Specific Considerations

A.10.1.5.1 The classification criteria refer to kinematic viscosity. The following provides the conversion between dynamic and kinematic viscosity:

A.10.1.5.2 Although the definition of aspiration in A.10.1.1 includes the entry of solids into the respiratory system, classification according to (b) in table A.10.1 for Category 1 is intended to apply to liquid substances and mixtures only.

A.10.1.5.3 Classification of aerosol/mist products.

Aerosol and mist products are usually dispensed in containers such as self-pressurized containers, trigger and pump sprayers. Classification for these products shall be considered if their use may form a pool of product in the mouth, which then may be aspirated. If the mist or aerosol from a pressurized container is fine, a pool may not be formed. On the other hand, if a pressurized container dispenses product in a stream, a pool may be formed that may then be aspirated. Usually, the mist produced by trigger and pump sprayers is coarse and therefore, a pool may be formed that then may be aspirated. When the pump mechanism may be removed and contents are available to be swallowed then the classification of the products should be considered.

A.10.2 Classification Criteria for Substances

Table A.10.1
Criteria for Aspiration Toxicity

Category	Criteria
Category 1: Chemicals known to cause human aspiration toxicity hazards or to be regarded as if they cause human aspiration toxicity hazard	A substance shall be classified in Category 1: (a) If reliable and good quality human evidence indicates that it causes aspiration toxicity (See note); or (b) If it is a hydrocarbon and has a kinematic viscosity ≤20.5 mm^2/s, measured at 40 °C.

Note: Examples of substances included in Category 1 are certain hydrocarbons, turpentine and pine oil.

A.10.3 Classification Criteria for Mixtures

A.10.3.1 Classification When Data Are Available for the Complete Mixture

A mixture shall be classified in Category 1 based on reliable and good quality human evidence.

A.10.3.2 Classification of Mixtures When Data Are Not Available for the Complete Mixture: Bridging Principles

A.10.3.2.1 Where the mixture itself has not been tested to determine its aspiration toxicity, but there are sufficient data on both the individual ingredients and similar tested mixtures to adequately characterize the hazard of the mixture, these data shall be used in accordance with the following bridging principles as found in paragraph A.0.5 of this Appendix: Dilution; Batching; Concentration of mixtures; Interpolation within one toxicity category; and Substantially similar mixtures. For application of the dilution bridging principle, the concentration of aspiration toxicants shall not be less than 10%.

A.10.3.3 Classification of Mixtures When Data Are Available for All Ingredients or Only for Some Ingredients of the Mixture

A.10.3.3.1 A mixture which contains ≥10% of an ingredient or ingredients classified in Category 1, and has a kinematic viscosity ≤20.5 mm2 /s, measured at 40 °C, shall be classified in Category 1.

A.10.3.3.2 In the case of a mixture which separates into two or more distinct layers, one of which contains ≥10% of an ingredient or ingredients classified in Category 1 and has a kinematic viscosity ≤20.5 mm2 /s, measured at 40 °C, then the entire mixture shall be classified in Category 1.

§1910.1200 Appendix B
Physical criteria
(Mandatory)

B.1 EXPLOSIVES

B.1.1 Definitions and general considerations

B.1.1.1 An **explosive chemical** is a solid or liquid chemical which is in itself capable by chemical reaction of producing gas at such a temperature and pressure and at such a speed as to cause damage to the surroundings. Pyrotechnic chemicals are included even when they do not evolve gases.

A **pyrotechnic chemical** is a chemical designed to produce an effect by heat, light, sound, gas or smoke or a combination of these as the result of non-detonative self-sustaining exothermic chemical reactions.

An **explosive item** is an item containing one or more explosive chemicals.

A **pyrotechnic item** is an item containing one or more pyrotechnic chemicals.

An **unstable explosive** is an explosive which is thermally unstable and/or too sensitive for normal handling, transport, or use.

An **intentional explosive** is a chemical or item which is manufactured with a view to produce a practical explosive or pyrotechnic effect.

B.1.1.2 The class of explosives comprises:

(a) Exp.losive chemicals;
(b) Explosive items, except devices containing explosive chemicals in such quantity or of such a character that their inadvertent or accidental ignition or initiation shall not cause any effect external to the device either by projection, fire, smoke, heat or loud noise; and
(c) Chemicals and items not included under (a) and (b) above which are manufactured with the view to producing a practical explosive or pyrotechnic effect.

B.1.2 Classification criteria

Chemicals and items of this class shall be classified as unstable explosives or shall be assigned to one of the following six divisions depending on the type of hazard they present:

(a) Division 1.1 - Chemicals and items which have a mass explosion hazard (a mass explosion is one which affects almost the entire quantity present virtually instantaneously);
(b) Division 1.2 - Chemicals and items which have a projection hazard but not a mass explosion hazard;
(c) Division 1.3 - Chemicals and items which have a fire hazard and either a minor blast hazard or a minor projection hazard or both, but not a mass explosion hazard:
 (i) Combustion of which gives rise to considerable radiant heat; or
 (ii) Which burn one after another, producing minor blast or projection effects or both;
(d) Division 1.4 - Chemicals and items which present no significant hazard: chemicals and items which present only a small hazard in the event of ignition or initiation. The effects are largely confined to the package and no projection of fragments of appreciable size or range is to be expected. An external fire shall not cause virtually instantaneous explosion of almost the entire contents of the package;

(e) Division 1.5 - Very insensitive chemicals which have a mass explosion hazard: chemicals which have a mass explosion hazard but are so insensitive that there is very little probability of initiation or of transition from burning to detonation under normal conditions;

(f) Division 1.6 - Extremely insensitive items which do not have a mass explosion hazard: items which contain only extremely insensitive detonating chemicals and which demonstrate a negligible probability of accidental initiation or propagation.

B.1.3 Additional classification considerations

B.1.3.1 Explosives shall be classified as unstable explosives or shall be assigned to one of the six divisions identified in B.1.2 in accordance with the three step procedure in Part I of the UN ST/SG/AC.10 (incorporated by reference; See §1910.6). The first step is to ascertain whether the substance or mixture has explosive effects (Test Series 1). The second step is the acceptance procedure (Test Series 2 to 4) and the third step is the assignment to a hazard division (Test Series 5 to 7). The assessment whether a candidate for "ammonium nitrate emulsion or suspension or gel, intermediate for blasting explosives (ANE)" is insensitive enough for inclusion as an oxidizing liquid (See B.13) or an oxidizing solid (See B.14) is determined by Test Series 8 tests.

NOTE: Classification of solid chemicals shall be based on tests performed on the chemical as presented. If, for example, for the purposes of supply or transport, the same chemical is to be presented in a physical form different from that which was tested and which is considered likely to materially alter its performance in a classification test, classification must be based on testing of the chemical in the new form.

B.1.3.2 Explosive properties are associated with the presence of certain chemical groups in a molecule which can react to produce very rapid increases in temperature or pressure. The screening procedure in B.1.3.1 is aimed at identifying the presence of such reactive groups and the potential for rapid energy release. If the screening procedure identifies the chemical as a potential explosive, the acceptance procedure (See Section 10.3 of the UN ST/SG/AC.10 (incorporated by reference; See §1910.6)) is necessary for classification.

NOTE: Neither a Series 1 type (a) propagation of detonation test nor a Series 2 type (a) test of sensitivity to detonative shock is necessary if the exothermic decomposition energy of organic materials is less than 800 J/g.

B.1.3.3 If a mixture contains any known explosives, the acceptance procedure is necessary for classification.

B.1.3.4 A chemical is not classified as explosive if:

(a) There are no chemical groups associated with explosive properties present in the molecule. Examples of groups which may indicate explosive properties are given in Table A6.1 in Appendix 6 of the UN ST/SG/AC.10 (incorporated by reference; See §1910.6); or

(b) The substance contains chemical groups associated with explosive properties which include oxygen and the calculated oxygen balance is less than -200.

The oxygen balance is calculated for the chemical reaction:

$$C_xH_yO_z + [x + (y/4) - (z/2)]\ O_2 \rightarrow x.\ CO_2 + (y/2)\ H_2O$$

using the formula: oxygen balance = -1600 [2x +(y/2) -z]/ molecular weight; or

(c) The organic substance or a homogenous mixture of organic substances contains chemical groups associated with explosive properties but the exothermic decomposition energy is less than 500 J/g and the onset of exothermic decomposition is below 500 °C (932°F). The exothermic decomposition energy may be determined using a suitable calorimetric technique; or

(d) For mixtures of inorganic oxidizing substances with organic material(s), the concentration of the inorganic oxidizing substance is:

(i) less than 15%, by mass, if the oxidizing substance is assigned to Category 1 or 2;

(ii) less than 30%, by mass, if the oxidizing substance is assigned to Category 3.

B.2 FLAMMABLE GASES

B.2.1 Definition

Flammable gas means a gas having a flammable range with air at 20 °C (68 °F) and a standard pressure of 101.3 kPa (14.7 psi).

B.2.2 Classification criteria

A flammable gas shall be classified in one of the two categories for this class in accordance with Table B.2.1:

Table B.2.1
Criteria for flammable gases

Category	Criteria
1	Gases, which at 20 °C (68 °F) and a standard pressure of 101.3 kPa (14.7 psi): (a) are ignitable when in a mixture of 13% or less by volume in air; or (b) have a flammable range with air of at least 12 percentage points regardless of the lower flammable limit.
2	Gases, other than those of Category 1, which, at 20 °C (68 °F) and a standard pressure of 101.3 kPa (14.7 psi), have a flammable range while mixed in air.

NOTE: Aerosols should not be classified as flammable gases. See B.3.

B.2.3 Additional classification considerations

Flammability shall be determined by tests or by calculation in accordance with ISO 10156 (incorporated by reference; See §1910.6). Where insufficient data are available to use this method, equivalent validated methods may be used.

B.3 FLAMMABLE AEROSOLS

B.3.1 Definition

Aerosol means any non-refillable receptacle containing a gas compressed, liquefied or dissolved under pressure, and fitted with a release device allowing the contents to be ejected as particles in suspension in a gas, or as a foam, paste, powder, liquid or gas.

B.3.2 Classification criteria

B.3.2.1 Aerosols shall be considered for classification as flammable if they contain any component which is classified as flammable in accordance with this Appendix, i.e.:

Flammable liquids (See B.6);
Flammable gases (See B.2);
Flammable solids (See B.7).

NOTE 1: Flammable components do not include pyrophoric, self-heating or water-reactive chemicals.

NOTE 2: Flammable aerosols do not fall additionally within the scope of flammable gases, flammable liquids, or flammable solids.

B.3.2.2 A flammable aerosol shall be classified in one of the two categories for this class in accordance with Table B.3.1.

Table B.3.1
Criteria for flammable aerosols

Category	Criteria
1	Contains ≥85% flammable components and the chemical heat of combustion is ≥30 kJ/g; or a) For spray aerosols, in the ignition distance test, ignition occurs at a distance ≥75 cm (29.5 in), or b) For foam aerosols, in the aerosol foam flammability test (i) the flame height is ≥20 cm (7.87 in) and the flame duration ≥2 s; or (ii) the flame height is ≥4 cm (1.57 in) and the flame duration ≥7 s
2	Contains >1% flammable components, or the heat of combustion is ≥20 kJ/g; and a) For spray aerosols, in the ignition distance test, ignition occurs at a distance ≥15 cm (5.9 in), or in the enclosed space ignition test, the (i) time equivalent is ≤300 s/m^3; or (ii) Deflagration density is ≤300 g/m^3 b) For foam aerosols, in the aerosol foam flammability test, the flame height is ≥4 cm and the flame duration is ≥2 s and it does not meet the criteria for Category 1

NOTE: Aerosols not submitted to the flammability classification procedures in this Appendix shall be classified as extremely flammable (Category 1).

B.3.3 Additional classification considerations

B.3.3.1 To classify a flammable aerosol, data on its flammable components, on its chemical heat of combustion and, if applicable, the results of the aerosol foam flammability test (for foam aerosols) and of the ignition distance test and enclosed space test (for spray aerosols) are necessary.

B.3.3.2 The chemical heat of combustion (ΔHc), in kilojoules per gram (kJ/g), is the product of the theoretical heat of combustion (ΔHcomb), and a combustion efficiency, usually less than 1.0 (a typical combustion efficiency is 0.95 or 95%).

For a composite aerosol formulation, the chemical heat of combustion is the summation of the weighted heats of combustion for the individual components, as follows:

$$\Delta Hc\ (\text{product}) = \sum_{i}^{n} [wi\% \times \Delta Hc(i)]$$

where:
ΔHc = chemical heat of combustion (kJ/g);
wi% = mass fraction of component i in the product;
ΔHc(i) = specific heat of combustion (kJ/g) of component i in the product;

The chemical heats of combustion shall be found in literature, calculated or determined by tests (See ASTM D240-02, ISO 13943, Sections 86.1 to 86.3, and NFPA 30B (incorporated by reference; See §1910.6)).

B.3.3.3 The Ignition Distance Test, Enclosed Space Ignition Test and Aerosol Foam Flammability Test shall be performed in accordance with sub-sections 31.4, 31.5 and 31.6 of the of the UN ST/SG/AC.10 (incorporated by reference; See §1910.6).

B.4 OXIDIZING GASES

B.4.1 Definition

Oxidizing gas means any gas which may, generally by providing oxygen, cause or contribute to the combustion of other material more than air does.

NOTE: "Gases which cause or contribute to the combustion of other material more than air does" means pure gases or gas mixtures with an oxidizing power greater than 23.5% (as determined by a method specified in ISO 10156 or 10156-2 (incorporated by reference, See §1910.6)or an equivalent testing method.)

B.4.2 Classification criteria

An oxidizing gas shall be classified in a single category for this class in accordance with Table B.4.1:

Table B.4.1
Criteria for oxidizing gases

Category	Criteria
1	Any gas which may, generally by providing oxygen, cause or contribute to the combustion of other material more than air does.

B.4.3 Additional classification considerations

Classification shall be in accordance with tests or calculation methods as described in ISO 10156 (incorporated by reference; See §1910.6) and ISO 10156-2 (incorporated by reference; See §1910.6).

B.5 GASES UNDER PRESSURE

B.5.1 Definition

Gases under pressure are gases which are contained in a receptacle at a pressure of 200 kPa (29 psi) (gauge) or more, or which are liquefied or liquefied and refrigerated.

They comprise compressed gases, liquefied gases, dissolved gases and refrigerated liquefied gases.

B.5.2 Classification criteria

Gases under pressure shall be classified in one of four groups in accordance with Table B.5.1:

Table B.5.1
Criteria for gases under pressure

Category	Criteria
Compressed gas	A gas which when under pressure is entirely gaseous at -50 °C (-58 °F), including all gases with a critical temperature[1] ≤50 °C (-58 °F).
Liquefied gas	A gas which when under pressure is partially liquid at temperatures above -50 °C (-58 °F). A distinction is made between: (a) High pressure liquefied gas: a gas with a critical temperature[1] between -50 °C (-58 °F) and +65 °C (149 °F); and (b) Low pressure liquefied gas: a gas with a critical temperature[1] above +65 °C (149 °F).
Refrigerated liquefied gas	A gas which is made partially liquid because of its low temperature.
Dissolved gas	A gas which when under pressure is dissolved in a liquid phase solvent.

[1] The critical temperature is the temperature above which a pure gas cannot be liquefied, regardless of the degree of compression.

B.6 FLAMMABLE LIQUIDS

B.6.1 Definition

Flammable liquid means a liquid having a flash point of not more than 93 °C (199.4 °F).

Flash point means the minimum temperature at which a liquid gives off vapor in sufficient concentration to form an ignitable mixture with air near the surface of the liquid, as determined by a method identified in Section B.6.3.

B.6.2 Classification criteria

A flammable liquid shall be classified in one of four categories in accordance with Table B.6.1:

Table B.6.1:
Criteria for flammable liquids

Category	Criteria
1	Flash point <23 °C (73.4 °F) and initial boiling point ≤35 °C (95 °F)
2	Flash point <23 °C (73.4 °F) and initial boiling point >35 °C (95 °F)
3	Flash point ≥23 °C (73.4 °F) and ≤60 °C (140 °F)
4	Flash point >60 °C (140 °F) and ≤93 °C (199.4 °F)

B.6.3 Additional classification considerations

The flash point shall be determined in accordance with ASTM D56-05, ASTM D3278, ASTM D3828, ASTM D93-08 (incorporated by reference; See §1910.6), or any other method specified in GHS Revision 3, Chapter 2.6.

The initial boiling point shall be determined in accordance with ASTM D86-07a or ASTM D1078 (incorporated by reference; See §1910.6).

B.7 FLAMMABLE SOLIDS

B.7.1 Definitions

Flammable solid means a solid which is a readily combustible solid, or which may cause or contribute to fire through friction.

Readily combustible solids are powdered, granular, or pasty chemicals which are dangerous if they can be easily ignited by brief contact with an ignition source, such as a burning match, and if the flame spreads rapidly.

B.7.2 Classification criteria

B.7.2.1 Powdered, granular or pasty chemicals shall be classified as flammable solids when the time of burning of one or more of the test runs, performed in accordance with the test method described in the UN ST/SG/AC.10 (incorporated by reference; See §1910.6), Part III, Subsection §33.2.1, is less than 45 s or the rate of burning is more than 2.2 mm/s (0.0866 in/s).

B.7.2.2 Powders of metals or metal alloys shall be classified as flammable solids when they can be ignited and the reaction spreads over the whole length of the sample in 10 min or less.

B.7.2.3 Solids which may cause fire through friction shall be classified in this class by analogy with existing entries (e.g., matches) until definitive criteria are established.

B.7.2.4 A flammable solid shall be classified in one of the two categories for this class using Method N.1 as described in Part III, sub-section 33.2.1 of the UN ST/SG/AC.10 (incorporated by reference; See §1910.6), in accordance with Table B.7.1:

Table B.7.1:
Criteria for flammable solids

Category	Criteria
1	Burning rate test: Chemicals other than metal powders: (a) wetted zone does not stop fire; and (b) burning time <45 s or burning rate >2.2 mm/s Metal powders: burning time ≤5 min
2	Burning rate test: Chemicals other than metal powders: (a) wetted zone stops the fire for at least 4 min; and (b) burning time <45 s or burning rate >2.2 mm/s Metal powders: burning time >5 min and ≤10 min

NOTE: Classification of solid chemicals shall be based on tests performed on the chemical as presented. If, for example, for the purposes of supply or transport, the same chemical is to be presented in a physical form different from that which was tested and which is considered likely to materially alter its performance in a classification test, classification must be based on testing of the chemical in the new form.

B.8 SELF-REACTIVE CHEMICALS

B.8.1 Definitions

Self-reactive chemicals are thermally unstable liquid or solid chemicals liable to undergo a strongly exothermic decomposition even without participation of oxygen (air). This definition excludes chemicals classified under this Section as explosives, organic peroxides, oxidizing liquids or oxidizing solids.

A self-reactive chemical is regarded as possessing explosive properties when in laboratory testing the formulation is liable to detonate, to deflagrate rapidly or to show a violent effect when heated under confinement.

B.8.2 Classification criteria

B.8.2.1 A self-reactive chemical shall be considered for classification in this class unless:

(a) It is classified as an explosive according to B.1 of this Appendix;
(b) It is classified as an oxidizing liquid or an oxidizing solid according to B.13 or B.14 of this Appendix, except that a mixture of oxidizing

substances which contains 5% or more of combustible organic substances shall be classified as a self-reactive chemical according to the procedure defined in B.8.2.2;

(c) It is classified as an organic peroxide according to B.15 of this Appendix;
(d) Its heat of decomposition is less than 300 J/g; or
(e) Its self-accelerating decomposition temperature (SADT) is greater than 75 °C (167 °F) for a 50 kg (110 lb) package.

B.8.2.2 Mixtures of oxidizing substances, meeting the criteria for classification as oxidizing liquids or oxidizing solids, which contain 5% or more of combustible organic substances and which do not meet the criteria mentioned in B.8.2.1 (a), (c), (d) or (e), shall be subjected to the self-reactive chemicals classification procedure in B.8.2.3. Such a mixture showing the properties of a self-reactive chemical type B to F shall be classified as a self-reactive chemical.

B.8.2.3 Self-reactive chemicals shall be classified in one of the seven categories of "types A to G" for this class, according to the following principles:

(a) Any self-reactive chemical which can detonate or deflagrate rapidly, as packaged, will be defined as self-reactive chemical TYPE A;
(b) Any self-reactive chemical possessing explosive properties and which, as packaged, neither detonates nor deflagrates rapidly, but is liable to undergo a thermal explosion in that package will be defined as self-reactive chemical TYPE B;
(c) Any self-reactive chemical possessing explosive properties when the chemical as packaged cannot detonate or deflagrate rapidly or undergo a thermal explosion will be defined as self-reactive chemical TYPE C;
(d) Any self-reactive chemical which in laboratory testing meets the criteria in (d)(i), (ii), or (iii) will be defined as self-reactive chemical TYPE D:
    (i) Detonates partially, does not deflagrate rapidly and shows no violent effect when heated under confinement; or
    (ii) Does not detonate at all, deflagrates slowly and shows no violent effect when heated under confinement; or
    (iii) Does not detonate or deflagrate at all and shows a medium effect when heated under confinement;
(e) Any self-reactive chemical which, in laboratory testing, neither detonates nor deflagrates at all and shows low or no effect when heated under confinement will be defined as self-reactive chemical TYPE E;
(f) Any self-reactive chemical which, in laboratory testing, neither detonates in the cavitated state nor deflagrates at all and shows only a low or no effect when heated under confinement as well as low or no explosive power will be defined as self-reactive chemical TYPE F;
(g) Any self-reactive chemical which, in laboratory testing, neither detonates in the cavitated state nor deflagrates at all and shows no effect when heated under confinement nor any explosive power, provided that it is thermally stable (self-accelerating decomposition temperature is 60 °C (140 °F) to 75 °C (167 °F) for a 50 kg (110 lb) package), and, for liquid mixtures, a diluent having a boiling point greater than or equal to 150 °C (302 °F) is used for desensitization will be defined as self-reactive chemical TYPE G. If the mixture is not thermally stable or a diluent having a boiling point less than 150 °C (302 °F) is used for desensitization, the mixture shall be defined as self-reactive chemical TYPE F.

B.8.3 Additional classification considerations

B.8.3.1 For purposes of classification, the properties of self-reactive chemicals shall be determined in accordance with test series A to H as described in Part II of the UN ST/SG/AC.10 (incorporated by reference; See §1910.6).

B.8.3.2 Self-accelerating decomposition temperature (SADT) shall be determined in accordance with the UN ST/SG/AC.10, Part II, Section 28 (incorporated by reference; See §1910.6).

B.8.3.3 The classification procedures for self-reactive substances and mixtures need not be applied if:

(a) There are no chemical groups present in the molecule associated with explosive or self-reactive properties; examples of such groups are given in Tables A6.1 and A6.2 in the Appendix 6 of the UN ST/SG/AC.10 (incorporated by reference; See §1910.6); or
(b) For a single organic substance or a homogeneous mixture of organic substances, the estimated SADT is greater than 75 °C (167 °F) or the exothermic decomposition energy is less than 300 J/g. The onset temperature and decomposition energy may be estimated using a suitable calorimetric technique (See 20.3.3.3 in Part II of the UN ST/SG/AC.10 (incorporated by reference; See §1910.6)).

B.9 PYROPHORIC LIQUIDS

B.9.1 Definition

Pyrophoric liquid means a liquid which, even in small quantities, is liable to ignite within five minutes after coming into contact with air.

B.9.2 Classification criteria

A pyrophoric liquid shall be classified in a single category for this class using test N.3 in Part III, sub-section 33.3.1.5 of the UN ST/SG/AC.10 (incorporated by reference; See §1910.6), in accordance with Table B.9.1:

Table B.9.1: Criteria for pyrophoric liquids

Category	Criteria
1	The liquid ignites within 5 min when added to an inert carrier and exposed to air, or it ignites or chars a filter paper on contact with air within 5 min.

B.9.3 Additional classification considerations

The classification procedure for pyrophoric liquids need not be applied when experience in production or handling shows that the chemical does not ignite spontaneously on coming into contact with air at normal temperatures (i.e., the substance is known to be stable at room temperature for prolonged periods of time (days)).

B.10 PYROPHORIC SOLIDS

B.10.1 Definition

Pyrophoric solid means a solid which, even in small quantities, is liable to ignite within five minutes after coming into contact with air.

B.10.2 Classification criteria

A pyrophoric solid shall be classified in a single category for this class using test N.2 in Part III, sub-section 33.3.1.4 of the UN ST/SG/AC.10 (incorporated by reference; See §1910.6), in accordance with Table B.10.1:

Table B.10.1: Criteria for pyrophoric solids

Category	Criteria
1	The solid ignites within 5 min of coming into contact with air.

NOTE: Classification of solid chemicals shall be based on tests performed on the chemical as presented. If, for example, for the purposes of supply or transport, the same chemical is to be presented in a physical form different from that which was tested and which is considered likely to materially alter its performance in a classification test, classification must be based on testing of the chemical in the new form.

B.10.3 Additional classification considerations

The classification procedure for pyrophoric solids need not be applied when experience in production or handling shows that the chemical does not ignite spontaneously on coming into contact with air at normal temperatures (i.e., the chemical is known to be stable at room temperature for prolonged periods of time (days)).

B.11 SELF-HEATING CHEMICALS

B.11.1 Definition

A **self-heating chemical** is a solid or liquid chemical, other than a pyrophoric liquid or solid, which, by reaction with air and without energy supply, is liable to self-heat; this chemical differs from a pyrophoric liquid or solid in that it will ignite only when in large amounts (kilograms) and after long periods of time (hours or days).

NOTE: Self-heating of a substance or mixture is a process where the gradual reaction of that substance or mixture with oxygen (in air) generates heat. If the rate of heat production exceeds the rate of heat loss, then the temperature of the substance or mixture will rise which, after an induction time, may lead to self-ignition and combustion.

B.11.2 Classification criteria

B.11.2.1 A self-heating chemical shall be classified in one of the two categories for this class if, in tests performed in accordance with test method N.4 in Part III, sub-section 33.3.1.6 of the UN ST/SG/AC.10 (incorporated by reference; See §1910.6), the result meets the criteria shown in Table B.11.1.

Table B.11.1: Criteria for self-heating chemicals

Category	Criteria
1	A positive result is obtained in a test using a 25 mm sample cube at 140 °C (284 °F)
2	A negative result is obtained in a test using a 25 mm cube sample at 140 °C (284 °F), a positive result is obtained in a test using a 100 mm sample cube at 140 °C (284 °F), and: (a) The unit volume of the chemical is more than 3 m^3; or (b) Apositive result is obtained in a test using a 100 mm cube sample at 120 °C (248 °F) and the unit volume of the chemical is more than 450 liters; or (c) Apositive result is obtained in a test using a 100 mm cube sample at 100 °C (212 °F).

B.11.2.2 Chemicals with a temperature of spontaneous combustion higher than 50 °C (122 °F) for a volume of 27 m^3 shall not be classified as self-heating chemicals.

B.11.2.3 Chemicals with a spontaneous ignition temperature higher than 50 °C (122 °F) for a volume of 450 liters shall not be classified in Category 1 of this class.

B.11.3 Additional classification considerations

B.11.3.1 The classification procedure for self-heating chemicals need not be applied if the results of a screening test can be adequately correlated with the classification test and an appropriate safety margin is applied.

B.11.3.2 Examples of screening tests are:

(a) The Grewer Oven test (VDI guideline 2263, Part 1, 1990, Test methods for the Determination of the Safety Characteristics of Dusts) with an onset temperature 80°K above the reference temperature for a volume of 1 l;

(b) The Bulk Powder Screening Test (Gibson, N. Harper, D. J. Rogers, R. Evaluation of the fire and explosion risks in drying powders, Plant Operations Progress, 4 (3), 181-189, 1985) with an onset temperature 60 °K above the reference temperature for a volume of 1 l.

B.12 CHEMICALS WHICH, IN CONTACT WITH WATER, EMIT FLAMMABLE GASES

B.12.1 Definition

Chemicals which, in contact with water, emit flammable gases are solid or liquid chemicals which, by interaction with water, are liable to become spontaneously flammable or to give off flammable gases in dangerous quantities.

B.12.2 Classification criteria

B.12.2.1 A chemical which, in contact with water, emits flammable gases shall be classified in one of the three categories for this class, using test N.5 in Part III, sub-section 33.4.1.4 of the UN ST/SG/AC.10 (incorporated by reference; See §1910.6), in accordance with Table B.12.1:

Table B.12.1: Criteria for chemicals which, in contact with water, emit flammable gases

Category	Criteria
1	Any chemical which reacts vigorously with water at ambient temperatures and demonstrates generally a tendency for the gas produced to ignite spontaneously, or which reacts readily with water at ambient temperatures such that the rate of evolution of flammable gas is equal to or greater than 10 liters per kilogram of chemical over any one minute.
2	Any chemical which reacts readily with water at ambient temperatures such that the maximum rate of evolution of flammable gas is equal to or greater than 20 liters per kilogram of chemical per hour, and which does not meet the criteria for Category 1.
3	Any chemical which reacts slowly with water at ambient temperatures such that the maximum rate of evolution of flammable gas is equal to or greater than 1 liter per kilogram of chemical per hour, and which does not meet the criteria for Categories 1 and 2.

NOTE: Classification of solid chemicals shall be based on tests performed on the chemical as presented. If, for example, for the purposes of supply or transport, the same chemical is to be presented in a physical form different from that which was tested and which is considered likely to materially alter its performance in a classification test, classification must be based on testing of the chemical in the new form.

B.12.2.2 A chemical is classified as a chemical which, in contact with water, emits flammable gases if spontaneous ignition takes place in any step of the test procedure.

B.12.3 Additional classification considerations

The classification procedure for this class need not be applied if:

(a) The chemical structure of the chemical does not contain metals or metalloids;

(b) Experience in production or handling shows that the chemical does not react with water, (e.g., the chemical is manufactured with water or washed with water); or

(c) The chemical is known to be soluble in water to form a stable mixture.

B.13 OXIDIZING LIQUIDS

B.13.1 Definition

Oxidizing liquid means a liquid which, while in itself not necessarily combustible, may, generally by yielding oxygen, cause, or contribute to, the combustion of other material.

B.13.2 Classification criteria

An oxidizing liquid shall be classified in one of the three categories for this class using test O.2 in Part III, sub-section 34.4.2 of the UN ST/SG/AC.10 (incorporated by reference; See §1910.6), in accordance with Table B.13.1:

Table B.13.1: Criteria for oxidizing liquids

Category	Criteria
1	Any chemical which, in the 1:1 mixture, by mass, of chemical and cellulose tested, spontaneously ignites; or the mean pressure rise time of a 1:1 mixture, by mass, of chemical and cellulose is less than that of a 1:1 mixture, by mass, of 50% perchloric acid and cellulose;
2	Any chemical which, in the 1:1 mixture, by mass, of chemical and cellulose tested, exhibits a mean pressure rise time less than or equal to the mean pressure rise time of a 1:1 mixture, by mass, of 40% aqueous sodium chlorate solution and cellulose; and the criteria for Category 1 are not met;
3	Any chemical which, in the 1:1 mixture, by mass, of chemical and cellulose tested, exhibits a mean pressure rise time less than or equal to the mean pressure rise time of a 1:1 mixture, by mass, of 65% aqueous nitric acid and cellulose; and the criteria for Categories 1 and 2 are not met.

B.13.3 Additional classification considerations

B.13.3.1 For organic chemicals, the classification procedure for this class shall not be applied if:

(a) The chemical does not contain oxygen, fluorine or chlorine; or

(b) The chemical contains oxygen, fluorine or chlorine and these elements are chemically bonded only to carbon or hydrogen.

B.13.3.2 For inorganic chemicals, the classification procedure for this class shall not be applied if the chemical does not contain oxygen or halogen atoms.

B.13.3.3 In the event of divergence between test results and known experience in the handling and use of chemicals which shows them to be oxidizing, judgments based on known experience shall take precedence over test results.

B.13.3.4 In cases where chemicals generate a pressure rise (too high or too low), caused by chemical reactions not characterizing the oxidizing properties of the chemical, the test described in Part III, sub-section 34.4.2 of the UN ST/SG/AC.10 (incorporated by reference; See §1910.6) shall be repeated with an inert substance (e.g., diatomite (kieselguhr)) in place of the cellulose in order to clarify the nature of the reaction.

B.14 OXIDIZING SOLIDS

B.14.1 Definition

Oxidizing solid means a solid which, while in itself is not necessarily combustible, may, generally by yielding oxygen, cause, or contribute to, the combustion of other material.

B.14.2 Classification criteria

An oxidizing solid shall be classified in one of the three categories for this class using test O.1 in Part III, sub-section 34.4.1 of the UN ST/SG/AC.10 (incorporated by reference; See §1910.6), in accordance with Table B.14.1:

Table B.14.1: Criteria for oxidizing solids

Category	Criteria
1	Any chemical which, in the 4:1 or 1:1 sample-to-cellulose ratio (by mass) tested, exhibits a mean burning time less than the mean burning time of a 3:2 mixture, by mass, of potassium bromate and cellulose.
2	Any chemical which, in the 4:1 or 1:1 sample-to-cellulose ratio (by mass) tested, exhibits a mean burning time equal to or less than the mean burning time of a 2:3 mixture (by mass) of potassium bromate and cellulose and the criteria for Category 1 are not met.
3	Any chemical which, in the 4:1 or 1:1 sample-to-cellulose ratio (by mass) tested, exhibits a mean burning time equal to or less than the mean burning time of a 3:7 mixture (by mass) of potassium bromate and cellulose and the criteria for Categories 1 and 2 are not met.

NOTE 1: Some oxidizing solids may present explosion hazards under certain conditions (e.g., when stored in large quantities). For example, some types of ammonium nitrate may give rise to an explosion hazard under extreme conditions and the "Resistance to detonation test" (IMO: Code of Safe Practice for Solid Bulk Cargoes, 2005, Annex 3, Test 5) may be used to assess this hazard. When information indicates that an oxidizing solid may present an explosion hazard, it shall be indicated on the Safety Data Sheet.
NOTE 2: Classification of solid chemicals shall be based on tests performed on the chemical as presented. If, for example, for the purposes of supply or transport, the same chemical is to be presented in a physical form different from that which was tested and which is considered likely to materially alter its performance in a classification test, classification must be based on testing of the chemical in the new form.

B.14.3 Additional classification considerations

B.14.3.1 For organic chemicals, the classification procedure for this class shall not be applied if:

(a) The chemical does not contain oxygen, fluorine or chlorine; or

(b) The chemical contains oxygen, fluorine or chlorine and these elements are chemically bonded only to carbon or hydrogen.

B.14.3.2 For inorganic chemicals, the classification procedure for this class shall not be applied if the chemical does not contain oxygen or halogen atoms.

B.14.3.3 In the event of divergence between test results and known experience in the handling and use of chemicals which shows them to be oxidizing, judgements based on known experience shall take precedence over test results.

B.15 ORGANIC PEROXIDES

B.15.1 Definition

B.15.1.1 **Organic peroxide** means a liquid or solid organic chemical which contains the bivalent -0-0- structure and as such is considered a derivative of hydrogen peroxide, where one or both of the hydrogen atoms have been replaced by organic radicals. The term organic peroxide includes organic peroxide mixtures containing at least one organic peroxide. Organic peroxides are thermally unstable chemicals, which may undergo exothermic self-accelerating decomposition. In addition, they may have one or more of the following properties:

(a) Be liable to explosive decomposition;
(b) Burn rapidly;
(c) Be sensitive to impact or friction;
(d) React dangerously with other substances.

B.15.1.2 An organic peroxide is regarded as possessing explosive properties when in laboratory testing the formulation is liable to detonate, to deflagrate rapidly or to show a violent effect when heated under confinement.

B.15.2 Classification criteria

B.15.2.1 Any organic peroxide shall be considered for classification in this class, unless it contains:

(a) Not more than 1.0% available oxygen from the organic peroxides when containing not more than 1.0% hydrogen peroxide; or
(b) Not more than 0.5% available oxygen from the organic peroxides when containing more than 1.0% but not more than 7.0% hydrogen peroxide.

NOTE: The available oxygen content (%) of an organic peroxide mixture is given by the formula:

$$16 \times \sum_{i}^{n} \left(\frac{n_i \times c_i}{m_i} \right)$$

where:
ni = number of peroxygen groups per molecule of organic peroxide i;
ci = concentration (mass %) of organic peroxide i;
mi = molecular mass of organic peroxide i.

B.15.2.2 Organic peroxides shall be classified in one of the seven categories of "Types A to G" for this class, according to the following principles:

(a) Any organic peroxide which, as packaged, can detonate or deflagrate rapidly shall be defined as organic peroxide TYPE A;
(b) Any organic peroxide possessing explosive properties and which, as packaged, neither detonates nor deflagrates rapidly, but is liable to undergo a thermal explosion in that package shall be defined as organic peroxide TYPE B;
(c) Any organic peroxide possessing explosive properties when the chemical as packaged cannot detonate or deflagrate rapidly or undergo a thermal explosion shall be defined as organic peroxide TYPE C;
(d) Any organic peroxide which in laboratory testing meets the criteria in (d)(i), (ii), or (iii) shall be defined as organic peroxide TYPE D:
  (i) detonates partially, does not deflagrate rapidly and shows no violent effect when heated under confinement; or
  (ii) does not detonate at all, deflagrates slowly and shows no violent effect when heated under confinement; or
  (iii) does not detonate or deflagrate at all and shows a medium effect when heated under confinement;
(e) Any organic peroxide which, in laboratory testing, neither detonates nor deflagrates at all and shows low or no effect when heated under confinement shall be defined as organic peroxide TYPE E;
(f) Any organic peroxide which, in laboratory testing, neither detonates in the cavitated state nor deflagrates at all and shows only a low or no effect when heated under confinement as well as low or no explosive power shall be defined as organic peroxide TYPE F;
(g) Any organic peroxide which, in laboratory testing, neither detonates in the cavitated state nor deflagrates at all and shows no effect when heated under confinement nor any explosive power, provided that it is thermally stable (self-accelerating decomposition temperature is 60 °C (140 °F) or higher for a 50 kg (110 lb) package), and, for liquid mixtures, a diluent having a boiling point of not less than 150 °C (302 °F) is used for desensitization, shall be defined as organic peroxide TYPE G. If the organic peroxide is not thermally stable or a diluent having a boiling point less than 150 °C (302 °F) is used for desensitization, it shall be defined as organic peroxide TYPE F.

B.15.3 Additional classification considerations

B.15.3.1 For purposes of classification, the properties of organic peroxides shall be determined in accordance with test series A to H as described in Part II of the UN ST/SG/AC.10 (incorporated by reference; See §1910.6).

B.15.3.2 Self-accelerating decomposition temperature (SADT) shall be determined in accordance with the UN ST/SG/AC.10 (incorporated by reference; See §1910.6), Part II, Section 28.

B.15.3.3 Mixtures of organic peroxides may be classified as the same type of organic peroxide as that of the most dangerous ingredient. However, as two stable ingredients can form a thermally less stable mixture, the SADT of the mixture shall be determined.

B.16 CORROSIVE TO METALS

B.16.1 Definition

A **chemical which is corrosive to metals** means a chemical which by chemical action will materially damage, or even destroy, metals.

B.16.2 Classification criteria

A chemical which is corrosive to metals shall be classified in a single category for this class, using the test in Part III, sub-section 37.4 of the UN ST/SG/AC.10 (incorporated by reference; See §1910.6), in accordance with Table B.16.1:

Table B.16.1:
Criteria for chemicals corrosive to metal

Category	Criteria
1	Corrosion rate on either steel or aluminium surfaces exceeding 6.25 mm per year at a test temperature of 55 °C (131 °F) when tested on both materials.

NOTE: Where an initial test on either steel or aluminium indicates the chemical being tested is corrosive the follow-up test on the other metal is not necessary.

B.16.3 Additional classification considerations

The specimen to be used for the test shall be made of the following materials:

(a) For the purposes of testing steel, steel types S235JR+CR (1.0037 resp. St 37-2), S275J2G3+CR (1.0144 resp.St 44-3), ISO 3574, Unified Numbering System (UNS) G 10200, or SAE 1020;
(b) For the purposes of testing aluminium: non-clad types 7075-T6 or AZ5GU-T6.

§1910.1200 Appendix C
Allocation of label elements
(Mandatory)

C.1 The label for each hazardous chemical shall include the product identifier used on the safety data sheet.

C.1.1 The labels on shipped containers shall also include the name, address, and telephone number of the chemical manufacturer, importer, or responsible party.

C.2 The label for each hazardous chemical that is classified shall include the signal word, hazard statement(s), pictogram(s), and precautionary statement(s) specified in C.4 for each hazard class and associated hazard category, except as provided for in C.2.1 through C.2.4.

C.2.1 Precedence of hazard information

C.2.1.1 If the signal word "Danger" is included, the signal word "Warning" shall not appear;

C.2.1.2 If the skull and crossbones pictogram is included, the exclamation mark pictogram shall not appear where it is used for acute toxicity;

C.2.1.3 If the corrosive pictogram is included, the exclamation mark pictogram shall not appear where it is used for skin or eye irritation;

C.2.1.4 If the health hazard pictogram is included for respiratory sensitization, the exclamation mark pictogram shall not appear where it is used for skin sensitization or for skin or eye irritation.

C.2.2 Hazard statement text

C.2.2.1 The text of all applicable hazard statements shall appear on the label, except as otherwise specified. The information in italics shall be included as part of the hazard statement as provided. For example: "causes damage to organs (*state all organs affected*) through prolonged or repeated exposure (*state route of exposure if no other routes of exposure cause the hazard*)". Hazard statements may be combined where appropriate to reduce the information on the label and improve readability, as long as all of the hazards are conveyed as required.

C.2.2.2 If the chemical manufacturer, importer, or responsible party can demonstrate that all or part of the hazard statement is inappropriate to a specific substance or mixture, the corresponding statement may be omitted from the label.

C.2.3 Pictograms

C.2.3.1 Pictograms shall be in the shape of a square set at a point and shall include a black hazard symbol on a white background with a red frame sufficiently wide to be clearly visible. A square red frame set at a point without a hazard symbol is not a pictogram and is not permitted on the label.

C.2.3.2 One of eight standard hazard symbols shall be used in each pictogram. The eight hazard symbols are depicted in Figure C.1. A pictogram using the exclamation mark symbol is presented in Figure C.2, for the purpose of illustration.

Figure C.1
Hazard Symbols and Classes

Flame	Flame Over Circle	Exclamation Mark	Exploding Bomb
			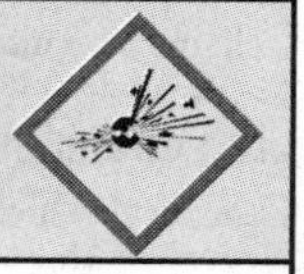
Flammables Self-Reactives Pyrophorics Self-Heating Emits Flammable Gas Organic Peroxides	Oxidizers	Irritant Dermal Sensitizer Acute Toxicity (harmful) Narcotic Effects Respiratory Tract Irritant	Explosives Self-Reactives Organic Peroxides

Corrosion	Gas Cylinder	Health Hazard	Skull and Crossbones

Corrosives	Gases Under Pressure	Carcinogen Respiratory Sensitizer Reproductive Toxicity Target Organ Toxicity Mutagenicity Aspiration Toxicity	Acute Toxicity (severe)

Figure C.2
Exclamation Mark Pictogram

C.2.3.3 Where a pictogram required by the Department of Transportation under Title 49 of the Code of Federal Regulations appears on a shipped container, the pictogram specified in C.4 for the same hazard shall not appear.

C.2.4 Precautionary statement text

C.2.4.1 There are four types of precautionary statements presented, "prevention," "response," "storage," and "disposal." The core part of the precautionary statement is presented in bold print. This is the text, except as otherwise specified, that shall appear on the label. Where additional information is required, it is indicated in plain text.

C.2.4.2 When a backslash or diagonal mark (/) appears in the precautionary statement text, it indicates that a choice has to be made between the separated phrases. In such cases, the chemical manufacturer, importer, or responsible party can choose the most appropriate phrase(s). For example, "Wear protective gloves/protective clothing/eye protection/face protection" could read "wear eye protection".

C.2.4.3 When three full stops (…) appear in the precautionary statement text, they indicate that all applicable conditions are not listed. For example, in "Use explosion-proof electrical/ventilating/lighting/.../equipment", the use of "..." indicates that other equipment may need to be specified. In such cases, the chemical manufacturer, importer, or responsible party can choose the other conditions to be specified.

C.2.4.4 When text in italics is used in a precautionary statement, this indicates specific conditions applying to the use or allocation of the precautionary statement. For example, "Use explosion-proof electrical/ventilating/lighting/.../equipment" is only required for flammable solids "*if dust clouds can occur*". Text in italics is intended to be an explanatory, conditional note and is not intended to appear on the label.

C.2.4.5 Where square brackets ([ ]) appear around text in a precautionary statement, this indicates that the text in square brackets is not appropriate in every case and should be used only in certain circumstances. In these cases, conditions for use explaining when the text should be used are provided. For example, one precautionary statement states: "[In case of inadequate ventilation] wear respiratory protection." This statement is given with the condition for use "– text in square brackets may be used if additional information is provided with the chemical at the point of use that explains what type of ventilation would be adequate for safe use". This means that, if additional information is provided with the chemical explaining what type of ventilation would be adequate for safe use, the text in square brackets should be used and the statement would read: "In case of inadequate ventilation wear respiratory protection." However, if the chemical is supplied without such ventilation information, the text in square brackets should not be used, and the precautionary statement should read: "Wear respiratory protection."

C.2.4.6 Precautionary statements may be combined or consolidated to save label space and improve readability. For example, "Keep away from heat, sparks and open flame," "Store in a well-ventilated place" and "Keep cool" can be combined to read "Keep away from heat, sparks and open flame and store in a cool, well-ventilated place."

C.2.4.7 In most cases, the precautionary statements are independent (e.g., the phrases for explosive hazards do not modify those related to certain health hazards, and products that are classified for both hazard classes shall bear appropriate precautionary statements for both). Where a chemical is classified for a number of hazards, and the precautionary statements are similar, the most stringent shall be included on the label (this will be applicable mainly to preventive measures). An order of precedence may be imposed by the chemical manufacturer, importer or responsible party in situations where phrases concern "Response." Rapid action may be crucial. For example, if a chemical is carcinogenic and acutely toxic, rapid action may be crucial, and first aid measures for acute toxicity will take precedence over those for long-term effects. In addition, medical attention to delayed health effects may be required in cases of incidental exposure, even if not associated with immediate symptoms of intoxication.

C.2.4.8 If the chemical manufacturer, importer, or responsible party can demonstrate that a precautionary statement is inappropriate to a specific substance or mixture, the precautionary statement may be omitted from the label.

C.3 Supplementary hazard information

C.3.1 To ensure that non-standardized information does not lead to unnecessarily wide variation or undermine the required information, supplementary information on the label is limited to when it provides further detail and does not contradict or cast doubt on the validity of the standardized hazard information.

C.3.2 Where the chemical manufacturer, importer, or distributor chooses to add supplementary information on the label, the placement of supplemental information shall not impede identification of information required by this Section.

C.3.3 Where an ingredient with unknown acute toxicity is used in a mixture at a concentration $\geq$ 1%, and the mixture is not classified based on testing of the mixture as a whole, a statement that X% of the mixture consists of ingredient(s) of unknown acute toxicity is required on the label.

C.4 Requirements for Signal Words, Hazard Statements, Pictograms, and Precautionary Statements.

C.4.1 Acute Toxicity - Oral
(Classified In Accordance With Appendix A.1)

Pictogram
Skull and Crossbones

Hazard category	Signal word	Hazard statement
1	Danger	Fatal if swallowed
2	Danger	Fatal if swallowed
3	Danger	Toxic if swallowed

Precautionary statements

Prevention	Response	Storage	Disposal
Wash ... thoroughly after handling. ... Chemical manufacturer, importer, or distributor to specify parts of the body to be washed after handling. **Do not eat, drink or smoke when using this product.**	**If swallowed: Immediately call a poison center/ doctor/...** **... Chemical manufacturer, importer, or distributor to specify the appropriate source of emergency medical advice.** Specific treatment (see ... on this label) ... Reference to supplemental first aid instruction. - *if immediate administration of antidote is required*. **Rinse mouth.**	**Store locked up.**	**Dispose of contents/ container to...** ... in accordance with local/ regional/national/ international regulations (to be specified).

Pictogram
Exclamation Mark

Hazard category	Signal word	Hazard statement
4	Warning	Harmful if swallowed

Precautionary statements

Prevention	Response	Storage	Disposal
Wash ... thoroughly after handling. ... Chemical manufacturer, importer, or distributor to specify parts of the body to be washed after handling. **Do not eat, drink or smoke when using this product.**	**If swallowed: Call a poison center/ doctor/.../ if you feel unwell.** ... Chemical manufacturer, importer, or distributor to specify the appropriate source of emergency medical advice. **Rinse mouth.**	**Store locked up.**	**Dispose of contents/ container to...** ... in accordance with local/ regional/national/ international regulations (to be specified).

C.4.2 Acute Toxicity Dermal
(Classified In Accordance With Appendix A.1)

Pictogram
Skull and Crossbones

Hazard category	Signal word	Hazard statement
1	Danger	Fatal in contact with skin
2	Danger	Fatal in contact with skin

Precautionary statements

Prevention	Response	Storage	Disposal
Do not get in eyes, on skin, or on clothing. **Wash ... thoroughly after handling.** ... Chemical manufacturer, importer, or distributor to specify parts of the body to be washed after handling. **Do not eat, drink or smoke when using this product.** **Wear protective gloves/ protective clothing.** Chemical manufacturer, importer, or distributor to specify type of equipment.	**If on skin: Wash with plenty of water/... ...** Chemical manufacturer, importer, or distributor may specify a cleansing agent if appropriate, or may recommend an alternative agent in exceptional cases if water is clearly inappropriate. **Immediately call a poison center/ doctor/...** ... Chemical manufacturer, importer, or distributor to specify the appropriate source of emergency medical advice. **Specific treatment (see ... on this label)** ... Reference to supplemental first aid instruction. - *if immediate measures such as specific cleansing agent is advised*. **Take off immediately all contaminated clothing and wash it before reuse.**	**Store locked up.**	**Dispose of contents/ container to...** ... in accordance with local/ regional/national/ international regulations (to be specified).

Pictogram
Skull and Crossbones

Hazard category	Signal word	Hazard statement
3	Danger	Toxic in contact with skin

Precautionary statements

Prevention	Response	Storage	Disposal
Wear protective gloves/ protective clothing. Chemical manufacturer, importer, or distributor to specify type of equipment.	**If on skin: Wash with plenty of water/...** ... Chemical manufacturer, importer, or distributor may specify a cleansing agent if appropriate, or may recommend an alternative agent in exceptional cases if water is clearly inappropriate. **Call a poison center/ doctor/.../ if you feel unwell.** ... Chemical manufacturer, importer, or distributor to specify the appropriate source of emergency medical advice. **Specific measures (see ... on this label)** ... Reference to supplemental first aid instruction. - *if measures such as specific cleansing agent is advised*. **Take off immediately all contaminated clothing and wash it before reuse.**	**Store locked up.**	**Dispose of contents/ container to...** ... in accordance with local/ regional/national/ international regulations (to be specified).

Pictogram
Exclamation Mark

Hazard category	Signal word	Hazard statement
4	Warning	Harmful in contact with skin

Precautionary statements

Prevention	Response	Storage	Disposal
Wear protective gloves/ protective clothing. Chemical manufacturer, importer, or distributor to specify type of equipment.	**If on skin: Wash with plenty of water/...** ... Chemical manufacturer, importer, or distributor may specify a cleansing agent if appropriate, or may recommend an alternative agent in exceptional cases if water is clearly inappropriate. **Call a poison center/ doctor/.../if you feel unwell.** ... Chemical manufacturer, importer, or distributor to specify the appropriate source of emergency medical advice. **Specific treatment (see ... on this label)** ... Reference to supplemental first aid instruction. - *if measures such as specific cleansing agent is advised*. **Take off contaminated clothing and wash it before reuse.**		**Dispose of contents/ container to...** ... in accordance with local/ regional/national/ international regulations (to be specified).

C.4.3 Acute Toxicity – Inhalation (Classified In Accordance With Appendix A.1)

Pictogram
Skull and Crossbones

Hazard category	Signal word	Hazard statement
1	Danger	Fatal if inhaled
2	Danger	Fatal if inhaled

Precautionary statements

Prevention	Response	Storage	Disposal
Do not breathe dust/fume/gas/ mist/ vapors/spray. Chemical manufacturer, importer, or distributor to specify applicable conditions. **Use only outdoors or in a well-ventilated area.** **[In case of inadequate ventilation] wear respiratory protection.** Chemical manufacturer, importer, or distributor to specify equipment. - *Text in square brackets may be used if additional information is provided with the chemical at the point of use that explains what type of ventilation would be adequate for safe use*.	**If inhaled: Remove person to fresh air and keep comfortable for breathing.** **Immediately call a poison center/ doctor/...** ... Chemical manufacturer, importer, or distributor to specify the appropriate source of emergency medical advice. **Specific treatment is urgent (see ... on this label)** ... Reference to supplemental first aid instruction. - *if immediate administration of antidote is required*.	**Store in a well-ventilated place. Keep container tightly closed.** - *if product is volatile as to generate hazardous atmosphere*. **Store locked up.**	**Dispose of contents/ container to...** ... in accordance with local/ regional/national/ international regulations (to be specified).

Pictogram
Skull and Crossbones

Hazard category	Signal word	Hazard statement
3	Danger	Toxic if inhaled

Precautionary statements

Prevention	Response	Storage	Disposal
Avoid breathing dust/fume/gas/ mist/vapors/ spray. Chemical manufacturer, importer, or distributor to specify applicable conditions. **Use only outdoors or in a well-ventilated area.**	**If inhaled: Remove victim to fresh air and keep at rest in a position comfortable for breathing.** **Call a poison center/doctor/...** ... Chemical manufacturer, importer, or distributor to specify the appropriate source of emergency medical advice. **Specific treatment (see ... on this label)** ... Reference to supplemental first aid instruction. - *if immediate specific measures are required*.	**Store in a well-ventilated place. Keep container tightly closed.** - *if product is volatile as to generate hazardous atmosphere*. **Store locked up.**	**Dispose of contents/ container to...** ... in accordance with local/ regional/national/ international regulations (to be specified).

Pictogram
Exclamation Mark

Hazard category	Signal word	Hazard statement
4	Warning	Harmful if inhaled

Precautionary statements

Prevention	Response	Storage	Disposal
Avoid breathing dust/fume/gas/ mist/vapors/ spray. Chemical manufacturer, importer, or distributor to specify applicable conditions. **Use only outdoors or in a well-ventilated area.**	**If inhaled: Remove person to fresh air and keep comfortable for breathing.** **Call a poison center/doctor/.../ if you feel unwell.** ... Chemical manufacturer, importer, or distributor to specify the appropriate source of emergency medical advice.		

C.4.4 Skin Corrosion/Irritation (Classified In Accordance With Appendix A.2)

Pictogram
Corrosive

Hazard category	Signal word	Hazard statement
1A to 1C	Danger	Causes severe skin burns and eye damage

Precautionary statements

Prevention	Response	Storage	Disposal
Do not breathe dusts or mists. - *if inhalable particles of dusts or mists may occur during use*. **Wash ... thoroughly after handling.** ... Chemical manufacturer, importer, or distributor to specify parts of the body to be washed after handling. **Wear protective gloves/protective clothing/eye protection/face protection.** Chemical manufacturer, importer, or distributor to specify type of equipment.	**If swallowed: Rinse mouth. Do NOT induce vomiting.** **If on skin (or hair): Take off immediately all contaminated clothing. Rinse skin with water/shower.** **Wash contaminated clothing before reuse.** **If inhaled: Remove person to fresh air and keep comfortable for breathing.** **Immediately call a poison center/ doctor/...** ... Chemical manufacturer, importer, or distributor to specify the appropriate source of emergency medical advice. **Specific treatment (see ... on this label)** ... Reference to supplemental first aid instruction. - *Manufacturer, importer, or distributor may specify a cleansing agent if appropriate*. **If in eyes: Rinse cautiously with water for several minutes. Remove contact lenses, if present and easy to do. Continue rinsing.**	**Store locked up.**	**Dispose of contents/ container to...** ... in accordance with local/ regional/ national/ international regulations (to be specified).

Pictogram
Exclamation Mark

Hazard category	Signal word	Hazard statement
2	Warning	Causes skin irritation

Precautionary statements

Prevention	Response	Storage	Disposal
Wash ... thoroughly after handling. ... Chemical manufacturer, importer, or distributor to specify parts of the body to be washed after handling. **Wear protective gloves.** Chemical manufacturer, importer, or distributor to specify type of equipment.	**If on skin: Wash with plenty water/...** ... Chemical manufacturer, importer, or distributor may specify a cleansing agent if appropriate, or may recommend as alternative agent in exceptional cases if water is clearly inappropriate. **Specific treatment (see ... on this label)** ... Reference to supplemental first aid instruction. - *Manufacturer, importer, or distributor may specify a cleansing agent if appropriate*. **If skin irritation occurs: Get medical advice/ attention.** **Take off contaminated clothing and wash before reuse.**		

C.4.5 Eye Damage/Irritation (Classified In Accordance With Appendix A.3)

Pictogram
Corrosive

Hazard category	Signal word	Hazard statement
1	Danger	Causes serious eye damage

Precautionary statements

Prevention	Response	Storage	Disposal
Wear eye protection/face protection. Chemical manufacturer, importer, or distributor to specify type of equipment.	**If in eyes: Rinse cautiously with water for several minutes. Remove contact lenses, if present and easy to do. Continue rinsing.** **Immediately call a poison center/doctor/...** ... Chemical manufacturer, importer, or distributor to specify the appropriate source of emergency medical advice.		

Pictogram
Exclamation Mark

Hazard category	Signal word	Hazard statement
2A	Warning	Causes serious eye irritation

Precautionary statements

Prevention	Response	Storage	Disposal
Wash ... thoroughly after handling. ... Chemical manufacturer, importer, or distributor to specify parts of the body to be washed after handling. **Wear eye protection/ face protection.** Chemical Manufacturer, importer, or distributor to specify type of equipment.	**If in eyes: Rinse cautiously with water for several minutes. Remove contact lenses, if present and easy to do. Continue rinsing.** **If eye irritation persists: Get medical advice/ attention.**		

Pictogram
No Pictogram

Hazard category	Signal word	Hazard statement
2B	Warning	Causes eye irritation

Precautionary statements

Prevention	Response	Storage	Disposal
Wash ... thoroughly after handling. ... Chemical manufacturer, importer, or distributor to specify parts of the body to be washed after handling.	**If in eyes: Rinse with water for several minutes. Remove contact lenses, if present and easy to do. Continue rinsing.** **If eye irritation persists: Get medical advice/attention.**		

C.4.6 Sensitization – Respiratory (Classified In Accordance With Appendix A.4)

Pictogram
Health Hazard

Hazard category	Signal word	Hazard statement
1 (including both subcategories 1A and 1B)	Danger	May cause allergy symptoms or breathing difficulty if inhaled

Precautionary statements

Prevention	Response	Storage	Disposal
Avoid breathing dust/fume/gas/mist/ vapors/spray. Chemical manufacturer, importer, or distributor to specify applicable conditions. **[In case of inadequate ventilation] wear respiratory protection.** Chemical manufacturer, importer, or distributor to specify equipment - *Text in square brackets may be used if additional information is provided with the chemical at the point of use that explains what type of ventilation would be adequate for safe use.*	**If inhaled: If breathing is difficult, remove person to fresh air and keep comfortable for breathing.** **If experiencing respiratory symptoms: Call a poison center/ doctor/...** ... Chemical manufacturer, importer, or distributor to specify the appropriate source of emergency medical advice.		**Dispose of contents/ container to...** ... in accordance with local/ regional/ national/ international regulations (to be specified).

C.4.7 Sensitization – Skin (Classified In Accordance With Appendix A.4)

Pictogram
Exclamation Mark

Hazard category	Signal word	Hazard statement
1 (including both subcategories 1A and 1B)	Warning	May cause an allergic skin reaction

Precautionary statements

Prevention	Response	Storage	Disposal
Avoid breathing dust/fume/gas/ mist/ vapors/ spray. Chemical manufacturer, importer, or distributor to specify applicable conditions. **Contaminated work clothing must not be allowed out of the workplace.** **Wear protective gloves.** Manufacturer, importer, or distributor to specify type of equipment.	**If on skin: Wash with plenty of water/...** ... Chemical manufacturer, importer, or distributor may specify a cleansing agent if appropriate, or may recommend an alternative agent in exceptional cases if water is clearly inappropriate. **If skin irritation or rash occurs: Get medical advice/attention.** **Specific treatment (see ... on this label)** ... Reference to supplemental first aid instruction. - *Manufacturer, importer, or distributor may specify a cleansing agent if appropriate*. **Wash contaminated clothing before reuse.**		**Dispose of contents/ container to...** ... in accordance with local/ regional/ national/ international regulations (to be specified).

C.4.8 Germ Cell Mutagenicity (Classified In Accordance With Appendix A.5)

Pictogram
Health Hazard

Hazard category	Signal word	Hazard statement
1A and 1B	Danger	May cause genetic defects <...>
2	Warning	Suspected of causing genetic defects
<...>		*(state route of exposure if no other routes of exposure cause the hazard)*

Precautionary statements

Prevention	Response	Storage	Disposal
Obtain special instructions before use. **Do not handle until all safety precautions have been read and understood.** **Wear protective gloves/protective clothing/eye protection/face protection.** Chemical manufacturer, importer, or distributor to specify type of equipment, as required.	**If exposed or concerned: Get medical advice/ attention.**	**Store locked up.**	**Dispose of contents/ container to...** ... in accordance with local/ regional/ national/ international regulations (to be specified).

C.4.9 Carcinogenicity (Classified In Accordance With Appendix A.6)

Pictogram
Health Hazard

Hazard category	Signal word	Hazard statement
1A and 1B	Danger	May cause cancer <...>
2	Warning	Suspected of causing cancer <...> *(state route of exposure if no other routes of exposure cause the hazard)*

Precautionary statements

Prevention	Response	Storage	Disposal
Obtain special instructions before use. **Do not handle until all safety precautions have been read and understood.** **Wear protective gloves/protective clothing/eye protection/face protection.** Chemical manufacturer, importer, or distributor to specify type of equipment, as required.	**If exposed or concerned: Get medical advice/ attention.**	**Store locked up.**	**Dispose of contents/ container to...** ... in accordance with local/ regional/ national/ international regulations (to be specified).

Note: If a Category 2 carcinogen ingredient is present in the mixture at a concentration between 0.1% and 1%, information is required on the SDS for a product; however, a label warning is optional. If a Category 2 carcinogen ingredient is present in the mixture at a concentration of ≥1%, both an SDS and a label is required and the information must be included on each.

C.4.10 Toxic to Reproduction (Classified In Accordance With Appendix A.7)

Pictogram
Health Hazard

Hazard category	Signal word	Hazard statement
1A and 1B	Danger	May damage fertility or the unborn child <...><<...>>
2	Warning	Suspected of damaging fertility or the unborn child <...><<...>> *(state route if known) (state route of exposure if no other routes of exposure cause the hazard)*

Precautionary statements			
Prevention	**Response**	**Storage**	**Disposal**
Obtain special instructions before use. **Do not handle until all safety precautions have been read and understood.** **Wear protective gloves/protective clothing/eye protection/face protection.** Chemical manufacturer, importer, or distributor to specify type of equipment, as required.	**If exposed or concerned: Get medical advice/ attention.**	**Store locked up.**	**Dispose of contents/ container to...** ... in accordance with local/ regional/national/ international regulations (to be specified).

Pictogram
No Pictogram

Hazard category	Signal word	Hazard statement
No designated number	*No signal word*	May cause harm to breast-fed children

(See Table A.7.1 in Appendix A.7)

Precautionary statements			
Prevention	**Response**	**Storage**	**Disposal**
Obtain special instructions before use. **Do not breathe dusts or mists.** - *if inhalable particles of dusts or mists may occur during use.* **Avoid contact during pregnancy/while nursing.** **Wash ... thoroughly after handling.** ...Chemical manufacturer, importer, or distributor to specify parts of the body to be washed after handling. **Do not eat, drink or smoke when using this product.**	**If exposed or concerned: Get medical advice/ attention.**		

C.4.11 Specific Target Organ Toxicity (Single Exposure) (Classified In Accordance With Appendix A.8)

Pictogram
Health Hazard

Hazard category	Signal word	Hazard statement
1	Danger	Causes damage to organs <...><<...>> *(or state all organs affected if known)* *(state route of exposure if no other routes of exposure cause the hazard)*

Precautionary statements			
Prevention	**Response**	**Storage**	**Disposal**
Do not breathe dust/ fume/gas/mist/ vapors/spray. Chemical manufacturer, importer, or distributor to specify applicable conditions. **Wash ...thoroughly after handling.** ... Chemical manufacturer, importer, or distributor to specify parts of the body to be washed after handling. **Do not eat, drink or smoke when using this product.**	**If exposed: Call a poison center/ doctor/...** ... Chemical manufacturer, importer, or distributor to specify the appropriate source of emergency medical advice. **Specific treatment (see ... on this label)** ... Reference to supplemental first aid instruction. - *if immediate measures are required.*	**Store locked up.**	**Dispose of contents/ container to...** ... in accordance with local/ regional/ national/ international regulations (to be specified).

Pictogram
Health Hazard

Hazard category	Signal word	Hazard statement
2 <...><<...>>	Warning	May cause damage to organs *(or state all organs affected if known)* *(state route of exposure if no other routes of exposure cause the hazard)*

Precautionary statements			
Prevention	**Response**	**Storage**	**Disposal**
Do not breathe dust/ fume/gas/mist/ vapors/spray. Chemical manufacturer, importer, or distributor to specify applicable conditions. **Wash ...thoroughly after handling.** ... Chemical manufacturer, importer, or distributor to specify parts of the body to be washed after handling. **Do not eat, drink or smoke when using this product.**	**If exposed or concerned: Call a poison center/ doctor/...** ... Chemical manufacturer, importer, or distributor to specify the appropriate source of emergency medical advice.	**Store locked up.**	**Dispose of contents/ container to...** ... in accordance with local/ regional/ national/ international regulations (to be specified).

Pictogram
Exclamation Mark

Hazard category	Signal word	Hazard statement
3	Warning	May cause respiratory irritation; or May cause drowsiness or dizziness

Precautionary statements			
Prevention	**Response**	**Storage**	**Disposal**
Avoid breathing dust/fume/gas/ mist/ vapors/ spray. Chemical manufacturer, importer, or distributor to specify applicable conditions. **Use only outdoors or in a well-ventilated area.**	**If Inhaled: Remove person to fresh air and keep comfortable for breathing.** **Call a poison center/doctor/... if you feel unwell.** ... Chemical manufacturer, importer, or distributor to specify the appropriate source of emergency medical advice.	**Store in a well-ventilated place. Keep container tightly closed.** - *if product is volatile so as to generate hazardous atmosphere.* **Store locked up.**	**Dispose of contents/ container to...** ... in accordance with local/ regional/national/ international regulations (to be specified).

C.4.12 Specific Target Organ Toxicity (Repeated Exposure) (Classified In Accordance With Appendix A.9)

Pictogram
Health Hazard

Hazard category	Signal word	Hazard statement
1	Danger	Causes damage to organs <...> through prolonged or repeated exposure <<...>> *(or state all organs affected if known)* *(state route of exposure if no other routes of exposure cause the hazard)*

Precautionary statements			
Prevention	**Response**	**Storage**	**Disposal**
Do not breathe dust/ fume/gas/mist/ vapors/ spray. Chemical manufacturer, importer, or distributor to specify applicable conditions. **Wash ...thoroughly after handling.** ... Chemical manufacturer, importer, or distributor to specify parts of the body to be washed after handling. **Do not eat, drink or smoke when using this product.**	**Get medical advice/ attention if you feel unwell.**		**Dispose of contents/ container to...** ... in accordance with local/ regional/national/ international regulations (to be specified).

Pictogram
Health Hazard

Hazard category	Signal word	Hazard statement
2	Warning	May cause damage to organs <...> through prolonged or repeated exposure <<...>> (state all organs affected if known) (state route of exposure if no other routes of exposure cause the hazard)

Precautionary statements			
Prevention	**Response**	**Storage**	**Disposal**
Do not breathe dust/fume/gas/ mist/ vapors/ spray. Chemical manufacturer, importer, or distributor to specify applicable conditions.	**Get medical advice/attention if you feel unwell.**		**Dispose of contents/container to...** ... in accordance with local/ regional/national/ international regulations (to be specified).

C.4.13 Aspiration Hazard (Classified In Accordance With Appendix A.10)

Pictogram
Health Hazard

Hazard category	Signal word	Hazard statement
1	Danger	May be fatal if swallowed and enters airways.

Precautionary statements			
Prevention	**Response**	**Storage**	**Disposal**
	If Swallowed: Immediately call a poison center/ doctor/... ... Chemical manufacturer, importer, or distributor to specify the appropriate source of emergency medical advice. **Do NOT induce vomiting.**	**Store locked up.**	**Dispose of contents/ container to...** ... in accordance with local/ regional/national/ international regulations (to be specified).

C.4.14 Explosives (Classified In Accordance With Appendix B.1)

Pictogram
Exploding Bomb

Hazard category	Signal word	Hazard statement
Unstable Explosive	Danger	Unstable Explosive

Precautionary statements			
Prevention	**Response**	**Storage**	**Disposal**
Obtain special instructions before use. **Do not handle until all safety precautions have been read and understood.** **Wear personal protective equipment/face protection** Chemical manufacturer, importer, or distributor to specify type of equipment, as required.	**Explosion risk in case of fire.** **Do NOT fight fire when fire reaches explosives.** **Evacuate area.**	**Store ...** ...in accordance with local/ regional/ national/ international regulations (to be specified).	**Dispose of contents/ container to ...** ...in accordance with local/ regional/ national/ international regulations (to be specified).

Pictogram
Exploding Bomb

Hazard category	Signal word	Hazard statement
Division 1.1	Danger	Explosive; mass explosion hazard
Division 1.2	Danger	Explosive; severe projection hazard
Division 1.3	Danger	Explosive: fire, blast or projection hazard

Precautionary statements			
Prevention	**Response**	**Storage**	**Disposal**
Keep away from heat/ sparks/open flames/ hot surfaces. - No smoking. Chemical manufacturer, importer, or distributor to specify applicable ignition source(s). **Keep wetted with...** ... Chemical Manufacturer, importer, or distributor to specify appropriate material. - *if drying out increases explosion hazard, except as needed for manufacturing or operating processes (e.g. nitrocellulose).* **Ground/bond container and receiving equipment.** - *if the explosive is electrostatically sensitive.* **Do not subject to grinding/shock/.../ friction.** ... Chemical manufacturer, importer, or distributor to specify applicable rough handling. **Wear face protection.** Chemical Manufacturer, importer, or distributor to specify type of equipment.	**In case of fire: evacuate area.** **Explosion risk in case of fire.** **Do NOT fight fire when fire reaches explosives.**	**Store ...** ...in accordance with local/ regional/ national/ international regulations (to be specified).	**Dispose of contents/ container to ...** ...in accordance with local/ regional/ national/ international regulations (to be specified).

Note: Unpackaged explosives or explosives repacked in packagings other than the original or similar packaging shall have the label elements assigned to Division 1.1 unless the hazard is shown to correspond to one of the hazard categories in Appendix B.1, in which case the corresponding symbol, signal word and/or the hazard statement shall be assigned.

Pictogram
Exploding Bomb[1]

Hazard category	Signal word	Hazard statement
Division 1.4	Warning	Fire or projection hazard

Precautionary statements[1]			
Prevention	**Response**	**Storage**	**Disposal**
Keep away from heat/sparks/ open flames/hot surfaces. - No smoking. Chemical manufacturer, importer, or distributor to specify applicable ignition source(s). **Ground/bond container and receiving equipment.** - _if the explosive is electrostatically sensitive._ **Do not subject to grinding/shock/.../ friction.** Chemical manufacturer, importer, or distributor to specify applicable rough handling. **Wear face protection.** Chemical Manufacturer, importer, or distributor to specify type of equipment.	**In case of fire: Evacuate area.** **Explosion risk in case of fire.** - _except if explosives are 1.4S ammunition and components thereof._ **Do NOT fight fire when fire reaches explosives.** **Fight fire with normal precautions from a reasonable distance** - _if explosives are 1.4S ammunition and components thereof._	**Store ...** ...in accordance with local/ regional/ national/ international regulations (to be specified).	**Dispose of contents/ container to ...** ...in accordance with local/ regional/ national/ international regulations (to be specified).

Note: Unpackaged explosives or explosives repacked in packagings other than the original or similar packaging shall have the label elements assigned to Division 1.1 unless the hazard is shown to correspond to one of the hazard categories in Appendix B.1, in which case the corresponding symbol, signal word and/or the hazard statement shall be assigned.[1]

---

[1] Except no pictogram is required for explosives that are 1.4S small arms ammunition and components thereof. Labels for 1.4S small arms ammunition and components shall include appropriate precautionary statements.

Pictogram
No Pictogram

Hazard category	Signal word	Hazard statement
Division 1.5	Danger	May mass explode in fire

Precautionary statements			
Prevention	**Response**	**Storage**	**Disposal**
Keep away from heat/sparks/open flames/hot surfaces. - No smoking. Chemical manufacturer, importer, or distributor to specify applicable ignition source(s). **Keep wetted with...** ... Chemical manufacturer, importer, or distributor to specify appropriate material. - _if drying out increases explosion hazard, except as needed for manufacturing or operating processes (e.g., nitrocellulose)._ **Ground/bond container and receiving equipment.** - _if the explosive is electrostatically sensitive._ **Do not subject to grinding/shock/.../ friction.** Chemical manufacturer, importer, or distributor to specify applicable rough handling. **Wear face protection.** Chemical manufacturer, importer, or distributor to specify type of equipment.	**In case of fire: Evacuate area.** **Explosion risk in case of fire.** **Do NOT fight fire when fire reaches explosives.**	**Store ...** ...in accordance with local/ regional/ national/ international regulations (to be specified).	**Dispose of contents/ container to ...** ...in accordance with local/ regional/ national/ international regulations (to be specified).

Note: Unpackaged explosives or explosives repacked in packagings other than the original or similar packaging shall have the label elements assigned to Division 1.1 unless the hazard is shown to correspond to one of the hazard categories in Appendix B.1, in which case the corresponding symbol, signal work and/or the hazard statement shall be assigned.

Pictogram
No Pictogram

Hazard category	Signal word	Hazard statement
Division 1.6	_No signal word_	_No hazard statement_

Precautionary statements			
Prevention	**Response**	**Storage**	**Disposal**
None assigned.	None assigned.	None assigned.	None assigned.

Note: Unpackaged explosives or explosives repacked in packagings other than the original or similar packaging shall have the label elements assigned to Division 1.1 unless the hazard is shown to correspond to one of the hazard categories in Appendix B.1, in which case the corresponding symbol, signal work and/or the hazard statement shall be assigned.

C.4.15 Flammable Gases (Classified In Accordance With Appendix B.2)

Pictogram
Flame

Hazard category	Signal word	Hazard statement
1	Danger	Extremely flammable gas

Precautionary statements			
Prevention	**Response**	**Storage**	**Disposal**
Keep away from heat/sparks/ open flames/hot surfaces. -No smoking. Chemical manufacturer, importer, or distributor to specify applicable ignition source(s).	**Leaking gas fire:** **Do not extinguish, unless leak can be stopped safely.** **Eliminate all ignition sources if safe to do so.**	Store in well-ventilated place.	

Pictogram
No Pictogram

Hazard category	Signal word	Hazard statement
2	Warning	Flammable gas

Precautionary statements			
Prevention	**Response**	**Storage**	**Disposal**
Keep away from heat/sparks/ open flames/hot surfaces. -No smoking. Chemical manufacturer, importer, or distributor to specify applicable ignition sources(s).	**Leaking gas fire: Do not extinguish, unless leak can be stopped safely.** **Eliminate all ignition sources if safe to do so.**	Store in well-ventilated place.	

C.4.16 Flammable Aerosols (Classified In Accordance With Appendix B.3)

Pictogram
Flame

Hazard category	Signal word	Hazard statement
1	Danger	Extremely flammable aerosol
2	Warning	Flammable aerosol

Precautionary statements			
Prevention	**Response**	**Storage**	**Disposal**
Keep away from heat/ sparks/open flames/hot surfaces. -No smoking. Chemical manufacturer, importer, or distributor to specify applicable ignition source(s). **Do not spray on an open flame or other ignition source.** **Pressurized container: Do not pierce or burn, even after use.**		Protect from sunlight. Do not expose to temperatures exceeding 50 °C/122 °F.	

C.4.17 Oxidizing Gases (Classified In Accordance With Appendix B.4)

Pictogram
Flame over Circle

Hazard category	Signal word	Hazard statement
1	Danger	May cause or intensify fire; oxidizer

Precautionary statements			
Prevention	**Response**	**Storage**	**Disposal**
Keep/Store away from clothing/.../combustible materials. ...Chemical manufacturer, importer, or distributor to specify other incompatible materials. **Keep reduction valves/ valves and fittings free from oil and grease.**	**In case of fire: Stop leak if safe to do so.**	**Store in well-ventilated place.**	

C.4.18 Gases Under Pressure (Classified In Accordance With Appendix B.5)

Pictogram
Gas Cylinder

Hazard category	Signal word	Hazard statement
Compressed gas	Warning	Contains gas under pressure; may explode if heated
Liquefied gas	Warning	Contains gas under pressure; may explode if heated
Dissolved gas	Warning	Contains gas under pressure; may explode if heated

Precautionary statements			
Prevention	**Response**	**Storage**	**Disposal**
		Protect from sunlight. Store in a well-ventilated place.	

Pictogram
Gas Cylinder

Hazard category	Signal word	Hazard statement
Refrigerated liquefied gas	Warning	Contains refrigerated gas; may cause cryogenic burns or injury

Precautionary statements			
Prevention	**Response**	**Storage**	**Disposal**
Wear cold insulating gloves/face shield/eye protection.	**Thaw frosted parts with lukewarm water. Do not rub affected area.** **Get immediate medical advice/ attention**	**Store in well-ventilated place.**	

C.4.19 Flammable Liquids (Classified In Accordance With Appendix B.6)

Pictogram
Flame

Hazard category	Signal word	Hazard statement
1	Danger	Extremely flammable liquid and vapor
2	Danger	Highly flammable liquid and vapor
3	Warning	Flammable liquid and vapor

Precautionary statements			
Prevention	**Response**	**Storage**	**Disposal**
Keep away from heat/sparks/ open flames/hot surfaces.– No smoking. Chemical manufacturer, importer, or distributor to specify applicable ignition source(s). **Keep container tightly closed.** **Ground/Bond container and receiving equipment.** - *if electrostatically sensitive material is for reloading* *- if product is volatile so as to generate hazardous atmosphere*. **Use explosion-proof electrical/ ventilating/ lighting/.../ equipment.** ... Chemical manufacturer, importer, or distributor to specify other equipment. **Use only non-sparking tools.** **Take precautionary measures against static discharge.** **Wear protective gloves/eye protection/face protection** Chemical Manufacturer, importer, or distributor to specify type of equipment.	**If on skin (or hair): Remove/Take off immediately all contaminated clothing. Rinse skin with water/ shower.** **In case of fire: Use ... for extinction.** ... Chemical manufacturer, importer, or distributor to specify appropriate media. - *if water increases risk.*	**Store in a well-ventilated place. Keep cool.**	**Dispose of contents/ container to...** ... in accordance with local/regional/ national/ international regulations (to be specified).

Pictogram
No Pictogram

Hazard category	Signal word	Hazard statement
4	Warning	Combustible liquid

Precautionary statements

Prevention	Response	Storage	Disposal
Keep away from flames and hot surfaces. – No smoking. **Wear protective gloves/eye protection/face protection** Chemical manufacturer, importer, or distributor to specify type of equipment.	**In case of fire: Use ... for extinction.** ... Chemical manufacturer, importer, or distributor to specify appropriate media. - *if water increases risk.*	**Store in a well-ventilated place. Keep cool.**	**Dispose of contents/ container to...** ... in accordance with local/ regional/national/ international regulations (to be specified).

C.4.20 Flammable Solids (Classified In Accordance With Appendix B.6)

Pictogram
Flame

Hazard category	Signal word	Hazard statement
1	Danger	Flammable solid
2	Warning	Flammable solid

Precautionary statements

Prevention	Response	Storage	Disposal
Keep away from heat/sparks/ open flames/hot surfaces.– No smoking. Chemical Manufacturer, importer, or distributor to specify applicable ignition source(s). **Ground/Bond container and receiving equipment** - *if electrostatically sensitive material is for reloading.* **Use explosion-proof electrical/ventilating/ lighting/.../equipment.** ... Chemical Manufacturer, importer, or distributor to specify other equipment. - *if dust clouds can occur.* **Wear protective gloves/eye protection/face protection** Chemical Manufacturer, importer, or distributor to specify type of equipment.	**In case of fire: Use ... for extinction** ... Chemical Manufacturer, importer, or distributor to specify appropriate media. - *if water increases risk.*		

C.4.21 Self-Reactive Substances and Mixtures (Classified In Accordance With Appendix B.8)

Pictogram
Exploding Bomb

Hazard category	Signal word	Hazard statement
Type A	Danger	Heating may cause an explosion

Precautionary statements

Prevention	Response	Storage	Disposal
Keep away from heat/sparks/open flames/hot surfaces. - No smoking. Chemical manufacturer, importer, or distributor to specify applicable ignition source(s). **Keep/Store away from clothing/.../ combustible materials.** ... Chemical manufacturer, importer, or distributor to specify other incompatible materials.	**In case of fire: Use ... for extinction** ... Chemical Manufacturer, importer, or distributor to specify appropriate media. - *if water increases risk.* **In case of fire: Evacuate area. Fight fire remotely due to the risk of explosion.**	**Store in a well-ventilated place. Keep cool.** **Store at temperatures not exceeding ...°C/...°F.** ... Chemical Manufacturer, importer, or distributor to specify temperature.	**Dispose of contents/ container to ...** ...in accordance with local/ regional/ national/ international regulations (to be specified).

Note: Data continues at the top of the next column.

Note: Data continues from the previous column.

Precautionary statements

Prevention	Response	Storage	Disposal
Keep only in original container. **Wear protective gloves/eye protection/face protection.** Chemical manufacturer, importer, or distributor to specify type of equipment.		**Store away from other materials.**	

Pictogram
Exploding Bomb and Flame

Hazard category	Signal word	Hazard statement
Type B	Danger	Heating may cause fire or explosion

Precautionary statements

Prevention	Response	Storage	Disposal
Keep away from heat/sparks/open flames/hot surfaces. - No smoking. Chemical manufacturer, importer, or distributor to specify applicable ignition source(s). **Keep/Store away from clothing/.../ combustible materials.** ... Chemical manufacturer, importer, or distributor to specify other incompatible materials. **Keep only in original container.** **Wear protective gloves/eye protection/face protection.** Chemical manufacturer, importer, or distributor to specify type of equipment.	**In case of fire: Use ... for extinction** ... Chemical manufacturer, importer, or distributor to specify appropriate media. - *if water increases risk.* **In case of fire: Evacuate area. Fight fire remotely due to the risk of explosion.**	**Store in a well-ventilated place. Keep cool.** **Store at temperatures not exceeding ...°C/...°F.** ... Chemical Manufacturer, importer, or distributor to specify temperature. **Store away from other materials.**	**Dispose of contents/ container to ...** ...in accordance with local/ regional/ national/ international regulations (to be specified).

Pictogram
Flame

Hazard category	Signal word	Hazard statement
Type C	Danger	Heating may cause fire
Type D	Danger	Heating may cause fire
Type E	Warning	Heating may cause fire
Type F	Warning	Heating may cause fire

Precautionary statements

Prevention	Response	Storage	Disposal
Keep away from heat/sparks/open flames/hot surfaces. - No smoking. Chemical manufacturer, importer, or distributor to specify applicable ignition source(s). **Keep/Store away from clothing/.../ combustible materials.** ... Chemical manufacturer, importer, or distributor to specify other incompatible materials.	**In case of fire: Use ... for extinction** ... Chemical manufacturer, importer, or distributor to specify appropriate media. - *if water increases risk.*	**Store in a well-ventilated place. Keep cool.** **Store at temperatures not exceeding ...°C/...°F.** ... Chemical manufacturer, importer, or distributor to specify temperature.	**Dispose of contents/ container to ...** ...in accordance with local/ regional/ national/ international regulations (to be specified).

Note: Data continues at the top of the next column, on next page.

Note: Data continues from the previous column, on previous page.

Precautionary statements			
Prevention	**Response**	**Storage**	**Disposal**
Keep only in original container. **Wear protective gloves/eye protection/face protection.** Chemical manufacturer, importer, or distributor to specify type of equipment.		**Store away from other materials.**	

C.4.22 Pyrophoric Liquids (Classified In Accordance With Appendix B.9)

Pictogram: Flame

Hazard category	Signal word	Hazard statement
1	Danger	Catches fire spontaneously if exposed to air

Precautionary statements			
Prevention	**Response**	**Storage**	**Disposal**
Keep away from heat/sparks/open flames/hot surfaces. - No smoking. Chemical manufacturer, importer, or distributor to specify applicable ignition sources(s). **Do not allow contact with air.** **Wear protective gloves/eye protection/face protection.** Chemical manufacturer, importer, or distributor to specify type of equipment.	**If on skin: Immerse in cool water/wrap with wet bandages** **In case of fire: Use ... for extinction** ... Chemical manufacturer, importer, or distributor to specify appropriate media. - *if water increases risk*	**Store contents under ...** ... Chemical manufacturer, importer, or distributor to specify appropriate liquid or inert gas.	

C.4.23 Pyrophoric Solids (Classified In Accordance With Appendix B.10)

Pictogram: Flame

Hazard category	Signal word	Hazard statement
1	Danger	Catches fire spontaneously if exposed to air

Precautionary statements			
Prevention	**Response**	**Storage**	**Disposal**
Keep away from heat/sparks/open flames/hot surfaces. - No smoking. Chemical manufacturer, importer, or distributor to specify applicable ignition sources(s). **Do not allow contact with air.** **Wear protective gloves/eye protection/face protection.** Chemical manufacturer, importer, or distributor to specify type of equipment.	**Brush off loose particles from skin. Immerse in cool water/wrap in wet bandages.** **In case of fire: Use ... for extinction** ... Chemical manufacturer, importer, or distributor to specify appropriate media. - *if water increases risk.*	**Store contents under ...** ... Chemical manufacturer, importer, or distributor to specify appropriate liquid or inert gas.	

C.4.24 Self-Heating Substances and Mixtures (Classified In Accordance With Appendix B.11)

Pictogram: Flame

Hazard category	Signal word	Hazard statement
1	Danger	Self-heating; may catch fire
2	Warning	Self-heating in large quantities; may catch fire

Precautionary statements			
Prevention	**Response**	**Storage**	**Disposal**
Keep cool. Protect from sunlight. **Wear protective gloves/eye protection/face protection.** Chemical manufacturer, importer, or distributor to specify type of equipment.		**Maintain air gap between stacks/pallets.** **Store bulk masses greater than ... kg/...lbs at temperatures not exceeding ...°C/...°F.** ... Chemical manufacturer, importer, or distributor to specify mass and temperature. **Store away from other materials.**	

C.4.25 Substances and Mixtures which, in Contact with Water, Emit Flammable Gas (Classified In Accordance With Appendix B.12)

Pictogram: Flame

Hazard category	Signal word	Hazard statement
1	Danger	In contact with water releases flammable gases, which may ignite spontaneously
2	Danger	In contact with water releases flammable gas

Precautionary statements			
Prevention	**Response**	**Storage**	**Disposal**
Do not allow contact with water. **Handle under inert gas. Protect from moisture.** **Wear protective gloves/eye protection/face protection.** Chemical manufacturer, importer, or distributor to specify type of equipment.	**Brush off loose particles from skin and immerse in cool water/wrap in wet bandages.** **In case of fire: Use ... for extinction** ... Chemical manufacturer, importer, or distributor to specify appropriate media. - *if water increases risk.*	**Store in a dry place. Store in a closed container.**	**Dispose of contents/ container to...** ...in accordance with local/ regional/national/ international regulations (to be specified).

Pictogram: Flame

Hazard category	Signal word	Hazard statement
3	Warning	In contact with water releases flammable gas

Precautionary statements			
Prevention	**Response**	**Storage**	**Disposal**
Handle under inert gas. Protect from moisture. **Wear protective gloves/eye protection/face protection.** Chemical manufacturer, importer, or distributor to specify type of equipment.	**In case of fire: Use ... for extinction** ... Chemical manufacturer, importer, or distributor to specify appropriate media. - *if water increases risk.*	**Store in a dry place. Store in a closed container.**	**Dispose of contents/ container to...** ...in accordance with local/ regional/national/ international regulations (to be specified).

C.4.26 Oxidizing Liquids (Classified In Accordance With Appendix B.13)

Pictogram
Flame over Circle

Hazard category	Signal word	Hazard statement
1	Danger	May cause fire or explosion; strong oxidizer

Precautionary statements

Prevention	Response	Storage	Disposal
Keep away from heat. **Keep/Store away from clothing and other combustible materials.** **Take any precaution to avoid mixing with combustibles/...** ... Chemical manufacturer, importer, or distributor to specify other incompatible materials. **Wear protective gloves /eye protection/face protection.** Chemical manufacturer, importer, or distributor to specify type of equipment. **Wear fire/flame resistant/retardant clothing.**	**If on clothing: Rinse immediately contaminated clothing and skin with plenty of water before removing clothes.** **In case of major fire and large quantities: Evacuate area. Fight fire remotely due to the risk of explosion.** **In case of fire: Use ... for extinction** ... Chemical manufacturer, importer, or distributor to specify appropriate media. - *if water increases risk.*		**Dispose of contents/ container to...** ...in accordance with local/ regional/national/ international regulations (to be specified).

Pictogram
Flame over Circle

Hazard category	Signal word	Hazard statement
2	Danger	May intensify fire; oxidizer
3	Warning	May intensify fire; oxidizer

Precautionary statements

Prevention	Response	Storage	Disposal
Keep away from heat. **Keep/Store away from clothing/.../combustible materials.** ...Chemical manufacturer, importer, or distributor to specify other incompatible materials. **Take any precaution to avoid mixing with combustibles/...** ... Chemical manufacturer, importer, or distributor to specify other incompatible materials. **Wear protective gloves /eye protection/face protection.** Chemical manufacturer, importer, or distributor to specify type of equipment.	**In case of fire: Use ... for extinction** ... Chemical manufacturer, importer, or distributor to specify appropriate media. - *if water increases risk.*		**Dispose of contents/ container to...** ...in accordance with local/ regional/national/ international regulations (to be specified).

C.4.27 Oxidizing Solids (Classified In Accordance With Appendix B.14)

Pictogram
Flame over Circle

Hazard category	Signal word	Hazard statement
1	Danger	May cause fire or explosion; strong oxidizer

Precautionary statements

Prevention	Response	Storage	Disposal
Keep away from heat. **Keep away from clothing and other combustable materials** **Take any precaution to avoid mixing with combustibles/...** ... Chemical manufacturer, importer, or distributor to specify other incompatible materials. **Wear protective gloves /eye protection/face protection.** Chemical manufacturer, importer, or distributor to specify type of equipment. **Wear fire/flame resistant/retardant clothing.**	**If on clothing: Rinse immediately contaminated clothing and skin with plenty of water before removing clothes.** **In case of major fire and large quantities: Evacuate area. Fight fire remotely due to the risk of explosion.** **In case of fire: Use ... for extinction** ... Chemical manufacturer, importer, or distributor to specify appropriate media. - *if water increases risk.*		**Dispose of contents/ container to...** ...in accordance with local/ regional/national/ international regulations (to be specified).

Pictogram
Flame over Circle

Hazard category	Signal word	Hazard statement
2	Danger	May intensify fire; oxidizer
3	Warning	May intensify fire; oxidizer

Precautionary statements

Prevention	Response	Storage	Disposal
Keep away from heat. **Keep/Store away from clothing/.../ combustible materials.** ... Chemical manufacturer, importer, or distributor to specify other incompatible materials. **Take any precaution to avoid mixing with combustibles/...** ... Chemical manufacturer, importer, or distributor to specify other incompatible materials. **Wear protective gloves /eye protection/ face protection.** Chemical manufacturer, importer, or distributor to specify type of equipment.	**In case of fire: Use ... for extinction** ... Chemical manufacturer, importer, or distributor to specify appropriate media. - *if water increases risk.*		**Dispose of contents/ container to...** ...in accordance with local/ regional/national/ international regulations (to be specified).

C.4.28 Organic Peroxides (Classified In Accordance With Appendix B.15)

Pictogram
Exploding Bomb

Hazard category	Signal word	Hazard statement
Type A	Danger	Heating may cause explosion

Precautionary statements

Prevention	Response	Storage	Disposal
Keep away from heat/sparks/ open flames/ hot surfaces.- No smoking. Chemical manufacturer, importer, or distributor to specify applicable ignition source(s). **Keep/Store away from clothing/.../ combustible materials.** ... Chemical manufacturer, importer, or distributor to specify incompatible materials. **Keep only in original container.** **Wear protective gloves/eye protection/face protection.** Chemical manufacturer, importer, or distributor to specify type of equipment.		**Store at temperatures not exceeding ...°C/...°F. Keep cool.** ... Chemical manufacturer, importer, or distributor to specify temperature. **Protect from sunlight.** **Store away from other materials.**	**Dispose of contents/ container to...** ...in accordance with local/ regional/national/ international regulations (to be specified).

Pictogram
Exploding Bomb and Flame

Hazard category	Signal word	Hazard statement
Type B	Danger	Heating may cause an explosion

Precautionary statements

Prevention	Response	Storage	Disposal
Keep away from heat/ sparks/open flames/ hot surfaces. - No smoking. Chemical manufacturer, importer, or distributor to specify applicable ignition source(s). **Keep/Store away from clothing/.../ combustible materials.** ... Chemical manufacturer, importer, or distributor to specify other incompatible materials. **Keep only in original container.** **Wear protective gloves/eye protection/ face protection.** Chemical manufacturer, importer, or distributor to specify type of equipment.		**Store at temperatures not exceeding ...°C/...°F. Keep cool.** Chemical manufacturer, importer, or distributor to specify temperature. **Protect from sunlight.** **Store away from other materials.**	**Dispose of contents/ container to ...** ...in accordance with local/ regional/ national/ international regulations (to be specified).

Pictogram
Flame

Hazard category	Signal word	Hazard statement
Type C	Danger	Heating may cause fire
Type D	Danger	Heating may cause fire
Type E	Warning	Heating may cause fire
Type F	Warning	Heating may cause fire

Precautionary statements

Prevention	Response	Storage	Disposal
Keep away from heat/ sparks/open flames/ hot surfaces. - No smoking. Chemical manufacturer, importer, or distributor to specify applicable ignition source(s). **Keep/Store away from clothing/.../ combustible materials.** ... Chemical manufacturer, importer, or distributor to specify other incompatible materials. **Keep only in original container.** **Wear protective gloves/eye protection/face protection.** Chemical manufacturer, importer, or distributor to specify type of equipment.	.	**Store at temperatures not exceeding ...°C/...°F. Keep cool.** Chemical manufacturer, importer, or distributor to specify temperature. **Protect from sunlight.** **Store away from other materials.**	**Dispose of contents/ container to ...** ...in accordance with local/ regional/national/ international regulations (to be specified).

C.4.29 Corrosive to Metals (Classified In Accordance With Appendix B.16)

Pictogram
Corrosive

Hazard category	Signal word	Hazard statement
1	Warning	May be corrosive to metals

Precautionary statements

Prevention	Response	Storage	Disposal
Keep only in original containers.	**Absorb spillage to prevent material damage.**	**Store in corrosive resistant/... container with a resistant inner liner.** ... Chemical manufacturer, importer, or distributor to specify other compatible materials.	

C.4.30 Label elements for OSHA defined hazards

Pictogram
Flame

Hazard	Signal word	Hazard statement
Pyrophoric Gas	Danger	Catches fire spontaneously if exposed to air

Pictogram
No Pictogram

Hazard	Signal word	Hazard statement
Simple Asphyxiant	Warning	May displace oxygen and cause rapid suffocation

Pictogram
No Pictogram

Hazard	Signal word	Hazard statement
Combustible Dust[2]	Warning	May form combustible dust concentrations in air

[2] *The chemical manufacturer or importer shall label chemicals that are shipped in dust form, and present a combustible dust hazard in that form when used downstream, under paragraph (f)(1); 2) the chemical manufacturer or importer shipping chemicals that are in a form that is not yet a dust must provide a label to customers under paragraph (f)(4) if, under normal conditions of use, the chemicals are processed in a downstream workplace in such a way that they present a combustible dust hazard; and 3) the employer shall follow the workplace labeling requirements under paragraph (f)(6) where combustible dust hazards are present.*

§1910.1200 Appendix D
Safety data sheets
(Mandatory)

A safety data sheet (SDS) shall include the information specified in Table D.1 under the Section number and heading indicated for Sections 1-11 and 16. If no relevant information is found for any given subheading within a Section, the SDS shall clearly indicate that no applicable information is available. Sections 12-15 may be included in the SDS, but are not mandatory.

Table D.1.
Minimum Information for an SDS

	Heading	Subheading
1	Identification	(a) Product identifier used on the label; (b) Other means of identification; (c) Recommended use of the chemical and restrictions on use; (d) Name, address, and telephone number of the chemical manufacturer, importer, or other responsible party; (e) Emergency phone number.
2	Hazard(s) identification	(a) Classification of the chemical in accordance with paragraph (d) of §1910.1200; (b) Signal word, hazard statement(s), symbol(s) and precautionary statement(s) in accordance with paragraph (f) of §1910.1200. (Hazard symbols may be provided as graphical reproductions in black and white or the name of the symbol, e.g., flame, skull and crossbones); (c) Describe any hazards not otherwise classified that have been identified during the classification process; (d) Where an ingredient with unknown acute toxicity is used in a mixture at a concentration ≥ 1% and the mixture is not classified based on testing of the mixture as a whole, a statement that X% of the mixture consists of ingredient(s) of unknown acute toxicity is required.
3	Composition/ information on ingredients	Except as provided for in paragraph (i) of §1910.1200 on trade secrets: **For Substances** (a) Chemical name; (b) Common name and synonyms; (c) CAS number and other unique identifiers; (d) Impurities and stabilizing additives which are themselves classified and which contribute to the classification of the substance. **For Mixtures** In addition to the information required for substances: (a) The chemical name and concentration (exact percentage) or concentration ranges of all ingredients which are classified as health hazards in accordance with paragraph (d) of §1910.1200 and (1) are present above their cut-off/concentration limits; or (2) present a health risk below the cut-off/ concentration limits. (b) The concentration (exact percentage) shall be specified unless a trade secret claim is made in accordance with paragraph (i) of §1910.1200, when there is batch-to-batch variability in the production of a mixture, or for a group of substantially similar mixtures (See A.0.5.1.2) with similar chemical composition. In these cases, concentration ranges may be used. **For All Chemicals Where a Trade Secret is Claimed** Where a trade secret is claimed in accordance with paragraph (i) of §1910.1200, a statement that the specific chemical identity and/or exact percentage (concentration) of composition has been withheld as a trade secret is required.
4	First-aid measures	(a) Description of necessary measures, subdivided according to the different routes of exposure, i.e., inhalation, skin and eye contact, and ingestion; (b) Most important symptoms/effects, acute and delayed. (c) Indication of immediate medical attention and special treatment needed, if necessary.
5	Fire-fighting measures	(a) Suitable (and unsuitable) extinguishing media. (b) Specific hazards arising from the chemical (e.g., nature of any hazardous combustion products). (c) Special protective equipment and precautions for fire-fighters.
6	Accidental release measures	(a) Personal precautions, protective equipment, and emergency procedures. (b) Methods and materials for containment and cleaning up.
7	Handling and storage	(a) Precautions for safe handling. (b) Conditions for safe storage, including any incompatibilities.
8	Exposure controls/ personal protection	(a) OSHA permissible exposure limit (PEL), American Conference of Governmental Industrial Hygienists (ACGIH) Threshold Limit Value (TLV), and any other exposure limit used or recommended by the chemical manufacturer, importer, or employer preparing the safety data sheet, where available. (b) Appropriate engineering controls. (c) Individual protection measures, such as personal protective equipment.
9	Physical and chemical properties	(a) Appearance (physical state, color, etc.); (b) Odor; (c) Odor threshold; (d) pH; (e) Melting point/freezing point; (f) Initial boiling point and boiling range; (g) Flash point; (h) Evaporation rate; (i) Flammability (solid, gas); (j) Upper/lower flammability or explosive limits; (k) Vapor pressure; (l) Vapor density; (m) Relative density; (n) Solubility(ies); (o) Partition coefficient: n-octanol/water; (p) Auto-ignition temperature; (q) Decomposition temperature; (r) Viscosity.
10	Stability and reactivity	(a) Reactivity; (b) Chemical stability; (c) Possibility of hazardous reactions; (d) Conditions to avoid (e.g., static discharge, shock, or vibration); (e) Incompatible materials; (f) Hazardous decomposition products.
11	Toxicological information	Description of the various toxicological (health) effects and the available data used to identify those effects, including: (a) Information on the likely routes of exposure (inhalation, ingestion, skin and eye contact); (b) Symptoms related to the physical, chemical and toxicological characteristics; (c) Delayed and immediate effects and also chronic effects from short- and long-term exposure; (d) Numerical measures of toxicity (such as acute toxicity estimates). (e) Whether the hazardous chemical is listed in the National Toxicology Program (NTP) Report on Carcinogens (latest edition) or has been found to be a potential carcinogen in the International Agency for Research on Cancer (IARC) Monographs (latest edition), or by OSHA.
12	Ecological information (Non-mandatory)	(a) Ecotoxicity (aquatic and terrestrial, where available); (b) Persistence and degradability; (c) Bioaccumulative potential; (d) Mobility in soil; (e) Other adverse effects (such as hazardous to the ozone layer).
13	Disposal considerations (Non-mandatory)	Description of waste residues and information on their safe handling and methods of disposal, including the disposal of any contaminated packaging.
14	Transport information (Non-mandatory)	(a) UN number; (b) UN proper shipping name; (c) Transport hazard class(es); (d) Packing group, if applicable; (e) Environmental hazards (e.g., Marine pollutant (Yes/No)); (f) Transport in bulk (according to Annex II of MARPOL 73/78 and the IBC Code); (g) Special precautions which a user needs to be aware of, or needs to comply with, in connection with transport or conveyance either within or outside their premises.
15	Regulatory information (Non-mandatory)	Safety, health and environmental regulations specific for the product in question.
16	Other information, including date of preparation or last revision	The date of preparation of the SDS or the last change to it

§1910.1200 Appendix E Definition of "Trade Secret" (Mandatory)

The following is a reprint of the Restatement of Torts Section 757, Comment B (1939):

b. "Definition of trade secret." A trade secret may consist of any formula, pattern, device or compilation of information which is used in one's business, and which gives him an opportunity to obtain an advantage over competitors who do not know or use it. It may be a formula for a chemical compound, a process of manufacturing, treating or preserving materials, a pattern for a machine or other device, or a list of customers. It differs from other secret information in a business (see s759 of the Restatement of Torts which is not included in this Appendix) in that it is not simply information as to single or ephemeral events in the conduct of the business, as, for example, the amount or other terms of a secret bid for a contract or the salary of certain employees, or the security investments made or contemplated, or the date fixed for the announcement of a new policy or for bringing out a new model or the like. A trade secret is a process or device for continuous use in the operations of the business. Generally it relates to the production of goods, as, for example, a machine or formula for the production of an article. It may, however, relate to the sale of goods or to other operations in the business, such as a code for determining discounts, rebates or other concessions in a price list or catalogue, or a list of specialized customers, or a method of bookkeeping or other office management.

"Secrecy." The subject matter of a trade secret must be secret. Matters of public knowledge or of general knowledge in an industry cannot be appropriated by one as his secret. Matters which are completely disclosed by the goods which one markets cannot be his secret. Substantially, a trade secret is known only in the particular business in which it is used. It is not requisite that only the proprietor of the business know it. He may, without losing his protection, communicate it to employees involved in its use. He may likewise communicate it to others pledged to secrecy. Others may also know of it independently, as, for example, when they have discovered the process or formula by independent invention and are keeping it secret. Nevertheless, a substantial element of secrecy must exist, so that, except by the use of improper means, there would be difficulty in acquiring the information. An exact definition of a trade secret is not possible. Some factors to be considered in determining whether given information is one's trade secret are:

(1) The extent to which the information is known outside of his business;
(2) the extent to which it is known by employees and others involved in his business;
(3) the extent of measures taken by him to guard the secrecy of the information;
(4) the value of the information to him and his competitors;
(5) the amount of effort or money expended by him in developing the information;
(6) the ease or difficulty with which the information could be properly acquired or duplicated by others.

"Novelty and prior art." A trade secret may be a device or process which is patentable; but it need not be that. It may be a device or process which is clearly anticipated in the prior art or one which is merely a mechanical improvement that a good mechanic can make. Novelty and invention are not requisite for a trade secret as they are for patentability. These requirements are essential to patentability because a patent protects against unlicensed use of the patented device or process even by one who discovers it properly through independent research. The patent monopoly is a reward to the inventor. But such is not the case with a trade secret. Its protection is not based on a policy of rewarding or otherwise encouraging the development of secret processes or devices. The protection is merely against breach of faith and reprehensible means of learning another's secret. For this limited protection it is not appropriate to require also the kind of novelty and invention which is a requisite of patentability. The nature of the secret is, however, an important factor in determining the kind of relief that is appropriate against one who is subject to liability under the rule stated in this Section. Thus, if the secret consists of a device or process which is a novel invention, one who acquires the secret wrongfully is ordinarily enjoined from further use of it and is required to account for the profits derived from his past use. If, on the other hand, the secret consists of mechanical improvements that a good mechanic can make without resort to the secret, the wrongdoer's liability may be limited to damages, and an injunction against future use of the improvements made with the aid of the secret may be inappropriate.

§1910.1200 Appendix F Guidance for hazard classifications Re: Carcinogenicity (Nonandatory)

The mandatory criteria for classification of a chemical for carcinogenicity under HCS are found in Appendix A.6 to this Section. This non-mandatory Appendix provides additional guidance on hazard classification for carcinogenicity. Part A of Appendix F includes background guidance provided by GHS based on the Preamble of the International Agency for Research on Cancer (IARC) "Monographs on the Evaluation of Carcinogenic Risks to Humans" (2006). Part B provides IARC classification information. Part C provides background guidance from the National Toxicology Program (NTP) "Report on Carcinogens" (RoC), and Part D is a table that compares GHS carcinogen hazard categories to carcinogen classifications under IARC and NTP, allowing classifiers to be able to use information from IARC and NTP RoC carcinogen classifications to complete their classifications under the GHS, and thus the HCS.

Part A: Background Guidance[1]

As noted in Footnote 6 of Appendix A.6., the GHS includes as guidance for classifiers information taken from the Preamble of the International Agency for Research on Cancer (IARC) "Monographs on the Evaluation of Carcinogenic Risks to Humans" (2006), providing guidance on the evaluation of the strength and evidence of carcinogenic risks to humans. This guidance also discusses some additional considerations in classification and an approach to analysis, rather than hard-and-fast rules. Part A is consistent with Appendix A.6, and should help in evaluating information to determine carcinogenicity.

Carcinogenicity in humans:

The evidence relevant to carcinogenicity from studies in humans is classified into one of the following categories:

(a) Sufficient evidence of carcinogenicity: A causal relationship has been established between exposure to the agent and human cancer. That is, a positive relationship has been observed between the exposure and cancer in studies in which chance, bias and confounding could be ruled out with reasonable confidence.
(b) Limited evidence of carcinogenicity: A positive association has been observed between exposure to the agent and cancer for which a causal interpretation is considered by the Working Group to be credible, but chance, bias or confounding could not be ruled out with reasonable confidence.

In some instances, the above categories may be used to classify the degree of evidence related to carcinogenicity in specific organs or tissues.

Carcinogenicity in experimental animals:

The evidence relevant to carcinogenicity in experimental animals is classified into one of the following categories:

(a) Sufficient evidence of carcinogenicity: A causal relationship has been established between the agent and an increased incidence of malignant neoplasms or of an appropriate combination of benign and malignant neoplasms in two or more species of animals or two or more independent studies in one species carried out at different times or in different laboratories or under different protocols. An increased incidence of tumors in both sexes of a single species in a well-conducted study, ideally conducted under Good Laboratory Practices, can also provide sufficient evidence.

Exceptionally, a single study in one species and sex might be considered to provide sufficient evidence of carcinogenicity when malignant neoplasms occur to an unusual degree with regard to incidence, site, type of tumor or age at onset, or when there are strong findings of tumors at multiple sites.

(b) Limited evidence of carcinogenicity: The data suggest a carcinogenic effect but are limited for making a definitive evaluation because, e.g. the evidence of carcinogenicity is restricted to a single experiment; there are unresolved questions regarding the adequacy of the design, conduct or interpretation of the studies; the agent increases the incidence only of benign neoplasms or lesions of uncertain neoplastic potential; or the evidence of carcinogenicity is restricted to studies that demonstrate only promoting activity in a narrow range of tissues or organs.

[1] The text of Appendix F, Part A, on the IARC Monographs, is paraphrased from the 2006 Preamble to the "Monographs on the Evaluation of Carcinogenic Risks to Humans" the Classifier is referred to the full IARC Preamble for the complete text. The text is not part of the agreed GHS text on the harmonized system developed by the OECD Task Force-HCL.

Guidance on how to consider important factors in classification of carcinogenicity (See Reference Section)

The weight of evidence analysis called for in GHS and the HCS (§1910.1200) is an integrative approach that considers important factors in determining carcinogenic potential along with the strength of evidence analysis. The IPCS "*Conceptual Framework for Evaluating a Mode of Action for Chemical Carcinogenesis*" (2001), International Life Sciences Institute (ILSI) "*Framework for Human Relevance Analysis of Information on Carcinogenic Modes of Action*" (Meek, et al., 2003; Cohen et al., 2003, 2004), and Preamble to the IARC Monographs (2006; Section B.6. (Scientific Review and Evaluation; Evaluation and Rationale)) provide a basis for systematic assessments that may be performed in a consistent fashion. The IPCS also convened a panel in 2004 to further develop and clarify the human relevance framework. However, the above documents are not intended to dictate answers, nor provide lists of criteria to be checked off.

Mode of action

Various documents on carcinogen assessment all note that mode of action in and of itself, or consideration of comparative metabolism, should be evaluated on a case-by-case basis and are part of an analytic evaluative approach. One must look closely at any mode of action in animal experiments, taking into consideration comparative toxicokinetics/toxicodynamics between the animal test species and humans to determine the relevance of the results to humans. This may lead to the possibility of discounting very specific effects of certain types of substances. Life stage-dependent effects on cellular differentiation may also lead to qualitative differences between animals and humans. Only if a mode of action of tumor development is conclusively determined not to be operative in humans may the carcinogenic evidence for that tumor be discounted. However, a weight of evidence evaluation for a substance calls for any other tumorigenic activity to be evaluated, as well.

Responses in multiple animal experiments

Positive responses in several species add to the weight of evidence that a substance is a carcinogen. Taking into account all of the factors listed in A.6.2.5.2 and more, such chemicals with positive outcomes in two or more species would be provisionally considered to be classified in GHS Category 1B until human relevance of animal results are assessed in their entirety. It should be noted, however, that positive results for one species in at least two independent studies, or a single positive study showing unusually strong evidence of malignancy may also lead to Category 1B.

Responses are in one sex or both sexes

Any case of gender-specific tumors should be evaluated in light of the total tumorigenic response to the substance observed at other sites (multi-site responses or incidence above background) in determining the carcinogenic potential of the substance.

If tumors are seen only in one sex of an animal species, the mode of action should be carefully evaluated to see if the response is consistent with the postulated mode of action. Effects seen only in one sex in a test species may be less convincing than effects seen in both sexes, unless there is a clear patho-physiological difference consistent with the mode of action to explain the single sex response.

Confounding effects of excessive toxicity or localized effects

Tumors occurring only at excessive doses associated with severe toxicity generally have doubtful potential for carcinogenicity in humans. In addition, tumors occurring only at sites of contact and/or only at excessive doses need to be carefully evaluated for human relevance for carcinogenic hazard. For example, forestomach tumors, following administration by gavage of an irritating or corrosive, non-mutagenic chemical, may be of questionable relevance. However, such determinations must be evaluated carefully in justifying the carcinogenic potential for humans; any occurrence of other tumors at distant sites must also be considered.

Tumor type, reduced tumor latency

Unusual tumor types or tumors occurring with reduced latency may add to the weight of evidence for the carcinogenic potential of a substance, even if the tumors are not statistically significant.

Toxicokinetic behavior is normally assumed to be similar in animals and humans, at least from a qualitative perspective. On the other hand, certain tumor types in animals may be associated with toxicokinetics or toxicodynamics that are unique to the animal species tested and may not be predictive of carcinogenicity in humans. Very few such examples have been agreed internationally. However, one example is the lack of human relevance of kidney tumors in male rats associated with compounds causing a2u-globulin nephropathy (IARC, Scientific Publication N° 147[2]). Even when a particular tumor type may be discounted, expert judgment must be used in assessing the total tumor profile in any animal experiment.

[2] While most international agencies do not consider kidney tumors coincident with a2u-globulin nephropathy to be a predictor of risk in humans, this view is not universally held. (See: Doi et al., 2007)

Part B: International Agency for Research on Cancer (IARC)[3]

IARC Carcinogen Classification Categories:

Group 1: The agent is carcinogenic to humans.

This category is used when there is ***sufficient evidence of carcinogenicity*** in humans. Exceptionally, an agent may be placed in this category when evidence of carcinogenicity in humans is less than ***sufficient*** but there is ***sufficient evidence of carcinogenicity*** in experimental animals and strong evidence in exposed humans that the agent acts through a relevant mechanism of carcinogenicity.

Group 2:

This category includes agents for which, at one extreme, the degree of evidence of carcinogenicity in humans is almost ***sufficient***, as well as those for which, at the other extreme, there are no human data but for which there is evidence of carcinogenicity in experimental animals. Agents are assigned to either Group 2A (***probably carcinogenic to humans***) or Group 2B (***possibly carcinogenic to humans***) on the basis of epidemiological and experimental evidence of carcinogenicity and mechanistic and other relevant data. The terms ***probably carcinogenic*** and ***possibly carcinogenic*** have no quantitative significance and are used simply as descriptors of different levels of evidence of human carcinogenicity, with ***probably carcinogenic*** signifying a higher level of evidence than possibly carcinogenic.

Group 2A: The agent is probably carcinogenic to humans.

This category is used when there is ***limited evidence of carcinogenicity*** in humans and ***sufficient evidence of carcinogenicity*** in experimental animals. In some cases, an agent may be classified in this category when there is ***inadequate evidence of carcinogenicity*** in humans and ***sufficient evidence of carcinogenicity*** in experimental animals and strong evidence that the carcinogenesis is mediated by a mechanism that also operates in humans. Exceptionally, an agent may be classified in this category solely on the basis of ***limited evidence of carcinogenicity*** in humans. An agent may be assigned to this category if it clearly belongs, based on mechanistic considerations, to a class of agents for which one or more members have been classified in Group 1 or Group 2A.

Group 2B: The agent is possibly carcinogenic to humans.

This category is used for agents for which there is ***limited evidence of carcinogenicity*** in humans and less than ***sufficient evidence of carcinogenicity*** in experimental animals. It may also be used when there is ***inadequate evidence of carcinogenicity*** in humans but there is ***sufficient evidence of carcinogenicity*** in experimental animals. In some instances, an agent for which there is ***inadequate evidence of carcinogenicity*** in humans and less than ***sufficient evidence of carcinogenicity*** in experimental animals together with supporting evidence from mechanistic and other relevant data may be placed in this group. An agent may be classified in this category solely on the basis of strong evidence from mechanistic and other relevant data.

Part C: National Toxicology Program (NTP), "Report on Carcinogens", Background Guidance

NTP Listing Criteria[4]:

The criteria for listing an agent, substance, mixture, or exposure circumstance in the Report on Carcinogens (RoC) are as follows:

Known To Be A Human Carcinogen: There is sufficient evidence of carcinogenicity from studies in humans[5] that indicates a causal relationship between exposure to the agent, substance, or mixture, and human cancer.

Reasonably Anticipated To Be A Human Carcinogen: There is limited evidence of carcinogenicity from studies in humans that indicates that a causal interpretation is credible, but that alternative explanations, such as chance, bias, or confounding factors, could not adequately be excluded,

or

there is sufficient evidence of carcinogenicity from studies in experimental animals that indicates there is an increased incidence of malignant and/or a combination of malignant and benign tumors (1) in multiple species or at multiple tissue sites, or (2) by multiple routes of exposure, or (3) to an unusual degree with regard to incidence, site, or type of tumor, or age at onset,

or

there is less than sufficient evidence of carcinogenicity in humans or laboratory animals; however, the agent, substance, or mixture belongs to a well-defined, structurally-related class of substances whose members are listed in a previous Report on Carcinogens as either known to be a human carcinogen or reasonably anticipated to be a human carcinogen, or there is convincing relevant information that the agent acts through mechanisms indicating it would likely cause cancer in humans.

[3] Preamble of the International Agency for Research on Cancer (IARC) "Monographs on the Evaluation of Carcinogenic Risks to Humans" (2006)

[4] See: http://ntp.niehs.nih.gov/go/15209

[5] This evidence can include traditional cancer epidemiology studies, data from clinical studies, and/or data derived from the study of tissues or cells from humans exposed to the substance in question that can be useful for evaluating whether a relevant cancer mechanism is operating in people.

Conclusions regarding carcinogenicity in humans or experimental animals are based on scientific judgment, with consideration given to all relevant information. Relevant information includes, but is not limited to, dose response, route of exposure, chemical structure, metabolism, pharmacokinetics, sensitive sub-populations, genetic effects, or other data relating to mechanism of action or factors that may be unique to a given substance. For example, there may be substances for which there is evidence of carcinogenicity in laboratory animals, but there are compelling data indicating that the agent acts through mechanisms that do not operate in humans and would therefore not reasonably be anticipated to cause cancer in humans.

Part D. Table Relating Approximate Equivalences among IARC, NTP RoC, and GHS Carcinogenicity Classifications

The following table may be used to perform hazard classifications for carcinogenicity under the HCS (§1910.1200). It relates the approximated GHS hazard categories for carcinogenicity to the classifications provided by IARC and NTP, as described in Parts B and C of this Appendix.

Approximate Equivalences Among Carcinogen Classification Schemes		
IARC	GHS	NTP RoC
Group 1	Category 1A	Known
Group 2A	Category 1B	Reasonably Anticipated (See Note 1)
Group 2B	Category 2	Reasonably Anticipated (See Note 1)

Note 1:

1. Limited evidence of carcinogenicity from studies in humans (corresponding to IARC 2A / GHS 1B);
2. Sufficient evidence of carcinogenicity from studies in experimental animals (again, essentially corresponding to IARC 2A / GHS 1B);
3. Less than sufficient evidence of carcinogenicity in humans or laboratory animals; however:
   (a) The agent, substance, or mixture belongs to a well-defined, structurally-related class of substances whose members are listed in a previous RoC as either "Known" or "Reasonably Anticipated" to be a human carcinogen, or
   (b) There is convincing relevant information that the agent acts through mechanisms indicating it would likely cause cancer in humans.

***References:**

Cohen, S.M., J. Klaunig, M.E. Meek, R.N. Hill, T. Pastoor, L. Lehman-McKeeman, J. Bucher, D.G. Longfellow, J. Seed, V. Dellarco, P. Fenner-Crisp, and D. Patton. 2004. Evaluating the human relevance of chemically induced animal tumors. Toxicol. Sci. 78(2):181-186.

Cohen, S.M., M.E. Meek, J.E. Klaunig, D.E. Patton, P.A. Fenner-Crisp. 2003. The human relevance of information on carcinogenic modes of action: Overview. Crit. Rev. Toxicol. 33(6):581-9.

Meek, M.E., J.R. Bucher, S.M. Cohen, V. Dellarco, R.N. Hill, L. Lehman-McKeeman, D.G. Longfellow, T. Pastoor, J. Seed, D.E. Patton. 2003. A framework for human relevance analysis of information on carcinogenic modes of action. Crit. Rev. Toxicol. 33(6):591-653.

Sonich-Mullin, C., R. Fielder, J. Wiltse, K. Baetcke, J. Dempsey, P. Fenner-Crisp, D. Grant, M. Hartley, A. Knapp, D. Kroese, I. Mangelsdorf, E. Meek, J.M. Rice, and M. Younes. 2001. The conceptual framework for evaluating a mode of action for chemical carcinogenesis. Reg. Toxicol. Pharm. 34:146-152.

International Programme on Chemical Safety Harmonization Group. 2004. Report of the First Meeting of the Cancer Working Group. World Health Organization. Report IPCS/HSC-CWG-1/04. Geneva.

International Agency for Research on Cancer. IARC Monographs on the Evaluation of Carcinogenic Risks to Human. Preambles to Volumes. World Health Organization. Lyon, France.

Cohen, S.M., P.A. Fenner-Crisp, and D.E. Patton. 2003. Special Issue: Cancer Modes of Action and Human Relevance. Critical Reviews in Toxicology, R.O. McClellan, ed., Volume 33/Issue 6. CRC Press.

Capen, C.C., E. Dybing, and J.D. Wilbourn. 1999. Species differences in thyroid, kidney and urinary bladder carcinogenesis. International Agency for Research on Cancer, Scientific Publication N° 147.

Doi, A.M., G. Hill, J. Seely, J.R. Hailey, G. Kissling, and J.R. Buchera. 2007. a2u-Globulin nephropathy and renal tumors in National Toxicology Program studies. Toxicol. Pathol. 35:533-540

Explanation of the Letter of Interpretation notes for §1910.1200

The Standard Interpretations for §1910.1200 have not been updated since OSHA updated the Hazard Communication Standard.

When looking for a Standard Interpretation (indicated by the (Letter of Interpretation notation) in the main text), reference the chart below. For the "Current" citation, see the Interpretation referenced by the "Previous" citation.

Where the chart indicates "No change", the Current and Previous Standard citation(s) are the same. Once you have the correct "citation", see www.oshainterpretation.us for the Standard Interpretation details.

Standard Interpretation	
Current	Previous
1910.1200	No change
(a)(2)	No change
(b)	No change
(b)(1)	No change
(b)(2)	No change
(b)(3)(iv)	No change
(b)(5)(ii)	No change
(b)()5)(iii)	No change
(b)(6)	No change
(b)(6)(i)	No change
(b)(6)(iv)	No change
(b)(6)(v)	No change
(b)(6)(vi)	No change
(b)(6)(vii)	No change
(b)(6)(viii)	No change
(b)(6)(ix)	No change
(c)	No change
(d)	No change
(d)(1)	No change
(d)(2)	No change
(d)(3)(i)	(d)(3) (d)(4) (d)(4)(iii) (d)(5) (d)(5)(ii)
(e)	No change
(e)(1)	No change
(e)(1)(i)	No change
(e)(2)	No change
(e)(4)	No change

Standard Interpretation	
Current	Previous
(f)	No change
(f)(1)	No change
(f)(1)(i)	No change
(f)(1)(vi)	(f)(1)(iii)
(f)(4)	(f)(2)
(f)(4)(i)	(f)(2)(i)
(f)(6)	(f)(4) (f)(5)
(f)(6)(i)	(f)(5)(i)
(f)(6)(ii)	(f)(5)(ii)
(f)(7)	(f)(6)
(f)(10)	(f)(9)
(f)(11)	No change
(g)	No change
(g)(1)	No change
(g)(2)	(g)(2)(i)(C)(2) (g)(2)(vi) (g)(2)(xi) (g)(2)(xii)
(g)(4)	No change
(g)(5)	No change
(g)(6)	No change
(g)(6)(i)	No change
(g)(7)	No change
(g)(7)(iii)	No change
(g)(8)	No change
(g)(9)	No change
(g)(10)	No change
(h)	No change
(h)(3)	No change
(i)	No change

§1910.1201 Retention of DOT markings, placards and labels

(a) Any employer who receives a package of hazardous material which is required to be marked, labeled or placarded in accordance with the U. S. Department of Transportation's Hazardous Materials Regulations (49 CFR Parts 171 through 180) shall retain those markings, labels and placards on the package until the packaging is sufficiently cleaned of residue and purged of vapors to remove any potential hazards.

(b) Any employer who receives a freight container, rail freight car, motor vehicle, or transport vehicle that is required to be marked or placarded in accordance with the Hazardous Materials Regulations shall retain those markings and placards on the freight container, rail freight car, motor vehicle or transport vehicle until the hazardous materials which require the marking or placarding are sufficiently removed to prevent any potential hazards.

(c) Markings, placards and labels shall be maintained in a manner that ensures that they are readily visible.

(d) For non-bulk packages which will not be reshipped, the provisions of this Section are met if a label or other acceptable marking is affixed in accordance with the Hazard Communication Standard (29 CFR §1910.1200).

(e) For the purposes of this Section, the term "hazardous material" and any other terms not defined in this Section have the same definition as in the Hazardous Materials Regulations (49 CFR Parts 171 through 180).

[59 FR 36700, July 19, 1994]

§1910.1450 Occupational exposure to hazardous chemicals in laboratories

(a) Scope and application

(a)(1) This Section shall apply to all employers engaged in the laboratory use of hazardous chemicals as defined below.

(a)(2) Where this Section applies, it shall supersede, for laboratories, the requirements of all other OSHA health standards in 29 CFR Part §1910, Subpart Z, except as follows:

(a)(2)(i) For any OSHA health standard, only the requirement to limit employee exposure to the specific permissible exposure limit shall apply for laboratories, unless that particular standard states otherwise or unless the conditions of paragraph (a)(2)(iii) of this Section apply.

(a)(2)(ii) Prohibition of eye and skin contact where specified by any OSHA health standard shall be observed.

(a)(2)(iii) Where the action level (or in the absence of an action level, the permissible exposure limit) is routinely exceeded for an OSHA regulated substance with exposure monitoring and medical surveillance requirements, paragraphs (d) and (g)(1)(ii) of this Section shall apply.

(a)(3) This Section shall not apply to:

(a)(3)(i) Uses of hazardous chemicals which do not meet the definition of laboratory use, and in such cases, the employer shall comply with the relevant standard in 29 CFR Part §1910, Subpart Z, even if such use occurs in a laboratory.

(a)(3)(ii) Laboratory uses of hazardous chemicals which provide no potential for employee exposure. Examples of such conditions might include:

(a)(3)(ii)(A) Procedures using chemically-impregnated test media such as Dip-and-Read tests where a reagent strip is dipped into the specimen to be tested and the results are interpreted by comparing the color reaction to a color chart supplied by the manufacturer of the test strip; and

(a)(3)(ii)(B) Commercially prepared kits such as those used in performing pregnancy tests in which all of the reagents needed to conduct the test are contained in the kit.

(b) **Definitions.**

Action level means a concentration designated in 29 CFR Part §1910 for a specific substance, calculated as an eight (8)-hour time-weighted average, which initiates certain required activities such as exposure monitoring and medical surveillance.

Assistant Secretary means the Assistant Secretary of Labor for Occupational Safety and Health, U.S. Department of Labor, or designee.

Carcinogen (see select carcinogen).

Chemical Hygiene Officer means an employee who is designated by the employer, and who is qualified by training or experience, to provide technical guidance in the development and implementation of the provisions of the Chemical Hygiene Plan. This definition is not intended to place limitations on the position description or job classification that the designated individual shall hold within the employer's organizational structure.

Chemical Hygiene Plan means a written program developed and implemented by the employer which sets forth procedures, equipment, personal protective equipment and work practices that (i) are capable of protecting employees from the health hazards presented by hazardous chemicals used in that particular workplace and (ii) meets the requirements of paragraph (e) of this Section.

Designated area means an area which may be used for work with "select carcinogens," reproductive toxins or substances which have a high degree of acute toxicity. A designated area may be the entire laboratory, an area of a laboratory or a device such as a laboratory hood.

Emergency means any occurrence such as, but not limited to, equipment failure, rupture of containers or failure of control equipment which results in an uncontrolled release of a hazardous chemical into the workplace.

Employee means an individual employed in a laboratory workplace who may be exposed to hazardous chemicals in the course of his or her assignments.

Hazardous chemical means any chemical which is classified as health hazard or simple asphyxiant in accordance with the Hazard Communication Standard (§1910.1200).

Health hazard means a chemical that is classified as posing one of the following hazardous effects: Acute toxicity (any route of exposure); skin corrosion or irritation; serious eye damage or eye irritation; respiratory or skin sensitization; germ cell mutagenicity; carcinogenicity; reproductive toxicity; specific target organ toxicity (single or repeated exposure); aspiration hazard. The criteria for determining whether a chemical is classified as a health hazard are detailed in Appendix A of the hazard Communication Standard (§1910.1200) and §1910.1200(c) (definition of "simple asphyxiant").

Laboratory means a facility where the "laboratory use of hazardous chemicals" occurs. It is a workplace where relatively small quantities of hazardous chemicals are used on a= non-production basis.

Laboratory scale means work with substances in which the containers used for reactions, transfers, and other handling of substances are designed to be easily and safely manipulated by one person. "Laboratory scale" excludes those workplaces whose function is to produce commercial quantities of materials.

Laboratory-type hood means a device located in a laboratory, enclosure on five sides with a moveable sash or fixed partial enclosed on the remaining side; constructed and maintained to draw air from the laboratory and to prevent or minimize the escape of air contaminants into the laboratory; and allows chemical manipulations to be conducted in the enclosure without insertion of any portion of the employee's body other than hands and arms.

Walk-in hoods with adjustable sashes meet the above definition provided that the sashes are adjusted during use so that the airflow and the exhaust of air contaminants are not compromised and employees do not work inside the enclosure during the release of airborne hazardous chemicals.

Laboratory use of hazardous chemicals means handling or use of such chemicals in which all of the following conditions are met:

(i) Chemical manipulations are carried out on a "laboratory scale;"
(ii) Multiple chemical procedures or chemicals are used;
(iii) The procedures involved are not part of a production process, nor in any way simulate a production process; and
(iv) "Protective laboratory practices and equipment" are available and in common use to minimize the potential for employee exposure to hazardous chemicals.

Medical consultation means a consultation which takes place between an employee and a licensed physician for the purpose of determining what medical examinations or procedures, if any, are appropriate in cases where a significant exposure to a hazardous chemical may have taken place.

Mutagen means chemicals that cause permanent changes in the amount or structure of the genetic material in a cell. Chemicals classified as mutagens in accordance with the Hazard Communication Standard (§1910.1200) shall be considered mutagens for purposes of this Section.

Physical hazard means a chemical that is classified as posing one of the following hazardous effects; Explosive; flammable (gases, aerosols, liquids, or solids); oxidizer (liquid, solid, or gas); self reactive; pyrophoric (gas, liquid or solid); self-heating; organic peroxide; corrosive to metal; gas under pressure; in contact with water emits flammable gas; or combustible dust. The criteria for determining whether a chemical is classified as a physical hazard are in Appendix B of the Hazard Communication Standard (§1910.1200) and §1910.1200(c) (definitions of "combustible dust" and "pyrophoric gas").

Protective laboratory practices and equipment means those laboratory procedures, practices and equipment accepted by laboratory health and safety experts as effective, or that the employer can show to be effective, in minimizing the potential for employee exposure to hazardous chemicals.

Reproductive toxins mean chemicals that affect the reproductive capabilities including adverse effects on sexual function and fertility in adult males and females, as well as adverse effects on the development of the offspring. Chemicals classified as reproductive toxins in accordance with the Hazard Communication Standard (§1910.1200) shall be considered reproductive toxins for purposes of this Section.

Select carcinogen means any substance which meets one of the following criteria:

(i) It is regulated by OSHA as a carcinogen; or

(ii) It is listed under the category, "known to be carcinogens," in the Annual Report on Carcinogens published by the National Toxicology Program (NTP) (latest edition); or

(iii) It is listed under Group 1 ("carcinogenic to humans") by the International Agency for Research on Cancer Monographs (IARC) (latest editions); or

(iv) It is listed in either Group 2A or 2B by IARC or under the category, "reasonably anticipated to be carcinogens" by NTP, and causes statistically significant tumor incidence in experimental animals in accordance with any of the following criteria:

(A) After inhalation exposure of 6–7 hours per day, 5 days per week, for a significant portion of a lifetime to dosages of less than 10 mg/m^3;

(B) After repeated skin application of less than 300 (mg/kg of body weight) per week; or

(C) After oral dosages of less than 50 mg/kg of body weight per day.

(c) **Permissible exposure limits** For laboratory uses of OSHA regulated substances, the employer shall assure that laboratory employees' exposures to such substances do not exceed the permissible exposure limits specified in 29 CFR Part §1910, Subpart Z.

(d) **Employee exposure determination**

(d)(1) **Initial monitoring** The employer shall measure the employee's exposure to any substance regulated by a standard which requires monitoring if there is reason to believe that exposure levels for that substance routinely exceed the action level (or in the absence of an action level, the PEL).

(d)(2) **Periodic monitoring** If the initial monitoring prescribed by paragraph (d)(1) of this Section discloses employee exposure over the action level (or in the absence of an action level, the PEL), the employer shall immediately comply with the exposure monitoring provisions of the relevant standard.

(d)(3) **Termination of monitoring** Monitoring may be terminated in accordance with the relevant standard.

(d)(4) **Employee notification of monitoring results** The employer shall, within 15 working days after the receipt of any monitoring results, notify the employee of these results in writing either individually or by posting results in an appropriate location that is accessible to employees.

(e) **Chemical hygiene plan—General** (Appendix A of this Section is non-mandatory but provides guidance to assist employers in the development of the Chemical Hygiene Plan.)

(e)(1) Where hazardous chemicals as defined by this Standard are used in the workplace, the employer shall develop and carry out the provisions of a written Chemical Hygiene Plan which is:

- (e)(1)(i) Capable of protecting employees from health hazards associated with hazardous chemicals in that laboratory and
- (e)(1)(ii) Capable of keeping exposures below the limits specified in paragraph (c) of this Section.

(e)(2) The Chemical Hygiene Plan shall be readily available to employees, employee representatives and, upon request, to the Assistant Secretary.

(e)(3) The Chemical Hygiene Plan shall include each of the following elements and shall indicate specific measures that the employer will take to ensure laboratory employee protection:

- (e)(3)(i) Standard operating procedures relevant to safety and health considerations to be followed when laboratory work involves the use of hazardous chemicals;
- (e)(3)(ii) Criteria that the employer will use to determine and implement control measures to reduce employee exposure to hazardous chemicals including engineering controls, the use of personal protective equipment and hygiene practices; particular attention shall be given to the selection of control measures for chemicals that are known to be extremely hazardous;
- (e)(3)(iii) A requirement that fume hoods and other protective equipment are functioning properly and specific measures that shall be taken to ensure proper and adequate performance of such equipment;
- (e)(3)(iv) Provisions for employee information and training as prescribed in paragraph (f) of this Section;
- (e)(3)(v) The circumstances under which a particular laboratory operation, procedure or activity shall require prior approval from the employer or the employer's designee before implementation;
- (e)(3)(vi) Provisions for medical consultation and medical examinations in accordance with paragraph (g) of this Section;
- (e)(3)(vii) OI Designation of personnel responsible for implementation of the Chemical Hygiene Plan including the assignment of a Chemical Hygiene Officer and, if appropriate, establishment of a Chemical Hygiene Committee; and
- (e)(3)(viii) OI Provisions for additional employee protection for work with particularly hazardous substances. These include "select carcinogens," reproductive toxins and substances which have a high degree of acute toxicity. Specific consideration shall be given to the following provisions which shall be included where appropriate:
  - (e)(3)(viii)(A) Establishment of a designated area;
  - (e)(3)(viii)(B) Use of containment devices such as fume hoods or glove boxes;
  - (e)(3)(viii)(C) Procedures for safe removal of contaminated waste; and
  - (e)(3)(viii)(D) Decontamination procedures.

(e)(4) The employer shall review and evaluate the effectiveness of the Chemical Hygiene Plan at least annually and update it as necessary.

(f) **Employee information and training**

(f)(1) The employer shall provide employees with information and training to ensure that they are apprised of the hazards of chemicals present in their work area.

(f)(2) Such information shall be provided at the time of an employee's initial assignment to a work area where hazardous chemicals are present and prior to assignments involving new exposure situations. The frequency of refresher information and training shall be determined by the employer.

(f)(3) **Information** Employees shall be informed of:

- (f)(3)(i) The contents of this Standard and its Appendices which shall be made available to employees;
- (f)(3)(ii) The location and availability of the employer's Chemical Hygiene Plan;
- (f)(3)(iii) The permissible exposure limits for OSHA regulated substances or recommended exposure limits for other hazardous chemicals where there is no applicable OSHA standard;
- (f)(3)(iv) Signs and symptoms associated with exposures to hazardous chemicals used in the laboratory; and
- (f)(3)(v) The location and availability of known reference material on the hazards, safe handling, storage and disposal of hazardous chemicals found in the laboratory including, but not limited to, Safety Data Sheets received from the chemical supplier.

(f)(4) **Training**

- (f)(4)(i) Employee training shall include:
  - (f)(4)(i)(A) Methods and observations that may be used to detect the presence or release of a hazardous chemical (such as monitoring conducted by the employer, continuous monitoring devices, visual appearance or odor of hazardous chemicals when being released, etc.);
  - (f)(4)(i)(B) The physical and health hazards of chemicals in the work area; and
  - (f)(4)(i)(C) The measures employees can take to protect themselves from these hazards, including specific procedures the employer has implemented to protect employees from exposure to hazardous chemicals, such as appropriate work practices, emergency procedures, and personal protective equipment to be used.
- (f)(4)(ii) The employee shall be trained on the applicable details of the employer's written Chemical Hygiene Plan.

(g) **Medical consultation and medical examinations**

(g)(1) The employer shall provide all employees who work with hazardous chemicals an opportunity to receive medical attention, including any follow-up examinations which the examining physician determines to be necessary, under the following circumstances:

- (g)(1)(i) Whenever an employee develops signs or symptoms associated with a hazardous chemical to which the employee may have been exposed in the laboratory, the employee shall be provided an opportunity to receive an appropriate medical examination.
- (g)(1)(ii) Where exposure monitoring reveals an exposure level routinely above the action level (or in the absence of an action level, the PEL) for an OSHA regulated substance for which there are exposure monitoring and medical surveillance requirements, medical surveillance shall be established for the affected employee as prescribed by the particular standard.
- (g)(1)(iii) Whenever an event takes place in the work area such as a spill, leak, explosion or other occurrence resulting in the likelihood of a hazardous exposure, the affected employee shall be provided an opportunity for a medical consultation. Such consultation shall be for the purpose of determining the need for a medical examination.

(g)(2) All medical examinations and consultations shall be performed by or under the direct supervision of a licensed physician and shall be provided without cost to the employee, without loss of pay and at a reasonable time and place.

(g)(3) **Information provided to the physician** The employer shall provide the following information to the physician:

- (g)(3)(i) The identity of the hazardous chemical(s) to which the employee may have been exposed;
- (g)(3)(ii) A description of the conditions under which the exposure occurred including quantitative exposure data, if available; and
- (g)(3)(iii) A description of the signs and symptoms of exposure that the employee is experiencing, if any.

(g)(4) **Physician's written opinion**

- (g)(4)(i) For examination or consultation required under this Standard, the employer shall obtain a written opinion from the examining physician which shall include the following:
  - (g)(4)(i)(A) Any recommendation for further medical follow-up;
  - (g)(4)(i)(B) The results of the medical examination and any associated tests;
  - (g)(4)(i)(C) Any medical condition which may be revealed in the course of the examination which may place the employee at increased risk as a result of exposure to a hazardous chemical found in the workplace; and
  - (g)(4)(i)(D) A statement that the employee has been informed by the physician of the results of the consultation or medical examination and any medical condition that may require further examination or treatment.

(g)(4)(ii) The written opinion shall not reveal specific findings of diagnoses unrelated to occupational exposure.

(h) **Hazard identification**

(h)(1) With respect to labels and safety data sheets:

(h)(1)(i) OI Employers shall ensure that labels on incoming containers of hazardous chemicals are not removed or defaced.

(h)(1)(ii) Employers shall maintain any safety data sheets that are received with incoming shipments of hazardous chemicals, and ensure that they are readily accessible to laboratory employees.

(h)(2) The following provisions shall apply to chemical substances developed in the laboratory:

(h)(2)(i) If the composition of the chemical substance which is produced exclusively for the laboratory's use is known, the employer shall determine if it is a hazardous chemical as defined in paragraph (b) of this Section. If the chemical is determined to be hazardous, the employer shall provide appropriate training as required under paragraph (f) of this Section.

(h)(2)(ii) If the chemical produced is a byproduct whose composition is not known, the employer shall assume that the substance is hazardous and shall implement paragraph (e) of this Section.

(h)(2)(iii) If the chemical substance is produced for another user outside of the laboratory, the employer shall comply with the Hazard Communication Standard (29 CFR §1910.1200) including the requirements for preparation of safety data sheets and labeling.

(i) **Use of respirators** Where the use of respirators is necessary to maintain exposure below permissible exposure limits, the employer shall provide, at no cost to the employee, the proper respiratory equipment. Respirators shall be selected and used in accordance with the requirements of 29 CFR §1910.134.

(j) **Recordkeeping**

(j)(1) The employer shall establish and maintain for each employee an accurate record of any measurements taken to monitor employee exposures and any medical consultation and examinations including tests or written opinions required by this Standard.

(j)(2) The employer shall assure that such records are kept, transferred, and made available in accordance with 29 CFR §1910.1020.

(k) [Reserved]

(l) **Appendices** The information contained in the Appendices is not intended, by itself, to create any additional obligations not otherwise imposed or to detract from any existing obligation.

§1910.1450 Appendix A National Research Council recommendations concerning chemical hygiene in laboratories (Nonmandatory)

To assist employers in developing an appropriate laboratory Chemical Hygiene Plan (CHP), the following non-mandatory recommendations were based on the National Research Council's (NRC) 2011 edition of "Prudent Practices in the Laboratory: Handling and Management of Chemical Hazards." This reference, henceforth referred to as "Prudent Practices," is available from the National Academies Press, 500 Fifth Street NW., Washington DC 20001 (www.nap.edu). "Prudent Practices" is cited because of its wide distribution and acceptance and because of its preparation by recognized authorities in the laboratory community through the sponsorship of the NRC. However, these recommendations do not modify any requirements of the OSHA Laboratory standard. This Appendix presents pertinent recommendations from "Prudent Practices," organized into a form convenient for quick reference during operation of a laboratory and during development and application of a CHP. For a detailed explanation and justification for each recommendation, consult "Prudent Practices."

"Prudent Practices" deals with both general laboratory safety and many types of chemical hazards, while the Laboratory standard is concerned primarily with chemical health hazards as a result of chemical exposures. The recommendations from "Prudent Practices" have been paraphrased, combined, or otherwise reorganized in order to adapt them for this purpose. However, their sense has not been changed.

Section F contains information from the U.S. Chemical Safety Board's (CSB) Fiscal Year 2011 Annual Performance and Accountability report and Section F contains recommendations extracted from the CSB's 2011 case study, "Texas Tech University Laboratory Explosion," available from: http://www.csb.gov/.

Culture of Safety

With the promulgation of the Occupational Safety and Health Administration (OSHA) Laboratory standard (29 CFR §1910.1450), a culture of safety consciousness, accountability, organization, and education has developed in industrial, governmental, and academic laboratories. Safety and training programs have been implemented to promote the safe handling of chemicals from ordering to disposal, and to train laboratory personnel in safe practices. Laboratory personnel must realize that the welfare and safety of each individual depends on clearly defined attitudes of teamwork and personal responsibility. Learning to participate in this culture of habitual risk assessment, experiment planning, and consideration of worst-case possibilities—for oneself and one's fellow workers—is as much part of a scientific education as learning the theoretical background of experiments or the step-by-step protocols for doing them in a professional manner. A crucial component of chemical education for all personnel is to nurture basic attitudes and habits of prudent behavior so that safety is a valued and inseparable part of all laboratory activities throughout their career.

Over the years, special techniques have been developed for handling chemicals safely. Local, state, and federal regulations hold institutions that sponsor chemical laboratories accountable for providing safe working environments. Beyond regulation, employers and scientists also hold themselves personally responsible for their own safety, the safety of their colleagues and the safety of the general public. A sound safety organization that is respected by all requires the participation and support of laboratory administrators, workers, and students. A successful health and safety program requires a daily commitment from everyone in the organization. To be most effective, safety and health must be balanced with, and incorporated into, laboratory processes. A strong safety and health culture is the result of positive workplace attitudes—from the chief executive officer to the newest hire; involvement and buy-in of all members of the workforce; mutual, meaningful, and measurable safety and health improvement goals; and policies and procedures that serve as reference tools, rather than obscure rules.

In order to perform their work in a prudent manner, laboratory personnel must consider the health, physical, and environmental hazards of the chemicals they plan to use in an experiment. However, the ability to accurately identify and assess laboratory hazards must be taught and encouraged through training and ongoing organizational support. This training must be at the core of every good health and safety program. For management to lead, personnel to assess worksite hazards, and hazards to be eliminated or controlled, everyone involved must be trained.

A. General Principles

1. Minimize All Chemical Exposures and Risks

Because few laboratory chemicals are without hazards, general precautions for handling all laboratory chemicals should be adopted. In addition to these general guidelines, specific guidelines for chemicals that are used frequently or are particularly hazardous should be adopted.

Laboratory personnel should conduct their work under conditions that minimize the risks from both known and unknown hazardous substances. Before beginning any laboratory work, the hazards and risks associated with an experiment or activity should be determined and the necessary safety precautions implemented. Every laboratory should develop facility-specific policies and procedures for the highest-risk materials and procedures used in their laboratory. To identify these, consideration should be given to past accidents, process conditions, chemicals used in large volumes, and particularly hazardous chemicals.

Perform Risk Assessments for Hazardous Chemicals and Procedures Prior to Laboratory Work:

(a) Identify chemicals to be used, amounts required, and circumstances of use in the experiment. Consider any special employee or laboratory conditions that could create or increase a hazard. Consult sources of safety and health information and experienced scientists to ensure that those conducting the risk assessment have sufficient expertise.

(b) Evaluate the hazards posed by the chemicals and the experimental conditions. The evaluation should cover toxic, physical, reactive, flammable, explosive, radiation, and biological hazards, as well as any other potential hazards posed by the chemicals.

(c) For a variety of physical and chemical reasons, reaction scale-ups pose special risks, which merit additional prior review and precautions.

(d) Select appropriate controls to minimize risk, including use of engineering controls, administrative controls, and personal protective equipment (PPE) to protect workers from hazards. The controls must ensure that OSHA's Permissible Exposure Limits (PELs) are not exceeded. Prepare for contingencies and be aware of the institutional procedures in the event of emergencies and accidents.

One sample approach to risk assessment is to answer these five questions:

(a) What are the hazards?

(b) What is the worst thing that could happen?

(c) What can be done to prevent this from happening?

(d) What can be done to protect from these hazards?

(e) What should be done if something goes wrong?

2. Avoid Underestimation of Risk

Even for substances of no known significant hazard, exposure should be minimized; when working with substances that present special hazards, special precautions should be taken. Reference should be made to the safety data sheet (SDS) that is provided for each chemical. Unless otherwise known, one should assume that any mixture will be more toxic than its most toxic component and that all substances of unknown toxicity are toxic.

Determine the physical and health hazards associated with chemicals before working with them. This determination may involve consulting literature references, laboratory chemical safety summaries (LCSSs), SDSs, or other reference materials. Consider how the chemicals will be processed and determine whether the changing states or forms will change the nature of the hazard. Review your plan, operating limits, chemical evaluations and detailed risk assessment with other chemists, especially those with experience with similar materials and protocols.

Before working with chemicals, know your facility's policies and procedures for how to handle an accidental spill or fire. Emergency telephone numbers should be posted in a prominent area. Know the location of all safety equipment and the nearest fire alarm and telephone.

3. Adhere to the Hierarchy of Controls

The hierarchy of controls prioritizes intervention strategies based on the premise that the best way to control a hazard is to systematically remove it from the workplace, rather than relying on employees to reduce their exposure. The types of measures that may be used to protect employees (listed from most effective to least effective) are: engineering controls, administrative controls, work practices, and PPE. Engineering controls, such as chemical hoods, physically separate the employee from the hazard. Administrative controls, such as employee scheduling, are established by management to help minimize the employees' exposure time to hazardous chemicals. Work practice controls are tasks that are performed in a designated way to minimize or eliminate hazards. Personal protective equipment and apparel are additional protection provided under special circumstances and when exposure is unavoidable.

Face and eye protection is necessary to prevent ingestion and skin absorption of hazardous chemicals. At a minimum, safety glasses, with side shields, should be used for all laboratory work. Chemical splash goggles are more appropriate than regular safety glasses to protect against hazards such as projectiles, as well as when working with glassware under reduced or elevated pressures (e.g., sealed tube reactions), when handling potentially explosive compounds (particularly during distillations), and when using glassware in high-temperature operations. Do not allow laboratory chemicals to come in contact with skin. Select gloves carefully to ensure that they are impervious to the chemicals being used and are of correct thickness to allow reasonable dexterity while also ensuring adequate barrier protection.

Lab coats and gloves should be worn when working with hazardous materials in a laboratory. Wear closed-toe shoes and long pants or other clothing that covers the legs when in a laboratory where hazardous chemicals are used. Additional protective clothing should be used when there is significant potential for skin-contact exposure to chemicals. The protective characteristics of this clothing must be matched to the hazard. Never wear gloves or laboratory coats outside the laboratory or into areas where food is stored and consumed.

4. Provide Laboratory Ventilation

The best way to prevent exposure to airborne substances is to prevent their escape into the working atmosphere by the use of hoods and other ventilation devices. To determine the best choice for laboratory ventilation using engineering controls for personal protection, employers are referred to Table 9.3 of the 2011 edition of "Prudent Practices." Laboratory chemical hoods are the most important components used to protect laboratory personnel from exposure to hazardous chemicals.

- (a) Toxic or corrosive chemicals that require vented storage should be stored in vented cabinets instead of in a chemical hood.
- (b) Chemical waste should not be disposed of by evaporation in a chemical hood.
- (c) Keep chemical hood areas clean and free of debris at all times.
- (d) Solid objects and materials, such as paper, should be prevented from entering the exhaust ducts as they can reduce the air flow.
- (e) Chemical hoods should be maintained, monitored and routinely tested for proper performance.

A laboratory ventilation system should include the following characteristics and practices:

- (a) Heating and cooling should be adequate for the comfort of workers and operation of equipment. Before modification of any building HVAC, the impact on laboratory or hood ventilation should be considered, as well as how laboratory ventilation changes may affect the building HVAC.
- (b) A negative pressure differential should exist between the amount of air exhausted from the laboratory and the amount supplied to the laboratory to prevent uncontrolled chemical vapors from leaving the laboratory.
- (c) Local exhaust ventilation devices should be appropriate to the materials and operations in the laboratory.
- (d) The air in chemical laboratories should be continuously replaced so that concentrations of odoriferous or toxic substances do not increase during the workday.
- (e) Laboratory air should not be recirculated but exhausted directly outdoors.
- (f) Air pressure should be negative with respect to the rest of the building. Local capture equipment and systems should be designed only by an experienced engineer or industrial hygienist.
- (g) Ventilation systems should be inspected and maintained on a regular basis. There should be no areas where air remains static or areas that have unusually high airflow velocities.

Before work begins, laboratory workers should be provided with proper training that includes how to use the ventilation equipment, how to ensure that it is functioning properly, the consequences of improper use, what to do in the event of a system failure or power outage, special considerations, and the importance of signage and postings.

5. Institute a Chemical Hygiene Program

A comprehensive chemical hygiene program is required. It should be designed to minimize exposures, injuries, illnesses and incidents. There should be a regular, continuing effort that includes program oversight, safe facilities, chemical hygiene planning, training, emergency preparedness and chemical security. The chemical hygiene program must be reviewed annually and updated as necessary whenever new processes, chemicals, or equipment is implemented. Its recommendations should be followed in all laboratories.

6. Observe the PELs and TLVs

OSHA's Permissible Exposure Limits (PELs) must not be exceeded. The American Conference of Governmental Industrial Hygienists' Threshold Limit Values (TLVs) should also not be exceeded.

B. Responsibilities

Persons responsible for chemical hygiene include, but are not limited to, the following:

1. Chemical Hygiene Officer
   - (a) Establishes, maintains, and revises the chemical hygiene plan (CHP).
   - (b) Creates and revises safety rules and regulations.
   - (c) Monitors procurement, use, storage, and disposal of chemicals.
   - (d) Conducts regular inspections of the laboratories, preparations rooms, and chemical storage rooms, and submits detailed laboratory inspection reports to administration.
   - (e) Maintains inspection, personnel training, and inventory records.
   - (f) Assists laboratory supervisors in developing and maintaining adequate facilities.
   - (g) Seeks ways to improve the chemical hygiene program.
2. Department Chairperson or Director
   - (a) Assumes responsibility for personnel engaged in the laboratory use of hazardous chemicals.
   - (b) Provides the chemical hygiene officer (CHO) with the support necessary to implement and maintain the CHP.
   - (c) After receipt of laboratory inspection report from the CHO, meets with laboratory supervisors to discuss cited violations and to ensure timely actions to protect trained laboratory personnel and facilities and to ensure that the department remains in compliance with all applicable federal, state, university, local and departmental codes and regulations.
   - (d) Provides budgetary arrangements to ensure the health and safety of the departmental personnel, visitors, and students.
3. Departmental Safety Committee reviews accident reports and makes appropriate recommendations to the department chairperson regarding proposed changes in the laboratory procedures.
4. Laboratory Supervisor or Principal Investigator has overall responsibility for chemical hygiene in the laboratory, including responsibility to:
   - (a) Ensure that laboratory personnel comply with the departmental CHP and do not operate equipment or handle hazardous chemicals without proper training and authorization.
   - (b) Always wear personal protective equipment (PPE) that is compatible to the degree of hazard of the chemical.
   - (c) Follow all pertinent safety rules when working in the laboratory to set an example.
   - (d) Review laboratory procedures for potential safety problems before assigning to other laboratory personnel.
   - (e) Ensure that visitors follow the laboratory rules and assumes responsibility for laboratory visitors.
   - (f) Ensure that PPE is available and properly used by each laboratory employee and visitor.
   - (g) Maintain and implement safe laboratory practices.
   - (h) Provide regular, formal chemical hygiene and housekeeping inspections, including routine inspections of emergency equipment;
   - (i) Monitor the facilities and the chemical fume hoods to ensure that they are maintained and function properly. Contact the appropriate person, as designated by the department chairperson, to report problems with the facilities or the chemical fume hoods.
5. Laboratory Personnel
   - (a) Read, understand, and follow all safety rules and regulations that apply to the work area;

(b) Plan and conduct each operation in accordance with the institutional chemical hygiene procedures;
(c) Promote good housekeeping practices in the laboratory or work area.
(d) Notify the supervisor of any hazardous conditions or unsafe work practices in the work area.
(e) Use PPE as appropriate for each procedure that involves hazardous chemicals.

C. The Laboratory Facility

General Laboratory Design Considerations

Wet chemical spaces and those with a higher degree of hazard should be separated from other spaces by a wall or protective barrier wherever possible. If the areas cannot be separated, then workers in lower hazard spaces may require additional protection from the hazards in connected spaces.

1. Laboratory Layout and Furnishing
   (a) Work surfaces should be chemically resistant, smooth, and easy to clean.
   (b) Hand washing sinks for hazardous materials may require elbow, foot, or electronic controls for safe operation.
   (c) Wet laboratory areas should have chemically resistant, impermeable, slip-resistant flooring.
   (d) Walls should be finished with a material that is easy to clean and maintain.
   (e) Doors should have view panels to prevent accidents and should open in the direction of egress.
   (f) Operable windows should not be present in laboratories, particularly if there are chemical hoods or other local ventilation systems present.
2. Safety Equipment and Utilities
   (a) An adequate number and placement of safety showers, eyewash units, and fire extinguishers should be provided for the laboratory.
   (b) Use of water sprinkler systems is resisted by some laboratories because of the presence of electrical equipment or water-reactive materials, but it is still generally safer to have sprinkler systems installed. A fire large enough to trigger the sprinkler system would have the potential to cause far more destruction than the local water damage.

D. Chemical Hygiene Plan (CHP)

The OSHA Laboratory standard defines a CHP as "a written program developed and implemented by the employer which sets forth procedures, equipment, personal protective equipment and work practices that are capable of protecting employees from the health hazards presented by hazardous chemicals used in that particular workplace." (29 CFR §1910.1450(b)). The Laboratory Standard requires a CHP: "Where hazardous chemicals as defined by this Standard are used in the workplace, the employer shall develop and carry out the provisions of a written Chemical Hygiene Plan." (29 CFR §1910.1450(e)(1)). The CHP is the foundation of the laboratory safety program and must be reviewed and updated, as needed, and at least on an annual basis to reflect changes in policies and personnel. A CHP should be facility specific and can assist in promoting a culture of safety to protect workers from exposure to hazardous materials.

1. The Laboratory's CHP must be readily available to workers and capable of protecting workers from health hazards and minimizing exposure. Include the following topics in the CHP:
   (a) Individual chemical hygiene responsibilities;
   (b) Standard operating procedures;
   (c) Personal protective equipment, engineering controls and apparel;
   (d) Laboratory equipment;
   (e) Safety equipment;
   (f) Chemical management;
   (g) Housekeeping;
   (h) Emergency procedures for accidents and spills;
   (i) Chemical waste;
   (j) Training;
   (k) Safety rules and regulations;
   (l) Laboratory design and ventilation;
   (m) Exposure monitoring;
   (n) Compressed gas safety;
   (o) Medical consultation and examination.

It should be noted that the nature of laboratory work may necessitate addressing biological safety, radiation safety and security issues.

2. Chemical Procurement, Distribution, and Storage

Prudent chemical management includes the following processes:

Chemical Procurement:
   (a) Information on proper handling, storage, and disposal should be known to those who will be involved before a substance is received.
   (b) Only containers with adequate identifying labels should be accepted.
   (c) Ideally, a central location should be used for receiving all chemical shipments.
   (d) Shipments with breakage or leakage should be refused or opened in a chemical hood.
   (e) Only the minimum amount of the chemical needed to perform the planned work should be ordered.
   (f) Purchases of high risk chemicals should be reviewed and approved by the CHO.
   (g) Proper protective equipment and handling and storage procedures should be in place before receiving a shipment.

Chemical Storage:
   (a) Chemicals should be separated and stored according to hazard category and compatibility.
   (b) SDS and label information should be followed for storage requirements.
   (c) Maintain existing labels on incoming containers of chemicals and other materials.
   (d) Labels on containers used for storing hazardous chemicals must include the chemical identification and appropriate hazard warnings.
   (e) The contents of all other chemical containers and transfer vessels, including, but not limited to, beakers, flasks, reaction vessels, and process equipment, should be properly identified.
   (f) Chemical shipments should be dated upon receipt and stock rotated.
   (g) Peroxide formers should be dated upon receipt, again dated upon opening, and stored away from heat and light with tight-fitting, nonmetal lids.
   (h) Open shelves used for chemical storage should be secured to the wall and contain 3⁄4 -inch lips. Secondary containment devices should be used as necessary.
   (i) Consult the SDS and keep incompatibles separate during transport, storage, use, and disposal.
   (j) Oxidizers, reducing agents, and fuels should be stored separately to prevent contact in the event of an accident.
   (k) Chemicals should not be stored in the chemical hood, on the floor, in areas of egress, on the benchtop, or in areas near heat or in direct sunlight.
   (l) Laboratory-grade, flammable-rated refrigerators and freezers should be used to store sealed chemical containers of flammable liquids that require cool storage. Do not store food or beverages in the laboratory refrigerator.
   (m) Highly hazardous chemicals should be stored in a well-ventilated and secure area designated for that purpose.
   (n) Flammable chemicals should be stored in a spark-free environment and in approved flammable-liquid containers and storage cabinets. Grounding and bonding should be used to prevent static charge buildups when dispensing solvents.
   (o) Chemical storage and handling rooms should be controlled-access areas. They should have proper ventilation, appropriate signage, diked floors, and fire suppression systems.

Chemical Handling:
   (a) As described above, a risk assessment should be conducted prior to beginning work with any hazardous chemical for the first time.
   (b) All SDS and label information should be read before using a chemical for the first time.
   (c) Trained laboratory workers should ensure that proper engineering controls (ventilation) and PPE are in place.

Chemical Inventory:
   (a) Prudent management of chemicals in any laboratory is greatly facilitated by keeping an accurate inventory of the chemicals stored.
   (b) Unneeded items should be discarded or returned to the storeroom.

Transporting Chemicals:
   (a) Secondary containment devices should be used when transporting chemicals.
   (b) When transporting chemicals outside of the laboratory or between stockrooms and laboratories, the transport container should be break-resistant.
   (c) High-traffic areas should be avoided.

Transferring Chemicals:
   (a) Use adequate ventilation (such as a fume hood) when transferring even a small amount of a particularly hazardous substance (PHS).
   (b) While drum storage is not appropriate for laboratories, chemical stockrooms may purchase drum quantities of solvents used in high volumes. Ground and bond the drum and receiving vessel when transferring flammable liquids from a drum to prevent static charge buildup.
   (c) If chemicals from commercial sources are repackaged into transfer vessels, the new containers should be labeled with all essential information on the original container.

Shipping Chemicals: Outgoing chemical shipments must meet all applicable Department of Transportation (DOT) regulations and should be authorized and handled by the institutional shipper.

3. Waste Management

A waste management plan should be in place before work begins on any laboratory activity. The plan should utilize the following hierarchy of practices:
   (a) Reduce waste sources. The best approach to minimize waste generation is by reducing the scale of operations, reducing its formation during operations, and, if possible, substituting less hazardous chemicals for a particular operation.

(b) Reuse surplus materials. Only the amount of material necessary for an experiment should be purchased, and, if possible, materials should be reused.

(c) Recycle waste. If waste cannot be prevented or minimized, the organization should consider recycling chemicals that can be safely recovered or used as fuel.

(d) Dispose of waste properly. Sink disposal may not be appropriate. Proper waste disposal methods include incineration, treatment, and land disposal. The organization's environmental health and safety (EHS) office should be consulted in determining which methods are appropriate for different types of waste.

Collection and Storage of Waste:

(a) Chemical waste should be accumulated at or near the point of generation, under the control of laboratory workers.

(b) Each waste type should be stored in a compatible container pending transfer or disposal. Waste containers should be clearly labeled and kept sealed when not in use.

(c) Incompatible waste types should be kept separate to ensure that heat generation, gas evolution, or another reaction does not occur.

(d) Waste containers should be segregated by how they will be managed. Waste containers should be stored in a designated location that does not interfere with normal laboratory operations. Ventilated storage and secondary containment may be appropriate for certain waste types.

(e) Waste containers should be clearly labeled and kept sealed when not in use. Labels should include the accumulation start date and hazard warnings as appropriate.

(f) Non-explosive electrical systems, grounding and bonding between floors and containers, and non-sparking conductive floors and containers should be used in the central waste accumulation area to minimize fire and explosion hazards. Fire suppression systems, specialized ventilation systems, and dikes should be installed in the central waste accumulation area. Waste management workers should be trained in proper waste handling procedures as well as contingency planning and emergency response. Trained laboratory workers most familiar with the waste should be actively involved in waste management decisions to ensure that the waste is managed safely and efficiently. Engineering controls should be implemented as necessary, and personal protective equipment should be worn by workers involved in waste management.

4. Inspection Program

Maintenance and regular inspection of laboratory equipment are essential parts of the laboratory safety program. Management should participate in the design of a laboratory inspection program to ensure that the facility is safe and healthy, workers are adequately trained, and proper procedures are being followed.

Types of inspections: The program should include an appropriate combination of routine inspections, self-audits, program audits, peer inspections, EHS inspections, and inspections by external entities.

Elements of an inspection:

(a) Inspectors should bring a checklist to ensure that all issues are covered and a camera to document issues that require correction.

(b) Conversations with workers should occur during the inspection, as they can provide valuable information and allow inspectors an opportunity to show workers how to fix problems.

(c) Issues resolved during the inspection should be noted.

(d) An inspection report containing all findings and recommendations should be prepared for management and other appropriate workers.

(e) Management should follow-up on the inspection to ensure that all corrections are implemented.

5. Medical Consultation and Examination

The employer must provide all employees who work with hazardous chemicals an opportunity to receive medical attention, including any follow-up examinations that the examining physician determines to be necessary, whenever an employee develops signs or symptoms associated with a hazardous chemical to which the employee may have been exposed in the laboratory. If an employee encounters a spill, leak, explosion or other occurrence resulting in the likelihood of a hazardous exposure, the affected employee must be provided an opportunity for a medical consultation by a licensed physician. All medical examinations and consultations must be performed by or under the direct supervision of a licensed physician and must be provided without cost to the employee, without loss of pay and at a reasonable time and place. The identity of the hazardous chemical, a description of the incident, and any signs and symptoms that the employee may experience must be relayed to the physician.

6. Records

All accident, fatality, illness, injury, and medical records and exposure monitoring records must be retained by the institution in accordance with the requirements of state and federal regulations (see 29 CFR Part §1904 and §1910.1450(j)). Any exposure monitoring results must be provided to affected laboratory staff within 15 working days after receipt of the results (29 CFR §1910.1450(d)(4)).

7. Signs

Prominent signs of the following types should be posted:

(a) Emergency telephone numbers of emergency personnel/facilities, supervisors, and laboratory workers;

(b) Location signs for safety showers, eyewash stations, other safety and first aid equipment, and exits; and

(c) Warnings at areas or equipment where special or unusual hazards exist.

8. Spills and Accidents

Before beginning an experiment, know your facility's policies and procedures for how to handle an accidental release of a hazardous substance, a spill or a fire. Emergency response planning and training are especially important when working with highly toxic compounds. Emergency telephone numbers should be posted in a prominent area. Know the location of all safety equipment and the nearest fire alarm and telephone. Know who to notify in the event of an emergency. Be prepared to provide basic emergency treatment. Keep your co-workers informed of your activities so they can respond appropriately. Safety equipment, including spill control kits, safety shields, fire safety equipment, PPE, safety showers and eyewash units, and emergency equipment should be available in well-marked highly visible locations in all chemical laboratories. The laboratory supervisor or CHO is responsible for ensuring that all personnel are aware of the locations of fire extinguishers and are trained in their use. After an extinguisher has been used, designated personnel must promptly recharge or replace it (29 CFR §1910.157(c)(4)). The laboratory supervisor or CHO is also responsible for ensuring proper training and providing supplementary equipment as needed.

Special care must be used when handling solutions of chemicals in syringes with needles. Do not recap needles, especially when they have been in contact with chemicals. Remove the needle and discard it immediately after use in the appropriate sharps containers. Blunt-tip needles are available from a number of commercial sources and should be used unless a sharp needle is required to puncture rubber septa or for subcutaneous injection.

For unattended operations, laboratory lights should be left on, and signs should be posted to identify the nature of the experiment and the hazardous substances in use. Arrangements should be made, if possible, for other workers to periodically inspect the operation. Information should be clearly posted indicating who to contact in the event of an emergency. Depending on the nature of the hazard, special rules, precautions, and alert systems may be necessary.

9. Training and Information

Personnel training at all levels within the organization, is essential. Responsibility and accountability throughout the organization are key elements in a strong safety and health program. The employer is required to provide employees with information and training to ensure that they are apprised of the hazards of chemicals present in their work area (29 CFR §1910.1450(f)). This information must be provided at the time of an employee's initial assignment to a work area where hazardous chemicals are present and prior to assignments involving new exposure situations. The frequency of refresher information and training should be determined by the employer. At a minimum, laboratory personnel should be trained on their facility's specific CHP, methods and observations that may be used to detect the presence or release of a hazardous chemical (such as monitoring conducted by the employer, continuous monitoring devices, visual appearance or odor of hazardous chemicals when being released), the physical and health hazards of chemicals in the work area and means to protect themselves from these hazards. Trained laboratory personnel must know shut-off procedures in case of an emergency. All SDSs must be made available to the employees.

E. General Procedures for Working With Chemicals

The risk of laboratory injuries can be reduced through adequate training, improved engineering, good housekeeping, safe work practice and personal behavior.

1. General Rules for Laboratory Work With Chemicals

(a) Assigned work schedules should be followed unless a deviation is authorized by the laboratory supervisor.

(b) Unauthorized experiments should not be performed.

(c) Plan safety procedures before beginning any operation.

(d) Follow standard operating procedures at all times.

(e) Always read the SDS and label before using a chemical.

(f) Wear appropriate PPE at all times.

(g) To protect your skin from splashes, spills and drips, always wear long pants and closed-toe shoes.

(h) Use appropriate ventilation when working with hazardous chemicals.

(i) Pipetting should never be done by mouth.

(j) Hands should be washed with soap and water immediately after working with any laboratory chemicals, even if gloves have been worn.

(k) Eating, drinking, smoking, gum chewing, applying cosmetics, and taking medicine in laboratories where hazardous chemicals are used or stored should be strictly prohibited.

(l) Food, beverages, cups, and other drinking and eating utensils should not be stored in areas where hazardous chemicals are handled or stored.

(m) Laboratory refrigerators, ice chests, cold rooms, and ovens should not be used for food storage or preparation.
(n) Contact the laboratory supervisor, Principal Investigator, CHO or EHS office with all safety questions or concerns.
(o) Know the location and proper use of safety equipment.
(p) Maintain situational awareness.
(q) Make others aware of special hazards associated with your work.
(r) Notify supervisors of chemical sensitivities or allergies.
(s) Report all injuries, accidents, incidents, and near misses.
(t) Unauthorized persons should not be allowed in the laboratory.
(u) Report unsafe conditions to the laboratory supervisor or CHO.
(v) Properly dispose of chemical wastes.

Working Alone in the Laboratory

Working alone in a laboratory is dangerous and should be strictly avoided. There have been many tragic accidents that illustrate this danger. Accidents are unexpected by definition, which is why coworkers should always be present. Workers should coordinate schedules to avoid working alone.

Housekeeping

Housekeeping can help reduce or eliminate a number of laboratory hazards. Proper housekeeping includes appropriate labeling and storage of chemicals, safe and regular cleaning of the facility, and proper arrangement of laboratory equipment.

2. Nanoparticles and Nanomaterials

Nanoparticles and nanomaterials have different reactivities and interactions with biological systems than bulk materials, and understanding and exploiting these differences is an active area of research. However, these differences also mean that the risks and hazards associated with exposure to engineered nanomaterials are not well known. Because this is an area of ongoing research, consult trusted sources for the most up to date information available. Note that the higher reactivity of many nanoscale materials suggests that they should be treated as potential sources of ignition, accelerants, and fuel that could result in fire or explosion. Easily dispersed dry nanomaterials may pose the greatest health hazard because of the risk of inhalation. Operations involving these nanomaterials deserve more attention and more stringent controls than those where the nanomaterials are embedded in solid or suspended in liquid matrixes.

Consideration should be given to all possible routes of exposure to nanomaterials including inhalation, ingestion, injection, and dermal contact (including eye and mucous membranes). Avoid handling nanomaterials in the open air in a free-particle state. Whenever possible, handle and store dispersible nanomaterials, whether suspended in liquids or in a dry particle form, in closed (tightly-sealed) containers. Unless cutting or grinding occurs, nanomaterials that are not in a free form (encapsulated in a solid or a nanocomposite) typically will not require engineering controls. If a synthesis is being performed to create nanomaterials, it is not enough to only consider the final material in the risk assessment, but consider the hazardous properties of the precursor materials as well.

To minimize laboratory personnel exposure, conduct any work that could generate engineered nanoparticles in an enclosure that operates at a negative pressure differential compared to the laboratory personnel breathing zone. Limited data exist regarding the efficacy of PPE and ventilation systems against exposure to nanoparticles. However, until further information is available, it is prudent to follow standard chemical hygiene practices. Conduct a hazard evaluation to determine PPE appropriate for the level of hazard according to the requirements set forth in OSHA's Personal Protective Equipment standard (29 CFR §1910.132).

3. Highly Toxic and Explosive/Reactive Chemicals/Materials

The use of highly toxic and explosive/reactive chemicals and materials has been an area of growing concern. The frequency of academic laboratory incidents in the U.S. is an area of significant concern for the Chemical Safety Board (CSB). The CSB issued a case study on an explosion at Texas Tech University in Lubbock, Texas, which severely injured a graduate student handling a high-energy metal compound. Since 2001, the CSB has gathered preliminary information on 120 different university laboratory incidents that resulted in 87 evacuations, 96 injuries, and three deaths.

It is recommended that each facility keep a detailed inventory of highly toxic chemicals and explosive/reactive materials. There should be a record of the date of receipt, amount, location, and responsible individual for all acquisitions, syntheses, and disposal of these chemicals. A physical inventory should be performed annually to verify active inventory records. There should be a procedure in place to report security breaches, inventory discrepancies, losses, diversions, or suspected thefts.

Procedures for disposal of highly toxic materials should be established before any experiments begin, possibly even before the chemicals are ordered. The procedures should address methods for decontamination of any laboratory equipment that comes into contact with highly toxic chemicals. All waste should be accumulated in clearly labeled impervious containers that are stored in unbreakable secondary containment.

Highly reactive and explosive materials that may be used in the laboratory require appropriate procedures and training. An explosion can occur when a material undergoes a rapid reaction that results in a violent release of energy. Such reactions can happen spontaneously and can produce pressures, gases, and fumes that are hazardous. Some reagents pose a risk on contact with the atmosphere. It is prudent laboratory practice to use a safer alternative whenever possible.

If at all possible, substitutes for highly acute, chronic, explosive, or reactive chemicals should be considered prior to beginning work and used whenever possible.

4. Compressed Gas

Compressed gases expose laboratory personnel to both chemical and physical hazards. It is essential that these are monitored for leaks and have the proper labeling. By monitoring compressed gas inventories and disposing of or returning gases for which there is no immediate need, the laboratory can substantially reduce these risks. Leaking gas cylinders can cause serious hazards that may require an immediate evacuation of the area and activation of the emergency response system. Only appropriately trained hazmat responders may respond to stop a leaking gas cylinder under this situation.

F. Safety Recommendations—Physical Hazards

Physical hazards in the laboratory include combustible liquids, compressed gases, reactives, explosives and flammable chemicals, as well as high pressure/energy procedures, sharp objects and moving equipment. Injuries can result from bodily contact with rotating or moving objects, including mechanical equipment, parts, and devices. Personnel should not wear loose-fitting clothing, jewelry, or unrestrained long hair around machinery with moving parts.

The Chemical Safety Board has identified the following key lessons for laboratories that address both physical and other hazards:

(1) Ensure that research-specific hazards are evaluated and then controlled by developing specific written protocols and training.
(2) Expand existing laboratory safety plans to ensure that all safety hazards, including physical hazards of chemicals, are addressed.
(3) Ensure that the organization's EHS office reports directly to an identified individual/office with organizational authority to implement safety improvements.
(4) Develop a verification program that ensures that the safety provisions of the CHP are communicated, followed, and enforced at all levels within the organization.
(5) Document and communicate all laboratory near-misses and previous incidents to track safety, provide opportunities for education and improvement to drive safety changes at the university.
(6) Manage the hazards unique to laboratory chemical research in the academic environment. Utilize available practice guidance that identifies and describes methodologies to assess and control hazards.
(7) Written safety protocols and training are necessary to manage laboratory risk.

G. Emergency Planning

In addition to laboratory safety issues, laboratory personnel should be familiar with established facility policies and procedures regarding emergency situations. Topics may include, but are not limited to:

(1) Evacuation procedures—when it is appropriate and alternate routes;
(2) Emergency shutdown procedures—equipment shutdown and materials that should be stored safely;
(3) Communications during an emergency—what to expect, how to report, where to call or look for information;
(4) How and when to use a fire extinguisher;
(5) Security issues—preventing tailgating and unauthorized access;
(6) Protocol for absences due to travel restrictions or illness;
(7) Safe practices for power outage;
(8) Shelter in place—when it is appropriate;
(9) Handling suspicious mail or phone calls;
(10) Laboratory-specific protocols relating to emergency planning and response;
(11) Handling violent behavior in the workplace; and
(12) First-aid and CPR training, including automated external defibrillator training if available.

It is prudent that laboratory personnel are also trained in how to respond to short-term, long-term and large-scale emergencies. Laboratory security can play a role in reducing the likelihood of some emergencies and assisting in preparation and response for others. Every institution, department, and individual laboratory should consider having an emergency preparedness plan. The level of detail of the plan will vary depending on the function of the group and institutional planning efforts already in place.

Emergency planning is a dynamic process. As personnel, operations, and events change, plans will need to be updated and modified. To determine the type and level of emergency planning needed, laboratory personnel need to perform a vulnerability assessment. Periodic drills to assist in training and evaluation of the emergency plan are recommended as part of the training program.

H. Emergency Procedures

(1) Fire alarm policy. Most organizations use fire alarms whenever a building needs to be evacuated—for any reason. When a fire alarm sounds in the facility, evacuate immediately after extinguishing all equipment flames. Check on and assist others who may require help evacuating.

(2) Emergency safety equipment. The following safety elements should be met:

a. A written emergency action plan has been provided to workers;

b. Fire extinguishers, eyewash units, and safety showers are available and tested on a regular basis; and

c. Fire blankets, first-aid equipment, fire alarms, and telephones are available and accessible.

(3) Chemical spills. Workers should contact the CHO or EHS office for instructions before cleaning up a chemical spill. All SDS and label instructions should be followed, and appropriate PPE should be worn during spill cleanup.

(4) Accident procedures. In the event of an accident, immediately notify appropriate personnel and local emergency responders. Provide an SDS of any chemical involved to the attending physician. Complete an accident report and submit it to the appropriate office or individual within 24 hours.

(5) Employee safety training program. New workers should attend safety training before they begin any activities. Additional training should be provided when they advance in their duties or are required to perform a task for the first time. Training documents should be recorded and maintained. Training should include hands-on instruction of how to use safety equipment appropriately.

(6) Conduct drills. Practice building evacuations, including the use of alternate routes. Practice shelter-in-place, including plans for extended stays. Walk the fastest route from your work area to the nearest fire alarm, emergency eye wash and emergency shower. Learn how each is activated. In the excitement of an actual emergency, people rely on what they learned from drills, practice and training.

(7) Contingency plans. All laboratories should have long-term contingency plans in place (e.g., for pandemics). Scheduling, workload, utilities and alternate work sites may need to be considered.

I. Laboratory Security

Laboratory security has evolved in the past decade, reducing the likelihood of some emergencies and assisting in preparation and response for others. Most security measures are based on the laboratory's vulnerability. Risks to laboratory security include, but are not limited to:

(1) Theft or diversion of chemicals, biologicals, and radioactive or proprietary materials, mission-critical or high-value equipment;
(2) Threats from activist groups;
(3) Intentional release of, or exposure to, hazardous materials;
(4) Sabotage or vandalism of chemicals or high-value equipment;
(5) Loss or release of sensitive information; and
(6) Rogue work or unauthorized laboratory experimentation. Security systems in the laboratory are used to detect and respond to a security breach, or a potential security breach, as well as to delay criminal activity by imposing multiple layered barriers of increasing stringency. A good laboratory security system will increase overall safety for laboratory personnel and the public, improve emergency preparedness by assisting with preplanning, and lower the organization's liability by incorporating more rigorous planning, staffing, training, and command systems and implementing emergency communications protocols, drills, background checks, card access systems, video surveillance, and other measures. The security plan should clearly delineate response to security issues, including the coordination of institution and laboratory personnel with both internal and external responders.

§1910.1450 Appendix B References (Nonmandatory)

The following references are provided to assist the employer in the development of a Chemical Hygiene Plan. The materials listed below are offered as non-mandatory guidance. References listed here do not imply specific endorsement of a book, opinion, technique, policy or a specific solution for a safety or health problem. Other references not listed here may better meet the needs of a specific laboratory.

(a) Materials for the development of the Chemical Hygiene Plan:

1. American Chemical Society, Safety in Academic Chemistry Laboratories, 4th edition, 1985.
2. Fawcett, H.H. and W. S. Wood, Safety and Accident Prevention in Chemical Operations, 2nd edition, Wiley-Interscience, New York, 1982.
3. Flury, Patricia A., Environmental Health and Safety in the Hospital Laboratory, Charles C. Thomas Publisher, Springfield IL, 1978.
4. Green, Michael E. and Turk, Amos, Safety in Working with Chemicals, Macmillan Publishing Co., NY, 1978.
5. Kaufman, James A., Laboratory Safety Guidelines, Dow Chemical Co., Box 1713, Midland, MI 48640, 1977.
6. National Institutes of Health, NIH Guidelines for the Laboratory use of Chemical Carcinogens, NIH Pub. No. 81–2385, GPO, Washington, DC 20402, 1981.
7. National Research Council, Prudent Practices for Disposal of Chemicals from Laboratories, National Academy Press, Washington, DC, 1983.
8. National Research Council, Prudent Practices for Handling Hazardous Chemicals in Laboratories, National Academy Press, Washington, DC, 1981.
9. Renfrew, Malcolm, Ed., Safety in the Chemical Laboratory, Vol. IV, J. Chem. Ed., American Chemical Society, Easlon, PA, 1981.
10. Steere, Norman V., Ed., Safety in the Chemical Laboratory, J. Chem. Ed. American Chemical Society, Easlon, PA, 18042, Vol. I, 1967, Vol. II, 1971, Vol. III 1974.
11. Steere, Norman V., Handbook of Laboratory Safety, the Chemical Rubber Company Cleveland, OH, 1971.
12. Young, Jay A., Ed., Improving Safety in the Chemical Laboratory, John Wiley & Sons, Inc. New York, 1987.

(b) Hazardous Substances Information:

1. American Conference of Governmental Industrial Hygienists, Threshold Limit Values for Chemical Substances and Physical Agents in the Workroom Environment with Intended Changes, 6500 Glenway Avenue, Bldg. D–7 Cincinnati, OH 45211–4438 (latest edition).
2. Annual Report on Carcinogens, National Toxicology Program U.S. Department of Health and Human Services, Public Health Service, U.S. Government Printing Office, Washington, DC, (latest edition).
3. Best Company, Best Safety Directory, Vols. I and II, Oldwick, N.J., 1981.
4. Bretherick, L., Handbook of Reactive Chemical Hazards, 2nd edition, Butterworths, London, 1979.
5. Bretherick, L., Hazards in the Chemical Laboratory, 3rd edition, Royal Society of Chemistry, London, 1986.
6. Code of Federal Regulations, 29 CFR Part §1910 Subpart Z. U.S. Govt. Printing Office, Washington, DC 20402 (latest edition).
7. IARC Monographs on the Evaluation of the Carcinogenic Risk of Chemicals to Man, World Health Organization Publications Center, 49 Sheridan Avenue, Albany, New York 12210 (latest editions).
8. NIOSH/OSHA Pocket Guide to Chemical Hazards. NIOSH Pub. No. 85–114, U.S. Government Printing Office, Washington, DC, 1985 (or latest edition).
9. Occupational Health Guidelines, NIOSH/OSHA NIOSH Pub. No. 81–123 U.S. Government Printing Office, Washington, DC, 1981.
10. Patty, F.A., Industrial Hygiene and Toxicology, John Wiley & Sons, Inc., New York, NY (Five Volumes).
11. Registry of Toxic Effects of Chemical Substances, U.S. Department of Health and Human Services, Public Health Service, Centers for Disease Control, National Institute for Occupational Safety and Health, Revised Annually, for sale from Superintendent of Documents U.S. Govt. Printing Office, Washington, DC 20402.
12. The Merck Index: An Encyclopedia of Chemicals and Drugs. Merck and Company Inc. Rahway, N.J., 1976 (or latest edition).
13. Sax, N.I. Dangerous Properties of Industrial Materials, 5th edition, Van Nostrand Reinhold, NY., 1979.
14. Sittig, Marshall, Handbook of Toxic and Hazardous Chemicals, Noyes Publications, Park Ridge, NJ, 1981.

(c) Information on Ventilation:

1. American Conference of Governmental Industrial Hygienists Industrial Ventilation (latest edition), 6500 Glenway Avenue, Bldg. D–7, Cincinnati, Ohio 45211–4438.
2. American National Standards Institute, Inc. American National Standards Fundamentals Governing the Design and Operation of Local Exhaust Systems ANSI Z 9.2–1979 American National Standards Institute, N.Y. 1979.
3. Imad, A.P. and Watson, C.L. Ventilation Index: An Easy Way to Decide about Hazardous Liquids, Professional Safety pp 15–18, April 1980.
4. National Fire Protection Association, Fire Protection for Laboratories Using Chemicals NFPA–45, 1982.
Safety Standard for Laboratories in Health Related Institutions, NFPA, 56c, 1980.
Fire Protection Guide on Hazardous Materials, 7th edition, 1978.
National Fire Protection Association, Batterymarch Park, Quincy, MA 02269.
5. Scientific Apparatus Makers Association (SAMA), Standard for Laboratory Fume Hoods, SAMA LF7–1980, 1101 16th Street, NW., Washington, DC 20036.

(d) Information on Availability of Referenced Material:

1. American National Standards Institute (ANSI), 1430 Broadway, New York, NY 10018.
2. American Society for Testing and Materials (ASTM), 1916 Race Street, Philadelphia, PA 19103.

[55 FR 3327, Jan. 31, 1990; 55 FR 7967, Mar. 6, 1990; 55 FR 12111, Mar. 30, 1990; 57 FR 29204, July 1, 1992; 61 FR 5508, Feb. 13, 1996; 71 FR 16674, Apr. 3, 2006; 76 FR 33609, June 8, 2011

29 CFR PART 1910
Recommended Practices for Safety and Health Programs

OSHA has recently updated the Guidelines for Safety and Health Programs. The Recommended Practices present a step-by-step approach to implementing a safety and health program, built around seven core elemens that make up a successful progam.

To view the new 40-page publication from OSHA click on the QRC Code below.

10 EASY THINGS TO GET YOUR PROGRAM STARTED

If these recommended practices appear challenging, here are some simple steps you can take to get started. Completing these steps will give you a solid base from which to take on some of the more structured actions presented in the recommended practices.

1. SET SAFETY AND HEALTH AS A TOP PRIORITY

Always set safety and health as the top priority. Tell your workers that making sure they finish the day and go home safely is the way you do business. Assure them that you will work with them to find and fix any hazards that could injure them or make them sick.

2. LEAD BY EXAMPLE

Practice safe behaviors yourself and make safety part of your daily conversations with workers.

3. IMPLEMENT A REPORTING SYSTEM

Develop and communicate a simple procedure for workers to report any injuries, illnesses, incidents (including near misses/close calls), hazards, or safety and health concerns without fear of retaliation. Include an option for reporting hazards or concerns anonymously.

4. PROVIDE TRAINING

Train workers on how to identify and control hazards using, for example, OSHA's Hazard Identification Training Tool.

5. CONDUCT INSPECTIONS

Inspect the workplace with workers and ask them to identify any activity, piece of equipment, or material that concerns them. Use checklists, such as those included in OSHA's Small Business Handbook, to help identify problems.

6. COLLECT HAZARD CONTROL IDEAS

Ask workers for ideas on improvements and follow up on their suggestions. Provide them time during work hours, if necessary, to research solutions.

7. IMPLEMENT HAZARD CONTROLS

Assign workers the task of choosing, implementing, and evaluating the solutions they come up with.

8. ADDRESS EMERGENCIES

Identify foreseeable emergency scenarios and develop instructions on what to do in each case. Meet to discuss these procedures and post them in a visible location in the workplace.

9. SEEK INPUT ON WORKPLACE CHANGES

Before making significant changes to the workplace, work organization, equipment, or materials, consult with workers to identify potential safety or health issues.

10. MAKE IMPROVEMENTS

Set aside a regular time to discuss safety and health issues, with the goal of identifying ways to improve the program.

CORE ELEMENTS OF THE SAFETY AND HEALTH PROGRAM RECOMMENDED PRACTICES

MANAGEMENT LEADERSHIP

- Top management demonstrates its commitment to continuous improvement in safety and health, communicates that commitment to workers, and sets program expectations and responsibilities.
- Managers at all levels make safety and health a core organizational value, establish safety and health goals and objectives, provide adequate resources and support for the program, and set a good example.

WORKER PARTICIPATION

- Workers and their representatives are involved in all aspects of the program—including setting goals, identifying and reporting hazards, investigating incidents, and tracking progress.
- All workers, including contractors and temporary workers, understand their roles and responsibilities under the program and what they need to do to effectively carry them out.
- Workers are encouraged and have means to communicate openly with management and to report safety and health concerns without fear of retaliation.
- Any potential barriers or obstacles to worker participation in the program (for example, language, lack of information, or disincentives) are removed or addressed.

HAZARD IDENTIFICATION & ASSESSMENT

- Procedures are put in place to continually identify workplace hazards and evaluate risks.
- Safety and health hazards from routine, nonroutine, and emergency situations are identified and assessed.
- An initial assessment of existing hazards, exposures, and control measures is followed by periodic inspections and reassessments, to identify new hazards.
- Any incidents are investigated with the goal of identifying the root causes.
- Identified hazards are prioritized for control.

HAZARD PREVENTION & CONTROL

- Employers and workers cooperate to identify and select methods for eliminating, preventing, or controlling workplace hazards.
- Controls are selected according to a hierarchy that uses engineering solutions first, followed by safe work practices, administrative controls, and finally personal protective equipment (PPE).
- A plan is developed to ensure that controls are implemented, interim protection is provided, progress is tracked, and the effectiveness of controls is verified.

EDUCATION & TRAINING

- All workers are trained to understand how the program works and how to carry out the responsibilities assigned to them under the program.
- Employers, managers, and supervisors receive training on safety concepts and their responsibility for protecting workers' rights and responding to workers' reports and concerns.
- All workers are trained to recognize workplace hazards and to understand the control measures that have been implemented.

PROGRAM EVALUATION & IMPROVEMENT

- Control measures are periodically evaluated for effectiveness.
- Processes are established to monitor program performance, verify program implementation, and identify program shortcomings and opportunities for improvement.
- Necessary actions are taken to improve the program and overall safety and health performance.

COMMUNICATION AND COORDINATION FOR HOST EMPLOYERS, CONTRACTORS, AND STAFFING AGENCIES

- Host employers, contractors, and staffing agencies commit to providing the same level of safety and health protection to all employees.
- Host employers, contractors, and staffing agencies commmunicate the hazards present at the worksite and the hazards that work of contract workers may create on site.
- Host employers establish specifications and qualifications for contractors and staffing agencies.
- Before beginning work, host employers, contractors, and staffing agencies coordinate on work planning and scheduling to identify and resolve any conflicts that could affect safety or health.

GLOSSARY

This glossary provides a single location to find the definition(s) for each of the terms that OSHA has previously defined in each Section or Subpart of this book. Please refer to the individual Section or Subpart for more information or context about each term. Please note that OSHA has provided more than one definition for some of the included terms.

#

1,2-dibromo-3-chloropropane See "DBCP"

1,3–Butadiene organic compound with chemical formula CH_2=CH-CH=CH_2 that has a molecular weight of approximately 54.15 gm/mole. (§1910.1051(b))

4,4′ Methylenedianiline or MDA chemical, 4,4′-diaminodiphenyl-methane, Chemical Abstract Service Registry number 101–77–9, in the form of a vapor, liquid, or solid. The definition also includes the salts of MDA. (§1910.1050(b))

A

A-frame structure made of two independent columns fastened together at the top and separated at the bottom for stability. (§1910.265(b)(1))

A-frame derrick derrick in which the boom is hinged from a cross member between the bottom ends of two upright members spread apart at the lower ends and joined at the top; the boom point secured to the junction of the side members, and the side members are braced or guyed from this junction point. (§1910.181(a)(2))

Abatement action by an employer to comply with a cited Standard or regulation or to eliminate a recognized hazard identified by OSHA during an inspection. (§1903.19(b)(1))

Abatement date means:
(i) For an uncontested citation item, the later of:
(A) the date in the citation for abatement of the violation;
(B) the date approved by OSHA or established in litigation as a result of a petition for modification of the abatement date (PMA); or
(C) the date established in a citation by an informal settlement agreement.
(ii) For a contested citation item for which the Occupational Safety and Health Review Commission (OSHRC) has issued a final order affirming the violation, the later of:
(A) the date identified in the final order for abatement; or
(B) the date computed by adding the period allowed in the citation for abatement to the final order date;
(C) the date established by a formal settlement agreement. (§1903.19(b)(2))

Abrasive solid substance used in an abrasive blasting operation. (§1910.94(a)(1)(i))

Abrasive blasting forcible application of an abrasive to a surface by pneumatic pressure, hydraulic pressure, or centrifugal force. (§1910.94(a)(1)(xii))

Abrasive-blasting respirator respirator constructed so that it covers the wearer's head, neck, and shoulders to protect the wearer from rebounding abrasive. (§1910.94(a)(1)(ii))

Abrasive cutting-off wheels organic-bonded wheels, the thickness of which is not more than one forty-eighth of their diameter for those up to, and including, 20 inches in diameter, and not more than one-sixtieth of their diameter for those larger than 20 inches in diameter, used for a multitude of operations variously known as cutting, cutting off, grooving, slotting, coping, and jointing, and the like. The wheels may be "solid" consisting of organic-bonded abrasive material throughout, "steel centered" consisting of a steel disc with a rim of organic-bonded material moulded around the periphery, or of the "inserted tooth" type consisting of a steel disc with organic-bonded abrasive teeth or inserts mechanically secured around the periphery. (§1910.94(b)(1)(i))

Abrasive wheel cutting tool consisting of abrasive grains held together by organic or inorganic bonds. Diamond and reinforced wheels are included. (§1910.211(b)(14))

Absolute filter one capable of retaining 99.97 percent of a mono disperse aerosol of 0.3 µm particles. (§1910.1003(b))

Acceptable installation or equipment is acceptable to the Assistant Secretary of Labor, and approved within the meaning of this Subpart S:
(1) if it is accepted, or certified, or listed, or labeled, or otherwise determined to be safe by a nationally recognized testing laboratory recognized pursuant to §1910.7; or
(2) with respect to an installation or equipment of a kind that no nationally recognized testing laboratory accepts, certifies, lists, labels, or determines to be safe, if it is inspected or tested by another Federal agency, or by a state, municipal, or other local authority responsible for enforcing occupational safety provisions of the National Electrical Code, and found in compliance with the provisions of the National Electrical Code as applied in this Subpart; or
(3) with respect to custom-made equipment or related installations that are designed, fabricated for, and intended for use by a particular customer, if it is determined to be safe for its intended use by its manufacturer on the basis of test data which the employer keeps and makes available for inspection to the Assistant Secretary and his authorized representatives. (§1910.399)

Acceptable entry conditions conditions that must exist in a permit space to allow entry and to ensure that employees involved with a permit-required confined space entry can safely enter into and work within the space. (§1910.146(b))

Accepted an installation is "accepted" if it has been inspected and found by a nationally recognized testing laboratory to conform to specified plans or to procedures of applicable codes. (§1910.399)

Access right and opportunity to examine and copy. (§1910.1020(c)(1))

Accessible
(As applied to equipment.) (See Also "Readily accessible") admitting close approach; not guarded by locked doors, elevation, or other effective means. (§1910.399)
(As applied to wiring methods.) (See Also: "Concealed;" "Exposed") capable of being removed or exposed without damaging the building structure or finish, or not permanently closed in by the structure or finish of the building. (§1910.399)

Accessory secondary part or assembly of parts which contributes to the overall function and usefulness of a machine. (§1910.180(a)(5))

Accuracy measure of the bias of a data set. Bias is a systematic error that is either inherent in a method or caused by some artifact or idiosyncrasy of the measurement system. Bias is characterized by a consistent deviation (positive or negative) in the results from an accepted reference value. (Appendix F to §1910.1027)

Acfm Actual cubic feet per minute. (§1910.402)

Acrylonitrile or AN acrylonitrile monomer, chemical formula CH_2=CHCN. (§1910.1045(b))

Act
(1903) (1910) Williams-Steiger Occupational Safety and Health Act of 1970. (84 Stat. 1590 et seq., 29 U.S.C. 651 et seq.). (§1903.22(a)) (§1910.2(a))
(1904) The Act means the Occupational Safety and Health Act of 1970 (29 U.S.C. 651 et seq.). The definitions contained in Section 3 of the Act (29 U.S.C. 652) and related interpretations apply to such terms when used in this Part §1904. (§1903.46)

Actinolite See "Tremolite, Anthophyllite, and Actinolite"

Action level
(1,3-Butadiene) concentration of airborne BD of 0.5 ppm calculated as an 8-hour time-weighted average. (§1910.1051(b))
(Acrylonitrile) concentration of AN of 1 ppm as an 8-hour time-weighted average. (§1910.1045(b))
(Benzene) airborne concentration of benzene of 0.5 ppm calculated as an 8-hour time-weighted average. (§1910.1028(b))
(Cadmium (AL)) airborne concentration of cadmium of 2.5 micrograms per cubic meter of air (2.5 µg/m^3), calculated as an 8-hour time-weighted average (TWA). (§1910.1027(b))
(Chromium (VI)) concentration of airborne chromium (VI) of 2.5 micrograms per cubic meter of air (2.5 µgm/m^3) calculated as an 8-hour time-weighted average (TWA). (§1910.1026(b))
(Ethylene oxide) concentration of airborne EtO of 0.5 ppm calculated as an 8-hour time-weighted average. (§1910.1047(b))
(Formaldehyde) concentration of 0.5 part formaldehyde per million parts of air (0.5 ppm) calculated as an 8-hour time-weighted average (TWA) concentration. (§1910.1048(b))
(Inorganic arsenic) concentration of inorganic arsenic of 5 micrograms per cubic meter of air (5 µg/m^3) averaged over any 8-hour period. (§1910.1018(b))
(Lead) employee exposure, without regard to the use of respirators, to an airborne concentration of lead of 30 micrograms per cubic meter of air (30 µg/m^3) averaged over an 8-hour period. (§1910.1025(b))
(Methylene chloride) concentration of airborne MC of 12.5 parts per million (ppm) calculated as an 8-hour time-weighted average (TWA). (§1910.1052(b))

(Methylenedianiline) concentration of airborne MDA of 5 ppb as an 8-hour time-weighted average. (§1910.1050(b))
(Occupational exposure to hazardous chemicals in laboratories) concentration designated in 29 CFR Part §1910 for a specific substance, calculated as an 8-hour time-weighted average, which initiates certain required activities such as exposure monitoring and medical surveillance. (§1910.1450(b))
(Occupational noise exposure) an 8-hour time-weighted average of 85 decibels measured on the A-scale, slow response, or equivalently, a dose of fifty percent. (Appendix I to §1910.95)
(Respirable crystalline silica) concentration of vinyl chloride of 0.5 ppm averaged over an 8-hour work day. (§1910.1053(b))
(Vinyl chloride) concentration of vinyl chloride of 0.5 ppm averaged over an 8-hour work day. (§1910.1017(b)(1))

Acute toxicity those adverse effects occurring following oral or dermal administration of a single dose of a substance, or multiple doses given within 24 hours, or an inhalation exposure of 4 hours. (Appendix A to §1910.1200(A.1.1))

Adjacent area any area within 20 feet (6.1 m) of a vapor area that is not separated from the vapor area by tight partitions. (§1910.123(d))

Adjustable barrier guard barrier requiring adjustment for each job or die setup. (§1910.211(d)(36))

Adverse effects on development of the offspring any effect of chemicals which interferes with normal development of the conceptus either before or after birth, which is induced during pregnancy or results from parental exposure. These effects can be manifested at any point in the life span of the organism. The major manifestations of developmental toxicity include death of the developing organism, structural abnormality, altered growth and functional deficiency. (Appendix A to §1910.1200(A.7.1.3))

Adverse effects on sexual function and fertility any effect of chemicals that interferes with reproductive ability or sexual capacity. This includes, but is not limited to, alterations to the female and male reproductive system, adverse effects on onset of puberty, gamete production and transport, reproductive cycle normality, sexual behavior, fertility, parturition, pregnancy outcomes, premature reproductive senescence, or modifications in other functions that are dependent on the integrity of the reproductive systems. (Appendix A to §1910.1200(A.7.1.2))

Aerated solid powders any powdered material used as a coating material which shall be fluidized within a container by passing air uniformly from below. It is common practice to fluidize such materials to form a fluidized powder bed and then dip the part to be coated into the bed in a manner similar to that used in liquid dipping. Such beds are also used as sources for powder spray operations. (§1910.107(a)(1))

Aerial device any vehicle-mounted device, telescoping or articulating, or both, which is used to position personnel. (§1910.67(a)(1))

Aerial ladder aerial device consisting of a single- or multiple-section extensible ladder. (§1910.67(a)(2))

Aerial lifts aerial lifts include the following types of vehicle-mounted aerial devices used to elevate personnel to jobsites above ground:
(i) extensible boom platforms,
(ii) aerial ladders,
(iii) articulating boom platforms,
(iv) vertical towers,
(v) combination of any of the above defined in ANSI A92.2–1969, which is incorporated by reference as specified in §1910.6. These devices are made of metal, wood, fiberglass reinforced plastic (FRP), or other material; are powered or manually operated; and are deemed to be aerial lifts whether or not they are capable of rotating about a substantially vertical axis. (§1910.268(s)(1))

Aerial splicing platform platform, approximately 3 ft.×4 ft., used to perform aerial cable work. It is furnished with fiber or synthetic ropes for supporting the platform from aerial strand, detachable guy ropes for anchoring it, and a device for raising and lowering it with a handline. (§1910.268(s)(2))

Aerial tent small tent usually constructed of vinyl-coated canvas which is usually supported by light metal or plastic tubing. It is designed to protect employees in inclement weather while working on ladders, aerial splicing platforms, or aerial devices. (§1910.268(s)(3))

Aerosol
(Flammable liquids) material which is dispensed from its container as a mist, spray, or foam by a propellant under pressure. (§1910.106(a)(1))
(Hazard Communication) any non-refillable receptacle containing a gas compressed, liquefied or dissolved under pressure, and fitted with a release device allowing the contents to be ejected as particles in suspension in a gas, or as a foam, paste, powder, liquid or gas. (Appendix B to §1910.1200(B.3.1))

Affected employee employee whose job requires him/her to operate or use a machine or equipment on which servicing or maintenance is being performed under lockout or tagout, or whose job requires him/her to work in an area in which such servicing or maintenance is being performed. (§1910.147(b)); (§1910.269(x))

Affected employees those employees who are exposed to the hazard(s) identified as violation(s) in a citation. (§1903.19(b)(3))

After-flame time a test specimen continues to flame after the flame source has been removed. (§1910.155(c)(1))

Air-purifying respirator respirator with an air-purifying filter, cartridge, or canister that removes specific air contaminants by passing ambient air through the air-purifying element. (§1910.134(b))

Airline respirator See "Supplied-air respirator (SAR) or airline respirator"

Alive or live (energized) electrically connected to a source of potential difference, or electrically charged so as to have a potential significantly different from that of the earth in the vicinity. The term live is sometimes used in the place of the term current-carrying, where the intent is clear, to avoid repetition of the longer term. (§1910.268(s)(4))

Alternating tread-type stair type of stairway consisting of a series of treads that usually are attached to a center support in an alternating manner such that an employee typically does not have both feet on the same level while using the stairway. (§1910.21(b))

Ampacity current, in amperes, that a conductor can carry continuously under the conditions of use without exceeding its temperature rating. (§1910.399)

Amphibole a family of minerals whose crystals are formed by long, thin units which have two thin ribbons of double chain silicate with a brucite ribbon in between. The shape of each unit is similar to an "I-beam". Minerals important in asbestos analysis include cummingtonite-grunerite, crocidolite, tremolite-actinolite and anthophyllite. (Appendix J to §1910.1001)

Analysis using exposure or medical records any compilation of data or any statistical study based at least in part on information collected from individual employee exposure or medical records or information collected from health insurance claims records, provided that either the analysis has been reported to the employer or no further work is currently being done by the person responsible for preparing the analysis. (§1910.1020(c)(2))

Anchorage
(Walking-working surfaces) secure point of attachment for equipment such as lifelines, lanyards, deceleration devices, and rope descent systems. (§1910.21(b))
(Powered platforms for building maintenance) secure point of attachment for lifelines, lanyards or deceleration devices, and which is independent of the means of supporting or suspending the employee. (Appendix C to §1910.66(b))

Anemometer instrument for measuring wind velocity. (§1910.66(d))

Angle indicator (boom) accessory which measures the angle of the boom to the horizontal. (§1910.180(a)(8))

Angle of loading inclination of a leg or branch of a sling measured from the horizontal or vertical plane as shown in Fig. N–184–5; provided that an angle of loading of five degrees or less from the vertical may be considered a vertical angle of loading. (§1910.184(b))

Angulated roping
(Powered platforms for building maintenance) suspension method where the upper point of suspension is inboard from the attachments on the suspended unit, thus causing the suspended unit to bear against the face of the building. (§1910.66(d))
(Powered platforms for building maintenance/Existing installations (mandatory)) system of platform suspension in which the upper wire rope sheaves or suspension points are closer to the plane of the building face than the corresponding attachment points on the platform, thus causing the platform to press against the face of the building during its vertical travel.(Appendix D to §1910.66(a)(1))

Annealing heating then cooling to soften and render less brittle. (§1910.265(b)(2))

ANSI American National Stardards Institute. (Appendix D to §1910.66(a)(2)); (§1910.179(a)(16)); (§1910.180(a)(7)); (§1910.181(a)(11))

Anthophyllite See "Tremolite, Anthophyllite, and Actinolite"

Antirepeat part of the clutch/brake control system designed to limit the press to a single stroke if the tripping means is held operated. Antirepeat requires release of all tripping mechanisms before another stroke can be initiated. Antirepeat is also called single stroke reset or reset circuit. (§1910.211(d)(1))

API-ASME container container constructed in accordance with the requirements of paragraph (b)(3)(iii) of §1910.110. (§1910.110(a)(1))

Appliances utilization equipment, generally other than industrial, normally built in standardized sizes or types, that is installed or connected as a unit to perform one or more functions. (§1910.399)

Appointed assigned specific responsibilities by the employer or the employer's representative. (§1910.179(a)(15)) (§1910.180(a)(6)) (§1910.181(a)(10))

Approved (See Also "Listed")
(Dipping and coating operations) equipment so designated is listed or approved by a nationally recognized testing laboratory, as defined by §1910.7. (§1910.123(d))
(Electrical) acceptable to the authority enforcing this Subpart S. The authority enforcing this Subpart is the Assistant Secretary of Labor for Occupational Safety and Health. The definition of "acceptable" indicates what is acceptable to the Assistant Secretary of Labor, and therefore approved within the meaning of this Subpart. (§1910.399)
(Fire protection) acceptable to the Assistant Secretary under the following criteria:
(i) if it is accepted, or certified, or listed, or labeled or otherwise determined to be safe by a nationally recognized testing laboratory; or
(ii) with respect to an installation or equipment of a kind which no nationally recognized testing laboratory accepts, certifies, lists, labels, or determines to be safe, if it is inspected or tested by another Federal agency and found in compliance with the provisions of the applicable National Fire Protection Association Fire Code; or
(iii) with respect to custom-made equipment or related installations which are designed, fabricated for, and intended for use by its manufacturer on the basis of test data which the employer keeps and makes available for inspection to the Assistant Secretary.
(iv) for the purposes of paragraph (c)(3) of this Section:
(A) equipment is listed if it is of a kind mentioned in a list which is published by a nationally recognized testing laboratory which makes periodic inspections of the production of such equipment and which states that such equipment meets nationally recognized standards or has been tested and found safe for use in a specified manner;
(B) equipment is labeled if there is attached to it a label, symbol, or other identifying mark of a nationally recognized testing laboratory which makes periodic inspections of the production of such equipment, and whose labeling indicates compliance with nationally recognized standards or tests to determine safe use in a specified manner;
(C) equipment is accepted if it has been inspected and found by a nationally recognized testing laboratory to conform to specified plans or to procedures of applicable codes; and
(D) equipment is certified if it has been tested and found by a nationally recognized testing laboratory to meet nationally recognized standards or to be safe for use in a specified manner or is of a kind whose production is periodically inspected by a nationally recognized testing laboratory, and if it bears a label, tag, or other record of certification. (§1910.155(c)(3))
(Hydrogen); (Flammable liquids); (Spray finishing using flammable and combustible materials); (Storage and handling of liquefied petroleum gases); (Welding, cutting and brazing) unless otherwise indicated, listed or approved by a nationally recognized testing laboratory. Refer to "Approved (Fire Protection)" for definitions of listed and approved, and §1910.7 for definition of nationally recognized testing laboratory. (§1910.103(a)(1)(ii)); (§1910.106(a)(35)); (§1910.107(a)(8)); (§1910.110(a)(14)); (§1910.251(b))

Approved truck or approved industrial truck as used in §1910.178, a truck that is listed or approved for fire safety purposes for the intended use by a nationally recognized testing laboratory, using nationally recognized testing standards. Refer to §1910.155(c)(3)(iv)(A) for definition of listed, and to §1910.7 for definition of nationally recognized testing laboratory. (§1910.178(a)(7))

Approved for the purpose (See Also "Labeled;" "Listed") approved for a specific purpose, environment, or application described in a particular standard requirement. Suitability of equipment or materials for a specific purpose, environment or application may be determined by a nationally recognized testing laboratory, inspection agency, or other organization condemned with product evaluation as part of its listing and labeling program. (§1910.399).

Appurtenances all devices such as pumps, compressors, safety relief devices, liquid-level gaging devices, valves and pressure gages. (§1910.111(a)(2)(i))

Aqueous film forming foam (AFFF) fluorinated surfactant with a foam stabilizer which is diluted with water to act as a temporary barrier to exclude air from mixing with the fuel vapor by developing an aqueous film on the fuel surface of some hydrocarbons which is capable of suppressing the generation of fuel vapors. (§1910.155(c)(2))

Arch open-framed trailer or built-up framework used to suspend the leading ends of trees or logs when they are skidded. (§1910.266(c))

Area Director employee or officer regularly or temporarily in charge of an Area Office of the Occupational Safety and Health Administration, U.S. Department of Labor, or any other person or persons who are authorized to act for such employee or officer. The latter authorizations may include general delegations of the authority of an Area Director under this Part to a Compliance Safety and Health Officer or delegations to such an officer for more limited purposes, such as the exercise of the Area Director's duties under §1903.14(a). The term also includes any employee or officer exercising supervisory responsibilities over an Area Director. A supervisory employee or officer is considered to exercise concurrent authority with the Area Director. (§1903.22(e))

Arithmetic Mean sum of measurements in a set divided by the number of measurements in a set. (Appendix F to §1910.1027)

Armored cable (Type AC) fabricated assembly of insulated conductors in a flexible metallic enclosure. (§1910.399)

Article manufactured item other than a fluid or particle:
(i) which is formed to a specific shape or design during manufacture;
(ii) which has end use function(s) dependent in whole or in part upon its shape or design during end use; and
(iii) which under normal conditions of use does not release more than very small quantities, e.g., minute or trace amounts of a hazardous chemical (as determined under paragraph (d) of this Section), and does not pose a physical hazard or health risk to employees. (§1910.1200(c))

Articulating boom platform aerial device with two or more hinged boom sections. (§1910.67(a)(3))

Asbestos includes chrysotile, amosite, crocidolite, tremolite asbestos, anthophyllite asbestos, actinolite asbestos, and any of these minerals that have been chemically treated and/or altered.

A term for naturally occurring fibrous minerals. Asbestos includes chrysotile, crocidolite, amosite (cummingtonite-grunerite asbestos), tremolite asbestos, actinolite asbestos, anthophyllite asbestos, and any of these minerals that have been chemically treated and/or altered. The precise chemical formulation of each species will vary with the location from which it was mined. Nominal compositions are listed:

Chrysotile	$Mg_3Si_2O_5(OH)_4$
Crocidolite	$Na_2Fe_3{}^2+ Fe_2{}^3 + Si_8O_{22}(OH)_2$
Amosite	$(Mg,Fe)_7Si_8O_{22}(OH)_2$
Tremolite-actinolite	$Ca_2(Mg,Fe)_5Si_8O_{22}(OH)_2$
Anthophyllite	$(Mg,Fe)_7Si_8O_{22}(OH)_2$

(§1910.1001(b)); (Appendix B to §1910.1001); (Appendix J to §1910.1001)

Asbestos fiber A fiber of asbestos which meets the criteria for a fiber. (Appendix B to §1910.1001); (Appendix J to §1910.1001)

Asbestos-containing material (ACM) any material containing more than 1% asbestos. (§1910.1001(b))

Askarel generic term for a group of nonflammable synthetic chlorinated hydrocarbons used as electrical insulating media. Askarels of various compositional types are used. Under arcing conditions, the gases produced, while consisting predominantly of noncombustible hydrogen chloride, can include varying amounts of combustible gases depending upon the askarel type. (§1910.399)

ASME American Society of Mechanical Engineers. (§1910.103(a)(1)(iv))

ASME Code or equivalent ASME (American Society of Mechanical Engineers) Boiler and Pressure Vessel Code, Section VIII, or an equivalent code which the employer can demonstrate to be equally effective. (§1910.402)

ASME container container constructed in accordance with the requirements of paragraph (b)(3)(i) of §1910.110. (§1910.110(a)(2))

Aspect Ratio ratio of the length of a fiber to it's diameter (e.g. 3:1, 5:1 aspect ratios). (Appendix B to §1910.1001); (Appendix J to §1910.1001)

Aspiration entry of a liquid or solid chemical directly through the oral or nasal cavity, or indirectly from vomiting, into the trachea and lower respiratory system. (Appendix A to §1910.1200(A.10.1.1))

Assigned protection factor (APF) workplace level of respiratory protection that a respirator or class of respirators is expected to provide to employees when the employer implements a continuing, effective respiratory protection program as specified by this Section. (§1910.134(b))

Assistant Regional Director employee or officer regularly or temporarily in charge of a Region of the Occupational Safety and Health Administration, U.S. Department of Labor, or any other person or persons who are specifically designated to act for such employee or officer in his absence. The term also includes any employee or officer in the Occupational Safety and Health Administration exercising supervisory responsibilities over the Assistant Regional Director. Such supervisory employee or officer is considered to exercise concurrent authority with the Assistant Regional Director. No delegation of authority under this paragraph shall adversely affect the procedures for independent informal review of investigative determinations prescribed under §1903.12 of this Part. (§1903.22(f))

Assistant Secretary Assistant Secretary of Labor for Occupational Safety and Health or designee. (§1910.155(c)(4)); (§1910.1001(b)); (§1910.1017(b)(2)); (§1910.1018(b)); (§1910.1025(b)); (§1910.1026(b)); (§1910.1027(b)); (§1910.1028(b)); (§1910.1030(b)); (§1910.1043(b)); (§1910.1044(b)); (§1910.1045(b)); (§1910.1047(b)); (§1910.1048(b)); (§1910.1050(b)); (§1910.1051(b)); (§1910.1052(b)); (§1910.1053(b)); (§1910.1450(b)); (§1910.1200(c))

Assistant Secretary of Labor Assistant Secretary of Labor for Occupational Safety and Health; (§1910.2(b))

ATA Atmosphere absolute. (§1910.402)

Atmosphere-supplying respirator respirator that supplies the respirator user with breathing air from a source independent of the ambient atmosphere, and includes supplied-air respirators (SARs) and self-contained breathing apparatus (SCBA) units. (§1910.134(b))

Atmospheric tank storage tank which has been designed to operate at pressures from atmospheric through 0.5 p.s.i.g. (pounds per square inch gauge, 3.45 Kpa). (§1910.106(a)(2)); (§1910.119(b))

Attachment plug (Plug cap)(Cap) device that, by insertion in a receptacle, establishes a connection between the conductors of the attached flexible cord and the conductors connected permanently to the receptacle. (§1910.399)

Attendant

(Electric power generation, transmission and distribution) employee assigned to remain immediately outside the entrance to an enclosed or other space to render assistance as needed to employees inside the space. (§1910.269(x))

(Permit-required confined spaces) individual stationed outside one or more permit spaces who monitors the authorized entrants and who performs all attendant's duties assigned in the employer's permit space program. (§1910.146(b))

Audiogram chart, graph, or table resulting from an audiometric test showing an individual's hearing threshold levels as a function of frequency. (Appendix I to §1910.95)

Audiologist A professional, specializing in the study and rehabilitation of hearing, who is certified by the American Speech-Language-Hearing Association or licensed by a state board of examiners. (Appendix I to §1910.95)

Authorized employee who the employer assigns to perform a specific type of duty, or allows in a specific location or area. (§1910.21(b))

Authorized employee

(13 Carcinogens) employee whose duties require him to be in the regulated area and who has been specifically assigned by the employer. (§1910.1003(b))

(The control of hazardous energy (lockout/tagout)) (Electric power generation, transmission, and distribution) person who locks out or tags out machines or equipment in order to perform servicing or maintenance on that machine or equipment. An affected employee becomes an authorized employee when that employee's duties include performing servicing or maintenance covered under this Section. (§1910.147(b)); (§1910.269(x))

Authorized entrant employee who is authorized by the employer to enter a permit space. (§1910.146(b))

Authorized person

(1,2-dibromo-3-chloropropane (DBCP)) any person required by his duties to be present in regulated areas and authorized to do so by his employer, by this Section, or by the Act. Authorized person also includes any person entering such areas as a designated representative of employees exercising an opportunity to observe employee exposure monitoring. (§1910.1044(b))

(1,3,-Butadiene) any person specifically designated by the employer, whose duties require entrance into a regulated area, or a person entering such an area as a designated representative of employees to exercise the right to observe monitoring and measuring procedures under paragraph (d)(8) of this Section, or a person designated under the Act or regulations issued under the Act to enter a regulated area. (§1910.1051(b))

(Acrylonitrile) any person specifically authorized by the employer whose duties require the person to enter a regulated area, or any person entering such an area as a designated representative of employees for the purpose of exercising the opportunity to observe monitoring procedures under paragraph (r) of this Section. (§1910.1045(b))

(Asbestos) any person authorized by the employer and required by work duties to be present in regulated areas. (§1910.1001(b))

(Benzene) any person specifically authorized by the employer whose duties require the person to enter a regulated area, or any person entering such an area as a designated representative of employees for the purpose of exercising the right to observe monitoring and measuring procedures under paragraph (l) of this Section, or any other person authorized by the Act or regulations issued under the Act. (§1910.1028(b))

(Cadmium) any person authorized by the employer and required by work duties to be present in regulated areas or any person authorized by the OSH Act or regulations issued under it to be in regulated areas. (§1910.1027(b))

(Coke oven emissions) any person specifically authorized by the employer whose duties require the person to enter a regulated area, or any person entering such an area as a designated representative of employees for the purpose of exercising the opportunity to observe monitoring and measuring procedures under paragraph (n) of this Section. (§1910.1029(b))

(Ethylene oxide) any person specifically authorized by the employer whose duties require the person to enter a regulated area, or any person entering such an area as a designated representative of employees for the purpose of exercising the right to observe monitoring and measuring procedures under paragraph (l) of this Section, or any other person authorized by the Act or regulations issued under the Act. (§1910.1047(b))

(Formaldehyde) any person required by work duties to be present in regulated areas, or authorized to do so by the employer, by this Section, or by the OSH Act of 1970. (§1910.1048(b))

(Inorganic arsenic) any person specifically authorized by the employer whose duties require the person to enter a regulated area, or any person entering such an area as a designated representative of employees for the purpose of exercising the right to observe monitoring and measuring procedures under paragraph (e) of this Section. (§1910.1018(b))

(Mechanical power presses) one to whom the authority and responsibility to perform a specific assignment has been given by the employer. (§1910.211(d)(63))

(Methylene chloride) any person specifically authorized by the employer and required by work duties to be present in regulated areas, or any person entering such an area as a designated representative of employees for the purpose of exercising the right to observe monitoring and measuring procedures under paragraph (d) of this Section, or any other person authorized by the OSH Act or regulations issued under the Act. (§1910.1052(b))

(Methylenedianiline) any person specifically authorized by the employer whose duties require the person to enter a regulated area, or any person entering such an area as a designated representative of employees, for the purpose of exercising the right to observe monitoring and measuring procedures under paragraph (o) of this Section, or any other person authorized by the Act or regulations issued under the Act. (§1910.1050(b))

(Vinyl chloride) any person specifically authorized by the employer whose duties require him to enter a regulated area or any person entering such an area as a designated representative of employees for the purpose of exercising an opportunity to observe monitoring and measuring procedures. (§1910.1017(b)(3))

Autoignition temperature minimum temperature required to cause self-sustained combustion, independent of any other source of heat. (§1910.123(d))

Automatic self-acting, operating by its own mechanism when actuated by some impersonal influence, as, for example, a change in current strength, pressure, temperature, or mechanical configuration. (§1910.399)

Automatic circuit recloser self-controlled device for interrupting and reclosing an alternating current circuit with a predetermined sequence of opening and reclosing followed by resetting, hold-closed, or lockout operation. (§1910.269(x))

Automatic crane crane which, when activated, operates through a preset cycle or cycles. (§1910.179(a)(2))

Automatic feeding (See Also "Feeding;" "Manual feeding;" "Semiautomatic feeding") feeding wherein the material or part being processed is placed within or removed from the point of operation by a method or means not requiring action by an operator on each stroke of the press. (§1910.211(d)(27))

Automatic fire detection device device designed to automatically detect the presence of fire by heat, flame, light, smoke or other products of combustion. (§1910.155(c)(5))

Automotive service station that portion of property where flammable liquids used as motor fuels are stored and dispensed from fixed equipment into the fuel tanks of motor vehicles and shall include any facilities available for the sale and service of tires, batteries, and accessories, and for minor automotive maintenance work. Major automotive repairs, painting, body and fender work are excluded. (§1910.106(a)(3))

Auxiliary hoist auxiliary hoist is a supplemental hoisting unit of lighter capacity and usually higher speed than provided for the main hoist. (§1910.179(a)(17))

Axis of rotation vertical axis around which the crane superstructure rotates. (§1910.180(a)(9))

Axle shaft or spindle with which or about which a wheel rotates. On truck- and wheel-mounted cranes it refers to an automotive type of axle assembly including housings, gearing, differential, bearings, and mounting appurtenances. (§1910.180(a)(10))

Axle (bogie) two or more automotive-type axles mounted in tandem in a frame so as to divide the load between the axles and permit vertical oscillation of the wheels. (§1910.180(a)(11))

B

Babbitted fastenings method of providing wire rope attachments in which the ends of the wire strands are bent back and are held in a tapered socket by means of poured molten babbitt metal. (Appendix D to §1910.66(a)(3))

Backcut (felling cut) final cut in a felling operation. (§1910.266(c))

Ballistic nylon nylon fabric of high tensile properties designed to provide protection from lacerations. (§1910.266(c))

Bare conductor See "Conductor"

Barrel volume of 42 U.S. gallons. (§1910.106(a)(33))

Barricade

(Electric power generation, transmission, and distribution) A physical obstruction such as tapes, cones, or A-frame type wood or metal structures intended to provide a warning about and to limit access to a hazardous area. (§1910.269(x))

(Telecommunications) physical obstruction such as tapes, cones, or "A" frame type wood and/or metal structure intended to warn and limit access to a work area. (§1910.268(s)(5))

Barrier

(Servicing multi-piece and single piece rim wheels) fence, wall or other structure or object placed between a single piece rim wheel and an employee during tire inflation, to contain the rim wheel components in the event of the sudden release of the contained air of the single piece rim wheel. (§1910.177(b))

(Telecommunications); (Electric power generation, transmission, and distribution) (Electrical) physical obstruction which is intended to prevent contact with energized lines or equipment, or to prevent unauthorized access to work area. (§1910.268(s)(6)); (§1910.269(x)); (§1910.399)

Base (mounting) base (mounting) is the traveling base or carrier on which the rotating superstructure is mounted such as a car, truck, crawlers, or wheel platform. (§1910.180(a)(12))

Baseline audiogram (See Also "Audiogram") audiogram against which future audiograms are compared. (Appendix I to §1910.95)

Basement story of a building or structure having one-half or more of its height below ground level and to which access for fire fighting purposes is unduly restricted. (§1910.106(a)(4))

Basket derrick basket derrick is a derrick without a boom, similar to a gin pole, with its base supported by ropes attached to corner posts or other parts of the structure. The base is at a lower elevation than its supports. The location of the base of a basket derrick can be changed by varying the length of the rope supports. The top of the pole is secured with multiple reeved guys to position the top of the pole to the desired location by varying the length of the upper guy lines. The load is raised and lowered by ropes through a sheave or block secured to the top of the pole. (§1910.181(a)(3))

Basket hitch sling configuration whereby the sling is passed under the load and has both ends, end attachments, eyes or handles on the hook or a single master link. (§1910.184(b))

Bathroom area including a basin with one or more of the following: a toilet, a tub, or a shower. (§1910.399)

Beehive oven coke oven in which the products of carbonization other than coke are not recovered, but are released into the ambient air. (§1910.1029(b))

Bell enclosed compartment, pressurized (closed bell) or unpressurized (open bell), which allows the diver to be transported to and from the underwater work area and which may be used as a temporary refuge during diving operations. (§1910.402)

Belt pole (sometimes called a belt shipper or shipper pole) device used in shifting belts on and off fixed pulleys on line or countershaft where there are no loose pulleys. (§1910.211(f)(3))

Belt shifter

(Mechanical power-transmission apparatus) device for mechanically shifting belts from tight to loose pulleys or vice versa, or for shifting belts on cones of speed pulleys. (§1910.211(f)(2))

(Textiles) belt shifter is a device for mechanically shifting a belt from one pulley to another. (§1910.262(b)(1))

Belt shifter lock device for positively locking the belt shifter in position while the machine is stopped and the belt is idling on the loose pulleys. (§1910.262(b)(2))

Belt shipper See "Belt pole"

Belts

(Ventilation) all power-driven, flexible, coated bands used for grinding, polishing, or buffing purposes. (§1910.94(b)(1)(ii))

((Machinery and Machine guarding) include all power transmission belts, such as flat belts, round belts, V-belts, etc., unless otherwise specified. (§1910.211(f)(1))

Benzene (C6H6) (CAS Registry No. 71–43–2) liquefied or gaseous benzene. It includes benzene contained in liquid mixtures and the benzene vapors released by these liquids. It does not include trace amounts of unreacted benzene contained in solid materials. (§1910.1028(b))

Binder chain, cable, rope, or other approved material used for binding loads. (§1910.265(b)(3))

Biological hazard or BIOHAZARD those infectious agents presenting a risk of death, injury or illness to employees. (§1910.145(f)(2))

Bite nip point between any two inrunning rolls. (§1910.211(c)(1))

Blacksmith hammers See "Open framehammers or blacksmith hammers"

Blanking or blinding absolute closure of a pipe, line, or duct by the fastening of a solid plate (such as a spectacle blind or a skillet blind) that completely covers the bore and that is capable of withstanding the maximum pressure of the pipe, line, or duct with no leakage beyond the plate. (§1910.146(b))

Blasting agent material or mixture, consisting of a fuel and oxidizer, intended for blasting, not otherwise classified as an explosive and in which none of the ingredients are classified as an explosive, provided that the finished product, as mixed and packaged for use or shipment, cannot be detonated by means of a No. 8 test blasting cap when unconfined. (§1910.109(a)(1))

Blasting cabinet enclosure where the operator stands outside and operates the blasting nozzle through an opening or openings in the enclosure. (§1910.94(a)(1)(v))

Blast cleaning barrel complete enclosure which rotates on an axis, or which has an internal moving tread to tumble the parts, in order to expose various surfaces of the parts to the action of an automatic blast spray. (§1910.94(a)(1)(iii))

Blast cleaning room complete enclosure in which blasting operations are performed and where the operator works inside of the room to operate the blasting nozzle and direct the flow of the abrasive material. (§1910.94(a)(1)(iv))

Blind samples quality control procedure in which the concentration of analyte in the samples should be unknown to the analyst at the time that the analysis is performed. (Appendix F to §1910.1027)

Blinding See "Blanking or blinding"

Block short block of wood, provided with a handle similar to that of a plane and a shoulder at the rear end, which is used for pushing short stock over revolving cutters. (§1910.211(a)(2))

Blood human blood, human blood components, and products made from human blood. (§1910.1030(b))

Bloodborne pathogens pathogenic microorganisms that are present in human blood and can cause disease in humans. These pathogens include, but are not limited to, hepatitis B virus (HBV) and human immunodeficiency virus (HIV). (§1910.1030(b))

Blow down general cleaning of a room or a part of a room by the use of compressed air. (§1910.1043(b))

Blow off use of compressed air for cleaning of short duration and usually for a specific machine or any portion of a machine. (§1910.1043(b))

Body belt (safety belt) strap with means both for securing it about the waist and for attaching it to a lanyard, lifeline, or deceleration device. (Appendix C to §1910.66(b))

Body harness design of straps which may be secured about the employee in a manner to distribute the fall arrest forces over at least the thighs, pelvis, waist, chest and shoulders with means for attaching it to other components of a personal fall arrest system. (Appendix C to §1910.66(b))

Boiling point boiling point of a liquid at a pressure of 14.7 pounds per square inch absolute (p.s.i.a.) (760 mm.). For the purposes of this Section, where an accurate boiling point is unavailable for the material in question, or for mixtures which do not have a constant boiling point, the 10 percent point of a distillation performed in accordance with the Standard Method of Test for Distillation of Petroleum Products, ASTM D–86–62, which is incorporated by reference as specified in §1910.6, may be used as the boiling point of the liquid. (§1910.106(a)(5)); (§1910.119(b))

Boilover expulsion of crude oil (or certain other liquids) from a burning tank. The light fractions of the crude oil burnoff producing a heat wave in the residue, which on reaching a water strata may result in the expulsion of a portion of the contents of the tank in the form of froth. (§1910.106(a)(6))

Bolster plate plate attached to the top of the bed of the press having drilled holes or T-slots for attaching the lower die or die shoe. (§1910.211(d)(3))

Bolt-headers same as an upsetter or forging machine except that the diameter of stock fed into the machine is much smaller, i.e., commonly three-fourths inch or less. (§1910.211(e)(10))

Bond
(Electric power generation, transmission, and distribution) electrical interconnection of conductive parts designed to maintain a common electrical potential. (§1910.269(x))
(Telecommunications); (Power transmission and distribution) electrical connection from one conductive element to another for the purpose of minimizing potential differences or providing suitable conductivity for fault current or for mitigation of leakage current and electrolytic action. (§1910.268(s)(7))

Bonding (Bonded) permanent joining of metallic parts to form an electrically conductive path that ensures electrical continuity and the capacity to conduct safely any current likely to be imposed. (§1910.399)

Bonding jumper conductor that assures the necessary electrical conductivity between metal parts required to be electrically connected. (§1910.399)

Boom (See Also "Angle indicator (Boom);" "Side loading;" "Stiff boom")
(Derricks) timber or metal section or strut, pivoted or hinged at the heel (lower end) at a location fixed in height on a frame or mast or vertical member, and with its point (upper end) supported by chains, ropes, or rods to the upper end of the frame, mast, or vertical member. A rope for raising and lowering the load is reeved through sheaves or a block at the boom point. The length of the boom shall be taken as the straight line distance between the axis of the foot pin and the axis of the boom point sheave pin, or where used, the axis of the upper load block attachment pin. (§1910.181(a)(12))
(Sawmills) logs or timbers fastened together end to end and used to contain floating logs. The term includes enclosed logs. (§1910.265(b)(4))

Boom (crane) member hinged to the front of the rotating superstructure with the outer end supported by ropes leading to a gantry or A-frame and used for supporting the hoisting tackle. (§1910.180(a)(13))

Boom angle angle between the longitudinal centerline of the boom and the horizontal. The boom longitudinal centerline is a straight line between the boom foot pin (heel pin) centerline and boom point sheave pin centerline. (§1910.180(a)(14))

Boom harness block and sheave arrangement on the boom point to which the topping lift cable is reeved for lowering and raising the boom. (§1910.181(a)(13))

Boom hoist boom hoist is a hoist drum and rope reeving system used to raise and lower the boom. The rope system may be all live reeving or a combination of live reeving and pendants. (§1910.180(a)(15))

Boom point boom point is the outward end of the top section of the boom. (§1910.181(a)(14))

Boom stop boom stop is a device used to limit the angle of the boom at the highest position. (§1910.180(a)(16))

Bottom time total elapsed time measured in minutes from the time when the diver leaves the surface in descent to the time that the diver begins ascent. (§1910.402)

Braided wire rope wire rope formed by plaiting component wire ropes. (§1910.184(b))

Brake
(Mechanical power presses) mechanism used on a mechanical power press to stop and/or hold the crankshaft, either directly or through a gear train, when the clutch is disengaged. (§1910.211(d)(2))
(Overhead and gantry cranes) (Crawler, locomotive, and truck cranes) brake is a device used for retarding or stopping motion by friction or power means. (§1910.179(a)(18)); (§1910.180(a)(17))

Brake monitor sensor designed, constructed, and arranged to monitor the effectiveness of the press braking system. (§1910.211(d)(60))

Brake—disc type brake in which the holding effect is obtained by frictional resistance between one or more faces of discs keyed to the rotating member to be held and fixed discs keyed to the stationary or housing member (pressure between the discs being applied axially). (Appendix D to §1910.66(a)(4))

Brake—self-energizing band type essentially undirectional brake in which the holding effect is obtained by the snubbing action of a flexible band wrapped about a cylindrical wheel or drum affixed to the rotating member to be held, the connections and linkages being so arranged that the motion of the brake wheel or drum will act to increase the tension or holding force of the band. (Appendix D to §1910.66(a)(5))

Brake—shoe type brake in which the holding effect is obtained by applying the direct pressure of two or more segmental friction elements held to a stationary member against a cylindrical wheel or drum affixed to the rotating member to be held. (Appendix D to §1910.66(a)(6))

Branch circuit circuit conductors between the final overcurrent device protecting the circuit and the outlets. (§1910.399)

Branch pipe part of an exhaust system piping that is connected directly to the hood or enclosure. (§1910.94(b)(1)(iii))

Breast derrick derrick without boom. The mast consists of two side members spread farther apart at the base than at the top and tied together at top and bottom by rigid members. The mast is prevented from tipping forward by guys connected to its top. The load is raised and lowered by ropes through a sheave or block secured to the top crosspiece. (§1910.181(a)(4))

Bridge that part of a crane consisting of girders, trucks, end ties, footwalks, and drive mechanism which carries the trolley or trolleys. (§1910.179(a)(21))

Bridge conductors See "Conductors, bridge"

Bridge travel crane movement in a direction parallel to the crane runway. (§1910.179(a)(22))

Bridle wire rope sling sling composed of multiple wire rope legs with the top ends gathered in a fitting that goes over the lifting hook. (§1910.184(b))

Bromochlorodifluoromethane See "Halon 1211"

Bromotrifluoromethane See "Halon 1301"

Brow log log placed parallel to a roadway at a landing or dump to protect vehicles while loading or unloading. (§1910.265(b)(5))

Brucite sheet mineral with the composition $Mg(OH)_2$. (Appendix J to §1910.1001)

Buck to cut a felled tree into logs. (§1910.266(c))

Buckle any device for holding the body belt or body harness closed around the employee's body. (Appendix C to §1910.66(b))

Buddy-breathing device accessory to self-contained breathing apparatus which permits a second person to share the same air supply as that of the wearer of the apparatus. (§1910.155(c)(6))

Buddy system system of organizing employees into work groups in such a manner that each employee of the work group is designated to be observed by at least one other employee in the work group. The purpose of the buddy system is to provide rapid assistance to employees in the event of an emergency. (§1910.120(a)(3))

Buffer See "Bumper (Buffer)"

Building structure that stands alone or is cut off from adjoining structures by fire walls with all openings therein protected by approved fire doors. (§1910.399)

Building face roller(s)
(Powered platforms for building maintenance) rotating cylindrical member designed to ride on the face of the building wall to prevent the platform from abrading the face of the building and to assist in stabilizing the platform. (§1910.66(d))
(Powered platforms for building maintenance/Existing installations (Mandatory) specialized form of guide roller designed to contact a portion of the outer face or wall structure of the building, and to assist in stabilizing the operators' platform during vertical travel. (Appendix D to §1910.66(a)(7))

Building/facility owner legal entity, including a lessee, which exercises control over management and record keeping functions relating to a building and/or facility in which activities covered by this Standard take place. (§1910.1001(b))

Building maintenance operations such as window cleaning, caulking, metal polishing, reglazing, and general maintenance on building surfaces. (§1910.66(d))

Bulk oxygen system bulk oxygen system is an assembly of equipment, such as oxygen storage containers, pressure regulators, safety devices, vaporizers, manifolds, and interconnecting piping, which has storage capacity of more than 13,000 cubic feet of oxygen, Normal Temperature and Pressure (NTP), connected in service or ready for service, or more than 25,000 cubic feet of oxygen (NTP) including unconnected reserves on hand at the site. The bulk oxygen system terminates at the point where oxygen at service pressure first enters the supply line. The oxygen containers may be stationary or movable, and the oxygen may be stored as gas or liquid. (§1910.104(b)(1))

Bulk plant that portion of a property where flammable liquids are received by tank vessel, pipelines, tank car, or tank vehicle, and are stored or blended in bulk for the purpose of distributing such liquids by tank vessel, pipeline, tank car, tank vehicle, or container. (§1910.106(a)(7))

Bulk wholesale storage facility bulk terminal or bulk plant where fuel is stored prior to its delivery to wholesale customers. (§1910.1028(b))

Bumper (buffer) energy absorbing device for reducing impact when a moving crane or trolley reaches the end of its permitted travel; or when two moving cranes or trolleys come in contact. (§1910.179(a)(23))

Bunk cross support for a load. (§1910.265(b)(6))

Bunk block See "Chock (Bunk block) (Cheese block)"

Bursting pressure pressure at which a pressure containment device would fail structurally. (§1910.402)

Bus conductor or a group of conductors that serve as a common connection for two or more circuits. (§1910.269(x))

Bushing insulating structure, including a through conductor or providing a passageway for such a conductor, with provision for mounting on a barrier, conducting or otherwise, for the purposes of insulating the conductor from the barrier and conducting current from one side of the barrier to the other. (§1910.269(x))

Business day any Monday through Friday, except those days designated as federal, state, local or company specific holidays. (§1910.1051(b))

Butt bottom of the felled part of a tree. (§1910.266(c))

C

Cab
(Crawler, locomotive, and truck cranes) housing which covers the rotating superstructure machinery and/or operator's station. On truck-crane trucks a separate cab covers the driver's station. (§1910.180(a)(18))
(Overhead and gantry cranes) operator's compartment on a crane. (§1910.179(a)(24))

Cab-operated crane crane controlled by an operator in a cab located on the bridge or trolley. (§1910.179(a)(3))

Cabinet enclosure designed either for surface or flush mounting, and provided with a frame, mat, or trim in which a swinging door or doors are or can be hung. (§1910.399)

Cable (See Also "Service-entrance cable"; "Shielded non metallic-sheath cable")
(Power platforms for building maintenance) conductor, or group of conductors, enclosed in a weatherproof sheath, that may be used to supply electrical power and/or control current for equipment or to provide voice communication circuits. (§1910.66(d))
(Telecommunications); (Electric power generation, transmission, and distribution) conductor with insulation, or a stranded conductor with or without insulation and other coverings (single-conductor cable), or a combination of conductors insulated from one another (multiple-conductor cable). (§1910.268(s)(8)); (§1910.269)(x))

Cable laid endless sling-mechanical joint wire rope sling made endless by joining the ends of a single length of cable laid rope with one or more metallic fittings. (§1910.184(b))

Cable laid grommet-hand tucked endless wire rope sling made from one length of rope wrapped six times around a core formed by hand tucking the ends of the rope inside the six wraps. (§1910.184(b))

Cable laid rope wire rope composed of six wire ropes wrapped around a fiber or wire rope core. (§1910.184(b))

Cable laid rope sling-mechanical joint wire rope sling made from a cable laid rope with eyes fabricated by pressing or swaging one or more metal sleeves over the rope junction. (§1910.184(b))

Cable sheath
(Electric power generation, transmission, and distribution) conductive protective covering applied to cables.
Note: *A cable sheath may consist of multiple layers of which one or more is conductive.* (§1910.269(x))

(Telecommunications) protective covering applied to cables.
Note: *A cable sheath may consist of multiple layers of which one or more is conductive.* (§1910.268(s)(9))

Cable tray system unit or assembly of units or sections and associated fittings forming a rigid structural system used to securely fasten or support cables and raceways. Cable tray systems include ladders, troughs, channels, solid bottom trays, and other similar structures. (§1910.399)

Cable yarding movement of felled trees or logs from the area where they are felled to the landing on a system composed of a cable suspended from spars and/or towers. The trees or logs may be either dragged across the ground on the cable or carried while suspended from the cable. (§1910.266(c))

Cablebus assembly of insulated conductors with fittings and conductor terminations in a completely enclosed, ventilated, protective metal housing. (§1910.399)

Cage enclosure mounted on the side rails of a fixed ladder or fastened to a structure behind the fixed ladder that is designed to surround the climbing space of the ladder. A cage also is called a "cage guard" or "basket guard." (§1910.21(b))

Calender
(Mills and calenders in the rubber and plastics industries) machine equipped with two or more metal rolls revolving in opposite directions and used for continuously sheeting or plying up rubber and plastics compounds and for frictioning or coating materials with rubber and plastics compounds. (§1910.211(c)(2))
(Textiles) calender in essence consists of a set of heavy rollers mounted on vertical side frames and arranged to pass cloth between them. Calenders may have two to ten rollers, or bowls, some of which can be heated. (§1910.262(b)(3))

Canister or cartridge container with a filter, sorbent, or catalyst, or combination of these items, which removes specific contaminants from the air passed through the container. (§1910.134(b))

Cans (drying) hollow cylindrical drums mounted in a frame so they can rotate. They are heated with steam and are used to dry fabrics or yarn as it passes around the perimeter of the can. (§1910.262(b)(5)).

Cant log slabbed on one or more sides. (§1910.265(b)(7))

Cantilever gantry crane gantry or semigantry crane in which the bridge girders or trusses extend transversely beyond the crane runway on one or both sides. (§1910.179(a)(4))

Cap See "Attachment plug (Plug cap) (Cap)"

Capable of being locked out energy isolating device is capable of being locked out if it has a hasp or other means of attachment to which, or through which, a lock can be affixed, or it has a locking mechanism built into it. Other energy isolating devices are capable of being locked out, if lockout can be achieved without the need to dismantle, rebuild, or replace the energy isolating device or permanently alter its energy control capability. (§1910.147(b))

Capacity total volume of the container in standard U.S. gallons. (§1910.111(a)(2)(xi))

Carbon dioxide colorless, odorless, electrically nonconductive inert gas (chemical formula CO_2) that is a medium for extinguishing fires by reducing the concentration of oxygen or fuel vapor in the air to the point where combustion is impossible. (§1910.155(c)(7))

Carbonizing removing of vegetable matter such as burns, straws, etc., from wool by treatment with acid, followed by heat. The undesired matter is reduced to a carbon-like form which may be removed by dusting or shaking. (§1910.262(b)(6))

Carcinogen (See Also "Select carcinogen") substance or a mixture of substances which induce cancer or increase its incidence. Substances and mixtures which have induced benign and malignant tumors in well-performed experimental studies on animals are considered also to be presumed or suspected human carcinogens unless there is strong evidence that the mechanism of tumor formation is not relevant for humans. (Appendix A to §1910.1200(A.6.1))

Card consists of cylinders of various sizes—and in certain cases flats—covered with card clothing and set in relation to each other so that fibers in staple form may be separated into individual relationship. The speed of the cylinders and their direction of rotation varies. The finished product is delivered as a sliver. Cards of different types are: The revolving flat card, the roller-and-clearer card, etc. (§1910.262(b)(7))

Card clothing material with which many of the surfaces of a card are covered; e.g., the cylinder, doffer, etc. It consists of a thick foundation material, usually made of textile fabrics, through which are pressed many fine, closely spaced, specially bent wires. (§1910.262(b)(8))

Carriage wheeled vehicle used for the horizontal movement and support of other equipment. (§1910.66(d))

Carriage (log carriage) framework mounted on wheels which runs on tracks or in grooves in a direction parallel to the face of the saw, and which contains apparatus to hold a log securely and advance it towards the saw. (§1910.265(b)(8))

Carriage dog See "Dog (Carriage dog)"

Carrier
(Walking-working surfaces) track of a ladder safety system that consists of a flexible cable or rigid rail attached to the fixed ladder or immediately adjacent to it. (§1910.21(b)
(Sawmills) industrial truck so designed and constructed that it straddles the load to be transported with mechanisms to pick up the load and support it during transportation. (§1910.265(b)(9))

Cartridge See "Canister or cartridge"

Catastrophic release major uncontrolled emission, fire, or explosion, involving one or more highly hazardous chemicals, that presents serious danger to employees in the workplace. (§1910.119(b))

Cell line assembly of electrically interconnected electrolytic cells supplied by a source of direct current power. (§1910.399)

Cell line attachments and auxiliary equipment include, but are not limited to, auxiliary tanks, process piping, ductwork, structural supports, exposed cell line conductors, conduits and other raceways, pumps, positioning equipment, and cell cutout or bypass electrical devices. Auxiliary equipment also includes tools, welding machines, crucibles, and other portable equipment used for operation and maintenance within the electrolytic cell line working zone. In the cell line working zone, auxiliary equipment includes the exposed conductive surfaces of ungrounded cranes and crane-mounted cell-servicing equipment. (§1910.399)

Cell line working zone space envelope wherein operation or maintenance is normally performed on or in the vicinity of exposed energized surfaces of cellins or their attachments. (§1910.306(h)(2))

Center of gravity point on an object at which all of the object's weight is concentrated. For symmetrical loads, the center of gravity is at the middle of the load. (Appendix A to §1910.178)

Center pivot irrigation machine multi-motored irrigation machine that revolves around a central pivot and employs alignment switches or similar devices to control individual motors. (§1910.399)

Central Stop Dispersion Staining (microscope) dark field microscope technique that images particles using only light refracted by the particle, excluding light that travels through the particle unrefracted. This is usually accomplished with a McCrone objective or other arrangement which places a circular stop with apparent aperture equal to the objective aperture in the back focal plane of the microscope. (Appendix J to §1910.1001)

Certification

(Mechanical power presses) in the case of design certification/validation, that the manufacturer has reviewed and tested the design and manufacture, and in the case of installation certification/validation and annual recertification/revalidation, that the employer has reviewed and tested the installation, and concludes in both cases that the requirements of §1910.217 (a) through (h) and Appendix A have been met. The certifications are made to the validation organization. (§1910.211(d)(64))
(Powered platforms for building maintenance) written, signed and dated statement confirming the performance of a requirement of this Section. (§1910.66(d))

Certification/validation and certify/validate combined process of certification and validation. (§1910.211(d)(66))

Certified equipment is "certified" if it bears a label, tag, or other record of certification that the equipment:
(1) has been tested and found by a nationally recognized testing laboratory to meet nationally recognized standards or to be safe for use in a specified manner; or
(2) is of a kind whose production is periodically inspected by a nationally recognized testing laboratory and is accepted by the laboratory as safe for its intended use. (§1910.399)

Certified industrial hygienist (CIH) one certified in the practice of industrial hygiene by the American Board of Industrial Hygiene. (§1910.1001(b))

CFR means Code of Federal Regulations.

Chamber See "To chamber"

Charts U.S. Department of Labor, Occupational Safety and Health Administration publications entitled "Demounting and Mounting Procedures for Truck/Bus Tires" and "Multi-piece Rim Matching Chart," the National Highway Traffic Safety Administration (NHTSA) publications entitled "Demounting and Mounting Procedures Truck/Bus Tires" and "Multi-piece Rim Matching Chart," or any other poster which contains at least the same instructions, safety precautions and other information contained in the charts that is applicable to the types of wheels being serviced. (§1910.177(b))

Chemical any substance, or mixture of substances. (§1910.1200(c))

Chemical Hygiene Officer employee who is designated by the employer, and who is qualified by training or experience, to provide technical guidance in the development and implementation of the provisions of the Chemical Hygiene Plan. This definition is not intended to place limitations on the position description or job classification that the designated individual shall hold within the employer's organizational structure. (§1910.1450(b))

Chemical Hygiene Plan written program developed and implemented by the employer which sets forth procedures, equipment, personal protective equipment and work practices that
(i) are capable of protecting employees from the health hazards presented by hazardous chemicals used in that particular workplace and
(ii) meets the requirements of paragraph (e) of this Section. (§1910.1450(b))

Chock

(Bunk block) (Cheese block) (Sawmills) wedge that prevents logs or loads from moving. (§1910.265(b)(11))
(Logging operations) block, often wedge shaped, which is used to prevent movement; e.g., a log from rolling, a wheel from turning. (§1910.266(c))

Choked leg condition of material buildup in the bucket elevator that results in the stoppage of material flow and bucket movement. A bucket elevator is not considered choked that has the up-leg partially or fully loaded and has the boot and discharge cleared allowing bucket movement. (§1910.272(c))

Choker sling used to encircle the end of a log for yarding. One end is passed around the load, then through a loop eye, end fitting or other device at the other end of the sling. The end that passed through the end fitting or other device is then hooked to the lifting or pulling machine. (§1910.266(c))

Choker hitch See Also "Female handle (choker)" sling configuration with one end of the sling passing under the load and through an end attachment, handle or eye on the other end of the sling. (§1910.184(b))

Chromium (VI) [hexavalent chromium or Cr(VI)] chromium with a valence of positive six, in any form and in any compound. (§1910.1026(b))

Circuit conductor or system of conductors through which an electric current is intended to flow. (§1910.268(s)(10); (§1910.269(x))

Circuit breaker device designed to open and close a circuit by nonautomatic means and to open the circuit automatically on a predetermined overcurrent without damage to itself when properly applied within its rating. (§1910.399)

Class See "Combustible liquid (Flammable liquids);" Flammable liquid (Flammable liquids)"

Class A fire fire involving ordinary combustible materials such as paper, wood, cloth, and some rubber and plastic materials. (§1910.155(c)(8))

Class B fire fire involving flammable or combustible liquids, flammable gases, greases and similar materials, and some rubber and plastic materials. (§1910.155(c)(9))

Class C fire fire involving energized electrical equipment where safety to the employee requires the use of electrically nonconductive extinguishing media. (§1910.155(c)(10))

Class D fire fire involving combustible metals such as magnesium, titanium, zirconium, sodium, lithium and potassium. (§1910.155(c)(11))

Class I locations those in which flammable gases or vapors are or may be present in the air in quantities sufficient to produce explosive or ignitable mixtures. Class I locations include the following:
(1) Class I, Division 1 location:
(i) in which ignitable concentrations of flammable gases or vapors may exist under normal operating conditions; or
(ii) in which ignitable concentrations of such gases or vapors may exist frequently because of repair or maintenance operations or because of leakage; or
(iii) in which breakdown or faulty operation of equipment or processes might release ignitable concentrations of flammable gases or vapors, and might also cause simultaneous failure of electric equipment.
Note to the definition of "Class I, Division 1:" *This classification usually includes locations where volatile flammable liquids or liquefied flammable gases are transferred from one container to another; interiors of spray booths and areas in the vicinity of spraying and painting operations where volatile flammable solvents are used; locations containing open tanks or vats of volatile flammable liquids; drying rooms or compartments for the evaporation of flammable solvents; locations containing fat and oil extraction equipment using volatile flammable solvents; portions of cleaning and dyeing plants where flammable liquids are used; gas generator rooms and other portions of gas manufacturing plants where flammable gas may escape; inadequately ventilated pump rooms for flammable gas or for volatile flammable liquids; the interiors of refrigerators and freezers in which volatile flammable materials are stored in open, lightly stoppered, or easily ruptured containers; and all other locations where ignitable concentrations of flammable vapors or gases are likely to occur in the course of normal operations.*
(2) Class I, Division 2 location:
(i) in which volatile flammable liquids or flammable gases are handled, processed, or used, but in which the hazardous liquids, vapors, or gases will normally be confined within closed containers or closed systems from which they can escape only in the event of accidental rupture or breakdown of such containers or systems, or as a result of abnormal operation of equipment; or
(ii) in which ignitable concentrations of gases or vapors are normally prevented by positive mechanical ventilation, and which might become hazardous through failure or abnormal operations of the ventilating equipment; or

(iii) that is adjacent to a Class I, Division 1 location, and to which ignitable concentrations of gases or vapors might occasionally be communicated unless such communication is prevented by adequate positive-pressure ventilation from a source of clean air, and effective safeguards against ventilation failure are provided.

Note to the definition of "Class I, Division 2:" *This classification usually includes locations where volatile flammable liquids or flammable gases or vapors are used, but which would become hazardous only in case of an accident or of some unusual operating condition. The quantity of flammable material that might escape in case of accident, the adequacy of ventilating equipment, the total area involved, and the record of the industry or business with respect to explosions or fires are all factors that merit consideration in determining the classification and extent of each location.*

Piping without valves, checks, meters, and similar devices would not ordinarily introduce a hazardous condition even though used for flammable liquids or gases. Locations used for the storage of flammable liquids or liquefied or compressed gases in sealed containers would not normally be considered hazardous unless also subject to other hazardous conditions.

Electrical conduits and their associated enclosures separated from process fluids by a single seal or barrier are classed as a Division 2 location if the outside of the conduit and enclosures is a nonhazardous location.

(3) Class I, Zone 0 location in which one of the following conditions exists:

(i) ignitable concentrations of flammable gases or vapors are present continuously; or

(ii) ignitable concentrations of flammable gases or vapors are present for long periods of time.

Note to the definition of "Class I, Zone 0:" *As a guide in determining when flammable gases or vapors are present continuously or for long periods of time, refer to Recommended Practice for Classification of Locations for Electrical Installations of Petroleum Facilities Classified as Class I, Zone 0, Zone 1 or Zone 2, API RP 505–1997; Electrical Apparatus for Explosive Gas Atmospheres, Classifications of Hazardous Areas, IEC 79–10–1995; Area Classification Code for Petroleum Installations, Model Code—Part 15, Institute for Petroleum; and Electrical Apparatus for Explosive Gas Atmospheres, Classifications of Hazardous (Classified) Locations, ISA S12.24.01–1997. (§1910.399)*

(4) Class I, Zone 1 location in which one of the following conditions exists:

(i) ignitable concentrations of flammable gases or vapors are likely to exist under normal operating conditions; or

(ii) ignitable concentrations of flammable gases or vapors may exist frequently because of repair or maintenance operations or because of leakage; or

(iii) equipment is operated or processes are carried on of such a nature that equipment breakdown or faulty operations could result in the release of ignitable concentrations of flammable gases or vapors and also cause simultaneous failure of electric equipment in a manner that would cause the electric equipment to become a source of ignition; or

(iv) location that is adjacent to a Class I, Zone 0 location from which ignitable concentrations of vapors could be communicated, unless communication is prevented by adequate positive pressure ventilation from a source of clean air and effective safeguards against ventilation failure are provided.

(5) Class I, Zone 2 location in which one of the following conditions exists:

(i) ignitable concentrations of flammable gases or vapors are not likely to occur in normal operation and if they do occur will exist only for a short period; or

(ii) volatile flammable liquids, flammable gases, or flammable vapors are handled, processed, or used, but in which the liquids, gases, or vapors are normally confined within closed containers or closed systems from which they can escape only as a result of accidental rupture or breakdown of the containers or system or as the result of the abnormal operation of the equipment with which the liquids or gases are handled, processed, or used; or

(iii) ignitable concentrations of flammable gases or vapors normally are prevented by positive mechanical ventilation, but which may become hazardous as the result of failure or abnormal operation of the ventilation equipment; or

(iv) location that is adjacent to a Class I, Zone 1 location, from which ignitable concentrations of flammable gases or vapors could be communicated, unless such communication is prevented by adequate positive-pressure ventilation from a source of clean air, and effective safeguards against ventilation failure are provided. (§1910.399)

Class II locations those that are hazardous because of the presence of combustible dust. Class II locations include the following:

(1) Class II, Division 1 location:

(i) in which combustible dust is or may be in suspension in the air under normal operating conditions, in quantities sufficient to produce explosive or ignitable mixtures; or

(ii) where mechanical failure or abnormal operation of machinery or equipment might cause such explosive or ignitable mixtures to be produced, and might also provide a source of ignition through simultaneous failure of electric equipment, through operation of protection devices, or from other causes; or

(iii) in which combustible dusts of an electrically conductive nature may be present.

Note to the definition of "Class II, Division 1:" *This classification may include areas of grain handling and processing plants, starch plants, sugar-pulverizing plants, malting plants, hay-grinding plants, coal pulverizing plants, areas where metal dusts and powders are produced or processed, and other similar locations that contain dust producing machinery and equipment (except where the equipment is dust-tight or vented to the outside). These areas would have combustible dust in the air, under normal operating conditions, in quantities sufficient to produce explosive or ignitable mixtures. Combustible dusts that are electrically nonconductive include dusts produced in the handling and processing of grain and grain products, pulverized sugar and cocoa, dried egg and milk powders, pulverized spices, starch and pastes, potato and wood flour, oil meal from beans and seed, dried hay, and other organic materials which may produce combustible dusts when processed or handled. Dusts containing magnesium or aluminum are particularly hazardous, and the use of extreme caution is necessary to avoid ignition and explosion.*

(2) Class II, Division 2 location where:

(i) combustible dust will not normally be in suspension in the air in quantities sufficient to produce explosive or ignitable mixtures, and dust accumulations will normally be insufficient to interfere with the normal operation of electric equipment or other apparatus, but combustible dust may be in suspension in the air as a result of infrequent malfunctioning of handling or processing equipment; and

(ii) resulting combustible dust accumulations on, in, or in the vicinity of the electric equipment may be sufficient to interfere with the safe dissipation of heat from electric equipment or may be ignitable by abnormal operation or failure of electric equipment.

Note to the definition of "Class II, Division 2:" *This classification includes locations where dangerous concentrations of suspended dust would not be likely, but where dust accumulations might form on or in the vicinity of electric equipment. These areas may contain equipment from which appreciable quantities of dust would escape under abnormal operating conditions or be adjacent to a Class II Division 1 location, as described above, into which an explosive or ignitable concentration of dust may be put into suspension under abnormal operating conditions.* (§1910.399)

Class III locations are those that are hazardous because of the presence of easily ignitable fibers or flyings, but in which such fibers or flyings are not likely to be in suspension in the air in quantities sufficient to produce ignitable mixtures. Class III locations include the following:

(1) Class III, Division 1 location in which easily ignitable fibers or materials producing combustible flyings are handled, manufactured, or used.

Note to the definition of "Class III, Division 1:" *Such locations usually include some parts of rayon, cotton, and other textile mills; combustible fiber manufacturing and processing plants; cotton gins and cotton-seed mills; flax-processing plants; clothing manufacturing plants; woodworking plants, and establishments; and industries involving similar hazardous processes or conditions.*

Easily ignitable fibers and flyings include rayon, cotton (including cotton linters and cotton waste), sisal or henequen, istle, jute, hemp, tow, cocoa fiber, oakum, baled waste kapok, Spanish moss, excelsior, and other materials of similar nature.

(2) Class III, Division 2 location in which easily ignitable fibers are stored or handled, other than in the process of manufacture. (§1910.399)

Classification to identify the relevant data regarding the hazards of a chemical; review those data to ascertain the hazards associated with the chemical; and decide whether the chemical will be classified as hazardous according to the definition of hazardous chemical in this Section. In addition, classification for health and physical hazards includes the determination of the degree of hazard, where appropriate, by comparing the data with the criteria for health and physical hazards. (§1910.1200(c))

Clean air air of such purity that it will not cause harm or discomfort to an individual if it is inhaled for extended periods of time. (§1910.94(a)(1)(vi))

Clean change room room where employees put on clean clothing and/or protective equipment in an environment free of the 13 carcinogens addressed by §1910.1003. The clean change room shall be contiguous to and have an entry from a shower room, when the shower room facilities are otherwise required in §1910.1003. (§1910.1003(b))

Clean-up operation operation where hazardous substances are removed, contained, incinerated, neutralized, stabilized, cleared-up, or in any other manner processed or handled with the ultimate goal of making the site safer for people or the environment. (§1910.120(a)(3))

Clearance distance from any part of the crane to a point of the nearest obstruction (§1910.179(a)(25))

Clearance (between objects) clear distance between two objects measured surface to surface. (§1910.269(x))

Clearance (for work) authorization to perform specified work or permission to enter a restricted area. (§1910.269(x))

Cleavage Fragments mineral particles formed by comminution of minerals, especially those characterized by parallel sides and a moderate aspect ratio (usually less than 20:1). (Appendix B to §1910.1001); (Appendix J to §1910.1001)

Clinical Laboratory workplace where diagnostic or other screening procedures are performed on blood or other potentially infectious materials. (§1910.1030(b))

Closed container container as herein defined, so sealed by means of a lid or other device that neither liquid nor vapor will escape from it at ordinary temperatures. (§1910.106(a)(9))

Closed system operation involving a carcinogen addressed by §1910.1003 where containment prevents the release of the material into regulated areas, non-regulated areas, or the external environment. (§1910.1003(b))

Closed type cup-shaped device, open at the top in the direction of travel of the step for which it is to be used, and closed at the bottom, into which the passenger may place his fingers. (§1910.68(a)(3))

Clutch (See Also "Continuous;" "Full revolution clutch;" "Part revolution clutch")
(Crawler locomotive and truck cranes) clutch is a friction, electromagnetic, hydraulic, pneumatic, or positive mechanical device for engagement or disengagement of power. (§1910.180(a)(19))
(Mechanical power presses) coupling mechanism used on a mechanical power press to couple the flywheel to the crankshaft, either directly or through a gear train. (§1910.211(d)(4))

Coating elastomer or other suitable material applied to a sling or to a sling component to impart desirable properties. (§1910.184(b))

Code Boiler and Pressure Vessel Code, Section VIII, Unfired Pressure Vessels of the American Society of Mechanical Engineers (ASME)—1968. (§1910.111(a)(2)(iii))

Coefficient of Variation ratio of the standard deviation of a set of measurements to the mean (arithmetic or geometric) of the measurements. (Appendix F to §1910.1027)

Coke oven retort in which coke is produced by the destructive distillation or carbonization of coal. (§1910.1029(b))

Coke oven battery structure containing a number of slot-type coke ovens. (§1910.1029(b))

Coke oven emissions benzene-soluble fraction of total particulate matter present during the destructive distillation or carbonization of coal for the production of coke. (§1910.1029(b))

Cold deck pile of logs stored for future removal. (§1910.265(b)(12))

Collector ring assembly of slip rings for transferring electric energy from a stationary to a rotating member. (§1910.399)

Collectors current contacting devices for collecting current from runway or bridge conductors. (§1910.179(a)(26))

Comber machine for combing fibers of cotton, wool, etc. The essential parts are a device for feeding forward a fringe of fibers at regular intervals and an arrangement of combs or pins which, at the right time, pass through the fringe. All tangled fibers, short fibers, and neps are removed and the long fibers are laid parallel. (§1910.262(b)(9))

Combination cable cable having both steel structural members capable of supporting the platform, and copper or other electrical conductors insulated from each other and the structural members by nonconductive barriers. (§1910.66(d))

Combination ladder portable ladder that can be used as a stepladder, extension ladder, trestle ladder, or stairway ladder. The components of a combination ladder also may be used separately as a single ladder. (§1910.21(b))

Combing machinery general classification, including combers, sliver lap machines, ribbon lap machines and gill boxes, but excluding cards (§1910.262(b)(10))

Combustible liquid (See Also "Flammable liquid")
(Dipping and coating operations) means a liquid having a flash point of 100 °F (37.8 °C) or above. (§1910.123(d))
(Flammable liquids) any liquid having a flashpoint at or below 199.4 °F (93 °C). Flammable liquids are divided into four categories as follows:
(i) Category 1 shall include liquids having flashpoints below 73.4 °F (23 °C) and having a boiling point at or below 95 °F (35 °C);
(ii) Category 2 shall include liquids having flashpoints below 73.4 °F (23 °C) and having a boiling point above 95 °F (35 °C);
(iii) Category 3 shall include liquids having flashpoints at or above 73.4 °F (23 °C) and at or below 140 °F (60 °C). When a Category 3 liquid with a flashpoint at or above 100 °F (37.8 °C) is heated for use to within 30 °F (16.7 °C) of its flashpoint, it shall be handled in accordance with the requirements for a Category 3 liquid with a flashpoint below 100 °F (37.8 °C);
(iv) Category 4 shall include liquids having flashpoints above 140 °F (60 °C) and at or below 199.4 °F (93 °C). When a Category 4 flammable liquid is heated for use to within 30 °F (16.7 °C) of its flashpoint, it shall be handled in accordance with the requirements for a Category 3 liquid with a flashpoint at or above 100 °F (37.8 °C);
When liquid with a flashpoint greater than 199.4 °F (93 °C) is heated for use to within 30 °F (16.7 °C) of its flashpoint, it shall be handled in accordance with the requirements for a Category 4 flammable liquid. (§1910.106(a)(19))

Commerce trade, traffic, commerce, transportation, or communication among the several States, or between a State and any place outside thereof, or within the District of Columbia, or a possession of the United States (other than the Trust Territory of the Pacific Islands), or between points in the same State but through a point outside thereof; (§1910.2(e))

Commercial account arrangement whereby a retail distributor sells hazardous chemicals to an employer, generally in large quantities over time and/or at costs that are below the regular retail price. (§1910.1200(c))

Common name any designation or identification such as code name, code number, trade name, brand name or generic name used to identify a chemical other than by its chemical name. (§1910.1200(c))

Communication lines
(Telecommunications) conductors and their supporting or containing structures for telephone, telegraph, railroad signal, data, clock, fire, police-alarm, community television antenna and other systems which are used for public or private signal or communication service, and which operate at potentials not exceeding 400 volts to ground or 750 volts between any two points of the circuit, and the transmitted power of which does not exceed 150 watts. When communications lines operate at less than 150 volts to ground, no limit is placed on the capacity of the system. Specifically designed communications cables may include communication circuits not complying with the preceding limitations, where such circuits are also used incidentally to supply power to communication equipment. (§1910.268)(s)(11))
(Electric power generation, transmission and distribution) (See Lines, Communication lines) (§1910.269(x))

Competent possessing the skills, knowledge, experience, and judgment to perform assigned tasks or activities satisfactorily as determined by the employer. (Appendix E to §1910.120)

Competent person
(Electrical) one who is capable of identifying existing and predictable hazards in the surroundings or working conditions that are unsanitary, hazardous, or dangerous to employees and who has authorization to take prompt corrective measures to eliminate them. (§1910.399)
(Powered platforms for building maintenance) person who, because of training and experience, is capable of identifying hazardous or dangerous conditions in powered platform installations and of training employees to identify such conditions. (§1910.66(d))
(Powered platforms for building maintenance/Personal fall arrest system) person who is capable of identifying hazardous or dangerous conditions in the personal fall arrest system or any component thereof, as well as in their application and use with related equipment. (Appendix C to §1910.66(b))

Complete Blood Count (CBC) laboratory tests performed on whole blood specimens and includes the following: White blood cell count (WBC), hematocrit (Hct), red blood cell count (RBC), hemoglobin (Hgb), differential count of white blood cells, red blood cell morphology, red blood cell indices, and platelet count. (§1910.1051(b))

Compliance Safety and Health Officer person authorized by the Occupational Safety and Health Administration, U.S. Department of Labor, to conduct inspections. (§1903.22(d))

Compliance Samples samples from exposed workers sent to a participating laboratory for analysis. (Appendix F to §1910.1027)

Concealed (See Also "Accessible (As applied to wiring methods)") rendered inaccessible by the structure or finish of the building. Wires in concealed raceways are considered concealed, even though they may become accessible by withdrawing them. (§1910.399)

Concurrent acting in conjunction, and is used to describe a situation wherein two or more controls exist in an operated condition at the same time. (§1910.211(d)(8))

Conductor (See Also "Service-entrance conductors, overhead system;" "Service-entrance conductors, underground system")
(Electrical)
(1) Bare conductor having no covering or electrical insulation whatsoever.
(2) Covered conductor encased within material of composition or thickness that is not recognized as electrical insulation.
(3) Insulated conductor encased within material of composition and thickness that is recognized as electrical insulation (§1910.399)
(Telecommunications); (Electric power generation, transmission and distribution) material, usually in the form of a wire, cable, or bus bar, suitable for carrying an electric current. (§1910.268(s)(12)); (§1910.269(x))

Conductors, bridge electrical conductors located along the bridge structure of a crane to provide power to the trolley. (§1910.179(a)(27))

Conductors, runway (main) electrical conductors located along a crane runway to provide power to the crane. (§1910.179(a)(28))

Conduit body separate portion of a conduit or tubing system that provides access through one or more removable covers to the interior of the system at a junction of two or more sections of the system or at a terminal point of the system. Boxes such as FS and FD or larger cast or sheet metal boxes are not classified as conduit bodies. (§1910.399)

Confined space space that:
(1) is large enough and so configured that an employee can bodily enter and perform assigned work; and
(2) has limited or restricted means for entry or exit (for example, tanks, vessels, silos, storage bins, hoppers, vaults, and pits are spaces that may have limited means of entry.); and
(3) is not designed for continuous employee occupancy. (§1910.146(b))

Connector device which is used to couple (connect) parts of the system together. It may be an independent component of the system (such as a carabiner), or an integral component of part of the system (such as a buckle or dee-ring sewn into a body belt or body harness, or a snap-hook spliced or sewn to a lanyard or self-retracting lanyard). (Appendix C to §1910.66(b))

Container(s)
(Anhydrous ammonia) includes all vessels, tanks, cylinders, or spheres used for transportation, storage, or application of anhydrous ammonia. (§1910.111(a)(2)(iv))
(Benzene) any barrel, bottle, can, cylinder, drum, reaction vessel, storage tank, or the like, but does not include piping systems. (§1910.1028(b))
(Flammable liquids) any can, barrel, or drum. (§1910.106(a)(34))
(Hazard communication) any bag, barrel, bottle, box, can, cylinder, drum, reaction vessel, storage tank, or the like that contains a hazardous chemical. For purposes of this Section, pipes or piping systems, and engines, fuel tanks, or other operating systems in a vehicle, are not considered to be containers. (§1910.1200(c))
(Liquefied petroleum gases) all vessels, such as tanks, cylinders, or drums, used for transportation or storing liquefied petroleum gases. (§1910.110(a)(4))
(Methylenedianiline) any barrel, bottle, can, cylinder, drum, reaction vessel, storage tank, commercial packaging or the like, but does not include piping systems. (§1910.1050(b))

Container assembly assembly consisting essentially of the container and fittings for all container openings, including shutoff valves, excess flow valves, liquid-level gaging devices, safety relief devices, and protective housing. (§1910.110(a)(3))

Contaminated presence or the reasonably anticipated presence of blood or other potentially infectious materials on an item or surface. (§1910.1030(b))

Contaminated Laundry laundry which has been soiled with blood or other potentially infectious materials or may contain sharps. (§1910.1030(b))

Contaminated Sharps any contaminated object that can penetrate the skin including, but not limited to, needles, scalpels, broken glass, broken capillary tubes, and exposed ends of dental wires. (§1910.1030(b))

Continuous (See Also "Clutch") uninterrupted multiple strokes of the slide without intervening stops (or other clutch control action) at the end of individual strokes. (§1910.211(d)(9))

Continuous bleaching ranges See "Ranges (Bleaching continuous)"

Continuous pressure
(Powered platforms for building maintenance) need for constant manual actuation for a control to function. (§1910.66(d))
(Powered platforms for building maintenance/Existing installations (mandatory)) operation by means of buttons or switches, any one of which may be used to control the movement of the working platform or roof car, only as long as the button or switch is manually maintained in the actuating position. (Appendix D to §1910.66(a)(8))

Contract employer employer, other than a host employer, that performs work covered by this Section under contract. (§1910.269(x))

Control
(Powered platforms for building maintenance/Existing installations (mandatory)) mechanism used to regulate or guide the operation of the equipment. (§1910.66(d))
(Powered platforms for building maintenance) system governing starting, stopping, direction, acceleration, speed, and retardation of moving members. (Appendix D to §1910.66(a)(9))

Control braking method of controlling crane motor speed when it is in an overhauling condition. (§1910.179(a)(29))

Control Charts graphic representations of the results for quality control samples being analyzed by a participating laboratory. (Appendix F to §1910.1027)

Control Limits statistical limits which define when an analytic procedure exceeds acceptable parameters; control limits provide a method of assessing the accuracy of analysts, laboratories, and discrete analytic runs. (Appendix F to §1910.1027)

Control samples quality control samples. (Appendix F to §1910.1027)

Control system sensors, manual input and mode selection elements, interlocking and decision-making circuitry, and output elements to the press operating mechanism. (§1910.211(d)(59))

Controller
(Electrical) device or group of devices that serves to govern, in some predetermined manner, the electric power delivered to the apparatus to which it is connected. (§1910.399)
(Powered platforms for building maintenance) device or group of devices, usually contained in a single enclosure, which serves to control in some predetermined manner the apparatus to which it is connected. (Appendix D to §1910.66(a)(10))

Controller spring return controller which, when released, will return automatically to a neutral position. (§1910.179(a)(34))

Corrosive substance chemical that produces destruction of skin tissue, namely, visible necrosis through the epidermis and into the dermis, in at least 1 of 3 tested animals after exposure up to a 4-hour duration. Corrosive reactions are typified by ulcers, bleeding, bloody scabs and, by the end of observation at 14 days, by discoloration due to blanching of the skin, complete areas of alopecia and scars. Histopathology should be considered to discern questionable lesions. (Appendix A to §1910.1200(A.2.2.1.1))

Cotton dust dust present in the air during the handling or processing of cotton, which may contain a mixture of many substances including ground up plant matter, fiber, bacteria, fungi, soil, pesticides, non-cotton plant matter and other contaminants which may have accumulated with the cotton during the growing, harvesting and subsequent processing or storage periods. Any dust present during the handling and processing of cotton through the weaving or knitting of fabrics, and dust present in other operations or manufacturing processes using raw or waste cotton fibers or cotton fiber by-products from textile mills are considered cotton dust within this definition. Lubricating oil mist associated with weaving operations is not considered cotton dust. (§1910.1043(b))

Counterbalance mechanism that is used to balance or support the weight of the connecting rods, slide, and slide attachments. (§1910.211(d)(10))

Countertorque method of control by which the power to the motor is reversed to develop torque in the opposite direction. (§1910.179(a)(30))

Counterweight
(Crawler, locomotive, and truck cranes) is a weight used to supplement the weight of the machine in providing stability for lifting working loads. (§1910.180(a)(20))
(Powered industrial trucks/Stability of powered industrial truck (non-mandatory)) is the weight that is built into the truck's basic structure and is used to offset the load's weight and to maximize the vehicle's resistance to tipping over. (Appendix A to §1910.178)

Covered conductor (See Also "Conductor") conductor covered with a dielectric having no rated insulating strength or having a rated insulating strength less than the voltage of the circuit in which the conductor is used. (§1910.269(x))

Cradle movable fixture, upon which the part to be ground or polished is placed. (§1910.94(b)(1)(iv))

Crane See Also "Automatic crane;" Cantilever gantry crane;" "Crawler crane;" "Floor-operated crane;" "Gantry crane;" "Hot metal handling crane;" "Load ratings;" "Locomotive crane;" "Main switch;" "Overhead crane;" "Power-operated crane;" "Pulpit-operated crane:" "Remote-operated crane;" "Semigantry crane:" "Standby crane;" "Storage bridge crane;" "Transit;" "Truck crane;" "Wall crane;" "Wheel mounted crane (Wagon crane)". machine for lifting and lowering a load and moving it horizontally, with the hoisting mechanism an integral part of the machine. Cranes whether fixed or mobile are driven manually or by power. (§1910.179(a)(1))

Crawler crane crawler crane consists of a rotating superstructure with power plant, operating machinery, and boom, mounted on a base, equipped with crawler treads for travel. Its function is to hoist and swing loads at various radii. (§1910.180(a)(1))

Criterion sound level sound level of 90 decibels. (Appendix I to §1910.95)

Cross rod wire used to join spirals of metal mesh to form a complete fabric. (See Fig. N–184–2.) (§1910.184(b))

Crotch lines two short lines attached to a hoisting line by a ring or shackle, the lower ends being attached to loading hooks. (§1910.265(b)(13))

Crude petroleum hydrocarbon mixtures that have a flash point below 150 °F and which have not been processed in a refinery. (§1910.106(a)(10))

Current-carrying part conducting part intended to be connected in an electric circuit to a source of voltage. Non-current-carrying parts are those not intended to be so connected. (§1910.269(x))

Cutout (Over 600 volts, nominal.) assembly of a fuse support with either a fuseholder, fuse carrier, or disconnecting blade. The fuseholder or fuse carrier may include a conducting element (fuse link), or may act as the disconnecting blade by the inclusion of a nonfusible member. (§1910.399)

Cutout box (See Also "Cabinet") enclosure designed for surface mounting and having swinging doors or covers secured directly to and telescoping with the walls of the box proper. (§1910.399)

Cutter (rotary staple) machine consisting of one or more rotary blades used for the purpose of cutting textile fibers into staple lengths. (§1910.262(b)(11))

Cutting off wheels wheels having diameter thickness and hole size dimensions and are subject to all limitations of mounting and use listed for type 1 wheels, the definition in subparagraph (1) of this paragraph and paragraph (d) of §1910.215. They may be steel centered, diamond abrasive or organic bonded abrasive of the plain or reinforced type.

(i) Limitation: Cutting off wheels are recommended only for use on specially designed and fully guarded machines and are subject to the following maximum thickness and hole size limitations.

Wheel diameter	Max. thickness (inch)
6 inch and smaller	3⁄16
Larger than 6 inches to 12 inches	¼
Larger than 12 inches to 23 inches	⅜
Larger than 23 inches	½

(ii) Maximum hole size for cutting-off wheels should not be larger than ¼ wheel diameter. (§1910.211(b)(13))

Cylinder

(Storage and handling of Anhydrous ammonia) container of 1,000 pounds of water capacity or less constructed in accordance with Department of Transportation specifications. (§1910.111(a)(2)(ii))

(Commercial Diving Operations) A pressure vessel for the storage of gases. (§1910.402)

D

Damp location See "Location"

Danger tree standing tree that presents a hazard to employees due to conditions such as, but not limited to, deterioration or physical damage to the root system, trunk, stem or limbs, and the direction and lean of the tree. (§1910.266(c))

Dangerous equipment equipment, such as vats, tanks, electrical equipment, machinery, equipment or machinery with protruding parts, or other similar units, that, because of their function or form, may harm an employee who falls into or onto the equipment. (§1910.21(b))

Data quality See "Quality or data quality"

Davit device, used singly or in pairs, for suspending a powered platform from work, storage and rigging locations on the building being serviced. Unlike outriggers, a davit reacts its operating load into a single roof socket or carriage attachment. (§1910.66(d))

Day any part of a calendar day. (§1910.1028(b)); (§1910.1051(b))

DBCP 1,2-dibromo-3-chloropropane, Chemical Abstracts Service Registry Number 96–12–8, and includes all forms of DBCP. (§1910.1044(b))

Dead front without live parts exposed to a person on the operating side of the equipment (§1910.399)

Debark to remove bark from trees or logs. (§1910.266(c))

Deceleration device any mechanism, such as a rope grab, ripstitch lanyard, specially woven lanyard, tearing or deforming lanyard, or automatic self retracting-lifeline/lanyard, which serves to dissipate a substantial amount of energy during a fall arrest, or otherwise limits the energy imposed on an employee during fall arrest. (Appendix C to §1910.66(b))

Deceleration distance additional vertical distance a falling employee travels, excluding lifeline elongation and free fall distance, before stopping, from the point at which the deceleration device begins to operate. It is measured as the distance between the location of an employee's body belt or body harness attachment point at the moment of activation (at the onset of fall arrest forces) of the deceleration device during a fall, and the location of that attachment point after the employee comes to a full stop. (Appendix C to §1910.66(b))

Decibel (dB) unit of measurement of sound level. (Appendix I to §1910.95)

Deck A stack of trees or logs. (§1910.266(c))

Decompression chamber pressure vessel for human occupancy such as a surface decompression chamber, closed bell, or deep diving system used to decompress divers and to treat decompression sickness. (§1910.402)

Decompression sickness condition with a variety of symptoms which may result from gas or bubbles in the tissues of divers after pressure reduction. (§1910.402)

Decompression table profile or set of profiles of depth-time relationships for ascent rates and breathing mixtures to be followed after a specific depth-time exposure or exposures. (§1910.402)

Decontamination (See Also "Clean change room")

(13 Carcinogens) inactivation of a carcinogen addressed by this Section or its safe disposal. (§1910.1003(b))

(Acrylonitrile) treatment of materials and surfaces by water washdown, ventilation, or other means, to assure that the materials will not expose employees to airborne concentrations of AN above 1 means the Director, National Institute for Occupational Safety and Health, U.S. Department of Health and Human Services, or designee. (§1910.1045(b))

(Bloodborne pathogens) use of physical or chemical means to remove, inactivate, or destroy bloodborne pathogens on a surface or item to the point where they are no longer capable of transmitting infectious particles and the surface or item is rendered safe for handling, use, or disposal. (§1910.1030(b))

(Hazardous waste operations and emergency response) removal of hazardous substances from employees and their equipment to the extent necessary to preclude the occurrence of foreseeable adverse health effects. (§1910.120(a)(3))

Deenergized free from any electrical connection to a source of potential difference and from electrical charge; not having a potential different from that of the earth.

***Note:** The term is used only with reference to current-carrying parts, which are sometimes energized (alive).* (§1910.269(x)); (§1910.399)

Demand respirator atmosphere-supplying respirator that admits breathing air to the facepiece only when a negative pressure is created inside the facepiece by inhalation. (§1910.134(b))

Demonstration showing by actual use of equipment or procedures. (Appendix E to §1910.120)

Dermal exposure to MDA occurs where employees are engaged in the handling, application or use of mixtures or materials containing MDA, with any of the following non-airborne forms of MDA:

(i) liquid, powdered, granular, or flaked mixtures containing MDA in concentrations greater than 0.1% by weight or volume; and

(ii) materials other than "finished articles" containing MDA in concentrations greater than 0.1% by weight or volume. (§1910.1050(b))

Derrick derrick is an apparatus consisting of a mast or equivalent member held at the head by guys or braces, with or without a boom, for use with a hoisting mechanism and operating ropes. (§1910.181(a)(1))

Derrick bullwheel horizontal ring or wheel, fastened to the foot of a derrick, for the purpose of turning the derrick by means of ropes leading from this wheel to a powered drum. (§1910.181(a)(15))

Design pressure identical to the term Maximum Allowable Working Pressure used in the Code. (§1910.111(a)(2)(vi))

Designated selected or assigned by the employer or the employer's representative as being qualified to perform specific duties. (§1910.179(a)(35)); (§1910.180(a)(21)); (§1910.181(a)(16)); (§1910.184(b))

Designated area
(Walking-working surfaces) distinct portion of a walking-working surface delineated by a warning line in which employees may perform work without additional fall protection . (§1910.21(b))
(Occupational exposure to hazardous chemicals in laboratories) area which may be used for work with "select carcinogens," reproductive toxins or substances which have a high degree of acute toxicity. A designated area may be the entire laboratory, an area of a laboratory or a device such as a laboratory hood. (§1910.1450(b))

Designated employee (designated person) employee (or person) who is designated by the employer to perform specific duties under the terms of §1910.269 and who is knowledgeable in the construction and operation of the equipment and the hazards involved. (§1910.269(x))

Designated person employee who has the requisite knowledge, training and experience to perform specific duties. (§1910.266(c))

Designated representative
(Access to employees exposure and medical records) any individual or organization to whom an employee gives written authorization to exercise a right of access. For the purposes of access to employee exposure records and analyses using exposure or medical records, a recognized or certified collective bargaining agent shall be treated automatically as a designated representative without regard to written employee authorization. (§1910.1020(c)(3))
(Hazard communication) any individual or organization to whom an employee gives written authorization to exercise such employee's rights under this Section. A recognized or certified collective bargaining agent shall be treated automatically as a designated representative without regard to written employee authorization. (§1910.1200(c))

Detection limit number of fibers necessary to be 95% certain that the result is greater than zero. (Appendix B to §1910.1001)

Device
(Electrical) unit of an electrical system which is intended to carry but not utilize electric energy. (§1910.399)
(Mechanical power presses) means a press control or attachment that:
(i) restrains the operator from inadvertently reaching into the point of operation, or
(ii) prevents normal press operation if the operator's hands are inadvertently within the point of operation, or
(iii) automatically withdraws the operator's hands if the operator's hands are inadvertently within the point of operation as the dies close, or
(iv) prevents the initiation of a stroke, or stops of stroke in progress, when there is an intrusion through the sensing field by any part of the operator's body or by any other object. (§1910.211(d)(11))

Die tooling used in a press for cutting or forming material. An upper and a lower die make a complete set. (§1910.211(d)(18))

Die builder any person who builds dies for power presses. (§1910.211(d)(19))

Die enclosure guard enclosure attached to the die shoe or stripper, or both, in a fixed position. (§1910.211(d)(33))

Die set tool holder held in alignment by guide posts and bushings and consisting of a lower shoe, an upper shoe or punch holder, and guide posts and bushings. (§1910.211(d)(20))

Die setter individual who places or removes dies in or from mechanical power presses, and who, as a part of his duties, makes the necessary adjustments to cause the tooling to function properly and safely. (§1910.211(d)(21))

Die setting process of placing or removing dies in or from a mechanical power press, and the process of adjusting the dies, other tooling and safeguarding means to cause them to function properly and safely. (§1910.211(d)(22))

Die shoe plate or block upon which a die holder is mounted. A die shoe functions primarily as a base for the complete die assembly, and, when used, is bolted or clamped to the bolster plate or the face of slide. (§1910.211(d)(23))

Dielectric heating heating of a nominally insulating material due to its own dielectric losses when the material is placed in a varying electric field. (§1910.399)

Differential Counting
(Detailed procedures for sampling and analysis of Asbestos (Non-mandatory)): term applied to the practice of excluding certain kinds of fibers from the fiber count because they do not appear to be asbestos. (Appendix B to §1910.1001)
(Polarized Light Microscopy of Asbestos (Non-mandatory)) term applied to the practice of excluding certain kinds of fibers from a phase contrast asbestos count because they are not asbestos. (Appendix J to §1910.1001)

Dip tank container holding a liquid other than water and that is used for dipping or coating. An object may be immersed (or partially immersed) in a dip tank or it may be suspended in a vapor coming from the tank. (§1910.123(d))

Direct drive type of driving arrangement wherein no clutch is used; coupling and decoupling of the driving torque is accomplished by energization and deenergization of a motor. Even though not employing a clutch, direct drives match the operational characteristics of "part revolution clutches" because the driving power may be disengaged during the stroke of the press. (§1910.211(d)(7))

Director Director of the National Institute for Occupational Safety and Health (NIOSH), U.S. Department of Health and Human Services, or designee. (§1910.1001(b)); (§1910.1003(b)); (§1910.1017(b)(4)); (§1910.1018(b)); (§1910.1025(b)); (§1910.1026(b)); (§1910.1027(b)); (§1910.1028(b)); (§1910.1029(b)); (§1910.1030(b)); (§1910.1043(b)); (§1910.1044(b)); (§1910.1047(b)); (§1910.1048(b)); (§1910.1050(b)); (§1910.1051(b)); (§1910.1052(b)); (§1910.1053(b)); (§1910.1200(c))

Disc wheels. all power-driven rotatable discs faced with abrasive materials, artificial or natural, and used for grinding or polishing on the side of the assembled disc. (§1910.94(b)(1)(v))

Disconnecting means device, or group of devices, or other means by which the conductors of a circuit can be disconnected from their source of supply. (§1910.399)

Disconnecting (or Isolating) switch (Over 600 volts, nominal.) mechanical switching device used for isolating a circuit or equipment from a source of power. (§1910.399)

Disposal (See Also "Clean change room") safe removal of the carcinogens addressed by this Section from the work environment. (§1910.1003(b))

Distillery plant or that portion of a plant where flammable liquids produced by fermentation are concentrated, and where the concentrated products may also be mixed, stored, or packaged. (§1910.106(a)(11))

Distributor business, other than a chemical manufacturer or importer, which supplies hazardous chemicals to other distributors or to employers. (§1910.1200(c))

Dive location surface or vessel from which a diving operation is conducted. (§1910.402)

Dive-guiding operations leading groups of sports divers, who use an open-circuit, semi-closed-circuit, or closed-circuit self-contained underwater breathing apparatus, to local undersea diving locations for recreational purposes. (§1910.402)

Dive-location reserve breathing gas supply system of air or mixed-gas (as appropriate) at the dive location which is independent of the primary supply system and sufficient to support divers during the planned decompression. (§1910.402)

Dive team divers and support employees involved in a diving operation, including the designated person-in-charge. (§1910.402)

Diver employee working in water using underwater apparatus which supplies compressed breathing gas at the ambient pressure. (§1910.402)

Diver-carried reserve breathing gas diver-carried supply of air or mixed gas (as appropriate) sufficient under standard operating conditions to allow the diver to reach the surface, or another source of breathing gas, or to be reached by a standby diver. (§1910.402)

Diving mode type of diving requiring specific equipment, procedures and techniques (SCUBA, surface-supplied air, or mixed gas). (§1910.402)

Dockboard portable or fixed device that spans a gap or compensates for a difference in elevation between a loading platform and a transport vehicle. Dockboards include, but are not limited to, bridge plates, dock plates, and dock levelers. (§1910.21(b))

Dog (carriage dog) steel tooth, one or more of which are attached to each carriage knee to hold log firmly in place on carriage. (§1910.265(b)(14))

Domino felling partial cutting of multiple trees which are left standing and then pushed over with a pusher tree. (§1910.266(c))

Dose (See Also "Rem;" "Rad") quantity of ionizing radiation absorbed, per unit of mass, by the body or by any portion of the body. When the provisions in §1910.1096 specify a dose during a period of time, the dose is the total quantity of radiation absorbed, per unit of mass, by the body or by any portion of the body during such period of time. Several different units of dose are in current use. Definitions of units used in this Section are set forth in paragraphs §1910.1096(a)(6) and §1910.1096 (7) of this Section. (§1910.1096(a)(5))

DOT U.S. Department of Transportation. (§1910.110(a)(5)); (§1910.111(a)(2)(v))

Dote See "Decay"

DOT container container constructed in accordance with the applicable requirements of 49 CFR chapter 1. (§1910.110(a)(6))

DOT cylinders cylinders meeting the requirements of 49 CFR chapter I. (§1910.110(a)(19))

DOT Specifications regulations of the Department of Transportation published in 49 CFR chapter I. (§1910.103(a)(1)(v)); (§1910.109(a)(19)); (§1910.110(a)(16)); (§1910.111(a)(2)(xii))

DOT regulations See "DOT Specifications"

Double block and bleed closure of a line, duct, or pipe by closing and locking or tagging two in-line valves and by opening and locking or tagging a drain or vent valve in the line between the two closed valves. (§1910.146(b))

Drag brake brake which provides retarding force without external control. (§1910.179(a)(19))

Drag saw power-driven, reciprocating crosscut saw mounted on suitable frame and used for bucking logs. (§1910.265(b)(15))

Drift point drift point means a point on a travel motion controller which releases the brake while the motor is not energized. This allows for coasting before the brake is set. (§1910.179(a)(36))

Drum drum is the cylindrical members around which ropes are wound for raising and lowering the load or boom. (§1910.179(a)(37)) (§1910.180(a)(22))

Dry chemical extinguishing agent composed of very small particles of chemicals such as, but not limited to, sodium bicarbonate, potassium bicarbonate, urea-based potassium bicarbonate, potassium chloride, or monoammonium phosphate supplemented by special treatment to provide resistance to packing and moisture absorption (caking) as well as to provide proper flow capabilities. Dry chemical does not include dry powders. (§1910.155(c)(12))

Dry location See "Location."

Dry powder compound used to extinguish or control Class D fires. (§1910.155(c)(13))

Dry spray booth spray booth not equipped with a water washing system as described in paragraph (a)(4) of this Section. A dry spray booth may be equipped with

(i) distribution or baffle plates to promote an even flow of air through the booth or cause the deposit of overspray before it enters the exhaust duct; or

(ii) overspray dry filters to minimize dusts; or

(iii) overspray dry filters to minimize dusts or residues entering exhaust ducts; or

(iv) overspray dry filter rolls designed to minimize dusts or residues entering exhaust ducts; or

(v) where dry powders are being sprayed, with powder collection systems so arranged in the exhaust to capture oversprayed material. (§1910.107(a)(5))

Dust collector device or combination of devices for separating dust from the air handled by an exhaust ventilation system. (§1910.94(a)(1)(vii))

Dynamic method of controlling crane motor speeds when in the overhauling condition to provide a retarding force. (§1910.179(a)(31))

Dynamic (loading) loads introduced into the machine or its components by forces in motion. (§1910.180(a)(23))

E

Education process of imparting knowledge or skill through systematic instruction. It does not require formal classroom instruction. (§1910.155(c)(14))

Effectively grounded intentionally connected to earth through a ground connection or connections of sufficiently low impedance and having sufficient current-carrying capacity to prevent the build-up of voltages which may result in undue hazard to connected equipment or to persons. (§1910.268(s)(13))

Ejector mechanism for removing work or material from between the dies. (§1910.211(d)(24))

Electric line truck truck used to transport personnel, tools, and material for electric supply line work. (§1910.269(x))

Electric supply equipment equipment that produces, modifies, regulates, controls, or safeguards a supply of electric energy. (§1910.269(x))

Electric supply lines See "Lines, electric supply"

Electric utility organization responsible for the installation, operation, or maintenance of an electric supply system. (§1910.269(x))

Electrical ground conducting connection between an electrical circuit or equipment and the earth, or some conducting body which serves in place of the earth. (Appendix D to §1910.66(a)(11))

Electroluminescent light-emitting capacitor. Alternating current excites phosphor atoms when placed between the electrically conductive surfaces to produce light. This light source is typically contained inside the device. (§1910.34(c))

Electrolytic cell line working zone cell line working zone is the space envelope wherein operation or maintenance is normally performed on or in the vicinity of exposed energized surfaces of electrolytic cell lines or their attachments. (§1910.399)

Electrolytic cells tank or vat in which electrochemical reactions are caused by applying energy for the purpose of refining or producing usable materials. (§1910.399)

Electromagnetic radiation is restricted to that portion of the spectrum commonly defined as the radio frequency region, which for the purpose of this specification shall include the microwave frequency region. (§1910.97(a)(1)(i))

Electrostatic fluidized bed container holding powder coating material which is aerated from below so as to form an air-supported expanded cloud of such material which is electrically charged with a charge opposite to the charge of the object to be coated; such object is transported, through the container immediately above the charged and aerated materials in order to be coated. (§1910.107(a)(7))

Embossing calender calender with two or more rolls, one of which is engraved for producing figured effects of various kinds on a fabric. (§1910.262(b)(4))

Emergency

(1,2-dibromo-3-chloropropane) any occurrence such as, but not limited to equipment failure, rupture of containers, or failure of control equipment which may, or does, result in an unexpected release of DBCP. (§1910.1044(b))

(13 Carcinogens) unforeseen circumstance or set of circumstances resulting in the release of a carcinogen addressed by this Section that may result in exposure to or contact with the material. (§1910.1003(b))

(Acrylonitrile) any occurrence such as, but not limited to, equipment failure, rupture of containers, or failure of control equipment, which results in an unexpected massive release of AN. (§1910.1045(b))

(Benzene) any occurrence such as, but not limited to, equipment failure, rupture of containers, or failure of control equipment which may or does result in an unexpected significant release of benzene. (§1910.1028(b))

(Chromium (VI)) any occurrence that results, or is likely to result, in an uncontrolled release of chromium (VI). If an incidental release of chromium (VI) can be controlled at the time of release by employees in the immediate release area, or by maintenance personnel, it is not an emergency. (§1910.1026(b))

(Coke oven emissions) any occurrence such as, but not limited to, equipment failure which is likely to, or does, result in any massive release of coke oven emissions. (§1910.1029(b))

(Ethylene oxide) any occurrence such as, but not limited to, equipment failure, rupture of containers, or failure of control equipment that is likely to or does result in an unexpected significant release of EtO. (§1910.1047(b))

(Formaldehyde) any occurrence, such as but not limited to equipment failure, rupture of containers, or failure of control equipment that results in an uncontrolled release of a significant amount of formaldehyde. (§1910.1048(b))

(Methylene chloride) any occurrence, such as, but not limited to, equipment failure, rupture of containers, or failure of control equipment, which results, or is likely to result in an uncontrolled release of MC. If an incidental release of MC can be controlled by employees such as maintenance personnel at the time of release and in accordance with the leak/spill provisions required by paragraph (f) of this Section, it is not considered an emergency as defined by this Standard. (§1910.1052(b))

(Methylenedianiline) any occurrence such as, but not limited to, equipment failure, rupture of containers, or failure of control equipment which results in an unexpected and potentially hazardous release of MDA. (§1910.1050(b))

(Occupational exposure to hazardous chemicals in laboratories) any occurrence such as, but not limited to, equipment failure, rupture of containers or failure of control equipment which results in an uncontrolled release of a hazardous chemical into the workplace. (§1910.1450(b))

(Permit-required confined spaces) any occurrence (including any failure of hazard control or monitoring equipment) or event internal or external to the permit space that could endanger entrants. (§1910.146(b)

(Vinyl chloride) any occurrence such as, but not limited to, equipment failure, or operation of a relief device which is likely to, or does, result in massive release of vinyl chloride. (§1910.1017(b)(5))

Emergency response or responding to emergencies response effort by employees from outside the immediate release area or by other designated responders (i.e., mutual-aid groups, local fire departments, etc.) to an occurrence which results, or is likely to result, in an uncontrolled release of a hazardous substance. Responses to incidental releases of hazardous substances where the substance can be absorbed, neutralized, or otherwise controlled at the time of release by employees in the immediate release area, or by maintenance personnel are not considered to be emergency responses within the scope of this Standard. Responses to releases of hazardous substances where there is no potential safety or health hazard (i.e., fire, explosion, or chemical exposure) are not considered to be emergency responses. (§1910.120(a)(3))

Emergency situation
1,3-Butadiene any occurrence such as, but not limited to, equipment failure, rupture of containers, or failure of control equipment that may or does result in an uncontrolled significant release of BD. (§1910.1051(b))
(Respiratory protection) any occurrence such as, but not limited to, equipment failure, rupture of containers, or failure of control equipment that may or does result in an uncontrolled significant release of an airborne contaminant. (§1910.134(b))

Emergency stop emergency stop switch is a manually or automatically operated electric switch to cut off electric power independently of the regular operating controls. (§1910.179(a)(59))

Employee
(Access to employee exposure and medical records) current employee, a former employee, or an employee being assigned or transferred to work where there will be exposure to toxic substances or harmful physical agents. In the case of a deceased or legally incapacitated employee, the employee's legal representative may directly exercise all the employee's rights under this Section. (§1910.1020(c)(4))
(General) employee of an employer who is employed in a business of his employer which affects commerce; (§1910.2(d))
(Hazard communication) worker who may be exposed to hazardous chemicals under normal operating conditions or in foreseeable emergencies. Workers such as office workers or bank tellers who encounter hazardous chemicals only in non-routine, isolated instances are not covered. (§1910.1200(c))
(Occupational exposure to hazardous chemicals in laboratories) individual employed in a laboratory workplace who may be exposed to hazardous chemicals in the course of his or her assignments. (§1910.1450(b))

Employee exposure (See Also "Exposure or exposed")
(1,3-Butadiene) exposure of a worker to airborne concentrations of BD which would occur if the employee were not using respiratory protective equipment. (§1910.1051(b))
(Asbestos) that exposure to airborne asbestos that would occur if the employee were not using respiratory protective equipment. (§1910.1001(b))
(Benzene) exposure to airborne benzene which would occur if the employee were not using respiratory protective equipment. (§1910.1028(b))
(Cadmium) and similar language referring to the air cadmium level to which an employee is exposed means the exposure to airborne cadmium that would occur if the employee were not using respiratory protective equipment. (§1910.1027(b))
(Chromium (VI)) exposure to airborne chromium (VI) that would occur if the employee were not using a respirator. (§1910.1026(b))
(Ethylene oxide) exposure to airborne EtO which would occur if the employee were not using respiratory protective equipment. (§1910.1047(b))
(Formaldehyde) exposure to airborne formaldehyde which would occur without corrections for protection provided by any respirator that is in use. (§1910.1048(b))
(Methylene chloride) exposure to airborne MC which occurs or would occur if the employee were not using respiratory protection. (§1910.1052(b))
(Methylenedianiline) exposure to MDA which would occur if the employee were not using respirators or protective work clothing and equipment. (§1910.1050(b))
(Respirable crystalline silica) exposure to airborne respirable crystalline silica that would occur if the employee were not using a respirator. (§1910.1053(b))
(Respiratory protection) exposure to a concentration of an airborne contaminant that would occur if the employee were not using respiratory protection. (§1910.134(b))

Employee exposure record record containing any of the following kinds of information:
(i) Environmental (workplace) monitoring or measuring of a toxic substance or harmful physical agent, including personal, area, grab, wipe, or other form of sampling, as well as related collection and analytical methodologies, calculations, and other background data relevant to interpretation of the results obtained;
(ii) Biological monitoring results which directly assess the absorption of a toxic substance or harmful physical agent by body systems (e.g., the level of a chemical in the blood, urine, breath, hair, fingernails, etc) but not including results which assess the biological effect of a substance or agent or which assess an employee's use of alcohol or drugs;
(iii) Safety data sheets indicating that the material may pose a hazard to human health; or
(iv) In the absence of the above, a chemical inventory or any other record which reveals where and when used and the identity (e.g., chemical, common, or trade name) of a toxic substance or harmful physical agent. (§1910.1020(c)(5))

Employee medical record record concerning the health status of an employee which is made or maintained by a physician, nurse, or other health care personnel or technician, including:
(A) Medical and employment questionnaires or histories (including job description and occupational exposures),
(B) The results of medical examinations (pre-employment, pre-assignment, periodic, or episodic) and laboratory tests (including chest and other X-ray examinations taken for the purposes of establishing a base-line or detecting occupational illness, and all biological monitoring not defined as an "employee exposure record"),
(C) Medical opinions, diagnoses, progress notes, and recommendations,
(D) First aid records,
(E) Descriptions of treatments and prescriptions, and
(F) Employee medical complaints.
(ii) "Employee medical record" does not include medical information in the form of:
(A) Physical specimens (e.g., blood or urine samples) which are routinely discarded as a part of normal medical practice; or
(B) Records concerning health insurance claims if maintained separately from the employer's medical program and its records, and not accessible to the employer by employee name or other direct personal identifier (e.g., social security number, payroll number, etc.); or
(C) Records created solely in preparation for litigation which are privileged from discovery under the applicable rules of procedure or evidence; or
(D) Records concerning voluntary employee assistance programs (alcohol, drug abuse, or personal counseling programs) if maintained separately from the employer's medical program and its records. (§1910.1020(c)(6)(i))

Employer
(Access to employee exposure and medical records) current employer, a former employer, or a successor employer. (§1910.1020(c)(7))
(General) means a person engaged in a business affecting commerce who has employees, but does not include the United States or any State or political subdivision of a State; (§1910.2(c))
(Hazard communication) person engaged in a business where chemicals are either used, distributed, or are produced for use or distribution, including a contractor or subcontractor. (§1910.1200(c))

Enclosed surrounded by a case, housing, fence, or walls that will prevent persons from accidentally contacting energized parts. (§1910.399)

Enclosed space working space, such as a manhole, vault, tunnel, or shaft, that has a limited means of egress or entry, that is designed for periodic employee entry under normal operating conditions, and that under normal conditions does not contain a hazardous atmosphere, but that may contain a hazardous atmosphere under abnormal conditions.
Note: *Spaces that are enclosed but not designed for employee entry under normal operating conditions are not considered to be enclosed spaces for the purposes of this Section. Similarly, spaces that are enclosed and that are expected to contain a hazardous atmosphere are not considered to be enclosed spaces for the purposes of this Section. Such spaces meet the definition of permit spaces in §1910.146 of this Part, and entry into them must be performed in accordance with that Standard.* (§1910.269(x))

Enclosed structure structure with a roof or ceiling and at least two walls which may present fire hazards to employees, such as accumulations of smoke, toxic gases and heat, similar to those found in buildings. (§1910.155(c)(15))

Enclosure case or housing of apparatus, or the fence or walls surrounding an installation to prevent personnel from accidentally contacting energized parts, or to protect the equipment from physical damage. (§1910.399)

End-of-service-life indicator (ESLI) system that warns the respirator user of the approach of the end of adequate respiratory protection, for example, that the sorbent is approaching saturation or is no longer effective. (§1910.134(b))

Energized (alive, live)
(The control of hazardous energy (lockout/tagout) connected to an energy source or containing residual or stored energy. (§1910.147(b))
(Electric power generation, transmission and distribution) (Alive, live) electrically connected to a source of potential difference, or electrically charged so as to have a potential significantly different from that of earth in the vicinity. (§1910.269(x)); (§1910.399)

Energy isolating device
(The control of hazardous energy (lockout/tagout) mechanical device that physically prevents the transmission or release of energy, including

but not limited to the following: A manually operated electrical circuit breaker; a disconnect switch; a manually operated switch by which the conductors of a circuit can be disconnected from all ungrounded supply conductors, and, in addition, no pole can be operated independently; a line valve; a block; and any similar device used to block or isolate energy. Push buttons, selector switches and other control circuit type devices are not energy isolating devices. (§1910.147(b))

(Electric power generation, transmission and distribution) physical device that prevents the transmission or release of energy, including, but not limited to, the following: a manually operated electric circuit breaker, a disconnect switch, a manually operated switch, a slide gate, a slip blind, a line valve, blocks, and any similar device with a visible indication of the position of the device. (Push buttons, selector switches, and other control-circuit-type devices are not energy isolating devices.) (§1910.269(x))

Energy source

(The control of hazardous energy (lockout/tagout) any source of electrical, mechanical, hydraulic, pneumatic, chemical, thermal, or other energy source that could cause injury to employees. (§1910.147(b))

(Electric power generation, transmission and distribution) any electrical, mechanical, hydraulic, pneumatic, chemical, nuclear, thermal, or other energy source that could cause injury to personnel. (§1910.269(x))

Engineering controls controls (e.g., sharps disposal containers, self-sheathing needles, safer medical devices, such as sharps with engineered sharps injury protections and needleless systems) that isolate or remove the bloodborne pathogens hazard from the workplace. (§1910.1030(b))

Engulfment surrounding and effective capture of a person by a liquid or finely divided (flowable) solid substance that can be aspirated to cause death by filling or plugging the respiratory system or that can exert enough force on the body to cause death by strangulation, constriction, or crushing. (§1910.146(b))

Entry action by which a person passes through an opening into a permit-required confined space. Entry includes ensuing work activities in that space and is considered to have occurred as soon as any part of the entrant's body breaks the plane of an opening into the space. (§1910.146(b)); (§1910.269(x))

Entry loss loss in static pressure caused by air flowing into a duct or hood. It is usually expressed in inches of water gauge. (§1910.94(b)(1)(vi))

Entry permit (permit) (See Also "Permit") written or printed document that is provided by the employer to allow and control entry into a permit space and that contains the information specified in paragraph (f) of this Section. (§1910.146(b))

Entry supervisor person (such as the employer, foreman, or crew chief) responsible for determining if acceptable entry conditions are present at a permit space where entry is planned, for authorizing entry and overseeing entry operations, and for terminating entry as required by this Section.

Note: *An entry supervisor also may serve as an attendant or as an authorized entrant, as long as that person is trained and equipped as required by this Section for each role he or she fills. Also, the duties of entry supervisor may be passed from one individual to another during the course of an entry operation.* (§1910.146(b))

Equalizer device which compensates for unequal length or stretch of a rope. (§1910.179(a)(38))

Equipment

(Electric power generation, transmission and distribution) general term including material, fittings, devices, appliances, fixtures, apparatus, and the like used as part of or in connection with an electrical installation. (§1910.269(x)); (§1910.399)

(Telecommunications) general term which includes materials, fittings, devices, appliances, fixtures, apparatus, and similar items used as part of, or in connection with, a supply or communications installation. (§1910.268(s)(14))

Equipment grounding conductor See "Grounding conductor, equipment"

Equivalent

(Walking-working surgaces) alternative designs, equipment, materials, or methods, that the employer can demonstrate will provide an equal or greater degree of safety for employees compared to the designs, equipment, materials, or methods specified in this subpart. (§1910.21(b))

(Powered platforms for building maintenance) (Powered platfroms for building maintenance/Personal fall arrest system) alternative designs, materials or methods which the employer can demonstrate will provide an equal or greater degree of safety for employees than the methods, materials or designs specified in the Standard. (§1910.66(d)); (Appendix C to §1910.66(b))

Equivalent entity person or organization (including an employer) which, by possession of equipment, technical knowledge and skills, can perform with equal competence the same repairs and tests as the person or organization with which it is equated. (§1910.184(b))

Equivalent Instrument cotton dust sampling device that meets the vertical elutriator equivalency requirements as described in paragraph (d)(1)(iii) of §1910.1043. (§1910.1043(b))

Escape-only respirator respirator intended to be used only for emergency exit. (§1910.134(b))

Establishment

(1903) single physical location where business is conducted or where services or industrial operations are performed. (For example: A factory, mill, store, hotel, restaurant, movie theatre, farm, ranch, bank, sales office, warehouse, or central administrative office.) Where distinctly separate activities are performed at a single physical location (such as contract construction activities from the same physical location as a lumber yard), each activity shall be treated as a separate physical establishment, and a separate notice or notices shall be posted in each such establishment, to the extent that such notices have been furnished by the Occupational Safety and Health Administration, U.S. Department of Labor. Where employers are engaged in activities which are physically dispersed, such as agriculture, construction, transportation, communications, and electric, gas and sanitary services, the notice or notices required by this Section shall be posted at the location to which employees report each day. Where employees do not usually work at, or report to, a single establishment, such as longshoremen, traveling salesmen, technicians, engineers, etc., such notice or notices shall be posted at the location from which the employees operate to carry out their activities. In all cases, such notice or notices shall be posted in accordance with the requirements of paragraph (a) of this Section. (§1903.2(b))

(1904) establishment is a single physical location where business is conducted or where services or industrial operations are performed. For activities where employees do not work at a single physical location, such as construction; transportation; communications, electric, gas and sanitary services; and similar operations, the establishment is represented by main or branch offices, terminals, stations, etc. that either supervise such activities or are the base from which personnel carry out these activities.

(1) *Can one business location include two or more establishments?* Normally, one business location has only one establishment. Under limited conditions, the employer may consider two or more separate businesses that share a single location to be separate establishments. An employer may divide one location into two or more establishments only when:

(i) Each of the establishments represents a distinctly separate business;

(ii) Each business is engaged in a different economic activity;

(iii) No one industry description in the Standard Industrial Classification Manual (1987) applies to the joint activities of the establishments; and

(iv) Separate reports are routinely prepared for each establishment on the number of employees, their wages and salaries, sales or receipts, and other business information. For example, if an employer operates a construction company at the same location as a lumber yard, the employer may consider each business to be a separate establishment.

(2) *Can an establishment include more than one physical location?* Yes, but only under certain conditions. An employer may combine two or more physical locations into a single establishment only when:

(i) The employer operates the locations as a single business operation under common management;

(ii) The locations are all located in close proximity to each other; and

(iii) The employer keeps one set of business records for the locations, such as records on the number of employees, their wages and salaries, sales or receipts, and other kinds of business information. For example, one manufacturing establishment might include the main plant, a warehouse a few blocks away, and an administrative services building across the street.

(3) *If an employee telecommutes from home, is his or her home considered a separate establishment?* No, for employees who telecommute from home, the employee's home is not a business establishment and a separate 300 Log is not required. Employees who telecommute must be linked to one of your establishments under §1904.30(b)(3). (§1904.46)

Established Federal Standard any operative standard established by any agency of the United States and in effect on April 28, 1971, or contained in any Act of Congress in force on the date of enactment of the Williams-Steiger Occupational Safety and Health Act. (§1910.2(h))

Ethylene oxide or EtO three-membered ring organic compound with chemical formula C_2H_4O. (§1910.1047(b))

Exhaust system system consisting of branch pipes connected to hoods or enclosures, one or more header pipes, an exhaust fan, means for separating solid contaminants from the air flowing in the system, and a discharge stack to outside. (§1910.94(b)(1)(vii))

Exhaust ventilation system system for removing contaminated air from a space, comprising two or more of the following elements (a) enclosure or hood, (b) duct work, (c) dust collecting equipment, (d) exhauster, and (e) discharge stack. (§1910.94(a)(1)(viii))

Existing coke oven battery battery in operation or under construction on January 20, 1977, and which is not a rehabilitated coke oven battery. (§1910.1029(b))

Exit that portion of an exit route that is generally separated from other areas to provide a protected way of travel to the exit discharge. An example of an exit is a two-hour fire resistance-rated enclosed stairway that leads from the fifth floor of an office building to the outside of the building. (§1910.34(c))

Exit access that portion of an exit route that leads to an exit. An example of an exit access is a corridor on the fifth floor of an office building that leads to a two-hour fire resistance-rated enclosed stairway (the Exit). (§1910.34(c))

Exit discharge part of the exit route that leads directly outside or to a street, walkway, refuge area, public way, or open space with access to the outside. An example of an exit discharge is a door at the bottom of a two-hour fire resistance-rated enclosed stairway that discharges to a place of safety outside the building. (§1910.34(c))

Exit route continuous and unobstructed path of exit travel from any point within a workplace to a place of safety (including refuge areas). An exit route consists of three parts: The exit access; the exit; and, the exit discharge. (An exit route includes all vertical and horizontal areas along the route.) (§1910.34(c))

Explosion-proof apparatus apparatus enclosed in a case that is capable of withstanding an explosion of a specified gas or vapor that may occur within it and of preventing the ignition of a specified gas or vapor surrounding the enclosure by sparks, flashes, or explosion of the gas or vapor within, and that operates at such an external temperature that it will not ignite a surrounding flammable atmosphere. (§1910.399)

Explosive

(Explosive and blasting agents) any chemical compound, mixture, or device, the primary or common purpose of which is to function by explosion, i.e., with substantially instantaneous release of gas and heat, unless such compound, mixture, or device is otherwise specifically classified by the U.S. Department of Transportation; see 49 CFR chapter I. The term "explosives" shall include all material which is classified as Class A, Class B, and Class C explosives by the U.S. Department of Transportation, and includes, but is not limited to dynamite, black powder, pellet powders, initiating explosives, blasting caps, electric blasting caps, safety fuse, fuse lighters, fuse igniters, squibs, cordeau detonant fuse, instantaneous fuse, igniter cord, igniters, small arms ammunition, small arms ammunition primers, smokeless propellant, cartridges for propellant-actuated power devices, and cartridges for industrial guns. Commercial explosives are those explosives which are intended to be used in commercial or industrial operations.

Note 1: *Classification of explosives is described by the U.S. Department of Transportation as follows (See 49 CFR chapter I):*

(i) Class A explosives. Possessing, detonating, or otherwise maximum hazard; such as dynamite, nitroglycerin, picric acid, lead azide, fulminate of mercury, black powder, blasting caps, and detonating primers.

(ii) Class B explosives. Possessing flammable hazard, such as propellant explosives (including some smokeless propellants), photographic flash powders, and some special fireworks.

(iii) Class C explosives. Includes certain types of manufactured articles which contain Class A or Class B explosives, or both, as components but in restricted quantities.

(iv) Forbidden or not acceptable explosives. Explosives which are forbidden or not acceptable for transportation by common carriers by rail freight, rail express, highway, or water in accordance with the regulations of the U.S. Department of Transportation, 49 CFR chapter I. (§1910.109(a)(3))

Explosive chemical solid or liquid chemical which is in itself capable by chemical reaction of producing gas at such a temperature and pressure and at such a speed as to cause damage to the surroundings. Pyrotechnic chemicals are included even when they do not evolve gases. (Appendix B to §1910.1200(B.1.1.1))

Explosive item item containing one or more explosive chemicals. (Appendix B to §1910.1200(B.1.1.1))

Explosive powerload also known as load (See Also "Load") any substance in any form capable of producing a propellant force. (§1910.241(a)(6))

Explosive-actuated power devices explosive-actuated power device—any tool or special mechanized device which is actuated by explosives, but not including propellant-actuated power devices. Examples of explosive-actuated power devices are jet tappers and jet perforators. (§1910.109(a)(2))

Exposed

(Electric power generation, transmission, and distribution) not isolated or guarded. (§1910.269(x)); (Appendix B to §1910.269)

(Electrical)

(As applied to live parts.) (See Also "Accessible;" "Concealed") capable of being inadvertently touched or approached nearer than a safe distance by a person. It is applied to parts not suitably guarded, isolated, or insulated. (§1910.399)

(As applied to wiring methods.) (See Also "Accessible. (As applied to wiring methods)") on or attached to the surface, or behind panels designed to allow access. (§1910.399)

(For the purposes of §1910.308(e).) where the circuit is in such a position that in case of failure of supports or insulation, contact with another circuit may result. (§1910.399)

(Overhead and gantry cranes) capable of being contacted inadvertently. Applied to hazardous objects not adequately guarded or isolated. (§1910.179(a)(39))

Exposed to contact

(Mechanical power-transmission apparatus) that the location of an object is such that a person is likely to come into contact with it and be injured. (§1910.211(f)(4))

(Textiles) Exposed to contact. Exposed to contact shall mean that the location of an object, material, nip point, or point of operation is such that a person is liable to come in contact with it in his normal course of employment. (§1910.262(b)(12))

Exposure or exposed (See Also "Employee exposure")

(Access to employee exposure and medical records) that an employee is subjected to a toxic substance or harmful physical agent in the course of employment through any route of entry (inhalation, ingestion, skin contact or absorption, etc.), and includes past exposure and potential (e.g., accidental or possible) exposure, but does not include situations where the employer can demonstrate that the toxic substance or harmful physical agent is not used, handled, stored, generated, or present in the workplace in any manner different from typical non-occupational situations. (§1910.1020(c)(8))

(Hazard communication) that an employee is subjected in the course of employment to a chemical that is a physical or health hazard, and includes potential (e.g. accidental or possible) exposure. "Subjected" in terms of health hazards includes any route of entry (e.g. inhalation, ingestion, skin contact or absorption.) (§1910.1200(c))

Exposure Incident (See Also ""Sharps with engineered sharps injury protections") specific eye, mouth, other mucous membrane, non-intact skin, or parenteral contact with blood or other potentially infectious materials that results from the performance of an employee's duties. (§1910.1030(b))

Extensible boom platform aerial device (except ladders) with a telescopic or extensible boom. Telescopic derricks with personnel platform attachments shall be considered to be extensible boom platforms when used with a personnel platform. (§1910.67(a)(4))

Extension ladder non-self-supporting portable ladder that is adjustable in length. (§1910.21(b))

External environment any environment external to regulated and nonregulated areas. (§1910.1003(b))

Externally operable. capable of being operated without exposing the operator to contact with live parts. (§1910.399)

Extinguisher classification letter classification given an extinguisher to designate the class or classes of fire on which an extinguisher will be effective. (§1910.155(c)(16))

Extinguisher rating numerical rating given to an extinguisher which indicates the extinguishing potential of the unit based on standardized tests developed by Underwriters' Laboratories, Inc. (§1910.155(c)(17))

Eye loop formed at the end of a rope by securing the dead end to the live end at the base of the loop. (§1910.181(a)(17))

Eye irritation production of changes in the eye following the application of test substance to the anterior surface of the eye, which are fully reversible within 21 days of application. (Appendix A to §1910.1200(A.3.1.1))

F

F/T measured amount of an analyte divided by the theoretical value (See "Theoretical Value or theoretical amount") for that analyte in the sample analyzed; this ratio is a measure of the recovery for a quality control sample. (Appendix F to §1910.1027)

Fabric (metal mesh) (See Also "Sling") flexible portion of a metal mesh sling consisting of a series of transverse coils and cross rods. (§1910.184(b))

Fabricated product product made wholly or partly from polyvinyl chloride, and which does not require further processing at temperatures, and for times, sufficient to cause mass melting of the polyvinyl chloride resulting in the release of vinyl chloride. (§1910.1017(b)(6))

Face of slide bottom surface of the slide to which the punch or upper die is generally attached. (§1910.211(d)(25))

Facility

(Hazardous waste operations and emergency response)

(A) any building, structure, installation, equipment, pipe or pipeline (including any pipe into a sewer or publicly owned treatment works), well, pit, pond, lagoon, impoundment, ditch, storage container, motor vehicle, rolling stock, or aircraft, or

(B) any site or area where a hazardous substance has been deposited, stored, disposed of, or placed, or otherwise come to be located; but does not include any consumer product in consumer use or any water-borne vessel. (§1910.120(a)(3))

(Process safety management of highly hazardous chemicals) means the buildings, containers or equipment which contain a process. (§1910.119(b))

Fail-safe provision designed to automatically stop or safely control any motion in which a malfunction occurs. (§1910.179(a)(40))

Failure load refusal, breakage, or separation of component parts. A load refusal is the point at which the ultimate strength of a component or object is exceeded. (§1910.21(b))

Fall See "Fell (Fall)"

Fall hazard any condition on a walking-working surface that exposes an employee to a risk of harm from a fall on the same level or to a lower level. (§1910.21(b))

Fall protection any equipment, device, or system that prevents an employee from falling from an elevation or mitigates the effect of such a fall. (§1910.21(b))

Fall restraint system fall protection system that prevents the user from falling any distance. (§1910.269(x))

Farm carts See "Movable fuel storage tenders or farm carts"

Farm vehicle (implement of husbandry) vehicle for use on a farm on which is mounted a container of not over 1,200 gallons water capacity. (§1910.111(a)(2)(vii))

Feeder all circuit conductors between the service equipment, the source of a separate derived system, or other power supply source and the final branch-circuit overcurrent device. (§1910.399)

Feeding (See Also "Automatic feeding;" "Manual feeding;" "Semiautomatic feeding") process of placing or removing material within or from the point of operation. (§1910.211(d)(26))

Fell (fall) to cut down trees. (§1910.266(c))

Feller (faller) employee who fells trees. (§1910.266(c))

Female handle (choker) handle with a handle eye and a slot of such dimension as to permit passage of a male handle thereby allowing the use of a metal mesh sling in a choker hitch. (See §1910.184, Fig. N–184–1.) (§1910.184(b))

Fiber

(Asbestos) particulate form of asbestos 5 micrometers or longer,with a length-to-diameter ratio of at least 3 to 1. (§1910.1001(b))

(Detailed procedures for sampling and analysis of Asbestos (Non-mandatory)) particle that is 5 µm or longer, with a length-to-width ratio of 3 to 1 or longer. (Appendix B to §1910.1001)

(Polarized Light Microscopy of Asbestos (Non-mandatory)) particle longer than or equal to 5 µm with a length to width ratio greater than or equal to 3:1. This may include cleavage fragments. (See Section 3.5 of this Appendix). (Appendix J to §1910.1001)

Fiddle block block consisting of two sheaves in the same plane held in place by the same cheek plates. (§1910.181(a)(18))

Field area within the graticule circle that is superimposed on the microscope image. (Appendix B to §1910.1001)

Filling density percent ratio of the weight of the gas in a container to the weight of water at 60 °F that the container will hold. (§1910.111(a)(2)(viii))

Filter or air purifying element component used in respirators to remove solid or liquid aerosols from the inspired air. (§1910.134(b))

Filtering facepiece (dust mask) negative pressure particulate respirator with a filter as an integral part of the facepiece or with the entire facepiece composed of the filtering medium. (§1910.134(b))

Final medical determination written medical opinion of the employee's health status by the examining physician under paragraphs §1910.1027(l)(3)-(12) of this Section or, if multiple physician review under paragraph (l)(13) of this Section or the alternative physician determination under §1910.1027(l)(14) of this Section is invoked, it is the final, written medical finding, recommendation or determination that emerges from that process. (§1910.1027(b))

Final order date means:

(i) for an uncontested citation item, the fifteenth working day after the employer's receipt of the citation;

(ii) for a contested citation item:

(A) The thirtieth day after the date on which a decision or order of a commission administrative law judge has been docketed with the commission, unless a member of the commission has directed review; or

(B) Where review has been directed, the thirtieth day after the date on which the Commission issues its decision or order disposing of all or pertinent part of a case; or

(C) The date on which a federal appeals court issues a decision affirming the violation in a case in which a final order of OSHRC has been stayed. (§1903.19(b)(4))

Finished article containing MDA manufactured item:

(i) which is formed to a specific shape or design during manufacture;

(ii) which has end use function(s) dependent in whole or part upon its shape or design during end use; and

(iii) where applicable, is an item which is fully cured by virtue of having been subjected to the conditions (temperature, time) necessary to complete the desired chemical reaction. (§1910.1050(b))

Fire See "Class A fire;" "Class B fire;" Class C fire;" "Class D fire;" "Incipient stage fire"

Fire area area of a building separated from the remainder of the building by construction having a fire resistance of at least 1 hour and having all communicating openings properly protected by an assembly having a fire resistance rating of at least 1 hour. (§1910.106(a)(12))

Fire brigade (private fire department industrial fire department) organized group of employees who are knowledgeable, trained, and skilled in at least basic fire fighting operations. (§1910.155(c)(18))

First aid for the purposes of Part §1904, "first aid" means the following:

(A) using a non-prescription medication at nonprescription strength (for medications available in both prescription and non-prescription form, a recommendation by a physician or other licensed health care professional to use a non-prescription medication at prescription strength is considered medical treatment for recordkeeping purposes);

(B) administering tetanus immunizations (other immunizations, such as Hepatitis B vaccine or rabies vaccine, are considered medical treatment);

(C) cleaning, flushing or soaking wounds on the surface of the skin;

(D) using wound coverings such as bandages, Band-AidsTM , gauze pads, etc.; or using butterfly bandages or Steri-StripsTM (other wound closing devices such as sutures, staples, etc., are considered medical treatment);

(E) using hot or cold therapy;

(F) using any non-rigid means of support, such as elastic bandages, wraps, non-rigid back belts, etc. (devices with rigid stays or other systems designed to immobilize parts of the body are considered medical treatment for recordkeeping purposes);

(G) using temporary immobilization devices while transporting an accident victim (e.g., splints, slings, neck collars, back boards, etc.).

(H) drilling of a fingernail or toenail to relieve pressure, or draining fluid from a blister;

(I) using eye patches;

(J) removing foreign bodies from the eye using only irrigation or a cotton swab;

(K) removing splinters or foreign material from areas other than the eye by irrigation, tweezers, cotton swabs or other simple means;

(L) rsing finger guards;

(M) using massages (physical therapy or chiropractic treatment are considered medical treatment for recordkeeping purposes); or

(N) drinking fluids for relief of heat stress. (§1904.7(b)(5)(ii))

First aid training training in the initial care, including cardiopulmonary resuscitation (which includes chest compressions, rescue breathing, and, as appropriate, other heart and lung resuscitation techniques), performed by a person who is not a medical practitioner, of a sick or injured person until definitive medical treatment can be administered. (§1910.269(x))

Fit factor quantitative estimate of the fit of a particular respirator to a specific individual, and typically estimates the ratio of the concentration of a substance in ambient air to its concentration inside the respirator when worn. (§1910.134(b))

Fit test use of a protocol to qualitatively or quantitatively evaluate the fit of a respirator on an individual. (See Also Qualitative fit test QLFT and Quantitative fit test QNFT.) (§1910.134(b))

Fitting accessory such as a locknut, bushing, or other part of a wiring system that is intended primarily to perform a mechanical rather than an electrical function. (§1910.399)

Fixed barrier guard die space barrier attached to the press frame. (§1910.211(d)(34))

Fixed extinguishing system permanently installed system that either extinguishes or controls a fire at the location of the system. (§1910.155(c)(1))

Fixed ladder ladder with rails or individual rungs that is permanently attached to a structure, building, or equipment. Fixed ladders include individual-rung ladders, but not ship stairs, step bolts, or manhole steps. (§1910.21(b))

Flame resistance property of materials, or combinations of component materials, to retard ignition and restrict the spread of flame. (§1910.155(c)(20))

Flammable aerosol flammable aerosol as defined by Appendix B to §1910.1200—Physical Hazard Criteria. For the purposes of paragraph (d) of this Section, such aerosols are considered Category 1 flammable liquids. (§1910.106(a)(13))

Flammable gas gas having a flammable range with air at 20°C (68 °F) and a standard pressure of 101.3 kPa (14.7 psi). (Appendix B to §1910.1200(B.2.1))

Flammable liquid (See Also "Combustible liquid")
(Dipping and coating operations) any liquid having a flashpoint at or below 199.4 °F (93 °C). (§1910.123(d))
(Flammable liquids) any liquid having a flashpoint at or below 199.4 °F (93 °C). Flammable liquids are divided into four categories as follows:
(i) Category 1 shall include liquids having flashpoints below 73.4 °F (23 °C) and having a boiling point at or below 95 °F (35 °C);
(ii) Category 2 shall include liquids having flashpoints below 73.4 °F (23 °C) and having a boiling point above 95 °F (35 °C);
(iii) Category 3 shall include liquids having flashpoints at or above 73.4 °F (23 °C) and at or below 140 °F (60 °C). When a Category 3 liquid with a flashpoint at or above 100 °F (37.8 °C) is heated for use to within 30 °F (16.7 °C) of its flashpoint, it shall be handled in accordance with the requirements for a Category 3 liquid with a flashpoint below 100 °F (37.8 °C);
(iv) Category 4 shall include liquids having flashpoints above 140 °F (60 °C) and at or below 199.4 °F (93 °C). When a Category 4 flammable liquid is heated for use to within 30 °F (16.7 °C) of its flashpoint, it shall be handled in accordance with the requirements for a Category 3 liquid with a flashpoint at or above 100 °F (37.8 °C);
When liquid with a flashpoint greater than 199.4 °F (93 °C) is heated for use to within 30 °F (16.7 °C) of its flashpoint, it shall be handled in accordance with the requirements for a Category 4 flammable liquid. (§1910.106(a)(19))
(Hazard Communication) liquid having a flash point of not more than 93°C (199.4°F). (Appendix B to §1910.1200(B.6.1))

Flammable solid solid which is a readily combustible solid, or which may cause or contribute to fire through friction. (Appendix B to §1910.1200(B.7.1))

Flanges collars, discs or plates between which wheels are mounted and are referred to as adaptor, sleeve, or back up type. See paragraph (c) of §1910.215 for full description. (§1910.211(b)(9))

Flashpoint
(Dipping and coating operations) (Hazard communication) (Occupational exposure to hazardous chemicals in laboratories) (Hazard communication) minimum temperature at which a liquid gives off a vapor in sufficient concentration to ignite if tested in accordance with the test methods in Appendix B to §1910.1200—Physical Hazard Criteria (§1910.123(d):
(Flammable liquids)
(i) For a liquid which has a viscosity of less than 45 SUS at 100 °F (37.8 °C), does not contain suspended solids, and does not have a tendency to form a surface film while under test, the procedure specified in the Standard Method of Test for Flashpoint by Tag Closed Tester (ASTM D–56–70), which is incorporated by reference as specified in §1910.6, or an equivalent test method as defined in Appendix B to §1910.1200—Physical Hazard Criteria, shall be used.
(ii) For a liquid which has a viscosity of 45 SUS or more at 100 °F (37.8 °C), or contains suspended solids, or has a tendency to form a surface film while under test, the Standard Method of Test for Flashpoint by Pensky-Martens Closed Tester (ASTM D–93–71) or an equivalent method as defined by Appendix B to §1910.1200—Physical Hazard Criteria, shall be used except that the methods specified in Note 1 to Section 1.1 of ASTM D–93–71 may be used for the respective materials specified in the Note. The preceding ASTM standard is incorporated by reference as specified in §1910.6.
(iii) For a liquid that is a mixture of compounds that have different volatilities and flashpoints, its flashpoint shall be determined by using the procedure specified in paragraph (a)(14)(i) or (ii) of this Section on the liquid in the form it is shipped.
(iv) Organic peroxides, which undergo autoaccelerating thermal decomposition, are excluded from any of the flashpoint determination methods specified in this subparagraph. (§1910.106(a)(14)(i)-(iv))

Flat storage structure grain storage building or structure that will not empty completely by gravity, has an unrestricted ground level opening for entry, and must be entered to reclaim the residual grain using powered equipment or manual means. (§1910.272(c))

Floor-operated crane crane which is pendant or nonconductive rope controlled by an operator on the floor or an independent platform. (§1910.179(a)(5))

Fluidized bed container holding powder coating material which is aerated from below so as to form an air-supported expanded cloud of such material through which the preheated object to be coated is immersed and transported. (§1910.107(a)(6))

Flywheels include flywheels, balance wheels, and flywheel pulleys mounted and revolving on crankshaft of engine or other shafting. (§1910.211(f)(5))

Foam stable aggregation of small bubbles which flow freely over a burning liquid surface and form a coherent blanket which seals combustible vapors and thereby extinguishes the fire. (§1910.155(c)(21))

Foot bearing or foot block (sill block) lower support on which the mast rotates. (§1910.181(a)(19))

Foot control foot operated control mechanism designed to be used with a clutch or clutch/brake control system. (§1910.211(d)(30))

Foot pedal foot operated lever designed to operate the mechanical linkage that trips a full revolution clutch. (§1910.211(d)(31))

Footwalk walkway with handrail, attached to the bridge or trolley for access purposes. (§1910.179(a)(41))

Foreseeable emergency any potential occurrence such as, but not limited to, equipment failure, rupture of containers, or failure of control equipment which could result in an uncontrolled release of a hazardous chemical into the workplace. (§1910.1200(c))

Forging product of work on metal formed to a desired shape by impact or pressure in hammers, forging machines (upsetters), presses, rolls, and related forming equipment. Forging hammers, counterblow equipment and high-energy-rate forging machines impart impact to the workpiece, while most other types of forging equipment impart squeeze pressure in shaping the stock. Some metals can be forged at room temperature, but the majority of metals are made more plastic for forging by heating. (§1910.211(e)(1))

Forging machine See "Upsetters (or forging machines, or headers)"

Forging presses class of forging equipment wherein the shaping of metal between dies is performed by mechanical or hydraulic pressure, and usually is accomplished with a single workstroke of the press for each die station. (§1910.211(e)(5))

Forging rolls class of auxiliary forging equipment wherein stock is shaped between power driven rolls bearing contoured dies. Usually used for preforming, roll forging is often employed to reduce thickness and increase length of stock. (§1910.211(e)(8))

Formaldehyde chemical substance, HCHO, Chemical Abstracts Service Registry No. 50–00–0. (§1910.1048(b))

Fountain fountains, ornamental pools, display pools, and reflection pools.
Note to the definition of "fountain:" *This definition does not include drinking fountains.* (§1910.399)

Free fall act of falling before the personal fall arrest system begins to apply force to arrest the fall. (Appendix C to §1910.66(b))

Free fall distance vertical displacement of the fall arrest attachment point on the employee's body belt or body harness between onset of the fall and just before the system begins to apply force to arrest the fall. This distance excludes deceleration distance, lifeline and lanyard elongation but includes any deceleration device slide distance or self-retracting lifeline/lanyard extension before they operate and fall arrest forces occur. (Appendix C to §1910.66(b))

Fsw Feet of seawater (or equivalent static pressure head). (§1910.402)

Fugitive grain dust combustible dust particles, emitted from the stock handling system, of such size as will pass through a U.S. Standard 40 mesh sieve (425 microns or less). (§1910.272(c))

Fulcrum truck's axis of rotation when it tips over. (Appendix A to §1910.178)

Full revolution clutch type of clutch that, when tripped, cannot be disengaged until the crankshaft has completed a full revolution and the press slide a full stroke. (§1910.211(d)(5))

Full stop or no movement of the slide or ram when the crankshaft rotation has slowed to two or less revolutions per minute, just before stopping completely. (Appendix A to §1910.217)

Function completion for electrical, electromechanical and electronic devices, when the circuit produces a change of state in the output element of the device. (Appendix A to §1910.217)

Fuse (Over 600 volts, nominal) overcurrent protective device with a circuit opening fusible part that is heated and severed by the passage of overcurrent through it. A fuse comprises all the parts that form a unit capable of performing the prescribed functions. It may or may not be the complete device necessary to connect it into an electrical circuit. (§1910.399)

G

Gantry crane crane similar to an overhead crane except that the bridge for carrying the trolley or trolleys is rigidly supported on two or more legs running on fixed rails or other runway. (§1910.179(a)(6))

Gantry (A-frame) structural frame, extending above the superstructure, to which the boom support ropes are reeved. (§1910.180(a)(24))

Garnett machine any of a number of types of machines for opening hard twisted waste of wool, cotton, silk, etc. Essentially, such machines consist of a lickerin; one or more cylinders, each having a complement worker and stripper rolls; and a fancy roll and doffer. The action of such machines is somewhat like that of a wool card, but it is much more severe in that the various rolls are covered with garnett wire instead of card clothing. (§1910.262(b)(13))

Gas anhydrous ammonia in either the gaseous or liquefied state. (§1910.111(a)(2)(ix))

Gas masks gas masks must be approved by the National Institute for Occupational Safety and Health (NIOSH) under 42 CFR Part 84 for use with anhydrous ammonia. (§1910.111(a)(2)(x))

Gas tight (See Also " Totally-encapsulated chemical protective suit (TECP suit)") for the purpose of the test method, the limited flow of a gas under pressure from the inside of a TECP suit to atmosphere at a prescribed pressure and time interval. (Appendix A to §1910.120(2.3))

Gaseous agent fire extinguishing agent which is in the gaseous state at normal room temperature and pressure. It has low viscosity, can expand or contract with changes in pressure and temperature, and has the ability to diffuse readily and to distribute itself uniformly throughout an enclosure. (§1910.155(c)(22))

Gaseous hydrogen system one in which the hydrogen is delivered, stored and discharged in the gaseous form to consumer's piping. The system includes stationary or movable containers, pressure regulators, safety relief devices, manifolds, interconnecting piping and controls. The system terminates at the point where hydrogen at service pressure first enters the consumer's distribution piping. (§1910.103(a)(1)(i))

Gases under pressure gases which are contained in a receptacle at a pressure of 200 kPa (29 psi) (gauge) or more, or which are liquefied or liquefied and refrigerated. (Appendix B to §1910.1200(B.5.1))

Gate or movable barrier device movable barrier arranged to enclose the point of operation before the press stroke can be started. (§1910.211(d)(13))

Gathering ring See "Master link or gathering ring"

Genotoxic and genotoxicity apply to agents or processes which alter the structure, information content, or segregation of DNA, including those which cause DNA damage by interfering with normal replication processes, or which in a non-physiological manner (temporarily) alter its replication. Genotoxicity test results are usually taken as indicators for mutagenic effects. (Appendix A to §1910.1200(A.5.1.2))

Geometric Mean natural antilog of the mean of a set of natural log-transformed data. (Appendix F to §1910.1027)

Geometric standard deviation antilog of the standard deviation of a set of natural log-transformed data. (Appendix F to §1910.1027)

Gill box machine used in the worsted system of manufacturing yarns. Its function is to arrange the fibers in a parallel order. Essentially, it consists of a pair of feed rolls and a series of followers where the followers move at a faster surface speed and perform a combing action. (§1910.262(b)(14))

Gin pole derrick derrick without a boom. Its guys are so arranged from its top as to permit leaning the mast in any direction. The load is raised and lowered by ropes reeved through sheaves or blocks at the top of the mast. (§1910.181(a)(6))

Grab bars individual horizontal or vertical handhold installed to provide access above the height of the ladder. (§1910.21(b))

Grade (See Also "Slope (Grade") slope of a surface, which is usually measured as the number of feet of rise or fall over a hundred foot horizontal distance (the slope is expressed as a percent). (Appendix A to §1910.178)

Grain elevator facility engaged in the receipt, handling, storage, and shipment of bulk raw agricultural commodities such as corn, wheat, oats, barley, sunflower seeds, and soybeans. (§1910.272(c))

Gravity hammers class of forging hammer wherein energy for forging is obtained by the mass and velocity of a freely falling ram and the attached upper die. Examples: board hammers and air-lift hammers. (§1910.211(e)(4))

Green plush coke which when removed rom the oven results in emissions due to the presence of unvolatilied coal. (§1910.1029(b))

Grinding wheels all power-driven rotatable grinding or abrasive wheels, except disc wheels as defined in this Standard, consisting of abrasive particles held together by artificial or natural bonds and used for peripheral grinding. (§1910.94(b)(1)(viii))

Ground conducting connection, whether intentional or accidental, between an electric circuit or equipment and the earth, or to some conducting body that serves in place of the earth. (§1910.269(x)); (§1910.399)

Ground (as a noun) conductive connection, whether intentional or accidental, by which an electric circuit or equipment is connected to reference ground. (§1910.268(s)(16))

Ground (as a verb) connecting or establishment of a connection, whether by intention or accident, of an electric circuit or equipment to reference ground. (§1910.268(s)(17))

Ground (reference) that conductive body, usually earth, to which an electric potential is referenced. (§1910.268(s)(15))

Ground rigged davit davit which cannot be used to raise a suspended working platform above the building face being serviced. (§1910.66(d))

Ground rigging method of suspending a working platform starting from a safe surface to a point of suspension above the safe surface. (§1910.66(d))

Ground tent small tent usually constructed of vinyl coated canvas supported by a metal or plastic frame. Its purpose is to protect employees from inclement weather while working at buried cable pedestal sites or similar locations. (§1910.268(s)(18))

Grounded

(Electric power generation, transmission, and distribution; Electrical) connected to earth or to some conducting body that serves in place of the earth. (§1910.269(x)); (§1910.399)

(Logging operations) placement of a component of a machine on the ground or on a device where it is firmly supported. (§1910.266(c))

Grounded conductor system or circuit conductor that is intentionally grounded. (§1910.268(s)(19)); (§1910.399)

Grounded, effectively intentionally connected to earth through a ground connection or connections of sufficiently low impedance and having sufficient current-carrying capacity to prevent the buildup of voltages that may result in undue hazards to connected equipment or to persons. (§1910.399)

Grounded systems system of conductors in which at least one conductor or point (usually the middle wire, or the neutral point of transformer or generator windings) is intentionally grounded, either solidly or through a current-limiting device (not a current-interrupting device). (§1910.268(s)(20))

Ground-fault circuit-interrupter device intended for the protection of personnel that functions to deenergize a circuit or a portion of a circuit within an established period of time when a current to ground exceeds some predetermined value that is less than that required to operate the overcurrent protective device of the supply circuit. (§1910.399)

Grounding conductor conductor used to connect equipment or the grounded circuit of a wiring system to a grounding electrode or electrodes. (§1910.399)

Grounding conductor, equipment conductor used to connect the noncurrent-carrying metal parts of equipment, raceways, and other enclosures to the system grounded conductor, the grounding electrode conductor, or both, at the service equipment or at the source of a separately derived system. (§1910.399)

Grounding electrode conductor (Grounding conductor)

(Electrical) conductor used to connect the grounding electrode to the equipment grounding conductor, to the grounded conductor, or to both, of the circuits at the service equipment or at the source of a separately derived system. (§1910.399)

(Telecommunications) conductor used to connect equipment or the grounded circuit of a wiring system to a grounding electrode. (§1910.268(s)(21))

Guard barrier that prevents entry of the operator's hands or fingers into the point of operation. (§1910.211(d)(32))

Guarded

(Electric power generation, transmission and distribution) covered, fenced, enclosed, or otherwise protected, by means of suitable covers or casings, barrier rails or screens, mats, or platforms, designed to minimize the possibility, under normal conditions, of dangerous approach or inadvertent contact by persons or objects.

Note: *Wires that are insulated, but not otherwise protected, are not guarded.* (§1910.269(x)); (Appendix B to §1910.269)

(Electrical) covered, shielded, fenced, enclosed, or otherwise protected by means of suitable covers, casings, barriers, rails, screens, mats, or platforms to remove the likelihood of approach to a point of danger or contact by persons or objects. (§1910.399)

(Logging operations) covered, shielded, fenced, enclosed, or otherwise protected by means of suitable enclosures, covers, casings, shields, troughs, railings, screens, mats, or platforms, or by location, to prevent injury. (§1910.266)(c))

Guardrail system barrier erected along an unprotected or exposed side, edge, or other area of a walking-working surface to prevent employees from falling to a lower level. (§1910.21(b))

Gudgeon pin pin connecting the mast cap to the mast allowing rotation of the mast. (§1910.181(a)(20))

Guide button building face anchor designed to engage a guide track mounted on a platform. (§1910.66(d))

Guide post pin attached to the upper or lower die shoe operating within the bushing on the opposing die shoe, to maintain the alignment of the upper and lower dies. (§1910.211(d)(37))

Guide roller
(Powered platforms for building maintenance) rotating cylindrical member, operating separately or as part of a guide assembly, designed to provide continuous engagement between the platform and the building guides or guideways. (§1910.66(d))
(Powered platforms for building maintenance/Existing installations (mandatory)) rotating, bearing-mounted, generally cylindrical member, operating separately or as part of a guide shoe assembly, attached to the platform, and providing rolling contact with building guideways, or other building contact members. (Appendix D to §1910.66(a)(12))

Guide shoe
(Powered platforms for building maintenance) assembly of rollers, slide members, or the equivalent, attached as a unit to the operators' platform, and designed to engage with the building members provided for the vertical guidance of the operators' platform. (§1910.66(d))
(Powered platforms for building maintenance/Existing installations (mandatory)) device attached to the platform designed to provide a sliding contact between the platform and the building guides. (Appendix D to §1910.66(a)(13))

Guy (See Also "Standing (guy) rope") rope used to steady or secure the mast or other member in the desired position. (§1910.181(a)(21))

Guy derrick fixed derrick consisting of a mast capable of being rotated, supported in a vertical position by guys, and a boom whose bottom end is hinged or pivoted to move in a vertical plane with a reeved rope between the head of the mast and the boom point for raising and lowering the boom, and a reeved rope from the boom point for raising and lowering the load. (§1910.181(a)(7))

H

Halon 1211 colorless, faintly sweet smelling, electrically nonconductive liquefied gas (chemical formula $CBrC_1F_2$) which is a medium for extinguishing fires by inhibiting the chemical chain reaction of fuel and oxygen. It is also known as bromochlorodifluoromethane. (§1910.155(c)(23))

Halon 1301 colorless, odorless, electrically nonconductive gas (chemical formula $CBrF_3$) which is a medium for extinguishing fires by inhibiting the chemical chain reaction of fuel and oxygen. It is also known as bromotrifluoromethane. (§1910.155(c)(24))

Hammer-operated piston tool — low-velocity type tool which, by means of a heavy mass hammer supplemented by a load, moves a piston designed to be captive to drive a stud, pin, or fastener into a work surface, always starting the fastener at rest and in contact with the work surface. It shall be so designed that when used with any load that accurately chambers in it and that is commercially available at the time the tool is submitted for approval, it will not cause such stud, pin, or fastener to have a mean velocity in excess of 300 feet per second when measured 6.5 feet from the muzzle end of the barrel. (§1910.241(a)(1))

Hand feeding tool any hand held tool designed for placing or removing material or parts to be processed within or from the point of operation. (§1910.211(d)(38))

Handhold (Handgrip) device attached to the belt which can be grasped by the passenger to provide a means of maintaining balance. (§1910.68(a)(1))

Handle terminal fitting to which metal mesh fabric is attached. (See §1910.184, Fig. N–184–1.) (§1910.184(b))

Handle eye opening in a handle of a metal mesh sling shaped to accept a hook, shackle or other lifting device. (See§1910.184, Fig. N–184–1.) (§1910.184(b))

Handrail
(Fixed industrial stairs) single bar or pipe supported on brackets from a wall or partition to provide a continuous handhold for persons using a stair. (§1910.21(b)(1))
(Guarding floor and wall openings and holes) single bar or pipe supported on brackets from a wall or partition, as on a stairway or ramp, to furnish persons with a handhold in case of tripping. (§1910.21(a)(3))
(Walking-working surfaces) rail used to provide employees with a handhold for support. (§1910.21(b))

Hands-on training training in a simulated work environment that permits each student to have experience performing tasks, making decisions, or using equipment appropriate to the job assignment for which the training is being conducted. (Appendix E to §1910.120)

Handwashing facilities facility providing an adequate supply of running potable water, soap, and single-use towels or air-drying machines. (§1910.1030(b))

Harmful physical agent See "Toxic substance or harmful physical agent"

Hazard category division of criteria within each hazard class, e.g., oral acute toxicity and flammable liquids include four hazard categories. These categories compare hazard severity within a hazard class and should not be taken as a comparison of hazard categories more generally. (§1910.1200(c))

Hazard class nature of the physical or health hazards, e.g., flammable solid, carcinogen, oral acute toxicity. (§1910.1200(c))

Hazard not otherwise classified (HNOC) adverse physical or health effect identified through evaluation of scientific evidence during the classification process that does not meet the specified criteria for the physical and health hazard classes addressed in this Section. This does not extend coverage to adverse physical and health effects for which there is a hazard class addressed in this Section, but the effect either falls below the cut-off value/concentration limit of the hazard class or is under a GHS hazard category that has not been adopted by OSHA (e.g., acute toxicity Category 5). (§1910.1200(c))

Hazard statement statement assigned to a hazard class and category that describes the nature of the hazard(s) of a chemical, including, where appropriate, the degree of hazard. (§1910.1200(c))

Hazardous atmosphere atmosphere that may expose employees to the risk of death, incapacitation, impairment of ability to self-rescue (that is, escape unaided from a permit space), injury, or acute illness from one or more of the following causes:
(1) Flammable gas, vapor, or mist in excess of 10 percent of its lower flammable limit (LFL);
(2) Airborne combustible dust at a concentration that meets or exceeds its LFL;
Note: *This concentration may be approximated as a condition in which the dust obscures vision at a distance of 5 feet (1.52 m) or less.*
(3) Atmospheric oxygen concentration below 19.5 percent or above 23.5 percent;
(4) Atmospheric concentration of any substance for which a dose or a permissible exposure limit is published in Subpart G, Occupational Health and Environmental Control, or in Subpart Z, Toxic and Hazardous Substances, of this Part and which could result in employee exposure in excess of its dose or permissible exposure limit;
Note: *An atmospheric concentration of any substance that is not capable of causing death, incapacitation, impairment of ability to self-rescue, injury, or acute illness due to its health effects is not covered by this provision.*
(5) Any other atmospheric condition that is immediately dangerous to life or health.
Note: *For air contaminants for which OSHA has not determined a dose or permissible exposure limit, other sources of information, such as Safety Data Sheets that comply with the Hazard Communication Standard, §1910.1200 of this Part, published information, and internal documents can provide guidance in establishing acceptable atmospheric conditions.* (§1910.146(b)); (§1910.269(x))

Hazardous chemical
(Hazard communication) any chemical which is classified as a physical hazard or a health hazard, a simple asphyxiant, combustible dust, pyrophoric gas, or hazard not otherwise classified. (§1910.1200(c))
(Occupational exposure to hazardous chemicals in laboratories) any chemical which is classified as health hazard or simple asphyxiant in accordance with the Hazard Communication Standard (§1910.1200).§1910.1450(b)

Appendices A and B of the Hazard Communication Standard (29 CFR §1910.1200) provide further guidance in defining the scope of health hazards and determining whether or not a chemical is to be considered hazardous for purposes of this Standard. (§1910.1450(b))

Hazardous materials response (HAZMAT) team organized group of employees, designated by the employer, who are expected to perform work to handle and control actual or potential leaks or spills of hazardous substances requiring possible close approach to the substance. The team members perform responses to releases or potential releases of hazardous substances for the purpose of control or stabilization of the incident. A HAZMAT team is not a fire brigade nor is a typical fire brigade a HAZMAT team. A HAZMAT team, however, may be a separate component of a fire brigade or fire department. (§1910.120(a)(3))

Hazardous operation any operation, procedure, or activity where a release of either vinyl chloride liquid or gas might be expected as a consequence of the operation or because of an accident in the operation, which would result in an employee exposure in excess of the permissible exposure limit. (§1910.1017(b)(7))

Hazardous substance any substance designated or listed under paragraphs (A) through (D) of this definition, exposure to which results or may result in adverse affects on the health or safety of employees:
(A) any substance defined under Section 101(14) of CERCLA;
(B) any biological agent and other disease-causing agent which after release into the environment and upon exposure, ingestion, inhalation, or assimilation into any person, either directly from the environment or indirectly by ingestion through food chains, will or may reasonably be anticipated to cause death, disease, behavioral abnormalities, cancer, genetic mutation, physiological malfunctions (including malfunctions in reproduction) or physical deformations in such persons or their offspring;
(C) any substance listed by the U.S. Department of Transportation as hazardous materials under 49 CFR §172.101 and Appendices; and
(D) hazardous waste as herein defined. (§1910.120(a)(3))

Hazardous waste means
(A) waste or combination of wastes as defined in 40 CFR 261.3, or
(B) those substances defined as hazardous wastes in 49 CFR §171.8. (§1910.120(a)(3))

Hazardous waste operation any operation conducted within the scope of this Standard. (§1910.120(a)(3))

Hazardous waste site or Site any facility or location within the scope of this Standard at which hazardous waste operations take place. (§1910.120(a)(3))

HBV hepatitis B virus. (§1910.1030(b))

Head block that part of a carriage which holds the log and upon which it rests. It generally consists of base, knee, taper set, and mechanism. (§1910.265(b)(16))

Head rig combination of head saw and log carriage used for the initial breakdown of logs into timbers, cants, and boards. (§1910.265(b)(17))

Headers See "Upsetters (or forging machines, or headers)"

Header pipe (main pipe) pipe into which one or more branch pipes enter and which connects such branch pipes to the remainder of the exhaust system. (§1910.94(b)(1)(ix))

Health care facilities buildings or portions of buildings in which medical, dental, psychiatric, nursing, obstetrical, or surgical care are provided.

Note to the definition of "health care facilities:" *Health care facilities include, but are not limited to, hospitals, nursing homes, limited care facilities, clinics, medical and dental offices, and ambulatory care centers, whether permanent or movable.* (§1910.399)

Health care provider health care practitioner operating with the scope of his/her license, certificate, registration or legally authorized practice. (§1910.266(c))

Health hazard
(Hazard communication) chemical which is classified as posing one of the following hazardous effects: acute toxicity (any route of exposure); skin corrosion or irritation; serious eye damage or eye irritation; respiratory or skin sensitization; germ cell mutagenicity; carcinogenicity; reproductive toxicity; specific target organ toxicity (single or repeated exposure); or aspiration hazard. The criteria for determining whether a chemical is classified as a health hazard are detailed in Appendix A to §1910.1200 -- Health Hazard Criteria. (§1910.1200(c))
(Hazardous waste operations and emergency response) chemical or a pathogen where acute or chronic health effects may occur in exposed employees. It also includes stress due to temperature extremes. The term health hazard includes chemicals that are classified in accordance with the Hazard Communication Standard, 29 CFR §1910.1200, as posing one of the following hazardous effects: Acute toxicity (any route of exposure); skin corrosion or irritation; serious eye damage or eye irritation; respiratory or skin sensitization; germ cell mutagenicity; carcinogenicity; reproductive toxicity; specific target organ toxicity (single or repeated exposure); aspiration toxicity or simple asphyxiant. (See Appendix A to §1910.1200—Health Hazard Criteria (Mandatory) for the criteria for determining whether a chemical is classified as a health hazard.). (§1910.120(a)(3))
(Occupational exposure to hazardous chemicals in laboratories) chemical that is classified as posing one of the following hazardous effects: Acute toxicity (any route of exposure); skin corrosion or irritation; serious eye damage or eye irritation; respiratory or skin sensitization; germ cell mutagenicity; carcinogenicity; reproductive toxicity; specific target organ toxicity (single or repeated exposure); aspiration hazard. The criteria for determining whether a chemical is classified as a health hazard are detailed in Appendix A of the hazard Communication Standard (§1910.1200) and §1910.1200(c) (definition of "simple asphyxiant") §1910.1450(b)

Health Professional physician, occupational health nurse, industrial hygienist, toxicologist, or epidemiologist, providing medical or other occupational health services to exposed employees. (§1910.1020(c)(9))

Heating equipment for the purposes of §1910.306(g), the term "heating equipment" includes any equipment used for heating purposes if heat is generated by induction or dielectric methods. (§1910.399)

Heavy gear diver-worn deep-sea dress including helmet, breastplate, dry suit, and weighted shoes. (§1910.402)

Helmet
(Fire protection) head protective device consisting of a rigid shell, energy absorption system and chin strap intended to be worn to provide protection for the head or portions thereof, against impact, flying or falling objects, electric shock, penetration, heat and flame. (§1910.155(c)(25))
(Respiratory protection) rigid respiratory inlet covering that also provides head protection against impact and penetration. (§1910.134(b))

Hertz (Hz) unit of measurement of frequency, numerically equal to cycles per second. (Appendix I to §1910.95)

High hazard area area inside a workplace in which operations include high hazard materials, processes, or contents. (§1910.34(c))

High radiation area any area, accessible to personnel, in which there exists radiation at such levels that a major portion of the body could receive in any one hour a dose in excess of 100 millirem. (§1910.1096(d)(3)(iii))

High wind wind of such velocity that the following hazards would be present:
(1) the wind could blow an employee from an elevated location,, or
(2) yhe wind could cause an employee or equipment handling material to lose control of the material, or
(3) the wind would expose an employee to other hazards not controlled by the standard involved.

Note: *The Occupational Safety and Health Administration normally considers winds exceeding 64.4 kilometers per hour (40 miles per hour), or 48.3 kilometers per hour (30 miles per hour) if the work involves material handling, as meeting this criteria, unless the employer takes precautions to protect employees from the hazardous effects of the wind.* (§1910.269(x))

High-efficiency particulate air (HEPA) filter
(Asbestos) means a filter capable of trapping and retaining at least 99.97 percent of 0.3 micrometer diameter mono-disperse particles. (§1910.1001(b))
(Cadmium) filter capable of trapping and retaining at least 99.97 percent of mono-dispersed particles of 0.3 micrometers in diameter. (§1910.1027(b))
(Chromium (VI)) filter that is at least 99.97 percent efficient in removing mono-dispersed particles of 0.3 micrometers in diameter or larger. (§1910.1026(b))
(Respiratory protection) (Respirable crystalline silica) filter that is at least 99.97% efficient in removing monodisperse particles of 0.3 micrometers in diameter. The equivalent NIOSH 42 CFR 84 particulate filters are the N100, R100, and P100 filters. (§1910.134(b)); (§1910.1053(b))

High-energy-rate forging machines class of forging equipment wherein high ram velocities resulting from the sudden release of a compressed gas against a free piston impart impact to the workpiece. (§1910.211(e)(7))

High-power tests tests in which fault currents, load currents, magnetizing currents, and line-dropping currents are used to test equipment, either at the equipment's rated voltage or at lower voltages. (§1910.269(x))

High-velocity tool tool or machine which, when used with a load, propels or discharges a stud, pin, or fastener, at velocities in excess of 300 feet per second when measured 6.5 feet from the muzzle end of the barrel, for the purpose of impinging it upon, affixing it to, or penetrating another object or material. (§1910.241(a)(2))

High-voltage tests tests in which the employer uses voltages of approximately 1,000 volts as a practical minimum and in which the voltage source has sufficient energy to cause injury. (§1910.269(x))

Highly hazardous chemical substance possessing toxic, reactive, flammable, or explosive properties and specified by paragraph §1910.119(a)(1) of this Section. (§1910.119(b))

Highway any public street, public alley, or public road. (§1910.109(a)(4))

Historical monitoring data data from chromium (VI) monitoring conducted prior to May 30, 2006, obtained during work operations conducted under workplace conditions closely resembling the processes, types of material, control methods, work practices, and environmental conditions in the employer's current operations. (§1910.1026(b))

Hitch sling configuration whereby the sling is fastened to an object or load, either directly to it or around it. (§1910.184(b))

HIV human immunodeficiency virus. (§1910.1030(b))

Hog machine for cutting or grinding slabs and other coarse residue from the mill. (§1910.265(b)(18))

Hoist hoist is an apparatus which may be a part of a crane, exerting a force for lifting or lowering. (§1910.179(a)(42))

Hoist area any elevated access opening to a walking-working surface through which equipment or materials are loaded or received. (§1910.21(b))

Hoist chain load bearing chain in a hoist.

Note: *Chain properties do not conform to those shown in ANSI B30.9–1971, Safety Code for Slings.* (§1910.179(a)(43))

Hoist motion that motion of a crane which raises and lowers a load. (§1910.179(a)(44))

Hoist rated load hoist manufacturer's maximum allowable operating load. (§1910.66(d))

Hoisting machine device intended to raise and lower a suspended or supported unit. (§1910.66(d))

Hoistway any shaftway, hatchway, well hole, or other vertical opening or space that is designed for the operation of an elevator or dumbwaiter. (§1910.399)

Holding brake brake that automatically prevents motion when power is off. (§1910.179(a)(20))

Holdout or restraint device mechanism, including attachments for operator's hands, that when anchored and adjusted prevent the operator's hands from entering the point of operation. (§1910.211(d)(14))

Hole gap or open space in a floor, roof, horizontal walking-working surface, or similar surface that is at least 2 inches (5 cm) in its least dimension. (§1910.21(b))

Homogeneous area area of surfacing material or thermal system insulation that is uniform in color and texture. (§1910.1001(b))

Hood respiratory inlet covering that completely covers the head and neck and may also cover portions of the shoulders and torso. (§1910.134(b))

Hoods and enclosures partial or complete enclosure around the wheel or disc through which air enters an exhaust system during operation. (§1910.94(b)(1)(x))

Horizontal double-spindle disc grinder grinding machine carrying two power-driven, rotatable, coaxial, horizontal spindles upon the inside ends of which are mounted abrasive disc wheels used for grinding two surfaces simultaneously. (§1910.94(b)(1)(xi))

Horizontal single-spindle disc grinder grinding machine carrying an abrasive disc wheel upon one or both ends of a power-driven, rotatable single horizontal spindle. (§1910.94(b)(1)(xii))

Host employer employer that operates, or that controls the operating procedures for, an electric power generation, transmission, or distribution installation on which a contract employer is performing work covered by this Section.

Note: *The Occupational Safety and Health Administration will treat the electric utility or the owner of the installation as the host employer if it operates or controls operating procedures for the installation. If the electric utility or installation owner neither operates nor controls operating procedures for the installation, the Occupational Safety and Health Administration will treat the employer that the utility or owner has contracted with to operate or control the operating procedures for the installation as the host employer. In no case will there be more than one host employer. (§1910.269(x))*

Hot metal handling crane overhead crane used for transporting or pouring molten material. (§1910.179(a)(7))

Hot tap procedure used in the repair, maintenance and services activities which involves welding on a piece of equipment (pipelines, vessels or tanks) under pressure, in order to install connections or appurtenances. It is commonly used to replace or add sections of pipeline without the interruption of service for air, gas, water, steam, and petrochemical distribution systems. (§1910.147(b))

Hot work work involving electric or gas welding, cutting, brazing, or similar flame or spark-producing operations. (§1910.119(b)); (§1910.272(c))

Hot work permit employer's written authorization to perform operations (for example, riveting, welding, cutting, burning, and heating) capable of providing a source of ignition. (§1910.146(b))

Hotel buildings or groups of buildings under the same management in which there are sleeping accommodations for hire, primarily used by transients who are lodged with or without meals, including but not limited to inns, clubs, motels, and apartment hotels. (§1910.106(a)(15))

Hung tree See "Lodged tree (hung tree)"

Husk head saw framework on a circular mill. (§1910.265(b)(19))

Hyperbaric conditions pressure conditions in excess of surface pressure. (§1910.402)

I

Identified (As applied to equipment) approved as suitable for the specific purpose, function, use, environment, or application, where described in a particular requirement.

Note to the definition of "identified:" *Some examples of ways to determine suitability of equipment for a specific purpose, environment, or application include investigations by a nationally recognized testing laboratory (through listing and labeling), inspection agency, or other organization recognized under the definition of "acceptable."* (§1910.399)

IDLH See " Immediately dangerous to life or health (IDLH)"

Immediate use that the hazardous chemical will be under the control of and used only by the person who transfers it from a labeled container and only within the work shift in which it is transferred. (§1910.1200(c))

Immediately dangerous to life or health (IDLH)

(Hazardous waste operations and emergency response) atmospheric concentration of any toxic, corrosive or asphyxiant substance that poses an immediate threat to life or would cause irreversible or delayed adverse health effects or would interfere with an individual's ability to escape from a dangerous atmosphere. (§1910.120(a)(3))

(Permit-required confined spaces); (Electric power generation, transmission, and distribution) any condition that poses an immediate or delayed threat to life or that would cause irreversible adverse health effects or that would interfere with an individual's ability to escape unaided from a permit space.

Note: *Some materials—hydrogen fluoride gas and cadmium vapor, for example—may produce immediate transient effects that, even if severe, may pass without medical attention, but are followed by sudden, possibly fatal collapse 12–72 hours after exposure. The victim "feels normal" from recovery from transient effects until collapse. Such materials in hazardous quantities are considered to be "immediately" dangerous to life or health.* (§1910.146(b)); (§1910.269(x))

(Respiratory protection) atmosphere that poses an immediate threat to life, would cause irreversible adverse health effects, or would impair an individual's ability to escape from a dangerous atmosphere. (§1910.134(b))

Importer first business with employees within the Customs Territory of the United States which receives hazardous chemicals produced in other countries for the purpose of supplying them to distributors or employers within the United States. (§1910.1200(c))

Inch intermittent motion imparted to the slide (on machines using part revolution clutches) by momentary operation of the Inch operating means. Operation of the Inch operating means engages the driving clutch so that a small portion of one stroke or indefinite stroking can occur, depending upon the length of time the Inch operating means is held operated. Inch is a function used by the die setter for setup of dies and tooling, but is not intended for use during production operations by the operator. (§1910.211(d)(39))

Incipient stage fire fire which is in the initial or beginning stage and which can be controlled or extinguished by portable fire extinguishers, Class II standpipe or small hose systems without the need for protective clothing or breathing apparatus. (§1910.155(c)(26))

Individual-rung ladder ladder that has rungs individually attached to a building or structure. An individual-rung ladder does not include manhole steps. (§1910.21(b))

Induction heating heating of a nominally conductive material due to its own I2 R losses when the material is placed in a varying electromagnetic field. (§1910.399)

Industrial hygienist professional qualified by education, training, and experience to anticipate, recognize, evaluate and develop controls for occupational health hazards. (§1910.1001(b))

Industrial organic solvent See "Solvent (Industrial organic)"

Industrial truck mobile power-driven truck or tractor. (§1910.265(b)(2))

Inerting displacement of the atmosphere in a permit space by a noncombustible gas (such as nitrogen) to such an extent that the resulting atmosphere is noncombustible.

Note: *This procedure produces an IDLH oxygen-deficient atmosphere.* (§1910.146(b))

Initial training training required prior to beginning work. (Appendix E to §1910.120)

Injury or illness injury or illness is an abnormal condition or disorder. Injuries include cases such as, but not limited to, a cut, fracture, sprain, or amputation. Illnesses include both acute and chronic illnesses, such as, but not limited to, a skin disease, respiratory disorder, or poisoning.
Note: *Injuries and illnesses are recordable only if they are new, work-related cases that meet one or more of the Part §1904 recording criteria.* (§1904.46)

Inorganic arsenic copper aceto-arsenite and all inorganic compounds containing arsenic except arsine, measured as arsenic (As). (§1910.1018(b))

Inorganic wheels wheels which are bonded by means of inorganic material such as clay, glass, porcelain, sodium silicate, magnesium oxychloride, or metal. Wheels bonded with clay, glass, porcelain or related ceramic materials are characterized as vitrified bonded wheels. (§1910.211(b)(16))

Inside bucket elevator bucket elevator that has the boot and more than 20 percent of the total leg height (above grade or ground level) inside the grain elevator structure. Bucket elevators with leg casings that are inside (and pass through the roofs) of rail or truck dump sheds with the remainder of the leg outside of the grain elevator structure, are not considered inside bucket elevators. (§1910.272(c))

Inspection
(1903) any inspection of an employer's factory, plant, establishment, construction site, or other area, workplace or environment where work is performed by an employee of an employer, and includes any inspection conducted pursuant to a complaint filed under §1903.11 (a) and (c), any reinspection, followup inspection, accident investigation or other inspection conducted under Section 8(a) of the Act. (§1903.22(g))
(1910) visual check of fire protection systems and equipment to ensure that they are in place, charged, and ready for use in the event of a fire. (§1910.155(c)(27))

Installation all the equipment and all affected parts of a building which are associated with the performance of building maintenance using powered platforms. (§1910.66(d))

Installing a rim wheel transfer and attachment of an assembled rim wheel onto a vehicle axle hub. Removing means the opposite of installing. (§1910.177(b))

Institutional occupancy occupancy or use of a building or structure or any portion thereof by persons harbored or detained to receive medical, charitable or other care or treatment, or by persons involuntarily detained. (§1910.106(a)(16))

Insulated separated from other conducting surfaces by a dielectric substance (including air space) offering a high resistance to the passage of current.
Note: *When any object is said to be insulated, it is understood to be insulated in suitable manner for the conditions to which it is subjected. Otherwise, it is, within the purpose of these rules, uninsulated. Insulating coverings of conductors in one means of making the conductor insulated.* (§1910.268(s)(22)); (§1910.269(x)); (Appendix B to §1910.269); (§1910.399)

Insulated aerial device aerial device designed for work on energized lines and apparatus. (§1910.67(a)(5))

Insulated conductor See "Conductor (Electrical), insulated"

Insulation (as applied to cable) that which is relied upon to insulate the conductor from other conductors or conducting parts or from ground. (§1910.268(s)(23)); (§1910.269(x))

Intentional explosive chemical or item which is manufactured with a view to produce a practical explosive or pyrotechnic effect. (Appendix B to §1910.1200(B.1.1.1)

Interior structural firefighting physical activity of fire suppression, rescue or both, inside of buildings or enclosed structures which are involved in a fire situation beyond the incipient stage. (§1910.134(b)); (§1910.155(c)(28))

Interlock
(Powered platforms for building maintenance) device designed to ensure that operations or motions occur in proper sequence. (§1910.66(d))
(Powered platforms for building maintenance/Existing installations)) device actuated by the operation of some other device with which it is directly associated, to govern succeeding operations of the same or allied devices. (Appendix D to §1910.66(a)(14))
(Textiles) interlock is a device that operates to prevent the operation of machine while the cover or door of the machine is open or unlocked, and which will also hold the cover or door closed and locked while the machine is in motion. (§1910.262(b)(15))

Interlocked press barrier guard barrier attached to the press frame and interlocked so that the press stroke cannot be started normally unless the guard itself, or its hinged or movable sections, enclose the point of operation. (§1910.211(d)(35))

Intermittent stabilization method of platform stabilization in which the angulated suspension wire rope(s) are secured to regularly spaced building anchors. (§1910.66(d))

Interrupter switch (Over 600 volts, nominal) switch capable of making, carrying, and interrupting specified currents. (§1910.399)

Intrusion coefficient number expressing the level of protection provided by a gas tight totally-encapsulating chemical protective suit. The intrusion coefficient is calculated by dividing the test room challenge agent concentration by the concentration of challenge agent found inside the suit. The accuracy of the intrusion coefficient is dependent on the challenge agent monitoring methods. The larger the intrusion coefficient the greater the protection provided by the TECP suit. (Appendix A to §1910.120(2.4))

Inwater stage suspended underwater platform which supports a diver in the water. (§1910.402)

Irrigation machine electrically driven or controlled machine, with one or more motors, not hand portable, and used primarily to transport and distribute water for agricultural purposes. (§1910.399)

Isolated not readily accessible to persons unless special means for access are used. (§1910.269)(x); (§1910.399)

Isolated power system system comprising an isolating transformer or its equivalent, a line isolation monitor, and its ungrounded circuit conductors. (§1910.399)

Isolated system fully enclosed structure other than the vessel of containment of a carcinogen addressed by this Section that is impervious to the passage of the material and would prevent the entry of the carcinogen addressed by this Section into regulated areas, nonregulated areas, or the external environment, should leakage or spillage from the vessel of containment occur. (§1910.1003(b))

Isolation process by which a permit space is removed from service and completely protected against the release of energy and material into the space by such means as: blanking or blinding; misaligning or removing sections of lines, pipes, or ducts; a double block and bleed system; lockout or tagout of all sources of energy; or blocking or disconnecting all mechanical linkages. (§1910.146(b))

J

Jack (See Also "Rating") appliance for lifting and lowering or moving horizontally a load by application of a pushing force.
Note: *Jacks may be of the following types: Lever and ratchet, screw and hydraulic.* (§1910.241(d)(1))

Jib extension attached to the boom point to provide added boom length for lifting specified loads. The jib may be in line with the boom or offset to various angles. (§1910.180(a)(25))

Jig (dye) machine for dyeing piece goods. The cloth, at full width, passes from a roller through the dye liquor in an open vat and is then wound on another roller. The operation is repeated until the desired shade is obtained. (§1910.262(b)(16))

Jog intermittent motion imparted to the slide by momentary operation of the drive motor, after the clutch is engaged with the flywheel at rest. (§1910.211(d)(40))

Jogging repeated starting and stopping of drive motors in an attempt to clear choked legs. (§1910.272(c))

Joint use sharing of a common facility, such as a manhole, trench or pole, by two or more different kinds of utilities (e.g., power and telecommunications). (§1910.268(s)(24))

K

Kier large mental vat, usually a pressure type, in which fabrics may be boiled out, bleached, etc. (§1910.262(b)(17))

Kiln tender operator of a kiln. (§1910.265(b)(21))

Knockout mechanism for releasing material from either die. (§1910.211(d)(41))

L

Label appropriate group of written, printed or graphic information elements concerning a hazardous chemical that is affixed to, printed on, or attached to the immediate container of a hazardous chemical, or to the outside packaging. (§1910.1200(c))

Label elements specified pictogram, hazard statement, signal word and precautionary statement for each hazard class and category. (§1910.1200(c))

Labeled Equipment is "labeled" if there is attached to it a label, symbol, or other identifying mark of a nationally recognized testing laboratory:
(1) that makes periodic inspections of the production of such equipment, and
(2) whose labeling indicates compliance with nationally recognized standards or tests to determine safe use in a specified manner. (§1910.399)

Laboratory facility where the "laboratory use of hazardous chemicals" occurs. It is a workplace where relatively small quantities of hazardous chemicals are used on a non-production basis. (§1910.1450(b))

Laboratory scale work with substances in which the containers used for reactions, transfers, and other handling of substances are designed to be easily and safely manipulated by one person. "Laboratory scale" excludes those workplaces whose function is to produce commercial quantities of materials. (§1910.1450(b))

Laboratory use of hazardous chemicals handling or use of such chemicals in which all of the following conditions are met:
(i) chemical manipulations are carried out on a "laboratory scale;"
(ii) multiple chemical procedures or chemicals are used;
(iii) the procedures involved are not part of a production process, nor in any way simulate a production process; and
(iv) "protective laboratory practices and equipment" are available and in common use to minimize the potential for employee exposure to hazardous chemicals. (§1910.1450(b))

Laboratory-type hood
(13 Carcinogens) device enclosed on the three sides and the top and bottom, designed and maintained so as to draw air inward at an average linear face velocity of 150 feet per minute with a minimum of 125 feet per minute; designed, constructed, and maintained in such a way that an operation involving a carcinogen addressed by this Section within the hood does not require the insertion of any portion of any employee's body other than his hands and arms. (§1910.1003(b))
(Occupational exposure to hazardous chemicals in laboratories) device located in a laboratory, enclosure on five sides with a moveable sash or fixed partial enclosed on the remaining side; constructed and maintained to draw air from the laboratory and to prevent or minimize the escape of air contaminants into the laboratory; and allows chemical manipulations to be conducted in the enclosure without insertion of any portion of the employee's body other than hands and arms. (§1910.1450(b))

Ladder device with rungs, steps, or cleats used to gain access to a different elevation. (§1910.21(b))

Ladder platform device designed to facilitate working aloft from an extension ladder. A typical device consists of a platform (approximately 9"×18") hinged to a welded pipe frame. The rear edge of the platform and the bottom cross-member of the frame are equipped with latches to lock the platform to ladder rungs. (§1910.268(s)(25))

Ladder safety system system designed to eliminate or reduce the possibility of falling from a ladder. A ladder safety system usually consists of a carrier, safety sleeve, lanyard, connectors, and body harness. Cages and wells are not ladder safety systems. (§1910.21(b))

Ladder seat removable seat used to facilitate work at an elevated position on rolling ladders in telecommunication centers. (§1910.268(s)(26))

Ladder stand mobile fixed size self-supporting ladder consisting of a wide flat tread ladder in the form of stairs. The assembly may include handrails. (§1910.21(g)(9))

Lagging covering on drive pulleys used to increase the coefficient of friction between the pulley and the belt. (§1910.272(c))

Landing any place where logs are laid after being yarded, and before transport from the work site. (§1910.266(c))

Lanyard (See Also "Self-retracting lifeline/lanyard") flexible line of rope, wire rope or strap which is used to secure the body belt or body harness to a deceleration device, lifeline or anchorage. (§1910.66(d)); (Appendix C to §1910.66(b))

Lapper (ribbon) machine used to prepare laps for feeding a cotton comb; its purpose is to provide a uniform lap in which the fibers have been straightened as much as possible. (§1910.262(b)(18))

Lapper (sliver) machine in which a number of parallel card slivers are drafted slightly, laid side by side in a compact sheet, and wound into a cylindrical package. (§1910.262(b)(19))

Lateral stability truck's resistance to overturning sideways. (Appendix A to §1910.178)

Lead metallic lead, all inorganic lead compounds, and organic lead soaps. Excluded from this definition are all other organic lead compounds. (§1910.1025(b))

Licensed Healthcare Professional person whose legally permitted scope of practice allows him or her to independently perform the activities required by paragraph (f) Hepatitis B Vaccination and Post-exposure Evaluation and Follow-up. (§1910.1030(b))

Lifeline (See Also "Self-retracting lifeline/lanyard") component consisting of a flexible line for connection to an anchorage at one end to hang vertically (vertical lifeline), or for connection to anchorages at both ends to stretch horizontally (horizontal lifeline), and which serves as a means for connecting other components of a personal fall arrest system to the anchorage. (§1910.66(d)); (Appendix C to §1910.66(b))

Lift truck industrial truck used for lateral transportation and equipped with a power-operated lifting device, usually in the form of forks, for piling or unpiling lumber units or packages. (§1910.265(b)(22))

Liftout mechanism also known as knockout. (§1910.211(d)(42))

Lighting outlet outlet intended for the direct connection of a lampholder, a lighting fixture, or a pendant cord terminating in a lampholder. (§1910.399)

Limbing to cut branches off felled trees. (§1910.266(c))

Limit of Detection using a predefined level of confidence, this is the lowest measured value at which some of the measured material is likely to have come from the sample. (Appendix F to §1910.1027)

Limit switch
(Manlifts) device, the purpose of which is to cut off the power to the motor and apply the brake to stop the carrier in the event that a loaded step passes the terminal landing. (§1910.68(a)(4))
(Overhead and gantry cranes) limit switch is a switch which is operated by some part or motion of a power-driven machine or equipment to alter the electric circuit associated with the machine or equipment. (§1910.179(a)(60))

Line breaking intentional opening of a pipe, line, or duct that is or has been carrying flammable, corrosive, or toxic material, an inert gas, or any fluid at a volume, pressure, or temperature capable of causing injury. (§1910.146(b))

Line of action imaginary vertical line through an object's center of gravity. (Appendix A to §1910.178)

Line-clearance tree trimmer employee who, through related training or on-the-job experience or both is familiar with the special techniques and hazards involved in line-clearance tree trimming.
Note 1: *An employee who is regularly assigned to a line-clearance tree-trimming crew and who is undergoing on-the-job training and who, in the course of such training, has demonstrated and ability to perform duties safely at his or her level of training and who is under the direct supervision of a line-clearance tree trimmer is considered to be a line-clearance tree trimmer for the performance of those duties.*
Note 2: *A line-clearance tree trimmer is not considered to be a "qualified employee" under §1910.269 unless he or she has the training required for a qualified employee under §1910.269(a)(2)(ii). However, under the electrical safety-related work practices Standard in Subpart S of this Part, a line-clearance tree trimmer is considered to be a "qualified employee." Tree trimming performed by such "qualified employees" is not subject to the electrical safety-related work practice requirements contained in §1910.331 through §1910.335 of this Part. (See Also the note following §1910.332(b)(3) of this Part for information regarding the training an employee must have to be considered a qualified employee under §1910.331 through §1910.335 of this Part.)* (§1910.269(x))

Line-clearance tree trimming pruning, trimming, repairing, maintaining, removing, or clearing of trees, or the cutting of brush, that is within the following distance of electric supply lines and equipment:
(1) For voltages to ground of 50 kilovolts or less—3.05 meters (10 feet);
(2) For voltages to ground of more than 50 kilovolts—3.05 meters (10 feet) plus 0.10 meters (4 inches) for every 10 kilovolts over 50 kilovolts. (§1910.269(x))

Lines (See Also "Communication lines")
(1) Communication lines The conductors and their supporting or containing structures which are used for public or private signal or communication service, and which operate at potentials not exceeding 400 volts to ground or 750 volts between any two points of the circuit, and the transmitted power of which does not exceed 150 watts. If the lines are operating at less than 150 volts, no limit is placed on the transmitted power of the system. Under certain conditions, communication cables may include communication circuits exceeding these limitations where such circuits are also used to supply power solely to communication equipment.
Note: *Telephone, telegraph, railroad signal, data, clock, fire, police alarm, cable television, and other systems conforming to this definition are included. Lines used for signaling purposes, but not included under this definition, are considered as electric supply lines of the same voltage.*
(2) Electric supply lines Conductors used to transmit electric energy and their necessary supporting or containing structures. Signal lines of more than 400 volts are always supply lines within this section, and those of less than 400 volts are considered as supply lines, if so run and operated throughout. (§1910.269(x))

Lining material permanently attached to the inside of the outer shell of a garment for the purpose of thermal protection and padding. (§1910.155(c)(29))

Link single ring of a chain. (§1910.184(b))

Lint-free respirable cotton dust particles of cotton dust of approximately 15 micrometers or less aerodynamic equivalent diameter; (§1910.1043(b))

Liquid for the purpose of this Section, any material which has a fluidity greater than that of 300 penetration asphalt when tested in accordance with ASTM Test for Penetration for Bituminous Materials, D–5–65, which is incorporated by reference as specified in §1910.6. (§1910.106(a)(17))

Liquid AN AN monomer in liquid form, and liquid or semiliquid polymer intermediates, including slurries, suspensions, emulsions, and solutions, produced during the polymerization of AN. (§1910.1045(b))

Liquefied petroleum gases "LPG" and "LP-Gas" mean and include any material which is composed predominantly of any of the following hydrocarbons, or mixtures of them, such as propane, propylene, butane (normal butane or iso-butane), and butylenes. (§1910.110(a)(7))

Listed (See Also "Approved") equipment is "listed" if it is of a kind mentioned in a list that:
(1) is published by a nationally recognized laboratory that makes periodic inspection of the production of such equipment, and
(2) states that such equipment meets nationally recognized standards or has been tested and found safe for use in a specified manner. (§1910.399)

Live See "Alive or live (Energized)"

Live load total static weight of workers, tools, parts, and supplies that the equipment is designed to support. (§1910.66(d))

Live parts energized conductive components. (§1910.399)

Live rolls cylinders of wood or metal mounted on horizontal axes and rotated by power, which are used to convey slabs, lumber, and other wood products. (§1910.265(b)(23))

Liveboating practice of supporting a surfaced-supplied air or mixed gas diver from a vessel which is underway. (§1910.402)

Load (See Also "Explosive powerload") total superimposed weight on the load block or hook. (§1910.179(a)(45))

Load block assembly of hook or shackle, swivel, bearing, sheaves, pins, and frame suspended by the hoisting rope. (§1910.179(a)(46))

Load block (lower)
(Crawler, locomotive, and truck cranes) assembly of hook or shackle, swivel, sheaves, pins, and frame suspended by the hoisting ropes. (§1910.180(a)(28)
(Derricks) assembly of sheaves, pins, and frame suspended by the hoisting rope. (§1910.181(a)(23))

Load block (upper)
(Crawler, locomotive, and truck cranes) assembly of hook or shackle, swivel, sheaves, pins, and frame suspended from the boom point. (§1910.181(a)(27)
(Derricks) assembly of sheaves, pins, and frame suspended from the boom. (§1910.181(a)(24))

Load center horizontal distance from the load's edge (or the fork's or other attachment's vertical face) to the line of action through the load's center of gravity. (Appendix A to §1910.178)

Load hoist hoist drum and rope reeving system used for hoisting and lowering loads. (§1910.180(a)(29))

Load ratings crane ratings in pounds established by the manufacturer in accordance with paragraph (c) of this Section. (§1910.180(a)(30))

Load (working)
(Crawler, locomotive, and truck cranes) external load, in pounds, applied to the crane, including the weight of load-attaching equipment such as load blocks, shackles, and slings. (§1910.180(a)(26))
(Derricks) external load, in pounds, applied to the derrick, including the weight of load attaching equipment such as load blocks, shackles, and slings. (§1910.181(a)(22))

Loading boom any structure projecting from a pivot point to guide a log when lifted. (§1910.265(b)(24))

Local application system fixed fire suppression system which has a supply of extinguishing agent, with nozzles arranged to automatically discharge extinguishing agent directly on the burning material to extinguish or control a fire. (§1910.155(c)(30))

Location
(1) Damp location partially protected locations under canopies, marquees, roofed open porches, and like locations, and interior locations subject to moderate degrees of moisture, such as some basements, some barns, and some cold-storage warehouses.
(2) Dry location location not normally subject to dampness or wetness. A location classified as dry may be temporarily subject to dampness or wetness, as in the case of a building under construction.
(3) Wet location installations underground or in concrete slabs or masonry in direct contact with the earth, and locations subject to saturation with water or other liquids, such as vehicle-washing areas, and locations unprotected and exposed to weather. (§1910.399)

Locations See "Class I locations;" "Class II locations;" "Class III locations"

Lockout placement of a lockout device on an energy isolating device, in accordance with an established procedure, ensuring that the energy isolating device and the equipment being controlled cannot be operated until the lockout device is removed. (§1910.147(b))

Lockout device device that utilizes a positive means such as a lock, either key or combination type, to hold an energy isolating device in a safe position and prevent the energizing of a machine or equipment. Included are blank flanges and bolted slip blinds. (§1910.147(b))

Locomotive crane locomotive crane consists of a rotating superstructure with power-plant, operating machinery and boom, mounted on a base or car equipped for travel on railroad track. It may be self-propelled or propelled by an outside source. Its function is to hoist and swing loads at various radii. (§1910.180(a)(2))

Lodged tree (hung tree) tree leaning against another tree or object which prevents it from falling to the ground. (§1910.266(c))

Log segment sawed or split from a felled tree, such as, but not limited to, a section, bolt, or tree length. (§1910.266(c))

Log carriage See "Carriage (Log carriage)"

Log deck platform in the sawmill on which the logs remain until needed for sawing. (§1910.265(b)(25))

Log haul conveyor for transferring logs to mill. (§1910.265(b)(27))

Logging operations operations associated with felling and moving trees and logs from the stump to the point of delivery, such as, but not limited to, marking danger trees and trees/logs to be cut to length, felling, limbing, bucking, debarking, chipping, yarding, loading, unloading, storing, and transporting machines, equipment and personnel to, from and between logging sites. (§1910.266(c))

Longitudinal stability truck's resistance to overturning forward or rearward. (Appendix A to §1910.178)

Longshoring operation loading, unloading, moving, or handling of, cargo, ship's stores, gear, etc., into, in, on, or out of any vessel. (§1910.16(c)(1))

Loom for effecting the interlacing of two series of yarns crossing one another at right angles. The warp yarns are wound on a warp beam and pass through heddles and reed. The filling is shot across in a shuttle and settled in place by reed and lay, and the fabric is wound on a cloth beam. (§1910.262(b)(20))

Loose-fitting facepiece respiratory inlet covering that is designed to form a partial seal with the face. (§1910.134(b))

Low-pressure tank storage tank which has been designed to operate at pressures above 0.5 p.s.i.g. but not more than 15 p.s.i.g. (§1910.106(a)(21))

Low-slope roof roof that has a slope less than or equal to a ratio of 4 in 12 (vertical to horizontal). (§1910.21(b))

Low-velocity piston tool tool that utilizes a piston designed to be captive to drive a stud, pin, or fastener into a work surface. It shall be so designed that when used with any load that accurately chambers in it and that is commercially available at the time the tool is submitted for approval, it will not cause such stud, pin, or fastener to have a mean velocity in excess of 300 feet per second when measured 6.5 feet from the muzzle end of the barrel. (§1910.241(a)(3))

Lower flammable limit (LFL) lowest concentration of a material that will propagate a flame. The LFL is usually expressed as a percent by volume of the material in air (or other oxidant). (§1910.123(d))

Lower level surface or area to which an employee could fall. Such surfaces or areas include, but are not limited to, ground levels, floors, roofs, ramps, runways, excavations, pits, tanks, materials, water, equipment, and similar surfaces and structures, or portions thereof. (§1910.21(b))

Lumber hauling truck industrial truck, other than a lift truck or a carrier, used for the transport of lumber. (§1910.265(b)(26))

M

Machine piece of stationary or mobile equipment having a self-contained powerplant, that is operated off-road and used for the movement of material. Machines include, but are not limited to, tractors, skidders, front-end loaders, scrapers, graders, bulldozers, swing yarders, log stackers, log loaders, and mechanical felling devices, such as tree shears and feller-bunchers. Machines do not include airplanes or aircraft (e.g., helicopters). (§1910.266(c))

Magazine any building or structure, other than an explosives manufacturing building, used for the storage of explosives. (§1910.109(a)(6))

Magnet electromagnetic device carried on a crane hook to pick up loads magnetically. (§1910.179(a)(47))

Main hoist hoist mechanism provided for lifting the maximum rated load. (§1910.179(a)(48))

Main switch switch controlling the entire power supply to the crane. (§1910.179(a)(61))

Maintenance (See Also "Servicing and/or maintenance") performance of service on fire protection equipment and systems to assure that they will perform as expected in the event of a fire. Maintenance differs from inspection in that maintenance requires the checking of internal fittings, devices, and agent supplies. (§1910.155(c)(31))

Maintenance runway any permanent runway or platform used for oiling, maintenance, running adjustment, or repair work, but not for passageway. (§1910.211(f)(6))

Major message that portion of a tag's inscription that is more specific than the signal word and that indicates the specific hazardous condition or the instruction to be communicated to the employee. Examples include: "High Voltage," "Close Clearance," "Do Not Start," or "Do Not Use" or a corresponding pictograph used with a written text or alone. (§1910.141(a)(2))

Male handle (triangle) (See Also "Handle eye") is a handle with a handle eye. (§1910.184(b))

Man trolley trolley having an operator's cab attached thereto. (§1910.179(a)(49))

Mangle (starch) starch mangle is a mangle that is used specifically for starching cotton goods. It commonly consists of two large rolls and a shallow open vat with several immersion rolls. The vat contains the starch solution. (§1910.262(b)(21))

Mangle (water) water mangle is a calender having two or more rolls used for squeezing water from fabrics before drying. Water mangles also may be used in other ways during the finishing of various fabrics. (§1910.262(b)(22))

Manhole subsurface enclosure which personnel may enter and which is used for the purpose of installing, operating, and maintaining submersible equipment and/or cable. (§1910.268(s)(27)); (§1910.269(x))

Manhole platform platform consisting of separate planks which are laid across steel platform supports. The ends of the supports are engaged in the manhole cable racks. (§1910.268(s)(28))

Manhole steps

(Walking-working sufaces) steps that are individually attached to, or set into, the wall of a manhole structure. (§1910.21(b))

(Electric power generation, transmission, and distribution) series of steps individually attached to or set into the walls of a manhole structure. (§1910.269(x))

Manlift device consisting of a power-driven endless belt moving in one direction only, and provided with steps or platforms and handholds attached to it for the transportation of personnel from floor to floor. (§1910.68(a)(5))

Manual feeding (See Also "Automatic feeding;" "Feeding;" "Semiautomatic feeding") feeding wherein the material or part being processed is handled by the operator on each stroke of the press. (§1910.211(d)(29))

Marine service station that portion of a property where flammable liquids used as fuels are stored and dispensed from fixed equipment on shore, piers, wharves, or floating docks into the fuel tanks of self-propelled craft, and shall include all facilities used in connection therewith. (§1910.106(a)(22))

Marine terminal wharves, bulkheads, quays, piers, docks and other berthing locations and adjacent storage or adjacent areas and structures associated with the primary movement of cargo or materials from vessel to shore or shore to vessel including structures which are devoted to receiving, handling, holding, consolidation and loading or delivery of waterborne shipments or passengers, including areas devoted to the maintenance of the terminal or equipment. The term does not include production or manufacturing areas having their own docking facilities and located at a marine terminal nor does the term include storage facilities directly associated with those production or manufacturing areas. (§1910.16(c)(4))

Mast upright member of the derrick. (§1910.181(a)(25))

Mast cap (spider) fitting at the top of the mast to which the guys are connected. (§1910.181(a)(26))

Master coupling link alloy steel welded coupling link used as an intermediate link to join alloy steel chain to master links. (See §1910.184, Fig. N–184–3.) (§1910.184(b))

Master link or gathering ring forged or welded steel link used to support all members (legs) of an alloy steel chain sling or wire rope sling. (See §1910.184, Fig. N–184–3.) (§1910.184(b))

Master switch switch which dominates the operation of contactors, relays, or other remotely operated devices. (§1910.179(a)(62))

Maximum intended load total load (weight and force) of all employees, equipment, vehicles, tools, materials, and other loads the employer reasonably anticipates to be applied to a walking-working surface at any one time. (§1910.21(b))

Maximum use concentration (MUC) the maximum atmospheric concentration of a hazardous substance from which an employee can be expected to be protected when wearing a respirator, and is determined by the assigned protection factor of the respirator or class of respirators and the exposure limit of the hazardous substance. The MUC can be determined mathematically by multiplying the assigned protection factor specified for a respirator by the required OSHA permissible exposure limit, short-term exposure limit, or ceiling limit. When no OSHA exposure limit is available for a hazardous substance, an employer must determine an MUC on the basis of relevant available information and informed professional judgment. (§1910.134(b))

Mean (See Also "Arithmetic mean") central tendency of a set of data; in this protocol, this mean is defined as the arithmetic mean unless stated otherwise. (Appendix F to §1910.1027)

Measurement value See "Value or measurement value"

Mechanical method of control by friction. (§1910.179(a)(33))

Mechanical coupling link nonwelded, mechanically closed steel link used to attach master links, hooks, etc., to alloy steel chain. (§1910.184(b))

Medical consultation consultation which takes place between an employee and a licensed physician for the purpose of determining what medical examinations or procedures, if any, are appropriate in cases where a significant exposure to a hazardous chemical may have taken place. (§1910.1450(b))

Medical pathology disorder or disease. For purposes of this regulation, a condition or disease affecting the ear, which should be treated by a physician specialist. (Appendix I to §1910.95)

Medical removal protection benefits

(Benzene) for the purposes of §1910.1028, the requirement that an employer provide medical removal protection benefits means that the employer shall maintain the current wage rate, seniority and other benefits of an employee as though the employee had not been removed. (§1910.1028(i)(9)(ii))

(Cadmium) for purposes of §1910.1027, the requirement that the employer provide MRPB means that the employer shall maintain the total normal earnings, seniority, and all other employee rights and benefits of the removed employee, including the employee's right to his/her former job status, as if the employee had not been removed from the employee's job or otherwise medically limited. (§1910.1027(l)(12)(ii))

(Lead) for the purposes of §1910.1025, the requirement that an employer provide medical removal protection benefits means that the employer shall maintain the earnings, seniority and other employment rights and benefits of an employee as though the employee had not been removed from normal exposure to lead or otherwise limited. (§1910.1025(k)(2)(ii))

(Methylene Chloride) for purposes of this paragraph (§1910.1052(j), the term medical removal protection benefits means that, for each removal, an employer must maintain for up to six months the earnings, seniority, and other employment rights and benefits of the employee as though the employee had not been removed from MC exposure or transferred to a comparable job. (§1910.1052(j)(12)(i))

(Methylenedianiline) for the purposes of 910.1050, the requirement that an employer provide medical removal protection benefits means that the employer shall maintain the earnings, seniority, and other employment rights and benefits of an employee as though the employee had not been removed from normal exposure to MDA or otherwise limited. (§1910.1050(m)(9)(v)(B))

Medical treatment management and care of a patient to combat disease or disorder. For the purposes of Part §1904, medical treatment does not include:

(A) visits to a physician or other licensed health care professional solely for observation or counseling;

(B) the conduct of diagnostic procedures, such as x-rays and blood tests, including the administration of prescription medications used solely for diagnostic purposes (e.g., eye drops to dilate pupils); (§1904.7(b)(5)(i))

Medium voltage cable (Type MV) single or multiconductor solid dielectric insulated cable rated 2000 volts or higher. (§1910.399)

Mercantile occupancy occupancy or use of a building or structure or any portion thereof for the displaying, selling, or buying of goods, wares, or merchandise. (§1910.106(a)(23))

Mercerizing range See "Ranges (mercerizing)"

Metal-clad cable (Type MC) factory assembly of one or more insulated circuit conductors with or without optical fiber members enclosed in an armor of interlocking metal tape, or a smooth or corrugated metallic sheath. (§1910.399)

Methylene chloride (MC) organic compound with chemical formula, CH_2Cl_2. Its Chemical Abstracts Service Registry Number is 75–09–2. Its molecular weight is 84.9 g/mole. (§1910.1052(b))

Microwave transmission act of communicating or signaling utilizing a frequency between 1 GHz(gigahertz) and 300 GHz inclusively. (§1910.268(s)(29))

Mill machine consisting of two adjacent metal rolls, set horizontally, which revolve in opposite directions (i.e., toward each other as viewed from above) used for the mechanical working of rubber and plastics compounds. (§1910.211(c)(3))

Mineral-insulated metal-sheathed cable (Type MI) factory assembly of one or more conductors insulated with a highly compressed refractory mineral insulation and enclosed in a liquid-tight and gas-tight continuous copper or alloy steel sheath. (§1910.399)

Minimum approach distance closest distance an employee may approach an energized or a grounded object.

Note: *Paragraph (l)(3)(i) of this §1910.269 requires employers to establish minimum approach distances.* (§1910.269(x))

Minimum maintained velocity velocity of air movement which must be maintained in order to meet minimum specified requirements for health and safety. (§1910.94(c)(1)(iv))

Mixed-gas diving diving mode in which the diver is supplied in the water with a breathing gas other than air. (§1910.402)

Mixture combination or a solution composed of two or more substances in which they do not react. (§1910.1200(c))

Mobile manually propelled or moveable. (§1910.21(b))

Mobile ladder stand (ladder stand) mobile, fixed-height, self-supporting ladder that usually consists of wheels or casters on a rigid base and steps leading to a top step. A mobile ladder stand also may have handrails and is designed for use by one employee at a time. (§1910.21(b))

Mobile ladder stand platform mobile, fixed-height, self-supporting unit having one or more standing platforms that are provided with means of access or egress manually propelled or moveable. (§1910.21(b))

Mobile unit combination of an aerial device, its vehicle, and related equipment. (§1910.67(a)(6))

Mobile X-ray (See Also "Portable X-ray;" "Transportable X-ray") X-ray equipment mounted on a permanent base with wheels and/or casters for moving while completely assembled. (§1910.399)

Modified types 6 and 11 wheels (terrazzo) some type 6 and 11 cup wheels used in the terrazzo trade having tapered K dimensions to match a special tapered flange furnished by the machine builder.

Limitation: *These wheels shall be mounted only with a special tapered flange.* (§1910.211(b)(5), Fig. No. 0-5.)

Moment product of the object's weight times the distance from a fixed point (usually the fulcrum). In the case of a powered industrial truck, the distance is measured from the point at which the truck will tip over to the object's line of action. The distance is always measured perpendicular to the line of action. (Appendix A to §1910.178)

Motor control center assembly of one or more enclosed sections having a common power bus and principally containing motor control units. (§1910.399)

Motor vehicle any self-propelled vehicle, truck, tractor, semitrailer, or truck-full trailers used for the transportation of freight over public highways. (§1910.109(a)(7))

Mounted wheels mounted wheels, usually 2-inch diameter or smaller, and of various shapes, may be either organic or inorganic bonded abrasive wheels. They are secured to plain or threaded steel mandrels. (§1910.241(b)(1))

Mounting a tire assembly or putting together of the wheel and tire components to form a rim wheel, including inflation. "Demounting" means the opposite of mounting. (§1910.177(b))

Movable barrier device See "Gate or movable barrier device"

Movable equipment hand-held or non-hand-held machine or device, powered or unpowered, that is used to do work and is moved within or between worksites. (§1903.19(b)(5))

Movable fuel storage tenders or farm carts containers not in excess of 1,200 gallons water capacity, equipped with wheels to be towed from one location of usage to another. They are basically non-highway vehicles, but may occasionally be moved over public roads or highways. They are used as a fuel supply for farm tractors, construction machinery and similar equipment. (§1910.110(a)(8))

Mule type of spinning frame having a head stock and a carriage as its two main sections. The head stock is stationary. The carriage is movable and it carries the spindles which draft and spin the roving into the yarn. The carriage extends over the whole width of the machine and moves slowly toward and away from the head stock during the spinning operation. (§1910.262(b)(23))

Multi-piece rim wheel assemblage of a multi-piece wheel with the tire tube and other components. (§1910.177(b))

Multi-piece wheel vehicle wheel consisting of two or more parts, one of which is a side or locking ring designed to hold the tire on the wheel by interlocking components when the tire is inflated. (§1910.177(b))

Multipurpose dry chemical dry chemical which is approved for use on Class A, Class B, and Class C fires. (§1910.155(c)(1))

Mutagen chemicals that cause permanent changes in the amount or structure of the genetic material in a cell. Chemicals classified as mutagens in accordance with the Hazard Communication Standard (§1910.1200) shall be considered mutagens for purposes of this Section. §1910.1450(b)

Mutation permanent change in the amount or structure of the genetic material in a cell. The term mutation applies both to heritable genetic changes that may be manifested at the phenotypic level and to the underlying DNA modifications when known (including, for example, specific base pair changes and chromosomal translocations). The term mutagenic and mutagen will be used for agents giving rise to an increased occurrence of mutations in populations of cells and/or organisms. (Appendix A to §1910.1200(A.5.1.1))

N

National consensus standard any standard or modification thereof which:
(1) has been adopted and promulgated by a nationally recognized standards-producing organization under procedures whereby it can be determined by the Secretary of Labor or by the Assistant Secretary of Labor that persons interested and affected by the scope or provisions of the standard have reached substantial agreement on its adoption,
(2) was formulated in a manner which afforded an opportunity for diverse views to be considered, and
(3) has been designated as such a standard by the Secretary or the Assistant Secretary, after consultation with other appropriate Federal agencies; (§1910.2(g))

Needleless systems device that does not use needles for:
(1) the collection of bodily fluids or withdrawal of body fluids after initial venous or arterial access is established;
(2) the administration of medication or fluids; or
(3) any other procedure involving the potential for occupational exposure to bloodborne pathogens due to percutaneous injuries from contaminated sharps. (§1910.1030(b))

Negative pressure respirator (tight fitting) (See Also "Pressure demand respirator;" "Supplied-air respirator (SAR or airline respirator;" "User seal check") respirator in which the air pressure inside the facepiece is negative during inhalation with respect to the ambient air pressure outside the respirator. (§1910.134(b))

Nip point of contact between two in-running rolls. (§1910.262(b)(24))

Nip-point belt and pulley guard device which encloses the pulley and is provided with rounded or rolled edge slots through which the belt passes. (§1910.211(f)(7))

No movement of the slide or ram See "Full stop or movement of the slide or ram"

No-decompression limits the depth-time limits of the "no-decompression limits and repetitive dive group designation table for no-decompression air dives", U.S. Navy Diving Manual or equivalent limits which the employer can demonstrate to be equally effective. (§1910.402)

Noise dose ratio, expressed as a percentage, of
(1) the time integral, over a stated time or event, of the 0.6 power of the measured SLOW exponential time-averaged, squared A-weighted sound pressure and
(2) the product of the criterion duration (8 hours) and the 0.6 power of the squared sound pressure corresponding to the criterion sound level (90 dB). (Appendix I to §1910.95)

Noise dosimeter instrument that integrates a function of sound pressure over a period of time in such a manner that it directly indicates a noise dose. (Appendix I to §1910.95)

Nominal voltage nominal voltage of a system or circuit is the value assigned to a system or circuit of a given voltage class for the purpose of convenient designation. The actual voltage may vary above or below this value. (§1910.268(s)(30))

Non-permit confined space confined space that does not contain or, with respect to atmospheric hazards, have the potential to contain any hazard capable of causing death or serious physical harm. (§1910.146(b))

Nonmetallic-sheathed cable (Types NM, NMC, and NMS) factory assembly of two or more insulated conductors having an outer sheath of moisture resistant, flame-retardant, nonmetallic material. (§1910.399)

Nonregulated area any area under the control of the employer where entry and exit is neither restricted nor controlled. (§1910.1003(b))

Nonwater carriage toilet facility toilet facility not connected to a sewer. (§1910.141(a)(2))

Normal production operations the utilization of a machine or equipment to perform its intended production function. (§1910.147(b))

Normally unoccupied remote facility facility which is operated, maintained or serviced by employees who visit the facility only periodically to check its operation and to perform necessary operating or maintenance tasks. No employees are permanently stationed at the facility. Facilities meeting this definition are not contiguous with, and must be geographically remote from all other buildings, processes or persons. (§1910.119(b))

Number of employees unless otherwise specified, the maximum number of employees present at any one time on a regular shift. (§1910.141(a)(2))

O

Objective data
(1,3-Butadiene) monitoring data, or mathematical modelling or calculations based on composition, chemical and physical properties of a material, stream or product. (§1910.1051(b))
(Chromium (VI)) information such as air monitoring data from industry-wide surveys or calculations based on the composition or chemical and physical properties of a substance demonstrating the employee exposure to chromium (VI) associated with a particular product or material or a specific process, operation, or activity. The data must reflect workplace conditions closely resembling the processes, types of material, control methods, work practices, and environmental conditions in the employer's current operations. (§1910.1026(b))
(Respirable crystalline silica) information, such as air monitoring data from industry-wide surveys or calculations based on the composition of a substance, demonstrating employee exposure to respirable crystalline silica associated with a particular product or material or a specific process, task, or activity. The data must reflect workplace conditions closely resembling or with a higher exposure potential than the processes, types of material, control methods, work practices, and environmental conditions in the employer's current operations. (§1910.1053(b))

Obstruction detector control that will stop the suspended or supported unit in the direction of travel if an obstruction is encountered, and will allow the unit to move only in a direction away from the obstruction. (§1910.66(d))

Occupant load total number of persons that may occupy a workplace or portion of a workplace at any one time. The occupant load of a workplace is calculated by dividing the gross floor area of the workplace or portion of the workplace by the occupant load factor for that particular type of workplace occupancy. Information regarding the "Occupant load" is located in NFPA 101–2009, Life Safety Code, and in IFC–2009, International Fire Code (incorporated by reference, See §1910.6). (§1910.34(c))

Occupational Exposure reasonably anticipated skin, eye, mucous membrane, or parenteral contact with blood or other potentially infectious materials that may result from the performance of an employee's duties. (§1910.1030(b))

Off-hand grinding grinding of any material or part which is held in the operator's hand. (§1910.211(b)(11))

Office occupancy occupancy or use of a building or structure or any portion thereof for the transaction of business, or the rendering or receiving of professional services. (§1910.106(a)(24))

Oil (filled) cutout (Over 600 volts, nominal) cutout in which all or part of the fuse support and its fuse link or disconnecting blade are mounted in oil with complete immersion of the contacts and the fusible portion of the conducting element (fuse link), so that arc interruption by severing of the fuse link or by opening of the contacts will occur under oil. (§1910.399)

Open framehammers (or blacksmith hammers) hammers used primarily for the shaping of forgings by means of impact with flat dies. Open frame hammers generally are so constructed that the anvil assembly is separate from the operating mechanism and machine supports; it rests on its own independent foundation. Certain exceptions are forging hammers made with frame mounted on the anvil; e.g., the smaller, single-frame hammers are usually made with the anvil and frame in one piece. (§1910.211(e)(2))

Open riser gap or space between treads of stairways that do not have upright or inclined members (risers). (§1910.21(b))

Open type (Manlift) which has a handgrip surface fully exposed and capable of being encircled by the passenger's fingers. (§1910.68(a)(2))

Open wiring on insulators open wiring on insulators is an exposed wiring method using cleats, knobs, tubes, and flexible tubing for the protection and support of single insulated conductors run in or on buildings, and not concealed by the building structure. (§1910.399)

Open-vessel system operation involving a carcinogen addressed by this Section in an open vessel that is not in an isolated system, a laboratory-type hood, nor in any other system affording equivalent protection against the entry of the material into regulated areas, non-regulated areas, or the external environment. (§1910.1003(b))

Openers and pickers openers and pickers means a general classification which includes breaker pickers, intermediate pickers, finisher pickers, single process pickers, multiple process pickers, willow machines, card and picker waste cleaners, thread extractors, shredding machines, roving waste openers, shoddy pickers, bale breakers, feeders, vertical openers, lattice cleaners, horizontal cleaners, and any similar machinery equipped with either cylinders, screen section, calender section, rolls, or beaters used for the preparation of stock for further processing. (§1910.262(b)(25))

Opening gap or open space in a wall, partition, vertical walking-working surface, or similar surface that is at least 30 inches (76 cm) high and at least 18 inches (46 cm) wide, through which an employee can fall to a lower level. (§1910.21(b))

Operating control mechanism regulating or guiding the operation of equipment that ensures a specific operating mode. (§1910.66(d))

Operating device
(Powered platforms for building maintenance) device actuated manually to activate a control (§1910.66(d))
Powered platforms for building maintenance/Existing installations (Mandatory)) push-button, lever, or other manual device used to actuate a control. (Appendix D to §1910.66(a)(15))

Operator's station complete complement of controls used by or available to an operator on a given operation for stroking the press. (§1910.211(d)(43))

Organic bonded wheels organic wheels are wheels which are bonded by means of an organic material such as resin, rubber, shellac, or other similar bonding agent. (§1910.241(b)(5))

Organic peroxide liquid or solid organic chemical which contains the bivalent -0-0- structure and as such is considered a derivative of hydrogen peroxide, where one or both of the hydrogen atoms have been replaced by organic radicals. The term organic peroxide includes organic peroxide mixtures containing at least one organic peroxide. Organic peroxides are thermally unstable chemicals, which may undergo exothermic self-accelerating decomposition. In addition, they may have one or more of the following properties:
(a) be liable to explosive decomposition;
(b) burn rapidly;
(c) be sensitive to impact or friction;
(d) react dangerously with other substances. (Appendix B to §1910.1200(B.15.1.1))

Organic wheels which are bonded by means of an organic material such as resin, rubber, shellac, or other similar bonding agent. (§1910.211(b)(15))

OSHA Area Director Director for the Occupational Safety and Health Administration Area Office having jurisdiction over the geographic area in which the employer's establishment is located. (§1910.1017(b)(8))

OSHA Area Office Area Office of the Occupational Safety and Health Administration having jurisdiction over the geographic area where the affected workplace is located. (§1910.1044(b)); (§1910.1045(b))

Other Potentially Infectious Materials
(1) the following human body fluids: semen, vaginal secretions, cerebrospinal fluid, synovial fluid, pleural fluid, pericardial fluid, peritoneal fluid, amniotic fluid, saliva in dental procedures, any body fluid that is visibly contaminated with blood, and all body fluids in situations where it is difficult or impossible to differentiate between body fluids;
(2) any unfixed tissue or organ (other than intact skin) from a human (living or dead); and
(3) HIV-containing cell or tissue cultures, organ cultures, and HIV- or HBV-containing culture medium or other solutions; and blood, organs, or other tissues from experimental animals infected with HIV or HBV. (§1910.1030(b))

Otolaryngologist physician specializing in diagnosis and treatment of disorders of the ear, nose and throat. (Appendix I to §1910.95)

Outer shell exterior layer of material on the fire coat and protective trousers which forms the outermost barrier between the fire fighter and the environment. It is attached to the vapor barrier and liner and is usually constructed with a storm flap, suitable closures and pockets. (§1910.155(c)(33))

Outlet point on the wiring system at which current is taken to supply utilization equipment. (§1910.399)

Outline lighting arrangement of incandescent lamps or electric discharge lighting to outline or call attention to certain features, such as the shape of a building or the decoration of a window. (§1910.399)

Outrigger

(Crawler, locomotive, and truck cranes) extendable or fixed metal arms, attached to the mounting base, which rest on supports at the outer ends. (§1910.180(a)(31))

(Power platforms for building maintenance) device, used singly or in pairs, for suspending a working platform from work, storage, and rigging locations on the building being serviced. Unlike davits, an outrigger reacts its operating moment load as at least two opposing vertical components acting into two or more distinct roof points and/or attachments. (§1910.66(d))

Overcurrent (See Also "Overload") any current in excess of the rated current of equipment or the ampacity of a conductor. It may result from overload, short circuit, or ground fault. (§1910.399)

Overhaul to perform a major replacement, modification, repair, or rehabilitation similar to that involved when a new building or facility is built, a new wing is added, or an entire floor is renovated. (§1910.399)

Overhead crane crane with a movable bridge carrying a movable or fixed hoisting mechanism and traveling on an overhead fixed runway structure. (§1910.179(a)(8))

Overload (See Also "Overcurrent") operation of equipment in excess of normal, full-load rating, or of a conductor in excess of rated ampacity that, when it persists for a sufficient length of time, would cause damage or dangerous overheating. A fault, such as a short circuit or ground fault, is not an overload. (§1910.399)

Oxidizing gas any gas which may, generally by providing oxygen, cause or contribute to the combustion of other material more than air does.

Note: *Gases which cause or contribute to the combustion of other material more than air does" means pure gases or gas mixtures with an oxidizing power greater than 23.5% (as determined by a method specified in ISO 10156 or 10156-2 (incorporated by reference, See §1910.6)or an equivalent testing method.)* (Appendix B to §1910.1200(B.4.1))

Oxidizing liquid liquid which, while in itself not necessarily combustible, may, generally by yielding oxygen, cause, or contribute to, the combustion of other material. (Appendix B to §1910.1200(B.13.1))

Oxidizing solid solid which, while in itself is not necessarily combustible, may, generally by yielding oxygen, cause, or contribute to, the combustion of other material. (Appendix B to §1910.1200(B.14.1))

Oxygen deficiency that concentration of oxygen by volume below which atmosphere supplying respiratory protection must be provided. It exists in atmospheres where the percentage of oxygen by volume is less than 19.5 percent oxygen. (§1910.120(a)(3))

Oxygen deficient atmosphere atmosphere with an oxygen content below 19.5% by volume. (§1910.134(b)); (§1910.146(b))

Oxygen enriched atmosphere atmosphere containing more than 23.5 percent oxygen by volume. (§1910.146(b))

P

Package unit of lumber. (§1910.265(b)(28))

PACM "presumed asbestos containing material." (§1910.1001(b))

Paddler trough for a solution and two or more squeeze rolls between which cloth passes after being passed through a mordant or dye bath. (§1910.262(b)(26))

Panelboard (See Also "Switchboard) single panel or group of panel units designed for assembly in the form of a single panel; including buses, automatic overcurrent devices, and with or without switches for the control of light, heat, or power circuits; designed to be placed in a cabinet or cutout box placed in or against a wall or partition and accessible only from the front. (§1910.399)

Parenteral piercing mucous membranes or the skin barrier through such events as needlesticks, human bites, cuts, and abrasions. (§1910.1030(b))

Part revolution clutch type of clutch that can be disengaged at any point before the crankshaft has completed a full revolution and the press slide a full stroke. (§1910.211(d)(6))

Partial body irradiation pertains to the case in which part of the body is exposed to the incident electromagnetic energy. (§1910.97(a)(1)(ii))

Particulate-filter respirator air purifying respirator, commonly referred to as a dust or a fume respirator, which removes most of the dust or fume from the air passing through the device. (§1910.94(a)(1)(ix))

Peavy stout wooden handle fitted with a spike and hook and used for rolling logs. (§1910.265(b)(29))

Performance measure of the overall quality of data reported by a laboratory. (Appendix F to §1910.1027)

Permanently installed decorative fountains and reflection pools pools that are constructed in the ground, on the ground, or in a building in such a manner that the fountain or pool cannot be readily disassembled for storage, whether or not served by electrical circuits of any nature. These units are primarily constructed for their aesthetic value and are not intended for swimming or wading. (§1910.399)

Permanently installed swimming, wading, and therapeutic pools pools that are constructed in the ground or partially in the ground, and all other capable of holding water in a depth greater than 1.07 m (42 in.). The definition also applies to all pools installed inside of a building, regardless of water depth, whether or not served by electric circuits of any nature. (§1910.399)

Permissible exposure limit exposure, inhalation or dermal permissible exposure limit specified in 29 CFR Part §1910, Subparts G and Z. (§1910.120(a)(3))

Permissible Exposure Limits, PELs either the 8 hour Time Weighted Average (8-hr TWA) exposure or the Short-Term Exposure Limit (STEL). (§1910.1051(b))

Permit (See Also "Entry permit (Permit)") written certification by the employer authorizing employees to perform identified work operations subject to specified precautions. (§1910.272(c))

Permit-required confined space (permit space) (See Also "Rescue service") confined space that has one or more of the following characteristics:

(1) contains or has a potential to contain a hazardous atmosphere;

(2) contains a material that has the potential for engulfing an entrant;

(3) has an internal configuration such that an entrant could be trapped or asphyxiated by inwardly converging walls or by a floor which slopes downward and tapers to a smaller cross- section; or

(4) contains any other recognized serious safety or health hazard. (§1910.146(b))

Permit-required confined space program (permit space program) (See Also "Rescue service") employer's overall program for controlling, and, where appropriate, for protecting employees from, permit space hazards and for regulating employee entry into permit spaces. (§1910.146(b))

Permit system employer's written procedure for preparing and issuing permits for entry and for returning the permit space to service following termination of entry. (§1910.146(b))

Personal fall arrest system

(Walking-working surfaces) system used to arrest an employee in a fall from a walking-working surface. It consists of a body harness, anchorage, and connector. The means of connection may include a lanyard, deceleration device, lifeline, or a suitable combination of these. (§1910.21(b))

(Powered platforms for building maintenance) (Electric power generation, transmission, and distribution) system used to arrest an employee in a fall from a working level. It consists of an anchorage, connectors, a body belt or body harness and may include a lanyard, deceleration device, lifeline, or suitable combinations of these. (Appendix C to §1910.66(b)); (§1910.269(x))

Personal fall protection system system (including all components) an employer uses to provide protection from falling or to safely arrest an employee's fall if one occurs. Examples of personal fall protection systems include personal fall arrest systems, positioning systems, and travel restraint systems. (§1910.21(b))

Personal Protective Equipment specialized clothing or equipment worn by an employee for protection against a hazard. General work clothes (e.g., uniforms, pants, shirts or blouses) not intended to function as protection against a hazard are not considered to be personal protective equipment. (§1910.1030(b))

Personal service room room used for activities not directly connected with the production or service function performed by the establishment. Such activities include, but are not limited to, first-aid, medical services, dressing, showering, toilet use, washing, and eating. (§1910.141(a)(2))

Personnel monitoring equipment devices designed to be worn or carried by an individual for the purpose of measuring the dose received (e.g., film badges, pocket chambers, pocket dosimeters, film rings, etc.); (§1910.1096(d)(3)(i))

Phase Contrast contrast obtained in the microscope by causing light scattered by small particles to destructively interfere with unscattered light, thereby enhancing the visibility of very small particles and particles with very low intrinsic contrast. (Appendix J to §1910.1001)

Phase Contrast Microscope microscope configured with a phase mask pair to create phase contrast. The technique which uses this is called Phase Contrast Microscopy (PCM). (Appendix J to §1910.1001)

Phase-Polar Analysis use of polarized light in a phase contrast microscope. It is used to see the same size fibers that are visible in air filter analysis. Although fibers finer than 1 µm are visible, analysis of these is inferred from analysis of larger bundles that are usually present. (Appendix J to §1910.1001)

Phase-Polar Microscope phase-polar microscope is a phase contrast microscope which has an analyzer, a polarizer, a first order red plate and a rotating phase condenser all in place so that the polarized light image is enhanced by phase contrast. (Appendix J to §1910.1001)

Physical hazard

(Hazard communication) chemical that is classified as posing one of the following hazardous effects: explosive; flammable (gases, aerosols, liquids, or solids); oxidizer (liquid, solid or gas); self-reactive; pyrophoric (liquid or solid); self-heating; organic peroxide; corrosive to metal; gas under pressure; or in contact with water emits flammable gas. See Appendix B to §1910.1200—Physical Hazard Criteria. (§1910.1200(c))

(Occupational exposure to hazardous chemicals in laboratories) chemical that is classified as posing one of the following hazardous effects; Explosive; flammable (gases, aerosols, liquids, or solids); oxidizer (liquid, solid, or gas); self reactive; pyrophoric (gas, liquid or solid); self-heating; organic peroxide; corrosive to metal; gas under pressure; in contact with water emits flammable gas; or combustible dust. The criteria for determing whether a chemical is classified as a physical hazard are in Appendix B of the Hazard Communication Standard (§1910.1200) and §1910.1200(c) (definitions of "combustible dust" and "pyrophoric gas"). (§1910.1450(b))

Physician or Other Licensed Health Care Professional

1,3-Butadiene individual whose legally permitted scope of practice (i.e., license, registration, or certification) allows him or her to independently provide or be delegated the responsibility to provide one or more of the specific health care services required by paragraph (k) of §1910.1051. (§1910.1051(b))

(Chromium (VI)) individual whose legally permitted scope of practice (i.e. , license, registration, or certification) allows him or her to independently provide or be delegated the responsibility to provide some or all of the particular health care services required by paragraph (k) of §1910.1026. (§1910.1026(b))

(Methylene chloride) individual whose legally permitted scope of practice (i.e., license, registration, or certification) allows him or her to independently provide or be delegated the responsibility to provide some or all of the health care services required by paragraph (j) of §1910.1052. (§1910.1052(b))

(PLHCP (Respiratory protection)) individual whose legally permitted scope of practice (i.e., license, registration, or certification) allows him or her to independently provide, or be delegated the responsibility to provide, some or all of the health care services required by paragraph (e) of §1910.134. (§1910.134(b))

(Recording and reporting occupational injuries and illnesses) physician or other licensed health care professional is an individual whose legally permitted scope of practice (i.e., license, registration, or certification) allows him or her to independently perform, or be delegated the responsibility to perform, the activities described by this regulation. (§1904.46)

(Respirable crystalline silica) individual whose legally permitted scope of practice (i.e., license, registration, or certification) allows him or her to independently provide or be delegated the responsibility to provide some or all of the particular health care services required by paragraph (i) of §1910.1053. (§1904.1053(b))

Pictogram composition that may include a symbol plus other graphic elements, such as a border, background pattern, or color, that is intended to convey specific information about the hazards of a chemical. Eight pictograms are designated under this Standard for application to a hazard category. (§1910.1200(c))

Pictograph pictorial representation used to identify a hazardous condition or to convey a safety instruction. (§1910.145(f)(2))

Pike pole long pole whose end is shod with a sharp pointed spike. (§1910.265(b)(30))

Pinch point any point other than the point of operation at which it is possible for a part of the body to be caught between the moving parts of a press or auxiliary equipment, or between moving and stationary parts of a press or auxiliary equipment or between the material and moving part or parts of the press or auxiliary equipment. (§1910.211(d)(44))

Pipeline charging any apparatus used to introduce coal into an oven which uses a pipe or duct permanently mounted onto an oven and through which coal is charged. (§1910.1029(b))

Pitman rod connecting rod. (§1910.265(b)(31))

Platform (See Also "Ladder platform;" "Step (platform)")

(Fixed industrial stairs) extended step or landing breaking a continuous run of stairs. (§1910.21(b)(4))

(Guarding floor and wall openings and holes) working space for persons, elevated above the surrounding floor or ground; such as a balcony or platform for the operation of machinery and equipment. (§1910.21(a)(4))

(Vehicle mounted elevating and rotating work platforms) any personnel-carrying device (basket or bucket) which is a component of an aerial device. (§1910.67(a)(7))

(Walking-working surfaces) walking-working surface that is elevated above the surrounding area. (§1910.21(b))

Platen See "Slide"

Plug cap See "Attachment plug (Plug cap) (Cap)"

Plunger See "Slide"

Platform rated load combined weight of workers, tools, equipment and other material which is permitted to be carried by the working platform at the installation, as stated on the load rating plate. (§1910.66(d))

Point of operation

(Mechanical power presses) area of the press where material is actually positioned and work is being performed during any process such as shearing, punching, forming, or assembling. (§1910.211(d)(45))

(Mechanical power-transmission apparatus) that point at which cutting, shaping, or forming is accomplished upon the stock and shall include such other points as may offer a hazard to the operator in inserting or manipulating the stock in the operation of the machine. (§1910.211(f)(8))

(Textiles) that part of the machine where the work of cutting, shearing, squeezing, drawing, or manipulating the stock in any other way is done. (§1910.262(b)(27))

(Woodworking machinery requirements) that point at which cutting, shaping, boring, or forming is accomplished upon the stock. (§1910.211(a)(1))

Pole balcony or seat balcony or seat used as a support for workmen at pole-mounted equipment or terminal boxes. A typical device consists of a bolted assembly of steel details and a wooden platform. Steel braces run from the pole to the underside of the balcony. A guard rail (approximately 30" high) may be provided. (§1910.268(s)(31))

Pole platform platform intended for use by a workman in splicing and maintenance operations in an elevated position adjacent to a pole. It consists of a platform equipped at one end with a hinged chain binder for securing the platform to a pole. A brace from the pole to the underside of the platform is also provided. (§1910.268(s)(32))

Pole scaffold (See "Single-pole scaffold;" "Double pole or independent scaffold").

Polishing and buffing wheels all power-driven rotatable wheels composed all or in part of textile fabrics, wood, felt, leather, paper, and may be coated with abrasives on the periphery of the wheel for purposes of polishing, buffing, and light grinding. (§1910.94(b)(1)(xiii))

Polyvinyl chloride polyvinyl chloride homopolymer or copolymer before such is converted to a fabricated product. (§1910.1017(b)(9))

Pools groups of quality-control samples to be established for each target value (defined below) of an analyte. For the protocol provided in attachment 3, for example, the theoretical value of the quality control samples of the pool must be within a range defined as ± 50% of the target value. Within each analyte pool, there must be quality control samples of at least 4 theoretical values. (Appendix F to §1910.1027)

Portable grinder any power-driven rotatable grinding, polishing, or buffing wheel mounted in such manner that it may be manually manipulated. (§1910.94(b)(1)(xiv))

Portable grinding grinding operation where the grinding machine is designed to be hand held and may be easily moved from one location to another. (§1910.241(b)(4))

Portable ladder ladder that can readily be moved or carried, and usually consists of side rails joined at intervals by steps, rungs, or cleats. (§1910.21(b))

Portable tank closed container having a liquid capacity over 60 U.S. gallons and not intended for fixed installation. (§1910.106(a)(25))

Portable X-ray (See Also "Mobile X-ray;" "Transportable X-ray") X-ray equipment designed to be hand-carried. (§1910.399)

Positioning system (Work-positioning system) system of equipment and connectors that, when used with a body harness or body belt, allows an employee to be supported on an elevated vertical surface, such as a wall or window sill, and work with both hands free. Positioning systems also are called "positioning system devices" and "work-positioning equipment." (§1910.21(b))

Positive-pressure breathing apparatus self-contained breathing apparatus in which the pressure in the breathing zone is positive in relation to the immediate environment during inhalation and exhalation. (§1910.155(c)(34))

Positive pressure respirator respirator in which the pressure inside the respiratory inlet covering exceeds the ambient air pressure outside the respirator. (§1910.134(b))

Post emergency response that portion of an emergency response performed after the immediate threat of a release has been stabilized or eliminated and clean-up of the site has begun. If post emergency response is performed by an employer's own employees who were part of the initial emergency response, it is considered to be part of the initial response and not post emergency response. However, if a group of an employer's own employees, separate from the group providing initial response, performs the clean-up operation, then the separate group of employees would be considered to be performing post-emergency response and subject to paragraph (q)(11) of §1910.120. (§1910.120(a)(3))

Potable water water that meets the standards for drinking purposes of the State or local authority having jurisdiction, or water that meets the quality standards prescribed by the U.S. Environmental Protection Agency's National Primary Drinking Water Regulations (40 CFR §141). (§1910.141(a)(2))

Poured socket method of providing wire rope terminations in which the ends of the rope are held in a tapered socket by means of poured spelter or resins. (§1910.66(d))

Power and control tray cable (Type TC) factory assembly of two or more insulated conductors, with or without associated bare or covered grounding conductors under a nonmetallic sheath, approved for installation in cable trays, in raceways, or where supported by a messenger wire. (§1910.399)

Power fuse (Over 600 volts, nominal.) See "Fuse"

Power outlet enclosed assembly, which may include receptacles, circuit breakers, fuseholders, fused switches, buses, and watt-hour meter mounting means, that is intended to supply and control power to mobile homes, recreational vehicles, or boats or to serve as a means for distributing power needed to operate mobile or temporarily installed equipment. (§1910.399)

Power-limited tray cable (Type PLTC) factory assembly of two or more insulated conductors under a nonmetallic jacket. (§1910.399)

Power-operated crane crane whose mechanism is driven by electric, air, hydraulic, or internal combustion means. (§1910.179(a)(9))

Powered air-purifying respirator (PAPR) air-purifying respirator that uses a blower to force the ambient air through air-purifying elements to the inlet covering. (§1910.134(b))

Powered platform equipment to provide access to the exterior of a building for maintenance, consisting of a suspended power-operated working platform, a roof car, or other suspension means, and the requisite operating and control devices. (Appendix D to §1910.66(a)(16))

PPE See "Personal Protective Equipment"

Precautionary statement phrase that describes recommended measures that should be taken to minimize or prevent adverse effects resulting from exposure to a hazardous chemical, or improper storage or handling. (§1910.1200(c))

Precision extent of agreement between repeated, independent measurements of the same quantity of an analyte. (Appendix F to §1910.1027)

Pre-discharge employee alarm alarm which will sound at a set time prior to actual discharge of an extinguishing system so that employees may evacuate the discharge area prior to system discharge. (§1910.155(c)(35))

Premises wiring (Premises wiring system.) interior and exterior wiring, including power, lighting, control, and signal circuit wiring together with all of their associated hardware, fittings, and wiring devices, both permanently and temporarily installed, that extends from the service point of utility conductors or source of power (such as a battery, a solar photovoltaic system, or a generator, transformer, or converter) to the outlets. Such wiring does not include wiring internal to appliances, fixtures, motors, controllers, motor control centers, and similar equipment. (§1910.399)

Presence sensing device device designed, constructed and arranged to create a sensing field or area that signals the clutch/brake control to deactivate the clutch and activate the brake of the press when any part of the operator's body or a hand tool is within such field or area. (§1910.211(d)(12))

Presence sensing device initiation operating mode of indirect manual initiation of a single stroke by a presence sensing device when it senses that work motions of the operator, related to feeding and/or removing parts, are completed and all parts of the operator's body or hand tools are safely clear of the point of operation. (§1910.211(d)(61))

Press mechanically powered machine that shears, punches, forms or assembles metal or other material by means of cutting, shaping, or combination dies attached to slides. A press consists of a stationary bed or anvil, and a slide (or slides) having a controlled reciprocating motion toward and away from the bed surface, the slide being guided in a definite path by the frame of the press. (§1910.211(d)(46))

Pressure demand respirator (See Also "Negative pressure respirator (tight fitting);" "Supplied-air respirator (SAR) or airline respirator;" "User seal check") positive pressure atmosphere-supplying respirator that admits breathing air to the facepiece when the positive pressure is reduced inside the facepiece by inhalation. (§1910.134(b))

Pressure vessel storage tank or vessel which has been designed to operate at pressures above 15 p.s.i.g. (§1910.106(a)(26))

Presumed asbestos containing material means thermal system insulation and surfacing material found in buildings constructed no later than 1980. The designation of a material as "PACM" may be rebutted pursuant to paragraph (j)(8) of this Section. (§1910.1001(b))

Primary brake brake designed to be applied automatically whenever power to the prime mover is interrupted or discontinued. (§1910.66(d))

Prime mover(s)
(Mechanical power-transmission apparatus) include steam, gas, oil, and air engines, motors, steam and hydraulic turbines, and other equipment used as a source of power. (§1910.211(f)(9))
(Powered platforms for building maintenance) source of mechanical power for a machine. (§1910.66(d))

Printing machine (roller type) machine consisting of a large central cylinder, or pressure bowl, around the lower part of the perimeter of which is placed a series of engraved color rollers (each having a color trough), a furnisher roller, doctor blades, etc. The machine is used for printing fabrics. (§1910.262(b)(28))

Process any activity involving a highly hazardous chemical including any use, storage, manufacturing, handling, or the on-site movement of such chemicals, or combination of these activities. For purposes of this definition, any group of vessels which are interconnected and separate vessels which are located such that a highly hazardous chemical could be involved in a potential release shall be considered a single process. (§1910.119(b))

Produce to manufacture, process, formulate, blend, extract, generate, emit, or repackage. (§1910.1200(c))

Product identifier name or number used for a hazardous chemical on a label or in the SDS. It provides a unique means by which the user can identify the chemical. The product identifier used shall permit cross-references to be made among the list of hazardous chemicals required in the written hazard communication program, the label and the SDS. (§1910.1200(c))

Production facility facility engaged in industrial-scale, large-volume or high concentration production of HIV or HBV. (§1910.1030(b))

Proficiency ability to satisfy a specified level of analyte performance. (Appendix F to §1910.1027)

Proficiency Samples specimens, the values of which are unknown to anyone at a participating laboratory, and which are submitted by a participating laboratory for proficiency testing. (Appendix F to §1910.1027)

Proficient meeting a stated level of achievement. (Appendix E to §1910.120)

Prohibited condition any condition in a permit space that is not allowed by the permit during the period when entry is authorized. (§1910.146(b))

Proof load is the load applied in performance of a proof test. (§1910.184(b))

Proof test nondestructive tension test performed by the sling manufacturer or an equivalent entity to verify construction and workmanship of a sling. (§1910.184(b))

Propellant-actuated power devices any tool or special mechanized device or gas generator system which is actuated by a smokeless propellant or which releases and directs work through a smokeless propellant charge. (§1910.109(a)(8))

Protection for exposure adequate fire protection for structures on property adjacent to tanks, where there are employees of the establishment. (§1910.106(a)(27))

Protective clothing clothing designed to protect an employee against contact with or exposure to a carcinogen addressed by this Section. (§1910.1003(b))

Protective clothing material any material or combination of materials used in an item of clothing for the purpose of isolating parts of the body from direct contact with a potentially hazardous liquid or gaseous chemicals. (Appendix A to §1910.120(2.2))

Protective laboratory practices and equipment those laboratory procedures, practices and equipment accepted by laboratory health and safety experts as effective, or that the employer can show to be effective, in minimizing the potential for employee exposure to hazardous chemicals. (§1910.1450(b))

Protective shield or guard device or guard attached to the muzzle end of the tool, which is designed to confine flying particles. (§1910.241(a)(8))

P.S.I.A. pounds per square inch absolute. (§1910.110(a)(10))

P.S.I.G. or Psi(g) pounds per square inch gauge. (§1910.110(a)(9)); (§1910.402)

Published exposure level exposure limits published in "NIOSH Recommendations for Occupational Health Standards" dated 1986, which is incorporated by reference as specified in §1910.6 or if none is specified, the exposure limits published in the standards specified by the American Conference of Governmental Industrial Hygienists in their publication "Threshold Limit Values and Biological Exposure Indices for 1987–88" dated 1987, which is incorporated by reference as specified in §1910.6. (§1910.120(a)(3))

Pull-out device mechanism attached to the operator's hands and connected to the upper die or slide of the press, that is designed, when properly adjusted, to withdraw the operator's hands as the dies close, if the operator's hands are inadvertently within the point of operation. (§1910.211(d)(15))

Pulpit-operated crane crane operated from a fixed operator station not attached to the crane. (§1910.179(a)(10))

Push stick narrow strip of wood or other soft material with a notch cut into one end and which is used to push short pieces of material through saws. (§1910.211(a)(2))

Pyrophoric gas chemical in a gaseous state that will ignite spontaneously in air at a temperature of 130 degrees F (54.4 degrees C) or below. (§1910.1200(c))

Pyrophoric liquid liquid which, even in small quantities, is liable to ignite within five minutes after coming into contact with air. (Appendix B to §1910.1200(B.9.1))

Pyrophoric solid solid which, even in small quantities, is liable to ignite within five minutes after coming into contact with air. (Appendix B to §1910.1200(B.10.1))

Pyrotechnic chemical is a chemical designed to produce an effect by heat, light, sound, gas or smoke or a combination of these as the result of non-detonative self-sustaining exothermic chemical reactions. (Appendix B to §1910.1200(B.1.1.1))

Pyrotechnic item item containing one or more pyrotechnic chemicals. (Appendix B to §1910.1200(B.1.1.1))

Pyrotechnics any combustible or explosive compositions or manufactured articles designed and prepared for the purpose of producing audible or visible effects which are commonly referred to as fireworks. (§1910.109(a)(10))

Q

Qualified; Qualified employee (qualified person); Qualified person

(Electrical power generation, transmission, and distribution) employee (person) knowledgeable in the construction and operation of the electric power generation, transmission, and distribution equipment involved, along with the associated hazards.

Note 1: An employee must have the training required by §1926.950(b)(2) to be a qualified employee.

Note 2: *Except under §1926.954(b)(3)(iii), an employee who is undergoing on-the-job training and who has demonstrated, in the course of such training, an ability to perform duties safely at his or her level of training and who is under the direct supervision of a qualified person is a qualified person for the performance of those duties. (§1926.968)*

(Electrical) one who has received training in and has demonstrated skills and knowledge in the construction and operation of electric equipment and installations and the hazards involved.

Note 1 *to the definition of "qualified person:" Whether an employee is considered to be a "qualified person" will depend upon various circumstances in the workplace. For example, it is possible and, in fact, likely for an individual to be considered "qualified" with regard to certain equipment in the workplace, but "unqualified" as to other equipment. (See §1910.332(b)(3) for training requirements that specifically apply to qualified persons.)*

Note 2 *to the definition of "qualified person:" An employee who is undergoing on-the-job training and who, in the course of such training, has demonstrated an ability to perform duties safely at his or her level of training and who is under the direct supervision of a qualified person is considered to be a qualified person for the performance of those duties.* (§1910.399)

(Hazardous waste operations and emergency response) person with specific training, knowledge and experience in the area for which the person has the responsibility and the authority to control. (§1910.120(a)(3))

(Powered platforms for building maintenance/Personal fall arrest systems) one with a recognized degree or professional certificate and extensive knowledge and experience in the subject field who is capable of design, analysis, evaluation and specifications in the subject work, project, or product. (Appendix C to §1910.66(b))

(Telecommunications) any worker who by reason of his training and experience has demonstrated his ability to safely perform his duties. (§1910.268(s)(33))

(Walking-working surfaces) describes a person who, by possession of a recognized degree, certificate, or professional standing, or who by extensive knowledge, training, and experience has successfully demonstrated the ability to solve or resolve problems relating to the subject matter, the work, or the project. (1910.21(b))

Qualified line-clearance tree trimmer tree worker who through related training and on-the-job experience is familiar with the special techniques and hazards involved in line clearance. (§1910.268(s)(34))

Qualified line-clearance tree-trimmer trainee any worker regularly assigned to a line-clearance tree-trimming crew and undergoing on-the-job training who, in the course of such training, has demonstrated his ability to perform his duties safely at his level of training. (§1910.268(s)(35))

Qualitative fit test (QLFT) pass/fail fit test to assess the adequacy of respirator fit that relies on the individual's response to the test agent. (§1910.134(b))

Quality or Data Quality measure of the confidence in the measurement value. (Appendix F to §1910.1027)

Quality Control (QC) Samples specimens, the value of which is unknown to the analyst, but is known to the appropriate QA/QC personnel of a participating laboratory; when used as part of a laboratory QA/QC program, the theoretical values of these samples should not be known to the analyst until the analyses are complete. QC samples are to be run in sets consisting of one QC sample from each pool (Seedefinition of "Pools" above). (Appendix F to §1910.1027)

Quantitative fit test (QNFT) assessment of the adequacy of respirator fit by numerically measuring the amount of leakage into the respirator. (§1910.134(b))

Quick disconnect value device which starts the flow of air by inserting of the hose (which leads from the facepiece) into the regulator of self-contained breathing apparatus, and stops the flow of air by disconnection of the hose from the regulator. (§1910.155(c)(35))

R

Raceway enclosed channel of metal or nonmetallic materials designed expressly for holding wires, cables, or busbars, with additional functions as permitted in this Standard. Raceways include, but are not limited to, rigid metal conduit, rigid nonmetallic conduit, intermediate metal conduit, liquid-tight flexible conduit, flexible metallic tubing, flexible metal conduit, electrical metallic tubing, electrical nonmetallic tubing, under-floor raceways, cellular concrete floor raceways, cellular metal floor raceways, surface raceways, wireways, and busways. (§1910.399)

Rad (See Also "Dose;" "Rem") measure of the dose of any ionizing radiation to body tissues in terms of the energy absorbed per unit of mass of the tissue. One rad is the dose corresponding to the absorption of 100 ergs per gram of tissue (1 millirad (mrad) = 0.001 rad). (§1910.1096(a)(6))

Radiation includes alpha rays, beta rays, gamma rays, X-rays, neutrons, high-speed electrons, high-speed protons, and other atomic particles; but such term does not include sound or radio waves, or visible light, or infrared or ultraviolet light. (§1910.1096(a)(1))

Radiation area any area, accessible to personnel, in which there exists radiation at such levels that a major portion of the body could receive in any 1 hour a dose in excess of 5 millirem, or in any 5 consecutive days a dose in excess of 100 millirem; (§1910.1096(d)(3)(ii))

Radiation protection guide radiation level which should not be exceeded without careful consideration of the reasons for doing so. (§1910.97(a)(1)(iii))

Radioactive material any material which emits, by spontaneous nuclear disintegration, corpuscular or electromagnetic emanations. (§1910.1096(a)(2))

Rail clamp tong-like metal device, mounted on a locomotive crane car, which can be connected to the track. (§1910.180(a)(32))

Ram See "Slide"

Ramp inclined walking-working surface used to access another level. (1910.21(b))

Ranges (bleaching continuous) continuous bleaching ranges are of several types and may be made for cloth in rope or open-width form. The goods, after wetting out, pass through a squeeze roll into a saturator containing a solution of caustic soda and then to an enclosed J-box. A V-shaped arrangement is attached to the front part of the J-box for uniform and rapid saturation of the cloth with steam before it is packed down in the J-box. The cloth, in a single strand rope form, passes over a guide roll down the first arm of the "V" and up the second. Steam is injected into the "V" at the upper end of the second arm so that the cloth is rapidly saturated with steam at this point. The J-box capacity is such that cloth will remain hot for a sufficient time to complete the scouring action. It then passes a series of washers with a squeeze roll in between. The cloth then passes through a second set of saturator, J-box, and washer, where it is treated with the peroxide solution. By slight modification of the form of the unit, the same process can be applied to open-width cloth. (§1910.262(b)(29))

Range (mercerizing) consists generally of a 3-bowl mangle, a tenter frame, and a number of boxes for washing and scouring. The whole setup is in a straight line and all parts operate continuously. The combination is used to saturate the cloth with sodium hydroxide, stretch it while saturated, and washing out most of the caustic before releasing tension. (§1910.262(b)(30))

Rated capacity

(Logging operations) maximum load a system, vehicle, machine or piece of equipment was designed by the manufacturer to handle. (§1910.266(c))

(Slings) or **working load limit** maximum working load permitted by the provisions of §1910.184). (§1910.184(b))

Rated load

(Overhead and gantry cranes) maximum load for which a crane or individual hoist is designed and built by the manufacturer and shown on the equipment nameplate(s). (§1910.179(a)(50))

(Powered platforms for building maintenance) manufacturer's recommended maximum load. (§1910.66(d))

(Powered platforms for building maintenance/Existing installations (Mandatory)) combined weight of employees, tools, equipment, and other material which the working platform is designed and installed to lift. (Appendix D to §1910.66(a)(17))

Rated speed rated speed is the speed for which the device is designed and installed. (§1910.68(a)(6))

Rated strength strength of wire rope, as designated by its manufacturer or vendor, based on standard testing procedures or acceptable engineering design practices. (§1910.66(d))

Rated working load combined static weight of men, materials, and suspended or supported equipment. (§1910.66(d))

Rating (See Also "Jack") rating of a jack is the maximum working load for which it is designed to lift safely that load throughout its specified amount of travel.

Note: *To raise the rated load of a jack, the point of application of the load, the applied force, and the length of lever arm should be those designated by the manufacturer for the particular jack considered.* (§1910.241(d)(2))

Reach effective length of an alloy steel chain sling measured from the top bearing surface of the upper terminal component to the bottom bearing surface of the lower terminal component. (§1910.184(b))

Reaction time time, in seconds, it takes the signal, required to activate/deactivate the system, to travel through the system, measured from the time of signal initiation to the time the function being measured is completed. (Appendix A to §1910.217)

Readily accessible (See Also "Accessible") capable of being reached quickly for operation, renewal, or inspections, without requiring those to whom ready access is requisite to climb over or remove obstacles or to resort to portable ladders, chairs, etc. (§1910.399)

Readily combustible solids powdered, granular, or pasty chemicals which are dangerous if they can be easily ignited by brief contact with an ignition source, such as a burning match, and if the flame spreads rapidly. (Appendix B to §1910.1200(B.7.1))

Receptacle contact device installed at the outlet for the connection of an attachment plug. A single receptacle is a single contact device with no other contact device on the same yoke. A multiple receptacle is two or more contact devices on the same yoke. (§1910.399)

Receptacle outlet outlet where one or more receptacles are installed. (§1910.399)

Record any item, collection, or grouping of information regardless of the form or process by which it is maintained (e.g., paper document, microfiche, microfilm, X-ray film, or automated data processing). (§1910.1020(c)(10))

Recreational diving instruction training diving students in the use of recreational diving procedures and the safe operation of diving equipment, including an open-circuit, semi-closed-circuit, or closed-circuit self-contained underwater breathing apparatus, during dives. (§1910.402)

Reeving rope system in which the rope travels around drums and sheaves. (§1910.180(a)(33)); (§1910.181(a)(27))

Refinery plant in which flammable liquids are produced on a commercial scale from crude petroleum, natural gasoline, or other hydrocarbon sources. (§1910.106(a)(28))

Refuge area either:

(1) a space along an exit route that is protected from the effects of fire by separation from other spaces within the building by a barrier with at least a one-hour fire resistance-rating; or

(2) a floor with at least two spaces, separated from each other by smoke-resistant partitions, in a building protected throughout by an automatic sprinkler system that complies with §1910.159 of this Part. (§1910.34(c))

Regenerative form of dynamic braking in which the electrical energy generated is fed back into the power system. (§1910.179(a)(32))

Registered professional engineer person who has been duly and currently registered and licensed by an authority within the United States or its territories to practice the profession of engineering. (§1910.66(d))

Regulated area

(1,3-Butadiene) any area where airborne concentrations of BD exceed or can reasonably be expected to exceed the 8-hour time weighted average (8-hr TWA) exposure of 1 ppm or the short-term exposure limit (STEL) of 5 ppm for 15 minutes. (§1910.1051(b))

(13 Carcinogens) area where entry and exit is restricted and controlled. (§1910.1003(b))

(Asbestos) area established by the employer to demarcate areas where airborne concentrations of asbestos exceed, or there is a reasonable possibility they may exceed, the permissible exposure limits. (§1910.1001(b))

(Benzene) any area where airborne concentrations of benzene exceed or can reasonably be expected to exceed, the permissible exposure limits, either the 8-hour time weighted average exposure of 1 ppm or the short-term exposure limit of 5 ppm for 15 minutes. (§1910.1028(b))

(Cadmium) area demarcated by the employer where an employee's exposure to airborne concentrations of cadmium exceeds, or can reasonably be expected to exceed the permissible exposure limit (PEL). (§1910.1027(b))

(Chromium (VI)) area, demarcated by the employer, where an employee's exposure to airborne concentrations of chromium (VI) exceeds, or can reasonably be expected to exceed, the PEL. (§1910.1026(b))

(Methylene chloride) area, demarcated by the employer, where an employee's exposure to airborne concentrations of MC exceeds or can reasonably be expected to exceed either the 8-hour TWA PEL or the STEL. (§1910.1052(b))

(Methylenedianiline) areas where airborne concentrations of MDA exceed or can reasonably be expected to exceed, the permissible exposure limits, or where dermal exposure to MDA can occur. (§1910.1050(b))

(Respirable crystalline silica) area, demarcated by the employer, where an employee's exposure to airborne concentrations of respirable crystalline silica exceeds, or can reasonably be expected to exceed, the PEL. (§1910.1053(b))

Regulated Waste liquid or semi-liquid blood or other potentially infectious materials; contaminated items that would release blood or other potentially infectious materials in a liquid or semi-liquid state if compressed; items that are caked with dried blood or other potentially infectious materials and are capable of releasing these materials during handling; contaminated sharps; and pathological and microbiological wastes containing blood or other potentially infectious materials. (§1910.1030(b))

Rehabilitated coke oven battery battery which is rebuilt, overhauled, renovated, or restored such as from the pad up, after January 20, 1977. (§1910.1029(b))

Reinforced wheels as applied to grinding wheels shall define a class of organic wheels which contain strengthening fabric or filament. The term reinforced does not cover wheels using such mechanical additions as steel rings, steel cup backs or wire or tape winding. (§1910.241(b)(7))

Related employment

(Longshoring and maine terminals) any employment performed as in incident to or in conjunction with, longshoring operations including, but not restricted to, securing cargo, rigging, and employment as a porter, checker, or watchman. (§1910.16(c)(2))

(Shipyard employment) any employment performed as an incident to, or in conjunction with, ship repair, shipbreaking, and shipbuilding work, including, but not restricted to, inspection, testing, and employment as a watchman. (§1910.15(b)(4))

Relay, direction electrically energized contactor responsive to an initiating control circuit, which in turn causes a moving member to travel in a particular direction. (Appendix D to §1910.66(a)(18))

Relay, potential for vertical travel electrically energized contactor responsive to initiating control circuit, which in turn controls the operation of a moving member in both directions. This relay usually operates in conjunction with direction relays, as covered under the definition, "relay, direction." (Appendix D to §1910.66(a)(19))

Rem (See Also "Dose;" "Ram") measure of the dose of any ionizing radiation to body tissue in terms of its estimated biological effect relative to a dose of 1 roentgen (r) of X-rays (1 millirem (mrem) = 0.001 rem). The relation of the rem to other dose units depends upon the biological effect under consideration and upon the conditions for irradiation. Each of the following is considered to be equivalent to a dose of 1 rem:

(i) a dose of 1 roentgen due to X- or gamma radiation;
(ii) a dose of 1 rad due to X-, gamma, or beta radiation;
(iii) a dose of 0.1 rad due to neutrons or high energy protons;
(iv) a dose of 0.05 rad due to particles heavier than protons and with sufficient energy to reach the lens of the eye;
(v) if it is more convenient to measure the neutron flux, or equivalent, than to determine the neutron dose in rads, as provided in paragraph (a)(7)(iii) of this Section, 1 rem of neutron radiation may, for purposes of the provisions in this Section be assumed to be equivalent to 14 million neutrons per square centimeter incident upon the body; or, if there is sufficient information to estimate with reasonable accuracy the approximate distribution in energy of the neutrons, the incident number of neutrons per square centimeter equivalent to 1 rem may be estimated from Table G–17:

Table G–17
Neutron Flux Dose Equivalents

Neutron energy (million electron volts (Mev))	Number of neutrons per square centimeter equivalent to a dose of 1 rem (neutrons/cm^2)	Average flux to deliver 100 millirem in 40 hours (neutrons/cm^2 per sec.)
Thermal	970×10^6	670
0.0001	720×10^6	500
0.005	820×10^6	570
0.02	400×10^6	280
0.1	120×10^6	80
0.5	43×10^6	30
1.0	26×10^6	18
2.5	29×10^6	20
5.0	26×10^6	18
7.5	24×10^6	17
10	24×10^6	17
10 to 30	14×10^6	10

(§1910.1096(a)(7))

Remote-control circuit any electric circuit that controls any other circuit through a relay or an equivalent device. (§1910.399)

Remote-operated crane remote-operated crane is a crane controlled by an operator not in a pulpit or in the cab attached to the crane, by any method other than pendant or rope control. (§1910.179(a)(11))

Repeat unintended or unexpected successive stroke of the press resulting from a malfunction. (§1910.211(d)(47))

Replacement in kind replacement which satisfies the design specification. (§1910.119(b))

Representative exposure measurements of an employee's noise dose or 8-hour time-weighted average sound level that the employers deem to be representative of the exposures of other employees in the workplace. (Appendix I to §1910.95)

Reproductive toxicity chemicals that affect the reproductive capabilities including adverse effects on sexual function and fertility in adult males and females, as well as adverse effects on the development of the offspring. Chemicals classified as reproductive toxins in accordance with the Hazard Communication Standard (§1910.1200) shall be considered reproductive toxins for purposes of this Section. (§1910.1450(b))

Reproductive toxins chemicals which affect the reproductive capabilities including chromosomal damage (mutations) and effects on fetuses (teratogenesis). (§1910.1450(b))

Resaw band, circular, or sash gang saws used to break down slabs, cants, or flitches into lumber. (§1910.265(b)(32))

Rescue service (See Also "Permit-required confined space (permit space);" "Permit-required confined space program (permit space program)") personnel designated to rescue employees from permit spaces. (§1910.146(b))

Research Laboratory laboratory producing or using research-laboratory-scale amounts of HIV or HBV. Research laboratories may produce high concentrations of HIV or HBV but not in the volume found in production facilities. (§1910.1030(b))

Reset circuit See "Antirepeat"

Respirable crystalline silica quartz, cristobalite, and/or tridymite contained in airborne particles that are determined to be respirable by a sampling device designed to meet the characteristics for respirable-particle-size-selective samplers specified in the International Organization for Standardization (ISO) 7708:1995: Air Quality—Particle Size Fraction Definitions for Health-Related Sampling. (§1910.1053(b))

Respirable dust airborne dust in sizes capable of passing through the upper respiratory system to reach the lower lung passages. (§1910.94(a)(1)(x))

Respirator See "Negative pressure respirator (Tight fitting);" "Pressure demand respirator;" "Supplied-air respirator (SAR) or airline respirator;" "User seal check."

Respiratory inlet covering that portion of a respirator that forms the protective barrier between the user's respiratory tract and an air-purifying device or breathing air source, or both. It may be a facepiece, helmet, hood, suit, or a mouthpiece respirator with nose clamp. (§1910.134(b))

Respiratory sensitizer chemical that will lead to hypersensitivity of the airways following inhalation of the chemical. (Appendix A to §1910.1200(A.4.1.1))

Responsible party someone who can provide additional information on the hazardous chemical and appropriate emergency procedures, if necessary. (§1910.1200(c))

Restraining device apparatus such as a cage, rack, assemblage of bars and other components that will constrain all rim wheel components during an explosive separation of a multi-piece rim wheel, or during the sudden release of the contained air of a single piece rim wheel. (§1910.177(c))

Restraint device See "Holdout or restraint device"

Restricted area any area access to which is controlled by the employer for purposes of protection of individuals from exposure to radiation or radioactive materials. (§1910.1096(a)(3))

Retrieval system equipment (including a retrieval line, chest or full-body harness, wristlets, if appropriate, and a lifting device or anchor) used for non-entry rescue of persons from permit spaces. (§1910.146(b))

Ribbon lapper See "Lapper (ribbon)"

Rim manual publication containing instructions from the manufacturer or other qualified organization for correct mounting, demounting, maintenance, and safety precautions peculiar to the type of wheel being serviced. (§1910.177(b))

Rim wheel assemblage of tire, tube and liner (where appropriate), and wheel components. (§1910.177(b))

Ring rolls class for forging equipment used for shaping weldless rings from pierced discs or thick-walled, ring-shaped blanks between rolls which control wall thickness, ring diameter, height and contour. (§1910.211(e)(9))

Riser upright (vertical) or inclined member of a stair that is located at the back of a stair tread or platform and connects close to the front edge of the next higher tread, platform, or landing. (§1910.21(b))

Rivet making machine same as upsetters and boltheaders when producing rivets with stock diameter of 1-inch or more. Rivet making with less than 1-inch diameter is usually a cold forging operation and therefore not included in Subpart O. (§1910.211(e)(11))

Roof car structure for the suspension of a working platform, providing for its horizontal movement to working positions. (Appendix D to §1910.66(a)(20))

Roof powered platform
(Powered platforms for building maintenance) working platform where the hoist(s) used to raise or lower the platform is located on the roof. (§1910.66(d))
(Powered platforms for building maintenance/Existing installations (Mandatory)) powered platform having the raising and lowering mechanism located on a roof car. (Appendix D to §1910.66(a)(21))

Roof rigged davit davit used to raise the suspended working platform above the building face being serviced. This type of davit can also be used to raise a suspended working platform which has been ground-rigged. (§1910.66(d))

Root wad ball of a tree root and dirt that is pulled from the ground when a tree is uprooted. (§1910.266(c))

Rope
(Overhead and gantry cranes; Crawler, locomotive and truck cranes; Derricks)) refers to wire rope, unless otherwise specified. (§1910.179(a)(51)); (§1910.180(a)(34)); (§1910.181(a)(28))
(Powered platforms for building maintenance) equipment used to suspend a component of an equipment installation, i.e., wire rope. (§1910.66(d))

Rope descent system suspension system that allows an employee to descend in a controlled manner and, as needed, stop at any point during the descent. A rope descent system usually consists of a roof anchorage, support rope, a descent device, carabiner(s) or shackle(s), and a chair (seatboard). A rope descent system also is called controlled descent equipment or apparatus. Rope descent systems do not include industrial rope access systems. (§1910.21(b))

Rope grab deceleration device which travels on a lifeline and automatically, by friction, engages the lifeline and locks so as to arrest the fall of an employee. A rope grab usually employs the principle of inertial locking, cam/level locking, or both. (Appendix C to §1910.66(b))

Rot See "Decay"

Rotary blast cleaning table enclosure where the pieces to be cleaned are positioned on a rotating table and are passed automatically through a series of blast sprays. (§1910.94(a)(1)(xi))

Rung, step, or cleat cross-piece of a ladder on which an employee steps to climb up and down. (§1910.21(b))

Running line any moving rope as distinguished from a stationary rope such as a guyline. (§1910.265(b)(33))

Running sheave sheave which rotates as the load block is raised or lowered. (§1910.179(a)(52))

Runway
(Overhead and gantry cranes) assembly of rails, beams, girders, brackets, and framework on which the crane or trolley travels. (§1910.179(a)(53))
(Walking-working surfaces) elevated walking-working surface, such as a catwalk, a foot walk along shafting, or an elevated walkway between buildings. (§1910.21(b))

S

Safe surface horizontal surface intended to be occupied by personnel, which is so protected by a fall protection system that it can be reasonably assured that said occupants will be protected against falls. (§1910.66(d))

Safety block prop that, when inserted between the upper and lower dies or between the bolster plate and the face of the slide, prevents the slide from falling of its own deadweight. (§1910.211(d)(48))

Safety can approved container, of not more than 5 gallons capacity, having a spring-closing lid and spout cover and so designed that it will safely relieve internal pressure when subjected to fire exposure. (§1910.106(a)(29))

Safety data sheet (SDS) written or printed material concerning a hazardous chemical that is prepared in accordance with paragraph (g) of this Section. (§1910.1200(c))

Safety factor calculated reduction factor which may be applied to laboratory test values to obtain safe working stresses for wooden beams and other mechanical members; ratio of breaking load to safe load. (§1910.265(b)(34))

Safety guard enclosure designed to restrain the pieces of the grinding wheel and furnish all possible protection in the event that the wheel is broken in operation. See paragraph (b) of §1910.215. (§1910.211(b)(12)); (§1910.241(b)(6))

Safety hook hook with a latch to prevent slings or load from accidentally slipping off the hook. (§1910.181(a)(29))

Safety system integrated total system, including the pertinent elements of the press, the controls, the safeguarding and any required supplemental safeguarding, and their interfaces with the operator, and the environment, designed, constructed and arranged to operate together as a unit, such that a single failure or single operating error will not cause injury to personnel due to point of operation hazards. (§1910.211(d)(62))

Sanforizing machine machine consisting of a large steam-heated cylinder, and endless, thick, woolen felt blanket which is in close contact with the cylinder for most of its perimeter, and an electrically heated shoe which presses the clothe against the blanket wile the latter is in a stretched condition as it curves around feed-in roll. (§1910.262(b)(31))

Saw guide device for steadying a circular or bandsaw. (§1910.265(b)(35))

Scaffold any temporary elevated or suspended platform and its supporting structure, including anchorage points, used to support employees, equipment, materials, and other items. For purposes of this subpart, a scaffold does not include a crane-suspended or derrick-suspended personnel platform or a rope descent system. (§1910.21(b))

Scientific diving diving performed solely as a necessary part of a scientific, research, or educational activity by employees whose sole purpose for diving is to perform scientific research tasks. Scientific diving does not include performing any tasks usually associated with commercial diving such as: Placing or removing heavy objects underwater; inspection of pipelines and similar objects; construction; demolition; cutting or welding; or the use of explosives. (§1910.402)

Scratch brush wheels all power-driven rotatable wheels made from wire or bristles, and used for scratch cleaning and brushing purposes. (§1910.94(b)(1)(xv))

SCUBA diving diving mode independent of surface supply in which the diver uses open circuit self-contained underwater breathing apparatus. (§1910.402)

Sealable equipment equipment enclosed in a case or cabinet that is provided with a means of sealing or locking so that live parts cannot be made accessible without opening the enclosure. The equipment may or may not be operable without opening the enclosure. (§1910.399)

Sealing Encapsulant product which can be applied, preferably by spraying, onto an asbestos surface which will seal the surface so that fibers cannot be released. (Appendix J to §1910.1001)

Secondary brake brake designed to arrest the descent of the suspended or supported equipment in the event of an overspeed condition. (§1910.66(d))

Secretary Secretary of Labor, U.S. Department of Labor, or his or her designee. (§1910.1029(b))

Select carcinogen any substance which meets one of the following criteria:
(i) it is regulated by OSHA as a carcinogen; or
(ii) it is listed under the category, "known to be carcinogens," in the Annual Report on Carcinogens published by the National Toxicology Program (NTP) (latest edition); or
(iii) it is listed under Group 1 ("carcinogenic to humans") by the International Agency for Research on Cancer Monographs (IARC) (latest editions); or
(iv) it is listed in either Group 2A or 2B by IARC or under the category, "reasonably anticipated to be carcinogens" by NTP, and causes statistically significant tumor incidence in experimental animals in accordance with any of the following criteria:
(A) after inhalation exposure of 6–7 hours per day, 5 days per week, for a significant portion of a lifetime to dosages of less than 10 mg/m^3 ;
(B) after repeated skin application of less than 300 (mg/kg of body weight) per week; or
(C) after oral dosages of less than 50 mg/kg of body weight per day. (§1910.1450(b))

Self-contained breathing apparatus (SCBA) atmosphere-supplying respirator for which the breathing air source is designed to be carried by the user. (§1910.134(b))

Self-heating chemical solid or liquid chemical, other than a pyrophoric liquid or solid, which, by reaction with air and without energy supply, is liable to self-heat; this chemical differs from a pyrophoric liquid or solid in that it will ignite only when in large amounts (kilograms) and after long periods of time (hours or days).

Note: *Self-heating of a substance or mixture is a process where the gradual reaction of that substance or mixture with oxygen (in air) generates heat. If the rate of heat production exceeds the rate of heat loss, then the temperature of the substance or mixture will rise which, after an induction time, may lead to self-ignition and combustion.* (Appendix B to §1910.1200(B.11.1))

Self-luminous light source that is illuminated by a self-contained power source (e.g. tritium) and that operates independently from external power sources. Batteries are not acceptable self-contained power sources. The light source is typically contained inside the device. (§1910.34(c))

Self-powered platform working platform where the hoist(s) used to raise or lower the platform is mounted on the platform. (§1910.66(d)); (Appendix D to §1910.66(a)(22))

Self-reactive chemicals thermally unstable liquid or solid chemicals liable to undergo a strongly exothermic decomposition even without participation of oxygen (air). This definition excludes chemicals classified under this Section as explosives, organic peroxides, oxidizing liquids or oxidizing solids. (Appendix B to §1910.1200(B.8.1))

Self-retracting lifeline/lanyard deceleration device which contains a drum-wound line which may be slowly extracted from, or retracted onto, the drum under slight tension during normal employee movement, and which, after onset of a fall, automatically locks the drum and arrests the fall. (Appendix C to §1910.66(b))

Selvage edge finished edge of synthetic webbing designed to prevent unraveling. (§1910.184(b))

Semiautomatic feeding (See Also "Automatic feeding;" "Feeding;" "Manual feeding;") feeding wherein the material or part being processed is placed within or removed from the point of operation by an auxiliary means controlled by operator on each stroke of the press. (§1910.211(d)(28))

Semiconductive hose hose with an electrical resistance high enough to limit flow of stray electric currents to safe levels, yet not so high as to prevent drainage of static electric charges to ground; hose of not more than 2 megohms resistance over its entire length and of not less than 5,000 ohms per foot meets the requirement. (§1910.109(a)(12))

Semigantry crane gantry crane with one end of the bridge rigidly supported on one or more legs that run on a fixed rail or runway, the other end of the bridge being supported by a truck running on an elevated rail or runway. (§1910.179(a)(12))

Sensitivity for the purposes of this protocol, the limit of detection. (Appendix F to §1910.1027)

Separately derived system premises wiring system whose power is derived from a battery, a solar photovoltaic system, or from a generator, transformer, or converter windings, and that has no direct electrical connection, including a solidly connected grounded circuit conductor, to supply conductors originating in another system. (§1910.399)

Sequential charging procedure, usually automatically timed, by which a predetermined volume of coal in each larry car hopper is introduced into an oven such that no more than two hoppers commence or finish discharging simultaneously although, at some point, all hoppers are discharging simultaneously. (§1910.1029(b))

Serious eye damage production of tissue damage in the eye, or serious physical decay of vision, following application of a test substance to the anterior surface of the eye, which is not fully reversible within 21 days of application. (Appendix A to §1910.1200(A.3.1.1))

Serpentine mineral family consisting of minerals with the general composition $Mg_3(Si_2O_5(OH)_4$ having the magnesium in brucite layer over a silicate layer. Minerals important in asbestos analysis included in this family are chrysotile, lizardite, antigorite. (Appendix J to §1910.1001)

Service or servicing

(Electrical) conductors and equipment for delivering electric energy from the serving utility to the wiring system of the premises served. (§1910.399)

(Servicing multi-piece and single-piece rim wheels) mounting and demounting of rim wheels, and related activities such as inflating, deflating, installing, removing, and handling. (§1910.177(b))

Service area that part of an employer's premises used for the servicing of rim wheels, or any other place where an employee services rim wheels. (§1910.177(b))

Service cable service conductors made up in the form of a cable. (§1910.399)

Service conductors conductors from the service point to the service disconnecting means. (§1910.399)

Service drop overhead service conductors from the last pole or other aerial support to and including the splices, if any, connecting to the service-entrance conductors at the building or other structure. (§1910.399)

Service equipment necessary equipment, usually consisting of one or more circuit breakers or switches and fuses, and their accessories, connected to the load end of service conductors to a building or other structure, or an otherwise designated area, and intended to constitute the main control and cutoff of the supply. (§1910.399)

Service life period of time that a respirator, filter or sorbent, or other respiratory equipment provides adequate protection to the wearer. (§1910.134(b))

Service point point of connection between the facilities of the serving utility and the premises wiring. (§1910.399)

Service-entrance cable single conductor or multiconductor assembly provided with or without an overall covering, primarily used for services, and is of the following types:

(1) Type SE, having a flame-retardant, moisture resistant covering; and

(2) Type USE, identified for underground use, having a moisture-resistant covering, but not required to have a flame-retardant covering. Cabled, single-conductor, Type USE constructions recognized for underground use may have a bare copper conductor cabled with the assembly. Type USE single, parallel, or cable conductor assemblies recognized for underground use may have a bare copper concentric conductor applied. These constructions do not require an outer overall covering. (§1910.399)

Service-entrance conductors, overhead system service conductors between the terminals of the service equipment and a point usually outside the building, clear of building walls, where joined by tap or splice to the service drop. (§1910.399)

Service-entrance conductors, underground system service conductors between the terminals of the service equipment and the point of connection to the service lateral. (§1910.399)

Serviceable condition state or ability of a tool, machine, vehicle or other device to operate as it was intended by the manufacturer to operate. (§1910.266(c))

Servicing and/or maintenance workplace activities such as constructing, installing, setting up, adjusting, inspecting, modifying, and maintaining and/or servicing machines or equipment. These activities include lubrication, cleaning or unjamming of machines or equipment and making adjustments or tool changes, where the employee may be exposed to the unexpected energization or startup of the equipment or release of hazardous energy. (§1910.147(b))

Set samples which are taken, submitted to the laboratory, analyzed, and for which, interim or final result reports are generated. (Appendix B to §1910.1001)

Setting up any work performed to prepare a machine or equipment to perform its normal production operation. (§1910.147(b))

Setwork mechanism on a sawmill carriage which enables an operator to move the log into position for another cut. (§1910.265(b)(36))

Sharps with engineered sharps injury protections (See Also "Exposure incident") non-needle sharp or a needle device used for withdrawing body fluids, accessing a vein or artery, or administering medications or other fluids, with a built-in safety feature or mechanism that effectively reduces the risk of an exposure incident. (§1910.1030(b))

Shearing machine machine used in shearing cloth. Cutting action is provided by a number of steel blades spirally mounted on a roller. The roller rotates in close contact with a fixed ledger blade. There may be from one to six such rollers on a machine. (§1910.262(b)(32))

Shearleg derrick derrick without a boom and similar to a breast derrick. The mast, wide at the bottom and narrow at the top, is hinged at the bottom and has its top secured by a multiple reeved guy to permit handling loads at various radii by means of load tackle suspended from the mast top. (§1910.181(a)(8))

Sheaves grooved pulleys, and shall be so classified unless used as flywheels. (§1910.211(f)(10))

Shielded nonmetallic-sheathed cable (Type SNM) factory assembly of two or more insulated conductors in an extruded core of moisture-resistant, flame-resistant nonmetallic material, covered with an overlapping spiral metal tape and wire shield and jacketed with an extruded moisture-, flame-, oil-, corrosion-, fungus-, and sunlight-resistant nonmetallic material. (§1910.399)

Ship repair any repair of a vessel, including, but not restricted to, alterations, conversions, installations, cleaning, painting, and maintenance work. (§1910.15(b)(1))

Ship stair (ship ladder) stairway that is equipped with treads, stair rails, and open risers, and has a slope that is between 50 and 70 degrees from the horizontal. (1910.21(b))

Shipbreaking any breaking down of a vessel's structure for the purpose of scrapping the vessel, including the removal of gear, equipment, or any component of a vessel. (§1910.15(b)(2))

Shipbuilding construction of a vessel, including the installation of machinery and equipment. (§1910.15(b)(3))

Shipper pole See "Belt pole"

Short term exposure limit See "STEL"

Show window any window used or designed to be used for the display of goods or advertising material, whether it is fully or partly enclosed or entirely open at the rear and whether or not it has a platform raised higher than the street floor level. (§1910.399)

Side loading means a load applied at an angle to the vertical plane of the boom. (§1910.180(a)(35)); (§1910.181(a)(30))

Side pull means that portion of the hoist pull acting horizontally when the hoist lines are not operated vertically. (§1910.179(a)(54))

Side-step ladder type of fixed ladder that requires an employee to step sideways from it in order to reach a walking-working surface, such as a landing. (§1910.21(b))

Signal word
(Hazard Communication) means a word used to indicate the relative level of severity of hazard and alert the reader to a potential hazard on the label. The signal words used in this Section are "danger" and "warning." "Danger" is used for the more severe hazards, while "warning" is used for the less severe. (§1910.1200(c))
(Specifications for accident prevention signs and tags) means that portion of a tag's inscription that contains the word or words that are intended to capture the employee's immediate attention. (§1910.145(f)(2))

Signaling circuit Any electric circuit that energizes signaling equipment. (§1910.399)

Sill A member connecting the foot block and stiff leg or a member connecting the lower ends of a double member mast. (§1910.181(a)(31))

Sill block See "Foot bearing or foot block (Sill block)"

Simple asphxyiant means a substance or mixture that displaces oxygen in the ambient atmosphere, and can thus cause oxygen deprivation in those who are exposed, leading to unconsciousness and death. (§1910.1200(c))

Singeing machine A machine used particularly with cotton; it comprises of a heated roller, plate, or an open gas flame. The material is rapidly passed over the roller or the plate or through the open gas flame to remove, fuzz or hairiness on yarn or cloth by burning. (§1910.262(b)(33))

Single piece rim wheel means the assemblage of single piece rim wheel with the tire and other components. (§1910.177(b))

Single piece wheel means a vehicle wheel consisting of one part, designed to hold the tire on the wheel when the tire is inflated. (§1910.177(b))

Single stroke means one complete stroke of the slide, usually initiated from a full open (or up) position, followed by closing (or down), and then a return to the full open position. (§1910.211(d)(49))

Single stroke mechanism means an arrangement used on a full revolution clutch to limit the travel of the slide to one complete stroke at each engagement of the clutch. (§1910.211(d)(50))

Single stroke reset See "Antirepeat"

Site safety and health supervisor (or official) means the individual located on a hazardous waste site who is responsible to the employer and has the authority and knowledge necessary to implement the site safety and health plan and verify compliance with applicable safety and health requirements. (§1910.120(a)(3))

Site-specific means individual training directed to the operations of a specific job site. (Appendix E to §1910.120)

Skidding The yarding of trees or logs by pulling or towing them across the ground. (§1910.266(c))

Skin corrosion is the production of irreversible damage to the skin; namely, visible necrosis through the epidermis and into the dermis, following the application of a test substance for up to 4 hours. Corrosive reactions are typified by ulcers, bleeding, bloody scabs, and, by the end of observation at 14 days, by discoloration due to blanching of the skin, complete areas of alopecia, and scars. Histopathology should be considered to evaluate questionable lesions. (Appendix A to §1910.1200(A.2.1.1))

Skin irritation is the production of reversible damage to the skin following the application of a test substance for up to 4 hours. (Appendix A to §1910.1200(A.2.1.1))

Skin sensitizer means a chemical that will lead to an allergic response following skin contact. (Appendix A to §1910.1200(A.4.1.1))

Slasher A slasher is a machine used for applying a size mixture to warp yarns. Essentially, it consists of a stand for holding section beams, a size box, one or more cylindrical dryers or an enclosed hot air dryer, and a beaming end for finding the yarn on the loom beams. (§1910.262(b)(34))

Slide means the main reciprocating press member. A slide is also called a ram, plunger, or platen. (§1910.211(d)(51))

Sling (See Also "Cross rod;" "Fabric (Metal mesh)") is an assembly which connects the load to the material handling equipment. (§1910.184(b))

Sling manufacturer is a person or organization that assembles sling components into their final form for sale to users. (§1910.184(b))

Sliver lapper See "Lapper (sliver)"

Slope (grade) (See Also "Grade") increase or decrease in altitude over a horizontal distance expressed as a percentage. For example, a change of altitude of 20 feet (6 m) over a horizontal distance of 100 feet (30 m) is expressed as a 20 percent slope. (§1910.266(c))

Small arms ammunition any shotgun, rifle, pistol, or revolver cartridge, and cartridges for propellant-actuated power devices and industrial guns. Military-type ammunition containing explosive-bursting charges, incendiary, tracer, spotting, or pyrotechnic projectiles is excluded from this definition. (§1910.109(a)(13))

Small arms ammunition primers small percussion-sensitive explosive charges, encased in a cup, used to ignite propellant powder. (§1910.109(a)(14))

Small quantity generator generator of hazardous wastes who in any calendar month generates no more than 1,000 kilograms (2,205 pounds) of hazardous waste in that month. (§1910.120(a)(3))

Smokeless propellants solid propellants, commonly called smokeless powders in the trade, used in small arms ammunition, cannon, rockets, propellant-actuated power devices, etc. (§1910.109(a)(15))

Snag any standing dead tree or portion thereof. (§1910.266(c))

Snagging grinding which removes relatively large amounts of material without regard to close tolerances or surface finish requirements. (§1910.211(b)(10))

Snaphook or (Snap-hook) connector comprised of a hook-shaped member with a normally closed keeper, or similar arrangement, which may be opened to permit the hook to receive an object and, when released, automatically closes to retain the object. Snaphooks are generally one of two types:
(1) the locking type with a self-closing, self-locking keeper which remains closed and locked until unlocked and pressed open for connection or disconnection; or
(2) the non-locking type with a self-closing keeper which remains closed until pressed open for connection or disconnection. As of January 1, 1998, the use of a non-locking snaphook as part of personal fall arrest systems and positioning device systems is prohibited. (Appendix C to §1910.66(b))

Solvent (industrial organic) industrial organic solvent means any organic volatile liquid or compound, or any combination of these substances which are used to dissolve or suspend a nonvolatile or slightly volatile substance for industrial utilization. It shall also apply to such substances when used as detergents or cleansing agents. It shall not apply to petroleum products when such products are used as fuel. (§1910.262(b)(35))

Sorting gaps areas on a log pond enclosed by boom sticks into which logs are sorted. (§1910.265(b)(37))

Sound level ten times the common logarithm of the ratio of the square of the measured A-weighted sound pressure to the square of the standard reference pressure of 20 micropascals. Unit: decibels (dB). For use with this regulation, SLOW time response, in accordance with ANSI S1.4–1971 (R1976), is required. (Appendix I to §1910.95)

Sound level meter instrument for the measurement of sound level. (Appendix I to §1910.95)

Source Individual any individual, living or dead, whose blood or other potentially infectious materials may be a source of occupational exposure to the employee. Examples include, but are not limited to, hospital and clinic patients; clients in institutions for the developmentally disabled; trauma victims; clients of drug and alcohol treatment facilities; residents of hospices and nursing homes; human remains; and individuals who donate or sell blood or blood components. (§1910.1030(b))

Span horizontal distance center to center of runway rails. (§1910.179(a)(55))

Special industrial explosives devices explosive-actuated power devices and propellant-actuated power devices. (§1910.109(a)(16))

Special industrial explosives materials shaped materials and sheet forms and various other extrusions, pellets, and packages of high explosives, which include dynamite, trinitrotoluene (TNT), pentaerythritol tetranitrate (PETN), hexahydro-1,3,5-trinitro-s-triazine (RDX), and other similar compounds used for high-energy-rate forming, expanding, and shaping in metal fabrication, and for dismemberment and quick reduction of scrap metal. (§1910.109(a)(17))

Specialist American Board Certified Specialist in Pulmonary Disease or an American Board Certified Specialist in Occupational Medicine. (§1910.1053(b))

Specific chemical identity chemical name, Chemical Abstracts Service (CAS) Registry Number, or any other information that reveals the precise chemical designation of the substance. (§1910.1020(c)(11)); (§1910.1200(c))

Specific target organ toxicity–repeated exposure (STOT-RE) specific target organ toxicity arising from repeated exposure to a substance or mixture. All significant health effects that can impair function, both reversible and irreversible, immediate and/or delayed and not specifically addressed in A.1 to A.7 and A.10 of this Appendix are included. Specific target organ toxicity following a single-event exposure is classified in accordance with SPECIFIC TARGET ORGAN TOXICITY – SINGLE EXPOSURE (A.8 of this Appendix) and is therefore not included here. (Appendix A to §1910.1200(A.9.1.1))

Specific target organ toxicity–single exposure, (STOT-SE) specific, non-lethal target organ toxicity arising from a single exposure to a chemical.

All significant health effects that can impair function, both reversible and irreversible, immediate and/or delayed and not specifically addressed in A.1 to A.7 and A.10 of this Appendix are included. Specific target organ toxicity following repeated exposure is classified in accordance with SPECIFIC TARGET ORGAN TOXICITY – REPEATED EXPOSURE (A.9 of this Appendix) and is therefore not included here. (Appendix A to §1910.1200(A.8.1.1))

Specific written consent written authorization containing the following:
(A) the name and signature of the employee authorizing the release of medical information,
(B) the date of the written authorization,
(C) the name of the individual or organization that is authorized to release the medical information,
(D) the name of the designated representative (individual or organization) that is authorized to receive the released information,
(E) a general description of the medical information that is authorized to be released,
(F) a general description of the purpose for the release of the medical information, and
(G) a date or condition upon which the written authorization will expire (if less than one year).
(ii) A written authorization does not operate to authorize the release of medical information not in existence on the date of written authorization, unless the release of future information is expressly authorized, and does not operate for more than one year from the date of written authorization.
(iii) A written authorization may be revoked in writing prospectively at any time. (§1910.1020(c)(12)(i))

Speed reducer positive type speed reducing machine. (§1910.66(d))

Spider See "Mast cap (spider)"

Spiral single transverse coil that is the basic element from which metal mesh is fabricated. (See §1910.184, Fig. N–184–2.) (§1910.184(b))

Spiral stairs series of treads attached to a vertical pole in a winding fashion, usually within a cylindrical space. (§1910.21(b))

Split-rail switch electric limit switch operated mechanically by the rollers on the manlift steps. It consists of an additional hinged or "split" rail, mounted on the regular guide rail, over which the step rollers pass. It is spring loaded in the "split" position. If the step supports no load, the rollers will "bump" over the switch; if a loaded step should pass over the section, the split rail will be forced straight, tripping the switch and opening the electrical circuit. (§1910.68(a)(7))

Splitter knife-type, non-rotating spreader. (§1910.265(b)(39))

Spray booth power-ventilated structure provided to enclose or accommodate a spraying operation to confine and limit the escape of spray, vapor, and residue, and to safely conduct or direct them to an exhaust system. (§1910.94(c)(1)(ii)); (§1910.107(a)(3))

Spray room room in which spray-finishing operations not conducted in a spray booth are performed separately from other areas. (§1910.94(c)(1)(iii))

Spray-finishing operations spray-finishing operations are employment of methods wherein organic or inorganic materials are utilized in dispersed form for deposit on surfaces to be coated, treated, or cleaned. Such methods of deposit may involve either automatic, manual, or electrostatic deposition but do not include metal spraying or metallizing, dipping, flow coating, roller coating, tumbling, centrifuging, or spray washing and degreasing as conducted in self-contained washing and degreasing machines or systems. (§1910.94(c)(1)(i))

Spraying area any area in which dangerous quantities of flammable vapors or mists, or combustible residues, dusts, or deposits are present due to the operation of spraying processes. (§1910.107(a)(2))

Spreader wheel metal wheel that separates the board from the log in back of circular saws to prevent binding. (§1910.265(b)(38))

Spring pole tree, segment of a tree, limb, or sapling which is under stress or tension due to the pressure or weight of another object. (§1910.266)(c))

Sprinkler alarm approved device installed so that any water flow from a sprinkler system equal to or greater than that from single automatic sprinkler will result in an audible alarm signal on the premises. (§1910.155(c)(37))

Sprinkler system system of piping designed in accordance with fire protection engineering standards and installed to control or extinguish fires. The system includes an adequate and reliable water supply, and a network of specially sized piping and sprinklers which are interconnected. The system also includes a control valve and a device for actuating an alarm when the system is in operation. (§1910.155(c)(38))

Stability factor ratio of the stabilizing moment to the overturning moment. (§1910.66(d))

Stabilizer tie flexible line connecting the building anchor and the suspension wire rope supporting the platform. (§1910.66(d))

Stage charging procedure by which a predetermined volume of coal in each larry car hopper is introduced into an oven such that no more than two hoppers are discharging simultaneously. (§1910.1029(b))

Stair rail or stair rail system barrier erected along the exposed or open side of stairways to prevent employees from falling to a lower level. (§1910.21(b))

Stairway (stairs) risers and treads that connect one level with another, and includes any landings and platforms in between those levels. Stairways include standard, spiral, alternating tread-type, and ship stairs. (§1910.21(b))

Standard standard which requires conditions, or the adoption or use of one or more practices, means, methods, operations, or processes, reasonably necessary or appropriate to provide safe or healthful employment and places of employment; (§1910.2(f))

Standard Deviation measure of the distribution or spread of a data set about the mean; the standard deviation is equal to the positive square root of the variance, and is expressed in the same units as the original measurements in the data set. (Appendix F to §1910.1027)

Standard stairs fixed or permanently installed stairway. Ship, spiral, and alternating tread-type stairs are not considered standard stairs (§1910.21(b))

Standards samples with values known by the analyst and used to calibrate equipment and to check calibration throughout an analytic run. In a laboratory QA/QC program, the values of the standards must exceed the values obtained for compliance samples such that the lowest standard value is near the limit of detection and the highest standard is higher than the highest compliance sample or QC sample. Standards of at least three different values are to be used for calibration, and should be constructed from at least 2 different sources. (Appendix F to §1910.1027)

Standby crane crane which is not in regular service but which is used occasionally or intermittently as required. (§1910.179(a)(56)); (§1910.180(a)(36))

Standby derrick derrick not in regular service which is used occasionally or intermittently as required. (§1910.181(a)(32))

Standby diver diver at the dive location available to assist a diver in the water. (§1910.402)

Standing (guy) rope (See Also "Guy") supporting rope which maintains a constant distance between the points of attachment to the two components connected by the rope. (§1910.180(a)(37))

Standpipe systems
Class I standpipe system a 2½-inch (6.3 cm) hose connection for use by fire departments and those trained in handling heavy fire streams. (§1910.155(c)(39)(i))
Class II standpipe system a 1½-inch (3.8 cm) hose system which provides a means for the control or extinguishment of incipient stage fires. (§1910.155(c)(39)(ii))
Class III standpipe system combined system of hose which is for the use of employees trained in the use of hose operations and which is capable of furnishing effective water discharge during the more advanced stages of fire (beyond incipient state) in the interior of workplaces. Hose outlets are available for both 1½-inch (3.8 cm) and 2½-inch (6.3 cm) hose. (§1910.155(c)(39)(iii))
Small hose system system of hose ranging in diameter from ⅝-inch (1.6 cm) up to 1½-inch (3.8 cm) which is for the use of employees and which provides a means for the control and extinguishment of incipient stage fires. (§1910.155(c)(39)(iv))

Starch mangle See "Mangle (starch)"

Statistical sparkover voltage transient overvoltage level that produces a 97.72-percent probability of sparkover (that is, two standard deviations above the voltage at which there is a 50-percent probability of sparkover) (§1910.269(x))

Statistical withstand voltage transient overvoltage level that produces a 0.14-percent probability of sparkover (that is, three standard deviations below the voltage at which there is a 50-percent probability of sparkover) (§1910.269(x))

Steam hammers type of drop hammer where the ram is raised for each stroke by a double-action steam cylinder and the energy delivered to the workpiece is supplied by the velocity and weight of the ram and attached upper die driven downward by steam pressure. Energy delivered during each stroke may be varied. (§1910.211(e)(3))

STEL short term exposure limit as determined by any 15 minute sample period. (§1910.1050(b))

Step bolt bolt or rung attached at intervals along a structural member and used for foot placement during climbing or standing. (§1910.269(x))

Step bolt (pole step) bolt or rung attached at intervals along a structural member used for foot placement and as a handhold when climbing or standing. (§1910.21(b))

Step (platform) passenger carrying unit. (§1910.68(a)(8))

Step potential voltage between the feet of a person standing near an energized grounded object. It is equal to the difference in voltage, given by the voltage distribution curve, between two points at different distances from the "electrode". A person could be at risk of injury during a fault simply by standing near the grounding point. (Appendix C to §1910.269)

Stepladder self-supporting, portable ladder that has a fixed height, flat steps, and a hinged back. (§1910.21(b))

Stepstool self-supporting, portable ladder that has flat steps and side rails. For purposes of the final rule, stepstool includes only those ladders that have a fixed height, do not have a pail shelf, and do not exceed 32 inches (81 cm) in overall height to the top cap, although side rails may extend above the top cap. A stepstool is designed so an employee can climb and stand on all of the steps and the top cap. (§1910.21(b))

Sterilize use of a physical or chemical procedure to destroy all microbial life including highly resistant bacterial endospores. (§1910.1030(b))

Sticker strip of wood or other material used to separate layers of lumber. (§1910.265(b)(40))

Stiff boom anchored, stationary boom sticks which are tied together and on which boom men work. (§1910.265(b)(41))

Stiff leg rigid member supporting the mast at the head. (§1910.181(a)(33))

Stiff leg derrick derrick similar to a guy derrick except that the mast is supported or held in place by two or more stiff members, called stiff legs, which are capable of resisting either tensile or compressive forces. Sills are generally provided to connect the lower ends of the stiff legs to the foot of the mast. (§1910.181(a)(9))

Stop device to limit travel of a trolley or crane bridge. This device normally is attached to a fixed structure and normally does not have energy absorbing ability. (§1910.179(a)(57))

Stop control operator control designed to immediately deactivate the clutch control and activate the brake to stop slide motion. (§1910.211(d)(52))

Storable swimming or wading pool pool that is constructed on or above the ground and is capable of holding water to a maximum depth of 1.07 m (42 in.), or a pool with nonmetallic, molded polymeric walls or inflatable fabric walls regardless of dimension. (§1910.399)

Storage flammable liquids shall be stored in a tank or in a container that complies with paragraph (d)(2) of Section §1910.106. (§1910.106(a)(32))

Storage bridge crane gantry type crane of long span usually used for bulk storage of material; the bridge girders or trusses are rigidly or non-rigidly supported on one or more legs. It may have one or more fixed or hinged cantilever ends. (§1910.179(a)(13))

Strand laid endless sling-mechanical joint wire rope sling made endless from one length of rope with the ends joined by one or more metallic fittings. (§1910.184(b))

Strand laid grommet-hand tucked endless wire rope sling made from one length of strand wrapped six times around a core formed by hand tucking the ends of the strand inside the six wraps. (§1910.184(b))

Strand laid rope wire rope made with strands (usually six or eight) wrapped around a fiber core, wire strand core, or independent wire rope core (IWRC). (§1910.184(b))

Stripper mechanism or die part for removing the parts or material from the punch. (§1910.211(d)(53))

Stroking selector part of the clutch/brake control that determines the type of stroking when the operating means is actuated. The stroking selector generally includes positions for "Off" (Clutch Control), "Inch," "Single Stroke," and "Continuous" (when Continuous is furnished). (§1910.211(d)(54))

Structural competence ability of the machine and its components to withstand the stresses imposed by applied loads. (§1910.180(a)(38))

Stud, pin, or fastener fastening device specifically designed and manufactured for use in explosive-actuated fastening tools. (§1910.241(a)(4))

Substance chemical elements and their compounds in the natural state or obtained by any production process, including any additive necessary to preserve the stability of the product and any impurities deriving from the process used, but excluding any solvent which may be separated without affecting the stability of the substance or changing its composition. (§1910.1200(c))

Superstructure rotating upper frame structure of the machine and the operating machinery mounted thereon. (§1910.180(a)(39))

Supplied-air respirator (SAR) or airline respirator (See Also "Negative pressure respirator (Tight fitting);" "Pressure demand respirator;" "User seal check") atmosphere-supplying respirator for which the source of breathing air is not designed to be carried by the user. (§1910.134(b))

Supported equipment building maintenance equipment that is held or moved to its working position by means of attachment directly to the building or extensions of the building being maintained. (§1910.66(d))

Surface feet per minute (s.f.p.m.) distance in feet any one abrasive grain on the peripheral surface of a grinding wheel travels in 1 minute.

Surface Feet Per Minute = 3.1416 × diameter in inches × r.p.m. ÷ 12 or .262 × diameter in inches × r.p.m.

Examples:

(a) 24-inch diameter wheel, 1,000 revolutions per minute. Surface Feet per minute .262 × 24 × 1,000 = 6,288 s.f.p.m.

(b) 12-inch diameter wheel, 1,000 revolutions per minute. Surface Feet per minute .262 × 12 × 1,000 = 3,144 s.f.p.m. (§1910.211(b)(8))

Surface-supplied air diving diving mode in which the diver in the water is supplied from the dive location with compressed air for breathing. (§1910.402)

Surfacing ACM surfacing material which contains more than 1% asbestos. (§1910.1001(b))

Surfacing material material that is sprayed, troweled-on or otherwise applied to surfaces (such as acoustical plaster on ceilings and fireproofing materials on structural members, or other materials on surfaces for acoustical, fireproofing, and other purposes). (§1910.1001(b))

SUS Saybolt Universal Seconds as determined by the Standard Method of Test for Saybolt Viscosity (ASTM D–88–56), and may be determined by use of the SUS conversion tables specified in ASTM Method D2161–66 following determination of viscosity in accordance with the procedures specified in the Standard Method of Test for Viscosity of Transparent and Opaque Liquids (ASTM D445–65). (§1910.106(a)(37))

Suspended equipment building maintenance equipment that is suspended and raised or lowered to its working position by means of ropes or combination cables attached to some anchorage above the equipment. (§1910.66(d))

Suspended scaffold (swinging scaffold) scaffold supported on wire or other ropes, used for work on, or for providing access to, vertical sides of structures on a temporary basis. Such scaffold is not designed for use on a specific structure or group of structures. (§1910.66(d))

Sweep device single or double arm (rod) attached to the upper die or slide of the press and designed to move the operator's hands to a safe position as the dies close, if the operator's hands are inadvertently within the point of operation. (§1910.211(d)(16))

Swifter means of tying boom sticks together to prevent them from spreading while being towed. (§1910.265(b)(42))

Swing

(Crawler, locomotive, and truck cranes) rotation of the superstructure for movement of loads in a horizontal direction about the axis of rotation. (§1910.180(a)(40))

(Derricks) rotation of the mast and/or boom for movements of loads in a horizontal direction about the axis of rotation. (§1910.181(a)(34))

Swing mechanism machinery involved in providing rotation of the superstructure. (§1910.180(a)(41))

Swing-frame grinder any power-driven rotatable grinding, polishing, or buffing wheel mounted in such a manner that the wheel with its supporting framework can be manipulated over stationary objects. (§1910.94(b)(1)(xvi))

Switch

(Electric power generation, transmission and distribution) device for opening and closing or for changing the connection of a circuit. In this Section, a switch is manually operable, unless otherwise stated. (§1910.269(x))

(Electrical)

(1) General-use switch switch intended for use in general distribution and branch circuits. It is rated in amperes, and it is capable of interrupting its rated current at its rated voltage.

(2) General-use snap switch form of general-use switch constructed so that it can be installed in device boxes or on box covers, or otherwise used in conjunction with wiring systems recognized by this Subpart.

(3) Isolating switch switch intended for isolating an electric circuit from the source of power. It has no interrupting rating, and it is intended to be operated only after the circuit has been opened by some other means.

(4) Motor-circuit switch switch, rated in horsepower, capable of interrupting the maximum operating overload current of a motor of the same horsepower rating as the switch at the rated voltage. (§1910.399)

(Overhead and gantry cranes) switch is a device for making, breaking, or for changing the connections in an electric circuit. (§1910.179(a)(58))

Switchboard (See Also "Panelboard") large single panel, frame, or assembly of panels on which are mounted, on the face or back, or both, switches, overcurrent and other protective devices, buses, and (usually) instruments. Switchboards are generally accessible from the rear as well as from the front and are not intended to be installed in cabinets.

Switch

(1) General-use switch switch intended for use in genera distribution and branch circuits. It is rated in amperes, and it is capable of interrupting its rated current at its rated voltage.

(2) General-use snap switch form of general-use switch constructed so that it can be installed in device boxes or on box covers, or otherwise used in conjunction with wiring systems recognized by this Subpart.

(3) Isolating switch switch intended for isolating an electric circuit from the source of power. It has no interrupting rating, and it is intended to be operated only after the circuit has been opened by some other means.

(4) Motor-circuit switch switch, rated in horsepower, capable of interrupting the maximum operating overload current of a motor of the same horsepower rating as the switch at the rated voltage. (§1910.399)

Switching devices (Over 600 volts, nominal) Devices designed to close and open one or more electric circuits. Included in this category are circuit breakers, cutouts, disconnecting (or isolating) switches, disconnecting means, interrupter switches, and oil (filled) cutouts. (§1910.399)

Symbol as used in this specification refers to the overall design, shape, and coloring of the rf radiation sign shown in figure G–11. (§1910.97(a)(1)(iv))

Symptom central nervous system effects such as headaches, disorientation, dizziness, fatigue, and decreased attention span; skin effects such as chapping, erythema, cracked skin, or skin burns; and cardiac effects such as chest pain or shortness of breath. (§1910.1052(b))

System operator qualified person designated to operate the system or its parts. (§1910.269(x))

System operator/owner person or organization that operates or controls the electrical conductors involved. (§1910.268(s)(36))

Systems assembly of equipment consisting essentially of the container or containers, major devices such as vaporizers, safety relief valves, excess flow valves, regulators, and piping connecting such parts. (§1910.110(a)(11))

T

Tackle assembly of ropes and sheaves arranged for hoisting and pulling. (§1910.180(a)(42))

Tag device usually made of card, paper, pasteboard, plastic or other material used to identify a hazardous condition. (§1910.145(f)(2))

Tagout placement of a tagout device on an energy isolating device, in accordance with an established procedure, to indicate that the energy isolating device and the equipment being controlled may not be operated until the tagout device is removed. (§1910.147(b))

Tagout device prominent warning device, such as a tag and a means of attachment, which can be securely fastened to an energy isolating device in accordance with an established procedure, to indicate that the energy isolating device and the equipment being controlled may not be operated until the tagout device is removed. (§1910.147(b))

Tail line non-supporting end of the wire rope used to suspend the platform. (§1910.66(d))

Target Value those values of CDB, CDU or B_2MU which trigger some action as prescribed in the medical surveillance section of the regulatory text of the final cadmium rule. For CDB, the target values are 5, 10 and 15 µg/l. For CDU, the target values are 3, 7, and 15 µg/g CRTU. For B2MU, the target values are 300, 750 and 1500 µg/g CRTU. (Note that target values may vary as a function of time.) (Appendix F to §1910.1027)

Telecommunication line truck truck used to transport men, tools, and material, and to serve as a traveling workshop for telecommunication installation and maintenance work. It is sometimes equipped with a boom and auxiliary equipment for setting poles, digging holes, and elevating material or men. (§1910.268(s)(39))

Telecommunication service furnishing of a capability to signal or communicate at a distance by means such as telephone, telegraph, police and fire alarm, community antenna television, or similar system, using wire, conventional cable, coaxial cable, wave guides, microwave transmission, or other similar means. (§1910.268(s)(40))

Telecommunications center installation of communication equipment under the exclusive control of an organization providing telecommunications service, that is located outdoors or in a vault, chamber, or a building space used primarily for such installations.

Note: *Telecommunication centers are facilities established, equipped and arranged in accordance with engineered plans for the purpose of providing telecommunications service. They may be located on premises owned or leased by the organization providing telecommunication service, or on the premises owned or leased by others. This definition includes switch rooms (whether electromechanical, electronic, or computer controlled), terminal rooms, power rooms, repeater rooms, transmitter and receiver rooms, switchboard operating rooms, cable vaults, and miscellaneous communications equipment rooms. Simulation rooms of telecommunication centers for training or developmental purposes are also included.* (§1910.268(s)(37))

Telecommunications derricks Rotating or non-rotating derrick structures permanently mounted on vehicles for the purpose of lifting, lowering, or positioning hardware and materials used in telecommunications work. (§1910.268(s)(38))

Telltale device used to serve as a warning for overhead objects. (§1910.265(b)(43))

Tenter frame machine for drying cloth under tension. It essentially consists of a pair of endless traveling chains fitted with clips of fine pins and carried on tracks. The cloth is firmly held at the selvages by the two chains which diverge as they move forward so that the cloth is brought to the desired width. (§1910.262(b)(36))

Terrazzo See "Modified types 6 and 11 wheels (terrazzo)"

Testing process by which the hazards that may confront entrants of a permit space are identified and evaluated. Testing includes specifying the tests that are to be performed in the permit space.

Note: *Testing enables employers both to devise and implement adequate control measures for the protection of authorized entrants and to determine if acceptable entry conditions are present immediately prior to, and during, entry.* (§1910.146(b))

Theoretical Value (or Theoretical Amount) reported concentration of a quality-control sample (or calibration standard) derived from prior characterizations of the sample. (Appendix F to §1910.1027)

Thermal system insulation ACM thermal system insulation which contains more than 1% asbestos. (§1910.1001(b))

Thermal System Insulation (TSI) ACM applied to pipes, fittings, boilers, breeching, tanks, ducts or other structural components to prevent heat loss or gain. (§1910.1001(b))

Through fixed ladder See "Fixed ladder."

Through ladder type of fixed ladder that allows the employee to step through the side rails at the top of the ladder to reach a walking-working surface, such as a landing. (§1910.21(b))

Tie down chain, cable, steel strips or fiber webbing and binders attached to a truck, trailer or other conveyance as a means to secure loads and to prevent them from shifting or moving when they are being transported. (§1910.266(c))

Tieback attachment between an anchorage (e.g., structural member) and a supporting device (e.g., parapet clamp or cornice hook). (§1910.21(b))

Tie-in guides portion of a building that provides continuous positive engagement between the building and a suspended or supported unit during its vertical travel on the face of the building. (§1910.66(d))

Tie-off act of an employee, wearing personal fall protection equipment, connecting directly or indirectly to an anchorage. It also means the condition of an employee being connected to an anchorage. (Appendix C to §1910.66(b))

Tight-fitting facepiece respiratory inlet covering that forms a complete seal with the face. (§1910.134(b))

Time-weighted average sound level that sound level, which if constant over an 8-hour exposure, would result in the same noise dose as is measured. (Appendix I to §1910.95)

To chamber to fit properly without the use of excess force, the case being duly supported. (§1910.241(a)(5))

Toeboard

(Guarding floor and wall openings and holes) vertical barrier at floor level erected along exposed edges of a floor opening, wall opening, platform, runway, or ramp to prevent falls of materials. (§1910.21(a)(9))

(Manually propelled mobile ladder stands and scaffolds (towers)) barrier at platform level erected along the exposed sides and ends of a scaffold platform to prevent falls of materials. (§1910.21(g)(16))

(Safety requirements for scaffolding) barrier secured along the sides and ends of a platform, to guard against the falling of material. (§1910.21(f)(31))

(Walking-working surfaces) low protective barrier that is designed to prevent materials, tools, and equipment from falling to a lower level, and protect employees from falling. (§1910.21(b))

Toilet facility fixture maintained within a toilet room for the purpose of defecation or urination, or both. (§1910.141(a)(2))

Toilet room room maintained within or on the premises of any place of employment, containing toilet facilities for use by employees. (§1910.141(a)(2))

Tool explosive-actuated fastening tool, unless otherwise indicated, and all accessories pertaining thereto. (§1910.241(a)(7))

Top saw upper of two circular saws on a head rig, both being on the same husk. (§1910.265(b)(44))

Total flooding system fixed suppression system which is arranged to automatically discharge a predetermined concentration of agent into an enclosed space for the purpose of fire extinguishment or control. (§1910.155(c)(40))

Totally-encapsulated chemical protective suit (TECP suit) (See Also "Gas tight") full body garment which is constructed of protective clothing materials; covers the wearer's torso, head, arms, legs and respirator; may cover the wearer's hands and feet with tightly attached gloves and boots; completely encloses the wearer and respirator by itself or in combination with the wearer's gloves and boots. (Appendix A to §1910.120(2.1))

Touch potential voltage between the energized object and the feet of a person in contact with the object. It is equal to the difference in voltage between the object (which is at a distance of 0 feet) and a point some distance away. It should be noted that the touch potential could be nearly the full voltage across the grounded object if that object is grounded at a point remote from the place where the person is in contact with it. For example, a crane that was grounded to the system neutral and that contacted an energized line would expose any person in contact with the crane or its uninsulated load line to a touch potential nearly equal to the full fault voltage. (Appendix C to §1910.269)

Toxic material material in concentration or amount which exceeds the applicable limit established by a Standard, such as §1910.1000 and §1910.1001 or, in the absence of an applicable Standard, which is of such toxicity so as to constitute a recognized hazard that is causing or is likely to cause death or serious physical harm. (§1910.141(a)(2))

Toxic substance or harmful physical agent any chemical substance, biological agent (bacteria, virus, fungus, etc.), or physical stress (noise, heat, cold, vibration, repetitive motion, ionizing and non-ionizing radiation, hypo-or hyperbaric pressure, etc.) which:

(i) is listed in the latest printed edition of the National Institute for Occupational Safety and Health (NIOSH) Registry of Toxic Effects of Chemical Substances (RTECS), which is incorporated by reference as specified in §1910.6; or

(ii) has yielded positive evidence of an acute or chronic health hazard in testing conducted by, or known to, the employer; or

(iii) is the subject of a safety data sheet kept by or known to the employer indicating that the material may pose a hazard to human health. (§1910.1020(c)(13))

Track distance between the wheels on the same axle of the truck. (Appendix A to §1910.178)

Traction hoist type of hoisting machine that does not accumulate the suspension wire rope on the hoisting drum or sheave, and is designed to raise and lower a suspended load by the application of friction forces between the suspension wire rope and the drum or sheave. (§1910.66(d))

Trade secret any confidential formula, pattern, process, device, information or compilation of information that is used in an employer's business, and that gives the employer an opportunity to obtain an advantage over competitors who do not know or use it. See Appendix E to §1910.1200—Definition of a Trade Secret (which sets out the criteria to be used in evaluating trade secrets). (§1910.119(b)); (§1910.1020(c)(14)); (§1910.1200(c)); (Appendix E to §1910.1200(b))

Training process of making proficient through instruction and hands-on practice in the operation of equipment, including respiratory protection equipment that is expected to be used and in the performance of assigned duties. (§1910.155(c)(41))

Training hours number of hours devoted to lecture, learning activities, small group work sessions, demonstration, evaluations, or hands-on experience. (Appendix E to §1910.120)

Trajectory any potential path or route that a rim wheel component may travel during an explosive separation, or the sudden release of the pressurized air, or an area at which an airblast from a single piece rim wheel may be released. The trajectory may deviate from paths which are perpendicular to the assembled position of the rim wheel at the time of separation or explosion. (See Appendix A to §1910.177 for examples of trajectories.) (§1910.177(b))

Tramway way for trams, usually consisting of parallel tracks laid on wooden beams. (§1910.265(b)(45))

Transit moving or transporting of a crane from one jobsite to another. (§1910.180(a)(43))

Transportable outriggers outriggers designed to be moved from one work location to another. (§1910.66(d))

Transportable X-ray (See Also "Mobile X-ray;" "Portable X-ray") X-ray equipment installed in a vehicle or that may readily be disassembled for transport in a vehicle. (§1910.399)

Travel

(Crawler, locomotive, and truck cranes) function of the machine moving from one location to another, on a jobsite. (§1910.180(a)(44))

(Manlifts) travel is the distance between the centers of the top and bottom pulleys. (§1910.68(a)(9))

Travel mechanism travel mechanism is the machinery involved in providing travel. (§1910.180(a)(45))

Traveling cable cable made up of electrical or communication conductors or both, and providing electrical connection between the working platform and the roof car or other fixed point. (Appendix D to §1910.66(a)(23))

Travel restraint system combination of an anchorage, anchorage connector, lanyard (or other means of connection), and body support that an employer uses to eliminate the possibility of an employee going over the edge of a walking-working surface. (§1910.21(b))

Tread horizontal member of a stair or stairway, but does not include landings or platforms. (§1910.21(b))

Treatment table depth-time and breathing gas profile designed to treat decompression sickness. (§1910.402)

Trestle braced framework of timbers, piles or steelwork for carrying a road or railroad over a depression. (§1910.265(b)(46))

Tremolite, Anthophyllite, and Actinolite non-asbestos form of these minerals which meet the definition of a fiber. It includes any of these minerals that have been chemically treated and/or altered. (Appendix B to §1910.1001)

Trimming presses class of auxiliary forging equipment which removes flash or excess metal from a forging. This trimming operation can also be done cold, as can coining, a product sizing operation. (§1910.211(e)(6))

Trip or (tripping) activation of the clutch to "run" the press. (§1910.211(d)(55))

Trolley unit which travels on the bridge rails and carries the hoisting mechanism. (§1910.179(a)(63))

Trolley carriage carriage suspended from an overhead track structure. (§1910.66(d))

Trolly travel trolley movement at right angles to the crane runway. (§1910.179(a)(64))

Truck unit consisting of a frame, wheels, bearings, and axles which supports the bridge girders or trolleys. (§1910.179(a)(65))

Truck crane consists of a rotating superstructure with power plant, operating machinery and boom, mounted on an automotive truck equipped with a power plant for travel. Its function is to hoist and swing loads at various radii. (§1910.180(a)(3))

Tuck pointing removal, by grinding, of cement, mortar, or other nonmetallic jointing material. (§1910.241(b)(2))

Tuck pointing wheels (See Also "Type 1 straight wheels") tuck pointing wheels, usually Type 1, reinforced organic bonded wheels have diameter, thickness and hole size dimension. They are subject to the same limitations of use and mounting as Type 1 wheels defined in (b)(10) of §1910.211.

Limitation: Wheels used for tuck pointing should be reinforced, organic bonded. (§1910.243(c)(1)(ii)(c)); (§1910.241(b)(3))

Turnover bar bar used in die setting to manually turn the crankshaft of the press. (§1910.211(d)(56))

Two hand control device two hand trip that further requires concurrent pressure from both hands of the operator during a substantial part of the die-closing portion of the stroke of the press. (§1910.211(d)(17))

Two-hand trip clutch actuating means requiring the concurrent use of both hands of the operator to trip the press. (§1910.211(d)(57))

Two-point suspension scaffold scaffold, the platform of which is supported by hangers (stirrups) at two points, suspended from overhead supports so as to permit the raising or lowering of the platform to the desired working position by tackle or hoisting machines. (§1910.21(f)(34))

Type 1 straight wheels (See Also "Tuck pointing wheels") wheels having diameter, thickness, and hole size dimensions, and they should be used only on the periphery. Type 1 wheels shall be mounted between flanges.

Limitation: Hole dimension (H) should not be greater than two-thirds of wheel diameter dimension (D) for precision, cylindrical, centerless, or surface grinding applications. Maximum hole size for all other applications should not exceed one-half wheel diameter. (§1910.211(b)(1), Fig. No. 0-1; §1910.241(b)10))

Type 2 cylinder wheels wheels having diameter, wheel thickness, and rim thickness dimensions. Grinding is performed on the rim face only, dimension W. Cylinder wheels may be plain, plate mounted, inserted nut, or of the projecting stud type.

Limitation: Rim height, T dimension, is generally equal to or greater than rim thickness, W dimension. (§1910.211(b)(2), Fig. No. 0-2)

Type 6 straight cup wheels wheels having diameter, thickness, hole size, rim thickness, and back thickness dimensions. Grinding is always performed on rim face, W dimension.

Limitation: Minimum back thickness, E dimension, should not be less than one-fourth T dimension. In addition, when unthreaded hole wheels are specified, the inside flat, K dimension, must be large enough to accommodate a suitable flange. (§1910.211(b)(3), Fig. No. 0-3); §1910.241(b)(9))

Type 11 flaring cup wheels wheels having double diameter dimensions D and J, and in addition have thickness, hole size, rim and back thickness dimensions. Grinding is always performed on rim face, W dimension. Type 11 wheels are subject to all limitations of use and mounting listed for type 6 straight sided cup wheels definition.

Limitation: Minimum back thickness, E dimension, should not be less than one-fourth T dimension. In addition when unthreaded hole wheels are specified the inside flat, K dimension, shall be large enough to accommodate a suitable flange. (§1910.211(b)(4), Fig. No. 0-1; §1910.241(b)(8))

Types 6 and 11 wheels modified (terrazzo) See "Modified types 7 and 11 wheels (terrazzo)"

Types 27 and 28 depressed center wheels wheels having diameter, thickness, and hole size dimensions. Both types are reinforced, organic bonded wheels having offset hubs which permit side and peripheral grinding operations without interference with the mounting. Type 27 wheels are manufactured with flat grinding rims permitting notching and cutting operations. Type 28 wheels have saucer shaped grinding rims.

(i) ***Limitations:*** *Special supporting, back adapter and inside flange nuts are required for the proper mounting of these types of wheels subject to limitations of §1910.215(c)(4) (i) and (ii).*

(ii) Mounts which are affixed to the wheel by the manufacturer may not require an inside nut and shall not be reused. (§1910.211(b)(6))

Type 27A depressed center, cutting-off wheels wheels having diameter, thickness, and hole size dimensions. They are reinforced, organic bonded, offset hub type wheels, usually 16 inches diameter and larger, specially designed for use on cutting-off machines where mounting nut or outer flange interference cannot be tolerated. (§1910.211(b)(7))

U

Umbilical composite hose bundle between a dive location and a diver or bell, or between a diver and a bell, which supplies the diver or bell with breathing gas, communications, power, or heat as appropriate to the diving mode or conditions, and includes a safety line between the diver and the dive location. (§1910.402)

Uncontrolled hazardous waste site area identified as an uncontrolled hazardous waste site by a governmental body, whether Federal, state, local or other where an accumulation of hazardous substances creates a threat to the health and safety of individuals or the environment or both. Some sites are found on public lands such as those created by former municipal, county or state landfills where illegal or poorly managed waste disposal has taken place. Other sites are found on private property, often belonging to generators or former generators of hazardous substance wastes. Examples of such sites include, but are not limited to, surface impoundments, landfills, dumps, and tank or drum farms. Normal operations at TSD sites are not covered by this definition. (§1910.120(a)(3))

Undercut notch cut in a tree to guide the direction of the tree fall and to prevent splitting or kickback. (§1910.266(c))

Unitized tooling type of die in which the upper and lower members are incorporated into a self-contained unit so arranged as to hold the die members in alignment. (§1910.211(d)(58))

Universal Precautions approach to infection control. According to the concept of Universal Precautions, all human blood and certain human body fluids are treated as if known to be infectious for HIV, HBV, and other bloodborne pathogens. (§1910.1030(b))

Unprotected sides and edges any side or edge of a walking-working surface (except at entrances and other points of access) where there is no wall, guardrail system, or stair rail system to protect an employee from falling to a lower level. (§1910.21(b))

Unrestricted area any area access to which is not controlled by the employer for purposes of protection of individuals from exposure to radiation or radioactive materials. (§1910.1096(a)(4))

Unstable explosive explosive which is thermally unstable and/or too sensitive for normal handling, transport, or use. (Appendix B to §1910.1200(B.1.1.1))

Unstable (reactive) liquid liquid which in the pure state or as commercially produced or transported will vigorously polymerize, decompose, condense, or will become self-reactive under conditions of shocks, pressure, or temperature. (§1910.106(a)(20))

Unvented vault (See Also "Vault;" Vented vault") enclosed vault in which the only openings are access openings. (§1910.268(s)(41))

Upsetters (or forging machines, or headers) type of forging equipment, related to the mechanical press, in which the main forming energy is applied horizontally to the workpiece which is gripped and held by prior action of the dies. (§1910.211(e)(12))

Urinal toilet facility maintained within a toilet room for the sole purpose of urination. (§1910.141(a)(2))

Use to package, handle, react, emit, extract, generate as a byproduct, or transfer. (§1910.1200(c))

User seal check (See Also "Negative pressure respirator (Tight fitting);" "Pressure demand respirator;" "Supplied-air respirator (SAR) or airline respirator") action conducted by the respirator user to determine if the respirator is properly seated to the face. (§1910.134(b))

Utilization equipment equipment that utilizes electric energy for electronic, electromechanical, chemical, heating, lighting, or similar purposes. (§1910.399)

V

Validation or validate for PSDI safety systems that an OSHA recognized third-party validation organization:

(i) for design certification/validation has reviewed the manufacturer's certification that the PSDI safety system meets the requirements of §1910.217(a)-(h) and Appendix A and the underlying tests and analyses performed by the manufacturer, has performed additional tests and analyses which may be required by §1910.217(a)-(h) and Appendix A, and concludes that the requirements of §1910.217(a)-(h) and Appendix A have been met; and

(ii) for installation certification/validation and annual recertification/revalidation has reviewed the employer's certification that the PSDI safety system meets the requirements of §1910.217(a)-(h) and Appendix A and the underlying tests performed by the employer, has performed additional tests and analyses which may be required by §1910.217(a)-(h) and Appendix A, and concludes that the requirements of §1910.217(a)-(h) and Appendix A have been met. (§1910.211(d)(65))

Value or Measurement Value numerical result of a measurement. (Appendix F to §1910.1027)

Vapor area any space containing a dip tank, including its drain boards, associated drying or conveying equipment, and any surrounding area where the vapor concentration exceeds 25% of the LFL of the liquid in the tank. (§1910.123(d))

Vapor barrier that material used to prevent or substantially inhibit the transfer of water, corrosive liquids and steam or other hot vapors from the outside of a garment to the wearer's body. (§1910.155(c)(42))

Vapor control system any equipment used for containing the total vapors displaced during the loading of gasoline, motor fuel or other fuel tank trucks and the displacing of these vapors through a vapor processing system or balancing the vapor with the storage tank. This equipment also includes systems containing the vapors displaced from the storage tank during the unloading of the tank truck which balance the vapors back to the tank truck. (§1910.1028(b))

Vapor pressure pressure, measured in pounds per square inch (absolute) exerted by a volatile liquid as determined by the "Standard Method of Test for Vapor Pressure of Petroleum Products (Reid Method)," American Society for Testing and Materials ASTM D323–68, which is incorporated by reference as specified in §1910.6. (§1910.106(a)(30))

Vaporizer-burner integral vaporizer-burner unit, dependent upon the heat generated by the burner as the source of heat to vaporize the liquid used for dehydrators or dryers. (§1910.110(a)(12))

Variance measure of the distribution or spread of a data set about the mean; the variance is the sum of the squares of the differences between the mean and each discrete measurement divided by one less than the number of measurements in the data set. (Appendix F to §1910.1027)

Vault (See Also "Unvented vault;" "Vented vault")
(Electric power generation, transmission, and distribution) enclosure, above or below ground, that personnel may enter and that is used for installing, operating, or maintaining equipment or cable. (§1910.269(x))
(Telecommunications) enclosure above or below ground which personnel may enter, and which is used for the purpose of installing, operating, and/or maintaining equipment and/or cable which need not be of submersible design. (§1910.268(s)(42))

Vehicle
(Logging operations) car, bus, truck, trailer or semi-trailer owned, leased or rented by the employer that is used for transportation of employees or movement of material. (§1910.266(c))
(Vehicle mounted elevating and rotating work platforms) any carrier that is not manually propelled. (§1910.67(a)(8))

Velocity pressure (vp) kinetic pressure in the direction of flow necessary to cause a fluid at rest to flow at a given velocity. It is usually expressed in inches of water gauge. (§1910.94(b)(1)(xvii))

Vented vault (See Also "Unvented vault;" Vault)
(Electric power generation, transmission, and distribution) vault that has provision for air changes using exhaust-flue stacks and low-level air intakes operating on pressure and temperature differentials that provide for airflow that precludes a hazardous atmosphere from developing. (§1910.269(x))
(Telecommunications) enclosure as described in paragraph (s)(42) of this Section, with provision for air changes using exhaust flue stack(s) and low level air intake(s), operating on differentials of pressure and temperature providing for air flow. (§1910.268(s)(43))

Ventilated provided with a means to permit circulation of air sufficient to remove an excess of heat, fumes, or vapors. (§1910.399)

Ventilation as specified in §1910.106 is for the prevention of fire and explosion. It is considered adequate if it is sufficient to prevent accumulation of significant quantities of vapor-air mixtures in concentration over one-fourth of the lower flammable limit. (§1910.106(a)(31))

Ventilation adequate when specified for the prevention of fire during normal operation, ventilation shall be considered adequate when the concentration of the gas in a gas-air mixture does not exceed 25 percent of the lower flammable limit. (§1910.110(a)(13))

Verified accepted by design, evaluation, or inspection by a registered professional engineer. (§1910.66(d))

Vertical elutriator cotton dust sampler or vertical elutriator dust sampler which has a particle size cut-off at approximately 15 micrometers aerodynamic equivalent diameter when operating at the flow rate of 7.4 ±0.2 liters of air per minute; (§1910.1043(b))

Vertical hitch method of supporting a load by a single, vertical part or leg of the sling. (§1910.184(b))

Vertical spindle disc grinder grinding machine having a vertical, rotatable power-driven spindle carrying a horizontal abrasive disc wheel. (§1910.94(b)(1)(xvii))

Vertical tower aerial device designed to elevate a platform in a substantially vertical axis. (§1910.67(a)(9))

Vessel (See Also "Ship repair;" Shipbreaking;" "Shipbuilding") includes every description of watercraft or other artificial contrivance used, or capable of being used, as a means of transportation on water, including special purpose floating structures not primarily designed for, or used as a means of, transportation on water. (§1910.15(b)(5)); (§1910.16(c)(3))

Vinyl chloride vinyl chloride monomer. (§1910.1017(b)(10))

Viscous viscosity of 45 SUS or more. (§1910.106(a)(38))

Volatile flammable liquid flammable liquid having a flash point below 38 °C (100 °F), or a flammable liquid whose temperature is above its flash point, or a Class II combustible liquid having a vapor pressure not exceeding 276 kPa (40 psia) at 38 °C (100 °F) and whose temperature is above its flash point. (§1910.399)

Voltage effective (root mean square, or rms) potential difference between any two conductors or between a conductor and ground. This section expresses voltages in nominal values, unless otherwise indicated. The nominal voltage of a system or circuit is the value assigned to a system or circuit of a given voltage class for the purpose of convenient designation. The operating voltage of the system may vary above or below this value. (§1910.269(x))

Voltage, nominal nominal value assigned to a circuit or system for the purpose of conveniently designating its voltage class (as 120/240 volts, 480Y/277 volts, 600 volts). The actual voltage at which a circuit operates can vary from the nominal within a range that permits satisfactory operation of equipment. (§1910.399)

Voltage (of a circuit) greatest root-mean-square (rms) (effective) difference of potential between any two conductors of the circuit concerned. (§1910.399)

Voltage of a circuit not effectively grounded voltage between any two conductors. If one circuit is directly connected to and supplied from another circuit of higher voltage (as in the case of an autotransformer), both are considered as of the higher voltage, unless the circuit of lower voltage is effectively grounded, in which case its voltage is not determined by the circuit of higher voltage. Direct connection implies electric connection as distinguished from connection merely through electromagnetic or electrostatic induction. (§1910.268(s)(45))

Voltage of an effectively grounded circuit voltage between any conductor and ground unless otherwise indicated. (§1910.268(s)(44))

Voltage to ground for grounded circuits, the voltage between the given conductor and that point or conductor of the circuit that is grounded; for ungrounded circuits, the greatest voltage between the given conductor and any other conductor of the circuit. (§1910.399)

Volume tank pressure vessel connected to the outlet of a compressor and used as an air reservoir. (§1910.402)

W

Wagon crane See "Wheel mounted crane (wagon crane)"

Walking-working surface any horizontal or vertical surface on or through which an employee walks, works, or gains access to a work area or workplace location. (§1910.21(b))

Wall crane crane having a jib with or without trolley and supported from a side wall or line of columns of a building. It is a traveling type and operates on a runway attached to the side wall or columns. (§1910.179(a)(14))

Walton-Beckett Graticule eyepiece graticule specifically designed for asbestos fiber counting. It consists of a circle with a projected diameter of 100±2 µm (area of about 0.00785 mm^2) with a cross-hair having tic-marks at 3-µm intervals in one direction and 5-µm in the orthogonal direction. There are marks around the periphery of the circle to demonstrate the proper sizes and shapes of fibers. This design is reproduced in Figure 1. The disk is placed in one of the microscope eyepieces so that the design is superimposed on the field of view. (Appendix B to §1910.1001)

Warning line barrier erected to warn employees that they are approaching an unprotected side or edge, and which designates an area in which work may take place without the use of other means of fall protection. (§1910.21(b))

Warper any machine for preparing and arranging the yarns intended for the warp of a fabric, specifically, a beam warper. (§1910.262(b)(37))

Waste processing waste recycling (sorting, blending, cleaning and willowing) and garnetting. (§1910.1043(b))

Water closet toilet facility maintained within a toilet room for the purpose of both defecation and urination and which is flushed with water. (§1910.141(a)(2))

Water gels, or slurry explosives wide variety of materials used for blasting. They all contain substantial proportions of water and high proportions of ammonium nitrate, some of which is in solution in the water. Two broad classes of water gels are:
(i) those which are sensitized by a material classed as an explosive, such as TNT or smokeless powder, and
(ii) those which contain no ingredient classified as an explosive; these are sensitized with metals such as aluminum or with other fuels. Water gels may be premixed at an explosives plant or mixed at the site immediately before delivery into the bore hole. (§1910.109(a)(18))

Water mangle See "Mangle (water)"

Watertight so constructed that moisture will not enter the enclosure. (§1910.399)

Waterwash spray booth (See Also "Dry spray booth") spray booth equipped with a water washing system designed to minimize dusts or residues entering exhaust ducts and to permit the recovery of overspray finishing material. (§1910.107(a)(4))

Water-reactive chemical that reacts with water to release a gas that is either flammable or presents a health hazard. (§1910.1450(b))

Weatherproof
(Electrical) so constructed or protected that exposure to the weather will not interfere with successful operation. Rainproof, raintight, or watertight equipment can fulfill the requirements for weatherproof where varying weather conditions other than wetness, such as snow, ice, dust, or temperature extremes, are not a factor. (§1910.399)

(Powered platforms for building maintenance) equipment so constructed or protected that exposure to the weather will not interfere with its proper operation. (§1910.66(d)); (Appendix D to §1910.66(a)(24))

Welder and welding operator any operator of electric or gas welding and cutting equipment. (§1910.251(a))

Well permanent, complete enclosure around a fixed ladder. (§1910.21(b))

Wet location See "Location"

Wet process any process or operation in a workroom which normally results in surfaces upon which employees may walk or stand becoming wet. (§1910.141(a)(2))

Wharf shall mean any wharf, pier, bulkhead, or other structure over or contiguous to navigable water used in conjunction with a bulk plant, the primary function of which is the transfer of flammable liquid cargo in bulk between the bulk plant and any tank vessel, ship, barge, lighter boat, or other mobile floating craft; and this subparagraph shall apply to all such installations except Marine Service Stations as covered in paragraph (g) of this Section. (§1910.106(f)(4)(i))

Wheel that portion of a rim wheel which provides the method of attachment of the assembly to the axle of a vehicle and also provides the means to contain the inflated portion of the assembly (i.e., the tire and/or tube). (§1910.177(b))

Wheel mounted crane (wagon crane) consists of a rotating superstructure with power plant, operating machinery and boom, mounted on a base or platform equipped with axles and rubber-tired wheels for travel. The base is usually propelled by the engine in the superstructure, but it may be equipped with a separate engine controlled from the superstructure. Its function is to hoist and swing loads at various radii. (§1910.180(a)(4))

Wheelbase

(Crawler, locomotive, and truck cranes) distance between centers of front and rear axles. For a multiple axle assembly the axle center for wheelbase measurement is taken as the midpoint of the assembly. (§1910.180(a)(46))

(Powered industrial trucks/Stability of powered industrial trucks (non-mandatory)) distance between the center line of the vehicle's front and rear wheels. (Appendix A to §1910.178)

Whipline (auxiliary hoist) separate hoist rope system of lighter load capacity and higher speed than provided by the main hoist. (§1910.180(a)(47))

Whole body irradiation pertains to the case in which the entire body is exposed to the incident electromagnetic energy or in which the cross section of the body is smaller than the cross section of the incident radiation beam. (§1910.97(a)(1)(v))

Winch head power-driven spool for handling of loads by means of friction between fiber or wire rope and spool. (§1910.180(a)(48))

Winching winding of cable or rope onto a spool or drum. (§1910.266(c))

Winding drum hoist type of hoisting machine that accumulates the suspension wire rope on the hoisting drum. (§1910.66(d))

Wireways sheet-metal troughs with hinged or removable covers for housing and protecting electric wires and cable and in which conductors are laid in place after the wireway has been installed as a complete system. (§1910.399)

Work area room or defined space in a workplace where hazardous chemicals are produced or used, and where employees are present. (§1910.1200(c))

Work Practice Controls controls that reduce the likelihood of exposure by altering the manner in which a task is performed (e.g., prohibiting recapping of needles by a two-handed technique). (§1910.1030(b))

Work-positioning equipment body belt or body harness system rigged to allow an employee to be supported on an elevated vertical surface, such as a utility pole or tower leg, and work with both hands free while leaning. (§1910.269(x))

Working days Mondays through Fridays but shall not include Saturdays, Sundays, or Federal holidays. In computing 15 working days, the day of receipt of any notice shall not be included, and the last day of the 15 working days shall be included. (§1903.22(c))

Working platform

(Powered platforms for building maintenance) suspended or supported equipment intended to provide access to the face of a building and manned by persons engaged in building maintenance. (§1910.66(d))

(Powered platforms for building maintenance/Existing installations (mandatory)) suspended structure arranged for vertical travel which provides access to the exterior of the building or structure. (Appendix D to §1910.66(a)(25))

Working pressure maximum pressure to which a pressure containment device may be exposed under standard operating conditions. (§1910.402)

Workplace establishment, job site, or project, at one geographical location containing one or more work areas. (§1910.1200(c))

Wrap one complete turn of the suspension wire rope around the surface of a hoist drum. (§1910.66(d))

X

Y

Yarding movement of logs from the place they are felled to a landing. (§1910.266)(c))

Yarn manufacturing all textile mill operations from opening to, but not including, slashing and weaving. (§1910.1043(b))

Yield point stress at which the material exhibits a permanent set of 0.2 percent. (Appendix D to §1910.66(a)(26))

You

(1904) employer as defined in Section 3 of the Occupational Safety and Health Act of 1970 (29 U.S.C. 652). (§1904.46)

(1910) employer, as defined by the Occupational Safety and Health Act of 1970 (29 U.S.C. 651 et seq.). (§1910.123(d))

Z

Zinced fastenings method of providing wire rope attachments in which the splayed or fanned wire ends are held in a tapered socket by means of poured molten zinc. (Appendix D to §1910.66(a)(27))

This page intentionally left blank.

Subject Index

C

D

E

F

M

T

U

V

W

X

Z